MACHINERY'S
HANDBOOK

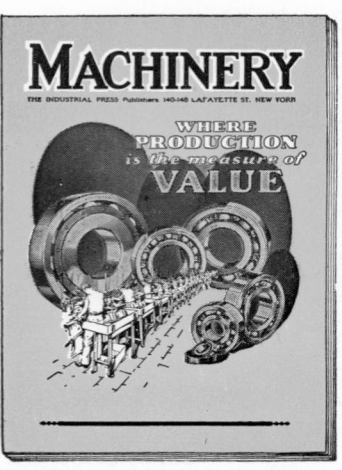

MACHINERY'S HANDBOOK

FOR MACHINE SHOP AND DRAFTING-ROOM

A REFERENCE BOOK ON MACHINE DE-
SIGN AND SHOP PRACTICE FOR THE
MECHANICAL ENGINEER, DRAFTS-
MAN, TOOLMAKER, AND MACHINIST

BY

ERIK OBERG AND F. D. JONES

FOURTEENTH EDITION

SECOND PRINTING

TOTAL ISSUE 929,000

THE INDUSTRIAL PRESS
148 Lafayette Street, New York 13, N. Y.

Sole Distributors for the British Empire:
MACHINERY PUBLISHING CO., Ltd.
National House, West St., Brighton, 1, England

1950

COMPOSITION AND ELECTROTYPING BY THE TECHNICAL COMPOSITION CO., BOSTON, MASS.

PREFACE

MACHINERY'S HANDBOOK, since the publication of its first edition in 1914, has continually increased in popularity throughout the world. It is now used extensively as a work of reference in all countries where machines or other mechanical products are manufactured. The aim of the publishers is to make each new edition of greater practical value than the preceding one. This has been accomplished by revising the HANDBOOK as frequently as is practicable for a voluminous work which must necessarily be printed in large editions to meet the constant demand for it both here and abroad.

The new material covers a large variety of subjects that are important to designers and builders of everything mechanical. Recent or revised engineering standards are included, together with a large amount of general information and mechanical data representing the latest designing and manufacturing practice.

In selecting material from the almost limitless supply of data pertaining to mechanical subjects, the plan is to consider primarily the needs and requirements in both the designing and manufacturing departments of machine-building plants. The editors have received many practical suggestions from friends throughout the mechanical field, and this coöperation, which has proved to be invaluable, is highly appreciated. The HANDBOOK user who directs the publisher's attention to some defect or to the omission of matter considered of general value, often renders valuable service to the entire mechanical industry. For this reason and also because we desire to perfect the HANDBOOK as far as possible, all criticisms and suggestions either about revisions or the inclusion of new matter are welcome.

ERIK OBERG AND FRANKLIN D. JONES, EDITORS

GENERAL CONTENTS

GENERAL CONTENTS

GENERAL CONTENTS

MACHINERY'S HANDBOOK
FOR MACHINE SHOP AND
DRAFTING ROOM

MATHEMATICAL TABLES
Square and Cube Roots of Decimal Numbers

Decimal	Square Root	Cube Root	Decimal	Square Root	Cube Root	Decimal	Square Root	Cube Root
0.01	0.1000	0.2154	0.34	0.5831	0.6980	0.67	0.8185	0.8750
0.02	0.1414	0.2714	0.35	0.5916	0.7047	0.68	0.8246	0.8794
0.03	0.1732	0.3107	0.36	0.6000	0.7114	0.69	0.8307	0.8837
0.04	0.2000	0.3420	0.37	0.6083	0.7179	0.70	0.8367	0.8879
0.05	0.2236	0.3684	0.38	0.6164	0.7243	0.71	0.8426	0.8921
0.06	0.2449	0.3915	0.39	0.6245	0.7306	0.72	0.8485	0.8963
0.07	0.2646	0.4121	0.40	0.6325	0.7368	0.73	0.8544	0.9004
0.08	0.2828	0.4309	0.41	0.6403	0.7429	0.74	0.8602	0.9045
0.09	0.3000	0.4481	0.42	0.6481	0.7489	0.75	0.8660	0.9086
0.10	0.3162	0.4642	0.43	0.6557	0.7548	0.76	0.8718	0.9126
0.11	0.3317	0.4791	0.44	0.6633	0.7606	0.77	0.8775	0.9166
0.12	0.3464	0.4932	0.45	0.6708	0.7663	0.78	0.8832	0.9205
0.13	0.3606	0.5066	0.46	0.6782	0.7719	0.79	0.8888	0.9244
0.14	0.3742	0.5192	0.47	0.6856	0.7775	0.80	0.8944	0.9283
0.15	0.3873	0.5313	0.48	0.6928	0.7830	0.81	0.9000	0.9322
0.16	0.4000	0.5429	0.49	0.7000	0.7884	0.82	0.9055	0.9360
0.17	0.4123	0.5540	0.50	0.7071	0.7937	0.83	0.9110	0.9398
0.18	0.4243	0.5646	0.51	0.7141	0.7990	0.84	0.9165	0.9435
0.19	0.4359	0.5749	0.52	0.7211	0.8041	0.85	0.9220	0.9473
0.20	0.4472	0.5848	0.53	0.7280	0.8093	0.86	0.9274	0.9510
0.21	0.4583	0.5944	0.54	0.7348	0.8143	0.87	0.9327	0.9546
0.22	0.4690	0.6037	0.55	0.7416	0.8193	0.88	0.9381	0.9583
0.23	0.4796	0.6127	0.56	0.7483	0.8243	0.89	0.9434	0.9619
0.24	0.4899	0.6214	0.57	0.7550	0.8291	0.90	0.9487	0.9655
0.25	0.5000	0.6300	0.58	0.7616	0.8340	0.91	0.9539	0.9691
0.26	0.5099	0.6383	0.59	0.7681	0.8387	0.92	0.9592	0.9726
0.27	0.5196	0.6463	0.60	0.7746	0.8434	0.93	0.9644	0.9761
0.28	0.5292	0.6542	0.61	0.7810	0.8481	0.94	0.9695	0.9796
0.29	0.5385	0.6619	0.62	0.7874	0.8527	0.95	0.9747	0.9830
0.30	0.5477	0.6694	0.63	0.7937	0.8573	0.96	0.9798	0.9865
0.31	0.5568	0.6768	0.64	0.8000	0.8618	0.97	0.9849	0.9899
0.32	0.5657	0.6840	0.65	0.8062	0.8662	0.98	0.9899	0.9933
0.33	0.5745	0.6910	0.66	0.8124	0.8707	0.99	0.9950	0.9967

Powers, Roots and Reciprocals

No.	Square	Cube	Sq. Root	Cube Root	Reciprocal	No.
1	1	1	1.00000	1.00000	1.0000000	1
2	4	8	1.41421	1.25992	0.5000000	2
3	9	27	1.73205	1.44225	0.3333333	3
4	16	64	2.00000	1.58740	0.2500000	4
5	25	125	2.23607	1.70998	0.2000000	5
6	36	216	2.44949	1.81712	0.1666667	6
7	49	343	2.64575	1.91293	0.1428571	7
8	64	512	2.82843	2.00000	0.1250000	8
9	81	729	3.00000	2.08008	0.1111111	9
10	100	1,000	3.16228	2.15443	0.1000000	10
11	121	1,331	3.31662	2.22398	0.0909091	11
12	144	1,728	3.46410	2.28943	0.0833333	12
13	169	2,197	3.60555	2.35133	0.0769231	13
14	196	2,744	3.74166	2.41014	0.0714286	14
15	225	3,375	3.87298	2.46621	0.0666667	15
16	256	4,096	4.00000	2.51984	0.0625000	16
17	289	4,913	4.12311	2.57128	0.0588235	17
18	324	5,832	4.24264	2.62074	0.0555556	18
19	361	6,859	4.35890	2.66840	0.0526316	19
20	400	8,000	4.47214	2.71442	0.0500000	20
21	441	9,261	4.58258	2.75892	0.0476190	21
22	484	10,648	4.69042	2.80204	0.0454545	22
23	529	12,167	4.79583	2.84387	0.0434783	23
24	576	13,824	4.89898	2.88450	0.0416667	24
25	625	15,625	5.00000	2.92402	0.0400000	25
26	676	17,576	5.09902	2.96250	0.0384615	26
27	729	19,683	5.19615	3.00000	0.0370370	27
28	784	21,952	5.29150	3.03659	0.0357143	28
29	841	24,389	5.38516	3.07232	0.0344828	29
30	900	27,000	5.47723	3.10723	0.0333333	30
31	961	29,791	5.56776	3.14138	0.0322581	31
32	1,024	32,768	5.65685	3.17480	0.0312500	32
33	1,089	35,937	5.74456	3.20753	0.0303030	33
34	1,156	39,304	5.83095	3.23961	0.0294118	34
35	1,225	42,875	5.91608	3.27107	0.0285714	35
36	1,296	46,656	6.00000	3.30193	0.0277778	36
37	1,369	50,653	6.08276	3.33222	0.0270270	37
38	1,444	54,872	6.16441	3.36198	0.0263158	38
39	1,521	59,319	6.24500	3.39121	0.0256410	39
40	1,600	64,000	6.32456	3.41995	0.0250000	40
41	1,681	68,921	6.40312	3.44822	0.0243902	41
42	1,764	74,088	6.48074	3.47603	0.0238095	42
43	1,849	79,507	6.55744	3.50340	0.0232558	43
44	1,936	85,184	6.63325	3.53035	0.0227273	44
45	2,025	91,125	6.70820	3.55689	0.0222222	45
46	2,116	97,336	6.78233	3.58305	0.0217391	46
47	2,209	103,823	6.85565	3.60883	0.0212766	47
48	2,304	110,592	6.92820	3.63424	0.0208333	48
49	2,401	117,649	7.00000	3.65931	0.0204082	49
50	2,500	125,000	7.07107	3.68403	0.0200000	50

Powers, Roots and Reciprocals

No.	Square	Cube	Sq. Root	Cube Root	Reciprocal	No.
51	2,601	132,651	7.14143	3.70843	0.0196078	51
52	2,704	140,608	7.21110	3.73251	0.0192308	52
53	2,809	148,877	7.28011	3.75629	0.0188679	53
54	2,916	157,464	7.34847	3.77976	0.0185185	54
55	3,025	166,375	7.41620	3.80295	0.0181818	55
56	3,136	175,616	7.48331	3.82586	0.0178571	56
57	3,249	185,193	7.54983	3.84850	0.0175439	57
58	3,364	195,112	7.61577	3.87088	0.0172414	58
59	3,481	205,379	7.68115	3.89300	0.0169492	59
60	3,600	216,000	7.74597	3.91487	0.0166667	60
61	3,721	226,981	7.81025	3.93650	0.0163934	61
62	3,844	238,328	7.87401	3.95789	0.0161290	62
63	3,969	250,047	7.93725	3.97906	0.0158730	63
64	4,096	262,144	8.00000	4.00000	0.0156250	64
65	4,225	274,625	8.06226	4.02073	0.0153846	65
66	4,356	287,496	8.12404	4.04124	0.0151515	66
67	4,489	300,763	8.18535	4.06155	0.0149254	67
68	4,624	314,432	8.24621	4.08166	0.0147059	68
69	4,761	328,509	8.30662	4.10157	0.0144928	69
70	4,900	343,000	8.36660	4.12129	0.0142857	70
71	5,041	357,911	8.42615	4.14082	0.0140845	71
72	5,184	373,248	8.48528	4.16017	0.0138889	72
73	5,329	389,017	8.54400	4.17934	0.0136986	73
74	5,476	405,224	8.60233	4.19834	0.0135135	74
75	5,625	421,875	8.66025	4.21716	0.0133333	75
76	5,776	438,976	8.71780	4.23582	0.0131579	76
77	5,929	456,533	8.77496	4.25432	0.0129870	77
78	6,084	474,552	8.83176	4.27266	0.0128205	78
79	6,241	493,039	8.88819	4.29084	0.0126582	79
80	6,400	512,000	8.94427	4.30887	0.0125000	80
81	6,561	531,441	9.00000	4.32675	0.0123457	81
82	6,724	551,368	9.05539	4.34448	0.0121951	82
83	6,889	571,787	9.11043	4.36207	0.0120482	83
84	7,056	592,704	9.16515	4.37952	0.0119048	84
85	7,225	614,125	9.21954	4.39683	0.0117647	85
86	7,396	636,056	9.27362	4.41400	0.0116279	86
87	7,569	658,503	9.32738	4.43105	0.0114943	87
88	7,744	681,472	9.38083	4.44797	0.0113636	88
89	7,921	704,969	9.43398	4.46475	0.0112360	89
90	8,100	729,000	9.48683	4.48140	0.0111111	90
91	8,281	753,571	9.53939	4.49794	0.0109890	91
92	8,464	778,688	9.59166	4.51436	0.0108696	92
93	8,649	804,357	9.64365	4.53065	0.0107527	93
94	8,836	830,584	9.69536	4.54684	0.0106383	94
95	9,025	857,375	9.74679	4.56290	0.0105263	95
96	9,216	884,736	9.79796	4.57886	0.0104167	96
97	9,409	912,673	9.84886	4.59470	0.0103093	97
98	9,604	941,192	9.89949	4.61044	0.0102041	98
99	9,801	970,299	9.94987	4.62607	0.0101010	99
100	10,000	1,000,000	10.00000	4.64159	0.0100000	100

Powers, Roots and Reciprocals

No.	Square	Cube	Sq. Root	Cube Root	Reciprocal	No.
101	10,201	1,030,301	10.0499	4.65701	0.0099010	101
102	10,404	1,061,208	10.0995	4.67233	0.0098039	102
103	10,609	1,092,727	10.1489	4.68755	0.0097087	103
104	10,816	1,124,864	10.1980	4.70267	0.0096154	104
105	11,025	1,157,625	10.2470	4.71769	0.0095238	105
106	11,236	1,191,016	10.2956	4.73262	0.0094340	106
107	11,449	1,225,043	10.3441	4.74746	0.0093458	107
108	11,664	1,259,712	10.3923	4.76220	0.0092593	108
109	11,881	1,295,029	10.4403	4.77686	0.0091743	109
110	12,100	1,331,000	10.4881	4.79142	0.0090909	110
111	12,321	1,367,631	10.5357	4.80590	0.0090090	111
112	12,544	1,404,928	10.5830	4.82028	0.0089286	112
113	12,769	1,442,897	10.6301	4.83459	0.0088496	113
114	12,996	1,481,544	10.6771	4.84881	0.0087719	114
115	13,225	1,520,875	10.7238	4.86294	0.0086957	115
116	13,456	1,560,896	10.7703	4.87700	0.0086207	116
117	13,689	1,601,613	10.8167	4.89097	0.0085470	117
118	13,924	1,643,032	10.8628	4.90487	0.0084746	118
119	14,161	1,685,159	10.9087	4.91868	0.0084034	119
120	14,400	1,728,000	10.9545	4.93242	0.0083333	120
121	14,641	1,771,561	11.0000	4.94609	0.0082645	121
122	14,884	1,815,848	11.0454	4.95968	0.0081967	122
123	15,129	1,860,867	11.0905	4.97319	0.0081301	123
124	15,376	1,906,624	11.1355	4.98663	0.0080645	124
125	15,625	1,953,125	11.1803	5.00000	0.0080000	125
126	15,876	2,000,376	11.2250	5.01330	0.0079365	126
127	16,129	2,048,383	11.2694	5.02653	0.0078740	127
128	16,384	2,097,152	11.3137	5.03968	0.0078125	128
129	16,641	2,146,689	11.3578	5.05277	0.0077519	129
130	16,900	2,197,000	11.4018	5.06580	0.0076923	130
131	17,161	2,248,091	11.4455	5.07875	0.0076336	131
132	17,424	2,299,968	11.4891	5.09164	0.0075758	132
133	17,689	2,352,637	11.5326	5.10447	0.0075188	133
134	17,956	2,406,104	11.5758	5.11723	0.0074627	134
135	18,225	2,460,375	11.6190	5.12993	0.0074074	135
136	18,496	2,515,456	11.6619	5.14256	0.0073529	136
137	18,769	2,571,353	11.7047	5.15514	0.0072993	137
138	19,044	2,628,072	11.7473	5.16765	0.0072464	138
139	19,321	2,685,619	11.7898	5.18010	0.0071942	139
140	19,600	2,744,000	11.8322	5.19249	0.0071429	140
141	19,881	2,803,221	11.8743	5.20483	0.0070922	141
142	20,164	2,863,288	11.9164	5.21710	0.0070423	142
143	20,449	2,924,207	11.9583	5.22932	0.0069930	143
144	20,736	2,985,984	12.0000	5.24148	0.0069444	144
145	21,025	3,048,625	12.0416	5.25359	0.0068966	145
146	21,316	3,112,136	12.0830	5.26564	0.0068493	146
147	21,609	3,176,523	12.1244	5.27763	0.0068027	147
148	21,904	3,241,792	12.1655	5.28957	0.0067568	148
149	22,201	3,307,949	12.2066	5.30146	0.0067114	149
150	22,500	3,375,000	12.2474	5.31329	0.0066667	150

Powers, Roots and Reciprocals

No.	Square	Cube	Sq. Root	Cube Root	Reciprocal	No.
151	22,801	3,442,951	12.2882	5.32507	0.0066225	151
152	23,104	3,511,808	12.3288	5.33680	0.0065789	152
153	23,409	3,581,577	12.3693	5.34848	0.0065359	153
154	23,716	3,652,264	12.4097	5.36011	0.0064935	154
155	24,025	3,723,875	12.4499	5.37169	0.0064516	155
156	24,336	3,796,416	12.4900	5.38321	0.0064103	156
157	24,649	3,869,893	12.5300	5.39469	0.0063694	157
158	24,964	3,944,312	12.5698	5.40612	0.0063291	158
159	25,281	4,019,679	12.6095	5.41750	0.0062893	159
160	25,600	4,096,000	12.6491	5.42884	0.0062500	160
161	25,921	4,173,281	12.6886	5.44012	0.0062112	161
162	26,244	4,251,528	12.7279	5.45136	0.0061728	162
163	26,569	4,330,747	12.7671	5.46256	0.0061350	163
164	26,896	4,410,944	12.8062	5.47370	0.0060976	164
165	27,225	4,492,125	12.8452	5.48481	0.0060606	165
166	27,556	4,574,296	12.8841	5.49586	0.0060241	166
167	27,889	4,657,463	12.9228	5.50688	0.0059880	167
168	28,224	4,741,632	12.9615	5.51785	0.0059524	168
169	28,561	4,826,809	13.0000	5.52877	0.0059172	169
170	28,900	4,913,000	13.0384	5.53966	0.0058823	170
171	29,241	5,000,211	13.0767	5.55050	0.0058480	171
172	29,584	5,088,448	13.1149	5.56130	0.0058140	172
173	29,929	5,177,717	13.1529	5.57205	0.0057803	173
174	30,276	5,268,024	13.1909	5.58277	0.0057471	174
175	30,625	5,359,375	13.2288	5.59344	0.0057143	175
176	30,976	5,451,776	13.2665	5.60408	0.0056818	176
177	31,329	5,545,233	13.3041	5.61467	0.0056497	177
178	31,684	5,639,752	13.3417	5.62523	0.0056180	178
179	32,041	5,735,339	13.3791	5.63574	0.0055866	179
180	32,400	5,832,000	13.4164	5.64622	0.0055556	180
181	32,761	5,929,741	13.4536	5.65665	0.0055249	181
182	33,124	6,028,568	13.4907	5.66705	0.0054945	182
183	33,489	6,128,487	13.5277	5.67741	0.0054645	183
184	33,856	6,229,504	13.5647	5.68773	0.0054348	184
185	34,225	6,331,625	13.6015	5.69802	0.0054054	185
186	34,596	6,434,856	13.6382	5.70827	0.0053763	186
187	34,969	6,539,203	13.6748	5.71848	0.0053476	187
188	35,344	6,644,672	13.7113	5.72865	0.0053191	188
189	35,721	6,751,269	13.7477	5.73879	0.0052910	189
190	36,100	6,859,000	13.7840	5.74890	0.0052632	190
191	36,481	6,967,871	13.8203	5.75897	0.0052356	191
192	36,864	7,077,888	13.8564	5.76900	0.0052083	192
193	37,249	7,189,057	13.8924	5.77900	0.0051813	193
194	37,636	7,301,384	13.9284	5.78896	0.0051546	194
195	38,025	7,414,875	13.9642	5.79889	0.0051282	195
196	38,416	7,529,536	14.0000	5.80879	0.0051020	196
197	38,809	7,645,373	14.0357	5.81865	0.0050761	197
198	39,204	7,762,392	14.0712	5.82849	0.0050505	198
199	39,601	7,880,599	14.1067	5.83827	0.0050251	199
200	40,000	8,000,000	14.1421	5.84804	0.0050000	200

Powers, Roots and Reciprocals

No.	Square	Cube	Sq. Root	Cube Root	Reciprocal	No.
201	40,401	8,120,601	14.1774	5.85777	0.0049751	201
202	40,804	8,242,408	14.2127	5.86747	0.0049505	202
203	41,209	8,365,427	14.2478	5.87713	0.0049261	203
204	41,616	8,489,664	14.2829	5.88677	0.0049020	204
205	42,025	8,615,125	14.3178	5.89637	0.0048780	205
206	42,436	8,741,816	14.3527	5.90594	0.0048544	206
207	42,849	8,869,743	14.3875	5.91548	0.0048309	207
208	43,264	8,998,912	14.4222	5.92499	0.0048077	208
209	43,681	9,129,329	14.4568	5.93447	0.0047847	209
210	44,100	9,261,000	14.4914	5.94392	0.0047619	210
211	44,521	9,393,931	14.5258	5.95334	0.0047393	211
212	44,944	9,528,128	14.5602	5.96273	0.0047170	212
213	45,369	9,663,597	14.5945	5.97209	0.0046948	213
214	45,796	9,800,344	14.6287	5.98142	0.0046729	214
215	46,225	9,938,375	14.6629	5.99073	0.0046512	215
216	46,656	10,077,696	14.6969	6.00000	0.0046296	216
217	47,089	10,218,313	14.7309	6.00925	0.0046083	217
218	47,524	10,360,232	14.7648	6.01846	0.0045872	218
219	47,961	10,503,459	14.7986	6.02765	0.0045662	219
220	48,400	10,648,000	14.8324	6.03681	0.0045455	220
221	48,841	10,793,861	14.8661	6.04594	0.0045249	221
222	49,284	10,941,048	14.8997	6.05505	0.0045045	222
223	49,729	11,089,567	14.9332	6.06413	0.0044843	223
224	50,176	11,239,424	14.9666	6.07318	0.0044643	224
225	50,625	11,390,625	15.0000	6.08220	0.0044444	225
226	51,076	11,543,176	15.0333	6.09120	0.0044248	226
227	51,529	11,697,083	15.0665	6.10017	0.0044053	227
228	51,984	11,852,352	15.0997	6.10911	0.0043860	228
229	52,441	12,008,989	15.1327	6.11803	0.0043668	229
230	52,900	12,167,000	15.1658	6.12693	0.0043478	230
231	53,361	12,326,391	15.1987	6.13579	0.0043290	231
232	53,824	12,487,168	15.2315	6.14463	0.0043103	232
233	54,289	12,649,337	15.2643	6.15345	0.0042918	233
234	54,756	12,812,904	15.2971	6.16224	0.0042735	234
235	55,225	12,977,875	15.3297	6.17101	0.0042553	235
236	55,696	13,144,256	15.3623	6.17975	0.0042373	236
237	56,169	13,312,053	15.3948	6.18846	0.0042194	237
238	56,644	13,481,272	15.4272	6.19715	0.0042017	238
239	57,121	13,651,919	15.4596	6.20582	0.0041841	239
240	57,600	13,824,000	15.4919	6.21447	0.0041667	240
241	58,081	13,997,521	15.5242	6.22308	0.0041494	241
242	58,564	14,172,488	15.5563	6.23168	0.0041322	242
243	59,049	14,348,907	15.5885	6.24025	0.0041152	243
244	59,536	14,526,784	15.6205	6.24880	0.0040984	244
245	60,025	14,706,125	15.6525	6.25732	0.0040816	245
246	60,516	14,886,936	15.6844	6.26583	0.0040650	246
247	61,009	15,069,223	15.7162	6.27431	0.0040486	247
248	61,504	15,252,992	15.7480	6.28276	0.0040323	248
249	62,001	15,438,249	15.7797	6.29119	0.0040161	249
250	62,500	15,625,000	15.8114	6.29961	0.0040000	250

Powers, Roots and Reciprocals

No.	Square	Cube	Sq. Root	Cube Root	Reciprocal	No.
251	63,001	15,813,251	15.8430	6.30799	0.0039841	251
252	63,504	16,003,008	15.8745	6.31636	0.0039683	252
253	64,009	16,194,277	15.9060	6.32470	0.0039526	253
254	64,516	16,387,064	15.9374	6.33303	0.0039370	254
255	65,025	16,581,375	15.9687	6.34133	0.0039216	255
256	65,536	16,777,216	16.0000	6.34960	0.0039063	256
257	66,049	16,974,593	16.0312	6.35786	0.0038911	257
258	66,564	17,173,512	16.0624	6.36610	0.0038760	258
259	67,081	17,373,979	16.0935	6.37431	0.0038610	259
260	67,600	17,576,000	16.1245	6.38250	0.0038462	260
261	68,121	17,779,581	16.1555	6.39068	0.0038314	261
262	68,644	17,984,728	16.1864	6.39883	0.0038168	262
263	69,169	18,191,447	16.2173	6.40696	0.0038023	263
264	69,696	18,399,744	16.2481	6.41507	0.0037879	264
265	70,225	18,609,625	16.2788	6.42316	0.0037736	265
266	70,756	18,821,096	16.3095	6.43123	0.0037594	266
267	71,289	19,034,163	16.3401	6.43928	0.0037453	267
268	71,824	19,248,832	16.3707	6.44731	0.0037313	268
269	72,361	19,465,109	16.4012	6.45531	0.0037175	269
270	72,900	19,683,000	16.4317	6.46330	0.0037037	270
271	73,441	19,902,511	16.4621	6.47127	0.0036900	271
272	73,984	20,123,648	16.4924	6.47922	0.0036765	272
273	74,529	20,346,417	16.5227	6.48715	0.0036630	273
274	75,076	20,570,824	16.5529	6.49507	0.0036496	274
275	75,625	20,796,875	16.5831	6.50296	0.0036364	275
276	76,176	21,024,576	16.6132	6.51083	0.0036232	276
277	76,729	21,253,933	16.6433	6.51868	0.0036101	277
278	77,284	21,484,952	16.6733	6.52652	0.0035971	278
279	77,841	21,717,639	16.7033	6.53434	0.0035842	279
280	78,400	21,952,000	16.7332	6.54213	0.0035714	280
281	78,961	22,188,041	16.7631	6.54991	0.0035587	281
282	79,524	22,425,768	16.7929	6.55767	0.0035461	282
283	80,089	22,665,187	16.8226	6.56541	0.0035336	283
284	80,656	22,906,304	16.8523	6.57314	0.0035211	284
285	81,225	23,149,125	16.8819	6.58084	0.0035088	285
286	81,796	23,393,656	16.9115	6.58853	0.0034965	286
287	82,369	23,639,903	16.9411	6.59620	0.0034843	287
288	82,944	23,887,872	16.9706	6.60385	0.0034722	288
289	83,521	24,137,569	17.0000	6.61149	0.0034602	289
290	84,100	24,389,000	17.0294	6.61911	0.0034483	290
291	84,681	24,642,171	17.0587	6.62671	0.0034364	291
292	85,264	24,897,088	17.0880	6.63429	0.0034247	292
293	85,849	25,153,757	17.1172	6.64185	0.0034130	293
294	86,436	25,412,184	17.1464	6.64940	0.0034014	294
295	87,025	25,672,375	17.1756	6.65693	0.0033898	295
296	87,616	25,934,336	17.2047	6.66444	0.0033784	296
297	88,209	26,198,073	17.2337	6.67194	0.0033670	297
298	88,804	26,463,592	17.2627	6.67942	0.0033557	298
299	89,401	26,730,899	17.2916	6.68688	0.0033445	299
300	90,000	27,000,000	17.3205	6.69433	0.0033333	300

Powers, Roots and Reciprocals

No.	Square	Cube	Sq. Root	Cube Root	Reciprocal	No.
301	90,601	27,270,901	17.3494	6.70176	0.0033223	301
302	91,204	27,543,608	17.3781	6.70917	0.0033113	302
303	91,809	27,818,127	17.4069	6.71657	0.0033003	303
304	92,416	28,094,464	17.4356	6.72395	0.0032895	304
305	93,025	28,372,625	17.4642	6.73132	0.0032787	305
306	93,636	28,652,616	17.4929	6.73866	0.0032680	306
307	94,249	28,934,443	17.5214	6.74600	0.0032573	307
308	94,864	29,218,112	17.5499	6.75331	0.0032468	308
309	95,481	29,503,629	17.5784	6.76061	0.0032362	309
310	96,100	29,791,000	17.6068	6.76790	0.0032258	310
311	96,721	30,080,231	17.6352	6.77517	0.0032154	311
312	97,344	30,371,328	17.6635	6.78242	0.0032051	312
313	97,969	30,664,297	17.6918	6.78966	0.0031949	313
314	98,596	30,959,144	17.7200	6.79688	0.0031847	314
315	99,225	31,255,875	17.7482	6.80409	0.0031746	315
316	99,856	31,554,496	17.7764	6.81128	0.0031646	316
317	100,489	31,855,013	17.8045	6.81846	0.0031546	317
318	101,124	32,157,432	17.8326	6.82562	0.0031447	318
319	101,761	32,461,759	17.8606	6.83277	0.0031348	319
320	102,400	32,768,000	17.8885	6.83990	0.0031250	320
321	103,041	33,076,161	17.9165	6.84702	0.0031153	321
322	103,684	33,386,248	17.9444	6.85412	0.0031056	322
323	104,329	33,698,267	17.9722	6.86121	0.0030960	323
324	104,976	34,012,224	18.0000	6.86829	0.0030864	324
325	105,625	34,328,125	18.0278	6.87534	0.0030769	325
326	106,276	34,645,976	18.0555	6.88239	0.0030675	326
327	106,929	34,965,783	18.0831	6.88942	0.0030581	327
328	107,584	35,287,552	18.1108	6.89643	0.0030488	328
329	108,241	35,611,289	18.1384	6.90344	0.0030395	329
330	108,900	35,937,000	18.1659	6.91042	0.0030303	330
331	109,561	36,264,691	18.1934	6.91740	0.0030211	331
332	110,224	36,594,368	18.2209	6.92436	0.0030120	332
333	110,889	36,926,037	18.2483	6.93131	0.0030030	333
334	111,556	37,259,704	18.2757	6.93823	0.0029940	334
335	112,225	37,595,375	18.3030	6.94515	0.0029851	335
336	112,896	37,933,056	18.3303	6.95205	0.0029762	336
337	113,569	38,272,753	18.3576	6.95894	0.0029674	337
338	114,244	38,614,472	18.3848	6.96582	0.0029586	338
339	114,921	38,958,219	18.4120	6.97268	0.0029499	339
340	115,600	39,304,000	18.4391	6.97953	0.0029412	340
341	116,281	39,651,821	18.4662	6.98637	0.0029326	341
342	116,964	40,001,688	18.4932	6.99319	0.0029240	342
343	117,649	40,353,607	18.5203	7.00000	0.0029155	343
344	118,336	40,707,584	18.5472	7.00680	0.0029070	344
345	119,025	41,063,625	18.5742	7.01358	0.0028986	345
346	119,716	41,421,736	18.6011	7.02035	c.0028902	346
347	120,409	41,781,923	18.6279	7.02711	0.0028818	347
348	121,104	42,144,192	18.6548	7.03385	0.0028736	348
349	121,801	42,508,549	18.6815	7.04059	0.0028653	349
350	122,500	42,875,000	18.7083	7.04730	0.0028571	350

Powers, Roots and Reciprocals

No.	Square	Cube	Sq. Root	Cube Root	Reciprocal	No.
351	123,201	43,243,551	18.7350	7.05400	0.0028490	351
352	123,904	43,614,208	18.7617	7.06070	0.0028409	352
353	124,609	43,986,977	18.7883	7.06738	0.0028329	353
354	125,316	44,361,864	18.8149	7.07404	0.0028249	354
355	126,025	44,738,875	18.8414	7.08070	0.0028169	355
356	126,736	45,118,016	18.8680	7.08734	0.0028090	356
357	127,449	45,499,293	18.8944	7.09397	0.0028011	357
358	128,164	45,882,712	18.9209	7.10059	0.0027933	358
359	128,881	46,268,279	18.9473	7.10719	0.0027855	359
360	129,600	46,656,000	18.9737	7.11379	0.0027778	360
361	130,321	47,045,881	19.0000	7.12037	0.0027701	361
362	131,044	47,437,928	19.0263	7.12694	0.0027624	362
363	131,769	47,832,147	19.0526	7.13349	0.0027548	363
364	132,496	48,228,544	19.0788	7.14004	0.0027473	364
365	133,225	48,627,125	19.1050	7.14657	0.0027397	365
366	133,956	49,027,896	19.1311	7.15309	0.0027322	366
367	134,689	49,430,863	19.1572	7.15960	0.0027248	367
368	135,424	49,836,032	19.1833	7.16610	0.0027174	368
369	136,161	50,243,409	19.2094	7.17258	0.0027100	369
370	136,900	50,653,000	19.2354	7.17905	0.0027027	370
371	137,641	51,064,811	19.2614	7.18552	0.0026954	371
372	138,384	51,478,848	19.2873	7.19197	0.0026882	372
373	139,129	51,895,117	19.3132	7.19841	0.0026810	373
374	139,876	52,313,624	19.3391	7.20483	0.0026738	374
375	140,625	52,734,375	19.3649	7.21125	0.0026667	375
376	141,376	53,157,376	19.3907	7.21765	0.0026596	376
377	142,129	53,582,633	19.4165	7.22405	0.0026525	377
378	142,884	54,010,152	19.4422	7.23043	0.0026455	378
379	143,641	54,439,939	19.4679	7.23680	0.0026385	379
380	144,400	54,872,000	19.4936	7.24316	0.0026316	380
381	145,161	55,306,341	19.5192	7.24950	0.0026247	381
382	145,924	55,742,968	19.5448	7.25584	0.0026178	382
383	146,689	56,181,887	19.5704	7.26217	0.0026110	383
384	147,456	56,623,104	19.5959	7.26848	0.0026042	384
385	148,225	57,066,625	19.6214	7.27479	0.0025974	385
386	148,996	57,512,456	19.6469	7.28108	0.0025907	386
387	149,769	57,960,603	19.6723	7.28736	0.0025840	387
388	150,544	58,411,072	19.6977	7.29363	0.0025773	388
389	151,321	58,863,869	19.7231	7.29989	0.0025707	389
390	152,100	59,319,000	19.7484	7.30614	0.0025641	390
391	152,881	59,776,471	19.7737	7.31238	0.0025575	391
392	153,664	60,236,288	19.7990	7.31861	0.0025510	392
393	154,449	60,698,457	19.8242	7.32483	0.0025445	393
394	155,236	61,162,984	19.8494	7.33104	0.0025381	394
395	156,025	61,629,875	19.8746	7.33723	0.0025316	395
396	156,816	62,099,136	19.8997	7.34342	0.0025253	396
397	157,609	62,570,773	19.9249	7.34960	0.0025189	397
398	158,404	63,044,792	19.9499	7.35576	0.0025126	398
399	159,201	63,521,199	19.9750	7.36192	0.0025063	399
400	160,000	64,000,000	20.0000	7.36806	0.0025000	400

Powers, Roots and Reciprocals

No.	Square	Cube	Sq. Root	Cube Root	Reciprocal	No.
401	160,801	64,481,201	20.0250	7.37420	0.0024938	401
402	161,604	64,964,808	20.0499	7.38032	0.0024876	402
403	162,409	65,450,827	20.0749	7.38644	0.0024814	403
404	163,216	65,939,264	20.0998	7.39254	0.0024752	404
405	164,025	66,430,125	20.1246	7.39864	0.0024691	405
406	164,836	66,923,416	20.1494	7.40472	0.0024631	406
407	165,649	67,419,143	20.1742	7.41080	0.0024570	407
408	166,464	67,917,312	20.1990	7.41686	0.0024510	408
409	167,281	68,417,929	20.2237	7.42291	0.0024450	409
410	168,100	68,921,000	20.2485	7.42896	0.0024390	410
411	168,921	69,426,531	20.2731	7.43499	0.0024331	411
412	169,744	69,934,528	20.2978	7.44102	0.0024272	412
413	170,569	70,444,997	20.3224	7.44703	0.0024213	413
414	171,396	70,957,944	20.3470	7.45304	0.0024155	414
415	172,225	71,473,375	20.3715	7.45904	0.0024096	415
416	173,056	71,991,296	20.3961	7.46502	0.0024038	416
417	173,889	72,511,713	20.4206	7.47100	0.0023981	417
418	174,724	73,034,632	20.4450	7.47697	0.0023923	418
419	175,561	73,560,059	20.4695	7.48292	0.0023866	419
420	176,400	74,088,000	20.4939	7.48887	0.0023810	420
421	177,241	74,618,461	20.5183	7.49481	0.0023753	421
422	178,084	75,151,448	20.5426	7.50074	0.0023697	422
423	178,929	75,686,967	20.5670	7.50666	0.0023641	423
424	179,776	76,225,024	20.5913	7.51257	0.0023585	424
425	180,625	76,765,625	20.6155	7.51847	0.0023529	425
426	181,476	77,308,776	20.6398	7.52437	0.0023474	426
427	182,329	77,854,483	20.6640	7.53025	0.0023419	427
428	183,184	78,402,752	20.6882	7.53612	0.0023364	428
429	184,041	78,953,589	20.7123	7.54199	0.0023310	429
430	184,900	79,507,000	20.7364	7.54784	0.0023256	430
431	185,761	80,062,991	20.7605	7.55369	0.0023202	431
432	186,624	80,621,568	20.7846	7.55953	0.0023148	432
433	187,489	81,182,737	20.8087	7.56535	0.0023095	433
434	188,356	81,746,504	20.8327	7.57117	0.0023041	434
435	189,225	82,312,875	20.8567	7.57698	0.0022989	435
436	190,096	82,881,856	20.8806	7.58279	0.0022936	436
437	190,969	83,453,453	20.9045	7.58858	0.0022883	437
438	191,844	84,027,672	20.9284	7.59436	0.0022831	438
439	192,721	84,604,519	20.9523	7.60014	0.0022779	439
440	193,600	85,184,000	20.9762	7.60590	0.0022727	440
441	194,481	85,766,121	21.0000	7.61166	0.0022676	441
442	195,364	86,350,888	21.0238	7.61741	0.0022624	442
443	196,249	86,938,307	21.0476	7.62315	0.0022573	443
444	197,136	87,528,384	21.0713	7.62888	0.0022523	444
445	198,025	88,121,125	21.0950	7.63461	0.0022472	445
446	198,916	88,716,536	21.1187	7.64032	0.0022422	446
447	199,809	89,314,623	21.1424	7.64603	0.0022371	447
448	200,704	89,915,392	21.1660	7.65172	0.0022321	448
449	201,601	90,518,849	21.1896	7.65741	0.0022272	449
450	202,500	91,125,000	21.2132	7.66309	0.0022222	450

Powers, Roots and Reciprocals

No.	Square	Cube	Sq. Root	Cube Root	Reciprocal	No.
451	203,401	91,733,851	21.2368	7.66877	0.0022173	451
452	204,304	92,345,408	21.2603	7.67443	0.0022124	452
453	205,209	92,959,677	21.2838	7.68009	0.0022075	453
454	206,116	93,576,664	21.3073	7.68573	0.0022026	454
455	207,025	94,196,375	21.3307	7.69137	0.0021978	455
456	207,936	94,818,816	21.3542	7.69700	0.0021930	456
457	208,849	95,443,993	21.3776	7.70262	0.0021882	457
458	209,764	96,071,912	21.4009	7.70824	0.0021834	458
459	210,681	96,702,579	21.4243	7.71384	0.0021786	459
460	211,600	97,336,000	21.4476	7.71944	0.0021739	460
461	212,521	97,972,181	21.4709	7.72503	0.0021692	461
462	213,444	98,611,128	21.4942	7.73061	0.0021645	462
463	214,369	99,252,847	21.5174	7.73619	0.0021598	463
464	215,296	99,897,344	21.5407	7.74175	0.0021552	464
465	216,225	100,544,625	21.5639	7.74731	0.0021505	465
466	217,156	101,194,696	21.5870	7.75286	0.0021459	466
467	218,089	101,847,563	21.6102	7.75840	0.0021413	467
468	219,024	102,503,232	21.6333	7.76394	0.0021368	468
469	219,961	103,161,709	21.6564	7.76946	0.0021322	469
470	220,900	103,823,000	21.6795	7.77498	0.0021277	470
471	221,841	104,487,111	21.7025	7.78049	0.0021231	471
472	222,784	105,154,048	21.7256	7.78599	0.0021186	472
473	223,729	105,823,817	21.7486	7.79149	0.0021142	473
474	224,676	106,496,424	21.7715	7.79697	0.0021097	474
475	225,625	107,171,875	21.7945	7.80245	0.0021053	475
476	226,576	107,850,176	21.8174	7.80793	0.0021008	476
477	227,529	108,531,333	21.8403	7.81339	0.0020964	477
478	228,484	109,215,352	21.8632	7.81885	0.0020921	478
479	229,441	109,902,239	21.8861	7.82429	0.0020877	479
480	230,400	110,592,000	21.9089	7.82974	0.0020833	480
481	231,361	111,284,641	21.9317	7.83517	0.0020790	481
482	232,324	111,980,168	21.9545	7.84059	0.0020747	482
483	233,289	112,678,587	21.9773	7.84601	0.0020704	483
484	234,256	113,379,904	22.0000	7.85142	0.0020661	484
485	235,225	114,084,125	22.0227	7.85683	0.0020619	485
486	236,196	114,791,256	22.0454	7.86222	0.0020576	486
487	237,169	115,501,303	22.0681	7.86761	0.0020534	487
488	238,144	116,214,272	22.0907	7.87299	0.0020492	488
489	239,121	116,930,169	22.1133	7.87837	0.0020450	489
490	240,100	117,649,000	22.1359	7.88374	0.0020408	490
491	241,081	118,370,771	22.1585	7.88909	0.0020367	491
492	242,064	119,095,488	22.1811	7.89445	0.0020325	492
493	243,049	119,823,157	22.2036	7.89979	0.0020284	493
494	244,036	120,553,784	22.2261	7.90513	0.0020243	494
495	245,025	121,287,375	22.2486	7.91046	0.0020202	495
496	246,016	122,023,936	22.2711	7.91578	0.0020161	496
497	247,009	122,763,473	22.2935	7.92110	0.0020121	497
498	248,004	123,505,992	22.3159	7.92641	0.0020080	498
499	249,001	124,251,499	22.3383	7.93171	0.0020040	499
500	250,000	125,000,000	22.3607	7.93701	0.0020000	500

Powers, Roots and Reciprocals

No.	Square	Cube	Sq. Root	Cube Root	Reciprocal	No.
501	251,001	125,751,501	22.3830	7.94229	0.0019960	501
502	252,004	126,506,008	22.4054	7.94757	0.0019920	502
503	253,009	127,263,527	22.4277	7.95285	0.0019881	503
504	254,016	128,024,064	22.4499	7.95811	0.0019841	504
505	255,025	128,787,625	22.4722	7.96337	0.0019802	505
506	256,036	129,554,216	22.4944	7.96863	0.0019763	506
507	257,049	130,323,843	22.5167	7.97387	0.0019724	507
508	258,064	131,096,512	22.5389	7.97911	0.0019685	508
509	259,081	131,872,229	22.5610	7.98434	0.0019646	509
510	260,100	132,651,000	22.5832	7.98957	0.0019608	510
511	261,121	133,432,831	22.6053	7.99479	0.0019569	511
512	262,144	134,217,728	22.6274	8.00000	0.0019531	512
513	263,169	135,005,697	22.6495	8.00520	0.0019493	513
514	264,196	135,796,744	22.6716	8.01040	0.0019455	514
515	265,225	136,590,875	22.6936	8.01559	0.0019417	515
516	266,256	137,388,096	22.7156	8.02078	0.0019380	516
517	267,289	138,188,413	22.7376	8.02596	0.0019342	517
518	268,324	138,991,832	22.7596	8.03113	0.0019305	518
519	269,361	139,798,359	22.7816	8.03629	0.0019268	519
520	270,400	140,608,000	22.8035	8.04145	0.0019231	520
521	271,441	141,420,761	22.8254	8.04660	0.0019194	521
522	272,484	142,236,648	22.8473	8.05175	0.0019157	522
523	273,529	143,055,667	22.8692	8.05689	0.0019120	523
524	274,576	143,877,824	22.8910	8.06202	0.0019084	524
525	275,625	144,703,125	22.9129	8.06714	0.0019048	525
526	276,676	145,531,576	22.9347	8.07226	0.0019011	526
527	277,729	146,363,183	22.9565	8.07737	0.0018975	527
528	278,784	147,197,952	22.9783	8.08248	0.0018939	528
529	279,841	148,035,889	23.0000	8.08758	0.0018904	529
530	280,900	148,877,000	23.0217	8.09267	0.0018868	530
531	281,961	149,721,291	23.0434	8.09776	0.0018832	531
532	283,024	150,568,768	23.0651	8.10284	0.0018797	532
533	284,089	151,419,437	23.0868	8.10791	0.0018762	533
534	285,156	152,273,304	23.1084	8.11298	0.0018727	534
535	286,225	153,130,375	23.1301	8.11804	0.0018692	535
536	287,296	153,990,656	23.1517	8.12310	0.0018657	536
537	288,369	154,854,153	23.1733	8.12814	0.0018622	537
538	289,444	155,720,872	23.1948	8.13319	0.0018587	538
539	290,521	156,590,819	23.2164	8.13822	0.0018553	539
540	291,600	157,464,000	23.2379	8.14325	0.0018519	540
541	292,681	158,340,421	23.2594	8.14828	0.0018484	541
542	293,764	159,220,088	23.2809	8.15329	0.0018450	542
543	294,849	160,103,007	23.3024	8.15831	0.0018416	543
544	295,936	160,989,184	23.3238	8.16331	0.0018382	544
545	297,025	161,878,625	23.3452	8.16831	0.0018349	545
546	298,116	162,771,336	23.3666	8.17330	0.0018315	546
547	299,209	163,667,323	23.3880	8.17829	0.0018282	547
548	300,304	164,566,592	23.4094	8.18327	0.0018248	548
549	301,401	165,469,149	23.4307	8.18824	0.0018215	549
550	302,500	166,375,000	23.4521	8.19321	0.0018182	550

Powers, Roots and Reciprocals

No.	Square	Cube	Sq. Root	Cube Root	Reciprocal	No.
551	303,601	167,284,151	23.4734	8.19818	0.0018149	551
552	304,704	168,196,608	23.4947	8.20313	0.0018116	552
553	305,809	169,112,377	23.5160	8.20808	0.0018083	553
554	306,916	170,031,464	23.5372	8.21303	0.0018051	554
555	308,025	170,953,875	23.5584	8.21797	0.0018018	555
556	309,136	171,879,616	23.5797	8.22290	0.0017986	556
557	310,249	172,808,693	23.5008	8.22783	0.0017953	557
558	311,364	173,741,112	23.6220	8.23275	0.0017921	558
559	312,481	174,676,879	23.6432	8.23766	0.0017889	559
560	313,600	175,616,000	23.6643	8.24257	0.0017857	560
561	314,721	176,558,481	23.6854	8.24747	0.0017825	561
562	315,844	177,504,328	23.7065	8.25237	0.0017794	562
563	316,969	178,453,547	23.7276	8.25726	0.0017762	563
564	318,096	179,406,144	23.7487	8.26215	0.0017731	564
565	319,225	180,362,125	23.7697	8.26703	0.0017699	565
566	320,356	181,321,496	23.7908	8.27190	0.0017668	566
567	321,489	182,284,263	23.8118	8.27677	0.0017637	567
568	322,624	183,250,432	23.8328	8.28163	0.0017606	568
569	323,761	184,220,009	23.8537	8.28649	0.0017575	569
570	324,900	185,193,000	23.8747	8.29134	0.0017544	570
571	326,041	186,169,411	23.8956	8.29619	0.0017513	571
572	327,184	187,149,248	23.9165	8.30103	0.0017483	572
573	328,329	188,132,517	23.9374	8.30587	0.0017452	573
574	329,476	189,119,224	23.9583	8.31069	0.0017422	574
575	330,625	190,109,375	23.9792	8.31552	0.0017391	575
576	331,776	191,102,976	24.0000	8.32034	0.0017361	576
577	332,929	192,100,033	24.0208	8.32515	0.0017331	577
578	334,084	193,100,552	24.0416	8.32995	0.0017301	578
579	335,241	194,104,539	24.0624	8.33476	0.0017271	579
580	336,400	195,112,000	24.0832	8.33955	0.0017241	580
581	337,561	196,122,941	24.1039	8.34434	0.0017212	581
582	338,724	197,137,368	24.1247	8.34913	0.0017182	582
583	339,889	198,155,287	24.1454	8.35390	0.0017153	583
584	341,056	199,176,704	24.1661	8.35868	0.0017123	584
585	342,225	200,201,625	24.1868	8.36345	0.0017094	585
586	343,396	201,230,056	24.2074	8.36821	0.0017065	586
587	344,569	202,262,003	24.2281	8.37297	0.0017036	587
588	345,744	203,297,472	24.2487	8.37772	0.0017007	588
589	346,921	204,336,469	24.2693	8.38247	0.0016978	589
590	348,100	205,379,000	24.2899	8.38721	0.0016949	590
591	349,281	206,425,071	24.3105	8.39194	0.0016920	591
592	350,464	207,474,688	24.3311	8.39667	0.0016892	592
593	351,649	208,527,857	24.3516	8.40140	0.0016863	593
594	352,836	209,584,584	24.3721	8.40612	0.0016835	594
595	354,025	210,644,875	24.3926	8.41083	0.0016807	595
596	355,216	211,708,736	24.4131	8.41554	0.0016779	596
597	356,409	212,776,173	24.4336	8.42025	0.0016750	597
598	357,604	213,847,192	24.4540	8.42494	0.0016722	598
599	358,801	214,921,799	24.4745	8.42964	0.0016694	599
600	360,000	216,000,000	24.4949	8.43433	0.0016667	600

Powers, Roots and Reciprocals

No.	Square	Cube	Sq. Root	Cube Root	Reciprocal	No.
601	361,201	217,081,801	24.5153	8.43901	0.0016639	601
602	362,404	218,167,208	24.5357	8.44369	0.0016611	602
603	363,609	219,256,227	24.5561	8.44836	0.0016584	603
604	364,816	220,348,864	24.5764	8.45303	0.0016556	604
605	366,025	221,445,125	24.5967	8.45769	0.0016529	605
606	367,236	222,545,016	24.6171	8.46235	0.0016502	606
607	368,449	223,648,543	24.6374	8.46700	0.0016474	607
608	369,664	224,755,712	24.6577	8.47165	0.0016447	608
609	370,881	225,866,529	24.6779	8.47629	0.0016420	609
610	372,100	226,981,000	24.6982	8.48093	0.0016393	610
611	373,321	228,099,131	24.7184	8.48556	0.0016367	611
612	374,544	229,220,928	24.7386	8.49018	0.0016340	612
613	375,769	230,346,397	24.7588	8.49481	0.0016313	613
614	376,996	231,475,544	24.7790	8.49942	0.0016287	614
615	378,225	232,608,375	24.7992	8.50404	0.0016260	615
616	379,456	233,744,896	24.8193	8.50864	0.0016234	616
617	380,689	234,885,113	24.8395	8.51324	0.0016207	617
618	381,924	236,029,032	24.8596	8.51784	0.0016181	618
619	383,161	237,176,659	24.8797	8.52243	0.0016155	619
620	384,400	238,328,000	24.8998	8.52702	0.0016129	620
621	385,641	239,483,061	24.9199	8.53160	0.0016103	621
622	386,884	240,641,848	24.9399	8.53618	0.0016077	622
623	388,129	241,804,367	24.9600	8.54075	0.0016051	623
624	389,376	242,970,624	24.9800	8.54532	0.0016026	624
625	390,625	244,140,625	25.0000	8.54988	0.0016000	625
626	391,876	245,314,376	25.0200	8.55444	0.0015974	626
627	393,129	246,491,883	25.0400	8.55899	0.0015949	627
628	394,384	247,673,152	25.0599	8.56354	0.0015924	628
629	395,641	248,858,189	25.0799	8.56808	0.0015898	629
630	396,900	250,047,000	25.0998	8.57262	0.0015873	630
631	398,161	251,239,591	25.1197	8.57715	0.0015848	631
632	399,424	252,435,968	25.1396	8.58168	0.0015823	632
633	400,689	253,636,137	25.1595	8.58620	0.0015798	633
634	401,956	254,840,104	25.1794	8.59072	0.0015773	634
635	403,225	256,047,875	25.1992	8.59524	0.0015748	635
636	404,496	257,259,456	25.2190	8.59975	0.0015723	636
637	405,769	258,474,853	25.2389	8.60425	0.0015699	637
638	407,044	259,694,072	25.2587	8.60875	0.0015674	638
639	408,321	260,917,119	25.2784	8.61325	0.0015649	639
640	409,600	262,144,000	25.2982	8.61774	0.0015625	640
641	410,881	263,374,721	25.3180	8.62222	0.0015601	641
642	412,164	264,609,288	25.3377	8.62671	0.0015576	642
643	413,449	265,847,707	25.3574	8.63118	0.0015552	643
644	414,736	267,089,984	25.3772	8.63566	0.0015528	644
645	416,025	268,336,125	25.3969	8.64012	0.0015504	645
646	417,316	269,586,136	25.4165	8.64459	0.0015480	646
647	418,609	270,840,023	25.4362	8.64904	0.0015456	647
648	419,904	272,097,792	25.4558	8.65350	0.0015432	648
649	421,201	273,359,449	25.4755	8.65795	0.0015408	649
650	422,500	274,625,000	25.4951	8.66239	0.0015385	650

Powers, Roots and Reciprocals

No.	Square	Cube	Sq. Root	Cube Root	Reciprocal	No.
651	423,801	275,894,451	25.5147	8.66683	0.0015361	651
652	425,104	277,167,808	25.5343	8.67127	0.0015337	652
653	426,409	278,445,077	25.5539	8.67570	0.0015314	653
654	427,716	279,726,264	25.5734	8.68012	0.0015291	654
655	429,025	281,011,375	25.5930	8.68455	0.0015267	655
656	430,336	282,300,416	25.6125	8.68896	0.0015244	656
657	431,649	283,593,393	25.6320	8.69338	0.0015221	657
658	432,964	284,890,312	25.6515	8.69778	0.0015198	658
659	434,281	286,191,179	25.6710	8.70219	0.0015175	659
660	435,600	287,496,000	25.6905	8.70659	0.0015152	660
661	436,921	288,804,781	25.7099	8.71098	0.0015129	661
662	438,244	290,117,528	25.7294	8.71537	0.0015106	662
663	439,569	291,434,247	25.7488	8.71976	0.0015083	663
664	440,896	292,754,944	25.7682	8.72414	0.0015060	664
665	442,225	294,079,625	25.7876	8.72852	0.0015038	665
666	443,556	295,408,296	25.8070	8.73289	0.0015015	666
667	444,889	296,740,963	25.8263	8.73726	0.0014993	667
668	446,224	298,077,632	25.8457	8.74162	0.0014970	668
669	447,561	299,418,309	25.8650	8.74598	0.0014948	669
670	448,900	300,763,000	25.8844	8.75034	0.0014925	670
671	450,241	302,111,711	25.9037	8.75469	0.0014903	671
672	451,584	303,464,448	25.9230	8.75904	0.0014881	672
673	452,929	304,821,217	25.9422	8.76338	0.0014859	673
674	454,276	306,182,024	25.9615	8.76772	0.0014837	674
675	455,625	307,546,875	25.9808	8.77205	0.0014815	675
676	456,976	308,915,776	26.0000	8.77638	0.0014793	676
677	458,329	310,288,733	26.0192	8.78071	0.0014771	677
678	459,684	311,665,752	26.0384	8.78503	0.0014749	678
679	461,041	313,046,839	26.0576	8.78935	0.0014728	679
680	462,400	314,432,000	26.0768	8.79366	0.0014706	680
681	463,761	315,821,241	26.0960	8.79797	0.0014684	681
682	465,124	317,214,568	26.1151	8.80227	0.0014663	682
683	466,489	318,611,987	26.1343	8.80657	0.0014641	683
684	467,856	320,013,504	26.1534	8.81087	0.0014620	684
685	469,225	321,419,125	26.1725	8.81516	0.0014599	685
686	470,596	322,828,856	26.1916	8.81945	0.0014577	686
687	471,969	324,242,703	26.2107	8.82373	0.0014556	687
688	473,344	325,660,672	26.2298	8.82801	0.0014535	688
689	474,721	327,082,769	26.2488	8.83229	0.0014514	689
690	476,100	328,509,000	26.2679	8.83656	0.0014493	690
691	477,481	329,939,371	26.2869	8.84082	0.0014472	691
692	478,864	331,373,888	26.3059	8.84509	0.0014451	692
693	480,249	332,812,557	26.3249	8.84934	0.0014430	693
694	481,636	334,255,384	26.3439	8.85360	0.0014409	694
695	483,025	335,702,375	26.3629	8.85785	0.0014388	695
696	484,416	337,153,536	26.3818	8.86210	0.0014368	696
697	485,809	338,608,873	26.4008	8.86634	0.0014347	697
698	487,204	340,068,392	26.4197	8.87058	0.0014327	698
699	488,601	341,532,099	26.4386	8.87481	0.0014306	699
700	490,000	343,000,000	26.4575	8.87904	0.0014286	700

Powers, Roots and Reciprocals

No.	Square	Cube	Sq. Root	Cube Root	Reciprocal	No.
701	491,401	344,472,101	26.4764	8.88327	0.0014265	701
702	492,804	345,948,408	26.4953	8.88749	0.0014245	702
703	494,209	347,428,927	26.5141	8.89171	0.0014225	703
704	495,616	348,913,664	26.5330	8.89592	0.0014205	704
705	497,025	350,402,625	26.5518	8.90013	0.0014184	705
706	498,436	351,895,816	26.5707	8.90434	0.0014164	706
707	499,849	353,393,243	26.5895	8.90854	0.0014144	707
708	501,264	354,894,912	26.6083	8.91274	0.0014124	708
709	502,681	356,400,829	26.6271	8.91693	0.0014104	709
710	504,100	357,911,000	26.6458	8.92112	0.0014085	710
711	505,521	359,425,431	26.6646	8.92531	0.0014065	711
712	506,944	360,944,128	26.6833	8.92949	0.0014045	712
713	508,369	362,467,097	26.7021	8.93367	0.0014025	713
714	509,796	363,994,344	26.7208	8.93784	0.0014006	714
715	511,225	365,525,875	26.7395	8.94201	0.0013986	715
716	512,656	367,061,696	26.7582	8.94618	0.0013966	716
717	514,089	368,601,813	26.7769	8.95034	0.0013947	717
718	515,524	370,146,232	26.7955	8.95450	0.0013928	718
719	516,961	371,694,959	26.8142	8.95866	0.0013908	719
720	518,400	373,248,000	26.8328	8.96281	0.0013889	720
721	519,841	374,805,361	26.8514	8.96696	0.0013870	721
722	521,284	376,367,048	26.8701	8.97110	0.0013850	722
723	522,729	377,933,067	26.8887	8.97524	0.0013831	723
724	524,176	379,503,424	26.9072	8.97938	0.0013812	724
725	525,625	381,078,125	26.9258	8.98351	0.0013793	725
726	527,076	382,657,176	26.9444	8.98764	0.0013774	726
727	528,529	384,240,583	26.9629	8.99176	0.0013755	727
728	529,984	385,828,352	26.9815	8.99589	0.0013736	728
729	531,441	387,420,489	27.0000	9.00000	0.0013717	729
730	532,900	389,017,000	27.0185	9.00411	0.0013699	730
731	534,361	390,617,891	27.0370	9.00822	0.0013680	731
732	535,824	392,223,168	27.0555	9.01233	0.0013661	732
733	537,289	393,832,837	27.0740	9.01643	0.0013643	733
734	538,756	395,446,904	27.0924	9.02053	0.0013624	734
735	540,225	397,065,375	27.1109	9.02462	0.0013605	735
736	541,696	398,688,256	27.1293	9.02871	0.0013587	736
737	543,169	400,315,553	27.1477	9.03280	0.0013569	737
738	544,644	401,947,272	27.1662	9.03689	0.0013550	738
739	546,121	403,583,419	27.1846	9.04097	0.0013532	739
740	547,600	405,224,000	27.2029	9.04504	0.0013514	740
741	549,081	406,869,021	27.2213	9.04911	0.0013495	741
742	550,564	408,518,488	27.2397	9.05318	0.0013477	742
743	552,049	410,172,407	27.2580	9.05725	0.0013459	743
744	553,536	411,830,784	27.2764	9.06131	0.0013441	744
745	555,025	413,493,625	27.2947	9.06537	0.0013423	745
746	556,516	415,160,936	27.3130	9.06942	0.0013405	746
747	558,009	416,832,723	27.3313	9.07347	0.0013387	747
748	559,504	418,508,992	27.3496	9.07752	0.0013369	748
749	561,001	420,189,749	27.3679	9.08156	0.0013351	749
750	562,500	421,875,000	27.3861	9.08560	0.0013333	750

Powers, Roots and Reciprocals

No.	Square	Cube	Sq. Root	Cube Root	Reciprocal	No.
751	564,001	423,564,751	27.4044	9.08964	0.0013316	751
752	565,504	425,259,008	27.4226	9.09367	0.0013298	752
753	567,009	426,957,777	27.4408	9.09770	0.0013280	753
754	568,516	428,661,064	27.4591	9.10173	0.0013263	754
755	570,025	430,368,875	27.4773	9.10575	0.0013245	755
756	571,536	432,081,216	27.4955	9.10977	0.0013228	756
757	573,049	433,798,093	27.5136	9.11378	0.0013210	757
758	574,564	435,519,512	27.5318	9.11779	0.0013193	758
759	576,081	437,245,479	27.5500	9.12180	0.0013175	759
760	577,600	438,976,000	27.5681	9.12581	0.0013158	760
761	579,121	440,711,081	27.5862	9.12981	0.0013141	761
762	580,644	442,450,728	27.6043	9.13380	0.0013123	762
763	582,169	444,194,947	27.6225	9.13780	0.0013106	763
764	583,696	445,943,744	27.6405	9.14179	0.0013089	764
765	585,225	447,697,125	27.6586	9.14577	0.0013072	765
766	586,756	449,455,096	27.6767	9.14976	0.0013055	766
767	588,289	451,217,663	27.6948	9.15374	0.0013038	767
768	589,824	452,984,832	27.7128	9.15771	0.0013021	768
769	591,361	454,756,609	27.7308	9.16169	0.0013004	769
770	592,900	456,533,000	27.7489	9.16566	0.0012987	770
771	594,441	458,314,011	27.7669	9.16962	0.0012970	771
772	595,984	460,099,648	27.7849	9.17359	0.0012953	772
773	597,529	461,889,917	27.8029	9.17754	0.0012937	773
774	599,076	463,684,824	27.8209	9.18150	0.0012920	774
775	600,625	465,484,375	27.8388	9.18545	0.0012903	775
776	602,176	467,288,576	27.8568	9.18940	0.0012887	776
777	603,729	469,097,433	27.8747	9.19335	0.0012870	777
778	605,284	470,910,952	27.8927	9.19729	0.0012853	778
779	606,841	472,729,139	27.9106	9.20123	0.0012837	779
780	608,400	474,552,000	27.9285	9.20516	0.0012821	780
781	609,961	476,379,541	27.9464	9.20910	0.0012804	781
782	611,524	478,211,768	27.9643	9.21303	0.0012788	782
783	613,089	480,048,687	27.9821	9.21695	0.0012771	783
784	614,656	481,890,304	28.0000	9.22087	0.0012755	784
785	616,225	483,736,625	28.0179	9.22479	0.0012739	785
786	617,796	485,587,656	28.0357	9.22871	0.0012723	786
787	619,369	487,443,403	28.0535	9.23262	0.0012706	787
788	620,944	489,303,872	28.0713	9.23653	0.0012690	788
789	622,521	491,169,069	28.0891	9.24043	0.0012674	789
790	624,100	493,039,000	28.1069	9.24434	0.0012658	790
791	625,681	494,913,671	28.1247	9.24823	0.0012642	791
792	627,264	496,793,088	28.1425	9.25213	0.0012626	792
793	628,849	498,677,257	28.1603	9.25602	0.0012610	793
794	630,436	500,566,184	28.1780	9.25991	0.0012594	794
795	632,025	502,459,875	28.1957	9.26380	0.0012579	795
796	633,616	504,358,336	28.2135	9.26768	0.0012563	796
797	635,209	506,261,573	28.2312	9.27156	0.0012547	797
798	636,804	508,169,592	28.2489	9.27544	0.0012531	798
799	638,401	510,082,399	28.2666	9.27931	0.0012516	799
800	640,000	512,000,000	28.2843	9.28318	0.0012500	800

Powers, Roots and Reciprocals

No.	Square	Cube	Sq. Root	Cube Root	Reciprocal	No.
801	641,601	513,922,401	28.3019	9.28704	0.0012484	801
802	643,204	515,849,608	28.3196	9.29091	0.0012469	802
803	644,809	517,781,627	28.3373	9.29477	0.0012453	803
804	646,416	519,718,464	28.3549	9.29862	0.0012438	804
805	648,025	521,660,125	28.3725	9.30248	0.0012422	805
806	649,636	523,606,616	28.3901	9.30633	0.0012407	806
807	651,249	525,557,943	28.4077	9.31018	0.0012392	807
808	652,864	527,514,112	28.4253	9.31402	0.0012376	808
809	654,481	529,475,129	28.4429	9.31786	0.0012361	809
810	656,100	531,441,000	28.4605	9.32170	0.0012346	810
811	657,721	533,411,731	28.4781	9.32553	0.0012330	811
812	659,344	535,387,328	28.4956	9.32936	0.0012315	812
813	660,969	537,367,797	28.5132	9.33319	0.0012300	813
814	662,596	539,353,144	28.5307	9.33702	0.0012285	814
815	664,225	541,343,375	28.5482	9.34084	0.0012270	815
816	665,856	543,338,496	28.5657	9.34466	0.0012255	816
817	667,489	545,338,513	28.5832	9.34847	0.0012240	817
818	669,124	547,343,432	28.6007	9.35229	0.0012225	818
819	670,761	549,353,259	28.6182	9.35610	0.0012210	819
820	672,400	551,368,000	28.6356	9.35990	0.0012195	820
821	674,041	553,387,661	28.6531	9.36370	0.0012180	821
822	675,684	555,412,248	28.6705	9.36751	0.0012165	822
823	677,329	557,441,767	28.6880	9.37130	0.0012151	823
824	678,976	559,476,224	28.7054	9.37510	0.0012136	824
825	680,625	561,515,625	28.7228	9.37889	0.0012121	825
826	682,276	563,559,976	28.7402	9.38268	0.0012107	826
827	683,929	565,609,283	28.7576	9.38646	0.0012092	827
828	685,584	567,663,552	28.7750	9.39024	0.0012077	828
829	687,241	569,722,789	28.7924	9.39402	0.0012063	829
830	688,900	571,787,000	28.8097	9.39780	0.0012048	830
831	690,561	573,856,191	28.8271	9.40157	0.0012034	831
832	692,224	575,930,368	28.8444	9.40534	0.0012019	832
833	693,889	578,009,537	28.8617	9.40911	0.0012005	833
834	695,556	580,093,704	28.8791	9.41287	0.0011990	834
835	697,225	582,182,875	28.8964	9.41663	0.0011976	835
836	698,896	584,277,056	28.9137	9.42039	0.0011962	836
837	700,569	586,376,253	28.9310	9.42414	0.0011947	837
838	702,244	588,480,472	28.9482	9.42789	0.0011933	838
839	703,921	590,589,719	28.9655	9.43164	0.0011919	839
840	705,600	592,704,000	28.9828	9.43538	0.0011905	840
841	707,281	594,823,321	29.0000	9.43913	0.0011891	841
842	708,964	596,947,688	29.0172	9.44287	0.0011876	842
843	710,649	599,077,107	29.0345	9.44661	0.0011862	843
844	712,336	601,211,584	29.0517	9.45034	0.0011848	844
845	714,025	603,351,125	29.0689	9.45407	0.0011834	845
846	715,716	605,495,736	29.0861	9.45780	0.0011820	846
847	717,409	607,645,423	29.1033	9.46152	0.0011806	847
848	719,104	609,800,192	29.1204	9.46525	0.0011792	848
849	720,801	611,960,049	29.1376	9.46897	0.0011779	849
850	722,500	614,125,000	29.1548	9.47268	0.0011765	850

Powers, Roots and Reciprocals

No.	Square	Cube	Sq. Root	Cube Root	Reciprocal	No.
851	724,201	616,295,051	29.1719	9.47640	0.0011751	851
852	725,904	618,470,208	29.1890	9.48011	0.0011737	852
853	727,609	620,650,477	29.2062	9.48381	0.0011723	853
854	729,316	622,835,864	29.2233	9.48752	0.0011710	854
855	731,025	625,026,375	29.2404	9.49122	0.0011696	855
856	732,736	627,222,016	29.2575	9.49492	0.0011682	856
857	734,449	629,422,793	29.2746	9.49861	0.0011669	857
858	736,164	631,628,712	29.2916	9.50231	0.0011655	858
859	737,881	633,839,779	29.3087	9.50600	0.0011641	859
860	739,600	636,056,000	29.3258	9.50969	0.0011628	860
861	741,321	638,277,381	29.3428	9.51337	0.0011614	861
862	743,044	640,503,928	29.3598	9.51705	0.0011601	862
863	744,769	642,735,647	29.3769	9.52073	0.0011587	863
864	746,496	644,972,544	29.3939	9.52441	0.0011574	864
865	748,225	647,214,625	29.4109	9.52808	0.0011561	865
866	749,956	649,461,896	29.4279	9.53175	0.0011547	866
867	751,689	651,714,363	29.4449	9.53542	0.0011534	867
868	753,424	653,972,032	29.4618	9.53908	0.0011521	868
869	755,161	656,234,909	29.4788	9.54274	0.0011507	869
870	756,900	658,503,000	29.4958	9.54640	0.0011494	870
871	758,641	660,776,311	29.5127	9.55006	0.0011481	871
872	760,384	663,054,848	29.5296	9.55371	0.0011468	872
873	762,129	665,338,617	29.5466	9.55736	0.0011455	873
874	763,876	667,627,624	29.5635	9.56101	0.0011442	874
875	765,625	669,921,875	29.5804	9.56466	0.0011429	875
876	767,376	672,221,376	29.5973	9.56830	0.0011416	876
877	769,129	674,526,133	29.6142	9.57194	0.0011403	877
878	770,884	676,836,152	29.6311	9.57557	0.0011390	878
879	772,641	679,151,439	29.6479	9.57921	0.0011377	879
880	774,400	681,472,000	29.6648	9.58284	0.0011364	880
881	776,161	683,797,841	29.6816	9.58647	0.0011351	881
882	777,924	686,128,968	29.6985	9.59009	0.0011338	882
883	779,689	688,465,387	29.7153	9.59372	0.0011325	883
884	781,456	690,807,104	29.7321	9.59734	0.0011312	884
885	783,225	693,154,125	29.7489	9.60095	0.0011299	885
886	784,996	695,506,456	29.7658	9.60457	0.0011287	886
887	786,769	697,864,103	29.7825	9.60818	0.0011274	887
888	788,544	700,227,072	29.7993	9.61179	0.0011261	888
889	790,321	702,595,369	29.8161	9.61540	0.0011249	889
890	792,100	704,969,000	29.8329	9.61900	0.0011236	890
891	793,881	707,347,971	29.8496	9.62260	0.0011223	891
892	795,664	709,732,288	29.8664	9.62620	0.0011211	892
893	797,449	712,121,957	29.8831	9.62980	0.0011198	893
894	799,236	714,516,984	29.8998	9.63339	0.0011186	894
895	801,025	716,917,375	29.9166	9.63698	0.0011173	895
896	802,816	719,323,136	29.9333	9.64057	0.0011161	896
897	804,609	721,734,273	29.9500	9.64415	0.0011148	897
898	806,404	724,150,792	29.9666	9.64774	0.0011136	898
899	808,201	726,572,699	29.9833	9.65132	0.0011123	899
900	810,000	729,000,000	30.0000	9.65489	0.0011111	900

Powers, Roots and Reciprocals

No.	Square	Cube	Sq. Root	Cube Root	Reciprocal	No.
901	811,801	731,432,701	30.0167	9.65847	0.0011099	901
902	813,604	733,870,808	30.0333	9.66204	0.0011086	902
903	815,409	736,314,327	30.0500	9.66561	0.0011074	903
904	817,216	738,763,264	30.0666	9.66918	0.0011062	904
905	819,025	741,217,625	30.0832	9.67274	0.0011050	905
906	820,836	743,677,416	30.0998	9.67630	0.0011038	906
907	822,649	746,142,643	30.1164	9.67986	0.0011025	907
908	824,464	748,613,312	30.1330	9.68342	0.0011013	908
909	826,281	751,089,429	30.1496	9.68697	0.0011001	909
910	828,100	753,571,000	30.1662	9.69052	0.0010989	910
911	829,921	756,058,031	30.1828	9.69407	0.0010977	911
912	831,744	758,550,528	30.1993	9.69762	0.0010965	912
913	833,569	761,048,497	30.2159	9.70116	0.0010953	913
914	835,396	763,551,944	30.2324	9.70470	0.0010941	914
915	837,225	766,060,875	30.2490	9.70824	0.0010929	915
916	839,056	768,575,296	30.2655	9.71177	0.0010917	916
917	840,889	771,095,213	30.2820	9.71531	0.0010905	917
918	842,724	773,620,632	30.2985	9.71884	0.0010893	918
919	844,561	776,151,559	30.3150	9.72236	0.0010881	919
920	846,400	778,688,000	30.3315	9.72589	0.0010870	920
921	848,241	781,229,961	30.3480	9.72941	0.0010858	921
922	850,084	783,777,448	30.3645	9.73293	0.0010846	922
923	851,929	786,330,467	30.3809	9.73645	0.0010834	923
924	853,776	788,889,024	30.3974	9.73996	0.0010823	924
925	855,625	791,453,125	30.4138	9.74348	0.0010811	925
926	857,476	794,022,776	30.4302	9.74699	0.0010799	926
927	859,329	796,597,983	30.4467	9.75049	0.0010787	927
928	861,184	799,178,752	30.4631	9.75400	0.0010776	928
929	863,041	801,765,089	30.4795	9.75750	0.0010764	929
930	864,900	804,357,000	30.4959	9.76100	0.0010753	930
931	866,761	806,954,491	30.5123	9.76450	0.0010741	931
932	868,624	809,557,568	30.5287	9.76799	0.0010730	932
933	870,489	812,166,237	30.5450	9.77148	0.0010718	933
934	872,356	814,780,504	30.5614	9.77497	0.0010707	934
935	874,225	817,400,375	30.5778	9.77846	0.0010695	935
936	876,096	820,025,856	30.5941	9.78195	0.0010684	936
937	877,969	822,656,953	30.6105	9.78543	0.0010672	937
938	879,844	825,293,672	30.6268	9.78891	0.0010661	938
939	881,721	827,936,019	30.6431	9.79239	0.0010650	939
940	883,600	830,584,000	30.6594	9.79586	0.0010638	940
941	885,481	833,237,621	30.6757	9.79933	0.0010627	941
942	887,364	835,896,888	30.6920	9.80280	0.0010616	942
943	889,249	838,561,807	30.7083	9.80627	0.0010604	943
944	891,136	841,232,384	30.7246	9.80974	0.0010593	944
945	893,025	843,908,625	30.7409	9.81320	0.0010582	945
946	894,916	846,590,536	30.7571	9.81666	0.0010571	946
947	896,809	849,278,123	30.7734	9.82012	0.0010560	947
948	898,704	851,971,392	30.7896	9.82357	0.0010549	948
949	900,601	854,670,349	30.8058	9.82703	0.0010537	949
950	902,500	857,375,000	30.8221	9.83048	0.0010526	950

Powers, Roots and Reciprocals

No.	Square	Cube	Sq. Root	Cube Root	Reciprocal	No.
951	904,401	860,085,351	30.8383	9.83392	0.0010515	951
952	906,304	862,801,408	30.8545	9.83737	0.0010504	952
953	908,209	865,523,177	30.8707	9.84081	0.0010493	953
954	910,116	868,250,664	30.8869	9.84425	0.0010482	954
955	912,025	870,983,875	30.9031	9.84769	0.0010471	955
956	913,936	873,722,816	30.9192	9.85113	0.0010460	956
957	915,849	876,467,493	30.9354	9.85456	0.0010449	957
958	917,764	879,217,912	30.9516	9.85799	0.0010438	958
959	919,681	881,974,079	30.9677	9.86142	0.0010428	959
960	921,600	884,736,000	30.9839	9.86485	0.0010417	960
961	923,521	887,503,681	31.0000	9.86827	0.0010406	961
962	925,444	890,277,128	31.0161	9.87169	0.0010395	962
963	927,369	893,056,347	31.0322	9.87511	0.0010384	963
964	929,296	895,841,344	31.0483	9.87853	0.0010373	964
965	931,225	898,632,125	31.0644	9.88195	0.0010363	965
966	933,156	901,428,696	31.0805	9.88536	0.0010352	966
967	935,089	904,231,063	31.0966	9.88877	0.0010341	967
968	937,024	907,039,232	31.1127	9.89217	0.0010331	968
969	938,961	909,853,209	31.1288	9.89558	0.0010320	969
970	940,900	912,673,000	31.1448	9.89898	0.0010309	970
971	942,841	915,498,611	31.1609	9.90238	0.0010299	971
972	944,784	918,330,048	31.1769	9.90578	0.0010288	972
973	946,729	921,167,317	31.1929	9.90918	0.0010277	973
974	948,676	924,010,424	31.2090	9.91257	0.0010267	974
975	950,625	926,859,375	31.2250	9.91596	0.0010256	975
976	952,576	929,714,176	31.2410	9.91935	0.0010246	976
977	954,529	932,574,833	31.2570	9.92274	0.0010235	977
978	956,484	935,441,352	31.2730	9.92612	0.0010225	978
979	958,441	938,313,739	31.2890	9.92950	0.0010215	979
980	960,400	941,192,000	31.3050	9.93288	0.0010204	980
981	962,361	944,076,141	31.3209	9.93626	0.0010194	981
982	964,324	946,966,168	31.3369	9.93964	0.0010183	982
983	966,289	949,862,087	31.3528	9.94301	0.0010173	983
984	968,256	952,763,904	31.3688	9.94638	0.0010163	984
985	970,225	955,671,625	31.3847	9.94975	0.0010152	985
986	972,196	958,585,256	31.4006	9.95311	0.0010142	986
987	974,169	961,504,803	31.4166	9.95648	0.0010132	987
988	976,144	964,430,272	31.4325	9.95984	0.0010121	988
989	978,121	967,361,669	31.4484	9.96320	0.0010111	989
990	980,100	970,299,000	31.4643	9.96655	0.0010101	990
991	982,081	973,242,271	31.4802	9.96991	0.0010091	991
992	984,064	976,191,488	31.4960	9.97326	0.0010081	992
993	986,049	979,146,657	31.5119	9.97661	0.0010070	993
994	988,036	982,107,784	31.5278	9.97996	0.0010060	994
995	990,025	985,074,875	31.5436	9.98331	0.0010050	995
996	992,016	988,047,936	31.5595	9.98665	0.0010040	996
997	994,009	991,026,973	31.5753	9.98999	0.0010030	997
998	996,004	994,011,992	31.5911	9.99333	0.0010020	998
999	998,001	997,002,999	31.6070	9.99667	0.0010010	999
1000	1,000,000	1,000,000,000	31.6228	10.00000	0.0010000	1000

Powers, Roots and Reciprocals

No.	Square	Cube	Sq. Root	Cube Root	Reciprocal	No.
1001	1,002,001	1,003,003,001	31.6386	10.0033	0.0009990	1001
1002	1,004,004	1,006,012,008	31.6544	10.0067	0.0009980	1002
1003	1,006,009	1,009,027,027	31.6702	10.0100	0.0009970	1003
1004	1,008,016	1,012,048,064	31.6860	10.0133	0.0009960	1004
1005	1,010,025	1,015,075,125	31.7017	10.0166	0.0009950	1005
1006	1,012,036	1,018,108,216	31.7175	10.0200	0.0009940	1006
1007	1,014,049	1,021,147,343	31.7333	10.0233	0.0009930	1007
1008	1,016,064	1,024,192,512	31.7490	10.0266	0.0009921	1008
1009	1,018,081	1,027,243,729	31.7648	10.0299	0.0009911	1009
1010	1,020,100	1,030,301,000	31.7805	10.0332	0.0009901	1010
1011	1,022,121	1,033,364,331	31.7962	10.0365	0.0009891	1011
1012	1,024,144	1,036,433,728	31.8119	10.0398	0.0009881	1012
1013	1,026,169	1,039,509,197	31.8277	10.0431	0.0009872	1013
1014	1,028,196	1,042,590,744	31.8434	10.0465	0.0009862	1014
1015	1,030,225	1,045,678,375	31.8591	10.0498	0.0009852	1015
1016	1,032,256	1,048,772,096	31.8748	10.0531	0.0009843	1016
1017	1,034,289	1,051,871,913	31.8904	10.0563	0.0009833	1017
1018	1,036,324	1,054,977,832	31.9061	10.0596	0.0009823	1018
1019	1,038,361	1,058,089,859	31.9218	10.0629	0.0009814	1019
1020	1,040,400	1,061,208,000	31.9374	10.0662	0.0009804	1020
1021	1,042,441	1,064,332,261	31.9531	10.0695	0.0009794	1021
1022	1,044,484	1,067,462,648	31.9687	10.0728	0.0009785	1022
1023	1,046,529	1,070,599,167	31.9844	10.0761	0.0009775	1023
1024	1,048,576	1,073,741,824	32.0000	10.0794	0.0009766	1024
1025	1,050,625	1,076,890,625	32.0156	10.0826	0.0009756	1025
1026	1,052,676	1,080,045,576	32.0312	10.0859	0.0009747	1026
1027	1,054,729	1,083,206,683	32.0468	10.0892	0.0009737	1027
1028	1,056,784	1,086,373,952	32.0624	10.0925	0.0009728	1028
1029	1,058,841	1,089,547,389	32.0780	10.0957	0.0009718	1029
1030	1,060,900	1,092,727,000	32.0936	10.0990	0.0009709	1030
1031	1,062,961	1,095,912,791	32.1092	10.1023	0.0009699	1031
1032	1,065,024	1,099,104,768	32.1248	10.1055	0.0009690	1032
1033	1,067,089	1,102,302,937	32.1403	10.1088	0.0009681	1033
1034	1,069,156	1,105,507,304	32.1559	10.1121	0.0009671	1034
1035	1,071,225	1,108,717,875	32.1714	10.1153	0.0009662	1035
1036	1,073,296	1,111,934,656	32.1870	10.1186	0.0009653	1036
1037	1,075,369	1,115,157,653	32.2025	10.1218	0.0009643	1037
1038	1,077,444	1,118,386,872	32.2180	10.1251	0.0009634	1038
1039	1,079,521	1,121,622,319	32.2335	10.1283	0.0009625	1039
1040	1,081,600	1,124,864,000	32.2490	10.1316	0.0009615	1040
1041	1,083,681	1,128,111,921	32.2645	10.1348	0.0009606	1041
1042	1,085,764	1,131,366,088	32.2800	10.1381	0.0009597	1042
1043	1,087,849	1,134,626,507	32.2955	10.1413	0.0009588	1043
1044	1,089,936	1,137,893,184	32.3110	10.1446	0.0009579	1044
1045	1,092,025	1,141,166,125	32.3265	10.1478	0.0009569	1045
1046	1,094,116	1,144,445,336	32.3419	10.1510	0.0009560	1046
1047	1,096,209	1,147,730,823	32.3574	10.1543	0.0009551	1047
1048	1,098,304	1,151,022,592	32.3728	10.1575	0.0009542	1048
1049	1,100,401	1,154,320,649	32.3883	10.1607	0.0009533	1049
1050	1,102,500	1,157,625,000	32.4037	10.1640	0.0009524	1050

Powers, Roots and Reciprocals

No.	Square	Cube	Sq. Root	Cube Root	Reciprocal	No.
1051	1,104,601	1,160,935,651	32.4191	10.1672	0.0009515	1051
1052	1,106,704	1,164,252,608	32.4345	10.1704	0.0009506	1052
1053	1,108,809	1,167,575,877	32.4500	10.1736	0.0009497	1053
1054	1,110,916	1,170,905,464	32.4654	10.1769	0.0009488	1054
1055	1,113,025	1,174,241,375	32.4808	10.1801	0.0009479	1055
1056	1,115,136	1,177,583,616	32.4962	10.1833	0.0009470	1056
1057	1,117,249	1,180,932,193	32.5115	10.1865	0.0009461	1057
1058	1,119,364	1,184,287,112	32.5269	10.1897	0.0009452	1058
1059	1,121,481	1,187,648,379	32.5423	10.1929	0.0009443	1059
1060	1,123,600	1,191,016,000	32.5576	10.1961	0.0009434	1060
1061	1,125,721	1,194,389,981	32.5730	10.1993	0.0009425	1061
1062	1,127,844	1,197,770,328	32.5883	10.2025	0.0009416	1062
1063	1,129,969	1,201,157,047	32.6037	10.2057	0.0009407	1063
1064	1,132,096	1,204,550,144	32.6190	10.2089	0.0009398	1064
1065	1,134,225	1,207,949,625	32.6343	10.2121	0.0009390	1065
1066	1,136,356	1,211,355,496	32.6497	10.2153	0.0009381	1066
1067	1,138,489	1,214,767,763	32.6650	10.2185	0.0009372	1067
1068	1,140,624	1,218,186,432	32.6803	10.2217	0.0009363	1068
1069	1,142,761	1,221,611,509	32.6956	10.2249	0.0009355	1069
1070	1,144,900	1,225,043,000	32.7109	10.2281	0.0009346	1070
1071	1,147,041	1,228,480,911	32.7261	10.2313	0.0009337	1071
1072	1,149,184	1,231,925,248	32.7414	10.2345	0.0009328	1072
1073	1,151,329	1,235,376,017	32.7567	10.2376	0.0009320	1073
1074	1,153,476	1,238,833,224	32.7719	10.2408	0.0009311	1074
1075	1,155,625	1,242,296,875	32.7872	10.2440	0.0009302	1075
1076	1,157,776	1,245,766,976	32.8024	10.2472	0.0009294	1076
1077	1,159,929	1,249,243,533	32.8177	10.2503	0.0009285	1077
1078	1,162,084	1,252,726,552	32.8329	10.2535	0.0009276	1078
1079	1,164,241	1,256,216,039	32.8481	10.2567	0.0009268	1079
1080	1,166,400	1,259,712,000	32.8634	10.2599	0.0009259	1080
1081	1,168,561	1,263,214,441	32.8786	10.2630	0.0009251	1081
1082	1,170,724	1,266,723,368	32.8938	10.2662	0.0009242	1082
1083	1,172,889	1,270,238,787	32.9090	10.2693	0.0009234	1083
1084	1,175,056	1,273,760,704	32.9242	10.2725	0.0009225	1084
1085	1,177,225	1,277,289,125	32.9393	10.2757	0.0009217	1085
1086	1,179,396	1,280,824,056	32.9545	10.2788	0.0009208	1086
1087	1,181,569	1,284,365,503	32.9697	10.2820	0.0009200	1087
1088	1,183,744	1,287,913,472	32.9848	10.2851	0.0009191	1088
1089	1,185,921	1,291,467,969	33.0000	10.2883	0.0009183	1089
1090	1,188,100	1,295,029,000	33.0151	10.2914	0.0009174	1090
1091	1,190,281	1,298,596,571	33.0303	10.2946	0.0009166	1091
1092	1,192,464	1,302,170,688	33.0454	10.2977	0.0009158	1092
1093	1,194,649	1,305,751,357	33.0606	10.3009	0.0009149	1093
1094	1,196,836	1,309,338,584	33.0757	10.3040	0.0009141	1094
1095	1,199,025	1,312,932,375	33.0908	10.3071	0.0009132	1095
1096	1,201,216	1,316,532,736	33.1059	10.3103	0.0009124	1096
1097	1,203,409	1,320,139,673	33.1210	10.3134	0.0009116	1097
1098	1,205,604	1,323,753,192	33.1361	10.3165	0.0009107	1098
1099	1,207,801	1,327,373,299	33.1512	10.3197	0.0009099	1099
1100	1,210,000	1,331,000,000	33.1662	10.3228	0.0009091	1100

Powers, Roots and Reciprocals

No.	Square	Cube	Sq. Root	Cube Root	Reciprocal	No.
1101	1,212,201	1,334,633,301	33.1813	10.3259	0.0009083	1101
1102	1,214,404	1,338,273,208	33.1964	10.3291	0.0009074	1102
1103	1,216,609	1,341,919,727	33.2114	10.3322	0.0009066	1103
1104	1,218,816	1,345,572,864	33.2265	10.3353	0.0009058	1104
1105	1,221,025	1,349,232,625	33.2415	10.3384	0.0009050	1105
1106	1,223,236	1,352,899,016	33.2566	10.3415	0.0009042	1106
1107	1,225,449	1,356,572,043	33.2716	10.3447	0.0009033	1107
1108	1,227,664	1,360,251,712	33.2866	10.3478	0.0009025	1108
1109	1,229,881	1,363,938,029	33.3017	10.3509	0.0009017	1109
1110	1,232,100	1,367,631,000	33.3167	10.3540	0.0009009	1110
1111	1,234,321	1,371,330,631	33.3317	10.3571	0.0009001	1111
1112	1,236,544	1,375,036,928	33.3467	10.3602	0.0008993	1112
1113	1,238,769	1,378,749,897	33.3617	10.3633	0.0008985	1113
1114	1,240,996	1,382,469,544	33.3766	10.3664	0.0008977	1114
1115	1,243,225	1,386,195,875	33.3916	10.3695	0.0008969	1115
1116	1,245,456	1,389,928,896	33.4066	10.3726	0.0008961	1116
1117	1,247,689	1,393,668,613	33.4215	10.3757	0.0008953	1117
1118	1,249,924	1,397,415,032	33.4365	10.3788	0.0008945	1118
1119	1,252,161	1,401,168,159	33.4515	10.3819	0.0008937	1119
1120	1,254,400	1,404,928,000	33.4664	10.3850	0.0008929	1120
1121	1,256,641	1,408,694,561	33.4813	10.3881	0.0008921	1121
1122	1,258,884	1,412,467,848	33.4963	10.3912	0.0008913	1122
1123	1,261,129	1,416,247,867	33.5112	10.3943	0.0008905	1123
1124	1,263,376	1,420,034,624	33.5261	10.3973	0.0008897	1124
1125	1,265,625	1,423,828,125	33.5410	10.4004	0.0008889	1125
1126	1,267,876	1,427,628,376	33.5559	10.4035	0.0008881	1126
1127	1,270,129	1,431,435,383	33.5708	10.4066	0.0008873	1127
1128	1,272,384	1,435,249,152	33.5857	10.4097	0.0008865	1128
1129	1,274,641	1,439,069,689	33.6006	10.4127	0.0008857	1129
1130	1,276,900	1,442,897,000	33.6155	10.4158	0.0008850	1130
1131	1,279,161	1,446,731,091	33.6303	10.4189	0.0008842	1131
1132	1,281,424	1,450,571,968	33.6452	10.4219	0.0008834	1132
1133	1,283,689	1,454,419,637	33.6601	10.4250	0.0008826	1133
1134	1,285,956	1,458,274,104	33.6749	10.4281	0.0008818	1134
1135	1,288,225	1,462,135,375	33.6898	10.4311	0.0008811	1135
1136	1,290,496	1,466,003,456	33.7046	10.4342	0.0008803	1136
1137	1,292,769	1,469,878,353	33.7194	10.4373	0.0008795	1137
1138	1,295,044	1,473,760,072	33.7342	10.4403	0.0008787	1138
1139	1,297,321	1,477,648,619	33.7491	10.4434	0.0008780	1139
1140	1,299,600	1,481,544,000	33.7639	10.4464	0.0008772	1140
1141	1,301,881	1,485,446,221	33.7787	10.4495	0.0008764	1141
1142	1,304,164	1,489,355,288	33.7935	10.4525	0.0008757	1142
1143	1,306,449	1,493,271,207	33.8083	10.4556	0.0008749	1143
1144	1,308,736	1,497,193,984	33.8231	10.4586	0.0008741	1144
1145	1,311,025	1,501,123,625	33.8378	10.4617	0.0008734	1145
1146	1,313,316	1,505,060,136	33.8526	10.4647	0.0008726	1146
1147	1,315,609	1,509,003,523	33.8674	10.4678	0.0008718	1147
1148	1,317,904	1,512,953,792	33.8821	10.4708	0.0008711	1148
1149	1,320,201	1,516,910,949	33.8969	10.4739	0.0008703	1149
1150	1,322,500	1,520,875,000	33.9116	10.4769	0.0008696	1150

Powers, Roots and Reciprocals

No.	Square	Cube	Sq. Root	Cube Root	Reciprocal	No.
1151	1,324,801	1,524,845,951	33.9264	10.4799	0.0008688	1151
1152	1,327,104	1,528,823,808	33.9411	10.4830	0.0008681	1152
1153	1,329,409	1,532,808,577	33.9559	10.4860	0.0008673	1153
1154	1,331,716	1,536,800,264	33.9706	10.4890	0.0008666	1154
1155	1,334,025	1,540,798,875	33.9853	10.4921	0.0008658	1155
1156	1,336,336	1,544,804,416	34.0000	10.4951	0.0008651	1156
1157	1,338,649	1,548,816,893	34.0147	10.4981	0.0008643	1157
1158	1,340,964	1,552,836,312	34.0294	10.5011	0.0008636	1158
1159	1,343,281	1,556,862,679	34.0441	10.5042	0.0008628	1159
1160	1,345,600	1,560,896,000	34.0588	10.5072	0.0008621	1160
1161	1,347,921	1,564,936,281	34.0735	10.5102	0.0008613	1161
1162	1,350,244	1,568,983,528	34.0881	10.5132	0.0008606	1162
1163	1,352,569	1,573,037,747	34.1028	10.5162	0.0008598	1163
1164	1,354,896	1,577,098,944	34.1174	10.5192	0.0008591	1164
1165	1,357,225	1,581,167,125	34.1321	10.5223	0.0008584	1165
1166	1,359,556	1,585,242,296	34.1467	10.5253	0.0008576	1166
1167	1,361,889	1,589,324,463	34.1614	10.5283	0.0008569	1167
1168	1,364,224	1,593,413,632	34.1760	10.5313	0.0008562	1168
1169	1,366,561	1,597,509,809	34.1906	10.5343	0.0008554	1169
1170	1,368,900	1,601,613,000	34.2053	10.5373	0.0008547	1170
1171	1,371,241	1,605,723,211	34.2199	10.5403	0.0008540	1171
1172	1,373,584	1,609,840,448	34.2345	10.5433	0.0008532	1172
1173	1,375,929	1,613,964,717	34.2491	10.5463	0.0008525	1173
1174	1,378,276	1,618,096,024	34.2637	10.5493	0.0008518	1174
1175	1,380,625	1,622,234,375	34.2783	10.5523	0.0008511	1175
1176	1,382,976	1,626,379,776	34.2929	10.5553	0.0008503	1176
1177	1,385,329	1,630,532,233	34.3074	10.5583	0.0008496	1177
1178	1,387,684	1,634,691,752	34.3220	10.5612	0.0008489	1178
1179	1,390,041	1,638,858,339	34.3366	10.5642	0.0008482	1179
1180	1,392,400	1,643,032,000	34.3511	10.5672	0.0008475	1180
1181	1,394,761	1,647,212,741	34.3657	10.5702	0.0008467	1181
1182	1,397,124	1,651,400,568	34.3802	10.5732	0.0008460	1182
1183	1,399,489	1,655,595,487	34.3948	10.5762	0.0008453	1183
1184	1,401,856	1,659,797,504	34.4093	10.5791	0.0008446	1184
1185	1,404,225	1,664,006,625	34.4238	10.5821	0.0008439	1185
1186	1,406,596	1,668,222,856	34.4384	10.5851	0.0008432	1186
1187	1,408,969	1,672,446,203	34.4529	10.5881	0.0008425	1187
1188	1,411,344	1,676,676,672	34.4674	10.5910	0.0008418	1188
1189	1,413,721	1,680,914,269	34.4819	10.5940	0.0008410	1189
1190	1,416,100	1,685,159,000	34.4964	10.5970	0.0008403	1190
1191	1,418,481	1,689,410,871	34.5109	10.6000	0.0008396	1191
1192	1,420,864	1,693,669,888	34.5254	10.6029	0.0008389	1192
1193	1,423,249	1,697,936,057	34.5398	10.6059	0.0008382	1193
1194	1,425,636	1,702,209,384	34.5543	10.6088	0.0008375	1194
1195	1,428,025	1,706,489,875	34.5688	10.6118	0.0008368	1195
1196	1,430,416	1,710,777,536	34.5832	10.6148	0.0008361	1196
1197	1,432,809	1,715,072,373	34.5977	10.6177	0.0008354	1197
1198	1,435,204	1,719,374,392	34.6121	10.6207	0.0008347	1198
1199	1,437,601	1,723,683,599	34.6266	10.6236	0.0008340	1199
1200	1,440,000	1,728,000,000	34.6410	10.6266	0.0008333	1200

Powers, Roots and Reciprocals

No.	Square	Cube	Sq. Root	Cube Root	Reciprocal	No.
1201	1,442,401	1,732,323,601	34.6554	10.6295	0.0008326	1201
1202	1,444,804	1,736,654,408	34.6699	10.6325	0.0008319	1202
1203	1,447,209	1,740,992,427	34.6843	10.6354	0.0008313	1203
1204	1,449,616	1,745,337,664	34.6987	10.6384	0.0008306	1204
1205	1,452,025	1,749,690,125	34.7131	10.6413	0.0008299	1205
1206	1,454,436	1,754,049,816	34.7275	10.6443	0.0008292	1206
1207	1,456,849	1,758,416,743	34.7419	10.6472	0.0008285	1207
1208	1,459,264	1,762,790,912	34.7563	10.6501	0.0008278	1208
1209	1,461,681	1,767,172,329	34.7707	10.6531	0.0008271	1209
1210	1,464,100	1,771,561,000	34.7851	10.6560	0.0008264	1210
1211	1,466,521	1,775,956,931	34.7994	10.6590	0.0008258	1211
1212	1,468,944	1,780,360,128	34.8138	10.6619	0.0008251	1212
1213	1,471,369	1,784,770,597	34.8281	10.6648	0.0008244	1213
1214	1,473,796	1,789,188,344	34.8425	10.6678	0.0008237	1214
1215	1,476,225	1,793,613,375	34.8569	10.6707	0.0008230	1215
1216	1,478,656	1,798,045,696	34.8712	10.6736	0.0008224	1216
1217	1,481,089	1,802,485,313	34.8855	10.6765	0.0008217	1217
1218	1,483,524	1,806,932,232	34.8999	10.6795	0.0008210	1218
1219	1,485,961	1,811,386,459	34.9142	10.6824	0.0008203	1219
1220	1,488,400	1,815,848,000	34.9285	10.6853	0.0008197	1220
1221	1,490,841	1,820,316,861	34.9428	10.6882	0.0008190	1221
1222	1,493,284	1,824,793,048	34.9571	10.6911	0.0008183	1222
1223	1,495,729	1,829,276,567	34.9714	10.6940	0.0008177	1223
1224	1,498,176	1,833,767,424	34.9857	10.6970	0.0008170	1224
1225	1,500,625	1,838,265,625	35.0000	10.6999	0.0008163	1225
1226	1,503,076	1,842,771,176	35.0143	10.7028	0.0008157	1226
1227	1,505,529	1,847,284,083	35.0286	10.7057	0.0008150	1227
1228	1,507,984	1,851,804,352	35.0428	10.7086	0.0008143	1228
1229	1,510,441	1,856,331,989	35.0571	10.7115	0.0008137	1229
1230	1,512,900	1,860,867,000	35.0714	10.7144	0.0008130	1230
1231	1,515,361	1,865,409,391	35.0856	10.7173	0.0008123	1231
1232	1,517,824	1,869,959,168	35.0999	10.7202	0.0008117	1232
1233	1,520,289	1,874,516,337	35.1141	10.7231	0.0008110	1233
1234	1,522,756	1,879,080,904	35.1283	10.7260	0.0008104	1234
1235	1,525,225	1,883,652,875	35.1426	10.7289	0.0008097	1235
1236	1,527,696	1,888,232,256	35.1568	10.7318	0.0008091	1236
1237	1,530,169	1,892,819,053	35.1710	10.7347	0.0008084	1237
1238	1,532,644	1,897,413,272	35.1852	10.7376	0.0008078	1238
1239	1,535,121	1,902,014,919	35.1994	10.7405	0.0008071	1239
1240	1,537,600	1,906,624,000	35.2136	10.7434	0.0008065	1240
1241	1,540,081	1,911,240,521	35.2278	10.7463	0.0008058	1241
1242	1,542,564	1,915,864,488	35.2420	10.7491	0.0008052	1242
1243	1,545,049	1,920,495,907	35.2562	10.7520	0.0008045	1243
1244	1,547,536	1,925,134,784	35.2704	10.7549	0.0008039	1244
1245	1,550,025	1,929,781,125	35.2846	10.7578	0.0008032	1245
1246	1,552,516	1,934,434,936	35.2987	10.7607	0.0008026	1246
1247	1,555,009	1,939,096,223	35.3129	10.7635	0.0008019	1247
1248	1,557,504	1,943,764,992	35.3270	10.7664	0.0008013	1248
1249	1,560,001	1,948,441,249	35.3412	10.7693	0.0008006	1249
1250	1,562,500	1,953,125,000	35.3553	10.7722	0.0008000	1250

Powers, Roots and Reciprocals

No.	Square	Cube	Sq. Root	Cube Root	Reciprocal	No.
1251	1,565,001	1,957,816,251	35.3695	10.7750	0.0007994	1251
1252	1,567,504	1,962,515,008	35.3836	10.7779	0.0007987	1252
1253	1,570,009	1,967,221,277	35.3977	10.7808	0.0007981	1253
1254	1,572,516	1,971,935,064	35.4119	10.7837	0.0007974	1254
1255	1,575,025	1,976,656,375	35.4260	10.7865	0.0007968	1255
1256	1,577,536	1,981,385,216	35.4401	10.7894	0.0007962	1256
1257	1,580,049	1,986,121,593	35.4542	10.7922	0.0007955	1257
1258	1,582,564	1,990,865,512	35.4683	10.7951	0.0007949	1258
1259	1,585,081	1,995,616,979	35.4824	10.7980	0.0007943	1259
1260	1,587,600	2,000,376,000	35.4965	10.8008	0.0007937	1260
1261	1,590,121	2,005,142,581	35.5106	10.8037	0.0007930	1261
1262	1,592,644	2,009,916,728	35.5246	10.8065	0.0007924	1262
1263	1,595,169	2,014,698,447	35.5387	10.8094	0.0007918	1263
1264	1,597,696	2,019,487,744	35.5528	10.8122	0.0007911	1264
1265	1,600,225	2,024,284,625	35.5668	10.8151	0.0007905	1265
1266	1,602,756	2,029,089,096	35.5809	10.8179	0.0007899	1266
1267	1,605,289	2,033,901,163	35.5949	10.8208	0.0007893	1267
1268	1,607,824	2,038,720,832	35.6090	10.8236	0.0007886	1268
1269	1,610,361	2,043,548,109	35.6230	10.8265	0.0007880	1269
1270	1,612,900	2,048,383,000	35.6371	10.8293	0.0007874	1270
1271	1,615,441	2,053,225,511	35.6511	10.8322	0.0007868	1271
1272	1,617,984	2,058,075,648	35.6651	10.8350	0.0007862	1272
1273	1,620,529	2,062,933,417	35.6791	10.8378	0.0007855	1273
1274	1,623,076	2,067,798,824	35.6931	10.8407	0.0007849	1274
1275	1,625,625	2,072,671,875	35.7071	10.8435	0.0007843	1275
1276	1,628,176	2,077,552,576	35.7211	10.8463	0.0007837	1276
1277	1,630,729	2,082,440,933	35.7351	10.8492	0.0007831	1277
1278	1,633,284	2,087,336,952	35.7491	10.8520	0.0007825	1278
1279	1,635,841	2,092,240,639	35.7631	10.8548	0.0007819	1279
1280	1,638,400	2,097,152,000	35.7771	10.8577	0.0007813	1280
1281	1,640,961	2,102,071,041	35.7911	10.8605	0.0007806	1281
1282	1,643,524	2,106,997,768	35.8050	10.8633	0.0007800	1282
1283	1,646,089	2,111,932,187	35.8190	10.8661	0.0007794	1283
1284	1,648,656	2,116,874,304	35.8329	10.8690	0.0007788	1284
1285	1,651,225	2,121,824,125	35.8469	10.8718	0.0007782	1285
1286	1,653,796	2,126,781,656	35.8608	10.8746	0.0007776	1286
1287	1,656,369	2,131,746,903	35.8748	10.8774	0.0007770	1287
1288	1,658,944	2,136,719,872	35.8887	10.8802	0.0007764	1288
1289	1,661,521	2,141,700,569	35.9026	10.8831	0.0007758	1289
1290	1,664,100	2,146,689,000	35.9166	10.8859	0.0007752	1290
1291	1,666,681	2,151,685,171	35.9305	10.8887	0.0007746	1291
1292	1,669,264	2,156,689,088	35.9444	10.8915	0.0007740	1292
1293	1,671,849	2,161,700,757	35.9583	10.8943	0.0007734	1293
1294	1,674,436	2,166,720,184	35.9722	10.8971	0.0007728	1294
1295	1,677,025	2,171,747,375	35.9861	10.8999	0.0007722	1295
1296	1,679,616	2,176,782,336	36.0000	10.9027	0.0007716	1296
1297	1,682,209	2,181,825,073	36.0139	10.9055	0.0007710	1297
1298	1,684,804	2,186,875,592	36.0278	10.9083	0.0007704	1298
1299	1,687,401	2,191,933,899	36.0416	10.9111	0.0007698	1299
1300	1,690,000	2,197,000,000	36.0555	10.9139	0.0007692	1300

Powers, Roots and Reciprocals

No.	Square	Cube	Sq. Root	Cube Root	Reciprocal	No.
1301	1,692,601	2,202,073,901	36.0694	10.9167	0.0007686	1301
1302	1,695,204	2,207,155,608	36.0832	10.9195	0.0007680	1302
1303	1,697,809	2,212,245,127	36.0971	10.9223	0.0007675	1303
1304	1,700,416	2,217,342,464	36.1109	10.9251	0.0007669	1304
1305	1,703,025	2,222,447,625	36.1248	10.9279	0.0007663	1305
1306	1,705,636	2,227,560,616	36.1386	10.9307	0.0007657	1306
1307	1,708,249	2,232,681,443	36.1525	10.9335	0.0007651	1307
1308	1,710,864	2,237,810,112	36.1663	10.9363	0.0007645	1308
1309	1,713,481	2,242,946,629	36.1801	10.9391	0.0007639	1309
1310	1,716,100	2,248,091,000	36.1939	10.9418	0.0007634	1310
1311	1,718,721	2,253,243,231	36.2077	10.9446	0.0007628	1311
1312	1,721,344	2,258,403,328	36.2215	10.9474	0.0007622	1312
1313	1,723,969	2,263,571,297	36.2353	10.9502	0.0007616	1313
1314	1,726,596	2,268,747,144	36.2491	10.9530	0.0007610	1314
1315	1,729,225	2,273,930,875	36.2629	10.9557	0.0007605	1315
1316	1,731,856	2,279,122,496	36.2767	10.9585	0.0007599	1316
1317	1,734,489	2,284,322,013	36.2905	10.9613	0.0007593	1317
1318	1,737,124	2,289,529,432	36.3043	10.9641	0.0007587	1318
1319	1,739,761	2,294,744,759	36.3180	10.9668	0.0007582	1319
1320	1,742,400	2,299,968,000	36.3318	10.9696	0.0007576	1320
1321	1,745,041	2,305,199,161	36.3456	10.9724	0.0007570	1321
1322	1,747,684	2,310,438,248	36.3593	10.9752	0.0007564	1322
1323	1,750,329	2,315,685,267	36.3731	10.9779	0.0007559	1323
1324	1,752,976	2,320,940,224	36.3868	10.9807	0.0007553	1324
1325	1,755,625	2,326,203,125	36.4005	10.9834	0.0007547	1325
1326	1,758,276	2,331,473,976	36.4143	10.9862	0.0007541	1326
1327	1,760,929	2,336,752,783	36.4280	10.9890	0.0007536	1327
1328	1,763,584	2,342,039,552	36.4417	10.9917	0.0007530	1328
1329	1,766,241	2,347,334,289	36.4555	10.9945	0.0007524	1329
1330	1,768,900	2,352,637,000	36.4692	10.9972	0.0007519	1330
1331	1,771,561	2,357,947,691	36.4829	11.0000	0.0007513	1331
1332	1,774,224	2,363,266,368	36.4966	11.0028	0.0007508	1332
1333	1,776,889	2,368,593,037	36.5103	11.0055	0.0007502	1333
1334	1,779,556	2,373,927,704	36.5240	11.0083	0.0007496	1334
1335	1,782,225	2,379,270,375	36.5377	11.0110	0.0007491	1335
1336	1,784,896	2,384,621,056	36.5513	11.0138	0.0007485	1336
1337	1,787,569	2,389,979,753	36.5650	11.0165	0.0007479	1337
1338	1,790,244	2,395,346,472	36.5787	11.0193	0.0007474	1338
1339	1,792,921	2,400,721,219	36.5923	11.0220	0.0007468	1339
1340	1,795,600	2,406,104,000	36.6060	11.0247	0.0007463	1340
1341	1,798,281	2,411,494,821	36.6197	11.0275	0.0007457	1341
1342	1,800,964	2,416,893,688	36.6333	11.0302	0.0007452	1342
1343	1,803,649	2,422,300,607	36.6470	11.0330	0.0007446	1343
1344	1,806,336	2,427,715,584	36.6606	11.0357	0.0007440	1344
1345	1,809,025	2,433,138,625	36.6742	11.0384	0.0007435	1345
1346	1,811,716	2,438,569,736	36.6879	11.0412	0.0007429	1346
1347	1,814,409	2,444,008,923	36.7015	11.0439	0.0007424	1347
1348	1,817,104	2,449,456,192	36.7151	11.0466	0.0007418	1348
1349	1,819,801	2,454,911,549	36.7287	11.0494	0.0007413	1349
1350	1,822,500	2,460,375,000	36.7423	11.0521	0.0007407	1350

Powers, Roots and Reciprocals

No.	Square	Cube	Sq. Root	Cube Root	Reciprocal	No.
1351	1,825,201	2,465,846,551	36.7560	11.0548	0.0007402	1351
1352	1,827,904	2,471,326,208	36.7696	11.0575	0.0007396	1352
1353	1,830,609	2,476,813,977	36.7831	11.0603	0.0007391	1353
1354	1,833,316	2,482,309,864	36.7967	11.0630	0.0007386	1354
1355	1,836,025	2,487,813,875	36.8103	11.0657	0.0007380	1355
1356	1,838,736	2,493,326,016	36.8239	11.0684	0.0007375	1356
1357	1,841,449	2,498,846,293	36.8375	11.0712	0.0007369	1357
1358	1,844,164	2,504,374,712	36.8511	11.0739	0.0007364	1358
1359	1,846,881	2,509,911,279	36.8646	11.0766	0.0007358	1359
1360	1,849,600	2,515,456,000	36.8782	11.0793	0.0007353	1360
1361	1,852,321	2,521,008,881	36.8917	11.0820	0.0007348	1361
1362	1,855,044	2,526,569,928	36.9053	11.0847	0.0007342	1362
1363	1,857,769	2,532,139,147	36.9188	11.0875	0.0007337	1363
1364	1,860,496	2,537,716,544	36.9324	11.0902	0.0007331	1364
1365	1,863,225	2,543,302,125	36.9459	11.0929	0.0007326	1365
1366	1,865,956	2,548,895,896	36.9594	11.0956	0.0007321	1366
1367	1,868,689	2,554,497,863	36.9730	11.0983	0.0007315	1367
1368	1,871,424	2,560,108,032	36.9865	11.1010	0.0007310	1368
1369	1,874,161	2,565,726,409	37.0000	11.1037	0.0007305	1369
1370	1,876,900	2,571,353,000	37.0135	11.1064	0.0007299	1370
1371	1,879,641	2,576,987,811	37.0270	11.1091	0.0007294	1371
1372	1,882,384	2,582,630,848	37.0405	11.1118	0.0007289	1372
1373	1,885,129	2,588,282,117	37.0540	11.1145	0.0007283	1373
1374	1,887,876	2,593,941,624	37.0675	11.1172	0.0007278	1374
1375	1,890,625	2,599,609,375	37.0810	11.1199	0.0007273	1375
1376	1,893,376	2,605,285,376	37.0945	11.1226	0.0007267	1376
1377	1,896,129	2,610,969,633	37.1080	11.1253	0.0007262	1377
1378	1,898,884	2,616,662,152	37.1214	11.1280	0.0007257	1378
1379	1,901,641	2,622,362,939	37.1349	11.1307	0.0007252	1379
1380	1,904,400	2,628,072,000	37.1484	11.1334	0.0007246	1380
1381	1,907,161	2,633,789,341	37.1618	11.1361	0.0007241	1381
1382	1,909,924	2,639,514,968	37.1753	11.1387	0.0007236	1382
1383	1,912,689	2,645,248,887	37.1887	11.1414	0.0007231	1383
1384	1,915,456	2,650,991,104	37.2022	11.1441	0.0007225	1384
1385	1,918,225	2,656,741,625	37.2156	11.1468	0.0007220	1385
1386	1,920,996	2,662,500,456	37.2290	11.1495	0.0007215	1386
1387	1,923,769	2,668,267,603	37.2424	11.1522	0.0007210	1387
1388	1,926,544	2,674,043,072	37.2559	11.1548	0.0007205	1388
1389	1,929,321	2,679,826,869	37.2693	11.1575	0.0007199	1389
1390	1,932,100	2,685,619,000	37.2827	11.1602	0.0007194	1390
1391	1,934,881	2,691,419,471	37.2961	11.1629	0.0007189	1391
1392	1,937,664	2,697,228,288	37.3095	11.1655	0.0007184	1392
1393	1,940,449	2,703,045,457	37.3229	11.1682	0.0007179	1393
1394	1,943,236	2,708,870,984	37.3363	11.1709	0.0007174	1394
1395	1,946,025	2,714,704,875	37.3497	11.1736	0.0007168	1395
1396	1,948,816	2,720,547,136	37.3631	11.1762	0.0007163	1396
1397	1,951,609	2,726,397,773	37.3765	11.1789	0.0007158	1397
1398	1,954,404	2,732,256,792	37.3898	11.1816	0.0007153	1398
1399	1,957,201	2,738,124,199	37.4032	11.1842	0.0007148	1399
1400	1,960,000	2,744,000,000	37.4166	11.1869	0.0007143	1400

Powers, Roots and Reciprocals

No.	Square	Cube	Sq. Root	Cube Root	Reciprocal	No.
1401	1,962,801	2,749,884,201	37.4299	11.1896	0.0007138	1401
1402	1,965,604	2,755,776,808	37.4433	11.1922	0.0007133	1402
1403	1,968,409	2,761,677,827	37.4566	11.1949	0.0007128	1403
1404	1,971,216	2,767,587,264	37.4700	11.1975	0.0007123	1404
1405	1,974,025	2,773,505,125	37.4833	11.2002	0.0007117	1405
1406	1,976,836	2,779,431,416	37.4967	11.2028	0.0007112	1406
1407	1,979,649	2,785,366,143	37.5100	11.2055	0.0007107	1407
1408	1,982,464	2,791,309,312	37.5233	11.2082	0.0007102	1408
1409	1,985,281	2,797,260,929	37.5366	11.2108	0.0007097	1409
1410	1,988,100	2,803,221,000	37.5500	11.2135	0.0007092	1410
1411	1,990,921	2,809,189,531	37.5633	11.2161	0.0007087	1411
1412	1,993,744	2,815,166,528	37.5766	11.2188	0.0007082	1412
1413	1,996,569	2,821,151,997	37.5899	11.2214	0.0007077	1413
1414	1,999,396	2,827,145,944	37.6032	11.2241	0.0007072	1414
1415	2,002,225	2,833,148,375	37.6165	11.2267	0.0007067	1415
1416	2,005,056	2,839,159,296	37 6298	11.2293	0.0007062	1416
1417	2,007,889	2,845,178,713	37.6431	11.2320	0.0007057	1417
1418	2,010,724	2,851,206,632	37.6563	11.2346	0.0007052	1418
1419	2,013,561	2,857,243,059	37.6696	11.2373	0.0007047	1419
1420	2,016,400	2,863,288,000	37.6829	11.2399	0.0007042	1420
1421	2,019,241	2,869,341,461	37.6962	11.2425	0.0007037	1421
1422	2,022,084	2,875,403,448	37.7094	11.2452	0.0007032	1422
1423	2,024,929	2,881,473,967	37.7227	11.2478	0.0007027	1423
1424	2,027,776	2,887,553,024	37.7359	11.2504	0.0007022	1424
1425	2,030,625	2,893,640,625	37.7492	11.2531	0.0007018	1425
1426	2,033,476	2,899,736,776	37.7624	11.2557	0.0007013	1426
1427	2,036,329	2,905,841,483	37.7757	11.2583	0.0007008	1427
1428	2,039,184	2,911,954,752	37.7889	11.2610	0.0007003	1428
1429	2,042,041	2,918,076,589	37.8021	11.2636	0.0006998	1429
1430	2,044,900	2,924,207,000	37.8153	11.2662	0.0006993	1430
1431	2,047,761	2,930,345,991	37.8286	11.2689	0.0006988	1431
1432	2,050,624	2,936,493,568	37.8418	11.2715	0.0006983	1432
1433	2,053,489	2,942,649,737	37.8550	11.2741	0.0006978	1433
1434	2,056,356	2,948,814,504	37.8682	11.2767	0.0006974	1434
1435	2,059,225	2,954,987,875	37.8814	11.2793	0.0006969	1435
1436	2,062,096	2,961,169,856	37.8946	11.2820	0.0006964	1436
1437	2,064,969	2,967,360,453	37.9078	11.2846	0.0006959	1437
1438	2,067,844	2,973,559,672	37.9210	11.2872	0.0006954	1438
1439	2,070,721	2,979,767,519	37.9342	11.2898	0.0006949	1439
1440	2,073,600	2,985,984,000	37.9473	11.2924	0.0006944	1440
1441	2,076,481	2,992,209,121	37.9605	11.2950	0.0006940	1441
1442	2,079,364	2,998,442,888	37.9737	11.2977	0.0006935	1442
1443	2,082,249	3,004,685,307	37.9868	11.3003	0.0006930	1443
1444	2,085,136	3,010,936,384	38.0000	11.3029	0.0006925	1444
1445	2,088,025	3,017,196,125	38.0132	11.3055	0.0006920	1445
1446	2,090,916	3,023,464,536	38.0263	11.3081	0.0006916	1446
1447	2,093,809	3,029,741,623	38.0395	11.3107	0.0006911	1447
1448	2,096,704	3,036,027,392	38.0526	11.3133	0.0006906	1448
1449	2,099,601	3,042,321,849	38.0657	11.3159	0.0006901	1449
1450	2,102,500	3,048,625,000	38.0789	11.3185	0.0006897	1450

Powers, Roots and Reciprocals

No.	Square	Cube	Sq. Root	Cube Root	Reciprocal	No.
1451	2,105,401	3,054,936,851	38.0920	11.3211	0.0006892	1451
1452	2,108,304	3,061,257,408	38.1051	11.3237	0.0006887	1452
1453	2,111,209	3,067,586,677	38.1182	11.3263	0.0006882	1453
1454	2,114,116	3,073,924,664	38.1314	11.3289	0.0006878	1454
1455	2,117,025	3,080,271,375	38.1445	11.3315	0.0006873	1455
1456	2,119,936	3,086,626,816	38.1576	11.3341	0.0006868	1456
1457	2,122,849	3,092,990,993	38.1707	11.3367	0.0006863	1457
1458	2,125,764	3,099,363,912	38.1838	11.3393	0.0006859	1458
1459	2,128,681	3,105,745,579	38.1969	11.3419	0.0006854	1459
1460	2,131,600	3,112,136,000	38.2099	11.3445	0.0006849	1460
1461	2,134,521	3,118,535,181	38.2230	11.3471	0.0006845	1461
1462	2,137,444	3,124,943,128	38.2361	11.3496	0.0006840	1462
1463	2,140,369	3,131,359,847	38.2492	11.3522	0.0006835	1463
1464	2,143,296	3,137,785,344	38.2623	11.3548	0.0006831	1464
1465	2,146,225	3,144,219,625	38.2753	11.3574	0.0006826	1465
1466	2,149,156	3,150,662,696	38.2884	11.3600	0.0006821	1466
1467	2,152,089	3,157,114,563	38.3014	11.3626	0.0006817	1467
1468	2,155,024	3,163,575,232	38.3145	11.3652	0.0006812	1468
1469	2,157,961	3,170,044,709	38.3275	11.3677	0.0006807	1469
1470	2,160,900	3,176,523,000	38.3406	11.3703	0.0006803	1470
1471	2,163,841	3,183,010,111	38.3536	11.3729	0.0006798	1471
1472	2,166,784	3,189,506,048	38.3667	11.3755	0.0006793	1472
1473	2,169,729	3,196,010,817	38.3797	11.3780	0.0006789	1473
1474	2,172,676	3,202,524,424	38.3927	11.3806	0.0006784	1474
1475	2,175,625	3,209,046,875	38.4057	11.3832	0.0006780	1475
1476	2,178,576	3,215,578,176	38.4187	11.3858	0.0006775	1476
1477	2,181,529	3,222,118,333	38.4318	11.3883	0.0006770	1477
1478	2,184,484	3,228,667,352	38.4448	11.3909	0.0006766	1478
1479	2,187,441	3,235,225,239	38.4578	11.3935	0.0006761	1479
1480	2,190,400	3,241,792,000	38.4708	11.3960	0.0006757	1480
1481	2,193,361	3,248,367,641	38.4838	11.3986	0.0006752	1481
1482	2,196,324	3,254,952,168	38.4968	11.4012	0.0006748	1482
1483	2,199,289	3,261,545,587	38.5097	11.4037	0.0006743	1483
1484	2,202,256	3,268,147,904	38.5227	11.4063	0.0006739	1484
1485	2,205,225	3,274,759,125	38.5357	11.4089	0.0006734	1485
1486	2,208,196	3,281,379,256	38.5487	11.4114	0.0006729	1486
1487	2,211,169	3,288,008,303	38.5616	11.4140	0.0006725	1487
1488	2,214,144	3,294,646,272	38.5746	11.4165	0.0006720	1488
1489	2,217,121	3,301,293,169	38.5876	11.4191	0.0006716	1489
1490	2,220,100	3,307,949,000	38.6005	11.4216	0.0006711	1490
1491	2,223,081	3,314,613,771	38.6135	11.4242	0.0006707	1491
1492	2,226,064	3,321,287,488	38.6264	11.4268	0.0006702	1492
1493	2,229,049	3,327,970,157	38.6394	11.4293	0.0006698	1493
1494	2,232,036	3,334,661,784	38.6523	11.4319	0.0006693	1494
1495	2,235,025	3,341,362,375	38.6652	11.4344	0.0006689	1495
1496	2,238,016	3,348,071,936	38.6782	11.4370	0.0006684	1496
1497	2,241,009	3,354,790,473	38.6911	11.4395	0.0006680	1497
1498	2,244,004	3,361,517,992	38.7040	11.4421	0.0006676	1498
1499	2,247,001	3,368,254,499	38.7169	11.4446	0.0006671	1499
1500	2,250,000	3,375,000,000	38.7298	11.4471	0.0006667	1500

Powers, Roots and Reciprocals

No.	Square	Cube	Sq. Root	Cube Root	Reciprocal	No.
1501	2,253,001	3,381,754,501	38.7427	11.4497	0.0006662	1501
1502	2,256,004	3,388,518,008	38.7556	11.4522	0.0006658	1502
1503	2,259,009	3,395,290,527	38.7685	11.4548	0.0006653	1503
1504	2,262,016	3,402,072,064	38.7814	11.4573	0.0006649	1504
1505	2,265,025	3,408,862,625	38.7943	11.4598	0.0006645	1505
1506	2,268,036	3,415,662,216	38.8072	11.4624	0.0006640	1506
1507	2,271,049	3,422,470,843	38.8201	11.4649	0.0006636	1507
1508	2,274,064	3,429,288,512	38.8330	11.4675	0.0006631	1508
1509	2,277,081	3,436,115,229	38.8458	11.4700	0.0006627	1509
1510	2,280,100	3,442,951,000	38.8587	11.4725	0.0006623	1510
1511	2,283,121	3,449,795,831	38.8716	11.4751	0.0006618	1511
1512	2,286,144	3,456,649,728	38.8844	11.4776	0.0006614	1512
1513	2,289,169	3,463,512,697	38.8973	11.4801	0.0006609	1513
1514	2,292,196	3,470,384,744	38.9102	11.4826	0.0006605	1514
1515	2,295,225	3,477,265,875	38.9230	11.4852	0.0006601	1515
1516	2,298,256	3,484,156,096	38.9358	11.4877	0.0006596	1516
1517	2,301,289	3,491,055,413	38.9487	11.4902	0.0006592	1517
1518	2,304,324	3,497,963,832	38.9615	11.4927	0.0006588	1518
1519	2,307,361	3,504,881,359	38.9744	11.4953	0.0006583	1519
1520	2,310,400	3,511,808,000	38.9872	11.4978	0.0006579	1520
1521	2,313,441	3,518,743,761	39.0000	11.5003	0.0006575	1521
1522	2,316,484	3,525,688,648	39.0128	11.5028	0.0006570	1522
1523	2,319,529	3,532,642,667	39.0256	11.5054	0.0006566	1523
1524	2,322,576	3,539,605,824	39.0384	11.5079	0.0006562	1524
1525	2,325,625	3,546,578,125	39.0512	11.5104	0.0006557	1525
1526	2,328,676	3,553,559,576	39.0640	11.5129	0.0006553	1526
1527	2,331,729	3,560,550,183	39.0768	11.5154	0.0006549	1527
1528	2,334,784	3,567,549,952	39.0896	11.5179	0.0006545	1528
1529	2,337,841	3,574,558,889	39.1024	11.5204	0.0006540	1529
1530	2,340,900	3,581,577,000	39.1152	11.5230	0.0006536	1530
1531	2,343,961	3,588,604,291	39.1280	11.5255	0.0006532	1531
1532	2,347,024	3,595,640,768	39.1408	11.5280	0.0006527	1532
1533	2,350,089	3,602,686,437	39.1535	11.5305	0.0006523	1533
1534	2,353,156	3,609,741,304	39.1663	11.5330	0.0006519	1534
1535	2,356,225	3,616,805,375	39.1791	11.5355	0.0006515	1535
1536	2,359,296	3,623,878,656	39.1918	11.5380	0.0006510	1536
1537	2,362,369	3,630,961,153	39.2046	11.5405	0.0006506	1537
1538	2,365,444	3,638,052,872	39.2173	11.5430	0.0006502	1538
1539	2,368,521	3,645,153,819	39.2301	11.5455	0.0006498	1539
1540	2,371,600	3,652,264,000	39.2428	11.5480	0.0006494	1540
1541	2,374,681	3,659,383,421	39.2556	11.5505	0.0006489	1541
1542	2,377,764	3,666,512,088	39.2683	11.5530	0.0006485	1542
1543	2,380,849	3,673,650,007	39.2810	11.5555	0.0006481	1543
1544	2,383,936	3,680,797,184	39.2938	11.5580	0.0006477	1544
1545	2,387,025	3,687,953,625	39.3065	11.5605	0.0006472	1545
1546	2,390,116	3,695,119,336	39.3192	11.5630	0.0006468	1546
1547	2,393,209	3,702,294,323	39.3319	11.5655	0.0006464	1547
1548	2,396,304	3,709,478,592	39.3446	11.5680	0.0006460	1548
1549	2,399,401	3,716,672,149	39.3573	11.5705	0.0006456	1549
1550	2,402,500	3,723,875,000	39.3700	11.5729	0.0006452	1550

Powers, Roots and Reciprocals

No.	Square	Cube	Sq. Root	Cube Root	Reciprocal	No.
1551	2,405,601	3,731,087,151	39.3827	11.5754	0.0006447	1551
1552	2,408,704	3,738,308,608	39.3954	11.5779	0.0006443	1552
1553	2,411,809	3,745,539,377	39.4081	11.5804	0.0006439	1553
1554	2,414,916	3,752,779,464	39.4208	11.5829	0.0006435	1554
1555	2,418,025	3,760,028,875	39.4335	11.5854	0.0006431	1555
1556	2,421,136	3,767,287,616	39.4462	11.5879	0.0006427	1556
1557	2,424,249	3,774,555,693	39.4588	11.5903	0.0006423	1557
1558	2,427,364	3,781,833,112	39.4715	11.5928	0.0006418	1558
1559	2,430,481	3,789,119,879	39.4842	11.5953	0.0006414	1559
1560	2,433,600	3,796,416,000	39.4968	11.5978	0.0006410	1560
1561	2,436,721	3,803,721,481	39.5095	11.6003	0.0006406	1561
1562	2,439,844	3,811,036,328	39.5221	11.6027	0.0006402	1562
1563	2,442,969	3,818,360,547	39.5348	11.6052	0.0006398	1563
1564	2,446,096	3,825,694,144	39.5474	11.6077	0.0006394	1564
1565	2,449,225	3,833,037,125	39.5601	11.6102	0.0006390	1565
1566	2,452,356	3,840,389,496	39.5727	11.6126	0.0006386	1566
1567	2,455,489	3,847,751,263	39.5854	11.6151	0.0006382	1567
1568	2,458,624	3,855,122,432	39.5980	11.6176	0.0006378	1568
1569	2,461,761	3,862,503,009	39.6106	11.6200	0.0006373	1569
1570	2,464,900	3,869,893,000	39.6232	11.6225	0.0006369	1570
1571	2,468,041	3,877,292,411	39.6358	11.6250	0.0006365	1571
1572	2,471,184	3,884,701,248	39.6485	11.6274	0.0006361	1572
1573	2,474,329	3,892,119,517	39.6611	11.6299	0.0006357	1573
1574	2,477,476	3,899,547,224	39.6737	11.6324	0.0006353	1574
1575	2,480,625	3,906,984,375	39.6863	11.6348	0.0006349	1575
1576	2,483,776	3,914,430,976	39.6989	11.6373	0.0006345	1576
1577	2,486,929	3,921,887,033	39.7115	11.6398	0.0006341	1577
1578	2,490,084	3,929,352,552	39.7240	11.6422	0.0006337	1578
1579	2,493,241	3,936,827,539	39.7366	11.6447	0.0006333	1579
1580	2,496,400	3,944,312,000	39.7492	11.6471	0.0006329	1580
1581	2,499,561	3,951,805,941	39.7618	11.6496	0.0006325	1581
1582	2,502,724	3,959,309,368	39.7744	11.6520	0.0006321	1582
1583	2,505,889	3,966,822,287	39.7869	11.6545	0.0006317	1583
1584	2,509,056	3,974,344,704	39.7995	11.6570	0.0006313	1584
1585	2,512,225	3,981,876,625	39.8121	11.6594	0.0006309	1585
1586	2,515,396	3,989,418,056	39.8246	11.6619	0.0006305	1586
1587	2,518,569	3,996,969,003	39.8372	11.6643	0.0006301	1587
1588	2,521,744	4,004,529,472	39.8497	11.6668	0.0006297	1588
1589	2,524,921	4,012,099,469	39.8623	11.6692	0.0006293	1589
1590	2,528,100	4,019,679,000	39.8748	11.6717	0.0006289	1590
1591	2,531,281	4,027,268,071	39.8873	11.6741	0.0006285	1591
1592	2,534,464	4,034,866,688	39.8999	11.6765	0.0006281	1592
1593	2,537,649	4,042,474,857	39.9124	11.6790	0.0006277	1593
1594	2,540,836	4,050,092,584	39.9249	11.6814	0.0006274	1594
1595	2,544,025	4,057,719,875	39.9375	11.6839	0.0006270	1595
1596	2,547,216	4,065,356,736	39.9500	11.6863	0.0006266	1596
1597	2,550,409	4,073,003,173	39.9625	11.6887	0.0006262	1597
1598	2,553,604	4,080,659,192	39.9750	11.6912	0.0006258	1598
1599	2,556,801	4,088,324,799	39.9875	11.6936	0.0006254	1599
1600	2,560,000	4,096,000,000	40.0000	11.6961	0.0006250	1600

Powers, Roots and Reciprocals

No.	Square	Cube	Sq. Root	Cube Root	Reciprocal	No.
1601	2,563,201	4,103,684,801	40.0125	11.6985	0.0006246	1601
1602	2,566,404	4,111,379,208	40.0250	11.7009	0.0006242	1602
1603	2,569,609	4,119,083,227	40.0375	11.7034	0.0006238	1603
1604	2,572,816	4,126,796,864	40.0500	11.7058	0.0006234	1604
1605	2,576,025	4,134,520,125	40.0625	11.7082	0.0006231	1605
1606	2,579,236	4,142,253,016	40.0749	11.7107	0.0006227	1606
1607	2,582,449	4,149,995,543	40.0874	11.7131	0.0006223	1607
1608	2,585,664	4,157,747,712	40.0999	11.7155	0.0006219	1608
1609	2,588,881	4,165,509,529	40.1123	11.7180	0.0006215	1609
1610	2,592,100	4,173,281,000	40.1248	11.7204	0.0006211	1610
1611	2,595,321	4,181,062,131	40.1373	11.7228	0.0006207	1611
1612	2,598,544	4,188,852,928	40.1497	11.7252	0.0006203	1612
1613	2,601,769	4,196,653,397	40.1622	11.7277	0.0006200	1613
1614	2,604,996	4,204,463,544	40.1746	11.7301	0.0006196	1614
1615	2,608,225	4,212,283,375	40.1871	11.7325	0.0006192	1615
1616	2,611,456	4,220,112,896	40.1995	11.7349	0.0006188	1616
1617	2,614,689	4,227,952,113	40.2119	11.7373	0.0006184	1617
1618	2,617,924	4,235,801,032	40.2244	11.7398	0.0006180	1618
1619	2,621,161	4,243,659,659	40.2368	11.7422	0.0006177	1619
1620	2,624,400	4,251,528,000	40.2492	11.7446	0.0006173	1620
1621	2,627,641	4,259,406,061	40.2616	11.7470	0.0006169	1621
1622	2,630,884	4,267,293,848	40.2741	11.7494	0.0006165	1622
1623	2,634,129	4,275,191,367	40.2865	11.7518	0.0006161	1623
1624	2,637,376	4,283,098,624	40.2989	11.7543	0.0006158	1624
1625	2,640,625	4,291,015,625	40.3113	11.7567	0.0006154	1625
1626	2,643,876	4,298,942,376	40.3237	11.7591	0.0006150	1626
1627	2,647,129	4,306,878,883	40.3361	11.7615	0.0006146	1627
1628	2,650,384	4,314,825,152	40.3485	11.7639	0.0006143	1628
1629	2,653,641	4,322,781,189	40.3609	11.7663	0.0006139	1629
1630	2,656,900	4,330,747,000	40.3733	11.7687	0.0006135	1630
1631	2,660,161	4,338,722,591	40.3856	11.7711	0.0006131	1631
1632	2,663,424	4,346,707,968	40.3980	11.7735	0.0006127	1632
1633	2,666,689	4,354,703,137	40.4104	11.7759	0.0006124	1633
1634	2,669,956	4,362,708,104	40.4228	11.7783	0.0006120	1634
1635	2,673,225	4,370,722,875	40.4351	11.7807	0.0006116	1635
1636	2,676,496	4,378,747,456	40.4475	11.7831	0.0006112	1636
1637	2,679,769	4,386,781,853	40.4599	11.7855	0.0006109	1637
1638	2,683,044	4,394,826,072	40.4722	11.7879	0.0006105	1638
1639	2,686,321	4,402,880,119	40.4846	11.7903	0.0006101	1639
1640	2,689,600	4,410,944,000	40.4969	11.7927	0.0006098	1640
1641	2,692,881	4,419,017,721	40.5093	11.7951	0.0006094	1641
1642	2,696,164	4,427,101,288	40.5216	11.7975	0.0006090	1642
1643	2,699,449	4,435,194,707	40.5339	11.7999	0.0006086	1643
1644	2,702,736	4,443,297,984	40.5463	11.8023	0.0006083	1644
1645	2,706,025	4,451,411,125	40.5586	11.8047	0.0006079	1645
1646	2,709,316	4,459,534,136	40.5709	11.8071	0.0006075	1646
1647	2,712,609	4,467,667,023	40.5832	11.8095	0.0006072	1647
1648	2,715,904	4,475,809,792	40.5956	11.8119	0.0006068	1648
1649	2,719,201	4,483,962,449	40.6079	11.8143	0.0006064	1649
1650	2,722,500	4,492,125,000	40.6202	11.8167	0.0006061	1650

Powers, Roots and Reciprocals

No.	Square	Cube	Sq. Root	Cube Root	Reciprocal	No.
1651	2,725,801	4,500,297,451	40.6325	11.8190	0.0006057	1651
1652	2,729,104	4,508,479,808	40.6448	11.8214	0.0006053	1652
1653	2,732,409	4,516,672,077	40.6571	11.8238	0.0006050	1653
1654	2,735,716	4,524,874,264	40.6694	11.8262	0.0006046	1654
1655	2,739,025	4,533,086,375	40.6817	11.8286	0.0006042	1655
1656	2,742,336	4,541,308,416	40.6940	11.8310	0.0006039	1656
1657	2,745,649	4,549,540,393	40.7063	11.8333	0.0006035	1657
1658	2,748,964	4,557,782,312	40.7185	11.8357	0.0006031	1658
1659	2,752,281	4,566,034,179	40.7308	11.8381	0.0006028	1659
1660	2,755,600	4,574,296,000	40.7431	11.8405	0.0006024	1660
1661	2,758,921	4,582,567,781	40.7554	11.8429	0.0006020	1661
1662	2,762,244	4,590,849,528	40.7676	11.8452	0.0006017	1662
1663	2,765,569	4,599,141,247	40.7799	11.8476	0.0006013	1663
1664	2,768,896	4,607,442,944	40.7922	11.8500	0.0006010	1664
1665	2,772,225	4,615,754,625	40.8044	11.8524	0.0006006	1665
1666	2,775,556	4,624,076,296	40.8167	11.8547	0.0006002	1666
1667	2,778,889	4,632,407,963	40.8289	11.8571	0.0005999	1667
1668	2,782,224	4,640,749,632	40.8412	11.8595	0.0005995	1668
1669	2,785,561	4,649,101,309	40.8534	11.8618	0.0005992	1669
1670	2,788,900	4,657,463,000	40.8656	11.8642	0.0005988	1670
1671	2,792,241	4,665,834,711	40.8779	11.8666	0.0005984	1671
1672	2,795,584	4,674,216,448	40.8901	11.8689	0.0005981	1672
1673	2,798,929	4,682,608,217	40.9023	11.8713	0.0005977	1673
1674	2,802,276	4,691,010,024	40.9145	11.8737	0.0005974	1674
1675	2,805,625	4,699,421,875	40.9268	11.8760	0.0005970	1675
1676	2,808,976	4,707,843,776	40.9390	11.8784	0.0005967	1676
1677	2,812,329	4,716,275,733	40.9512	11.8808	0.0005963	1677
1678	2,815,684	4,724,717,752	40.9634	11.8831	0.0005959	1678
1679	2,819,041	4,733,169,839	40.9756	11.8855	0.0005956	1679
1680	2,822,400	4,741,632,000	40.9878	11.8878	0.0005952	1680
1681	2,825,761	4,750,104,241	41.0000	11.8902	0.0005949	1681
1682	2,829,124	4,758,586,568	41.0122	11.8926	0.0005945	1682
1683	2,832,489	4,767,078,987	41.0244	11.8949	0.0005942	1683
1684	2,835,856	4,775,581,504	41.0366	11.8973	0.0005938	1684
1685	2,839,225	4,784,094,125	41.0487	11.8996	0.0005935	1685
1686	2,842,596	4,792,616,856	41.0609	11.9020	0.0005931	1686
1687	2,845,969	4,801,149,703	41.0731	11.9043	0.0005928	1687
1688	2,849,344	4,809,692,672	41.0853	11.9067	0.0005924	1688
1689	2,852,721	4,818,245,769	41.0974	11.9090	0.0005921	1689
1690	2,856,100	4,826,809,000	41.1096	11.9114	0.0005917	1690
1691	2,859,481	4,835,382,371	41.1218	11.9137	0.0005914	1691
1692	2,862,864	4,843,965,888	41.1339	11.9161	0.0005910	1692
1693	2,866,249	4,852,559,557	41.1461	11.9184	0.0005907	1693
1694	2,869,636	4,861,163,384	41.1582	11.9208	0.0005903	1694
1695	2,873,025	4,869,777,375	41.1704	11.9231	0.0005900	1695
1696	2,876,416	4,878,401,536	41.1825	11.9255	0.0005896	1696
1697	2,879,809	4,887,035,873	41.1947	11.9278	0.0005893	1697
1698	2,883,204	4,895,680,392	41.2068	11.9301	0.0005889	1698
1699	2,886,601	4,904,335,099	41.2189	11.9325	0.0005886	1699
1700	2,890,000	4,913,000,000	41.2311	11.9348	0.0005882	1700

Powers, Roots and Reciprocals

No.	Square	Cube	Sq. Root	Cube Root	Reciprocal	No.
1701	2,893,401	4,921,675,101	41.2432	11.9372	0.0005879	1701
1702	2,896,804	4,930,360,408	41.2553	11.9395	0.0005875	1702
1703	2,900,209	4,939,055,927	41.2674	11.9418	0.0005872	1703
1704	2,903,616	4,947,761,664	41.2795	11.9442	0.0005869	1704
1705	2,907,025	4,956,477,625	41.2916	11.9465	0.0005865	1705
1706	2,910,436	4,965,203,816	41.3038	11.9489	0.0005862	1706
1707	2,913,849	4,973,940,243	41.3159	11.9512	0.0005858	1707
1708	2,917,264	4,982,686,912	41.3280	11.9535	0.0005855	1708
1709	2,920,681	4,991,443,829	41.3401	11.9559	0.0005851	1709
1710	2,924,100	5,000,211,000	41.3521	11.9582	0.0005848	1710
1711	2,927,521	5,008,988,431	41.3642	11.9605	0.0005845	1711
1712	2,930,944	5,017,776,128	41.3763	11.9628	0.0005841	1712
1713	2,934,369	5,026,574,097	41.3884	11.9652	0.0005838	1713
1714	2,937,796	5,035,382,344	41.4005	11.9675	0.0005834	1714
1715	2,941,225	5,044,200,875	41.4126	11.9698	0.0005831	1715
1716	2,944,656	5,053,029,696	41.4246	11.9722	0.0005828	1716
1717	2,948,089	5,061,868,813	41.4367	11.9745	0.0005824	1717
1718	2,951,524	5,070,718,232	41.4488	11.9768	0.0005821	1718
1719	2,954,961	5,079,577,959	41.4608	11.9791	0.0005817	1719
1720	2,958,400	5,088,448,000	41.4729	11.9815	0.0005814	1720
1721	2,961,841	5,097,328,361	41.4849	11.9838	0.0005811	1721
1722	2,965,284	5,106,219,048	41.4970	11.9861	0.0005807	1722
1723	2,968,729	5,115,120,067	41.5090	11.9884	0.0005804	1723
1724	2,972,176	5,124,031,424	41.5211	11.9907	0.0005800	1724
1725	2,975,625	5,132,953,125	41.5331	11.9931	0.0005797	1725
1726	2,979,076	5,141,885,176	41.5452	11.9954	0.0005794	1726
1727	2,982,529	5,150,827,583	41.5572	11.9977	0.0005790	1727
1728	2,985,984	5,159,780,352	41.5692	12.0000	0.0005787	1728
1729	2,989,441	5,168,743,489	41.5812	12.0023	0.0005784	1729
1730	2,992,900	5,177,717,000	41.5933	12.0046	0.0005780	1730
1731	2,996,361	5,186,700,891	41.6053	12.0069	0.0005777	1731
1732	2,999,824	5,195,695,168	41.6173	12.0093	0.0005774	1732
1733	3,003,289	5,204,699,837	41.6293	12.0116	0.0005770	1733
1734	3,006,756	5,213,714,904	41.6413	12.0139	0.0005767	1734
1735	3,010,225	5,222,740,375	41.6533	12.0162	0.0005764	1735
1736	3,013,696	5,231,776,256	41.6653	12.0185	0.0005760	1736
1737	3,017,169	5,240,822,553	41.6773	12.0208	0.0005757	1737
1738	3,020,644	5,249,879,272	41.6893	12.0231	0.0005754	1738
1739	3,024,121	5,258,946,419	41.7013	12.0254	0.0005750	1739
1740	3,027,600	5,268,024,000	41.7133	12.0277	0.0005747	1740
1741	3,031,081	5,277,112,021	41.7253	12.0300	0.0005744	1741
1742	3,034,564	5,286,210,488	41.7373	12.0323	0.0005741	1742
1743	3,038,049	5,295,319,407	41.7493	12.0346	0.0005737	1743
1744	3,041,536	5,304,438,784	41.7612	12.0369	0.0005734	1744
1745	3,045,025	5,313,568,625	41.7732	12.0392	0.0005731	1745
1746	3,048,516	5,322,708,936	41.7852	12.0415	0.0005727	1746
1747	3,052,009	5,331,859,723	41.7971	12.0438	0.0005724	1747
1748	3,055,504	5,341,020,992	41.8091	12.0461	0.0005721	1748
1749	3,059,001	5,350,192,749	41.8210	12.0484	0.0005718	1749
1750	3,062,500	5,359,375,000	41.8330	12.0507	0.0005714	1750

Powers, Roots and Reciprocals

No.	Square	Cube	Sq. Root	Cube Root	Reciprocal	No.
1751	3,066,001	5,368,567,751	41.8450	12.0530	0.0005711	1751
1752	3,069,504	5,377,771,008	41.8569	12.0553	0.0005708	1752
1753	3,073,009	5,386,984,777	41.8688	12.0576	0.0005705	1753
1754	3,076,516	5,396,209,064	41.8808	12.0599	0.0005701	1754
1755	3,080,025	5,405,443,875	41.8927	12.0622	0.0005698	1755
1756	3,083,536	5,414,689,216	41.9047	12.0645	0.0005695	1756
1757	3,087,049	5,423,945,093	41.9166	12.0668	0.0005692	1757
1758	3,090,564	5,433,211,512	41.9285	12.0690	0.0005688	1758
1759	3,094,081	5,442,488,479	41.9404	12.0713	0.0005685	1759
1760	3,097,600	5,451,776,000	41.9524	12.0736	0.0005682	1760
1761	3,101,121	5,461,074,081	41.9643	12.0759	0.0005679	1761
1762	3,104,644	5,470,382,728	41.9762	12.0782	0.0005675	1762
1763	3,108,169	5,479,701,947	41.9881	12.0805	0.0005672	1763
1764	3,111,696	5,489,031,744	42.0000	12.0828	0.0005669	1764
1765	3,115,225	5,498,372,125	42.0119	12.0850	0.0005666	1765
1766	3,118,756	5,507,723,096	42.0238	12.0873	0.0005663	1766
1767	3,122,289	5,517,084,663	42.0357	12.0896	0.0005659	1767
1768	3,125,824	5,526,456,832	42.0476	12.0919	0.0005656	1768
1769	3,129,361	5,535,839,609	42.0595	12.0942	0.0005653	1769
1770	3,132,900	5,545,233,000	42.0714	12.0964	0.0005650	1770
1771	3,136,441	5,554,637,011	42.0833	12.0987	0.0005647	1771
1772	3,139,984	5,564,051,648	42.0951	12.1010	0.0005643	1772
1773	3,143,529	5,573,476,917	42.1070	12.1033	0.0005640	1773
1774	3,147,076	5,582,912,824	42.1189	12.1056	0.0005637	1774
1775	3,150,625	5,592,359,375	42.1307	12.1078	0.0005634	1775
1776	3,154,176	5,601,816,576	42.1426	12.1101	0.0005631	1776
1777	3,157,729	5,611,284,433	42.1545	12.1124	0.0005627	1777
1778	3,161,284	5,620,762,952	42.1663	12.1146	0.0005624	1778
1779	3,164,841	5,630,252,139	42.1782	12.1169	0.0005621	1779
1780	3,168,400	5,639,752,000	42.1900	12.1192	0.0005618	1780
1781	3,171,961	5,649,262,541	42.2019	12.1215	0.0005615	1781
1782	3,175,524	5,658,783,768	42.2137	12.1237	0.0005612	1782
1783	3,179,089	5,668,315,687	42.2256	12.1260	0.0005609	1783
1784	3,182,656	5,677,858,304	42.2374	12.1283	0.0005605	1784
1785	3,186,225	5,687,411,625	42.2493	12.1305	0.0005602	1785
1786	3,189,796	5,696,975,656	42.2611	12.1328	0.0005599	1786
1787	3,193,369	5,706,550,403	42.2729	12.1350	0.0005596	1787
1788	3,196,944	5,716,135,872	42.2847	12.1373	0.0005593	1788
1789	3,200,521	5,725,732,069	42.2966	12.1396	0.0005590	1789
1790	3,204,100	5,735,339,000	42.3084	12.1418	0.0005587	1790
1791	3,207,681	5,744,956,671	42.3202	12.1441	0.0005585	1791
1792	3,211,264	5,754,585,088	42.3320	12.1464	0.0005580	1792
1793	3,214,849	5,764,224,257	42.3438	12.1486	0.0005577	1793
1794	3,218,436	5,773,874,184	42.3556	12.1509	0.0005574	1794
1795	3,222,025	5,783,534,875	42.3674	12.1531	0.0005571	1795
1796	3,225,616	5,793,206,336	42.3792	12.1554	0.0005568	1796
1797	3,229,209	5,802,888,573	42.3910	12.1576	0.0005565	1797
1798	3,232,804	5,812,581,592	42.4028	12.1599	0.0005562	1798
1799	3,236,401	5,822,285,399	42.4146	12.1622	0.0005559	1799
1800	3,240,000	5,832,000,000	42.4264	12.1644	0.0005556	1800

Powers, Roots and Reciprocals

No.	Square	Cube	Sq. Root	Cube Root	Reciprocal	No.
1801	3,243,601	5,841,725,401	42.4382	12.1667	0.0005552	1801
1802	3,247,204	5,851,461,608	42.4500	12.1689	0.0005549	1802
1803	3,250,809	5,861,208,627	42.4617	12.1712	0.0005546	1803
1804	3,254,416	5,870,966,464	42.4735	12.1734	0.0005543	1804
1805	3,258,025	5,880,735,125	42.4853	12.1757	0.0005540	1805
1806	3,261,636	5,890,514,616	42.4971	12.1779	0.0005537	1806
1807	3,265,249	5,900,304,943	42.5088	12.1802	0.0005534	1807
1808	3,268,864	5,910,106,112	42.5206	12.1824	0.0005531	1808
1809	3,272,481	5,919,918,129	42.5323	12.1846	0.0005528	1809
1810	3,276,100	5,929,741,000	42.5441	12.1869	0.0005525	1810
1811	3,279,721	5,939,574,731	42.5558	12.1891	0.0005522	1811
1812	3,283,344	5,949,419,328	42.5676	12.1914	0.0005519	1812
1813	3,286,969	5,959,274,797	42.5793	12.1936	0.0005516	1813
1814	3,290,596	5,969,141,144	42.5911	12.1959	0.0005513	1814
1815	3,294,225	5,979,018,375	42.6028	12.1981	0.0005510	1815
1816	3,297,856	5,988,906,496	42.6146	12.2003	0.0005507	1816
1817	3,301,489	5,998,805,513	42.6263	12.2026	0.0005504	1817
1818	3,305,124	6,008,715,432	42.6380	12.2048	0.0005501	1818
1819	3,308,761	6,018,636,259	42.6497	12.2071	0.0005498	1819
1820	3,312,400	6,028,568,000	42.6615	12.2093	0.0005495	1820
1821	3,316,041	6,038,510,661	42.6732	12.2115	0.0005491	1821
1822	3,319,684	6,048,464,248	42.6849	12.2138	0.0005488	1822
1823	3,323,329	6,058,428,767	42.6966	12.2160	0.0005485	1823
1824	3,326,976	6,068,404,224	42.7083	12.2182	0.0005482	1824
1825	3,330,625	6,078,390,625	42.7200	12.2205	0.0005479	1825
1826	3,334,276	6,088,387,976	42.7317	12.2227	0.0005476	1826
1827	3,337,929	6,098,396,283	42.7434	12.2249	0.0005473	1827
1828	3,341,584	6,108,415,552	42.7551	12.2272	0.0005470	1828
1829	3,345,241	6,118,445,789	42.7668	12.2294	0.0005467	1829
1830	3,348,900	6,128,487,000	42.7785	12.2316	0.0005464	1830
1831	3,352,561	6,138,539,191	42.7902	12.2338	0.0005461	1831
1832	3,356,224	6,148,602,368	42.8019	12.2361	0.0005459	1832
1833	3,359,889	6,158,676,537	42.8135	12.2383	0.0005456	1833
1834	3,363,556	6,168,761,704	42.8252	12.2405	0.0005453	1834
1835	3,367,225	6,178,857,875	42.8369	12.2427	0.0005450	1835
1836	3,370,896	6,188,965,056	42.8486	12.2450	0.0005447	1836
1837	3,374,569	6,199,083,253	42.8602	12.2472	0.0005444	1837
1838	3,378,244	6,209,212,472	42.8719	12.2494	0.0005441	1838
1839	3,381,921	6,219,352,719	42.8836	12.2516	0.0005438	1839
1840	3,385,600	6,229,504,000	42.8952	12.2539	0.0005435	1840
1841	3,389,281	6,239,666,321	42.9069	12.2561	0.0005432	1841
1842	3,392,964	6,249,839,688	42.9185	12.2583	0.0005429	1842
1843	3,396,649	6,260,024,107	42.9302	12.2605	0.0005426	1843
1844	3,400,336	6,270,219,584	42.9418	12.2627	0.0005423	1844
1845	3,404,025	6,280,426,125	42.9535	12.2649	0.0005420	1845
1846	3,407,716	6,290,643,736	42.9651	12.2672	0.0005417	1846
1847	3,411,409	6,300,872,423	42.9767	12.2694	0.0005414	1847
1848	3,415,104	6,311,112,192	42.9884	12.2716	0.0005411	1848
1849	3,418,801	6,321,363,049	43.0000	12.2738	0.0005408	1849
1850	3,422,500	6,331,625,000	43.0116	12.2760	0.0005405	1850

Powers, Roots and Reciprocals

No.	Square	Cube	Sq. Root	Cube Root	Reciprocal	No.
1851	3,426,201	6,341,898,051	43.0232	12.2782	0.0005402	1851
1852	3,429,904	6,352,182,208	43.0349	12.2804	0.0005400	1852
1853	3,433,609	6,362,477,477	43.0465	12.2826	0.0005397	1853
1854	3,437,316	6,372,783,864	43.0581	12.2849	0.0005394	1854
1855	3,441,025	6,383,101,375	43.0697	12.2871	0.0005391	1855
1856	3,444,736	6,393,430,016	43.0813	12.2893	0.0005388	1856
1857	3,448,449	6,403,769,793	43.0929	12.2915	0.0005385	1857
1858	3,452,164	6,414,120,712	43.1045	12.2937	0.0005382	1858
1859	3,455,881	6,424,482,779	43.1161	12.2959	0.0005379	1859
1860	3,459,600	6,434,856,000	43.1277	12.2981	0.0005376	1860
1861	3,463,321	6,445,240,381	43.1393	12.3003	0.0005373	1861
1862	3,467,044	6,455,635,928	43.1509	12.3025	0.0005371	1862
1863	3,470,769	6,466,042,647	43.1625	12.3047	0.0005368	1863
1864	3,474,496	6,476,460,544	43.1741	12.3069	0.0005365	1864
1865	3,478,225	6,486,889,625	43.1856	12.3091	0.0005362	1865
1866	3,481,956	6,497,329,896	43.1972	12.3113	0.0005359	1866
1867	3,485,689	6,507,781,363	43.2088	12.3135	0.0005356	1867
1868	3,489,424	6,518,244,032	43.2204	12.3157	0.0005353	1868
1869	3,493,161	6,528,717,909	43.2319	12.3179	0.0005350	1869
1870	3,496,900	6,539,203,000	43.2435	12.3201	0.0005348	1870
1871	3,500,641	6,549,699,311	43.2551	12.3223	0.0005345	1871
1872	3,504,384	6,560,206,848	43.2666	12.3245	0.0005342	1872
1873	3,508,129	6,570,725,617	43.2782	12.3267	0.0005339	1873
1874	3,511,876	6,581,255,624	43.2897	12.3289	0.0005336	1874
1875	3,515,625	6,591,796,875	43.3013	12.3311	0.0005333	1875
1876	3,519,376	6,602,349,376	43.3128	12.3333	0.0005330	1876
1877	3,523,129	6,612,913,133	43.3244	12.3354	0.0005328	1877
1878	3,526,884	6,623,488,152	43.3359	12.3376	0.0005325	1878
1879	3,530,641	6,634,074,439	43.3474	12.3398	0.0005322	1879
1880	3,534,400	6,644,672,000	43.3590	12.3420	0.0005319	1880
1881	3,538,161	6,655,280,841	43.3705	12.3442	0.0005316	1881
1882	3,541,924	6,665,900,968	43.3820	12.3464	0.0005313	1882
1883	3,545,689	6,676,532,387	43.3935	12.3486	0.0005311	1883
1884	3,549,456	6,687,175,104	43.4051	12.3508	0.0005308	1884
1885	3,553,225	6,697,829,125	43.4166	12.3529	0.0005305	1885
1886	3,556,996	6,708,494,456	43.4281	12.3551	0.0005302	1886
1887	3,560,769	6,719,171,103	43.4396	12.3573	c 0005299	1887
1888	3,564,544	6,729,859,072	43.4511	12.3595	0.0005297	1888
1889	3,568,321	6,740,558,369	43.4626	12.3617	0.0005294	1889
1890	3,572,100	6,751,269,000	43.4741	12.3639	0.0005291	1890
1891	3,575,881	6,761,990,971	43.4856	12 3660	0.0005288	1891
1892	3,579,664	6,772,724,288	43.4971	12.3682	0.0005285	1892
1893	3,583,449	6,783,468,957	43.5086	12.3704	0.0005283	1893
1894	3,587,236	6,794,224,984	43.5201	12.3726	0.0005280	1894
1895	3,591,025	6,804,992,375	43.5316	12.3747	0.0005277	1895
1896	3,594,816	6,815,771,136	43.5431	12.3769	0.0005274	1896
1897	3,598,609	6,826,561,273	43.5546	12.3791	0.0005271	1897
1898	3,602,404	6,837,362,792	43.5660	12.3813	0.0005269	1898
1899	3,606,201	6,848,175,699	43.5775	12.3835	0.0005266	1899
1900	3,610,000	6,859,000,000	43.5890	12.3856	0.0005263	1900

Powers, Roots and Reciprocals

No.	Square	Cube	Sq. Root	Cube Root	Reciprocal	No.
1901	3,613,801	6,869,835,701	43.6005	12.3878	0.0005260	1901
1902	3,617,604	6,880,682,808	43.6119	12.3900	0.0005258	1902
1903	3,621,409	6,891,541,327	43.6234	12.3921	0.0005255	1903
1904	3,625,216	6,902,411,264	43.6348	12.3943	0.0005252	1904
1905	3,629,025	6,913,292,625	43.6463	12.3965	0.0005249	1905
1906	3,632,836	6,924,185,416	43.6578	12.3986	0.0005247	1906
1907	3,636,649	6,935,089,643	43.6692	12.4008	0.0005244	1907
1908	3,640,464	6,946,005,312	43.6807	12.4030	0.0005241	1908
1909	3,644,281	6,956,932,429	43.6921	12.4051	0.0005238	1909
1910	3,648,100	6,967,871,000	43.7035	12.4073	0.0005236	1910
1911	3,651,921	6,978,821,031	43.7150	12.4095	0.0005233	1911
1912	3,655,744	6,989,782,528	43.7264	12.4116	0.0005230	1912
1913	3,659,569	7,000,755,497	43.7379	12.4138	0.0005227	1913
1914	3,663,396	7,011,739,944	43.7493	12.4160	0.0005225	1914
1915	3,667,225	7,022,735,875	43.7607	12.4181	0.0005222	1915
1916	3,671,056	7,033,743,296	43.7721	12.4203	0.0005219	1916
1917	3,674,889	7,044,762,213	43.7836	12.4225	0.0005216	1917
1918	3,678,724	7,055,792,632	43.7950	12.4246	0.0005214	1918
1919	3,682,561	7,066,834,559	43.8064	12.4268	0.0005211	1919
1920	3,686,400	7,077,888,000	43.8178	12.4289	0.0005208	1920
1921	3,690,241	7,088,952,961	43.8292	12.4311	0.0005206	1921
1922	3,694,084	7,100,029,448	43.8406	12.4332	0.0005203	1922
1923	3,697,929	7,111,117,467	43.8520	12.4354	0.0005200	1923
1924	3,701,776	7,122,217,024	43.8634	12.4376	0.0005198	1924
1925	3,705,625	7,133,328,125	43.8748	12.4397	0.0005195	1925
1926	3,709,476	7,144,450,776	43.8862	12.4419	0.0005192	1926
1927	3,713,329	7,155,584,983	43.8976	12.4440	0.0005189	1927
1928	3,717,184	7,166,730,752	43.9090	12.4462	0.0005187	1928
1929	3,721,041	7,177,888,089	43.9204	12.4483	0.0005184	1929
1930	3,724,900	7,189,057,000	43.9318	12.4505	0.0005181	1930
1931	3,728,761	7,200,237,491	43.9431	12.4526	0.0005179	1931
1932	3,732,624	7,211,429,568	43.9545	12.4548	0.0005176	1932
1933	3,736,489	7,222,633,237	43.9659	12.4569	0.0005173	1933
1934	3,740,356	7,233,848,504	43.9773	12.4591	0.0005171	1934
1935	3,744,225	7,245,075,375	43.9886	12.4612	0.0005168	1935
1936	3,748,096	7,256,313,856	44.0000	12.4634	0.0005165	1936
1937	3,751,969	7,267,563,953	44.0114	12.4655	0.0005163	1937
1938	3,755,844	7,278,825,672	44.0227	12.4676	0.0005160	1938
1939	3,759,721	7,290,099,019	44.0341	12.4698	0.0005157	1939
1940	3,763,600	7,301,384,000	44.0454	12.4719	0.0005155	1940
1941	3,767,481	7,312,680,621	44.0568	12.4741	0.0005152	1941
1942	3,771,364	7,323,988,888	44.0681	12.4762	0.0005149	1942
1943	3,775,249	7,335,308,807	44.0795	12.4784	0.0005147	1943
1944	3,779,136	7,346,640,384	44.0908	12.4805	0.0005144	1944
1945	3,783,025	7,357,983,625	44.1022	12.4826	0.0005141	1945
1946	3,786,916	7,369,338,536	44.1135	12.4848	0.0005139	1946
1947	3,790,809	7,380,705,123	44.1248	12.4869	0.0005136	1947
1948	3,794,704	7,392,083,392	44.1362	12.4891	0.0005133	1948
1949	3,798,601	7,403,473,349	44.1475	12.4912	0.0005131	1949
1950	3,802,500	7,414,875,000	44.1588	12.4933	0.0005128	1950

Powers, Roots and Reciprocals

No.	Square	Cube	Sq. Root	Cube Root	Reciprocal	No.
1951	3,806,401	7,426,288,351	44.1701	12.4955	0.0005126	1951
1952	3,810,304	7,437,713,408	44.1814	12.4976	0.0005123	1952
1953	3,814,209	7,449,150,177	44.1928	12.4997	0.0005120	1953
1954	3,818,116	7,460,598,664	44.2041	12.5019	0.0005118	1954
1955	3,822,025	7,472,058,875	44.2154	12.5040	0.0005115	1955
1956	3,825,936	7,483,530,816	44.2267	12.5061	0.0005112	1956
1957	3,829,849	7,495,014,493	44.2380	12.5083	0.0005110	1957
1958	3,833,764	7,506,509,912	44.2493	12.5104	0.0005107	1958
1959	3,837,681	7,518,017,079	44.2606	12.5125	0.0005105	1959
1960	3,841,600	7,529,536,000	44.2719	12.5146	0.0005102	1960
1961	3,845,521	7,541,066,681	44.2832	12.5168	0.0005099	1961
1962	3,849,444	7,552,609,128	44.2945	12.5189	0.0005097	1962
1963	3,853,369	7,564,163,347	44.3058	12.5210	0.0005094	1963
1964	3,857,296	7,575,729,344	44.3170	12.5232	0.0005092	1964
1965	3,861,225	7,587,307,125	44.3283	12.5253	0.0005089	1965
1966	3,865,156	7,598,896,696	44.3396	12.5274	0.0005086	1966
1967	3,869,089	7,610,498,063	44.3509	12.5295	0.0005084	1967
1968	3,873,024	7,622,111,232	44.3621	12.5317	0.0005081	1968
1969	3,876,961	7,633,736,209	44.3734	12.5338	0.0005079	1969
1970	3,880,900	7,645,373,000	44.3847	12.5359	0.0005076	1970
1971	3,884,841	7,657,021,611	44.3959	12.5380	0.0005074	1971
1972	3,888,784	7,668,682,048	44.4072	12.5401	0.0005071	1972
1973	3,892,729	7,680,354,317	44.4185	12.5423	0.0005068	1973
1974	3,896,676	7,692,038,424	44.4297	12.5444	0.0005066	1974
1975	3,900,625	7,703,734,375	44.4410	12.5465	0.0005063	1975
1976	3,904,576	7,715,442,176	44.4522	12.5486	0.0005061	1976
1977	3,908,529	7,727,161,833	44.4635	12.5507	0.0005058	1977
1978	3,912,484	7,738,893,352	44.4747	12.5528	0.0005056	1978
1979	3,916,441	7,750,636,739	44.4860	12.5550	0.0005053	1979
1980	3,920,400	7,762,392,000	44.4972	12.5571	0.0005051	1980
1981	3,924,361	7,774,159,141	44.5084	12.5592	0.0005048	1981
1982	3,928,324	7,785,938,168	44.5197	12.5613	0.0005045	1982
1983	3,932,289	7,797,729,087	44.5309	12.5634	0.0005043	1983
1984	3,936,256	7,809,531,904	44.5421	12.5655	0.0005040	1984
1985	3,940,225	7,821,346,625	44.5533	12.5676	0.0005038	1985
1986	3,944,196	7,833,173,256	44.5646	12.5697	0.0005035	1986
1987	3,948,169	7,845,011,803	44.5758	12.5719	0.0005033	1987
1988	3,952,144	7,856,862,272	44.5870	12.5740	0.0005030	1988
1989	3,956,121	7,858,724,669	44.5982	12.5761	0.0005028	1989
1990	3,960,100	7,880,599,000	44.6094	12.5782	0.0005025	1990
1991	3,964,081	7,892,485,271	44.6206	12.5803	0.0005023	1991
1992	3,968,064	7,904,383,488	44.6318	12.5824	0.0005020	1992
1993	3,972,049	7,916,293,657	44.6430	12.5845	0.0005018	1993
1994	3,976,036	7,928,215,784	44.6542	12.5866	0.0005015	1994
1995	3,980,025	7,940,149,875	44.6654	12.5887	0.0005013	1995
1996	3,984,016	7,952,095,936	44.6766	12.5908	0.0005010	1996
1997	3,988,009	7,964,053,973	44.6878	12.5929	0.0005008	1997
1998	3,992,004	7,976,023,992	44.6990	12.5950	0.0005005	1998
1999	3,996,001	7,988,005,999	44.7102	12.5971	0.0005003	1999
2000	4,000,000	8,000,000,000	44.7214	12.5992	0.0005000	2000

Squares of Mixed Numbers from 1/64 to 12, by 64ths

I. Squares of Mixed Numbers from 1/64 to 6

	0	1	2	3	4	5
1/64	0.00024	1.03149	4.06274	9.09399	16.12524	25.15649
1/32	0.00098	1.06348	4.12598	9.18848	16.25098	25.31348
3/64	0.00220	1.09595	4.18970	9.28345	16.37720	25.47095
1/16	0.00391	1.12891	4.25391	9.37891	16.50391	25.62891
5/64	0.00610	1.16235	4.31860	9.47485	16.63110	25.78735
3/32	0.00879	1.19629	4.38379	9.57129	16.75879	25.94629
7/64	0.01196	1.23071	4.44946	9.66821	16.88696	26.10571
1/8	0.01562	1.26562	4.51562	9.76562	17.01562	26.26562
9/64	0.01978	1.30103	4.58228	9.86353	17.14478	26.42603
5/32	0.02441	1.33691	4.64941	9.96191	17.27441	26.58691
11/64	0.02954	1.37329	4.71704	10.06079	17.40454	26.74829
3/16	0.03516	1.41016	4.78516	10.16016	17.53516	26.91016
13/64	0.04126	1.44751	4.85376	10.26001	17.66626	27.07251
7/32	0.04785	1.48535	4.92285	10.36035	17.79785	27.23535
15/64	0.05493	1.52368	4.99243	10.46118	17.92993	27.39868
1/4	0.06250	1.56250	5.06250	10.56250	18.06250	27.56250
17/64	0.07056	1.60181	5.13306	10.66431	18.19556	27.72681
9/32	0.07910	1.64160	5.20410	10.76660	18.32910	27.89160
19/64	0.08813	1.68188	5.27563	10.86938	18.46313	28.05688
5/16	0.09766	1.72266	5.34766	10.97266	18.59766	28.22266
21/64	0.10767	1.76392	5.42017	11.07642	18.73267	28.38892
11/32	0.11816	1.80566	5.49316	11.18066	18.86816	28.55566
23/64	0.12915	1.84790	5.56663	11.28540	19.00415	28.72290
3/8	0.14062	1.89062	5.64062	11.39062	19.14062	28.89062
25/64	0.15259	1.93384	5.71509	11.49634	19.27759	29.05884
13/32	0.16504	1.97754	5.79004	11.60254	19.41504	29.22754
27/64	0.17798	2.02173	5.86548	11.70923	19.55298	29.39673
7/16	0.19141	2.06641	5.94141	11.81641	19.69141	29.56641
29/64	0.20532	2.11157	6.01782	11.92407	19.83032	29.73657
15/32	0.21973	2.15723	6.09473	12.03223	19.96973	29.90723
31/64	0.23462	2.20337	6.17212	12.14087	20.10962	30.07837
1/2	0.25000	2.25000	6.25000	12.25000	20.25000	30.25000
33/64	0.26587	2.29712	6.32837	12.35962	20.39087	30.42212
17/32	0.28223	2.34473	6.40723	12.46973	20.53223	30.59473
35/64	0.29907	2.39282	6.48657	12.58032	20.67407	30.76782
9/16	0.31641	2.44141	6.56641	12.69141	20.81641	30.94141
37/64	0.33423	2.49048	6.64673	12.80298	20.95923	31.11548
19/32	0.35254	2.54004	6.72754	12.91504	21.10254	31.29004
39/64	0.37134	2.59009	6.80884	13.02759	21.24634	31.46509
5/8	0.39062	2.64062	6.89062	13.14062	21.39062	31.64062
41/64	0.41040	2.69165	6.97290	13.25415	21.53540	31.81665
21/32	0.43066	2.74316	7.05566	13.36816	21.68066	31.99316

The tables of squares of mixed numbers from 1/64 to 12 are arranged in as compact a manner as possible, and a few words may be necessary to explain their use. Assume, for example, that the square of 8%4 is required; 8 is located at the

Squares of Mixed Numbers from 1/64 to 6 (Continued)

	0	1	2	3	4	5
43/64	0.45142	2.79517	7.13892	13.48267	21.82642	32.17017
11/16	0.47266	2.84766	7.22266	13.59766	21.97266	32.34766
45/64	0.49438	2.90063	7.30688	13.71313	22.11938	32.52563
23/32	0.51660	2.95410	7.39160	13.82910	22.26660	32.70410
47/64	0.53931	3.00806	7.47681	13.94556	22.41431	32.88306
3/4	0.56250	3.06250	7.56250	14.06250	22.56250	33.06250
49/64	0.58618	3.11743	7.64868	14.17993	22.71118	33.24243
25/32	0.61035	3.17285	7.73535	14.29785	22.86035	33.42285
51/64	0.63501	3.22876	7.82251	14.41626	23.01001	33.60376
13/16	0.66016	3.28516	7.91016	14.53516	23.16016	33.78516
53/64	0.68579	3.34204	7.99829	14.65454	23.31079	33.96704
27/32	0.71191	3.39941	8.08691	14.77441	23.46191	34.14941
55/64	0.73853	3.45728	8.17603	14.89478	23.61363	34.33228
7/8	0.76562	3.51562	8.26562	15.01562	23.76562	34.51562
57/64	0.79321	3.57446	8.35571	15.13696	23.91821	34.69946
29/32	0.82129	3.63379	8.44629	15.25879	24.07129	34.88379
59/64	0.84985	3.69360	8.53735	15.38110	24.22485	35.06860
15/16	0.87891	3.75391	8.62891	15.50391	24.37891	35.25391
61/64	0.90845	3.81470	8.72095	15.62720	24.53345	35.43970
31/32	0.93848	3.87598	8.81348	15.75098	24.68848	35.62598
63/64	0.96899	3.93774	8.90649	15.87524	24.84399	35.81274

II. Squares of Mixed Numbers from 6 1/64 to 12

	6	7	8	9	10	11
1/64	36.18774	49.21899	64.25024	81.28149	100.31274	121.34399
1/32	36.37598	49.43848	64.50098	81.56348	100.62598	121.68848
3/64	36.56470	49.65845	64.75220	81.84595	100.93970	122.03345
1/16	36.75391	49.87891	65.00391	82.12891	101.25391	122.37891
5/64	36.94360	50.09985	65.25610	82.41235	101.56860	122.72485
3/32	37.13379	50.32129	65.50879	82.69629	101.88379	123.07129
7/64	37.32446	50.54321	65.76196	82.98071	102.19946	123.41821
1/8	37.51562	50.76562	66.01562	83.26562	102.51562	123.76562
9/64	37.70728	50.98853	66.26978	83.55103	102.83228	124.11353
5/32	37.89941	51.21191	66.52441	83.83691	103.14941	124.46191
11/64	38.09204	51.43579	66.77954	84.12329	103.46704	124.81079
3/16	38.28516	51.66016	67.03516	84.41016	103.78516	125.16016
13/64	38.47876	51.88501	67.29126	84.69751	104.10376	125.51001
7/32	38.67285	52.11035	67.54785	84.98535	104.42285	125.86035
15/64	38.86743	52.33618	67.80493	85.27368	104.74243	126.21110
1/4	39.06250	52.56250	68.06250	85.56250	105.06250	126.56250

top of its column, and 5/64 in the left-hand column. The square is then found to equal 65.25610. In the same way, the square of 3 3/16 is found to equal 10.16016.

Squares of Mixed Numbers from 6¹⁄₆₄ to 12 (Continued)

	6	7	8	9	10	11
1⁷⁄₆₄	39.25806	52.78931	68.32056	85.85181	105.38306	126.91431
⁹⁄₃₂	39.45410	53.01660	68.57910	86.14160	105.70410	127.26660
1⁹⁄₆₄	39.65063	53.24438	68.83813	86.43188	106.02563	127.61938
⁵⁄₁₆	39.84766	53.47266	69.09766	86.72266	106.34766	127.97266
2¹⁄₆₄	40.04517	53.70142	69.35767	87.01392	106.67017	128.32642
11⁄₃₂	40.24316	53.93066	69.61816	87.30566	106.99316	128.68066
2³⁄₆₄	40.44165	54.16040	69.87915	87.59790	107.31665	129.03540
³⁄₈	40.64062	54.39062	70.14062	87.89062	107.64062	129.39062
2⁵⁄₆₄	40.84009	54.62134	70.40259	88.18384	107.96509	129.74634
13⁄₃₂	41.04004	54.85254	70.66504	88.47754	108.29004	130.10254
2⁷⁄₆₄	41.24048	55.08423	70.92798	88.77173	108.61548	130.45923
⁷⁄₁₆	41.44141	55.31641	71.19141	89.06641	108.94141	130.81641
2⁹⁄₆₄	41.64282	55.54907	71.45532	89.36157	109.26782	131.17407
15⁄₃₂	41.84473	55.78223	71.71973	89.65723	109.59473	131.53223
3¹⁄₆₄	42.04712	56.01587	71.98462	89.95337	109.92212	131.89087
¹⁄₂	42.25000	56.25000	72.25000	90.25000	110.25000	132.25000
33⁄₆₄	42.45337	56.48462	72.51587	90.54712	110.57837	132.60962
1⁷⁄₃₂	42.65723	56.71973	72.78223	90.84473	110.90723	132.96973
35⁄₆₄	42.86157	56.95532	73.04907	91.14282	111.23657	133.33032
⁹⁄₁₆	43.06641	57.19141	73.31641	91.44141	111.56641	133.69141
37⁄₆₄	43.27173	57.42798	73.58423	91.74048	111.89673	134.05298
1⁹⁄₃₂	43.47754	57.66504	73.85254	92.04004	112.22754	134.41504
39⁄₆₄	43.68384	57.90259	74.12134	92.34009	112.55884	134.77759
⁵⁄₈	43.89062	58.14062	74.39062	92.64062	112.89062	135.14062
41⁄₆₄	44.09790	58.37915	74.66040	92.94165	113.22290	135.50415
21⁄₃₂	44.30566	58.61816	74.93066	93.24316	113.55566	135.86816
43⁄₆₄	44.51392	58.85767	75.20142	93.54517	113.88892	136.23267
11⁄₁₆	44.72266	59.09766	75.47266	93.84766	114.22266	136.59766
45⁄₆₄	44.93188	59.33813	75.74438	94.15063	114.55688	136.96313
23⁄₃₂	45.14160	59.57910	76.01660	94.45410	114.89160	137.32910
47⁄₆₄	45.35181	59.82056	76.28931	94.75806	115.22681	137.69556
³⁄₄	45.56250	60.06250	76.56250	95.06250	115.56250	138.06250
49⁄₆₄	45.77368	60.30493	76.83618	95.36743	115.89868	138.42993
25⁄₃₂	45.98535	60.54785	77.11035	95.67285	116.23535	138.79785
51⁄₆₄	46.19751	60.79126	77.38501	95.97876	116.57251	139.16626
13⁄₁₆	46.41016	61.03516	77.66016	96.28516	116.91016	139.53516
53⁄₆₄	46.62329	61.27954	77.93579	96.59204	117.24829	139.90454
27⁄₃₂	46.83691	61.52441	78.21191	96.89941	117.58691	140.27441
55⁄₆₄	47.05103	61.76978	78.48853	97.20728	117.92603	140.64478
⁷⁄₈	47.26562	62.01562	78.76562	97.51562	118.26562	141.01562
57⁄₆₄	47.48071	62.26196	79.04321	97.82446	118.60571	141.38696
29⁄₃₂	47.69629	62.50879	79.32129	98.13379	118.94629	141.75879
59⁄₆₄	47.91235	62.75610	79.59985	98.44360	119.28735	142.13110
15⁄₁₆	48.12891	63.00391	79.87891	98.75391	119.62891	142.50391
61⁄₆₄	48.34595	63.25220	80.15845	99.06470	119.97095	142.87720
31⁄₃₂	48.56348	63.50098	80.43848	99.37598	120.31348	143.25098
63⁄₆₄	48.78149	63.75024	80.71899	99.68774	120.65649	143.62524

Squares and Cubes of Numbers from 1/32 to 100
Advancing by 32nds to 2; from 2 to 10 by 16ths; from 10 to 100 by 8ths

No.	Square	Cube	No.	Square	Cube	No.	Square	Cube
1/32	0.000976	0.000031	1 17/32	2.344727	3.590363	4	16.0000	64.0000
1/16	0.003906	0.000244	9/16	2.441406	3.814697	1/16	16.5039	67.0471
3/32	0.008789	0.000824	1 19/32	2.540039	4.048187	1/8	17.0156	70.1895
1/8	0.015625	0.001953	5/8	2.640625	4.291016	3/16	17.5352	73.4285
5/32	0.024414	0.003815	21/32	2.743164	4.543365	1/4	18.0625	76.7656
3/16	0.035156	0.006592	11/16	2.847656	4.805419	5/16	18.5977	80.2024
7/32	0.047852	0.010468	23/32	2.954102	5.077362	3/8	19.1406	83.7402
1/4	0.062500	0.015625	3/4	3.062500	5.359375	7/16	19.6914	87.3806
9/32	0.079102	0.022247	25/32	3.172852	5.651642	1/2	20.2500	91.1250
5/16	0.097656	0.030518	13/16	3.285156	5.954346	9/16	20.8164	94.9749
11/32	0.118164	0.040619	27/32	3.399414	6.267660	5/8	21.3906	98.9316
3/8	0.140625	0.052734	7/8	3.515625	6.591797	11/16	21.9727	102.9968
13/32	0.165039	0.067047	29/32	3.633789	6.926910	3/4	22.5625	107.1719
7/16	0.191406	0.083740	15/16	3.753966	7.273193	13/16	23.1602	111.4583
15/32	0.219727	0.102997	31/32	3.875977	7.630828	7/8	23.7656	115.8574
1/2	0.250000	0.125000	2	4.00000	8.00000	15/16	24.3789	120.3708
17/32	0.282227	0.149933	1/2	4.12598	8.38089	5	25.0000	125.0000
9/16	0.316406	0.177979	1/16	4.25391	8.77368	1/16	25.6289	129.7463
19/32	0.352539	0.209320	1/8	4.51563	9.59570	1/8	26.2656	134.6113
5/8	0.390625	0.244141	3/16	4.78516	10.46754	3/16	26.9102	139.5964
21/32	0.430664	0.282623	1/4	5.06250	11.39063	1/4	27.5625	144.7031
11/16	0.472656	0.324951	5/16	5.34766	12.36646	5/16	28.2227	149.9329
23/32	0.516602	0.371307	3/8	5.64063	13.39648	3/8	28.8906	155.2871
3/4	0.562500	0.421875	7/16	5.94141	14.48218	7/16	29.5664	160.7673
25/32	0.610352	0.476837	1/2	6.25000	15.62500	1/2	30.2500	166.3750
13/16	0.660156	0.536377	9/16	6.56641	16.82642	9/16	30.9414	172.1116
27/32	0.711914	0.600678	5/8	6.89063	18.08789	5/8	31.6406	177.9785
7/8	0.765625	0.669922	11/16	7.22266	19.41089	11/16	32.3477	183.9773
29/32	0.821289	0.744293	3/4	7.56250	20.79688	3/4	33.0625	190.1094
15/16	0.878906	0.823975	13/16	7.91016	22.24731	13/16	33.7852	196.3762
31/32	0.938477	0.909149	7/8	8.26563	23.76367	7/8	34.5156	202.7793
1	1.000000	1.000000	15/16	8.62891	25.34741	15/16	35.2539	209.3201
1/32	1.063477	1.096800	3	9.00000	27.00000	6	36.0000	216.0000
1/16	1.128906	1.199463	1/16	9.37891	28.72290	1/16	36.7539	222.8206
3/32	1.196289	1.308441	1/8	9.76563	30.51758	1/8	37.5156	229.7832
1/8	1.265625	1.423828	3/16	10.16016	32.38550	3/16	38.2852	236.8894
5/32	1.336914	1.545807	1/4	10.56250	34.32813	1/4	39.0625	244.1406
3/16	1.410156	1.674561	5/16	10.97266	36.34692	5/16	39.8477	251.5383
7/32	1.485352	1.810272	3/8	11.39063	38.44336	3/8	40.6406	259.0840
1/4	1.562500	1.953125	7/16	11.81641	40.61889	7/16	41.4414	266.7791
9/32	1.641602	2.103302	1/2	12.25000	42.87500	1/2	42.2500	274.6250
5/16	1.722656	2.260986	9/16	12.69141	45.21313	9/16	43.0664	282.6233
11/32	1.805664	2.426361	5/8	13.14063	47.63477	5/8	43.8906	290.7754
3/8	1.890625	2.599609	11/16	13.59766	50.14135	11/16	44.7227	299.0828
13/32	1.977539	2.780914	3/4	14.06250	52.73438	3/4	45.5625	307.5469
7/16	2.066406	2.970459	13/16	14.53516	55.41528	13/16	46.4102	316.1692
15/32	2.157227	3.168927	7/8	15.01563	58.18555	7/8	47.2656	324.9512
1/2	2.250000	3.375000	15/16	15.50391	61.04663	15/16	48.1289	333.8943

Squares and Cubes of Numbers from 1/32 to 100 (Continued)

No.	Square	Cube	No.	Square	Cube	No.	Square	Cube
7	49.0000	343.0000	10	100.0000	1000.0000	16	256.0000	4096.000
1/16	49.8789	352.2698	1/8	102.5156	1037.9707	1/8	260.0156	4192.752
1/8	50.7656	361.7051	1/4	105.0625	1076.8906	1/4	264.0625	4291.015
3/16	51.6602	371.3074	3/8	107.6406	1116.7715	3/8	268.1406	4390.802
1/4	52.5625	381.0781	1/2	110.2500	1157.6250	1/2	272.2500	4492.125
5/16	53.4727	391.0188	5/8	112.8906	1199.4629	5/8	276.3906	4594.994
3/8	54.3906	401.1309	3/4	115.5625	1242.2969	3/4	280.5625	4699.421
7/16	55.3164	411.4158	7/8	118.2656	1286.1387	7/8	284.7656	4805.419
1/2	56.2500	421.8750	11	121.0000	1331.0000	17	289.0000	4913.000
9/16	57.1914	432.5100	1/8	123.7656	1376.8926	1/8	293.2656	5022.173
5/8	58.1406	443.3223	1/4	126.5625	1423.8281	1/4	297.5625	5132.953
11/16	59.0977	454.3132	3/8	129.3906	1471.8184	3/8	301.8906	5245.349
3/4	60.0625	465.4844	1/2	132.2500	1520.8750	1/2	306.2500	5359.375
13/16	61.0352	476.8372	5/8	135.1406	1571.0098	5/8	310.6406	5475.041
7/8	62.0156	488.3730	3/4	138.0625	1622.2344	3/4	315.0625	5592.359
15/16	63.0039	500.0935	7/8	141.0156	1674.5605	7/8	319.5156	5711.341
8	64.0000	512.0000	12	144.0000	1728.0000	18	324.0000	5832.000
1/16	65.0039	524.0940	1/8	147.0156	1782.5645	1/8	328.5156	5954.345
1/8	66.0156	536.3770	1/4	150.0625	1838.2656	1/4	333.0625	6078.390
3/16	67.0352	548.8503	3/8	153.1406	1895.1152	3/8	337.6406	6204.146
1/4	68.0625	561.5156	1/2	156.2500	1953.1250	1/2	342.2500	6331.625
5/16	69.0977	574.3743	5/8	159.3906	2012.3066	5/8	346.8906	6460.837
3/8	70.1406	587.4277	3/4	162.5625	2072.6719	3/4	351.5625	6591.796
7/16	71.1914	600.6775	7/8	165.7656	2134.2324	7/8	356.2656	6724.513
1/2	72.2500	614.1250	13	169.0000	2197.0000	19	361.0000	6859.000
9/16	73.3164	627.7717	1/8	172.2656	2260.9863	1/8	365.7656	6995.267
5/8	74.3906	641.6191	1/4	175.5625	2326.2031	1/4	370.5625	7133.328
11/16	75.4727	655.6687	3/8	178.8906	2392.6621	3/8	375.3906	7273.193
3/4	76.5625	669.9219	1/2	182.2500	2460.3750	1/2	380.2500	7414.875
13/16	77.6602	684.3801	5/8	185.6406	2529.3535	5/8	385.1406	7558.384
7/8	78.7656	699.0449	3/4	189.0625	2599.6094	3/4	390.0625	7703.734
15/16	79.8789	713.9177	7/8	192.5156	2671.1543	7/8	395.0156	7850.935
9	81.0000	729.0000	14	196.0000	2744.0000	20	400.0000	8000.000
1/16	82.1289	744.2932	1/8	199.5156	2818.1582	1/8	405.0156	8150.939
1/8	83.2656	759.7988	1/4	203.0625	2893.6406	1/4	410.0625	8303.765
3/16	84.4102	775.5183	3/8	206.6406	2970.4590	3/8	415.1406	8458.490
1/4	85.5625	791.4531	1/2	210.2500	3048.6250	1/2	420.2500	8615.125
5/16	86.7227	807.6047	5/8	213.8906	3128.1504	5/8	425.3906	8773.681
3/8	87.8906	823.9746	3/4	217.5625	3209.0469	3/4	430.5625	8934.171
7/16	89.0664	840.5642	7/8	221.2656	3291.3262	7/8	435.7656	9096.607
1/2	90.2500	857.3750	15	225.0000	3375.0000	21	441.0000	9261.000
9/16	91.4414	874.4084	1/8	228.7656	3460.0801	1/8	446.2656	9427.361
5/8	92.6406	891.6660	1/4	232.5625	3546.5781	1/4	451.5625	9595.703
11/16	93.8477	909.1492	3/8	236.3906	3634.5059	3/8	456.8906	9766.037
3/4	95.0625	926.8594	1/2	240.2500	3723.8750	1/2	462.2500	9,938.375
13/16	96.2852	944.7981	5/8	244.1406	3814.6973	5/8	467.6406	10,112.728
7/8	97.5156	962.9668	3/4	248.0625	3906.9844	3/4	473.0625	10,289.109
15/16	98.7539	981.3669	7/8	252.0156	4000.7480	7/8	478.5156	10,467.529

Squares and Cubes of Numbers from 1/32 to 100 (Continued)

No.	Square	Cube	No.	Square	Cube	No.	Square	Cube
22	484.0000	10,648.000	28	784.000	21,952.000	34	1156.000	39,304.000
1/8	489.5156	10,830.533	1/8	791.015	22,247.314	1/8	1164.515	39,739.095
1/4	495.0625	11,015.140	1/4	798.062	22,545.265	1/4	1173.062	40,177.390
3/8	500.6406	11,201.834	3/8	805.140	22,845.865	3/8	1181.640	40,618.896
1/2	506.2500	11,390.625	1/2	812.250	23,149.125	1/2	1190.250	41,063.625
5/8	511.8906	11,581.525	5/8	819.390	23,455.056	5/8	1198.890	41,511.587
3/4	517.5625	11,774.546	3/4	826.562	23,763.671	3/4	1207.562	41,962.796
7/8	523.2656	11,969.701	7/8	833.765	24,074.982	7/8	1216.265	42,417.263
23	529.0000	12,167.000	29	841.000	24,389.000	35	1225.000	42,875.000
1/8	534.7656	12,366.455	1/8	848.265	24,705.736	1/8	1233.765	43,336.017
1/4	540.5625	12,568.078	1/4	855.562	25,025.203	1/4	1242.562	43,800.328
3/8	546.3906	12,771.880	3/8	862.890	25,347.412	3/8	1251.390	44,267.943
1/2	552.2500	12,977.875	1/2	870.250	25,672.375	1/2	1260.250	44,738.875
5/8	558.1406	13,186.072	5/8	877.640	26,000.103	5/8	1269.140	45,213.134
3/4	564.0625	13,396.484	3/4	885.062	26,330.609	3/4	1278.062	45,690.734
7/8	570.0156	13,609.123	7/8	892.515	26,663.904	7/8	1287.015	46,171.685
24	576.0000	13,824.000	30	900.000	27,000.000	36	1296.000	46,656.000
1/8	582.0156	14,041.127	1/8	907.515	27,338.908	1/8	1305.015	47,143.689
1/4	588.0625	14,260.515	1/4	915.062	27,680.640	1/4	1314.062	47,634.765
3/8	594.1406	14,482.177	3/8	922.640	28,025.209	3/8	1323.140	48,129.240
1/2	600.2500	14,706.125	1/2	930.250	28,372.625	1/2	1332.250	48,627.125
5/8	606.3906	14,932.369	5/8	937.890	28,722.900	5/8	1341.390	49,128.431
3/4	612.5625	15,160.921	3/4	945.562	29,076.046	3/4	1350.562	49,633.171
7/8	618.7656	15,391.794	7/8	953.265	29,432.076	7/8	1359.765	50,141.357
25	625.0000	15,625.000	31	961.000	29,791.000	37	1369.000	50,653.000
1/8	631.2656	15,860.548	1/8	968.765	30,152.830	1/8	1378.265	51,168.111
1/4	637.5625	16,098.453	1/4	976.562	30,517.578	1/4	1387.562	51,686.703
3/8	643.8906	16,338.724	3/8	984.390	30,885.255	3/8	1396.890	52,208.787
1/2	650.2500	16,581.375	1/2	992.250	31,255.875	1/2	1406.250	52,734.375
5/8	656.6406	16,826.416	5/8	1000.140	31,629.447	5/8	1415.640	53,263.478
3/4	663.0625	17,073.859	3/4	1008.062	32,005.984	3/4	1425.062	53,796.109
7/8	669.5156	17,323.716	7/8	1016.015	32,385.498	7/8	1434.515	54,332.279
26	676.0000	17,576.000	32	1024.000	32,768.000	38	1444.000	54,872.000
1/8	682.5156	17,830.720	1/8	1032.015	33,153.502	1/8	1453.515	55,415.283
1/4	689.0625	18,087.890	1/4	1040.062	33,542.015	1/4	1463.062	55,962.140
3/8	695.6406	18,347.521	3/8	1048.140	33,933.552	3/8	1472.640	56,512.584
1/2	702.2500	18,609.625	1/2	1056.250	34,328.125	1/2	1482.250	57,066.625
5/8	708.8906	18,874.212	5/8	1064.390	34,725.744	5/8	1491.890	57,624.275
3/4	715.5625	19,141.296	3/4	1072.562	35,126.421	3/4	1501.562	58,185.546
7/8	722.2656	19,410.888	7/8	1080.765	35,530.169	7/8	1511.265	58,750.451
27	729.0000	19,683.000	33	1089.000	35,937.000	39	1521.000	59,319.000
1/8	735.7656	19,957.642	1/8	1097.265	36,346.923	1/8	1530.765	59,891.205
1/4	742.5625	20,234.828	1/4	1105.562	36,759.953	1/4	1540.562	60,467.078
3/8	749.3906	20,514.568	3/8	1113.890	37,176.099	3/8	1550.390	61,046.630
1/2	756.2500	20,796.875	1/2	1122.250	37,595.375	1/2	1560.250	61,629.875
5/8	763.1406	21,081.759	5/8	1130.640	38,017.791	5/8	1570.140	62,216.822
3/4	770.0625	21,369.234	3/4	1139.062	38,443.359	3/4	1580.062	62,807.484
7/8	777.0156	21,659.310	7/8	1147.515	38,872.091	7/8	1590.015	63,401.873

Squares and Cubes of Numbers from 1/32 to 100 (Continued)

No.	Square	Cube	No.	Square	Cube	No.	Square	Cube
40	1600.000	64,000.000	46	2116.000	97,336.00	52	2704.000	140,608.00
1/8	1610.015	64,601.877	1/8	2127.515	98,131.65	1/8	2717.015	141,624.43
1/4	1620.062	65,207.516	1/4	2139.062	98,931.64	1/4	2730.062	142,645.76
3/8	1630.140	65,816.928	3/8	2150.640	99,735.95	3/8	2743.140	143,671.99
1/2	1640.250	66,430.125	1/2	2162.250	100,544.62	1/2	2756.250	144,703.12
5/8	1650.390	67,047.119	5/8	2173.890	101,357.65	5/8	2769.390	145,739.18
3/4	1660.562	67,667.922	3/4	2185.562	102,175.04	3/4	2782.562	146,780.17
7/8	1670.765	68,292.545	7/8	2197.265	102,996.82	7/8	2795.765	147,826.10
41	1681.000	68,921.000	47	2209.000	103,823.00	53	2809.000	148,877.00
1/8	1691.265	69,553.299	1/8	2220.765	104,653.58	1/8	2822.265	149,932.86
1/4	1701.562	70,189.453	1/4	2232.562	105,488.57	1/4	2835.562	150,993.70
3/8	1711.890	70,829.475	3/8	2244.390	106,328.00	3/8	2848.890	152,059.53
1/2	1722.250	71,473.375	1/2	2256.250	107,171.87	1/2	2862.250	153,130.37
5/8	1732.640	72,121.166	5/8	2268.140	108,020.19	5/8	2875.640	154,206.22
3/4	1743.062	72,772.859	3/4	2280.062	108,872.98	3/4	2889.062	155,287.10
7/8	1753.515	73,428.467	7/8	2292.015	109,730.24	7/8	2902.515	156,373.02
42	1764.000	74,088.000	48	2304.000	110,592.00	54	2916.000	157,464.00
1/8	1774.515	74,751.471	1/8	2316.015	111,458.25	1/8	2929.515	158,560.03
1/4	1785.062	75,418.891	1/4	2328.062	112,329.01	1/4	2943.062	159,661.14
3/8	1795.640	76,090.271	3/8	2340.140	113,204.30	3/8	2956.640	160,767.33
1/2	1806.250	76,765.625	1/2	2352.250	114,084.12	1/2	2970.250	161,878.62
5/8	1816.890	77,444.963	5/8	2364.390	114,968.49	5/8	2983.890	162,995.02
3/4	1827.562	78,128.297	3/4	2376.562	115,857.42	3/4	2997.562	164,116.54
7/8	1838.265	78,815.639	7/8	2388.765	116,750.92	7/8	3011.265	165,243.20
43	1849.000	79,507.000	49	2401.000	117,649.00	55	3025.000	166,375.00
1/8	1859.765	80,202.393	1/8	2413.265	118,551.67	1/8	3038.765	167,511.95
1/4	1870.562	80,901.828	1/4	2425.562	119,458.95	1/4	3052.562	168,654.07
3/8	1881.390	81,605.318	3/8	2437.890	120,370.85	3/8	3066.390	169,801.38
1/2	1892.250	82,312.875	1/2	2450.250	121,287.37	1/2	3080.250	170,953.87
5/8	1903.140	83,024.510	5/8	2462.640	122,208.54	5/8	3094.140	172,111.57
3/4	1914.062	83,740.234	3/4	2475.062	123,134.35	3/4	3108.062	173,274.48
7/8	1925.015	84,460.061	7/8	2487.515	124,064.84	7/8	3122.015	174,442.62
44	1936.000	85,184.000	50	2500.000	125,000.00	56	3136.000	175,616.00
1/8	1947.015	85,912.064	1/8	2512.515	125,939.84	1/8	3150.015	176,794.62
1/4	1958.062	86,644.266	1/4	2525.062	126,884.39	1/4	3164.062	177,978.51
3/8	1969.140	87,380.615	3/8	2537.640	127,833.64	3/8	3178.140	179,167.67
1/2	1980.250	88,121.125	1/2	2550.250	128,787.62	1/2	3192.250	180,362.12
5/8	1991.390	88,865.807	5/8	2562.890	129,746.33	5/8	3206.390	181,561.86
3/4	2002.562	89,614.672	3/4	2575.562	130,709.79	3/4	3220.562	182,766.92
7/8	2013.765	90,367.732	7/8	2588.265	131,678.01	7/8	3234.765	183,977.29
45	2025.000	91,125.000	51	2601.000	132,651.00	57	3249.000	185,193.00
1/8	2036.265	91,886.486	1/8	2613.765	133,628.76	1/8	3263.265	186,414.04
1/4	2047.562	92,652.203	1/4	2626.562	134,611.32	1/4	3277.562	187,640.45
3/8	2058.890	93,422.162	3/8	2639.390	135,598.69	3/8	3291.890	188,872.22
1/2	2070.250	94,196.375	1/2	2652.250	136,590.87	1/2	3306.250	190,109.37
5/8	2081.640	94,974.854	5/8	2665.140	137,587.88	5/8	3320.640	191,351.91
3/4	2093.062	95,757.609	3/4	2678.062	138,589.73	3/4	3335.062	192,599.85
7/8	2104.515	96,544.654	7/8	2691.015	139,596.43	7/8	3349.515	193,853.21

Squares and Cubes of Numbers from 1/32 to 100 (Continued)

No.	Square	Cube	No.	Square	Cube	No.	Square	Cube
58	3364.000	195,112.00	64	4096.000	262,144.00	70	4900.000	343,000.00
⅛	3378.515	196,376.22	⅛	4112.015	263,683.00	⅛	4917.515	344,840.78
¼	3393.062	197,645.89	¼	4128.062	265,228.01	¼	4935.062	346,688.14
⅜	3407.640	198,921.02	⅜	4144.140	266,779.05	⅜	4952.640	348,542.08
½	3422.250	200,201.62	½	4160.250	268,336.12	½	4970.250	350,402.62
⅝	3436.890	201,487.71	⅝	4176.390	269,899.24	⅝	4987.890	352,269.77
¾	3451.562	202,779.29	¾	4192.562	271,468.42	¾	5005.562	354,143.54
⅞	3466.265	204,076.38	⅞	4208.765	273,043.67	⅞	5023.265	356,023.95
59	3481.000	205,379.00	65	4225.000	274,625.00	71	5041.000	357,911.00
⅛	3495.765	206,687.14	⅛	4241.265	276,212.42	⅛	5058.765	359,804.70
¼	3510.562	208,000.82	¼	4257.562	277,805.95	¼	5076.562	361,705.07
⅜	3525.390	209,320.06	⅜	4273.890	279,405.60	⅜	5094.390	363,612.13
½	3540.250	210,644.87	½	4290.250	281,011.37	½	5112.250	365,525.87
⅝	3555.140	211,975.25	⅝	4306.640	282,623.29	⅝	5130.140	367,446.32
¾	3570.062	213,311.23	¾	4323.062	284,241.35	¾	5148.062	369,373.48
⅞	3585.015	214,652.81	⅞	4339.515	285,865.59	⅞	5166.015	371,307.37
60	3600.000	216,000.00	66	4356.000	287,496.00	72	5184.000	373,248.00
⅛	3615.015	217,352.81	⅛	4372.515	289,132.59	⅛	5202.015	375,195.37
¼	3630.062	218,711.26	¼	4389.062	290,775.39	¼	5220.062	377,149.51
⅜	3645.140	220,075.36	⅜	4405.640	292,424.39	⅜	5238.140	379,110.42
½	3660.250	221,445.12	½	4422.250	294,079.62	½	5256.250	381,078.12
⅝	3675.390	222,820.55	⅝	4438.890	295,741.08	⅝	5274.390	383,052.61
¾	3690.562	224,201.67	¾	4455.562	297,408.79	¾	5292.562	385,033.92
⅞	3705.765	225,588.48	⅞	4472.265	299,082.76	⅞	5310.765	387,022.04
61	3721.000	226,981.00	67	4489.000	300,763.00	73	5329.000	389,017.00
⅛	3736.265	228,379.23	⅛	4505.765	302,449.51	⅛	5347.265	391,018.79
¼	3751.562	229,783.20	¼	4522.562	304,142.32	¼	5365.562	393,027.45
⅜	3766.890	231,192.91	⅜	4539.390	305,841.44	⅜	5383.890	395,042.97
½	3782.250	232,608.37	½	4556.250	307,546.87	½	5402.250	397,065.37
⅝	3797.640	234,029.60	⅝	4573.140	309,258.63	⅝	5420.635	399,094.29
¾	3813.062	235,456.60	¾	4590.062	310,976.73	¾	5439.062	401,130.85
⅞	3828.515	236,889.40	⅞	4607.015	312,701.18	⅞	5457.515	403,173.96
62	3844.000	238,328.00	68	4624.000	314,432.00	74	5476.000	405,224.00
⅛	3859.515	239,772.40	⅛	4641.015	316,169.18	⅛	5494.515	407,280.97
¼	3875.062	241,222.64	¼	4658.062	317,912.76	¼	5513.062	409,344.89
⅜	3890.640	242,678.70	⅜	4675.140	319,662.74	⅜	5531.640	411,415.77
½	3906.250	244,140.62	½	4692.250	321,419.12	½	5550.250	413,493.62
⅝	3921.890	245,608.40	⅝	4709.390	323,181.93	⅝	5568.890	415,578.46
¾	3937.562	247,082.04	¾	4726.562	324,951.17	¾	5587.562	417,670.29
⅞	3953.265	248,561.57	⅞	4743.765	326,726.85	⅞	5606.265	419,769.13
63	3969.000	250,047.00	69	4761.000	328,509.00	75	5625.000	421,875.00
⅛	3984.765	251,538.33	⅛	4778.265	330,297.61	⅛	5643.765	423,987.89
¼	4000.562	253,035.57	¼	4795.562	332,092.70	¼	5662.562	426,107.82
⅜	4016.390	254,538.75	⅜	4812.890	333,894.28	⅜	5681.390	428,234.81
½	4032.250	256,047.87	½	4830.250	335,702.37	½	5700.250	430,368.87
⅝	4048.140	257,562.94	⅝	4847.640	337,516.97	⅝	5719.140	432,510.01
¾	4064.062	259,083.98	¾	4865.062	339,338.10	¾	5738.062	434,658.23
⅞	4080.015	260,610.99	⅞	4882.515	341,165.77	⅞	5757.015	436,813.56

Squares and Cubes of Numbers from 1/32 to 100 (Continued)

No.	Square	Cube	No.	Square	Cube	No.	Square	Cube
76	5776.000	438,976.00	82	6724.000	551,368.00	88	7744.000	681,472.00
⅛	5795.015	441,145.56	⅛	6744.515	553,893.34	⅛	7766.015	684,380.12
¼	5814.062	443,322.26	¼	6765.062	556,426.39	¼	7788.062	687,296.51
⅜	5833.140	445,506.11	⅜	6785.640	558,967.14	⅜	7810.140	690,221.17
½	5852.250	447,697.12	½	6806.250	561,515.62	½	7832.250	693,154.12
⅝	5871.390	449,895.30	⅝	6826.890	564,071.83	⅝	7854.390	696,095.36
¾	5890.562	452,100.67	¾	6847.562	566,635.79	¾	7876.562	699,044.92
⅞	5909.765	454,313.23	⅞	6868.265	569,207.51	⅞	7898.765	702,002.79
77	5929.000	456,533.00	83	6889.000	571,787.00	89	7921.000	704,969.00
⅛	5948.265	458,759.98	⅛	6909.765	574,374.26	⅛	7943.265	707,943.54
¼	5967.562	460,994.20	¼	6930.562	576,969.32	¼	7965.562	710,926.45
⅜	5986.890	463,235.66	⅜	6951.390	579,572.19	⅜	7987.890	713,917.72
½	6006.250	465,484.37	½	6972.250	582,182.87	½	8010.250	716,917.37
⅝	6025.640	467,740.35	⅝	6993.140	584,801.38	⅝	8032.640	719,925.41
¾	6045.062	470,003.60	¾	7014.062	587,427.73	¾	8055.062	722,941.85
⅞	6064.515	472,274.15	⅞	7035.015	590,061.93	⅞	8077.515	725,966.71
78	6084.000	474,552.00	84	7056.000	592,704.00	90	8100.000	729,000.00
⅛	6103.515	476,837.15	⅛	7077.015	595,353.93	⅛	8122.515	732,041.72
¼	6123.062	479,129.64	¼	7098.062	598,011.76	¼	8145.062	735,091.89
⅜	6142.640	481,429.45	⅜	7119.140	600,677.49	⅜	8167.640	738,150.52
½	6162.250	483,736.62	½	7140.250	603,351.12	½	8190.250	741,217.62
⅝	6181.890	486,051.15	⅝	7161.390	606,032.68	⅝	8212.890	744,293.21
¾	6201.562	488,373.04	¾	7182.562	608,722.17	¾	8235.562	747,377.29
⅞	6221.265	490,702.32	⅞	7203.765	611,419.60	⅞	8258.265	750,469.88
79	6241.000	493,039.00	85	7225.000	614,125.00	91	8281.000	753,571.00
⅛	6260.765	495,383.08	⅛	7246.265	616,838.36	⅛	8303.765	756,680.64
¼	6280.562	497,734.57	¼	7267.562	619,559.70	¼	8326.562	759,798.82
⅜	6300.390	500,093.50	⅜	7288.890	622,289.03	⅜	8349.390	762,925.56
½	6320.250	502,459.87	½	7310.250	625,026.37	½	8372.250	766,060.87
⅝	6340.140	504,833.69	⅝	7331.640	627,771.72	⅝	8395.140	769,204.76
¾	6360.062	507,214.98	¾	7353.062	630,525.10	¾	8418.062	772,357.23
⅞	6380.015	509,603.74	⅞	7374.515	633,286.52	⅞	8441.015	775,518.31
80	6400.000	512,000.00	86	7396.000	636,056.00	92	8464.000	778,688.00
⅛	6420.015	514,403.75	⅛	7417.515	638,833.53	⅛	8487.015	781,866.31
¼	6440.062	516,815 01	¼	7439.062	641,619.14	¼	8510.062	785,053.26
⅜	6460.140	519,233.80	⅜	7460.640	644,412.83	⅜	8533.140	788,248.86
½	6480.250	521,660.12	½	7482.250	647,214.62	½	8556.250	791,453.12
⅝	6500.390	524,093.99	⅝	7503.890	650,024.52	⅝	8579.390	794,666.05
¾	6520.562	526,535.42	¾	7525.562	652,842.54	¾	8602.562	797,887.67
⅞	6540.765	528,984.42	⅞	7547.265	655,668.70	⅞	8625.765	801,117.98
81	6561.000	531,441.00	87	7569.000	658,503.00	93	8649.000	804,357.00
⅛	6581.265	533,905.17	⅛	7590.765	661,345.45	⅛	8672.265	807,604.73
¼	6601.562	536,376.95	¼	7612.562	664,196.07	¼	8695 562	810,861.20
⅜	6621.890	538,856.35	⅜	7634.390	667,054.88	⅜	8718.890	814,126.41
½	6642.250	541,343.37	½	7656.250	669,921.87	½	8742.250	817,400.37
⅝	6662.640	543,838.04	⅝	7678.140	672,797.07	⅝	8765.640	820,683.10
¾	6683.062	546,340.35	¾	7700.062	675,680.48	¾	8789.062	823,974.61
⅞	6703.515	548,850.34	⅞	7722.015	678,572.12	⅞	8812.515	827,274.90

Squares and Cubes of Numbers from 1/32 to 100 (Continued)

No.	Square	Cube	No.	Square	Cube	No.	Square	Cube
94	8836.000	830,584.00	96	9216.000	884,736.00	98	9604.00	941,192.0
1/8	8859.515	833,901.90	1/8	9240.015	888,196.50	1/8	9628.51	944,798.0
1/4	8883.062	837,228.64	1/4	9264.062	891,666.01	1/4	9653.06	948,413.3
3/8	8906.640	840,564.20	3/8	9288.140	895,144.55	3/8	9677.64	952,037.8
1/2	8930.250	843,908.62	1/2	9312.250	898,632.12	1/2	9702.25	955,671.6
5/8	8953.890	847,261.90	5/8	9336.390	902,128.74	5/8	9726.89	959,314.5
3/4	8977.562	850,624.04	3/4	9360.562	905,634.42	3/4	9751.56	962,966.7
7/8	9001.265	853,995.07	7/8	9384.765	909,149.17	7/8	9776.26	966,628.2
95	9025.000	857,375.00	97	9409.000	912,673.00	99	9801.00	970,299.0
1/8	9048.765	860,763.83	1/8	9433.265	916,205.92	1/8	9825.76	973,979.0
1/4	9072.562	864,161.57	1/4	9457.562	919,747.95	1/4	9850.56	977,668.3
3/8	9096.390	867,568.25	3/8	9481.890	923,299.10	3/8	9875.39	981,366.9
1/2	9120.250	870,983.87	1/2	9506.250	926,859.37	1/2	9900.25	985,074.8
5/8	9144.140	874,408.44	5/8	9530.640	930,428.79	5/8	9925.14	988,792.1
3/4	9168.062	877,841.98	3/4	9555.062	934,007.35	3/4	9950.06	992,518.7
7/8	9192.015	881,284.49	7/8	9579.515	937,595.09	7/8	9975.01	996,254.6
						100	10,000.00	1,000,000.0

Table of Fractions of $\pi = 3.14159265$

a	$\frac{\pi}{a}$	a	$\frac{\pi}{a}$	a	$\frac{\pi}{a}$	a	$\frac{\pi}{a}$	a	$\frac{\pi}{a}$
1	3.14159	21	0.14960	41	0.07662	61	0.05150	81	0.03879
2	1.57080	22	0.14280	42	0.07480	62	0.05067	82	0.03831
3	1.04720	23	0.13659	43	0.07306	63	0.04987	83	0.03785
4	0.78540	24	0.13090	44	0.07140	64	0.04909	84	0.03740
5	0.62832	25	0.12566	45	0.06981	65	0.04833	85	0.03696
6	0.52360	26	0.12083	46	0.06830	66	0.04760	86	0.03653
7	0.44880	27	0.11636	47	0.06684	67	0.04689	87	0.03611
8	0.39270	28	0.11220	48	0.06545	68	0.04620	88	0.03570
9	0.34907	29	0.10833	49	0.06411	69	0.04553	89	0.03530
10	0.31416	30	0.10472	50	0.06283	70	0.04488	90	0.03491
11	0.28560	31	0.10134	51	0.06160	71	0.04425	91	0.03452
12	0.26180	32	0.09817	52	0.06042	72	0.04363	92	0.03415
13	0.24166	33	0.09520	53	0.05928	73	0.04304	93	0.03378
14	0.22440	34	0.09240	54	0.05818	74	0.04245	94	0.03342
15	0.20944	35	0.08976	55	0.05712	75	0.04189	95	0.03307
16	0.19635	36	0.08727	56	0.05610	76	0.04134	96	0.03272
17	0.18480	37	0.08491	57	0.05512	77	0.04080	97	0.03239
18	0.17453	38	0.08267	58	0.05417	78	0.04028	98	0.03206
19	0.16535	39	0.08055	59	0.05325	79	0.03977	99	0.03173
20	0.15708	40	0.07854	60	0.05236	80	0.03927	100	0.03142

Pi (π). — The ratio of the circumference of a circle to its diameter, which is represented by the Greek letter pi (π), is an incommensurable quantity. The value 3.1416 is accurate enough for ordinary purposes and the value 22/7 is convenient for rough calculations. The fractions of π given in the above table will be found convenient in certain calculations and also the values in the table of constants on page 79.

Table of Decimal Equivalents, Squares, Cubes, Square Roots, Cube Roots and Logarithms of Fractions from 1/64 to 1, by 64ths

Fraction	Decimal Equivalent	Log.	Square	Log.	Cube	Log.	Sq. Root	Log.	Cube Root	Log.
1/64	0.015625	$\bar{2}$.19382	0.0002441	$\bar{4}$.38764	0.000003815	$\bar{6}$.58146	0.1250	$\bar{1}$.09691	0.2500	$\bar{1}$.39794
1/32	0.03125	$\bar{2}$.49485	0.0009765	$\bar{4}$.98970	0.00003052	$\bar{5}$.48455	0.1768	$\bar{1}$.24743	0.3150	$\bar{1}$.49828
3/64	0.046875	$\bar{2}$.67094	0.002197	$\bar{3}$.34188	0.0001030	$\bar{4}$.01282	0.2165	$\bar{1}$.33547	0.3606	$\bar{1}$.55698
1/16	0.0625	$\bar{2}$.79588	0.003906	$\bar{3}$.59176	0.0002442	$\bar{4}$.38764	0.2500	$\bar{1}$.39794	0.3968	$\bar{1}$.59863
5/64	0.078125	$\bar{2}$.89279	0.006104	$\bar{3}$.78558	0.0004768	$\bar{4}$.67837	0.2795	$\bar{1}$.44639	0.4275	$\bar{1}$.63093
3/32	0.09375	$\bar{2}$.97197	0.008789	$\bar{3}$.94394	0.0008240	$\bar{4}$.91591	0.3062	$\bar{1}$.48598	0.4543	$\bar{1}$.65732
7/64	0.109375	$\bar{1}$.03892	0.01196	$\bar{2}$.07784	0.001308	$\bar{3}$.11676	0.3307	$\bar{1}$.51946	0.4782	$\bar{1}$.67964
1/8	0.125	$\bar{1}$.09691	0.015625	$\bar{2}$.19382	0.001953	$\bar{3}$.29073	0.3535	$\bar{1}$.54845	0.5000	$\bar{1}$.69897
9/64	0.140625	$\bar{1}$.14807	0.01978	$\bar{2}$.29614	0.002781	$\bar{3}$.44421	0.3750	$\bar{1}$.57403	0.5200	$\bar{1}$.71602
5/32	0.15625	$\bar{1}$.19382	0.02441	$\bar{2}$.38764	0.003815	$\bar{3}$.58146	0.3953	$\bar{1}$.59691	0.5386	$\bar{1}$.73127
11/64	0.171875	$\bar{1}$.23532	0.02954	$\bar{2}$.47044	0.005078	$\bar{3}$.70566	0.4146	$\bar{1}$.61761	0.5560	$\bar{1}$.74597
3/16	0.1875	$\bar{1}$.27300	0.03516	$\bar{2}$.54600	0.006592	$\bar{3}$.81900	0.4330	$\bar{1}$.63650	0.5724	$\bar{1}$.75767
13/64	0.203125	$\bar{1}$.30776	0.04126	$\bar{2}$.61553	0.008381	$\bar{3}$.93329	0.4507	$\bar{1}$.65388	0.5878	$\bar{1}$.76925
7/32	0.21875	$\bar{1}$.33995	0.04786	$\bar{2}$.67990	0.01047	$\bar{2}$.01985	0.4677	$\bar{1}$.66998	0.6025	$\bar{1}$.77998
15/64	0.234375	$\bar{1}$.36992	0.05493	$\bar{2}$.73984	0.01287	$\bar{2}$.10976	0.4841	$\bar{1}$.68496	0.6166	$\bar{1}$.78997
1/4	0.250	$\bar{1}$.39794	0.06250	$\bar{2}$.79588	0.01562	$\bar{2}$.19382	0.5000	$\bar{1}$.69897	0.6300	$\bar{1}$.79931
17/64	0.265625	$\bar{1}$.42427	0.07056	$\bar{2}$.84854	0.01874	$\bar{2}$.27281	0.5154	$\bar{1}$.71213	0.6428	$\bar{1}$.80809
9/32	0.28125	$\bar{1}$.44910	0.07910	$\bar{2}$.89820	0.02225	$\bar{2}$.34730	0.5303	$\bar{1}$.72455	0.6552	$\bar{1}$.81636
19/64	0.296875	$\bar{1}$.47258	0.08813	$\bar{2}$.94516	0.02616	$\bar{2}$.41774	0.5449	$\bar{1}$.73629	0.6671	$\bar{1}$.82419
5/16	0.3125	$\bar{1}$.49485	0.09766	$\bar{2}$.98970	0.03052	$\bar{2}$.48455	0.5590	$\bar{1}$.74742	0.6786	$\bar{1}$.83161

Table of Decimal Equivalents, Squares, Cubes, Etc., of Fractions

Fraction	Decimal Equivalent	Log.	Square	Log.	Cube	Log.	Sq. Root	Log.	Cube Root	Log.
21/64	0.328125	$\bar{1}$.51604	0.1077	$\bar{1}$.03208	0.03533	$\bar{2}$.54812	0.5728	$\bar{1}$.75802	0.6897	$\bar{1}$.83868
11/32	0.34375	$\bar{1}$.53625	0.1182	$\bar{1}$.07250	0.04062	$\bar{2}$.60875	0.5863	$\bar{1}$.76812	0.7005	$\bar{1}$.84541
23/64	0.359375	$\bar{1}$.55555	0.1291	$\bar{1}$.11110	0.04641	$\bar{2}$.66665	0.5995	$\bar{1}$.77777	0.7110	$\bar{1}$.85185
3/8	0.375	$\bar{1}$.57403	0.1406	$\bar{1}$.14806	0.05273	$\bar{2}$.72209	0.6124	$\bar{1}$.78701	0.7211	$\bar{1}$.85801
25/64	0.390625	$\bar{1}$.59176	0.1526	$\bar{1}$.18352	0.05960	$\bar{2}$.77528	0.6250	$\bar{1}$.79588	0.7310	$\bar{1}$.86392
13/32	0.40625	$\bar{1}$.60879	0.1650	$\bar{1}$.21758	0.06705	$\bar{2}$.82637	0.6374	$\bar{1}$.80439	0.7406	$\bar{1}$.86959
27/64	0.421875	$\bar{1}$.62519	0.1780	$\bar{1}$.25037	0.07508	$\bar{2}$.87555	0.6495	$\bar{1}$.81259	0.7500	$\bar{1}$.87506
7/16	0.4375	$\bar{1}$.64098	0.1914	$\bar{1}$.28196	0.08374	$\bar{2}$.92294	0.6614	$\bar{1}$.82049	0.7592	$\bar{1}$.88032
29/64	0.453125	$\bar{1}$.65622	0.2053	$\bar{1}$.31244	0.09304	$\bar{2}$.96866	0.6732	$\bar{1}$.82811	0.7681	$\bar{1}$.88540
15/32	0.46875	$\bar{1}$.67094	0.2197	$\bar{1}$.34188	0.1030	$\bar{1}$.01282	0.6847	$\bar{1}$.83547	0.7768	$\bar{1}$.89031
31/64	0.484375	$\bar{1}$.68518	0.2346	$\bar{1}$.37036	0.1136	$\bar{1}$.05554	0.6960	$\bar{1}$.84259	0.7853	$\bar{1}$.89506
1/2	0.500	$\bar{1}$.69897	0.2500	$\bar{1}$.39794	0.1250	$\bar{1}$.09691	0.7071	$\bar{1}$.84948	0.7937	$\bar{1}$.89966
33/64	0.515625	$\bar{1}$.71233	0.2659	$\bar{1}$.42466	0.1371	$\bar{1}$.13699	0.7181	$\bar{1}$.85616	0.8019	$\bar{1}$.90411
17/32	0.53125	$\bar{1}$.72530	0.2822	$\bar{1}$.45066	0.1499	$\bar{1}$.17590	0.7289	$\bar{1}$.86265	0.8099	$\bar{1}$.90843
35/64	0.546875	$\bar{1}$.73789	0.2991	$\bar{1}$.47578	0.1636	$\bar{1}$.21367	0.7395	$\bar{1}$.86894	0.8178	$\bar{1}$.91263
9/16	0.5625	$\bar{1}$.75012	0.3164	$\bar{1}$.50024	0.1780	$\bar{1}$.25036	0.7500	$\bar{1}$.87506	0.8255	$\bar{1}$.91670
37/64	0.578125	$\bar{1}$.76202	0.3342	$\bar{1}$.52404	0.1932	$\bar{1}$.28606	0.7603	$\bar{1}$.88101	0.8331	$\bar{1}$.92067
19/32	0.59375	$\bar{1}$.77361	0.3525	$\bar{1}$.54722	0.2093	$\bar{1}$.32083	0.7706	$\bar{1}$.88680	0.8405	$\bar{1}$.92453
39/64	0.609375	$\bar{1}$.78488	0.3713	$\bar{1}$.56976	0.2263	$\bar{1}$.35464	0.7806	$\bar{1}$.89244	0.8478	$\bar{1}$.92829
5/8	0.625	$\bar{1}$.79588	0.3906	$\bar{1}$.59176	0.2441	$\bar{1}$.38764	0.7906	$\bar{1}$.89794	0.8550	$\bar{1}$.93196
41/64	0.640625	$\bar{1}$.80661	0.4104	$\bar{1}$.61322	0.2629	$\bar{1}$.41983	0.8004	$\bar{1}$.90330	0.8621	$\bar{1}$.93553
21/32	0.65625	$\bar{1}$.81707	0.4307	$\bar{1}$.63414	0.2826	$\bar{1}$.45121	0.8101	$\bar{1}$.90853	0.8699	$\bar{1}$.93902

Table of Decimal Equivalents, Squares, Cubes, Etc., of Fractions

Fraction	Decimal Equivalent	Log.	Square	Log.	Cube	Log.	Sq. Root	Log.	Cube Root	Log.
43/64	0.671875	$\bar{1}$.82729	0.4514	$\bar{1}$.65458	0.3033	$\bar{1}$.48187	0.8197	$\bar{1}$.91364	0.8758	$\bar{1}$.94243
11/16	0.6875	$\bar{1}$.83727	0.4727	$\bar{1}$.67454	0.3250	$\bar{1}$.51181	0.8292	$\bar{1}$.91864	0.8826	$\bar{1}$.94575
45/64	0.703125	$\bar{1}$.84704	0.4944	$\bar{1}$.69408	0.3476	$\bar{1}$.54112	0.8385	$\bar{1}$.92352	0.8892	$\bar{1}$.94901
23/32	0.71875	$\bar{1}$.85658	0.5166	$\bar{1}$.71316	0.3713	$\bar{1}$.56974	0.8478	$\bar{1}$.92829	0.8958	$\bar{1}$.95219
47/64	0.734375	$\bar{1}$.86592	0.5393	$\bar{1}$.73184	0.3961	$\bar{1}$.59776	0.8569	$\bar{1}$.93296	0.9022	$\bar{1}$.95530
3/4	0.750	$\bar{1}$.87506	0.5625	$\bar{1}$.75012	0.4219	$\bar{1}$.62518	0.8660	$\bar{1}$.93753	0.9086	$\bar{1}$.95835
49/64	0.765625	$\bar{1}$.88402	0.5862	$\bar{1}$.76804	0.4488	$\bar{1}$.65206	0.8750	$\bar{1}$.94201	0.9148	$\bar{1}$.96134
25/32	0.78125	$\bar{1}$.89279	0.6104	$\bar{1}$.78558	0.4768	$\bar{1}$.67837	0.8839	$\bar{1}$.94640	0.9210	$\bar{1}$.96426
51/64	0.796875	$\bar{1}$.90139	0.6350	$\bar{1}$.80278	0.5060	$\bar{1}$.70417	0.8927	$\bar{1}$.95069	0.9271	$\bar{1}$.96713
13/16	0.8125	$\bar{1}$.90982	0.6602	$\bar{1}$.81964	0.5364	$\bar{1}$.72946	0.9014	$\bar{1}$.95491	0.9331	$\bar{1}$.96994
53/64	0.828125	$\bar{1}$.91810	0.6858	$\bar{1}$.83620	0.5679	$\bar{1}$.75430	0.9100	$\bar{1}$.95905	0.9391	$\bar{1}$.97270
27/32	0.84375	$\bar{1}$.92622	0.7119	$\bar{1}$.85244	0.6007	$\bar{1}$.77866	0.9186	$\bar{1}$.96311	0.9449	$\bar{1}$.97540
55/64	0.859375	$\bar{1}$.93419	0.7385	$\bar{1}$.86838	0.6347	$\bar{1}$.80257	0.9270	$\bar{1}$.96709	0.9507	$\bar{1}$.97806
7/8	0.875	$\bar{1}$.94201	0.7656	$\bar{1}$.88402	0.6699	$\bar{1}$.82603	0.9354	$\bar{1}$.97101	0.9565	$\bar{1}$.98067
57/64	0.890625	$\bar{1}$.94969	0.7932	$\bar{1}$.89938	0.7064	$\bar{1}$.84907	0.9437	$\bar{1}$.97484	0.9621	$\bar{1}$.98323
29/32	0.90625	$\bar{1}$.95725	0.8213	$\bar{1}$.91450	0.7443	$\bar{1}$.87175	0.9520	$\bar{1}$.97862	0.9677	$\bar{1}$.98575
59/64	0.921875	$\bar{1}$.96467	0.8499	$\bar{1}$.92934	0.7835	$\bar{1}$.89401	0.9601	$\bar{1}$.98233	0.9732	$\bar{1}$.98822
15/16	0.9375	$\bar{1}$.97197	0.8789	$\bar{1}$.94394	0.8240	$\bar{1}$.91591	0.9682	$\bar{1}$.98598	0.9787	$\bar{1}$.99065
61/64	0.953125	$\bar{1}$.97915	0.9084	$\bar{1}$.95830	0.8659	$\bar{1}$.93745	0.9763	$\bar{1}$.98957	0.9841	$\bar{1}$.99305
31/32	0.96875	$\bar{1}$.98621	0.9385	$\bar{1}$.97242	0.9091	$\bar{1}$.95863	0.9843	$\bar{1}$.99310	0.9895	$\bar{1}$.99540
63/64	0.984375	$\bar{1}$.99316	0.9690	$\bar{1}$.98632	0.9539	$\bar{1}$.97948	0.9922	$\bar{1}$.99658	0.9948	$\bar{1}$.99772
1	1	0	1	0	1	0	1	0	1	0

Circumferences and Areas of Circles

Diameter	Circumference	Area	Diameter	Circumference	Area	Diameter	Circumference	Area
1/64	0.0491	0.0002	2	6.2832	3.1416	5	15.7080	19.635
1/32	0.0982	0.0008	1/16	6.4795	3.3410	1/16	15.9043	20.129
1/16	0.1964	0.0031	1/8	6.6759	3.5466	1/8	16.1007	20.629
3/32	0.2945	0.0069	3/16	6.8722	3.7583	3/16	16.2970	21.135
1/8	0.3927	0.0123	1/4	7.0686	3.9761	1/4	16.4934	21.648
5/32	0.4909	0.0192	5/16	7.2649	4.2000	5/16	16.6897	22.166
3/16	0.5890	0.0276	3/8	7.4613	4.4301	3/8	16.8861	22.691
7/32	0.6872	0.0376	7/16	7.6576	4.6664	7/16	17.0824	23.221
1/4	0.7854	0.0491	1/2	7.8540	4.9087	1/2	17.2788	23.758
9/32	0.8836	0.0621	9/16	8.0503	5.1572	9/16	17.4751	24.301
5/16	0.9817	0.0767	5/8	8.2467	5.4119	5/8	17.6715	24.850
11/32	1.0799	0.0928	11/16	8.4430	5.6727	11/16	17.8678	25.406
3/8	1.1781	0.1105	3/4	8.6394	5.9396	3/4	18.0642	25.967
13/32	1.2763	0.1296	13/16	8.8357	6.2126	13/16	18.2605	26.535
7/16	1.3745	0.1503	7/8	9.0321	6.4918	7/8	18.4569	27.109
15/32	1.4726	0.1726	15/16	9.2284	6.7771	15/16	18.6532	27.688
1/2	1.5708	0.1964	3	9.4248	7.0686	6	18.8496	28.274
17/32	1.6690	0.2217	1/16	9.6211	7.3662	1/8	19.2423	29.465
9/16	1.7672	0.2485	1/8	9.8175	7.6699	1/4	19.6350	30.680
19/32	1.8653	0.2769	3/16	10.0138	7.9798	3/8	20.0277	31.919
5/8	1.9635	0.3068	1/4	10.2102	8.2958	1/2	20.4204	33.183
21/32	2.0617	0.3382	5/16	10.4065	8.6179	5/8	20.8131	34.472
11/16	2.1598	0.3712	3/8	10.6029	8.9462	3/4	21.2058	35.785
23/32	2.2580	0.4057	7/16	10.7992	9.2806	7/8	21.5984	37.122
3/4	2.3562	0.4418	1/2	10.9956	9.6211	7	21.9911	38.485
25/32	2.4544	0.4794	9/16	11.1919	9.9678	1/8	22.3838	39.871
13/16	2.5525	0.5185	5/8	11.3883	10.321	1/4	22.7765	41.282
27/32	2.6507	0.5591	11/16	11.5846	10.680	3/8	23.1692	42.718
7/8	2.7489	0.6013	3/4	11.7810	11.045	1/2	23.5619	44.179
29/32	2.8471	0.6450	13/16	11.9773	11.416	5/8	23.9546	45.664
15/16	2.9452	0.6903	7/8	12.1737	11.793	3/4	24.3473	47.173
31/32	3.0434	0.7371	15/16	12.3700	12.177	7/8	24.7400	48.707
1	3.1416	0.7854	4	12.5664	12.566	8	25.1327	50.265
1/16	3.3379	0.8866	1/16	12.7627	12.962	1/8	25.5254	51.849
1/8	3.5343	0.9940	1/8	12.9591	13.364	1/4	25.9181	53.456
3/16	3.7306	1.1075	3/16	13.1554	13.772	3/8	26.3108	55.088
1/4	3.9270	1.2272	1/4	13.3518	14.186	1/2	26.7035	56.745
5/16	4.1233	1.3530	5/16	13.5481	14.607	5/8	27.0962	58.426
3/8	4.3197	1.4849	3/8	13.7445	15.033	3/4	27.4889	60.132
7/16	4.5160	1.6230	7/16	13.9408	15.466	7/8	27.8816	61.862
1/2	4.7124	1.7671	1/2	14.1372	15.904	9	28.2743	63.617
9/16	4.9087	1.9175	9/16	14.3335	16.349	1/8	28.6670	65.397
5/8	5.1051	2.0739	5/8	14.5299	16.800	1/4	29.0597	67.201
11/16	5.3014	2.2365	11/16	14.7262	17.257	3/8	29.4524	69.029
3/4	5.4978	2.4053	3/4	14.9226	17.721	1/2	29.8451	70.882
13/16	5.6941	2.5802	13/16	15.1189	18.190	5/8	30.2378	72.760
7/8	5.8905	2.7612	7/8	15.3153	18.665	3/4	30.6305	74.662
15/16	6.0868	2.9483	15/16	15.5116	19.147	7/8	31.0232	76.589

Circumferences and Areas of Circles

Diameter	Circumference	Area	Diameter	Circumference	Area	Diameter	Circumference	Area
10	31.4159	78.540	16	50.2655	201.06	22	69.1150	380.13
1/8	31.8086	80.516	1/8	50.6582	204.22	1/8	69.5077	384.46
1/4	32.2013	82.516	1/4	51.0509	207.39	1/4	69.9004	388.82
3/8	32.5940	84.541	3/8	51.4436	210.60	3/8	70.2931	393.20
1/2	32.9867	86.590	1/2	51.8363	213.82	1/2	70.6858	397.61
5/8	33.3794	88.664	5/8	52.2290	217.08	5/8	71.0785	402.04
3/4	33.7721	90.763	3/4	52.6217	220.35	3/4	71.4712	406.49
7/8	34.1648	92.886	7/8	53.0144	223.65	7/8	71.8639	410.97
11	34.5575	95.033	17	53.4071	226.98	23	72.2566	415.48
1/8	34.9502	97.205	1/8	53.7998	230.33	1/8	72.6493	420.00
1/4	35.3429	99.402	1/4	54.1925	233.71	1/4	73.0420	424.56
3/8	35.7356	101.62	3/8	54.5852	237.10	3/8	73.4347	429.13
1/2	36.1283	103.87	1/2	54.9779	240.53	1/2	73.8274	433.74
5/8	36.5210	106.14	5/8	55.3706	243.98	5/8	74.2201	438.36
3/4	36.9137	108.43	3/4	55.7633	247.45	3/4	74.6128	443.01
7/8	37.3064	110.75	7/8	56.1560	250.95	7/8	75.0055	447.69
12	37.6991	113.10	18	56.5487	254.47	24	75.3982	452.39
1/8	38.0918	115.47	1/8	56.9414	258.02	1/8	75.7909	457.11
1/4	38.4845	117.86	1/4	57.3341	261.59	1/4	76.1836	461.86
3/8	38.8772	120.28	3/8	57.7268	265.18	3/8	76.5763	466.64
1/2	39.2699	122.72	1/2	58.1195	268.80	1/2	76.9690	471.44
5/8	39.6626	125.19	5/8	58.5122	272.45	5/8	77.3617	476.26
3/4	40.0553	127.68	3/4	58.9049	276.12	3/4	77.7544	481.11
7/8	40.4480	130.19	7/8	59.2976	279.81	7/8	78.1471	485.98
13	40.8407	132.73	19	59.6903	283.53	25	78.5398	490.87
1/8	41.2334	135.30	1/8	60.0830	287.27	1/8	78.9325	495.79
1/4	41.6261	137.89	1/4	60.4757	291.04	1/4	79.3252	500.74
3/8	42.0188	140.50	3/8	60.8684	294.83	3/8	79.7179	505.71
1/2	42.4115	143.14	1/2	61.2611	298.65	1/2	80.1106	510.71
5/8	42.8042	145.80	5/8	61.6538	302.49	5/8	80.5033	515.72
3/4	43.1969	148.49	3/4	62.0465	306.35	3/4	80.8960	520.77
7/8	43.5896	151.20	7/8	62.4392	310.24	7/8	81.2887	525.84
14	43.9823	153.94	20	62.8319	314.16	26	81.6814	530.93
1/8	44.3750	156.70	1/8	63.2246	318.10	1/8	82.0741	536.05
1/4	44.7677	159.48	1/4	63.6173	322.06	1/4	82.4668	541.19
3/8	45.1604	162.30	3/8	64.0100	326.05	3/8	82.8595	546.35
1/2	45.5531	165.13	1/2	64.4026	330.06	1/2	83.2522	551.55
5/8	45.9458	167.99	5/8	64.7953	334.10	5/8	83.6449	556.76
3/4	46.3385	170.87	3/4	65.1880	338.16	3/4	84.0376	562.00
7/8	46.7312	173.78	7/8	65.5807	342.25	7/8	84.4303	567.27
15	47.1239	176.71	21	65.9734	346.36	27	84.8230	572.56
1/8	47.5166	179.67	1/8	66.3661	350.50	1/8	85.2157	577.87
1/4	47.9093	182.65	1/4	66.7588	354.66	1/4	85.6084	583.21
3/8	48.3020	185.66	3/8	67.1515	358.84	3/8	86.0011	588.57
1/2	48.6947	188.69	1/2	67.5442	363.05	1/2	86.3938	593.96
5/8	49.0874	191.75	5/8	67.9369	367.28	5/8	86.7865	599.37
3/4	49.4801	194.83	3/4	68.3296	371.54	3/4	87.1792	604.81
7/8	49.8728	197.93	7/8	68.7223	375.83	7/8	87.5719	610.27

Circumferences and Areas of Circles

Diam-eter	Circum-ference	Area	Diam-eter	Circum-ference	Area	Diam-eter	Circum-ference	Area
28	87.9646	615.75	34	106.814	907.92	40	125.664	1256.6
1/8	88.3573	621.26	1/8	107.207	914.61	1/8	126.056	1264.5
1/4	88.7500	626.80	1/4	107.600	921.32	1/4	126.449	1272.4
3/8	89.1427	632.36	3/8	107.992	928.06	3/8	126.842	1280.3
1/2	89.5354	637.94	1/2	108.385	934.82	1/2	127.235	1288.2
5/8	89.9281	643.55	5/8	108.778	941.61	5/8	127.627	1296.2
3/4	90.3208	649.18	3/4	109.170	948.42	3/4	128.020	1304.2
7/8	90.7135	654.84	7/8	109.563	955.25	7/8	128.413	1312.2
29	91.1062	660.52	35	109.956	962.11	41	128.805	1320.3
1/8	91.4989	666.23	1/8	110.348	969.00	1/8	129.198	1328.3
1/4	91.8916	671.96	1/4	110.741	975.91	1/4	129.591	1336.4
3/8	92.2843	677.71	3/8	111.134	982.84	3/8	129.983	1344.5
1/2	92.6770	683.49	1/2	111.527	989.80	1/2	130.376	1352.7
5/8	93.0697	689.30	5/8	111.919	996.78	5/8	130.769	1360.8
3/4	93.4624	695.13	3/4	112.312	1003.8	3/4	131.161	1369.0
7/8	93.8551	700.98	7/8	112.705	1010.8	7/8	131.554	1377.2
30	94.2478	706.86	36	113.097	1017.9	42	131.947	1385.4
1/8	94.6405	712.76	1/8	113.490	1025.0	1/8	132.340	1393.7
1/4	95.0332	718.69	1/4	113.883	1032.1	1/4	132.732	1402.0
3/8	95.4259	724.64	3/8	114.275	1039.2	3/8	133.125	1410.3
1/2	95.8186	730.62	1/2	114.668	1046.3	1/2	133.518	1418.6
5/8	96.2113	736.62	5/8	115.061	1053.5	5/8	133.910	1427.0
3/4	96.6040	742.64	3/4	115.454	1060.7	3/4	134.303	1435.4
7/8	96.9967	748.69	7/8	115.846	1068.0	7/8	134.696	1443.8
31	97.3894	754.77	37	116.239	1075.2	43	135.088	1452.2
1/8	97.7821	760.87	1/8	116.632	1082.5	1/8	135.481	1460.7
1/4	98.1748	766.99	1/4	117.024	1089.8	1/4	135.874	1469.1
3/8	98.5675	773.14	3/8	117.417	1097.1	3/8	136.267	1477.6
1/2	98.9602	779.31	1/2	117.810	1104.5	1/2	136.659	1486.2
5/8	99.3529	785.51	5/8	118.202	1111.8	5/8	137.052	1494.7
3/4	99.7456	791.73	3/4	118.596	1119.2	3/4	137.445	1503.3
7/8	100.138	797.98	7/8	118.988	1126.7	7/8	137.837	1511.9
32	100.531	804.25	38	119.381	1134.1	44	138.230	1520.5
1/8	100.924	810.54	1/8	119.773	1141.6	1/8	138.623	1529.2
1/4	101.316	816.86	1/4	120.166	1149.1	1/4	139.015	1537.9
3/8	101.709	823.21	3/8	120.559	1156.6	3/8	139.408	1546.6
1/2	102.102	829.58	1/2	120.951	1164.2	1/2	139.801	1555.3
5/8	102.494	835.97	5/8	121.344	1171.7	5/8	140.194	1564.0
3/4	102.887	842.39	3/4	121.737	1179.3	3/4	140.586	1572.8
7/8	103.280	848.83	7/8	122.129	1186.9	7/8	140.979	1581.6
33	103.673	855.30	39	122.522	1194.6	45	141.372	1590.4
1/8	104.065	861.79	1/8	122.915	1202.3	1/8	141.764	1599.3
1/4	104.458	868.31	1/4	123.308	1210.0	1/4	142.157	1608.2
3/8	104.851	874.85	3/8	123.700	1217.7	3/8	142.550	1617.0
1/2	105.243	881.41	1/2	124.093	1225.4	1/2	142.942	1626.0
5/8	105.636	888.00	5/8	124.486	1233.2	5/8	143.335	1634.9
3/4	106.029	894.62	3/4	124.878	1241.0	3/4	143.728	1643.9
7/8	106.421	901.26	7/8	125.271	1248.8	7/8	144.121	1652.9

Circumferences and Areas of Circles

Diameter	Circumference	Area	Diameter	Circumference	Area	Diameter	Circumference	Area
46	144.513	1661.9	52	163.363	2123.7	58	182.212	2642.1
1/8	144.906	1670.9	1/8	163.756	2133.9	1/8	182.605	2653.5
1/4	145.299	1680.0	1/4	164.148	2144.2	1/4	182.998	2664.9
3/8	145.691	1689.1	3/8	164.541	2154.5	3/8	183.390	2676.4
1/2	146.084	1698.2	1/2	164.934	2164.8	1/2	183.783	2687.8
5/8	146.477	1707.4	5/8	165.326	2175.1	5/8	184.176	2699.3
3/4	146.869	1716.5	3/4	165.719	2185.4	3/4	184.569	2710.9
7/8	147.262	1725.7	7/8	166.112	2195.8	7/8	184.961	2722.4
47	147.655	1734.9	53	166.504	2206.2	59	185.354	2734.0
1/8	148.048	1744.2	1/8	166.897	2216.6	1/8	185.747	2745.6
1/4	148.440	1753.5	1/4	167.290	2227.0	1/4	186.139	2757.2
3/8	148.833	1762.7	3/8	167.683	2237.5	3/8	186.532	2768.8
1/2	149.226	1772.1	1/2	168.075	2248.0	1/2	186.925	2780.5
5/8	149.618	1781.4	5/8	168.468	2258.5	5/8	187.317	2792.2
3/4	150.011	1790.8	3/4	168.861	2269.1	3/4	187.710	2803.9
7/8	150.404	1800.1	7/8	169.253	2279.6	7/8	188.103	2815.7
48	150.796	1809.6	54	169.646	2290.2	60	188.496	2827.4
1/8	151.189	1819.0	1/8	170.039	2300.8	1/8	188.888	2839.2
1/4	151.582	1828.5	1/4	170.431	2311.5	1/4	189.281	2851.0
3/8	151.975	1837.9	3/8	170.824	2322.1	3/8	189.674	2862.9
1/2	152.367	1847.5	1/2	171.217	2332.8	1/2	190.066	2874.8
5/8	152.760	1857.0	5/8	171.609	2343.5	5/8	190.459	2886.6
3/4	153.153	1866.5	3/4	172.002	2354.3	3/4	190.852	2898.6
7/8	153.545	1876.1	7/8	172.395	2365.0	7/8	191.244	2910.5
49	153.938	1885.7	55	172.788	2375.8	61	191.637	2922.5
1/8	154.331	1895.4	1/8	173.180	2386.6	1/8	192.030	2934.5
1/4	154.723	1905.0	1/4	173.573	2397.5	1/4	192.423	2946.5
3/8	155.116	1914.7	3/8	173.966	2408.3	3/8	192.815	2958.5
1/2	155.509	1924.4	1/2	174.358	2419.2	1/2	193.208	2970.6
5/8	155.902	1934.2	5/8	174.751	2430.1	5/8	193.601	2982.7
3/4	156.294	1943.9	3/4	175.144	2441.1	3/4	193.993	2994.8
7/8	156.687	1953.7	7/8	175.536	2452.0	7/8	194.386	3006.9
50	157.080	1963.5	56	175.929	2463.0	62	194.779	3019.1
1/8	157.472	1973.3	1/8	176.322	2474.0	1/8	195.171	3031.3
1/4	157.865	1983.2	1/4	176.715	2485.0	1/4	195.564	3043.5
3/8	158.258	1993.1	3/8	177.107	2496.1	3/8	195.957	3055.7
1/2	158.650	2003.0	1/2	177.500	2507.2	1/2	196.350	3068.0
5/8	159.043	2012.9	5/8	177.893	2518.3	5/8	196.742	3080.3
3/4	159.436	2022.8	3/4	178.285	2529.4	3/4	197.135	3092.6
7/8	159.829	2032.8	7/8	178.678	2540.6	7/8	197.528	3104.9
51	160.221	2042.8	57	179.071	2551.8	63	197.920	3117.2
1/8	160.614	2052.8	1/8	179.463	2563.0	1/8	198.313	3129.6
1/4	161.007	2062.9	1/4	179.856	2574.2	1/4	198.706	3142.0
3/8	161.399	2073.0	3/8	180.249	2585.4	3/8	199.098	3154.5
1/2	161.792	2083.1	1/2	180.642	2596.7	1/2	199.491	3166.9
5/8	162.185	2093.2	5/8	181.034	2608.0	5/8	199.884	3179.4
3/4	162.577	2103.3	3/4	181.427	2619.4	3/4	200.277	3191.9
7/8	162.970	2113.5	7/8	181.820	2630.7	7/8	200.669	3204.4

Circumferences and Areas of Circles

Diameter	Circumference	Area	Diameter	Circumference	Area	Diameter	Circumference	Area
64	201.062	3217.0	70	219.911	3848.5	76	238.761	4536.5
1/8	201.455	3229.6	1/8	220.304	3862.2	1/8	239.154	4551.4
1/4	201.847	3242.2	1/4	220.697	3876.0	1/4	239.546	4566.4
3/8	202.240	3254.8	3/8	221.090	3889.8	3/8	239.939	4581.3
1/2	202.633	3267.5	1/2	221.482	3903.6	1/2	240.332	4596.3
5/8	203.025	3280.1	5/8	221.875	3917.5	5/8	240.725	4611.4
3/4	203.418	3292.8	3/4	222.268	3931.4	3/4	241.117	4626.4
7/8	203.811	3305.6	7/8	222.660	3945.3	7/8	241.510	4641.5
65	204.204	3318.3	71	223.053	3959.2	77	241.903	4656.6
1/8	204.596	3331.1	1/8	223.446	3973.1	1/8	242.295	4671.8
1/4	204.989	3343.9	1/4	223.838	3987.1	1/4	242.688	4686.9
3/8	205.382	3356.7	3/8	224.231	4001.1	3/8	243.081	4702.1
1/2	205.774	3369.6	1/2	224.624	4015.2	1/2	243.473	4717.3
5/8	206.167	3382.4	5/8	225.017	4029.2	5/8	243.866	4732.5
3/4	206.560	3395.3	3/4	225.409	4043.3	3/4	244.259	4747.8
7/8	206.952	3408.2	7/8	225.802	4057.4	7/8	244.652	4763.1
66	207.345	3421.2	72	226.195	4071.5	78	245.044	4778.4
1/8	207.738	3434.2	1/8	226.587	4085.7	1/8	245.437	4793.7
1/4	208.131	3447.2	1/4	226.980	4099.8	1/4	245.830	4809.0
3/8	208.523	3460.2	3/8	227.373	4114.0	3/8	246.222	4824.4
1/2	208.916	3473.2	1/2	227.765	4128.2	1/2	246.615	4839.8
5/8	209.309	3486.3	5/8	228.158	4142.5	5/8	247.008	4855.2
3/4	209.701	3499.4	3/4	228.551	4156.8	3/4	247.400	4870.7
7/8	210.094	3512.5	7/8	228.944	4171.1	7/8	247.793	4886.2
67	210.487	3525.7	73	229.336	4185.4	79	248.186	4901.7
1/8	210.879	3538.8	1/8	229.729	4199.7	1/8	248.579	4917.4
1/4	211.272	3552.0	1/4	230.122	4214.1	1/4	248.971	4932.7
3/8	211.665	3565.2	3/8	230.514	4228.5	3/8	249.364	4948.3
1/2	212.058	3578.5	1/2	230.907	4242.9	1/2	249.757	4963.9
5/8	212.450	3591.7	5/8	231.300	4257.4	5/8	250.149	4979.5
3/4	212.843	3605.0	3/4	231.692	4271.8	3/4	250.542	4995.2
7/8	213.236	3618.3	7/8	232.085	4286.3	7/8	250.935	5010.9
68	213.628	3631.7	74	232.478	4300.8	80	251.327	5026.5
1/8	214.021	3645.0	1/8	232.871	4315.4	1/8	251.720	5042.3
1/4	214.414	3658.4	1/4	233.263	4329.9	1/4	252.113	5058.0
3/8	214.806	3671.8	3/8	233.656	4344.5	3/8	252.506	5073.8
1/2	215.199	3685.3	1/2	234.049	4359.2	1/2	252.898	5089.6
5/8	215.592	3698.7	5/8	234.441	4373.8	5/8	253.291	5105.4
3/4	215.984	3712.2	3/4	234.834	4388.5	3/4	253.684	5121.2
7/8	216.377	3725.7	7/8	235.227	4403.1	7/8	254.076	5137.1
69	216.770	3739.3	75	235.619	4417.9	81	254.469	5153.0
1/8	217.163	3752.8	1/8	236.012	4432.6	1/8	254.862	5168.9
1/4	217.555	3766.4	1/4	236.405	4447.4	1/4	255.254	5184.9
3/8	217.948	3780.0	3/8	236.798	4462.2	3/8	255.647	5200.8
1/2	218.341	3793.7	1/2	237.190	4477.0	1/2	256.040	5216.8
5/8	218.733	3807.3	5/8	237.583	4491.8	5/8	256.433	5232.8
3/4	219.126	3821.0	3/4	237.976	4506.7	3/4	256.825	5248.9
7/8	219.519	3834.7	7/8	238.368	4521.5	7/8	257.218	5264.9

Circumferences and Areas of Circles

Diameter	Circumference	Area	Diameter	Circumference	Area	Diameter	Circumference	Area
82	257.611	5281.0	88	276.460	6082.1	94	295.310	6939.8
⅛	258.003	5297.1	⅛	276.853	6099.4	⅛	295.702	6958.2
¼	258.396	5313.3	¼	277.246	6116.7	¼	296.095	6976.7
⅜	258.789	5329.4	⅜	277.638	6134.1	⅜	296.488	6995.3
½	259.181	5345.6	½	278.031	6151.4	½	296.881	7013.8
⅝	259.574	5361.8	⅝	278.424	6168.8	⅝	297.273	7032.4
¾	259.967	5378.1	¾	278.816	6186.2	¾	297.666	7051.0
⅞	260.359	5394.3	⅞	279.209	6203.7	⅞	298.059	7069.6
83	260.752	5410.6	89	279.602	6221.1	95	298.451	7088.2
⅛	261.145	5426.9	⅛	279.994	6238.6	⅛	298.844	7106.9
¼	261.538	5443.3	¼	280.387	6256.1	¼	299.237	7125.6
⅜	261.930	5459.6	⅜	280.780	6273.7	⅜	299.629	7144.3
½	262.323	5476.0	½	281.173	6291.2	½	300.022	7163.0
⅝	262.716	5492.4	⅝	281.565	6308.8	⅝	300.415	7181.8
¾	263.108	5508.8	¾	281.958	6326.4	¾	300.807	7200.6
⅞	263.501	5525.3	⅞	282.351	6344.1	⅞	301.200	7219.4
84	263.894	5541.8	90	282.743	6361.7	96	301.593	7238.2
⅛	264.286	5558.3	⅛	283.136	6379.4	⅛	301.986	7257.1
¼	264.679	5574.8	¼	283.529	6397.1	¼	302.378	7276.0
⅜	265.072	5591.4	⅜	283.921	6414.9	⅜	302.771	7294.9
½	265.465	5607.9	½	284.314	6432.6	½	303.164	7313.8
⅝	265.857	5624.5	⅝	284.707	6450.4	⅝	303.556	7332.8
¾	266.250	5641.2	¾	285.100	6468.2	¾	303.949	7351.8
⅞	266.643	5657.8	⅞	285.492	6486.0	⅞	304.342	7370.8
85	267.035	5674.5	91	285.885	6503.9	97	304.734	7389.8
⅛	267.428	5691.2	⅛	286.278	6521.8	⅛	305.127	7408.9
¼	267.821	5707.9	¼	286.670	6539.7	¼	305.520	7428.0
⅜	268.213	5724.7	⅜	287.063	6557.6	⅜	305.913	7447.1
½	268.606	5741.5	½	287.456	6575.5	½	306.305	7466.2
⅝	268.999	5758.3	⅝	287.848	6593.5	⅝	306.698	7485.3
¾	269.392	5775.1	¾	288.241	6611.5	¾	307.091	7504.5
⅞	269.784	5791.9	⅞	288.634	6629.6	⅞	307.483	7523.7
86	270.177	5808.8	92	289.027	6647.6	98	307.876	7543.0
⅛	270.570	5825.7	⅛	289.419	6665.7	⅛	308.269	7562.2
¼	270.962	5842.6	¼	289.812	6683.8	¼	308.661	7581.5
⅜	271.355	5859.6	⅜	290.205	6701.9	⅜	309.054	7600.8
½	271.748	5876.5	½	290.597	6720.1	½	309.447	7620.1
⅝	272.140	5893.5	⅝	290.990	6738.2	⅝	309.840	7639.5
¾	272.533	5910.6	¾	291.383	6756.4	¾	310.232	7658.9
⅞	272.926	5927.6	⅞	291.775	6774.7	⅞	310.625	7678.3
87	273.319	5944.7	93	292.168	6792.9	99	311.018	7697.7
⅛	273.711	5961.8	⅛	292.561	6811.2	⅛	311.410	7717.1
¼	274.104	5978.9	¼	292.954	6829.5	¼	311.803	7736.6
⅜	274.497	5996.0	⅜	293.346	6847.8	⅜	312.196	7756.1
½	274.889	6013.2	½	293.739	6866.1	½	312.588	7775.6
⅝	275.282	6030.4	⅝	294.132	6884.5	⅝	312.981	7795.2
¾	275.675	6047.6	¾	294.524	6902.9	¾	313.374	7814.8
⅞	276.067	6064.9	⅞	294.917	6921.3	⅞	313.767	7834.4

Circumferences and Areas of Circles

Diameter	Circumference	Area	Diameter	Circumference	Area	Diameter	Circumference	Area
100	314.16	7,854.0	150	471.24	17,671.5	200	628.32	31,415.9
101	317.30	8,011.8	151	474.38	17,907.9	201	631.46	31,730.9
102	320.44	8,171.3	152	477.52	18,145.8	202	634.60	32,047.4
103	323.58	8,332.3	153	480.66	18,385.4	203	637.74	32,365.5
104	326.73	8,494.9	154	483.81	18,626.5	204	640.88	32,685.1
105	329.87	8,659.0	155	486.95	18,869.2	205	644.03	33,006.4
106	333.01	8,824.7	156	490.09	19,113.4	206	647.17	33,329.2
107	336.15	8,992.0	157	493.23	19,359.3	207	650.31	33,653.5
108	339.29	9,160.9	158	496.37	19,606.7	208	653.45	33,979.5
109	342.43	9,331.3	159	499.51	19,855.7	209	656.59	34,307.0
110	345.58	9,503.3	160	502.65	20,106.2	210	659.73	34,636.1
111	348.72	9,676.9	161	505.80	20,358.3	211	662.88	34,966.7
112	351.86	9,852.0	162	508.94	20,612.0	212	666.02	35,298.9
113	355.00	10,028.7	163	512.08	20,867.2	213	669.16	35,632.7
114	358.14	10,207.0	164	515.22	21,124.1	214	672.30	35,968.1
115	361.28	10,386.9	165	518.36	21,382.5	215	675.44	36,305.0
116	364.42	10,568.3	166	521.50	21,642.4	216	678.58	36,643.5
117	367.57	10,751.3	167	524.65	21,904.0	217	681.73	36,983.6
118	370.71	10,935.9	168	527.79	22,167.1	218	684.87	37,325.3
119	373.85	11,122.0	169	530.93	22,431.8	219	688.01	37,668.5
120	376.99	11,309.7	170	534.07	22,698.0	220	691.15	38,013.3
121	380.13	11,499.0	171	537.21	22,965.8	221	694.29	38,359.6
122	383.27	11,689.9	172	540.35	23,235.2	222	697.43	38,707.6
123	386.42	11,882.3	173	543.50	23,506.2	223	700.58	39,057.1
124	389.56	12,076.3	174	546.64	23,778.7	224	703.72	39,408.1
125	392.70	12,271.8	175	549.78	24,052.8	225	706.86	39,760.8
126	395.84	12,469.0	176	552.92	24,328.5	226	710.00	40,115.0
127	398.98	12,667.7	177	556.06	24,605.7	227	713.14	40,470.8
128	402.12	12,868.0	178	559.20	24,884.6	228	716.28	40,828.1
129	405.27	13,069.8	179	562.35	25,164.9	229	719.42	41,187.1
130	408.41	13,273.2	180	565.49	25,446.9	230	722.57	41,547.6
131	411.55	13,478.2	181	568.63	25,730.4	231	725.71	41,909.6
132	414.69	13,684.8	182	571.77	26,015.5	232	728.85	42,273.3
133	417.83	13,892.9	183	574.91	26,302.2	233	731.99	42,638.5
134	420.97	14,102.6	184	578.05	26,590.4	234	735.13	43,005.3
135	424.12	14,313.9	185	581.19	26,880.3	235	738.27	43,373.6
136	427.26	14,526.7	186	584.34	27,171.6	236	741.42	43,743.5
137	430.40	14,741.1	187	587.48	27,464.6	237	744.56	44,115.0
138	433.54	14,957.1	188	590.62	27,759.1	238	747.70	44,488.1
139	436.68	15,174.7	189	593.76	28,055.2	239	750.84	44,862.7
140	439.82	15,393.8	190	596.90	28,352.9	240	753.98	45,238.9
141	442.96	15,614.5	191	600.04	28,652.1	241	757.12	45,616.7
142	446.11	15,836.8	192	603.19	28,952.9	242	760.27	45,996.1
143	449.25	16,060.6	193	606.33	29,255.3	243	763.41	46,377.0
144	452.39	16,286.0	194	609.47	29,559.2	244	766.55	46,759.5
145	455.53	16,513.0	195	612.61	29,864.8	245	769.69	47,143.5
146	458.67	16,741.5	196	615.75	30,171.9	246	772.83	47,529.2
147	461.81	16,971.7	197	618.89	30,480.5	247	775.97	47,916.4
148	464.96	17,203.4	198	622.04	30,790.7	248	779.11	48,305.1
149	468.10	17,436.6	199	625.18	31,102.6	249	782.26	48,695.5

Circumferences and Areas of Circles

Diameter	Circumference	Area	Diameter	Circumference	Area	Diameter	Circumference	Area
250	785.40	49,087.4	300	942.48	70,685.8	350	1099.56	96,211.3
251	788.54	49,480.9	301	945.62	71,157.9	351	1102.70	96,761.8
252	791.68	49,875.9	302	948.76	71,631.5	352	1105.84	97,314.0
253	794.82	50,272.6	303	951.90	72,106.6	353	1108.98	97,867.7
254	797.96	50,670.7	304	955.04	72,583.4	354	1112.12	98,423.0
255	801.11	51,070.5	305	958.19	73,061.7	355	1115.27	98,979.8
256	804.25	51,471.9	306	961.33	73,541.5	356	1118.41	99,538.2
257	807.39	51,874.8	307	964.47	74,023.0	357	1121.55	100,098
258	810.53	52,279.2	308	967.61	74,506.0	358	1124.69	100,660
259	813.67	52,685.3	309	970.75	74,990.6	359	1127.83	101,223
260	816.81	53,092.9	310	973.89	75,476.8	360	1130.97	101,788
261	819.96	53,502.1	311	977.04	75,964.5	361	1134.11	102,354
262	823.10	53,912.9	312	980.18	76,453.8	362	1137.26	102,922
263	826.24	54,325.2	313	983.32	76,944.7	363	1140.40	103,491
264	829.38	54,739.1	314	986.46	77,437.1	364	1143.54	104,062
265	832.52	55,154.6	315	989.60	77,931.1	365	1146.68	104,635
266	835.66	55,571.6	316	992.74	78,426.7	366	1149.82	105,209
267	838.81	55,990.2	317	995.88	78,923.9	367	1152.96	105,784
268	841.95	56,410.4	318	999.03	79,422.6	368	1156.11	106,362
269	845.09	56,832.2	319	1002.17	79,922.9	369	1159.25	106,941
270	848.23	57,255.5	320	1005.31	80,424.8	370	1162.39	107,521
271	851.37	57,680.4	321	1008.45	80,928.2	371	1165.53	108,103
272	854.51	58,106.9	322	1011.59	81,433.2	372	1168.67	108,687
273	857.65	58,534.9	323	1014.73	81,939.8	373	1171.81	109,272
274	860.80	58,964.6	324	1017.88	82,448.0	374	1174.96	109,858
275	863.94	59,395.7	325	1021.02	82,957.7	375	1178.10	110,447
276	867.08	59,828.5	326	1024.16	83,469.0	376	1181.24	111,036
277	870.22	60,262.8	327	1027.30	83,981.8	377	1184.38	111,628
278	873.36	60,698.7	328	1030.44	84,496.3	378	1187.52	112,221
279	876.50	61,136.2	329	1033.58	85,012.3	379	1190.66	112,815
280	879.65	61,575.2	330	1036.73	85,529.9	380	1193.81	113,411
281	882.79	62,015.8	331	1039.87	86,049.0	381	1196.95	114,009
282	885.93	62,458.0	332	1043.01	86,569.7	382	1200.09	114,608
283	889.07	62,901.8	333	1046.15	87,092.0	383	1203.23	115,209
284	892.21	63,347.1	334	1049.29	87,615.9	384	1206.37	115,812
285	895.35	63,794.0	335	1052.43	88,141.3	385	1209.51	116,416
286	898.50	64,242.4	336	1055.58	88,668.3	386	1212.65	117,021
287	901.64	64,692.5	337	1058.72	89,196.9	387	1215.80	117,628
288	904.78	65,144.1	338	1061.86	89,727.0	388	1218.94	118,237
289	907.92	65,597.2	339	1065.00	90,258.7	389	1222.08	118,847
290	911.06	66,052.0	340	1068.14	90,792.0	390	1225.22	119,459
291	914.20	66,508.3	341	1071.28	91,326.9	391	1228.36	120,072
292	917.35	66,966.2	342	1074.42	91,863.3	392	1231.50	120,687
293	920.49	67,425.6	343	1077.57	92,401.3	393	1234.65	121,304
294	923.63	67,886.7	344	1080.71	92,940.9	394	1237.79	121,922
295	926.77	68,349.3	345	1083.85	93,482.0	395	1240.93	122,542
296	929.91	68,813.4	346	1086.99	94,024.7	396	1244.07	123,163
297	933.05	69,279.2	347	1090.13	94,569.0	397	1247.21	123,786
298	936.19	69,746.5	348	1093.27	95,114.9	398	1250.35	124,410
299	939.34	70,215.4	349	1096.42	95,662.3	399	1253.50	125,036

Circumferences and Areas of Circles

Diameter	Circumference	Area	Diameter	Circumference	Area	Diameter	Circumference	Area
400	1256.64	125,664	450	1413.72	159,043	500	1570.80	196,350
401	1259.78	126,293	451	1416.86	159,751	501	1573.94	197,136
402	1262.92	126,923	452	1420.00	160,460	502	1577.08	197,923
403	1266.06	127,556	453	1423.14	161,171	503	1580.22	198,713
404	1269.20	128,190	454	1426.28	161,883	504	1583.36	199,504
405	1272.35	128,825	455	1429.42	162,597	505	1586.50	200,296
406	1275.49	129,462	456	1432.57	163,313	506	1589.65	201,090
407	1278.63	130,100	457	1435.71	164,030	507	1592.79	201,886
408	1281.77	130,741	458	1438.85	164,748	508	1595.93	202,683
409	1284.91	131,382	459	1441.99	165,468	509	1599.07	203,482
410	1288.05	132,025	460	1445.13	166,190	510	1602.21	204,282
411	1291.19	132,670	461	1448.27	166,914	511	1605.35	205,084
412	1294.34	133,317	462	1451.42	167,639	512	1608.50	205,887
413	1297.48	133,965	463	1454.56	168,365	513	1611.64	206,692
414	1300.62	134,614	464	1457.70	169,093	514	1614.78	207,499
415	1303.76	135,265	465	1460.84	169,823	515	1617.92	208,307
416	1306.90	135,918	466	1463.98	170,554	516	1621.06	209,117
417	1310.04	136,572	467	1467.12	171,287	517	1624.20	209,928
418	1313.19	137,228	468	1470.27	172,021	518	1627.35	210,741
419	1316.33	137,885	469	1473.41	172,757	519	1630.49	211,556
420	1319.47	138,544	470	1476.55	173,494	520	1633.63	212,372
421	1322.61	139,205	471	1479.69	174,234	521	1636.77	213,189
422	1325.75	139,867	472	1482.83	174,974	522	1639.91	214,008
423	1328.89	140,531	473	1485.97	175,716	523	1643.05	214,829
424	1332.04	141,196	474	1489.11	176,460	524	1646.20	215,651
425	1335.18	141,863	475	1492.26	177,205	525	1649.34	216,475
426	1338.32	142,531	476	1495.40	177,952	526	1652.48	217,301
427	1341.46	143,201	477	1498.54	178,701	527	1655.62	218,128
428	1344.60	143,872	478	1501.68	179,451	528	1658.76	218,956
429	1347.74	144,545	479	1504.82	180,203	529	1661.90	219,787
430	1350.88	145,220	480	1507.96	180,956	530	1665.04	220,618
431	1354.03	145,896	481	1511.11	181,711	531	1668.19	221,452
432	1357.17	146,574	482	1514.25	182,467	532	1671.33	222,287
433	1360.31	147,254	483	1517.39	183,225	533	1674.47	223,123
434	1363.45	147,934	484	1520.53	183,984	534	1677.61	223,961
435	1366.59	148,617	485	1523.67	184,745	535	1680.75	224,801
436	1369.73	149,301	486	1526.81	185,508	536	1683.89	225,642
437	1372.88	149,987	487	1529.96	186,272	537	1687.04	226,484
438	1376.02	150,674	488	1533.10	187,038	538	1690.18	227,329
439	1379.16	151,363	489	1536.24	187,805	539	1693.32	228,175
440	1382.30	152,053	490	1539.38	188,574	540	1696.46	229,022
441	1385.44	152,745	491	1542.52	189,345	541	1699.60	229,871
442	1388.58	153,439	492	1545.66	190,117	542	1702.74	230,722
443	1391.73	154,134	493	1548.81	190,890	543	1705.88	231,574
444	1394.87	154,830	494	1551.95	191,665	544	1709.03	232,428
445	1398.01	155,528	495	1555.09	192,442	545	1712.17	233,283
446	1401.15	156,228	496	1558.23	193,221	546	1715.31	234,140
447	1404.29	156,930	497	1561.37	194,000	547	1718.45	234,998
448	1407.43	157,633	498	1564.51	194,782	548	1721.59	235,858
449	1410.58	158,337	499	1567.65	195,565	549	1724.73	236,720

Circumferences and Areas of Circles

Diameter	Circumference	Area	Diameter	Circumference	Area	Diameter	Circumference	Area
550	1727.88	237,583	600	1884.96	282,743	650	2042.04	331,831
551	1731.02	238,448	601	1888.10	283,687	651	2045.18	332,853
552	1734.16	239,314	602	1891.24	284,631	652	2048.32	333,876
553	1737.30	240,182	603	1894.38	285,578	653	2051.46	334,901
554	1740.44	241,051	604	1897.52	286,526	654	2054.60	335,927
555	1743.58	241,922	605	1900.66	287,475	655	2057.74	336,955
556	1746.73	242,795	606	1903.81	288,426	656	2060.88	337,985
557	1749.87	243,669	607	1906.95	289,379	657	2064.03	339,016
558	1753.01	244,545	608	1910.09	290,333	658	2067.17	340,049
559	1756.15	245,422	609	1913.23	291,289	659	2070.31	341,083
560	1759.29	246,301	610	1916.37	292,247	660	2073.45	342,119
561	1762.43	247,181	611	1919.51	293,206	661	2076.59	343,157
562	1765.58	248,063	612	1922.65	294,166	662	2079.73	344,196
563	1768.72	248,947	613	1925.80	295,128	663	2082.88	345,237
564	1771.86	249,832	614	1928.94	296,092	664	2086.02	346,279
565	1775.00	250,719	615	1932.08	297,057	665	2089.16	347,323
566	1778.14	251,607	616	1935.22	298,024	666	2092.30	348,368
567	1781.28	252,497	617	1938.36	298,992	667	2095.44	349,415
568	1784.42	253,388	618	1941.50	299,962	668	2098.58	350,464
569	1787.57	254,281	619	1944.65	300,934	669	2101.73	351,514
570	1790.71	255,176	620	1947.79	301,907	670	2104.87	352,565
571	1793.85	256,072	621	1950.93	302,882	671	2108.01	353,618
572	1796.99	256,970	622	1954.07	303,858	672	2111.15	354,673
573	1800.13	257,869	623	1957.21	304,836	673	2114.29	355,730
574	1803.27	258,770	624	1960.35	305,815	674	2117.43	356,788
575	1806.42	259,672	625	1963.50	306,796	675	2120.58	357,847
576	1809.56	260,576	626	1966.64	307,779	676	2123.72	358,908
577	1812.70	261,482	627	1969.78	308,763	677	2126.86	359,971
578	1815.84	262,389	628	1972.92	309,748	678	2130.00	361,035
579	1818.98	263,298	629	1976.06	310,736	679	2133.14	362,101
580	1822.12	264,208	630	1979.20	311,725	680	2136.28	363,168
581	1825.27	265,120	631	1982.35	312,715	681	2139.42	364,237
582	1828.41	266,033	632	1985.49	313,707	682	2142.57	365,308
583	1831.55	266,948	633	1988.63	314,700	683	2145.71	366,380
584	1834.69	267,865	634	1991.77	315,696	684	2148.85	367,453
585	1837.83	268,783	635	1994.91	316,692	685	2151.99	368,528
586	1840.97	269,703	636	1998.05	317,690	686	2155.13	369,605
587	1844.11	270,624	637	2001.19	318,690	687	2158.27	370,684
588	1847.26	271,547	638	2004.34	319,692	688	2161.42	371,764
589	1850.40	272,471	639	2007.48	320,695	689	2164.56	372,845
590	1853.54	273,397	640	2010.62	321,699	690	2167.70	373,928
591	1856.68	274,325	641	2013.76	322,705	691	2170.84	375,013
592	1859.82	275,254	642	2016.90	323,713	692	2173.98	376,099
593	1862.96	276,184	643	2020.04	324,722	693	2177.12	377,187
594	1866.11	277,117	644	2023.19	325,733	694	2180.27	378,276
595	1869.25	278,051	645	2026.33	326,745	695	2183.41	379,367
596	1872.39	278,986	646	2029.47	327,759	696	2186.55	380,459
597	1875.53	279,923	647	2032.61	328,775	697	2189.69	381,554
598	1878.67	280,862	648	2035.75	329,792	698	2192.83	382,649
599	1881.81	281,802	649	2038.89	330,810	699	2195.97	383,746

Circumferences and Areas of Circles

Diameter	Circumference	Area	Diameter	Circumference	Area	Diameter	Circumference	Area
700	2199.11	384,845	750	2356.19	441,786	800	2513.27	502,655
701	2202.26	385,945	751	2359.34	442,965	801	2516.42	503,912
702	2205.40	387,047	752	2362.48	444,146	802	2519.56	505,171
703	2208.54	388,151	753	2365.62	445,328	803	2522.70	506,432
704	2211.68	389,256	754	2368.76	446,511	804	2525.84	507,694
705	2214.82	390,363	755	2371.90	447,697	805	2528.98	508,958
706	2217.96	391,471	756	2375.04	448,883	806	2532.12	510,223
707	2221.11	392,580	757	2378.19	450,072	807	2535.27	511,490
708	2224.25	393,692	758	2381.33	451,262	808	2538.41	512,758
709	2227.39	394,805	759	2384.47	452,453	809	2541.55	514,028
710	2230.53	395,919	760	2387.61	453,646	810	2544.69	515,300
711	2233.67	397,035	761	2390.75	454,841	811	2547.83	516,573
712	2236.81	398,153	762	2393.89	456,037	812	2550.97	517,848
713	2239.96	399,272	763	2397.04	457,234	813	2554.11	519,124
714	2243.10	400,393	764	2400.18	458,434	814	2557.26	520,402
715	2246.24	401,515	765	2403.32	459,635	815	2560.40	521,681
716	2249.38	402,639	766	2406.46	460,837	816	2563.54	522,962
717	2252.52	403,765	767	2409.60	462,041	817	2566.68	524,245
718	2255.66	404,892	768	2412.74	463,247	818	2569.82	525,529
719	2258.81	406,020	769	2415.88	464,454	819	2572.96	526,814
720	2261.95	407,150	770	2419.03	465,663	820	2576.11	528,102
721	2265.09	408,282	771	2422.17	466,873	821	2579.25	529,391
722	2268.23	409,416	772	2425.31	468,085	822	2582.39	530,681
723	2271.37	410,550	773	2428.45	469,298	823	2585.53	531,973
724	2274.51	411,687	774	2431.59	470,513	824	2588.67	533,267
725	2277.65	412,825	775	2434.73	471,730	825	2591.81	534,562
726	2280.80	413,965	776	2437.88	472,948	826	2594.96	535,858
727	2283.94	415,106	777	2441.02	474,168	827	2598.10	537,157
728	2287.08	416,248	778	2444.16	475,389	828	2601.24	538,456
729	2290.22	417,393	779	2447.30	476,612	829	2604.38	539,758
730	2293.36	418,539	780	2450.44	477,836	830	2607.52	541,061
731	2296.50	419,686	781	2453.58	479,062	831	2610.66	542,365
732	2299.65	420,835	782	2456.73	480,290	832	2613.81	543,671
733	2302.79	421,986	783	2459.87	481,519	833	2616.95	544,979
734	2305.93	423,138	784	2463.01	482,750	834	2620.09	546,288
735	2309.07	424,292	785	2466.15	483,982	835	2623.23	547,599
736	2312.21	425,447	786	2469.29	485,216	836	2626.37	548,912
737	2315.35	426,604	787	2472.43	486,451	837	2629.51	550,226
738	2318.50	427,762	788	2475.58	487,688	838	2632.65	551,541
739	2321.64	428,922	789	2478.72	488,927	839	2635.80	552,858
740	2324.78	430,084	790	2481.86	490,167	840	2638.94	554,177
741	2327.92	431,247	791	2485.00	491,409	841	2642.08	555,497
742	2331.06	432,412	792	2488.14	492,652	842	2645.22	556,819
743	2334.20	433,578	793	2491.28	493,897	843	2648.36	558,142
744	2337.34	434,746	794	2494.42	495,143	844	2651.50	559,467
745	2340.49	435,916	795	2497.57	496,391	845	2654.65	560,794
746	2343.63	437,087	796	2500.71	497,641	846	2657.79	562,122
747	2346.77	438,259	797	2503.85	498,892	847	2660.93	563,452
748	2349.91	439,433	798	2506.99	500,145	848	2664.07	564,783
749	2353.05	440,609	799	2510.13	501,399	849	2667.21	566,116

Circumferences and Areas of Circles

Diameter	Circumference	Area	Diameter	Circumference	Area	Diameter	Circumference	Area
850	2670.35	567,450	900	2827.43	636,173	950	2984.51	708,822
851	2673.50	568,786	901	2830.58	637,587	951	2987.65	710,315
852	2676.64	570,124	902	2833.72	639,003	952	2990.80	711,809
853	2679.78	571,463	903	2836.86	640,421	953	2993.94	713,306
854	2682.92	572,803	904	2840.00	641,840	954	2997.08	714,803
855	2686.06	574,146	905	2843.14	643,261	955	3000.22	716,303
856	2689.20	575,490	906	2846.28	644,683	956	3003.36	717,804
857	2692.34	576,835	907	2849.42	646,107	957	3006.50	719,306
858	2695.49	578,182	908	2852.57	647,533	958	3009.65	720,810
859	2698.63	579,530	909	2855.71	648,960	959	3012.79	722,316
860	2701.77	580,880	910	2858.85	650,388	960	3015.93	723,823
861	2704.91	582,232	911	2861.99	651,818	961	3019.07	725,332
862	2708.05	583,585	912	2865.13	653,250	962	3022.21	726,842
863	2711.19	584,940	913	2868.27	654,684	963	3025.35	728,354
864	2714.34	586,297	914	2871.42	656,118	964	3028.50	729,867
865	2717.48	587,655	915	2874.56	657,555	965	3031.64	731,382
866	2720.62	589,014	916	2877.70	658,993	966	3034.78	732,899
867	2723.76	590,375	917	2880.84	660,433	967	3037.92	734,417
868	2726.90	591,738	918	2883.98	661,874	968	3041.06	735,937
869	2730.04	593,102	919	2887.12	663,317	969	3044.20	737,458
870	2733.19	594,468	920	2890.27	664,761	970	3047.34	738,981
871	2736.33	595,835	921	2893.41	666,207	971	3050.49	740,506
872	2739.47	597,204	922	2896.55	667,654	972	3053.63	742,032
873	2742.61	598,575	923	2899.69	669,103	973	3056.77	743,559
874	2745.75	599,947	924	2902.83	670,554	974	3059.91	745,088
875	2748.89	601,320	925	2905.97	672,006	975	3063.05	746,619
876	2752.04	602,696	926	2909.11	673,460	976	3066.19	748,151
877	2755.18	604,073	927	2912.26	674,915	977	3069.34	749,685
878	2758.32	605,451	928	2915.40	676,372	978	3072.48	751,221
879	2761.46	606,831	929	2918.54	677,831	979	3075.62	752,758
880	2764.60	608,212	930	2921.68	679,291	980	3078.76	754,296
881	2767.74	609,595	931	2924.82	680,752	981	3081.90	755,837
882	2770.88	610,980	932	2927.96	682,216	982	3085.04	757,378
883	2774.03	612,366	933	2931.11	683,680	983	3088.19	758,922
884	2777.17	613,754	934	2934.25	685,147	984	3091.33	760,466
885	2780.31	615,143	935	2937.39	686,615	985	3094.47	762,013
886	2783.45	616,534	936	2940.53	688,084	986	3097.61	763,561
887	2786.59	617,927	937	2943.67	689,555	987	3100.75	765,111
888	2789.73	619,321	938	2946.81	691,028	988	3103.89	766,662
889	2792.88	620,717	939	2949.96	692,502	989	3107.04	768,214
890	2796.02	622,114	940	2953.10	693,978	990	3110.18	769,769
891	2799.16	623,513	941	2956.24	695,455	991	3113.32	771,325
892	2802.30	624,913	942	2959.38	696,934	992	3116.46	772,882
893	2805.44	626,315	943	2962.52	698,415	993	3119.60	774,441
894	2808.58	627,718	944	2965.66	699,897	994	3122.74	776,002
895	2811.73	629,124	945	2968.81	701,380	995	3125.88	777,564
896	2814.87	630,530	946	2971.95	702,865	996	3129.03	779,128
897	2818.01	631,938	947	2975.09	704,352	997	3132.17	780,693
898	2821.15	633,348	948	2978.23	705,840	998	3135.31	782,260
899	2824.29	634,760	949	2981.37	707,330	999	3138.45	783,828

Diameters, Circumferences and Areas of Circles in Feet and Inches

Diam. Ft.	In.	Circum.* Ft.	In.	Area Sq. In.	Area Sq. Ft.	Diam. Ft.	In.	Circum.* Ft.	In.	Area Sq. In.	Area Sq. Ft.
1	6	4	8½	254.469	1.7671	2	0	6	3⅜	452.390	3.1416
	6⅛	4	9	258.016	1.7918		0¼	6	4⅛	461.864	3.2074
	6¼	4	9⅜	261.587	1.8166		0½	6	5	471.436	3.2739
	6⅜	4	9¾	265.182	1.8415		0¾	6	5¾	481.106	3.3410
	6½	4	10⅛	268.803	1.8667	2	1	6	6½	490.875	3.4089
	6⅝	4	10½	272.447	1.8920		1¼	6	7⅜	500.741	3.4774
	6¾	4	10⅞	276.117	1.9175		1½	6	8⅛	510.706	3.5466
	6⅞	4	11¼	279.811	1.9431		1¾	6	8⅞	520.769	3.6165
1	7	4	11¾	283.529	1.9690	2	2	6	9⅝	530.930	3.6870
	7⅛	5	0⅛	287.272	1.9949		2¼	6	10½	541.189	3.7583
	7¼	5	0½	291.039	2.0211		2½	6	11¼	551.547	3.8302
	7⅜	5	0⅞	294.831	2.0474		2¾	7	0	562.002	3.9028
	7½	5	1¼	298.648	2.0739	2	3	7	0⅞	572.556	3.9761
	7⅝	5	1⅝	302.489	2.1006		3¼	7	1⅝	583.208	4.0501
	7¾	5	2	306.355	2.1275		3½	7	2⅜	593.958	4.1247
	7⅞	5	2½	310.245	2.1545		3¾	7	3⅛	604.807	4.2000
1	8	5	2⅞	314.160	2.1817	2	4	7	4	615.753	4.2761
	8⅛	5	3¼	318.099	2.2090		4¼	7	4¾	626.798	4.3528
	8¼	5	3⅝	322.063	2.2365		4½	7	5½	637.941	4.4301
	8⅜	5	4	326.051	2.2642		4¾	7	6⅜	649.182	4.5082
	8½	5	4⅜	330.064	2.2921	2	5	7	7⅛	660.521	4.5870
	8⅝	5	4¾	334.101	2.3201		5¼	7	7⅞	671.958	4.6665
	8¾	5	5¼	338.163	2.3480		5½	7	8⅝	683.494	4.7465
	8⅞	5	5⅝	342.250	2.3768		5¾	7	9½	695.128	4.8273
1	9	5	6	346.361	2.4053	2	6	7	10¼	706.860	4.9088
	9⅛	5	6⅜	350.497	2.4340		6¼	7	11	718.690	4.9909
	9¼	5	6¾	354.657	2.4629		6½	7	11⅞	730.618	5.0737
	9⅜	5	7⅛	358.841	2.4920		6¾	8	0⅝	742.644	5.1573
	9½	5	7½	363.051	2.5212	2	7	8	1⅜	754.769	5.2415
	9⅝	5	7⅞	367.284	2.5506		7¼	8	2⅛	766.992	5.3263
	9¾	5	8⅜	371.543	2.5802		7½	8	3	779.313	5.4112
	9⅞	5	8¾	375.826	2.6099		7¾	8	3¾	791.732	5.4995
1	10	5	9⅛	380.133	2.6398	2	8	8	4½	804.249	5.5851
	10⅛	5	9½	384.465	2.6699		8¼	8	5⅜	816.865	5.6727
	10¼	5	9⅞	388.822	2.7002		8½	8	6⅛	829.578	5.7610
	10⅜	5	10¼	393.203	2.7306		8¾	8	6⅞	842.390	5.8499
	10½	5	10⅝	397.608	2.7612	2	9	8	7⅝	855.300	5.9396
	10⅝	5	11⅛	402.038	2.7919		9¼	8	8½	868.308	6.0299
	10¾	5	11½	406.493	2.8229		9½	8	9¼	881.415	6.1209
	10⅞	5	11⅞	410.972	2.8540		9¾	8	10	894.619	6.2126
1	11	6	0¼	415.476	2.8853	2	10	8	10⅞	907.922	6.3050
	11⅛	6	0⅝	420.004	2.9167		10¼	8	11⅝	921.323	6.3981
	11¼	6	1	424.557	2.9483		10½	9	0⅜	934.822	6.4918
	11⅜	6	1⅜	429.135	2.9801		10¾	9	1⅛	948.419	6.5862
	11½	6	1⅞	433.737	3.0121	2	11	9	2	962.115	6.6814
	11⅝	6	2¼	438.363	3.0442		11¼	9	2¾	975.908	6.7771
	11¾	6	2⅝	443.014	3.0765		11½	9	3½	989.800	6.8736
	11⅞	6	3	447.690	3.1090		11¾	9	4¼	1003.790	6.9707

* Circumference to nearest ⅛ inch.

Diameters, Circumferences and Areas of Circles in Feet and Inches

Diam. Ft.	Diam. In.	Circum.* Ft.	Circum.* In.	Area Sq. In.	Area Sq. Ft.	Diam. Ft.	Diam. In.	Circum.* Ft.	Circum.* In.	Area Sq. In.	Area Sq. Ft.
3	0	9	5⅛	1017.87	7.068	4	0	12	6¾	1809.56	12.566
	0¼	9	5⅞	1032.06	7.167		0¼	12	7⅝	1828.46	12.697
	0½	9	6⅝	1046.35	7.266		0½	12	8⅜	1847.45	12.829
	0¾	9	7½	1060.73	7.366		0¾	12	9⅛	1866.55	12.962
3	1	9	8¼	1075.21	7.466	4	1	12	10	1885.74	13.095
	1¼	9	9	1089.79	7.568		1¼	12	10¾	1905.03	13.229
	1½	9	9¾	1104.46	7.669		1½	12	11½	1924.42	13.364
	1¾	9	10½	1119.24	7.772		1¾	13	0¼	1943.91	13.499
3	2	9	11⅜	1134.12	7.875	4	2	13	1⅛	1963.50	13.635
	2¼	10	0⅛	1149.09	7.979		2¼	13	1⅞	1983.18	13.772
	2½	10	1	1164.16	8.084		2½	13	2⅝	2002.96	13.909
	2¾	10	1¾	1179.32	8.189		2¾	13	3⅜	2022.84	14.047
3	3	10	2½	1194.59	8.295	4	3	13	4¼	2042.82	14.186
	3¼	10	3¼	1209.95	8.402		3¼	13	5	2062.90	14.325
	3½	10	4⅛	1225.42	8.509		3½	13	5¾	2083.07	14.465
	3¾	10	4⅞	1240.98	8.617		3¾	13	6⅝	2103.35	14.606
3	4	10	5⅝	1256.64	8.726	4	4	13	7⅜	2123.72	14.748
	4¼	10	6½	1272.39	8.836		4¼	13	8⅛	2144.19	14.890
	4½	10	7¼	1288.25	8.946		4½	13	8⅞	2164.75	15.033
	4¾	10	8	1304.20	9.056		4¾	13	9¾	2185.42	15.176
3	5	10	8¾	1320.25	9.168	4	5	13	10½	2206.18	15.320
	5¼	10	9⅝	1336.40	9.280		5¼	13	11¼	2227.05	15.465
	5½	10	10⅜	1352.65	9.393		5½	14	0⅛	2248.01	15.611
	5¾	10	11⅛	1369.00	9.506		5¾	14	0⅞	2269.06	15.757
3	6	11	0	1385.44	9.621	4	6	14	1⅝	2290.22	15.904
	6¼	11	0¾	1401.98	9.736		6¼	14	2⅜	2311.48	16.051
	6½	11	1½	1418.62	9.851		6½	14	3¼	2332.83	16.200
	6¾	11	2¼	1435.36	9.967		6¾	14	4	2354.28	16.349
3	7	11	3⅛	1452.20	10.084	4	7	14	4¾	2375.83	16.498
	7¼	11	3⅞	1469.14	10.202		7¼	14	5⅝	2397.48	16.649
	7½	11	4⅝	1486.17	10.320		7½	14	6⅜	2419.22	16.800
	7¾	11	5½	1503.30	10.439		7¾	14	7⅛	2441.07	16.951
3	8	11	6¼	1520.53	10.559	4	8	14	7⅞	2463.01	17.104
	8¼	11	7	1537.86	10.679		8¼	14	8¾	2485.05	17.257
	8½	11	7¾	1555.28	10.800		8½	14	9½	2507.19	17.411
	8¾	11	8⅝	1572.81	10.922		8¾	14	10¼	2529.42	17.565
3	9	11	9⅜	1590.43	11.044	4	9	14	11⅛	2551.76	17.720
	9¼	11	10⅛	1608.15	11.137		9¼	14	11⅞	2574.19	17.876
	9½	11	11	1625.97	11.291		9½	15	0⅝	2596.72	18.032
	9¾	11	11¾	1643.89	11.415		9¾	15	1⅜	2619.35	18.189
3	10	12	0½	1661.90	11.541	4	10	15	2¼	2642.08	18.347
	10¼	12	1¼	1680.02	11.666		10¼	15	3	2664.91	18.506
	10½	12	2⅛	1698.23	11.793		10½	15	3¾	2687.83	18.665
	10¾	12	2⅞	1716.54	11.920		10¾	15	4⅝	2710.85	18.825
3	11	12	3⅝	1734.94	12.048	4	11	15	5⅜	2733.97	18.985
	11¼	12	4½	1753.45	12.176		11¼	15	6⅛	2757.19	19.147
	11½	12	5¼	1772.05	12.305		11½	15	6⅞	2780.51	19.309
	11¾	12	6	1790.76	12.435		11¾	15	7¾	2803.92	19.471

* Circumference to nearest ⅛ inch.

Diameters, Circumferences and Areas of Circles in Feet and Inches

Diam. Ft.	Diam. In.	Circum.* Ft.	Circum.* In.	Area Sq. In.	Area Sq. Ft.	Diam. Ft.	Diam. In.	Circum.* Ft.	Circum.* In.	Area Sq. In.	Area Sq. Ft.
5	0	15	8½	2827.44	19.635	6	0	18	10¼	4071.51	28.274
	0¼	15	9¼	2851.05	19.798		0¼	18	11	4099.83	28.471
	0½	15	10⅛	2874.76	19.963		0½	18	11¾	4128.25	28.668
	0¾	15	10⅞	2898.56	20.128		0¾	19	0½	4156.77	28.866
5	1	15	11⅝	2922.47	20.294	6	1	19	1⅜	4185.39	29.065
	1¼	16	0⅜	2946.47	20.461		1¼	19	2⅛	4214.11	29.264
	1½	16	1¼	2970.57	20.629		1½	19	2⅞	4242.92	29.464
	1¾	16	2	2994.77	20.797		1¾	19	3¾	4271.83	29.665
5	2	16	2¾	3019.07	20.965	6	2	19	4½	4300.85	29.867
	2¼	16	3⅝	3043.47	21.135		2¼	19	5¼	4329.95	30.069
	2½	16	4⅜	3067.96	21.305		2½	19	6	4359.16	30.271
	2¾	16	5⅛	3092.56	21.476		2¾	19	6⅞	4388.47	30.475
5	3	16	5⅞	3117.25	21.647	6	3	19	7⅝	4417.87	30.679
	3¼	16	6¾	3142.04	21.819		3¼	19	8⅜	4447.37	30.884
	3½	16	7½	3166.92	21.992		3½	19	9¼	4476.97	31.090
	3¾	16	8¼	3191.91	22.166		3¾	19	10	4506.67	31.296
5	4	16	9	3216.99	22.340	6	4	19	10¾	4536.47	31.503
	4¼	16	9⅞	3242.17	22.512		4¼	19	11½	4566.36	31.710
	4½	16	10⅝	3267.46	22.690		4½	20	0⅜	4596.35	31.919
	4¾	16	11⅜	3292.83	22.866		4¾	20	1⅛	4626.44	32.128
5	5	17	0¼	3318.31	23.043	6	5	20	1⅞	4656.63	32.337
	5¼	17	1	3343.88	23.221		5¼	20	2¾	4686.92	32.548
	5½	17	1¾	3369.56	23.399		5½	20	3½	4717.30	32.759
	5¾	17	2½	3395.33	23.578		5¾	20	4¼	4747.79	32.970
5	6	17	3⅜	3421.20	23.758	6	6	20	5	4778.37	33.183
	6¼	17	4⅛	3447.16	23.938		6¼	20	5⅞	4809.05	33.396
	6½	17	4⅞	3473.23	24.119		6½	20	6⅝	4839.83	33.609
	6¾	17	5¾	3499.39	24.301		6¾	20	7⅜	4870.70	33.824
5	7	17	6½	3525.66	24.483	6	7	20	8⅛	4901.68	34.039
	7¼	17	7¼	3552.01	24.666		7¼	20	9	4932.75	34.255
	7½	17	8	3578.47	24.850		7½	20	9¾	4963.92	34.471
	7¾	17	8⅞	3605.03	25.034		7¾	20	10½	4995.19	34.688
5	8	17	9⅝	3631.68	25.220	6	8	20	11⅜	5026.56	34.906
	8¼	17	10⅜	3658.44	25.405		8¼	21	0⅛	5058.02	35.125
	8½	17	11¼	3685.29	25.592		8½	21	0⅞	5089.58	35.344
	8¾	18	0	3712.24	25.779		8¾	21	1⅝	5121.24	35.564
5	9	18	0¾	3739.28	25.967	6	9	21	2½	5153.00	35.784
	9¼	18	1½	3766.43	26.155		9¼	21	3¼	5184.86	36.006
	9½	18	2⅜	3793.67	26.344		9½	21	4	5216.82	36.227
	9¾	18	3⅛	3821.02	26.534		9¾	21	4⅞	5248.87	36.450
5	10	18	3⅞	3848.46	26.725	6	10	21	5⅝	5281.02	36.674
	10¼	18	4¾	3875.99	26.916		10¼	21	6⅜	5313.27	36.897
	10½	18	5½	3903.63	27.108		10½	21	7⅛	5345.62	37.122
	10¾	18	6¼	3931.36	27.301		10¾	21	8	5378.07	37.347
5	11	18	7⅛	3959.20	27.494	6	11	21	8¾	5410.62	37.573
	11¼	18	7⅞	3987.13	27.688		11¼	21	9½	5443.26	37.800
	11½	18	8⅝	4015.16	27.883		11½	21	10⅜	5476.00	38.027
	11¾	18	9⅜	4043.28	28.078		11¾	21	11⅛	5508.84	38.256

* Circumference to nearest ⅛ inch.

Diameters, Circumferences and Areas of Circles in Feet and Inches

Diam. Ft.	Diam. In.	Circum.* Ft.	Circum.* In.	Area Sq. Ft.	Diam. Ft.	Diam. In.	Circum.* Ft.	Circum.* In.	Area Sq. Ft.	Diam. Ft.	Diam. In.	Circum.* Ft.	Circum.* In.	Area Sq. Ft.
7	0	21	11⅞	38.48	11	0	34	6¾	95.03	15	0	47	1½	176.71
	1	22	3	39.40		1	34	9⅞	96.47		1	47	4⅝	178.68
	2	22	6⅛	40.33		2	35	1	97.93		2	47	7¾	180.66
	3	22	9⅜	41.28		3	35	4⅛	99.40		3	47	10⅞	182.65
	4	23	0½	42.23		4	35	7¼	100.87		4	48	2	184.65
	5	23	3⅝	43.20		5	35	10⅜	102.36		5	48	5¼	186.66
	6	23	6¾	44.17		6	36	1½	103.86		6	48	8⅜	188.69
	7	23	9⅞	45.16		7	36	4⅝	105.37		7	48	11½	190.72
	8	24	1	46.16		8	36	7⅞	106.90		8	49	2⅝	192.77
	9	24	4⅛	47.17		9	36	11	108.43		9	49	5¾	194.82
	10	24	7¼	48.19		10	37	2⅛	109.97		10	49	8⅞	196.89
	11	24	10½	49.22		11	37	5¼	111.53		11	50	0	198.97
8	0	25	1⅝	50.26	12	0	37	8⅜	113.09	16	0	50	3¼	201.06
	1	25	4¾	51.31		1	37	11½	114.67		1	50	6⅜	203.16
	2	25	7⅞	52.38		2	38	2⅝	116.26		2	50	9½	205.27
	3	25	11	53.45		3	38	5¾	117.85		3	51	0⅝	207.39
	4	26	2⅛	54.54		4	38	9	119.46		4	51	3¾	209.52
	5	26	5¼	55.63		5	39	0⅛	121.08		5	51	6⅞	211.67
	6	26	8½	56.74		6	39	3¼	122.71		6	51	10	213.82
	7	26	11⅝	57.86		7	39	6⅜	124.36		7	52	1⅛	215.99
	8	27	2¾	58.99		8	39	9½	126.01		8	52	4⅜	218.16
	9	27	5⅞	60.13		9	40	0⅝	127.67		9	52	7½	220.35
	10	27	9	61.28		10	40	3¾	129.35		10	52	10⅝	222.55
	11	28	0⅛	62.44		11	40	7	131.03		11	53	1¾	224.76
9	0	28	3¼	63.61	13	0	40	10⅛	132.73	17	0	53	4⅞	226.98
	1	28	6⅜	64.80		1	41	1¼	134.43		1	53	8	229.21
	2	28	9⅝	65.99		2	41	4⅜	136.15		2	53	11⅛	231.45
	3	29	0¾	67.20		3	41	7½	137.88		3	54	2¼	233.70
	4	29	3⅞	68.41		4	41	10⅝	139.62		4	54	5½	235.96
	5	29	7	69.64		5	42	1¾	141.37		5	54	8⅝	238.24
	6	29	10⅛	70.88		6	42	5	143.13		6	54	11¾	240.52
	7	30	1¼	72.13		7	42	8⅛	144.91		7	55	2⅞	242.82
	8	30	4⅜	73.39		8	42	11¼	146.69		8	55	6	245.13
	9	30	7⅝	74.66		9	43	2⅜	148.48		9	55	9⅛	247.45
	10	30	10¾	75.94		10	43	5½	150.29		10	56	0¼	249.77
	11	31	1⅞	77.23		11	43	8⅝	152.11		11	56	3½	252.11
10	0	31	5	78.54	14	0	43	11¾	153.93	18	0	56	6⅝	254.46
	1	31	8⅛	79.85		1	44	2⅞	155.77		1	56	9¾	256.83
	2	31	11¼	81.17		2	44	6⅛	157.62		2	57	0⅞	259.20
	3	32	2⅜	82.51		3	44	9¼	159.48		3	57	4	261.58
	4	32	5½	83.86		4	45	0⅜	161.35		4	57	7⅛	263.98
	5	32	8¾	85.22		5	45	3½	163.23		5	57	10¼	266.38
	6	32	11⅞	86.59		6	45	6⅝	165.13		6	58	1⅜	268.80
	7	33	3	87.97		7	45	9¾	167.03		7	58	4⅝	271.22
	8	33	6⅛	89.36		8	46	0⅞	168.94		8	58	7¾	273.66
	9	33	9¼	90.76		9	46	4	170.87		9	58	10⅞	276.11
	10	34	0⅜	92.17		10	46	7¼	172.80		10	59	2	278.57
	11	34	3½	93.59		11	46	10⅜	174.75		11	59	5⅛	281.04

* Circumference to nearest ⅛ inch.

Circumferences and Corresponding Diameters of Circles

Circum.	Diameter	Circum.	Diameter	Circum.	Diameter	Circum.	Diameter	Circum.	Diameter
1	0.3183	51	16.2338	101	32.149	151	48.065	201	63.980
2	0.6366	52	16.5521	102	32.468	152	48.383	202	64.299
3	0.9549	53	16.8704	103	32.786	153	48.701	203	64.617
4	1.2732	54	17.1887	104	33.104	154	49.020	204	64.935
5	1.5915	55	17.5070	105	33.422	155	49.338	205	65.253
6	1.9099	56	17.8254	106	33.741	156	49.656	206	65.572
7	2.2282	57	18.1437	107	34.059	157	49.975	207	65.890
8	2.5465	58	18.4620	108	34.377	158	50.293	208	66.208
9	2.8648	59	18.7803	109	34.696	159	50.611	209	66.527
10	3.1831	60	19.0986	110	35.014	160	50.930	210	66.845
11	3.5014	61	19.4169	111	35.332	161	51.248	211	67.163
12	3.8197	62	19.7352	112	35.651	162	51.566	212	67.482
13	4.1380	63	20.0535	113	35.969	163	51.884	213	67.800
14	4.4563	64	20.3718	114	36.287	164	52.203	214	68.118
15	4.7746	65	20.6901	115	36.606	165	52.521	215	68.437
16	5.0930	66	21.0085	116	36.924	166	52.839	216	68.755
17	5.4113	67	21.3268	117	37.242	167	53.158	217	69.073
18	5.7296	68	21.6451	118	37.561	168	53.476	218	69.392
19	6.0479	69	21.9634	119	37.879	169	53.794	219	69.710
20	6.3662	70	22.2817	120	38.197	170	54.113	220	70.028
21	6.6845	71	22.6000	121	38.515	171	54.431	221	70.346
22	7.0028	72	22.9183	122	38.834	172	54.749	222	70.665
23	7.3211	73	23.2366	123	39.152	173	55.068	223	70.983
24	7.6394	74	23.5549	124	39.470	174	55.386	224	71.301
25	7.9577	75	23.8732	125	39.789	175	55.704	225	71.620
26	8.2761	76	24.1916	126	40.107	176	56.022	226	71.938
27	8.5944	77	24.5099	127	40.425	177	56.341	227	72.256
28	8.9127	78	24.8282	128	40.744	178	56.659	228	72.575
29	9.2310	79	25.1465	129	41.062	179	56.977	229	72.893
30	9.5493	80	25.4648	130	41.380	180	57.296	230	73.211
31	9.8676	81	25.7831	131	41.699	181	57.614	231	73.530
32	10.1859	82	26.1014	132	42.017	182	57.932	232	73.848
33	10.5042	83	26.4197	133	42.335	183	58.251	233	74.166
34	10.8225	84	26.7380	134	42.653	184	58.569	234	74.484
35	11.1408	85	27.0563	135	42.972	185	58.887	235	74.803
36	11.4592	86	27.3747	136	43.290	186	59.206	236	75.121
37	11.7775	87	27.6930	137	43.608	187	59.524	237	75.439
38	12.0958	88	28.0113	138	43.927	188	59.842	238	75.758
39	12.4141	89	28.3296	139	44.245	189	60.161	239	76.076
40	12.7324	90	28.6479	140	44.563	190	60.479	240	76.394
41	13.0507	91	28.9662	141	44.882	191	60.797	241	76.713
42	13.3690	92	29.2845	142	45.200	192	61.115	242	77.031
43	13.6873	93	29.6028	143	45.518	193	61.434	243	77.349
44	14.0056	94	29.9211	144	45.837	194	61.752	244	77.668
45	14.3239	95	30.2394	145	46.155	195	62.070	245	77.986
46	14.6423	96	30.5577	146	46.473	196	62.389	246	78.304
47	14.9606	97	30.8761	147	46.792	197	62.707	247	78.622
48	15.2789	98	31.1944	148	47.110	198	63.025	248	78.941
49	15.5972	99	31.5127	149	47.428	199	63.344	249	79.259
50	15.9155	100	31.8310	150	47.746	200	63.662	250	79.577

Segments of Circles

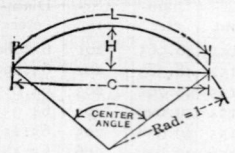

Length of Arc, Height of Segment, Length of Chord and Area of Segment for Angles from 1 to 180 degrees, and Radius = 1. — For other radii, multiply the values of L, H and C in the table by the given radius, and the values for areas, by the square of the radius.

Center Angle, Degrees	L	H	C	Area of Segment	Center Angle, Degrees	L	H	C	Area of Segment
1	0.01745	0.00004	0.01745	0.00000	46	0.803	0.0795	0.781	0.04176
2	0.03491	0.00015	0.03490	0.00000	47	0.820	0.0829	0.797	0.04448
3	0.05236	0.00034	0.05235	0.00001	48	0.838	0.0865	0.813	0.04731
4	0.06981	0.00061	0.06980	0.00003	49	0.855	0.0900	0.829	0.05025
5	0.08727	0.00095	0.08724	0.00006	50	0.873	0.0937	0.845	0.05331
6	0.10472	0.00137	0.10467	0.00010	51	0.890	0.0974	0.861	0.05649
7	0.12217	0.00186	0.12210	0.00015	52	0.908	0.1012	0.877	0.05978
8	0.13963	0.00243	0.13951	0.00023	53	0.925	0.1051	0.892	0.06319
9	0.15708	0.00308	0.15692	0.00032	54	0.942	0.1090	0.908	0.06673
10	0.17453	0.00380	0.17431	0.00044	55	0.960	0.1130	0.923	0.07039
11	0.19199	0.00460	0.19169	0.00059	56	0.977	0.1171	0.939	0.07417
12	0.20944	0.00548	0.20906	0.00076	57	0.995	0.1212	0.954	0.07808
13	0.22689	0.00643	0.22641	0.00097	58	1.012	0.1254	0.970	0.08212
14	0.24435	0.00745	0.24374	0.00121	59	1.030	0.1296	0.985	0.08629
15	0.26180	0.00855	0.26105	0.00149	60	1.047	0.1340	1.000	0.09059
16	0.27925	0.00973	0.27835	0.00181	61	1.065	0.1384	1.015	0.09502
17	0.29671	0.01098	0.29562	0.00217	62	1.082	0.1428	1.030	0.09958
18	0.31416	0.01231	0.31287	0.00257	63	1.100	0.1474	1.045	0.10428
19	0.33161	0.01371	0.33010	0.00302	64	1.117	0.1520	1.060	0.10911
20	0.34907	0.01519	0.34730	0.00352	65	1.134	0.1566	1.075	0.11408
21	0.36652	0.01674	0.36447	0.00408	66	1.152	0.1613	1.089	0.11919
22	0.38397	0.01837	0.38162	0.00468	67	1.169	0.1661	1.104	0.12443
23	0.40143	0.02007	0.39874	0.00535	68	1.187	0.1710	1.118	0.12982
24	0.41888	0.02185	0.41582	0.00607	69	1.204	0.1759	1.133	0.13535
25	0.43633	0.02370	0.43288	0.00686	70	1.222	0.1808	1.147	0.14102
26	0.45379	0.02563	0.44990	0.00771	71	1.239	0.1859	1.161	0.14683
27	0.47124	0.02763	0.46689	0.00862	72	1.257	0.1910	1.176	0.15279
28	0.48869	0.02970	0.48384	0.00961	73	1.274	0.1961	1.190	0.15889
29	0.50615	0.03185	0.50076	0.01067	74	1.291	0.2014	1.204	0.16514
30	0.52360	0.03407	0.51764	0.01180	75	1.309	0.2066	1.217	0.17154
31	0.54105	0.03637	0.53448	0.01301	76	1.326	0.2120	1.231	0.17808
32	0.55851	0.03874	0.55127	0.01429	77	1.344	0.2174	1.245	0.18477
33	0.57596	0.04118	0.56803	0.01566	78	1.361	0.2229	1.259	0.19160
34	0.59341	0.04369	0.58474	0.01711	79	1.379	0.2284	1.272	0.19859
35	0.61087	0.04628	0.60141	0.01864	80	1.396	0.2340	1.286	0.20573
36	0.62832	0.04894	0.61803	0.02027	81	1.414	0.2396	1.299	0.21301
37	0.64577	0.05168	0.63461	0.02198	82	1.431	0.2453	1.312	0.22045
38	0.66323	0.05448	0.65114	0.02378	83	1.449	0.2510	1.325	0.22804
39	0.68068	0.05736	0.66761	0.02568	84	1.466	0.2569	1.338	0.23578
40	0.69813	0.06031	0.68404	0.02767	85	1.483	0.2627	1.351	0.24367
41	0.71559	0.06333	0.70041	0.02976	86	1.501	0.2686	1.364	0.25171
42	0.73304	0.06642	0.71674	0.03195	87	1.518	0.2746	1.377	0.25990
43	0.75049	0.06958	0.73300	0.03425	88	1.536	0.2807	1.389	0.26825
44	0.76795	0.07282	0.74921	0.03664	89	1.553	0.2867	1.402	0.27677
45	0.78540	0.07612	0.76537	0.03915	90	1.571	0.2929	1.414	0.28540

Segments of Circles

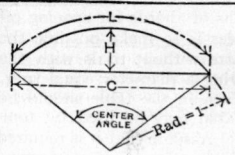

Length of Arc, Height of Segment, Length of Chord and Area of Segment for Angles from 1 to 180 degrees, and Radius = 1. — For other radii, multiply the values of L, H and C in the table by the given radius, and the values for areas, by the square of the radius.

Center Angle, Degrees	L	H	C	Area of Segment	Center Angle, Degrees	L	H	C	Area of Segment
91	1.588	0.2991	1.426	0.2942	136	2.374	0.6254	1.854	0.8395
92	1.606	0.3053	1.439	0.3032	137	2.391	0.6335	1.861	0.8545
93	1.623	0.3116	1.451	0.3123	138	2.409	0.6416	1.867	0.8697
94	1.641	0.3180	1.463	0.3215	139	2.426	0.6498	1.873	0.8850
95	1.658	0.3244	1.475	0.3309	140	2.443	0.6580	1.879	0.9003
96	1.675	0.3309	1.486	0.3405	141	2.461	0.6662	1.885	0.9158
97	1.693	0.3374	1.498	0.3502	142	2.478	0.6744	1.891	0.9313
98	1.710	0.3439	1.509	0.3601	143	2.496	0.6827	1.897	0.9470
99	1.728	0.3506	1.521	0.3701	144	2.513	0.6910	1.902	0.9627
100	1.745	0.3572	1.532	0.3803	145	2.531	0.6993	1.907	0.9786
101	1.763	0.3639	1.543	0.3906	146	2.548	0.7076	1.913	0.9945
102	1.780	0.3707	1.554	0.4010	147	2.566	0.7160	1.918	1.0105
103	1.798	0.3775	1.565	0.4117	148	2.583	0.7244	1.922	1.0266
104	1.815	0.3843	1.576	0.4224	149	2.600	0.7328	1.927	1.0427
105	1.833	0.3912	1.587	0.4333	150	2.618	0.7412	1.932	1.0590
106	1.850	0.3982	1.597	0.4444	151	2.635	0.7496	1.936	1.0753
107	1.867	0.4052	1.608	0.4556	152	2.653	0.7581	1.941	1.0917
108	1.885	0.4122	1.618	0.4669	153	2.670	0.7666	1.945	1.1082
109	1.902	0.4193	1.628	0.4784	154	2.688	0.7750	1.949	1.1247
110	1.920	0.4264	1.638	0.4901	155	2.705	0.7836	1.953	1.1413
111	1.937	0.4336	1.648	0.5019	156	2.723	0.7921	1.956	1.1580
112	1.955	0.4408	1.658	0.5138	157	2.740	0.8006	1.960	1.1747
113	1.972	0.4481	1.668	0.5259	158	2.758	0.8092	1.963	1.1915
114	1.990	0.4554	1.677	0.5381	159	2.775	0.8178	1.966	1.2083
115	2.007	0.4627	1.687	0.5504	160	2.792	0.8264	1.970	1.2252
116	2.025	0.4701	1.696	0.5629	161	2.810	0.8350	1.973	1.2422
117	2.042	0.4775	1.705	0.5755	162	2.827	0.8436	1.975	1.2592
118	2.059	0.4850	1.714	0.5883	163	2.845	0.8522	1.978	1.2763
119	2.077	0.4925	1.723	0.6012	164	2.862	0.8608	1.980	1.2933
120	2.094	0.5000	1.732	0.6142	165	2.880	0.8695	1.983	1.3105
121	2.112	0.5076	1.741	0.6273	166	2.897	0.8781	1.985	1.3277
122	2.129	0.5152	1.749	0.6406	167	2.915	0.8868	1.987	1.3449
123	2.147	0.5228	1.758	0.6540	168	2.932	0.8955	1.989	1.3621
124	2.164	0.5305	1.766	0.6676	169	2.950	0.9042	1.991	1.3794
125	2.182	0.5383	1.774	0.6812	170	2.967	0.9128	1.992	1.3967
126	2.199	0.5460	1.782	0.6950	171	2.984	0.9215	1.994	1.4140
127	2.217	0.5538	1.790	0.7090	172	3.002	0.9302	1.995	1.4314
128	2.234	0.5616	1.798	0.7230	173	3.019	0.9390	1.996	1.4488
129	2.251	0.5695	1.805	0.7372	174	3.037	0.9477	1.997	1.4662
130	2.269	0.5774	1.813	0.7514	175	3.054	0.9564	1.998	1.4836
131	2.286	0.5853	1.820	0.7658	176	3.072	0.9651	1.999	1.5010
132	2.304	0.5933	1.827	0.7803	177	3.089	0.9738	1.999	1.5185
133	2.321	0.6013	1.834	0.7950	178	3.107	0.9825	2.000	1.5359
134	2.339	0.6093	1.841	0.8097	179	3.124	0.9913	2.000	1.5533
135	2.356	0.6173	1.848	0.8245	180	3.142	1.0000	2.000	1.5708

Lengths of Chords for Spacing off the Circumference of Circles

On the following pages are given tables of the lengths of chords for spacing off the circumference of circles. The object of these tables is to make possible the division of the periphery into a number of equal parts without trials with the dividers. The first table is calculated for circles having a diameter equal to 1. For circles of other diameters, the length of chord given in the table should be multiplied by the diameter of the circle. This first table may be used by tool-makers when setting " buttons " in circular formation. Assume that it is required to divide the periphery of a circle of 20 inches diameter into thirty-two equal parts. From the table the length of the chord is found to be 0.098017 inch, if the diameter of the circle were 1 inch. With a diameter of 20 inches the length of the chord for one division would be 20 × 0.098017 = 1.9603 inch.

The two following pages give an additional table for the spacing off of circles, the table, in this case, being worked out for diameters from 1/16 inch to 14 inches. As an example, assume that it is required to divide a circle having a diameter of 6½ inches into seven equal parts. Find first, in the column headed "6" and in line with 7 divisions, the length of the chord for a 6-inch circle, which is 2.604 inches. Then find the length of the chord for a ½-inch diameter circle, 7 divisions, which is 0.217. The sum of these two values, 2.604 + 0.217 = 2.821 inches, is the length of the chord required for spacing off the circumference of a 6½-inch circle into seven equal divisions.

As another example, assume that it is required to divide a circle having a diameter of 9²³⁄₃₂ inches into 15 equal divisions. First find the length of the chord for a 9-inch circle, which is 1.871 inch. The length of the chord for a 2³⁄₃₂-inch circle can easily be estimated from the table by taking the value that is exactly between those given for 11/16 and 3/4 inch. The value for 11/16 inch is 0.143, and for 3/4 inch, 0.156. Hence for 2³⁄₃₂, the value would be 0.150. Then, 1.871 + 0.150 = 2.021 inches.

Rapid Proof of Multiplications and Divisions

To prove that the product of a multiplication is correct, add together the individual figures in each of the two factors (proceeding to add until a single digit is obtained, as indicated below), and multiply the sum of the figures of one of the factors by the sum of the other factor. This product, reduced by similar addition of digits to one figure, should then equal the sum of the digits in the product as shown by the following example. (Errors of 9 or multiples of 9 cannot be detected by this method.)

Example: $3617 \times 2034 = 7,356,978.$

Adding digits in one factor: $3 + 6 + 1 + 7 = 17$; $1 + 7 = 8$.
Adding digits in other factor: $2 + 0 + 3 + 4 = 9$.
Multiplying the sums: $8 \times 9 = 72$. Adding digits: $7 + 2 = 9$. Adding digits of product: $7 + 3 + 5 + 6 + 9 + 7 + 8 = 45$; $4 + 5 = 9$. The fact that the sum of the digits of the product equals the sum of the digits in the product of the sum of the digits in the factors, is an indication that the product is correct. If the final sums are not equal, the product is incorrect.

Division can be proved in a similar manner, (errors of 9 or multiples excepted) by considering divisor and quotient as factors, and dividend as the product.

Example: $131,872 \div 317 = 416.$

$3 + 1 + 7 = 11$; $1 + 1 = 2$. $4 + 1 + 6 = 11$; $1 + 1 = 2$.
Then $2 \times 2 = 4$, and $1 + 3 + 1 + 8 + 7 + 2 = 22$; $2 + 2 = 4$.

If there is a remainder, the sum of its digits (reduced to one digit as before) should be added to the product of the final digits of the divisor and quotient. The final digit of this sum should equal the final digit of the dividend.

Lengths of Chords for Spacing Off the Circumference of Circles with a Diameter Equal to 1

For Circles of Other Diameters Multiply Length Given in Table by Diameter of Circle

No. of Spaces	Length of Chord	No. of Spaces	Length of Chord	No. of Spaces	Length of Chord	No. of Spaces	Length of Chord
3	0.866025	51	0.061560	99	0.031727	147	0.021369
4	0.707106	52	0.060378	100	0.031410	148	0.021225
5	0.587785	53	0.059240	101	0.031099	149	0.021082
6	0.500000	54	0.058144	102	0.030795	150	0.020942
7	0.433883	55	0.057088	103	0.030496	151	0.020803
8	0.382683	56	0.056070	104	0.030202	152	0.020666
9	0.342020	57	0.055087	105	0.029915	153	0.020531
10	0.309017	58	0.054138	106	0.029633	154	0.020398
11	0.281732	59	0.053222	107	0.029356	155	0.020266
12	0.258819	60	0.052336	108	0.029084	156	0.020137
13	0.239315	61	0.051478	109	0.028817	157	0.020008
14	0.222520	62	0.050649	110	0.028556	158	0.019882
15	0.207911	63	0.049845	111	0.028296	159	0.019757
16	0.195090	64	0.049067	112	0.028046	160	0.019633
17	0.183749	65	0.048313	113	0.027798	161	0.019511
18	0.173648	66	0.047581	114	0.027554	162	0.019391
19	0.164594	67	0.046872	115	0.027314	163	0.019272
20	0.156434	68	0.046183	116	0.027079	164	0.019154
21	0.149042	69	0.045514	117	0.026847	165	0.019038
22	0.142314	70	0.044864	118	0.026620	166	0.018924
23	0.136166	71	0.044233	119	0.026396	167	0.018810
24	0.130526	72	0.043619	120	0.026176	168	0.018698
25	0.125333	73	0.043022	121	0.025960	169	0.018588
26	0.120536	74	0.042441	122	0.025747	170	0.018478
27	0.116092	75	0.041875	123	0.025538	171	0.018370
28	0.111964	76	0.041324	124	0.025332	172	0.018264
29	0.108118	77	0.040788	125	0.025130	173	0.018158
30	0.104528	78	0.040265	126	0.024930	174	0.018054
31	0.101168	79	0.039756	127	0.024734	175	0.017950
32	0.098017	80	0.039259	128	0.024541	176	0.017848
33	0.095056	81	0.038775	129	0.024350	177	0.017748
34	0.092268	82	0.038302	130	0.024163	178	0.017648
35	0.089639	83	0.037841	131	0.023979	179	0.017549
36	0.087155	84	0.037391	132	0.023797	180	0.017452
37	0.084805	85	0.036951	133	0.023618	181	0.017355
38	0.082579	86	0.036522	134	0.023442	182	0.017260
39	0.080466	87	0.036102	135	0.023268	183	0.017166
40	0.078459	88	0.035692	136	0.023097	184	0.017073
41	0.076549	89	0.035291	137	0.022929	185	0.016980
42	0.074730	90	0.034899	138	0.022763	186	0.016889
43	0.072995	91	0.034516	139	0.022599	187	0.016799
44	0.071339	92	0.034141	140	0.022438	188	0.016709
45	0.069756	93	0.033774	141	0.022278	189	0.016621
46	0.068242	94	0.033414	142	0.022122	190	0.016533
47	0.066792	95	0.033063	143	0.021967	191	0.016447
48	0.065403	96	0.032719	144	0.021814	192	0.016361
49	0.064070	97	0.032381	145	0.021664	193	0.016276
50	0.062790	98	0.032051	146	0.021516	194	0.016193

Table for Spacing Off the Circumference of Circles
(See page 74 for explanatory matter.)

No. of Divisions	Degrees in Arc	Diameter of Circle to be Spaced Off														
		Length of Chord														
		1/16	1/8	3/16	1/4	5/16	3/8	7/16	1/2	9/16	5/8	11/16	3/4	13/16	7/8	15/16
3	120	0.054	0.108	0.162	0.216	0.270	0.324	0.378	0.432	0.486	0.541	0.595	0.649	0.703	0.757	0.811
4	90	0.044	0.088	0.132	0.176	0.221	0.265	0.309	0.353	0.397	0.442	0.486	0.530	0.574	0.618	0.662
5	72	0.037	0.073	0.110	0.146	0.183	0.220	0.257	0.293	0.330	0.367	0.403	0.440	0.477	0.514	0.551
6	60	0.031	0.063	0.094	0.125	0.156	0.188	0.219	0.250	0.281	0.312	0.343	0.375	0.406	0.438	0.469
7	51 3/7	0.027	0.054	0.081	0.108	0.135	0.162	0.189	0.217	0.244	0.271	0.298	0.325	0.352	0.379	0.406
8	45	0.024	0.048	0.072	0.096	0.120	0.143	0.167	0.191	0.215	0.239	0.263	0.287	0.311	0.335	0.359
9	40	0.021	0.043	0.064	0.086	0.107	0.128	0.149	0.171	0.192	0.214	0.235	0.257	0.278	0.299	0.320
10	36	0.019	0.039	0.058	0.077	0.097	0.116	0.135	0.155	0.174	0.193	0.212	0.232	0.251	0.270	0.289
11	32 8/11	0.018	0.035	0.053	0.070	0.088	0.105	0.123	0.141	0.158	0.176	0.193	0.211	0.228	0.246	0.264
12	30	0.016	0.032	0.048	0.065	0.081	0.097	0.114	0.130	0.146	0.162	0.178	0.194	0.211	0.227	0.243
13	27 9/13	0.015	0.030	0.045	0.059	0.074	0.089	0.104	0.119	0.134	0.149	0.164	0.179	0.194	0.209	0.224
14	25 5/7	0.014	0.028	0.042	0.056	0.069	0.083	0.097	0.111	0.125	0.139	0.153	0.167	0.180	0.194	0.208
15	24	0.013	0.026	0.039	0.052	0.065	0.078	0.091	0.104	0.117	0.130	0.143	0.156	0.169	0.182	0.195
16	22 1/2	0.012	0.024	0.037	0.049	0.061	0.073	0.085	0.098	0.109	0.122	0.134	0.146	0.158	0.170	0.183
17	21 3/17	0.011	0.023	0.034	0.046	0.057	0.069	0.080	0.092	0.103	0.115	0.126	0.138	0.149	0.160	0.172
18	20	0.011	0.022	0.032	0.043	0.054	0.065	0.076	0.087	0.097	0.108	0.119	0.130	0.141	0.152	0.163
19	18 18/19	0.010	0.021	0.031	0.041	0.051	0.062	0.072	0.082	0.092	0.103	0.113	0.123	0.133	0.144	0.154
20	18	0.010	0.020	0.029	0.039	0.049	0.059	0.068	0.078	0.088	0.098	0.107	0.117	0.127	0.136	0.146
21	17 1/7	0.009	0.019	0.028	0.037	0.047	0.056	0.065	0.075	0.084	0.093	0.102	0.112	0.121	0.130	0.139
22	16 4/11	0.009	0.018	0.027	0.036	0.045	0.053	0.062	0.071	0.080	0.089	0.098	0.107	0.115	0.124	0.133
23	15 15/23	0.009	0.017	0.026	0.034	0.043	0.051	0.059	0.068	0.077	0.085	0.094	0.102	0.111	0.119	0.128
24	15	0.008	0.016	0.024	0.033	0.041	0.049	0.057	0.065	0.073	0.082	0.090	0.098	0.106	0.114	0.122
25	14 2/5	0.008	0.016	0.023	0.031	0.039	0.047	0.055	0.063	0.070	0.078	0.086	0.094	0.102	0.109	0.117
26	13 11/13	0.008	0.015	0.023	0.030	0.038	0.045	0.053	0.060	0.068	0.075	0.083	0.090	0.098	0.105	0.113
28	12 6/7	0.007	0.014	0.021	0.028	0.035	0.042	0.049	0.056	0.063	0.070	0.077	0.084	0.091	0.098	0.105
30	12	0.007	0.013	0.019	0.026	0.033	0.039	0.046	0.052	0.059	0.065	0.072	0.078	0.085	0.091	0.098
32	11 1/4	0.006	0.012	0.018	0.024	0.031	0.037	0.043	0.049	0.055	0.061	0.067	0.074	0.080	0.086	0.092

Table for Spacing Off the Circumference of Circles

No. of Divisions	Degrees in Arc	Diameter of Circle to be Spaced Off													
		1	2	3	4	5	6	7	8	9	10	11	12	13	14
		Length of Chord													
3	120	0.866	1.732	2.598	3.464	4.330	5.196	6.062	6.928	7.794	8.660	9.526	10.392	11.258	12.124
4	90	0.707	1.414	2.121	2.828	3.536	4.243	4.950	5.657	6.364	7.071	7.778	8.485	9.192	9.900
5	72	0.588	1.176	1.763	2.351	2.939	3.527	4.115	4.702	5.290	5.878	6.465	7.053	7.641	8.229
6	60	0.500	1.000	1.500	2.000	2.500	3.000	3.500	4.000	4.500	5.000	5.500	6.000	6.500	7.000
7	51 3/7	0.434	0.868	1.302	1.736	2.170	2.604	3.037	3.471	3.905	4.339	4.773	5.207	5.641	6.075
8	45	0.383	0.765	1.148	1.531	1.913	2.296	2.679	3.061	3.444	3.827	4.210	4.592	4.975	5.358
9	40	0.342	0.684	1.026	1.368	1.710	2.052	2.394	2.736	3.078	3.420	3.762	4.104	4.446	4.788
10	36	0.309	0.618	0.927	1.236	1.545	1.854	2.163	2.472	2.781	3.090	3.399	3.708	4.017	4.326
11	32 8/11	0.282	0.564	0.845	1.127	1.409	1.691	1.973	2.254	2.536	2.818	3.100	3.381	3.663	3.945
12	30	0.259	0.518	0.776	1.035	1.294	1.553	1.812	2.070	2.329	2.588	2.847	3.106	3.365	3.624
13	27 9/13	0.239	0.479	0.718	0.958	1.197	1.436	1.676	1.915	2.154	2.393	2.633	2.873	3.112	3.352
14	25 5/7	0.222	0.445	0.667	0.890	1.112	1.334	1.557	1.779	2.001	2.224	2.446	2.669	2.891	3.114
15	24	0.208	0.416	0.624	0.832	1.040	1.247	1.455	1.663	1.871	2.079	2.287	2.495	2.703	2.911
16	22 1/2	0.195	0.390	0.585	0.780	0.975	1.171	1.366	1.561	1.756	1.951	2.146	2.341	2.536	2.731
17	21 3/17	0.184	0.367	0.551	0.735	0.918	1.102	1.286	1.469	1.653	1.837	2.020	2.204	2.388	2.571
18	20	0.174	0.347	0.521	0.695	0.868	1.041	1.215	1.389	1.563	1.736	1.910	2.084	2.257	2.431
19	18 18/19	0.165	0.329	0.493	0.658	0.822	0.987	1.151	1.316	1.480	1.645	1.809	1.974	2.138	2.303
20	18	0.156	0.313	0.469	0.626	0.782	0.938	1.095	1.251	1.408	1.564	1.721	1.877	2.033	2.190
21	17 1/7	0.149	0.298	0.447	0.596	0.745	0.894	1.043	1.192	1.341	1.490	1.639	1.788	1.936	2.085
22	16 4/11	0.142	0.286	0.428	0.570	0.712	0.855	0.997	1.139	1.281	1.423	1.566	1.708	1.850	1.993
23	15 15/23	0.136	0.273	0.409	0.545	0.681	0.818	0.954	1.091	1.227	1.362	1.499	1.635	1.772	1.908
24	15	0.131	0.261	0.392	0.522	0.653	0.783	0.914	1.044	1.175	1.305	1.436	1.566	1.697	1.827
25	14 2/5	0.125	0.251	0.376	0.501	0.627	0.752	0.877	1.003	1.128	1.253	1.379	1.504	1.629	1.755
26	13 11/13	0.120	0.241	0.361	0.482	0.602	0.723	0.843	0.964	1.084	1.205	1.325	1.445	1.566	1.686
28	12 6/7	0.112	0.224	0.336	0.448	0.560	0.672	0.784	0.896	1.008	1.120	1.232	1.344	1.456	1.568
30	12	0.105	0.209	0.314	0.418	0.523	0.627	0.732	0.836	0.941	1.045	1.150	1.254	1.359	1.463
32	11 1/4	0.098	0.196	0.294	0.392	0.490	0.588	0.686	0.784	0.882	0.980	1.078	1.176	1.274	1.372

Coordinates for Locating Equally-spaced Holes in Jig Boring

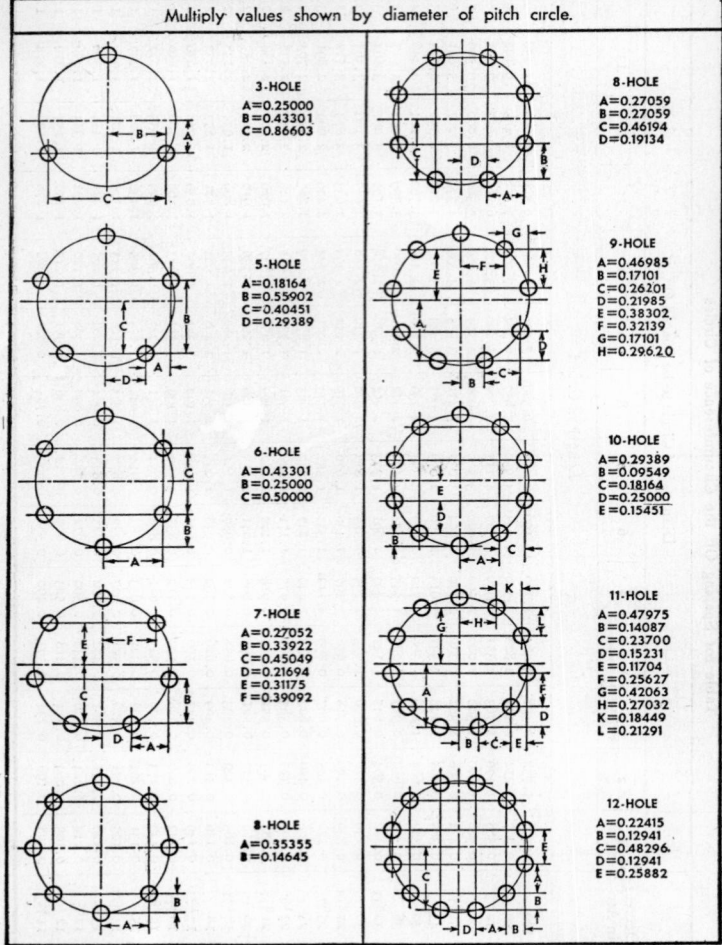

Multiply values shown by diameter of pitch circle.

3-HOLE
A=0.25000
B=0.43301
C=0.86603

5-HOLE
A=0.18164
B=0.55902
C=0.40451
D=0.29389

6-HOLE
A=0.43301
B=0.25000
C=0.50000

7-HOLE
A=0.27052
B=0.33922
C=0.45049
D=0.21694
E=0.31175
F=0.39092

8-HOLE
A=0.35355
B=0.14645

8-HOLE
A=0.27059
B=0.27059
C=0.46194
D=0.19134

9-HOLE
A=0.46985
B=0.17101
C=0.26201
D=0.21985
E=0.38302
F=0.32139
G=0.17101
H=0.29620

10-HOLE
A=0.29389
B=0.09549
C=0.18164
D=0.25000
E=0.15451

11-HOLE
A=0.47975
B=0.14087
C=0.23700
D=0.15231
E=0.11704
F=0.25627
G=0.42063
H=0.27032
K=0.18449
L=0.21291

12-HOLE
A=0.22415
B=0.12941
C=0.48296
D=0.12941
E=0.25882

The constants in the table are multiplied by the diameter of the bolt-hole pitch circle to obtain the longitudinal and lateral adjustments of the right-angle slides of the jig borer, in boring equally spaced holes. While holes may be located by these right-angular measurements, an auxiliary rotary table provides a more direct method. With a rotary table, the holes are spaced by precise angular movements after adjustment to the required radius.

Table of Commonly Used Constants

Constant	Numerical Value	Logarithm	Constant	Numerical Value	Logarithm
π	3.141593	0.49715	Weight in pounds of:		
2π	6.283185	0.79818	Water column, $1''\times1''\times1$ ft.	0.4335	$\bar{1}$.63699
$\pi\div4$	0.785398	$\bar{1}$.89509	1 U.S. gallon of water, 39.1°F.	8.34	0.92117
π^2	9.869604	0.99430	1 cu. ft. of water, 39.1° F...	62.4245	1.79535
π^3	31.006277	1.49145	1 cu. in. of water, 39.1° F...	0.0361	$\bar{2}$.55751
$1\div\pi$	0.318310	$\bar{1}$.50285	1 cu. ft. of air, 32° F., atmos-		
$1\div\pi^2$	0.101321	$\bar{1}$.00570	pheric pressure	0.08073	$\bar{2}$.90703
$1\div\pi^3$	0.032252	$\bar{2}$.50855	Volume in cu. ft. of:		
$\sqrt{\pi}$	1.772454	0.24858	1 pound of water, 39.1° F...	0.01602	$\bar{2}$.20465
$\sqrt[3]{\pi}$	1.464592	0.16572	1 pound of air, 32° F., atmos-		
g	32.16	1.50732	pheric pressure	12.387	1.09297
g^2	1034.266	3.01463	Volume in gallons of 1 pound		
$2g$	64.32	1.80835	of water, 39.1° F.........	0.1199	$\bar{1}$.07883
$1\div2g$	0.01555	$\bar{2}$.19165	Volume in cu. in. of 1 pound of		
$\sqrt{2g}$	8.01998	0.90417	water, 39.1° F.........	27.70	1.44249
$1\div\sqrt{g}$	0.17634	$\bar{1}$.24635	One cubic ft. in gallons	7.4805	0.87393
$\pi\div\sqrt{g}$	0.55399	$\bar{1}$.74350	Atmospheric pressure in		
e	2.71828	0.43429	pounds per sq. in........	14.696	1.16720

Useful Constants Multiplied and Divided by 1 to 10

Constant	Multiplied by:							
	2	3	4	5	6	7	8	9
0.7854	1.5708	2.3562	3.1416	3.9270	4.7124	5.4978	6.2832	7.0686
3.1416	6.2832	9.4248	12.566	15.708	18.850	21.991	25.133	28.274
14.7	29.4	44.1	58.8	73.5	88.2	102.9	117.6	132.3
32.16	64.32	96.48	128.64	160.80	192.96	225.12	257.28	289.44
64.32	128.64	192.96	257.28	321.60	385.92	450.24	514.56	578.88
144	288	432	576	720	864	1,008	1,152	1,296
778	1,556	2,334	3,112	3,890	4,668	5,446	6,224	7,002
1,728	3,456	5,184	6,912	8,640	10,368	12,096	13,824	15,552
33,000	66,000	99,000	132,000	165,000	198,000	231,000	264,000	297,000

Constant	Divided by:							
	2	3	4	5	6	7	8	9
0.7854	0.3927	0.2618	0.1964	0.1571	0.1309	0.1122	0.0982	0.0873
3.1416	1.5708	1.0472	0.7854	0.6283	0.5236	0.4488	0.3927	0.3490
14.7	7.350	4.900	3.625	2.940	2.450	2.100	1.838	1.633
32.16	16.080	10.720	8.040	6.432	5.360	4.594	4.020	3.573
64.32	32.160	21.440	16.080	12.864	10.720	9.189	8.040	7.147
144	72	48	36	28.800	24	20.571	18	16
778	389	259.33	194.50	155.60	129.67	111.14	97.25	86.44
1,728	864	576	432	345.60	288	246.86	216	192
33,000	16,500	11,000	8250	6600	5500	4714.3	4125	3666.7

Formulas and Table for Regular Polygons

N = number of sides.
S = length of side.
R = radius of circumscribed circle.
r = radius of inscribed circle.
A = area of polygon.
$\alpha = 180° \div N$ = one-half center angle of one side.

Formulas:

$$A = \frac{N \times \cot \alpha \times S^2}{4} = N \times \sin \alpha \times \cos \alpha \times R^2 = N \times \tan \alpha \times r^2$$

$$R = \frac{S}{2 \sin \alpha} = \frac{r}{\cos \alpha} \qquad S = 2R \times \sin \alpha = 2r \times \tan \alpha$$

$$r = \frac{S \times \cot \alpha}{2} = R \times \cos \alpha$$

Examples of Use of Table.

A regular hexagon is inscribed in a circle of 6 inches diameter. Find the area and the radius of the inscribed circle. — Here $R = 3$. From the table, area $(A) = 2.5981\,R^2 = 2.5981 \times 9 = 23.3829$ square inches. Radius of inscribed circle, $r = 0.866\,R = 0.866 \times 3 = 2.598$ inches.

Thirty-two bolts are to be equally spaced on the periphery of a bolt-circle, 16 inches in diameter. Find the chordal distance between the bolts. — Chordal distance equals the side (S) of a polygon with 32 sides. $R = 8$. Hence, $S = 0.196\,R = 0.196 \times 8 = 1.568$ inch.

No. of Sides	$A =$	$A =$	$A =$	$R =$	$R =$	$S =$	$S =$	$r =$	$r =$	No. of Sides
3	$0.4330\,S^2$	$1.2990\,R^2$	$5.1962\,r^2$	$0.5774\,S$	$2.0000\,r$	$1.7321\,R$	$3.4641\,r$	$0.5000\,R$	$0.2887\,S$	3
4	$1.0000\,S^2$	$2.0000\,R^2$	$4.0000\,r^2$	$0.7071\,S$	$1.4142\,r$	$1.4142\,R$	$2.0000\,r$	$0.7071\,R$	$0.5000\,S$	4
5	$1.7205\,S^2$	$2.3776\,R^2$	$3.6327\,r^2$	$0.8507\,S$	$1.2361\,r$	$1.1756\,R$	$1.4531\,r$	$0.8090\,R$	$0.6882\,S$	5
6	$2.5981\,S^2$	$2.5981\,R^2$	$3.4641\,r^2$	$1.0000\,S$	$1.1547\,r$	$1.0000\,R$	$1.1547\,r$	$0.8660\,R$	$0.8660\,S$	6
7	$3.6339\,S^2$	$2.736\,R^2$	$3.3710\,r^2$	$1.1524\,S$	$1.1099\,r$	$0.8678\,R$	$0.9631\,r$	$0.9010\,R$	$1.0383\,S$	7
8	$4.8284\,S^2$	$2.8284\,R^2$	$3.3137\,r^2$	$1.3066\,S$	$1.0824\,r$	$0.7654\,R$	$0.8284\,r$	$0.9239\,R$	$1.2071\,S$	8
9	$6.1818\,S^2$	$2.8925\,R^2$	$3.2757\,r^2$	$1.4619\,S$	$1.0642\,r$	$0.6840\,R$	$0.7279\,r$	$0.9397\,R$	$1.3737\,S$	9
10	$7.6942\,S^2$	$2.9389\,R^2$	$3.2492\,r^2$	$1.6180\,S$	$1.0515\,r$	$0.6180\,R$	$0.6498\,r$	$0.9511\,R$	$1.5388\,S$	10
12	$11.196\,S^2$	$3.0000\,R^2$	$3.2154\,r^2$	$1.9319\,S$	$1.0353\,r$	$0.5176\,R$	$0.5359\,r$	$0.9659\,R$	$1.8660\,S$	12
16	$20.109\,S^2$	$3.0615\,R^2$	$3.1826\,r^2$	$2.5629\,S$	$1.0196\,r$	$0.3902\,R$	$0.3978\,r$	$0.9808\,R$	$2.5137\,S$	16
20	$31.569\,S^2$	$3.0902\,R^2$	$3.1677\,r^2$	$3.1962\,S$	$1.0125\,r$	$0.3129\,R$	$0.3168\,r$	$0.9877\,R$	$3.1569\,S$	20
24	$45.575\,S^2$	$3.1058\,R^2$	$3.1597\,r^2$	$3.8306\,S$	$1.0086\,r$	$0.2611\,R$	$0.2633\,r$	$0.9914\,R$	$3.7979\,S$	24
32	$81.225\,S^2$	$3.1214\,R^2$	$3.1517\,r^2$	$5.1011\,S$	$1.0048\,r$	$0.1960\,R$	$0.1970\,r$	$0.9952\,R$	$5.0766\,S$	32
48	$183.08\,S^2$	$3.1326\,R^2$	$3.1461\,r^2$	$7.6449\,S$	$1.0021\,r$	$0.1308\,R$	$0.1311\,r$	$0.9979\,R$	$7.6285\,S$	48
64	$325.69\,S^2$	$3.1365\,R^2$	$3.1441\,r^2$	$10.190\,S$	$1.0012\,r$	$0.0981\,R$	$0.0983\,r$	$0.9988\,R$	$10.178\,S$	64

Distance Across Corners of Squares and Hexagons

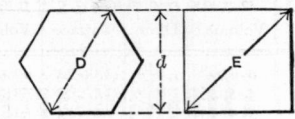

$$D = 1.1547\,d$$
$$E = 1.4142\,d$$

d	D	E	d	D	E	d	D	E
¼	0.2886	0.3535	1¼	1.4434	1.7677	2 5⁄16	2.6702	3.2703
9⁄32	0.3247	0.3977	1 9⁄32	1.4794	1.8119	2 3⁄8	2.7424	3.3587
5⁄16	0.3608	0.4419	1 5⁄16	1.5155	1.8561	2 7⁄16	2.8145	3.4471
11⁄32	0.3968	0.4861	1 11⁄32	1.5516	1.9003	2½	2.8867	3.5355
3⁄8	0.4329	0.5303	1 3⁄8	1.5877	1.9445	2 9⁄16	2.9589	3.6239
13⁄32	0.4690	0.5745	1 13⁄32	1.6238	1.9887	2 5⁄8	3.0311	3.7123
7⁄16	0.5051	0.6187	1 7⁄16	1.6598	2.0329	2 11⁄16	3.1032	3.8007
15⁄32	0.5412	0.6629	1 15⁄32	1.6959	2.0771	2 3⁄4	3.1754	3.8891
½	0.5773	0.7071	1½	1.7320	2.1213	2 13⁄16	3.2476	3.9794
17⁄32	0.6133	0.7513	1 17⁄32	1.7681	2.1655	2 7⁄8	3.3197	4.0658
9⁄16	0.6494	0.7955	1 9⁄16	1.8042	2.2097	2 15⁄16	3.3919	4.1542
19⁄32	0.6855	0.8397	1 19⁄32	1.8403	2.2539	3	3.4641	4.2426
5⁄8	0.7216	0.8839	1 5⁄8	1.8764	2.2981	3 1⁄16	3.5362	4.3310
21⁄32	0.7576	0.9281	1 21⁄32	1.9124	2.3423	3 1⁄8	3.6084	4.4194
11⁄16	0.7937	0.9723	1 11⁄16	1.9485	2.3865	3 3⁄16	3.6806	4.5078
23⁄32	0.8298	1.0164	1 23⁄32	1.9846	2.4306	3¼	3.7527	4.5962
3⁄4	0.8659	1.0606	1 3⁄4	2.0207	2.4748	3 5⁄16	3.8249	4.6846
25⁄32	0.9020	1.1048	1 25⁄32	2.0568	2.5190	3 3⁄8	3.8971	4.7729
13⁄16	0.9380	1.1490	1 13⁄16	2.0929	2.5632	3 7⁄16	3.9692	4.8613
27⁄32	0.9741	1.1932	1 27⁄32	2.1289	2.6074	3½	4.0414	4.9497
7⁄8	1.0102	1.2374	1 7⁄8	2.1650	2.6516	3 9⁄16	4.1136	5.0381
29⁄32	1.0463	1.2816	1 29⁄32	2.2011	2.6958	3 5⁄8	4.1857	5.1265
15⁄16	1.0824	1.3258	1 15⁄16	2.2372	2.7400	3 11⁄16	4.2579	5.2149
31⁄32	1.1184	1.3700	1 31⁄32	2.2733	2.7842	3 3⁄4	4.3301	5.3033
1	1.1547	1.4142	2	2.3094	2.8284	3 13⁄16	4.4023	5.3917
1 1⁄32	1.1907	1.4584	2 1⁄32	2.3453	2.8726	3 7⁄8	4.4744	5.4801
1 1⁄16	1.2268	1.5026	2 1⁄16	2.3815	2.9168	3 15⁄16	4.5466	5.5684
1 3⁄32	1.2629	1.5468	2 3⁄32	2.4176	2.9610	4	4.6188	5.6568
1 1⁄8	1.2990	1.5910	2 1⁄8	2.4537	3.0052	4 1⁄8	4.7631	5.8336
1 5⁄32	1.3351	1.6352	2 5⁄32	2.4898	3.0494	4¼	4.9074	6.0104
1 5⁄16	1.3712	1.6793	2 5⁄16	2.5259	3.0936	4 3⁄8	5.0518	6.1872
1 7⁄32	1.4073	1.7235	2¼	2.5981	3.1820	4½	5.1961	6.3639

Surface and Volume of Spheres

d = diameter.   Surface = $3.1416\,d^2$.   Volume = $0.5236\,d^3$.

Diam.	Surface	Volume	Diam.	Surface	Volume	Diam.	Surface	Volume
1/64	0.00077	0.000002	2	12.566	4.1888	6 1/2	132.73	143.79
1/32	0.00307	0.00002	2 1/16	13.364	4.5939	6 5/8	137.89	152.25
1/16	0.01227	0.00013	2 1/8	14.186	5.0243	6 3/4	143.14	161.03
3/32	0.02761	0.00043	2 3/16	15.033	5.4809	6 7/8	148.49	170.14
1/8	0.04909	0.00102	2 1/4	15.904	5.9641	7	153.94	179.59
5/32	0.07670	0.00200	2 5/16	16.800	6.4751	7 1/8	159.49	189.39
3/16	0.11045	0.00345	2 3/8	17.721	7.0144	7 1/4	165.13	199.53
7/32	0.15033	0.00548	2 7/16	18.666	7.5829	7 3/8	170.87	210.03
1/4	0.19635	0.00818	2 1/2	19.635	8.1813	7 1/2	176.71	220.89
9/32	0.24851	0.01165	2 9/16	20.629	8.8103	7 5/8	182.66	232.13
5/16	0.30680	0.01598	2 5/8	21.648	9.4708	7 3/4	188.69	243.73
11/32	0.37123	0.02127	2 11/16	22.691	10.164	7 7/8	194.83	255.72
3/8	0.44179	0.02761	2 3/4	23.758	10.889	8	201.06	268.08
13/32	0.51848	0.03511	2 13/16	24.850	11.649	8 1/8	207.39	280.85
7/16	0.60132	0.04385	2 7/8	25.967	12.443	8 1/4	213.82	294.01
15/32	0.69028	0.05393	2 15/16	27.109	13.272	8 3/8	220.36	307.58
1/2	0.78540	0.06545	3	28.274	14.137	8 1/2	226.98	321.56
17/32	0.88664	0.07850	3 1/16	29.465	15.039	8 5/8	233.71	335.95
9/16	0.99403	0.09319	3 1/8	30.680	15.979	8 3/4	240.53	350.77
19/32	1.1075	0.10960	3 3/16	31.919	16.957	8 7/8	247.45	366.02
5/8	1.2272	0.12783	3 1/4	33.183	17.974	9	254.47	381.70
21/32	1.3530	0.14798	3 5/16	34.472	19.031	9 1/8	261.59	397.83
11/16	1.4849	0.17014	3 3/8	35.784	20.129	9 1/4	268.81	414.41
23/32	1.6230	0.19442	3 7/16	37.122	21.268	9 3/8	276.12	431.44
3/4	1.7671	0.22089	3 1/2	38.484	22.449	9 1/2	283.53	448.92
25/32	1.9175	0.24967	3 5/8	41.283	24.942	9 5/8	291.04	466.87
13/16	2.0739	0.28084	3 3/4	44.179	27.611	9 3/4	298.65	485.31
27/32	2.2365	0.31451	3 7/8	47.173	30.466	9 7/8	306.36	504.21
7/8	2.4053	0.35077	4	50.265	33.510	10	314.16	523.60
29/32	2.5802	0.38971	4 1/8	53.456	36.751	10 1/4	330.06	563.86
15/16	2.7611	0.43143	4 1/4	56.745	40.195	10 1/2	346.36	606.13
31/32	2.9483	0.47603	4 3/8	60.133	43.847	10 3/4	363.05	650.46
1	3.1416	0.52360	4 1/2	63.617	47.713	11	380.13	696.91
1 1/16	3.5466	0.62804	4 5/8	67.201	51.801	11 1/4	397.61	745.51
1 1/8	3.9761	0.74551	4 3/4	70.883	56.116	11 1/2	415.48	796.33
1 3/16	4.4301	0.87681	4 7/8	74.663	60.663	11 3/4	433.73	849.40
1 1/4	4.9088	1.0227	5	78.540	65.450	12	452.39	904.78
1 5/16	5.4119	1.1839	5 1/8	82.516	70.482	12 1/4	471.44	962.52
1 3/8	5.9396	1.3611	5 1/4	86.591	75.767	12 1/2	490.87	1022.7
1 7/16	6.4919	1.5553	5 3/8	90.763	81.308	12 3/4	510.71	1085.3
1 1/2	7.0686	1.7671	5 1/2	95.033	87.113	13	530.93	1150.3
1 9/16	7.6699	1.9974	5 5/8	99.401	93.189	13 1/4	551.55	1218.0
1 5/8	8.2957	2.2468	5 3/4	103.87	99.541	13 1/2	572.55	1288.3
1 11/16	8.9461	2.5161	5 7/8	108.44	106.18	13 3/4	593.95	1361.2
1 3/4	9.6211	2.8062	6	113.10	113.10	14	615.75	1436.8
1 13/16	10.321	3.1177	6 1/8	117.87	120.31	14 1/4	637.95	1515.1
1 7/8	11.044	3.4514	6 1/4	122.72	127.83	14 1/2	660.52	1596.3
1 15/16	11.793	3.8083	6 3/8	127.68	135.66	14 3/4	683.49	1680.3

Surface and Volume of Spheres

Diam.	Surface	Volume	Diam.	Surface	Volume	Diam.	Surface	Volume
15	706.85	1,767.2	27½	2375.8	10,889	51	8,171.2	69,456
15¼	730.63	1,857.0	27¾	2419.2	11,189	51½	8,332.3	71,519
15½	754.77	1,949.8	28	2463.0	11,494	52	8,494.8	73,622
15¾	779.32	2,045.7	28¼	2507.2	11,805	52½	8,658.9	75,767
16	804.25	2,144.7	28½	2551.8	12,121	53	8,824.8	77,952
16¼	829.57	2,246.8	28¾	2596.7	12,443	53½	8,992.0	80,178
16½	855.29	2,352.1	29	2642.1	12,770	54	9,160.8	82,448
16¾	881.42	2,460.6	29½	2734.0	13,442	54½	9,331.2	84,760
17	907.93	2,572.4	30	2827.4	14,137	55	9,503.2	87,114
17¼	934.83	2,687.6	30½	2922.5	14,856	55½	9,676.8	89,511
17½	962.12	2,806.2	31	3019.1	15,599	56	9,852.0	91,953
17¾	989.80	2,928.2	31½	3117.3	16,366	56½	10,029	94,438
18	1017.9	3,053.6	32	3217.0	17,157	57	10,207	96,967
18¼	1046.4	3,182.6	32½	3318.3	17,974	57½	10,387	99,541
18½	1075.2	3,315.3	33	3421.2	18,817	58	10,568	102,161
18¾	1104.5	3,451.5	33½	3525.7	19,685	58½	10,751	104,826
19	1134.1	3,591.4	34	3631.7	20,580	59	10,936	107,536
19¼	1164.2	3,735.0	34½	3739.3	21,501	59½	11,122	110,294
19½	1194.6	3,882.5	35	3848.5	22,449	60	11,310	113,098
19¾	1225.4	4,033.7	35½	3959.2	23,425	60½	11,499	115,949
20	1256.7	4,188.8	36	4071.5	24,429	61	11,690	118,847
20¼	1288.3	4,347.8	36½	4185.5	25,461	61½	11,882	121,794
20½	1320.3	4,510.9	37	4300.9	26,522	62	12,076	124,789
20¾	1352.7	4,677.9	37½	4417.9	27,612	62½	12,272	127,832
21	1385.5	4,849.1	38	4536.5	28,731	63	12,469	130,925
21¼	1418.6	5,024.3	38½	4656.7	29,880	63½	12,668	134,067
21½	1452.2	5,203.7	39	4778.4	31,059	64	12,868	137,259
21¾	1486.2	5,387.4	39½	4901.7	32,270	64½	13,070	140,501
22	1520.5	5,575.3	40	5026.5	33,510	65	13,273	143,794
22¼	1555.3	5,767.6	40½	5153.1	34,783	65½	13,478	147,138
22½	1590.4	5,964.1	41	5281.1	36,087	66	13,685	150,533
22¾	1626.0	6,165.2	41½	5410.7	37,423	66½	13,893	153,980
23	1661.9	6,370.6	42	5541.9	38,792	67	14,103	157,480
23¼	1698.2	6,580.6	42½	5674.5	40,194	67½	14,314	161,032
23½	1735.0	6,795.2	43	5808.8	41,630	68	14,527	164,637
23¾	1772.1	7,014.3	43½	5944.7	43,099	68½	14,741	168,295
24	1809.6	7,238.2	44	6082.1	44,602	69	14,957	172,007
24¼	1847.5	7,466.7	44½	6221.2	46,141	59½	15,175	175,774
24½	1885.8	7,700.1	45	6361.7	47,713	70	15,394	179,595
24¾	1924.4	7,938.3	45½	6503.9	49,321	70½	15,615	183,471
25	1963.5	8,181.3	46	6647.6	50,965	71	15,837	187,402
25¼	2002.9	8,429.2	46½	6792.9	52,645	71½	16,061	191,389
25½	2042.8	8,682.0	47	6939.9	54,362	72	16,286	195,433
25¾	2083.0	8,939.9	47½	7088.3	56,115	72½	16,513	199,532
26	2123.7	9,202.8	48	7238.3	57,906	73	16,742	203,689
26¼	2164.7	9,470.8	48½	7389.9	59,734	73½	16,972	207,903
26½	2206.2	9,744.0	49	7543.1	61,601	74	17,204	212,175
26¾	2248.0	10,022	49½	7697.7	63,506	74½	17,437	216,505
27	2290.2	10,306	50	7854.0	65,450	75	17,672	220,894
27¼	2332.8	10,595	50½	8011.8	67,433	75½	17,908	225,341

Surface and Volume of Spheres

Diam.	Surface	Volume	Diam.	Surface	Volume	Diam.	Surface	Volume
76	18,146	229,848	101	32,047	539,464	151	71,631	1,802,725
76½	18,386	234,414	102	32,685	555,647	152	72,583	1,838,778
77	18,626	239,041	103	33,329	572,150	153	73,542	1,875,309
77½	18,869	243,728	104	33,979	588,977	154	74,506	1,912,321
78	19,114	248,475	105	34,636	606,131	155	75,477	1,949,816
78½	19,360	253,284	106	35,299	623,614	156	76,454	1,987,799
79	19,607	258,155	107	35,968	641,431	157	77,437	2,026,271
79½	19,856	263,088	108	36,644	659,584	158	78,427	2,065,237
80	20,106	268,083	109	37,325	678,076	159	79,423	2,104,699
80½	20,358	273,141	110	38,013	696,910	160	80,425	2,144,660
81	20,612	278,263	111	38,708	716,090	161	81,433	2,185,125
81½	20,867	283,447	112	39,408	735,619	162	82,448	2,226,094
82	21,124	288,696	113	40,115	755,499	163	83,469	2,267,574
82½	21,382	294,010	114	40,828	775,735	164	84,496	2,309,565
83	21,642	299,388	115	41,548	796,328	165	85,530	2,352,071
83½	21,904	304,831	116	42,273	817,283	166	86,569	2,395,096
84	22,167	310,340	117	43,005	838,603	167	87,616	2,438,642
84½	22,432	315,915	118	43,744	860,289	168	88,668	2,482,713
85	22,698	321,556	119	44,488	882,347	169	89,729	2,527,311
85½	22,966	327,264	120	45,239	904,779	170	90,792	2,572,441
86	23,235	333,039	121	45,996	927,587	171	91,863	2,618,104
86½	23,506	338,882	122	46,759	950,776	172	92,941	2,664,305
87	23,779	344,792	123	47,529	974,348	173	94,025	2,711,046
87½	24,053	350,771	124	48,305	998,306	174	95,115	2,758,331
88	24,328	356,819	125	49,087	1,022,654	175	96,211	2,806,162
88½	24,606	362,935	126	49,876	1,047,394	176	97,314	2,854,543
89	24,885	369,122	127	50,671	1,072,531	177	98,423	2,903,477
89½	25,165	375,378	128	51,472	1,098,066	178	99,538	2,952,967
90	25,447	381,704	129	52,279	1,124,004	179	100,660	3,003,006
90½	25,730	388,102	130	53,093	1,150,347	180	101,788	3,053,628
91	26,016	394,570	131	53,913	1,177,098	181	102,922	3,104,805
91½	26,302	401,109	132	54,739	1,204,260	182	104,062	3,156,551
92	26,590	407,721	133	55,572	1,231,838	183	105,209	3,208,869
92½	26,880	414,405	134	56,410	1,259,833	184	106,362	3,261,761
93	27,172	421,161	135	57,256	1,288,249	185	107,521	3,315,231
93½	27,464	427,991	136	58,107	1,317,090	186	108,687	3,369,282
94	27,759	434,894	137	58,965	1,346,357	187	109,858	3,423,919
94½	28,055	441,871	138	59,829	1,376,055	188	111,090	3,479,142
95	28,353	448,920	139	60,699	1,406,187	189	112,221	3,534,956
95½	28,652	456,047	140	61,575	1,436,755	190	113,411	3,591,364
96	28,953	463,248	141	62,458	1,467,763	191	114,609	3,648,369
96½	29,255	470,524	142	63,347	1,499,214	192	115,812	3,705,973
97	29,559	477,874	143	64,242	1,531,112	193	117,021	3,764,181
97½	29,865	485,302	144	65,144	1,563,457	194	118,237	3,822,996
98	30,172	492,808	145	66,052	1,596,256	195	119,459	3,882,419
98½	30,481	500,388	146	66,966	1,629,511	196	120,687	3,942,456
99	30,791	508,047	147	67,887	1,663,224	197	121,922	4,003,108
99½	31,103	515,785	148	68,813	1,697,398	198	123,163	4,064,379
100	31,416	523,598	149	69,747	1,732,038	199	124,420	4,126,272
100½	31,731	531,492	150	70,686	1,767,146	200	125,664	4,188,790

Table for Finding Volume of Spherical Segments

Multiply factor C in table by the cube of the length of the chord of the segment; the product equals the volume.

Center Angle of Segment, Deg.	C	Center Angle of Segment, Deg.	C	Center Angle of Segment, Deg.	C	Center Angle of Segment, Deg.	C	Center Angle of Segment, Deg.	C
3	0.0026	39	0.0341	75	0.0692	111	0.1128	147	0.1739
6	0.0051	42	0.0368	78	0.0724	114	0.1171	150	0.1802
9	0.0077	45	0.0396	81	0.0757	117	0.1215	153	0.1869
12	0.0103	48	0.0424	84	0.0791	120	0.1260	156	0.1937
15	0.0129	51	0.0452	87	0.0825	123	0.1306	159	0.2010
18	0.0155	54	0.0480	90	0.0860	126	0.1354	162	0.2085
21	0.0181	57	0.0509	93	0.0895	129	0.1403	165	0.2163
24	0.0207	60	0.0539	96	0.0932	132	0.1454	168	0.2246
27	0.0233	63	0.0568	99	0.0969	135	0.1507	171	0.2332
30	0.0260	66	0.0599	102	0.1008	138	0.1562	174	0.2423
33	0.0287	69	0.0629	105	0.1047	141	0.1619	177	0.2518
36	0.0314	72	0.0660	108	0.1087	144	0.1678	180	0.2618

Example: Find the volume of a spherical segment having a center angle of 30 degrees, if the length of the chord is 10 inches.

$$10^3 \times 0.026 = 1000 \times 0.026 = 26 \text{ cubic inches}$$

Prime Numbers—Factors

The *factors* of a given number are those numbers which when multiplied together give a product equal to that number; thus, 2 and 3 are factors of 6; and 5 and 7 are factors of 35.

A *prime number* is one which has no factors except itself and 1. Thus, 3, 5, 7, 11, etc., are prime numbers. A factor which is a prime number is called a *prime factor*.

The accompanying "Prime Number and Factor Table" gives the smallest prime factor of all odd numbers from 1 to 9600, and can be used for finding all the factors for numbers up to this limit. For example, find the factors of 931. In the column headed "900," and in the line indicated by "31" in the left-hand column, the smallest prime factor is found to be 7. As this leaves another factor 133 (since $931 \div 7 = 133$), find the smallest prime factor of this number. In the column headed "100" and in the line "33," this is found to be 7, leaving a factor 19. This latter is a prime number; hence, the factors of 931 are $7 \times 7 \times 19$. Where no factor is given for a number in the factor table, it indicates that the number is a prime number. Tables of prime numbers and factors are especially useful in calculating the gearing for unusual gear ratios and for spiral gear generating machines. etc.

For factoring, the following general rules will be found useful:

2 is a factor of any number the right-hand figure of which is an even number or 0. Thus, $28 = 2 \times 14$, and $210 = 2 \times 105$.

3 is a factor of any number the sum of the figures of which is evenly divisible by 3. Thus, 3 is a factor of 1869, because $1 + 8 + 6 + 9 = 24$, and $24 \div 3 = 8$.

4 is a factor of any number the two right-hand figures of which, considered as one number, are evenly divisible by 4. Thus, 1844 has a factor 4, because $44 \div 4 = 11$.

5 is a factor of any number the right-hand figure of which is 0 or 5. Thus, $85 = 5 \times 17$; $70 = 5 \times 14$.

Prime Number and Factor Table

From to	0 100	100 200	200 300	300 400	400 500	500 600	600 700	700 800	800 900	900 1000	1000 1100	1100 1200
1	P	P	3	7	P	3	P	P	3	17	7	3
3	P	P	7	3	13	P	3	19	11	3	17	P
5	P	3	5	5	3	5	5	3	5	5	3	5
7	P	P	3	P	11	3	P	7	3	P	19	3
9	3	P	11	3	P	P	3	P	P	3	P	P
11	P	3	P	P	3	7	13	3	P	P	3	11
13	P	P	3	P	7	3	P	23	3	11	P	3
15	3	5	5	3	5	5	3	5	5	3	5	5
17	P	3	7	P	3	11	P	3	19	7	3	P
19	P	7	3	11	P	3	P	P	3	P	P	3
21	3	11	13	3	P	P	3	7	P	3	P	19
23	P	3	P	17	3	P	7	3	P	13	3	P
25	5	5	3	5	5	3	5	5	3	5	5	3
27	3	P	P	3	7	17	3	P	P	3	13	7
29	P	3	P	7	3	23	17	3	P	P	3	P
31	P	P	3	P	P	3	P	17	3	7	P	3
33	3	7	P	3	P	13	3	P	7	3	P	11
35	5	3	5	5	3	5	5	3	5	5	3	5
37	P	P	3	P	19	3	7	11	3	P	17	3
39	3	P	P	3	P	7	3	P	P	3	P	17
41	P	3	P	11	3	P	P	3	29	P	3	7
43	P	11	3	7	P	3	P	P	3	23	7	3
45	3	5	5	3	5	5	3	5	5	3	5	5
47	P	3	13	P	3	P	P	3	7	P	3	31
49	7	P	3	P	P	3	11	7	3	13	P	3
51	3	P	P	3	11	19	3	P	23	3	P	P
53	P	3	11	P	3	7	P	3	P	P	3	P
55	5	5	3	5	5	3	5	5	3	5	5	3
57	3	P	P	3	P	P	3	P	P	3	7	13
59	P	3	7	P	3	13	P	3	P	7	3	19
61	P	7	3	19	P	3	P	P	3	31	P	3
63	3	P	P	3	P	P	3	7	P	3	P	P
65	5	3	5	5	3	5	5	3	5	5	3	5
67	P	P	3	P	P	3	23	13	3	P	11	3
69	3	13	P	3	7	P	3	P	11	3	P	7
71	P	3	P	7	3	P	11	3	13	P	3	P
73	P	P	3	P	11	3	P	P	3	7	29	3
75	3	5	5	3	5	5	3	5	5	3	5	5
77	7	3	P	13	3	P	P	3	P	P	3	11
79	P	P	3	P	P	3	7	19	3	11	13	3
81	3	P	P	3	13	7	3	11	P	3	23	P
83	P	3	P	P	3	11	P	3	P	P	3	7
85	5	5	3	5	5	3	5	5	3	5	5	3
87	3	11	7	3	P	P	3	P	P	3	P	P
89	P	3	17	P	3	19	13	3	7	23	3	29
91	7	P	3	17	P	3	P	7	3	P	P	3
93	3	P	P	3	17	P	3	13	19	3	P	P
95	5	3	5	5	3	5	5	3	5	5	3	5
97	P	P	3	P	7	3	17	P	3	P	P	3
99	3	P	13	3	P	P	3	17	29	3	7	11

Prime Number and Factor Table

From to	1200 1300	1300 1400	1400 1500	1500 1600	1600 1700	1700 1800	1800 1900	1900 2000	2000 2100	2100 2200	2200 2300	2300 2400
1	P	P	3	19	P	3	P	P	3	11	31	3
3	3	P	23	3	7	13	3	11	P	3	P	7
5	5	3	5	5	3	5	5	3	5	5	3	5
7	17	P	3	11	P	3	13	P	3	7	P	3
9	3	7	P	3	P	P	3	23	7	3	47	P
11	7	3	17	P	3	29	P	3	P	P	3	P
13	P	13	3	17	P	3	7	P	3	P	P	3
15	3	5	5	3	5	5	3	5	5	3	5	5
17	P	3	13	37	3	17	23	3	P	29	3	7
19	23	P	3	7	P	3	17	19	3	13	7	3
21	3	P	7	3	P	P	3	17	43	3	P	11
23	P	3	P	P	3	P	P	3	7	11	3	23
25	5	5	3	5	5	3	5	5	3	5	5	3
27	3	P	P	3	P	11	3	41	P	3	17	13
29	P	3	P	11	3	7	31	3	P	P	3	17
31	P	11	3	P	7	3	P	P	3	P	23	3
33	3	31	P	3	23	P	3	P	19	3	7	P
35	5	3	5	5	3	5	5	3	5	5	3	5
37	P	7	3	29	P	3	11	13	3	P	P	3
39	3	13	P	3	11	37	3	7	P	3	P	P
41	17	3	11	23	3	P	7	3	13	P	3	P
43	11	17	3	P	31	3	19	29	3	P	P	3
45	3	5	5	3	5	5	3	5	5	3	5	5
47	29	3	P	7	3	P	P	3	23	19	3	P
49	P	19	3	P	17	3	43	P	3	7	13	3
51	3	7	P	3	13	17	3	P	7	3	P	P
53	7	3	P	P	3	P	17	3	P	P	3	13
55	5	5	3	5	5	3	5	5	3	5	5	3
57	3	23	31	3	P	7	3	19	11	3	37	P
59	P	3	P	P	3	P	11	3	29	17	3	7
61	13	P	3	7	11	3	P	37	3	P	7	3
63	3	29	7	3	P	41	3	13	P	3	31	17
65	5	3	5	5	3	5	5	3	5	5	3	5
67	7	P	3	P	P	3	P	7	3	11	P	3
69	3	37	13	3	P	29	3	11	P	3	P	23
71	31	3	P	P	3	7	P	3	19	13	3	P
73	19	P	3	11	P	3	P	P	3	41	P	3
75	3	5	5	3	5	5	3	5	5	3	5	5
77	P	3	7	19	3	P	P	3	31	7	3	P
79	P	7	3	P	23	3	P	P	3	P	43	3
81	3	P	P	3	41	13	3	7	P	3	P	P
83	P	3	P	P	3	P	7	3	P	37	3	P
85	5	5	3	5	5	3	5	5	3	5	5	3
87	3	19	P	3	7	P	3	P	P	3	P	7
89	P	3	P	7	3	P	P	3	P	11	3	P
91	P	13	3	37	19	3	31	11	3	7	29	3
93	3	7	P	3	P	11	3	P	7	3	P	P
95	5	3	5	5	3	5	5	3	5	5	3	5
97	P	11	3	P	P	3	7	P	3	13	P	3
99	3	P	P	3	P	7	3	P	P	3	11	P

Prime Number and Factor Table

From to	2400 2500	2500 2600	2600 2700	2700 2800	2800 2900	2900 3000	3000 3100	3100 3200	3200 3300	3300 3400	3400 3500	3500 3600
1	7	41	3	37	P	3	P	7	3	P	19	3
3	3	P	19	3	P	P	3	29	P	3	41	31
5	5	3	5	5	3	5	5	3	5	5	3	5
7	29	23	3	P	7	3	31	13	3	P	P	3
9	3	13	P	3	53	P	3	P	P	3	7	11
11	P	3	7	P	3	41	P	3	13	7	3	P
13	19	7	3	P	29	3	23	11	3	P	P	3
15	3	5	5	3	5	5	3	5	5	3	5	5
17	P	3	P	11	3	P	7	3	P	31	3	P
19	41	11	3	P	P	3	P	P	3	P	13	3
21	3	P	P	3	7	23	3	P	P	3	11	7
23	P	3	43	7	3	37	P	3	11	P	3	13
25	5	5	3	5	5	3	5	5	3	5	5	3
27	3	7	37	3	11	P	3	53	7	3	23	P
29	7	3	11	P	3	29	13	3	P	P	3	P
31	11	P	3	P	19	3	7	31	3	P	47	3
33	3	17	P	3	P	7	3	13	53	3	P	P
35	5	3	5	5	3	5	5	3	5	5	3	5
37	P	43	3	7	P	3	P	P	3	47	7	3
39	3	P	7	3	17	P	3	43	41	3	19	P
41	P	3	19	P	3	17	P	3	7	13	3	P
43	7	P	3	13	P	3	17	7	3	P	11	3
45	3	5	5	3	5	5	3	5	5	3	5	5
47	P	3	P	41	3	7	11	3	17	P	3	P
49	31	P	3	P	7	3	P	47	3	17	P	3
51	3	P	11	3	P	13	3	23	P	3	7	53
53	11	3	7	P	3	P	43	3	P	7	3	11
55	3	5	5	3	5	5	3	5	5	3	5	5
57	3	P	P	3	P	P	3	7	P	3	P	P
59	P	3	P	31	3	11	7	3	P	P	3	P
61	23	13	3	11	P	3	P	29	3	P	P	3
63	3	11	P	3	7	P	3	P	13	3	P	7
65	5	3	5	5	3	5	5	3	5	5	3	5
67	P	17	3	P	47	3	P	P	3	7	P	3
69	3	7	17	3	19	P	3	P	7	3	P	43
71	7	3	P	17	3	P	37	3	P	P	3	P
73	P	31	3	47	13	3	7	19	3	P	23	3
75	3	5	5	3	5	5	3	5	5	3	5	5
77	P	3	P	P	3	13	17	3	29	11	3	7
79	37	P	3	7	P	3	P	11	3	31	7	3
81	3	29	7	3	43	11	3	P	17	3	59	P
83	13	3	P	11	3	19	P	3	7	17	3	P
85	5	5	3	5	5	3	5	5	3	5	5	3
87	3	13	P	3	P	29	3	P	19	3	11	17
89	19	3	P	P	3	7	P	3	11	P	3	37
91	47	P	3	P	7	3	11	P	3	P	P	3
93	3	P	P	3	11	41	3	31	37	3	7	P
95	5	3	5	5	3	5	5	3	5	5	3	5
97	11	7	3	P	P	3	19	23	3	43	13	3
99	3	23	P	3	13	P	3	7	P	3	P	59

Prime Number and Factor Table

From to	3600 3700	3700 3800	3800 3900	3900 4000	4000 4100	4100 4200	4200 4300	4300 4400	4400 4500	4500 4600	4600 4700	4700 4800
1	13	P	3	47	P	3	P	11	3	7	43	3
3	3	7	P	3	P	11	3	13	7	3	P	P
5	5	3	5	5	3	5	5	3	5	5	3	5
7	P	11	3	P	P	3	7	59	3	P	17	3
9	3	P	13	3	19	7	3	31	P	3	11	17
11	23	3	37	P	3	P	P	3	11	13	3	7
13	P	47	3	7	P	3	11	19	3	P	7	3
15	3	5	5	3	5	5	3	5	5	3	5	5
17	P	3	11	P	3	23	P	3	7	P	3	53
19	7	P	3	P	P	3	P	7	3	P	31	3
21	3	61	P	3	P	13	3	29	P	3	P	P
23	P	3	P	P	3	7	41	3	P	P	3	P
25	5	5	3	5	5	3	5	5	3	5	5	3
27	3	P	43	3	P	P	3	P	19	3	7	29
29	19	3	7	P	3	P	P	3	43	7	3	P
31	P	7	3	P	29	3	P	61	3	23	11	3
33	3	P	P	3	37	P	3	7	11	3	41	P
35	5	3	5	5	3	5	5	3	5	5	3	5
37	P	37	3	31	11	3	19	P	3	13	P	3
39	3	P	11	3	7	P	3	P	23	3	P	7
41	11	3	23	7	3	41	P	3	P	19	3	11
43	P	19	3	P	13	3	P	43	3	7	P	3
45	3	5	5	3	5	5	3	5	5	3	5	5
47	7	3	P	P	3	11	31	3	P	P	3	47
49	41	23	3	11	P	3	7	P	3	P	P	3
51	3	11	P	3	P	7	3	19	P	3	P	P
53	13	3	P	59	3	P	P	3	61	29	3	7
55	5	5	3	5	5	3	5	5	3	5	5	3
57	3	13	7	3	P	P	3	P	P	3	P	67
59	P	3	17	37	3	P	P	3	7	47	3	P
61	7	P	3	17	31	3	P	7	3	P	59	3
63	3	53	P	3	17	23	3	P	P	3	P	11
65	5	3	5	5	3	5	5	3	5	5	3	5
67	19	P	3	P	7	3	17	11	3	P	13	3
69	3	P	53	3	13	11	3	17	41	3	7	19
71	P	3	7	11	3	43	P	3	17	7	3	13
73	P	7	3	29	P	3	P	P	3	17	P	3
75	3	5	5	3	5	5	3	5	5	3	5	5
77	P	3	P	41	3	P	7	3	11	23	3	17
79	13	P	3	23	P	3	11	29	3	19	P	3
81	3	19	P	3	7	37	3	13	P	3	31	7
83	29	3	11	7	3	47	P	3	P	P	3	P
85	5	5	3	5	5	3	5	5	3	5	5	3
87	3	7	13	3	61	53	3	41	7	3	43	P
89	7	3	P	P	3	59	P	3	67	13	3	P
91	P	17	3	13	P	3	7	P	3	P	P	3
93	3	P	17	3	P	7	3	23	P	3	13	P
95	5	3	5	5	3	5	5	3	5	5	3	5
97	P	P	3	7	17	3	P	P	3	P	7	3
99	3	29	7	3	P	13	3	53	11	3	37	P

MATHEMATICAL TABLES

Prime Number and Factor Table

From to	4800 4900	4900 5000	5000 5100	5100 5200	5200 5300	5300 5400	5400 5500	5500 5600	5600 5700	5700 5800	5800 5900	5900 6000
1	P	13	3	P	7	3	11	P	3	P	P	3
3	3	P	P	3	11	P	3	P	13	3	7	P
5	5	3	5	5	3	5	5	3	5	5	3	5
7	11	7	3	P	41	3	P	P	3	13	P	3
9	3	P	P	3	P	P	3	7	71	3	37	19
11	17	3	P	19	3	47	7	3	31	P	3	23
13	P	17	3	P	13	3	P	37	3	29	P	3
15	3	5	5	3	5	5	3	5	5	3	5	5
17	P	3	29	7	3	13	P	3	41	P	3	61
19	61	P	3	P	17	3	P	P	3	7	11	3
21	3	7	P	3	23	17	3	P	7	3	P	31
23	7	3	P	47	3	P	11	3	P	59	3	P
25	5	5	3	5	5	3	5	5	3	5	5	3
27	3	13	11	3	P	7	3	P	17	3	P	P
29	11	3	47	23	3	73	61	3	13	17	3	7
31	P	P	3	7	P	3	P	P	3	11	7	3
33	3	P	7	3	P	P	3	11	43	3	19	17
35	5	3	5	5	3	5	5	3	5	5	3	5
37	7	P	3	11	P	3	P	7	3	P	13	3
39	3	11	P	3	13	19	3	29	P	3	P	P
41	47	3	71	53	3	7	P	3	P	P	3	13
43	29	P	3	37	7	3	P	23	3	P	P	3
45	3	5	5	3	5	5	3	5	5	3	5	5
47	37	3	7	P	3	P	13	3	P	7	3	19
49	13	7	3	19	29	3	P	31	3	P	P	3
51	3	P	P	3	59	P	3	7	P	3	P	11
53	23	3	31	P	3	53	7	3	P	11	3	P
55	5	5	3	5	5	3	5	5	3	5	5	3
57	3	P	13	3	7	11	3	P	P	3	P	7
59	43	3	P	7	3	23	53	3	P	13	3	59
61	P	11	3	13	P	3	43	67	3	7	P	3
63	3	7	61	3	19	31	3	P	7	3	11	67
65	5	3	5	5	3	5	5	3	5	5	3	5
67	31	P	3	P	23	3	7	19	3	73	P	3
69	3	P	37	3	11	7	3	P	P	3	P	47
71	P	3	11	P	3	41	P	3	53	29	3	7
73	11	P	3	7	P	3	13	P	3	23	7	3
75	3	5	5	3	5	5	3	5	5	3	5	5
77	P	3	P	31	3	19	P	3	7	53	3	43
79	7	13	3	P	P	3	P	7	3	P	P	3
81	3	17	P	3	P	P	3	P	13	3	P	P
83	19	3	13	71	3	7	P	3	P	P	3	31
85	5	5	3	5	5	3	5	5	3	5	5	3
87	3	P	P	3	17	P	3	37	11	3	7	P
89	P	3	7	P	3	17	11	3	P	7	3	53
91	67	7	3	29	11	3	17	P	3	P	43	3
93	3	P	11	3	67	P	3	7	P	3	71	13
95	5	3	5	5	3	5	5	3	5	5	3	5
97	59	19	3	P	P	3	23	29	3	11	P	3
99	3	P	P	3	7	P	3	11	41	3	17	7

Prime Number and Factor Table

From to	6000 6100	6100 6200	6200 6300	6300 6400	6400 6500	6500 6600	6600 6700	6700 6800	6800 6900	6900 7000	7000 7100	7100 7200
1	17	P	3	P	37	3	7	P	3	67	P	3
3	3	17	P	3	19	7	3	P	P	3	47	P
5	5	3	5	5	3	5	5	3	5	5	3	5
7	P	31	3	7	43	3	P	19	3	P	7	3
9	3	41	7	3	13	23	3	P	11	3	43	P
11	P	3	P	P	3	17	11	3	7	P	3	13
13	7	P	3	59	11	3	17	7	3	31	P	3
15	3	5	5	3	5	5	3	5	5	3	5	5
17	11	3	P	P	3	7	13	3	17	P	3	11
19	13	29	3	71	7	3	P	P	3	11	P	3
21	3	P	P	3	P	P	3	11	19	3	7	P
23	19	3	7	P	3	11	37	3	P	7	3	17
25	5	5	3	5	5	3	5	5	3	5	5	3
27	3	11	13	3	P	61	3	7	P	3	P	P
29	P	3	P	P	3	P	7	3	P	13	3	P
31	37	P	3	13	59	3	19	53	3	29	79	3
33	3	P	23	3	7	47	3	P	P	3	13	7
35	5	3	5	5	3	5	5	3	5	5	3	5
37	P	17	3	P	41	3	P	P	3	7	31	3
39	3	7	17	3	47	13	3	23	7	3	P	11
41	7	3	79	17	3	31	29	3	P	11	3	37
43	P	P	3	P	17	3	7	11	3	53	P	3
45	3	5	5	3	5	5	3	5	5	3	5	5
47	P	3	P	11	3	P	17	3	41	P	3	7
49	23	11	3	7	P	3	61	17	3	P	7	3
51	3	P	7	3	P	P	3	43	13	3	11	P
53	P	3	13	P	3	P	P	3	7	17	3	23
55	5	5	3	5	5	3	5	5	3	5	5	3
57	3	47	P	3	11	79	3	29	P	3	P	17
59	73	3	11	P	3	7	P	3	19	P	3	P
61	11	61	3	P	7	3	P	P	3	P	23	3
63	3	P	P	P	23	P	3	P	P	3	7	13
65	5	3	5	5	3	5	5	3	5	5	3	5
67	P	7	3	P	29	3	59	67	3	P	37	3
69	3	31	P	3	P	P	3	7	P	3	P	67
71	13	3	P	23	3	P	7	3	P	P	3	71
73	P	P	3	P	P	3	P	13	3	19	11	3
75	3	5	5	3	5	5	3	5	5	3	5	5
77	59	3	P	7	3	P	11	3	13	P	3	P
79	P	37	3	P	11	3	P	P	3	7	P	3
81	3	7	11	3	P	P	3	P	7	3	73	43
83	7	3	61	13	3	29	41	3	P	P	3	11
85	5	5	3	5	5	3	5	5	3	5	5	3
87	3	23	P	3	13	7	3	11	71	3	19	P
89	P	3	19	P	3	11	P	3	83	29	3	7
91	P	41	3	7	P	3	P	P	3	P	7	3
93	3	11	7	3	43	19	3	P	61	3	41	P
95	5	3	5	5	3	5	5	3	5	5	3	5
97	7	P	3	P	73	3	37	7	3	P	47	3
99	3	P	P	3	67	P	3	13	P	3	31	23

Prime Number and Factor Table

From to	7200 7300	7300 7400	7400 7500	7500 7600	7600 7700	7700 7800	7800 7900	7900 8000	8000 8100	8100 8200	8200 8300	8300 8400
1	19	7	3	13	11	3	29	P	3	P	59	3
3	3	67	11	3	P	P	3	7	53	3	13	19
5	5	3	5	5	3	5	5	3	5	5	3	5
7	P	P	3	P	P	3	37	P	3	11	29	3
9	3	P	31	3	7	13	3	11	P	3	P	7
11	P	3	P	7	3	11	73	3	P	P	3	P
13	P	71	3	11	23	3	13	41	3	7	43	3
15	3	5	5	3	5	5	3	5	5	3	5	5
17	7	3	P	P	3	P	P	3	P	P	3	P
19	P	13	3	73	19	3	7	P	3	23	P	3
21	3	P	41	3	P	7	3	89	13	3	P	53
23	31	3	13	P	3	P	P	3	71	P	3	7
25	5	5	3	5	5	3	5	5	3	5	5	3
27	3	17	7	3	29	P	3	P	23	3	19	11
29	P	3	17	P	3	59	P	3	7	11	3	P
31	7	P	3	17	13	3	41	7	3	47	P	3
33	3	P	P	3	17	11	3	P	29	3	P	13
35	5	3	5	5	3	5	5	3	5	5	3	5
37	P	11	3	P	7	3	17	P	3	79	P	3
39	3	41	43	3	P	71	3	17	P	3	7	31
41	13	3	7	P	3	P	P	3	11	7	3	19
43	P	7	3	19	P	3	11	13	3	17	P	3
45	3	5	5	3	5	5	3	5	5	3	5	5
47	P	3	11	P	3	61	7	3	13	P	3	17
49	11	P	3	P	P	3	47	P	3	29	73	3
51	3	P	P	3	7	23	3	P	83	3	37	7
53	P	3	29	7	3	P	P	3	P	31	3	P
55	5	5	3	5	5	3	5	5	3	5	5	3
57	3	7	P	3	13	P	3	73	7	3	23	61
59	7	3	P	P	3	P	29	3	P	41	3	13
61	53	17	3	P	47	3	7	19	3	P	11	3
63	3	37	17	3	79	7	3	P	11	3	P	P
65	5	3	5	5	3	5	5	3	5	5	3	5
67	13	53	3	7	11	3	P	31	3	P	7	3
69	3	P	7	3	P	17	3	13	P	3	P	11
71	11	3	31	67	3	19	17	3	7	P	3	P
73	7	73	3	P	P	3	P	7	3	11	P	3
75	3	5	5	3	5	5	3	5	5	3	5	5
77	19	3	P	P	3	7	P	3	41	13	3	P
79	29	47	3	11	7	3	P	79	3	P	17	3
81	3	11	P	3	P	37	3	23	P	3	7	17
83	P	3	7	P	3	43	P	3	59	7	3	83
85	5	5	3	5	5	3	5	5	3	5	5	3
87	3	83	P	3	P	13	3	7	P	3	P	P
89	37	3	P	P	3	P	7	3	P	19	3	P
91	23	19	3	P	P	3	13	61	3	P	P	3
93	3	3	59	3	7	P	3	P	P	3	P	7
95	5	3	5	5	3	5	5	3	5	5	3	5
97	P	13	3	71	43	3	53	11	3	7	P	3
99	3	7	P	3	P	11	3	19	7	3	43	37

Prime Number and Factor Table

From to	8400 8500	8500 8600	8600 8700	8700 8800	8800 8900	8900 9000	9000 9100	9100 9200	9200 9300	9300 9400	9400 9500	9500 9600
1	31	P	3	7	13	3	P	19	3	71	7	3
3	3	11	7	3	P	29	3	P	P	3	P	13
5	5	3	5	5	3	5	5	3	5	5	3	5
7	7	47	3	P	P	3	P	7	3	41	23	3
9	3	67	P	3	23	59	3	P	P	3	97	37
11	13	3	79	31	3	7	P	3	61	P	3	P
13	47	P	3	P	7	3	P	13	3	67	P	3
15	3	5	5	3	5	5	3	5	5	3	5	5
17	19	3	7	23	3	37	71	3	13	7	3	31
19	P	7	3	P	P	3	29	11	3	P	P	3
21	3	P	37	3	P	11	3	7	P	3	P	P
23	P	3	P	11	3	P	7	3	23	P	3	89
25	5	5	3	5	5	3	5	5	3	5	5	3
27	3	P	P	3	7	79	3	P	P	3	11	7
29	P	3	P	7	3	P	P	3	11	19	3	13
31	P	19	3	P	P	3	11	23	3	7	P	3
33	3	7	89	3	11	P	3	P	7	3	P	P
35	5	3	5	5	3	5	5	3	5	5	3	5
37	11	P	3	P	P	3	7	P	3	P	P	3
39	3	P	53	3	P	7	3	13	P	3	P	P
41	23	3	P	P	3	P	P	3	P	P	3	7
43	P	P	3	7	37	3	P	41	3	P	7	3
45	3	5	5	3	5	5	3	5	5	3	5	5
47	P	3	P	P	3	23	83	3	7	13	3	P
49	7	83	3	13	P	3	P	7	3	P	11	3
51	3	17	41	3	53	P	3	P	11	3	13	P
53	79	3	17	P	3	7	11	3	19	47	3	41
55	5	5	3	5	5	3	5	5	3	5	5	3
57	3	43	11	3	17	13	3	P	P	3	7	19
59	11	3	7	19	3	17	P	3	47	7	3	11
61	P	7	3	P	P	3	13	P	3	11	P	3
63	3	P	P	3	P	P	3	7	59	3	P	73
65	5	3	5	5	3	5	5	3	5	5	3	5
67	P	13	3	11	P	3	P	89	3	19	P	3
69	3	11	P	3	7	P	3	53	13	3	17	7
71	43	3	13	7	3	P	47	3	73	P	3	17
73	37	P	3	31	19	3	43	P	3	7	P	3
75	3	5	5	3	5	5	3	5	5	3	5	5
77	7	3	P	67	3	47	29	3	P	P	3	61
79	61	23	3	P	13	3	7	67	3	83	P	3
81	3	P	P	3	83	7	3	P	P	3	19	11
83	17	3	19	P	3	13	31	3	P	11	3	7
85	5	5	3	5	5	3	5	5	3	5	5	3
87	3	31	7	3	P	11	3	P	37	3	53	P
89	13	3	P	11	3	89	61	3	7	41	3	43
91	7	11	3	59	17	3	P	7	3	P	P	3
93	3	13	P	3	P	17	3	29	P	3	11	53
95	5	3	5	5	3	5	5	3	5	5	3	5
97	29	P	3	19	7	3	11	17	3	P	P	3
99	3	P	P	3	11	P	3	P	17	3	7	29

Transposition of Formulas

A formula is a rule for a calculation expressed by using letters and signs instead of writing out the rule in words; by this means it is possible to condense, in a very small space, the essentials of long and cumbersome rules. The letters used in formulas simply stand in place of the figures which are to be substituted when solving a specific problem.

An important method for facilitating the use of formulas is known as *transposition*. As an example, the formula for the horsepower transmitted by belting may be written:

$$\text{H.P.} = \frac{SVW}{33,000}$$

in which

H.P. = horsepower transmitted;
S = working stress of belt per inch of width, in pounds;
V = velocity of belt in feet per minute;
W = width of belt in inches.

If the working stress S, the velocity V, and the width W, are known, the horsepower can be found directly from this formula by inserting the given values. Assume $S = 33$; $V = 600$; and $W = 5$. Then:

$$\text{H.P.} = \frac{33 \times 600 \times 5}{33,000} = 3.$$

Assume, however, that the horsepower, the stress S, and the velocity V are known, and that the width of belt, W, is to be found. The formula must then be transposed so that the symbol W will be on one side of the equals sign and all the known quantities on the other. The transposed formula is as follows:

$$\frac{\text{H.P.} \times 33,000}{SV} = W.$$

The quantities (S and V) that were in the numerator on the right side of the equals sign are transposed to the denominator on the left side, and "33,000" which was in the denominator on the right side of the equals sign is transposed to the numerator on the other side. This is in conformity with the general rule for transposition. Symbols which are not part of a fraction, like "H.P." in the formula first given, are to be considered as being numerators (having the denominator 1).

According to the rule given, any formula of the form $A = \frac{B}{C}$ can be transposed as below:

$$A \times C = B, \quad \text{and} \quad C = \frac{B}{A}$$

Suppose a formula to be of the form:

$$A = \frac{B \times C}{D}$$

Then:

$$D = \frac{B \times C}{A}; \quad \frac{A \times D}{C} = B; \quad \frac{A \times D}{B} = C.$$

The method given is only directly applicable when all the quantities in the numerator or denominator are standing independently or are *factors of a product*. If connected by $+$ or $-$ signs, the transposition can be made by the method shown only when the *whole sum* or *difference* is transposed.

Example:

$$A = \frac{B + C}{D}; \quad \text{then} \quad D = \frac{B + C}{A} \quad \text{and} \quad A \times D = B + C.$$

A quantity preceded by a + or − sign can be transposed to the opposite side of the equals sign by changing its sign; if the sign is +, change it to − on the other side; if it is −, change it to +.

Example:

$$B + C = A - D; \text{ then } B + C + D = A;$$
$$B = A - D - C;$$
$$C = A - D - B;$$
$$D = A - B - C.$$

When several numbers or quantities in a formula are connected with signs indicating that additions, subtractions, multiplications or divisions are to be made, the multiplications should be carried out before any of the other operations. Division also precedes addition and subtraction if written in line with these. The other operations are carried out in the order written.

Examples:

$$10 + 26 \times 7 - 2 = 10 + 182 - 2 = 190.$$
$$18 \div 6 + 15 \times 3 = 3 + 45 = 48.$$
$$12 + 14 \div 2 - 4 = 12 + 7 - 4 = 15.$$

When it is required that certain additions and subtractions should precede multiplications and divisions, use is made of parentheses ( ) and brackets [ ]. These indicate that the calculation inside the parentheses or brackets should be carried out complete by itself before the remaining calculations are commenced. If one bracket is placed inside of another, the one inside is first calculated.

Examples:

$$(6 - 2) \times 5 + 8 = 4 \times 5 + 8 = 20 + 8 = 28.$$
$$6 \times (4 + 7) \div 22 = 6 \times 11 \div 22 = 66 \div 22 = 3.$$
$$2 + [10 \times 6(8 + 2) - 4] \times 2 = 2 + [10 \times 6 \times 10 - 4] \times 2$$
$$= 2 + [600 - 4] \times 2 = 2 + 596 \times 2 = 2 + 1192 = 1194.$$

The parentheses are considered as a sign of multiplication; for example, $6 (8 + 2) = 6 \times (8 + 2)$.

The line or bar between the numerator and denominator in a fractional expression is to be considered as a division sign. For example,

$$\frac{12 + 16 + 22}{10} = (12 + 16 + 22) \div 10 = 50 \div 10 = 5.$$

In formulas the multiplication sign (×) is often left out between symbols or letters, the values of which are to be multiplied. Thus

$$AB = A \times B, \text{ and } \frac{ABC}{D} = (A \times B \times C) \div D$$

Ratio and Proportion

The *ratio* between two quantities is the quotient obtained by dividing the first quantity by the second. For example, the ratio between 3 and 12 is $\frac{1}{4}$, and the ratio between 12 and 3 is 4. Ratio is generally indicated by the sign (:); thus 12 : 3 indicates the ratio of 12 to 3.

A *reciprocal* or *inverse* ratio is the reciprocal of the original ratio. Thus, the inverse ratio of 5 : 7 is 7 : 5.

In a *compound* ratio each term is the product of the corresponding terms in two or more simple ratios. Thus, when

$$8 : 2 = 4, \qquad 9 : 3 = 3, \qquad 10 : 5 = 2,$$

then the compound ratio is:

$$8 \times 9 \times 10 : 2 \times 3 \times 5 = 4 \times 3 \times 2,$$
$$720 : 30 = 24.$$

Proportion is the equality of ratios. Thus,

$$6 : 3 = 10 : 5, \quad \text{or} \quad 6 : 3 :: 10 : 5.$$

The first and last terms in a proportion are called the *extremes;* the second and third, the *means.* The product of the extremes is equal to the product of the means. Thus,

$$25 : 2 = 100 : 8 \quad \text{and} \quad 25 \times 8 = 2 \times 100.$$

If three terms in a proportion are known, the remaining term may be found by the following rules:

The first term is equal to the product of the second and third terms, divided by the fourth.

The second term is equal to the product of the first and fourth terms, divided by the third.

The third term is equal to the product of the first and fourth terms, divided by the second.

The fourth term is equal to the product of the second and third terms, divided by the first.

Examples: — Let x be the term to be found, then,

$$x : 12 = 3.5 : 21 \qquad x = \frac{12 \times 3.5}{21} = \frac{42}{21} = 2.$$

$$\tfrac{1}{4} : x = 14 : 42 \qquad x = \frac{\tfrac{1}{4} \times 42}{14} = \frac{1}{4} \times 3 = \frac{3}{4}$$

$$5 : 9 = x : 63 \qquad x = \frac{5 \times 63}{9} = \frac{315}{9} = 35$$

$$\tfrac{1}{4} : \tfrac{7}{8} = 4 : x \qquad x = \frac{\tfrac{7}{8} \times 4}{\tfrac{1}{4}} = \frac{3\tfrac{1}{2}}{\tfrac{1}{4}} = 14.$$

If the second and third terms are the same, either is said to be the *mean proportional* between the other two. Thus, $8 : 4 = 4 : 2$, and 4 is the mean proportional between 8 and 2. The mean proportional between two numbers may be found by multiplying the numbers together, and extracting the square root of the product. Thus, the mean proportional between 3 and 12 is found as below:

$$3 \times 12 = 36, \quad \text{and} \quad \sqrt{36} = 6,$$

which is the mean proportional.

Practical Examples Involving Simple Proportion. — If it takes 18 days to assemble 4 lathes, how long would it require to assemble 14 lathes?

Let the number of days to be found be x. Then write out the proportion as below:

$$4 \; : \; 18 \; = \; 14 \; : \; x$$
$$(\text{lathes} : \text{days} = \text{lathes} : \text{days})$$

Find now the fourth term by the rule given:

$$x = \frac{18 \times 14}{4} = 63 \text{ days.}$$

Thirty-four linear feet of bar stock are required for the blanks for 100 clamping bolts. How many feet of stock would be required for 912 bolts?

Let x = total length of stock required for 912 bolts.

$$34 \; : \; 100 \; = \; x \; : \; 912$$
$$(\text{feet} : \text{bolts} = \text{feet} : \text{bolts})$$

Then, the third term $x = \dfrac{34 \times 912}{100} = 310$ feet, approximately.

Example of Inverse Proportion. — A factory employing 270 men completes a given number of typewriters weekly, the number of working hours being 60 per week. How many men would be required for the same production if the working hours were reduced to 54 per week?

The time per week is in an inverse proportion to the number of men employed; the *shorter* the time, the *more* men. The inverse proportion is written:

$$270 \quad : \quad x \quad = \quad 54 \quad : \quad 60$$
(men, 10-hour basis : men, 9-hour basis = time, 9-hour basis : time, 10-hour basis)

The second term $x = \dfrac{270 \times 60}{54} = 300$ men.

Example of Compound Proportion. — If a man capable of turning 65 studs in a day of 10 hours is paid 32.5 cents per hour, how much ought a man be paid who turns 72 studs in a 9-hour day, if compensated in the same proportion?

When solving problems involving compound proportion, the following method of analysis tends to simplify the solution. Make up a table with four columns headed, "First Cause," "First Effect," "Second Cause," "Second Effect," and place under each the respective factors given in the problem. In the example above, the table would be arranged as below:

First Cause	First Effect	Second Cause	Second Effect
1 man 10 hours 32.5 cents	65 studs	1 man 9 hours x cents	72 studs

Consider as *causes* the number of men working, the length of time they work, and their capacity for work; the pay received or the amount of product turned out in a unit of time indicates the capacity for work. The effect is the total product given either in numbers, or by the dimensions of the work carried out. The unknown quantity is called x.

When the table is completed, take all the quantities in the first and fourth columns and place them as the numerator of a fraction with multiplication signs between them, and all the quantities in the second and third columns and place them as the denominator of a fraction with multiplication signs between them. Put this fraction equal to 1. Then cancel and reduce the fraction to its simplest form as below.

$$\frac{1 \times 10 \times 32.5 \times 72}{65 \times 1 \times 9 \times x} = 1; \quad \frac{40}{x} = 1, \text{ or } x = 40 \text{ cents.}$$

Percentage

If out of 100 pieces made, 12 do not pass inspection, it is said that 12 per cent (12 on the hundred) are rejected. If a quantity of steel is bought for $100 and sold for $140, the profit is 40 per cent.

The per cent of gain or loss is found by dividing the amount of gain or loss by the *original* number of which the percentage is wanted, and multiplying the quotient by 100.

Examples: — Out of a total output of 280 castings a day, 30 castings are, on an average, rejected. What is the percentage of bad castings?

$$\frac{30}{280} \times 100 = 10.7 \text{ per cent}$$

If by a new process 100 pieces can be made in the same time as 60 could formerly be made, what is the gain in output of the new process over the old, expressed in per cent?

Original number, 60; gain $100 - 60 = 40$. Hence,

$$\frac{40}{60} \times 100 = 66.7 \text{ per cent.}$$

Care should be taken always to use the original number, or the number of which the percentage is wanted, as the divisor in all percentage calculations. In the example just given, it is the percentage of gain over the old output 60 that is wanted, and not the percentage with relation to the new output 100. Mistakes are often made by overlooking this important point.

Interest

Interest is the money paid for the use of money lent for a certain time. *Simple* interest is the interest paid on the principal (money lent) only. When simple interest that is due is not paid, and its amount is added to the interest-bearing principal, the interest calculated on this new principal is called *compound* interest. The compounding of the interest into the principal may take place yearly or oftener, according to circumstances.

Simple Interest. — The following formulas are applicable to the calculations involving simple interest. Let:

P = principal or amount of money lent;
p = per cent of interest;
r = interest rate = the interest, expressed decimally, on \$1.00 for one year
   = the per cent of interest divided by 100; thus, if the interest is 6 per cent, the rate $r = \frac{6}{100} = 0.06$;
n = the number of years for which interest is calculated;
I = the amount of interest for n years at the given rate;
P_n = principal with interest for n years added, or the total amount after n years.

Then:
Interest for n years, $I = Prn$.
Total amount after n years, $P_n = P + Prn = P(1 + rn)$.
Interest rate $r = I \div Pn$.
Number of years $n = I \div Pr$.
Principal, or amount lent = $I \div rn$.

Example: — Assume that \$250 has been loaned for three years at 6 per cent simple interest. Then: $P = 250$; $p = 6$; $r = p \div 100 = 0.06$; $n = 3$.

$$I = Prn = 250 \times 0.06 \times 3 = \$45.$$
$$P_n = P + I = 250 + 45 = \$295.$$

The accurate interest for one day is $\frac{1}{365}$ of the interest for one year. Banks, however, customarily take the year as composed of 12 months of 30 days, making a total of 360 days to a year.

Compound Interest. — The following formulas are applicable when compound interest is to be computed, using the same notation as for simple interest, and assuming that the interest is compounded annually.

The total amount after n years, $P_n = P(1 + r)^n$.

The principal $P = \dfrac{P_n}{(1 + r)^n}$ The rate $r = \sqrt[n]{\dfrac{P_n}{P}} - 1$

The number of years during which the money is lent

$$n = \frac{\log P_n - \log P}{\log (1 + r)}$$

Logarithms are especially useful in calculating compound interest. To find the total amount P_n of principal and interest after n years, the formula just given can be transcribed as below:

$$\log P_n = \log P + n \log (1 + r).$$

If the interest is payable q times a year, it will be computed q times during each year, or nq times during n years. The rate for each compounding will be $r \div q$, if r is the annual rate. Hence, at the end of n years the amount due will be:

$$P_n = P \left(1 + \frac{r}{q} \right)^{nq}$$

Thus, if the term be five years, the interest be payable quarterly, and the annual rate be 6 per cent, then, $n = 5$; $q = 4$; $r = 0.06$; $r \div q = 0.06 \div 4 = 0.015$; and $nq = 5 \times 4 = 20$.

Example: — In what time will $500 become $1000 at 6 per cent interest compounded yearly?

$$P_n = 1000; \quad P = 500; \quad r = 0.06.$$

Substituting these values in the formula:

$$1000 = 500 \, (1 + 0.06)^n, \quad \text{or} \quad 2 = 1.06^n, \quad \text{and} \quad n \times \log 1.06 = \log 2.$$

Hence
$$n = \frac{0.30103}{0.02531} = 11.9 \text{ years.}$$

This is the number of years in which any principal will double itself at 6 per cent compound interest.

Present Value and Discount. — The present value V of a given amount due in a given time, is the sum which placed at interest for the given time, will produce the given amount. Hence,

At simple interest, $V = \dfrac{P_n}{1 + nr}$

At compound interest, $V = \dfrac{P_n}{(1 + r)^n}$

in which P_n is the amount due in n years time, and r is the rate of simple interest, or the per cent divided by 100.

The *true discount* D is the difference between the amount due at the end of n years and the present value, or,

At simple interest, $D = P_n - V = \dfrac{P_n nr}{1 + nr}$

At compound interest, $D = P_n - V = P_n \left[1 - \dfrac{1}{(1 + r)^n} \right]$

These formulas are for interest compounded annually. If the interest is payable and compounded semi-annually, or quarterly, modify the formulas as indicated in the formulas for compound interest.

Example: — Required the present value and discount of $500 due in six months at 6 per cent simple interest. Here, $P_n = 500$; $n = \frac{6}{12}$ years $= \frac{1}{2}$; $r = 0.06$; then,

$$V = \frac{500}{1 + 0.5 \times 0.06} = \$485.44.$$

$$D = 500 - 485.44 = \$14.56.$$

Example: — Required the sum which placed at 5 per cent compound interest, will in three years produce $5000. Here, $P_n = 5000$; $r = 0.05$; $n = 3$. Then,

$$V = \frac{5000}{(1 + 0.05)^3} = 4319.19.$$

Bank discount is calculated at simple interest on the total amount of a promissory note for the term of the note and on the basis of a year of 360 days.

Annuities. — An annuity is a fixed sum paid at regular intervals. In the formulas given below, yearly payments are assumed. It is customary to calculate annuities on the basis of compound interest.

If an annuity A is to be paid out for n consecutive years, the interest rate being r, then the present value P of the annuity is:

$$P = A \frac{(1 + r)^n - 1}{(1 + r)^n r}$$

Example: — If an annuity of $200 is to be paid for 10 years, what is the present amount of money that need be deposited if the interest is 5 per cent? Here,

$$A = 200; \quad r = 5 \div 100 = 0.05; \quad n = 10.$$

$$P = 200 \frac{1.05^{10} - 1}{1.05^{10} \times 0.05} = 1544.36.$$

The annuity that a principal P, drawing interest at the rate r, will give for a period of n years, is:

$$A = \frac{Pr(1 + r)^n}{(1 + r)^n - 1}$$

Example: — A sum of $10,000 is placed at 4 per cent interest. What is the amount of the annuity which can be paid for 20 years out of this sum? Here,

$$P = 10,000; \quad r = 0.04; \quad n = 20.$$

$$A = \frac{10,000 \times 0.04 \times 1.04^{20}}{1.04^{20} - 1} = 735.82.$$

If at the beginning of each year a sum A is set aside at an interest rate r, then the total value of the sum set aside, with interest, will be at the end of n years:

$$P_n = A \frac{(1 + r)[(1 + r)^n - 1]}{r}$$

If at the end of each year a sum A is set aside at an interest rate r, then the total value of the principal, with interest, at the end of n years will be:

$$P_n = A \frac{(1 + r)^n - 1}{r}$$

If a principal P is increased or decreased by a sum A at the end of each year, then the value of the principal after n years will be:

$$P_n = P(1 + r)^n \pm A \frac{(1 + r)^n - 1}{r}$$

If the sum A by which the principal P is decreased each year is greater than the total yearly interest on the principal, then the principal, with the accumulated interest, will be entirely used up in n years:

$$n = \frac{\log A - \log (A - Pr)}{\log (1 + r)}$$

Sinking Funds.—Amortization is "the extinction of a debt, usually by means of a sinking fund." The sinking fund is created by a fixed investment S placed annually at compound interest for a term of years, and is hence an annuity of sufficient size to produce at the end of the term of years the amount necessary for the repayment of the principal of the debt, or to provide a definite sum for other purposes. Let:

S = the annual investment;

r = rate of interest (the per cent divided by 100);

P = the amount of the sinking fund;

n = the number of years for its creation.

Then:

$$P = S \frac{(1 + r)^n - 1}{r}, \quad \text{and} \quad S = \frac{Pr}{(1 + r)^n - 1}$$

which formulas correspond to those given above, where a sum A was laid aside at the end of each year.

Example: — If $2000 is invested annually for 10 years, at 4 per cent compound interest, as a sinking fund, what would be the total amount of the fund at the expiration of the term? Here, $S = 2000$; $n = 10$; $r = 0.04$.

$$P = 2000 \frac{1.04^{10} - 1}{0.04} = 24{,}012.25$$

Alligation

When an alloy is composed of several metals varying in price, the price per pound of the alloy can be found as in the following example: An alloy is composed of 50 pounds of copper at 14 cents a pound, 10 pounds of tin at 29 cents a pound, 20 pounds of zinc at 5 cents a pound, and 5 pounds of lead at 4 cents a pound. What is the cost of the alloy per pound, no account being taken of the cost of mixing it?

Multiply the number of pounds of each of the ingredients by its price per pound, add these products together, and divide the sum by the total weight of all the ingredients. The quotient is the price per pound of the alloy.

$50 \times 14 + 10 \times 29 + 20 \times 5 + 5 \times 4 = 700 + 290 + 100 + 20 = 1110$.

Total weight of metal in alloy = $50 + 10 + 20 + 5 = 85$.

Price per pound of alloy = $1110/85 = 13$ cents, approximately.

In general, let a, b, c and d be the weights of each of the ingredients, and w, x, y and z be their respective values per unit weight. Then the average price P per unit weight of the alloy is found by the formula:

$$P = \frac{aw + bx + cy + dz}{a + b + c + d}$$

Example: — Find the average price per pound of an alloy containing 40 pounds of tin at 30 cents per pound, 48 pounds of lead at 4 cents per pound, 10 pounds of antimony at 8 cents per pound, and 2 pounds of copper at 15 cents per pound.

$$P = \frac{40 \times 30 + 48 \times 4 + 10 \times 8 + 2 \times 15}{40 + 48 + 10 + 2} = \frac{1502}{100} = 15.02 \text{ cents.}$$

Formulas for Arithmetical Progression

To Find	Given			Use Equation
a	d	l	n	$a = l - (n-1)\,d$
	d	n	S	$a = \dfrac{S}{n} - \dfrac{n-1}{2} \times d$
	d	l	S	$a = \dfrac{d}{2} \pm \dfrac{1}{2}\sqrt{(2\,l+d)^2 - 8\,dS}$
	l	n	S	$a = \dfrac{2\,S}{n} - l$
d	a	l	n	$d = \dfrac{l-a}{n-1}$
	a	n	S	$d = \dfrac{2\,S - 2\,an}{n\,(n-1)}$
	a	l	S	$d = \dfrac{l^2 - a^2}{2\,S - l - a}$
	l	n	S	$d = \dfrac{2\,nl - 2\,S}{n\,(n-1)}$
l	a	d	n	$l = a + (n-1)\,d$
	a	d	S	$l = -\dfrac{d}{2} \pm \dfrac{1}{2}\sqrt{8\,dS + (2\,a-d)^2}$
	a	n	S	$l = \dfrac{2\,S}{n} - a$
	d	n	S	$l = \dfrac{S}{n} + \dfrac{n-1}{2} \times d$
n	a	d	l	$n = 1 + \dfrac{l-a}{d}$
	a	d	S	$n = \dfrac{d - 2\,a}{2\,d} \pm \dfrac{1}{2\,d}\sqrt{8\,dS + (2\,a-d)^2}$
	a	l	S	$n = \dfrac{2\,S}{a+l}$
	d	l	S	$n = \dfrac{2\,l+d}{2\,d} \pm \dfrac{1}{2\,d}\sqrt{(2\,l+d)^2 - 8\,dS}$
S	a	d	n	$S = \dfrac{n}{2}\,[2\,a + (n-1)\,d]$
	a	d	l	$S = \dfrac{a+l}{2} + \dfrac{l^2 - a^2}{2\,d} = \dfrac{a+l}{2\,d}\,(l+d-a)$
	a	l	n	$S = \dfrac{n}{2}\,(a+l)$
	d	l	n	$S = \dfrac{n}{2}\,[2\,l - (n-1)\,d]$

Arithmetical Progression

An arithmetical progression is a series of numbers in which each consecutive term differs from the preceding one by a fixed amount called the *common difference,* *d*. Thus, 1, 3, 5, 7, etc., is an arithmetical progression where the difference *d* is 2. The difference in this case is *added* to the preceding term, and the progression is called increasing. In the series 13, 10, 7, 4, etc., the difference is (-3), and the progression is called decreasing. In any arithmetical progression (or part of progression) let

a = the first term considered;
l = the last term considered;
n = the number of terms;
d = the common difference;
S = the sum of n terms.

Then the general formulas are:

$$l = a + (n - 1)\,d \quad \text{and} \quad S = \frac{a + l}{2} \times n$$

In these formulas d is positive in an increasing and negative in a decreasing progression. When any three of the five quantities above are given, the other two can be found by the formulas in the accompanying table of arithmetical progression.
Example: — In an arithmetical progression, the first term equals 5, and the last term 40. The difference is 7. Find the sum of the progression.

$$S = \frac{a + l}{2\,d}\,(l + d - a) = \frac{5 + 40}{2 \times 7}\,(40 + 7 - 5) = 135.$$

Geometrical Progression

A geometrical progression or a geometrical series is a series in which each term is derived by multiplying the preceding term by a constant multiplier called the *ratio.* When the ratio is greater than 1, the progression is increasing; when smaller than 1, it is decreasing. Thus, 2, 6, 18, 54, etc., is an increasing geometrical progression with a ratio of 3, while 24, 12, 6, etc., is a decreasing progression with a ratio of ½.
In any geometrical progression (or part of progression) let

a = the first term;
l = the last (or nth) term;
n = the number of terms;
r = the ratio of the progression;
S = the sum of n terms.

Then the general formulas are:

$$l = ar^{n-1} \quad \text{and} \quad S = \frac{rl - a}{r - 1}$$

When any three of the five quantities above are given, the other two can be found by the formulas tabulated in the accompanying table. Geometrical progressions are used for finding the successive speeds in machine tool drives, in interest calculations, etc.
Example: — The lowest speed of a lathe is 20 R.P.M. The highest speed is 225 R.P.M. There are 18 speeds. Find the ratio between successive speeds.

$$\text{Ratio, } r = \sqrt[n-1]{\frac{l}{a}} = \sqrt[17]{\frac{225}{20}} = \sqrt[17]{11.25} = 1.153.$$

Formulas for Geometrical Progression

To Find	Given			Use Equation
a	l	n	r	$a = \dfrac{l}{r^{n-1}}$
	n	r	S	$a = \dfrac{(r-1)S}{r^n-1}$
	l	r	S	$a = lr - (r-1)S$
	l	n	S	$a(S-a)^{n-1} = l(S-l)^{n-1}$
l	a	n	r	$l = ar^{n-1}$
	a	r	S	$l = \dfrac{1}{r}[a + (r-1)S]$
	a	n	S	$l(S-l)^{n-1} = a(S-a)^{n-1}$
	n	r	S	$l = \dfrac{S(r-1)r^{n-1}}{r^n-1}$
n	a	l	r	$n = \dfrac{\log l - \log a}{\log r} + 1$
	a	r	S	$n = \dfrac{\log[a+(r-1)S] - \log a}{\log r}$
	a	l	S	$n = \dfrac{\log l - \log a}{\log(S-a)-\log(S-l)} + 1$
	l	r	S	$n = \dfrac{\log l - \log[lr-(r-1)S]}{\log r} + 1$
r	a	l	n	$r = \sqrt[n-1]{\dfrac{l}{a}}$
	a	n	S	$r^n = \dfrac{Sr}{a} + \dfrac{a-S}{a}$
	a	l	S	$r = \dfrac{S-a}{S-l}$
	l	n	S	$r^n = \dfrac{Sr^{n-1}}{S-l} - \dfrac{l}{S-l}$
S	a	n	r	$S = \dfrac{a(r^n-1)}{r-1}$
	a	l	r	$S = \dfrac{lr-a}{r-1}$
	a	l	n	$S = \dfrac{\sqrt[n-1]{l^n} - \sqrt[n-1]{a^n}}{\sqrt[n-1]{l} - \sqrt[n-1]{a}}$
	l	n	r	$S = \dfrac{l(r^n-1)}{(r-1)r^{n-1}}$

Greek Letters

The Greek letters are frequently used in mathematical expressions and formulas. The Greek alphabet is given below.

A	α	Alpha	H	η	Eta	N	ν	Nu	T	τ	Tau
B	β	Beta	Θ	ϑ θ	Theta	Ξ	ξ	Xi	Υ	υ	Upsilon
Γ	γ	Gamma	I	ι	Iota	O	o	Omicron	Φ	ϕ	Phi
Δ	δ	Delta	K	κ	Kappa	Π	π	Pi	X	χ	Chi
E	ϵ	Epsilon	Λ	λ	Lambda	P	ρ	Rho	Ψ	ψ	Psi
Z	ζ	Zeta	M	μ	Mu	Σ	σ s	Sigma	Ω	ω	Omega

Positive and Negative Numbers

The degrees on a thermometer scale extending upward from the zero point may be called *positive* and may be preceded by a plus sign; thus $+5$ degrees means 5 degrees above zero. The degrees below zero may be called *negative* and may be preceded by a minus sign; thus -5 degrees means 5 degrees below zero. In the same way, the ordinary numbers 1, 2, 3, etc., which are larger than 0, are called positive numbers; but numbers can be conceived of as extending in the other direction from 0, numbers that, in fact, are less than 0, and these are called negative. As these numbers must be expressed by the same figures as the positive numbers they are designated by a minus sign placed before them, thus: (-3). A negative number should always be enclosed within parentheses whenever it is written in line with other numbers; for example: $17 + (-13) - 3 \times (-0.76)$.

Negative numbers are most commonly met with in the use of logarithms and natural trigonometric functions. The following rules govern calculations with negative numbers.

A negative number can be added to a positive number by subtracting its numerical value from the positive number.

Example: $\qquad 4 + (-3) = 4 - 3 = 1.$

A negative number can be subtracted from a positive number by adding its numerical value to the positive number.

Example: $\qquad 4 - (-3) = 4 + 3 = 7.$

A negative number can be added to a negative number by adding the numerical values and making the sum negative.

Example: $\qquad (-4) + (-3) = -7.$

A negative number can be subtracted from a negative number by subtracting the numerical values and making the difference negative.

Example: $\qquad (-4) - (-3) = -1.$

If in a subtraction the number to be subtracted is larger than the number from which it is to be subtracted, the calculation can be carried out by subtracting the smaller number from the larger, and indicating that the remainder is negative.

Example: $\qquad 3 - 5 = -(5 - 3) = -2.$

When a positive number is to be multiplied or divided by a negative number, multiply or divide the numerical values as usual; the product or quotient, respectively, is negative. The same rule is true if a negative number is multiplied or divided by a positive number.

Examples: $\qquad 4 \times (-3) = -12; \quad (-4) \times 3 = -12;$
$\qquad\qquad 15 (-3) = -5; \quad (-15) \div 3 = -5.$

When two negative numbers are to be multiplied by each other, the product is positive. When a negative number is divided by a negative number, the quotient is positive.

Examples: $(-4) \times (-3) = 12$; $(-4) \div (-3) = 1.333$.

The two last rules are often expressed for memorizing as follows: "Equal signs make plus, unequal signs make minus."

Powers and Roots

The *square* of a number (or quantity) is the product of that number multiplied by itself. Thus, the square of 9 is $9 \times 9 = 81$. The square of a number is indicated by the *exponent* (^{2}), thus: $9^2 = 9 \times 9 = 81$.

The *cube* or *third power* of a number is the product obtained by using that number as a factor three times. Thus, the cube of 4 is $4 \times 4 \times 4 = 64$, and is written 4^3.

If a number is used as a factor four or five times, respectively, the product is the fourth or fifth power. Thus $3^4 = 3 \times 3 \times 3 \times 3 = 81$, and $2^5 = 2 \times 2 \times 2 \times 2 \times 2 = 32$. A number can be raised to any power by using it as a factor the required number of times.

The *square root* of a given number is that number which, when multiplied by itself, will give a product equal to the given number. The square root of 16 (written $\sqrt{16}$) equals 4, because $4 \times 4 = 16$.

The *cube root* of a given number is that number which, when used as a factor three times, will give a product equal to the given number. Thus, the cube root of 64 (written $\sqrt[3]{64}$) equals 4, because $4 \times 4 \times 4 = 64$.

The fourth, fifth, etc., roots of a given number are those numbers which when used as factors four, five, etc., times, will give as a product the given number. Thus $\sqrt[4]{16} = 2$, because $2 \times 2 \times 2 \times 2 = 16$.

The multiplications required for raising numbers to powers and the extracting of roots are greatly facilitated by the use of logarithms. The extracting of the square root and cube root by the regular arithmetical methods is a slow and cumbersome operation, and any roots can be more rapidly found by using logarithms.

The tables of squares and cubes, and square roots and cube roots, found at the beginning of this book, give these values directly for all whole numbers up to 2000. For ordinary practical calculations the squares, cubes, etc., for fractional values between whole numbers can usually be estimated. These tables also give the *reciprocals* of numbers from 1 to 2000. The reciprocal of a number is the quotient obtained by dividing 1 by the number. Thus the reciprocal of 4 is $1 \div 4 = 0.25$. The reciprocal values given in the tables can be used to save labor in division, as the quotient can be obtained by multiplying the dividend by the reciprocal of the divisor. Thus, the reciprocal of 244 is 0.0040984. To divide 13 by 244, or to reduce $13\frac{3}{244}$ to a decimal, multiply as follows: $13 \times 0.0040984 = 0.0532792$.

As the numbers in the second column of the tables, are the *squares* of the numbers in the first, it follows that the numbers in the first column are the *square roots* of the numbers in the second column. Similarly the numbers in the first column are the *cube roots* of the numbers or *cubes* in the third column. Hence the tables may be used for finding the roots of numbers beyond the direct range of the tables.

Example: — Find the square root of 9253 using the table. The table shows that 9216 is the square of 96; hence it is evident that the square root of the given number is a little over 96.

In the column of squares of numbers find a number the first four figures of which are nearest to the four figures in the given number. Thus, on page 21 we find in the column of squares the number 925444. The first four figures are within one of equalling the given number and this is the square of a number beginning with the figures 9 and 6; therefore the square root of 9253 is 96.2 nearly. The square root of 9253, accurate to three decimal places, is 96.192 so that the result obtained by the table is nearly correct. The indirect method of using the tables for determining *cube roots* is similar in principle to that just described for square roots.

Preferred Numbers

Preferred numbers are series of numbers selected to be used for standardization purposes in preference to any other numbers. Their use will lead to simplified practice and they should be employed whenever possible for individual standard sizes and ratings, or for a series, in applications similar to the following:

1. Important or characteristic linear dimensions, such as diameters and lengths, areas, volume, weights, capacities.

2. Ratings of machinery and apparatus in horsepower, kilowatts, kilovolt-amperes, voltages, currents, speeds, power-factors, pressures, heat units, temperatures, gas or liquid-flow units, weight-handling capacities, etc.

3. Characteristic ratios of figures for all kinds of units.

Preferred Numbers System: In order to facilitate the standardization of a series of sizes or ratings along logical and rational lines, preferred numbers have been selected to have definite relations to one another. The International System, which has been approved by the American Standards Association, covers the so-called " 5-, 10-, 20- and 40-series," and in the range from 10 to 100, the numbers are as follows:

5-series: This series gives 5 numbers approximately 60 per cent apart. These are 10, 16, 25, 40, and 63.

10-series: This series gives 10 numbers approximately 25 per cent apart. These are 10, 12.5, 16, 20, 25, 31.5, 40, 50, 63, and 80.

20-series: This series gives 20 numbers approximately 12 per cent apart. These are 10, 11.2, 12.5, 14, 16, 18, 20, 22.4, 25, 28, 31.5, 35.5, 40, 45, 50, 56, 63, 71, 80, and 90.

40-series: This series gives 40 numbers approximately 6 per cent apart. These are 10, 10.6, 11.2, 11.8, 12.5, 13.2, 14, 15, 16, 17, 18, 19, 20, 21.2, 22.4, 23.6, 25, 26.5, 28, 30, 31.5, 33.5, 35.5, 37.5, 40, 42.5, 45, 47.5, 50, 53, 56, 60, 63, 67, 71, 75, 80, 85, 90, and 95.

Preferred numbers above 100 are obtained by multiplying the given numbers by 10, 100, etc. Numbers below 10 are obtained by dividing by 10, 100, etc.

The American Standard includes a fractional system of preferred numbers over a limited range. It is based on the same general principle and may be used for linear dimensions in inches, where fractions are in such common use that decimals could not be applied readily. There is also an 80-series having 3 per cent steps and a supplementary series.

Theoretical Basis for the Preferred Numbers System: Preferred numbers are based on geometrical series. Using 10 as the first number of the series, the other theoretically exact numbers of any series are obtained by multiplying (or dividing) the first number by the constant factor applying to the particular series and repeating this operation with each resultant number. These factors are established as follows:

For the 5 series, the factor is the fifth root of 10, or 1.5849.
For the 10 series, the factor is the tenth root of 10, or 1.2589.
For the 20 series, the factor is the twentieth root of 10, or 1.1220.
For the 40 series, the factor is the fortieth root of 10, or 1.0593.

Principal Algebraic Expressions and Formulas

$$a \times a = aa = a^2$$
$$a \times a \times a = aaa = a^3$$
$$a \times b = ab$$

$$a^2b^2 = (ab)^2$$

$$a^2a^3 = a^{2+3} = a^5$$
$$a^4 \div a^3 = a^{4-3} = a$$
$$a^0 = 1$$
$$a^2 - b^2 = (a+b)(a-b)$$
$$(a+b)^2 = a^2 + 2ab + b^2$$

$$(a-b)^2 = a^2 - 2ab + b^2$$

$$\frac{a^3}{b^3} = \left(\frac{a}{b}\right)^3$$

$$\frac{1}{a^3} = \left(\frac{1}{a}\right)^3 = a^{-3}$$

$$(a^2)^3 = a^{2 \times 3} = (a^3)^2 = a^6$$
$$a^3 + b^3 = (a+b)(a^2 - ab + b^2)$$
$$a^3 - b^3 = (a-b)(a^2 + ab + b^2)$$
$$(a+b)^3 = a^3 + 3a^2b + 3ab^2 + b^3$$
$$(a-b)^3 = a^3 - 3a^2b + 3ab^2 - b^3$$

$$\sqrt{a} \times \sqrt{a} = a$$
$$\sqrt[3]{a} \times \sqrt[3]{a} \times \sqrt[3]{a} = a$$
$$(\sqrt[3]{a})^3 = a$$
$$\sqrt[3]{a^2} = (\sqrt[3]{a})^2 = a^{\frac{2}{3}}$$
$$\sqrt[4]{\sqrt[3]{a}} = \sqrt[4 \times 3]{a} = \sqrt[3]{\sqrt[4]{a}}$$

$$\sqrt{a} + \sqrt{b} = \sqrt{a + b + 2\sqrt{ab}}$$
$$\sqrt[3]{ab} = \sqrt[3]{a} \times \sqrt[3]{b}$$
$$\sqrt[3]{\frac{a}{b}} = \frac{\sqrt[3]{a}}{\sqrt[3]{b}}$$
$$\sqrt[3]{\frac{1}{a}} = \frac{1}{\sqrt[3]{a}} = a^{-\frac{1}{3}}$$

When
$$a \times b = x, \quad \text{then} \quad \log a + \log b = \log x$$
$$a \div b = x, \quad \text{then} \quad \log a - \log b = \log x$$
$$a^3 = x, \quad \text{then} \quad 3 \log a = \log x$$
$$\sqrt[3]{a} = x, \quad \text{then} \quad \frac{\log a}{3} = \log x$$

Equations

An equation is a statement of equality between two expressions, as $5x = 105$. The unknown quantity in an equation is generally designated by the letter x. If there is more than one unknown quantity, the others are designated by letters also selected at the end of the alphabet, as y, z, u, t, etc.

An equation of the first degree is one which contains the unknown quantity only in the first power, as $3x = 9$. A quadratic equation is one which contains the unknown quantity in the second, but no higher, power, as $x^2 + 3x = 10$.

Solving Equations of the First Degree with One Unknown. — Transpose all the terms containing the unknown x to one side of the equals sign, and all the other terms to the other side. Combine and simplify the expressions as far as possible, and divide both sides by the coefficient of the unknown x. (See the rules given for transposition of formulas.)

Example:
$$22x - 11 = 15x + 10$$
$$22x - 15x = 10 + 11$$
$$7x = 21$$
$$x = 3$$

Solution of Equations of the First Degree with Two Unknowns. — The form of the simplified equations is:

$$ax + by = c$$
$$a_1x + b_1y = c_1$$

Then,

$$x = \frac{cb_1 - c_1b}{ab_1 - a_1b} \qquad y = \frac{ac_1 - a_1c}{ab_1 - a_1b}$$

Example:

$$3x + 4y = 17$$
$$5x - 2y = 11$$

$$x = \frac{17 \times (-2) - 11 \times 4}{3 \times (-2) - 5 \times 4} = \frac{-34 - 44}{-6 - 20} = \frac{-78}{-26} = 3.$$

The value of y can now be most easily found by inserting the value of x in one of the equations:

$$5 \times 3 - 2y = 11; \quad 2y = 15 - 11 = 4; \quad y = 2.$$

Solution of Quadratic Equations with One Unknown. — If the form of the equation is $ax^2 + bx + c = 0$, then

$$x = \frac{-b \pm \sqrt{b^2 - 4ac}}{2a}$$

Example: Given the equation, $1x^2 + 6x + 5 = 0$, then $a = 1$; $b = 6$ and $c = 5$.

$$x = \frac{-6 \pm \sqrt{6^2 - 4 \times 1 \times 5}}{2 \times 1} = \frac{(-6) + 4}{2} = -1; \text{ or } \frac{(-6) - 4}{2} = -5$$

If the form of the equation is $ax^2 + bx = c$, then

$$x = \frac{-b \pm \sqrt{b^2 + 4ac}}{2a}$$

Example: A right-angle triangle has a hypotenuse 5 inches long and one side which is one inch longer than the other; find the lengths of the two sides.

Let x = one side and $x + 1$ = other side; then $x^2 + (x + 1)^2 = 5^2$ or $x^2 + x^2 + 2x + 1 = 25$; or $2x^2 + 2x = 24$; or $x^2 + x = 12$. Now referring to the basic formula, $ax^2 + bx = c$, we find, in this case, that $a = 1$; $b = 1$, and $c = 12$; hence

$$x = \frac{-1 \pm \sqrt{1 + 4 \times 1 \times 12}}{2 \times 1} = \frac{(-1) + 7}{2} = 3 \text{ or } x = \frac{(-1) - 7}{2} = -4$$

Since the positive value (3) would apply in this case, the lengths of the two sides are $x = 3$ inches and $x + 1 = 4$ inches.

Cubic Equations. — If the given equation has the form: $x^3 + ax + b = 0$, then

$$x = \left(-\frac{b}{2} + \sqrt{\frac{a^3}{27} + \frac{b^2}{4}}\right)^{\frac{1}{3}} + \left(-\frac{b}{2} - \sqrt{\frac{a^3}{27} + \frac{b^2}{4}}\right)^{\frac{1}{3}}$$

The equation $x^3 + px^2 + qx + r = 0$, may be reduced to the form $x_1^3 + ax_1 + b = 0$ by substituting $x_1 - \frac{p}{3}$ for x in the given equation.

THE SLIDE-RULE

By means of the slide-rule, various calculations may be made mechanically with greater ease and rapidity than by ordinary arithmetical methods, and usually with sufficient accuracy for all practical requirements. Slide-rules are used principally for performing multiplication and division, but they may also be used for finding powers, roots, and trigonometrical functions, and for various other purposes. The slide-rule in its most common form consists of three main parts. There is a main body or rule, a slide, and a runner or "cursor." Scales *A* and *D* (see Fig. 1) are on the rule, and scales *B* and *C* on the slide. Fig. 1 shows the right-hand half of the rule and the left-hand half of the slide, this sectional view being shown in order to secure a larger reproduction. The runner, which is in the form of a light metal frame that is free to slide endwise along the rule, is also shown in Fig. 1. Scales *A* and *B* are alike, as are scales *C* and *D*. All four scales are of the same length, but the graduations on scales *A* and *B* are different from those on scales *C* and *D*. The graduation 1 (seen at the extreme left in Fig. 1) is in the center of the rule, and scale *A* has two parts on opposite sides of this middle point 1 that are graduated exactly alike. The left-hand half from 1 to 1 is called the *left-hand A scale*, and the right-hand half from 1 to 1, the *right-hand A scale*. As scale *B* is exactly like scale *A*, its sections are designated as the *left-hand B scale* and the *right-hand B scale*. Each end of each scale is marked by the figure 1 which is known as the *index*. Thus, the figure 1 at the left-hand end of a scale is called the *left-hand index*, and figure 1 at the right-hand end is called the *right-hand index*.

As will be seen, the divisions on a slide-rule are not uniform. For example, that part of the left-hand *D* scale between divisions 1 and 2 (see enlarged detailed view, Fig. 2) is divided into ten main parts, no two of which are equal. Nevertheless, each of these main spaces represents 0.1. Each main space is subdivided into ten unequal parts, each of which represents one-tenth of 0.1, or 0.01. On the scales *A* and *B*, each of the ten main spaces between 1 and 2 is divided into only five parts; therefore, each subdivision represents 0.02. It is not possible to divide the spaces between graduations 4 and 5, 6 and 7, 8 and 9, etc., into as many parts as between 1 and 2, or 2 and 3, because the graduation lines would be too close together; therefore, the subdivisions near the right-hand end of any of the scales represent greater values than those near the left-hand end. This fact must be kept in mind or errors will result in the use of the slide-rule.

Reading the Slide-rule Graduations. — The method of reading the graduations is indicated in Fig. 2. A small figure 1 to the right of the left-hand index 1, represents the value 1.1, the small figure 2 marks the line that represents 1.2, and so on, to the small figure 9, which denotes 1.9. The second line to the right of the left-hand index denotes 1.02, as it is the second of the ten marks between 1 and 1.1. Several other lines at different points of the scale have the values indicated. It will be noticed that in each case the reading is accurate to at least three figures, and in some cases to four. The divisions on all four of the scales on the slide-rule are such that values can be read correctly to three figures; but beyond this it is not possible to proceed accurately, although the fourth figure may be obtained by estimating with the eye the fractional part of the subdivision. For instance, the fourth figure of the reading 1.535 is possible because the point is halfway between 1.53 and 1.54.

The values of these readings are based on the assumption that the left-hand index represents 1. The value of the left-hand index of any scale may be taken as any power of 0.1 or of 10; that is, it may be taken to represent 0.1, 0.01, 0.001, etc., or 10, 100, 1000, etc. If the left-hand index of the *D* scale represents 0.01, the readings in Fig. 2 must be multiplied by 0.01, so that they become 0.0102,

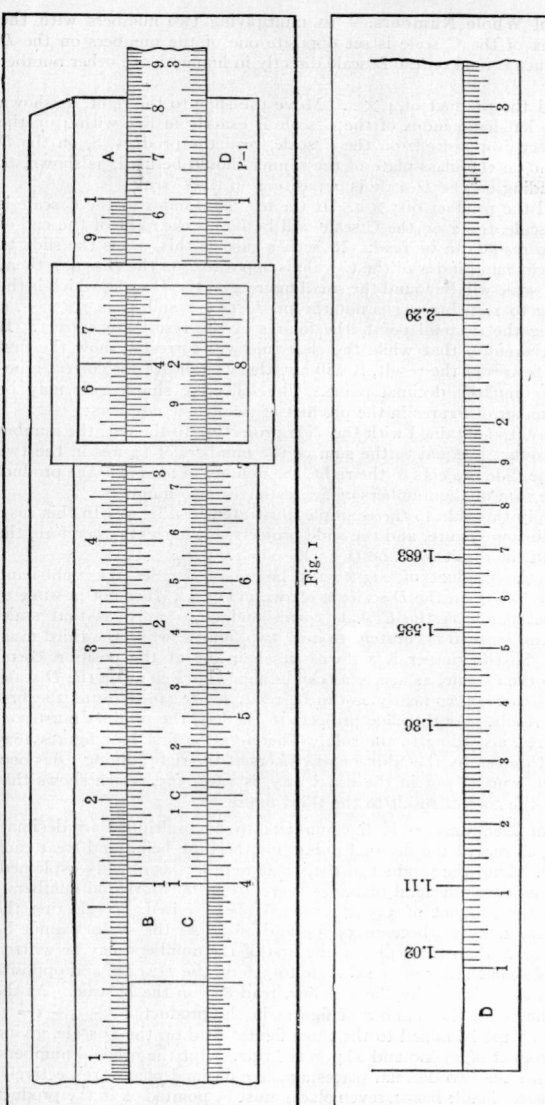

Fig. 1

Fig. 2

0.0111, 0.0136, 0.01535, 0.01683, and 0.0229. If the left-hand index represents 1000, the readings must be multiplied by 1000. When a value has been assigned to the index, the same ratio must be maintained throughout the remainder of the scale, a line on any scale always representing the same sequence of figures, but not always the same value. The scales C and D have a greater number of subdivisions between two consecutive numbers than have the scales A and B between the same numbers; therefore, it is customary to use the C and D scales for multiplications and divisions, as they can be read with greater ease and accuracy.

Multiplication of Whole Numbers. — In multiplying two numbers with the slide-rule, one index of the C scale is set opposite one of the numbers on the D scale, and the product is read on the D scale directly in line with the other number on the C scale.

Example: — Find the product of 4×2. Move the slide to the right, as shown in Fig. 1, until the left-hand index of the C scale is exactly in line with 4 on the D scale; then, directly opposite 2 on the C scale, read the product, 8, on the D scale. The hair-line on the glass plate of the runner should be used, as shown, to determine what reading on the D scale is opposite 2 on the C scale.

Example: — Find the product of 7×2. If the left-hand index of the C scale is set to 7 on the D scale, the 2 on the C scale will be far to the right of the end of the D scale, and no result can be read. In such a case as this, move the slide to the left until the right-hand index of the C scale is opposite 2 on the D scale; then, opposite 7 on the C scale will be found the small figure 4 on the D scale, which is the point corresponding to 1.4; but 1.4 is not the product of 7 and 2, as $7 \times 2 = 14$. However, neglecting the decimal point, the figures of the result are correct. It becomes evident, therefore, that while the slide-rule will correctly show the first two, three, or four figures of the result, it will not always indicate the correct number of figures preceding the decimal point. The following simple rule may be used to find the number of figures in the product of two whole numbers:

Rule: — If the result is obtained with the slide projecting to the left, the number of figures in the product is equal to the sum of the numbers of figures in the two numbers; but, if the slide projects to the right, the number of figures in the product is one less than the sum of the numbers of figures in the two numbers.

For instance, apply this rule to the example illustrated by Fig. 1. In this case, each number contains one figure, and the slide projects to the right; therefore, the number of figures in the result must be $(1 + 1) - 1 = 1$.

Example: — Let the product of 223×7285 be required. Set the right-hand index of the C scale to 223 on the D scale, as shown in Fig. 3. It is not possible to determine the exact point on the C scale corresponding to 7285, as that scale, between 7 and 8, can be read accurately to only two figures, while the third must be approximated. So the runner is set with its hair-line at the position corresponding to 729 on the C scale, as nearly as can be judged. Below, on the D scale, the hair-line points to 1625, as nearly as can be read; hence, 1625 forms the first four figures of the result. As the slide projects to the left, the product must contain $3 + 4 = 7$ figures, according to the rule. Therefore the first four figures 1625 must be increased to seven by the addition of ciphers at the right, giving 1,625,000. The actual product, worked out in the usual way, is 1,624,555, which shows that the slide-rule gives the correct result to the third figure.

Multiplication of Decimals. — If the numbers to be multiplied are decimals or mixed numbers, disregard the decimal points for the time being and treat each as a whole number. Find the product of the whole numbers as already explained, and then point off as many decimal places as there are in both original numbers.

Example: — Let the product of 335.75×0.00264 be required. Neglecting the decimal points, these numbers become 33,575 and 264. As the scales cannot be read accurately to more than three places, the first of the numbers may be written 33,600. Set the left-hand index of the C scale to 336 on the D scale, and opposite 264 on the C scale, as indicated by the hair-line, read 886 on the D scale. As the slide projects to the right, the number of figures in the product is $5 + 3 - 1 = 7$; that is, four ciphers must be added to the three figures read on the D scale, giving 8,860,000 as the product of 33,600 and 264 on the rule. But the original numbers, 335.75 and 0.00264, have two decimal places and five decimal places, respectively, or seven decimal places in all; hence, seven places must be pointed off in the product of the whole numbers, giving 0.8860000, or simply 0.886, as the required result.

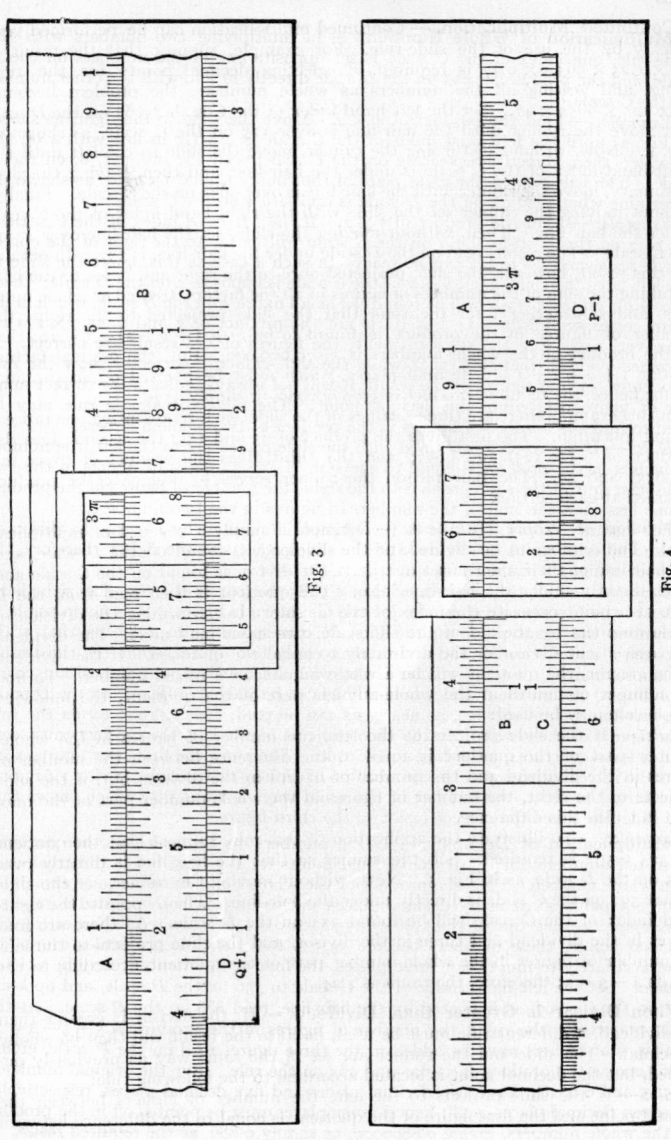

Fig. 3

Fig. 4

Continued Multiplication. — Continued multiplication can be performed very quickly by the use of the slide-rule. For example, suppose that the result of 6.3 × 1.25 × 965.5 × 0.47 is required. Neglecting decimal points for the time being, and writing all the numbers as whole numbers, the problem becomes 63 × 125 × 9655 × 47. Set the left-hand index of the C scale to 63 on the D scale and move the runner until the hair-line is over 125 on the C scale, as shown in Fig. 4. Now, without disturbing the runner, move the slide to the left until the right-hand index of the C scale is under the hair-line, and then, leaving the slide stationary, move the runner until the hair-line is over 9655 on the C scale. Finally, without moving the runner set the slide with the right-hand index of the C scale under the hair-line. Then, without moving the slide, set the hair-line over 47 on the C scale. The result, read on the D scale under the hair-line, is 357. In obtaining this result, however, the slide projected once to the right and twice to the left; so taking the sum of the numbers of figures in all the factors, treated as whole numbers, and subtracting 1 for the time that the slide projected to the right, the number of figures in the product is found to be $(2 + 3 + 4 + 2) - 1 = 10$; that is, the product of the whole numbers is 3,570,000,000. But, the original factors contain $1 + 2 + 1 + 2 = 6$ decimal places, which must be pointed off in the final result; hence, the required product is 3570.000000, or simply 3570.

In this example there are three settings of the slide, each representing one process of multiplication. The first gives the product of 63 and 125; the second gives the product of (63 × 125) and 9655; and the third gives the product of (63 × 125 × 9655) and 47. The hair-line on the runner serves to designate the product obtained at each setting.

Division of Whole Numbers. — Division is simply a reversal of multiplication. The number to be divided, or the dividend, is found on the D scale, and the hair-line of the runner is set over it. The divisor is found on the C scale and is set directly under the hair-line, also. The quotient is then read from the D scale at a point opposite the index of the C scale. In performing the division of whole numbers by the aid of the slide-rule, two cases may arise: The dividend may exceed the divisor or the divisor may exceed the dividend. If the dividend is the greater, the quotient will be a whole number or a mixed number. To find the number of figures in the whole-number part of the quotient, the following simple rule may be used:

Rule: — If the slide projects to the left, the number of figures in the whole-number part of the quotient is equal to the difference between the number of figures in the dividend and the number of figures in the divisor; but, if the slide projects to the right, the number of figures in the whole-number part of the quotient is 1 plus this difference.

Example: — To illustrate the application of this rule, suppose that the quotient of 1325 ÷ 592 is required. Set the runner so that the hair-line is directly over 1325 on the D scale, as in Fig. 5. Next, without moving the runner, set the slide so that 592 on the C scale is directly under the hair-line. Then, opposite the right-hand index of the C scale will be found 224 on the D scale. As there are four figures in the dividend and three in the divisor, and the slide projects to the left, the number of figures in the whole-number part of the quotient, according to the rule, is $4 - 3 = 1$; therefore, the result is 2.24.

When Divisor is Greater than Dividend. — If the divisor is greater than the dividend, a different rule must be used, because the result will then be wholly a decimal. The slide and the runner are set in the same way as previously described, but the decimal point is located according to the following rule:

Rule: — If the slide projects to the left, the number of ciphers between the decimal point and the first figure of the quotient is equal to the difference between

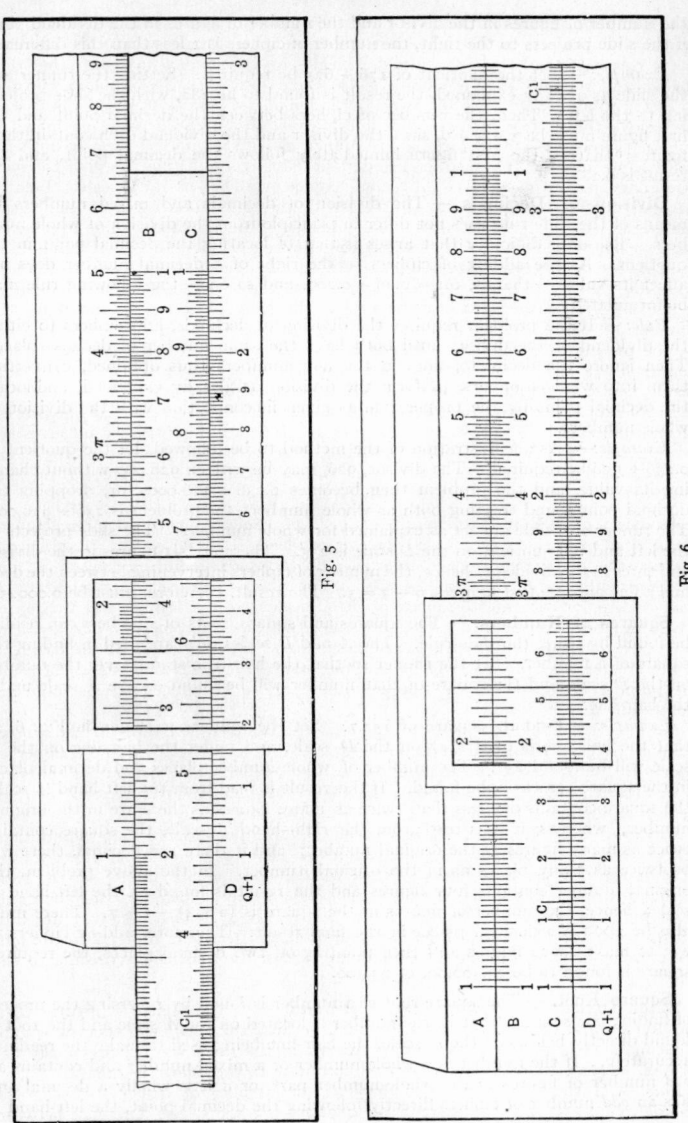

Fig. 5

Fig. 6

the number of figures in the divisor and the number of figures in the dividend; but, if the slide projects to the right, the number of ciphers is 1 less than this difference.

Example: — Let the quotient of 176 ÷ 625 be required. Setting the runner and the slide as already explained, the result is found to be 282, with the slide projecting to the left. Then, the number of ciphers between the decimal point and the first figure must be 3 − 3 = 0, since the divisor and the dividend each contain three figures; that is, the first figure immediately follows the decimal point, and the result is 0.282.

Division of Decimals. — The division of decimals and mixed numbers by means of the slide-rule does not differ in principle from the division of whole numbers. The only difficulty that arises is that of locating the decimal point in the quotient. As the adding of ciphers to the right of a decimal number does not affect its value — that is, 0.2 = 0.20 = 0.200, and so on — the following rule may be formulated:

Rule: — If the problem requires the division of decimals, add ciphers to either the dividend or the divisor until both have the same number of decimal places. Then ignore the decimal points in the new numbers thus obtained, converting them into whole numbers, perform the division as already explained, and locate the decimal point by the proper rule as given in connection with the division of whole numbers.

Example: — As an illustration of the method to be followed, let the quotient of 0.236 ÷ 926 be required. The divisor, 926, may be written 926.000 without changing its value, and the problem then becomes 0.236 ÷ 926.000; or, dropping the decimal points, and treating both as whole numbers, the problem is 236 ÷ 926,000. The runner and slide are set as explained for whole numbers. The slide projects to the left and the quotient on the *D* scale is 255. There are six figures in the divisor and three in the dividend; hence, the number of ciphers intervening between the decimal point and the first figure is 6 − 3 = 3. The result, therefore, must be 0.000255.

Squares of Numbers. — The squares and square roots of numbers can readily be found by using the slide-rule. The *A* and *D* scales only are used in finding the square of a number. Set the runner so that the hair-line stands over the number on the *D* scale and the square of that number will be found on the *A* scale under the hair-line.

Example: — Find the square of 152.7. Set the runner, as shown in Fig. 6, so that the hair-line is over 1527 on the *D* scale, and under the hair-line on the *A* scale will be found 233. The number of whole-number places and decimal places in the square can easily be found. If the result is read from the left-hand *A* scale, the square contains one less than twice as many figures as there are in the original number; whereas, if it is read from the right-hand *A* scale, the square contains twice as many figures as the original number; and if there is a decimal, there will be twice as many places as in the original number. In the above problem, the original number contains four figures and the result is found on the left-hand *A* scale; hence, the number of figures in the square is (2 × 4) − 1 = 7. There must also be 2 × 1 = 2 decimal places in the final result. Therefore, adding ciphers to 233 to make seven figures and then pointing off two decimal places, the required square is found to be 23,300.00, or 23,300.

Square Root. — The square root of a number is found by reversing the process of finding the square; that is, the number is located on the *A* scale and the root is found directly below, on the *D* scale, the hair-line being used to make the readings accurately. If the number is a whole number or a mixed number and contains an *odd* number of figures in the whole-number part, or if it is wholly a decimal and has an *odd* number of ciphers directly following the decimal point, the left-hand *A* scale must be used; in all other cases, the right-hand A scale is used. Let N represent the number of figures in the whole-number part, N' the number of ciphers directly following the decimal point, in the root, and n the same numbers in the original number. Then, if the left-hand A scale is used, $N = \frac{n+1}{2}$, and $N' = \frac{n-1}{2}$.

If the right-hand A scale is used, $N = N' = \frac{n}{2}$.

The finding of a square root is illustrated in Fig. 6.

Example: — Let the square root of 2.33 be required. As there is an odd number of figures in the whole-number part, the left-hand A scale is used, and below, on the D scale, 1527 is read. With the left-hand A scale in use, $N = \frac{n+1}{2} = \frac{1+1}{2} = 1$; hence, the square root is 1.527.

It is very probable that the number of figures preceding the decimal point, or the number of ciphers following the decimal point, in a square root can be determined more easily and quickly by inspection than by the foregoing rules, because by pointing off the given number into periods of two figures each, as taught in arithmetic, the desired information as to the location of the decimal point in the root can be seen at a glance. It is absolutely necessary, however, to use some form of rule, such as that given, to determine whether the left-hand or the right-hand A scale is to be used.

Cubes of Numbers. — Finding the cube of a number requires the use of all four scales. The index of the C scale is set to the given number on the D scale and, opposite the same number on the *left-hand* B scale, the cube is read from the A scale. Three cases may arise, as follows:

Case I. — The slide may project to the left and the cube be found on the left-hand A scale.

Case II. — The slide may project to the right and the cube be found on the right-hand A scale.

Case III. — The slide may project to the right and the cube be found on the left-hand A scale.

If the number contains a decimal, ignore the decimal point for the time being and treat it as a whole number. Let N represent the number of figures in the cube and n the number of figures in the given number. Then:

$$N = 3\,n, \text{ for Case I;}$$
$$N = 3\,n - 1, \text{ for Case II;}$$
$$N = 3\,n - 2, \text{ for Case III.}$$

After the total number of figures has been found by one of these rules, point off three times as many places as there are decimal places in the given number, and the result will be the required cube of the given number.

Example: — To illustrate, suppose that 36.8^3 is to be found. Treat it as a whole number, 368, and set the left-hand index of the C scale to 368 on the D scale, as in Fig. 7. Then, opposite 368 on the left-hand B scale will be found 5 on the A scale. As this setting falls under Case II, $N = (3 \times 3) - 1 = 8$; hence, the reading is 50,000,000. There is one decimal place in the given number, so that three places must be pointed off in the result, giving 50,000.000, or simply 50,000, as the required cube.

The cube can be found quite as readily by multiplying the number together three times; that is, $36.8^3 = 36.8 \times 36.8 \times 36.8$. This continued multiplication can be performed as previously described, and the position of the decimal point be determined by the rules given in that connection. This method will doubtless be found easier to remember than the one outlined above, involving three cases with as many different rules.

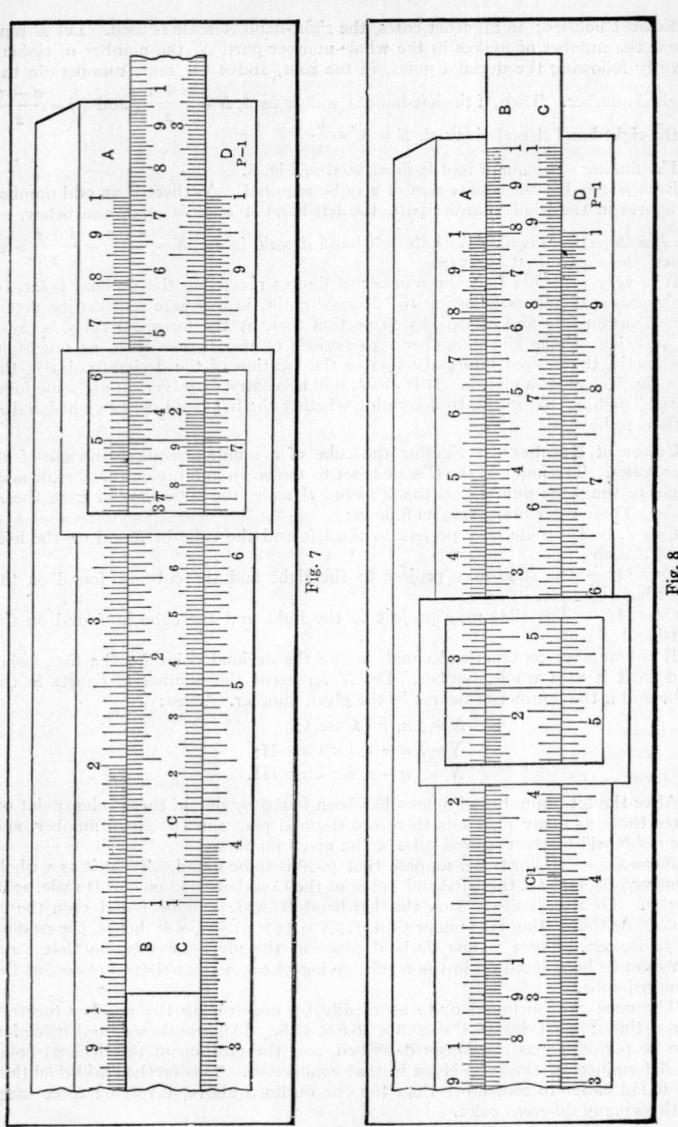

Fig. 7

Fig. 8

Cube Root. — The operation of finding the cube root is the reverse of finding the cube, and the method of determining the number of figures in the root, preceding or following the decimal point, is the same as that used in arithmetic; that is, the number is pointed off into periods of three figures each, beginning at the decimal point, and the root then contains one figure for each period or part of a period. If the number contains a decimal, add ciphers to the right of it, if necessary, so that the number of figures in the decimal part will be exactly divisible by 3, without a remainder. The scales and indexes to be used in finding the cube root depend upon the number of figures in the first period at the left, not counting ciphers when they *immediately* follow the decimal point. The rules to be followed are:

Case I. — If there are three figures in the first period, use the left-hand A scale and the right-hand index of the C scale.

Case II. — If there are two figures in the first period, use the right-hand A scale and the left-hand index of the C scale.

Case III. — If there is one figure in the first period, use the left-hand A scale and the left-hand index of the C scale.

Example: — Find the cube root of 0.05. Add ciphers to make three figures, giving 0.050, thus forming one period of three figures. This indicates that the first figure of the root immediately follows the decimal point. As there are two figures, 50, in the first period, "050," the right-hand A scale and the left-hand index of the C scale are used. Set the runner so that the hair-line is across 5 on the right-hand A scale, as in Fig. 7. Then move the slide until the reading on the B scale under the hair-line is exactly equal to that on the D scale opposite the left-hand index of the C scale. This reading on the D scale, 368, is the result required. The first figure of the root must follow the decimal point; therefore, the root is 0.368.

Diameters and Circumferences of Circles. — The ratio of the circumference of a circle to the diameter is $3.1416 = \pi$, and this value is marked by an extra line on the A and B scales, on many rules. It is used in finding the circumference from the diameter by multiplication, or the diameter from the circumference by division. In either instance, the A and B scales are used. The left-hand index of the B scale is set to π on the A scale, and opposite the given diameter on the B scale is read the circumference on the A scale; or, the value π on the B scale is set to the given circumference on the A scale, and opposite the index of the B scale the required diameter is read from the A scale. This multiplication or division is performed in exactly the same way as in using the C and D scales for the same kind of operation.

Areas of Circles. — The area of a circle is equal to 0.7854 times the square of the diameter; consequently, the value 0.7854 is marked by an extra line on the right-hand A and B scales on many rules. To find the area of a circle, having given the diameter, set the line 0.7854 of the B scale to either the left-hand or the right-hand index of the A scale and read the area from the B scale, above the given diameter on the D scale, the hair-line on the runner being used to transfer from D to B. If the area is given, set the slide as before, and read the required diameter from the D scale directly below the given area on the B scale. If the number of figures preceding the decimal point, or the number of ciphers immediately following the decimal point, in the area, is odd, use the left-hand B scale; otherwise, use the right-hand B scale.

Example: — Find the area of a circle $5\frac{1}{4}$ inches in diameter. Set the line marking 0.7854 on the B scale to the right-hand index of the A scale, as in Fig. 8, and above 5.25 on the D scale will be found 21.6 on the B scale; hence, the area is 21.6 square inches. The same setting, taken in reverse order, can be used to illustrate the method of finding the diameter of a circle the area of which is 21.6 square inches.

LOGARITHMS

The object of logarithms is to facilitate and shorten calculations involving multiplication, division, the extraction of roots and the obtaining of powers of numbers. A logarithm consists of two parts, a whole number and a decimal. The whole number, which may be either a positive or negative number, or zero, is called the *characteristic;* the decimal is called the *mantissa.* As a rule, the decimal or mantissa only is given in tables of logarithms. The characteristic is prefixed to the mantissa according to the following rules:

For 1 and for all numbers greater than 1, the characteristic is one less than the number of places to the left of the decimal point in the given number. For example, the characteristic of the logarithm of 237 is 2, and of 2536.5 is 3.

For numbers smaller than 1, that is for numbers wholly decimal, the characteristic is negative and its numerical value is one more than the number of ciphers between the decimal point and the first decimal which is not a cipher. For example, the characteristic of the logarithm of 0.036 is (− 2), and the characteristic of the logarithm of 0.0006 is (− 4). Instead of writing the minus sign (−) in front of the figure, as (− 2), it is frequently written over the figure, thus: ($\bar{2}$). This method

N.	L.	0	1	☐2	3	4		5	6	7	8	9		P. P.
400	☐60	206	217	228	239	249		260	271	282	293	304		
401		314	325	336	347	358		369	379	390	401	412		
402		423	433	444	455	466		477	487	498	509	520		
☐403		531	541	☐552	563	574		584	595	606	617	627		
404		638	649	660	670	681		692	703	713	724	735		

Fig. 1

is used because the minus sign refers only to the characteristic and not to the mantissa, which is always positive.

The logarithmic tables in the following give, in the body of the tables, the mantissa of the logarithms of numbers from 1 to 10,000. When finding the mantissa, the decimal point in a number is disregarded. The mantissa of the logarithms of 2716, 271.6, 27.16, 2.716, or 0.02716, for example, is the same. The tables give directly the mantissa of logarithms of numbers with four figures or less; the logarithms for numbers with more than four figures can be approximated.

To find the logarithm of a number from the tables, locate the first three figures of the number in the left-hand column, and then find the fourth figure at the top of the columns of the page. Then follow the column down from this last figure until opposite the three first figures in the left-hand column. The figure thus found in the body of the table is the mantissa of the logarithm. If the number of which the logarithm is required does not contain four figures, annex ciphers to the right so as to obtain four figures. If the mantissa of the logarithm of 6 is required, for example, find the mantissa for 6000.

Example: — Find the logarithm of 4032. Locate 403 in the left-hand column of the logarithmic tables, then follow downward the column headed "2" at the top of the page, and find the required mantissa opposite 403. The mantissa is .60552 the "group" figures 60 being found in the column under "L" and prefixed to the figures 552 found directly in the column under "2." The characteristic of the logarithm being 3, log 4032 = 3.60552. (See Fig. 1.)

All the mantissas, or the numbers in the tables, are decimals, and the decimal point has, therefore, been omitted in the tables, since no confusion could arise from this; but it should always be put before the figures of the mantissa as soon as taken from the table.

In the tables it will be found that, in some cases, the figures are preceded by the sign (∗). The sign (∗) indicates that the two figures to be prefixed are those given in the next line below that in which the last three figures are read. For example the logarithm of 5018 is 3.70053, the two figures to be prefixed being 70 and not 69 as would ordinarily be the case. (See Fig. 2.)

Finding a Number the Logarithm of which is Given.—When a logarithm is given and it is required to find the corresponding number, find the first two figures of the mantissa in the column headed " L " in the tables; then find in the group of mantissas, all having the same first two figures, the remaining three figures. These may appear in any of the columns headed "0" to "9". The number heading the column in which the last three figures of the mantissa are found is the last figure in the number sought, and the number in the left-hand column, headed " N," in line with the last three figures of the mantissa, gives the three first figures in the number sought. When the actual figures in the number sought have been deter-

N.	L. 0	1	2	3	4	5	6	7	8	9	P. P.
500	69 897	906	914	923	932	940	949	958	966	975	
501	984	992	∗001	∗010	∗018	∗027	∗036	∗044	∗053	∗062	
502	70 070	079	088	096	105	114	122	131	140	148	
503	157	165	174	183	191	200	209	217	226	234	
504	243	252	260	269	278	286	295	303	312	321	

Fig. 2

mined, locate the decimal point according to the rules given for the characteristic of logarithms. If the characteristic is greater than 3, add ciphers. For example, if the figures corresponding to a given mantissa are 3765 and the characteristic is 5, then the number sought has 6 figures to the left of the decimal point, and is 376,500. If the characteristic had been 3̄, then the number sought would, in this case, have been 0.003765. If the mantissa is not exactly obtainable in the tables, find the mantissa in the table which is the nearest to the one given and determine the number corresponding to this. In most cases, this gives results accurate enough. By interpolation, as will be explained later, more accurate results can be obtained.

If the three last figures of the mantissa, as found in the table, are preceded by a (∗), it indicates that these three figures belong to the group preceded by the two figures in the " L " column in the line next below.

Example: — Find the number the logarithm of which is 2.70053.

First find the two figures of the mantissa (70) in the column headed " L " in the tables. Then find the remaining three figures (053) in the mantissas which all have 70 for their first two figures. The (∗) in front of the figure ∗053 in the line next above that in which 70 is found indicates that these figures belong to the group preceded by 70. Therefore, the number corresponding to the logarithm 2.70053 is 501.8. (See Fig. 2.)

Avoiding Use of Negative Characteristics. — As previously explained, the logarithm of any number less than 1 has a negative characteristic and a positive mantissa. In many computations, the use of logarithms having negative characteristics is troublesome and frequently a source of error. A simple way to avoid this difficulty is to convert each logarithm having a negative characteristic into an equivalent logarithm having a positive characteristic. This is done according to the following method which is based on the principle that any number can be simultaneously added to and subtracted from the characteristic of a logarithm without changing its value, thus: Log $1 = 0.00000 = 10.00000 - 10$; log $0.3 = \overline{1}.47712 = 9.47712 - 10$; log $0.000478 = \overline{4}.67943 = 6.67943 - 10$. Usually 10 or 20 are added to and subtracted from the logarithmic characteristic, but any convenient number may be so used.

Multiplication by Logarithms. — If two or more numbers are to be multiplied together, find the logarithms of the numbers to be multiplied, and add these logarithms. The sum is the logarithm of the product, and the number corresponding to this logarithm, as found from the logarithmic tables, is the required product.

Example: — Find the product of $2831 \times 2.692 \times 29.69 \times 19.4$.

This calculation is carried out by means of logarithms as follows:

$$
\begin{array}{rl}
\log 2831. & = 3.45194 \\
\log \quad 2.692 & = 0.43008 \\
\log \quad 29.69 & = 1.47261 \\
\log \quad 19.4 & = 1.28780 \\
\hline
& 6.64243
\end{array}
$$

The product, as found from the tables, with ciphers added, then is 4,390,000.

In multiplication problems involving numbers less than 1, the method of avoiding the use of negative characteristics, previously outlined, simplifies the addition and tends to reduce the possibility of error. *Example:* Find the product of $0.002656 \times 155.1 \times 0.5853 \times 7.968$.

$$
\begin{array}{rll}
\log \quad 0.002656 & = \overline{3}.42423 = & 7.42423 - 10 \\
\log 155.1 & = 2.19061 = & 2.19061 \\
\log \quad 0.5853 & = \overline{1}.76738 = & 9.76738 - 10 \\
\log \quad 7.968 & = 0.90135 = & \underline{0.90135} \\
& & 20.28357 - 20 = 0.28357
\end{array}
$$

Hence $0.002656 \times 155.1 \times 0.5853 \times 7.968 = 1.9212$

Division by Logarithms. — When dividing one number by another, subtract the logarithm of the divisor from the logarithm of the dividend; the remainder is the logarithm of the quotient. *Example:* — To find the quotient of $7658 \div 935.3$.

$$
\begin{array}{rl}
\log 7658 & = \quad 3.88412 \\
-\log \ 935.3 & = \ -2.97095 \\
\hline
\log (7658 \div 935.3) & = \quad 0.91317
\end{array}
$$

Hence $7658 \div 935.3 = \quad 8.188$

Instead of dividing 7658 by 935.3, the same answer would be obtained if 7658 were *multiplied* by the reciprocal of 935.3 or $1 \div 935.3$. To do this by logarithms, the log of 7658 and the log of the reciprocal of 935.3 would be *added* together.

In order to use the method just outlined, it is necessary to know how to find the logarithm of the reciprocal of a number. This is done by simply subtracting the log of the number from the log of 1. To do this conveniently, some number, such as 10, is first added to and subtracted from the characteristic of the log of 1.

Example: — Find the log of the reciprocal of 935.3.

$$\begin{aligned}
\log \ 1 \ &= \ 0.00000 \ = \ 10.00000 \ - \ 10 \\
-\log 935.3 \ &= \ -2.97095 \ = \ -2.97095 \\
\hline
\log (1 \div 935.3) \ &= \qquad\quad 7.02905 \ - \ 10 \\
\log (1 \div 935.3) \ &= \qquad\quad \overline{3}.02905 \\
1 \div 935.3 \ &= \qquad\quad 0.001069
\end{aligned}$$

Thus the quotient of 7658 ÷ 935.3 can be found by adding the log of 7658 and the log of the reciprocal of 935.3:

$$\begin{aligned}
\log 7658 \ = \ 3.88412 \ &= \qquad 3.88412 \\
\log (1 \div 935.3) \ = \ \overline{3}.02905 \ &= \qquad 7.02905 \ - \ 10 \\
\hline
&\quad 10.91317 \ - \ 10 = 0.91317
\end{aligned}$$

Hence $7658 \div 935.3 = 8.188$

As is readily seen, this method is more cumbersome than the direct method, where there is only one factor each in the dividend and divisor, but it does greatly facilitate the solution of probems in division involving several factors in the dividend and the divisor. In such a problem the logarithm of each factor in the dividend is added to the logarithm of the reciprocal of each factor in the divisor.

Example: — Find the product of $\dfrac{0.0272 \times 27.1 \times 12.6}{2.371 \times 0.007}$

$$\begin{aligned}
\log \ 0.0272 \ &= \ \overline{2}.43457 \ = \ \ 8.43457 \ - \ 10 \\
\log \ 27.1 \ &= \ 1.43297 \ = \ \ 1.43297 \\
\log \ 12.6 \ &= \ 1.10037 \ = \ \ 1.10037 \\
\log (1 \div 2.371) \ &= \qquad\qquad\ \ 9.62507 \ - \ 10 \\
\log (1 \div 0.007) \ &= \qquad\qquad\ \ 2.15490 \\
\hline
&\qquad\qquad 22.74788 \ - \ 20 = 2.74788
\end{aligned}$$

Hence the result is 559.6.

In problems in division where the divisor is larger than the dividend, the subtraction of logarithms is facilitated if some number is added to and subtracted from the log of the dividend. (This is the same method used to convert a logarithm with a negative characteristic to an equivalent logarithm with a positive characteristic except that in this case it serves to convert a logarithm with a positive characteristic to one with a larger positive characteristic but having the same value.)

Example: — To find the quotient of 43.2 ÷ 971.4.

$$\begin{aligned}
\log \ 43.2 \ = \ \ 1.63548 \ &= \ 11.63548 \ - \ 10 \\
-\log 971.4 \ = \ -2.98740 \ &= \ -2.98740 \\
\hline
\log (43.2 \div 971.4) \ &= \ \ \ 8.64808 \ - \ 10 = \overline{2}.64808
\end{aligned}$$

Hence $43.2 \div 971.4 = 0.04447$

Obtaining the Powers of Numbers. — A number may be raised to any power by simply multiplying the logarithm of the number by the exponent of the number. The product gives the logarithm of the value of the power.

Example 1. — Find the value of 6.51^3.

$$\begin{aligned}
\log 6.51 \ &= \ 0.81358 \\
3 \times 0.81358 \ &= \ 2.44074
\end{aligned}$$

The logarithm 2.44074 is then the logarithm of 6.51^3. Hence 6.51^3 equals the number corresponding to this logarithm, as found from the tables, or $6.51^3 = 275.9$.

Example 2. — Find the value of $12^{1.29}$.

$$\log 12 = 1.07918$$

$$1.29 \times 1.07918 = 1.39214$$

Hence, $12^{1.29} = 24.67$.

The multiplication 1.29×1.07918 is carried out in the usual arithmetical way. The example above is one of a type which cannot be solved by any means except by the use of logarithms.

One difficulty is met with when raising a number less than 1 to a given power. The logarithm is then composed of a negative term, the characteristic, and a positive term, the mantissa. For example: Find the value 0.31^5. The logarithm of $0.31 = \bar{1}.49136$. The method, previously outlined, of avoiding the use of negative characteristics is helpful here. Thus $\bar{1}.49136 = 9.49136 - 10$. Then

$$9.49136 - 10$$
$$\underline{\times\ 5}$$
$$\log 0.31^5 = 47.45680 - 50 = \bar{3}.45680$$

Hence $0.31^5 = 0.002863$

Extracting Roots by Logarithms. — Roots of numbers, as for example $\sqrt[5]{37}$, can easily be extracted by means of logarithms. The small (5) in the radical ($\sqrt{\ }$) of the root-sign is called the index of the root. Any root of a number may be found by dividing its logarithm by the index of the root; the quotient is the logarithm of the root.

Example 1. —Find $\sqrt[3]{276}$.

$$\log 276 = 2.44091$$

$$2.44091 \div 3 = 0.81364$$

Hence $\log \sqrt[3]{276} = 0.81364$, and $\sqrt[3]{276} = 6.511$.

Example 2. — Find $\sqrt[3]{0.67}$.

$$\log 0.67 = \bar{1}.82607$$

In this case it is not possible to divide directly, because there is a negative characteristic and a positive mantissa. Here is another instance where the method of avoiding the use of negative characteristics, previously outlined, is helpful. The procedure in this case is to add and subtract some number to the characteristic which is evenly divisible by the index of the root. In this case the root index is 3. Thus 9 can be added to and subtracted from the characteristic, and the resulting logarithm divided by 3.

$$\log 0.67 = \bar{1}.82607 = 8.82607 - 9$$

$$\log \sqrt[3]{0.67} = \frac{8.82607 - 9}{3} = 2.94202 - 3$$

$$\log \sqrt[3]{0.67} = 2.94202 - 3 = \bar{1}.94202$$

Hence $\sqrt[3]{0.67} = 0.875$

Example 3. — Find $\sqrt[1.7]{0.2}$

$$\log 0.2 = \bar{1}.30103 = 16.30103 - 17$$

$$\log \sqrt[1.7]{0.2} = \frac{16.30103 - 17}{1.7} = 9.58884 - 10 = \bar{1}.58884$$

Hence $\sqrt[1.7]{0.2} = 0.388$

Interpolation. — If the number for which the logarithm is required consists of five figures, it is possible by means of the small tables in the right-hand column of the logarithmic tables, headed "P.P." (proportional parts), to obtain the logarithm more accurately than by taking the nearest value for four figures. The logarithm of 1524.2, for example, is found as follows:

First find the difference between the nearest larger and the nearest smaller logarithms in the table. Log 1524 = 3.18298 and log 1525 = 3.18327. (See Fig. 3.) The difference is 0.00029. Then in the small table headed "29" in the right-hand

N.	L. 0	1	2	3	4	5	6	7	8	9	P. P.	
150	17 609	638	667	696	725	754	782	811	840	869		
151	898	926	955	984	*013	*041	*070	*099	*127	*156	**29**	28
152	18 184	213	241	270	298	327	355	384	412	441	1 2,9	2,8
153	469	498	526	554	583	611	639	667	696	724	2 5,8	5,6
154	752	780	808	837	865	893	921	949	977	*005	3 8,7	8,4

Fig. 3

column, find the figure opposite 2 (2 being the last or fifth figure in the given number). This figure is 5.8. Add this to the mantissa of the smaller of the two logarithms already found, disregarding the decimal point in the mantissa, and considering it, for the while being, as a whole number. Then, 18298 + 5.8 = 18303.8, or approximately, 18304. This is the mantissa of the logarithm of 1524.2 and the complete logarithm is 3.18304.

To find a number more accurately than to four figures, when the mantissa cannot be found exactly in tne tables, find the mantissa which is nearest to, but less than, the given mantissa. Subtract this mantissa from the nearest larger mantissa in the tables and find in the right-hand column the small table headed by this differ-ence. Then subtract the nearest smaller mantissa from the given logarithm and find the exact or approximate difference in the "proportional part" table. The corresponding figure in the left-hand column of the "proportional part" table is the fifth figure in the number sought, the other four figures being those corresponding to the logarithm next smaller than the given logarithm. In accordance with this rule, the number corresponding to the logarithm 4.46262 is found to be 29,015.

Hyperbolic Logarithms. — In many calculations, notably those involving calculations of the mean effective pressure of steam in engine cylinders, use is made of logarithms termed *hyperbolic, Napierian*, or *natural*; the preferable name, and that most commonly used in the United States, is hyperbolic logarithms. The hyperbolic logarithms are usually designated "hyp. log." Sometimes the hyperbolic logarithm is also designated "$\log_e$" and "nat. log." Tables are given in the following for hyperbolic logarithms from 1 to 100.

To convert the common logarithms to hyperbolic logarithms, the former should be multiplied by 2.30258. To convert hyperbolic logarithms to common logarithms, multiply by 0.43429. Hyperbolic logarithms find extensive use in higher mathematics.

Tables of Logarithms

N.	L.	0	1	2	3	4	5	6	7	8	9
100	00	000	043	087	130	173	217	260	303	346	389
101		432	475	518	561	604	647	689	732	775	817
102		860	903	945	988	*030	*072	*115	*157	*199	*242
103	01	284	326	368	410	452	494	536	578	620	662
104		703	745	787	828	870	912	953	995	*036	*078
105	02	119	160	202	243	284	325	366	407	449	490
106		531	572	612	653	694	735	776	816	857	898
107		938	979	*019	*060	*100	*141	*181	*222	*262	*302
108	03	342	383	423	463	503	543	583	623	663	703
109		743	782	822	862	902	941	981	*021	*060	*100
110	04	139	179	218	258	297	336	376	415	454	493
111		532	571	610	650	689	727	766	805	844	883
112		922	961	999	*038	*077	*115	*154	*192	*231	*269
113	05	308	346	385	423	461	500	538	576	614	652
114		690	729	767	805	843	881	918	956	994	*032
115	06	070	108	145	183	221	258	296	333	371	408
116		446	483	521	558	595	633	670	707	744	781
117		819	856	893	930	967	*004	*041	*078	*115	*151
118	07	188	225	262	298	335	372	408	445	482	518
119		555	591	628	664	700	737	773	809	846	882
120		918	954	990	*027	*063	*099	*135	*171	*207	*243
121	08	279	314	350	386	422	458	493	529	565	600
122		636	672	707	743	778	814	849	884	920	955
123		991	*026	*061	*096	*132	*167	*202	*237	*272	*307
124	09	342	377	412	447	482	517	552	587	621	656
125		691	726	760	795	830	864	899	934	968	*003
126	10	037	072	106	140	175	209	243	278	312	346
127		380	415	449	483	517	551	585	619	653	687
128		721	755	789	823	857	890	924	958	992	*025
129	11	059	093	126	160	193	227	261	294	327	361
130		394	428	461	494	528	561	594	628	661	694
131		727	760	793	826	860	893	926	959	992	*024
132	12	057	090	123	156	189	222	254	287	320	352
133		385	418	450	483	516	548	581	613	646	678
134		710	743	775	808	840	872	905	937	969	*001
135	13	033	066	098	130	162	194	226	258	290	322
136		354	386	418	450	481	513	545	577	609	640
137		672	704	735	767	799	830	862	893	925	956
138		988	*019	*051	*082	*114	*145	*176	*208	*239	*270
139	14	301	333	364	395	426	457	489	520	551	582
140		613	644	675	706	737	768	799	829	860	891
141		922	953	983	*014	*045	*076	*106	*137	*168	*198
142	15	229	259	290	320	351	381	412	442	473	503
143		534	564	594	625	655	685	715	746	776	806
144		836	866	897	927	957	987	*017	*047	*077	*107
145	16	137	167	197	227	256	286	316	346	376	406
146		435	465	495	524	554	584	613	643	673	702
147		732	761	791	820	850	879	909	938	967	997
148	17	026	056	085	114	143	173	202	231	260	289
149		319	348	377	406	435	464	493	522	551	580
150		609	638	667	696	725	754	782	811	840	869

P.P.

	44	43	42
1	4.4	4.3	4.2
2	8.8	8.6	8.4
3	13.2	12.9	12.6
4	17.6	17.2	16.8
5	22.0	21.5	21.0
6	26.4	25.8	25.2
7	30.8	30.1	29.4
8	35.2	34.4	33.6
9	39.6	38.7	37.8

	41	40	39
1	4.1	4.0	3.9
2	8.2	8.0	7.8
3	12.3	12.0	11.7
4	16.4	16.0	15.6
5	20.5	20.0	19.5
6	24.6	24.0	23.4
7	28.7	28.0	27.3
8	32.8	32.0	31.2
9	36.9	36.0	35.1

	38	37	36
1	3.8	3.7	3.6
2	7.6	7.4	7.2
3	11.4	11.1	10.8
4	15.2	14.8	14.4
5	19.0	18.5	18.0
6	22.8	22.2	21.6
7	26.6	25.9	25.2
8	30.4	29.6	28.8
9	34.2	33.3	32.4

	35	34	33
1	3.5	3.4	3.3
2	7.0	6.8	6.6
3	10.5	10.2	9.9
4	14.0	13.6	13.2
5	17.5	17.0	16.5
6	21.0	20.4	19.8
7	24.5	23.8	23.1
8	28.0	27.2	26.4
9	31.5	30.6	29.7

	32	31	30
1	3.2	3.1	3.0
2	6.4	6.2	6.0
3	9.6	9.3	9.0
4	12.8	12.4	12.0
5	16.0	15.5	15.0
6	19.2	18.6	18.0
7	22.4	21.7	21.0
8	25.6	24.8	24.0
9	28.8	27.9	27.0

Tables of Logarithms

N.	L.	0	1	2	3	4	5	6	7	8	9
150	17	609	638	667	696	725	754	782	811	840	869
151		898	926	955	984	*013	*041	*070	*099	*127	*156
152	18	184	213	241	270	298	327	355	384	412	441
153		469	498	526	554	583	611	639	667	696	724
154		752	780	808	837	865	893	921	949	977	*005
155	19	033	061	089	117	145	173	201	229	257	285
156		312	340	368	396	424	451	479	507	535	562
157		590	618	645	673	700	728	756	783	811	838
158		866	893	921	948	976	*003	*030	*058	*085	*112
159	20	140	167	194	222	249	276	303	330	358	385
160		412	439	466	493	520	548	575	602	629	656
161		683	710	737	763	790	817	844	871	898	925
162		952	978	*005	*032	*059	*085	*112	*139	*165	*192
163	21	219	245	272	299	325	352	378	405	431	458
164		484	511	537	564	590	617	643	669	696	722
165		748	775	801	827	854	880	906	932	958	985
166	22	011	037	063	089	115	141	167	194	220	246
167		272	298	324	350	376	401	427	453	479	505
168		531	557	583	608	634	660	686	712	737	763
169		789	814	840	866	891	917	943	968	994	*019
170	23	045	070	096	121	147	172	198	223	249	274
171		300	325	350	376	401	426	452	477	502	528
172		553	578	603	629	654	679	704	729	754	779
173		805	830	855	880	905	930	955	980	*005	*030
174	24	055	080	105	130	155	180	204	229	254	279
175		304	329	353	378	403	428	452	477	502	527
176		551	576	601	625	650	674	699	724	748	773
177		797	822	846	871	895	920	944	969	993	*018
178	25	042	066	091	115	139	164	188	212	237	261
179		285	310	334	358	382	406	431	455	479	503
180		527	551	575	600	624	648	672	696	720	744
181		768	792	816	840	864	888	912	935	959	983
182	26	007	031	055	079	102	126	150	174	198	221
183		245	269	293	316	340	364	387	411	435	458
184		482	505	529	553	576	600	623	647	670	694
185		717	741	764	788	811	834	858	881	905	928
186		951	975	998	*021	*045	*068	*091	*114	*138	*161
187	27	184	207	231	254	277	300	323	346	370	393
188		416	439	462	485	508	531	554	577	600	623
189		646	669	692	715	738	761	784	807	830	852
190		875	898	921	944	967	989	*012	*035	*058	*081
191	28	103	126	149	171	194	217	240	262	285	307
192		330	353	375	398	421	443	466	488	511	533
193		556	578	601	623	646	668	691	713	735	758
194		780	803	825	847	870	892	914	937	959	981
195	29	003	026	048	070	092	115	137	159	181	203
196		226	248	270	292	314	336	358	380	403	425
197		447	469	491	513	535	557	579	601	623	645
198		667	688	710	732	754	776	798	820	842	863
199		885	907	929	951	973	994	*016	*038	*060	*081
200	30	103	125	146	168	190	211	233	255	276	298

P. P.

	29	28
1	2.9	2.8
2	5.8	5.6
3	8.7	8.4
4	11.6	11.2
5	14.5	14.0
6	17.4	16.8
7	20.3	19.6
8	23.2	22.4
9	26.1	25.2

	27	26
1	2.7	2.6
2	5.4	5.2
3	8.1	7.8
4	10.8	10.4
5	13.5	13.0
6	16.2	15.6
7	18.9	18.2
8	21.6	20.8
9	24.3	23.4

	25
1	2.5
2	5.0
3	7.5
4	10.0
5	12.5
6	15.0
7	17.5
8	20.0
9	22.5

	24	23
1	2.4	2.3
2	4.8	4.6
3	7.2	6.9
4	9.6	9.2
5	12.0	11.5
6	14.4	13.8
7	16.8	16.1
8	19.2	18.4
9	21.6	20.7

	22	21
1	2.2	2.1
2	4.4	4.2
3	6.6	6.3
4	8.8	8.4
5	11.0	10.5
6	13.2	12.6
7	15.4	14.7
8	17.6	16.8
9	19.8	18.9

Tables of Logarithms

N.	L.	0	1	2	3	4	5	6	7	8	9
200	30	103	125	146	168	190	211	233	255	276	298
201		320	341	363	384	406	428	449	471	492	514
202		535	557	578	600	621	643	664	685	707	728
203		750	771	792	814	835	856	878	899	920	942
204		963	984	*006	*027	*048	*069	*091	*112	*133	*154
205	31	175	197	218	239	260	281	302	323	345	366
206		387	408	429	450	471	492	513	534	555	576
207		597	618	639	660	681	702	723	744	765	785
208		806	827	848	869	890	911	931	952	973	994
209	32	015	035	056	077	098	118	139	160	181	201
210		222	243	263	284	305	325	346	366	387	408
211		428	449	469	490	510	531	552	572	593	613
212		634	654	675	695	715	736	756	777	797	818
213		838	858	879	899	919	940	960	980	*001	*021
214	33	041	062	082	102	122	143	163	183	203	224
215		244	264	284	304	325	345	365	385	405	425
216		445	465	486	506	526	546	566	586	606	626
217		646	666	686	706	726	746	766	786	806	826
218		846	866	885	905	925	945	965	985	*005	*025
219	34	044	064	084	104	124	143	163	183	203	223
220		242	262	282	301	321	341	361	380	400	420
221		439	459	479	498	518	537	557	577	596	616
222		635	655	674	694	713	733	753	772	792	811
223		830	850	869	889	908	928	947	967	986	*005
224	35	025	044	064	083	102	122	141	160	180	199
225		218	238	257	276	295	315	334	353	372	392
226		411	430	449	468	488	507	526	545	564	583
227		603	622	641	660	679	698	717	736	755	774
228		793	813	832	851	870	889	908	927	946	965
229		984	*003	*021	*040	*059	*078	*097	*116	*135	*154
230	36	173	192	211	229	248	267	286	305	324	342
231		361	380	399	418	436	455	474	493	511	530
232		549	568	586	605	624	642	661	680	698	717
233		736	754	773	791	810	829	847	866	884	903
234		922	940	959	977	996	*014	*033	*051	*070	*088
235	37	107	125	144	162	181	199	218	236	254	273
236		291	310	328	346	365	383	401	420	438	457
237		475	493	511	530	548	566	585	603	621	639
238		658	676	694	712	731	749	767	785	803	822
239		840	858	876	894	912	931	949	967	985	*003
240	38	021	039	057	075	093	112	130	148	166	184
241		202	220	238	256	274	292	310	328	346	364
242		382	399	417	435	453	471	489	507	525	543
243		561	578	596	614	632	650	668	686	703	721
244		739	757	775	792	810	828	846	863	881	899
245		917	934	952	970	987	*005	*023	*041	*058	*076
246	39	094	111	129	146	164	182	199	217	235	252
247		270	287	305	322	340	358	375	393	410	428
248		445	463	480	498	515	533	550	568	585	602
249		620	637	655	672	690	707	724	742	759	777
250		794	811	829	846	863	881	898	915	933	950

P. P.

	22	21
1	2.2	2.1
2	4.4	4.2
3	6.6	6.3
4	8.8	8.4
5	11.0	10.5
6	13.2	12.6
7	15.4	14.7
8	17.6	16.8
9	19.8	18.9

	20
1	2.0
2	4.0
3	6.0
4	8.0
5	10.0
6	12.0
7	14.0
8	16.0
9	18.0

	19
1	1.9
2	3.8
3	5.7
4	7.6
5	9.5
6	11.4
7	13.3
8	15.2
9	17.1

	18
1	1.8
2	3.6
3	5.4
4	7.2
5	9.0
6	10.8
7	12.6
8	14.4
9	16.2

	17
1	1.7
2	3.4
3	5.1
4	6.8
5	8.5
6	10.2
7	11.9
8	13.6
9	15.3

Tables of Logarithms

N.	L. 0	1	2	3	4	5	6	7	8	9
250	39 794	811	829	846	863	881	898	915	933	950
251	967	985	*002	*019	*037	*054	*071	*088	*106	*123
252	40 140	157	175	192	209	226	243	261	278	295
253	312	329	346	364	381	398	415	432	449	466
254	483	500	518	535	552	569	586	603	620	637
255	654	671	688	705	722	739	756	773	790	807
256	824	841	858	875	892	909	926	943	960	976
257	993	*010	*027	*044	*061	*078	*095	*111	*128	*145
258	41 162	179	196	212	229	246	263	280	296	313
259	330	347	363	380	397	414	430	447	464	481
260	497	514	531	547	564	581	597	614	631	647
261	664	681	697	714	731	747	764	780	797	814
262	830	847	863	880	896	913	929	946	963	979
263	996	*012	*029	*045	*062	*078	*095	*111	*127	*144
264	42 160	177	193	210	226	243	259	275	292	308
265	325	341	357	374	390	406	423	439	455	472
266	488	504	521	537	553	570	586	602	619	635
267	651	667	684	700	716	732	749	765	781	797
268	813	830	846	862	878	894	911	927	943	959
269	975	991	*008	*024	*040	*056	*072	*088	*104	*120
270	43 136	152	169	185	201	217	233	249	265	281
271	297	313	329	345	361	377	393	409	425	441
272	457	473	489	505	521	537	553	569	584	600
273	616	632	648	664	680	696	712	727	743	759
274	775	791	807	823	838	854	870	886	902	917
275	933	949	965	981	996	*012	*028	*044	*059	*075
276	44 091	107	122	138	154	170	185	201	217	232
277	248	264	279	295	311	326	342	358	373	389
278	404	420	436	451	467	483	498	514	529	545
279	560	576	592	607	623	638	654	669	685	700
280	716	731	747	762	778	793	809	824	840	855
281	871	886	902	917	932	948	963	979	994	*010
282	45 025	040	056	071	086	102	117	133	148	163
283	179	194	209	225	240	255	271	286	301	317
284	332	347	362	378	393	408	423	439	454	469
285	484	500	515	530	545	561	576	591	606	621
286	637	652	667	682	697	712	728	743	758	773
287	788	803	818	834	849	864	879	894	909	924
288	939	954	969	984	*000	*015	*030	*045	*060	*075
289	46 090	105	120	135	150	165	180	195	210	225
290	240	255	270	285	300	315	330	345	359	374
291	389	404	419	434	449	464	479	494	509	523
292	538	553	568	583	598	613	627	642	657	672
293	687	702	716	731	746	761	776	790	805	820
294	835	850	864	879	894	909	923	938	953	967
295	982	997	*012	*026	*041	*056	*070	*085	*100	*114
296	47 129	144	159	173	188	202	217	232	246	261
297	276	290	305	319	334	349	363	378	392	407
298	422	436	451	465	480	494	509	524	538	553
299	567	582	596	611	625	640	654	669	683	698
300	712	727	741	756	770	784	799	813	828	842

P. P.

	18
1	1.8
2	3.6
3	5.4
4	7.2
5	9.0
6	10.8
7	12.6
8	14.4
9	16.2

	17
1	1.7
2	3.4
3	5.1
4	6.8
5	8.5
6	10.2
7	11.9
8	13.6
9	15.3

	16
1	1.6
2	3.2
3	4.8
4	6.4
5	8.0
6	9.6
7	11.2
8	12.8
9	14.4

	15
1	1.5
2	3.0
3	4.5
4	6.0
5	7.5
6	9.0
7	10.5
8	12.0
9	13.5

	14
1	1.4
2	2.8
3	4.2
4	5.6
5	7.0
6	8.4
7	9.8
8	11.2
9	12.6

Tables of Logarithms

N.	L. 0	1	2	3	4	5	6	7	8	9
300	47 712	727	741	756	770	784	799	813	828	842
301	857	871	885	900	914	929	943	958	972	986
302	48 001	015	029	044	058	073	087	101	116	130
303	144	159	173	187	202	216	230	244	259	273
304	287	302	316	330	344	359	373	387	401	416
305	430	444	458	473	487	501	515	530	544	558
306	572	586	601	615	629	643	657	671	686	700
307	714	728	742	756	770	785	799	813	827	841
308	855	869	883	897	911	926	940	954	968	982
309	996	*010	*024	*038	*052	*066	*080	*094	*108	*122
310	49 136	150	164	178	192	206	220	234	248	262
311	276	290	304	318	332	346	360	374	388	402
312	415	429	443	457	471	485	499	513	527	541
313	554	568	582	596	610	624	638	651	665	679
314	693	707	721	734	748	762	776	790	803	817
315	831	845	859	872	886	900	914	927	941	955
316	969	982	996	*010	*024	*037	*051	*065	*079	*092
317	50 106	120	133	147	161	174	188	202	215	229
318	243	256	270	284	297	311	325	338	352	365
319	379	393	406	420	433	447	461	474	488	501
320	515	529	542	556	569	583	596	610	623	637
321	651	664	678	691	705	718	732	745	759	772
322	786	799	813	826	840	853	866	880	893	907
323	920	934	947	961	974	987	*001	*014	*028	*041
324	51 055	068	081	095	108	121	135	148	162	175
325	188	202	215	228	242	255	268	282	295	308
326	322	335	348	362	375	388	402	415	428	441
327	455	468	481	495	508	521	534	548	561	574
328	587	601	614	627	640	654	667	680	693	706
329	720	733	746	759	772	786	799	812	825	838
330	851	865	878	891	904	917	930	943	957	970
331	983	996	*009	*022	*035	*048	*061	*075	*088	*101
332	52 114	127	140	153	166	179	192	205	218	231
333	244	257	270	284	297	310	323	336	349	362
334	375	388	401	414	427	440	453	466	479	492
335	504	517	530	543	556	569	582	595	608	621
336	634	647	660	673	686	699	711	724	737	750
337	763	776	789	802	815	827	840	853	866	879
338	892	905	917	930	943	956	969	982	994	*007
339	53 020	033	046	058	071	084	097	110	122	135
340	148	161	173	186	199	212	224	237	250	263
341	275	288	301	314	326	339	352	364	377	390
342	403	415	428	441	453	466	479	491	504	517
343	529	542	555	567	580	593	605	618	631	643
344	656	668	681	694	706	719	732	744	757	769
345	782	794	807	820	832	845	857	870	882	895
346	908	920	933	945	958	970	983	995	*008	*020
347	54 033	045	058	070	083	095	108	120	133	145
348	158	170	183	195	208	220	233	245	258	270
349	283	295	307	320	332	345	357	370	382	394
350	407	419	432	444	456	469	481	494	506	518

P. P.

15		14		13		12	
1	1.5	1	1.4	1	1.3	1	1.2
2	3.0	2	2.8	2	2.6	2	2.4
3	4.5	3	4.2	3	3.9	3	3.6
4	6.0	4	5.6	4	5.2	4	4.8
5	7.5	5	7.0	5	6.5	5	6.0
6	9.0	6	8.4	6	7.8	6	7.2
7	10.5	7	9.8	7	9.1	7	8.4
8	12.0	8	11.2	8	10.4	8	9.6
9	13.5	9	12.6	9	11.7	9	10.8

Tables of Logarithms

N.	L. 0	1	2	3	4	5	6	7	8	9	P. P.	
350	54 407	419	432	444	456	469	481	494	506	518		
351	531	543	555	568	580	593	605	617	630	642		
352	654	667	679	691	704	716	728	741	753	765		
353	777	790	802	814	827	839	851	864	876	888		**13**
354	900	913	925	937	949	962	974	986	998	*011	1	1.3
355	55 023	035	047	060	072	084	096	108	121	133	2	2.6
356	145	157	169	182	194	206	218	230	242	255	3	3.9
357	267	279	291	303	315	328	340	352	364	376	4	5.2
358	388	400	413	425	437	449	461	473	485	497	5	6.5
359	509	522	534	546	558	570	582	594	606	618	6	7.8
360	630	642	654	666	678	691	703	715	727	739	7	9.1
361	751	763	775	787	799	811	823	835	847	859	8	10.4
362	871	883	895	907	919	931	943	955	967	979	9	11.7
363	991	*003	*015	*027	*038	*050	*062	*074	*086	*098		
364	56 110	122	134	146	158	170	182	194	205	217		
365	229	241	253	265	277	289	301	312	324	336		**12**
366	348	360	372	384	396	407	419	431	443	455	1	1.2
367	467	478	490	502	514	526	538	549	561	573	2	2.4
368	585	597	608	620	632	644	656	667	679	691	3	3.6
369	703	714	726	738	750	761	773	785	797	808	4	4.8
370	820	832	844	855	867	879	891	902	914	926	5	6.0
371	937	949	961	972	984	996	*008	*019	*031	*043	6	7.2
372	57 054	066	078	089	101	113	124	136	148	159	7	8.4
373	171	183	194	206	217	229	241	252	264	276	8	9.6
374	287	299	310	322	334	345	357	368	380	392	9	10.8
375	403	415	426	438	449	461	473	484	496	507		
376	519	530	542	553	565	576	588	600	611	623		**11**
377	634	646	657	669	680	692	703	715	726	738	1	1.1
378	749	761	772	784	795	807	818	830	841	852	2	2.2
379	864	875	887	898	910	921	933	944	955	967	3	3.3
380	978	990	*001	*013	*024	*035	*047	*058	*070	*081	4	4.4
381	58 092	104	115	127	138	149	161	172	184	195	5	5.5
382	206	218	229	240	252	263	274	286	297	309	6	6.6
383	320	331	343	354	365	377	388	399	410	422	7	7.7
384	433	444	456	467	478	490	501	512	524	535	8	8.8
385	546	557	569	580	591	602	614	625	636	647	9	9.9
386	659	670	681	692	704	715	726	737	749	760		
387	771	782	794	805	816	827	838	850	861	872		
388	883	894	906	917	928	939	950	961	973	984		**10**
389	995	*006	*017	*028	*040	*051	*062	*073	*084	*095	1	1.0
390	59 106	118	129	140	151	162	173	184	195	207	2	2.0
391	218	229	240	251	262	273	284	295	306	318	3	3.0
392	329	340	351	362	373	384	395	406	417	428	4	4.0
393	439	450	461	472	483	494	506	517	528	539	5	5.0
394	550	561	572	583	594	605	616	627	638	649	6	6.0
395	660	671	682	693	704	715	726	737	748	759	7	7.0
396	770	780	791	802	813	824	835	846	857	868	8	8.0
397	879	890	901	912	923	934	945	956	966	977	9	9.0
398	988	999	*010	*021	*032	*043	*054	*065	*076	*086		
399	60 097	108	119	130	141	152	163	173	184	195		
400	206	217	228	239	249	260	271	282	293	304		

Tables of Logarithms

N.	L.	0	1	2	3	4	5	6	7	8	9
400	60 206	217	228	239	249	260	271	282	293	304
401	314	325	336	347	358	369	379	390	401	412
402	423	433	444	455	466	477	487	498	509	520
403	531	541	552	563	574	584	595	606	617	627
404	638	649	660	670	681	692	703	713	724	735
405	746	756	767	778	788	799	810	821	831	842
406	853	863	874	885	895	906	917	927	938	949
407	959	970	981	991	*002	*013	*023	*034	*045	*055
408	61 066	077	087	098	109	119	130	140	151	162
409	172	183	194	204	215	225	236	247	257	268
410	278	289	300	310	321	331	342	352	363	374
411	384	395	405	416	426	437	448	458	469	479
412	490	500	511	521	532	542	553	563	574	584
413	595	606	616	627	637	648	658	669	679	690
414	700	711	721	731	742	752	763	773	784	794
415	805	815	826	836	847	857	868	878	888	899
416	909	920	930	941	951	962	972	982	993	*003
417	62 014	024	034	045	055	066	076	086	097	107
418	118	128	138	149	159	170	180	190	201	211
419	221	232	242	252	263	273	284	294	304	315
420	325	335	346	356	366	377	387	397	408	418
421	428	439	449	459	469	480	490	500	511	521
422	531	542	552	562	572	583	593	603	613	624
423	634	644	655	665	675	685	696	706	716	726
424	737	747	757	767	778	788	798	808	818	829
425	839	849	859	870	880	890	900	910	921	931
426	941	951	961	972	982	992	*002	*012	*022	*033
427	63 043	053	063	073	083	094	104	114	124	134
428	144	155	165	175	185	195	205	215	225	236
429	246	256	266	276	286	296	306	317	327	337
430	347	357	367	377	387	397	407	417	428	438
431	448	458	468	478	488	498	508	518	528	538
432	548	558	568	579	589	599	609	619	629	639
433	649	659	669	679	689	699	709	719	729	739
434	749	759	769	779	789	799	809	819	829	839
435	849	859	869	879	889	899	909	919	929	939
436	949	959	969	979	988	998	*008	*018	*028	*038
437	64 048	058	068	078	088	098	108	118	128	137
438	147	157	167	177	187	197	207	217	227	237
439	246	256	266	276	286	296	306	316	326	335
440	345	355	365	375	385	395	404	414	424	434
441	444	454	464	473	483	493	503	513	523	532
442	542	552	562	572	582	591	601	611	621	631
443	640	650	660	670	680	689	699	709	719	729
444	738	748	758	768	777	787	797	807	816	826
445	836	846	856	865	875	885	895	904	914	924
446	933	943	953	963	972	982	992	*002	*011	*021
447	65 031	040	050	060	070	079	089	099	108	118
448	128	137	147	157	167	176	186	196	205	215
449	225	234	244	254	263	273	283	292	302	312
450	321	331	341	350	360	369	379	389	398	408

P. P.

11

1	1.1
2	2.2
3	3.3
4	4.4
5	5.5
6	6.6
7	7.7
8	8.8
9	9.9

10

1	1.0
2	2.0
3	3.0
4	4.0
5	5.0
6	6.0
7	7.0
8	8.0
9	9.0

9

1	0.9
2	1.8
3	2.7
4	3.6
5	4.5
6	5.4
7	6.3
8	7.2
9	8.1

Tables of Logarithms

N.	L. 0	1	2	3	4	5	6	7	8	9	P. P.
450	65 321	331	341	350	360	369	379	389	398	408	
451	418	427	437	447	456	466	475	485	495	504	
452	514	523	533	543	552	562	571	581	591	600	
453	610	619	629	639	648	658	667	677	686	696	
454	706	715	725	734	744	753	763	772	782	792	
455	801	811	820	830	839	849	858	868	877	887	
456	896	906	916	925	935	944	954	963	973	982	**10**
457	992	*001	*011	*020	*030	*039	*049	*058	*068	*077	1|1.0
458	66 087	096	106	115	124	134	143	153	162	172	2|2.0
459	181	191	200	210	219	229	238	247	257	266	3|3.0
460	276	285	295	304	314	323	332	342	351	361	4|4.0
461	370	380	389	398	408	417	427	436	445	455	5|5.0
462	464	474	483	492	502	511	521	530	539	549	6|6.0
463	558	567	577	586	596	605	614	624	633	642	7|7.0
464	652	661	671	680	689	699	708	717	727	736	8|8.0
465	745	755	764	773	783	792	801	811	820	829	9|9.0
466	839	848	857	867	876	885	894	904	913	922	
467	932	941	950	960	969	978	987	997	*006	*015	
468	67 025	034	043	052	062	071	080	089	099	108	
469	117	127	136	145	154	164	173	182	191	201	
470	210	219	228	237	247	256	265	274	284	293	**9**
471	302	311	321	330	339	348	357	367	376	385	1|0.9
472	394	403	413	422	431	440	449	459	468	477	2|1.8
473	486	495	504	514	523	532	541	550	560	569	3|2.7
474	578	587	596	605	614	624	633	642	651	660	4|3.6
475	669	679	688	697	706	715	724	733	742	752	5|4.5
476	761	770	779	788	797	806	815	825	834	843	6|5.4
477	852	861	870	879	888	897	906	916	925	934	7|6.3
478	943	952	961	970	979	988	997	*006	*015	*024	8|7.2
479	68 034	043	052	061	070	079	088	097	106	115	9|8.1
480	124	133	142	151	160	169	178	187	196	205	
481	215	224	233	242	251	260	269	278	287	296	
482	305	314	323	332	341	350	359	368	377	386	
483	395	404	413	422	431	440	449	458	467	476	
484	485	494	502	511	520	529	538	547	556	565	
485	574	583	592	601	610	619	628	637	646	655	**8**
486	664	673	681	690	699	708	717	726	735	744	1|0.8
487	753	762	771	780	789	797	806	815	824	833	2|1.6
488	842	851	860	869	878	886	895	904	913	922	3|2.4
489	931	940	949	958	966	975	984	993	*002	*011	4|3.2
490	69 020	028	037	046	055	064	073	082	090	099	5|4.0
491	108	117	126	135	144	152	161	170	179	188	6|4.8
492	197	205	214	223	232	241	249	258	267	276	7|5.6
493	285	294	302	311	320	329	338	346	355	364	8|6.4
494	373	381	390	399	408	417	425	434	443	452	9|7.2
495	461	469	478	487	496	504	513	522	531	539	
496	548	557	566	574	583	592	601	609	618	627	
497	636	644	653	662	671	679	688	697	705	714	
498	723	732	740	749	758	767	775	784	793	801	
499	810	819	827	836	845	854	862	871	880	888	
500	897	906	914	923	932	940	949	958	966	975	

Tables of Logarithms

N.	L. 0	1	2	3	4	5	6	7	8	9	P. P.
500	69 897	906	914	923	932	940	949	958	966	975	
501	984	992	*001	*010	*018	*027	*036	*044	*053	*062	
502	70 070	079	088	096	105	114	122	131	140	148	
503	157	165	174	183	191	200	209	217	226	234	
504	243	252	260	269	278	286	295	303	312	321	
505	329	338	346	355	364	372	381	389	398	406	
506	415	424	432	441	449	458	467	475	484	492	**9**
507	501	509	518	526	535	544	552	561	569	578	1 0.9
508	586	595	603	612	621	629	638	646	655	663	2 1.8
509	672	680	689	697	706	714	723	731	740	749	3 2.7
510	757	766	774	783	791	800	808	817	825	834	4 3.6
511	842	851	859	868	876	885	893	902	910	919	5 4.5
512	927	935	944	952	961	969	978	986	995	*003	6 5.4
513	71 012	020	029	037	046	054	063	071	079	088	7 6.3
514	096	105	113	122	130	139	147	155	164	172	8 7.2
515	181	189	198	206	214	223	231	240	248	257	9 8.1
516	265	273	282	290	299	307	315	324	332	341	
517	349	357	366	374	383	391	399	408	416	425	
518	433	441	450	458	466	475	483	492	500	508	
519	517	525	533	542	550	559	567	575	584	592	
520	600	609	617	625	634	642	650	659	667	675	
521	684	692	700	709	717	725	734	742	750	759	**8**
522	767	775	784	792	800	809	817	825	834	842	1 0.8
523	850	858	867	875	883	892	900	908	917	925	2 1.6
524	933	941	950	958	966	975	983	991	999	*008	3 2.4
525	72 016	024	032	041	049	057	066	074	082	090	4 3.2
526	099	107	115	123	132	140	148	156	165	173	5 4.0
527	181	189	198	206	214	222	230	239	247	255	6 4.8
528	263	272	280	288	296	304	313	321	329	337	7 5.6
529	346	354	362	370	378	387	395	403	411	419	8 6.4
530	428	436	444	452	460	469	477	485	493	501	9 7.2
531	509	518	526	534	542	550	558	567	575	583	
532	591	599	607	616	624	632	640	648	656	665	
533	673	681	689	697	705	713	722	730	738	746	
534	754	762	770	779	787	795	803	811	819	827	
535	835	843	852	860	868	876	884	892	900	908	**7**
536	916	925	933	941	949	957	965	973	981	989	1 0.7
537	997	*006	*014	*022	*030	*038	*046	*054	*062	*070	2 1.4
538	73 078	086	094	102	111	119	127	135	143	151	3 2.1
539	159	167	175	183	191	199	207	215	223	231	4 2.8
540	239	247	255	263	272	280	288	296	304	312	5 3.5
541	320	328	336	344	352	360	368	376	384	392	6 4.2
542	400	408	416	424	432	440	448	456	464	472	7 4.9
543	480	488	496	504	512	520	528	536	544	552	8 5.6
544	560	568	576	584	592	600	608	616	624	632	9 6.3
545	640	648	656	664	672	679	687	695	703	711	
546	719	727	735	743	751	759	767	775	783	791	
547	799	807	815	823	830	838	846	854	862	870	
548	878	886	894	902	910	918	926	933	941	949	
549	957	965	973	981	989	997	*005	*013	*020	*028	
550	74 036	044	052	060	068	076	084	092	099	107	

Tables of Logarithms

N.	L. 0	1	2	3	4	5	6	7	8	9
550	74 036	044	052	060	068	076	084	092	099	107
551	115	123	131	139	147	155	162	170	178	186
552	194	202	210	218	225	233	241	249	257	265
553	273	280	288	296	304	312	320	327	335	343
554	351	359	367	374	382	390	398	406	414	421
555	429	437	445	453	461	468	476	484	492	500
556	507	515	523	531	539	547	554	562	570	578
557	586	593	601	609	617	624	632	640	648	656
558	663	671	679	687	695	702	710	718	726	733
559	741	749	757	764	772	780	788	796	803	811
560	819	827	834	842	850	858	865	873	881	889
561	896	904	912	920	927	935	943	950	958	966
562	974	981	989	997	*005	*012	*020	*028	*035	*043
563	75 051	059	066	074	082	089	097	105	113	120
564	128	136	143	151	159	166	174	182	189	197
565	205	213	220	228	236	243	251	259	266	274
566	282	289	297	305	312	320	328	335	343	351
567	358	366	374	381	389	397	404	412	420	427
568	435	442	450	458	465	473	481	488	496	504
569	511	519	526	534	542	549	557	565	572	580
570	587	595	603	610	618	626	633	641	648	656
571	664	671	679	686	694	702	709	717	724	732
572	740	747	755	762	770	778	785	793	800	808
573	815	823	831	838	846	853	861	868	876	884
574	891	899	906	914	921	929	937	944	952	959
575	967	974	982	989	997	*005	*012	*020	*027	*035
576	76 042	050	057	065	072	080	087	095	103	110
577	118	125	133	140	148	155	163	170	178	185
578	193	200	208	215	223	230	238	245	253	260
579	268	275	283	290	298	305	313	320	328	335
580	343	350	358	365	373	380	388	395	403	410
581	418	425	433	440	448	455	462	470	477	485
582	492	500	507	515	522	530	537	545	552	559
583	567	574	582	589	597	604	612	619	626	634
584	641	649	656	664	671	678	686	693	701	708
585	716	723	730	738	745	753	760	768	775	782
586	790	797	805	812	819	827	834	842	849	856
587	864	871	879	886	893	901	908	916	923	930
588	938	945	953	960	967	975	982	989	997	*004
589	77 012	019	026	034	041	048	056	063	070	078
590	085	093	100	107	115	122	129	137	144	151
591	159	166	173	181	188	195	203	210	217	225
592	232	240	247	254	262	269	276	283	291	298
593	305	313	320	327	335	342	349	357	364	371
594	379	386	393	401	408	415	422	430	437	444
595	452	459	466	474	481	488	495	503	510	517
596	525	532	539	546	554	561	568	576	583	590
597	597	605	612	619	627	634	641	648	656	663
598	670	677	685	692	699	706	714	721	728	735
599	743	750	757	764	772	779	786	793	801	808
600	815	822	830	837	844	851	859	866	873	880

P. P.

8

1	0.8
2	1.6
3	2.4
4	3.2
5	4.0
6	4.8
7	5.6
8	6.4
9	7.2

7

1	0.7
2	1.4
3	2.1
4	2.8
5	3.5
6	4.2
7	4.9
8	5.6
9	6.3

Tables of Logarithms

N.	L. 0	1	2	3	4	5	6	7	8	9	P. P.
600	77 815	822	830	837	844	851	859	866	873	880	
601	887	895	902	909	916	924	931	938	945	952	
602	960	967	974	981	988	996	*003	*010	*017	*025	
603	78 032	039	046	053	061	068	075	082	089	097	
604	104	111	118	125	132	140	147	154	161	168	
605	176	183	190	197	204	211	219	226	233	240	**8**
606	247	254	262	269	276	283	290	297	305	312	1 | 0.8
607	319	326	333	340	347	355	362	369	376	383	2 | 1.6
608	390	398	405	412	419	426	433	440	447	455	3 | 2.4
609	462	469	476	483	490	497	504	512	519	526	4 | 3.2
610	533	540	547	554	561	569	576	583	590	597	5 | 4.0
611	604	611	618	625	633	640	647	654	661	668	6 | 4.8
612	675	682	689	696	704	711	718	725	732	739	7 | 5.6
613	746	753	760	767	774	781	789	796	803	810	8 | 6.4
614	817	824	831	838	845	852	859	866	873	880	9 | 7.2
615	888	895	902	909	916	923	930	937	944	951	
616	958	965	972	979	986	993	*000	*007	*014	*021	
617	79 029	036	043	050	057	064	071	078	085	092	
618	099	106	113	120	127	134	141	148	155	162	
619	169	176	183	190	197	204	211	218	225	232	
620	239	246	253	260	267	274	281	288	295	302	
621	309	316	323	330	337	344	351	358	365	372	**7**
622	379	386	393	400	407	414	421	428	435	442	1 | 0.7
623	449	456	463	470	477	484	491	498	505	511	2 | 1.4
624	518	525	532	539	546	553	560	567	574	581	3 | 2.1
625	588	595	602	609	616	623	630	637	644	650	4 | 2.8
626	657	664	671	678	685	692	699	706	713	720	5 | 3.5
627	727	734	741	748	754	761	768	775	782	789	6 | 4.2
628	796	803	810	817	824	831	837	844	851	858	7 | 4.9
629	865	872	879	886	893	900	906	913	920	927	8 | 5.6
630	934	941	948	955	962	969	975	982	989	996	9 | 6.3
631	80 003	010	017	024	030	037	044	051	058	065	
632	072	079	085	092	099	106	113	120	127	134	
633	140	147	154	161	168	175	182	188	195	202	
634	209	216	223	229	236	243	250	257	264	271	
635	277	284	291	298	305	312	318	325	332	339	
636	346	353	359	366	373	380	387	393	400	407	**6**
637	414	421	428	434	441	448	455	462	468	475	1 | 0.6
638	482	489	496	502	509	516	523	530	536	543	2 | 1.2
639	550	557	564	570	577	584	591	598	604	611	3 | 1.8
640	618	625	632	638	645	652	659	665	672	679	4 | 2.4
641	686	693	699	706	713	720	726	733	740	747	5 | 3.0
642	754	760	767	774	781	787	794	801	808	814	6 | 3.6
643	821	828	835	841	848	855	862	868	875	882	7 | 4.2
644	889	895	902	909	916	922	929	936	943	949	8 | 4.8
645	956	963	969	976	983	990	996	*003	*010	*017	9 | 5.4
646	81 023	030	037	043	050	057	064	070	077	084	
647	090	097	104	111	117	124	131	137	144	151	
648	158	164	171	178	184	191	198	204	211	218	
649	224	231	238	245	251	258	265	271	278	285	
650	291	298	305	311	318	325	331	338	345	351	

Tables of Logarithms

N.	L. 0	1	2	3	4	5	6	7	8	9	P. P.
650	81 291	298	305	311	318	325	331	338	345	351	
651	358	365	371	378	385	391	398	405	411	418	
652	425	431	438	445	451	458	465	471	478	485	
653	491	498	505	511	518	525	531	538	544	551	
654	558	564	571	578	584	591	598	604	611	617	
655	624	631	637	644	651	657	664	671	677	684	
656	690	697	704	710	717	723	730	737	743	750	
657	757	763	770	776	783	790	796	803	809	816	
658	823	829	836	842	849	856	862	869	875	882	
659	889	895	902	908	915	921	928	935	941	948	
660	954	961	968	974	981	987	994	*000	*007	*014	**7**
661	82 020	027	033	040	046	053	060	066	073	079	1 | 0.7
662	086	092	099	105	112	119	125	132	138	145	2 | 1.4
663	151	158	164	171	178	184	191	197	204	210	3 | 2.1
664	217	223	230	236	243	249	256	263	269	276	4 | 2.8
665	282	289	295	302	308	315	321	328	334	341	5 | 3.5
666	347	354	360	367	373	380	387	393	400	406	6 | 4.2
667	413	419	426	432	439	445	452	458	465	471	7 | 4.9
668	478	484	491	497	504	510	517	523	530	536	8 | 5.6
669	543	549	556	562	569	575	582	588	595	601	9 | 6.3
670	607	614	620	627	633	640	646	653	659	666	
671	672	679	685	692	698	705	711	718	724	730	
672	737	743	750	756	763	769	776	782	789	795	
673	802	808	814	821	827	834	840	847	853	860	
674	866	872	879	885	892	898	905	911	918	924	
675	930	937	943	950	956	963	969	975	982	988	
676	995	*001	*008	*014	*020	*027	*033	*040	*046	*052	
677	83 059	065	072	078	085	091	097	104	110	117	
678	123	129	136	142	149	155	161	168	174	181	
679	187	193	200	206	213	219	225	232	238	245	
680	251	257	264	270	276	283	289	296	302	308	**6**
681	315	321	327	334	340	347	353	359	366	372	1 | 0.6
682	378	385	391	398	404	410	417	423	429	436	2 | 1.2
683	442	448	455	461	467	474	480	487	493	499	3 | 1.8
684	506	512	518	525	531	537	544	550	556	563	4 | 2.4
685	569	575	582	588	594	601	607	613	620	626	5 | 3.0
686	632	639	645	651	658	664	670	677	683	689	6 | 3.6
687	696	702	708	715	721	727	734	740	746	753	7 | 4.2
688	759	765	771	778	784	790	797	803	809	816	8 | 4.8
689	822	828	835	841	847	853	860	866	872	879	9 | 5.4
690	885	891	897	904	910	916	923	929	935	942	
691	948	954	960	967	973	979	985	992	998	*004	
692	84 011	017	023	029	036	042	048	055	061	067	
693	073	080	086	092	098	105	111	117	123	130	
694	136	142	148	155	161	167	173	180	186	192	
695	198	205	211	217	223	230	236	242	248	255	
696	261	267	273	280	286	292	298	305	311	317	
697	323	330	336	342	348	354	361	367	373	379	
698	386	392	398	404	410	417	423	429	435	442	
699	448	454	460	466	473	479	485	491	497	504	
700	510	516	522	528	535	541	547	553	559	566	

LOGARITHMS

Tables of Logarithms

N.	L. 0	1	2	3	4	5	6	7	8	9
700	84 510	516	522	528	535	541	547	553	559	566
701	572	578	584	590	597	603	609	615	621	628
702	634	640	646	652	658	665	671	677	683	689
703	696	702	708	714	720	726	733	739	745	751
704	757	763	770	776	782	788	794	800	807	813
705	819	825	831	837	844	850	856	862	868	874
706	880	887	893	899	905	911	917	924	930	936
707	942	948	954	960	967	973	979	985	991	997
708	85 003	009	016	022	028	034	040	046	052	058
709	065	071	077	083	089	095	101	107	114	120
710	126	132	138	144	150	156	163	169	175	181
711	187	193	199	205	211	217	224	230	236	242
712	248	254	260	266	272	278	285	291	297	303
713	309	315	321	327	333	339	345	352	358	364
714	370	376	382	388	394	400	406	412	418	425
715	431	437	443	449	455	461	467	473	479	485
716	491	497	503	509	516	522	528	534	540	546
717	552	558	564	570	576	582	588	594	600	606
718	612	618	625	631	637	643	649	655	661	667
719	673	679	685	691	697	703	709	715	721	727
720	733	739	745	751	757	763	769	775	781	788
721	794	800	806	812	818	824	830	836	842	848
722	854	860	866	872	878	884	890	896	902	908
723	914	920	926	932	938	944	950	956	962	968
724	974	980	986	992	998	*004	*010	*016	*022	*028
725	86 034	040	046	052	058	064	070	076	082	088
726	094	100	106	112	118	124	130	136	141	147
727	153	159	165	171	177	183	189	195	201	207
728	213	219	225	231	237	243	249	255	261	267
729	273	279	285	291	297	303	308	314	320	326
730	332	338	344	350	356	362	368	374	380	386
731	392	398	404	410	415	421	427	433	439	445
732	451	457	463	469	475	481	487	493	499	504
733	510	516	522	528	534	540	546	552	558	564
734	570	576	581	587	593	599	605	611	617	623
735	629	635	641	646	652	658	664	670	676	682
736	688	694	700	705	711	717	723	729	735	741
737	747	753	759	764	770	776	782	788	794	800
738	806	812	817	823	829	835	841	847	853	859
739	864	870	876	882	888	894	900	906	911	917
740	923	929	935	941	947	953	958	964	970	976
741	982	988	994	999	*005	*011	*017	*023	*029	*035
742	87 040	046	052	058	064	070	075	081	087	093
743	099	105	111	116	122	128	134	140	146	151
744	157	163	169	175	181	186	192	198	204	210
745	216	221	227	233	239	245	251	256	262	268
746	274	280	286	291	297	303	309	315	320	326
747	332	338	344	349	355	361	367	373	379	384
748	390	396	402	408	413	419	425	431	437	442
749	448	454	460	466	471	477	483	489	495	500
750	506	512	518	523	529	535	541	547	552	558

P. P.

7
1	0.7
2	1.4
3	2.1
4	2.8
5	3.5
6	4.2
7	4.9
8	5.6
9	6.3

6
1	0.6
2	1.2
3	1.8
4	2.4
5	3.0
6	3.6
7	4.2
8	4.8
9	5.4

5
1	0.5
2	1.0
3	1.5
4	2.0
5	2.5
6	3.0
7	3.5
8	4.0
9	4.5

Tables of Logarithms

N.	L. 0	1	2	3	4	5	6	7	8	9
750	87 506	512	518	523	529	535	541	547	552	558
751	564	570	576	581	587	593	599	604	610	616
752	622	628	633	639	645	651	656	662	668	674
753	679	685	691	697	703	708	714	720	726	731
754	737	743	749	754	760	766	772	777	783	789
755	795	800	806	812	818	823	829	835	841	846
756	852	858	864	869	875	881	887	892	898	904
757	910	915	921	927	933	938	944	950	955	961
758	967	973	978	984	990	996	*001	*007	*013	*018
759	88 024	030	036	041	047	053	058	064	070	076
760	081	087	093	098	104	110	116	121	127	133
761	138	144	150	156	161	167	173	178	184	190
762	195	201	207	213	218	224	230	235	241	247
763	252	258	264	270	275	281	287	292	298	304
764	309	315	321	326	332	338	343	349	355	360
765	366	372	377	383	389	395	400	406	412	417
766	423	429	434	440	446	451	457	463	468	474
767	480	485	491	497	502	508	513	519	525	530
768	536	542	547	553	559	564	570	576	581	587
769	593	598	604	610	615	621	627	632	638	643
770	649	655	660	666	672	677	683	689	694	700
771	705	711	717	722	728	734	739	745	750	756
772	762	767	773	779	784	790	795	801	807	812
773	818	824	829	835	840	846	852	857	863	868
774	874	880	885	891	897	902	908	913	919	925
775	930	936	941	947	953	958	964	969	975	981
776	986	992	997	*003	*009	*014	*020	*025	*031	*037
777	89 042	048	053	059	064	070	076	081	087	092
778	098	104	109	115	120	126	131	137	143	148
779	154	159	165	170	176	182	187	193	198	204
780	209	215	221	226	232	237	243	248	254	260
781	265	271	276	282	287	293	298	304	310	315
782	321	326	332	337	343	348	354	360	365	371
783	376	382	387	393	398	404	409	415	421	426
784	432	437	443	448	454	459	465	470	476	481
785	487	492	498	504	509	515	520	526	531	537
786	542	548	553	559	564	570	575	581	586	592
787	597	603	609	614	620	625	631	636	642	647
788	653	658	664	669	675	680	686	691	697	702
789	708	713	719	724	730	735	741	746	752	757
790	763	768	774	779	785	790	796	801	807	812
791	818	823	829	834	840	845	851	856	862	867
792	873	878	883	889	894	900	905	911	916	922
793	927	933	938	944	949	955	960	966	971	977
794	982	988	993	998	*004	*009	*015	*020	*026	*031
795	90 037	042	048	053	059	064	069	075	080	086
796	091	097	102	108	113	119	124	129	135	140
797	146	151	157	162	168	173	179	184	189	195
798	200	206	211	217	222	227	233	238	244	249
799	255	260	266	271	276	282	287	293	298	304
800	309	314	320	325	331	336	342	347	352	358

P. P.

6

1	0.6
2	1.2
3	1.8
4	2.4
5	3.0
6	3.6
7	4.2
8	4.8
9	5.4

5

1	0.5
2	1.0
3	1.5
4	2.0
5	2.5
6	3.0
7	3.5
8	4.0
9	4.5

Tables of Logarithms

N.	L. 0	1	2	3	4	5	6	7	8	9	P. P.
800	90 309	314	320	325	331	336	342	347	352	358	
801	363	369	374	380	385	390	396	401	407	412	
802	417	423	428	434	439	445	450	455	461	466	
803	472	477	482	488	493	499	504	509	515	520	
804	526	531	536	542	547	553	558	563	569	574	
805	580	585	590	596	601	607	612	617	623	628	
806	634	639	644	650	655	660	666	671	677	682	
807	687	693	698	703	709	714	720	725	730	736	
808	741	747	752	757	763	768	773	779	784	789	
809	795	800	806	811	816	822	827	832	838	843	
810	849	854	859	865	870	875	881	886	891	897	**6**
811	902	907	913	918	924	929	934	940	945	950	1 | 0.6
812	956	961	966	972	977	982	988	993	998	*004	2 | 1.2
813	91 009	014	020	025	030	036	041	046	052	057	3 | 1.8
814	062	068	073	078	084	089	094	100	105	110	4 | 2.4
815	116	121	126	132	137	142	148	153	158	164	5 | 3.0
816	169	174	180	185	190	196	201	206	212	217	6 | 3.6
817	222	228	233	238	243	249	254	259	265	270	7 | 4.2
818	275	281	286	291	297	302	307	312	318	323	8 | 4.8
819	328	334	339	344	350	355	360	365	371	376	9 | 5.4
820	381	387	392	397	403	408	413	418	424	429	
821	434	440	445	450	455	461	466	471	477	482	
822	487	492	498	503	508	514	519	524	529	535	
823	540	545	551	556	561	566	572	577	582	587	
824	593	598	603	609	614	619	624	630	635	640	
825	645	651	656	661	666	672	677	682	687	693	
826	698	703	709	714	719	724	730	735	740	745	
827	751	756	761	766	772	777	782	787	793	798	
828	803	808	814	819	824	829	834	840	845	850	
829	855	861	866	871	876	882	887	892	897	903	
830	908	913	918	924	929	934	939	944	950	955	**5**
831	960	965	971	976	981	986	991	997	*002	*007	1 | 0.5
832	92 012	018	023	028	033	038	044	049	054	059	2 | 1.0
833	065	070	075	080	085	091	096	101	106	111	3 | 1.5
834	117	122	127	132	137	143	148	153	158	163	4 | 2.0
835	169	174	179	184	189	195	200	205	210	215	5 | 2.5
836	221	226	231	236	241	247	252	257	262	267	6 | 3.0
837	273	278	283	288	293	298	304	309	314	319	7 | 3.5
838	324	330	335	340	345	350	355	361	366	371	8 | 4.0
839	376	381	387	392	397	402	407	412	418	423	9 | 4.5
840	428	433	438	443	449	454	459	464	469	474	
841	480	485	490	495	500	505	511	516	521	526	
842	531	536	542	547	552	557	562	567	572	578	
843	583	588	593	598	603	609	614	619	624	629	
844	634	639	645	650	655	660	665	670	675	681	
845	686	691	696	701	706	711	716	722	727	732	
846	737	742	747	752	758	763	768	773	778	783	
847	788	793	799	804	809	814	819	824	829	834	
848	840	845	850	855	860	865	870	875	881	886	
849	891	896	901	906	911	916	921	927	932	937	
850	942	947	952	957	962	967	973	978	983	988	

Tables of Logarithms

N.	L.	0	1	2	3	4	5	6	7	8	9	P. P.
850	92	942	947	952	957	962	967	973	978	983	988	
851		993	998	*003	*008	*013	*018	*024	*029	*034	*039	
852	93	044	049	054	059	064	069	075	080	085	090	
853		095	100	105	110	115	120	125	131	136	141	
854		146	151	156	161	166	171	176	181	186	192	
855		197	202	207	212	217	222	227	232	237	242	**6**
856		247	252	258	263	268	273	278	283	288	293	1|0.6
857		298	303	308	313	318	323	328	334	339	344	2|1.2
858		349	354	359	364	369	374	379	384	389	394	3|1.8
859		399	404	409	414	420	425	430	435	440	445	4|2.4
860		450	455	460	465	470	475	480	485	490	495	5|3.0
861		500	505	510	515	520	526	531	536	541	546	6|3.6
862		551	556	561	566	571	576	581	586	591	596	7|4.2
863		601	606	611	616	621	626	631	636	641	646	8|4.8
864		651	656	661	666	671	676	682	687	692	697	9|5.4
865		702	707	712	717	722	727	732	737	742	747	
866		752	757	762	767	772	777	782	787	792	797	
867		802	807	812	817	822	827	832	837	842	847	
868		852	857	862	867	872	877	882	887	892	897	
869		902	907	912	917	922	927	932	937	942	947	
870		952	957	962	967	972	977	982	987	992	997	
871	94	002	007	012	017	022	027	032	037	042	047	**5**
872		052	057	062	067	072	077	082	086	091	096	1|0.5
873		101	106	111	116	121	126	131	136	141	146	2|1.0
874		151	156	161	166	171	176	181	186	191	196	3|1.5
875		201	206	211	216	221	226	231	236	240	245	4|2.0
876		250	255	260	265	270	275	280	285	290	295	5|2.5
877		300	305	310	315	320	325	330	335	340	345	6|3.0
878		349	354	359	364	369	374	379	384	389	394	7|3.5
879		399	404	409	414	419	424	429	433	438	443	8|4.0
880		448	453	458	463	468	473	478	483	488	493	9|4.5
881		498	503	507	512	517	522	527	532	537	542	
882		547	552	557	562	567	571	576	581	586	591	
883		596	601	606	611	616	621	626	630	635	640	
884		645	650	655	660	665	670	675	680	685	689	
885		694	699	704	709	714	719	724	729	734	738	
886		743	748	753	758	763	768	773	778	783	787	**4**
887		792	797	802	807	812	817	822	827	832	836	1|0.4
888		841	846	851	856	861	866	871	876	880	885	2|0.8
889		890	895	900	905	910	915	919	924	929	934	3|1.2
890		939	944	949	954	959	963	968	973	978	983	4|1.6
891		988	993	998	*002	*007	*012	*017	*022	*027	*032	5|2.0
892	95	036	041	046	051	056	061	066	071	075	080	6|2.4
893		085	090	095	100	105	109	114	119	124	129	7|2.8
894		134	139	143	148	153	158	163	168	173	177	8|3.2
895		182	187	192	197	202	207	211	216	221	226	9|3.6
896		231	236	240	245	250	255	260	265	270	274	
897		279	284	289	294	299	303	308	313	318	323	
898		328	332	337	342	347	352	357	361	366	371	
899		376	381	386	390	395	400	405	410	415	419	
900		424	429	434	439	444	448	453	458	463	468	

Tables of Logarithms

N.	L. 0	1	2	3	4	5	6	7	8	9	P. P.
900	95 424	429	434	439	444	448	453	458	463	468	
901	472	477	482	487	492	497	501	506*	511	516	
902	521	525	530	535	540	545	550	554	559	564	
903	569	574	578	583	588	593	598	602	607	612	
904	617	622	626	631	636	641	646	650	655	660	
905	665	670	674	679	684	689	694	698	703	708	
906	713	718	722	727	732	737	742	746	751	756	
907	761	766	770	775	780	785	789	794	799	804	
908	809	813	818	823	828	832	837	842	847	852	
909	856	861	866	871	875	880	885	890	895	899	
910	904	909	914	918	923	928	933	938	942	947	
911	952	957	961	966	971	976	980	985	990	995	**5**
912	999	*004	*009	*014	*019	*023	*028	*033	*038	*042	1 | 0.5
913	96 047	052	057	061	066	071	076	080	085	090	2 | 1.0
914	095	099	104	109	114	118	123	128	133	137	3 | 1.5
915	142	147	152	156	161	166	171	175	180	185	4 | 2.0
916	190	194	199	204	209	213	218	223	227	232	5 | 2.5
917	237	242	246	251	256	261	265	270	275	280	6 | 3.0
918	284	289	294	298	303	308	313	317	322	327	7 | 3.5
919	332	336	341	346	350	355	360	365	369	374	8 | 4.0
920	379	384	388	393	398	402	407	412	417	421	9 | 4.5
921	426	431	435	440	445	450	454	459	464	468	
922	473	478	483	487	492	497	501	506	511	515	
923	520	525	530	534	539	544	548	553	558	562	
924	567	572	577	581	586	591	595	600	605	609	
925	614	619	624	628	633	638	642	647	652	656	
926	661	666	670	675	680	685	689	694	699	703	
927	708	713	717	722	727	731	736	741	745	750	
928	755	759	764	769	774	778	783	788	792	797	
929	802	806	811	816	820	825	830	834	839	844	
930	848	853	858	862	867	872	876	881	886	890	
931	895	900	904	909	914	918	923	928	932	937	
932	942	946	951	956	960	965	970	974	979	984	**4**
933	988	993	997	*002	*007	*011	*016	*021	*025	*030	1 | 0.4
934	97 035	039	044	049	053	058	063	067	072	077	2 | 0.8
935	081	086	090	095	100	104	109	114	118	123	3 | 1.2
936	128	132	137	142	146	151	155	160	165	169	4 | 1.6
937	174	179	183	188	192	197	202	206	211	216	5 | 2.0
938	220	225	230	234	239	243	248	253	257	262	6 | 2.4
939	267	271	276	280	285	290	294	299	304	308	7 | 2.8
940	313	317	322	327	331	336	340	345	350	354	8 | 3.2
941	359	364	368	373	377	382	387	391	396	400	9 | 3.6
942	405	410	414	419	424	428	433	437	442	447	
943	451	456	460	465	470	474	479	483	488	493	
944	497	502	506	511	516	520	525	529	534	539	
945	543	548	552	557	562	566	571	575	580	585	
946	589	594	598	603	607	612	617	621	626	630	
947	635	640	644	649	653	658	663	667	672	676	
948	681	685	690	695	699	704	708	713	717	722	
949	727	731	736	740	745	749	754	759	763	768	
950	772	777	782	786	791	795	800	804	809	813	

Tables of Logarithms

N.	L. 0	1	2	3	4	5	6	7	8	9
950	97 772	777	782	786	791	795	800	804	809	813
951	818	823	827	832	836	841	845	850	855	859
952	864	868	873	877	882	886	891	896	900	905
953	909	914	918	923	928	932	937	941	946	950
954	955	959	964	968	973	978	982	987	991	996
955	98 000	005	009	014	019	023	028	032	037	041
956	046	050	055	059	064	068	073	078	082	087
957	091	096	100	105	109	114	118	123	127	132
958	137	141	146	150	155	159	164	168	173	177
959	182	186	191	195	200	204	209	214	218	223
960	227	232	236	241	245	250	254	259	263	268
961	272	277	281	286	290	295	299	304	308	313
962	318	322	327	331	336	340	345	349	354	358
963	363	367	372	376	381	385	390	394	399	403
964	408	412	417	421	426	430	435	439	444	448
965	453	457	462	466	471	475	480	484	489	493
966	498	502	507	511	516	520	525	529	534	538
967	543	547	552	556	561	565	570	574	579	583
968	588	592	597	601	605	610	614	619	623	628
969	632	637	641	646	650	655	659	664	668	673
970	677	682	686	691	695	700	704	709	713	717
971	722	726	731	735	740	744	749	753	758	762
972	767	771	776	780	784	789	793	798	802	807
973	811	816	820	825	829	834	838	843	847	851
974	856	860	865	869	874	878	883	887	892	896
975	900	905	909	914	918	923	927	932	936	941
976	945	949	954	958	963	967	972	976	981	985
977	989	994	998	*003	*007	*012	*016	*021	*025	*029
978	99 034	038	043	047	052	056	061	065	069	074
979	078	083	087	092	096	100	105	109	114	118
980	123	127	131	136	140	145	149	154	158	162
981	167	171	176	180	185	189	193	198	202	207
982	211	216	220	224	229	233	238	242	247	251
983	255	260	264	269	273	277	282	286	291	295
984	300	304	308	313	317	322	326	330	335	339
985	344	348	352	357	361	366	370	374	379	383
986	388	392	396	401	405	410	414	419	423	427
987	432	436	441	445	449	454	458	463	467	471
988	476	480	484	489	493	498	502	506	511	515
989	520	524	528	533	537	542	546	550	555	559
990	564	568	572	577	581	585	590	594	599	603
991	607	612	616	621	625	629	634	638	642	647
992	651	656	660	664	669	673	677	682	686	691
993	695	699	704	708	712	717	721	726	730	734
994	739	743	747	752	756	760	765	769	774	778
995	782	787	791	795	800	804	808	813	817	822
996	826	830	835	839	843	848	852	856	861	865
997	870	874	878	883	887	891	896	900	904	909
998	913	917	922	926	930	935	939	944	948	952
999	957	961	965	970	974	978	983	987	991	996
1000	00 000	004	009	013	017	022	026	030	035	039

P. P.

5		4	
1	0.5	1	0.4
2	1.0	2	0.8
3	1.5	3	1.2
4	2.0	4	1.6
5	2.5	5	2.0
6	3.0	6	2.4
7	3.5	7	2.8
8	4.0	8	3.2
9	4.5	9	3.6

Hyperbolic Logarithms

No.	H. Log.	No.	H. Log.	No.	H. Log.	No.	H. Log.	No.	H. Log.
1.01	0.0099	1.51	0.4121	2.01	0.6981	2.51	0.9203	3.01	1.1019
1.02	0.0198	1.52	0.4187	2.02	0.7031	2.52	0.9243	3.02	1.1053
1.03	0.0296	1.53	0.4253	2.03	0.7080	2.53	0.9282	3.03	1.1086
1.04	0.0392	1.54	0.4318	2.04	0.7129	2.54	0.9322	3.04	1.1119
1.05	0.0488	1.55	0.4383	2.05	0.7178	2.55	0.9361	3.05	1.1151
1.06	0.0583	1.56	0.4447	2.06	0.7227	2.56	0.9400	3.06	1.1184
1.07	0.0677	1.57	0.4511	2.07	0.7275	2.57	0.9439	3.07	1.1216
1.08	0.0770	1.58	0.4574	2.08	0.7324	2.58	0.9478	3.08	1.1249
1.09	0.0862	1.59	0.4637	2.09	0.7372	2.59	0.9517	3.09	1.1282
1.10	0.0953	1.60	0.4700	2.10	0.7419	2.60	0.9555	3.10	1.1314
1.11	0.1044	1.61	0.4762	2.11	0.7467	2.61	0.9594	3.11	1.1346
1.12	0.1133	1.62	0.4824	2.12	0.7514	2.62	0.9632	3.12	1.1378
1.13	0.1222	1.63	0.4886	2.13	0.7561	2.63	0.9670	3.13	1.1410
1.14	0.1310	1.64	0.4947	2.14	0.7608	2.64	0.9708	3.14	1.1442
1.15	0.1398	1.65	0.5008	2.15	0.7655	2.65	0.9746	3.15	1.1474
1.16	0.1484	1.66	0.5068	2.16	0.7701	2.66	0.9783	3.16	1.1506
1.17	0.1570	1.67	0.5128	2.17	0.7747	2.67	0.9821	3.17	1.1537
1.18	0.1655	1.68	0.5188	2.18	0.7793	2.68	0.9858	3.18	1.1569
1.19	0.1740	1.69	0.5247	2.19	0.7839	2.69	0.9895	3.19	1.1600
1.20	0.1823	1.70	0.5306	2.20	0.7885	2.70	0.9933	3.20	1.1632
1.21	0.1906	1.71	0.5365	2 21	0.7930	2.71	0.9969	3.21	1.1663
1.22	0.1988	1.72	0.5423	2.22	0.7975	2.72	1.0006	3.22	1.1694
1.23	0.2070	1.73	0.5481	2.23	0.8020	2.73	1.0043	3.23	1.1725
1.24	0.2151	1.74	0.5539	2.24	0.8065	2.74	1.0080	3.24	1.1756
1.25	0.2231	1.75	0.5596	2.25	0.8109	2.75	1.0116	3.25	1.1787
1.26	0.2311	1.76	0.5653	2.26	0.8154	2.76	1.0152	3.26	1.1817
1.27	0.2390	1.77	0.5710	2.27	0.8198	2.77	1.0188	3.27	1.1848
1.28	0.2469	1.78	0.5766	2.28	0.8242	2.78	1.0225	3.28	1.1878
1.29	0.2546	1.79	0.5822	2.29	0.8286	2.79	1.0260	3.29	1.1909
1.30	0.2624	1.80	0.5878	2.30	0.8329	2.80	1.0296	3.30	1.1939
1.31	0.2700	1.81	0.5933	2.31	0.8372	2.81	1.0332	3.31	1.1969
1.32	0.2776	1.82	0.5988	2.32	0.8416	2.82	1.0367	3.32	1.1999
1.33	0.2852	1.83	0.6043	2.33	0.8458	2.83	1.0403	3.33	1.2030
1.34	0.2927	1.84	0.6098	2.34	0.8502	2.84	1.0438	3.34	1.2060
1.35	0.3001	1.85	0.6152	2.35	0.8544	2.85	1.0473	3.35	1.2090
1.36	0.3075	1.86	0.6206	2.36	0.8587	2.86	1.0508	3.36	1.2119
1.37	0.3148	1.87	0.6259	2.37	0.8629	2.87	1.0543	3.37	1.2149
1.38	0.3221	1.88	0.6313	2.38	0.8671	2.88	1.0578	3.38	1.2179
1.39	0.3293	1.89	0.6366	2.39	0.8713	2.89	1.0613	3.39	1.2208
1.40	0.3365	1.90	0.6419	2.40	0.8755	2.90	1.0647	3.40	1.2238
1.41	0.3436	1.91	0.6471	2.41	0.8796	2.91	1.0682	3.41	1.2267
1.42	0.3507	1.92	0.6523	2.42	0.8838	2.92	1.0716	3.42	1.2296
1.43	0.3577	1.93	0.6575	2.43	0.8879	2.93	1.0750	3.43	1.2326
1.44	0.3646	1.94	0.6627	2.44	0.8920	2.94	1.0784	3.44	1.2355
1.45	0.3716	1.95	0.6678	2.45	0.8961	2.95	1.0818	3.45	1.2384
1.46	0.3784	1.96	0.6729	2.46	0.9002	2.96	1.0852	3.46	1.2413
1.47	0.3853	1.97	0.6780	2.47	0.9042	2.97	1.0886	3.47	1.2442
1.48	0.3920	1.98	0.6831	2.48	0.9083	2.98	1.0919	3.48	1.2470
1.49	0.3988	1.99	0.6881	2.49	0.9123	2.99	1.0953	3.49	1.2499
1.50	0.4055	2.00	0.6931	2.50	0.9163	3.00	1.0986	3.50	1.2528

Hyperbolic Logarithms

No.	H. Log.	No.	H. Log.	No.	H. Log.	No.	H. Log.	No.	H. Log.
3.51	1.2556	4.01	1.3888	4.51	1.5063	5.01	1.6114	5.51	1.7066
3.52	1.2585	4.02	1.3913	4.52	1.5085	5.02	1.6134	5.52	1.7084
3.53	1.2613	4.03	1.3938	4.53	1.5107	5.03	1.6154	5.53	1.7102
3.54	1.2641	4.04	1.3962	4.54	1.5129	5.04	1.6174	5.54	1.7120
3.55	1.2669	4.05	1.3987	4.55	1.5151	5.05	1.6194	5.55	1.7138
3.56	1.2698	4.06	1.4012	4.56	1.5173	5.06	1.6214	5.56	1.7156
3.57	1.2726	4.07	1.4036	4.57	1.5195	5.07	1.6233	5.57	1.7174
3.58	1.2754	4.08	1.4061	4.58	1.5217	5.08	1.6253	5.58	1.7192
3.59	1.2782	4.09	1.4085	4.59	1.5239	5.09	1.6273	5.59	1.7210
3.60	1.2809	4.10	1.4110	4.60	1.5261	5.10	1.6292	5.60	1.7228
3.61	1.2837	4.11	1.4134	4.61	1.5282	5.11	1.6312	5.61	1.7246
3.62	1.2865	4.12	1.4159	4.62	1.5304	5.12	1.6332	5.62	1.7263
3.63	1.2892	4.13	1.4183	4.63	1.5326	5.13	1.6351	5.63	1.7281
3.64	1.2920	4.14	1.4207	4.64	1.5347	5.14	1.6371	5.64	1.7299
3.65	1.2947	4.15	1.4231	4.65	1.5369	5.15	1.6390	5.65	1.7317
3.66	1.2975	4.16	1.4255	4.66	1.5390	5.16	1.6409	5.66	1.7334
3.67	1.3002	4.17	1.4279	4.67	1.5412	5.17	1.6429	5.67	1.7352
3.68	1.3029	4.18	1.4303	4.68	1.5433	5.18	1.6448	5.68	1.7370
3.69	1.3056	4.19	1.4327	4.69	1.5454	5.19	1.6467	5.69	1.7387
3.70	1.3083	4.20	1.4351	4.70	1.5476	5.20	1.6487	5.70	1.7405
3.71	1.3110	4.21	1.4375	4.71	1.5497	5.21	1.6506	5.71	1.7422
3.72	1.3137	4.22	1.4398	4.72	1.5518	5.22	1.6525	5.72	1.7440
3.73	1.3164	4.23	1.4422	4.73	1.5539	5.23	1.6544	5.73	1.7457
3.74	1.3191	4.24	1.4446	4.74	1.5560	5.24	1.6563	5.74	1.7475
3.75	1.3218	4.25	1.4469	4.75	1.5581	5.25	1.6582	5.75	1.7492
3.76	1.3244	4.26	1.4493	4.76	1.5602	5.26	1.6601	5.76	1.7509
3.77	1.3271	4.27	1.4516	4.77	1.5623	5.27	1.6620	5.77	1.7527
3.78	1.3297	4.28	1.4540	4.78	1.5644	5.28	1.6639	5.78	1.7544
3.79	1.3324	4.29	1.4563	4.79	1.5665	5.29	1.6658	5.79	1.7561
3.80	1.3350	4.30	1.4586	4.80	1.5686	5.30	1.6677	5.80	1.7579
3.81	1.3376	4.31	1.4609	4.81	1.5707	5.31	1.6696	5.81	1.7596
3.82	1.3403	4.32	1.4633	4.82	1.5728	5.32	1.6715	5.82	1.7613
3.83	1.3429	4.33	1.4656	4.83	1.5748	5.33	1.6734	5.83	1.7630
3.84	1.3455	4.34	1.4679	4.84	1.5769	5.34	1.6752	5.84	1.7647
3.85	1.3481	4.35	1.4702	4.85	1.5790	5.35	1.6771	5.85	1.7664
3.86	1.3507	4.36	1.4725	4.86	1.5810	5.36	1.6790	5.86	1.7681
3.87	1.3533	4.37	1.4748	4.87	1.5831	5.37	1.6808	5.87	1.7699
3.88	1.3558	4.38	1.4770	4.88	1.5851	5.38	1.6827	5.88	1.7716
3.89	1.3584	4.39	1.4793	4.89	1.5872	5.39	1.6845	5.89	1.7733
3.90	1.3610	4.40	1.4816	4.90	1.5892	5.40	1.6864	5.90	1.7750
3.91	1.3635	4.41	1.4839	4.91	1.5913	5.41	1.6882	5.91	1.7766
3.92	1.3661	4.42	1.4861	4.92	1.5933	5.42	1.6901	5.92	1.7783
3.93	1.3686	4.43	1.4884	4.93	1.5953	5.43	1.6919	5.93	1.7800
3.94	1.3712	4.44	1.4907	4.94	1.5974	5.44	1.6938	5.94	1.7817
3.95	1.3737	4.45	1.4929	4.95	1.5994	5.45	1.6956	5.95	1.7834
3.96	1.3762	4.46	1.4951	4.96	1.6014	5.46	1.6974	5.96	1.7851
3.97	1.3788	4.47	1.4974	4.97	1.6034	5.47	1.6993	5.97	1.7867
3.98	1.3813	4.48	1.4996	4.98	1.6054	5.48	1.7011	5.98	1.7884
3.99	1.3838	4.49	1.5019	4.99	1.6074	5.49	1.7029	5.99	1.7901
4.00	1.3863	4.50	1.5041	5.00	1.6094	5.50	1.7047	6.00	1.7918

LOGARITHMS

Hyperbolic Logarithms

No.	H. Log.	No.	H. Log.	No.	H. Log.	No.	H. Log.	No.	H. Log.
6.01	1.7934	6.51	1.8733	7.01	1.9473	7.51	2.0162	8.01	2.0807
6.02	1.7951	6.52	1.8749	7.02	1.9488	7.52	2.0176	8.02	2.0819
6.03	1.7967	6.53	1.8764	7.03	1.9502	7.53	2.0189	8.03	2.0832
6.04	1.7984	6.54	1.8779	7.04	1.9516	7.54	2.0202	8.04	2.0844
6.05	1.8001	6.55	1.8795	7.05	1.9530	7.55	2.0215	8.05	2.0857
6.06	1.8017	6.56	1.8810	7.06	1.9544	7.56	2.0229	8.06	2.0869
6.07	1.8034	6.57	1.8825	7.07	1.9559	7.57	2.0242	8.07	2.0882
6.08	1.8050	6.58	1.8840	7.08	1.9573	7.58	2.0255	8.08	2.0894
6.09	1.8066	6.59	1.8856	7.09	1.9587	7.59	2.0268	8.09	2.0906
6.10	1.8083	6.60	1.8871	7.10	1.9601	7.60	2.0281	8.10	2.0919
6.11	1.8099	6.61	1.8886	7.11	1.9615	7.61	2.0295	8.11	2.0931
6.12	1.8116	6.62	1.8901	7.12	1.9629	7.62	2.0308	8.12	2.0943
6.13	1.8132	6.63	1.8916	7.13	1.9643	7.63	2.0321	8.13	2.0956
6.14	1.8148	6.64	1.8931	7.14	1.9657	7.64	2.0334	8.14	2.0968
6.15	1.8165	6.65	1.8946	7.15	1.9671	7.65	2.0347	8.15	2.0980
6.16	1.8181	6.66	1.8961	7.16	1.9685	7.66	2.0360	8.16	2.0992
6.17	1.8197	6.67	1.8976	7.17	1.9699	7.67	2.0373	8.17	2.1005
6.18	1.8213	6.68	1.8991	7.18	1.9713	7.68	2.0386	8.18	2.1017
6.19	1.8229	6.69	1.9006	7.19	1.9727	7.69	2.0399	8.19	2.1029
6.20	1.8245	6.70	1.9021	7.20	1.9741	7.70	2.0412	8.20	2.1041
6.21	1.8262	6.71	1.9036	7.21	1.9755	7.71	2.0425	8.21	2.1054
6.22	1.8278	6.72	1.9051	7.22	1.9769	7.72	2.0438	8.22	2.1066
6.23	1.8294	6.73	1.9066	7.23	1.9782	7.73	2.0451	8.23	2.1078
6.24	1.8310	6.74	1.9081	7.24	1.9796	7.74	2.0464	8.24	2.1090
6.25	1.8326	6.75	1.9095	7.25	1.9810	7.75	2.0477	8.25	2.1102
6.26	1.8342	6.76	1.9110	7.26	1.9824	7.76	2.0490	8.26	2.1114
6.27	1.8358	6.77	1.9125	7.27	1.9838	7.77	2.0503	8.27	2.1126
6.28	1.8374	6.78	1.9140	7.28	1.9851	7.78	2.0516	8.28	2.1138
6.29	1.8390	6.79	1.9155	7.29	1.9865	7.79	2.0528	8.29	2.1150
6.30	1.8405	6.80	1.9169	7.30	1.9879	7.80	2.0541	8.30	2.1163
6.31	1.8421	6.81	1.9184	7.31	1.9892	7.81	2.0554	8.31	2.1175
6.32	1.8437	6.82	1.9199	7.32	1.9906	7.82	2.0567	8.32	2.1187
6.33	1.8453	6.83	1.9213	7.33	1.9920	7.83	2.0580	8.33	2.1199
6.34	1.8469	6.84	1.9228	7.34	1.9933	7.84	2.0592	8.34	2.1211
6.35	1.8485	6.85	1.9242	7.35	1.9947	7.85	2.0605	8.35	2.1223
6.36	1.8500	6.86	1.9257	7.36	1.9961	7.86	2.0618	8.36	2.1235
6.37	1.8516	6.87	1.9272	7.37	1.9974	7.87	2.0631	8.37	2.1247
6.38	1.8532	6.88	1.9286	7.38	1.9988	7.88	2.0643	8.38	2.1258
6.39	1.8547	6.89	1.9301	7.39	2.0001	7.89	2.0656	8.39	2.1270
6.40	1.8563	6.90	1.9315	7.40	2.0015	7.90	2.0669	8.40	2.1282
6.41	1.8579	6.91	1.9330	7.41	2.0028	7.91	2.0681	8.41	2.1294
6.42	1.8594	6.92	1.9344	7.42	2.0041	7.92	2.0694	8.42	2.1306
6.43	1.8610	6.93	1.9359	7.43	2.0055	7.93	2.0707	8.43	2.1318
6.44	1.8625	6.94	1.9373	7.44	2.0069	7.94	2.0719	8.44	2.1330
6.45	1.8641	6.95	1.9387	7.45	2.0082	7.95	2.0732	8.45	2.1342
6.46	1.8656	6.96	1.9402	7.46	2.0096	7.96	2.0744	8.46	2.1353
6.47	1.8672	6.97	1.9416	7.47	2.0109	7.97	2.0757	8.47	2.1365
6.48	1.8687	6.98	1.9430	7.48	2.0122	7.98	2.0769	8.48	2.1377
6.49	1.8703	6.99	1.9445	7.49	2.0136	7.99	2.0782	8.49	2.1389
6.50	1.8718	7.00	1.9459	7.50	2.0149	8.00	2.0794	8.50	2.1401

Hyperbolic Logarithms

No.	H. Log.	No.	H. Log.	No.	H. Log.	No.	H. Log.	No.	H. Log.
8.51	2.1412	9.01	2.1983	9.51	2.2523	10.25	2.3273	41	3.7136
8.52	2.1424	9.02	2.1994	9.52	2.2534	10.50	2.3514	42	3.7377
8.53	2.1436	9.03	2.2006	9.53	2.2544	10.75	2.3749	43	3.7612
8.54	2.1448	9.04	2.2017	9.54	2.2555	11.00	2.3979	44	3.7842
8.55	2.1459	9.05	2.2028	9.55	2.2565	11.25	2.4204	45	3.8067
8.56	2.1471	9.06	2.2039	9.56	2.2576	11.50	2.4423	46	3.8286
8.57	2.1483	9.07	2.2050	9.57	2.2586	11.75	2.4638	47	3.8501
8.58	2.1494	9.08	2.2061	9.58	2.2597	12.00	2.4849	48	3.8712
8.59	2.1506	9.09	2.2072	9.59	2.2607	12.25	2.5055	49	3.8918
8.60	2.1518	9.10	2.2083	9.60	2.2618	12.50	2.5257	50	3.9120
8.61	2.1529	9.11	2.2094	9.61	2.2628	12.75	2.5455	51	3.9318
8.62	2.1541	9.12	2.2105	9.62	2.2638	13.00	2.5649	52	3.9512
8.63	2.1552	9.13	2.2116	9.63	2.2649	13.25	2.5840	53	3.9703
8.64	2.1564	9.14	2.2127	9.64	2.2659	13.50	2.6027	54	3.9890
8.65	2.1576	9.15	2.2138	9.65	2.2670	13.75	2.6210	55	4.0073
8.66	2.1587	9.16	2.2148	9.66	2.2680	14.00	2.6391	56	4.0254
8.67	2.1599	9.17	2.2159	9.67	2.2690	14.25	2.6568	57	4.0431
8.68	2.1610	9.18	2.2170	9.68	2.2701	14.50	2.6741	58	4.0604
8.69	2.1622	9.19	2.2181	9.69	2.2711	14.75	2.6912	59	4.0775
8.70	2.1633	9.20	2.2192	9.70	2.2721	15.00	2.7081	60	4.0943
8.71	2.1645	9.21	2.2203	9.71	2.2732	15.50	2.7408	61	4.1109
8.72	2.1656	9.22	2.2214	9.72	2.2742	16.00	2.7726	62	4.1271
8.73	2.1668	9.23	2.2225	9.73	2.2752	16.50	2.8034	63	4.1431
8.74	2.1679	9.24	2.2235	9.74	2.2762	17.00	2.8332	64	4.1589
8.75	2.1691	9.25	2.2246	9.75	2.2773	17.50	2.8622	65	4.1744
8.76	2.1702	9.26	2.2257	9.76	2.2783	18.00	2.8904	66	4.1897
8.77	2.1713	9.27	2.2268	9.77	2.2793	18.50	2.9178	67	4.2047
8.78	2.1725	9.28	2.2279	9.78	2.2803	19.00	2.9444	68	4.2195
8.79	2.1736	9.29	2.2289	9.79	2.2814	19.50	2.9704	69	4.2341
8.80	2.1748	9.30	2.2300	9.80	2.2824	20.00	2.9957	70	4.2485
8.81	2.1759	9.31	2.2311	9.81	2.2834	21	3.0445	71	4.2627
8.82	2.1770	9.32	2.2322	9.82	2.2844	22	3.0910	72	4.2767
8.83	2.1782	9.33	2.2332	9.83	2.2854	23	3.1355	73	4.2905
8.84	2.1793	9.34	2.2343	9.84	2.2865	24	3.1781	74	4.3041
8.85	2.1804	9.35	2.2354	9.85	2.2875	25	3.2189	75	4.3175
8.86	2.1815	9.36	2.2364	9.86	2.2885	26	3.2581	76	4.3307
8.87	2.1827	9.37	2.2375	9.87	2.2895	27	3.2958	77	4.3438
8.88	2.1838	9.38	2.2386	9.88	2.2905	28	3.3322	78	4.3567
8.89	2.1849	9.39	2.2396	9.89	2.2915	29	3.3673	79	4.3694
8.90	2.1861	9.40	2.2407	9.90	2.2925	30	3.4012	80	4.3820
8.91	2.1872	9.41	2.2418	9.91	2.2935	31	3.4340	82	4.4067
8.92	2.1883	9.42	2.2428	9.92	2.2946	32	3.4657	84	4.4308
8.93	2.1894	9.43	2.2439	9.93	2.2956	33	3.4965	86	4.4543
8.94	2.1905	9.44	2.2450	9.94	2.2966	34	3.5264	88	4.4773
8.95	2.1917	9.45	2.2460	9.95	2.2976	35	3.5553	90	4.4998
8.96	2.1928	9.46	2.2471	9.96	2.2986	36	3.5835	92	4.5218
8.97	2.1939	9.47	2.2481	9.97	2.2996	37	3.6109	94	4.5433
8.98	2.1950	9.48	2.2492	9.98	2.3006	38	3.6376	96	4.5643
8.99	2.1961	9.49	2.2502	9.99	2.3016	39	3.6636	98	4.5850
9.00	2.1972	9.50	2.2513	10.00	2.3026	40	3.6889	100	4.6052

Mensuration

In the following tables are given the areas of plane figures, together with other formulas relating to their dimensions and properties; the surfaces of solids; and the volumes of solids. The notation used in the formulas is, as far as possible, given in the illustration accompanying them; where this has not been possible, it is given at the beginning of each set of formulas.

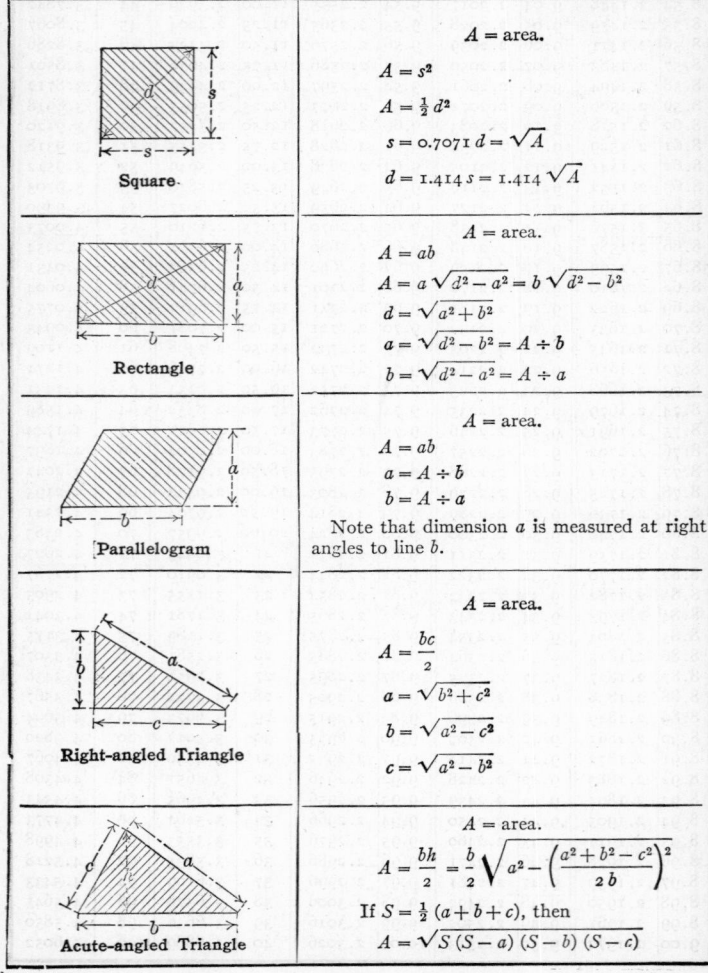

Square

A = area.

$A = s^2$

$A = \frac{1}{2} d^2$

$s = 0.7071\, d = \sqrt{A}$

$d = 1.414\, s = 1.414\, \sqrt{A}$

Rectangle

A = area.

$A = ab$

$A = a\sqrt{d^2 - a^2} = b\sqrt{d^2 - b^2}$

$d = \sqrt{a^2 + b^2}$

$a = \sqrt{d^2 - b^2} = A \div b$

$b = \sqrt{d^2 - a^2} = A \div a$

Parallelogram

A = area.

$A = ab$

$a = A \div b$

$b = A \div a$

Note that dimension a is measured at right angles to line b.

Right-angled Triangle

A = area.

$A = \dfrac{bc}{2}$

$a = \sqrt{b^2 + c^2}$

$b = \sqrt{a^2 - c^2}$

$c = \sqrt{a^2 - b^2}$

Acute-angled Triangle

A = area.

$A = \dfrac{bh}{2} = \dfrac{b}{2}\sqrt{a^2 - \left(\dfrac{a^2 + b^2 - c^2}{2b}\right)^2}$

If $S = \frac{1}{2}(a + b + c)$, then

$A = \sqrt{S\,(S - a)\,(S - b)\,(S - c)}$

Examples of the Use of the Formulas

Below are given a number of examples showing the use of the formulas on the opposite page. Each section of the page corresponds to the opposite section on the previous page, and the illustration on that page should be referred to. The notation used in the illustrations is also used in the examples given.

Square. — Assume that the side s of a square is 15 inches. Find the area and the length of the diagonal.

$$\text{Area} = A = s^2 = 15^2 = 225 \text{ square inches.}$$
$$\text{Diagonal} = d = 1.414 \, s = 1.414 \times 15 = 21.21 \text{ inches.}$$

The area of a square is 625 square inches. Find the length of the side s and the diagonal d.

$$s = \sqrt{A} = \sqrt{625} = 25 \text{ inches.}$$
$$d = 1.414 \sqrt{A} = 1.414 \times 25 = 35.35 \text{ inches.}$$

Rectangle. — The side a of a rectangle is 12 inches, and the area 70.5 square inches. Find the length of the side b, and the diagonal d.

$$b = A \div a = 70.5 \div 12 = 5.875 \text{ inches.}$$
$$d = \sqrt{a^2 + b^2} = \sqrt{12^2 + 5.875^2} = \sqrt{178.516} = 13.361 \text{ inches.}$$

The sides of a rectangle are 30.5 and 11 inches long. Find the area.

$$\text{Area} = a \times b = 30.5 \times 11 = 335.5 \text{ square inches.}$$

Parallelogram. — The base b of a parallelogram is 16 feet. The height a is 5.5 feet. Find the area.

$$\text{Area} = A = a \times b = 5.5 \times 16 = 88 \text{ square feet.}$$

The area of a parallelogram is 12 square inches. The height is 1.5 inch. Find the length of the base b.

$$b = A \div a = 12 \div 1.5 = 8 \text{ inches.}$$

Right-angled Triangle. — The sides b and c in a right-angled triangle are 6 and 8 inches. Find side a and the area.

$$a = \sqrt{b^2 + c^2} = \sqrt{6^2 + 8^2} = \sqrt{36 + 64} = \sqrt{100} = 10 \text{ inches.}$$
$$A = \frac{b \times c}{2} = \frac{6 \times 8}{2} = \frac{48}{2} = 24 \text{ square inches.}$$

If $a = 10$ and $b = 6$, had been known, but not c, the latter would have been found as follows:

$$c = \sqrt{a^2 - b^2} = \sqrt{10^2 - 6^2} = \sqrt{100 - 36} = \sqrt{64} = 8 \text{ inches.}$$

Acute-angled Triangle. — If $a = 10$, $b = 9$, and $c = 8$ inches, what is the area of the triangle?

$$A = \frac{b}{2} \sqrt{a^2 - \left(\frac{a^2 + b^2 - c^2}{2\,b}\right)^2} = \frac{9}{2} \sqrt{10^2 - \left(\frac{10^2 + 9^2 - 8^2}{2 \times 9}\right)^2} = 4.5 \sqrt{100 - \left(\frac{117}{18}\right)^2}$$
$$= 4.5 \sqrt{100 - 42.25} = 4.5 \sqrt{57.75} = 4.5 \times 7.60 = 34.20 \text{ square inches.}$$

Mensuration

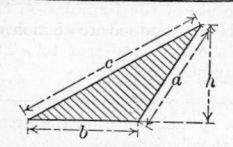

Obtuse-angled Triangle

A = area.

$$A = \frac{bh}{2} = \frac{b}{2}\sqrt{a^2 - \left(\frac{c^2 - a^2 - b^2}{2b}\right)^2}$$

If $S = \frac{1}{2}(a + b + c)$, then

$$A = \sqrt{S(S-a)(S-b)(S-c)}$$

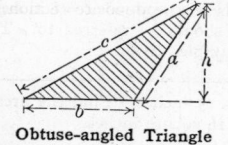

Trapezoid

A = area.

$$A = \frac{(a+b)h}{2}$$

Note: In England, this figure is called a *trapezium* and the one below it is known as a *trapezoid*, the terms being reversed.

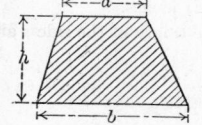

Trapezium

A = area.

$$A = \frac{(H+h)a + bh + cH}{2}$$

A trapezium can also be divided into two triangles as indicated by the dotted line. The area of each of these triangles is computed, and the results added to find the area of the trapezium.

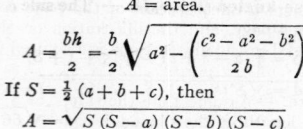

Regular Hexagon

A = area;
R = radius of circumscribed circle;
r = radius of inscribed circle.
$A = 2.598\,s^2 = 2.598\,R^2 = 3.464\,r^2$
$R = s = 1.155\,r$
$r = 0.866\,s = 0.866\,R$
$s = R = 1.155\,r$

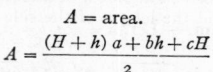

Regular Octagon

A = area;
R = radius of circumscribed circle;
r = radius of inscribed circle.
$A = 4.828\,s^2 = 2.828\,R^2 = 3.314\,r^2$
$R = 1.307\,s = 1.082\,r$
$r = 1.207\,s = 0.924\,R$
$s = 0.765\,R = 0.828\,r$

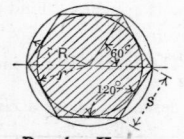

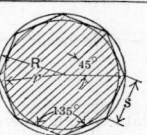

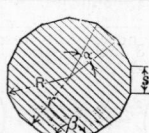

Regular Polygon

A = area; n = number of sides.
$\alpha = 360° \div n$ $\beta = 180° - \alpha$

$$A = \frac{nsr}{2} = \frac{ns}{2}\sqrt{R^2 - \frac{s^2}{4}}$$

$$R = \sqrt{r^2 + \frac{s^2}{4}}; \quad r = \sqrt{R^2 - \frac{s^2}{4}}; \quad s = 2\sqrt{R^2 - r^2}$$

Examples of the Use of the Formulas

Obtuse-angled Triangle. — The side $a = 5$, side $b = 4$, and side $c = 8$ inches. Find the area.

$$S = \tfrac{1}{2}(a + b + c) = \tfrac{1}{2}(5 + 4 + 8) = \tfrac{1}{2} \times 17 = 8.5$$

$$A = \sqrt{S(S-a)(S-b)(S-c)} = \sqrt{8.5\,(8.5-5)\,(8.5-4)\,(8.5-8)}$$

$$= \sqrt{8.5 \times 3.5 \times 4.5 \times 0.5} = \sqrt{66.937} = 8.18 \text{ square inches.}$$

Trapezoid. — Side $a = 23$ feet, side $b = 32$ feet, and height $h = 12$ feet. Find the area.

$$A = \frac{(a+b)h}{2} = \frac{(23+32)\,12}{2} = \frac{55 \times 12}{2} = \frac{660}{2} = 330 \text{ square feet.}$$

Trapezium. — Let $a = 10$, $b = 2$, $c = 3$, $h = 8$, and $H = 12$ inches. Find the area.

$$A = \frac{(H+h)\,a + bh + cH}{2} = \frac{(12+8)\,10 + 2 \times 8 + 3 \times 12}{2}$$

$$= \frac{20 \times 10 + 16 + 36}{2} = \frac{252}{2} = 126 \text{ square inches.}$$

Regular Hexagon. — The side s of a regular hexagon is 4 inches. Find the area and the radius r of the inscribed circle.

$$A = 2.598\,s^2 = 2.598 \times 4^2 = 2.598 \times 16 = 41.568 \text{ square inches.}$$

$$r = 0.866\,s = 0.866 \times 4 = 3.464 \text{ inches.}$$

What is the length of the side of a hexagon that is described about a circle of 5 inches radius? — Here $r = 5$. Hence,

$$s = 1.155\,r = 1.155 \times 5 = 5.775 \text{ inches.}$$

Regular Octagon. — Find the area and the length of the side of an octagon that is inscribed in a circle of 12 inches diameter.

Diameter of circumscribed circle = 12 inches; hence, $R = 6$ inches.

$$A = 2.828\,R^2 = 2.828 \times 6^2 = 2.828 \times 36 = 101.81 \text{ square inches.}$$

$$s = 0.765\,R = 0.765 \times 6 = 4.590 \text{ inches.}$$

Regular Polygon. — Find the area of a polygon having 12 sides, inscribed in a circle of 8 inches radius. The length of the side s is 4.141 inches.

$$A = \frac{ns}{2}\sqrt{R^2 - \frac{s^2}{4}} = \frac{12 \times 4.141}{2}\sqrt{8^2 - \frac{4.141^2}{4}} = 24.846\sqrt{59.713}$$

$$= 24.846 \times 7.727 = 191.98 \text{ square inches.}$$

Mensuration

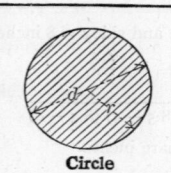 **Circle**	A = area; C = circumference. $A = \pi r^2 = 3.1416\, r^2 = 0.7854\, d^2$ $C = 2\,\pi r = 6.2832\, r = 3.1416\, d$ $r = C \div 6.2832 = \sqrt{A \div 3.1416} = 0.564\sqrt{A}$ $a = C \div 3.1416 = \sqrt{A \div 0.7854} = 1.128\sqrt{A}$ Length of arc for center-angle of $1° = 0.008727\, d$ Length of arc for center-angle of $n° = 0.008727\, nd$
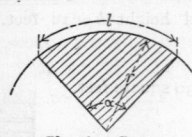 **Circular Sector**	A = area; l = length of arc; α = angle, in degrees. $l = \dfrac{r \times \alpha \times 3.1416}{180} = 0.01745\, r\alpha = \dfrac{2\,A}{r}$ $A = \frac{1}{2}\, rl = 0.008727\, \alpha r^2$ $\alpha = \dfrac{57.296\, l}{r} \qquad r = \dfrac{2\,A}{l} = \dfrac{57.296\, l}{\alpha}$
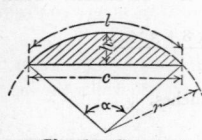 **Circular Segment**	A = area; l = length of arc; α = angle, in degrees. $c = 2\sqrt{h\,(2\,r - h)} \qquad A = \frac{1}{2}\,[rl - c\,(r - h)]$ $r = \dfrac{c^2 + 4\,h^2}{8\,h} \qquad\qquad l = 0.01745\, r\alpha$ $h = r - \frac{1}{2}\sqrt{4\,r^2 - c^2} \qquad \alpha = \dfrac{57.296\, l}{r}$
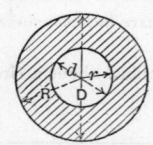 **Circular Ring**	A = area. $A = \pi\,(R^2 - r^2) = 3.1416\,(R^2 - r^2)$ $\quad = 3.1416\,(R + r)\,(R - r)$ $\quad = 0.7854\,(D^2 - d^2) = 0.7854\,(D + d)\,(D - d)$
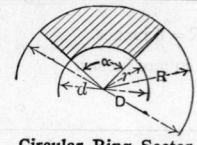 **Circular Ring Sector**	A = area; α = angle, in degrees. $A = \dfrac{\alpha\pi}{360}\,(R^2 - r^2) = 0.00873\,\alpha\,(R^2 - r^2)$ $\quad = \dfrac{\alpha\pi}{4 \times 360}\,(D^2 - d^2) = 0.00218\,\alpha\,(D^2 - d^2)$
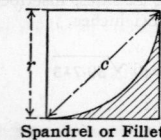 **Spandrel or Fillet**	A = area. $A = r^2 - \dfrac{\pi r^2}{4} = 0.215\, r^2$ $\quad = 0.1075\, c^2$

Examples of the Use of the Formulas

Circle. — Find the area A and circumference C of a circle with a diameter of $2\frac{3}{4}$ inches.

$A = 0.7854 \, d^2 = 0.7854 \times 2.75^2 = 0.7854 \times 2.75 \times 2.75 = 5.9396$ square inches.

$C = 3.1416 \, d = 3.1416 \times 2.75 = 8.6394$ inches.

The area of a circle is 16.8 square inches. Find its diameter.

$d = 1.128 \sqrt{A} = 1.128 \sqrt{16.8} = 1.128 \times 4.099 = 4.624$ inches.

Circular Sector. — The radius of a circle is $1\frac{1}{2}$ inch, and angle α of a sector of the circle is 60 degrees. Find the area of the sector and the length of arc l.

$A = 0.008727 \, \alpha r^2 = 0.008727 \times 60 \times 1.5^2 = 0.5236 \times 1.5 \times 1.5 = 1.178$ sq. inch.

$l = 0.01745 \, r\alpha = 0.01745 \times 1.5 \times 60 = 1.5705$ inch.

Circular Segment. — The radius r of a circular segment is 60 inches and the height h is 8 inches. Find the length of the chord c.

$c = 2 \sqrt{h \, (2\,r - h)} = 2 \sqrt{8 \times (2 \times 60 - 8)} = 2 \sqrt{896} = 2 \times 29.93 = 59.86$ inches.

If $c = 16$, and $h = 6$ inches, what is the radius of the circle of which the segment is a part?

$r = \dfrac{c^2 + 4\,h^2}{8\,h} = \dfrac{16^2 + 4 \times 6^2}{8 \times 6} = \dfrac{256 + 144}{48} = \dfrac{400}{48} = 8\frac{1}{3}$ inches.

Circular Ring. — Let the outside diameter $D = 12$ inches and the inside diameter $d = 8$ inches. Find area of ring.

$A = 0.7854 \, (D^2 - d^2) = 0.7854 \, (12^2 - 8^2) = 0.7854 \, (144 - 64) = 0.7854 \times 80$
$\quad = 62.83$ square inches.

By the alternative formula:

$A = 0.7854 \, (D + d) \, (D - d) = 0.7854 \, (12 + 8) \, (12 - 8) = 0.7854 \times 20 \times 4$
$\quad = 62.83$ square inches.

Circular Ring Sector. — Find the area, if the outside radius $R = 5$ inches, the inside radius $r = 2$ inches, and $\alpha = 72$ degrees.

$A = 0.00873 \, \alpha \, (R^2 - r^2) = 0.00873 \times 72 \, (5^2 - 2^2)$
$\quad = 0.6286 \, (25 - 4) = 0.6286 \times 21 = 13.2$ square inches.

Spandrel or Fillet. — Find the area of a spandrel, the radius of which is 0.7 inch.

$A = 0.215 \, r^2 = 0.215 \times 0.7^2 = 0.215 \times 0.7 \times 0.7 = 0.105$ square inch.

If chord c were given as 2.2 inches, what would be the area?

$A = 0.1075 \, c^2 = 0.1075 \times 2.2^2 = 0.1075 \times 4.84 = 0.520$ square inch.

Mensuration

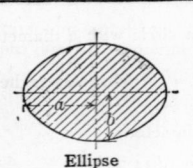

Ellipse

A = area; P = perimeter or circumference.

$A = \pi ab = 3.1416\,ab$.

An approximate formula for the perimeter is:

$P = 3.1416\sqrt{2\,(a^2+b^2)}$

A closer approximation is:

$P = 3.1416\sqrt{2\,(a^2+b^2) - \dfrac{(a-b)^2}{2.2}}$

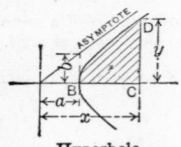

Hyperbola

A = area BCD.

$A = \dfrac{xy}{2} - \dfrac{ab}{2}\,\text{hyp. log}\left(\dfrac{x}{a} + \dfrac{y}{b}\right)$

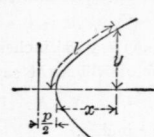

Parabola

l = length of arc.

$l = \dfrac{p}{2}\left[\sqrt{\dfrac{2x}{p}\left(1+\dfrac{2x}{p}\right)} + \text{hyp. log}\left(\sqrt{\dfrac{2x}{p}} + \sqrt{1+\dfrac{2x}{p}}\right)\right]$

When x is small in proportion to y, the following is a close approximation:

$l = y\left[1 + \dfrac{2}{3}\left(\dfrac{x}{y}\right)^2 - \dfrac{2}{5}\left(\dfrac{x}{y}\right)^4\right]$, or $l = \sqrt{y^2 + \dfrac{4}{3}x^2}$

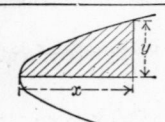

Parabola

A = area.

$A = \dfrac{2}{3}xy$

(The area is equal to two-thirds of the rectangle which has x for its base and y for its height.)

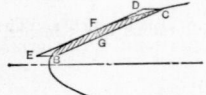

Segment of Parabola

A = area.

Area $BFC = A = \dfrac{2}{3}$ area of parallelogram $BCDE$.

If FG is the height of the segment, measured at right angles to BC, then:

Area of segment $BFC = \dfrac{2}{3}\,BC \times FG$

Cycloid

A = area; l = length of cycloid.

$A = 3\pi r^2 = 9.4248\,r^2 = 2.3562\,d^2$

$= 3 \times$ area of generating circle

$l = 8r = 4d$

Examples of the Use of the Formulas

Ellipse. — The larger or major axis is 8 inches. The smaller or minor axis is 6 inches. Find the area and the approximate circumference. Here, then, $a = 4$, and $b = 3$.

$$A = 3.1416\, ab = 3.1416 \times 4 \times 3 = 37.699 \text{ square inches.}$$

$$P = 3.1416 \sqrt{2\,(a^2 + b^2)} = 3.1416 \times \sqrt{2\,(4^2 + 3^2)} = 3.1416 \times \sqrt{2 \times 25}$$

$$= 3.1416 \sqrt{50} = 3.1416 \times 7.071 = 22.214 \text{ inches.}$$

Hyperbola. — The half-axes a and b are 3 and 2 inches, respectively. Find area shown shaded in illustration for $x = 8$ and $y = 5$.

Inserting the known values in the formula:

$$A = \frac{8 \times 5}{2} - \frac{3 \times 2}{2} \times \text{hyp. log} \left(\frac{8}{3} + \frac{5}{2} \right) = 20 - 3 \times \text{hyp. log } 5.167$$

$$= 20 - 3 \times 1.6423 = 20 - 4.927 = 15.073 \text{ square inches.}$$

Parabola. — If $x = 2$ and $y = 24$ feet, what is the approximate length l of the parabolic curve?

$$l = y \left[1 + \frac{2}{3} \left(\frac{x}{y} \right)^2 - \frac{2}{5} \left(\frac{x}{y} \right)^4 \right] = 24 \left[1 + \frac{2}{3} \left(\frac{2}{24} \right)^2 - \frac{2}{5} \left(\frac{2}{24} \right)^4 \right]$$

$$= 24 \left[1 + \frac{2}{3} \times \frac{1}{144} - \frac{2}{5} \times \frac{1}{20,736} \right] = 24 \times 1.0046 = 24.11 \text{ feet.}$$

Parabola. — Let the dimension x in the illustration be 15 inches, and y, 9 inches. Find the area of the shaded portion of the parabola.

$$A = \tfrac{2}{3} \times xy = \tfrac{2}{3} \times 15 \times 9 = 10 \times 9 = 90 \text{ square inches.}$$

Segment of Parabola. — The length of the chord $BC = 19.5$ inches. The distance between lines BC and DE, measured at right angles to BC, is 2.25 inches. This is the height of the segment. Find the area.

$$\text{Area} = A = \tfrac{2}{3}\, BC \times FG = \tfrac{2}{3} \times 19.5 \times 2.25 = 29.25 \text{ square inches.}$$

Cycloid. — The diameter of the generating circle of a cycloid is 6 inches. Find the length l of the cycloidal curve, and the area enclosed between the curve and the base line.

$$l = 4\,d = 4 \times 6 = 24 \text{ inches.}$$

$$A = 2.3562\, d^2 = 2.3562 \times 6^2 = 2.3562 \times 36 = 84.82 \text{ square inches.}$$

Volumes of Solids

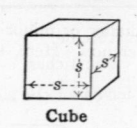

Cube

V = volume.
$$V = s^3$$
$$s = \sqrt[3]{V}$$

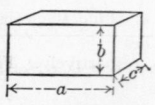

Square Prism

V = volume.
$$V = abc$$
$$a = \frac{V}{bc} \qquad b = \frac{V}{ac} \qquad c = \frac{V}{ab}$$

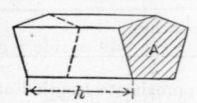

Prism

V = volume; A = area of end surface.
$$V = h \times A$$

The area A of the end surface is found by the formulas for areas of plane figures on the preceding pages. Height h must be measured perpendicular to end surface.

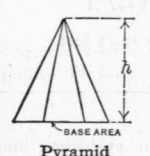

Pyramid

V = volume.
$$V = \tfrac{1}{3} h \times \text{area of base.}$$

If the base is a regular polygon with n sides, and s = length of side, r = radius of inscribed circle, and R = radius of circumscribed circle, then:
$$V = \frac{nsrh}{6} = \frac{nsh}{6}\sqrt{R^2 - \frac{s^2}{4}}$$

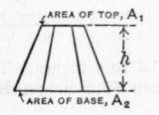

Frustum of Pyramid

V = volume.
$$V = \frac{h}{3}(A_1 + A_2 + \sqrt{A_1 \times A_2})$$

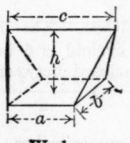

Wedge

V = volume.
$$V = \frac{(2a + c)bh}{6}$$

Examples of the Use of the Formulas

Cube. — The side of a cube equals 9.5 inches. Find its volume.

Volume $= V = s^3 = 9.5^3 = 9.5 \times 9.5 \times 9.5 = 857.375$ cubic inches.

The volume of a cube is 231 cubic inches. What is the length of the side?

$$s = \sqrt[3]{V} = \sqrt[3]{231} = 6.136 \text{ inches.}$$

Square Prism. — In a square prism, $a = 6$, $b = 5$, $c = 4$. Find the volume.

$$V = a \times b \times c = 6 \times 5 \times 4 = 120 \text{ cubic inches.}$$

How high should a box be made to contain 25 cubic feet, if it is 4 feet long and $2\frac{1}{2}$ feet wide? Here, $a = 4$, $c = 2.5$, and $V = 25$. Then,

$$b = \text{depth} = \frac{V}{ac} = \frac{25}{4 \times 2.5} = \frac{25}{10} = 2.5 \text{ feet.}$$

Prism. — A prism having for its base a regular hexagon with a side s of 3 inches, is 10 inches high. Find the volume.

Area of hexagon $= A = 2.598 \, s^2 = 2.598 \times 9 = 23.382$ square inches.

Volume of prism $= h \times A = 10 \times 23.382 = 233.82$ cubic inches.

Pyramid. —A pyramid, having a height of 9 feet, has a base formed by a rectangle, the sides of which are 2 and 3 feet, respectively. Find the volume.

Area of base $= 2 \times 3 = 6$ square feet; $h = 9$ feet.

Volume $= V = \frac{1}{3} h \times$ area of base $= \frac{1}{3} \times 9 \times 6 = 18$ cubic feet.

Frustum of Pyramid. — The pyramid in the previous example is cut off $4\frac{1}{2}$ feet from the base, the upper part being removed. The sides of the rectangle forming the top surface of the frustum are, then, 1 and $1\frac{1}{2}$ foot long, respectively. Find the volume of the frustum.

Area of top $= A_1 = 1 \times 1\frac{1}{2} = 1\frac{1}{2}$ sq. ft. Area of base $= A_2 = 2 \times 3 = 6$ sq. ft.

$$V = \frac{4.5}{3}(1.5 + 6 + \sqrt{1.5 \times 6}) = 1.5\,(7.5 + \sqrt{9}) = 1.5 \times 10.5 = 15.75 \text{ cubic feet.}$$

Wedge. — Let $a = 4$ inches, $b = 3$ inches, and $c = 5$ inches. The height $h = 4.5$ inches. Find the volume.

$$V = \frac{(2a + c)\,bh}{6} = \frac{(2 \times 4 + 5) \times 3 \times 4.5}{6} = \frac{(8 + 5) \times 13.5}{6} = \frac{13 \times 13.5}{6}$$

$$= \frac{175.5}{6} = 29.25 \text{ cubic inches.}$$

Volumes of Solids

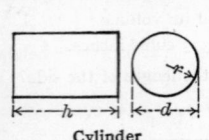

Cylinder

V = volume; S = area of cylindrical surface.
$V = 3.1416\,r^2h = 0.7854\,d^2h$
$S = 6.2832\,rh = 3.1416\,dh$

Total area A of cylindrical surface and end surfaces:
$A = 6.2832\,r\,(r + h) = 3.1416\,d\,(\tfrac{1}{2}\,d + h)$

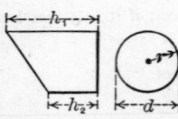

Portion of Cylinder

V = volume; S = area of cylindrical surface.
$V = 1.5708\,r^2\,(h_1 + h_2) = 0.3927\,d^2\,(h_1 + h_2)$
$S = 3.1416\,r\,(h_1 + h_2) = 1.5708\,d\,(h_1 + h_2)$

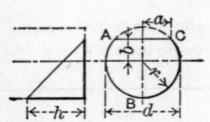

Portion of Cylinder

V = volume; S = area of cylindrical surface.
$$V = \left(\frac{2}{3}\,a^3 \pm b \times \text{area } ABC\right)\frac{h}{r \pm b}$$
$$S = (ad \pm b \times \text{length of arc } ABC)\,\frac{h}{r \pm b}$$

Use $+$ when base area is larger, and $-$ when base area is less than one-half the base circle.

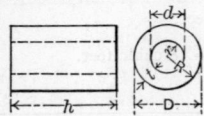

Hollow Cylinder

V = volume.
$V = 3.1416\,h\,(R^2 - r^2) = 0.7854\,h\,(D^2 - d^2)$
$\quad = 3.1416\,ht\,(2\,R - t) = 3.1416\,ht\,(D - t)$
$\quad = 3.1416\,ht\,(2\,r + t) = 3.1416\,ht\,(d + t)$
$\quad = 3.1416\,ht\,(R + r) = 1.5708\,ht\,(D + d)$

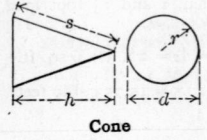

Cone

V = volume; A = area of conical surface.
$V = \dfrac{3.1416\,r^2h}{3} = 1.0472\,r^2h = 0.2618\,d^2h$
$A = 3.1416\,r\,\sqrt{r^2 + h^2} = 3.1416\,rs = 1.5708\,ds$
$s = \sqrt{r^2 + h^2} = \sqrt{\dfrac{d^2}{4} + h^2}$

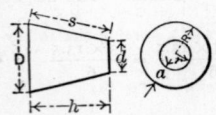

Frustum of Cone

V = volume; A = area of conical surface.
$V = 1.0472\,h\,(R^2 + Rr + r^2) = 0.2618\,h\,(D^2 + Dd + d^2)$
$A = 3.1416\,s\,(R + r) = 1.5708\,s\,(D + d)$
$a = R - r \qquad s = \sqrt{a^2 + h^2} = \sqrt{(R - r)^2 + h^2}$

Examples of the Use of the Formulas

Cylinder. — The diameter of a cylinder is $2\frac{1}{2}$ inches. The length or height is 20 inches. Find the volume, and the area of the cylindrical surface S.

$V = 0.7854\ d^2h = 0.7854 \times 2\frac{1}{2}^2 \times 20 = 0.7854 \times 6.25 \times 20 = 98.17$ cubic inches.
$S = 3.1416\ dh = 3.1416 \times 2\frac{1}{2} \times 20 = 157.08$ square inches.

Portion of Cylinder. — A cylinder 5 inches in diameter, is cut off at an angle, as shown in the illustration. Dimension $h_1 = 6$, and $h_2 = 4$ inches. Find the volume and the area S of the cylindrical surface.

$V = 0.3927\ d^2\ (h_1 + h_2) = 0.3927 \times 5^2 \times (6 + 4) = 0.3927 \times 25 \times 10$
$= 98.175$ cubic inches.
$S = 1.5708\ d\ (h_1 + h_2) = 1.5708 \times 5 \times 10 = 78.54$ square inches.

Portion of Cylinder. — Find the volume of a cylinder so cut off that line AC passes through the center of the base circle — that is, the base area is a half-circle. The diameter of the cylinder = 5 inches, and height $h = 2$ inches.
In this case $a = 2.5$; $b = 0$; area $ABC = \frac{1}{2} \times 0.7854 \times 5^2 = 9.82$; $r = 2.5$.

$V = \left(\dfrac{2}{3} \times 2.5^3 + 0 \times 9.82\right) \dfrac{2}{2.5 + 0} = \dfrac{2}{3} \times 15.625 \times 0.8 = 8.33$ cubic inches.

Hollow Cylinder. — A cylindrical shell, 28 inches high, is 36 inches in outside diameter, and 4 inches thick. Find its volume.

$V = 3.1416\ ht\ (D - t) = 3.1416 \times 28 \times 4\ (36 - 4) = 3.1416 \times 28 \times 4 \times 32$
$= 11,259.5$ cubic inches.

Cone. — Find the volume and area of conical surface of a cone, the base of which is a circle of 6 inches diameter, and the height of which is 4 inches.

$V = 0.2618\ d^2h = 0.2618 \times 6^2 \times 4 = 0.2618 \times 36 \times 4 = 37.7$ cubic inches.
$A = 3.1416\ r\ \sqrt{r^2 + h^2} = 3.1416 \times 3 \times \sqrt{3^2 + 4^2} = 9.4248 \times \sqrt{25}$
$= 47.124$ square inches.

Frustum of Cone. — Find the volume of a frustum of a cone of the following dimensions: $D = 8$ inches; $d = 4$ inches; $h = 5$ inches.

$V = 0.2618 \times 5\ (8^2 + 8 \times 4 + 4^2) = 0.2618 \times 5\ (64 + 32 + 16)$
$= 0.2618 \times 5 \times 112 = 146.61$ cubic inches.

Volumes of Solids

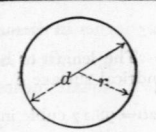 **Sphere**	V = volume; A = area of surface. $V = \dfrac{4\pi r^3}{3} = \dfrac{\pi d^3}{6} = 4.1888\,r^3 = 0.5236\,d^3$ $A = 4\pi r^2 = \pi d^2 = 12.5664\,r^2 = 3.1416\,d^2$ $r = \sqrt[3]{\dfrac{3\,V}{4\,\pi}} = 0.6204\,\sqrt[3]{V}$
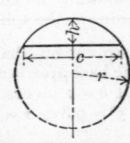 **Spherical Sector**	V = volume; A = total area of conical and spherical surface. $V = \dfrac{2\pi r^2 h}{3} = 2.0944\,r^2 h$ $A = 3.1416\,r\,(2\,h + \tfrac{1}{2}\,c)$ $c = 2\,\sqrt{h\,(2\,r - h)}$
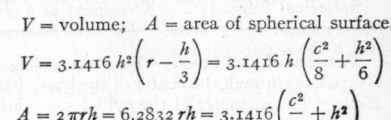 **Spherical Segment**	V = volume; A = area of spherical surface. $V = 3.1416\,h^2\left(r - \dfrac{h}{3}\right) = 3.1416\,h\left(\dfrac{c^2}{8} + \dfrac{h^2}{6}\right)$ $A = 2\,\pi r h = 6.2832\,rh = 3.1416\left(\dfrac{c^2}{4} + h^2\right)$ $c = 2\,\sqrt{h\,(2\,r - h)}; \quad r = \dfrac{c^2 + 4\,h^2}{8\,h}$
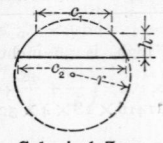 **Spherical Zone**	V = volume; A = area of spherical surface. $V = 0.5236\,h\left(\dfrac{3\,c_1{}^2}{4} + \dfrac{3\,c_2{}^2}{4} + h^2\right)$ $A = 2\,\pi r h = 6.2832\,rh$ $r = \sqrt{\dfrac{c_2{}^2}{4} + \left(\dfrac{c_2{}^2 - c_1{}^2 - 4\,h^2}{8\,h}\right)^2}$
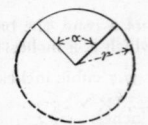 **Spherical Wedge**	V = volume; A = area of spherical surface; α = center angle in degrees. $V = \dfrac{\alpha}{360} \times \dfrac{4\,\pi r^3}{3} = 0.0116\,\alpha r^3$ $A = \dfrac{\alpha}{360} \times 4\,\pi r^2 = 0.0349\,\alpha r^2$
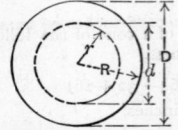 **Hollow Sphere**	V = volume. $V = \dfrac{4\,\pi}{3}\,(R^3 - r^3) = 4.1888\,(R^3 - r^3)$ $\quad = \dfrac{\pi}{6}\,(D^3 - d^3) = 0.5236\,(D^3 - d^3)$

Examples of the Use of the Formulas

Sphere. — Find the volume and surface of a sphere 6.5 inches in diameter.

$V = 0.5236\, d^3 = 0.5236 \times 6.5^3 = 0.5236 \times 6.5 \times 6.5 \times 6.5 = 143.79$ cubic inches.

$A = 3.1416\, d^2 = 3.1416 \times 6.5^2 = 3.1416 \times 6.5 \times 6.5 = 132.73$ square inches.

The volume of a sphere is 64 cubic inches. Find its radius.

$r = 0.6204 \sqrt[3]{64} = 0.6204 \times 4 = 2.4816$ inches.

Spherical Sector. — Find the volume of a sector of a sphere 6 inches in diameter, the height h of the sector being 1.5 inch. Also find length of chord c. — Here $r = 3$, and $h = 1.5$.

$V = 2.0944\, r^2 h = 2.0944 \times 3^2 \times 1.5 = 2.0944 \times 9 \times 1.5 = 28.27$ cubic inches.

$c = 2\sqrt{h\,(2\,r - h)} = 2\sqrt{1.5\,(2 \times 3 - 1.5)} = 2\sqrt{6.75} = 2 \times 2.598$
$= 5.196$ inches.

Spherical Segment. — A segment of a sphere has the following dimensions: $h = 2$ inches; $c = 5$ inches. Find the volume V and the radius of the sphere of which the segment is a part.

$V = 3.1416 \times 2 \times \left(\dfrac{5^2}{8} + \dfrac{2^2}{6} \right) = 6.2832 \times \left(\dfrac{25}{8} + \dfrac{4}{6} \right) = 6.2832 \times 3.792$
$= 23.825$ cubic inches.

$r = \dfrac{5^2 + 4 \times 2^2}{8 \times 2} = \dfrac{25 + 16}{16} = \dfrac{41}{16} = 2\frac{9}{16}$ inches.

Spherical Zone. — In a spherical zone, let $c_1 = 3$; $c_2 = 4$; and $h = 1.5$ inch. Find the volume.

$V = 0.5236 \times 1.5 \times \left(\dfrac{3 \times 3^2}{4} + \dfrac{3 \times 4^2}{4} + 1.5^2 \right) = 0.5236 \times 1.5 \times \left(\dfrac{27}{4} + \dfrac{48}{4} + 2.25 \right)$
$= 0.5236 \times 1.5 \times 21 = 16.493$ cubic inches.

Spherical Wedge. — Find the area of the spherical surface and the volume of a wedge of a sphere. The diameter of the sphere is 4 inches, and the center angle α is 45 degrees.

$V = 0.0116 \times 45 \times 2^3 = 0.0116 \times 45 \times 8 = 4.176$ cubic inches.

$A = 0.0349 \times 45 \times 2^2 = 0.0349 \times 45 \times 4 = 6.282$ square inches.

Hollow Sphere. — Find the volume of a hollow sphere, 8 inches in outside diameter, with a thickness of material of 1.5 inch.
Here $R = 4$; $r = 4 - 1.5 = 2.5$.

$V = 4.1888\,(4^3 - 2.5^3) = 4.1888\,(64 - 15.625) = 4.1888 \times 48.375$
$= 202.63$ cubic inches.

Volumes of Solids

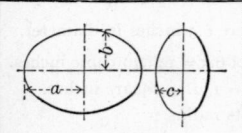

Ellipsoid

V = volume.

$$V = \frac{4\pi}{3}\,abc = 4.1888\,abc$$

In an ellipsoid of revolution, or spheroid, where $b = c$:

$$V = 4.1888\,ab^2$$

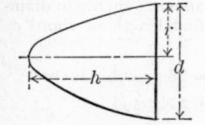

Paraboloid

V = volume; $V = \frac{1}{2}\,\pi r^2 h = 0.3927\,d^2 h$

A = area; $A = \dfrac{2}{3}\dfrac{\pi}{p}\left[\sqrt{\left(\dfrac{d^2}{4}+p^2\right)^3}-p^3\right]$ in which

$$p = \frac{d^2}{8\,h}$$

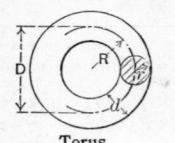

Paraboloidal Segment

V = volume.

$$V = \frac{\pi}{2}\,h\,(R^2 + r^2) = 1.5708\,h\,(R^2 + r^2)$$

$$= \frac{\pi}{8}\,h\,(D^2 + d^2) = 0.3927\,h\,(D^2 + d^2)$$

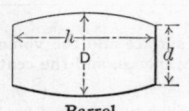

Torus

V = volume; A = area of surface.

$$V = 2\,\pi^2 Rr^2 = 19.739\,Rr^2$$

$$= \frac{\pi^2}{4}\,Dd^2 = 2.4674\,Dd^2$$

$$A = 4\,\pi^2 Rr = 39.478\,Rr$$

$$= \pi^2 Dd = 9.8696\,Dd$$

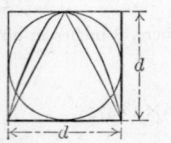

Barrel

V = approximate volume.

If the sides are bent to the arc of a circle:

$$V = \tfrac{1}{12}\pi h\,(2\,D^2 + d^2) = 0.262\,h\,(2\,D^2 + d^2)$$

If the sides are bent to the arc of a parabola:

$$V = 0.209\,h\,(2\,D^2 + Dd + \tfrac{3}{4}\,d^2)$$

If d = base diameter and height of a cone, a paraboloid and a cylinder, and the diameter of a sphere, then the volumes of these bodies are to each other as below:

Cone: paraboloid: sphere: cylinder = $\frac{1}{3} : \frac{1}{2} : \frac{2}{3} : 1$

Examples of the Use of the Formulas

Ellipsoid or Spheroid. — Find the volume of a spheroid in which $a = 5$, and $b = c = 1.5$ inch.

$$V = 4.1888 \times 5 \times 1.5^2 = 4.1888 \times 5 \times 2.25 = 47.124 \text{ cubic inches.}$$

Paraboloid. — Find the volume of a paraboloid in which $h = 12$ and $d = 5$ inches.

$$V = 0.3927 \, d^2 h = 0.3927 \times 5^2 \times 12 = 0.3927 \times 25 \times 12$$
$$= 0.3927 \times 300 = 117.81 \text{ cubic inches.}$$

Segment of Paraboloid. — Find the volume of a segment of a paraboloid in which $D = 5$ inches, $d = 3$ inches, and $h = 6$ inches.

$$V = 0.3927 \, h \, (D^2 + d^2) = 0.3927 \times 6 \times (5^2 + 3^2) = 0.3927 \times 6 \times (25 + 9)$$
$$= 0.3927 \times 6 \times 34 = 80.11 \text{ cubic inches.}$$

Torus. — Find the volume and area of surface of a torus in which $d = 1.5$ and $D = 5$ inches.

$$V = 2.4674 \times 5 \times 1.5^2 = 2.4674 \times 5 \times 2.25 = 27.76 \text{ cubic inches.}$$
$$A = 9.8696 \times 5 \times 1.5 = 74.022 \text{ square inches}$$

Barrel. — Find the approximate contents of a barrel, the inside dimensions of which are $D = 24$ inches; $d = 20$ inches; $h = 48$ inches.

$$V = 0.262 \, h \, (2 \, D^2 + d^2) = 0.262 \times 48 \times (2 \times 24^2 + 20^2) = 0.262 \times 48$$
$$\times (1152 + 400) = 0.262 \times 48 \times 1552 = 19,518 \text{ cubic inches.}$$

Assume, as an example, that the diameter of the base of a cone, paraboloid and cylinder is 2 inches, that the height is 2 inches, and that the diameter of a sphere is 2 inches. Then the volumes, written in formula-form, are as below:

Cone	Paraboloid	Sphere	Cylinder			

$$\frac{3.1416 \times 2^2 \times 2}{12} : \frac{3.1416 \times 2^2 \times 2}{8} : \frac{3.1416 \times 2^3}{6} : \frac{3.1416 \times 2^2 \times 2}{4} = \frac{1}{3} : \frac{1}{2} : \frac{2}{3} : 1$$

The Prismoidal Formula. — The prismoidal formula is a general formula by which the volume of any prism, pyramid or frustum of a pyramid may be found.

A_1 = area at one end of the body;
A_2 = area at the other end;
A_m = area of middle section between the two end surfaces;
h = height of body.

Then, volume V of the body is

$$V = \frac{h}{6} (A_1 + 4 A_m + A_2)$$

Pappus or Guldinus Rules. — By means of these rules the area of any surface of revolution and the volume of any solid of revolution may be found. The area of the surface swept out by the revolution of a line ABC (see illustration) about the axis DE equals the length of the line multiplied by the length of the path

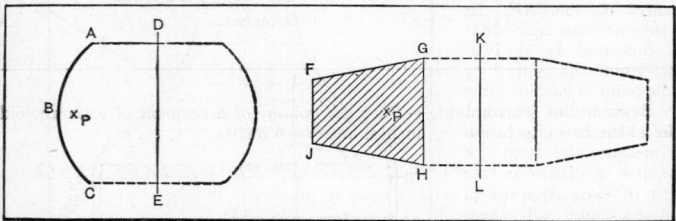

of its center of gravity, P. If the line is of such a shape that it is difficult to determine its center of gravity, then the line may be divided into a number of short sections, each of which may be considered as a straight line, and the areas swept out by these different sections, as computed by the rule given, may be added to find the total area. The line must lie wholly on one side of the axis of revolution and must be in the same plane.

The volume of a solid body formed by the revolution of a surface $FGHJ$ about axis KL equals the area of the surface multiplied by the length of the path of its center of gravity. The surface must lie wholly on one side of the axis of revolution and in the same plane.

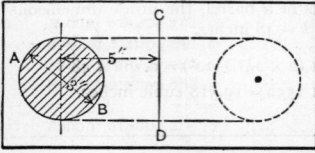

Example: — By means of these rules the area and volume of a cylindrical ring or torus may be found. The torus is formed by a circle AB being rotated about axis CD. The center of gravity of the circle is at its center. Hence, with the dimensions given in the illustration, the length of the path of the center of gravity of the circle is $3.1416 \times 10 = 31.416$ inches. This multiplied by the length of the circumference of the circle, which is $3.1416 \times 3 = 9.4248$ inches, equals:

$$31.416 \times 9.4248 = 296.089 \text{ square inches}$$

which is the area of the torus.

The volume equals the area of the circle, which is $0.7854 \times 9 = 7.0686$ square inches, multiplied by the path of the center of gravity, which is 31.416, as before; hence,

$$\text{volume} = 7.0686 \times 31.416 = 222.067 \text{ cubic inches.}$$

Example of Approximate Method for Finding the Area of a Surface of Revolution. — The accompanying illustration is shown in order to give an example of the approximate method based on Guldinus' rule, that can be used for finding the area of a symmetrical body. In the illustration, the dimensions in common fractions are the known dimensions; those in decimals are found by actual measurements on a figure drawn to scale. The method for finding the area is as follows: First separate such areas as are cylindrical, conical or spherical, as these can be found by exact formulas. In the illustration $ABCD$ is a cylinder, the area of the surface of which can be easily found. The top area EF is simply a circular area, and can thus be computed separately. The remainder of the surface generated by rotating line AF about the axis GH is found by the approximate method explained in the previous section. From point A, set off equal distances on line AF. In the present case each division indicated is ⅛ inch long. From the central or middle point of each of these parts draw a line at right angles to the axis of rotation GH, measure the length of these lines or diameters (the length of each is given in decimals), add all these lengths together and multiply the sum by the length of one division set off on line AF (in this case, ⅛ inch),

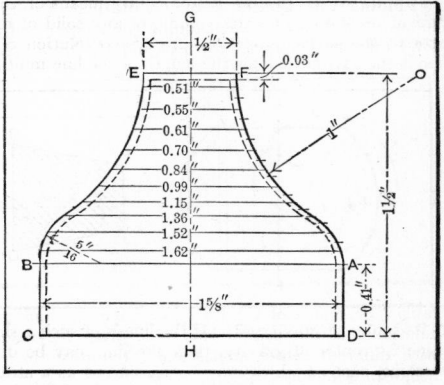

and multiply this product by π. This gives the approximate area of the surface of revolution.

In setting off divisions ⅛ inch long along line AF, the last division does not reach exactly to point F, but only to a point 0.03 inch below it. The part 0.03 inch high at the top of the cup, can be considered as a cylinder of ½ inch diameter and 0.03 inch height, the area of the cylindrical surface of which is easily computed. By adding the various surfaces together the total surface of the cup is found as below:

Cylinder, 1⅝ inch diameter, 0.41 inch high........	2.093 square inches
Circle, ½ inch diameter.........................	0.196 square inches
Cylinder, ½ inch diameter, 0.03 inch high.........	0.047 square inches
Irregular surface..............................	3.868 square inches
Total..................................	6.204 square inches

Plane Surfaces of Irregular Outline. — The areas of plane surfaces of irregular outline can best be found by dividing the surfaces into a number of geometrical figures, the areas of which can be found by the general rules and formulas. The most convenient method is, as a rule, to divide the area into a number of narrow strips which may be regarded as rectangles, the base of the rectangle being the width of the strip, and a line through the center of the strip its mean height. Surfaces of irregular outline, having straight boundary lines, are most conveniently divided into a number of triangles, the areas of which can be readily found and added together.

Areas Enclosed by Cycloidal Curves. — The area between a cycloid and the straight line upon which the generating circle rolls, equals three times the area of the generating circle (see diagram, page 154). The areas between epicycloidal and hypocycloidal curves and the "fixed circle" upon which the generating circle is rolled, may be determined by the following formulas, in which a = radius of the fixed circle upon which the generating circle rolls; b = radius of the generating circle; A = the area for the epicycloidal curve; and A_1 = the area for the hypocycloidal curve.

$$A = \frac{3.1416\, b^2\, (3\, a + 2\, b)}{a}; \qquad A_1 = \frac{3.1416\, b^2\, (3\, a - 2\, b)}{a}$$

Finding the Contents of Cylindrical Tanks at Different Levels. — The following method for determining the contents of a cylindrical tank at any given level may be employed for locating the graduations on gage sticks such as are

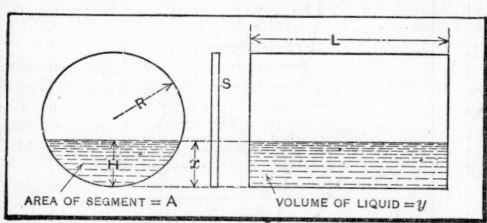

used for measuring approximately the contents, by inserting the gage vertically in the center of the tank with the lower end against the bottom and noting the relation between the level of the liquid and the graduation marks which indicate the number of gallons. The table "Segments of Circles" (see pages 72 and 73) is used to simplify the calculations. Column H of this table gives the values for the heights of segments with different center angles and for unit radius; or, in other words, the ratio: $\dfrac{\text{height of segment}}{\text{radius}}$. Another column gives the area of the segment in a circle of unit radius. The area of a similar segment of larger radius is this area multiplied by the given radius squared. Let

L = length of tank, in inches (see accompanying illustration);

R = radius in inches;

H = height of segment for unit radius = $\dfrac{\text{height}}{R}$;

y = capacity, in gallons, for which graduation is to be found on scale S;

x = distance from graduation mark to nearest end of scale;

$U = \dfrac{L}{231}$ gallons in one-inch square section, the length of which equals the length of the tank;

a = corresponding area in table giving areas for segments of unit radius;

A = area of segment of given radius.

As $H = \dfrac{\text{height}}{R} = \dfrac{x}{R}$, $x = HR$; also, by the rule at the head of the table, the area of a segment of given radius, or A, equals aR^2. The number of gallons represented by a graduation on the scale, or y, equals $AU = aR^2U$, and $a = \dfrac{y}{R^2U}$. Therefore, R^2U is a constant for any given tank. The method of procedure will be illustrated by a practical example.

Example: — A tank is 20 feet long and 6 feet in diameter, and the graduation mark representing 1000 gallons is to be located on a scale. Find the distance from the graduation mark to the nearest end of the scale.

As the radius of the tank is 36 inches and the length 240 inches, the total capacity, in this case, equals:

$$\frac{3.1416 \times 36^2 \times 240}{231} = 4230 \text{ gallons.}$$

As the graduation mark is to represent 1000 gallons, which is less than one-half the total capacity, this graduation will be located with reference to the lower end of the scale. The constant R^2U, for this tank, is $36^2 \times \frac{240}{231} = 1346$. As $a = \frac{y}{R^2U}$, the corresponding area of a segment of unit radius is $1000 \div 1346 = 0.743$. The table shows that this area is greater than the corresponding area of a segment of 129 degrees, and less than the area of a 130-degree segment. By interpolation, the value of H is found to be about 0.573. As $x = HR$, the graduation mark on the scale for 1000 gallons is $0.573 \times 36 = 20.62$ inches from the lower end.

In the preceding example, if a graduation mark were required to represent, say, 3000 gallons, this mark would be located from the top of the scale, because 3000 is more than one-half the total capacity of the tank. In this case, the value of y equals the difference between the total capacity and the number of gallons which the graduation is to represent. Thus, in this case, $y = 4230 - 3000 = 1230$, and $a = 1230 \div 1346 = 0.914$. By interpolation, the corresponding value of H is found to be 0.665. Therefore, $x = 0.665 \times 36 = 23.94$ inches for the 3000-gallon graduation mark.

Approximate Formulas for Finding Areas of Circular Segments. — An exact formula for area will be found on page 152, exact results being obtained provided the value of l is accurate. The formula for l (page 152) is used when angle a is in degrees, but if angle a is in seconds to obtain a more accurate result, then $l = .00000484814 \, ra$.

When approximate formulas for areas meet practical requirements, the following will prove useful. The notation used in these formulas is from the diagram on page 152; thus, A = area; h = height of segment; and c = length of chord.

Formula 1: If the segment is less than a semicircle, formula (1) gives results which are correct to three figures.

$$A = \frac{4\,h^2}{3}\sqrt{\frac{c^2}{4\,h^2} + 0.392} \tag{1}$$

Formula 2: The solution of this formula involves less work than formula (1), but the error is larger especially when the height of segment is large in proportion to length of the chord. For example, if $c = 2$ and $h = 1$, then the error in area with formula (1) is $+0.0023$, whereas with formula (2) it is $+0.0125$; whereas if $c = 40$ and $h = 1$, the error with formula (1) is -0.0062 and with formula (2) it is -0.0068.

$$A = \frac{h^3}{2\,c} + \frac{2\,ch}{3} \tag{2}$$

Formula (2) is accurate to within three figures when the height of the segment does not exceed one-fourth the length of the chord, and the error will be less than 1 per cent when the segment is a semicircle.

Formula 3: This formula gives results which are correct to four figures for a semicircle, but for general use it is less accurate than either of the other two approximate formulas.

$$A = \frac{h^3}{2\,c} + 0.6604\,ch \tag{3}$$

Diameters of Circles and Sides of Squares of Equal Area

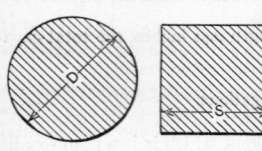

The table below will be found useful for determining the diameter of a circle of an area equal to that of a square, the side of which is known, or for determining the side of a square which has an area equal to that of a circle, the area or diameter of which is known. For example, if the diameter of a circle is 17½ inches, it is found from the table that the side of a square of the same area is 15.51 inches.

Diam. of Circle, D	Side of Square, S	Area of Circle or Square	Diam. of Circle, D	Side of Square, S	Area of Circle or Square	Diam. of Circle, D	Side of Square S	Area of Circle or Square
½	0.44	0.196	20½	18.17	330.06	40½	35.89	1288.25
1	0.89	0.785	21	18.61	346.36	41	36.34	1320.25
1½	1.33	1.767	21½	19.05	363.05	41½	36.78	1352.65
2	1.77	3.142	22	19.50	380.13	42	37.22	1385.44
2½	2.22	4.909	22½	19.94	397.61	42½	37.66	1418.63
3	2.66	7.069	23	20.38	415.48	43	38.11	1452.20
3½	3.10	9.621	23½	20.83	433.74	43½	38.55	1486.17
4	3.54	12.566	24	21.27	452.39	44	38.99	1520.53
4½	3.99	15.904	24½	21.71	471.44	44½	39.44	1555.28
5	4.43	19.635	25	22.16	490.87	45	39.88	1590.43
5½	4.87	23.758	25½	22.60	510.71	45½	40.32	1625.97
6	5.32	28.274	26	23.04	530.93	46	40.77	1661.90
6½	5.76	33.183	26½	23.49	551.55	46½	41.21	1698.23
7	6.20	38.485	27	23.93	572.56	47	41.65	1734.94
7½	6.65	44.179	27½	24.37	593.96	47½	42.10	1772.05
8	7.09	50.265	28	24.81	615.75	48	42.54	1809.56
8½	7.53	56.745	28½	25.26	637.94	48½	42.98	1847.45
9	7.98	63.617	29	25.70	660.52	49	43.43	1885.74
9½	8.42	70.882	29½	26.14	683.49	49½	43.87	1924.42
10	8.86	78.540	30	26.59	706.86	50	44.31	1963.50
10½	9.31	86.590	30½	27.03	730.62	50½	44.75	2002.96
11	9.75	95.033	31	27.47	754.77	51	45.20	2042.82
11½	10.19	103.87	31½	27.92	779.31	51½	45.64	2083.07
12	10.64	113.10	32	28.36	804.25	52	46.08	2123.72
12½	11.08	122.72	32½	28.80	829.58	52½	46.53	2164.75
13	11.52	132.73	33	29.25	855.30	53	46.97	2206.18
13½	11.96	143.14	33½	29.69	881.41	53½	47.41	2248.01
14	12.41	153.94	34	30.13	907.92	54	47.86	2290.22
14½	12.85	165.13	34½	30.57	934.82	54½	48.30	2332.83
15	13.29	176.71	35	31.02	962.11	55	48.74	2375.83
15½	13.74	188.69	35½	31.46	989.80	55½	49.19	2419.22
16	14.18	201.06	36	31.90	1017.88	56	49.63	2463.01
16½	14.62	213.82	36½	32.35	1046.35	56½	50.07	2507.19
17	15.07	226.98	37	32.79	1075.21	57	50.51	2551.76
17½	15.51	240.53	37½	33.23	1104.47	57½	50.96	2596.72
18	15.95	254.47	38	33.68	1134.11	58	51.40	2642.08
18½	16.40	268.80	38½	34.12	1164.16	58½	51.84	2687.83
19	16.84	283.53	39	34.56	1194.59	59	52.29	2733.97
19½	17.28	298.65	39½	35.01	1225.42	59½	52.73	2780.51
20	17.72	314.16	40	35.45	1256.64	60	53.17	2827.43

SOLUTION OF TRIANGLES

Any figure bounded by three straight lines is called a triangle. Any one of the three lines may be called the base, and the line drawn from the angle opposite the base at right angles to it is called the height or altitude of the triangle.

If all the three sides of a triangle are of equal length, the triangle is called *equilateral*. Each one of the three angles in an equilateral triangle equals 60 degrees. If two sides are of equal length, the triangle is an *isosceles* triangle. If one angle is a right or 90-degree angle, the triangle is a *right* or *right-angled* triangle. The side opposite the right angle is called the *hypotenuse*.

If all the angles are less than 90 degrees, the triangle is called an *acute* or *acute-angled* triangle. If one of the angles is larger than 90 degrees, the triangle is called an *obtuse-angled* triangle. Both acute and obtuse-angled triangles are known under the common name of *oblique-angled* triangles. The sum of the three angles in every triangle is 180 degrees.

The sides and angles of any triangle which are not known can be found when: 1. All the three sides; 2. Two sides and one angle; or, 3. One side and two angles, are given. In other words, if a triangle is considered as consisting of six parts, three angles and three sides, the unknown parts can be determined when any three parts are given, provided at least one of the given parts is a side.

Functions of Angles. — The functions of angles used in solving triangles are sine, cosine, tangent, cotangent, secant, and cosecant. These expressions are usually abbreviated as follows:

$$\begin{array}{ll} \sin = \text{sine}, & \cot = \text{cotangent}, \\ \cos = \text{cosine}, & \sec = \text{secant}, \\ \tan = \text{tangent}, & \text{cosec} = \text{cosecant}. \end{array}$$

If in a right-angled triangle (see the illustration in the table below), the lengths of the three sides are represented by a, b and c, and the angles opposite each of these sides by A, B and C, then the side a opposite the right angle is the hypotenuse;

Trigonometrical Functions of Angles

The *sine* of an angle equals the opposite side divided by the hypotenuse. Hence, $\sin B = b \div a$, and $\sin C = c \div a$.

The *cosine* of an angle equals the adjacent side divided by the hypotenuse. Hence, $\cos B = c \div a$, and $\cos C = b \div a$.

The *tangent* of an angle equals the opposite side divided by the adjacent side. Hence $\tan B = b \div c$, and $\tan C = c \div b$.

The *cotangent* of an angle equals the adjacent side divided by the opposite side. Hence, $\cot B = c \div b$, and $\cot C = b \div c$.

The *secant* of an angle equals the hypotenuse divided by the adjacent side. Hence, $\sec B = a \div c$, and $\sec C = a \div b$.

The *cosecant* of an angle equals the hypotenuse divided by the opposite side. Hence, cosec $B = a \div b$, and cosec $C = a \div c$.

It should be noted that the functions of the angles can be found in this manner only when the triangle is right-angled.

side *b* is called the *side adjacent* to angle *C* and is also the *side opposite* to angle *B*; side *c* is the side adjacent to angle *B* and the side opposite to angle *C*. The meanings of the various functions of angles can be explained by the aid of a right-angled triangle.

The following relation exists between the angular functions of the two acute angles in a right-angled triangle: The sine of angle *B* equals the cosine of angle *C*; the tangent of angle *B* equals the cotangent of angle *C*, and *vice versa*. The sum of the two acute angles in a right-angled triangle always equals 90 degrees; hence, when one angle is known, the other can easily be found. When any two angles together make 90 degrees, one is called the *complement* of the other, and in that case the sine of the one equals the cosine of the other, and the tangent of the one equals the cotangent of the other.

Graphic Illustrations of the Functions of Angles. — Draw a circle with a radius 1, as shown in the accompanying illustration. Draw two lines *AB* and *CD* at right angles to each other through the center of the circle; then draw a line *OE*

from the center *O* forming an angle *α* with line *OD*. The sine for this angle is represented by line *FG*, drawn from point *F* where *OE* intersects the periphery of the circle, at right angles to *CD*. The cosine of angle *α* is represented by line *OG*. The tangent of the angle is represented by line *DH* drawn from point *D* at right angles to *CD*. The cotangent is represented by line *AK* drawn from point *A* at right angles to *AB*. The secant is represented by *OH*, and the cosecant by *OK*.

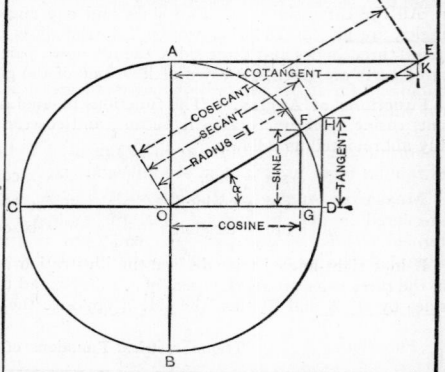

In graphically illustrating the functions of angles, it is assumed that all distances measured in the horizontal direction to the right of line *AB* are positive. Those measured horizontally to the left of *AB* are negative. All distances measured vertically, are positive above line *CD* and negative below it. It can then be readily seen that the sine is positive for all angles less than 180 degrees. For angles larger than 180 degrees, the sine would be measured below *CD*, and is negative. The cosine is positive up to 90 degrees, but for angles larger than 90 but less than 270 degrees, the cosine is measured to the left of line *AB* and is negative.

On the next page a table "Changes in Value and Sign of Trigonometrical Functions" is given. This table is arranged to show directly whether the function of any given angle is positive or negative. It also gives the limits between which the numerical values of the function vary. For example, it will be seen from the table that the cosine of an angle between 90 and 180 degrees is negative, and that its value will be somewhere between 0 and − 1. In the same way, the cotangent of an angle between 180 and 270 degrees is positive and has a value between infinity and 0; in other words, the cotangent for 180 degrees is infinitely large and then the cotangent gradually decreases for increasing angles, so that the cotangent for 270 degrees equals 0

Tables of Trigonometric Functions. — The numerical values for the natural or trigonometric functions for all degrees and minutes are given in the tables, pages 179 to 223 inclusive. The chart below shows how to find the functions of angles between 0 and 180 degrees.

How to Enter Table of Natural Trigonometric Functions

For Angles from	Enter Table for		For Angles from	Enter Table for	
	Degrees and Function	Minutes		Degrees and Function	Minutes
0° to 45°	at top	at left	90° to 135°	at bottom	at left
45° to 90°	at bottom	at right	135° to 180°	at top	at right

Exception· To obtain the versed sine of any angle from 90° to 180°, enter the table in column for cosine of required angle and add 1 to value shown.

Example: Find versed sine 102°10′. Versed sine = 1 − cos of angle. Between 90° and 180°, values of cosine are negative; hence,

$$1 - \cos 102°10' = 1 - (-0.21076) = 1 + 0.21076 = 1.21076$$

The sine is positive for all angles up to 180 degrees. The cosine, tangent and cotangent for angles between 90 and 180 degrees, while they have the same numerical values as for angles from 0 to 90 degrees, are negative. These should be preceded by a minus sign; thus tan 123 degrees 20 minutes = − 1.5204.

Formulas for the solution of right-angled and oblique-angled triangles, arranged in tabular form, are given on the following pages.

Measuring Angles in Radians. — While in practical work angles are always measured in degrees and minutes, the system for measuring angles in what is termed *circular measure* is often employed in theoretical investigations and in formulas relating to revolving bodies. In this system the unit of measurement is

Changes in Value and Sign of Trigonometrical Functions

Function	Between 0° and 90°	Between 90° and 180°	Between 180° and 270°	Between 270° and 360°
Sine	Positive From 0 to 1	Positive From 1 to 0	Negative From 0 to − 1	Negative From − 1 to 0
Cosine	Positive From 1 to 0	Negative From 0 to − 1	Negative From − 1 to 0	Positive From 0 to 1
Tangent	Positive From 0 to ∞	Negative From ∞ to 0	Positive From 0 to ∞	Negative From ∞ to 0
Cotangent	Positive From ∞ to 0	Negative From 0 to ∞	Positive From ∞ to 0	Negative From 0 to ∞
Secant	Positive From 1 to ∞	Negative From ∞ to − 1	Negative From − 1 to ∞	Positive From ∞ to 1
Cosecant	Positive From ∞ to 1	Positive From 1 to ∞	Negative From ∞ to − 1	Negative From − 1 to ∞

the *radian*, that is, the angle at the center of a circle which embraces an arc equal in length to the length of the radius. The value of the radian in degrees equals $180 \div \pi = 57.2958$ degrees. In this measurement, then, 3.1416 radians denotes an angle of 180 degrees, and 3.1416 radians $\div$ 2, an angle of 90 degrees.

It is especially convenient to measure angles in radians when dealing with angular velocity. If $\omega =$ angular velocity per second of the revolving body, in radians; $v =$ velocity of a point on the periphery of the body, in feet per second; and $r =$ the radius, in feet, then:

$$\omega = \frac{v}{r}$$

For example, assume that the velocity of a point on the periphery is 20 feet per second and the radius, 2 feet. Then the angular velocity is found as below:

$$\omega = \frac{20}{2} = 10 \text{ radians per second}$$

The simple manner in which the relation between the angular velocity, the linear velocity, and the radius or diameter of the revolving body can be expressed, is the reason for using the radian as a unit of angular measurement.

The Law of Sines. — In a triangle, any side is to any other side as the sine of the angle opposite the first side is to the sine of the angle opposite the other side; or, if a and b be the sides, and A and B the angles opposite them:

$$\frac{a}{b} = \frac{\sin A}{\sin B}$$

The Law of Cosines. — In a triangle, the square of any side is equal to the sum of the squares of the other two sides minus twice their product times the cosine of the included angle; or if a, b and c be the sides and the angle opposite side a be denoted A, then:

$$a^2 = b^2 + c^2 - 2\,bc \cos A$$

These two laws, together with the proposition that the sum of the three angles equals 180 degrees, are the basis of all formulas relating to the solution of triangles.

Use of Tables of Squares in Solving Right-angled Triangles. — The tables of squares at the beginning of the book may be used to advantage in solving right-angled triangles. Assume that the sides including the right angle are known, and that they are $1\frac{5}{8}$ and $1\frac{7}{8}$ inch, respectively. Find the side opposite the right angle.

$$\text{Side to be found} = \sqrt{1.625^2 + 1.875^2}$$

From tables of squares:

$$
\begin{array}{r}
1.625^2 = 2.640625 \\
1.875^2 = 3.515625 \\
\hline
6.156250
\end{array}
$$

By looking up the figures 615 in the number column in the tables, and finding the square root, we get the figures 24.799. The square root of 616 is 24.819. Hence, by estimating, the square root of 615.625 = 24.812. As we want the square root of 6.15625, move the decimal point in the root one step to the left; then $\sqrt{6.15625} = 2.4812$. This is the length of the side opposite the right angle.

Important Trigonometric Formulas

$$\sin^2 A + \cos^2 A = 1 \qquad\qquad \tan A = \frac{\sin A}{\cos A} = \frac{1}{\cot A}$$

$$\cot A = \frac{\cos A}{\sin A} = \frac{1}{\tan A} \qquad \sec A = \frac{1}{\cos A} \qquad \operatorname{cosec} A = \frac{1}{\sin A}$$

$$\sin A = \sqrt{1 - \cos^2 A} = \frac{\tan A}{\sqrt{1 + \tan^2 A}} = \frac{1}{\sqrt{1 + \cot^2 A}}$$

$$\cos A = \sqrt{1 - \sin^2 A} = \frac{1}{\sqrt{1 + \tan^2 A}} = \frac{\cot A}{\sqrt{1 + \cot^2 A}}$$

$$\sin (A + B) = \sin A \cos B + \cos A \sin B$$

$$\sin (A - B) = \sin A \cos B - \cos A \sin B$$

$$\cos (A + B) = \cos A \cos B - \sin A \sin B$$

$$\cos (A - B) = \cos A \cos B + \sin A \sin B$$

$$\tan (A + B) = \frac{\tan A + \tan B}{1 - \tan A \tan B} \qquad \tan (A - B) = \frac{\tan A - \tan B}{1 + \tan A \tan B}$$

$$\cot (A + B) = \frac{\cot A \cot B - 1}{\cot B + \cot A} \qquad \cot (A - B) = \frac{\cot A \cot B + 1}{\cot B - \cot A}$$

$$\tan A + \tan B = \frac{\sin (A + B)}{\cos A \cos B} \qquad \tan A - \tan B = \frac{\sin (A - B)}{\cos A \cos B}$$

$$\cot A + \cot B = \frac{\sin (B + A)}{\sin A \sin B} \qquad \cot A - \cot B = \frac{\sin (B - A)}{\sin A \sin B}$$

$$\sin^2 A - \sin^2 B = \cos^2 B - \cos^2 A = \sin (A + B) \sin (A - B)$$

$$\cos^2 A - \sin^2 B = \cos^2 B - \sin^2 A = \cos (A + B) \cos (A - B).$$

$$\sin A \sin B = \tfrac{1}{2} \cos (A - B) - \tfrac{1}{2} \cos (A + B).$$

$$\cos A \cos B = \tfrac{1}{2} \cos (A - B) + \tfrac{1}{2} \cos (A + B)$$

$$\sin A \cos B = \tfrac{1}{2} \sin (A + B) + \tfrac{1}{2} \sin (A - B)$$

$$\tan A \tan B = \frac{\tan A + \tan B}{\cot A + \cot B} \qquad \cot A \cot B = \frac{\cot A + \cot B}{\tan A + \tan B}$$

$$\sin A = 2 \sin \tfrac{1}{2} A \cos \tfrac{1}{2} A \qquad \sin 2 A = 2 \sin A \cos A$$

$$\cos 2 A = \cos^2 A - \sin^2 A = 1 - 2 \sin^2 A = 2 \cos^2 A - 1$$

$$\tan 2 A = \frac{2 \tan A}{1 - \tan^2 A} = \frac{2}{\cot A - \tan A}$$

$$\cot 2 A = \frac{\cot^2 A - 1}{2 \cot A} = \frac{\cot A - \tan A}{2}$$

$$\sin A = \frac{2 \tan \tfrac{1}{2} A}{1 + \tan^2 \tfrac{1}{2} A} \qquad\qquad \cos A = \frac{1 - \tan^2 \tfrac{1}{2} A}{1 + \tan^2 \tfrac{1}{2} A}$$

$$2 \sin^2 A = 1 - \cos 2 A \qquad\qquad 2 \cos^2 A = 1 + \cos 2 A$$

SOLUTION OF TRIANGLES

Solution of Right-angled Triangles

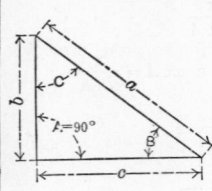

As shown in the illustration, the sides of the right-angled triangle are designated a, b and c. The angles opposite each of these sides are designated A, B and C, respectively.

Angle A, opposite the hypotenuse a is the right angle, and is therefore always one of the known quantities.

Sides and Angles Known	Formulas for Sides and Angles to be Found		
Sides a and b..........	$c = \sqrt{a^2 - b^2}$	$\sin B = \dfrac{b}{a}$	$C = 90° - B$
Sides a and c..........	$b = \sqrt{a^2 - c^2}$	$\sin C = \dfrac{c}{a}$	$B = 90° - C$
Sides b and c..........	$a = \sqrt{b^2 + c^2}$	$\tan B = \dfrac{b}{c}$	$C = 90° - B$
Side a; angle B........	$b = a \times \sin B$	$c = a \times \cos B$	$C = 90° - B$
Side a; angle C........	$b = a \times \cos C$	$c = a \times \sin C$	$B = 90° - C$
Side b; angle B........	$a = \dfrac{b}{\sin B}$	$c = b \times \cot B$	$C = 90° - B$
Side b; angle C........	$a = \dfrac{b}{\cos C}$	$c = b \times \tan C$	$B = 90° - C$
Side c; angle B........	$a = \dfrac{c}{\cos B}$	$b = c \times \tan B$	$C = 90° - B$
Side c; angle C........	$a = \dfrac{c}{\sin C}$	$b = c \times \cot C$	$B = 90° - C$

Examples of the Solution of Right-angled Triangles

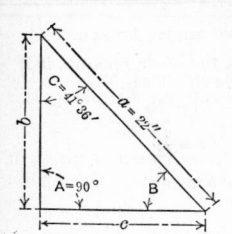

Sides and angles known:
$$a = 22 \text{ inches}; \quad C = 41° \ 36'.$$
Then, by the formulas given on the preceding page:
$$b = a \times \cos C = 22 \times \cos 41° \ 36' = 22 \times 0.74780$$
$$= 16.4516 \text{ inches.}$$
$$c = a \times \sin C = 22 \times \sin 41° \ 36' - 22 \times 0.66393$$
$$= 14.6065 \text{ inches.}$$
$$B = 90° - 41° \ 36' = 48° \ 24'.$$

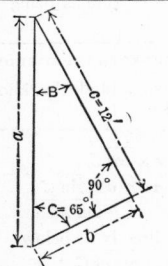

Sides and angles known:
$$c = 12 \text{ feet}; \quad C = 65°.$$
Then, by the formulas given on the preceding page:
$$a = \frac{c}{\sin C} = \frac{12}{\sin 65°} = \frac{12}{0.90631} = 13.2405 \text{ feet.}$$
$$b = c \times \cot C = 12 \times \cot 65° = 12 \times 0.46631$$
$$= 5.5957 \text{ feet.}$$
$$B = 90° - 65° = 25°.$$

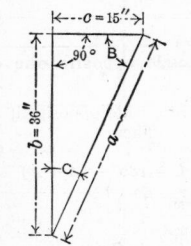

Sides known:
$$b = 36 \text{ inches}; \quad c = 15 \text{ inches.}$$
Then, by the formulas given on the preceding page:
$$a = \sqrt{b^2 + c^2} = \sqrt{36^2 + 15^2} = \sqrt{1296 + 225}$$
$$= \sqrt{1521} = 39 \text{ inches.}$$
$$\tan B = \frac{b}{c} = \frac{36}{15} = 2.4$$
Hence, $\quad B = 67° \ 23'.$
$$C = 90° - 67° \ 23' = 22° \ 37'.$$

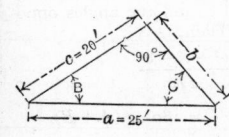

Sides known:
$$a = 25 \text{ feet}; \quad c = 20 \text{ feet.}$$
From the formulas on the preceding page:
$$b = \sqrt{a^2 - c^2} = \sqrt{25^2 - 20^2} = \sqrt{625 - 400}$$
$$= \sqrt{225} = 15 \text{ feet.}$$
$$\sin C = \frac{c}{a} = \frac{20}{25} = 0.8$$
Hence, $\quad C = 53° \ 8'.$
$$B = 90° - 53° \ 8' = 36° \ 52'.$$

Solution of Oblique-angled Triangles

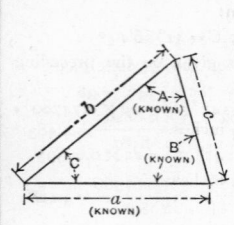

One side and two angles known.

Call the known side a, the angle opposite it A, and the other known angle B. Then:

$$C = 180° - (A + B)$$

$$b = \frac{a \times \sin B}{\sin A} \qquad c = \frac{a \times \sin C}{\sin A}$$

$$\text{Area} = \frac{a \times b \times \sin C}{2}$$

If angles B and C are given, but not A, then $A = 180° - (B + C)$, the other formulas being the same.

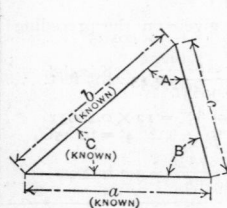

Two sides and the angle between them known.

Call the known sides a and b, and the known angle between them C. Then:

$$\tan A = \frac{a \times \sin C}{b - a \times \cos C}$$

$$B = 180° - (A + C) \qquad c = \frac{a \times \sin C}{\sin A}$$

Side c may also be found directly as below:

$$c = \sqrt{a^2 + b^2 - 2\,ab \times \cos C}$$

$$\text{Area} = \frac{a \times b \times \sin C}{2}$$

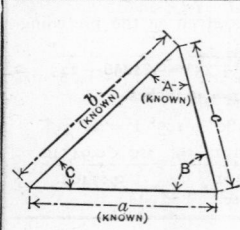

Two sides and the angle opposite one of the sides known.

Call the known angle A, the side opposite it a, and the other known side b. Then:

$$\sin B = \frac{b \times \sin A}{a} \qquad C = 180° - (A + B)$$

$$c = \frac{a \times \sin C}{\sin A}$$

$$\text{Area} = \frac{a \times b \times \sin C}{2}$$

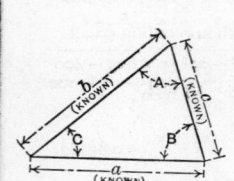

All three sides known.

Call the sides a, b and c, and the angles opposite them, A, B and C. Then:

$$\cos A = \frac{b^2 + c^2 - a^2}{2\,bc}$$

$$\sin B = \frac{b \times \sin A}{a} \qquad C = 180° - (A + B)$$

$$\text{Area} = \frac{a \times b \times \sin C}{2}$$

Examples of the Solution of Oblique-angled Triangles

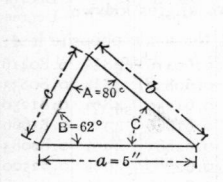

Sides and angles known:

$$a = 5 \text{ inches}; \quad A = 80°; \quad B = 62°.$$

Then, by the formulas on the opposite page:

$$C = 180° - (80° + 62°) = 180° - 142° = 38°.$$

$$b = \frac{a \times \sin B}{\sin A} = \frac{5 \times \sin 62°}{\sin 80°} = \frac{5 \times 0.88295}{0.98481} = 4.483$$

inches.

$$c = \frac{a \times \sin C}{\sin A} = \frac{5 \times \sin 38°}{\sin 80°} = \frac{5 \times 0.61566}{0.98481} = 3.126$$

inches.

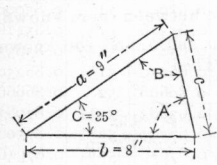

Sides and angles known:

$$a = 9 \text{ inches}; \quad b = 8 \text{ inches}; \quad C = 35°.$$

$$\tan A = \frac{a \times \sin C}{b - a \times \cos C} = \frac{9 \times \sin 35°}{8 - 9 \times \cos 35°}$$

$$= \frac{9 \times 0.57358}{8 - 9 \times 0.81915} = \frac{5.16222}{0.62765} = 8.22468.$$

Hence, $A = 83° 4'.$

$$B = 180° - (A + C) = 180° - 118° 4' = 61° 56'.$$

$$c = \frac{a \times \sin C}{\sin A} = \frac{9 \times 0.57358}{0.99269} = 5.2 \text{ inches.}$$

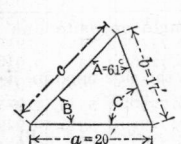

Sides and angles known:

$$a = 20 \text{ feet}; \quad b = 17 \text{ feet}; \quad A = 61°.$$

$$\sin B = \frac{b \times \sin A}{a} = \frac{17 \times \sin 61°}{20}$$

$$= \frac{17 \times 0.87462}{20} = 0.74343.$$

Hence, $B = 48° 1'.$

$$C = 180° - (A + B) = 180° - 109° 1' = 70° 59'.$$

$$c = \frac{a \times \sin C}{\sin A} = \frac{20 \times \sin 70° 59'}{\sin 61°} = \frac{20 \times 0.94542}{0.87462}$$

$$= 21.62 \text{ feet.}$$

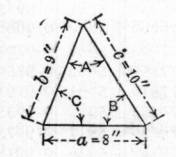

Sides known:

$$a = 8 \text{ inches}; \quad b = 9 \text{ inches}; \quad c = 10 \text{ inches.}$$

$$\cos A = \frac{b^2 + c^2 - a^2}{2\,bc} = \frac{9^2 + 10^2 - 8^2}{2 \times 9 \times 10}$$

$$= \frac{81 + 100 - 64}{180} = \frac{117}{180} = 0.65000.$$

Hence, $A = 49° 27'.$

$$\sin B = \frac{b \times \sin A}{a} = \frac{9 \times 0.75984}{8} = 0.85482.$$

Hence, $B = 58° 44'.$

$$C = 180° - (A + B) = 180° - 108° 11' = 71° 49'.$$

Table for Converting Minutes into Decimals of a Degree

Min.	Dec. of Degree	Min.	Dec. of Degree	Min.	Dec. of Degree	Min.	Dec. of Degree	Min.	Dec. of Degree
¼	0.00416	12¼	0.20416	24¼	0.40416	36¼	0.60416	48¼	0.80416
½	0.00833	12½	0.20833	24½	0.40833	36½	0.60833	48½	0.80833
¾	0.01250	12¾	0.21250	24¾	0.41250	36¾	0.61250	48¾	0.81250
1	0.01666	13	0.21666	25	0.41666	37	0.61666	49	0.81666
1¼	0.02083	13¼	0.22083	25¼	0.42083	37¼	0.62083	49¼	0.82083
1½	0.02500	13½	0.22500	25½	0.42500	37½	0.62500	49½	0.82500
1¾	0.02916	13¾	0.22916	25¾	0.42916	37¾	0.62916	49¾	0.82916
2	0.03333	14	0.23333	26	0.43333	38	0.63333	50	0.83333
2¼	0.03750	14¼	0.23750	26¼	0.43750	38¼	0.63750	50¼	0.83750
2½	0.04166	14½	0.24166	26½	0.44166	38½	0.64166	50½	0.84166
2¾	0.04583	14¾	0.24583	26¾	0.44583	38¾	0.64583	50¾	0.84583
3	0.05000	15	0.25000	27	0.45000	39	0.65000	51	0.85000
3¼	0.05416	15¼	0.25416	27¼	0.45416	39¼	0.65416	51¼	0.85416
3½	0.05833	15½	0.25833	27½	0.45833	39½	0.65833	51½	0.85833
3¾	0.06250	15¾	0.26250	27¾	0.46250	39¾	0.66250	51¾	0.86250
4	0.06666	16	0.26666	28	0.46666	40	0.66666	52	0.86666
4¼	0.07083	16¼	0.27083	28¼	0.47083	40¼	0.67083	52¼	0.87083
4½	0.07500	16½	0.27500	28½	0.47500	40½	0.67500	52½	0.87500
4¾	0.07916	16¾	0.27916	28¾	0.47916	40¾	0.67916	52¾	0.87916
5	0.08333	17	0.28333	29	0.48333	41	0.68333	53	0.88333
5¼	0.08750	17¼	0.28750	29¼	0.48750	41¼	0.68750	53¼	0.88750
5½	0.09166	17½	0.29166	29½	0.49166	41½	0.69166	53½	0.89166
5¾	0.09583	17¾	0.29583	29¾	0.49583	41¾	0.69583	53¾	0.89583
6	0.10000	18	0.30000	30	0.50000	42	0.70000	54	0.90000
6¼	0.10416	18¼	0.30416	30¼	0.50416	42¼	0.70416	54¼	0.90416
6½	0.10833	18½	0.30833	30½	0.50833	42½	0.70833	54½	0.90833
6¾	0.11250	18¾	0.31250	30¾	0.51250	42¾	0.71250	54¾	0.91250
7	0.11666	19	0.31666	31	0.51666	43	0.71666	55	0.91666
7¼	0.12083	19¼	0.32083	31¼	0.52083	43¼	0.72083	55¼	0.92083
7½	0.12500	19½	0.32500	31½	0.52500	43½	0.72500	55½	0.92500
7¾	0.12916	19¾	0.32916	31¾	0.52916	43¾	0.72916	55¾	0.92916
8	0.13333	20	0.33333	32	0.53333	44	0.73333	56	0.93333
8¼	0.13750	20¼	0.33750	32¼	0.53750	44¼	0.73750	56¼	0.93750
8½	0.14166	20½	0.34166	32½	0.54166	44½	0.74166	56½	0.94166
8¾	0.14583	20¾	0.34583	32¾	0.54583	44¾	0.74583	56¾	0.94583
9	0.15000	21	0.35000	33	0.55000	45	0.75000	57	0.95000
9¼	0.15416	21¼	0.35416	33¼	0.55416	45¼	0.75416	57¼	0.95416
9½	0.15833	21½	0.35833	33½	0.55833	45½	0.75833	57½	0.95833
9¾	0.16250	21¾	0.36250	33¾	0.56250	45¾	0.76250	57¾	0.96250
10	0.16666	22	0.36666	34	0.56666	46	0.76666	58	0.96666
10¼	0.17083	22¼	0.37083	34¼	0.57083	46¼	0.77083	58¼	0.97083
10½	0.17500	22½	0.37500	34½	0.57500	46½	0.77500	58½	0.97500
10¾	0.17916	22¾	0.37916	34¾	0.57916	46¾	0.77916	58¾	0.97916
11	0.18333	23	0.38333	35	0.58333	47	0.78333	59	0.98333
11¼	0.18750	23¼	0.38750	35¼	0.58750	47¼	0.78750	59¼	0.98750
11½	0.19166	23½	0.39166	35½	0.59166	47½	0.79166	59½	0.99166
11¾	0.19583	23¾	0.39583	35¾	0.59583	47¾	0.79583	59¾	0.99583
12	0.20000	24	0.40000	36	0.60000	48	0.80000	60	1.00000

0° **Natural Trigonometric Functions** 179°

M	Sine	Cosine	Tan.	Cotan.	Secant	Cosec.	Vrs. Sin.	Vrs. Cos.	M
0	0.00000	1.0000	0.00000	Infinite	1.0000	Infinite	0.00000	1.00000	60
1	.00029	.0000	.00029	3437.7	.0000	3437.7	.00000	0.99971	59
2	.00058	.0000	.00058	1718.9	.0000	1718.9	.00000	.99942	58
3	.00087	.0000	.00087	1145.9	.0000	1145.9	.00000	.99913	57
4	.00116	.0000	.00116	859.44	.0000	859.44	.00000	.99884	56
5	0.00145	1.0000	0.00145	687.55	1.0000	687.55	0.00000	0.99854	55
6	.00174	.0000	.00174	572.96	.0000	572.96	.00000	.99825	54
7	.00204	.0000	.00204	491.11	.0000	491.11	.00000	.99796	53
8	.00233	.0000	.00233	429.72	.0000	429.72	.00000	.99767	52
9	.00262	.0000	.00262	381.97	.0000	381.97	.00000	.99738	51
10	0.00291	0.99999	0.00291	343.77	1.0000	343.77	0.00000	0.99709	50
11	.00320	.99999	.00320	312.52	.0000	312.52	.00000	.99680	49
12	.00349	.99999	.00349	286.48	.0000	286.48	.00001	.99651	48
13	.00378	.99999	.00378	264.44	.0000	264.44	.00001	.99622	47
14	.00407	.99999	.00407	245.55	.0000	245.55	.00001	.99593	46
15	0.00436	0.99999	0.00436	229.18	1.0000	229.18	0.00001	0.99564	45
16	.00465	.99999	.00465	214.86	.0000	214.86	.00001	.99534	44
17	.00494	.99999	.00494	202.22	.0000	202.22	.00001	.99505	43
18	.00524	.99999	.00524	190.98	.0000	190.99	.00001	.99476	42
19	.00553	.99998	.00553	180.93	.0000	180.93	.00001	.99447	41
20	0.00582	0.99998	0.00582	171.88	1.0000	171.89	0.00002	0.99418	40
21	.00611	.99998	.00611	163.70	.0000	163.70	.00002	.99389	39
22	.00640	.99998	.00640	156.26	.0000	156.26	.00002	.99360	38
23	.00669	.99998	.00669	149.46	.0000	149.47	.00002	.99331	37
24	.00698	.99997	.00698	143.24	.0000	143.24	.00002	.99302	36
25	0.00727	0.99997	0.00727	137.51	1.0000	137.51	0.00003	0.99273	35
26	.00756	.99997	.00756	132.22	.0000	132.22	.00003	.99244	34
27	.00785	.99997	.00785	127.32	.0000	127.32	.00003	.99215	33
28	.00814	.99997	.00814	122.77	.0000	122.78	.00003	.99185	32
29	.00843	.99996	.00844	118.54	.0000	118.54	.00004	.99156	31
30	0.00873	0.99996	0.00873	114.59	1.0000	114.59	0.00004	0.99127	30
31	.00902	.99996	.00902	110.89	.0000	110.90	.00004	.99098	29
32	.00931	.99996	.00931	107.43	.0000	107.43	.00005	.99069	28
33	.00960	.99995	.00960	104.17	.0000	104.17	.00005	.99040	27
34	.00989	.99995	.00989	101.11	.0000	101.11	.00005	.99011	26
35	0.01018	0.99995	0.01018	98.218	1.0000	98.223	0.00005	0.98982	25
36	.01047	.99994	.01047	95.489	.0000	95.495	.00006	.98953	24
37	.01076	.99994	.01076	92.908	.0000	92.914	.00006	.98924	23
38	.01105	.99994	.01105	90.463	.0001	90.469	.00006	.98895	22
39	.01134	.99993	.01134	88.143	.0001	88.149	.00006	.98865	21
40	0.01163	0.99993	0.01164	85.940	1.0001	85.946	0.00007	0.98836	20
41	.01193	.99993	.01193	83.843	.0001	83.849	.00007	.98807	19
42	.01222	.99992	.01222	81.847	.0001	81.853	.00007	.98778	18
43	.01251	.99992	.01251	79.943	.0001	79.950	.00008	.98749	17
44	.01280	.99992	.01280	78.126	.0001	78.133	.00008	.98720	16
45	0.01309	0.99991	0.01309	76.390	1.0001	76.396	0.00008	0.98691	15
46	.01338	.99991	.01338	74.729	.0001	74.736	.00009	.98662	14
47	.01367	.99991	.01367	73.139	.0001	73.146	.00009	.98633	13
48	.01396	.99990	.01396	71.615	.0001	71.622	.00010	.98604	12
49	.01425	.99990	.01425	70.153	.0001	70.160	.00010	.98575	11
50	0.01454	0.99989	0.01454	68.750	1.0001	68.757	0.00010	0.98546	10
51	.01483	.99989	.01484	67.402	.0001	67.409	.00011	.98516	9
52	.01512	.99988	.01513	66.105	.0001	66.113	.00011	.98487	8
53	.01542	.99988	.01542	64.858	.0001	64.866	.00012	.98458	7
54	.01571	.99988	.01571	63.657	.0001	63.664	.00012	.98429	6
55	0.01600	0.99987	0.01600	62.499	1.0001	62.507	0.00013	0.98400	5
56	.01629	.99987	.01629	61.383	.0001	61.391	.00013	.98371	4
57	.01658	.99987	.01658	60.306	.0001	60.314	.00014	.98342	3
58	.01687	.99986	.01687	59.266	.0001	59.274	.00014	.98313	2
59	.01716	.99985	.01716	58.261	.0001	58.270	.00015	.98284	1
60	0.01745	0.99985	0.01745	57.290	1.0001	57.299	0.00015	0.98255	0
M	Cosine	Sine	Cotan.	Tan.	Cosec.	Secant	Vrs. Cos.	Vrs. Sin.	M

90° 89°

Natural Trigonometric Functions

M	Sine	Cosine	Tan.	Cotan.	Secant	Cosec.	Vrs. Sin.	Vrs. Cos.	M
0	0.01745	0.99985	0.01745	57.290	1.0001	57.299	0.00015	0.98255	60
1	.01774	.99984	.01775	56.350	.0001	56.359	.00016	.98226	59
2	.01803	.99984	.01804	55.441	.0001	55.450	.00016	.98196	58
3	.01832	.99983	.01833	54.561	.0002	54.570	.00017	.98167	57
4	.01861	.99983	.01862	53.708	.0002	53.718	.00017	.98138	56
5	0.01891	0.99982	0.01891	52.882	1.0002	52.891	0.00018	0.98109	55
6	.01920	.99981	.01920	52.081	.0002	52.090	.00018	.98080	54
7	.01949	.99981	.01949	51.303	.0002	51.313	.00019	.98051	53
8	.01978	.99980	.01978	50.548	.0002	50.558	.00019	.98022	52
9	.02007	.99980	.02007	49.816	.0002	49.826	.00020	.97993	51
10	0.02036	0.99979	0.02036	49.104	1.0002	49.114	0.00021	0.97964	50
11	.02065	.99979	.02066	48.412	.0002	48.422	.00021	.97935	49
12	.02094	.99978	.02095	47.739	.0002	47.750	.00022	.97906	48
13	.02123	.99977	.02124	47.085	.0002	47.096	.00022	.97877	47
14	.02152	.99977	.02153	46.449	.0002	46.460	.00023	.97847	46
15	0.02181	0.99976	0.02182	45.829	1.0002	45.840	0.00024	0.97818	45
16	.02210	.99975	.02211	45.226	.0002	45.237	.00024	.97789	44
17	.02240	.99975	.02240	44.638	.0002	44.650	.00025	.97760	43
18	.02269	.99974	.02269	44.066	.0002	44.077	.00026	.97731	42
19	.02298	.99974	.02298	43.508	.0003	43.520	.00026	.97702	41
20	0.02326	0.99973	0.02327	42.964	1.0003	42.976	0.00027	0.97673	40
21	.02356	.99972	.02357	42.433	.0003	42.445	.00028	.97644	39
22	.02385	.99971	.02386	41.916	.0003	41.928	.00028	.97615	38
23	.02414	.99971	.02415	41.410	.0003	41.423	.00029	.97586	37
24	.02443	.99970	.02444	40.917	.0003	40.930	.00030	.97557	36
25	0.02472	0.99969	0.02473	40.435	1.0003	40.448	0.00030	0.97528	35
26	.02501	.99969	.02502	39.965	.0003	39.978	.00031	.97499	34
27	.02530	.99968	.02531	39.506	.0003	39.518	.00032	.97469	33
28	.02559	.99967	.02560	39.057	.0003	39.069	.00033	.97440	32
29	.02589	.99966	.02589	38.618	.0003	38.631	.00033	.97411	31
30	0.02618	0.99966	0.02618	38.188	1.0003	38.201	0.00034	0.97382	30
31	.02647	.99965	.02648	37.769	.0003	37.782	.00035	.97353	29
32	.02676	.99964	.02677	37.358	.0003	37.371	.00036	.97324	28
33	.02705	.99963	.02706	36.956	.0004	36.969	.00036	.97295	27
34	.02734	.99963	.02735	36.563	.0004	36.576	.00037	.97266	26
35	0.02763	0.99962	0.02764	36.177	1.0004	36.191	0.00033	0.97237	25
36	.02792	.99961	.02793	35.800	.0004	35.814	.00039	.97208	24
37	.02821	.99960	.02822	35.431	.0004	35.445	.00040	.97179	23
38	.02850	.99959	.02851	35.069	.0004	35.084	.00041	.97150	22
39	.02879	.99958	.02881	34.715	.0004	34.729	.00041	.97121	21
40	0.02908	0.99958	0.02910	34.368	1.0004	34.382	0.00042	0.97091	20
41	.02937	.99957	.02939	34.027	.0004	34.042	.00043	.97062	19
42	.02967	.99956	.02963	33.693	.0004	33.708	.00044	.97033	18
43	.02996	.99955	.02997	33.366	.0004	33.381	.00045	.97004	17
44	.03025	.99954	.03026	33.045	.0004	33.060	.00045	.96975	16
45	0.03054	0.99953	0.03055	32.730	1.0005	32.745	0.00046	0.96946	15
46	.03083	.99952	.03084	32.421	.0005	32.437	.00047	.96917	14
47	.03112	.99951	.03113	32.118	.0005	32.134	.00048	.96888	13
48	.03141	.99951	.03143	31.820	.0005	31.836	.00049	.96859	12
49	.03170	.99950	.03172	31.528	.0005	31.544	.00050	.96830	11
50	0.03199	0.99949	0.03201	31.241	1.0005	31.257	0.00051	0.96801	10
51	.03228	.99948	.03230	30.960	.0005	30.976	.00052	.96772	9
52	.03257	.99947	.03259	30.633	.0005	30.699	.00053	.96743	8
53	.03286	.99946	.03288	30.411	.0005	30.428	.00054	.96713	7
54	.03315	.99945	.03317	30.145	.0005	30.161	.00055	.96684	6
55	0.03344	0.99944	0.03346	29.882	1.0005	29.899	0.00056	0.96655	5
56	.03374	.99943	.03375	29.624	.0006	29.641	.00057	.96626	4
57	.03403	.99942	.03405	29.371	.0006	29.388	.00058	.96597	3
58	.03432	.99941	.03434	29.122	.0006	29.139	.00059	.96568	2
59	.03461	.99940	.03463	28.877	.0006	28.894	.00060	.96539	1
60	0.03490	0.99939	0.03492	28.636	1.0006	28.654	0.00061	0.96510	0
M	Cosine	Sine	Cotan.	Tan.	Cosec.	Secant	Vrs. Cos.	Vrs. Sin.	M

M	Sine	Cosine	Tan.	Cotan.	Secant	Cosec.	Vrs. Sin.	Vrs. Cos.	M
0	0.03490	0.99939	0.03492	28.636	1.0006	28.654	0.00061	0.96510	60
1	.03519	.99938	.03521	28.399	.0006	28.417	.00062	.96481	59
2	.03548	.99937	.03550	28.166	.0006	28.184	.00063	.96452	58
3	.03577	.99936	.03579	27.937	.0006	27.955	.00064	.96423	57
4	.03606	.99935	.03608	27.712	.0006	27.730	.00065	.96394	56
5	0.03635	0.99934	0.03638	27.490	1.0007	27.508	0.00066	0.96365	55
6	.03664	.99933	.03667	27.271	.0007	27.290	.00067	.96336	54
7	.03693	.99932	.03696	27.056	.0007	27.075	.00068	.96306	53
8	.03722	.99931	.03725	26.845	.0007	26.864	.00069	.96277	52
9	.03751	.99930	.03754	26.637	.0007	26.655	.00070	.96248	51
10	0.03781	0.99928	0.03783	26.432	1.0007	26.450	0.00071	0.96219	50
11	.03810	.99927	.03812	26.230	.0007	26.249	.00073	.96190	49
12	.03839	.99926	.03842	26.031	.0007	26.050	.00074	.96161	48
13	.03868	.99925	.03871	25.835	.0007	25.854	.00075	.96132	47
14	.03897	.99924	.03900	25.642	.0008	25.661	.00076	.96103	46
15	0.03926	0.99923	0.03929	25.452	1.0008	25.471	0.00077	0.96074	45
16	.03955	.99922	.03958	25.264	.0008	25.284	.00078	.96045	44
17	.03984	.99921	.03987	25.080	.0008	25.100	.00079	.96016	43
18	.04013	.99919	.04016	24.898	.0008	24.918	.00080	.95987	42
19	.04042	.99918	.04045	24.718	.0008	24.739	.00082	.95958	41
20	0.04071	0.99917	0.04075	24.542	1.0008	24.562	0.00083	0.95929	40
21	.04100	.99916	.04104	24.367	.0008	24.388	.00084	.95900	39
22	.04129	.99915	.04133	24.196	.0008	24.216	.00085	.95870	38
23	.04158	.99913	.04162	24.026	.0009	24.047	.00086	.95841	37
24	.04187	.99912	.04191	23.859	.0009	23.880	.00088	.95812	36
25	0.04217	0.99911	0.04220	23.694	1.0009	23.716	0.00089	0.95783	35
26	.04246	.99910	.04249	23.532	.0009	23.553	.00090	.95754	34
27	.04275	.99908	.04279	23.372	.0009	23.393	.00091	.95725	33
28	.04304	.99907	.04308	23.214	.0009	23.235	.00093	.95696	32
29	.04333	.99906	.04337	23.058	.0009	23.079	.00094	.95667	31
30	0.04362	0.99905	0.04366	22.904	1.0009	22.925	0.00095	0.95638	30
31	.04391	.99903	.04395	22.752	.0010	22.774	.00096	.95609	29
32	.04420	.99902	.04424	22.602	.0010	22.624	.00098	.95580	28
33	.04449	.99901	.04453	22.454	.0010	22.476	.00099	.95551	27
34	.04478	.99900	.04483	22.308	.0010	22.330	.00100	.95522	26
35	0.04507	0.99898	0.04512	22.164	1.0010	22.186	0.00102	0.95493	25
36	.04536	.99897	.04541	22.022	.0010	22.044	.00103	.95464	24
37	.04565	.99896	.04570	21.881	.0010	21.904	.00104	.95435	23
38	.04594	.99894	.04599	21.742	.0010	21.765	.00106	.95405	22
39	.04623	.99893	.04628	21.606	.0011	21.629	.00107	.95376	21
40	0.04652	0.99882	0.04657	21.470	1.0011	21.494	0.00108	0.95347	20
41	.04681	.99890	.04687	21.337	.0011	21.360	.00110	.95318	19
42	.04711	.99889	.04716	21.205	.0011	21.228	.00111	.95289	18
43	.04740	.99888	.04745	21.075	.0011	21.098	.00112	.95260	17
44	.04769	.99886	.04774	20.946	.0011	20.970	.00114	.95231	16
45	0.04798	0.99885	0.04803	20.819	1.0011	20.843	0.00115	0.95202	15
46	.04827	.99883	.04832	20.693	.0012	20.717	.00116	.95173	14
47	.04856	.99882	.04862	20.569	.0012	20.593	.00118	.95144	13
48	.04885	.99881	.04891	20.446	.0012	20.471	.00119	.95115	12
49	.04914	.99879	.04920	20.325	.0012	20.350	.00121	.95086	11
50	0.04943	0.99878	0.04949	20.205	1.0012	20.230	0.00122	0.95057	10
51	.04972	.99876	.04978	20.087	.0012	20.112	.00124	.95028	9
52	.05001	.99875	.05007	19.970	.0013	19.995	.00125	.94999	8
53	.05030	.99873	.05037	19.854	.0013	19.880	.00127	.94970	7
54	.05059	.99872	.05066	19.740	.0013	19.766	.00128	.94941	6
55	0.05088	0.99870	0.05095	19.627	1.0013	19.653	0.00129	0.94912	5
56	.05117	.99869	.05124	19.515	.0013	19.541	.00131	.94883	4
57	.05146	.99867	.05153	19.405	.0013	19.431	.00132	.94853	3
58	.05175	.99866	.05182	19.296	.0013	19.322	.00134	.94824	2
59	.05204	.99864	.05212	19.188	.0013	19.214	.00135	.94795	1
60	0.05234	0.99863	0.05241	19.081	1.0014	19.107	0.00137	0.94766	0
M	Cosine	Sine	Cotan.	Tan.	Cosec.	Secant	Vrs. Cos.	Vrs. Sin.	M

3°　**Natural Trigonometric Functions**　176°

M	Sine	Cosine	Tan.	Cotan.	Secant	Cosec.	Vrs. Sin.	Vrs. Cos.	M
0	0.05234	0.99863	0.05241	19.081	1.0014	19.107	0.00137	0.94766	60
1	.05263	.99861	.05270	18.975	.0014	19.002	.00138	.94737	59
2	.05292	.99860	.05299	18.871	.0014	18.897	.00140	.94708	58
3	.05321	.99858	.05328	18.768	.0014	18.794	.00142	.94679	57
4	.05350	.99857	.05357	18.665	.0014	18.692	.00143	.94650	56
5	0.05379	0.99855	0.05387	18.564	1.0014	18.591	0.00145	0.94621	55
6	.05408	.99854	.05416	18.464	.0015	18.491	.00146	.94592	54
7	.05437	.99852	.05445	18.365	.0015	18.393	.00148	.94563	53
8	.05466	.99850	.05474	18.268	.0015	18.295	.00149	.94534	52
9	.05495	.99849	.05503	18.171	.0015	18.198	.00151	.94505	51
10	0.05524	0.99847	0.05532	18.075	1.0015	18.103	0.00153	0.94476	50
11	.05553	.99846	.05562	17.980	.0015	18.008	.00154	.94447	49
12	.05582	.99844	.05591	17.886	.0016	17.914	.00156	.94418	48
13	.05611	.99842	.05620	17.793	.0016	17.821	.00157	.94389	47
14	.05640	.99841	.05649	17.701	.0016	17.730	.00159	.94360	46
15	0.05669	0.99839	0.05678	17.610	1.0016	17.639	0.00161	0.94331	45
16	.05698	.99837	.05707	17.520	.0016	17.549	.00162	.94302	44
17	.05727	.99836	.05737	17.431	.0016	17.460	.00164	.94273	43
18	.05756	.99834	.05766	17.343	.0017	17.372	.00166	.94244	42
19	.05785	.99832	.05795	17.256	.0017	17.285	.00167	.94214	41
20	0.05814	0.99831	0.05824	17.169	1.0017	17.198	0.00169	0.94185	40
21	.05843	.99829	.05853	17.084	.0017	17.113	.00171	.94156	39
22	.05872	.99827	.05883	16.999	.0017	17.028	.00172	.94127	38
23	.05902	.99826	.05912	16.915	.0017	16.944	.00174	.94098	37
24	.05931	.99824	.05941	16.832	.0018	16.861	.00176	.94069	36
25	0.05960	0.99322	0.05970	16.750	1.0018	16.779	0.00178	0.94040	35
26	.05989	.99820	.05999	16.668	.0018	16.698	.00179	.94011	34
27	.06018	.99819	.06029	16.587	.0018	16.617	.00181	.93982	33
28	.06047	.99817	.06058	16.507	.0018	16.538	.00183	.93953	32
29	.06076	.99815	.06087	16.428	.0018	16.459	.00185	.93924	31
30	0.06105	0.99813	0.06116	16.350	1.0019	16.380	0.00186	0.93895	30
31	.06134	.99812	.06145	16.272	.0019	16.303	.00188	.93866	29
32	.06163	.99810	.06175	16.195	.0019	16.226	.00190	.93837	28
33	.06192	.99808	.06204	16.119	.0019	16.150	.00192	.93808	27
34	.06221	.99806	.06233	16.043	.0019	16.075	.00194	.93777	26
35	0.06250	0.99804	0.06262	15.969	1.0019	16.000	0.00195	0.93750	25
36	.06279	.99803	.06291	15.894	.0020	15.926	.00197	.93721	24
37	.06308	.99801	.06321	15.821	.0020	15.853	.00199	.93692	23
38	.06337	.99799	.06350	15.748	.0020	15.780	.00201	.93663	22
39	.06366	.99797	.06379	15.676	.0020	15.708	.00203	.93634	21
40	0.06395	0.99795	0.06408	15.605	1.0020	15.637	0.00205	0.93605	20
41	.06424	.99793	.06437	15.534	.0021	15.566	.00206	.93576	19
42	.06453	.99791	.06467	15.464	.0021	15.496	.00208	.93547	18
43	.06482	.99790	.06496	15.394	.0021	15.427	.00210	.93518	17
44	.06511	.99788	.06525	15.325	.0021	15.358	.00212	.93489	16
45	0.06540	0.99786	0.06554	15.257	1.0021	15.290	0.00214	0.93460	15
46	.06569	.99784	.06583	15.189	.0022	15.222	.00216	.93431	14
47	.06598	.99782	.06613	15.122	.0022	15.155	.00218	.93402	13
48	.06627	.99780	.06642	15.056	.0022	15.089	.00220	.93373	12
49	.06656	.99778	.06671	14.990	.0022	15.023	.00222	.93343	11
50	0.06685	0.99776	0.06700	14.924	1.0022	14.958	0.00224	0.93314	10
51	.06714	.99774	.06730	14.860	.0023	14.893	.00226	.93285	9
52	.06743	.99772	.06759	14.795	.0023	14.829	.00228	.93256	8
53	.06772	.99770	.06788	14.732	.0023	14.765	.00230	.93227	7
54	.06801	.99768	.06817	14.668	.0023	14.702	.00231	.93198	6
55	0.06830	0.99766	0.06846	14.606	1.0023	14.640	0.00233	0.93169	5
56	.06859	.99764	.06876	14.544	.0024	14.578	.00235	.93140	4
57	.06888	.99762	.06905	14.482	.0024	14.517	.00237	.93111	3
58	.06918	.99760	.06934	14.421	.0024	14.456	.00239	.93082	2
59	.06947	.99758	.06963	14.361	.0024	14.395	.00241	.93053	1
60	0.06976	0.99756	0.06993	14.301	1.0024	14.335	0.00243	0.93024	0
M	Cosine	Sine	Cotan.	Tan.	Cosec.	Secant	Vrs. Cos.	Vrs. Sin.	M

M	Sine	Cosine	Tan.	Cotan.	Secant	Cosec.	Vrs. Sin.	Vrs. Cos.	M
0	0.06976	0.99756	0.06993	14.301	1.0024	14.335	0.00243	0.93024	60
1	.07005	.99754	.07022	14.241	.0025	14.276	.00246	.92995	59
2	.07034	.99752	.07051	14.182	.0025	14.217	.00248	.92966	58
3	.07063	.99750	.07080	14.123	.0025	14.159	.00250	.92937	57
4	.07092	.99748	.07110	14.065	.0025	14.101	.00252	.92908	56
5	0.07121	0.99746	0.07139	14.008	1.0025	14.043	0.00254	0.92879	55
6	.07150	.99744	.07168	13.951	.0026	13.986	.00256	.92850	54
7	.07179	.99742	.07197	13.894	.0026	13.930	.00258	.92821	53
8	.07208	.99740	.07226	13.838	.0026	13.874	.00260	.92792	52
9	.07237	.99738	.07256	13.782	.0026	13.818	.00262	.92763	51
10	.07266	0.99736	0.07285	13.727	1.0026	13.763	0.00264	0.92734	50
11	.07295	.99733	.07314	13.672	.0027	13.708	.00266	.92705	49
12	.07324	.99731	.07343	13.617	.0027	13.654	.00268	.92676	48
13	.07353	.99729	.07373	13.563	.0027	13.600	.00271	.92647	47
14	.07382	.99727	.07402	13.510	.0027	13.547	.00273	.92618	46
15	0.07411	0.99725	0.07431	13.457	1.0027	13.494	0.00275	0.92589	45
16	.07440	.99723	.07460	13.404	.0028	13.441	.00277	.92560	44
17	.07469	.99721	.07490	13.351	.0028	13.389	.00279	.92531	43
18	.07498	.99718	.07519	13.299	.0028	13.337	.00281	.92502	42
19	.07527	.99716	.07548	13.248	.0028	13.286	.00284	.92473	41
20	0.07556	0.99714	0.07577	13.197	1.0029	13.235	0.00286	0.92444	40
21	.07585	.99712	.07607	13.146	.0029	13.184	.00288	.92415	39
22	.07614	.99710	.07636	13.096	.0029	13.134	.00290	.92386	38
23	.07643	.99707	.07665	13.046	.0029	13.084	.00292	.92357	37
24	.07672	.99705	.07694	12.996	.0029	13.034	.00295	.92328	36
25	0.07701	0.99703	0.07724	12.947	1.0030	12.985	0.00297	0.92299	35
26	.07730	.99701	.07753	12.898	.0030	12.937	.00299	.92270	34
27	.07759	.99698	.07782	12.849	.0030	12.888	.00301	.92241	33
28	.07788	.99696	.07812	12.801	.0030	12.840	.00304	.92212	32
29	.07817	.99694	.07841	12.754	.0031	12.793	.00306	.92183	31
30	0.07846	0.99692	0.07870	12.706	1.0031	12.745	0.00308	0.92154	30
31	.07875	.99689	.07899	12.659	.0031	12.698	.00310	.92125	29
32	.07904	.99687	.07929	12.612	.0031	12.652	.00313	.92096	28
33	.07933	.99685	.07958	12.566	.0032	12.606	.00315	.92067	27
34	.07962	.99683	.07987	12.520	.0032	12.560	.00317	.92038	26
35	0.07991	0.99680	0.08016	12.474	1.0032	12.514	0.00320	0.92009	25
36	.08020	.99678	.08046	12.429	.0032	12.469	.00322	.91980	24
37	.08049	.99675	.08075	12.384	.0032	12.424	.00324	.91951	23
38	.08078	.99673	.08104	12.339	.0033	12.379	.00327	.91922	22
39	.08107	.99671	.08134	12.295	.0033	12.335	.00329	.91893	21
40	0.08136	0.99668	0.08163	12.250	1.0033	12.291	0.00331	0.91864	20
41	.08165	.99666	.08192	12.207	.0033	12.248	.00334	.91835	19
42	.08194	.99664	.08221	12.163	.0034	12.204	.00336	.91806	18
43	.08223	.99661	.08251	12.120	.0034	12.161	.00339	.91777	17
44	.08252	.99659	.08280	12.077	.0034	12.118	.00341	.91748	16
45	0.08281	0.99656	0.08309	12.035	1.0034	12.076	0.00343	0.91719	15
46	.08310	.99654	.08339	11.992	.0035	12.034	.00346	.91690	14
47	.08339	.99652	.08368	11.950	.0035	11.992	.00348	.91661	13
48	.08368	.99649	.08397	11.909	.0035	11.950	.00351	.91632	12
49	.08397	.99647	.08426	11.867	.0035	11.909	.00353	.91603	11
50	0.08426	0.99644	0.08456	11.826	1.0036	11.868	0.00356	0.91574	10
51	.08455	.99642	.08485	11.785	.0036	11.828	.00358	.91545	9
52	.08484	.99639	.08514	11.745	.0036	11.787	.00360	.91516	8
53	.08513	.99637	.08544	11.704	.0036	11.747	.00363	.91487	7
54	.08542	.99634	.08573	11.664	.0037	11.707	.00365	.91458	6
55	0.08571	0.99632	0.08602	11.625	1.0037	11.668	0.00368	0.91429	5
56	.08600	.99629	.08632	11.585	.0037	11.628	.00370	.91400	4
57	.08629	.99627	.08661	11.546	.0037	11.589	.00373	.91371	3
58	.08658	.99624	.08690	11.507	.0038	11.550	.00375	.91342	2
59	.08687	.99622	.08719	11.468	.0038	11.512	.00378	.91313	1
60	0.08715	0.99619	0.08749	11.430	1.0038	11.474	0.00380	0.91284	0

M	Cosine	Sine	Cotan.	Tan.	Cosec.	Secant	Vrs. Cos.	Vrs. Sin.	M

Natural Trigonometric Functions

M	Sine	Cosine	Tan.	Cotan.	Secant	Cosec.	Vrs. Sin.	Vrs. Cos.	M
0	0.08715	0.99619	0.08749	11.430	1.0038	11.474	0.00380	0.91284	60
1	.08744	.99617	.08778	11.392	.0038	11.436	.00383	.91255	59
2	.08773	.99614	.08807	11.354	.0039	11.398	.00386	.91226	58
3	.08802	.99612	.08837	11.316	.0039	11.360	.00388	.91197	57
4	.08831	.99609	.08866	11.279	.0039	11.323	.00391	.91168	56
5	0.08860	0.99607	0.08895	11.242	1.0039	11.286	0.00393	0.91139	55
6	.08889	.99604	.08925	11.205	.0040	11.249	.00396	.91110	54
7	.08918	.99601	.08954	11.168	.0040	11.213	.00398	.91082	53
8	.08947	.99599	.08983	11.132	.0040	11.176	.00401	.91053	52
9	.08976	.99596	.09013	11.095	.0040	11.140	.00404	.91024	51
10	0.09005	0.99594	0.09042	11.059	1.0041	11.104	0.00406	0.90995	50
11	.09034	.99591	.09071	11.024	.0041	11.069	.00409	.90966	49
12	.09063	.99588	.09101	10.988	.0041	11.033	.00411	.90937	48
13	.09092	.99586	.09130	10.953	.0041	10.998	.00414	.90908	47
14	.09121	.99583	.09159	10.918	.0042	10.963	.00417	.90879	46
15	0.09150	0.99580	0.09189	10.883	1.0042	10.929	0.00419	0.90850	45
16	.09179	.99578	.09218	10.848	.0042	10.894	.00422	.90821	44
17	.09208	.99575	.09247	10.814	.0043	10.860	.00425	.90792	43
18	.09237	.99572	.09277	10.780	.0043	10.826	.00427	.90763	42
19	.09266	.99570	.09306	10.746	.0043	10.792	.00430	.90734	41
20	0.09295	0.99567	0.09335	10.712	1.0043	10.758	0.00433	0.90705	40
21	.09324	.99564	.09365	10.678	.0044	10.725	.00436	.90676	39
22	.09353	.99562	.09394	10.645	.0044	10.692	.00438	.90647	38
23	.09382	.99559	.09423	10.612	.0044	10.659	.00441	.90618	37
24	.09411	.99556	.09453	10.579	.0044	10.626	.00444	.90589	36
25	0.09440	0.99553	0.09482	10.546	1.0045	10.593	0.00446	0.90560	35
26	.09469	.99551	.09511	10.514	.0045	10.561	.00449	.90531	34
27	.09498	.99548	.09541	10.481	.0045	10.529	.00452	.90502	33
28	.09527	.99545	.09570	10.449	.0046	10.497	.00455	.90473	32
29	.09556	.99542	.09599	10.417	.0046	10.465	.00458	.90444	31
30	0.09584	0.99540	0.09629	10.385	1.0046	10.433	0.00460	0.90415	30
31	.09613	.99537	.09658	10.354	.0046	10.402	.00463	.90386	29
32	.09642	.99534	.09688	10.322	.0047	10.371	.00466	.90357	28
33	.09671	.99531	.09717	10.291	.0047	10.340	.00469	.90328	27
34	.09700	.99528	.09746	10.260	.0047	10.309	.00472	.90300	26
35	0.09729	0.99525	0.09776	10.229	1.0048	10.278	0.00474	0.90271	25
36	.09758	.99523	.09805	10.199	.0048	10.248	.00477	.90242	24
37	.09787	.99520	.09834	10.168	.0048	10.217	.00480	.90213	23
38	.09816	.99517	.09864	10.138	.0048	10.187	.00483	.90184	22
39	.09845	.99514	.09893	10.108	.0049	10.157	.00486	.90155	21
40	0.09874	0.99511	0.09922	10.078	1.0049	10.127	0.00489	0.90126	20
41	.09903	.99508	.09952	10.048	.0049	10.098	.00491	.90097	19
42	.09932	.99505	.09981	10.019	.0050	10.068	.00494	.90068	18
43	.09961	.99503	.10011	9.9893	.0050	10.039	.00497	.90039	17
44	.09990	.99500	.10040	9.9601	.0050	10.010	.00500	.90010	16
45	0.10019	0.99497	0.10069	9.9310	1.0050	9.9812	0.00503	0.89981	15
46	.10048	.99494	.10099	9.9021	.0051	9.9525	.00506	.89952	14
47	.10077	.99491	.10128	9.8734	.0051	9.9239	.00509	.89923	13
48	.10106	.99488	.10158	9.8448	.0051	9.8955	.00512	.89894	12
49	.10134	.99485	.10187	9.8164	.0052	9.8672	.00515	.89865	11
50	0.10163	0.99482	0.10216	9.7882	1.0052	9.8391	0.00518	0.89836	10
51	.10192	.99479	.10246	9.7601	.0052	9.8112	.00521	.89807	9
52	.10221	.99476	.10275	9.7322	.0053	9.7834	.00524	.89779	8
53	.10250	.99473	.10305	9.7044	.0053	9.7558	.00527	.89750	7
54	.10279	.99470	.10334	9.6768	.0053	9.7283	.00530	.89721	6
55	0.10308	0.99467	0.10363	9.6493	1.0053	9.7010	0.00533	0.89692	5
56	.10337	.99464	.10393	9.6220	.0054	9.6739	.00536	.89663	4
57	.10366	.99461	.10422	9.5949	.0054	9.6469	.00539	.89634	3
58	.10395	.99458	.10452	9.5679	.0054	9.6200	.00542	.89605	2
59	.10424	.99455	.10481	9.5411	.0055	9.5933	.00545	.89576	1
60	0.10453	0.99452	0.10510	9.5144	1.0055	9.5668	0.00548	0.89547	0

M	Cosine	Sine	Cotan.	Tan.	Cosec.	Secant	Vrs. Cos.	Vrs. Sin.	M

M	Sine	Cosine	Tan.	Cotan.	Secant	Cosec.	Vrs. Sin.	Vrs. Cos.	M
0	0.10453	0.99452	0.10510	9.5144	1.0055	9.5668	0.00548	0.89547	60
I	.10482	.99449	.10540	.4878	.0055	.5404	.00551	.89518	59
2	.10511	.99446	.10569	.4614	.0056	.5141	.00554	.89489	58
3	.10540	.99443	.10599	.4351	.0056	.4880	.00557	.89460	57
4	.10568	.99440	.10628	.4090	.0056	.4620	.00560	.89431	56
5	0.10597	0.99437	0.10657	9.3831	1.0057	9.4362	0.00563	0.89402	55
6	.10626	.99434	.10687	.3572	.0057	.4105	.00566	.89373	54
7	.10655	.99431	.10716	.3315	.0057	.3850	.00569	.89345	53
8	.10684	.99428	.10746	.3060	.0057	.3596	.00572	.89316	52
9	.10713	.99424	.10775	.2806	.0058	.3343	.00575	.89287	51
10	0.10742	0.99421	0.10805	9.2553	1.0058	9.3092	0.00579	0.89258	50
II	.10771	.99418	.10834	.2302	.0058	.2842	.00582	.89229	49
12	.10800	.99415	.10863	.2051	.0059	.2593	.00585	.89200	48
13	.10829	.99412	.10893	.1803	.0059	.2346	.00588	.89171	47
14	.10858	.99409	.10922	.1555	.0059	.2100	.00591	.89142	46
15	0.10887	0.99406	0.10952	9.1309	1.0060	9.1855	0.00594	0.89113	45
16	.10916	.99402	.10981	.1064	.0060	.1612	.00597	.89084	44
17	.10944	.99399	.11011	.0821	.0060	.1370	.00601	.89055	43
18	.10973	.99396	.11040	.0579	.0061	.1129	.00604	.89026	42
19	.11002	.99393	.11069	.0338	.0061	.0890	.00607	.88998	41
20	0.11031	0.99390	0.11099	9.0098	1.0061	9.0651	0.00610	0.88969	40
21	.11060	.99386	.11128	8.9860	.0062	.0414	.00613	.88940	39
22	.11089	.99383	.11158	.9623	.0062	.0179	.00617	.88911	38
23	.11118	.99380	.11187	.9387	.0062	8.9944	.00620	.88882	37
24	.11147	.99377	.11217	.9152	.0063	.9711	.00623	.88853	36
25	0.11176	0.99373	0.11246	8.8918	1.0063	8.9479	0.00626	0.88824	35
26	.11205	.99370	.11276	.8686	.0063	.9248	.00630	.88795	34
27	.11234	.99367	.11305	.8455	.0064	.9018	.00633	.88766	33
28	.11262	.99364	.11335	.8225	.0064	.8790	.00636	.88737	32
29	.11291	.99360	.11364	.7996	.0064	.8563	.00639	.88708	31
30	0.11320	0.99357	0.11393	8.7769	1.0065	8.8337	0.00643	0.88680	30
31	.11349	.99354	.11423	.7542	.0065	.8112	.00646	.88651	29
32	.11378	.99350	.11452	.7317	.0065	.7888	.00649	.88622	28
33	.11407	.99347	.11482	.7093	.0066	.7665	.00653	.88593	27
34	.11436	.99344	.11511	.6870	.0066	.7444	.00656	.88564	26
35	0.11465	0.99341	0.11541	8.6648	1.0066	8.7223	0.00659	0.88535	25
36	.11494	.99337	.11570	.6427	.0067	.7004	.00663	.88506	24
37	.11523	.99334	.11600	.6208	.0067	.6786	.00666	.88477	23
38	.11551	.99330	.11629	.5989	.0067	.6569	.00669	.88448	22
39	.11580	.99327	.11659	.5772	.0068	.6353	.00673	.88420	21
40	0.11609	0.99324	0.11688	8.5555	1.0068	8.6138	0.00676	0.88391	20
41	.11638	.99320	.11718	.5340	.0068	.5924	.00679	.88362	19
42	.11667	.99317	.11747	.5126	.0069	.5711	.00683	.88333	18
43	.11696	.99314	.11777	.4913	.0069	.5499	.00686	.88304	17
44	.11725	.99310	.11806	.4701	.0069	.5289	.00690	.88272	16
45	0.11754	0.99307	0.11836	8.4489	1.0070	8.5079	0.00693	0.88246	15
46	.11783	.99303	.11865	.4279	.0070	.4871	.00696	.88217	14
47	.11811	.99300	.11895	.4070	.0070	.4663	.00700	.88188	13
48	.11840	.99296	.11924	.3862	.0071	.4457	.00703	.88160	12
49	.11869	.99293	.11954	.3655	.0071	.4251	.00707	.88131	11
50	0.11898	0.99290	0.11983	8.3449	1.0071	8.4046	0.00710	0.88102	10
51	.11927	.99286	.12013	.3244	.0072	.3843	.00714	.88073	9
52	.11956	.99283	.12042	.3040	.0072	.3640	.00717	.88044	8
53	.11985	.99279	.12072	.2837	.0073	.3439	.00721	.88015	7
54	.12014	.99276	.12101	.2635	.0073	.3238	.00724	.87986	6
55	0.12042	0.99272	0.12131	8.2434	1.0073	8.3039	0.00728	0.87957	5
56	.12071	.99269	.12160	.2234	.0074	.2840	.00731	.87928	4
57	.12100	.99265	.12190	.2035	.0074	.2642	.00735	.87900	3
58	.12129	.99262	.12219	.1837	.0074	.2446	.00738	.87871	2
59	.12158	.99258	.12249	.1640	.0075	.2250	.00742	.87842	1
60	0.12187	0.99255	0.12278	8.1443	1.0075	8.2055	0.00745	0.87813	0
M	Cosine	Sine	Cotan.	Tan.	Cosec.	Secant	Vrs. Cos.	Vrs. Sin.	M

MATHEMATICAL TABLES
Natural Trigonometric Functions

M	Sine	Cosine	Tan.	Cotan.	Secant	Cosec.	Vrs. Sin.	Vrs. Cos.	M
0	0.12187	0.99255	0.12278	8.1443	1.0075	8.2055	0.00745	0.87813	60
1	.12216	.99251	.12308	.1248	.0075	.1861	.00749	.87787	59
2	.12245	.99247	.12337	.1053	.0076	.1668	.00752	.87755	58
3	.12273	.99244	.12367	.0860	.0076	.1476	.00756	.87726	57
4	.12302	.99240	.12396	.0667	.0076	.1285	.00760	.87697	56
5	0.12331	0.99237	0.12426	8.0476	1.0077	8.1094	.00763	.87669	55
6	.12360	.99233	.12456	.0285	.0077	.0905	.00767	.87640	54
7	.12389	.99229	.12485	.0095	.0078	.0717	.00770	.87611	53
8	.12418	.99226	.12515	7.9906	.0078	.0529	.00774	.87582	52
9	.12447	.99222	.12544	.9717	.0078	.0342	.00778	.87553	51
10	0.12476	0.99219	0.12574	7.9530	1.0079	8.0156	.00781	0.87524	50
11	.12504	.99215	.12603	.9344	.0079	7.9971	.00785	.87495	49
12	.12533	.99211	.12633	.9158	.0079	.9787	.00788	.87467	48
13	.12562	.99208	.12662	.8973	.0080	.9604	.00792	.87438	47
14	.12591	.99204	.12692	.8789	.0080	.9421	.00796	.87409	46
15	0.12620	0.99200	0.12722	7.8606	1.0080	7.9240	.00799	0.87380	45
16	.12649	.99197	.12751	.8424	.0081	.9059	.00803	.87351	44
17	.12678	.99193	.12781	.8243	.0081	.8879	.00807	.87322	43
18	.12706	.99189	.12810	.8062	.0082	.8700	.00810	.87293	42
19	.12735	.99186	.12840	.7882	.0082	.8522	.00814	.87265	41
20	0.12764	0.99182	0.12869	7.7703	1.0082	7.8344	.00818	0.87236	40
21	.12793	.99178	.12899	.7525	.0083	.8168	.00822	.87207	39
22	.12822	.99174	.12928	.7348	.0083	.7992	.00825	.87178	38
23	.12851	.99171	.12958	.7171	.0084	.7817	.00829	.87149	37
24	.12879	.99167	.12988	.6996	.0084	.7642	.00833	.87120	36
25	0.12908	0.99163	0.13017	7.6821	1.0084	7.7469	.00837	0.87091	35
26	.12937	.99160	.13047	.6646	.0085	.7296	.00840	.87063	34
27	.12966	.99156	.13076	.6473	.0085	.7124	.00844	.87034	33
28	.12995	.99152	.13106	.6300	.0085	.6953	.00848	.87005	32
29	.13024	.99148	.13136	.6129	.0086	.6783	.00852	.86976	31
30	0.13053	0.99144	0.13165	7.5957	1.0086	7.6613	.00855	0.86947	30
31	.13081	.99141	.13195	.5787	.0087	.6444	.00859	.86918	29
32	.13110	.99137	.13224	.5617	.0087	.6276	.00863	.86890	28
33	.13139	.99133	.13254	.5449	.0087	.6108	.00867	.86861	27
34	.13168	.99129	.13284	.5280	.0088	.5942	.00871	.86832	26
35	0.13197	0.99125	0.13313	7.5113	1.0088	7.5776	.00875	0.86803	25
36	.13226	.99121	.13343	.4946	.0089	.5611	.00878	.86774	24
37	.13254	.99118	.13372	.4780	.0089	.5446	.00882	.86745	23
38	.13283	.99114	.13402	.4615	.0089	.5282	.00886	.86717	22
39	.13312	.99110	.13432	.4451	.0090	.5119	.00890	.86688	21
40	0.13341	0.99106	0.13461	7.4287	1.0090	7.4957	.00894	0.86659	20
41	.13370	.99102	.13491	.4124	.0090	.4795	.00898	.86630	19
42	.13399	.99098	.13520	.3961	.0091	.4634	.00902	.86601	18
43	.13427	.99094	.13550	.3800	.0091	.4474	.00905	.86572	17
44	.13456	.99090	.13580	.3639	.0092	.4315	.00909	.86544	16
45	0.13485	0.99086	0.13609	7.3479	1.0092	7.4156	.00913	0.86515	15
46	.13514	.99083	.13639	.3319	.0092	.3998	.00917	.86486	14
47	.13543	.99079	.13669	.3160	.0093	.3840	.00921	.86457	13
48	.13571	.99075	.13698	.3002	.0093	.3683	.00925	.86428	12
49	.13600	.99071	.13728	.2844	.0094	.3527	.00929	.86400	11
50	0.13629	0.99067	0.13757	7.2687	1.0094	7.3372	.00933	0.86371	10
51	.13658	.99063	.13787	.2531	.0094	.3217	.00937	.86342	9
52	.13687	.99059	.13817	.2375	.0095	.3063	.00941	.86313	8
53	.13716	.99055	.13846	.2220	.0095	.2909	.00945	.86284	7
54	.13744	.99051	.13876	.2066	.0096	.2757	.00949	.86255	6
55	0.13773	0.99047	0.13906	7.1912	1.0096	7.2604	.00953	0.86227	5
56	.13802	.99043	.13935	.1759	.0097	.2453	.00957	.86198	4
57	.13831	.99039	.13965	.1607	.0097	.2302	.00961	.86169	3
58	.13860	.99035	.13995	.1455	.0097	.2152	.00965	.86140	2
59	.13888	.99031	.14024	.1304	.0098	.2002	.00969	.86111	1
60	0.13917	0.99027	0.14054	7.1154	1.0098	7.1853	.00973	0.86083	0
M	Cosine	Sine	Cotan.	Tan.	Cosec.	Secant	Vrs. Cos.	Vrs. Sin.	M

M	Sine	Cosine	Tan.	Cotan.	Secant	Cosec.	Vrs. Sin.	Vrs. Cos.	M
0	0.13917	0.99027	0.14054	7.1154	1.0098	7.1853	0.00973	0.86083	60
1	.13946	.99023	.14084	.1004	.0099	.1704	.00977	.86054	59
2	.13975	.99019	.14113	.0854	.0099	.1557	.00981	.86025	58
3	.14004	.99015	.14143	.0706	.0099	.1409	.00985	.85996	57
4	.14032	.99010	.14173	.0558	.0100	.1263	.00989	.85967	56
5	0.14061	0.99006	0.14202	7.0410	1.0100	7.1117	0.00993	0.85939	55
6	.14090	.99002	.14232	.0264	.0101	.0972	.00998	.85910	54
7	.14119	.98998	.14262	.0117	.0101	.0827	.01002	.85881	53
8	.14148	.98994	.14291	6.9972	.0102	.0683	.01006	.85852	52
9	.14176	.98990	.14321	.9827	.0102	.0539	.01010	.85823	51
10	0.14205	0.98986	0.14351	6.9682	1.0102	7.0396	0.01014	0.85795	50
11	.14234	.98982	.14380	.9538	.0103	.0254	.01018	.85766	49
12	.14263	.98978	.14410	.9395	.0103	.0112	.01022	.85737	48
13	.14292	.98973	.14440	.9252	.0104	6.9971	.01026	.85708	47
14	.14320	.98969	.14470	.9110	.0104	.9830	.01031	.85679	46
15	0.14349	0.98965	0.14499	6.8969	1.0104	6.9690	0.01035	0.85651	45
16	.14378	.98961	.14529	.8828	.0105	.9550	.01039	.85622	44
17	.14407	.98957	.14559	.8687	.0105	.9411	.01043	.85593	43
18	.14436	.98952	.14588	.8547	.0106	.9273	.01047	.85564	42
19	.14464	.98948	.14618	.8408	.0106	.9135	.01052	.85536	41
20	0.14493	0.98944	0.14648	6.8269	1.0107	6.8998	0.01056	0.85507	40
21	.14522	.98940	.14677	.8131	.0107	.8861	.01060	.85478	39
22	.14551	.98935	.14707	.7993	.0107	.8725	.01064	.85449	38
23	.14579	.98931	.14737	.7856	.0108	.8589	.01068	.85420	37
24	.14608	.98927	.14767	.7720	.0108	.8454	.01073	.85392	36
25	0.14637	0.98923	0.14796	6.7584	1.0109	6.8320	0.01077	0.85363	35
26	.14666	.98919	.14826	.7448	.0109	.8185	.01081	.85334	34
27	.14695	.98914	.14856	.7313	.0110	.8052	.01085	.85305	33
28	.14723	.98910	.14886	.7179	.0110	.7919	.01090	.85277	32
29	.14752	.98906	.14915	.7045	.0111	.7787	.01094	.85248	31
30	0.14781	0.98901	0.14945	6.6911	1.0111	6.7655	0.01098	0.85219	30
31	.14810	.98897	.14975	.6779	.0111	.7523	.01103	.85190	29
32	.14838	.98893	.15004	.6646	.0112	.7392	.01107	.85161	28
33	.14867	.98889	.15034	.6514	.0112	.7262	.01111	.85133	27
34	.14896	.98884	.15064	.6383	.0113	.7132	.01116	.85104	26
35	0.14925	0.98880	0.15094	6.6252	1.0113	6.7003	0.01120	0.85075	25
36	.14953	.98876	.15123	.6122	.0114	.6874	.01124	.85046	24
37	.14982	.98871	.15153	.5992	.0114	.6745	.01129	.85018	23
38	.15011	.98867	.15183	.5863	.0115	.6617	.01133	.84989	22
39	.15040	.98862	.15213	.5734	.0115	.6490	.01137	.84960	21
40	0.15068	0.98858	0.15243	6.5605	1.0115	6.6363	0.01142	0.84931	20
41	.15097	.98854	.15272	.5478	.0116	.6237	.01146	.84903	19
42	.15126	.98849	.15302	.5350	.0116	.6111	.01151	.84874	18
43	.15155	.98845	.15332	.5223	.0117	.5985	.01155	.84845	17
44	.15183	.98840	.15362	.5097	.0117	.5860	.01159	.84816	16
45	0.15212	0.98836	0.15391	6.4971	1.0118	6.5736	0.01164	0.84788	15
46	.15241	.98832	.15421	.4845	.0118	.5612	.01168	.84759	14
47	.15270	.98827	.15451	.4720	.0119	.5488	.01173	.84730	13
48	.15298	.98823	.15481	.4596	.0119	.5365	.01177	.84701	12
49	.15328	.98818	.15511	.4472	.0119	.5243	.01182	.84672	11
50	0.15356	0.98814	0.15540	6.4348	1.0120	6.5121	0.01186	0.84644	10
51	.15385	.98809	.15570	.4225	.0120	.4999	.01190	.84615	9
52	.15413	.98805	.15600	.4103	.0121	.4878	.01195	.84586	8
53	.15442	.98800	.15630	.3980	.0121	.4757	.01199	.84558	7
54	.15471	.98796	.15659	.3859	.0122	.4637	.01204	.84529	6
55	0.15500	0.98791	0.15689	6.3737	1.0122	6.4517	0.01208	0.84500	5
56	.15528	.98787	.15719	.3616	.0123	.4398	.01213	.84471	4
57	.15557	.98782	.15749	.3496	.0123	.4279	.01217	.84443	3
58	.15586	.98778	.15779	.3376	.0124	.4160	.01222	.84414	2
59	.15615	.98773	.15809	.3257	.0124	.4042	.01227	.84385	1
60	0.15643	0.98769	0.15838	6.3137	1.0125	6.3924	0.01231	0.84356	0
M	Cosine	Sine	Cotan.	Tan.	Cosec.	Secant	Vrs. Cos.	Vrs. Sin.	M

M	Sine	Cosine	Tan.	Cotan.	Secant	Cosec.	Vrs. Sin.	Vrs. Cos.	M
0	0.15643	0.98769	0.15838	6.3137	1.0125	6.3924	0.01231	0.84356	60
1	.15672	.98764	.15868	.3019	.0125	.3807	.01236	.84328	59
2	.15701	.98760	.15898	.2901	.0125	.3690	.01240	.84299	58
3	.15730	.98755	.15928	.2783	.0126	.3574	.01245	.84270	57
4	.15758	.98750	.15958	.2665	.0126	.3458	.01249	.84242	56
5	0.15787	0.98746	0.15987	6.2548	1.0127	6.3343	0.01254	0.84213	55
6	.15816	.98741	.16017	.2432	.0127	.3228	.01259	.84184	54
7	.15844	.98737	.16047	.2316	.0128	.3113	.01263	.84155	53
8	.15873	.98732	.16077	.2200	.0128	.2999	.01268	.84127	52
9	.15902	.98727	.16107	.2085	.0129	.2885	.01272	.84098	51
10	0.15931	0.98723	0.16137	6.1970	1.0129	6.2772	0.01277	0.84069	50
11	.15959	.98718	.16167	.1856	.0130	.2659	.01282	.84041	49
12	.15988	.98714	.16196	.1742	.0130	.2546	.01286	.84012	48
13	.16017	.98709	.16226	.1628	.0131	.2434	.01291	.83983	47
14	.16045	.98704	.16256	.1515	.0131	.2322	.01296	.83954	46
15	0.16074	0.98700	0.16286	6.1402	1.0132	6.2211	0.01300	0.83926	45
16	.16103	.98695	.16316	.1290	.0132	.2100	.01305	.83897	44
17	.16132	.98690	.16346	.1178	.0133	.1990	.01310	.83868	43
18	.16160	.98685	.16376	.1066	.0133	.1880	.01314	.83840	42
19	.16189	.98681	.16405	.0955	.0134	.1770	.01319	.83811	41
20	0.16218	0.98676	0.16435	6.0844	1.0134	6.1661	0.01324	0.83782	40
21	.16246	.98671	.16465	.0734	.0135	.1552	.01328	.83753	39
22	.16275	.98667	.16495	.0624	.0135	.1443	.01333	.83725	38
23	.16304	.98662	.16525	.0514	.0136	.1335	.01338	.83696	37
24	.16333	.98657	.16555	.0405	.0136	.1227	.01343	.83667	36
25	0.16361	0.98652	0.16585	6.0296	1.0136	6.1120	0.01347	0.83639	35
26	.16390	.98648	.16615	.0188	.0137	.1013	.01352	.83610	34
27	.16419	.98643	.16644	.0080	.0137	.0906	.01357	.83581	33
28	.16447	.98638	.16674	5.9972	.0138	.0800	.01362	.83553	32
29	.16476	.98633	.16704	.9865	.0138	.0694	.01367	.83524	31
30	0.16505	0.98628	0.16734	5.9758	1.0139	6.0588	0.01371	0.83495	30
31	.16533	.98624	.16764	.9651	.0139	.0483	.01376	.83466	29
32	.16562	.98619	.16794	.9545	.0140	.0379	.01381	.83438	28
33	.16591	.98614	.16824	.9439	.0140	.0274	.01386	.83409	27
34	.16619	.98609	.16854	.9333	.0141	.0170	.01391	.83380	26
35	0.16648	0.98604	0.16884	5.9228	1.0141	6.0066	0.01395	0.83352	25
36	.16677	.98600	.16914	.9123	.0142	5.9963	.01400	.83323	24
37	.16705	.98595	.16944	.9019	.0142	.9860	.01405	.83294	23
38	.16734	.98590	.16973	.8915	.0143	.9758	.01410	.83266	22
39	.16763	.98585	.17003	.8811	.0143	.9655	.01415	.83237	21
40	0.16791	0.98580	0.17033	5.8708	1.0144	5.9554	0.01420	0.83208	20
41	.16820	.98575	.17063	.8605	.0144	.9452	.01425	.83180	19
42	.16849	.98570	.17093	.8502	.0145	.9351	.01430	.83151	18
43	.16878	.98565	.17123	.8400	.0145	.9250	.01434	.83122	17
44	.16906	.98560	.17153	.8298	.0146	.9150	.01439	.83094	16
45	0.16935	0.98556	0.17183	5.8196	1.0146	5.9049	0.01444	0.83065	15
46	.16964	.98551	.17213	.8095	.0147	.8950	.01449	.83036	14
47	.16992	.98546	.17243	.7994	.0147	.8850	.01454	.83008	13
48	.17021	.98541	.17273	.7894	.0148	.8751	.01459	.82979	12
49	.17050	.98536	.17303	.7794	.0148	.8652	.01464	.82950	11
50	0.17078	0.98531	0.17333	5.7694	1.0149	5.8554	0.01469	0.82922	10
51	.17107	.98526	.17363	.7594	.0150	.8456	.01474	.82893	9
52	.17136	.98521	.17393	.7495	.0150	.8358	.01479	.82864	8
53	.17164	.98516	.17423	.7396	.0151	.8261	.01484	.82836	7
54	.17193	.98511	.17453	.7297	.0151	.8163	.01489	.82807	6
55	0.17221	0.98506	0.17483	5.7199	1.0152	5.8067	0.01494	0.82778	5
56	.17250	.98501	.17513	.7101	.0152	.7970	.01499	.82750	4
57	.17279	.98496	.17543	.7004	.0153	.7874	.01504	.82721	3
58	.17307	.98491	.17573	.6906	.0153	.7778	.01509	.82692	2
59	.17336	.98486	.17603	.6809	.0154	.7683	.01514	.82664	1
60	0.17365	0.98481	0.17633	5.6713	1.0154	5.7588	0.01519	0.82635	0
M	Cosine	Sine	Cotan.	Tan.	Cosec.	Secant	Vrs. Cos.	Vrs. Sin.	M

M	Sine	Cosine	Tan.	Cotan.	Secant	Cosec.	Vrs. Sin.	Vrs. Cos.	M
0	0.17365	0.98481	0.17633	5.6713	1.0154	5.7588	0.01519	0.82635	60
1	.17393	.98476	.17663	.6616	.0155	.7493	.01524	.82606	59
2	.17422	.98471	.17693	.6520	.0155	.7398	.01529	.82578	58
3	.17451	.98465	.17723	.6425	.0156	.7304	.01534	.82549	57
4	.17479	.98460	.17753	.6329	.0156	.7210	.01539	.82521	56
5	0.17508	0.98455	0.17783	5.6234	1.0157	5.7117	0.01544	0.82492	55
6	.17537	.98450	.17813	.6140	.0157	.7023	.01550	.82463	54
7	.17565	.98445	.17843	.6045	.0158	.6930	.01555	.82435	53
8	.17594	.98440	.17873	.5951	.0158	.6838	.01560	.82406	52
9	.17622	.98435	.17903	.5857	.0159	.6745	.01565	.82377	51
10	0.17651	0.98430	0.17933	5.5764	1.0159	5.6653	0.01570	0.82349	50
11	.17680	.98425	.17963	.5670	.0160	.6561	.01575	.82320	49
12	.17708	.98419	.17993	.5578	.0160	.6470	.01580	.82291	48
13	.17737	.98414	.18023	.5485	.0161	.6379	.01585	.82263	47
14	.17766	.98409	.18053	.5393	.0162	.6288	.01591	.82234	46
15	0.17794	0.98404	0.18083	5.5301	1.0162	5.6197	0.01596	0.82206	45
16	.17823	.98399	.18113	.5209	.0163	.6107	.01601	.82177	44
17	.17852	.98394	.18143	.5117	.0163	.6017	.01606	.82148	43
18	.17880	.98388	.18173	.5026	.0164	.5928	.01611	.82120	42
19	.17909	.98383	.18203	.4936	.0164	.5838	.01617	.82091	41
20	0.17937	0.98378	0.18233	5.4845	1.0165	5.5749	0.01622	0.82062	40
21	.17966	.98373	.18263	.4755	.0165	.5660	.01627	.82034	39
22	.17995	.98368	.18293	.4665	.0166	.5572	.01632	.82005	38
23	.18023	.98362	.18323	.4575	.0166	.5484	.01638	.81977	37
24	.18052	.98357	.18353	.4486	.0167	.5396	.01643	.81948	36
25	0.18080	0.98352	0.18383	5.4396	1.0167	5.5308	0.01648	0.81919	35
26	.18109	.98347	.18413	.4308	.0168	.5221	.01653	.81891	34
27	.18138	.98341	.18444	.4219	.0169	.5134	.01659	.81862	33
28	.18166	.98336	.18474	.4131	.0169	.5047	.01664	.81834	32
29	.18195	.98331	.18504	.4043	.0170	.4960	.01669	.81805	31
30	0.18223	0.98325	0.18534	5.3955	1.0170	5.4874	0.01674	0.81776	30
31	.18252	.98320	.18564	.3868	.0171	.4788	.01680	.81748	29
32	.18281	.98315	.18594	.3780	.0171	.4702	.01685	.81719	28
33	.18309	.98309	.18624	.3694	.0172	.4617	.01690	.81691	27
34	.18338	.98304	.18654	.3607	.0172	.4532	.01696	.81662	26
35	0.18366	0.98299	0.18684	5.3521	1.0173	5.4447	0.01701	0.81633	25
36	.18395	.98293	.18714	.3434	.0174	.4362	.01706	.81605	24
37	.18424	.98288	.18745	.3349	.0174	.4278	.01712	.81576	23
38	.18452	.98283	.18775	.3263	.0175	.4194	.01717	.81548	22
39	.18481	.98277	.18805	.3178	.0175	.4110	.01722	.81519	21
40	0.18509	0.98272	0.18835	5.3093	1.0176	5.4026	0.01728	0.81490	20
41	.18538	.98267	.18865	.3008	.0176	.3943	.01733	.81462	19
42	.18567	.98261	.18895	.2923	.0177	.3860	.01739	.81433	18
43	.18595	.98256	.18925	.2839	.0177	.3777	.01744	.81405	17
44	.18624	.98250	.18955	.2755	.0178	.3695	.01749	.81376	16
45	0.18652	0.98245	0.18985	5.2671	1.0179	5.3612	0.01755	0.81348	15
46	.18681	.98240	.19016	.2588	.0179	.3530	.01760	.81319	14
47	.18709	.98234	.19046	.2505	.0180	.3449	.01766	.81290	13
48	.18738	.98229	.19076	.2422	.0180	.3367	.01771	.81262	12
49	.18767	.98223	.19106	.2339	.0181	.3286	.01777	.81233	11
50	0.18795	0.98218	0.19136	5.2257	1.0181	5.3205	0.01782	0.81205	10
51	.18824	.98212	.19166	.2174	.0182	.3124	.01788	.81176	9
52	.18852	.98207	.19197	.2092	.0182	.3044	.01793	.81147	8
53	.18881	.98201	.19227	.2011	.0183	.2963	.01799	.81119	7
54	.18909	.98196	.19257	.1929	.0184	.2883	.01804	.81090	6
55	0.18938	0.98190	0.19287	5.1848	1.0184	5.2803	0.01810	0.81062	5
56	.18967	.98185	.19317	.1767	.0185	.2724	.01815	.81033	4
57	.18995	.98179	.19347	.1686	.0185	.2645	.01821	.81005	3
58	.19024	.98174	.19378	.1606	.0186	.2566	.01826	.80976	2
59	.19052	.98168	.19408	.1525	.0186	.2487	.01832	.80948	1
60	0.19081	0.98163	0.19438	5.1445	1.0187	5.2408	0.01837	0.80919	0
M	Cosine	Sine	Cotan.	Tan.	Cosec.	Secant	Vrs. Cos.	Vrs. Sin.	M

Natural Trigonometric Functions

M	Sine	Cosine	Tan.	Cotan.	Secant	Cosec.	Vrs. Sin.	Vrs. Cos.	M
0	0.19081	0.98163	0.19438	5.1445	1.0187	5.2408	0.01837	0.80919	60
1	.19109	.98157	.19468	.1366	.0188	.2330	.01843	.80890	59
2	.19138	.98152	.19498	.1286	.0188	.2252	.01848	.80862	58
3	.19166	.98146	.19529	.1207	.0189	.2174	.01854	.80833	57
4	.19195	.98140	.19559	.1128	.0189	.2097	.01859	.80805	56
5	0.19224	0.98135	0.19589	5.1049	1.0190	5.2019	0.01865	0.80776	55
6	.19252	.98129	.19619	.0970	.0191	.1942	.01871	.80748	54
7	.19281	.98124	.19649	.0892	.0191	.1865	.01876	.80719	53
8	.19309	.98118	.19680	.0814	.0192	.1788	.01882	.80691	52
9	.19338	.98112	.19710	.0736	.0192	.1712	.01887	.80662	51
10	0.19366	0.98107	0.19740	5.0658	1.0193	5.1636	0.01893	0.80634	50
11	.19395	.98101	.19770	.0581	.0193	.1560	.01899	.80605	49
12	.19423	.98095	.19800	.0504	.0194	.1484	.01904	.80576	48
13	.19452	.98090	.19831	.0427	.0195	.1409	.01910	.80548	47
14	.19480	.98084	.19861	.0350	.0195	.1333	.01916	.80519	46
15	0.19509	0.98078	0.19891	5.0273	1.0196	5.1258	0.01921	0.80491	45
16	.19537	.98073	.19921	.0197	.0196	.1183	.01927	.80462	44
17	.19566	.98067	.19952	.0121	.0197	.1109	.01933	.80434	43
18	.19595	.98061	.19982	.0045	.0198	.1034	.01938	.80405	42
19	.19623	.98056	.20012	4.9969	.0198	.0960	.01944	.80377	41
20	0.19652	0.98050	0.20042	4.9894	1.0199	5.0886	0.01950	0.80348	40
21	.19680	.98044	.20073	.9819	.0199	.0812	.01956	.80320	39
22	.19709	.98039	.20103	.9744	.0200	.0739	.01961	.80291	38
23	.19737	.98033	.20133	.9669	.0201	.0666	.01967	.80263	37
24	.19766	.98027	.20163	.9594	.0201	.0593	.01973	.80234	36
25	0.19794	0.98021	0.20194	4.9520	1.0202	5.0520	0.01979	0.80206	35
26	.19823	.98016	.20224	.9446	.0202	.0447	.01984	.80177	34
27	.19851	.98010	.20254	.9372	.0203	.0375	.01990	.80149	33
28	.19880	.98004	.20285	.9298	.0204	.0302	.01996	.80120	32
29	.19908	.97998	.20315	.9225	.0204	.0230	.02002	.80092	31
30	0.19937	0.97992	0.20345	4.9151	1.0205	5.0158	0.02007	0.80063	30
31	.19965	.97987	.20375	.9078	.0205	.0087	.02013	.80035	29
32	.19994	.97981	.20406	.9006	.0206	.0015	.02019	.80006	28
33	.20022	.97975	.20436	.8933	.0207	4.9944	.02025	.79978	27
34	.20051	.97969	.20466	.8860	.0207	.9873	.02031	.79949	26
35	0.20079	0.97963	0.20497	4.8788	1.0208	4.9802	0.02037	0.79921	25
36	.20108	.97957	.20527	.8716	.0208	.9732	.02042	.79892	24
37	.20136	.97952	.20557	.8644	.0209	.9661	.02048	.79863	23
38	.20165	.97946	.20588	.8573	.0210	.9591	.02054	.79835	22
39	.20193	.97940	.20618	.8501	.0210	.9521	.02060	.79807	21
40	0.20222	0.97934	0.20648	4.8430	1.0211	4.9452	0.02066	0.79778	20
41	.20250	.97928	.20679	.8359	.0211	.9382	.02072	.79750	19
42	.20279	.97922	.20709	.8288	.0212	.9313	.02078	.79721	18
43	.20307	.97916	.20739	.8217	.0213	.9243	.02084	.79693	17
44	.20336	.97910	.20770	.8147	.0213	.9175	.02089	.79664	16
45	0.20364	0.97904	0.20800	4.8077	1.0214	4.9106	0.02095	0.79636	15
46	.20393	.97899	.20830	.8007	.0215	.9037	.02101	.79607	14
47	.20421	.97893	.20861	.7937	.0215	.8969	.02107	.79579	13
48	.20450	.97887	.20891	.7867	.0216	.8901	.02113	.79550	12
49	.20478	.97881	.20921	.7798	.0216	.8833	.02119	.79522	11
50	0.20506	0.97875	0.20952	4.7728	1.0217	4.8765	0.02125	0.79493	10
51	.20535	.97869	.20982	.7659	.0218	.8697	.02131	.79465	9
52	.20563	.97863	.21012	.7591	.0218	.8630	.02137	.79436	8
53	.20592	.97857	.21043	.7522	.0219	.8563	.02143	.79408	7
54	.20620	.97851	.21073	.7453	.0220	.8496	.02149	.79379	6
55	0.20649	0.97845	0.21104	4.7385	1.0220	4.8429	0.02155	0.79351	5
56	.20677	.97839	.21134	.7317	.0221	.8362	.02161	.79323	4
57	.20706	.97833	.21164	.7249	.0221	.8296	.02167	.79294	3
58	.20734	.97827	.21195	.7181	.0222	.8229	.02173	.79266	2
59	.20763	.97821	.21225	.7114	.0223	.8163	.02179	.79237	1
60	0.20791	0.97815	0.21256	4.7046	1.0223	4.8097	0.02185	0.79209	0

| M | Cosine | Sine | Cotan. | Tan. | Cosec. | Secant | Vrs. Cos. | Vrs. Sin. | M |

Natural Trigonometric Functions

M	Sine	Cosine	Tan.	Cotan.	Secant	Cosec.	Vrs. Sin.	Vrs. Cos.	M
0	0.20791	0.97815	0.21256	4.7046	1.0223	4.8097	0.02185	0.79209	60
1	.20820	.97809	.21286	.6979	.0224	.8032	.02191	.79180	59
2	.20848	.97803	.21316	.6912	.0225	.7966	.02197	.79152	58
3	.20876	.97797	.21347	.6845	.0225	.7901	.02203	.79123	57
4	.20905	.97790	.21377	.6778	.0226	.7835	.02209	.79105	56
5	0.20933	0.97784	0.21408	4.6712	1.0226	4.7770	0.02215	0.79066	55
6	.20962	.97778	.21438	.6646	.0227	.7706	.02222	.79038	54
7	.20990	.97772	.21468	.6580	.0228	.7641	.02228	.79010	53
8	.21019	.97766	.21499	.6514	.0228	.7576	.02234	.78981	52
9	.21047	.97760	.21529	.6448	.0229	.7512	.02240	.78953	51
10	0.21076	0.97754	0.21560	4.6382	1.0230	4.7448	0.02246	0.78924	50
11	.21104	.97748	.21590	.6317	.0230	.7384	.02252	.78896	49
12	.21132	.97741	.21621	.6252	.0231	.7320	.02258	.78867	48
13	.21161	.97735	.21651	.6187	.0232	.7257	.02264	.78839	47
14	.21189	.97729	.21682	.6122	.0232	.7193	.02271	.78811	46
15	0.21218	0.97723	0.21712	4.6057	1.0233	4.7130	0.02277	0.78782	45
16	.21246	.97717	.21742	.5993	.0234	.7067	.02283	.78754	44
17	.21275	.97711	.21773	.5928	.0234	.7004	.02289	.78725	43
18	.21303	.97704	.21803	.5864	.0235	.6942	.02295	.78697	42
19	.21331	.97698	.21834	.5800	.0235	.6879	.02302	.78668	41
20	0.21360	0.97692	0.21864	4.5736	1.0236	4.6817	0.02308	0.78640	40
21	.21388	.97686	.21895	.5673	.0237	.6754	.02314	.78612	39
22	.21417	.97680	.21925	.5609	.0237	.6692	.02320	.78583	38
23	.21445	.97673	.21956	.5546	.0238	.6631	.02326	.78555	37
24	.21473	.97667	.21986	.5483	.0239	.6569	.02333	.78526	36
25	0.21502	0.97661	0.22017	4.5420	1.0239	4.6507	0.02339	0.78508	35
26	.21530	.97655	.22047	.5357	.0240	.6446	.02345	.78470	34
27	.21559	.97648	.22078	.5294	.0241	.6385	.02351	.78441	33
28	.21587	.97642	.22108	.5232	.0241	.6324	.02358	.78413	32
29	.21615	.97636	.22139	.5169	.0242	.6263	.02364	.78384	31
30	0.21644	0.97630	0.22169	4.5107	1.0243	4.6201	0.02370	0.78356	30
31	.21672	.97623	.22200	.5045	.0243	.6142	.02377	.78328	29
32	.21701	.97617	.22230	.4983	.0244	.6081	.02383	.78299	28
33	.21729	.97611	.22261	.4921	.0245	.6021	.02389	.78271	27
34	.21757	.97604	.22291	.4860	.0245	.5961	.02396	.78242	26
35	0.21786	0.97598	0.22322	4.4799	1.0246	4.5901	0.02402	0.78214	25
36	.21814	.97592	.22353	.4737	.0247	.5841	.02408	.78186	24
37	.21843	.97585	.22383	.4676	.0247	.5782	.02415	.78154	23
38	.21871	.97579	.22414	.4615	.0248	.5722	.02421	.78129	22
39	.21899	.97573	.22444	.4555	.0249	.5663	.02427	.78100	21
40	0.21928	0.97566	0.22475	4.4494	1.0249	4.5604	0.02434	0.78072	20
41	.21956	.97560	.22505	.4434	.0250	.5545	.02440	.78043	19
42	.21985	.97553	.22536	.4373	.0251	.5486	.02446	.78015	18
43	.22013	.97547	.22566	.4313	.0251	.5428	.02453	.77987	17
44	.22041	.97541	.22597	.4253	.0252	.5369	.02459	.77959	16
45	0.22070	0.97534	0.22628	4.4194	1.0253	4.5311	0.02466	0.77930	15
46	.22098	.97528	.22658	.4134	.0253	.5253	.02472	.77902	14
47	.22126	.97521	.22689	.4074	.0254	.5195	.02479	.77873	13
48	.22155	.97515	.22719	.4015	.0255	.5137	.02485	.77845	12
49	.22183	.97508	.22750	.3956	.0255	.5079	.02491	.77817	11
50	0.22211	0.97502	0.22781	4.3897	1.0256	4.5021	0.02498	0.77788	10
51	.22240	.97495	.22811	.3838	.0257	.4964	.02504	.77760	9
52	.22268	.97489	.22842	.3779	.0257	.4907	.02511	.77732	8
53	.22297	.97483	.22872	.3721	.0258	.4850	.02517	.77703	7
54	.22325	.97476	.22903	.3662	.0259	.4793	.02524	.77675	6
55	0.22353	0.97470	0.22934	4.3604	1.0260	4.4736	0.02530	0.77647	5
56	.22382	.97463	.22964	.3546	.0260	.4679	.02537	.77618	4
57	.22410	.97457	.22995	.3488	.0261	.4623	.02543	.77590	3
58	.22438	.97450	.23025	.3430	.0262	.4566	.02550	.77561	2
59	.22467	.97443	.23056	.3372	.0262	.4510	.02556	.77533	1
60	0.22495	0.97437	0.23087	4.3315	1.0263	4.4454	0.02563	0.77505	0
M	Cosine	Sine	Cotan.	Tan.	Cosec.	Secant	Vrs. Cos.	Vrs. Sin.	M

M	Sine	Cosine	Tan.	Cotan.	Secant	Cosec.	Vrs. Sin.	Vrs. Cos.	M
0	0.22495	0.97437	0.23087	4.3315	1.0263	4.4454	0.02563	0.77505	60
1	.22523	.97430	.23117	.3257	.0264	.4398	.02569	.77476	59
2	.22552	.97424	.23148	.3200	.0264	.4342	.02576	.77448	58
3	.22530	.97417	.23179	.3143	.0265	.4287	.02583	.77420	57
4	.22608	.97411	.23209	.3086	.0266	.4231	.02589	.77391	56
5	0.22637	0.97404	0.23240	4.3029	1.0266	4.4176	0.02596	0.77363	55
6	.22665	.97398	.23270	.2972	.0267	.4121	.02602	.77335	54
7	.22693	.97391	.23301	.2916	.0268	.4065	.02609	.77306	53
8	.22722	.97384	.23332	.2859	.0268	.4011	.02616	.77278	52
9	.22750	.97378	.23363	.2803	.0269	.3956	.02622	.77250	51
10	0.22778	0.97371	0.23393	4.2747	1.0270	4.3901	0.02629	0.77221	50
11	.22807	.97364	.23424	.2691	.0271	.3847	.02635	.77193	49
12	.22835	.97358	.23455	.2635	.0271	.3792	.02642	.77165	48
13	.22863	.97351	.23485	.2579	.0272	.3738	.02649	.77136	47
14	.22892	.97344	.23516	.2524	.0273	.3684	.02655	.77108	46
15	0.22920	0.97338	0.23547	4.2468	1.0273	4.3630	0.02662	0.77080	45
16	.22948	.97331	.23577	.2413	.0274	.3576	.02669	.77052	44
17	.22977	.97324	.23608	.2358	.0275	.3522	.02675	.77023	43
18	.23005	.97318	.23639	.2303	.0276	.3469	.02682	.76995	42
19	.23033	.97311	.23670	.2248	.0276	.3415	.02689	.76967	41
20	0.23061	0.97304	0.23700	4.2193	1.0277	4.3362	0.02695	0.76938	40
21	.23090	.97298	.23731	.2139	.0278	.3309	.02702	.76910	39
22	.23118	.97291	.23762	.2084	.0278	.3256	.02709	.76882	38
23	.23146	.97284	.23793	.2030	.0279	.3203	.02716	.76853	37
24	.23175	.97277	.23823	.1976	.0280	.3150	.02722	.76825	36
25	0.23203	0.97271	0.23854	4.1921	1.0280	4.3098	0.02729	0.76797	35
26	.23231	.97264	.23885	.1867	.0281	.3045	.02736	.76769	34
27	.23260	.97257	.23916	.1814	.0282	.2993	.02743	.76740	33
28	.23288	.97250	.23946	.1760	.0283	.2941	.02749	.76712	32
29	.23316	.97244	.23977	.1706	.0283	.2888	.02756	.76684	31
30	0.23344	0.97237	0.24008	4.1653	1.0284	4.2836	0.02763	0.76655	30
31	.23373	.97230	.24039	.1600	.0285	.2785	.02770	.76627	29
32	.23401	.97223	.24069	.1546	.0285	.2733	.02777	.76599	28
33	.23429	.97216	.24100	.1493	.0286	.2681	.02783	.76571	27
34	.23458	.97210	.24131	.1440	.0287	.2630	.02790	.76542	26
35	0.23486	0.97203	0.24162	4.1388	1.0288	4.2579	0.02797	0.76514	25
36	.23514	.97196	.24192	.1335	.0288	.2527	.02804	.76486	24
37	.23542	.97189	.24223	.1282	.0289	.2476	.02811	.76457	23
38	.23571	.97182	.24254	.1230	.0290	.2425	.02818	.76429	22
39	.23599	.97175	.24285	.1178	.0291	.2375	.02824	.76401	21
40	0.23627	0.97169	0.24316	4.1126	1.0291	4.2324	0.02831	0.76373	20
41	.23655	.97162	.24346	.1073	.0292	.2273	.02838	.76344	19
42	.23684	.97155	.24377	.1022	.0293	.2223	.02845	.76316	18
43	.23712	.97148	.24408	.0970	.0293	.2173	.02852	.76288	17
44	.23740	.97141	.24439	.0918	.0294	.2122	.02859	.76260	16
45	0.23768	0.97134	0.24470	4.0867	1.0295	4.2072	0.02866	0.76231	15
46	.23797	.97127	.24501	.0815	.0296	.2022	.02873	.76203	14
47	.23825	.97120	.24531	.0764	.0296	.1972	.02880	.76175	13
48	.23853	.97113	.24562	.0713	.0297	.1923	.02886	.76147	12
49	.23881	.97106	.24593	.0662	.0298	.1873	.02893	.76118	11
50	0.23910	0.97099	0.24624	4.0611	1.0299	4.1824	0.02900	0.76090	10
51	.23938	.97092	.24655	.0560	.0299	.1774	.02907	.76062	9
52	.23966	.97086	.24686	.0509	.0300	.1725	.02914	.76034	8
53	.23994	.97079	.24717	.0458	.0301	.1676	.02921	.76005	7
54	.24023	.97072	.24747	.0408	.0302	.1627	.02928	.75977	6
55	0.24051	0.97065	0.24778	4.0358	1.0302	4.1578	0.02935	0.75949	5
56	.24079	.97058	.24809	.0307	.0303	.1529	.02942	.75921	4
57	.24107	.97051	.24840	.0257	.0304	.1481	.02949	.75892	3
58	.24136	.97044	.24871	.0207	.0305	.1432	.02956	.75864	2
59	.24164	.97037	.24902	.0157	.0305	.1384	.02963	.75836	1
60	0.24192	0.97029	0.24933	4.0108	1.0306	4.1336	0.02970	0.75808	0
M	Cosine	Sine	Cotan.	Tan.	Cosec.	Secant	Vrs. Cos.	Vrs. Sin.	M

Natural Trigonometric Functions

M	Sine	Cosine	Tan.	Cotan.	Secant	Cosec.	Vrs. Sin.	Vrs. Cos.	M
0	0.24192	0.97029	0.24933	4.0108	1.0306	4.1336	0.02970	0.75808	60
1	.24220	.97022	.24964	.0058	.0307	.1287	.02977	.75779	59
2	.24249	.97015	.24995	.0009	.0308	.1239	.02934	.75751	58
3	.24277	.97008	.25025	3.9959	.0308	.1191	.02991	.75723	57
4	.24305	.97001	.25056	.9910	.0309	.1144	.02999	.75695	56
5	0.24333	0.96994	0.25087	3.9861	1.0310	4.1096	0.03006	0.75667	55
6	.24361	.96987	.25118	.9812	.0311	.1048	.03013	.75638	54
7	.24390	.96980	.25149	.9763	.0311	.1001	.03020	.75610	53
8	.24418	.96973	.25180	.9714	.0312	.0953	.03027	.75582	52
9	.24446	.96966	.25211	.9665	.0313	.0906	.03034	.75554	51
10	0.24474	0.96959	0.25242	3.9616	1.0314	4.0859	0.03041	0.75526	50
11	.24502	.96952	.25273	.9568	.0314	.0812	.03048	.75497	49
12	.24531	.96944	.25304	.9520	.0315	.0765	.03055	.75469	48
13	.24559	.96937	.25335	.9471	.0316	.0718	.03063	.75441	47
14	.24587	.96930	.25366	.9423	.0317	.0672	.03070	.75413	46
15	0.24615	0.96923	0.25397	3.9375	1.0317	4.0625	0.03077	0.75385	45
16	.24643	.96916	.25428	.9327	.0318	.0579	.03084	.75356	44
17	.24672	.96909	.25459	.9279	.0319	.0532	.03091	.75328	43
18	.24700	.96901	.25490	.9231	.0320	.0486	.03098	.75300	42
19	.24728	.96894	.25521	.9184	.0320	.0440	.03106	.75272	41
20	0.24756	0.96887	0.25552	3.9136	1.0321	4.0394	0.03113	0.75244	40
21	.24784	.96880	.25583	.9089	.0322	.0348	.03120	.75215	39
22	.24813	.96873	.25614	.9042	.0323	.0302	.03127	.75187	38
23	.24841	.96865	.25645	.8994	.0323	.0256	.03134	.75159	37
24	.24869	.96858	.25676	.8947	.0324	.0211	.03142	.75131	36
25	0.24897	0.96851	0.25707	3.8900	1.0325	4.0165	0.03149	0.75103	35
26	.24925	.96844	.25738	.8853	.0326	.0120	.03156	.75075	34
27	.24953	.96836	.25769	.8807	.0327	.0074	.03163	.75046	33
28	.24982	.96829	.25800	.8760	.0327	.0029	.03171	.75018	32
29	.25010	.96822	.25831	.8713	.0328	3.9984	.03178	.74990	31
30	0.25038	0.96815	0.25862	3.8667	1.0329	3.9939	0.03185	0.74962	30
31	.25066	.96807	.25893	.8621	.0330	.9894	.03192	.74934	29
32	.25094	.96800	.25924	.8574	.0330	.9850	.03200	.74906	28
33	.25122	.96793	.25955	.8528	.0331	.9805	.03207	.74877	27
34	.25151	.96785	.25986	.8482	.0332	.9760	.03214	.74849	26
35	0.25179	0.96778	0.26017	3.8436	1.0333	3.9716	0.03222	0.74821	25
36	.25207	.96771	.26048	.8390	.0334	.9672	.03229	.74793	24
37	.25235	.96763	.26079	.8345	.0334	.9627	.03236	.74765	23
38	.25263	.96756	.26110	.8299	.0335	.9583	.03244	.74737	22
39	.25291	.96749	.26141	.8254	.0336	.9539	.03251	.74709	21
40	0.25319	0.96741	0.26172	3.8208	1.0337	3.9495	0.03258	0.74680	20
41	.25348	.96734	.26203	.8163	.0338	.9451	.03266	.74652	19
42	.25376	.96727	.26234	.8118	.0338	.9408	.03273	.74624	18
43	.25404	.96719	.26266	.8073	.0339	.9364	.03281	.74596	17
44	.25432	.96712	.26297	.8027	.0340	.9320	.03288	.74568	16
45	0.25460	0.96704	0.26328	3.7983	1.0341	3.9277	0.03295	0.74540	15
46	.25488	.96697	.26359	.7938	.0341	.9234	.03303	.74512	14
47	.25516	.96690	.26390	.7893	.0342	.9190	.03310	.74483	13
48	.25544	.96682	.26421	.7848	.0343	.9147	.03318	.74455	12
49	.25573	.96675	.26452	.7804	.0344	.9104	.03325	.74427	11
50	0.25601	0.96667	0.26483	3.7759	1.0345	3.9061	0.03332	0.74399	10
51	.25629	.96660	.26514	.7715	.0345	.9018	.03340	.74371	9
52	.25657	.96652	.26546	.7671	.0346	.8976	.03347	.74344	8
53	.25685	.96645	.26577	.7627	.0347	.8933	.03355	.74315	7
54	.25713	.96638	.26608	.7583	.0348	.8890	.03362	.74287	6
55	0.25741	0.96630	0.26639	3.7539	1.0349	3.8848	0.03370	0.74259	5
56	.25769	.96623	.26670	.7495	.0349	.8805	.03377	.74230	4
57	.25798	.96615	.26701	.7451	.0350	.8763	.03385	.74202	3
58	.25826	.96608	.26732	.7407	.0351	.8721	.03392	.74174	2
59	.25854	.96600	.26764	.7364	.0352	.8679	.03400	.74146	1
60	0.25882	0.96592	0.26795	3.7320	1.0353	3.8637	0.03407	0.74118	0
M	Cosine	Sine	Cotan.	Tan.	Cosec.	Secant	Vrs. Cos.	Vrs. Sin.	M

M	Sine	Cosine	Tan.	Cotan.	Secant	Cosec.	Vrs. Sin.	Vrs. Cos.	M
0	0.25882	0.96592	0.26795	3.7320	1.0353	3.8637	0.03407	0.74118	60
1	.25910	.96585	.26826	.7277	.0353	.8595	.03415	.74090	59
2	.25938	.96577	.26857	.7234	.0354	.8553	.03422	.74062	58
3	.25966	.96570	.26888	.7191	.0355	.8512	.03430	.74034	57
4	.25994	.96562	.26920	.7147	.0356	.8470	.03438	.74006	56
5	0.26022	0.96555	0.26951	3.7104	1.0357	3.8428	0.03445	0.73978	55
6	.26050	.96547	.26982	.7062	.0358	.8387	.03453	.73949	54
7	.26078	.96540	.27013	.7019	.0358	.8346	.03460	.73921	53
8	.26107	.96532	.27044	.6976	.0359	.8304	.03468	.73893	52
9	.26135	.96524	.27076	.6933	.0360	.8263	.03475	.73865	51
10	0.26163	0.96517	0.27107	3.6891	1.0361	3.8222	0.03483	0.73837	50
11	.26191	.96509	.27138	.6848	.0362	.8181	.03491	.73809	49
12	.26219	.96502	.27169	.6806	.0362	.8140	.03498	.73781	48
13	.26247	.96494	.27201	.6764	.0363	.8100	.03506	.73753	47
14	.26275	.96486	.27232	.6722	.0364	.8059	.03514	.73725	46
15	0.26303	0.96479	0.27263	3.6679	1.0365	3.8018	0.03521	0.73697	45
16	.26331	.96471	.27294	.6637	.0366	.7978	.03529	.73669	44
17	.26359	.96463	.27326	.6596	.0367	.7937	.03536	.73641	43
18	.26387	.96456	.27357	.6554	.0367	.7897	.03544	.73613	42
19	.26415	.96448	.27388	.6512	.0368	.7857	.03552	.73585	41
20	0.26443	0.96440	0.27419	3.6470	1.0369	3.7816	0.03560	0.73556	40
21	.26471	.96433	.27451	.6429	.0370	.7776	.03567	.73528	39
22	.26499	.96425	.27482	.6387	.0371	.7736	.03575	.73500	38
23	.26527	.96417	.27513	.6346	.0371	.7697	.03583	.73472	37
24	.26556	.96409	.27544	.6305	.0372	.7657	.03590	.73444	36
25	0.26584	0.96402	0.27576	3.6263	1.0373	3.7617	0.03598	0.73416	35
26	.26612	.96394	.27607	.6222	.0374	.7577	.03606	.73388	34
27	.26640	.96386	.27638	.6181	.0375	.7538	.03614	.73360	33
28	.26668	.96378	.27670	.6140	.0376	.7498	.03621	.73332	32
29	.26696	.96371	.27701	.6100	.0376	.7459	.03629	.73304	31
30	0.26724	0.96363	0.27732	3.6059	1.0377	3.7420	0.03637	0.73276	30
31	.26752	.96355	.27764	.6018	.0378	.7380	.03645	.73248	29
32	.26780	.96347	.27795	.5977	.0379	.7341	.03652	.73220	28
33	.26808	.96340	.27826	.5937	.0380	.7302	.03660	.73192	27
34	.26836	.96332	.27858	.5896	.0381	.7263	.03668	.73164	26
35	0.26864	0.96324	0.27889	3.5856	1.0382	3.7224	0.03676	0.73136	25
36	.26892	.96316	.27920	.5816	.0382	.7186	.03684	.73108	24
37	.26920	.96308	.27952	.5776	.0383	.7147	.03691	.73080	23
38	.26948	.96301	.27983	.5736	.0384	.7108	.03699	.73052	22
39	.26976	.96293	.28014	.5696	.0385	.7070	.03707	.73024	21
40	0.27004	0.96285	0.28046	3.5656	1.0386	3.7031	0.03715	0.72996	20
41	.27032	.96277	.28077	.5616	.0387	.6993	.03723	.72968	19
42	.27060	.96269	.28109	.5576	.0387	.6955	.03731	.72940	18
43	.27088	.96261	.28140	.5536	.0388	.6917	.03739	.72912	17
44	.27116	.96253	.28171	.5497	.0389	.6878	.03746	.72884	16
45	0.27144	0.96245	0.28203	3.5457	1.0390	3.6840	0.03754	0.72856	15
46	.27172	.96238	.28234	.5418	.0391	.6802	.03762	.72828	14
47	.27200	.96230	.28266	.5378	.0392	.6765	.03770	.72800	13
48	.27228	.96222	.28297	.5339	.0393	.6727	.03778	.72772	12
49	.27256	.96214	.28328	.5300	.0393	.6689	.03786	.72744	11
50	0.27284	0.96206	0.28360	3.5261	1.0394	3.6651	0.03794	0.72716	10
51	.27312	.96198	.28391	.5222	.0395	.6614	.03802	.72688	9
52	.27340	.96190	.28423	.5183	.0396	.6576	.03810	.72660	8
53	.27368	.96182	.28454	.5144	.0397	.6539	.03818	.72632	7
54	.27396	.96174	.28486	.5105	.0398	.6502	.03826	.72604	6
55	0.27424	0.96166	0.28517	3.5066	1.0399	3.6464	0.03834	0.72576	5
56	.27452	.96158	.28549	.5028	.0399	.6427	.03842	.72548	4
57	.27480	.96150	.28580	.4989	.0400	.6390	.03850	.72520	3
58	.27508	.96142	.28611	.4951	.0401	.6353	.03858	.72492	2
59	.27536	.96134	.28643	.4912	.0402	.6316	.03866	.72464	1
60	0.27564	0.96126	0.28674	3.4874	1.0403	3.6279	0.03874	0.72436	0

| M | Cosine | Sine | Cotan. | Tan. | Cosec. | Secant | Vrs. Cos. | Vrs. Sin. | M |

Natural Trigonometric Functions

M	Sine	Cosine	Tan.	Cotan.	Secant	Cosec.	Vrs. Sin.	Vrs. Cos.	M
0	0.27564	0.96126	0.28674	3.4874	1.0403	3.6279	0.03874	0.72436	60
1	.27592	.96118	.28706	.4836	.0404	.6243	.03882	.72408	59
2	.27620	.96110	.28737	.4798	.0405	.6206	.03890	.72380	58
3	.27648	.96102	.28769	.4760	.0406	.6169	.03898	.72352	57
4	.27675	.96094	.28800	.4722	.0406	.6133	.03906	.72324	56
5	0.27703	0.96086	0.28832	3.4684	1.0407	3.6096	0.03914	0.72296	55
6	.27731	.96078	.28863	.4646	.0408	.6060	.03922	.72268	54
7	.27759	.96070	.28895	.4608	.0409	.6024	.03930	.72240	53
8	.27787	.96062	.28926	.4570	.0410	.5987	.03938	.72213	52
9	.27815	.96054	.28958	.4533	.0411	.5951	.03946	.72185	51
10	0.27843	0.96045	0.28990	3.4495	1.0412	3.5915	0.03954	0.72157	50
11	.27871	.96037	.29021	.4458	.0413	.5879	.03962	.72129	49
12	.27899	.96029	.29053	.4420	.0413	.5843	.03971	.72101	48
13	.27927	.96021	.29084	.4383	.0414	.5807	.03979	.72073	47
14	.27955	.96013	.29116	.4346	.0415	.5772	.03987	.72045	46
15	0.27983	0.96005	0.29147	3.4308	1.0416	3.5736	0.03995	0.72017	45
16	.28011	.95997	.29179	.4271	.0417	.5700	.04003	.71989	44
17	.28039	.95989	.29210	.4234	.0418	.5665	.04011	.71961	43
18	.28067	.95980	.29242	.4197	.0419	.5629	.04019	.71933	42
19	.28094	.95972	.29274	.4160	.0420	.5594	.04028	.71905	41
20	0.28122	0.95964	0.29305	3.4124	1.0420	3.5559	0.04036	0.71877	40
21	.28150	.95956	.29337	.4087	.0421	.5523	.04044	.71849	39
22	.28178	.95948	.29368	.4050	.0422	.5488	.04052	.71822	38
23	.28206	.95940	.29400	.4014	.0423	.5453	.04060	.71794	37
24	.28234	.95931	.29432	.3977	.0424	.5418	.04069	.71766	36
25	0.28262	0.95923	0.29463	3.3941	1.0425	3.5383	0.04077	0.71738	35
26	.28290	.95915	.29495	.3904	.0426	.5348	.04085	.71710	34
27	.28318	.95907	.29526	.3868	.0427	.5313	.04093	.71682	33
28	.28346	.95898	.29558	.3832	.0428	.5279	.04101	.71654	32
29	.28374	.95890	.29590	.3795	.0428	.5244	.04110	.71626	31
30	0.28401	0.95882	0.29621	3.3759	1.0429	3.5209	0.04118	0.71599	30
31	.28429	.95874	.29653	.3723	.0430	.5175	.04126	.71570	29
32	.28457	.95865	.29685	.3687	.0431	.5140	.04134	.71543	28
33	.28485	.95857	.29716	.3651	.0432	.5106	.04143	.71515	27
34	.28513	.95849	.29748	.3616	.0433	.5072	.04151	.71487	26
35	0.28541	0.95840	0.29780	3.3580	1.0434	3.5037	0.04159	0.71459	25
36	.28569	.95832	.29811	.3544	.0435	.5003	.04168	.71431	24
37	.28597	.95824	.29843	.3509	.0436	.4969	.04176	.71403	23
38	.28624	.95816	.29875	.3473	.0437	.4935	.04184	.71375	22
39	.28652	.95807	.29906	.3438	.0438	.4901	.04193	.71347	21
40	0.28680	0.95799	0.29938	3.3402	1.0438	3.4867	0.04201	0.71320	20
41	.28708	.95791	.29970	.3367	.0439	.4833	.04209	.71292	19
42	.28736	.95782	.30001	.3332	.0440	.4799	.04218	.71264	18
43	.28764	.95774	.30033	.3296	.0441	.4766	.04226	.71236	17
44	.28792	.95765	.30065	.3261	.0442	.4732	.04234	.71208	16
45	0.28820	0.95757	0.30096	3.3226	1.0443	3.4698	0.04243	0.71180	15
46	.28847	.95749	.30128	.3191	.0444	.4665	.04251	.71152	14
47	.28875	.95740	.30160	.3156	.0445	.4632	.04260	.71125	13
48	.28903	.95732	.30192	.3121	.0446	.4598	.04268	.71097	12
49	.28931	.95723	.30223	.3087	.0447	.4565	.04276	.71069	11
50	0.28959	0.95715	0.30255	3.3052	1.0448	3.4532	0.04285	0.71041	10
51	.28987	.95707	.30287	.3017	.0448	.4498	.04293	.71013	9
52	.29014	.95698	.30319	.2983	.0449	.4465	.04302	.70985	8
53	.29042	.95690	.30350	.2948	.0450	.4432	.04310	.70958	7
54	.29070	.95681	.30382	.2914	.0451	.4399	.04319	.70930	6
55	0.29098	0.95673	0.30414	3.2879	1.0452	3.4366	0.04327	0.70902	5
56	.29126	.95664	.30446	.2845	.0453	.4334	.04335	.70874	4
57	.29154	.95656	.30478	.2811	.0454	.4301	.04344	.70846	3
58	.29181	.95647	.30509	.2777	.0455	.4268	.04352	.70818	2
59	.29209	.95639	.30541	.2742	.0456	.4236	.04361	.70791	1
60	0.29237	0.95630	0.30573	3.2708	1.0457	3.4203	0.04369	0.70763	0
M	Cosine	Sine	Cotan.	Tan.	Cosec.	Secant	Vrs. Cos.	Vrs. Sin.	M

Natural Trigonometric Functions

M	Sine	Cosine	Tan.	Cotan.	Secant	Cosec.	Vrs. Sin.	Vrs. Cos.	M
0	0.29237	0.95630	0.30573	3.2708	1.0457	3.4203	0.04369	0.70763	60
1	.29265	.95622	.30605	.2674	.0458	.4170	.04378	.70735	59
2	.29293	.95613	.30637	.2640	.0459	.4138	.04386	.70707	58
3	.29321	.95605	.30668	.2607	.0460	.4106	.04395	.70679	57
4	.29348	.95596	.30700	.2573	.0461	.4073	.04404	.70651	56
5	0.29376	0.95588	0.30732	3.2539	1.0461	3.4041	0.04412	0.70624	55
6	.29404	.95579	.30764	.2505	.0462	.4009	.04421	.70596	54
7	.29432	.95571	.30796	.2472	.0463	.3977	.04429	.70568	53
8	.29460	.95562	.30828	.2438	.0464	.3945	.04438	.70540	52
9	.29487	.95554	.30859	.2405	.0465	.3913	.04446	.70512	51
10	0.29515	0.95545	0.30891	3.2371	1.0466	3.3881	0.04455	0.70485	50
11	.29543	.95536	.30923	.2338	.0467	.3849	.04463	.70457	49
12	.29571	.95528	.30955	.2305	.0468	.3817	.04472	.70429	48
13	.29598	.95519	.30987	.2271	.0469	.3785	.04481	.70401	47
14	.29626	.95511	.31019	.2238	.0470	.3754	.04489	.70374	46
15	0.29654	0.95502	0.31051	3.2205	1.0471	3.3722	0.04498	0.70346	45
16	.29682	.95493	.31083	.2172	.0472	.3690	.04507	.70318	44
17	.29710	.95485	.31115	.2139	.0473	.3659	.04515	.70290	43
18	.29737	.95476	.31146	.2106	.0474	.3627	.04524	.70262	42
19	.29765	.95467	.31178	.2073	.0475	.3596	.04532	.70235	41
20	0.29793	0.95459	0.31210	3.2041	1.0476	3.3565	0.04541	0.70207	40
21	.29821	.95450	.31242	.2008	.0477	.3534	.04550	.70179	39
22	.29848	.95441	.31274	.1975	.0478	.3502	.04558	.70151	38
23	.29876	.95433	.31306	.1942	.0478	.3471	.04567	.70124	37
24	.29904	.95424	.31338	.1910	.0479	.3440	.04576	.70096	36
25	0.29932	0.95415	0.31370	3.1877	1.0480	3.3409	0.04585	0.70068	35
26	.29959	.95407	.31402	.1845	.0481	.3378	.04593	.70040	34
27	.29987	.95398	.31434	.1813	.0482	.3347	.04602	.70013	33
28	.30015	.95389	.31466	.1780	.0483	.3316	.04611	.69982	32
29	.30043	.95380	.31498	.1748	.0484	.3286	.04619	.69957	31
30	0.30070	0.95372	0.31530	3.1716	1.0485	3.3255	0.04628	0.69929	30
31	.30098	.95363	.31562	.1684	.0486	.3224	.04637	.69902	29
32	.30126	.95354	.31594	.1652	.0487	.3194	.04646	.69874	28
33	.30154	.95345	.31626	.1620	.0488	.3163	.04654	.69846	27
34	.30181	.95337	.31658	.1588	.0489	.3133	.04663	.69818	26
35	0.30209	0.95328	0.31690	3.1556	1.0490	3.3102	0.04672	0.69791	25
36	.30237	.95319	.31722	.1524	.0491	.3072	.04681	.69763	24
37	.30265	.95310	.31754	.1492	.0492	.3042	.04690	.69735	23
38	.30292	.95301	.31786	.1460	.0493	.3011	.04698	.69707	22
39	.30320	.95293	.31818	.1429	.0494	.2981	.04707	.69680	21
40	0.30348	0.95284	0.31850	3.1397	1.0495	3.2951	0.04716	0.69652	20
41	.30375	.95275	.31882	.1366	.0496	.2921	.04725	.69624	19
42	.30403	.95266	.31914	.1334	.0497	.2891	.04734	.69597	18
43	.30431	.95257	.31946	.1303	.0498	.2861	.04743	.69569	17
44	.30459	.95248	.31978	.1271	.0499	.2831	.04751	.69541	16
45	0.30486	0.95239	0.32010	3.1240	1.0500	3.2801	0.04760	0.69513	15
46	.30514	.95231	.32042	.1209	.0501	.2772	.04769	.69486	14
47	.30542	.95222	.32074	.1177	.0502	.2742	.04778	.69458	13
48	.30569	.95213	.32106	.1146	.0503	.2712	.04787	.69430	12
49	.30597	.95204	.32138	.1115	.0504	.2683	.04796	.69403	11
50	0.30625	0.95195	0.32171	3.1084	1.0505	3.2653	0.04805	0.69375	10
51	.30653	.95186	.32203	.1053	.0506	.2624	.04814	.69347	9
52	.30680	.95177	.32235	.1022	.0507	.2594	.04823	.69320	8
53	.30708	.95168	.32267	.0991	.0508	.2565	.04832	.69292	7
54	.30736	.95159	.32299	.0960	.0509	.2535	.04840	.69264	6
55	0.30763	0.95150	0.32331	3.0930	1.0510	3.2506	0.04849	0.69237	5
56	.30791	.95141	.32363	.0899	.0511	.2477	.04858	.69209	4
57	.30819	.95132	.32395	.0868	.0512	.2448	.04867	.69181	3
58	.30846	.95124	.32428	.0838	.0513	.2419	.04876	.69154	2
59	.30874	.95115	.32460	.0807	.0514	.2390	.04885	.69126	1
60	0.30902	0.95106	0.32492	3.0777	1.0515	3.2361	0.04894	0.69098	0
M	Cosine	Sine	Cotan.	Tan.	Cosec.	Secant	Vrs. Cos.	Vrs. Sin.	M

M	Sine	Cosine	Tan.	Cotan.	Secant	Cosec.	Vrs. Sin.	Vrs. Cos.	M
0	0.30902	.95106	0.32492	3.0777	1.0515	3.2361	0.04894	0.69098	60
1	.30929	.95097	.32524	.0746	.0516	.2332	.04903	.69071	59
2	.30957	.95088	.32556	.0716	.0517	.2303	.04912	.69043	58
3	.30985	.95079	.32588	.0686	.0518	.2274	.04921	.69015	57
4	.31012	.95070	.32621	.0655	.0519	.2245	.04930	.68988	56
5	0.31040	.95061	0.32653	3.0625	1.0520	3.2216	0.04939	0.68960	55
6	.31068	.95051	.32685	.0595	.0521	.2188	.04948	.68932	54
7	.31095	.95042	.32717	.0565	.0522	.2159	.04957	.68905	53
8	.31123	.95033	.32749	.0535	.0523	.2131	.04966	.68877	52
9	.31150	.95024	.32782	.0505	.0524	.2102	.04975	.68849	51
10	0.31178	.95015	0.32814	3.0475	1.0525	3.2074	0.04985	0.68822	50
11	.31206	.95006	.32846	.0445	.0526	.2045	.04994	.68794	49
12	.31233	.94997	.32878	.0415	.0527	.2017	.05003	.68766	48
13	.31261	.94988	.32910	.0385	.0528	.1989	.05012	.68739	47
14	.31289	.94979	.32943	.0356	.0529	.1960	.05021	.68711	46
15	0.31316	.94970	0.32975	3.0326	1.0530	3.1932	0.05030	0.68684	45
16	.31344	.94961	.33007	.0296	.0531	.1904	.05039	.68656	44
17	.31372	.94952	.33039	.0267	.0532	.1876	.05048	.68628	43
18	.31399	.94942	.33072	.0237	.0533	.1848	.05057	.68601	42
19	.31427	.94933	.33104	.0208	.0534	.1820	.05066	.68573	41
20	0.31454	.94924	0.33136	3.0178	1.0535	3.1792	0.05076	0.68545	40
21	.31482	.94915	.33169	.0149	.0536	.1764	.05085	.68518	39
22	.31510	.94906	.33201	.0120	.0537	.1736	.05094	.68490	38
23	.31537	.94897	.33233	.0090	.0538	.1708	.05103	.68463	37
24	.31565	.94888	.33265	.0061	.0539	.1681	.05112	.68435	36
25	0.31592	.94878	0.33298	3.0032	1.0540	3.1653	0.05121	0.68407	35
26	.31620	.94869	.33330	.0003	.0541	.1625	.05131	.68380	34
27	.31648	.94860	.33362	2.9974	.0542	.1598	.05140	.68352	33
28	.31675	.94851	.33395	.9945	.0543	.1570	.05149	.68325	32
29	.31703	.94841	.33427	.9916	.0544	.1543	.05158	.68297	31
30	0.31730	.94832	0.33459	2.9887	1.0545	3.1515	0.05168	0.68269	30
31	.31758	.94823	.33492	.9858	.0546	.1488	.05177	.68242	29
32	.31786	.94814	.33524	.9829	.0547	.1461	.05186	.68214	28
33	.31813	.94805	.33557	.9800	.0548	.1433	.05195	.68187	27
34	.31841	.94795	.33589	.9772	.0549	.1406	.05205	.68159	26
35	0.31868	.94786	0.33621	2.9743	1.0550	3.1379	0.05214	0.68132	25
36	.31896	.94777	.33654	.9714	.0551	.1352	.05223	.68104	24
37	.31923	.94767	.33686	.9686	.0552	.1325	.05232	.68076	23
38	.31951	.94758	.33718	.9657	.0553	.1298	.05242	.68049	22
39	.31978	.94749	.33751	.9629	.0554	.1271	.05251	.68021	21
40	0.32006	.94740	0.33783	2.9600	1.0555	3.1244	0.05260	0.67994	20
41	.32034	.94730	.33816	.9572	.0556	.1217	.05270	.67966	19
42	.32061	.94721	.33848	.9544	.0557	.1190	.05279	.67939	18
43	.32089	.94712	.33880	.9515	.0558	.1163	.05288	.67911	17
44	.32116	.94702	.33913	.9487	.0559	.1137	.05297	.67884	16
45	0.32144	.94693	0.33945	2.9459	1.0560	3.1110	0.05307	0.67856	15
46	.32171	.94684	.33978	.9431	.0561	.1083	.05316	.67828	14
47	.32199	.94674	.34010	.9403	.0562	.1057	.05326	.67801	13
48	.32226	.94665	.34043	.9375	.0563	.1030	.05335	.67773	12
49	.32254	.94655	.34075	.9347	.0565	.1004	.05344	.67746	11
50	0.32282	.94646	0.34108	2.9319	1.0566	3.0977	0.05354	0.67718	10
51	.32309	.94637	.34140	.9291	.0567	.0951	.05363	.67691	9
52	.32337	.94627	.34173	.9263	.0568	.0925	.05373	.67663	8
53	.32364	.94618	.34205	.9235	.0569	.0898	.05382	.67636	7
54	.32392	.94608	.34238	.9208	.0570	.0872	.05391	.67608	6
55	0.32419	.94599	0.34270	2.9180	1.0571	3.0846	0.05401	0.67581	5
56	.32447	.94590	.34303	.9152	.0572	.0820	.05410	.67553	4
57	.32474	.94580	.34335	.9125	.0573	.0793	.05420	.67526	3
58	.32502	.94571	.34368	.9097	.0574	.0767	.05429	.67498	2
59	.32529	.94561	.34400	.9069	.0575	.0741	.05439	.67471	1
60	0.32557	.94552	0.34433	2.9042	1.0576	3.0715	0.05448	0.67443	0
M	Cosine	Sine	Cotan.	Tan.	Cosec.	Secant	Vrs. Cos.	Vrs. Sin.	M

M	Sine	Cosine	Tan.	Cotan.	Secant	Cosec.	Vrs. Sin.	Vrs. Cos.	M
0	0.32557	0.94552	0.34433	2.9042	1.0576	3.0715	0.05448	0.67443	60
1	.32584	.94342	.34465	.9015	.0577	.0690	.05458	.67416	59
2	.32612	.94533	.34498	.8987	.0578	.0664	.05467	.67388	58
3	.32639	.94523	.34530	.8960	.0579	.0638	.05476	.67361	57
4	.32667	.94514	.34563	.8933	.0580	.0612	.05486	.67333	56
5	0.32694	0.94504	.34595	2.8905	1.0581	3.0586	0.05495	0.67306	55
6	.32722	.94495	.34628	.8878	.0582	.0561	.05505	.67278	54
7	.32749	.94485	.34661	.8851	.0584	.0535	.05515	.67251	53
8	.32777	.94476	.34693	.8824	.0585	.0509	.05524	.67223	52
9	.32804	.94466	.34726	.8797	.0586	.0484	.05534	.67196	51
10	0.32832	0.94457	0.34758	2.8770	1.0587	3.0458	0.05543	0.67168	50
11	.32859	.94447	.34791	.8743	.0588	.0433	.05553	.67141	49
12	.32887	.94438	.34824	.8716	.0589	.0407	.05562	.67113	48
13	.32914	.94428	.34856	.8689	.0590	.0382	.05572	.67086	47
14	.32942	.94418	.34889	.8662	.0591	.0357	.05581	.67058	46
15	0.32969	0.94409	0.34921	2.8636	1.0592	3.0331	0.05591	0.67031	45
16	.32996	.94399	.34954	.8609	.0593	.0306	.05601	.67003	44
17	.33024	.94390	.34987	.8582	.0594	.0281	.05610	.66976	43
18	.33051	.94380	.35019	.8555	.0595	.0256	.05620	.66948	42
19	.33079	.94370	.35052	.8529	.0596	.0231	.05629	.66921	41
20	0.33106	0.94361	0.35085	2.8502	1.0598	3.0206	0.05639	0.66894	40
21	.33134	.94351	.35117	.8476	.0599	.0181	.05649	.66866	39
22	.33161	.94341	.35150	.8449	.0600	.0156	.05658	.66839	38
23	.33189	.94332	.35183	.8423	.0601	.0131	.05668	.66811	37
24	.33216	.94322	.35215	.8396	.0602	.0106	.05678	.66784	36
25	0.33243	0.94313	0.35248	2.8370	1.0603	3.0081	0.05687	0.66756	35
26	.33271	.94303	.35281	.8344	.0604	.0056	.05697	.66729	34
27	.33298	.94293	.35314	.8318	.0605	.0031	.05707	.66701	33
28	.33326	.94283	.35346	.8291	.0606	.0007	.05716	.66674	32
29	.33353	.94274	.35379	.8265	.0607	2.9982	.05726	.66647	31
30	0.33381	0.94264	0.35412	2.8239	1.0608	2.9957	0.05736	0.66619	30
31	.33408	.94254	.35445	.8213	.0609	.9933	.05745	.66592	29
32	.33435	.94245	.35477	.8187	.0611	.9908	.05755	.66564	28
33	.33463	.94235	.35510	.8161	.0612	.9884	.05765	.66537	27
34	.33490	.94225	.35543	.8135	.0613	.9859	.05775	.66510	26
35	0.33518	0.94215	0.35576	2.8109	1.0614	2.9835	0.05784	0.66482	25
36	.33545	.94206	.35608	.8083	.0615	.9810	.05794	.66455	24
37	.33572	.94196	.35641	.8057	.0616	.9786	.05804	.66427	23
38	.33600	.94186	.35674	.8032	.0617	.9762	.05814	.66400	22
39	.33627	.94176	.35707	.8006	.0618	.9738	.05823	.66373	21
40	0.33655	0.94167	0.35739	2.7980	1.0619	2.9713	0.05833	0.66345	20
41	.33682	.94157	.35772	.7954	.0620	.9689	.05843	.66318	19
42	.33709	.94147	.35805	.7929	.0622	.9665	.05853	.66290	18
43	.33737	.94137	.35838	.7903	.0623	.9641	.05863	.66263	17
44	.33764	.94127	.35871	.7878	.0624	.9617	.05872	.66236	16
45	0.33792	0.94118	0.35904	2.7852	1.0625	2.9593	0.05882	0.66208	15
46	.33819	.94108	.35936	.7827	.0626	.9569	.05892	.66181	14
47	.33846	.94098	.35969	.7801	.0627	.9545	.05902	.66153	13
48	.33874	.94088	.36002	.7776	.0628	.9521	.05912	.66126	12
49	.33901	.94078	.36035	.7751	.0629	.9497	.05922	.66099	11
50	0.33928	0.94068	0.36068	2.7725	1.0630	2.9474	0.05932	0.66071	10
51	.33956	.94058	.36101	.7700	.0632	.9450	.05941	.66044	9
52	.33983	.94049	.36134	.7675	.0633	.9426	.05951	.66017	8
53	.34011	.94039	.36167	.7650	.0634	.9402	.05961	.65989	7
54	.34038	.94029	.36199	.7625	.0635	.9379	.05971	.65962	6
55	0.34065	0.94019	0.36232	2.7600	1.0636	2.9355	0.05981	0.65935	5
56	.34093	.94009	.36265	.7575	.0637	.9332	.05991	.65907	4
57	.34120	.93999	.36298	.7550	.0638	.9308	.05999	.65880	3
58	.34147	.93989	.36331	.7525	.0639	.9285	.06001	.65853	2
59	.34175	.93979	.36364	.7500	.0641	.9261	.06021	.65825	1
60	0.34202	0.93969	0.36397	2.7475	1.0642	2.9238	0.06031	0.65798	0
M	Cosine	Sine	Cotan.	Tan.	Cosec.	Secant	Vrs. Cos.	Vrs. Sin.	M

Natural Trigonometric Functions

M	Sine	Cosine	Tan.	Cotan.	Secant	Cosec.	Vrs. Sin.	Vrs. Cos.	M
0	0.34202	.93969	0.36397	2.7475	1.0642	2.9238	0.06031	0.65798	60
1	.34229	.93959	.36430	.7450	.0643	.9215	.06041	.65771	59
2	.34257	.93949	.36463	.7425	.0644	.9191	.06051	.65743	58
3	.34284	.93939	.36496	.7400	.0645	.9168	.06061	.65716	57
4	.34311	.93929	.36529	.7376	.0646	.9145	.06071	.65689	56
5	0.34339	.93919	0.36562	2.7351	1.0647	2.9122	0.06080	0.65661	55
6	.34366	.93909	.36595	.7326	.0648	.9098	.06090	.65634	54
7	.34393	.93899	.36628	.7302	.0650	.9075	.06100	.65607	53
8	.34421	.93889	.36661	.7277	.0651	.9052	.06110	.65579	52
9	.34448	.93879	.36694	.7252	.0652	.9029	.06121	.65552	51
10	0.34475	.93869	0.36727	2.7228	1.0653	2.9006	0.06131	0.65525	50
11	.34502	.93859	.36760	.7204	.0654	.8983	.06141	.65497	49
12	.34530	.93849	.36793	.7179	.0655	.8960	.06151	.65470	48
13	.34557	.93839	.36826	.7155	.0656	.8937	.06161	.65443	47
14	.34584	.93829	.36859	.7130	.0658	.8915	.06171	.65415	46
15	0.34612	.93819	0.36892	2.7106	1.0659	2.8892	0.06181	0.65388	45
16	.34639	.93809	.36925	.7082	.0660	.8869	.06191	.65361	44
17	.34666	.93799	.36958	.7058	.0661	.8846	.06201	.65334	43
18	.34693	.93789	.36991	.7033	.0662	.8824	.06211	.65306	42
19	.34721	.93779	.37024	.7009	.0663	.8801	.06221	.65279	41
20	0.34748	.93769	0.37057	2.6985	1.0664	2.8778	0.06231	0.65252	40
21	.34775	.93758	.37090	.6961	.0666	.8756	.06241	.65225	39
22	.34803	.93748	.37123	.6937	.0667	.8733	.06251	.65197	38
23	.34830	.93738	.37156	.6913	.0668	.8711	.06262	.65170	37
24	.34857	.93728	.37190	.6889	.0669	.8688	.06272	.65143	36
25	0.34884	.93718	0.37223	2.6865	1.0670	2.8666	0.06282	0.65115	35
26	.34912	.93708	.37256	.6841	.0671	.8644	.06292	.65088	34
27	.34939	.93698	.37289	.6817	.0673	.8621	.06302	.65061	33
28	.34966	.93687	.37322	.6794	.0674	.8599	.06312	.65034	32
29	.34993	.93677	.37355	.6770	.0675	.8577	.06323	.65006	31
30	0.35021	.93667	0.37388	2.6746	1.0676	2.8554	0.06333	0.64979	30
31	.35048	.93657	.37422	.6722	.0677	.8532	.06343	.64952	29
32	.35075	.93647	.37455	.6699	.0678	.8510	.06353	.64925	28
33	.35102	.93637	.37488	.6675	.0679	.8488	.06363	.64897	27
34	.35130	.93626	.37521	.6652	.0681	.8466	.06373	.64870	26
35	0.35157	.93616	0.37554	2.6628	1.0682	2.8444	0.06384	0.64843	25
36	.35184	.93606	.37587	.6604	.0683	.8422	.06394	.64816	24
37	.35211	.93596	.37621	.6581	.0684	.8400	.06404	.64789	23
38	.35239	.93585	.37654	.6558	.0685	.8378	.06414	.64761	22
39	.35266	.93575	.37687	.6534	.0686	.8356	.06425	.64734	21
40	0.35293	.93565	0.37720	2.6511	1.0688	2.8334	0.06435	0.64707	20
41	.35320	.93555	.37754	.6487	.0689	.8312	.06445	.64680	19
42	.35347	.93544	.37787	.6464	.0690	.8290	.06456	.64652	18
43	.35375	.93534	.37820	.6441	.0691	.8269	.06466	.64625	17
44	.35402	.93524	.37853	.6418	.0692	.8247	.06476	.64598	16
45	0.35429	.93513	0.37887	2.6394	1.0694	2.8225	0.06486	0.64571	15
46	.35456	.93503	.37920	.6371	.0695	.8204	.06497	.64544	14
47	.35483	.93493	.37953	.6348	.0696	.8182	.06507	.64516	13
48	.35511	.93482	.37986	.6325	.0697	.8160	.06517	.64489	12
49	.35538	.93472	.38020	.6302	.0698	.8139	.06528	.64462	11
50	0.35565	.93462	0.38053	2.6279	1.0699	2.8117	0.06538	0.64435	10
51	.35592	.93451	.38086	.6256	.0701	.8096	.06548	.64408	9
52	.35619	.93441	.38120	.6233	.0702	.8074	.06559	.64380	8
53	.35647	.93431	.38153	.6210	.0703	.8053	.06569	.64353	7
54	.35674	.93420	.38186	.6187	.0704	.8032	.06579	.64326	6
55	0.35701	.93410	0.38220	2.6164	1.0705	2.8010	0.06590	0.64299	5
56	.35728	.93400	.38253	.6142	.0707	.7989	.06600	.64272	4
57	.35755	.93389	.38286	.6119	.0708	.7968	.06611	.64245	3
58	.35782	.93379	.38320	.6096	.0709	.7947	.06621	.64217	2
59	.35810	.93368	.38353	.6073	.0710	.7925	.06631	.64190	1
60	0.35837	.93358	0.38386	2.6051	1.0711	2.7904	0.06642	0.64163	0
M	Cosine	Sine	Cotan.	Tan.	Cosec.	Secant	Vrs. Cos.	Vrs. Sin.	M

M	Sine	Cosine	Tan.	Cotan.	Secant	Cosec.	Vrs. Sin.	Vrs. Cos.	M
0	0.35837	0.93358	0.38386	2.6051	1.0711	2.7904	0.06642	0.64163	60
1	.35864	.93348	.38420	.6028	.0713	.7883	.06652	.64136	59
2	.35891	.93337	.38453	.6006	.0714	.7862	.06663	.64109	58
3	.35918	.93327	.38486	.5983	.0715	.7841	.06673	.64082	57
4	.35945	.93316	.38520	.5960	.0716	.7820	.06684	.64055	56
5	0.35972	0.93306	0.38553	2.5938	1.0717	2.7799	0.06694	0.64027	55
6	.36000	.93295	.38587	.5916	.0719	.7778	.06705	.64000	54
7	.36027	.93285	.38620	.5893	.0720	.7757	.06715	.63973	53
8	.36054	.93274	.38654	.5871	.0721	.7736	.06726	.63946	52
9	.36081	.93264	.38687	.5848	.0722	.7715	.06736	.63919	51
10	0.36108	0.93253	0.38720	2.5826	1.0723	2.7694	0.06747	0.63892	50
11	.36135	.93243	.38754	.5804	.0725	.7674	.06757	.63865	49
12	.36162	.93232	.38787	.5781	.0726	.7653	.06768	.63837	48
13	.36189	.93222	.38821	.5759	.0727	.7632	.06778	.63810	47
14	.36217	.93211	.38854	.5737	.0728	.7611	.06789	.63783	46
15	0.36244	0.93201	0.38888	2.5715	1.0729	2.7591	0.06799	0.63756	45
16	.36271	.93190	.38921	.5693	.0731	.7570	.06810	.63729	44
17	.36298	.93180	.38955	.5671	.0732	.7550	.06820	.63702	43
18	.36325	.93169	.38988	.5649	.0733	.7529	.06831	.63675	42
19	.36352	.93159	.39022	.5627	.0734	.7509	.06841	.63648	41
20	0.36379	0.93148	0.39055	2.5605	1.0736	2.7488	0.06852	0.63621	40
21	.36406	.93137	.39089	.5583	.0737	.7468	.06863	.63593	39
22	.36433	.93127	.39122	.5561	.0738	.7447	.06873	.63566	38
23	.36460	.93116	.39156	.5539	.0739	.7427	.06884	.63539	37
24	.36488	.93105	.39189	.5517	.0740	.7406	.06894	.63512	36
25	0.36515	0.93095	0.39223	2.5495	1.0742	2.7386	0.06905	0.63485	35
26	.36542	.93084	.39257	.5473	.0743	.7366	.06916	.63458	34
27	.36569	.93074	.39290	.5451	.0744	.7346	.06926	.63431	33
28	.36596	.93063	.39324	.5430	.0745	.7325	.06937	.63404	32
29	.36623	.93052	.39357	.5408	.0747	.7305	.06947	.63377	31
30	0.36650	0.93042	0.39391	2.5386	1.0748	2.7285	0.06958	0.63350	30
31	.36677	.93031	.39425	.5365	.0749	.7265	.06969	.63323	29
32	.36704	.93020	.39458	.5343	.0750	.7245	.06979	.63296	28
33	.36731	.93010	.39492	.5322	.0751	.7225	.06990	.63269	27
34	.36758	.92999	.39525	.5300	.0753	.7205	.07001	.63242	26
35	0.36785	0.92988	0.39559	2.5278	1.0754	2.7185	0.07012	0.63214	25
36	.36812	.92978	.39593	.5257	.0755	.7165	.07022	.63187	24
37	.36839	.92967	.39626	.5236	.0756	.7145	.07033	.63160	23
38	.36866	.92956	.39660	.5214	.0758	.7125	.07044	.63133	22
39	.36893	.92945	.39694	.5193	.0759	.7105	.07054	.63106	21
40	0.36921	0.92935	0.39727	2.5171	1.0760	2.7085	0.07065	0.63079	20
41	.36948	.92924	.39761	.5150	.0761	.7065	.07076	.63052	19
42	.36975	.92913	.39795	.5129	.0763	.7045	.07087	.63025	18
43	.37002	.92902	.39828	.5108	.0764	.7026	.07097	.62998	17
44	.37029	.92892	.39862	.5086	.0765	.7006	.07108	.62971	16
45	0.37056	0.92881	0.39896	2.5065	1.0766	2.6986	0.07119	0.62944	15
46	.37083	.92870	.39930	.5044	.0768	.6967	.07130	.62917	14
47	.37110	.92859	.39963	.5023	.0769	.6947	.07141	.62890	13
48	.37137	.92848	.39997	.5002	.0770	.6927	.07151	.62863	12
49	.37164	.92838	.40031	.4981	.0771	.6908	.07162	.62836	11
50	0.37191	0.92827	0.40065	2.4960	1.0773	2.6888	0.07173	0.62809	10
51	.37218	.92816	.40098	.4939	.0774	.6869	.07184	.62782	9
52	.37245	.92805	.40132	.4918	.0775	.6849	.07195	.62755	8
53	.37272	.92794	.40166	.4897	.0776	.6830	.07205	.62728	7
54	.37299	.92784	.40200	.4876	.0778	.6810	.07216	.62701	6
55	0.37326	0.92773	0.40233	2.4855	1.0779	2.6791	0.07227	0.62674	5
56	.37353	.92762	.40267	.4834	.0780	.6772	.07238	.62647	4
57	.37380	.92751	.40301	.4813	.0781	.6752	.07249	.62620	3
58	.37407	.92740	.40335	.4792	.0783	.6733	.07260	.62593	2
59	.37434	.92729	.40369	.4772	.0784	.6714	.07271	.62566	1
60	0.37461	0.92718	0.40403	2.4751	1.0785	2.6695	0.07282	0.62539	0
M	Cosine	Sine	Cotan.	Tan.	Cosec.	Secant	Vrs. Cos.	Vrs. Sin.	M

M	Sine	Cosine	Tan.	Cotan.	Secant	Cosec.	Vrs. Sin.	Vrs. Cos.	M
0	0.37461	0.92718	0.40403	2.4751	1.0785	2.6695	0.07282	0.62539	60
1	.37488	.92707	.40436	.4730	.0787	.6675	.07292	.62512	59
2	.37514	.92696	.40470	.4709	.0788	.6656	.07303	.62485	58
3	.37541	.92686	.40504	.4689	.0789	.6637	.07314	.62458	57
4	.37568	.92675	.40538	.4668	.0790	.6618	.07325	.62431	56
5	0.37595	0.92664	0.40572	2.4647	1.0792	2.6599	0.07336	0.62404	55
6	.37622	.92653	.40606	.4627	.0793	.6580	.07347	.62377	54
7	.37649	.92642	.40640	.4606	.0794	.6561	.07358	.62351	53
8	.37676	.92631	.40673	.4586	.0795	.6542	.07369	.62324	52
9	.37703	.92620	.40707	.4565	.0797	.6523	.07380	.62297	51
10	0.37730	0.92609	0.40741	2.4545	1.0798	2.6504	0.07391	0.62270	50
11	.37757	.92598	.40775	.4525	.0799	.6485	.07402	.62243	49
12	.37784	.92587	.40809	.4504	.0801	.6466	.07413	.62216	48
13	.37811	.92576	.40843	.4484	.0802	.6447	.07424	.62189	47
14	.37838	.92565	.40877	.4463	.0803	.6428	.07435	.62162	46
15	0.37865	0.92554	0.40911	2.4443	1.0804	2.6410	0.07446	0.62135	45
16	.37892	.92543	.40945	.4423	.0806	.6391	.07457	.62108	44
17	.37919	.92532	.40979	.4403	.0807	.6372	.07468	.62081	43
18	.37946	.92521	.41013	.4382	.0808	.6353	.07479	.62054	42
19	.37972	.92510	.41047	.4362	.0810	.6335	.07490	.62027	41
20	0.37999	0.92499	0.41081	2.4342	1.0811	2.6316	0.07501	0.62000	40
21	.38026	.92488	.41115	.4322	.0812	.6297	.07512	.61974	39
22	.38053	.92477	.41149	.4302	.0813	.6279	.07523	.61947	38
23	.38080	.92466	.41183	.4282	.0815	.6260	.07534	.61920	37
24	.38107	.92455	.41217	.4262	.0816	.6242	.07545	.61893	36
25	0.38134	0.92443	0.41251	2.4242	1.0817	2.6223	0.07556	0.61866	35
26	.38151	.92432	.41285	.4222	.0819	.6205	.07567	.61839	34
27	.38188	.92421	.41319	.4202	.0820	.6186	.07579	.61812	33
28	.38214	.92410	.41353	.4182	.0821	.6168	.07590	.61785	32
29	.38241	.92399	.41387	.4162	.0823	.6150	.07601	.61758	31
30	0.38268	0.92388	0.41421	2.4142	1.0824	2.6131	0 07612	0.61732	30
31	.38295	.92377	.41455	.4122	.0826	.6113	.07623	.61705	29
32	.38322	.92366	.41489	.4102	.0826	.6095	.07634	.61678	28
33	.38349	.92354	.41524	.4083	.0828	.6076	.07645	.61651	27
34	.38376	.92343	.41558	.4063	.0829	.6058	.07657	.61624	26
35	0.38403	0.92332	0.41592	2.4043	1.0830	2.6040	0.07668	0.61597	25
36	.38429	.92321	.41626	.4023	.0832	.6022	.07679	.61570	24
37	.38456	.92310	.41660	.4004	.0833	.6003	.07690	.61544	23
38	.38483	.92299	.41694	.3984	.0834	.5985	.07701	.61517	22
39	.38510	.92287	.41728	.3964	.0836	.5967	.07712	.61490	21
40	0.38537	0.92276	0.41762	2.3945	1.0837	2.5949	0.07724	0.61463	20
41	.38564	.92265	.41797	.3925	.0838	.5931	.07735	.61436	19
42	.38591	.92254	.41831	.3906	.0840	.5913	.07746	.61409	18
43	.38617	.92242	.41865	.3886	.0841	.5895	.07757	.61382	17
44	.38644	.92231	.41899	.3867	.0842	.5877	.07769	.61356	16
45	0.38671	0.92220	0.41933	2.3847	1.0844	2.5859	0.07780	0.61329	15
46	.38698	.92209	.41968	.3828	.0845	.5841	.07791	.61302	14
47	.38725	.92197	.42002	.3808	.0846	.5823	.07802	.61275	13
48	.38751	.92186	.42036	.3789	.0847	.5805	.07814	.61248	12
49	.38778	.92175	.42070	.3770	.0849	.5787	.07825	.61222	11
50	0.38805	0.92164	0.42105	2.3750	1.0850	2.5770	0.07836	0.61195	10
51	.38832	.92152	.42139	.3731	.0851	.5752	.07847	.61168	9
52	.38859	.92141	.42173	.3712	.0853	.5734	.07859	.61141	8
53	.38886	.92130	.42207	.3692	.0854	.5716	.07870	.61114	7
54	.38912	.92118	.42242	.3673	.0855	.5699	.07881	.61088	6
55	0.38939	0.92107	0.42276	2.3654	1.0857	2.5681	0.07893	0.61061	5
56	.38966	.92096	.42310	.3635	.0858	.5663	.07904	.61034	4
57	.38993	.92084	.42344	.3616	.0859	.5646	.07915	.61007	3
58	.39019	.92073	.42379	.3597	.0861	.5628	.07927	.60980	2
59	.39046	.92062	.42413	.3577	.0862	.5610	.07938	.60954	1
60	0.39073	0.92050	0.42447	2.3558	1.0864	2.5593	0.07949	0.60927	0
M	Cosine	Sine	Cotan.	Tan.	Cosec.	Secant	Vrs. Cos.	Vrs. Sin.	M

M	Sine	Cosine	Tan.	Cotan.	Secant	Cosec.	Vrs. Sin.	Vrs. Cos.	M
0	0.39073	.92050	0.42447	2.3558	1.0864	2.5593	0.07949	0.60927	60
1	.39100	.92039	.42482	.3539	.0865	.5575	.07961	.60900	59
2	.39126	.92028	.42516	.3520	.0866	.5558	.07972	.60873	58
3	.39153	.92016	.42550	.3501	.0868	.5540	.07984	.60846	57
4	.39180	.92005	.42585	.3482	.0869	.5523	.07995	.60820	56
5	0.39207	.91993	0.42619	2.3463	1.0870	2.5506	0.08006	0.60793	55
6	.39234	.91982	.42654	.3445	.0872	.5488	.08018	.60766	54
7	.39260	.91971	.42688	.3426	.0873	.5471	.08029	.60739	53
8	.39287	.91959	.42722	.3407	.0874	.5453	.08041	.60713	52
9	.39314	.91948	.42757	.3388	.0876	.5436	.08052	.60686	51
10	0.39341	0.91936	0.42791	2.3369	1.0877	2.5419	0.08063	0.60659	50
11	.39367	.91925	.42826	.3350	.0878	.5402	.08075	.60632	49
12	.39394	.91913	.42860	.3332	.0880	.5384	.08086	.60606	48
13	.39421	.91902	.42894	.3313	.0881	.5367	.08098	.60579	47
14	.39448	.91891	.42929	.3294	.0882	.5350	.08109	.60552	46
15	0.39474	.91879	0.42963	2.3276	1.0884	2.5333	0.08121	0.60526	45
16	.39501	.91868	.42998	.3257	.0885	.5316	.08132	.60499	44
17	.39528	.91856	.43032	.3238	.0886	.5299	.08144	.60472	43
18	.39554	.91845	.43067	.3220	.0888	.5281	.08155	.60445	42
19	.39581	.91833	.43101	.3201	.0889	.5264	.08167	.60419	41
20	0.39608	0.91822	0.43136	2.3183	1.0891	2.5247	0.08178	0.60392	40
21	.39635	.91810	.43170	.3164	.0892	.5230	.08190	.60365	39
22	.39661	.91798	.43205	.3145	.0893	.5213	.08201	.60339	38
23	.39688	.91787	.43239	.3127	.0895	.5196	.08213	.60312	37
24	.39715	.91775	.43274	.3109	.0896	.5179	.08224	.60285	36
25	0.39741	0.91764	0.43308	2.3090	1.0897	2.5163	0.08236	0.60258	35
26	.39768	.91752	.43343	.3072	.0899	.5146	.08248	.60232	34
27	.39795	.91741	.43377	.3053	.0900	.5129	.08259	.60205	33
28	.39821	.91729	.43412	.3035	.0902	.5112	.08271	.60178	32
29	.39848	.91718	.43447	.3017	.0903	.5095	.08282	.60152	31
30	0.39875	0.91706	0.43481	2.2998	1.0904	2.5078	0.08294	0.60125	30
31	.39901	.91694	.43516	.2980	.0906	.5062	.08306	.60098	29
32	.39928	.91683	.43550	.2962	.0907	.5045	.08317	.60072	28
33	.39955	.91671	.43585	.2944	.0908	.5028	.08329	.60045	27
34	.39981	.91659	.43620	.2925	.0910	.5011	.08340	.60018	26
35	0.40008	0.91648	0.43654	2.2907	1.0911	2.4995	0.08352	0.59992	25
36	.40035	.91636	.43689	.2889	.0913	.4978	.08364	.59965	24
37	.40061	.91625	.43723	.2871	.0914	.4961	.08375	.59938	23
38	.40088	.91613	.43758	.2853	.0915	.4945	.08387	.59912	22
39	.40115	.91601	.43793	.2835	.0917	.4928	.08399	.59885	21
40	0.40141	0.91590	0.43827	2.2817	1.0918	2.4912	0.08410	0.59858	20
41	.40168	.91578	.43862	.2799	.0920	.4895	.08422	.59832	19
42	.40195	.91566	.43897	.2781	.0921	.4879	.08434	.59805	18
43	.40221	.91554	.43932	.2763	.0922	.4862	.08445	.59778	17
44	.40248	.91543	.43966	.2745	.0924	.4846	.08457	.59752	16
45	0.40275	0.91531	0.44001	2.2727	1.0925	2.4829	0.08469	0.59725	15
46	.40301	.91519	.44036	.2709	.0927	.4813	.08480	.59699	14
47	.40328	.91508	.44070	.2691	.0928	.4797	.08492	.59672	13
48	.40354	.91496	.44105	.2673	.0929	.4780	.08504	.59645	12
49	.40381	.91484	.44140	.2655	.0931	.4764	.08516	.59619	11
50	0.40408	0.91472	0.44175	2.2637	1.0932	2.4748	0.08527	0.59592	10
51	.40434	.91461	.44209	.2619	.0934	.4731	.08539	.59566	9
52	.40461	.91449	.44244	.2602	.0935	.4715	.08551	.59539	8
53	.40487	.91437	.44279	.2584	.0936	.4699	.08563	.59512	7
54	.40514	.91425	.44314	.2566	.0938	.4683	.08575	.59486	6
55	0.40541	0.91414	0.44349	2.2548	1.0939	2.4666	0.08586	0.59459	5
56	.40567	.91402	.44383	.2531	.0941	.4650	.08598	.59433	4
57	.40594	.91390	.44418	.2513	.0942	.4634	.08610	.59406	3
58	.40620	.91378	.44453	.2495	.0943	.4618	.08622	.59379	2
59	.40647	.91366	.44488	.2478	.0945	.4602	.08634	.59353	1
60	0.40674	0.91354	0.44523	2.2460	1.0946	2.4586	0.08645	0.59326	0
M	Cosine	Sine	Cotan.	Tan.	Cosec.	Secant	Vrs. Cos.	Vrs. Sin.	M

M	Sine	Cosine	Tan.	Cotan.	Secant	Cosec.	Vrs. Sin.	Vrs. Cos.	M
0	0.40674	0.91354	0.44523	2.2460	1.0946	2.4586	0.08645	0.59326	60
1	.40700	.91343	.44558	.2443	.0948	.4570	.08657	.59300	59
2	.40727	.91331	.44593	.2425	.0949	.4554	.08669	.59273	58
3	.40753	.91319	.44627	.2408	.0951	.4538	.08681	.59247	57
4	.40780	.91307	.44662	.2390	.0952	.4522	.08693	.59220	56
5	0.40806	0.91295	0.44697	2.2373	1.0953	2.4506	0.08705	0.59193	55
6	.40833	.91283	.44732	.2355	.0955	.4490	.08716	.59167	54
7	.40860	.91271	.44767	.2338	.0956	.4474	.08728	.59140	53
8	.40886	.91260	.44802	.2320	.0958	.4458	.08740	.59114	52
9	.40913	.91248	.44837	.2303	.0959	.4442	.08752	.59087	51
10	0.40939	0.91236	0.44872	2.2286	1.0961	2.4426	0.08764	0.59061	50
11	.40966	.91224	.44907	.2268	.0962	.4411	.08776	.59034	49
12	.40992	.91212	.44942	.2251	.0963	.4395	.08788	.59008	48
13	.41019	.91200	.44977	.2234	.0965	.4379	.08800	.58981	47
14	.41045	.91188	.45012	.2216	.0966	.4363	.08812	.58955	46
15	0.41072	0.91176	0.45047	2.2199	1.0968	2.4347	0.08824	0.58928	45
16	.41098	.91164	.45082	.2182	.0969	.4332	.08836	.58901	44
17	.41125	.91152	.45117	.2165	.0971	.4316	.08848	.58875	43
18	.41151	.91140	.45152	.2147	.0972	.4300	.08860	.58848	42
19	.41178	.91128	.45187	.2130	.0973	.4285	.08872	.58822	41
20	0.41204	0.91116	0.45222	2.2113	1.0975	2.4269	0.08884	0.58795	40
21	.41231	.91104	.45257	.2096	.0976	.4254	.08896	.58769	39
22	.41257	.91092	.45292	.2079	.0978	.4238	.08908	.58742	38
23	.41284	.91080	.45327	.2062	.0979	.4222	.08920	.58716	37
24	.41310	.91068	.45362	.2045	.0981	.4207	.08932	.58689	36
25	0.41337	0.91056	0.45397	2.2028	1.0982	2.4191	0.08944	0.58663	35
26	.41363	.91044	.45432	.2011	.0984	.4176	.08956	.58636	34
27	.41390	.91032	.45467	.1994	.0985	.4160	.08968	.58610	33
28	.41416	.91020	.45502	.1977	.0986	.4145	.08980	.58584	32
29	.41443	.91008	.45537	.1960	.0988	.4130	.08992	.58557	31
30	0.41469	0.90996	0.45573	2.1943	1.0989	2.4114	0.09004	0.58531	30
31	.41496	.90984	.45608	.1926	.0991	.4099	.09016	.58504	29
32	.41522	.90972	.45643	.1909	.0992	.4083	.09028	.58478	28
33	.41549	.90960	.45678	.1892	.0994	.4068	.09040	.58451	27
34	.41575	.90948	.45713	.1875	.0995	.4053	.09052	.58425	26
35	0.41602	0.90936	0.45748	2.1859	1.0997	2.4037	0.09064	0.58398	25
36	.41628	.90924	.45783	.1842	.0998	.4022	.09076	.58372	24
37	.41654	.90911	.45819	.1825	.1000	.4007	.09088	.58345	23
38	.41681	.90899	.45854	.1808	.1001	.3992	.09101	.58319	22
39	.41707	.90887	.45889	.1792	.1003	.3976	.09113	.58292	21
40	0.41734	0.90875	0.45924	2.1775	1.1004	2.3961	0.09125	0.58266	20
41	.41760	.90863	.45960	.1758	.1005	.3946	.09137	.58240	19
42	.41787	.90851	.45995	.1741	.1007	.3931	.09149	.58213	18
43	.41813	.90839	.46030	.1725	.1008	.3916	.09161	.58187	17
44	.41839	.90826	.46065	.1708	.1010	.3901	.09173	.58160	16
45	0.41866	0.90814	0.46101	2.1692	1.1011	2.3886	0.09186	0.58134	15
46	.41892	.90802	.46136	.1675	.1013	.3871	.09198	.58108	14
47	.41919	.90790	.46171	.1658	.1014	.3856	.09210	.58081	13
48	.41945	.90778	.46206	.1642	.1016	.3841	.09222	.58055	12
49	.41972	.90765	.46242	.1625	.1017	.3826	.09234	.58028	11
50	0.41998	0.90753	0.46277	2.1609	1.1019	2.3811	0.09247	0.58002	10
51	.42024	.90741	.46312	.1592	.1020	.3796	.09259	.57975	9
52	.42051	.90729	.46348	.1576	.1022	.3781	.09271	.57949	8
53	.42077	.90717	.46383	.1559	.1023	.3766	.09283	.57923	7
54	.42103	.90704	.46418	.1543	.1025	.3751	.09296	.57896	6
55	0.42130	0.90692	0.46454	2.1527	1.1026	2.3736	0.09308	0.57870	5
56	.42156	.90680	.46489	.1510	.1028	.3721	.09320	.57844	4
57	.42183	.90668	.46524	.1494	.1029	.3706	.09332	.57817	3
58	.42209	.90655	.46560	.1478	.1031	.3691	.09345	.57791	2
59	.42235	.90643	.46595	.1461	.1032	.3677	.09357	.57764	1
60	0.42262	0.90631	0.46631	2.1445	1.1034	2.3662	0.09369	0.57738	0
M	Cosine	Sine	Cotan.	Tan.	Cosec.	Secant	Vrs. Cos.	Vrs. Sin.	M

M	Sine	Cosine	Tan.	Cotan.	Secant	Cosec.	Vrs. Sin.	Vrs. Cos.	M
0	0.42262	0.90631	0.46631	2.1445	1.1034	2.3662	0.09369	0.57738	60
1	.42288	.90618	.46666	.1429	.1035	4.3647	.09381	.57712	59
2	.42314	.90606	.46702	.1412	.1037	.3632	.09394	.57685	58
3	.42341	.90594	.46737	.1396	.1038	.3618	.09406	.57659	57
4	.42367	.90581	.46772	.1380	.1040	.3603	.09418	.57633	56
5	0.42394	0.90569	0.46808	2.1364	1.1041	2.3588	0.09431	0.57606	55
6	.42420	.90557	.46843	.1348	.1043	.3574	.09443	.57580	54
7	.42446	.90544	.46879	.1331	.1044	.3559	.09455	.57554	53
8	.42473	.90532	.46914	.1315	.1046	.3544	.09468	.57527	52
9	.42499	.90520	.46950	.1299	.1047	.3530	.09480	.57501	51
10	0.42525	0.90507	0.46985	2.1283	1.1049	2.3515	0.09492	0.57475	50
11	.42552	.90495	.47021	.1267	.1050	.3501	.09505	.57448	49
12	.42578	.90483	.47056	.1251	.1052	.3486	.09517	.57422	48
13	.42604	.90470	.47092	.1235	.1053	.3472	.09530	.57396	47
14	.42630	.90458	.47127	.1219	.1055	.3457	.09542	.57369	46
15	0.42657	0.90445	0.47163	2.1203	1.1056	2.3443	0.09554	0.57343	45
16	.42683	.90433	.47199	.1187	.1058	.3428	.09567	.57317	44
17	.42709	.90421	.47234	.1171	.1059	.3414	.09579	.57290	43
18	.42736	.90408	.47270	.1155	.1061	.3399	.09592	.57264	42
19	.42762	.90396	.47305	.1139	.1062	.3385	.09604	.57238	41
20	0.42788	0.90383	0.47341	2.1123	1.1064	2.3371	0.09617	0.57212	40
21	.42815	.90371	.47376	.1107	.1065	.3356	.09629	.57185	39
22	.42841	.90358	.47412	.1092	.1067	.3342	.09641	.57159	38
23	.42867	.90346	.47448	.1076	.1068	.3328	.09654	.57133	37
24	.42893	.90333	.47483	.1060	.1070	.3313	.09666	.57106	36
25	0.42920	0.90321	0.47519	2.1044	1.1072	2.3299	0.09679	0.57080	35
26	.42946	.90308	.47555	.1028	.1073	.3285	.09691	.57054	34
27	.42972	.90296	.47590	.1013	.1075	.3271	.09704	.57028	33
28	.42998	.90283	.47626	.0997	.1076	.3256	.09716	.57001	32
29	.43025	.90271	.47662	.0981	.1078	.3242	.09729	.56975	31
30	0.43051	0.90258	0.47697	2.0965	1.1079	2.3228	0.09741	0.56949	30
31	.43077	.90246	.47733	.0950	.1081	.3214	.09754	.56923	29
32	.43104	.90233	.47769	.0934	.1082	.3200	.09766	.56896	28
33	.43130	.90221	.47805	.0918	.1084	.3186	.09779	.56870	27
34	.43156	.90208	.47840	.0903	.1085	.3172	.09792	.56844	26
35	0.43182	0.90196	0.47876	2.0887	1.1087	2.3158	0.09804	0.56818	25
36	.43208	.90183	.47912	.0872	.1088	.3143	.09817	.56791	24
37	.43235	.90171	.47948	.0856	.1090	.3129	.09829	.56765	23
38	.43261	.90158	.47983	.0840	.1092	.3115	.09842	.56739	22
39	.43287	.90145	.48019	.0825	.1093	.3101	.09854	.56713	21
40	0.43313	0.90133	0.48055	2.0809	1.1095	2.3087	0.09867	0.56686	20
41	.43340	.90120	.48091	.0794	.1096	.3073	.09880	.56660	19
42	.43366	.90108	.48127	.0778	.1098	.3059	.09892	.56634	18
43	.43392	.90095	.48162	.0763	.1099	.3046	.09905	.56608	17
44	.43418	.90082	.48198	.0747	.1101	.3032	.09917	.56582	16
45	0.43444	0.90070	0.48234	2.0732	1.1102	2.3018	0.09930	0.56555	15
46	.43471	.90057	.48270	.0717	.1104	.3004	.09943	.56529	14
47	.43497	.90044	.48306	.0701	.1106	.2990	.09955	.56503	13
48	.43523	.90032	.48342	.0686	.1107	.2976	.09968	.56477	12
49	.43549	.90019	.48378	.0671	.1109	.2962	.09981	.56451	11
50	0.43575	0.90006	0.48414	2.0655	1.1110	2.2949	0.09993	0.56424	10
51	.43602	.89994	.48449	.0640	.1112	.2935	.10006	.56398	9
52	.43628	.89981	.48485	.0625	.1113	.2921	.10019	.56372	8
53	.43654	.89968	.48521	.0609	.1115	.2907	.10031	.56346	7
54	.43680	.89956	.48557	.0594	.1116	.2894	.10044	.56320	6
55	0.43706	0.89943	0.48593	2.0579	1.1118	2.2880	0.10057	0.56294	5
56	.43732	.89930	.48629	.0564	.1120	.2866	.10070	.56267	4
57	.43759	.89918	.48665	.0548	.1121	.2853	.10082	.56241	3
58	.43785	.89905	.48701	.0533	.1123	.2839	.10095	.56215	2
59	.43811	.89892	.48737	.0518	.1124	.2825	.10108	.56189	1
60	0.43837	0.89879	0.48773	2.0503	1.1126	2.2812	0.10121	0.56163	0

| M | Cosine | Sine | Cotan. | Tan. | Cosec. | Secant | Vrs. Cos. | Vrs. Sin. | M |

M	Sine	Cosine	Tan.	Cotan.	Secant	Cosec.	Vrs. Sin.	Vrs. Cos.	M
0	0.43837	0.89879	0.48773	2.0503	1.1126	2.2812	0.10121	0.56163	60
1	.43863	.89867	.48809	.0488	.1127	.2798	.10133	.56137	59
2	.43889	.89854	.48845	.0473	.1129	.2784	.10146	.56111	58
3	.43915	.89841	.48881	.0458	.1131	.2771	.10159	.56084	57
4	.43942	.89828	.48917	.0443	.1132	.2757	.10172	.56058	56
5	0.43968	0.89815	0.48953	2.0427	1.1134	2.2744	0.10184	0.56032	55
6	.43994	.89803	.48989	.0412	.1135	.2730	.10197	.56006	54
7	.44020	.89790	.49025	.0397	.1137	.2717	.10210	.55980	53
8	.44046	.89777	.49062	.0382	.1139	.2703	.10223	.55954	52
9	.44072	.89764	.49098	.0367	.1140	.2690	.10236	.55928	51
10	0.44098	0.89751	0.49134	2.0352	1.1142	2.2676	0.10248	0.55902	50
11	.44124	.89739	.49170	.0338	.1143	.2663	.10261	.55875	49
12	.44150	.89726	.49206	.0323	.1145	.2650	.10274	.55849	48
13	.44177	.89713	.49242	.0308	.1147	.2636	.10287	.55823	47
14	.44203	.89700	.49278	.0293	.1148	.2623	.10300	.55797	46
15	0.44229	0.89687	0.49314	2.0278	1.1150	2.2610	0.10313	0.55771	45
16	.44255	.89674	.49351	.0263	.1151	.2596	.10326	.55745	44
17	.44281	.89661	.49387	.0248	.1153	.2583	.10338	.55719	43
18	.44307	.89649	.49423	.0233	.1155	.2570	.10351	.55693	42
19	.44333	.89636	.49459	.0219	.1156	.2556	.10364	.55667	41
20	0.44359	0.89623	0.49495	2.0204	1.1158	2.2543	0.10377	0.55641	40
21	.44385	.89610	.49532	.0189	.1159	.2530	.10390	.55615	39
22	.44411	.89597	.49568	.0174	.1161	.2517	.10403	.55589	38
23	.44437	.89584	.49604	.0159	.1163	.2503	.10416	.55562	37
24	.44463	.89571	.49640	.0145	.1164	.2490	.10429	.55536	36
25	0.44489	0.89558	0.49677	2.0130	1.1166	2.2477	0.10442	0.55510	35
26	.44516	.89545	.49713	.0115	.1167	.2464	.10455	.55484	34
27	.44542	.89532	.49749	.0101	.1169	.2451	.10468	.55458	33
28	.44568	.89519	.49785	.0086	.1171	.2438	.10481	.55432	32
29	.44594	.89506	.49822	.0071	.1172	.2425	.10493	.55406	31
30	0.44620	0.89493	0.49858	2.0057	1.1174	2.2411	0.10506	0.55380	30
31	.44646	.89480	.49894	.0042	.1176	.2398	.10519	.55354	29
32	.44672	.89467	.49931	.0028	.1177	.2385	.10532	.55328	28
33	.44698	.89454	.49967	.0013	.1179	.2372	.10545	.55302	27
34	.44724	.89441	.50003	1.9998	.1180	.2359	.10558	.55276	26
35	0.44750	0.89428	0.50040	1.9984	1.1182	2.2346	0.10571	0.55250	25
36	.44776	.89415	.50076	.9969	.1184	.2333	.10584	.55224	24
37	.44802	.89402	.50113	.9955	.1185	.2320	.10598	.55198	23
38	.44828	.89389	.50149	.9940	.1187	.2307	.10611	.55172	22
39	.44854	.89376	.50185	.9926	.1189	.2294	.10624	.55146	21
40	0.44880	0.89363	0.50222	1.9912	1.1190	2.2282	0.10637	0.55120	20
41	.44906	.89350	.50258	.9897	.1192	.2269	.10650	.55094	19
42	.44932	.89337	.50295	.9883	.1193	.2256	.10663	.55068	18
43	.44958	.89324	.50331	.9868	.1195	.2243	.10676	.55042	17
44	.44984	.89311	.50368	.9854	.1197	.2230	.10689	.55016	16
45	0.45010	0.89298	0.50404	1.9840	1.1198	2.2217	0.10702	0.54990	15
46	.45036	.89285	.50441	.9825	.1200	.2204	.10715	.54964	14
47	.45062	.89272	.50477	.9811	.1202	.2192	.10728	.54938	13
48	.45088	.89258	.50514	.9797	.1203	.2179	.10741	.54912	12
49	.45114	.89245	.50550	.9782	.1205	.2166	.10754	.54886	11
50	0.45140	0.89232	0.50587	1.9768	1.1207	2.2153	0.10768	0.54860	10
51	.45166	.89219	.50623	.9754	.1208	.2141	.10781	.54834	9
52	.45191	.89206	.50660	.9739	.1210	.2128	.10794	.54808	8
53	.45217	.89193	.50696	.9725	.1212	.2115	.10807	.54782	7
54	.45243	.89180	.50733	.9711	.1213	.2103	.10820	.54756	6
55	0.45269	0.89166	0.50769	1.9697	1.1215	2.2090	0.10833	0.54730	5
56	.45295	.89153	.50806	.9683	.1217	.2077	.10846	.54705	4
57	.45321	.89140	.50843	.9668	.1218	.2065	.10860	.54679	3
58	.45347	.89127	.50879	.9654	.1220	.2052	.10873	.54653	2
59	.45373	.89114	.50916	.9640	.1222	.2039	.10886	.54627	1
60	0.45399	0.89101	0.50952	1.9626	1.1223	2.2027	0.10899	0.54601	0

| M | Cosine | Sine | Cotan. | Tan. | Cosec. | Secant | Vrs. Cos. | Vrs. Sin. | M |

MATHEMATICAL TABLES

Natural Trigonometric Functions

M	Sine	Cosine	Tan.	Cotan.	Secant	Cosec.	Vrs. Sin.	Vrs. Cos.	M
0	0.45399	0.89101	0.50952	1.9626	1.1223	2.2027	0.10899	0.54601	60
1	.45425	.89087	.50989	.9612	.1225	.2014	.10912	.54575	59
2	.45451	.89074	.51026	.9598	.1226	.2002	.10926	.54549	58
3	.45477	.89061	.51062	.9584	.1228	.1989	.10939	.54523	57
4	.45503	.89048	.51099	.9570	.1230	.1977	.10952	.54497	56
5	0.45528	0.89034	0.51136	1.9556	1.1231	2.1964	0.10965	0.54471	55
6	.45554	.89021	.51172	.9542	.1233	.1952	.10979	.54445	54
7	.45580	.89008	.51209	.9528	.1235	.1939	.10992	.54420	53
8	.45606	.88995	.51246	.9514	.1237	.1927	.11005	.54394	52
9	.45632	.88981	.51283	.9500	.1238	.1914	.11018	.54368	51
10	0.45658	0.88968	0.51319	1.9486	1.1240	2.1902	0.11032	0.54342	50
11	.45684	.88955	.51356	.9472	.1242	.1889	.11045	.54316	49
12	.45710	.88942	.51393	.9458	.1243	.1877	.11058	.54290	48
13	.45736	.88928	.51430	.9444	.1245	.1865	.11072	.54264	47
14	.45761	.88915	.51466	.9430	.1247	.1852	.11085	.54238	46
15	0.45787	0.88902	0.51503	1.9416	1.1248	2.1840	0.11098	0.54213	45
16	.45813	.88888	.51540	.9402	.1250	.1828	.11112	.54187	44
17	.45839	.88875	.51577	.9388	.1252	.1815	.11125	.54161	43
18	.45865	.88862	.51614	.9375	.1253	.1803	.11138	.54135	42
19	.45891	.88848	.51651	.9361	.1255	.1791	.11152	.54109	41
20	0.45917	0.88835	0.51687	1.9347	1.1257	2.1778	0.11165	0.54083	40
21	.45942	.88822	.51724	.9333	.1258	.1766	.11178	.54057	39
22	.45968	.88808	.51761	.9319	.1260	.1754	.11192	.54032	38
23	.45994	.88795	.51798	.9306	.1262	.1742	.11205	.54006	37
24	.46020	.88781	.51835	.9292	.1264	.1730	.11218	.53980	36
25	0.46046	0.88768	0.51872	1.9278	1.1265	2.1717	0.11232	0.53954	35
26	.46072	.88755	.51909	.9264	.1267	.1705	.11245	.53928	34
27	.46097	.88741	.51946	.9251	.1269	.1693	.11259	.53902	33
28	.46123	.88728	.51983	.9237	.1270	.1681	.11272	.53877	32
29	.46149	.88714	.52020	.9223	.1272	.1669	.11285	.53851	31
30	0.46175	0.88701	0.52057	1.9210	1.1274	2.1657	0.11299	0.53825	30
31	.46201	.88688	.52094	.9196	.1275	.1645	.11312	.53799	29
32	.46226	.88674	.52131	.9182	.1277	.1633	.11326	.53773	28
33	.46252	.88661	.52168	.9169	.1279	.1620	.11339	.53748	27
34	.46278	.88647	.52205	.9155	.1281	.1608	.11353	.53722	26
35	0.46304	0.88634	0.52242	1.9142	1.1282	2.1596	0.11366	0.53696	25
36	.46330	.88620	.52279	.9128	.1284	.1584	.11380	.53670	24
37	.46355	.88607	.52316	.9115	.1286	.1572	.11393	.53645	23
38	.46381	.88593	.52353	.9101	.1287	.1560	.11407	.53619	22
39	.46407	.88580	.52390	.9088	.1289	.1548	.11420	.53593	21
40	0.46433	0.88566	0.52427	1.9074	1.1291	2.1536	0.11434	0.53567	20
41	.46458	.88553	.52464	.9061	.1293	.1525	.11447	.53541	19
42	.46484	.88539	.52501	.9047	.1294	.1513	.11461	.53516	18
43	.46510	.88526	.52538	.9034	.1296	.1501	.11474	.53490	17
44	.46536	.88512	.52575	.9020	.1298	.1489	.11488	.53464	16
45	0.46561	0.88499	0.52612	1.9007	1.1299	2.1477	0.11501	0.53438	15
46	.46587	.88485	.52650	.8993	.1301	.1465	.11515	.53413	14
47	.46613	.88472	.52687	.8980	.1303	.1453	.11528	.53387	13
48	.46639	.88458	.52724	.8967	.1305	.1441	.11542	.53361	12
49	.46664	.88444	.52761	.8953	.1306	.1430	.11555	.53336	11
50	0.46690	0.88431	0.52798	1.8940	1.1308	2.1418	0.11569	0.53310	10
51	.46716	.88417	.52836	.8927	.1310	.1406	.11583	.53284	9
52	.46741	.88404	.52873	.8913	.1312	.1394	.11596	.53258	8
53	.46767	.88390	.52910	.8900	.1313	.1382	.11610	.53233	7
54	.46793	.88376	.52947	.8887	.1315	.1371	.11623	.53207	6
55	0.46819	0.88363	0.52984	1.8873	1.1317	2.1359	0.11637	0.53181	5
56	.46844	.88349	.53022	.8860	.1319	.1347	.11651	.53156	4
57	.46870	.88336	.53059	.8847	.1320	.1335	.11664	.53130	3
58	.46896	.88322	.53096	.8834	.1322	.1324	.11678	.53104	2
59	.46921	.88308	.53134	.8820	.1324	.1312	.11691	.53078	1
60	0.46947	0.88295	0.53171	1.8807	1.1326	2.1300	0.11705	0.53053	0
M	Cosine	Sine	Cotan.	Tan.	Cosec.	Secant	Vrs. Cos.	Vrs. Sin.	M

M	Sine	Cosine	Tan.	Cotan.	Secant	Cosec.	Vrs. Sin.	Vrs. Cos.	M
0	0.46947	0.88295	0.53171	1.8807	1.1326	2.1300	0.11705	0.53053	60
1	.46973	.88281	.53208	.8794	.1327	.1289	.11719	.53027	59
2	.46998	.88267	.53245	.8781	.1329	.1277	.11732	.53001	58
3	.47024	.88254	.53283	.8768	.1331	.1266	.11746	.52976	57
4	.47050	.88240	.53320	.8754	.1333	.1254	.11760	.52950	56
5	0.47075	0.88226	0.53358	1.8741	1.1334	2.1242	0.11774	0.52924	55
6	.47101	.88213	.53395	.8728	.1336	.1231	.11787	.52899	54
7	.47127	.88199	.53432	.8715	.1338	.1219	.11801	.52873	53
8	.47152	.88185	.53470	.8702	.1340	.1208	.11815	.52847	52
9	.47178	.88171	.53507	.8689	.1341	.1196	.11828	.52822	51
10	0.47204	0.88158	0.53545	1.8676	1.1343	2.1185	0.11842	0.52796	50
11	.47229	.88144	.53582	.8663	.1345	.1173	.11856	.52770	49
12	.47255	.88130	.53619	.8650	.1347	.1162	.11870	.52745	48
13	.47281	.88117	.53657	.8637	.1349	.1150	.11883	.52719	47
14	.47306	.88103	.53694	.8624	.1350	.1139	.11897	.52694	46
15	0.47332	0.88089	0.53732	1.8611	1.1352	2.1127	0.11911	0.52668	45
16	.47357	.88075	.53769	.8598	.1354	.1116	.11925	.52642	44
17	.47383	.88061	.53807	.8585	.1356	.1104	.11938	.52617	43
18	.47409	.88048	.53844	.8572	.1357	.1093	.11952	.52591	42
19	.47434	.88034	.53882	.8559	.1359	.1082	.11966	.52565	41
20	0.47460	0.88020	0.53919	1.8546	1.1361	2.1070	0.11980	0.52540	40
21	.47486	.88006	.53957	.8533	.1363	.1059	.11994	.52514	39
22	.47511	.87992	.53995	.8520	.1365	.1048	.12007	.52489	38
23	.47537	.87979	.54032	.8507	.1366	.1036	.12021	.52463	37
24	.47562	.87965	.54070	.8495	.1368	.1025	.12035	.52437	36
25	0.47588	0.87951	0.54107	1.8482	1.1370	2.1014	0.12049	0.52412	35
26	.47613	.87937	.54145	.8469	.1372	.1002	.12063	.52386	34
27	.47639	.87923	.54183	.8456	.1373	.0991	.12077	.52361	33
28	.47665	.87909	.54220	.8443	.1375	.0980	.12090	.52335	32
29	.47690	.87895	.54258	.8430	.1377	.0969	.12104	.52310	31
30	0.47716	0.87882	0.54295	1.8418	1.1379	2.0957	0.12118	0.52284	30
31	.47741	.87868	.54333	.8405	.1381	.0946	.12132	.52258	29
32	.47767	.87854	.54371	.8392	.1382	.0935	.12146	.52233	28
33	.47792	.87840	.54409	.8379	.1384	.0924	.12160	.52207	27
34	.47818	.87826	.54446	.8367	.1386	.0912	.12174	.52182	26
35	.47844	0.87812	0.54484	1.8354	1.1388	2.0901	0.12188	0.52156	25
36	.47869	.87798	.54522	.8341	.1390	.0890	.12202	.52131	24
37	.47895	.87784	.54559	.8329	.1391	.0879	.12216	.52105	23
38	.47920	.87770	.54597	.8316	.1393	.0868	.12229	.52080	22
39	.47946	.87756	.54635	.8303	.1395	.0857	.12243	.52054	21
40	0.47971	0.87742	0.54673	1.8291	1.1397	2.0846	0.12257	0.52029	20
41	.47997	.87728	.54711	.8278	.1399	.0835	.12271	.52003	19
42	.48022	.87715	.54748	.8265	.1401	.0824	.12285	.51978	18
43	.48048	.87701	.54786	.8253	.1402	.0812	.12299	.51952	17
44	.48073	.87687	.54824	.8240	.1404	.0801	.12313	.51927	16
45	0.48099	0.87673	0.54862	1.8227	1.1406	2.0790	0.12327	0.51901	15
46	.48124	.87659	.54900	.8215	.1408	.0779	.12341	.51876	14
47	.48150	.87645	.54937	.8202	.1410	.0768	.12355	.51850	13
48	.48175	.87631	.54975	.8190	.1411	.0757	.12369	.51825	12
49	.48201	.87617	.55013	.8177	.1413	.0746	.12383	.51799	11
50	0.48226	0.87603	0.55051	1.8165	1.1415	2.0735	0.12397	0.51774	10
51	.48252	.87588	.55089	.8152	.1417	.0725	.12411	.51748	9
52	.48277	.87574	.55127	.8140	.1419	.0714	.12425	.51723	8
53	.48303	.87560	.55165	.8127	.1421	.0703	.12439	.51697	7
54	.48328	.87546	.55203	.8115	.1422	.0692	.12453	.51672	6
55	0.48354	0.87532	0.55241	1.8102	1.1424	2.0681	0.12468	0.51646	5
56	.48379	.87518	.55279	.8090	.1426	.0670	.12482	.51621	4
57	.48405	.87504	.55317	.8078	.1428	.0659	.12496	.51595	3
58	.48430	.87490	.55355	.8065	.1430	.0648	.12510	.51570	2
59	.48455	.87476	.55393	.8053	.1432	.0637	.12524	.51544	1
60	0.48481	0.87462	0.55431	1.8040	1.1433	2.0627	0.12538	0.51519	0
M	Cosine	Sine	Cotan.	Tan.	Cosec.	Secant	Vrs. Cos.	Vrs. Sin.	M

MATHEMATICAL TABLES

Natural Trigonometric Functions

M	Sine	Cosine	Tan.	Cotan.	Secant	Cosec.	Vrs. Sin.	Vrs. Cos.	M
0	0.48481	0.87462	0.55431	1.8040	1.1433	2.0627	0.12538	0.51519	60
1	.48506	.87448	.55469	.8028	.1435	.0616	.12552	.51493	59
2	.48532	.87434	.55507	.8016	.1437	.0605	.12566	.51468	58
3	.48557	.87420	.55545	.8003	.1439	.0594	.12580	.51443	57
4	.48583	.87405	.55583	.7991	.1441	.0583	.12594	.51417	56
5	0.48608	0.87391	0.55621	1.7979	1.1443	2.0573	0.12609	0.51392	55
6	.48633	.87377	.55659	.7966	.1445	.0562	.12623	.51366	54
7	.48659	.87363	.55697	.7954	.1446	.0551	.12637	.51341	53
8	.48684	.87349	.55735	.7942	.1448	.0540	.12651	.51316	52
9	.48710	.87335	.55774	.7930	.1450	.0530	.12665	.51290	51
10	0.48735	0.87320	0.55812	1.7917	1.1452	2.0519	0.12679	0.51265	50
11	.48760	.87306	.55850	.7905	.1454	.0508	.12694	.51239	49
12	.48786	.87292	.55888	.7893	.1456	.0498	.12708	.51214	48
13	.48811	.87278	.55926	.7881	.1458	.0487	.12722	.51189	47
14	.48837	.87264	.55964	.7868	.1459	.0476	.12736	.51163	46
15	0.48862	0.87250	0.56003	1.7856	1.1461	2.0466	0.12750	0.51138	45
16	.48887	.87235	.56041	.7844	.1463	.0455	.12765	.51112	44
17	.48913	.87221	.56079	.7832	.1465	.0444	.12779	.51087	43
18	.48938	.87207	.56117	.7820	.1467	.0434	.12793	.51062	42
19	.48964	.87193	.56156	.7808	.1469	.0423	.12807	.51036	41
20	0.48989	0.87178	0.56194	1.7795	1.1471	2.0413	0.12821	0.51011	40
21	.49014	.87164	.56232	.7783	.1473	.0402	.12836	.50986	39
22	.49040	.87150	.56270	.7771	.1474	.0392	.12850	.50960	38
23	.49065	.87136	.56309	.7759	.1476	.0381	.12864	.50935	37
24	.49090	.87121	.56347	.7747	.1478	.0370	.12879	.50910	36
25	0.49116	0.87107	0.56385	1.7735	1.1480	2.0360	0.12893	0.50884	35
26	.49141	.87093	.56424	.7723	.1482	.0349	.12907	.50859	34
27	.49166	.87078	.56462	.7711	.1484	.0339	.12921	.50834	33
28	.49192	.87064	.56500	.7699	.1486	.0329	.12936	.50808	32
29	.49217	.87050	.56539	.7687	.1488	.0318	.12950	.50783	31
30	0.49242	0.87035	0.56577	1.7675	1.1489	2.0308	0.12964	0.50758	30
31	.49268	.87021	.56616	.7663	.1491	.0297	.12979	.50732	29
32	.49293	.87007	.56654	.7651	.1493	.0287	.12993	.50707	28
33	.49318	.86992	.56692	.7639	.1495	.0276	.13007	.50682	27
34	.49343	.86978	.56731	.7627	.1497	.0266	.13022	.50656	26
35	0.49369	0.86964	0.56769	1.7615	1.1499	2.0256	0.13036	0.50631	25
36	.49394	.86949	.56808	.7603	.1501	.0245	.13050	.50606	24
37	.49419	.86935	.56846	.7591	.1503	.0235	.13065	.50580	23
38	.49445	.86921	.56885	.7579	.1505	.0224	.13079	.50555	22
39	.49470	.86906	.56923	.7567	.1507	.0214	.13094	.50530	21
40	0.49495	0.86892	0.56962	1.7555	1.1508	2.0204	0.13108	0.50505	20
41	.49521	.86877	.57000	.7544	.1510	.0194	.13122	.50479	19
42	.49546	.86863	.57039	.7532	.1512	.0183	.13137	.50454	18
43	.49571	.86849	.57077	.7520	.1514	.0173	.13151	.50429	17
44	.49596	.86834	.57116	.7508	.1516	.0163	.13166	.50404	16
45	0.49622	0.86820	0.57155	1.7496	1.1518	2.0152	0.13180	0.50378	15
46	.49647	.86805	.57193	.7484	.1520	.0142	.13194	.50353	14
47	.49672	.86791	.57232	.7473	.1522	.0132	.13209	.50328	13
48	.49697	.86776	.57270	.7461	.1524	.0122	.13223	.50303	12
49	.49723	.86762	.57309	.7449	.1526	.0111	.13238	.50277	11
50	0.49748	0.86748	0.57348	1.7437	1.1528	2.0101	0.13252	0.50252	10
51	.49773	.86733	.57386	.7426	.1530	.0091	.13267	.50227	9
52	.49798	.86719	.57425	.7414	.1531	.0081	.13281	.50202	8
53	.49823	.86704	.57464	.7402	.1533	.0071	.13296	.50176	7
54	.49849	.86690	.57503	.7390	.1535	.0061	.13310	.50151	6
55	0.49874	0.86675	0.57541	1.7379	1.1537	2.0050	0.13325	0.50126	5
56	.49899	.86661	.57580	.7367	.1539	.0040	.13339	.50101	4
57	.49924	.86646	.57619	.7355	.1541	.0030	.13354	.50076	3
58	.49950	.86632	.57657	.7344	.1543	.0020	.13368	.50050	2
59	.49975	.86617	.57696	.7332	.1545	.0010	.13383	.50025	1
60	0.50000	0.86603	0.57735	1.7320	1.1547	2.0000	0.13397	0.50000	0

| M | Cosine | Sine | Cotan. | Tan. | Cosec. | Secant | Vrs. Cos. | Vrs. Sin. | M |

Natural Trigonometric Functions

M	Sine	Cosine	Tan.	Cotan.	Secant	Cosec.	Vrs. Sin.	Vrs. Cos.	M
0	0.50000	0.86603	0.57735	1.7320	1.1547	2.0000	0.13397	0.50000	60
1	.50025	.86588	.57774	.7309	.1549	1.9990	.13412	.49975	59
2	.50050	.86573	.57813	.7297	.1551	.9980	.13426	.49950	58
3	.50075	.86559	.57851	.7286	.1553	.9970	.13441	.49924	57
4	.50101	.86544	.57890	.7274	.1555	.9960	.13456	.49899	56
5	0.50126	0.86530	0.57929	1.7262	.1557	1.9950	0.13470	0.49874	55
6	.50151	.86515	.57968	.7251	.1559	.9940	.13485	.49849	54
7	.50176	.86500	.58007	.7239	.1561	.9930	.13499	.49824	53
8	.50201	.86486	.58046	.7228	.1562	.9920	.13514	.49799	52
9	.50226	.86471	.58085	.7216	.1564	.9910	.13529	.49773	51
10	0.50252	0.86457	0.58123	1.7205	.1566	1.9900	0.13543	0.49748	50
11	.50277	.86442	.58162	.7193	.1568	.9890	.13558	.49723	49
12	.50302	.86427	.58201	.7182	.1570	.9880	.13572	.49698	48
13	.50327	.86413	.58240	.7170	.1572	.9870	.13587	.49673	47
14	.50352	.86398	.58279	.7159	.1574	.9860	.13602	.49648	46
15	0.50377	0.86383	0.58318	1.7147	.1576	1.9850	0.13616	0.49623	45
16	.50402	.86369	.58357	.7136	.1578	.9840	.13631	.49597	44
17	.50428	.86354	.58396	.7124	.1580	.9830	.13646	.49572	43
18	.50453	.86339	.58435	.7113	.1582	.9820	.13660	.49547	42
19	.50478	.86325	.58474	.7101	.1584	.9811	.13675	.49522	41
20	0.50503	0.86310	0.58513	1.7090	.1586	1.9801	0.13690	0.49497	40
21	.50528	.86295	.58552	.7079	.1588	.9791	.13704	.49472	39
22	.50553	.86281	.58591	.7067	.1590	.9781	.13719	.49447	38
23	.50578	.86266	.58630	.7056	.1592	.9771	.13734	.49422	37
24	.50603	.86251	.58670	.7044	.1594	.9761	.13749	.49397	36
25	0.50628	0.86237	0.58709	1.7033	.1596	1.9752	0.13763	0.49371	35
26	.50653	.86222	.58748	.7022	.1598	.9742	.13778	.49346	34
27	.50679	.86207	.58787	.7010	.1600	.9732	.13793	.49321	33
28	.50704	.86192	.58826	.6999	.1602	.9722	.13807	.49296	32
29	.50729	.86178	.58865	.6988	.1604	.9713	.13822	.49271	31
30	0.50754	0.86163	0.58904	1.6977	.1606	1.9703	0.13837	0.49246	30
31	.50779	.86148	.58944	.6965	.1608	.9693	.13852	.49221	29
32	.50804	.86133	.58983	.6954	.1610	.9633	.13867	.49196	28
33	.50829	.86118	.59022	.6943	.1612	.9674	.13881	.49171	27
34	.50854	.86104	.59061	.6931	.1614	.9664	.13896	.49146	26
35	0.50879	0.86089	0.59100	1.6920	.1616	1.9654	0.13911	0.49121	25
36	.50904	.86074	.59140	.6909	.1618	.9645	.13926	.49096	24
37	.50929	.86059	.59179	.6898	.1620	.9635	.13941	.49071	23
38	.50954	.86044	.59218	.6887	.1622	.9625	.13955	.49046	22
39	.50979	.86030	.59258	.6875	.1624	.9616	.13970	.49021	21
40	0.51004	0.86015	0.59297	1.6864	.1626	1.9606	0.13985	0.48996	20
41	.51029	.86000	.59336	.6853	.1628	.9596	.14000	.48971	19
42	.51054	.85985	.59376	.6842	.1630	.9587	.14015	.48946	18
43	.51079	.85970	.59415	.6831	.1632	.9577	.14030	.48921	17
44	.51104	.85955	.59454	.6820	.1634	.9563	.14044	.48896	16
45	0.51129	0.85941	0.59494	1.6808	.1636	1.9558	0.14059	0.48871	15
46	.51154	.85926	.59533	.6797	.1638	.9549	.14074	.48846	14
47	.51179	.85911	.59572	.6786	.1640	.9539	.14089	.48821	13
48	.51204	.85896	.59612	.6775	.1642	.9530	.14104	.48796	12
49	.51229	.85881	.59651	.6764	.1644	.9520	.14119	.48771	11
50	0.51254	0.85866	0.59691	1.6753	.1646	1.9510	0.14134	0.48746	10
51	.51279	.85851	.59730	.6742	.1648	.9501	.14149	.48721	9
52	.51304	.85836	.59770	.6731	.1650	.9491	.14164	.48696	8
53	.51329	.85821	.59809	.6720	.1652	.9482	.14178	.48671	7
54	.51354	.85806	.59849	.6709	.1654	.9473	.14193	.48646	6
55	0.51379	0.85791	0.59888	1.6698	.1656	1.9463	0.14208	0.48621	5
56	.51404	.85777	.59928	.6687	.1658	.9454	.14223	.48596	4
57	.51429	.85762	.59967	.6676	.1660	.9444	.14238	.48571	3
58	.51454	.85747	.60007	.6665	.1662	.9435	.14253	.48546	2
59	.51479	.85732	.60046	.6654	.1664	.9425	.14268	.48521	1
60	0.51504	0.85717	0.60086	1.6643	1.1666	1.9416	0.14283	0.48496	0
M	Cosine	Sine	Cotan.	Tan.	Cosec.	Secant	Vrs. Cos.	Vrs. Sin.	M

M	Sine	Cosine	Tan.	Cotan.	Secant	Cosec.	Vrs. Sin.	Vrs. Cos.	M
0	0.51504	0.85717	0.60086	1.6643	1.1666	1.9416	0.14283	0.48496	60
1	.51529	.85702	.60126	.6632	.1668	.9407	.14298	.48471	59
2	.51554	.85687	.60165	.6621	.1670	.9397	.14313	.48446	58
3	.51578	.85672	.60205	.6610	.1672	.9388	.14328	.48421	57
4	.51603	.85657	.60244	.6599	.1674	.9378	.14343	.48396	56
5	0.51628	0.85642	0.60284	1.6588	1.1676	1.9369	0.14358	0.48371	55
6	.51653	.85627	.60324	.6577	.1678	.9360	.14373	.48347	54
7	.51678	.85612	.60363	.6566	.1681	.9350	.14388	.48322	53
8	.51703	.85597	.60403	.6555	.1683	.9341	.14403	.48297	52
9	.51728	.85582	.60443	.6544	.1685	.9332	.14418	.48272	51
10	0.51753	0.85566	0.60483	1.6534	1.1687	1.9322	0.14433	0.48247	50
11	.51778	.85551	.60522	.6523	.1689	.9313	.14448	.48222	49
12	.51803	.85536	.60562	.6512	.1691	.9304	.14463	.48197	48
13	.51827	.85521	.60602	.6501	.1693	.9295	.14479	.48172	47
14	.51852	.85506	.60642	.6490	.1695	.9285	.14494	.48147	46
15	0.51877	0.85491	0.60681	1.6479	1.1697	1.9276	0.14509	0.48123	45
16	.51902	.85476	.60721	.6469	.1699	.9267	.14524	.48098	44
17	.51927	.85461	.60761	.6458	.1701	.9258	.14539	.48073	43
18	.51952	.85446	.60801	.6447	.1703	.9248	.14554	.48048	42
19	.51977	.85431	.60841	.6436	.1705	.9239	.14569	.48023	41
20	0.52002	0.85416	0.60881	1.6425	1.1707	1.9230	0.14584	0.47998	40
21	.52026	.85400	.60920	.6415	.1709	.9221	.14599	.47973	39
22	.52051	.85385	.60960	.6404	.1712	.9212	.14615	.47949	38
23	.52076	.85370	.61000	.6393	.1714	.9203	.14630	.47924	37
24	.52101	.85355	.61040	.6383	.1716	.9193	.14645	.47899	36
25	0.52126	0.85340	0.61080	1.6372	1.1718	1.9184	0.14660	0.47874	35
26	.52151	.85325	.61120	.6361	.1720	.9175	.14675	.47849	34
27	.52175	.85309	.61160	.6350	.1722	.9166	.14690	.47824	33
28	.52200	.85294	.61200	.6340	.1724	.9157	.14706	.47800	32
29	.52225	.85279	.61240	.6329	.1726	.9148	.14721	.47775	31
30	0.52250	0.85264	0.61280	1.6318	1.1728	1.9139	0.14736	0.47750	30
31	.52275	.85249	.61320	.6308	.1730	.9130	.14751	.47725	29
32	.52299	.85234	.61360	.6297	.1732	.9121	.14766	.47700	28
33	.52324	.85218	.61400	.6286	.1734	.9112	.14782	.47676	27
34	.52349	.85203	.61440	.6276	.1737	.9102	.14797	.47651	26
35	0.52374	0.85188	0.61480	1.6265	1.1739	1.9093	0.14812	0.47626	25
36	.52398	.85173	.61520	.6255	.1741	.9084	.14827	.47601	24
37	.52423	.85157	.61560	.6244	.1743	.9075	.14842	.47577	23
38	.52448	.85142	.61601	.6233	.1745	.9066	.14858	.47552	22
39	.52473	.85127	.61641	.6223	.1747	.9057	.14873	.47527	21
40	0.52498	0.85112	0.61681	1.6212	1.1749	1.9048	0.14888	0.47502	20
41	.52522	.85096	.61721	.6202	.1751	.9039	.14904	.47477	19
42	.52547	.85081	.61761	.6191	.1753	.9030	.14919	.47453	18
43	.52572	.85066	.61801	.6181	.1756	.9021	.14934	.47428	17
44	.52597	.85050	.61842	.6170	.1758	.9013	.14949	.47403	16
45	0.52621	0.85035	0.61882	1.6160	1.1760	1.9004	0.14965	0.47379	15
46	.52646	.85020	.61922	.6149	.1762	.8995	.14980	.47354	14
47	.52671	.85004	.61962	.6139	.1764	.8986	.14995	.47329	13
48	.52695	.84989	.62003	.6128	.1766	.8977	.15011	.47304	12
49	.52720	.84974	.62043	.6118	.1768	.8968	.15026	.47280	11
50	0.52745	0.84959	0.62083	1.6107	1.1770	1.8959	0.15041	0.47255	10
51	.52770	.84943	.62123	.6097	.1772	.8950	.15057	.47230	9
52	.52794	.84928	.62164	.6086	.1775	.8941	.15072	.47205	8
53	.52819	.84912	.62204	.6076	.1777	.8932	.15087	.47181	7
54	.52844	.84897	.62244	.6066	.1779	.8924	.15103	.47156	6
55	0.52868	0.84882	0.62285	1.6055	1.1781	1.8915	0.15118	0.47131	5
56	.52893	.84866	.62325	.6045	.1783	.8906	.15133	.47107	4
57	.52918	.84851	.62366	.6034	.1785	.8897	.15149	.47082	3
58	.52942	.84836	.62406	.6024	.1787	.8888	.15164	.47057	2
59	.52967	.84820	.62446	.6014	.1790	.8879	.15180	.47033	1
60	0.52992	0.84805	0.62487	1.6003	1.1792	1.8871	0.15195	0.47008	0

| M | Cosine | Sine | Cotan. | Tan. | Cosec. | Secant | Vrs. Cos. | Vrs. Sin. | M |

M	Sine	Cosine	Tan.	Cotan.	Secant	Cosec.	Vrs. Sin.	Vrs. Cos	M
0	0.52992	0.84805	0.62487	1.6003	1.1792	1.8871	0.15195	0.47008	60
1	.53016	.84789	.62527	.5993	.1794	.8862	.15211	.46983	59
2	.53041	.84774	.62568	.5983	.1796	.8853	.15226	.46959	58
3	.53066	.84758	.62608	.5972	.1798	.8844	.15241	.46934	57
4	.53090	.84743	.62649	.5962	.1800	.8836	.15257	.46909	56
5	0.53115	0.84728	0.62689	1.5952	1.1802	1.8827	0.15272	0.46885	55
6	.53140	.84712	.62730	.5941	.1805	.8818	.15288	.46860	54
7	.53164	.84697	.62770	.5931	.1807	.8809	.15303	.46835	53
8	.53189	.84681	.62811	.5921	.1809	.8801	.15319	.46811	52
9	.53214	.84666	.62851	.5910	.1811	.8792	.15334	.46786	51
10	0.53238	0.84650	0.62892	1.5900	1.1813	1.8783	0.15350	0.46762	50
11	.53263	.84635	.62933	.5890	.1815	.8775	.15365	.46737	49
12	.53288	.84619	.62973	.5880	.1818	.8766	.15381	.46712	48
13	.53312	.84604	.63014	.5869	.1820	.8757	.15396	.46688	47
14	.53337	.84588	.63055	.5859	.1822	.8749	.15412	.46663	46
15	0.53361	0.84573	0.63095	1.5849	1.1824	1.8740	0.15427	0.46638	45
16	.53386	.84557	.63136	.5839	.1826	.8731	.15443	.46614	44
17	.53411	.84542	.63177	.5829	.1828	.8723	.15458	.46589	43
18	.53435	.84526	.63217	.5818	.1831	.8714	.15474	.46565	42
19	.53460	.84511	.63258	.5808	.1833	.8706	.15489	.46540	41
20	0.53484	0.84495	0.63299	1.5798	1.1835	1.8697	0.15505	0.46516	40
21	.53509	.84479	.63339	.5788	.1837	.8688	.15520	.46491	39
22	.53533	.84464	.63380	.5778	.1839	.8680	.15536	.46466	38
23	.53558	.84448	.63421	.5768	.1841	.8671	.15552	.46442	37
24	.53583	.84433	.63462	.5757	.1844	.8663	.15567	.46417	36
25	0.53607	0.84417	0.63503	1.5747	1.1846	1.8654	0.15583	0.46393	35
26	.53632	.84402	.63543	.5737	.1848	.8646	.15598	.46368	34
27	.53656	.84386	.63584	.5727	.1850	.8637	.15614	.46344	33
28	.53681	.84370	.63625	.5717	.1852	.8629	.15630	.46319	32
29	.53705	.84355	.63666	.5707	.1855	.8620	.15645	.46294	31
30	0.53730	0.84339	0.63707	1.5697	1.1857	1.8611	0.15661	0.46270	30
31	.53754	.84323	.63748	.5687	.1859	.8603	.15676	.46245	29
32	.53779	.84308	.63789	.5677	.1861	.8595	.15692	.46221	28
33	.53803	.84292	.63830	.5667	.1863	.8586	.15708	.46196	27
34	.53828	.84276	.63871	.5657	.1866	.8578	.15723	.46172	26
35	0.53852	0.84261	0.63912	1.5646	1.1868	1.8569	0.15739	0.46147	25
36	.53877	.84245	.63953	.5636	.1870	.8561	.15755	.46123	24
37	.53901	.84229	.63994	.5626	.1872	.8552	.15770	.46098	23
38	.53926	.84214	.64035	.5616	.1874	.8544	.15786	.46074	22
39	.53950	.84198	.64076	.5606	.1877	.8535	.15802	.46049	21
40	0.53975	0.84182	0.64117	1.5596	1.1879	1.8527	0.15817	0.46025	20
41	.53999	.84167	.64158	.5586	.1881	.8519	.15833	.46000	19
42	.54024	.84151	.64199	.5577	.1883	.8510	.15849	.45976	18
43	.54048	.84135	.64240	.5567	.1886	.8502	.15865	.45951	17
44	.54073	.84120	.64281	.5557	.1888	.8493	.15880	.45927	16
45	0.54097	0.84104	0.64322	1.5547	1.1890	1.8485	0.15896	0.45902	15
46	.54122	.84088	.64363	.5537	.1892	.8477	.15912	.45878	14
47	.54146	.84072	.64404	.5527	.1894	.8468	.15927	.45854	13
48	.54171	.84057	.64446	.5517	.1897	.8460	.15943	.45829	12
49	.54195	.84041	.64487	.5507	.1899	.8452	.15959	.45805	11
50	0.54220	0.84025	0.64528	1.5497	1.1901	1.8443	0.15975	0.45780	10
51	.54244	.84009	.64569	.5487	.1903	.8435	.15991	.45756	9
52	.54268	.83993	.64610	.5477	.1906	.8427	.16006	.45731	8
53	.54293	.83978	.64652	.5467	.1908	.8418	.16022	.45707	7
54	.54317	.83962	.64693	.5458	.1910	.8410	.16038	.45682	6
55	0.54342	0.83946	0.64734	1.5448	1.1912	1.8402	0.16054	0.45658	5
56	.54366	.83930	.64775	.5438	.1915	.8394	.16070	.45634	4
57	.54391	.83914	.64817	.5428	.1917	.8385	.16085	.45609	3
58	.54415	.83899	.64858	.5418	.1919	.8377	.16101	.45585	2
59	.54439	.83883	.64899	.5408	.1921	.8369	.16117	.45560	1
60	0.54464	0.83867	0.64941	1.5399	1.1924	1.8361	0.16133	0.45536	0
M	Cosine	Sine	Cotan.	Tan.	Cosec.	Secant	Vrs. Cos.	Vrs. Sin.	M

M	Sine	Cosine	Tan.	Cotan.	Secant	Cosec.	Vrs. Sin.	Vrs. Cos.	M
0	0.54464	0.83867	0.64941	1.5399	1.1924	1.8361	0.16133	0.45536	60
1	.54488	.83851	.64982	.5389	.1926	.8352	.16149	.45512	59
2	.54513	.83835	.65023	.5379	.1928	.8344	.16165	.45487	58
3	.54537	.83819	.65065	.5369	.1930	.8336	.16180	.45463	57
4	.54561	.83804	.65106	.5359	.1933	.8328	.16196	.45438	56
5	0.54586	0.83788	0.65148	1.5350	1.1935	1.8320	0.16212	0.45414	55
6	.54610	.83772	.65189	.5340	.1937	.8311	.16228	.45390	54
7	.54634	.83756	.65231	.5330	.1939	.8303	.16244	.45365	53
8	.54659	.83740	.65272	.5320	.1942	.8295	.16260	.45341	52
9	.54683	.83724	.65314	.5311	.1944	.8287	.16276	.45317	51
10	0.54708	0.83708	0.65355	1.5301	1.1946	1.8279	0.16292	0.45292	50
11	.54732	.83692	.65397	.5291	.1948	.8271	.16308	.45268	49
12	.54756	.83676	.65438	.5282	.1951	.8263	.16323	.45244	48
13	.54781	.83660	.65480	.5272	.1953	.8255	.16339	.45219	47
14	.54805	.83644	.65521	.5262	.1955	.8246	.16355	.45195	46
15	0.54829	0.83629	0.65563	1.5252	1.1958	1.8238	0.16371	0.45171	45
16	.54854	.83613	.65604	.5243	.1960	.8230	.16387	.45146	44
17	.54878	.83597	.65646	.5233	.1962	.8222	.16403	.45122	43
18	.54902	.83581	.65688	.5223	.1964	.8214	.16419	.45098	42
19	.54926	.83565	.65729	.5214	.1967	.8206	.16435	.45073	41
20	0.54951	0.83549	0.65771	1.5204	1.1969	1.8198	0.16451	0.45049	40
21	.54975	.83533	.65813	.5195	.1971	.8190	.16467	.45025	39
22	.54999	.83517	.65854	.5185	.1974	.8182	.16483	.45000	38
23	.55024	.83501	.65896	.5175	.1976	.8174	.16499	.44976	37
24	.55048	.83485	.65938	.5166	.1978	.8166	.16515	.44952	36
25	0.55072	0.83469	0.65980	1.5156	1.1980	1.8158	0.16531	0.44928	35
26	.55097	.83453	.66021	.5147	.1983	.8150	.16547	.44903	34
27	.55121	.83437	.66063	.5137	.1985	.8142	.16563	.44879	33
28	.55145	.83421	.66105	.5127	.1987	.8134	.16579	.44855	32
29	.55169	.83405	.66147	.5118	.1990	.8126	.16595	.44830	31
30	0.55194	0.83388	0.66188	1.5108	1.1992	1.8118	0.16611	0.44806	30
31	.55218	.83372	.66230	.5099	.1994	.8110	.16627	.44782	29
32	.55242	.83356	.66272	.5089	.1997	.8102	.16643	.44758	28
33	.55266	.83340	.66314	.5080	.1999	.8094	.16660	.44733	27
34	.55291	.83324	.66356	.5070	.2001	.8086	.16676	.44709	26
35	0.55315	0.83308	0.66398	1.5061	1.2004	1.8078	0.16692	0.44685	25
36	.55339	.83292	.66440	.5051	.2006	.8070	.16708	.44661	24
37	.55363	.83276	.66482	.5042	.2008	.8062	.16724	.44637	23
38	.55388	.83260	.66524	.5032	.2010	.8054	.16740	.44612	22
39	.55412	.83244	.66566	.5023	.2013	.8047	.16756	.44588	21
40	0.55436	0.83228	0.66608	1.5013	1.2015	1.8039	0.16772	0.44564	20
41	.55460	.83211	.66650	.5004	.2017	.8031	.16788	.44540	19
42	.55484	.83195	.66692	.4994	.2020	.8023	.16804	.44515	18
43	.55509	.83179	.66734	.4985	.2022	.8015	.16821	.44491	17
44	.55533	.83163	.66776	.4975	.2024	.8007	.16837	.44467	16
45	0.55557	0.83147	0.66818	1.4966	1.2027	1.7999	0.16853	0.44443	15
46	.55581	.83131	.66860	.4957	.2029	.7992	.16869	.44419	14
47	.55605	.83115	.66902	.4947	.2031	.7984	.16885	.44395	13
48	.55629	.83098	.66944	.4938	.2034	.7976	.16901	.44370	12
49	.55654	.83082	.66986	.4928	.2036	.7968	.16918	.44346	11
50	0.55678	0.83066	0.67028	1.4919	1.2039	1.7960	0.16934	0.44322	10
51	.55702	.83050	.67071	.4910	.2041	.7953	.16950	.44298	9
52	.55726	.83034	.67113	.4900	.2043	.7945	.16966	.44274	8
53	.55750	.83017	.67155	.4891	.2046	.7937	.16982	.44250	7
54	.55774	.83001	.67197	.4881	.2048	.7929	.16999	.44225	6
55	0.55799	0.82985	0.67239	1.4872	1.2050	1.7921	0.17015	0.44201	5
56	.55823	.82969	.67282	.4863	.2053	.7914	.17031	.44177	4
57	.55847	.82952	.67324	.4853	.2055	.7906	.17047	.44153	3
58	.55871	.82936	.67366	.4844	.2057	.7898	.17064	.44129	2
59	.55895	.82920	.67408	.4835	.2060	.7891	.17080	.44105	1
60	0.55919	0.82904	0.67451	1.4826	1.2062	1.7883	0.17096	0.44081	0
M	Cosine	Sine	Cotan.	Tan.	Cosec.	Secant	Vrs. Cos.	Vrs. Sin.	M

M	Sine	Cosine	Tan.	Cotan.	Secant	Cosec.	Vrs. Sin.	Vrs. Cos.	M
0	0.55919	0.82904	0.67451	1.4826	1.2062	1.7883	0.17096	0.44081	60
1	.55943	.82887	.67493	.4816	.2064	.7875	.17112	.44057	59
2	.55967	.82871	.67535	.4807	.2067	.7867	.17129	.44032	58
3	.55992	.82855	.67578	.4798	.2069	.7860	.17145	.44008	57
4	.56016	.82839	.67620	.4788	.2072	.7852	.17161	.43984	56
5	0.56040	0.82822	0.67663	1.4779	1.2074	1.7844	0.17178	0.43960	55
6	.56064	.82806	.67705	.4770	.2076	.7837	.17194	.43936	54
7	.56088	.82790	.67747	.4761	.2079	.7829	.17210	.43912	53
8	.56112	.82773	.67790	.4751	.2081	.7821	.17227	.43888	52
9	.56136	.82757	.67832	.4742	.2083	.7814	.17243	.43864	51
10	0.56160	0.82741	0.67875	1.4733	1.2086	1.7806	0.17259	0.43840	50
11	.56184	.82724	.67917	.4724	.2088	.7798	.17276	.43816	49
12	.56208	.82708	.67960	.4714	.2091	.7791	.17292	.43792	48
13	.56232	.82692	.68002	.4705	.2093	.7783	.17308	.43768	47
14	.56256	.82675	.68045	.4696	.2095	.7776	.17325	.43743	46
15	0.56280	0.82659	0.68087	1.4687	1.2098	1.7768	0.17341	0.43719	45
16	.56304	.82643	.68130	.4678	.2100	.7760	.17357	.43695	44
17	.56328	.82626	.68173	.4669	.2103	.7753	.17374	.43671	43
18	.56353	.82610	.68215	.4659	.2105	.7745	.17390	.43647	42
19	.56377	.82593	.68258	.4650	.2107	.7738	.17406	.43623	41
20	0.56401	0.82577	0.68301	1.4641	1.2110	1.7730	0.17423	0.43599	40
21	.56425	.82561	.68343	.4632	.2112	.7723	.17439	.43575	39
22	.56449	.82544	.68386	.4623	.2115	.7715	.17456	.43551	38
23	.56473	.82528	.68429	.4614	.2117	.7708	.17472	.43527	37
24	.56497	.82511	.68471	.4605	.2119	.7700	.17489	.43503	36
25	0.56521	0.82495	0.68514	1.4595	1.2122	1.7693	0.17505	0.43479	35
26	.56545	.82478	.68557	.4586	.2124	.7685	.17521	.43455	34
27	.56569	.82462	.68600	.4577	.2127	.7678	.17538	.43431	33
28	.56593	.82445	.68642	.4568	.2129	.7670	.17554	.43407	32
29	.56617	.82429	.68685	.4559	.2132	.7663	.17571	.43383	31
30	.56641	0.82413	0.68728	1.4550	1.2134	1.7655	0.17587	0.43359	30
31	.56664	.82396	.68771	.4541	.2136	.7648	.17604	.43335	29
32	.56688	.82380	.68814	.4532	.2139	.7640	.17620	.43311	28
33	.56712	.82363	.68857	.4523	.2141	.7633	.17637	.43287	27
34	.56736	.82347	.68899	.4514	.2144	.7625	.17653	.43263	26
35	0.56760	0.82330	0.68942	1.4505	1.2146	1.7618	0.17670	0.43239	25
36	.56784	.82314	.68985	.4496	.2149	.7610	.17686	.43216	24
37	.56808	.82297	.69028	.4487	.2151	.7603	.17703	.43192	23
38	.56832	.82280	.69071	.4478	.2153	.7596	.17719	.43168	22
39	.56856	.82264	.69114	.4469	.2156	.7588	.17736	.43144	21
40	0.56880	0.82247	0.69157	1.4460	1.2158	1.7581	0.17752	0.43120	20
41	.56904	.82231	.69200	.4451	.2161	.7573	.17769	.43096	19
42	.56928	.82214	.69243	.4442	.2163	.7566	.17786	.43072	18
43	.56952	.82198	.69286	.4433	.2166	.7559	.17802	.43048	17
44	.56976	.82181	.69329	.4424	.2168	.7551	.17819	.43024	16
45	0.57000	0.82165	0.69372	1.4415	1.2171	1.7544	0.17835	0.43000	15
46	.57023	.82148	.69415	.4406	.2173	.7537	.17852	.42976	14
47	.57047	.82131	.69459	.4397	.2175	.7529	.17868	.42952	13
48	.57071	.82115	.69502	.4388	.2178	.7522	.17885	.42929	12
49	.57095	.82098	.69545	.4379	.2180	.7514	.17902	.42905	11
50	0.57119	0.82082	0.69588	1.4370	1.2183	1.7507	0.17918	0.42881	10
51	.57143	.82065	.69631	.4361	.2185	.7500	.17935	.42857	9
52	.57167	.82048	.69674	.4352	.2188	.7493	.17951	.42833	8
53	.57191	.82032	.69718	.4343	.2190	.7485	.17968	.42809	7
54	.57214	.82015	.69761	.4335	.2193	.7478	.17985	.42785	6
55	0.57238	0.81998	0.69804	1.4326	1.2195	1.7471	0.18001	0.42761	5
56	.57262	.81982	.69847	.4317	.2198	.7463	.18018	.42738	4
57	.57286	.81965	.69891	.4308	.2200	.7456	.18035	.42714	3
58	.57310	.81948	.69934	.4299	.2203	.7449	.18051	.42690	2
59	.57334	.81932	.69977	.4290	.2205	.7442	.18068	.42666	1
60	0.57358	0.81915	0.70021	1.4281	1.2208	1.7434	0.18085	0.42642	0
M	Cosine	Sine	Cotan.	Tan.	Cosec.	Secant	Vrs. Cos.	Vrs. Sin.	M

M	Sine	Cosine	Tan.	Cotan.	Secant	Cosec.	Vrs. Sin.	Vrs. Cos.	M
0	0.57358	0.81915	0.70021	1.4281	1.2208	1.7434	0.18085	0.42642	60
1	.57381	.81898	.70064	.4273	.2210	.7427	.18101	.42618	59
2	.57405	.81882	.70107	.4264	.2213	.7420	.18118	.42595	58
3	.57429	.81865	.70151	.4255	.2215	.7413	.18135	.42571	57
4	.57453	.81848	.70194	.4246	.2218	.7405	.18151	.42547	56
5	0.57477	0.81832	0.70238	1.4237	1.2220	1.7398	0.18168	0.42523	55
6	.57500	.81815	.70281	.4228	.2223	.7391	.18185	.42499	54
7	.57524	.81798	.70325	.4220	.2225	.7384	.18202	.42476	53
8	.57548	.81781	.70368	.4211	.2228	.7377	.18218	.42452	52
9	.57572	.81765	.70412	.4202	.2230	.7369	.18235	.42428	51
10	0.57596	0.81748	0.70455	1.4193	1.2233	1.7362	0.18252	0.42404	50
11	.57619	.81731	.70499	.4185	.2235	.7355	.18269	.42380	49
12	.57643	.81714	.70542	.4176	.2238	.7348	.18285	.42357	48
13	.57667	.81698	.70586	.4167	.2240	.7341	.18302	.42333	47
14	.57691	.81681	.70629	.4158	.2243	.7334	.18319	.42309	46
15	0.57714	0.81664	0.70673	1.4150	1.2245	1.7327	0.18336	0.42285	45
16	.57738	.81647	.70717	.4141	.2248	.7319	.18353	.42262	44
17	.57762	.81630	.70760	.4132	.2250	.7312	.18369	.42238	43
18	.57786	.81614	.70804	.4123	.2253	.7305	.18386	.42214	42
19	.57809	.81597	.70848	.4115	.2255	.7298	.18403	.42190	41
20	0.57833	0.81580	0.70891	1.4106	1.2258	1.7291	0.18420	0.42167	40
21	.57857	.81563	.70935	.4097	.2260	.7284	.18437	.42143	39
22	.57881	.81546	.70979	.4089	.2263	.7277	.18453	.42119	38
23	.57904	.81530	.71022	.4080	.2265	.7270	.18470	.42096	37
24	.57928	.81513	.71066	.4071	.2268	.7263	.18487	.42072	36
25	0.57952	0.81496	0.71110	1.4063	1.2270	1.7256	0.18504	0.42048	35
26	.57975	.81479	.71154	.4054	.2273	.7249	.18521	.42024	34
27	.57999	.81462	.71198	.4045	.2276	.7242	.18538	.42001	33
28	.58023	.81445	.71241	.4037	.2278	.7234	.18555	.41977	32
29	.58047	.81428	.71285	.4028	.2281	.7227	.18571	.41953	31
30	0.58070	0.81411	0.71329	1.4019	1.2283	1.7220	0.18588	0.41930	30
31	.58094	.81395	.71373	.4011	.2286	.7213	.18605	.41906	29
32	.58118	.81378	.71417	.4002	.2288	.7206	.18622	.41882	28
33	.58141	.81361	.71461	.3994	.2291	.7199	.18639	.41859	27
34	.58165	.81344	.71505	.3985	.2293	.7192	.18656	.41835	26
35	0.58189	0.81327	0.71549	1.3976	1.2296	1.7185	0.18673	0.41811	25
36	.58212	.81310	.71593	.3968	.2298	.7178	.18690	.41788	24
37	.58236	.81293	.71637	.3959	.2301	.7171	.18707	.41764	23
38	.58259	.81276	.71681	.3951	.2304	.7164	.18724	.41740	22
39	.58283	.81259	.71725	.3942	.2306	.7157	.18741	.41717	21
40	0.58307	0.81242	0.71769	1.3933	1.2309	1.7151	0.18758	0.41693	20
41	.58330	.81225	.71813	.3925	.2311	.7144	.18775	.41669	19
42	.58354	.81208	.71857	.3916	.2314	.7137	.18792	.41646	18
43	.58378	.81191	.71901	.3908	.2316	.7130	.18809	.41622	17
44	.58401	.81174	.71945	.3899	.2319	.7123	.18826	.41599	16
45	0.58425	0.81157	0.71990	1.3891	1.2322	1.7116	0.18843	0.41575	15
46	.58448	.81140	.72034	.3882	.2324	.7109	.18860	.41551	14
47	.58472	.81123	.72078	.3874	.2327	.7102	.18877	.41528	13
48	.58496	.81106	.72122	.3865	.2329	.7095	.18894	.41504	12
49	.58519	.81089	.72166	.3857	.2332	.7088	.18911	.41481	11
50	0.58543	0.81072	0.72211	1.3848	1.2335	1.7081	0.18928	0.41457	10
51	.58566	.81055	.72255	.3840	.2337	.7075	.18945	.41433	9
52	.58590	.81038	.72299	.3831	.2340	.7068	.18962	.41410	8
53	.58614	.81021	.72344	.3823	.2342	.7061	.18979	.41386	7
54	.58637	.81004	.72388	.3814	.2345	.7054	.18996	.41363	6
55	0.58661	0.80987	0.72432	1.3806	1.2348	1.7047	0.19013	0.41339	5
56	.58684	.80970	.72477	.3797	.2350	.7040	.19030	.41316	4
57	.58708	.80953	.72521	.3789	.2353	.7033	.19047	.41292	3
58	.58731	.80936	.72565	.3781	.2355	.7027	.19064	.41268	2
59	.58755	.80919	.72610	.3772	.2358	.7020	.19081	.41245	1
60	0.58778	0.80902	0.72654	1.3764	1.2361	1.7013	0.19098	0.41221	0
M	Cosine	Sine	Cotan.	Tan.	Cosec.	Secant	Vrs. Cos.	Vrs. Sin.	M

M	Sine	Cosine	Tan.	Cotan.	Secant	Cosec.	Vrs. Sin.	Vrs. Cos	M
0	0.58778	0.80902	0.72654	1.3764	1.2361	1.7013	0.19098	0.41221	60
1	.58802	.80885	.72699	.3755	.2363	.7006	.19115	.41198	59
2	.58825	.80867	.72743	.3747	.2366	.6999	.19132	.41174	58
3	.58849	.80850	.72788	.3738	.2368	.6993	.19150	.41151	57
4	.58873	.80833	.72832	.3730	.2371	.6986	.19167	.41127	56
5	0.58896	0.80816	0.72877	1.3722	1.2374	1.6979	0.19184	0.41104	55
6	.58920	.80799	.72921	.3713	.2376	.6972	.19201	.41080	54
7	.58943	.80782	.72966	.3705	.2379	.6965	.19218	.41057	53
8	.58967	.80765	.73010	.3697	.2382	.6959	.19235	.41033	52
9	.58990	.80747	.73055	.3688	.2384	.6952	.19252	.41010	51
10	0.59014	0.80730	0.73100	1.3680	1.2387	1.6945	0.19270	0.40986	50
11	.59037	.80713	.73144	.3672	.2389	.6938	.19287	.40963	49
12	.59060	.80696	.73189	.3663	.2392	.6932	.19304	.40939	48
13	.59084	.80679	.73234	.3655	.2395	.6925	.19321	.40916	47
14	.59107	.80662	.73278	.3647	.2397	.6918	.19338	.40892	46
15	0.59131	0.80644	0.73323	1.3638	1.2400	1.6912	0.19355	0.40869	45
16	.59154	.80627	.73368	.3630	.2403	.6905	.19373	.40845	44
17	.59178	.80610	.73412	.3622	.2405	.6898	.19390	.40822	43
18	.59201	.80593	.73457	.3613	.2408	.6891	.19407	.40799	42
19	.59225	.80576	.73502	.3605	.2411	.6885	.19424	.40775	41
20	0.59248	0.80558	0.73547	1.3597	1.2413	1.6878	0.19442	0.40752	40
21	.59272	.80541	.73592	.3588	.2416	.6871	.19459	.40728	39
22	.59295	.80524	.73637	.3580	.2419	.6865	.19476	.40705	38
23	.59318	.80507	.73681	.3572	.2421	.6858	.19493	.40681	37
24	.59342	.80489	.73726	.3564	.2424	.6851	.19511	.40658	36
25	0.59365	0.80472	0.73771	1.3555	1.2427	1.6845	0.19528	0.40635	35
26	.59389	.80455	.73816	.3547	.2429	.6838	.19545	.40611	34
27	.59412	.80437	.73861	.3539	.2432	.6831	.19562	.40588	33
28	.59435	.80420	.73906	.3531	.2435	.6825	.19580	.40564	32
29	.59459	.80403	.73951	.3522	.2437	.6818	.19597	.40541	31
30	0.59482	0.80386	0.73996	1.3514	1.2440	1.6812	0.19614	0.40518	30
31	.59506	.80368	.74041	.3506	.2443	.6805	.19632	.40494	29
32	.59529	.80351	.74086	.3498	.2445	.6798	.19649	.40471	28
33	.59552	.80334	.74131	.3489	.2448	.6792	.19666	.40447	27
34	.59576	.80316	.74176	.3481	.2451	.6785	.19683	.40424	26
35	0.59599	0.80299	0.74221	1.3473	1.2453	1.6779	0.19701	0.40401	25
36	.59622	.80282	.74266	.3465	.2456	.6772	.19718	.40377	24
37	.59646	.80264	.74312	.3457	.2459	.6766	.19736	.40354	23
38	.59669	.80247	.74357	.3449	.2461	.6759	.19753	.40331	22
39	.59692	.80230	.74402	.3440	.2464	.6752	.19770	.40307	21
40	0.59716	0.80212	0.74447	1.3432	1.2467	1.6746	0.19788	0.40284	20
41	.59739	.80195	.74492	.3424	.2470	.6739	.19805	.40261	19
42	.59762	.80177	.74538	.3416	.2472	.6733	.19822	.40237	18
43	.59786	.80160	.74583	.3408	.2475	.6726	.19840	.40214	17
44	.59809	.80143	.74628	.3400	.2478	.6720	.19857	.40191	16
45	0.59832	0.80125	0.74673	1.3392	1.2480	1.6713	0.19875	0.40167	15
46	.59856	.80108	.74719	.3383	.2483	.6707	.19892	.40144	14
47	.59879	.80090	.74764	.3375	.2486	.6700	.19909	.40121	13
48	.59902	.80073	.74809	.3367	.2488	.6694	.19927	.40098	12
49	.59926	.80056	.74855	.3359	.2491	.6687	.19944	.40074	11
50	0.59949	0.80038	0.74900	1.3351	1.2494	1.6681	0.19962	0.40051	10
51	.59972	.80021	.74946	.3343	.2497	.6674	.19979	.40028	9
52	.59995	.80003	.74991	.3335	.2499	.6668	.19997	.40004	8
53	.60019	.79986	.75037	.3327	.2502	.6661	.20014	.39981	7
54	.60042	.79968	.75082	.3319	.2505	.6655	.20031	.39958	6
55	0.60065	0.79951	0.75128	1.3311	1.2508	1.6648	0.20049	0.39935	5
56	.60088	.79933	.75173	.3303	.2510	.6642	.20066	.39911	4
57	.60112	.79916	.75219	.3294	.2513	.6636	.20084	.39888	3
58	.60135	.79898	.75264	.3286	.2516	.6629	.20101	.39865	2
59	.60158	.79881	.75310	.3278	.2519	.6623	.20119	.39842	1
60	0.60181	0.79863	0.75355	1.3270	1.2521	1.6616	0.20136	0.39818	0
M	Cosine	Sine	Cotan.	Tan.	Cosec.	Secant	Vrs. Cos.	Vrs. Sin.	M

M	Sine	Cosine	Tan.	Cotan.	Secant	Cosec.	Vrs. Sin.	Vrs. Cos.	M
0	0.60181	0.79863	0.75355	1.3270	1.2521	1.6616	0.20136	0.39818	60
1	.60205	.79846	.75401	.3262	.2524	.6610	.20154	.39795	59
2	.60228	.79828	.75447	.3254	.2527	.6603	.20171	.39772	58
3	.60251	.79811	.75492	.3246	.2530	.6597	.20189	.39749	57
4	.60274	.79793	.75538	.3238	.2532	.6591	.20206	.39726	56
5	0.60298	0.79776	0.75584	1.3230	1.2535	1.6584	0.20224	0.39702	55
6	.60320	.79758	.75629	.3222	.2538	.6578	.20242	.39679	54
7	.60344	.79741	.75675	.3214	.2541	.6572	.20259	.39656	53
8	.60367	.79723	.75721	.3206	.2543	.6565	.20277	.39633	52
9	.60390	.79706	.75767	.3198	.2546	.6559	.20294	.39610	51
10	0.60413	0.79688	0.75812	1.3190	1.2549	1.6552	0.20312	0.39586	50
11	.60437	.79670	.75858	.3182	.2552	.6546	.20329	.39563	49
12	.60460	.79653	.75904	.3174	.2554	.6540	.20347	.39540	48
13	.60483	.79635	.75950	.3166	.2557	.6533	.20365	.39517	47
14	.60506	.79618	.75996	.3159	.2560	.6527	.20382	.39494	46
15	0.60529	0.79600	0.76042	1.3151	1.2563	1.6521	0.20400	0.39471	45
16	.60552	.79582	.76088	.3143	.2565	.6514	.20417	.39447	44
17	.60576	.79565	.76134	.3135	.2568	.6508	.20435	.39424	43
18	.60599	.79547	.76179	.3127	.2571	.6502	.20453	.39401	42
19	.60622	.79530	.76225	.3119	.2574	.6496	.20470	.39378	41
20	0.60645	0.79512	0.76271	1.3111	1.2577	1.6489	0.20488	0.39355	40
21	.60668	.79494	.76317	.3103	.2579	.6483	.20505	.39332	39
22	.60691	.79477	.76364	.3095	.2582	.6477	.20523	.39309	38
23	.60714	.79459	.76410	.3087	.2585	.6470	.20541	.39285	37
24	.60737	.79441	.76456	.3079	.2588	.6464	.20558	.39262	36
25	0.60761	0.79424	0.76502	1.3071	1.2591	1.6458	0.20576	0.39239	35
26	.60784	.79406	.76548	.3064	.2593	.6452	.20594	.39216	34
27	.60807	.79388	.76594	.3056	.2596	.6445	.20611	.39193	33
28	.60830	.79371	.76640	.3048	.2599	.6439	.20629	.39170	32
29	.60853	.79353	.76686	.3040	.2602	.6433	.20647	.39147	31
30	0.60876	0.79335	0.76733	1.3032	1.2605	1.6427	0.20665	0.39124	30
31	.60899	.79318	.76779	.3024	.2607	.6420	.20682	.39101	29
32	.60922	.79300	.76825	.3016	.2610	.6414	.20700	.39078	28
33	.60945	.79282	.76871	.3009	.2613	.6408	.20718	.39055	27
34	.60968	.79264	.76918	.3001	.2616	.6402	.20735	.39031	26
35	0.60991	0.79247	0.76964	1.2993	1.2619	1.6396	0.20753	0.39008	25
36	.61014	.79229	.77010	.2985	.2622	.6389	.20771	.38985	24
37	.61037	.79211	.77057	.2977	.2624	.6383	.20789	.38962	23
38	.61061	.79193	.77103	.2970	.2627	.6377	.20806	.38939	22
39	.61084	.79176	.77149	.2962	.2630	.6371	.20824	.38916	21
40	0.61107	0.79158	0.77196	1.2954	1.2633	1.6365	0.20842	0.38893	20
41	.61130	.79140	.77242	.2946	.2636	.6359	.20860	.38870	19
42	.61153	.79122	.77289	.2938	.2639	.6352	.20878	.38847	18
43	.61176	.79104	.77335	.2931	.2641	.6346	.20895	.38824	17
44	.61199	.79087	.77382	.2923	.2644	.6340	.20913	.38801	16
45	0.61222	0.79069	0.77428	1.2915	1.2647	1.6334	0.20931	0.38778	15
46	.61245	.79051	.77475	.2907	.2650	.6328	.20949	.38755	14
47	.61268	.79033	.77521	.2900	.2653	.6322	.20967	.38732	13
48	.61290	.79015	.77568	.2892	.2656	.6316	.20984	.38709	12
49	.61314	.78998	.77614	.2884	.2659	.6309	.21002	.38686	11
50	0.61337	0.78980	0.77661	1.2876	1.2661	1.6303	0.21020	0.38663	10
51	.61360	.78962	.77708	.2869	.2664	.6297	.21038	.38640	9
52	.61383	.78944	.77754	.2861	.2667	.6291	.21056	.38617	8
53	.61405	.78926	.77801	.2853	.2670	.6285	.21074	.38594	7
54	.61428	.78908	.77848	.2845	.2673	.6279	.21091	.38571	6
55	0.61451	0.78890	0.77895	1.2838	1.2676	1.6273	0.21109	0.38548	5
56	.61474	.78873	.77941	.2830	.2679	.6267	.21127	.38525	4
57	.61497	.78855	.77988	.2822	.2681	.6261	.21145	.38503	3
58	.61520	.78837	.78035	.2815	.2684	.6255	.21163	.38480	2
59	.61543	.78819	.78082	.2807	.2687	.6249	.21181	.38457	1
60	0.61566	0.78801	0.78128	1.2799	1.2690	1.6243	0.21199	0.38434	0

| M | Cosine | Sine | Cotan. | Tan. | Cosec. | Secant | Vrs. Cos. | Vrs. Sin. | M |

M	Sine	Cosine	Tan.	Cotan.	Secant	Cosec.	Vrs. Sin.	Vrs. Cos.	M
0	0.61566	0.78801	0.78128	1.2799	1.2690	1.6243	0.21199	0.38434	60
1	.61589	.78783	.78175	.2792	.2693	.6237	.21217	.38411	59
2	.61612	.78765	.78222	.2784	.2696	.6231	.21235	.38388	58
3	.61635	.78747	.78269	.2776	.2699	.6224	.21253	.38365	57
4	.61658	.78729	.78316	.2769	.2702	.6218	.21271	.38342	56
5	0.61681	0.78711	0.78363	1.2761	1.2705	1.6212	0.21288	0.38319	55
6	.61703	.78693	.78410	.2753	.2707	.6206	.21306	.38296	54
7	.61726	.78675	.78457	.2746	.2710	.6200	.21324	.38273	53
8	.61749	.78657	.78504	.2738	.2713	.6194	.21342	.38251	52
9	.61772	.78640	.78551	.2730	.2716	.6188	.21360	.38228	51
10	0.61795	0.78622	0.78598	1.2723	1.2719	1.6182	0.21378	0.38205	50
11	.61818	.78604	.78645	.2715	.2722	.6176	.21396	.38182	49
12	.61841	.78586	.78692	.2708	.2725	.6170	.21414	.38159	48
13	.61864	.78568	.78739	.2700	.2728	.6164	.21432	.38136	47
14	.61886	.78550	.78786	.2692	.2731	.6159	.21450	.38113	46
15	0.61909	0.78532	0.78834	1.2685	1.2734	1.6153	0.21468	0.38091	45
16	.61932	.78514	.78881	.2677	.2737	.6147	.21486	.38068	44
17	.61955	.78496	.78928	.2670	.2739	.6141	.21504	.38045	43
18	.61978	.78478	.78975	.2662	.2742	.6135	.21522	.38022	42
19	.62001	.78460	.79022	.2655	.2745	.6129	.21540	.37999	41
20	0.62023	0.78441	0.79070	1.2647	1.2748	1.6123	0.21558	0.37976	40
21	.62046	.78423	.79117	.2639	.2751	.6117	.21576	.37954	39
22	.62069	.78405	.79164	.2632	.2754	.6111	.21594	.37931	38
23	.62092	.78387	.79212	.2624	.2757	.6105	.21612	.37908	37
24	.62115	.78369	.79259	.2617	.2760	.6099	.21631	.37885	36
25	0.62137	0.78351	0.79306	1.2609	1.2763	1.6093	0.21649	0.37862	35
26	.62160	.78333	.79354	.2602	.2766	.6087	.21667	.37840	34
27	.62183	.78315	.79401	.2594	.2769	.6081	.21685	.37817	33
28	.62206	.78297	.79449	.2587	.2772	.6077	.21703	.37794	32
29	.62229	.78279	.79496	.2579	.2775	.6070	.21721	.37771	31
30	0.62251	0.78261	0.79543	1.2572	1.2778	1.6064	0.21739	0.37748	30
31	.62274	.78243	.79591	.2564	.2781	.6058	.21757	.37726	29
32	.62297	.78224	.79639	.2557	.2784	.6052	.21775	.37703	28
33	.62320	.78206	.79686	.2549	.2787	.6046	.21793	.37680	27
34	.62342	.78188	.79734	.2542	.2790	.6040	.21812	.37657	26
35	0.62365	0.78170	0.79781	1.2534	1.2793	1.6034	0.21830	0.37635	25
36	.62388	.78152	.79829	.2527	.2795	.6029	.21848	.37612	24
37	.62411	.78134	.79876	.2519	.2798	.6023	.21866	.37589	23
38	.62433	.78116	.79924	.2512	.2801	.6017	.21884	.37566	22
39	.62456	.78097	.79972	.2504	.2804	.6011	.21902	.37544	21
40	0.62479	0.78079	0.80020	1.2497	1.2807	1.6005	0.21921	0.37521	20
41	.62501	.78061	.80067	.2489	.2810	.6000	.21939	.37498	19
42	.62524	.78043	.80115	.2482	.2813	.5994	.21957	.37476	18
43	.62547	.78025	.80163	.2475	.2816	.5988	.21975	.37453	17
44	.62570	.78007	.80211	.2467	.2819	.5982	.21993	.37430	16
45	0.62592	0.77983	0.80258	1.2460	1.2822	1.5976	0.22011	0.37408	15
46	.62615	.77970	.80306	.2452	.2825	.5971	.22030	.37385	14
47	.62638	.77952	.80354	.2445	.2828	.5965	.22048	.37362	13
48	.62660	.77934	.80402	.2437	.2831	.5959	.22066	.37340	12
49	.62683	.77915	.80450	.2430	.2834	.5953	.22084	.37317	11
50	0.62706	0.77897	0.80498	1.2423	1.2837	1.5947	0.22103	0.37294	10
51	.62728	.77879	.80546	.2415	.2840	.5942	.22121	.37272	9
52	.62751	.77861	.80594	.2408	.2843	.5936	.22139	.37249	8
53	.62774	.77842	.80642	.2400	.2846	.5930	.22157	.37226	7
54	.62796	.77824	.80690	.2393	.2849	.5924	.22176	.37204	6
55	0.62819	0.77806	0.80738	1.2386	1.2852	1.5919	0.22194	0.37181	5
56	.62841	.77788	.80786	.2378	.2855	.5913	.22212	.37158	4
57	.62864	.77769	.80834	.2371	.2858	.5907	.22230	.37136	3
58	.62887	.77751	.80882	.2364	.2861	.5901	.22249	.37113	2
59	.62909	.77733	.80930	.2356	.2864	.5896	.22267	.37090	1
60	0.62932	0.77715	0.80978	1.2349	1.2867	1.5890	0.22285	0.37068	0
M	Cosine	Sine	Cotan.	Tan.	Cosec.	Secant	Vrs. Cos.	Vrs. Sin.	M

M	Sine	Cosine	Tan.	Cotan.	Secant	Cosec.	Vrs. Sin.	Vrs. Cos.	M
0	0.62932	0.77715	0.80978	1.2349	1.2867	1.5890	0.22285	0.37068	60
1	.62955	.77696	.81026	.2342	.2871	.5884	.22304	.37045	59
2	.62977	.77678	.81075	.2334	.2874	.5879	.22322	.37023	58
3	.63000	.77660	.81123	.2327	.2877	.5873	.22340	.37000	57
4	.63022	.77641	.81171	.2320	.2880	.5867	.22359	.36977	56
5	0.63045	0.77623	0.81219	1.2312	1.2883	1.5862	0.22377	0.36955	55
6	.63067	.77605	.81268	.2305	.2886	.5856	.22395	.36932	54
7	.63090	.77586	.81316	.2297	.2889	.5850	.22414	.36910	53
8	.63113	.77568	.81364	.2290	.2892	.5845	.22432	.36887	52
9	.63135	.77549	.81413	.2283	.2895	.5839	.22450	.36865	51
10	0.63158	0.77531	0.81461	1.2276	1.2898	1.5833	0.22469	0.36842	50
11	.63180	.77513	.81509	.2268	.2901	.5828	.22487	.36820	49
12	.63203	.77494	.81558	.2261	.2904	.5822	.22505	.36797	48
13	.63225	.77476	.81606	.2254	.2907	.5816	.22524	.36774	47
14	.63248	.77458	.81655	.2247	.2910	.5811	.22542	.36752	46
15	0.63270	0.77439	0.81703	1.2239	1.2913	1.5805	0.22561	0.36729	45
16	.63293	.77421	.81752	.2232	.2916	.5799	.22579	.36707	44
17	.63315	.77402	.81800	.2225	.2919	.5794	.22597	.36684	43
18	.63338	.77384	.81849	.2218	.2922	.5788	.22616	.36662	42
19	.63360	.77365	.81898	.2210	.2926	.5783	.22634	.36639	41
20	0.63383	0.77347	0.81946	1.2203	1.2929	1.5777	0.22653	0.36617	40
21	.63405	.77329	.81995	.2196	.2932	.5771	.22671	.36594	39
22	.63428	.77310	.82043	.2189	.2935	.5766	.22690	.36572	38
23	.63450	.77292	.82092	.2181	.2938	.5760	.22708	.36549	37
24	.63473	.77273	.82141	.2174	.2941	.5755	.22727	.36527	36
25	0.63495	0.77255	0.82190	1.2167	1.2944	1.5749	0.22745	0.36504	35
26	.63518	.77236	.82238	.2160	.2947	.5743	.22763	.36482	34
27	.63540	.77218	.82287	.2152	.2950	.5738	.22782	.36459	33
28	.63563	.77199	.82336	.2145	.2953	.5732	.22800	.36437	32
29	.63585	.77181	.82385	.2138	.2956	.5727	.22819	.36415	31
30	0.63608	0.77162	0.82434	1.2131	1.2960	1.5721	0.22837	0.36392	30
31	.63630	.77144	.82482	.2124	.2963	.5716	.22856	.36370	29
32	.63653	.77125	.82531	.2117	.2966	.5710	.22874	.36347	28
33	.63675	.77107	.82580	.2109	.2969	.5705	.22893	.36325	27
34	.63697	.77088	.82629	.2102	.2972	.5699	.22912	.36302	26
35	0.63720	0.77070	0.82678	1.2095	1.2975	1.5694	0.22930	0.36280	25
36	.63742	.77051	.82727	.2088	.2978	.5688	.22949	.36258	24
37	.63765	.77033	.82776	.2081	.2981	.5683	.22967	.36235	23
38	.63787	.77014	.82825	.2074	.2985	.5677	.22986	.36213	22
39	.63810	.76996	.82874	.2066	.2988	.5672	.23004	.36190	21
40	0.63832	0.76977	0.82923	1.2059	1.2991	1.5666	0.23023	0.36168	20
41	.63854	.76958	.82972	.2052	.2994	.5661	.23041	.36146	19
42	.63877	.76940	.83022	.2045	.2997	.5655	.23060	.36123	18
43	.63899	.76921	.83071	.2038	.3000	.5650	.23079	.36101	17
44	.63921	.76903	.83120	.2031	.3003	.5644	.23097	.36078	16
45	0.63944	0.76884	0.83169	1.2024	1.3006	1.5639	0.23116	0.36056	15
46	.63966	.76865	.83218	.2016	.3010	.5633	.23134	.36034	14
47	.63989	.76847	.83267	.2009	.3013	.5628	.23153	.36011	13
48	.64011	.76828	.83317	.2002	.3016	.5622	.23172	.35989	12
49	.64033	.76810	.83366	.1995	.3019	.5617	.23190	.35967	11
50	0.64056	0.76791	0.83415	1.1988	1.3022	1.5611	0.23209	0.35944	10
51	.64078	.76772	.83465	.1981	.3025	.5606	.23227	.35922	9
52	.64100	.76754	.83514	.1974	.3029	.5600	.23246	.35900	8
53	.64123	.76735	.83563	.1967	.3032	.5595	.23265	.35877	7
54	.64145	.76716	.83613	.1960	.3035	.5590	.23283	.35855	6
55	0.64167	0.76698	0.83662	1.1953	1.3038	1.5584	0.23302	0.35833	5
56	.64189	.76679	.83712	.1946	.3041	.5579	.23321	.35810	4
57	.64212	.76660	.83761	.1939	.3044	.5573	.23339	.35788	3
58	.64234	.76642	.83811	.1932	.3048	.5568	.23358	.35766	2
59	.64256	.76623	.83860	.1924	.3051	.5563	.23377	.35743	1
60	0.64279	0.76604	0.83910	1.1917	1.3054	1.5557	0.23395	0.35721	0
M	Cosine	Sine	Cotan.	Tan.	Cosec.	Secant	Vrs. Cos.	Vrs. Sin.	M

M	Sine	Cosine	Tan.	Cotan.	Secant	Cosec.	Vrs. Sin.	Vrs. Cos.	M
0	0.64279	0.76604	0.83910	1.1917	1.3054	1.5557	0.23395	0.35721	60
1	.64301	.76586	.83959	.1910	.3057	.5552	.23414	.35699	59
2	.64323	.76567	.84009	.1903	.3060	.5546	.23433	.35677	58
3	.64345	.76548	.84059	.1896	.3064	.5541	.23452	.35654	57
4	.64368	.76530	.84108	.1889	.3067	.5536	.23470	.35632	56
5	0.64390	0.76511	0.84158	1.1882	1.3070	1.5530	0.23489	0.35610	55
6	.64412	.76492	.84208	.1875	.3073	.5525	.23508	.35588	54
7	.64435	.76473	.84257	.1868	.3076	.5520	.23527	.35565	53
8	.64457	.76455	.84307	.1861	.3080	.5514	.23545	.35543	52
9	.64479	.76436	.84357	.1854	.3083	.5509	.23564	.35521	51
10	0.64501	0.76417	0.84407	1.1847	1.3086	1.5503	0.23583	0.35499	50
11	.64523	.76398	.84457	.1840	.3089	.5498	.23602	.35476	49
12	.64546	.76380	.84506	.1833	.3092	.5493	.23620	.35454	48
13	.64568	.76361	.84556	.1826	.3096	.5487	.23639	.35432	47
14	.64590	.76342	.84606	.1819	.3099	.5482	.23658	.35410	46
15	0.64612	0.76323	0.84656	1.1812	1.3102	1.5477	0.23677	0.35388	45
16	.64635	.76304	.84706	.1805	.3105	.5471	.23695	.35365	44
17	.64657	.76286	.84756	.1798	.3109	.5466	.23714	.35343	43
18	.64679	.76267	.84806	.1791	.3112	.5461	.23733	.35321	42
19	.64701	.76248	.84856	.1785	.3115	.5456	.23752	.35299	41
20	0.64723	0.76229	0.84906	1.1778	1.3118	1.5450	0.23771	0.35277	40
21	.64745	.76210	.84956	.1771	.3121	.5445	.23790	.35254	39
22	.64768	.76191	.85006	.1764	.3125	.5440	.23808	.35232	38
23	.64790	.76173	.85056	.1757	.3128	.5434	.23827	.35210	37
24	.64812	.76154	.85107	.1750	.3131	.5429	.23846	.35188	36
25	0.64834	0.76135	0.85157	1.1743	1.3134	1.5424	0.23865	0.35166	35
26	.64856	.76116	.85207	.1736	.3138	.5419	.23884	.35144	34
27	.64878	.76097	.85257	.1729	.3141	.5413	.23903	.35121	33
28	.64900	.76078	.85307	.1722	.3144	.5408	.23922	.35099	32
29	.64923	.76059	.85358	.1715	.3148	.5403	.23940	.35077	31
30	0.64945	0.76041	0.85408	1.1708	1.3151	1.5398	0.23959	0.35055	30
31	.64967	.76022	.85458	.1702	.3154	.5392	.23978	.35033	29
32	.64989	.76003	.85509	.1695	.3157	.5387	.23997	.35011	28
33	.65011	.75984	.85559	.1688	.3161	.5382	.24016	.34989	27
34	.65033	.75965	.85609	.1681	.3164	.5377	.24035	.34967	26
35	0.65055	0.75946	0.85660	1.1674	1.3167	1.5371	0.24054	0.34945	25
36	.65077	.75927	.85710	.1667	.3170	.5366	.24073	.34922	24
37	.65100	.75908	.85761	.1660	.3174	.5361	.24092	.34900	23
38	.65121	.75889	.85811	.1653	.3177	.5356	.24111	.34878	22
39	.65144	.75870	.85862	.1647	.3180	.5351	.24130	.34856	21
40	0.65166	0.75851	0.85912	1.1640	1.3184	1.5345	0.24149	0.34834	20
41	.65188	.75832	.85963	.1633	.3187	.5340	.24168	.34812	19
42	.65210	.75813	.86013	.1626	.3190	.5335	.24186	.34790	18
43	.65232	.75794	.86064	.1619	.3193	.5330	.24205	.34768	17
44	.65254	.75775	.86115	.1612	.3197	.5325	.24224	.34746	16
45	0.65276	0.75756	0.86165	1.1605	1.3200	1.5319	0.24243	0.34724	15
46	.65298	.75737	.86216	.1599	.3203	.5314	.24262	.34702	14
47	.65320	.75718	.86267	.1592	.3207	.5309	.24281	.34680	13
48	.65342	.75700	.86318	.1585	.3210	.5304	.24300	.34658	12
49	.65364	.75680	.86368	.1578	.3213	.5299	.24319	.34636	11
50	0.65386	0.75661	0.86419	1.1571	1.3217	1.5294	0.24338	0.34614	10
51	.65408	.75642	.86470	.1565	.3220	.5289	.24357	.34592	9
52	.65430	.75623	.86521	.1558	.3223	.5283	.24376	.34570	8
53	.65452	.75604	.86572	.1551	.3227	.5278	.24396	.34548	7
54	.65474	.75585	.86623	.1544	.3230	.5273	.24415	.34526	6
55	0.65496	0.75566	0.86674	1.1537	1.3233	1.5268	0.24434	0.34504	5
56	.65518	.75547	.86725	.1531	.3237	.5263	.24453	.34482	4
57	.65540	.75528	.86775	.1524	.3240	.5258	.24472	.34460	3
58	.65562	.75509	.86826	.1517	.3243	.5253	.24491	.34438	2
59	.65584	.75490	.86878	.1510	.3247	.5248	.24510	.34416	1
60	0.65606	0.75471	0.86929	1.1504	1.3250	1.5242	0.24529	0.34394	0
M	Cosine	Sine	Cotan.	Tan.	Cosec.	Secant	Vrs. Cos.	Vrs. Sin.	M

M	Sine	Cosine	Tan.	Cotan.	Secant	Cosec.	Vrs. Sin.	Vrs. Cos.	M
0	0.65606	0.75471	0.86929	1.1504	1.3250	1.5242	0.24529	0.34394	60
1	.65628	.75452	.86980	.1497	.3253	.5237	.24548	.34372	59
2	.65650	.75433	.87031	.1490	.3257	.5232	.24567	.34350	58
3	.65672	.75414	.87082	.1483	.3260	.5227	.24586	.34328	57
4	.65694	.75394	.87133	.1477	.3263	.5222	.24605	.34306	56
5	0.65716	0.75375	0.87184	1.1470	1.3267	1.5217	0.24624	0.34284	55
6	.65737	.75356	.87235	.1463	.3270	.5212	.24644	.34262	54
7	.65759	.75337	.87287	.1456	.3274	.5207	.24663	.34240	53
8	.65781	.75318	.87338	.1450	.3277	.5202	.24682	.34219	52
9	.65803	.75299	.87389	.1443	.3280	.5197	.24701	.34197	51
10	0.65825	0.75280	0.87441	1.1436	1.3284	1.5192	0.24720	0.34175	50
11	.65847	.75261	.87492	.1430	.3287	.5187	.24739	.34153	49
12	.65869	.75241	.87543	.1423	.3290	.5182	.24758	.34131	48
13	.65891	.75222	.87595	.1416	.3294	.5177	.24778	.34109	47
14	.65913	.75203	.87646	.1409	.3297	.5171	.24797	.34087	46
15	0.65934	0.75184	0.87698	1.1403	1.3301	1.5166	0.24816	0.34065	45
16	.65956	.75165	.87749	.1396	.3304	.5161	.24835	.34043	44
17	.65978	.75146	.87801	.1389	.3307	.5156	.24854	.34022	43
18	.66000	.75126	.87852	.1383	.3311	.5151	.24873	.34000	42
19	.66022	.75107	.87904	.1376	.3314	.5146	.24893	.33978	41
20	0.66044	0.75088	0.87955	1.1369	1.3318	1.5141	0.24912	0.33956	40
21	.66066	.75069	.88007	.1363	.3321	.5136	.24931	.33934	39
22	.66087	.75049	.88058	.1356	.3324	.5131	.24950	.33912	38
23	.66109	.75030	.88110	.1349	.3328	.5126	.24970	.33891	37
24	.66131	.75011	.88162	.1343	.3331	.5121	.24989	.33869	36
25	0.66153	0.74992	0.88213	1.1336	1.3335	1.5116	0.25008	0.33847	35
26	.66175	.74973	.88265	.1329	.3338	.5111	.25027	.33825	34
27	.66197	.74953	.88317	.1323	.3342	.5106	.25047	.33803	33
28	.66218	.74934	.88369	.1316	.3345	.5101	.25066	.33781	32
29	.66240	.74915	.88421	.1309	.3348	.5096	.25085	.33760	31
30	0.66262	0.74895	0.88472	1.1303	1.3352	1.5092	0.25104	0.33738	30
31	.66284	.74876	.88524	.1296	.3355	.5087	.25124	.33716	29
32	.66305	.74857	.88576	.1290	.3359	.5082	.25143	.33694	28
33	.66327	.74838	.88628	.1283	.3362	.5077	.25162	.33673	27
34	.66349	.74818	.88680	.1276	.3366	.5072	.25181	.33651	26
35	0.66371	0.74799	0.88732	1.1270	1.3369	1.5067	0.25201	0.33629	25
36	.66393	.74780	.88784	.1263	.3372	.5062	.25220	.33607	24
37	.66414	.74760	.88836	.1257	.3376	.5057	.25239	.33586	23
38	.66436	.74741	.88888	.1250	.3379	.5052	.25259	.33564	22
39	.66458	.74722	.88940	.1243	.3383	.5047	.25278	.33542	21
40	0.66479	0.74702	0.88992	1.1237	1.3386	1.5042	0.25297	0.33520	20
41	.66501	.74683	.89044	.1230	.3390	.5037	.25317	.33499	19
42	.66523	.74664	.89097	.1224	.3393	.5032	.25336	.33477	18
43	.66545	.74644	.89149	.1217	.3397	.5027	.25355	.33455	17
44	.66566	.74625	.89201	.1211	.3400	.5022	.25375	.33433	16
45	0.66588	0.74606	0.89253	1.1204	1.3404	1.5018	0.25394	0.34412	15
46	.66610	.74586	.89306	.1197	.3407	.5013	.25414	.33390	14
47	.66631	.74567	.89358	.1191	.3411	.5008	.25433	.33368	13
48	.66653	.74548	.89410	.1184	.3414	.5003	.25452	.33347	12
49	.66675	.74528	.89463	.1178	.3418	.4998	.25472	.33325	11
50	0.66697	0.74509	0.89515	1.1171	1.3421	1.4993	0.25491	0.33303	10
51	.66718	.74489	.89567	.1165	.3425	.4988	.25510	.33282	9
52	.66740	.74470	.89620	.1158	.3428	.4983	.25530	.33260	8
53	.66762	.74450	.89672	.1152	.3432	.4979	.25549	.33238	7
54	.66783	.74431	.89725	.1145	.3435	.4974	.25569	.33217	6
55	0.66805	0.74412	0.89777	1.1139	1.3439	1.4969	0.25588	0.33195	5
56	.66826	.74392	.89830	.1132	.3442	.4964	.25608	.33173	4
57	.66848	.74373	.89882	.1126	.3446	.4959	.25627	.33152	3
58	.66870	.74353	.89935	.1119	.3449	.4954	.25647	.33130	2
59	.66891	.74334	.89988	.1113	.3453	.4949	.25666	.33108	1
60	0.66913	0.74314	0.90040	1.1106	1.3456	1.4945	0.25685	0.33087	0
M	Cosine	Sine	Cotan.	Tan.	Cosec.	Secant	Vrs. Cos.	Vrs. Sin.	M

M	Sine	Cosine	Tan.	Cotan.	Secant	Cosec.	Vrs. Sin.	Vrs. Cos.	M
0	0.66913	0.74314	0.90040	1.1106	1.3456	1.4945	0.25685	0.33087	60
1	.66935	.74295	.90093	.1100	.3460	.4940	.25705	.33065	59
2	.66956	.74275	.90146	.1093	.3463	.4935	.25724	.33044	58
3	.66978	.74256	.90198	.1086	.3467	.4930	.25744	.33022	57
4	.66999	.74236	.90251	.1080	.3470	.4925	.25763	.33000	56
5	0.67021	0.74217	0.90304	1.1074	1.3474	1.4921	0.25783	0.32979	55
6	.67043	.74197	.90357	.1067	.3477	.4916	.25802	.32957	54
7	.67064	.74178	.90410	.1061	.3481	.4911	.25822	.32936	53
8	.67086	.74158	.90463	.1054	.3485	.4906	.25841	.32914	52
9	.67107	.74139	.90515	.1048	.3488	.4901	.25861	.32893	51
10	0.67129	0.74119	0.90568	1.1041	1.3492	1.4897	0.25880	0.32871	50
11	.67150	.74100	.90621	.1035	.3495	.4892	.25900	.32849	49
12	.67172	.74080	.90674	.1028	.3499	.4887	.25919	.32828	48
13	.67194	.74061	.90727	.1022	.3502	.4882	.25939	.32806	47
14	.67215	.74041	.90780	.1015	.3506	.4877	.25959	.32785	46
15	0.67237	0.74022	0.90834	1.1009	1.3509	1.4873	0.25978	0.32763	45
16	.67258	.74002	.90887	.1003	.3513	.4868	.25998	.32742	44
17	.67280	.73983	.90940	.0996	.3517	.4863	.26017	.32720	43
18	.67301	.73963	.90993	.0990	.3520	.4858	.26037	.32699	42
19	.67323	.73943	.91046	.0983	.3524	.4854	.26056	.32677	41
20	0.67344	0.73924	0.91099	1.0977	1.3527	1.4849	0.26076	0.32656	40
21	.67366	.73904	.91153	.0971	.3531	.4844	.26096	.32634	39
22	.67387	.73885	.91206	.0964	.3534	.4839	.26115	.32613	38
23	.67409	.73865	.91259	.0958	.3538	.4835	.26135	.32591	37
24	.67430	.73845	.91312	.0951	.3542	.4830	.26154	.32570	36
25	0.67452	0.73826	0.91366	1.0945	1.3545	1.4825	0.26174	0.32548	35
26	.67473	.73806	.91419	.0939	.3549	.4821	.26194	.32527	34
27	.67495	.73787	.91473	.0932	.3552	.4816	.26213	.32505	33
28	.67516	.73767	.91526	.0926	.3556	.4811	.26233	.32484	32
29	.67537	.73747	.91580	.0919	.3560	.4806	.26253	.32462	31
30	0.67559	0.73728	0.91633	1.0913	1.3563	1.4802	0.26272	0.32441	30
31	.67580	.73708	.91687	.0907	.3567	.4797	.26292	.32419	29
32	.67602	.73688	.91740	.0900	.3571	.4792	.26311	.32398	28
33	.67623	.73669	.91794	.0894	.3574	.4788	.26331	.32377	27
34	.67645	.73649	.91847	.0888	.3578	.4783	.26351	.32355	26
35	0.67666	0.73629	0.91901	1.0881	1.3581	1.4778	0.26371	0.32334	25
36	.67688	.73610	.91955	.0875	.3585	.4774	.26390	.32312	24
37	.67709	.73590	.92008	.0868	.3589	.4769	.26410	.32291	23
38	.67730	.73570	.92062	.0862	.3592	.4764	.26430	.32269	22
39	.67752	.73551	.92116	.0856	.3596	.4760	.26449	.32248	21
40	0.67773	0.73531	0.92170	1.0849	1.3600	1.4755	0.26469	0.32227	20
41	.67794	.73511	.92223	.0843	.3603	.4750	.26489	.32205	19
42	.67816	.73491	.92277	.0837	.3607	.4746	.26508	.32184	18
43	.67837	.73472	.92331	.0830	.3611	.4741	.26528	.32163	17
44	.67859	.73452	.92385	.0824	.3614	.4736	.26548	.32141	16
45	0.67880	0.73432	0.92439	1.0818	1.3618	1.4732	0.26568	0.32120	15
46	.67901	.73412	.92493	.0812	.3622	.4727	.26587	.32098	14
47	.67923	.73393	.92547	.0805	.3625	.4723	.26607	.32077	13
48	.67944	.73373	.92601	.0799	.3629	.4718	.26627	.32056	12
49	.67965	.73353	.92655	.0793	.3633	.4713	.26647	.32034	11
50	0.67987	0.73333	0.92709	1.0786	1.3636	1.4709	0.26666	0.32013	10
51	.68008	.73314	.92763	.0780	.3640	.4704	.26686	.31992	9
52	.68029	.73294	.92817	.0774	.3644	.4699	.26706	.31970	8
53	.68051	.73274	.92871	.0767	.3647	.4695	.26726	.31949	7
54	.68072	.73254	.92926	.0761	.3651	.4690	.26746	.31928	6
55	0.68093	0.73234	0.92980	1.0755	1.3655	1.4686	0.26765	0.31907	5
56	.68115	.73215	.93034	.0749	.3658	.4681	.26785	.31885	4
57	.68136	.73195	.93088	.0742	.3662	.4676	.26805	.31864	3
58	.68157	.73175	.93143	.0736	.3666	.4672	.26825	.31843	2
59	.68178	.73155	.93197	.0730	.3669	.4667	.26845	.31821	1
60	0.68200	0.73135	0.93251	1.0724	1.3673	1.4663	0.26865	0.31800	0
M	Cosine	Sine	Cotan.	Tan.	Cosec.	Secant	Vrs. Cos.	Vrs. Sin.	M

M	Sine	Cosine	Tan.	Cotan.	Secant	Cosec.	Vrs. Sin.	Vrs. Cos.	M
0	0.68200	0.73135	0.93251	1.0724	1.3673	1.4663	0.26865	0.31800	60
1	.68221	.73115	.93306	.0717	.3677	.4658	.26884	.31779	59
2	.68242	.73096	.93360	.0711	.3681	.4654	.26904	.31758	58
3	.68264	.73076	.93415	.0705	.3684	.4649	.26924	.31736	57
4	.68285	.73056	.93469	.0699	.3688	.4644	.26944	.31715	56
5	0.68306	0.73036	0.93524	1.0692	1.3692	1.4640	0.26964	0.31694	55
6	.68327	.73016	.93578	.0686	.3695	.4635	.26984	.31673	54
7	.68349	.72996	.93633	.0680	.3699	.4631	.27004	.31651	53
8	.68370	.72976	.93687	.0674	.3703	.4626	.27023	.31630	52
9	.68391	.72956	.93742	.0667	.3707	.4622	.27043	.31609	51
10	0.68412	0.72937	0.93797	1.0661	1.3710	1.4617	0.27063	0.31588	50
11	.68433	.72917	.93851	.0655	.3714	.4613	.27083	.31566	49
12	.68455	.72897	.93906	.0649	.3718	.4608	.27103	.31545	48
13	.68476	.72877	.93961	.0643	.3722	.4604	.27123	.31524	47
14	.68497	.72857	.94016	.0636	.3725	.4599	.27143	.31503	46
15	0.68518	0.72837	0.94071	1.0630	1.3729	1.4595	0.27163	0.31482	45
16	.68539	.72817	.94125	.0624	.3733	.4590	.27183	.31460	44
17	.68561	.72797	.94180	.0618	.3737	.4586	.27203	.31439	43
18	.68582	.72777	.94235	.0612	.3740	.4581	.27223	.31418	42
19	.68603	.72757	.94290	.0605	.3744	.4577	.27243	.31397	41
20	0.68624	0.72737	0.94345	1.0599	1.3748	1.4572	0.27263	0.31376	40
21	.68645	.72717	.94400	.0593	.3752	.4568	.27283	.31355	39
22	.68666	.72697	.94455	.0587	.3756	.4563	.27302	.31333	38
23	.68688	.72677	.94510	.0581	.3759	.4559	.27322	.31312	37
24	.68709	.72657	.94565	.0575	.3763	.4554	.27342	.31291	36
25	0.68730	0.72637	0.94620	1.0568	1.3767	1.4550	0.27362	0.31270	35
26	.68751	.72617	.94675	.0562	.3771	.4545	.27382	.31249	34
27	.68772	.72597	.94731	.0556	.3774	.4541	.27402	.31228	33
28	.68793	.72577	.94786	.0550	.3778	.4536	.27422	.31207	32
29	.68814	.72557	.94841	.0544	.3782	.4532	.27442	.31186	31
30	0.68835	0.72537	0.94896	1.0538	1.3786	1.4527	0.27462	0.31164	30
31	.68856	.72517	.94952	.0532	.3790	.4523	.27482	.31143	29
32	.68878	.72497	.95007	.0525	.3794	.4518	.27503	.31122	28
33	.68899	.72477	.95062	.0519	.3797	.4514	.27523	.31101	27
34	.68920	.72457	.95118	.0513	.3801	.4510	.27543	.31080	26
35	0.68941	0.72437	0.95173	1.0507	1.3805	1.4505	0.27563	0.31059	25
36	.68962	.72417	.95229	.0501	.3809	.4501	.27583	.31038	24
37	.68983	.72397	.95284	.0495	.3813	.4496	.27603	.31017	23
38	.69004	.72377	.95340	.0489	.3816	.4492	.27623	.30996	22
39	.69025	.72357	.95395	.0483	.3820	.4487	.27643	.30975	21
40	0.69046	0.72337	0.95451	1.0476	1.3824	1.4483	0.27663	0.30954	20
41	.69067	.72317	.95506	.0470	.3828	.4479	.27683	.30933	19
42	.69088	.72297	.95562	.0464	.3832	.4474	.27703	.30912	18
43	.69109	.72277	.95618	.0458	.3836	.4470	.27723	.30891	17
44	.69130	.72256	.95673	.0452	.3839	.4465	.27743	.30870	16
45	0.69151	0.72236	0.95729	1.0446	1.3843	1.4461	0.27764	0.30849	15
46	.69172	.72216	.95785	.0440	.3847	.4457	.27784	.30828	14
47	.69193	.72196	.95841	.0434	.3851	.4452	.27804	.30807	13
48	.69214	.72176	.95896	.0428	.3855	.4448	.27824	.30786	12
49	.69235	.72156	.95952	.0422	.3859	.4443	.27844	.30765	11
50	0.69256	0.72136	0.96008	1.0416	1.3863	1.4439	0.27864	0.30744	10
51	.69277	.72115	.96064	.0410	.3867	.4435	.27884	.30723	9
52	.69298	.72095	.96120	.0404	.3870	.4430	.27904	.30702	8
53	.69319	.72075	.96176	.0397	.3874	.4426	.27925	.30681	7
54	.69340	.72055	.96232	.0391	.3878	.4422	.27945	.30660	6
55	0.69361	0.72035	0.96288	1.0385	1.3882	1.4417	0.27965	0.30639	5
56	.69382	.72015	.96344	.0379	.3886	.4413	.27985	.30618	4
57	.69403	.71994	.96400	.0373	.3890	.4408	.28005	.30597	3
58	.69424	.71974	.96456	.0367	.3894	.4404	.28026	.30576	2
59	.69445	.71954	.96513	.0361	.3898	.4400	.28046	.30555	1
60	0.69466	0.71934	0.96569	1.0355	1.3902	1.4395	0.28066	0.30534	0
M	Cosine	Sine	Cotan.	Tan.	Cosec.	Secant	Vrs. Cos.	Vrs. Sin.	M

M	Sine	Cosine	Tan.	Cotan.	Secant	Cosec.	Vrs. Sin.	Vrs. Cos.	M
0	0.69466	0.71934	0.96569	1.0355	1.3902	1.4395	0.28066	0.30534	60
1	.69487	.71914	.96625	.0349	.3905	.4391	.28086	.30513	59
2	.69508	.71893	.96681	.0343	.3909	.4387	.28106	.30492	58
3	.69528	.71873	.96738	.0337	.3913	.4382	.28127	.30471	57
4	.69549	.71853	.96794	.0331	.3917	.4378	.28147	.30450	56
5	0.69570	0.71833	0.96850	1.0325	1.3921	1.4374	0.28167	0.30430	55
6	.69591	.71813	.96907	.0319	.3925	.4370	.28187	.30409	54
7	.69612	.71792	.96963	.0313	.3929	.4365	.28208	.30388	53
8	.69633	.71772	.97020	.0307	.3933	.4361	.28228	.30367	52
9	.69654	.71752	.97076	.0301	.3937	.4357	.28248	.30346	51
10	0.69675	0.71732	0.97133	1.0295	1.3941	1.4352	0.28268	0.30325	50
11	.69696	.71711	.97189	.0289	.3945	.4348	.28289	.30304	49
12	.69716	.71691	.97246	.0283	.3949	.4344	.28309	.30283	48
13	.69737	.71671	.97302	.0277	.3953	.4339	.28329	.30263	47
14	.69758	.71650	.97359	.0271	.3957	.4335	.28349	.30242	46
15	0.69779	0.71630	0.97416	1.0265	1.3960	1.4331	0.28370	0.30221	45
16	.69800	.71610	.97472	.0259	.3964	.4327	.28390	.30200	44
17	.69821	.71589	.97529	.0253	.3968	.4322	.28410	.30179	43
18	.69841	.71569	.97586	.0247	.3972	.4318	.28431	.30158	42
19	.69862	.71549	.97643	.0241	.3976	.4314	.28451	.30138	41
20	0.69883	0.71529	0.97700	1.0235	1.3980	1.4310	0.28471	0.30117	40
21	.69904	.71508	.97756	.0229	.3984	.4305	.28492	.30096	39
22	.69925	.71488	.97813	.0223	.3988	.4301	.28512	.30075	38
23	.69945	.71468	.97870	.0218	.3992	.4297	.28532	.30054	37
24	.69966	.71447	.97927	.0212	.3996	.4292	.28553	.30034	36
25	0.69987	0.71427	0.97984	1.0206	1.4000	1.4288	0.28573	0.30013	35
26	.70008	.71406	.98041	.0200	.4004	.4284	.28593	.29992	34
27	.70029	.71386	.98098	.0194	.4008	.4280	.28614	.29971	33
28	.70049	.71366	.98155	.0188	.4012	.4276	.28634	.29950	32
29	.70070	.71345	.98212	.0182	.4016	.4271	.28654	.29930	31
30	0.70091	0.71325	0.98270	1.0176	1.4020	1.4267	0.28675	0.29909	30
31	.70112	.71305	.98327	.0170	.4024	.4263	.28695	.29888	29
32	.70132	.71284	.98384	.0164	.4028	.4259	.28716	.29867	28
33	.70153	.71264	.98441	.0158	.4032	.4254	.28736	.29847	27
34	.70174	.71243	.98499	.0152	.4036	.4250	.28756	.29826	26
35	0.70194	0.71223	0.98556	1.0146	1.4040	1.4246	0.28777	0.29805	25
36	.70215	.71203	.98613	.0141	.4044	.4242	.28797	.29785	24
37	.70236	.71182	.98671	.0135	.4048	.4238	.28818	.29764	23
38	.70257	.71162	.98728	.0129	.4052	.4233	.28838	.29743	22
39	.70277	.71141	.98786	.0123	.4056	.4229	.28859	.29722	21
40	0.70298	0.71121	0.98843	1.0117	1.4060	1.4225	0.28879	0.29702	20
41	.70319	.71100	.98901	.0111	.4065	.4221	.28899	.29681	19
42	.70339	.71080	.98958	.0105	.4069	.4217	.28920	.29660	18
43	.70360	.71059	.99016	.0099	.4073	.4212	.28940	.29640	17
44	.70381	.71039	.99073	.0093	.4077	.4208	.28961	.29619	16
45	0.70401	0.71018	0.99131	1.0088	1.4081	1.4204	0.28981	0.29598	15
46	.70422	.70998	.99189	.0082	.4085	.4200	.29002	.29578	14
47	.70443	.70977	.99246	.0076	.4089	.4196	.29022	.29557	13
48	.70463	.70957	.99304	.0070	.4093	.4192	.29043	.29536	12
49	.70484	.70936	.99362	.0064	.4097	.4188	.29063	.29516	11
50	0.70505	0.70916	0.99420	1.0058	1.4101	1.4183	0.29084	0.29495	10
51	.70525	.70895	.99478	.0052	.4105	.4179	.29104	.29475	9
52	.70546	.70875	.99536	.0047	.4109	.4175	.29125	.29454	8
53	.70566	.70854	.99593	.0041	.4113	.4171	.29145	.29433	7
54	.70587	.70834	.99651	.0035	.4117	.4167	.29166	.29413	6
55	0.70608	0.70813	0.99709	1.0029	1.4122	1.4163	0.29186	0.29392	5
56	.70628	.70793	.99767	.0023	.4126	.4159	.29207	.29372	4
57	.70649	.70772	.99826	.0017	.4130	.4154	.29228	.29351	3
58	.70669	.70752	.99884	.0012	.4134	.4150	.29248	.29330	2
59	.70690	.70731	.99942	.0006	.4138	.4146	.29269	.29310	1
60	0.70711	0.70711	1.00000	1.0000	1.4142	1.4142	0.29289	0.29289	0
M	Cosine	Sine	Cotan.	Tan.	Cosec.	Secant	Vrs. Cos.	Vrs. Sin.	M

Use of Logarithms in Solving Triangles

The following tables "Logarithms of Trigonometrical Functions" may be used in the solution of triangles. The calculations are worked out in the same manner as with logarithms in general. In these tables, the characteristic is given in all cases, together with the mantissa. The complete logarithm of the functions, therefore, is found directly from the tables; however, as the values of the natural functions of sines and cosines, and of tangents for angles less than 45 degrees, are always less than 1, the characteristics would always be negative for these functions. In order to avoid these negative characteristics, the logarithm, as generally given, has had 10 added to its value; consequently, the actual value of the logarithm for "cosine 3 degrees," for example, is 9.99940 − 10.

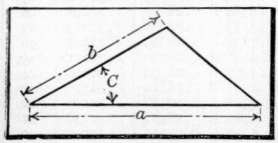

When using these logarithms in calculations with other logarithms, the calculations can be carried out exactly as explained under "LOGARITHMS." When writing down the logarithm taken from the tables of "Logarithms of Trigonometrical Functions," − 10 must be written after the value shown in the table if the computations are to be carried forward correctly. The examples which follow show the method of procedure.

Example. — Find the area of a triangle where the lengths of two sides are 53 and 82 inches, and the angle between them is 30 degrees.

The area is found by the formula (see accompanying illustration):

$$\text{Area} = \frac{a \times b \times \sin C}{2} = \frac{53 \times 82 \times \sin 30°}{2}$$

The logarithms of the numbers 53 and 82 are obtained from the regular tables in the usual manner. The logarithm for the sine of 30 degrees, as given in the table of "Logarithms of Trigonometrical Functions" is 9.69897 which, as previously explained, is written as 9.69897 − 10. The logarithms of the factors in the numerator are first added together and then the logarithm of the factor in the denominator is subtracted from their sum, as explained in the section on LOGARITHMS. (See "Division by Logarithms.") Proceed now to find the logarithm of the area.

First step: log 53   =   1.72428   Second step: 13.33706 − 10

            log 82   =   1.91381   −log 2 =   −0.30103

            log sin 30° =   9.69897 − 10   13.03603 − 10

                        13.33706 − 10   or   3.03603

The logarithm of the area thus is 3.03603, and from a logarithmic table it is found, by interpolation, that the area equals 1086.5 square inches.

Angles A and C and side a in a triangle are known. (See table "Solution of Oblique-angled Triangles.") $A = 37° 42'$; $C = 68° 12'$; $a = 12$ inches. Find side c.

$$c = \frac{a \times \sin C}{\sin A} = \frac{12 \times \sin 68° 12'}{\sin 37° 42'}$$

The solution is as follows:

            log 12   =   1.07918

            log sin 68° 12′   =   9.96778 − 10

                                  11.04696 − 10

     −log sin 37° 42′ = −(9.78642 − 10)

           Thus, log c =   1.26054, and hence, c = 18.22 inches.

M	Sine	Cosine	Tangent	Cotangent	Secant	Cosecant	M
0	Inf. Neg.	10.00000	Inf. Neg.	Infinite	10.00000	Infinite	60
1	6.46373	.00000	6.46373	13.53627	.00000	13.53627	59
2	.76476	.00000	.76476	.23524	.00000	.23524	58
3	.94085	.00000	.94085	.05915	.00000	.05915	57
4	7.06579	.00000	7.06579	12.93421	.00000	12.93421	56
5	7.16270	10.00000	7.16270	12.83730	10.00000	12.83730	55
6	.24188	.00000	.24188	.75812	.00000	.75812	54
7	.30882	.00000	.30882	.69118	.00000	.69118	53
8	.36682	.00000	.36682	.63318	.00000	.63318	52
9	.41797	.00000	.41797	.58203	.00000	.58203	51
10	7.46373	10.00000	7.46373	12.53627	10.00000	12.53627	50
11	.50512	.00000	.50512	.49488	.00000	.49488	49
12	.54291	.00000	.54291	.45709	.00000	.45709	48
13	.57767	.00000	.57767	.42233	.00000	.42233	47
14	.60985	.00000	.60986	.39014	.00000	.39015	46
15	7.63982	10.00000	7.63982	12.36018	10.00000	12.36018	45
16	.66784	.00000	.66785	.33215	.00000	.33216	44
17	.69417	9.99999	.69418	.30582	.00000	.30583	43
18	.71900	.99999	.71900	.28100	.00001	.28100	42
19	.74248	.99999	.74248	.25752	.00001	.25752	41
20	7.76475	9.99999	7.76476	12.23524	10.00001	12.23525	40
21	.78594	.99999	.78595	.21405	.00001	.21406	39
22	.80615	.99999	.80615	.19385	.00001	.19385	38
23	.82545	.99999	.82546	.17454	.00001	.17455	37
24	.84393	.99999	.84394	.15606	.00001	.15607	36
25	7.86166	9.99999	7.86167	12.13833	10.00001	12.13834	35
26	.87870	.99999	.87871	.12129	.00001	.12130	34
27	.89509	.99999	.89510	.10490	.00001	.10491	33
28	.91088	.99999	.91089	.08911	.00001	.08912	32
29	.92612	.99998	.92613	.07387	.00002	.07388	31
30	7.94084	9.99998	7.94086	12.05914	10.00002	12.05916	30
31	.95508	.99998	.95510	.04490	.00002	.04492	29
32	.96887	.99998	.96889	.03111	.00002	.03113	28
33	.98223	.99998	.98225	.01775	.00002	.01777	27
34	.99520	.99998	.99522	.00478	.00002	.00480	26
35	8.00779	9.99998	8.00781	11.99219	10.00002	11.99221	25
36	.02002	.99998	.02004	.97996	.00002	.97998	24
37	.03192	.99997	.03194	.96806	.00003	.96808	23
38	.04350	.99997	.04353	.95647	.00003	.95650	22
39	.05478	.99997	.05481	.94519	.00003	.94522	21
40	8.06578	9.99997	8.06581	11.93419	10.00003	11.93422	20
41	.07650	.99997	.07653	.92347	.00003	.92350	19
42	.08696	.99997	.08700	.91300	.00003	.91304	18
43	.09718	.99997	.09722	.90278	.00003	.90282	17
44	.10717	.99996	.10720	.89280	.00004	.89283	16
45	8.11693	9.99996	8.11696	11.88304	10.00004	11.88307	15
46	.12647	.99996	.12651	.87349	.00004	.87353	14
47	.13581	.99996	.13585	.86415	.00004	.86419	13
48	.14495	.99996	.14500	.85500	.00004	.85505	12
49	.15391	.99996	.15395	.84605	.00004	.84609	11
50	8.16268	9.99995	8.16273	11.83727	10.00005	11.83732	10
51	.17128	.99995	.17133	.82867	.00005	.82872	9
52	.17971	.99995	.17976	.82024	.00005	.82029	8
53	.18798	.99995	.18804	.81196	.00005	.81202	7
54	.19610	.99995	.19616	.80384	.00005	.80390	6
55	8.20407	9.99994	8.20413	11.79587	10.00006	11.79593	5
56	.21189	.99994	.21195	.78805	.00006	.78811	4
57	.21958	.99994	.21964	.78036	.00006	.78042	3
58	.22713	.99994	.22720	.77280	.00006	.77287	2
59	.23456	.99994	.23462	.76538	.00006	.76544	1
60	8.24186	9.99993	8.24192	11.75808	10.00007	11.75814	0

M	Cosine	Sine	Cotangent	Tangent	Cosecant	Secant	M

M	Sine	Cosine	Tangent	Cotangent	Secant	Cosecant	M
0	8.24186	9.99993	8.24192	11.75808	10.00007	11.75814	60
1	.24903	.99993	.24910	.75090	.00007	.75097	59
2	.25609	.99993	.25616	.74384	.00007	.74391	58
3	.26304	.99993	.26312	.73688	.00007	.73696	57
4	.26988	.99992	.26996	.73004	.00008	.73012	56
5	8.27661	9.99992	8.27669	11.72331	10.00008	11.72339	55
6	.28324	.99992	.28332	.71668	.00008	.71676	54
7	.28977	.99992	.28986	.71014	.00008	.71023	53
8	.29621	.99992	.29629	.70371	.00008	.70379	52
9	.30255	.99991	.30263	.69737	.00009	.69745	51
10	8.30879	9.99991	8.30888	11.69112	10.00009	11.69121	50
11	.31495	.99991	.31505	.68495	.00009	.68505	49
12	.32103	.99990	.32112	.67888	.00010	.67897	48
13	.32702	.99990	.32711	.67289	.00010	.67298	47
14	.33292	.99990	.33302	.66698	.00010	.66708	46
15	8.33875	9.99990	8.33886	11.66114	10.00010	11.66125	45
16	.34450	.99989	.34461	.65539	.00011	.65550	44
17	.35018	.99989	.35029	.64971	.00011	.64982	43
18	.35578	.99989	.35590	.64410	.00011	.64422	42
19	.36131	.99989	.36143	.63857	.00011	.63869	41
20	8.36678	9.99988	8.36689	11.63311	10.00012	11.63322	40
21	.37217	.99988	.37229	.62771	.00012	.62783	39
22	.37750	.99988	.37762	.62238	.00012	.62250	38
23	.38276	.99987	.38289	.61711	.00013	.61724	37
24	.38796	.99987	.38809	.61191	.00013	.61204	36
25	8.39310	9.99987	8.39323	11.60677	10.00013	11.60690	35
26	.39818	.99986	.39832	.60168	.00014	.60182	34
27	.40320	.99986	.40334	.59666	.00014	.59680	33
28	.40816	.99986	.40830	.59170	.00014	.59184	32
29	.41307	.99985	.41321	.58679	.00015	.58693	31
30	8.41792	9.99985	8.41807	11.58193	10.00015	11.58208	30
31	.42272	.99985	.42287	.57713	.00015	.57728	29
32	.42746	.99984	.42762	.57238	.00016	.57254	28
33	.43216	.99984	.43232	.56768	.00016	.56784	27
34	.43680	.99984	.43696	.56304	.00016	.56320	26
35	8.44139	9.99983	8.44156	11.55844	10.00017	11.55861	25
36	.44594	.99983	.44611	.55389	.00017	.55406	24
37	.45044	.99983	.45061	.54939	.00017	.54956	23
38	.45489	.99982	.45507	.54493	.00018	.54511	22
39	.45930	.99982	.45948	.54052	.00018	.54070	21
40	8.46366	9.99982	8.46385	11.53615	10.00018	11.53634	20
41	.46799	.99981	.46817	.53183	.00019	.53201	19
42	.47226	.99981	.47245	.52755	.00019	.52774	18
43	.47650	.99981	.47669	.52331	.00019	.52350	17
44	.48069	.99980	.48089	.51911	.00020	.51931	16
45	8.48485	9.99980	8.48505	11.51495	10.00020	11.51515	15
46	.48896	.99979	.48917	.51083	.00021	.51104	14
47	.49304	.99979	.49325	.50675	.00021	.50696	13
48	.49708	.99979	.49729	.50271	.00021	.50292	12
49	.50108	.99978	.50130	.49870	.00022	.49892	11
50	8.50504	9.99978	8.50527	11.49473	10.00022	11.49496	10
51	.50897	.99977	.50920	.49080	.00023	.49103	9
52	.51287	.99977	.51310	.48690	.00023	.48713	8
53	.51673	.99977	.51696	.48304	.00023	.48327	7
54	.52055	.99976	.52079	.47921	.00024	.47945	6
55	8.52434	9.99976	8.52459	11.47541	10.00024	11.47566	5
56	.52810	.99975	.52835	.47165	.00025	.47190	4
57	.53183	.99975	.53208	.46792	.00025	.46817	3
58	.53552	.99974	.53578	.46422	.00026	.46448	2
59	.53919	.99974	.53945	.46055	.00026	.46081	1
60	8.54282	9.99974	8.54308	11.45692	10.00026	11.45718	0

M	Cosine	Sine	Cotangent	Tangent	Cosecant	Secant	M

M	Sine	Cosine	Tangent	Cotangent	Secant	Cosecant	M
0	8.54282	9.99974	8.54308	11.45692	10.00026	11.45718	60
1	.54642	.99973	.54669	.45331	.00027	.45358	59
2	.54999	.99973	.55027	.44973	.00027	.45001	58
3	.55354	.99972	.55382	.44618	.00028	.44646	57
4	.55705	.99972	.55734	.44266	.00028	.44295	56
5	8.56054	9.99971	8.56083	11.43917	10.00029	11.43946	55
6	.56400	.99971	.56429	.43571	.00029	.43600	54
7	.56743	.99970	.56773	.43227	.00030	.43257	53
8	.57084	.99970	.57114	.42886	.00030	.42916	52
9	.57421	.99969	.57452	.42548	.00031	.42579	51
10	8.57757	9.99969	8.57788	11.42212	10.00031	11.42243	50
11	.58089	.99968	.58121	.41879	.00032	.41911	49
12	.58419	.99968	.58451	.41549	.00032	.41581	48
13	.58747	.99967	.58779	.41221	.00033	.41253	47
14	.59072	.99967	.59105	.40895	.00033	.40928	46
15	8.59395	9.99967	8.59428	11.40572	10.00033	11.40605	45
16	.59715	.99966	.59749	.40251	.00034	.40285	44
17	.60033	.99966	.60068	.39932	.00034	.39967	43
18	.60349	.99965	.60384	.39616	.00035	.39651	42
19	.60662	.99964	.60698	.39302	.00036	.39338	41
20	8.60973	9.99964	8.61009	11.38991	10.00036	11.39027	40
21	.61282	.99963	.61319	.38681	.00037	.38718	39
22	.61589	.99963	.61626	.38374	.00037	.38411	38
23	.61894	.99962	.61931	.38069	.00038	.38106	37
24	.62196	.99962	.62234	.37766	.00038	.37804	36
25	8.62497	9.99961	8.62535	11.37465	10.00039	11.37503	35
26	.62795	.99961	.62834	.37166	.00039	.37205	34
27	.63091	.99960	.63131	.36869	.00040	.36909	33
28	.63385	.99960	.63426	.36574	.00040	.36615	32
29	.63678	.99959	.63718	.36282	.00041	.36322	31
30	8.63968	9.99959	8.64009	11.35991	10.00041	11.36032	30
31	.64256	.99958	.64298	.35702	.00042	.35744	29
32	.64543	.99958	.64585	.35415	.00042	.35457	28
33	.64827	.99957	.64870	.35130	.00043	.35173	27
34	.65110	.99956	.65154	.34846	.00044	.34890	26
35	8.65391	9.99956	8.65435	11.34565	10.00044	11.34609	25
36	.65670	.99955	.65715	.34285	.00045	.34330	24
37	.65947	.99955	.65993	.34007	.00045	.34053	23
38	.66223	.99954	.66269	.33731	.00046	.33777	22
39	.66497	.99954	.66543	.33457	.00046	.33503	21
40	8.66769	9.99953	8.66816	11.33184	10.00047	11.33231	20
41	.67039	.99952	.67087	.32913	.00048	.32961	19
42	.67308	.99952	.67356	.32644	.00048	.32692	18
43	.67575	.99951	.67624	.32376	.00049	.32425	17
44	.67841	.99951	.67890	.32110	.00049	.32159	16
45	8.68104	9.99950	8.68154	11.31846	10.00050	11.31896	15
46	.68367	.99949	.68417	.31583	.00051	.31633	14
47	.68627	.99949	.68678	.31322	.00051	.31373	13
48	.68886	.99948	.68938	.31062	.00052	.31114	12
49	.69144	.99948	.69196	.30804	.00052	.30856	11
50	8.69400	9.99947	8.69453	11.30547	10.00053	11.30600	10
51	.69654	.99946	.69708	.30292	.00054	.30346	9
52	.69907	.99946	.69962	.30038	.00054	.30093	8
53	.70159	.99945	.70214	.29786	.00055	.29841	7
54	.70409	.99944	.70465	.29535	.00056	.29591	6
55	8.70658	9.99944	8.70714	11.29286	10.00056	11.29342	5
56	.70905	.99943	.70962	.29038	.00057	.29095	4
57	.71151	.99942	.71208	.28792	.00058	.28849	3
58	.71395	.99942	.71453	.28547	.00058	.28605	2
59	.71638	.99941	.71697	.28303	.00059	.28362	1
60	8.71880	9.99940	8.71940	11.28060	10.00060	11.28120	0

| M | Cosine | Sine | Cotangent | Tangent | Cosecant | Secant | M |

M	Sine	Cosine	Tangent	Cotangent	Secant	Cosecant	M
0	8.71880	9.99940	8.71940	11.28060	10.00060	11.28120	60
1	.72120	.99940	.72181	.27819	.00060	.27880	59
2	.72359	.99939	.72420	.27580	.00061	.27641	58
3	.72597	.99938	.72659	.27341	.00062	.27403	57
4	.72834	.99938	.72896	.27104	.00062	.27166	56
5	8.73069	9.99937	8.73132	11.26868	10.00063	11.26931	55
6	.73303	.99936	.73366	.26634	.00064	.26697	54
7	.73535	.99936	.73600	.26400	.00064	.26465	53
8	.73767	.99935	.73832	.26168	.00065	.26233	52
9	.73997	.99934	.74063	.25937	.00066	.26003	51
10	8.74226	9.99934	8.74292	11.25708	10.00066	11.25774	50
11	.74454	.99933	.74521	.25479	.00067	.25546	49
12	.74680	.99932	.74748	.25252	.00068	.25320	48
13	.74906	.99932	.74974	.25026	.00068	.25094	47
14	.75130	.99931	.75199	.24801	.00069	.24870	46
15	8.75353	9.99930	8.75423	11.24577	10.00070	11.24647	45
16	.75575	.99929	.75645	.24355	.00071	.24425	44
17	.75795	.99929	.75867	.24133	.00071	.24205	43
18	.76015	.99928	.76087	.23913	.00072	.23985	42
19	.76234	.99927	.76306	.23694	.00073	.23766	41
20	8.76451	9.99926	8.76525	11.23475	10.00074	11.23549	40
21	.76667	.99926	.76742	.23258	.00074	.23333	39
22	.76883	.99925	.76958	.23042	.00075	.23117	38
23	.77097	.99924	.77173	.22827	.00076	.22903	37
24	.77310	.99923	.77387	.22613	.00077	.22690	36
25	8.77522	9.99923	8.77600	11.22400	10.00077	11.22478	35
26	.77733	.99922	.77811	.22189	.00078	.22267	34
27	.77943	.99921	.78022	.21978	.00079	.22057	33
28	.78152	.99920	.78232	.21768	.00080	.21848	32
29	.78360	.99920	.78441	.21559	.00080	.21640	31
30	8.78568	9.99919	8.78649	11.21351	10.00081	11.21432	30
31	.78774	.99918	.78855	.21145	.00082	.21226	29
32	.78979	.99917	.79061	.20939	.00083	.21021	28
33	.79183	.99917	.79266	.20734	.00083	.20817	27
34	.79386	.99916	.79470	.20530	.00084	.20614	26
35	8.79588	9.99915	8.79673	11.20327	10.00085	11.20412	25
36	.79789	.99914	.79875	.20125	.00086	.20211	24
37	.79990	.99913	.80076	.19924	.00087	.20010	23
38	.80189	.99913	.80277	.19723	.00087	.19811	22
39	.80388	.99912	.80476	.19524	.00088	.19612	21
40	8.80585	9.99911	8.80674	11.19326	10.00089	11.19415	20
41	.80782	.99910	.80872	.19128	.00090	.19218	19
42	.80978	.99909	.81068	.18932	.00091	.19022	18
43	.81173	.99909	.81264	.18736	.00091	.18827	17
44	.81367	.99908	.81459	.18541	.00092	.18633	16
45	8.81560	9.99907	8.81653	11.18347	10.00093	11.18440	15
46	.81752	.99906	.81846	.18154	.00094	.18248	14
47	.81944	.99905	.82038	.17962	.00095	.18056	13
48	.82134	.99904	.82230	.17770	.00096	.17866	12
49	.82324	.99904	.82420	.17580	.00096	.17676	11
50	8.82513	9.99903	8.82610	11.17390	10.00097	11.17487	10
51	.82701	.99902	.82799	.17201	.00098	.17299	9
52	.82888	.99901	.82987	.17013	.00099	.17112	8
53	.83075	.99900	.83175	.16825	.00100	.16925	7
54	.83261	.99899	.83361	.16639	.00101	.16739	6
55	8.83446	9.99898	8.83547	11.16453	10.00102	11.16554	5
56	.83630	.99898	.83732	.16268	.00102	.16370	4
57	.83813	.99897	.83916	.16084	.00103	.16187	3
58	.83996	.99896	.84100	.15900	.00104	.16004	2
59	.84177	.99895	.84282	.15718	.00105	.15823	1
60	8.84358	9.99894	8.84464	11.15536	10.00106	11.15642	0

| M | Cosine | Sine | Cotangent | Tangent | Cosecant | Secant | M |

M	Sine	Cosine	Tangent	Cotangent	Secant	Cosecant	M
0	8.84358	9.99894	8.84464	11.15536	10.00106	11.15642	60
1	.84539	.99893	.84646	.15354	.00107	.15461	59
2	.84718	.99892	.84826	.15174	.00108	.15282	58
3	.84897	.99891	.85006	.14994	.00109	.15103	57
4	.85075	.99891	.85185	.14815	.00109	.14925	56
5	8.85252	9.99890	8.85363	11.14637	10.00110	11.14748	55
6	.85429	.99889	.85540	.14460	.00111	.14571	54
7	.85605	.99888	.85717	.14283	.00112	.14395	53
8	.85780	.99887	.85893	.14107	.00113	.14220	52
9	.85955	.99886	.86069	.13931	.00114	.14045	51
10	8.86128	9.99885	8.86243	11.13757	10.00115	11.13872	50
11	.86301	.99884	.86417	.13583	.00116	.13699	49
12	.86474	.99883	.86591	.13409	.00117	.13526	48
13	.86645	.99882	.86763	.13237	.00118	.13355	47
14	.86816	.99881	.86935	.13065	.00119	.13184	46
15	8.86987	9.99880	8.87106	11.12894	10.00120	11.13013	45
16	.87156	.99879	.87277	.12723	.00121	.12844	44
17	.87325	.99879	.87447	.12553	.00121	.12675	43
18	.87494	.99878	.87616	.12384	.00122	.12506	42
19	.87661	.99877	.87785	.12215	.00123	.12339	41
20	8.87829	9.99876	8.87953	11.12047	10.00124	11.12171	40
21	.87995	.99875	.88120	.11880	.00125	.12005	39
22	.88161	.99874	.88287	.11713	.00126	.11839	38
23	.88326	.99873	.88453	.11547	.00127	.11674	37
24	.88490	.99872	.88618	.11382	.00128	.11510	36
25	8.88654	9.99871	8.88783	11.11217	10.00129	11.11346	35
26	.88817	.99870	.88948	.11052	.00130	.11183	34
27	.88980	.99869	.89111	.10889	.00131	.11020	33
28	.89142	.99868	.89274	.10726	.00132	.10858	32
29	.89304	.99867	.89437	.10563	.00133	.10696	31
30	8.89464	9.99866	8.89598	11.10402	10.00134	11.10536	30
31	.89625	.99865	.89760	.10240	.00135	.10375	29
32	.89784	.99864	.89920	.10080	.00136	.10216	28
33	.89943	.99863	.90080	.09920	.00137	.10057	27
34	.90102	.99862	.90240	.09760	.00138	.09898	26
35	8.90260	9.99861	8.90399	11.09601	10.00139	11.09740	25
36	.90417	.99860	.90557	.09443	.00140	.09583	24
37	.90574	.99859	.90715	.09285	.00141	.09426	23
38	.90730	.99858	.90872	.09128	.00142	.09270	22
39	.90885	.99857	.91029	.08971	.00143	.09115	21
40	8.91040	9.99856	8.91185	11.08815	10.00144	11.08960	20
41	.91195	.99855	.91340	.08660	.00145	.08805	19
42	.91349	.99854	.91495	.08505	.00146	.08651	18
43	.91502	.99853	.91650	.08350	.00147	.08498	17
44	.91655	.99852	.91803	.08197	.00148	.08345	16
45	8.91807	9.99851	8.91957	11.08043	10.00149	11.08193	15
46	.91959	.99850	.92110	.07890	.00150	.08041	14
47	.92110	.99848	.92262	.07738	.00152	.07890	13
48	.92261	.99847	.92414	.07586	.00153	.07739	12
49	.92411	.99846	.92565	.07435	.00154	.07589	11
50	8.92561	9.99845	8.92716	11.07284	10.00155	11.07439	10
51	.92710	.99844	.92866	.07134	.00156	.07290	9
52	.92859	.99843	.93016	.06984	.00157	.07141	8
53	.93007	.99842	.93165	.06835	.00158	.06993	7
54	.93154	.99841	.93313	.06687	.00159	.06846	6
55	8.93301	9.99840	8.93462	11.06538	10.00160	11.06699	5
56	.93448	.99839	.93609	.06391	.00161	.06552	4
57	.93594	.99838	.93756	.06244	.00162	.06406	3
58	.93740	.99837	.93903	.06097	.00163	.06260	2
59	.93885	.99836	.94049	.05951	.00164	.06115	1
60	8.94030	9.99834	8.94195	11.05805	10.00166	11.05970	0
M	Cosine	Sine	Cotangent	Tangent	Cosecant	Secant	M

5°　Logarithms of Trigonometrical Functions　174°

M	Sine	Cosine	Tangent	Cotangent	Secant	Cosecant	M
0	8.94030	9.99834	8.94195	11.05805	10.00166	11.05970	60
1	.94174	.99833	.94340	.05660	.00167	.05826	59
2	.94317	.99832	.94485	.05515	.00168	.05683	58
3	.94461	.99831	.94630	.05370	.00169	.05539	57
4	.94603	.99830	.94773	.05227	.00170	.05397	56
5	8.94746	9.99829	8.94917	11.05083	10.00171	11.05254	55
6	.94887	.99828	.95060	.04940	.00172	.05113	54
7	.95029	.99827	.95202	.04798	.00173	.04971	53
8	.95170	.99825	.95344	.04656	.00175	.04830	52
9	.95310	.99824	.95486	.04514	.00176	.04690	51
10	8.95450	9.99823	8.95627	11.04373	10.00177	11.04550	50
11	.95589	.99822	.95767	.04233	.00178	.04411	49
12	.95728	.99821	.95908	.04092	.00179	.04272	48
13	.95867	.99820	.96047	.03953	.00180	.04133	47
14	.96005	.99819	.96187	.03813	.00181	.03995	46
15	8.96143	9.99817	8.96325	11.03675	10.00183	11.03857	45
16	.96280	.99816	.96464	.03536	.00184	.03720	44
17	.96417	.99815	.96602	.03398	.00185	.03583	43
18	.96553	.99814	.96739	.03261	.00186	.03447	42
19	.96689	.99813	.96877	.03123	.00187	.03311	41
20	8.96825	9.99812	8.97013	11.02987	10.00188	11.03175	40
21	.96960	.99810	.97150	.02850	.00190	.03040	39
22	.97095	.99809	.97285	.02715	.00191	.02905	38
23	.97229	.99808	.97421	.02579	.00192	.02771	37
24	.97363	.99807	.97556	.02444	.00193	.02637	36
25	8.97496	9.99806	8.97691	11.02309	10.00194	11.02504	35
26	.97629	.99804	.97825	.02175	.00196	.02371	34
27	.97762	.99803	.97959	.02041	.00197	.02238	33
28	.97894	.99802	.98092	.01908	.00198	.02106	32
29	.98026	.99801	.98225	.01775	.00199	.01974	31
30	8.98157	9.99800	8.98358	11.01642	10.00200	11.01843	30
31	.98288	.99798	.98490	.01510	.00202	.01712	29
32	.98419	.99797	.98622	.01378	.00203	.01581	28
33	.98549	.99796	.98753	.01247	.00204	.01451	27
34	.98679	.99795	.98884	.01116	.00205	.01321	26
35	8.98808	9.99793	8.99015	11.00985	10.00207	11.01192	25
36	.98937	.99792	.99145	.00855	.00208	.01063	24
37	.99066	.99791	.99275	.00725	.00209	.00934	23
38	.99194	.99790	.99405	.00595	.00210	.00806	22
39	.99322	.99788	.99534	.00466	.00212	.00678	21
40	8.99450	9.99787	8.99662	11.00338	10.00213	11.00550	20
41	.99577	.99786	.99791	.00209	.00214	.00423	19
42	.99704	.99785	.99919	.00081	.00215	.00296	18
43	.99830	.99783	9.00046	10.99954	.00217	.00170	17
44	.99956	.99782	.00174	.99826	.00218	.00044	16
45	9.00082	9.99781	9.00301	10.99699	10.00219	10.99918	15
46	.00207	.99780	.00427	.99573	.00220	.99793	14
47	.00332	.99778	.00553	.99447	.00222	.99668	13
48	.00456	.99777	.00679	.99321	.00223	.99544	12
49	.00581	.99776	.00805	.99195	.00224	.99419	11
50	9.00704	9.99775	9.00930	10.99070	10.00225	10.99296	10
51	.00828	.99773	.01055	.98945	.00227	.99172	9
52	.00951	.99772	.01179	.98821	.00228	.99049	8
53	.01074	.99771	.01303	.98697	.00229	.98926	7
54	.01196	.99769	.01427	.98573	.00231	.98804	6
55	9.01318	9.99768	9.01550	10.98450	10.00232	10.98682	5
56	.01440	.99767	.01673	.98327	.00233	.98560	4
57	.01561	.99765	.01796	.98204	.00235	.98439	3
58	.01682	.99764	.01918	.98082	.00236	.98318	2
59	.01803	.99763	.02040	.97960	.00237	.98197	1
60	9.01923	9.99761	9.02162	10.97838	10.00239	10.98077	0
M	Cosine	Sine	Cotangent	Tangent	Cosecant	Secant	M

M	Sine	Cosine	Tangent	Cotangent	Secant	Cosecant	M
0	9.01923	9.99761	9.02162	10.97838	10.00239	10.98077	60
1	.02043	.99760	.02283	.97717	.00240	.97957	59
2	.02163	.99759	.02404	.97596	.00241	.97837	58
3	.02283	.99757	.02525	.97475	.00243	.97717	57
4	.02402	.99756	.02645	.97355	.00244	.97598	56
5	9.02520	9.99755	9.02766	10.97234	10.00245	10.97480	55
6	.02639	.99753	.02885	.97115	.00247	.97361	54
7	.02757	.99752	.03005	.96995	.00248	.97243	53
8	.02874	.99751	.03124	.96876	.00249	.97126	52
9	.02992	.99749	.03242	.96758	.00251	.97008	51
10	9.03109	9.99748	9.03361	10.96639	10.00252	10.96891	50
11	.03226	.99747	.03479	.96521	.00253	.96774	49
12	.03342	.99745	.03597	.96403	.00255	.96658	48
13	.03458	.99744	.03714	.96286	.00256	.96542	47
14	.03574	.99742	.03832	.96168	.00258	.96426	46
15	9.03690	9.99741	9.03948	10.96052	10.00259	10.96310	45
16	.03805	.99740	.04065	.95935	.00260	.96195	44
17	.03920	.99738	.04181	.95819	.00262	.96080	43
18	.04034	.99737	.04297	.95703	.00263	.95966	42
19	.04149	.99736	.04413	.95587	.00264	.95851	41
20	9.04262	9.99734	9.04528	10.95472	10.00266	10.95738	40
21	.04376	.99733	.04643	.95357	.00267	.95624	39
22	.04490	.99731	.04758	.95242	.00269	.95510	38
23	.04603	.99730	.04873	.95127	.00270	.95397	37
24	.04715	.99728	.04987	.95013	.00272	.95285	36
25	9.04828	9.99727	9.05101	10.94899	10.00273	10.95172	35
26	.04940	.99726	.05214	.94786	.00274	.95060	34
27	.05052	.99724	.05328	.94672	.00276	.94948	33
28	.05164	.99723	.05441	.94559	.00277	.94836	32
29	.05275	.99721	.05553	.94447	.00279	.94725	31
30	9.05386	9.99720	9.05666	10.94334	10.00280	10.94614	30
31	.05497	.99718	.05778	.94222	.00282	.94503	29
32	.05607	.99717	.05890	.94110	.00283	.94393	28
33	.05717	.99716	.06002	.93998	.00284	.94283	27
34	.05827	.99714	.06113	.93887	.00286	.94173	26
35	9.05937	9.99713	9.06224	10.93776	10.00287	10.94063	25
36	.06046	.99711	.06335	.93665	.00289	.93954	24
37	.06155	.99710	.06445	.93555	.00290	.93845	23
38	.06264	.99708	.06556	.93444	.00292	.93736	22
39	.06372	.99707	.06666	.93334	.00293	.93628	21
40	9.06481	9.99705	9.06775	10.93225	10.00295	10.93519	20
41	.06589	.99704	.06885	.93115	.00296	.93411	19
42	.06696	.99702	.06994	.93006	.00298	.93304	18
43	.06804	.99701	.07103	.92897	.00299	.93196	17
44	.06911	.99699	.07211	.92789	.00301	.93089	16
45	9.07018	9.99698	9.07320	10.92680	10.00302	10.92982	15
46	.07124	.99696	.07428	.92572	.00304	.92876	14
47	.07231	.99695	.07536	.92464	.00305	.92769	13
48	.07337	.99693	.07643	.92357	.00307	.92663	12
49	.07442	.99692	.07751	.92249	.00308	.92558	11
50	9.07548	9.99690	9.07858	10.92142	10.00310	10.92452	10
51	.07653	.99689	.07964	.92036	.00311	.92347	9
52	.07758	.99687	.08071	.91929	.00313	.92242	8
53	.07863	.99686	.08177	.91823	.00314	.92137	7
54	.07968	.99684	.08283	.91717	.00316	.92032	6
55	9.08072	9.99683	9.08389	10.91611	10.00317	10.91928	5
56	.08176	.99681	.08495	.91505	.00319	.91824	4
57	.08280	.99680	.08600	.91400	.00320	.91720	3
58	.08383	.99678	.08705	.91295	.00322	.91617	2
59	.08486	.99677	.08810	.91190	.00323	.91514	1
60	9.08589	9.99675	9.08914	10.91086	10.00325	10.91411	0
M	Cosine	Sine	Cotangent	Tangent	Cosecant	Secant	M

M	Sine	Cosine	Tangent	Cotangent	Secant	Cosecant	M
0	9.08589	9.99675	9.08914	10.91086	10.00325	10.91411	60
1	.08692	.99674	.09019	.90981	.00326	.91308	59
2	.08795	.99672	.09123	.90877	.00328	.91205	58
3	.08897	.99670	.09227	.90773	.00330	.91103	57
4	.08999	.99669	.09330	.90670	.00331	.91001	56
5	9.09101	9.99667	9.09434	10.90566	10.00333	10.90899	55
6	.09202	.99666	.09537	.90463	.00334	.90798	54
7	.09304	.99664	.09640	.90360	.00336	.90696	53
8	.09405	.99663	.09742	.90258	.00337	.90595	52
9	.09506	.99661	.09845	.90155	.00339	.90494	51
10	9.09606	9.99659	9.09947	10.90053	10.00341	10.90394	50
11	.09707	.99658	.10049	.89951	.00342	.90293	49
12	.09807	.99656	.10150	.89850	.00344	.90193	48
13	.09907	.99655	.10252	.89748	.00345	.90093	47
14	.10006	.99653	.10353	.89647	.00347	.89994	46
15	9.10106	9.99651	9.10454	10.89546	10.00349	10.89894	45
16	.10205	.99650	.10555	.89445	.00350	.89795	44
17	.10304	.99648	.10656	.89344	.00352	.89696	43
18	.10402	.99647	.10756	.89244	.00353	.89598	42
19	.10501	.99645	.10856	.89144	.00355	.89499	41
20	9.10599	9.99643	9.10956	10.89044	10.00357	10.89401	40
21	.10697	.99642	.11056	.88944	.00358	.89303	39
22	.10795	.99640	.11155	.88845	.00360	.89205	38
23	.10893	.99638	.11254	.88746	.00362	.89107	37
24	.10990	.99637	.11353	.88647	.00363	.89010	36
25	9.11087	9.99635	9.11452	10.88548	10.00365	10.88913	35
26	.11184	.99633	.11551	.88449	.00367	.88816	34
27	.11281	.99632	.11649	.88351	.00368	.88719	33
28	.11377	.99630	.11747	.88253	.00370	.88623	32
29	.11474	.99629	.11845	.88155	.00371	.88526	31
30	9.11570	9.99627	9.11943	10.88057	10.00373	10.88430	30
31	.11666	.99625	.12040	.87960	.00375	.88334	29
32	.11761	.99624	.12138	.87862	.00376	.88239	28
33	.11857	.99622	.12235	.87765	.00378	.88143	27
34	.11952	.99620	.12332	.87668	.00380	.88048	26
35	9.12047	9.99618	9.12428	10.87572	10.00382	10.87953	25
36	.12142	.99617	.12525	.87475	.00383	.87858	24
37	.12236	.99615	.12621	.87379	.00385	.87764	23
38	.12331	.99613	.12717	.87283	.00387	.87669	22
39	.12425	.99612	.12813	.87187	.00388	.87575	21
40	9.12519	9.99610	9.12909	10.87091	10.00390	10.87481	20
41	.12612	.99608	.13004	.86996	.00392	.87388	19
42	.12706	.99607	.13099	.86901	.00393	.87294	18
43	.12799	.99605	.13194	.86806	.00395	.87201	17
44	.12892	.99603	.13289	.86711	.00397	.87108	16
45	9.12985	9.99601	9.13384	10.86616	10.00399	10.87015	15
46	.13078	.99600	.13478	.86522	.00400	.86922	14
47	.13171	.99598	.13573	.86427	.00402	.86829	13
48	.13263	.99596	.13667	.86333	.00404	.86737	12
49	.13355	.99595	.13761	.86239	.00405	.86645	11
50	9.13447	9.99593	9.13854	10.86146	10.00407	10.86553	10
51	.13539	.99591	.13948	.86052	.00409	.86461	9
52	.13630	.99589	.14041	.85959	.00411	.86370	8
53	.13722	.99588	.14134	.85866	.00412	.86278	7
54	.13813	.99586	.14227	.85773	.00414	.86187	6
55	9.13904	9.99584	9.14320	10.85680	10.00416	10.86096	5
56	.13994	.99582	.14412	.85588	.00418	.86006	4
57	.14085	.99581	.14504	.85496	.00419	.85915	3
58	.14175	.99579	.14597	.85403	.00421	.85825	2
59	.14266	.99577	.14688	.85312	.00423	.85734	1
60	9.14356	9.99575	9.14780	10.85220	10.00425	10.85644	0

M	Cosine	Sine	Cotangent	Tangent	Cosecant	Secant	M

M	Sine	Cosine	Tangent	Cotangent	Secant	Cosecant	M
0	9.14356	9.99575	9.14780	10.85220	10.00425	10.85644	60
1	.14445	.99574	.14872	.85128	.00426	.85555	59
2	.14535	.99572	.14963	.85037	.00428	.85465	58
3	.14624	.99570	.15054	.84946	.00430	.85376	57
4	.14714	.99568	.15145	.84855	.00432	.85286	56
5	9.14803	9.99566	9.15236	10.84764	10.00434	10.85197	55
6	.14891	.99565	.15327	.84673	.00435	.85109	54
7	.14980	.99563	.15417	.84583	.00437	.85020	53
8	.15069	.99561	.15508	.84492	.00439	.84931	52
9	.15157	.99559	.15598	.84402	.00441	.84843	51
10	9.15245	9.99557	9.15688	10.84312	10.00443	10.84755	50
11	.15333	.99556	.15777	.84223	.00444	.84667	49
12	.15421	.99554	.15867	.84133	.00446	.84579	48
13	.15508	.99552	.15956	.84044	.00448	.84492	47
14	.15596	.99550	.16046	.83954	.00450	.84404	46
15	9.15683	9.99548	9.16135	10.83865	10.00452	10.84317	45
16	.15770	.99546	.16224	.83776	.00454	.84230	44
17	.15857	.99545	.16312	.83688	.00455	.84143	43
18	.15944	.99543	.16401	.83599	.00457	.84056	42
19	.16030	.99541	.16489	.83511	.00459	.83970	41
20	9.16116	9.99539	9.16577	10.83423	10.00461	10.83884	40
21	.16203	.99537	.16665	.83335	.00463	.83797	39
22	.16289	.99535	.16753	.83247	.00465	.83711	38
23	.16374	.99533	.16841	.83159	.00467	.83626	37
24	.16460	.99532	.16928	.83072	.00468	.83540	36
25	9.16545	9.99530	9.17016	10.82984	10.00470	10.83455	35
26	.16631	.99528	.17103	.82897	.00472	.83369	34
27	.16716	.99526	.17190	.82810	.00474	.83284	33
28	.16801	.99524	.17277	.82723	.00476	.83199	32
29	.16886	.99522	.17363	.82637	.00478	.83114	31
30	9.16970	9.99520	9.17450	10.82550	10.00480	10.83030	30
31	.17055	.99518	.17536	.82464	.00482	.82945	29
32	.17139	.99517	.17622	.82378	.00483	.82861	28
33	.17223	.99515	.17708	.82292	.00485	.82777	27
34	.17307	.99513	.17794	.82206	.00487	.82693	26
35	9.17391	9.99511	9.17880	10.82120	10.00489	10.82609	25
36	.17474	.99509	.17965	.82035	.00491	.82526	24
37	.17558	.99507	.18051	.81949	.00493	.82442	23
38	.17641	.99505	.18136	.81864	.00495	.82359	22
39	.17724	.99503	.18221	.81779	.00497	.82276	21
40	9.17807	9.99501	9.18306	10.81694	10.00499	10.82193	20
41	.17890	.99499	.18391	.81609	.00501	.82110	19
42	.17973	.99497	.18475	.81525	.00503	.82027	18
43	.18055	.99495	.18560	.81440	.00505	.81945	17
44	.18137	.99494	.18644	.81356	.00506	.81863	16
45	9.18220	9.99492	9.18728	10.81272	10.00508	10.81780	15
46	.18302	.99490	.18812	.81188	.00510	.81698	14
47	.18383	.99488	.18896	.81104	.00512	.81617	13
48	.18465	.99486	.18979	.81021	.00514	.81535	12
49	.18547	.99484	.19063	.80937	.00516	.81453	11
50	9.18628	9.99482	9.19146	10.80854	10.00518	10.81372	10
51	.18709	.99480	.19229	.80771	.00520	.81291	9
52	.18790	.99478	.19312	.80688	.00522	.81210	8
53	.18871	.99476	.19395	.80605	.00524	.81129	7
54	.18952	.99474	.19478	.80522	.00526	.81048	6
55	9.19033	9.99472	9.19561	10.80439	10.00528	10.80967	5
56	.19113	.99470	.19643	.80357	.00530	.80887	4
57	.19193	.99468	.19725	.80275	.00532	.80807	3
58	.19273	.99466	.19807	.80193	.00534	.80727	2
59	.19353	.99464	.19889	.80111	.00536	.80647	1
60	9.19433	9.99462	9.19971	10.80029	10.00538	10.80567	0

M	Cosine	Sine	Cotangent	Tangent	Cosecant	Secant	M

M	Sine	Cosine	Tangent	Cotangent	Secant	Cosecant	M
0	9.19433	9.99462	9.19971	10.80029	10.00538	10.80567	60
1	.19513	.99460	.20053	.79947	.00540	.80487	59
2	.19592	.99458	.20134	.79866	.00542	.80408	58
3	.19672	.99456	.20216	.79784	.00544	.80328	57
4	.19751	.99454	.20297	.79703	.00546	.80249	56
5	9.19830	9.99452	9.20378	10.79622	10.00548	10.80170	55
6	.19909	.99450	.20459	.79541	.00550	.80091	54
7	.19988	.99448	.20540	.79460	.00552	.80012	53
8	.20067	.99446	.20621	.79379	.00554	.79933	52
9	.20145	.99444	.20701	.79299	.00556	.79855	51
10	9.20223	9.99442	9.20782	10.79218	10.00558	10.79777	50
11	.20302	.99440	.20862	.79138	.00560	.79698	49
12	.20380	.99438	.20942	.79058	.00562	.79620	48
13	.20458	.99436	.21022	.78978	.00564	.79542	47
14	.20535	.99434	.21102	.78898	.00566	.79465	46
15	9.20613	9.99432	9.21182	10.78818	10.00568	10.79387	45
16	.20691	.99429	.21261	.78739	.00571	.79309	44
17	.20768	.99427	.21341	.78659	.00573	.79232	43
18	.20845	.99425	.21420	.78580	.00575	.79155	42
19	.20922	.99423	.21499	.78501	.00577	.79078	41
20	9.20999	9.99421	9.21578	10.78422	10.00579	10.79001	40
21	.21076	.99419	.21657	.78343	.00581	.78924	39
22	.21153	.99417	.21736	.78264	.00583	.78847	38
23	.21229	.99415	.21814	.78186	.00585	.78771	37
24	.21306	.99413	.21893	.78107	.00587	.78694	36
25	9.21382	9.99411	9.21971	10.78029	10.00589	10.78618	35
26	.21458	.99409	.22049	.77951	.00591	.78542	34
27	.21534	.99407	.22127	.77873	.00593	.78466	33
28	.21610	.99404	.22205	.77795	.00596	.78390	32
29	.21685	.99402	.22283	.77717	.00598	.78315	31
30	9.21761	9.99400	9.22361	10.77639	10.00600	10.78239	30
31	.21836	.99398	.22438	.77562	.00602	.78164	29
32	.21912	.99396	.22516	.77484	.00604	.78088	28
33	.21987	.99394	.22593	.77407	.00606	.78013	27
34	.22062	.99392	.22670	.77330	.00608	.77938	26
35	9.22137	9.99390	9.22747	10.77253	10.00610	10.77863	25
36	.22211	.99388	.22824	.77176	.00612	.77789	24
37	.22286	.99385	.22901	.77099	.00615	.77714	23
38	.22361	.99383	.22977	.77023	.00617	.77639	22
39	.22435	.99381	.23054	.76946	.00619	.77565	21
40	9.22509	9.99379	9.23130	10.76870	10.00621	10.77491	20
41	.22583	.99377	.23206	.76794	.00623	.77417	19
42	.22657	.99375	.23283	.76717	.00625	.77343	18
43	.22731	.99372	.23359	.76641	.00628	.77269	17
44	.22805	.99370	.23435	.76565	.00630	.77195	16
45	9.22878	9.99368	9.23510	10.76490	10.00632	10.77122	15
46	.22952	.99366	.23586	.76414	.00634	.77048	14
47	.23025	.99364	.23661	.76339	.00636	.76975	13
48	.23098	.99362	.23737	.76263	.00638	.76902	12
49	.23171	.99359	.23812	.76188	.00641	.76829	11
50	9.23244	9.99357	9.23887	10.76113	10.00643	10.76756	10
51	.23317	.99355	.23962	.76038	.00645	.76683	9
52	.23390	.99353	.24037	.75963	.00647	.76610	8
53	.23462	.99351	.24112	.75888	.00649	.76538	7
54	.23535	.99348	.24186	.75814	.00652	.76465	6
55	9.23607	9.99346	9.24261	10.75739	10.00654	10.76393	5
56	.23679	.99344	.24335	.75665	.00656	.76321	4
57	.23752	.99342	.24410	.75590	.00658	.76248	3
58	.23823	.99340	.24484	.75516	.00660	.76177	2
59	.23895	.99337	.24558	.75442	.00663	.76105	1
60	9.23967	9.99335	9.24632	10.75368	10.00665	10.76033	0
M	Cosine	Sine	Cotangent	Tangent	Cosecant	Secant	M

10°   Logarithms of Trigonometrical Functions   **169°**

M	Sine	Cosine	Tangent	Cotangent	Secant	Cosecant	M
0	9.23967	9.99335	9.24632	10.75368	10.00665	10.76033	60
1	.24039	.99333	.24706	.75294	.00667	.75961	59
2	.24110	.99331	.24779	.75221	.00669	.75890	58
3	.24181	.99328	.24853	.75147	.00672	.75819	57
4	.24253	.99326	.24926	.75074	.00674	.75747	56
5	9.24324	9.99324	9.25000	10.75000	10.00676	10.75676	55
6	.24395	.99322	.25073	.74927	.00678	.75605	54
7	.24466	.99319	.25146	.74854	.00681	.75534	53
8	.24536	.99317	.25219	.74781	.00683	.75464	52
9	.24607	.99315	.25292	.74708	.00685	.75393	51
10	9.24677	9.99313	9.25365	10.74635	10.00687	10.75323	50
11	.24748	.99310	.25437	.74563	.00690	.75252	49
12	.24818	.99308	.25510	.74490	.00692	.75182	48
13	.24888	.99306	.25582	.74418	.00694	.75112	47
14	.24958	.99304	.25655	.74345	.00696	.75042	46
15	9.25028	9.99301	9.25727	10.74273	10.00699	10.74972	45
16	.25098	.99299	.25799	.74201	.00701	.74902	44
17	.25168	.99297	.25871	.74129	.00703	.74832	43
18	.25237	.99294	.25943	.74057	.00706	.74763	42
19	.25307	.99292	.26015	.73985	.00708	.74693	41
20	9.25376	9.99290	9.26086	10.73914	10.00710	10.74624	40
21	.25445	.99288	.26158	.73842	.00712	.74555	39
22	.25514	.99285	.26229	.73771	.00715	.74486	38
23	.25583	.99283	.26301	.73699	.00717	.74417	37
24	.25652	.99281	.26372	.73628	.00719	.74348	36
25	9.25721	9.99278	9.26443	10.73557	10.00722	10.74279	35
26	.25790	.99276	.26514	.73486	.00724	.74210	34
27	.25858	.99274	.26585	.73415	.00726	.74142	33
28	.25927	.99271	.26655	.73345	.00729	.74073	32
29	.25995	.99269	.26726	.73274	.00731	.74005	31
30	9.26063	9.99267	9.26797	10.73203	10.00733	10.73937	30
31	.26131	.99264	.26867	.73133	.00736	.73869	29
32	.26199	.99262	.26937	.73063	.00738	.73801	28
33	.26267	.99260	.27008	.72992	.00740	.73733	27
34	.26335	.99257	.27078	.72922	.00743	.73665	26
35	9.26403	9.99255	9.27148	10.72852	10.00745	10.73597	25
36	.26470	.99252	.27218	.72782	.00748	.73530	24
37	.26538	.99250	.27288	.72712	.00750	.73462	23
38	.26605	.99248	.27357	.72643	.00752	.73395	22
39	.26672	.99245	.27427	.72573	.00755	.73328	21
40	9.26739	9.99243	9.27496	10.72504	10.00757	10.73261	20
41	.26806	.99241	.27566	.72434	.00759	.73194	19
42	.26873	.99238	.27635	.72365	.00762	.73127	18
43	.26940	.99236	.27704	.72296	.00764	.73060	17
44	.27007	.99233	.27773	.72227	.00767	.72993	16
45	9.27073	9.99231	9.27842	10.72158	10.00769	10.72927	15
46	.27140	.99229	.27911	.72089	.00771	.72860	14
47	.27206	.99226	.27980	.72020	.00774	.72794	13
48	.27273	.99224	.28049	.71951	.00776	.72727	12
49	.27339	.99221	.28117	.71883	.00779	.72661	11
50	9.27405	9.99219	9.28186	10.71814	10.00781	10.72595	10
51	.27471	.99217	.28254	.71746	.00783	.72529	9
52	.27537	.99214	.28323	.71677	.00786	.72463	8
53	.27602	.99212	.28391	.71609	.00788	.72398	7
54	.27668	.99209	.28459	.71541	.00791	.72332	6
55	9.27734	9.99207	9.28527	10.71473	10.00793	10.72266	5
56	.27799	.99204	.28595	.71405	.00796	.72201	4
57	.27864	.99202	.28662	.71338	.00798	.72136	3
58	.27930	.99200	.28730	.71270	.00800	.72070	2
59	.27995	.99197	.28798	.71202	.00803	.72005	1
60	9.28060	9.99195	9.28865	10.71135	10.00805	10.71940	0
M	Cosine	Sine	Cotangent	Tangent	Cosecant	Secant	M

M	Sine	Cosine	Tangent	Cotangent	Secant	Cosecant	M
0	9.28060	9.99195	9.28865	10.71135	10.00805	10.71940	60
1	.28125	.99192	.28933	.71067	.00808	.71875	59
2	.28190	.99190	.29000	.71000	.00810	.71810	58
3	.28254	.99187	.29067	.70933	.00813	.71746	57
4	.28319	.99185	.29134	.70866	.00815	.71681	56
5	9.28384	9.99182	.29201	10.70799	10.00818	10.71616	55
6	.28448	.99180	.29268	.70732	.00820	.71552	54
7	.28512	.99177	.29335	.70665	.00823	.71488	53
8	.28577	.99175	.29402	.70598	.00825	.71423	52
9	.28641	.99172	.29468	.70532	.00828	.71359	51
10	9.28705	9.99170	9.29535	10.70465	10.00830	10.71295	50
11	.28769	.99167	.29601	.70399	.00833	.71231	49
12	.28833	.99165	.29668	.70332	.00835	.71167	48
13	.28896	.99162	.29734	.70266	.00838	.71104	47
14	.28960	.99160	.29800	.70200	.00840	.71040	46
15	9.29024	9.99157	9.29866	10.70134	10.00843	10.70976	45
16	.29087	.99155	.29932	.70068	.00845	.70913	44
17	.29150	.99152	.29998	.70002	.00848	.70850	43
18	.29214	.99150	.30064	.69936	.00850	.70786	42
19	.29277	.99147	.30130	.69870	.00853	.70723	41
20	9.29340	9.99145	9.30195	10.69805	10.00855	10.70660	40
21	.29403	.99142	.30261	.69739	.00858	.70597	39
22	.29466	.99140	.30326	.69674	.00860	.70534	38
23	.29529	.99137	.30391	.69609	.00863	.70471	37
24	.29591	.99135	.30457	.69543	.00865	.70409	36
25	9.29654	9.99132	9.30522	10.69478	10.00868	10.70346	35
26	.29716	.99130	.30587	.69413	.00870	.70284	34
27	.29779	.99127	.30652	.69348	.00873	.70221	33
28	.29841	.99124	.30717	.69283	.00876	.70159	32
29	.29903	.99122	.30782	.69218	.00878	.70097	31
30	9.29966	9.99119	9.30846	10.69154	10.00881	10.70034	30
31	.30028	.99117	.30911	.69089	.00883	.69972	29
32	.30090	.99114	.30975	.69025	.00886	.69910	28
33	.30151	.99112	.31040	.68960	.00888	.69849	27
34	.30213	.99109	.31104	.68896	.00891	.69787	26
35	9.30275	9.99106	9.31168	10.68832	10.00894	10.69725	25
36	.30336	.99104	.31233	.68767	.00896	.69664	24
37	.30398	.99101	.31297	.68703	.00899	.69602	23
38	.30459	.99099	.31361	.68639	.00901	.69541	22
39	.30521	.99096	.31425	.68575	.00904	.69479	21
40	9.30582	9.99093	9.31489	10.68511	10.00907	10.69418	20
41	.30643	.99091	.31552	.68448	.00909	.69357	19
42	.30704	.99088	.31616	.68384	.00912	69296	18
43	.30765	.99086	.31679	.68321	.00914	.69235	17
44	.30826	99083	.31743	.68257	.00917	.69174	16
45	9.30887	9.99080	9.31806	10.68194	10.00920	10.69113	15
46	.30947	.99078	.31870	.68130	.00922	.69053	14
47	.31008	.99075	.31933	.68067	.00925	.68992	13
48	.31068	.99072	.31996	.68004	.00928	.68932	12
49	.31129	.99070	.32059	.67941	.00930	.68871	11
50	9.31189	9.99067	9.32122	10.67878	10.00933	10.68811	10
51	.31250	.99064	.32185	.67815	.00936	.68750	9
52	.31310	.99062	.32248	.67752	.00938	.68690	8
53	.31370	.99059	.32311	.67689	.00941	.68630	7
54	.31430	.99056	.32373	.67627	.00944	.68570	6
55	9.31490	9.99054	9.32436	10.67564	10.00946	10.68510	5
56	.31549	.99051	.32498	.67502	.00949	.68451	4
57	.31609	.99048	.32561	.67439	.00952	.68391	3
58	.31669	.99046	.32623	.67377	.00954	.68331	2
59	.31728	.99043	.32685	.67315	.00957	.68272	1
60	9.31788	9.99040	9.32747	10.67253	10.00960	10.68212	0

M	Cosine	Sine	Cotangent	Tangent	Cosecant	Secant	M

M	Sine	Cosine	Tangent	Cotangent	Secant	Cosecant	M
0	9.31788	9.99040	9.32747	10.67253	10.00960	10.68212	60
1	.31847	.99038	.32810	.67190	.00962	.68153	59
2	.31907	.99035	.32872	.67128	.00965	.68093	58
3	.31966	.99032	.32933	.67067	.00968	.68034	57
4	.32025	.99030	.32995	.67005	.00970	.67975	56
5	9.32084	9.99027	9.33057	10.66943	10.00973	10.67916	55
6	.32143	.99024	.33119	.66881	.00976	.67857	54
7	.32202	.99022	.33180	.66820	.00978	.67798	53
8	.32261	.99019	.33242	.66758	.00981	.67739	52
9	.32319	.99016	.33303	.66697	.00984	.67681	51
10	9.32378	9.99013	9.33365	10.66635	10.00987	10.67622	50
11	.32437	.99011	.33426	.66574	.00989	.67563	49
12	.32495	.99008	.33487	.66513	.00992	.67505	48
13	.32553	.99005	.33548	.66452	.00995	.67447	47
14	.32612	.99002	.33609	.66391	.00998	.67388	46
15	9.32670	9.99000	9.33670	10.66330	10.01000	10.67330	45
16	.32728	.98997	.33731	.66269	.01003	.67272	44
17	.32786	.98994	.33792	.66208	.01006	.67214	43
18	.32844	.98991	.33853	.66147	.01009	.67156	42
19	.32902	.98989	.33913	.66087	.01011	.67098	41
20	9.32960	9.98986	9.33974	10.66026	10.01014	10.67040	40
21	.33018	.98983	.34034	.65966	.01017	.66982	39
22	.33075	.98980	.34095	.65905	.01020	.66925	38
23	.33133	.98978	.34155	.65845	.01022	.66867	37
24	.33190	.98975	.34215	.65785	.01025	.66810	36
25	9.33248	9.98972	9.34276	10.65724	10.01028	10.66752	35
26	.33305	.98969	.34336	.65664	.01031	.66695	34
27	.33362	.98967	.34396	.65604	.01033	.66638	33
28	.33420	.98964	.34456	.65544	.01036	.66580	32
29	.33477	.98961	.34516	.65484	.01039	.66523	31
30	9.33534	9.98958	9.34576	10.65424	10.01042	10.66466	30
31	.33591	.98955	.34635	.65365	.01045	.66409	29
32	.33647	.98953	.34695	.65305	.01047	.66353	28
33	.33704	.98950	.34755	.65245	.01050	.66296	27
34	.33761	.98947	.34814	.65186	.01053	.66239	26
35	9.33818	9.98944	9.34874	10.65126	10.01056	10.66182	25
36	.33874	.98941	.34933	.65067	.01059	.66126	24
37	.33931	.98938	.34992	.65008	.01062	.66069	23
38	.33987	.98936	.35051	.64949	.01064	.66013	22
39	.34043	.98933	.35111	.64889	.01067	.65957	21
40	9.34100	9.98930	9.35170	10.64830	10.01070	10.65900	20
41	.34156	.98927	.35229	.64771	.01073	.65844	19
42	.34212	.98924	.35288	.64712	.01076	.65788	18
43	.34268	.98921	.35347	.64653	.01079	.65732	17
44	.34324	.98919	.35405	.64595	.01081	.65676	16
45	9.34380	9.98916	9.35464	10.64536	10.01084	10.65620	15
46	.34436	.98913	35523	.64477	.01087	.65564	14
47	.34491	.98910	.35581	.64419	.01090	.65509	13
48	.34547	.98907	.35640	.64360	.01093	.65453	12
49	.34602	.98904	.35698	.64302	.01096	.65398	11
50	9.34658	9.98901	9.35757	10.64243	10.01099	10.65342	10
51	.34713	.98898	.35815	.64185	.01102	.65287	9
52	.34769	.98896	.35873	.64127	.01104	.65231	8
53	.34824	.98893	.35931	.64069	.01107	.65176	7
54	.34879	.98890	.35989	.64011	.01110	.65121	6
55	9.34934	9.98887	9.36047	10.63953	10.01113	10.65066	5
56	.34989	.98884	.36105	.63895	.01116	.65011	4
57	.35044	.98881	.36163	.63837	.01119	.64956	3
58	.35099	.98878	.36221	.63779	.01122	.64901	2
59	.35154	.98875	.36279	.63721	.01125	.64846	1
60	9.35209	9.98872	9.36336	10.63664	10.01128	10.64791	0

M	Cosine	Sine	Cotangent	Tangent	Cosecant	Secant	M

M	Sine	Cosine	Tangent	Cotangent	Secant	Cosecant	M
0	9.35209	9.98872	9.36336	10.63664	10.01128	10.64791	60
1	.35263	.98869	.36394	.63606	.01131	.64737	59
2	.35318	.98867	.36452	.63548	.01133	.64682	58
3	.35373	.98864	.36509	.63491	.01136	.64627	57
4	.35427	.98861	.36566	.63434	.01139	.64573	56
5	9.35481	9.98858	9.36624	10.63376	10.01142	10.64519	55
6	.35536	.98855	.36681	.63319	.01145	.64464	54
7	.35590	.98852	.36738	.63262	.01148	.64410	53
8	.35644	.98849	.36795	.63205	.01151	.64356	52
9	.35698	.98846	.36852	.63148	.01154	.64302	51
10	9.35752	9.98843	9.36909	10.63091	10.01157	10.64248	50
11	.35806	.98840	.36966	.63034	.01160	.64194	49
12	.35860	.98837	.37023	.62977	.01163	.64140	48
13	.35914	.98834	.37080	.62920	.01166	.64086	47
14	.35968	.98831	.37137	.62863	.01169	.64032	46
15	9.36022	9.98828	9.37193	10.62807	10.01172	10.63978	45
16	.36075	.98825	.37250	.62750	.01175	.63925	44
17	.36129	.98822	.37306	.62694	.01178	.63871	43
18	.36182	.98819	.37363	.62637	.01181	.63818	42
19	.36236	.98816	.37419	.62581	.01184	.63764	41
20	9.36289	9.98813	9.37476	10.62524	10.01187	10.63711	40
21	.36342	.98810	.37532	.62468	.01190	.63658	39
22	.36395	.98807	.37588	.62412	.01193	.63605	38
23	.36449	.98804	.37644	.62356	.01196	.63551	37
24	.36502	.98801	.37700	.62300	.01199	.63498	36
25	9.36555	9.98798	9.37756	10.62244	10.01202	10.63445	35
26	.36608	.98795	.37812	.62188	.01205	.63392	34
27	.36660	.98792	.37868	.62132	.01208	.63340	33
28	.36713	.98789	.37924	.62076	.01211	.63287	32
29	.36766	.98786	.37980	.62020	.01214	.63234	31
30	9.36819	9.98783	9.38035	10.61965	10.01217	10.63181	30
31	.36871	.98780	.38091	.61909	.01220	.63129	29
32	.36924	.98777	.38147	.61853	.01223	.63076	28
33	.36976	.98774	.38202	.61798	.01226	.63024	27
34	.37028	.98771	.38257	.61743	.01229	.62972	26
35	9.37081	9.98768	9.38313	10.61687	10.01232	10.62919	25
36	.37133	.98765	.38368	.61632	.01235	.62867	24
37	.37185	.98762	.38423	.61577	.01238	.62815	23
38	.37237	.98759	.38479	.61521	.01241	.62763	22
39	.37289	.98756	.38534	.61466	.01244	.62711	21
40	9.37341	9.98753	9.38589	10.61411	10.01247	10.62659	20
41	.37393	.98750	.38644	.61356	.01250	.62607	19
42	.37445	.98746	.38699	.61301	.01254	.62555	18
43	.37497	.98743	.38754	.61246	.01257	.62503	17
44	.37549	.98740	.38808	.61192	.01260	.62451	16
45	9.37600	9.98737	9.38863	10.61137	10.01263	10.62400	15
46	.37652	.98734	.38918	.61082	.01266	.62348	14
47	.37703	.98731	.38972	.61028	.01269	.62297	13
48	.37755	.98728	.39027	.60973	.01272	.62245	12
49	.37806	.98725	.39082	.60918	.01275	.62194	11
50	9.37858	9.98722	9.39136	10.60864	10.01278	10.62142	10
51	.37909	.98719	.39190	.60810	.01281	.62091	9
52	.37960	.98715	.39245	.60755	.01285	.62040	8
53	.38011	.98712	.39299	.60701	.01288	.61989	7
54	.38062	.98709	.39353	.60647	.01291	.61938	6
55	9.38113	9.98706	9.39407	10.60593	10.01294	10.61887	5
56	.38164	.98703	.39461	.60539	.01297	.61836	4
57	.38215	.98700	.39515	.60485	.01300	.61785	3
58	.38266	.98697	.39569	.60431	.01303	.61734	2
59	.38317	.98694	.39623	.60377	.01306	.61683	1
60	9.38368	9.98690	9.39677	10.60323	10.01310	10.61632	0
M	Cosine	Sine	Cotangent	Tangent	Cosecant	Secant	M

M	Sine	Cosine	Tangent	Cotangent	Secant	Cosecant	M
0	9.38368	9.98690	9.39677	10.60323	10.01310	10.61632	60
1	.38418	.98687	.39731	.60269	.01313	.61582	59
2	.38469	.98684	.39785	.60215	.01316	.61531	58
3	.38519	.98681	.39838	.60162	.01319	.61481	57
4	.38570	.98678	.39892	.60108	.01322	.61430	56
5	9.38620	9.98675	9.39945	10.60055	10.01325	10.61380	55
6	.38670	.98671	.39999	.60001	.01329	.61330	54
7	.38721	.98668	.40052	.59948	.01332	.61279	53
8	.38771	.98665	.40106	.59894	.01335	.61229	52
9	.38821	.98662	.40159	.59841	.01338	.61179	51
10	9.38871	9.98659	9.40212	10.59788	10.01341	10.61129	50
11	.38921	.98656	.40266	.59734	.01344	.61079	49
12	.38971	.98652	.40319	.59681	.01348	.61029	48
13	.39021	.98649	.40372	.59628	.01351	.60979	47
14	.39071	.98646	.40425	.59575	.01354	.60929	46
15	9.39121	9.98643	9.40478	10.59522	10.01357	10.60879	45
16	.39170	.98640	.40531	.59469	.01360	.60830	44
17	.39220	.98636	.40584	.59416	.01364	.60780	43
18	.39270	.98633	.40636	.59364	.01367	.60730	42
19	.39319	.98630	.40689	.59311	.01370	.60681	41
20	9.39369	9.98627	9.40742	10.59258	10.01373	10.60631	40
21	.39418	.98623	.40795	.59205	.01377	.60582	39
22	.39467	.98620	.40847	.59153	.01380	.60533	38
23	.39517	.98617	.40900	.59100	.01383	.60483	37
24	.39566	.98614	.40952	.59048	.01386	.60434	36
25	9.39615	9.98610	9.41005	10.58995	10.01390	10.60385	35
26	.39664	.98607	.41057	.58943	.01393	.60336	34
27	.39713	.98604	.41109	.58891	.01396	.60287	33
28	.39762	.98601	.41161	.58839	.01399	.60238	32
29	.39811	.98597	.41214	.58786	.01403	.60189	31
30	9.39860	9.98594	9.41266	10.58734	10.01406	10.60140	30
31	.39909	.98591	.41318	.58682	.01409	.60091	29
32	.39958	.98588	.41370	.58630	.01412	.60042	28
33	.40006	.98584	.41422	.58578	.01416	.59994	27
34	.40055	.98581	.41474	.58526	.01419	.59945	26
35	9.40103	9.98578	9.41526	10.58474	10.01422	10.59897	25
36	.40152	.98574	.41578	.58422	.01426	.59848	24
37	.40200	.98571	.41629	.58371	.01429	.59800	23
38	.40249	.98568	.41681	.58319	.01432	.59751	22
39	.40297	.98565	.41733	.58267	.01435	.59703	21
40	9.40346	9.98561	9.41784	10.58216	10.01439	10.59654	20
41	.40394	.98558	.41836	.58164	.01442	.59606	19
42	.40442	.98555	.41887	.58113	.01445	.59558	18
43	.40490	.98551	.41939	.58061	.01449	.59510	17
44	.40538	.98548	.41990	.58010	.01452	.59462	16
45	9.40586	9.98545	9.42041	10.57959	10.01455	10.59414	15
46	.40634	.98541	.42093	.57907	.01459	.59366	14
47	.40682	.98538	.42144	.57856	.01462	.59318	13
48	.40730	.98535	.42195	.57805	.01465	.59270	12
49	.40778	.98531	.42246	.57754	.01469	.59222	11
50	9.40825	9.98528	9.42297	10.57703	10.01472	10.59175	10
51	.40873	.98525	.42348	.57652	.01475	.59127	9
52	.40921	.98521	.42399	.57601	.01479	.59079	8
53	.40968	.98518	.42450	.57550	.01482	.59032	7
54	.41016	.98515	.42501	.57499	.01485	.58984	6
55	9.41063	9.98511	9.42552	10.57448	10.01489	10.58937	5
56	.41111	.98508	.42603	.57397	.01492	.58889	4
57	.41158	.98505	.42653	.57347	.01495	.58842	3
58	.41205	.98501	.42704	.57296	.01499	.58795	2
59	.41252	.98498	.42755	.57245	.01502	.58748	1
60	9.41300	9.98494	9.42805	10.57195	10.01506	10.58700	0

| M | Cosine | Sine | Cotangent | Tangent | Cosecant | Secant | M |

M	Sine	Cosine	Tangent	Cotangent	Secant	Cosecant	M
0	9.41300	9.98494	9.42805	10.57195	10.01506	10.58700	60
1	.41347	.98491	.42856	.57144	.01509	.58653	59
2	.41394	.98488	.42906	.57094	.01512	.58606	58
3	.41441	.98484	.42957	.57043	.01516	.58559	57
4	.41488	.98481	.43007	.56993	.01519	.58512	56
5	9.41535	9.98477	9.43057	10.56943	10.01523	10.58465	55
6	.41582	.98474	.43108	.56892	.01526	.58418	54
7	.41628	.98471	.43158	.56842	.01529	.58372	53
8	.41675	.98467	.43208	.56792	.01533	.58325	52
9	.41722	.98464	.43258	.56742	.01536	.58278	51
10	9.41768	9.98460	9.43308	10.56692	10.01540	10.58232	50
11	.41815	.98457	.43358	.56642	.01543	.58185	49
12	.41861	.98453	.43408	.56592	.01547	.58139	48
13	.41908	.98450	.43458	.56542	.01550	.58092	47
14	.41954	.98447	.43508	.56492	.01553	.58046	46
15	9.42001	9.98443	9.43558	10.56442	10.01557	10.57999	45
16	.42047	.98440	.43607	.56393	.01560	.57953	44
17	.42093	.98436	.43657	.56343	.01564	.57907	43
18	.42140	.98433	.43707	.56293	.01567	.57860	42
19	.42186	.98429	.43756	.56244	.01571	.57814	41
20	9.42232	9.98426	9.43806	10.56194	10.01574	10.57768	40
21	.42278	.98422	.43855	.56145	.01578	.57722	39
22	.42324	.98419	.43905	.56095	.01581	.57676	38
23	.42370	.98415	.43954	.56046	.01585	.57630	37
24	.42416	.98412	.44004	.55996	.01588	.57584	36
25	9.42461	9.98409	9.44053	10.55947	10.01591	10.57539	35
26	.42507	.98405	.44102	.55898	.01595	.57493	34
27	.42553	.98402	.44151	.55849	.01598	.57447	33
28	.42599	.98398	.44201	.55799	.01602	.57401	32
29	.42644	.98395	.44250	.55750	.01605	.57356	31
30	9.42690	9.98391	9.44299	10.55701	10.01609	10.57310	30
31	.42735	.98388	.44348	.55652	.01612	.57265	29
32	.42781	.98384	.44397	.55603	.01616	.57219	28
33	.42826	.98381	.44446	.55554	.01619	.57174	27
34	.42872	.98377	.44495	.55505	.01623	.57128	26
35	9.42917	9.98373	9.44544	10.55456	10.01627	10.57083	25
36	.42962	.98370	.44592	.55408	.01630	.57038	24
37	.43008	.98366	.44641	.55359	.01634	.56992	23
38	.43053	.98363	.44690	.55310	.01637	.56947	22
39	.43098	.98359	.44738	.55262	.01641	.56902	21
40	.43143	9.98356	9.44787	10.55213	10.01644	10.56857	20
41	.43188	.98352	.44836	.55164	.01648	.56812	19
42	.43233	.98349	.44884	.55116	.01651	.56767	18
43	.43278	.98345	.44933	.55067	.01655	.56722	17
44	.43323	.98342	.44981	.55019	.01658	.56677	16
45	9.43367	9.98338	9.45029	10.54971	10.01662	10.56633	15
46	.43412	.98334	.45078	.54922	.01666	.56588	14
47	.43457	.98331	.45126	.54874	.01669	.56543	13
48	.43502	.98327	.45174	.54826	.01673	.56498	12
49	.43546	.98324	.45222	.54778	.01676	.56454	11
50	9.43591	9.98320	9.45271	10.54729	10.01680	10.56409	10
51	.43635	.98317	.45319	.54681	.01683	.56365	9
52	.43680	.98313	.45367	.54633	.01687	.56320	8
53	.43724	.98309	.45415	.54585	.01691	.56276	7
54	.43769	.98306	.45463	.54537	.01694	.56231	6
55	9.43813	9.98302	9.45511	10.54489	10.01698	10.56187	5
56	.43857	.98299	.45559	.54441	.01701	.56143	4
57	.43901	.98295	.45606	.54394	.01705	.56099	3
58	.43946	.98291	.45654	.54346	.01709	.56054	2
59	.43990	.98288	.45702	.54298	.01712	.56010	1
60	9.44034	9.98284	9.45750	10.54250	10.01716	10.55966	0
M	Cosine	Sine	Cotangent	Tangent	Cosecant	Secant	M

M	Sine	Cosine	Tangent	Cotangent	Secant	Cosecant	M
0	9.44034	9.98284	9.45750	10.54250	10.01716	10.55966	60
1	.44078	.98281	.45797	.54203	.01719	.55922	59
2	.44122	.98277	.45845	.54155	.01723	.55878	58
3	.44166	.98273	.45892	.54108	.01727	.55834	57
4	.44210	.98270	.45940	.54060	.01730	.55790	56
5	9.44253	9.98266	9.45987	10.54013	10.01734	10.55747	55
6	.44297	.98262	.46035	.53965	.01738	.55703	54
7	.44341	.98259	.46082	.53918	.01741	.55659	53
8	.44385	.98255	.46130	.53870	.01745	.55615	52
9	.44428	.98251	.46177	.53823	.01749	.55572	51
10	9.44472	9.98248	9.46224	10.53776	10.01752	10.55528	50
11	.44516	.98244	.46271	.53729	.01756	.55484	49
12	.44559	.98240	.46319	.53681	.01760	.55441	48
13	.44602	.98237	.46366	.53634	.01763	.55398	47
14	.44646	.98233	.46413	.53587	.01767	.55354	46
15	9.44689	9.98229	9.46460	10.53540	10.01771	10.55311	45
16	.44733	.98226	.46507	.53493	.01774	.55267	44
17	.44776	.98222	.46554	.53446	.01778	.55224	43
18	.44819	.98218	.46601	.53399	.01782	.55181	42
19	.44862	.98215	.46648	.53352	.01785	.55138	41
20	9.44905	9.98211	9.46694	10.53306	10.01789	10.55095	40
21	.44948	.98207	.46741	.53259	.01793	.55052	39
22	.44992	.98204	.46788	.53212	.01796	.55008	38
23	.45035	.98200	.46835	.53165	.01800	.54965	37
24	.45077	.98196	.46881	.53119	.01804	.54923	36
25	9.45120	9.98192	9.46928	10.53072	10.01808	10.54880	35
26	.45163	.98189	.46975	.53025	.01811	.54837	34
27	.45206	.98185	.47021	.52979	.01815	.54794	33
28	.45249	.98181	.47068	.52932	.01819	.54751	32
29	.45292	.98177	.47114	.52886	.01823	.54708	31
30	9.45334	9.98174	9.47160	10.52840	10.01826	10.54666	30
31	.45377	.98170	.47207	.52793	.01830	.54623	29
32	.45419	.98166	.47253	.52747	.01834	.54581	28
33	.45462	.98162	.47299	.52701	.01838	.54538	27
34	.45504	.98159	.47346	.52654	.01841	.54496	26
35	9.45547	9.98155	9.47392	10.52608	10.01845	10.54453	25
36	.45589	.98151	.47438	.52562	.01849	.54411	24
37	.45632	.98147	.47484	.52516	.01853	.54368	23
38	.45674	.98144	.47530	.52470	.01856	.54326	22
39	.45716	.98140	.47576	.52424	.01860	.54284	21
40	9.45758	9.98136	9.47622	10.52378	10.01864	10.54242	20
41	.45801	.98132	.47668	.52332	.01868	.54199	19
42	.45843	.98129	.47714	.52286	.01871	.54157	18
43	.45885	.98125	.47760	.52240	.01875	.54115	17
44	.45927	.98121	.47806	.52194	.01879	.54073	16
45	9.45969	9.98117	9.47852	10.52148	10.01883	10.54031	15
46	.46011	.98113	.47897	.52103	.01887	.53989	14
47	.46053	.98110	.47943	.52057	.01890	.53947	13
48	.46095	.98106	.47989	.52011	.01894	.53905	12
49	.46136	.98102	.48035	.51965	.01898	.53864	11
50	9.46178	9.98098	9.48080	10.51920	10.01902	10.53822	10
51	.46220	.98094	.48126	.51874	.01906	.53780	9
52	.46262	.98090	.48171	.51829	.01910	.53738	8
53	.46303	.98087	.48217	.51783	.01913	.53697	7
54	.46345	.98083	.48262	.51738	.01917	.53655	6
55	9.46386	9.98079	9.48307	10.51693	10.01921	10.53614	5
56	.46428	.98075	.48353	.51647	.01925	.53572	4
57	.46469	.98071	.48398	.51602	.01929	.53531	3
58	.46511	.98067	.48443	.51557	.01933	.53489	2
59	.46552	.98063	.48489	.51511	.01937	.53448	1
60	9.46594	9.98060	9.48534	10.51466	10.01940	10.53406	0

| M | Cosine | Sine | Cotangent | Tangent | Cosecant | Secant | M |

M	Sine	Cosine	Tangent	Cotangent	Secant	Cosecant	M
0	9.46594	9.98060	9.48534	10.51466	10.01940	10.53406	60
1	.46635	.98056	.48579	.51421	.01944	.53365	59
2	.46676	.98052	.48624	.51376	.01948	.53324	58
3	.46717	.98048	.48669	.51331	.01952	.53283	57
4	.46758	.98044	.48714	.51286	.01956	.53242	56
5	9.46800	9.98040	9.48759	10.51241	10.01960	10.53200	55
6	.46841	.98036	.48804	.51196	.01964	.53159	54
7	.46882	.98032	.48849	.51151	.01968	.53118	53
8	.46923	.98029	.48894	.51106	.01971	.53077	52
9	.46964	.98025	.48939	.51061	.01975	.53036	51
10	9.47005	9.98021	9.48984	10.51016	10.01979	10.52995	50
11	.47045	.98017	.49029	.50971	.01983	.52955	49
12	.47086	.98013	.49073	.50927	.01987	.52914	48
13	.47127	.98009	.49118	.50882	.01991	.52873	47
14	.47168	.98005	.49163	.50837	.01995	.52832	46
15	9.47209	9.98001	9.49207	10.50793	10.01999	10.52791	45
16	.47249	.97997	.49252	.50748	.02003	.52751	44
17	.47290	.97993	.49296	.50704	.02007	.52710	43
18	.47330	.97989	.49341	.50659	.02011	.52670	42
19	.47371	.97986	.49385	.50615	.02014	.52629	41
20	9.47411	9.97982	9.49430	10.50570	10.02018	10.52589	40
21	.47452	.97978	.49474	.50526	.02022	.52548	39
22	.47492	.97974	.49519	.50481	.02026	.52508	38
23	.47533	.97970	.49563	.50437	.02030	.52467	37
24	.47573	.97966	.49607	.50393	.02034	.52427	36
25	9.47613	9.97962	9.49652	10.50348	10.02038	10.52387	35
26	.47654	.97958	.49696	.50304	.02042	.52346	34
27	.47694	.97954	.49740	.50260	.02046	.52306	33
28	.47734	.97950	.49784	.50216	.02050	.52266	32
29	.47774	.97946	.49828	.50172	.02054	.52226	31
30	9.47814	9.97942	9.49872	10.50128	10.02058	10.52186	30
31	.47854	.97938	.49916	.50084	.02062	.52146	29
32	.47894	.97934	.49960	.50040	.02066	.52106	28
33	.47934	.97930	.50004	.49996	.02070	.52066	27
34	.47974	.97926	.50048	.49952	.02074	.52026	26
35	9.48014	9.97922	9.50092	10.49908	10.02078	10.51986	25
36	.48054	.97918	.50136	.49864	.02082	.51946	24
37	.48094	.97914	.50180	.49820	.02086	.51906	23
38	.48133	.97910	.50223	.49777	.02090	.51867	22
39	.48173	.97906	.50267	.49733	.02094	.51827	21
40	9.48213	9.97902	9.50311	10.49689	10.02098	10.51787	20
41	.48252	.97898	.50355	.49645	.02102	.51748	19
42	.48292	.97894	.50398	.49602	.02106	.51708	18
43	.48332	.97890	.50442	.49558	.02110	.51668	17
44	.48371	.97886	.50485	.49515	.02114	.51629	16
45	9.48411	9.97882	9.50529	10.49471	10.02118	10.51589	15
46	.48450	.97878	.50572	.49428	.02122	.51550	14
47	.48490	.97874	.50616	.49384	.02126	.51510	13
48	.48529	.97870	.50659	.49341	.02130	.51471	12
49	.48568	.97866	.50703	.49297	.02134	.51432	11
50	9.48607	9.97861	9.50746	10.49254	10.02139	10.51393	10
51	.48647	.97857	.50789	.49211	.02143	.51353	9
52	.48686	.97853	.50833	.49167	.02147	.51314	8
53	.48725	.97849	.50876	.49124	.02151	.51275	7
54	.48764	.97845	.50919	.49081	.02155	.51236	6
55	9.48803	9.97841	9.50962	10.49038	10.02159	10.51197	5
56	.48842	.97837	.51005	.48995	.02163	.51158	4
57	.48881	.97833	.51048	.48952	.02167	.51119	3
58	.48920	.97829	.51092	.48908	.02171	.51080	2
59	.48959	.97825	.51135	.48865	.02175	.51041	1
60	9.48998	9.97821	9.51178	10.48822	10.02179	10.51002	0
M	Cosine	Sine	Cotangent	Tangent	Cosecant	Secant	M

M	Sine	Cosine	Tangent	Cotangent	Secant	Cosecant	M
0	9.48998	9.97821	9.51178	10.48822	10.02179	10.51002	60
1	.49037	.97817	.51221	.48779	.02183	.50963	59
2	.49076	.97812	.51264	.48736	.02188	.50924	58
3	.49115	.97808	.51306	.48694	.02192	.50885	57
4	.49153	.97804	.51349	.48651	.02196	.50847	56
5	9.49192	9.97800	9.51392	10.48608	10.02200	10.50808	55
6	.49231	.97796	.51435	.48565	.02204	.50769	54
7	.49269	.97792	.51478	.48522	.02208	.50731	53
8	.49308	.97788	.51520	.48480	.02212	.50692	52
9	.49347	.97784	.51563	.48437	.02216	.50653	51
10	9.49385	9.97779	9.51606	10.48394	10.02221	10.50615	50
11	.49424	.97775	.51648	.48352	.02225	.50576	49
12	.49462	.97771	.51691	.48309	.02229	.50538	48
13	.49500	.97767	.51734	.48266	.02233	.50500	47
14	.49539	.97763	.51776	.48224	.02237	.50461	46
15	9.49577	9.97759	9.51819	10.48181	10.02241	10.50423	45
16	.49615	.97754	.51861	.48139	.02246	.50385	44
17	.49654	.97750	.51903	.48097	.02250	.50346	43
18	.49692	.97746	.51946	.48054	.02254	.50308	42
19	.49730	.97742	.51988	.48012	.02258	.50270	41
20	9.49768	9.97738	9.52031	10.47969	10.02262	10.50232	40
21	.49806	.97734	.52073	.47927	.02266	.50194	39
22	.49844	.97729	.52115	.47885	.02271	.50156	38
23	.49882	.97725	.52157	.47843	.02275	.50118	37
24	.49920	.97721	.52200	.47800	.02279	.50080	36
25	9.49958	9.97717	9.52242	10.47758	10.02283	10.50042	35
26	.49996	.97713	.52284	.47716	.02287	.50004	34
27	.50034	.97708	.52326	.47674	.02292	.49966	33
28	.50072	.97704	.52368	.47632	.02296	.49928	32
29	.50110	.97700	.52410	.47590	.02300	.49890	31
30	9.50148	9.97696	9.52452	10.47548	10.02304	10.49852	30
31	.50185	.97691	.52494	.47506	.02309	.49815	29
32	.50223	.97687	.52536	.47464	.02313	.49777	28
33	.50261	.97683	.52578	.47422	.02317	.49739	27
34	.50298	.97679	.52620	.47380	.02321	.49702	26
35	9.50336	9.97674	9.52661	10.47339	10.02326	10.49664	25
36	.50374	.97670	.52703	.47297	.02330	.49626	24
37	.50411	.97666	.52745	.47255	.02334	.49589	23
38	.50449	.97662	.52787	.47213	.02338	.49551	22
39	.50486	.97657	.52829	.47171	.02343	.49514	21
40	9.50523	9.97653	9.52870	10.47130	10.02347	10.49477	20
41	.50561	.97649	.52912	.47088	.02351	.49439	19
42	.50598	.97645	.52953	.47047	.02355	.49402	18
43	.50635	.97640	.52995	.47005	.02360	.49365	17
44	.50673	.97636	.53037	.46963	.02364	.49327	16
45	9.50710	9.97632	9.53078	10.46922	10.02368	10.49290	15
46	.50747	.97628	.53120	.46880	.02372	.49253	14
47	.50784	.97623	.53161	.46839	.02377	.49216	13
48	.50821	.97619	.53202	.46798	.02381	.49179	12
49	.50858	.97615	.53244	.46756	.02385	.49142	11
50	9.50896	9.97610	9.53285	10.46715	10.02390	10.49104	10
51	.50933	.97606	.53327	.46673	.02394	.49067	9
52	.50970	.97602	.53368	.46632	.02398	.49030	8
53	.51007	.97597	.53409	.46591	.02403	.48993	7
54	.51043	.97593	.53450	.46550	.02407	.48957	6
55	9.51080	9.97589	9.53492	10.46508	10.02411	10.48920	5
56	.51117	.97584	.53533	.46467	.02416	.48883	4
57	.51154	.97580	.53574	.46426	.02420	.48846	3
58	.51191	.97576	.53615	.46385	.02424	.48809	2
59	.51227	.97571	.53656	.46344	.02429	.48773	1
60	9.51264	9.97567	9.53697	10.46303	10.02433	10.48736	0

| M | Cosine | Sine | Cotangent | Tangent | Cosecant | Secant | M |

M	Sine	Cosine	Tangent	Cotangent	Secant	Cosecant	M
0	9.51264	9.97567	9.53697	10.46303	10.02433	10.48736	60
1	.51301	.97563	.53738	.46262	.02437	.48699	59
2	.51338	.97558	.53779	.46221	.02442	.48662	58
3	.51374	.97554	.53820	.46180	.02446	.48626	57
4	.51411	.97550	.53861	.46139	.02450	.48589	56
5	9.51447	9.97545	9.53902	10.46098	10.02455	10.48553	55
6	.51484	.97541	.53943	.46057	.02459	.48516	54
7	.51520	.97536	.53984	.46016	.02464	.48480	53
8	.51557	.97532	.54025	.45975	.02468	.48443	52
9	.51593	.97528	.54065	.45935	.02472	.48407	51
10	9.51629	9.97523	9.54106	10.45894	10.02477	10.48371	50
11	.51666	.97519	.54147	.45853	.02481	.48334	49
12	.51702	.97515	.54187	.45813	.02485	.48298	48
13	.51738	.97510	.54228	.45772	.02490	.48262	47
14	.51774	.97506	.54269	.45731	.02494	.48226	46
15	9.51811	9.97501	9.54309	10.45691	10.02499	10.48189	45
16	.51847	.97497	.54350	.45650	.02503	.48153	44
17	.51883	.97492	.54390	.45610	.02508	.48117	43
18	.51919	.97488	.54431	.45569	.02512	.48081	42
19	.51955	.97484	.54471	.45529	.02516	.48045	41
20	9.51991	9.97479	9.54512	10.45488	10.02521	10.48009	40
21	.52027	.97475	.54552	.45448	.02525	.47973	39
22	.52063	.97470	.54593	.45407	.02530	.47937	38
23	.52099	.97466	.54633	.45367	.02534	.47901	37
24	.52135	.97461	.54673	.45327	.02539	.47865	36
25	9.52171	9.97457	9.54714	10.45286	10.02543	10.47829	35
26	.52207	.97453	.54754	.45246	.02547	.47793	34
27	.52242	.97448	.54794	.45206	.02552	.47758	33
28	.52278	.97444	.54835	.45165	.02556	.47722	32
29	.52314	.97439	.54875	.45125	.02561	.47686	31
30	9.52350	9.97435	9.54915	10.45085	10.02565	10.47650	30
31	.52385	.97430	.54955	.45045	.02570	.47615	29
32	.52421	.97426	.54995	.45005	.02574	.47579	28
33	.52456	.97421	.55035	.44965	.02579	.47544	27
34	.52492	.97417	.55075	.44925	.02583	.47508	26
35	9.52527	9.97412	9.55115	10.44885	10.02588	10.47473	25
36	.52563	.97408	.55155	.44845	.02592	.47437	24
37	.52598	.97403	.55195	.44805	.02597	.47402	23
38	.52634	.97399	.55235	.44765	.02601	.47366	22
39	.52669	.97394	.55275	.44725	.02606	.47331	21
40	9.52705	9.97390	9.55315	10.44685	10.02610	10.47295	20
41	.52740	.97385	.55355	.44645	.02615	.47260	19
42	.52775	.97381	.55395	.44605	.02619	.47225	18
43	.52811	.97376	.55434	.44566	.02624	.47189	17
44	.52846	.97372	.55474	.44526	.02628	.47154	16
45	9.52881	9.97367	9.55514	10.44486	10.02633	10.47119	15
46	.52916	.97363	.55554	.44446	.02637	.47084	14
47	.52951	.97358	.55593	.44407	.02642	.47049	13
48	.52986	.97353	.55633	.44367	.02647	.47014	12
49	.53021	.97349	.55673	.44327	.02651	.46979	11
50	9.53056	9.97344	9.55712	10.44288	10.02656	10.46944	10
51	.53092	.97340	.55752	.44248	.02660	.46908	9
52	.53126	.97335	.55791	.44209	.02665	.46874	8
53	.53161	.97331	.55831	.44169	.02669	.46839	7
54	.53196	.97326	.55870	.44130	.02674	.46804	6
55	9.53231	9.97322	9.55910	10.44090	10.02678	10.46769	5
56	.53266	.97317	.55949	.44051	.02683	.46734	4
57	.53301	.97312	.55989	.44011	.02688	.46699	3
58	.53336	.97308	.56028	.43972	.02692	.46664	2
59	.53370	.97303	.56067	.43933	.02697	.46630	1
60	9.53405	9.97299	9.56107	10.43893	10.02701	10.46595	0
M	Cosine	Sine	Cotangent	Tangent	Cosecant	Secant	M

M	Sine	Cosine	Tangent	Cotangent	Secant	Cosecant	M
0	9.53405	9.97299	9.56107	10.43893	10.02701	10.46595	60
1	.53440	.97294	.56146	.43854	.02706	.46560	59
2	.53475	.97289	.56185	.43815	.02711	.46525	58
3	.53509	.97285	.56224	.43776	.02715	.46491	57
4	.53544	.97280	.56264	.43736	.02720	.46456	56
5	9.53578	9.97276	9.56303	10.43697	10.02724	10.46422	55
6	.53613	.97271	.56342	.43658	.02729	.46387	54
7	.53647	97266	.56381	.43619	.02734	.46353	53
8	.53682	.97262	.56420	.43580	.02738	.46318	52
9	.53716	.97257	.56459	.43541	.02743	.46284	51
10	9.53751	9.97252	9.56498	10.43502	10.02748	10.46249	50
11	.53785	.97248	.56537	.43463	.02752	.46215	49
12	.53819	.97243	.56576	.43424	.02757	.46181	48
13	.53854	.97238	.56615	.43385	.02762	.46146	47
14	.53888	.97234	.56654	.43346	.02766	.46112	46
15	9.53922	9.97229	9.56693	10.43307	10.02771	10.46078	45
16	.53957	.97224	.56732	.43268	.02776	.46043	44
17	.53991	.97220	.56771	.43229	.02780	.46009	43
18	.54025	.97215	.56810	.43190	.02785	.45975	42
19	.54059	.97210	.56849	.43151	.02790	.45941	41
20	9.54093	9.97206	9.56887	10.43113	10.02794	10.45907	40
21	.54127	.97201	.56926	.43074	.02799	.45873	39
22	.54161	.97196	.56965	.43035	.02804	.45839	38
23	.54195	.97192	.57004	.42996	.02808	.45805	37
24	.54229	.97187	.57042	.42958	.02813	.45771	36
25	9.54263	9.97182	9.57081	10.42919	10.02818	10.45737	35
26	.54297	.97178	.57120	.42880	.02822	.45703	34
27	.54331	.97173	.57158	.42842	.02827	.45669	33
28	.54365	.97168	.57197	.42803	.02832	.45635	32
29	.54399	.97163	.57235	.42765	.02837	.45601	31
30	9.54433	9.97159	9.57274	10.42726	10.02841	10.45567	30
31	.54466	.97154	.57312	.42688	.02846	.45534	29
32	.54500	.97149	.57351	.42649	.02851	.45500	28
33	.54534	.97145	.57389	.42611	.02855	.45466	27
34	.54567	.97140	.57428	.42572	.02860	.45433	26
35	9.54601	9.97135	9.57466	10.42534	10.02865	10.45399	25
36	.54635	.97130	.57504	42496	.02870	.45365	24
37	.54668	.97126	.57543	.42457	.02874	.45332	23
38	.54702	.97121	.57581	.42419	.02879	.45298	22
39	.54735	.97116	.57619	.42381	.02884	.45265	21
40	9.54769	9.97111	9.57658	10.42342	10.02889	10.45231	20
41	.54802	.97107	.57696	.42304	.02893	.45198	19
42	.54836	.97102	.57734	.42266	.02898	.45164	18
43	.54869	.97097	.57772	.42228	.02903	.45131	17
44	.54903	.97092	.57810	.42190	.02908	.45097	16
45	9.54936	9.97087	9.57849	10.42151	10.02913	10.45064	15
46	.54969	.97083	.57887	.42113	.02917	.45031	14
47	.55003	.97078	.57925	.42075	.02922	.44997	13
48	.55036	.97073	.57963	.42037	.02927	.44964	12
49	.55069	.97068	.58001	.41999	.02932	.44931	11
50	9.55102	9.97063	9.58039	10.41961	10.02937	10.44898	10
51	.55136	.97059	.58077	.41923	.02941	.44864	9
52	.55169	.97054	.58115	.41885	.02946	.44831	8
53	.55202	.97049	.58153	.41847	.02951	.44798	7
54	.55235	.97044	.58191	.41809	.02956	.44765	6
55	9.55268	9.97039	9.58229	10.41771	10.02961	10.44732	5
56	.55301	.97035	.58267	.41733	.02965	.44699	4
57	.55334	.97030	.58304	.41696	.02970	.44666	3
58	.55367	.97025	.58342	.41658	.02975	.44633	2
59	.55400	.97020	.58380	.41620	.02980	.44600	1
60	9.55433	9.97015	9.58418	10.41582	10.02985	10.44567	0
M	Cosine	Sine	Cotangent	Tangent	Cosecant	Secant	M

M	Sine	Cosine	Tangent	Cotangent	Secant	Cosecant	M
0	9.55433	9.97015	9.58418	10.41582	10.02985	10.44567	60
1	.55466	.97010	.58455	.41545	.02990	.44534	59
2	.55499	.97005	.58493	.41507	.02995	.44501	58
3	.55532	.97001	.58531	.41469	.02999	.44468	57
4	.55564	.96996	.58569	.41431	.03004	.44436	56
5	9.55597	9.96991	9.58606	10.41394	10.03009	10.44403	55
6	.55630	.96986	.58644	.41356	.03014	.44370	54
7	.55663	.96981	.58681	.41319	.03019	.44337	53
8	.55695	.96976	.58719	.41281	.03024	.44305	52
9	.55728	.96971	.58757	.41243	.03029	.44272	51
10	9.55761	9.96966	9.58794	10.41206	10.03034	10.44239	50
11	.55793	.96962	.58832	.41168	.03038	.44207	49
12	.55826	.96957	.58869	.41131	.03043	.44174	48
13	.55858	.96952	.58907	.41093	.03048	.44142	47
14	.55891	.96947	.58944	.41056	.03053	.44109	46
15	9.55923	9.96942	9.58981	10.41019	10.03058	10.44077	45
16	.55956	.96937	.59019	.40981	.03063	.44044	44
17	.55988	.96932	.59056	.40944	.03068	.44012	43
18	.56021	.96927	.59094	.40906	.03073	.43979	42
19	.56053	.96922	.59131	.40869	.03078	.43947	41
20	9.56085	9.96917	9.59168	10.40832	10.03083	10.43915	40
21	.56118	.96912	.59205	.40795	.03088	.43882	39
22	.56150	.96907	.59243	.40757	.03093	.43850	38
23	.56182	.96903	.59280	.40720	.03097	.43818	37
24	.56215	.96898	.59317	.40683	.03102	.43785	36
25	9.56247	9.96893	9.59354	10.40646	10.03107	10.43753	35
26	.56279	.96888	.59391	.40609	.03112	.43721	34
27	.56311	.96883	.59429	.40571	.03117	.43689	33
28	.56343	.96878	.59466	.40534	.03122	.43657	32
29	.56375	.96873	.59503	.40497	.03127	.43625	31
30	9.56408	9.96868	9.59540	10.40460	10.03132	10.43592	30
31	.56440	.96863	.59577	.40423	.03137	.43560	29
32	.56472	.96858	.59614	.40386	.03142	.43528	28
33	.56504	.96853	.59651	.40349	.03147	.43496	27
34	.56536	.96848	.59688	.40312	.03152	.43464	26
35	9.56568	9.96843	9.59725	10.40275	10.03157	10.43432	25
36	.56599	.96838	.59762	.40238	.03162	.43401	24
37	.56631	.96835	.59799	.40201	.03167	.43369	23
38	.56663	.96828	.59835	.40165	.03172	.43337	22
39	.56695	.96823	.59872	.40128	.03177	.43305	21
40	9.56727	9.96818	9.59909	10.40091	10.03182	10.43273	20
41	.56759	.96813	.59946	.40054	.03187	.43241	19
42	.56790	.96808	.59983	.40017	.03192	.43210	18
43	.56822	.96803	.60019	.39981	.03197	.43178	17
44	.56854	.96798	.60056	.39944	.03202	.43146	16
45	9.56886	9.96793	9.60093	10.39907	10.03207	10.43114	15
46	.56917	.96788	.60130	.39870	.03212	.43083	14
47	.56949	.96783	.60166	.39834	.03217	.43051	13
48	.56980	.96778	.60203	.39797	.03222	.43020	12
49	.57012	.96772	.60240	.39760	.03228	.42988	11
50	9.57044	9.96767	9.60276	10.39724	10.03233	10.42956	10
51	.57075	.96762	.60313	.39687	.03238	.42925	9
52	.57107	.96757	.60349	.39651	.03243	.42893	8
53	.57138	.96752	.60386	.39614	.03248	.42862	7
54	.57169	.96747	.60422	.39578	.03253	.42831	6
55	9.57201	9.96742	9.60459	10.39541	10.03258	10.42799	5
56	.57232	.96737	.60495	.39505	.03263	.42768	4
57	.57264	.96732	.60532	.39468	.03268	.42736	3
58	.57295	.96727	.60568	.39432	.03273	.42705	2
59	.57326	.96722	.60605	.39395	.03278	.42674	1
60	9.57358	9.96717	9.60641	10.39359	10.03283	10.42642	0
M	Cosine	Sine	Cotangent	Tangent	Cosecant	Secant	M

M	Sine	Cosine	Tangent	Cotangent	Secant	Cosecant	M
0	9.57358	9.96717	9.60641	10.39359	10.03283	10.42642	60
1	.57389	.96711	.60677	.39323	.03289	.42611	59
2	.57420	.96706	.60714	.39286	.03294	.42580	58
3	.57451	.96701	.60750	.39250	.03299	.42549	57
4	.57482	.96696	.60786	.39214	.03304	.42518	56
5	9.57514	9.96691	9.60823	10.39177	10.03309	10.42486	55
6	.57545	.96686	.60859	.39141	.03314	.42455	54
7	.57576	.96681	.60895	.39105	.03319	.42424	53
8	.57607	.96676	.60931	.39069	.03324	.42393	52
9	.57638	.96670	.60967	.39033	.03330	.42362	51
10	9.57669	9.96665	9.61004	10.38996	10.03335	10.42331	50
11	.57700	.96660	.61040	.38960	.03340	.42300	49
12	.57731	.96655	.61076	.38924	.03345	.42269	48
13	.57762	.96650	.61112	.38888	.03350	.42238	47
14	.57793	.96645	.61148	.38852	.03355	.42207	46
15	9.57824	9.96640	9.61184	10.38816	10.03360	10.42176	45
16	.57855	.96634	.61220	.38780	.03366	.42145	44
17	.57885	.96629	.61256	.38744	.03371	.42115	43
18	.57916	.96624	.61292	.38708	.03376	.42084	42
19	.57947	.96619	.61328	.38672	.03381	.42053	41
20	9.57978	9.96614	9.61364	10.38636	10.03386	10.42022	40
21	.58008	.96608	.61400	.38600	.03392	.41992	39
22	.58039	.96603	.61436	.38564	.03397	.41961	38
23	.58070	.96598	.61472	.38528	.03402	.41930	37
24	.58101	.96593	.61508	.38492	.03407	.41899	36
25	9.58131	9.96588	9.61544	10.38456	10.03412	10.41869	35
26	.58162	.96582	.61579	.38421	.03418	.41838	34
27	.58192	.96577	.61615	.38385	.03423	.41808	33
28	.58223	.96572	.61651	.38349	.03428	.41777	32
29	.58253	.96567	.61687	.38313	.03433	.41747	31
30	9.58284	9.96562	9.61722	10.38278	10.03438	10.41716	30
31	.58314	.96556	.61758	.38242	.03444	.41686	29
32	.58345	.96551	.61794	.38206	.03449	.41655	28
33	.58375	.96546	.61830	.38170	.03454	.41625	27
34	.58406	.96541	.61865	.38135	.03459	.41594	26
35	9.58436	9.96535	9.61901	10.38099	10.03465	10.41564	25
36	.58467	.96530	.61936	.38064	.03470	.41533	24
37	.58497	.96525	.61972	.38028	.03475	.41503	23
38	.58527	.96520	.62008	.37992	.03480	.41473	22
39	.58557	.96514	.62043	.37957	.03486	.41443	21
40	9.58588	9.96509	9.62079	10.37921	10.03491	10.41412	20
41	.58618	.96504	.62114	.37886	.03496	.41382	19
42	.58648	.96498	.62150	.37850	.03502	.41352	18
43	.58678	.96493	.62185	.37815	.03507	.41322	17
44	.58709	.96488	.62221	.37779	.03512	.41291	16
45	9.58739	9.96483	9.62256	10.37744	10.03517	10.41261	15
46	.58769	.96477	.62292	.37708	.03523	.41231	14
47	.58799	.96472	.62327	.37673	.03528	.41201	13
48	.58829	.96467	.62362	.37638	.03533	.41171	12
49	.58859	.96461	.62398	.37602	.03539	.41141	11
50	9.58889	9.96456	9.62433	10.37567	10.03544	10.41111	10
51	.58919	.96451	.62468	.37532	.03549	.41081	9
52	.58949	.96445	.62504	.37496	.03555	.41051	8
53	.58979	.96440	.62539	.37461	.03560	.41021	7
54	.59009	.96435	.62574	.37426	.03565	.40991	6
55	9.59039	9.96429	9.62609	10.37391	10.03571	10.40961	5
56	.59069	.96424	.62645	.37355	.03576	.40931	4
57	.59098	.96419	.62680	.37320	.03581	.40902	3
58	.59128	.96413	.62715	.37285	.03587	.40872	2
59	.59158	.96408	.62750	.37250	.03592	.40842	1
60	9.59188	9.96403	9.62785	10.37215	10.03597	10.40812	0
M	Cosine	Sine	Cotangent	Tangent	Cosecant	Secant	M

M	Sine	Cosine	Tangent	Cotangent	Secant	Cosecant	M
0	9.59188	9.96403	9.62785	10.37215	10.03597	10.40812	60
1	.59218	.96397	.62820	.37180	.03603	.40782	59
2	.59247	.96392	.62855	.37145	.03608	.40753	58
3	.59277	.96387	.62890	.37110	.03613	.40723	57
4	.59307	.96381	.62926	.37074	.03619	.40693	56
5	9.59336	9.96376	9.62961	10.37039	10.03624	10.40664	55
6	.59366	.96370	.62996	.37004	.03630	.40634	54
7	.59396	.96365	.63031	.36969	.03635	.40604	53
8	.59425	.96360	.63066	.36934	.03640	.40575	52
9	.59455	.96354	.63101	.36899	.03646	.40545	51
10	9.59484	9.96349	9.63135	10.36865	10.03651	10.40516	50
11	.59514	.96343	.63170	.36830	.03657	.40486	49
12	.59543	.96338	.63205	.36795	.03662	.40457	48
13	.59573	.96333	.63240	.36760	.03667	.40427	47
14	.59602	.96327	.63275	.36725	.03673	.40398	46
15	9.59632	9.96322	9.63310	10.36690	10.03678	10.40368	45
16	.59661	.96316	.63345	.36655	.03684	.40339	44
17	.59690	.96311	.63379	.36621	.03689	.40310	43
18	.59720	.96305	.63414	.36586	.03695	.40280	42
19	.59749	.96300	.63449	.36551	.03700	.40251	41
20	9.59778	9.96294	9.63484	10.36516	10.03706	10.40222	40
21	.59808	.96289	.63519	.36481	.03711	.40192	39
22	.59837	.96284	.63553	.36447	.03716	.40163	38
23	.59866	.96278	.63588	.36412	.03722	.40134	37
24	.59895	.96273	.63623	.36377	.03727	.40105	36
25	9.59924	9.96267	9.63657	10.36343	10.03733	10.40076	35
26	.59954	.96262	.63692	.36308	.03738	.40046	34
27	.59983	.96256	.63726	.36274	.03744	.40017	33
28	.60012	.96251	.63761	.36239	.03749	.39988	32
29	.60041	.96245	.63796	.36204	.03755	.39959	31
30	9.60070	9.96240	9.63830	10.36170	10.03760	10.39930	30
31	.60099	.96234	.63865	.36135	.03766	.39901	29
32	.60128	.96229	.63899	.36101	.03771	.39872	28
33	.60157	.96223	.63934	.36066	.03777	.39843	27
34	.60186	.96218	.63968	.36032	.03782	.39814	26
35	9.60215	9.96212	9.64003	10.35997	10.03788	10.39785	25
36	.60244	.96207	.64037	.35963	.03793	.39756	24
37	.60273	.96201	.64072	.35928	.03799	.39727	23
38	.60302	.96196	.64106	.35894	.03804	.39698	22
39	.60331	.96190	.64140	.35860	.03810	.39669	21
40	9.60359	9.96185	9.64175	10.35825	10.03815	10.39641	20
41	.60388	.96179	.64209	.35791	.03821	.39612	19
42	.60417	.96174	.64243	.35757	.03826	.39583	18
43	.60446	.96168	.64278	.35722	.03832	.39554	17
44	.60474	.96162	.64312	.35688	.03838	.39526	16
45	9.60503	9.96157	9.64346	10.35654	10.03843	10.39497	15
46	.60532	.96151	.64381	.35619	.03849	.39468	14
47	.60561	.96146	.64415	.35585	.03854	.39439	13
48	.60589	.96140	.64449	.35551	.03860	.39411	12
49	.60618	.96135	.64483	.35517	.03865	.39382	11
50	9.60646	9.96129	9.64517	10.35483	10.03871	10.39354	10
51	.60675	.96123	.64552	.35448	.03877	.39325	9
52	.60704	.96118	.64586	.35414	.03882	.39296	8
53	.60732	.96112	.64620	.35380	.03888	.39268	7
54	.60761	.96107	.64654	.35346	.03893	.39239	6
55	9.60789	9.96101	9.64688	10.35312	10.03899	10.39211	5
56	.60818	.96095	.64722	.35278	.03905	.39182	4
57	.60846	.96090	.64756	.35244	.03910	.39154	3
58	.60875	.96084	.64790	.35210	.03916	.39125	2
59	.60903	.96079	.64824	.35176	.03921	.39097	1
60	9.60931	9.96073	9.64858	10.35142	10.03927	10.39069	0
M	Cosine	Sine	Cotangent	Tangent	Cosecant	Secant	M

M	Sine	Cosine	Tangent	Cotangent	Secant	Cosecant	M
0	9.60931	9.96073	9.64858	10.35142	10.03927	10.39069	60
1	.60960	.96067	.64892	.35108	.03933	.39040	59
2	.60988	.96062	.64926	.35074	.03938	.39012	58
3	.61016	.96056	.64960	.35040	.03944	.38984	57
4	.61045	.96050	.64994	.35006	.03950	.38955	56
5	9.61073	9.96045	9.65028	10.34972	10.03955	10.38927	55
6	.61101	.96039	.65062	.34938	.03961	.38899	54
7	.61129	.96034	.65096	.34904	.03966	.38871	53
8	.61158	.96028	.65130	.34870	.03972	.38842	52
9	.61186	.96022	.65164	.34836	.03978	.38814	51
10	9.61214	9.96017	9.65197	10.34803	10.03983	10.38786	50
11	.61242	.96011	.65231	.34769	.03989	.38758	49
12	.61270	.96005	.65265	.34735	.03995	.38730	48
13	.61298	.96000	.65299	.34701	.04000	.38702	47
14	.61326	.95994	.65333	.34667	.04006	.38674	46
15	9.61354	9.95988	9.65366	10.34634	10.04012	10.38646	45
16	.61382	.95982	.65400	.34600	.04018	.38618	44
17	.61411	.95977	.65434	.34566	.04023	.38589	43
18	.61438	.95971	.65467	.34533	.04029	.38562	42
19	.61466	.95965	.65501	.34499	.04035	.38534	41
20	9.61494	9.95960	9.65535	10.34465	10.04040	10.38506	40
21	.61522	.95954	.65568	.34432	.04046	.38478	39
22	.61550	.95948	.65602	.34398	.04052	.38450	38
23	.61578	.95942	.65636	.34364	.04058	.38422	37
24	.61606	.95937	.65669	.34331	.04063	.38394	36
25	9.61634	9.95931	9.65703	10.34297	10.04069	10.38366	35
26	.61662	.95925	.65736	.34264	.04075	.38338	34
27	.61689	.95920	.65770	.34230	.04080	.38311	33
28	.61717	.95914	.65803	.34197	.04086	.38283	32
29	.61745	.95908	.65837	.34163	.04092	.38255	31
30	9.61773	9.95902	9.65870	10.34130	10.04098	10.38227	30
31	.61800	.95897	.65904	.34096	.04103	.38200	29
32	.61828	.95891	.65937	.34063	.04109	.38172	28
33	.61856	.95885	.65971	.34029	.04115	.38144	27
34	.61883	.95879	.66004	.33996	.04121	.38117	26
35	9.61911	9.95873	9.66038	10.33962	10.04127	10.38089	25
36	.61939	.95868	.66071	.33929	.04132	.38061	24
37	.61966	.95862	.66104	.33896	.04138	.38034	23
38	.61994	.95856	.66138	.33862	.04144	.38006	22
39	.62021	.95850	.66171	.33829	.04150	.37979	21
40	9.62049	9.95844	9.66204	10.33796	10.04156	10.37951	20
41	.62076	.95839	.66238	.33762	.04161	.37924	19
42	.62104	.95833	.66271	.33729	.04167	.37896	18
43	.62131	.95827	.66304	.33696	.04173	.37869	17
44	.62159	.95821	.66337	.33663	.04179	.37841	16
45	9.62186	9.95815	9.66371	10.33629	10.04185	10.37814	15
46	.62214	.95810	.66404	.33596	.04190	.37786	14
47	.62241	.95804	.66437	.33563	.04196	.37759	13
48	.62268	.95798	.66470	.33530	.04202	.37732	12
49	.62296	.95792	.66503	.33497	.04208	.37704	11
50	9.62323	9.95786	9.66537	10.33463	10.04214	10.37677	10
51	.62350	.95780	.66570	.33430	.04220	.37650	9
52	.62377	.95775	.66603	.33397	.04225	.37623	8
53	.62405	.95769	.66636	.33364	.04231	.37595	7
54	.62432	.95763	.66669	.33331	.04237	.37568	6
55	9.62459	9.95757	9.66702	10.33298	10.04243	10.37541	5
56	.62486	.95751	.66735	.33265	.04249	.37514	4
57	.62513	.95745	.66768	.33232	.04255	.37487	3
58	.62541	.95739	.66801	.33199	.04261	.37459	2
59	.62568	.95733	.66834	.33166	.04267	.37432	1
60	9.62595	9.95728	9.66867	10.33133	10.04272	10.37405	0

M	Cosine	Sine	Cotangent	Tangent	Cosecant	Secant	M

M	Sine	Cosine	Tangent	Cotangent	Secant	Cosecant	M
0	9.62595	9.95728	9.66867	10.33133	10.04272	10.37405	60
1	.62622	.95722	.66900	.33100	.04278	.37378	59
2	.62649	.95716	.66933	.33067	.04284	.37351	58
3	.62676	.95710	.66966	.33034	.04290	.37324	57
4	.62703	.95704	.66999	.33001	.04296	.37297	56
5	9.62730	9.95698	9.67032	10.32968	10.04302	10.37270	55
6	.62757	.95692	.67065	.32935	.04308	.37243	54
7	.62784	.95686	.67098	.32902	.04314	.37216	53
8	.62811	.95680	.67131	.32869	.04320	.37189	52
9	.62838	.95674	.67163	.32837	.04326	.37162	51
10	9.62865	9.95668	9.67196	10.32804	10.04332	10.37135	50
11	.62892	.95663	.67229	.32771	.04337	.37108	49
12	.62918	.95657	.67262	.32738	.04343	.37082	48
13	.62945	.95651	.67295	.32705	.04349	.37055	47
14	.62972	.95645	.67327	.32673	.04355	.37028	46
15	9.62999	9.95639	9.67360	10.32640	10.04361	10.37001	45
16	.63026	.95633	.67393	.32607	.04367	.36974	44
17	.63052	.95627	.67426	.32574	.04373	.36948	43
18	.63079	.95621	.67458	.32542	.04379	.36921	42
19	.63106	.95615	.67491	.32509	.04385	.36894	41
20	9.63133	9.95609	9.67524	10.32476	10.04391	10.36867	40
21	.63159	.95603	.67556	.32444	.04397	.36841	39
22	.63186	.95597	.67589	.32411	.04403	.36814	38
23	.63213	.95591	.67622	.32378	.04409	.36787	37
24	.63239	.95585	.67654	.32346	.04415	.36761	36
25	9.63266	9.95579	9.67687	10.32313	10.04421	10.36734	35
26	.63292	.95573	.67719	.32281	.04427	.36708	34
27	.63319	.95567	.67752	.32248	.04433	.36681	33
28	.63345	.95561	.67785	.32215	.04439	.36655	32
29	.63372	.95555	.67817	.32183	.04445	.36628	31
30	9.63398	9.95549	9.67850	10.32150	10.04451	10.36602	30
31	.63425	.95543	.67882	.32118	.04457	.36575	29
32	.63451	.95537	.67915	.32085	.04463	.36549	28
33	.63478	.95531	.67947	.32053	.04469	.36522	27
34	.63504	.95525	.67980	.32020	.04475	.36496	26
35	9.63531	9.95519	9.68012	10.31988	10.04481	10.36469	25
36	.63557	.95513	.68044	.31956	.04487	.36443	24
37	.63583	.95507	.68077	.31923	.04493	.36417	23
38	.63610	.95500	.68109	.31891	.04500	.36390	22
39	.63636	.95494	.68142	.31858	.04506	.36364	21
40	9.63662	9.95488	9.68174	10.31826	10.04512	10.36338	20
41	.63689	.95482	.68206	.31794	.04518	.36311	19
42	.63715	.95476	.68239	.31761	.04524	.36285	18
43	.63741	.95470	.68271	.31729	.04530	.36259	17
44	.63767	.95464	.68303	.31697	.04536	.36233	16
45	9.63794	9.95458	9.68336	10.31664	10.04542	10.36206	15
46	.63820	.95452	.68368	.31632	.04548	.36180	14
47	.63846	.95446	.68400	.31600	.04554	.36154	13
48	.63872	.95440	.68432	.31568	.04560	.36128	12
49	.63898	.95434	.68465	.31535	.04566	.36102	11
50	9.63924	9.95427	9.68497	10.31503	10.04573	10.36076	10
51	.63950	.95421	.68529	.31471	.04579	.36050	9
52	.63976	.95415	.68561	.31439	.04585	.36024	8
53	.64002	.95409	.68593	.31407	.04591	.35998	7
54	.64028	.95403	.68626	.31374	.04597	.35972	6
55	.64054	9.95397	9.68658	10.31342	10.04603	10.35946	5
56	.64080	.95391	.68690	.31310	.04609	.35920	4
57	.64106	.95384	.68722	.31278	.04616	.35894	3
58	.64132	.95378	.68754	.31246	.04622	.35868	2
59	.64158	.95372	.68786	.31214	.04628	.35842	1
60	9.64184	9.95366	9.68818	10.31182	10.04634	10.35816	0

| M | Cosine | Sine | Cotangent | Tangent | Cosecant | Secant | M |

M	Sine	Cosine	Tangent	Cotangent	Secant	Cosecant	M
0	9.64184	9.95366	9.68818	10.31182	10.04634	10.35816	60
1	.64210	.95360	.68850	.31150	.04640	.35790	59
2	.64236	.95354	.68882	.31118	.04646	.35764	58
3	.64262	.95348	.68914	.31086	.04652	.35738	57
4	.64288	.95341	.68946	.31054	.04659	.35712	56
5	9.64313	9.95335	9.68978	10.31022	10.04665	10.35687	55
6	.64339	.95329	.69010	.30990	.04671	.35661	54
7	.64365	.95323	.69042	.30958	.04677	.35635	53
8	.64391	.95317	.69074	.30926	.04683	.35609	52
9	.64417	.95310	.69106	.30894	.04690	.35583	51
10	9.64442	9.95304	9.69138	10.30862	10.04696	10.35558	50
11	.64468	.95298	.69170	.30830	.04702	.35532	49
12	.64494	.95292	.69202	.30798	.04708	.35506	48
13	.64519	.95286	.69234	.30766	.04714	.35481	47
14	.64545	.95279	.69266	.30734	.04721	.35455	46
15	9.64571	9.95273	9.69298	10.30702	10.04727	10.35429	45
16	.64596	.95267	.69329	.30671	.04733	.35404	44
17	.64622	.95261	.69361	.30639	.04739	.35378	43
18	.64647	.95254	.69393	.30607	.04746	.35353	42
19	.64673	.95248	.69425	.30575	.04752	.35327	41
20	9.64698	9.95242	9.69457	10.30543	10.04758	10.35302	40
21	.64724	.95236	.69488	.30512	.04764	.35276	39
22	.64749	.95229	.69520	.30480	.04771	.35251	38
23	.64775	.95223	.69552	.30448	.04777	.35225	37
24	.64800	.95217	.69584	.30416	.04783	.35200	36
25	9.64826	9.95211	9.69615	10.30385	10.04789	10.35174	35
26	.64851	.95204	.69647	.30353	.04796	.35149	34
27	.64877	.95198	.69679	.30321	.04802	.35123	33
28	.64902	.95192	.69710	.30290	.04808	.35098	32
29	.64927	.95185	.69742	.30258	.04815	.35073	31
30	9.64953	9.95179	9.69774	10.30226	10.04821	10.35047	30
31	.64978	.95173	.69805	.30195	.04827	.35022	29
32	.65003	.95167	.69837	.30163	.04833	.34997	28
33	.65029	.95160	.69868	.30132	.04840	.34971	27
34	.65054	.95154	.69900	.30100	.04846	.34946	26
35	9.65079	9.95148	9.69932	10.30068	10.04852	10.34921	25
36	.65104	.95141	.69963	.30037	.04859	.34896	24
37	.65130	.95135	.69995	.30005	.04865	.34870	23
38	.65155	.95129	.70026	.29974	.04871	.34845	22
39	.65180	.95122	.70058	.29942	.04878	.34820	21
40	9.65205	9.95116	9.70089	10.29911	10.04884	10.34795	20
41	.65230	.95110	.70121	.29879	.04890	.34770	19
42	.65255	.95103	.70152	.29848	.04897	.34745	18
43	.65281	.95097	.70184	.29816	.04903	.34719	17
44	.65306	.95090	.70215	.29785	.04910	.34694	16
45	9.65331	9.95084	9.70247	10.29753	10.04916	10.34669	15
46	.65356	.95078	.70278	.29722	.04922	.34644	14
47	.65381	.95071	.70309	.29691	.04929	.34619	13
48	.65406	.95065	.70341	.29659	.04935	.34594	12
49	.65431	.95059	.70372	.29628	.04941	.34569	11
50	9.65456	9.95052	9.70404	10.29596	10.04948	10.34544	10
51	.65481	.95046	.70435	.29565	.04954	.34519	9
52	.65506	.95039	.70466	.29534	.04961	.34494	8
53	.65531	.95033	.70498	.29502	.04967	.34469	7
54	.65556	.95027	.70529	.29471	.04973	.34444	6
55	9.65580	9.95020	9.70560	10.29440	10.04980	10.34420	5
56	.65605	.95014	.70592	.29408	.04986	.34395	4
57	.65630	.95007	.70623	.29377	.04993	.34370	3
58	.65655	.95001	.70654	.29346	.04999	.34345	2
59	.65680	.94995	.70685	.29315	.05005	.34320	1
60	9.65705	9.94988	9.70717	10.29283	10.05012	10.34295	0

| M | Cosine | Sine | Cotangent | Tangent | Cosecant | Secant | M |

M	Sine	Cosine	Tangent	Cotangent	Secant	Cosecant	M
0	9.65705	9.94988	9.70717	10.29283	10.05012	10.34295	60
1	.65729	.94982	.70748	.29252	.05018	.34271	59
2	.65754	.94975	.70779	.29221	.05025	.34246	58
3	.65779	.94969	.70810	.29190	.05031	.34221	57
4	.65804	.94962	.70841	.29159	.05038	.34196	56
5	9.65828	9.94956	9.70873	10.29127	10.05044	10.34172	55
6	.65853	.94949	.70904	.29096	.05051	.34147	54
7	.65878	.94943	.70935	.29065	.05057	.34122	53
8	.65902	.94936	.70966	.29034	.05064	.34098	52
9	.65927	.94930	.70997	.29003	.05070	.34073	51
10	9.65952	9.94923	9.71028	10.28972	10.05077	10.34048	50
11	.65976	.94917	.71059	.28941	.05083	.34024	49
12	.66001	.94911	.71090	.28910	.05089	.33999	48
13	.66025	.94904	.71121	.28879	.05096	.33975	47
14	.66050	.94898	.71153	.28847	.05102	.33950	46
15	9.66075	9.94891	9.71184	10.28816	10.05109	10.33925	45
16	.66099	.94885	.71215	.28785	.05115	.33901	44
17	.66124	.94878	.71246	.28754	.05122	.33876	43
18	.66148	.94871	.71277	.28723	.05129	.33852	42
19	.66173	.94865	.71308	.28692	.05135	.33827	41
20	9.66197	9.94858	9.71339	10.28661	10.05142	10.33803	40
21	.66221	.94852	.71370	.28630	.05148	.33779	39
22	.66246	.94845	.71401	.28599	.05155	.33754	38
23	.66270	.94839	.71431	.28569	.05161	.33730	37
24	.66295	.94832	.71462	.28538	.05168	.33705	36
25	9.66319	9.94826	9.71493	10.28507	10.05174	10.33681	35
26	.66343	.94819	.71524	.28476	.05181	.33657	34
27	.66368	.94813	.71555	.28445	.05187	.33632	33
28	.66392	.94806	.71586	.28414	.05194	.33608	32
29	.66416	.94799	.71617	.28383	.05201	.33584	31
30	9.66441	9.94793	9.71648	10.28352	10.05207	10.33559	30
31	.66465	.94786	.71679	.28321	.05214	.33535	29
32	.66489	.94780	.71709	.28291	.05220	.33511	28
33	.66513	.94773	.71740	.28260	.05227	.33487	27
34	.66537	.94767	.71771	.28229	.05233	.33463	26
35	9.66562	9.94760	9.71802	10.28198	10.05240	10.33438	25
36	.66586	.94753	.71833	.28167	.05247	.33414	24
37	.66610	.94747	.71863	.28137	.05253	.33390	23
38	.66634	.94740	.71894	.28106	.05260	.33366	22
39	.66658	.94734	.71925	.28075	.05266	.33342	21
40	9.66682	9.94727	9.71955	10.28045	10.05273	10.33318	20
41	.66706	.94720	.71986	.28014	.05280	.33294	19
42	.66731	.94714	.72017	.27983	.05286	.33269	18
43	.66755	.94707	.72048	.27952	.05293	.33245	17
44	.66779	.94700	.72078	.27922	.05300	.33221	16
45	9.66803	9.94694	9.72109	10.27891	10.05306	10.33197	15
46	.66827	.94687	.72140	.27860	.05313	.33173	14
47	.66851	.94680	.72170	.27830	.05320	.33149	13
48	.66875	.94674	.72201	.27799	.05326	.33125	12
49	.66899	.94667	.72231	.27769	.05333	.33101	11
50	9.66922	9.94660	9.72262	10.27738	10.05340	10.33078	10
51	.66946	.94654	.72293	.27707	.05346	.33054	9
52	.66970	.94647	.72323	.27677	.05353	.33030	8
53	.66994	.94640	.72354	.27646	.05360	.33006	7
54	.67018	.94634	.72384	.27616	.05366	.32982	6
55	9.67042	9.94627	9.72415	10.27585	10.05373	10.32958	5
56	.67066	.94620	.72445	.27555	.05380	.32934	4
57	.67090	.94614	.72476	.27524	.05386	.32910	3
58	.67113	.94607	.72506	.27494	.05393	.32887	2
59	.67137	.94600	.72537	.27463	.05400	.32863	1
60	9.67161	9.94593	9.72567	10.27433	10.05407	10.32839	0

M	Cosine	Sine	Cotangent	Tangent	Cosecant	Secant	M

M	Sine	Cosine	Tangent	Cotangent	Secant	Cosecant	M
0	9.67161	9.94593	9.72567	10.27433	10.05407	10.32839	60
1	.67185	.94587	.72598	.27402	.05413	.32815	59
2	.67208	.94580	.72628	.27372	.05420	.32792	58
3	.67232	.94573	.72659	.27341	.05427	.32768	57
4	.67256	.94567	.72689	.27311	.05433	.32744	56
5	9.67280	9.94560	9.72720	10.27280	10.05440	10.32720	55
6	.67303	.94553	.72750	.27250	.05447	.32697	54
7	.67327	.94546	.72780	.27220	.05454	.32673	53
8	.67350	.94540	.72811	.27189	.05460	.32650	52
9	.67374	.94533	.72841	.27159	.05467	.32626	51
10	9.67398	9.94526	9.72872	10.27128	10.05474	10.32602	50
11	.67421	.94519	.72902	.27098	.05481	.32579	49
12	.67445	.94513	.72932	.27068	.05487	.32555	48
13	.67468	.94506	.72963	.27037	.05494	.32532	47
14	.67492	.94499	.72993	.27007	.05501	.32508	46
15	9.67515	9.94492	9.73023	10.26977	10.05508	10.32485	45
16	.67539	.94485	.73054	.26946	.05515	.32461	44
17	.67562	.94479	.73084	.26916	.05521	.32438	43
18	.67586	.94472	.73114	.26886	.05528	.32414	42
19	.67609	.94465	.73144	.26856	.05535	.32391	41
20	9.67633	9.94458	9.73175	10.26825	10.05542	10.32367	40
21	.67656	.94451	.73205	.26795	.05549	.32344	39
22	.67680	.94445	.73235	.26765	.05555	.32320	38
23	.67703	.94438	.73265	.26735	.05562	.32297	37
24	.67726	.94431	.73295	.26705	.05569	.32274	36
25	9.67750	9.94424	9.73326	10.26674	10.05576	10.32250	35
26	.67773	.94417	.73356	.26644	.05583	.32227	34
27	.67796	.94410	.73386	.26614	.05590	.32204	33
28	.67820	.94404	.73416	.26584	.05596	.32180	32
29	.67843	.94397	.73446	.26554	.05603	.32157	31
30	9.67866	9.94390	9.73476	10.26524	10.05610	10.32134	30
31	.67890	.94383	.73507	.26493	.05617	.32110	29
32	.67913	.94376	.73537	.26463	.05624	.32087	28
33	.67936	.94369	.73567	.26433	.05631	.32064	27
34	.67959	.94362	.73597	.26403	.05638	.32041	26
35	9.67982	9.94355	9.73627	10.26373	10.05645	10.32018	25
36	.68006	.94349	.73657	.26343	.05651	.31994	24
37	.68029	.94342	.73687	.26313	.05658	.31971	23
38	.68052	.94335	.73717	.26283	.05665	.31948	22
39	.68075	.94328	.73747	.26253	.05672	.31925	21
40	9.68098	9.94321	9.73777	10.26223	10.05679	10.31902	20
41	.68121	.94314	.73807	.26193	.05686	.31879	19
42	.68144	.94307	.73837	.26163	.05693	.31856	18
43	.68167	.94300	.73867	.26133	.05700	.31833	17
44	.68190	.94293	.73897	.26103	.05707	.31810	16
45	9.68213	9.94286	9.73927	10.26073	10.05714	10.31787	15
46	.68237	.94279	.73957	.26043	.05721	.31763	14
47	.68260	.94273	.73987	.26013	.05727	.31740	13
48	.68283	.94266	.74017	.25983	.05734	.31717	12
49	.68305	.94259	.74047	.25953	.05741	.31695	11
50	9.68328	9.94252	9.74077	10.25923	10.05748	10.31672	10
51	.68351	.94245	.74107	.25893	.05755	.31649	9
52	.68374	.94238	.74137	.25863	.05762	.31626	8
53	.68397	.94231	.74166	.25834	.05769	.31603	7
54	.68420	.94224	.74196	.25804	.05776	.31580	6
55	9.68443	9.94217	9.74226	10.25774	10.05783	10.31557	5
56	.68466	.94210	.74256	.25744	.05790	.31534	4
57	.68489	.94203	.74286	.25714	.05797	.31511	3
58	.68512	.94196	.74316	.25684	.05804	.31488	2
59	.68534	.94189	.74345	.25655	.05811	.31466	1
60	9.68557	9.94182	9.74375	10.25625	10.05818	10.31443	0

| M | Cosine | Sine | Cotangent | Tangent | Cosecant | Secant | M |

M	Sine	Cosine	Tangent	Cotangent	Secant	Cosecant	M
0	9.68557	9.94182	9.74375	10.25625	10.05818	10.31443	60
1	.68580	.94175	.74405	.25595	.05825	.31420	59
2	.68603	.94168	.74435	.25565	.05832	.31397	58
3	.68625	.94161	.74465	.25535	.05839	.31375	57
4	.68648	.94154	.74494	.25506	.05846	.31352	56
5	9.68671	9.94147	9.74524	10.25476	10.05853	10.31329	55
6	.68694	.94140	.74554	.25446	.05860	.31306	54
7	.68716	.94133	.74583	.25417	.05867	.31284	53
8	.68739	.94126	.74613	.25387	.05874	.31261	52
9	.68762	.94119	.74643	.25357	.05881	.31238	51
10	9.68784	9.94112	9.74673	10.25327	10.05888	10.31216	50
11	.68807	.94105	.74702	.25298	.05895	.31193	49
12	.68829	.94098	.74732	.25268	.05902	.31171	48
13	.68852	.94090	.74762	.25238	.05910	.31148	47
14	.68875	.94083	.74791	.25209	.05917	.31125	46
15	9.68897	9.94076	9.74821	10.25179	10.05924	10.31103	45
16	.68920	.94069	.74851	.25149	.05931	.31080	44
17	.68942	.94062	.74880	.25120	.05938	.31058	43
18	.68965	.94055	.74910	.25090	.05945	.31035	42
19	.68987	.94048	.74939	.25061	.05952	.31013	41
20	9.69010	9.94041	9.74969	10.25031	10.05959	10.30990	40
21	.69032	.94034	.74998	.25002	.05966	.30968	39
22	.69055	.94027	.75028	.24972	.05973	.30945	38
23	.69077	.94020	.75058	.24942	.05980	.30923	37
24	.69100	.94012	.75087	.24913	.05988	.30900	36
25	9.69122	9.94005	9.75117	10.24883	10.05995	10.30878	35
26	.69144	.93998	.75146	.24854	.06002	.30856	34
27	.69167	.93991	.75176	.24824	.06009	.30833	33
28	.69189	.93984	.75205	.24795	.06016	.30811	32
29	.69212	.93977	.75235	.24765	.06023	.30788	31
30	9.69234	9.93970	9.75264	10.24736	10.06030	10.30766	30
31	.69256	.93963	.75294	.24706	.06037	.30744	29
32	.69279	.93955	.75323	.24677	.06045	.30721	28
33	.69301	.93948	.75353	.24647	.06052	.30699	27
34	.69323	.93941	.75382	.24618	.06059	.30677	26
35	9.69345	9.93934	9.75411	10.24589	10.06066	10.30655	25
36	.69368	.93927	.75441	.24559	.06073	.30632	24
37	.69390	.93920	.75470	.24530	.06080	.30610	23
38	.69412	.93912	.75500	.24500	.06088	.30588	22
39	.69434	.93905	.75529	.24471	.06095	.30566	21
40	9.69456	9.93898	9.75558	10.24442	10.06102	10.30544	20
41	.69479	.93891	.75588	.24412	.06109	.30521	19
42	.69501	.93884	.75617	.24383	.06116	.30499	18
43	.69523	.93876	.75647	.24353	.06124	.30477	17
44	.69545	.93869	.75676	.24324	.06131	.30455	16
45	9.69567	9.93862	9.75705	10.24295	10.06138	10.30433	15
46	.69589	.93855	.75735	.24265	.06145	.30411	14
47	.69611	.93847	.75764	.24236	.06153	.30389	13
48	.69633	.93840	.75793	.24207	.06160	.30367	12
49	.69655	.93833	.75822	.24178	.06167	.30345	11
50	9.69677	9.93826	9.75852	10.24148	10.06174	10.30323	10
51	.69699	.93819	.75881	.24119	.06181	.30301	9
52	.69721	.93811	.75910	.24090	.06189	.30279	8
53	.69743	.93804	.75939	.24061	.06196	.30257	7
54	.69765	.93797	.75969	.24031	.06203	.30235	6
55	9.69787	9.93789	9.75998	10.24002	10.06211	10.30213	5
56	.69809	.93782	.76027	.23973	.06218	.30191	4
57	.69831	.93775	.76056	.23944	.06225	.30169	3
58	.69853	.93768	.76086	.23914	.06232	.30147	2
59	.69875	.93760	.76115	.23885	.06240	.30125	1
60	9.69897	9.93753	9.76144	10.23856	10.06247	10.30103	0

M	Cosine	Sine	Cotangent	Tangent	Cosecant	Secant	M

M	Sine	Cosine	Tangent	Cotangent	Secant	Cosecant	M
0	9.69897	9.93753	9.76144	10.23856	10.06247	10.30103	60
1	.69919	.93746	.76173	.23827	.06254	.30081	59
2	.69941	.93738	.76202	.23798	.06262	.30059	58
3	.69963	.93731	.76231	.23769	.06269	.30037	57
4	.69984	.93724	.76261	.23739	.06276	.30016	56
5	9.70006	9.93717	9.76290	10.23710	10.06283	10.29994	55
6	.70028	.93709	.76319	.23681	.06291	.29972	54
7	.70050	.93702	.76348	.23652	.06298	.29950	53
8	.70072	.93695	.76377	.23623	.06305	.29928	52
9	.70093	.93687	.76406	.23594	.06313	.29907	51
10	9.70115	9.93680	9.76435	10.23565	10.06320	10.29885	50
11	.70137	.93673	.76464	.23536	.06327	.29863	49
12	.70159	.93665	.76493	.23507	.06335	.29841	48
13	.70180	.93658	.76522	.23478	.06342	.29820	47
14	.70202	.93650	.76551	.23449	.06350	.29798	46
15	9.70224	9.93643	9.76580	10.23420	10.06357	10.29776	45
16	.70245	.93636	.76609	.23391	.06364	.29755	44
17	.70267	.93628	.76639	.23361	.06372	.29733	43
18	.70288	.93621	.76668	.23332	.06379	.29712	42
19	.70310	.93614	.76697	.23303	.06386	.29690	41
20	9.70332	9.93606	9.76725	10.23275	10.06394	10.29668	40
21	.70353	.93599	.76754	.23246	.06401	.29647	39
22	.70375	.93591	.76783	.23217	.06409	.29625	38
23	.70396	.93584	.76812	.23188	.06416	.29604	37
24	.70418	.93577	.76841	.23159	.06423	.29582	36
25	9.70439	9.93569	9.76870	10.23130	10.06431	10.29561	35
26	.70461	.93562	.76899	.23101	.06438	.29539	34
27	.70482	.93554	.76928	.23072	.06446	.29518	33
28	.70504	.93547	.76957	.23043	.06453	.29496	32
29	.70525	.93539	.76986	.23014	.06461	.29475	31
30	9.70547	9.93532	9.77015	10.22985	10.06468	10.29453	30
31	.70568	.93525	.77044	.22956	.06475	.29432	29
32	.70590	.93517	.77073	.22927	.06483	.29410	28
33	.70611	.93510	.77101	.22899	.06490	.29389	27
34	.70633	.93502	.77130	.22870	.06498	.29367	26
35	9.70654	9.93495	9.77159	10.22841	10.06505	10.29346	25
36	.70675	.93487	.77188	.22812	.06513	.29325	24
37	.70697	.93480	.77217	.22783	.06520	.29303	23
38	.70718	.93472	.77246	.22754	.06528	.29282	22
39	.70739	.93465	.77274	.22726	.06535	.29261	21
40	9.70761	9.93457	9.77303	10.22697	10.06543	10.29239	20
41	.70782	.93450	.77332	.22668	.06550	.29218	19
42	.70803	.93442	.77361	.22639	.06558	.29197	18
43	.70824	.93435	.77390	.22610	.06565	.29176	17
44	.70846	.93427	.77418	.22582	.06573	.29154	16
45	9.70867	9.93420	9.77447	10.22553	10.06580	10.29133	15
46	.70888	.93412	.77476	.22524	.06588	.29112	14
47	.70909	.93405	.77505	.22495	.06595	.29091	13
48	.70931	.93397	.77533	.22467	.06603	.29069	12
49	.70952	.93390	.77562	.22438	.06610	.29048	11
50	9.70973	9.93382	9.77591	10.22409	10.06618	10.29027	10
51	.70994	.93375	.77619	.22381	.06625	.29006	9
52	.71015	.93367	.77648	.22352	.06633	.28985	8
53	.71036	.93360	.77677	.22323	.06640	.28964	7
54	.71058	.93352	.77706	.22294	.06648	.28942	6
55	9.71079	9.93344	9.77734	10.22266	10.06656	10.28921	5
56	.71100	.93337	.77763	.22237	.06663	.28900	4
57	.71121	.93329	.77791	.22209	.06671	.28879	3
58	.71142	.93322	.77820	.22180	.06678	.28858	2
59	.71163	.93314	.77849	.22151	.06686	.28837	1
60	9.71184	9.93307	9.77877	10.22123	10.06693	10.28816	0

| M | Cosine | Sine | Cotangent | Tangent | Cosecant | Secant | M |

M	Sine	Cosine	Tangent	Cotangent	Secant	Cosecant	M
0	9.71184	9.93307	9.77877	10.22123	10.06693	10.28816	60
1	.71205	.93299	.77906	.22094	.06701	.28795	59
2	.71226	.93291	.77935	.22065	.06709	.28774	58
3	.71247	.93284	.77963	.22037	.06716	.28753	57
4	.71268	.93276	.77992	.22008	.06724	.28732	56
5	9.71289	9.93269	9.78020	10.21980	10.06731	10.28711	55
6	.71310	.93261	.78049	.21951	.06739	.28690	54
7	.71331	.93253	.78077	.21923	.06747	.28669	53
8	.71352	.93246	.78106	.21894	.06754	.28648	52
9	.71373	.93238	.78135	.21865	.06762	.28627	51
10	9.71393	9.93230	9.78163	10.21837	10.06770	10.28607	50
11	.71414	.93223	.78192	.21808	.06777	.28586	49
12	.71435	.93215	.78220	.21780	.06785	.28565	48
13	.71456	.93207	.78249	.21751	.06793	.28544	47
14	.71477	.93200	.78277	.21723	.06800	.28523	46
15	9.71498	9.93192	9.78306	10.21694	10.06808	10.28502	45
16	.71519	.93184	.78334	.21666	.06816	.28481	44
17	.71539	.93177	.78363	.21637	.06823	.28461	43
18	.71560	.93169	.78391	.21609	.06831	.28440	42
19	.71581	.93161	.78419	.21581	.06839	.28419	41
20	9.71602	9.93154	9.78448	10.21552	10.06846	10.28398	40
21	.71622	.93146	.78476	.21524	.06854	.28378	39
22	.71643	.93138	.78505	.21495	.06862	.28357	38
23	.71664	.93131	.78533	.21467	.06869	.28336	37
24	.71685	.93123	.78562	.21438	.06877	.28315	36
25	9.71705	9.93115	9.78590	10.21410	10.06885	10.28295	35
26	.71726	.93108	.78618	.21382	.06892	.28274	34
27	.71747	.93100	.78647	.21353	.06900	.28253	33
28	.71767	.93092	.78675	.21325	.06908	.28233	32
29	.71788	.93084	.78704	.21296	.06916	.28212	31
30	9.71809	9.93077	9.78732	10.21268	10.06923	10.28191	30
31	.71829	.93069	.78760	.21240	.06931	.28171	29
32	.71850	.93061	.78789	.21211	.06939	.28150	28
33	.71870	.93053	.78817	.21183	.06947	.28130	27
34	.71891	.93046	.78845	.21155	.06954	.28109	26
35	9.71911	9.93038	9.78874	10.21126	10.06962	10.28089	25
36	.71932	.93030	.78902	.21098	.06970	.28068	24
37	.71952	.93022	.78930	.21070	.06978	.28048	23
38	.71973	.93014	.78959	.21041	.06986	.28027	22
39	.71994	.93007	.78987	.21013	.06993	.28006	21
40	9.72014	9.92999	9.79015	10.20985	10.07001	10.27986	20
41	.72034	.92991	.79043	.20957	.07009	.27966	19
42	.72055	.92983	.79072	.20928	.07017	.27945	18
43	.72075	.92976	.79100	.20900	.07024	.27925	17
44	.72096	.92968	.79128	.20872	.07032	.27904	16
45	9.72116	9.92960	9.79156	10.20844	10.07040	10.27884	15
46	.72137	.92952	.79185	.20815	.07048	.27863	14
47	.72157	.92944	.79213	.20787	.07056	.27843	13
48	.72177	.92936	.79241	.20759	.07064	.27823	12
49	.72198	.92929	.79269	.20731	.07071	.27802	11
50	9.72218	9.92921	9.79297	10.20703	10.07079	10.27782	10
51	.72238	.92913	.79326	.20674	.07087	.27762	9
52	.72259	.92905	.79354	.20646	.07095	.27741	8
53	.72279	.92897	.79382	.20618	.07103	.27721	7
54	.72299	.92889	.79410	.20590	.07111	.27701	6
55	9.72320	9.92881	9.79438	10.20562	10.07119	10.27680	5
56	.72340	.92874	.79466	.20534	.07126	.27660	4
57	.72360	.92866	.79495	.20505	.07134	.27640	3
58	.72381	.92858	.79523	.20477	.07142	.27619	2
59	.72401	.92850	.79551	.20449	.07150	.27599	1
60	9.72421	9.92842	9.79579	10.20421	10.07158	10.27579	0
M	Cosine	Sine	Cotangent	Tangent	Cosecant	Secant	M

M	Sine	Cosine	Tangent	Cotangent	Secant	Cosecant	M
0	9.72421	9.92842	9.79579	10.20421	10.07158	10.27579	60
1	.72441	.92834	.79607	.20393	.07166	.27559	59
2	.72461	.92826	.79635	.20365	.07174	.27539	58
3	.72482	.92818	.79663	.20337	.07182	.27518	57
4	.72502	.92810	.79691	.20309	.07190	.27498	56
5	9.72522	9.92803	9.79719	10.20281	10.07197	10.27478	55
6	.72542	.92795	.79747	.20253	.07205	.27458	54
7	.72562	.92787	.79776	.20224	.07213	.27438	53
8	.72582	.92779	.79804	.20196	.07221	.27418	52
9	.72602	.92771	.79832	.20168	.07229	.27398	51
10	9.72622	9.92763	9.79860	10.20140	10.07237	10.27378	50
11	.72643	.92755	.79888	.20112	.07245	.27357	49
12	.72663	.92747	.79916	.20084	.07253	.27337	48
13	.72683	.92739	.79944	.20056	.07261	.27317	47
14	.72703	.92731	.79972	.20028	.07269	.27297	46
15	9.72723	9.92723	9.80000	10.20000	10.07277	10.27277	45
16	.72743	.92715	.80028	.19972	.07285	.27257	44
17	.72763	.92707	.80056	.19944	.07293	.27237	43
18	.72783	.92699	.80084	.19916	.07301	.27217	42
19	72803	.92691	.80112	.19888	.07309	.27197	41
20	9.72823	9.92683	9.80140	10.19860	10.07317	10.27177	40
21	.72843	.92675	.80168	.19832	.07325	.27157	39
22	.72863	.92667	.80195	.19805	.07333	.27137	38
23	.72883	.92659	.80223	.19777	.07341	.27117	37
24	.72902	.92651	.80251	.19749	.07349	.27098	36
25	9.72922	9.92643	9.80279	10.19721	10.07357	10.27078	35
26	.72942	.92635	.80307	.19693	.07365	.27058	34
27	.72962	.92627	.80335	.19665	.07373	.27038	33
28	.72982	.92619	.80363	.19637	.07381	.27018	32
29	.73002	.92611	.80391	.19609	.07389	.26998	31
30	9.73022	9.92603	9.80419	10.19581	10.07397	10.26978	30
31	.73041	.92595	.80447	.19553	.07405	26959	29
32	.73061	.92587	.80474	.19526	.07413	.26939	28
33	.73081	.92579	.80502	.19498	.07421	.26919	27
34	.73101	.92571	.80530	.19470	.07429	.26899	26
35	9.73121	9.92563	9.80558	10.19442	10.07437	10.26879	25
36	.73140	.92555	.80586	.19414	.07445	.26860	24
37	.73160	.92546	.80614	.19386	.07454	.26840	23
38	.73180	.92538	.80642	.19358	.07462	.26820	22
39	.73200	.92530	.80669	.19331	.07470	.26800	21
40	9.73219	9.92522	9.80697	10.19303	10.07478	10.26781	20
41	.73239	.92514	.80725	.19275	.07486	.26761	19
42	.73259	.92506	.80753	.19247	.07494	.26741	18
43	.73278	.92498	.80781	.19219	.07502	.26722	17
44	.73298	.92490	.80808	.19192	.07510	.26702	16
45	9.73318	9.92482	9.80836	10.19164	10.07518	10.26682	15
46	.73337	.92473	.80864	.19136	.07527	.26663	14
47	.73357	.92465	.80892	.19108	.07535	.26643	13
48	.73377	.92457	.80919	.19081	.07543	.26623	12
49	.73396	.92449	.80947	.19053	.07551	.26604	11
50	9.73416	9.92441	9.80975	10.19025	10.07559	10.26584	10
51	.73435	.92433	.81003	.18997	.07567	.26565	9
52	.73455	.92425	.81030	.18970	.07575	.26545	8
53	.73474	.92416	.81058	.18942	.07584	.26526	7
54	.73494	.92408	.81086	.18914	.07592	.26506	6
55	9.73513	9.92400	9.81113	10.18887	10.07600	10.26487	5
56	.73533	.92392	.81141	.18859	.07608	.26467	4
57	.73552	.92384	.81169	.18831	.07616	.26448	3
58	.73572	.92376	.81196	.18804	.07624	.26428	2
59	.73591	.92367	.81224	.18776	.07633	.26409	1
60	9.73611	9.92359	9.81252	10.18748	10.07641	10.26389	0
M	Cosine	Sine	Cotangent	Tangent	Cosecant	Secant	M

M	Sine	Cosine	Tangent	Cotangent	Secant	Cosecant	M
0	9.73611	9.92359	9.81252	10.18748	10.07641	10.26389	60
1	.73630	.92351	.81279	.18721	.07649	.26370	59
2	.73650	.92343	.81307	.18693	.07657	.26350	58
3	.73669	.92335	.81335	.18665	.07665	.26331	57
4	.73689	.92326	.81362	.18638	.07674	.26311	56
5	9.73708	9.92318	9.81390	10.18610	10.07682	10.26292	55
6	.73727	.92310	.81418	.18582	.07690	.26273	54
7	.73747	.92302	.81445	.18555	.07698	.26253	53
8	.73766	.92293	.81473	.18527	.07707	.26234	52
9	.73785	.92285	.81500	.18500	.07715	.26215	51
10	9.73805	9.92277	9.81528	10.18472	10.07723	10.26195	50
11	.73824	.92269	.81556	.18444	.07731	.26176	49
12	.73843	.92260	.81583	.18417	.07740	.26157	48
13	.73863	.92252	.81611	.18389	.07748	.26137	47
14	.73882	.92244	.81638	.18362	.07756	.26118	46
15	9.73901	9.92235	9.81666	10.18334	10.07765	10.26099	45
16	.73921	.92227	.81693	.18307	.07773	.26079	44
17	.73940	.92219	.81721	.18279	.07781	.26060	43
18	.73959	.92211	.81748	.18252	.07789	.26041	42
19	.73978	.92202	.81776	.18224	.07798	.26022	41
20	9.73997	9.92194	9.81803	10.18197	10.07806	10.26003	40
21	.74017	.92186	.81831	.18169	.07814	.25983	39
22	.74036	.92177	.81858	.18142	.07823	.25964	38
23	.74055	.92169	.81886	.18114	.07831	.25945	37
24	.74074	.92161	.81913	.18087	.07839	.25926	36
25	9.74093	9.92152	9.81941	10.18059	10.07848	10.25907	35
26	.74113	.92144	.81968	.18032	.07856	.25887	34
27	.74132	.92136	.81996	.18004	.07864	.25868	33
28	.74151	.92127	.82023	.17977	.07873	.25849	32
29	.74170	.92119	.82051	.17949	.07881	.25830	31
30	9.74189	9.92111	9.82078	10.17922	10.07889	10.25811	30
31	.74208	.92102	.82106	.17894	.07898	.25792	29
32	.74227	.92094	.82133	.17867	.07906	.25773	28
33	.74246	.92086	.82161	.17839	.07914	.25754	27
34	.74265	.92077	.82188	.17812	.07923	.25735	26
35	9.74284	9.92069	9.82215	10.17785	10.07931	10.25716	25
36	.74303	.92060	.82243	.17757	.07940	.25697	24
37	.74322	.92052	.82270	.17730	.07948	.25678	23
38	.74341	.92044	.82298	.17702	.07956	.25659	22
39	.74360	.92035	.82325	.17675	.07965	.25640	21
40	9.74379	9.92027	9.82352	10.17648	10.07973	10.25621	20
41	.74398	.92018	.82380	.17620	.07982	.25602	19
42	.74417	.92010	.82407	.17593	.07990	.25583	18
43	.74436	.92002	.82435	.17565	.07998	.25564	17
44	.74455	.91993	.82462	.17538	.08007	.25545	16
45	9.74474	9.91985	9.82489	10.17511	10.08015	10.25526	15
46	.74493	.91976	.82517	.17483	.08024	.25507	14
47	.74512	.91968	.82544	.17456	.08032	.25488	13
48	.74531	.91959	.82571	.17429	.08041	.25469	12
49	.74549	.91951	.82599	.17401	.08049	.25451	11
50	9.74568	9.91942	9.82626	10.17374	10.08058	10.25432	10
51	.74587	.91934	.82653	.17347	.08066	.25413	9
52	.74606	.91925	.82681	.17319	.08075	.25394	8
53	.74625	.91917	.82708	.17292	.08083	.25375	7
54	.74644	.91908	.82735	.17265	.08092	.25356	6
55	9.74662	9.91900	9.82762	10.17238	10.08100	10.25338	5
56	.74681	.91891	.82790	.17210	.08109	.25319	4
57	.74700	.91883	.82817	.17183	.08117	.25300	3
58	.74719	.91874	.82844	.17156	.08126	.25281	2
59	.74737	.91866	.82871	.17129	.08134	.25263	1
60	9.74756	9.91857	9.82899	10.17101	10.08143	10.25244	0
M	Cosine	Sine	Cotangent	Tangent	Cosecant	Secant	M

M	Sine	Cosine	Tangent	Cotangent	Secant	Cosecant	M
0	9.74756	9.91857	9.82899	10.17101	10.08143	10.25244	60
1	.74775	.91849	.82926	.17074	.08151	.25225	59
2	.74794	.91840	.82953	.17047	.08160	.25206	58
3	.74812	.91832	.82980	.17020	.08168	.25188	57
4	.74831	.91823	.83008	.16992	.08177	.25169	56
5	9.74850	9.91815	9.83035	10.16965	10.08185	10.25150	55
6	.74868	.91806	.83062	.16938	.08194	.25132	54
7	.74887	.91798	.83089	.16911	.08202	.25113	53
8	.74906	.91789	.83117	.16883	.08211	.25094	52
9	.74924	.91781	.83144	.16856	.08219	.25076	51
10	9.74943	9.91772	9.83171	10.16829	10.08228	10.25057	50
11	.74961	.91763	.83198	.16802	.08237	.25039	49
12	.74980	.91755	.83225	.16775	.08245	.25020	48
13	.74999	.91746	.83252	.16748	.08254	.25001	47
14	.75017	.91738	.83280	.16720	.08262	.24983	46
15	9.75036	9.91729	9.83307	10.16693	10.08271	10.24964	45
16	.75054	.91720	.83334	.16666	.08280	.24946	44
17	.75073	.91712	.83361	.16639	.08288	.24927	43
18	.75091	.91703	.83388	.16612	.08297	.24909	42
19	.75110	.91695	.83415	.16585	.08305	.24890	41
20	9.75128	9.91686	9.83442	10.16558	10.08314	10.24872	40
21	.75147	.91677	.83470	.16530	.08323	.24853	39
22	.75165	.91669	.83497	.16503	.08331	.24835	38
23	.75184	.91660	.83524	.16476	.08340	.24816	37
24	.75202	.91651	.83551	.16449	.08349	.24798	36
25	9.75221	9.91643	9.83578	10.16422	10.08357	10.24779	35
26	.75239	.91634	.83605	.16395	.08366	.24761	34
27	.75258	.91625	.83632	.16368	.08375	.24742	33
28	.75276	.91617	.83659	.16341	.08383	.24724	32
29	.75294	.91608	.83686	.16314	.08392	.24706	31
30	9.75313	9.91599	9.83713	10.16287	10.08401	10.24687	30
31	.75331	.91591	.83740	.16260	.08409	.24669	29
32	.75350	.91582	.83768	.16232	.08418	.24650	28
33	.75368	.91573	.83795	.16205	.08427	.24632	27
34	.75386	.91565	.83822	.16178	.08435	.24614	26
35	9.75405	9.91556	9.83849	10.16151	10.08444	10.24595	25
36	.75423	.91547	.83876	.16124	.08453	.24577	24
37	.75441	.91538	.83903	.16097	.08462	.24559	23
38	.75459	.91530	.83930	.16070	.08470	.24541	22
39	.75478	.91521	.83957	.16043	.08479	.24522	21
40	9.75496	9.91512	9.83984	10.16016	10.08488	10.24504	20
41	.75514	.91504	.84011	.15989	.08496	.24486	19
42	.75533	.91495	.84038	.15962	.08505	.24467	18
43	.75551	.91486	.84065	.15935	.08514	.24449	17
44	.75569	.91477	.84092	.15908	.08523	.24431	16
45	9.75587	9.91469	9.84119	10.15881	10.08531	10.24413	15
46	.75605	.91460	.84146	.15854	.08540	.24395	14
47	.75624	.91451	.84173	.15827	.08549	.24376	13
48	.75642	.91442	.84200	.15800	.08558	.24358	12
49	.75660	.91433	.84227	.15773	.08567	.24340	11
50	9.75678	9.91425	9.84254	10.15746	10.08575	10.24322	10
51	.75696	.91416	.84280	.15720	.08584	.24304	9
52	.75714	.91407	.84307	.15693	.08593	.24286	8
53	.75733	.91398	.84334	.15666	.08602	.24267	7
54	.75751	.91389	.84361	.15639	.08611	.24249	6
55	9.75769	9.91381	9.84388	10.15612	10.08619	10.24231	5
56	.75787	.91372	.84415	.15585	.08628	.24213	4
57	.75805	.91363	.84442	.15558	.08637	.24195	3
58	.75823	.91354	.84469	.15531	.08646	.24177	2
59	.75841	.91345	.84496	.15504	.08655	.24159	1
60	9.75859	9.91336	9.84523	10.15477	10.08664	10.24141	0
M	Cosine	Sine	Cotangent	Tangent	Cosecant	Secant	M

M	Sine	Cosine	Tangent	Cotangent	Secant	Cosecant	M
0	9.75859	9.91336	9.84523	10.15477	10.08664	10.24141	60
1	.75877	.91328	.84550	.15450	.08672	.24123	59
2	.75895	.91319	.84576	.15424	.08681	.24105	58
3	.75913	.91310	.84603	.15397	.08690	.24087	57
4	.75931	.91301	.84630	.15370	.08699	.24069	56
5	9.75949	9.91292	9.84657	10.15343	10.08708	10.24051	55
6	.75967	.91283	.84684	.15316	.08717	.24033	54
7	.75985	.91274	.84711	.15289	.08726	.24015	53
8	.76003	.91266	.84738	.15262	.08734	.23997	52
9	.76021	.91257	.84764	.15236	.08743	.23979	51
10	9.76039	9.91248	9.84791	10.15209	10.08752	10.23961	50
11	.76057	.91239	.84818	.15182	.08761	.23943	49
12	.76075	.91230	.84845	.15155	.08770	.23925	48
13	.76093	.91221	.84872	.15128	.08779	.23907	47
14	.76111	.91212	.84899	.15101	.08788	.23889	46
15	9.76129	9.91203	9.84925	10.15075	10.08797	10.23871	45
16	.76146	.91194	.84952	.15048	.08806	.23854	44
17	.76164	.91185	.84979	.15021	.08815	.23836	43
18	.76182	.91176	.85006	.14994	.08824	.23818	42
19	.76200	.91167	.85033	.14967	.08833	.23800	41
20	9.76218	9.91158	9.85059	10.14941	10.08842	10.23782	40
21	.76236	.91149	.85086	.14914	.08851	.23764	39
22	.76253	.91141	.85113	.14887	.08859	.23747	38
23	.76271	.91132	.85140	.14860	.08868	.23729	37
24	.76289	.91123	.85166	.14834	.08877	.23711	36
25	9.76307	9.91114	9.85193	10.14807	10.08886	10.23693	35
26	.76324	.91105	.85220	.14780	.08895	.23676	34
27	.76342	.91096	.85247	.14753	.08904	.23658	33
28	.76360	.91087	.85273	.14727	.08913	.23640	32
29	.76378	.91078	.85300	.14700	.08922	.23622	31
30	9.76395	9.91069	9.85327	10.14673	10.08931	10.23605	30
31	.76413	.91060	.85354	.14646	.08940	.23587	29
32	.76431	.91051	.85380	.14620	.08949	.23569	28
33	.76448	.91042	.85407	.14593	.08958	.23552	27
34	.76466	.91033	.85434	.14566	.08967	.23534	26
35	9.76484	9.91023	9.85460	10.14540	10.08977	10.23516	25
36	.76501	.91014	.85487	.14513	.08986	.23499	24
37	.76519	.91005	.85514	.14486	.08995	.23481	23
38	.76537	.90996	.85540	.14460	.09004	.23463	22
39	.76554	.90987	.85567	.14433	.09013	.23446	21
40	9.76572	9.90978	9.85594	10.14406	10.09022	10.23428	20
41	.76590	.90969	.85620	.14380	.09031	.23410	19
42	.76607	.90960	.85647	.14353	.09040	.23393	18
43	.76625	.90951	.85674	.14326	.09049	.23375	17
44	.76642	.90942	.85700	.14300	.09058	.23358	16
45	9.76660	9.90933	9.85727	10.14273	10.09067	10.23340	15
46	.76677	.90924	.85754	.14246	.09076	.23323	14
47	.76695	.90915	.85780	.14220	.09085	.23305	13
48	.76712	.90906	.85807	.14193	.09094	.23288	12
49	.76730	.90896	.85834	.14166	.09104	.23270	11
50	9.76747	9.90887	9.85860	10.14140	10.09113	10.23253	10
51	.76765	.90878	.85887	.14113	.09122	.23235	9
52	.76782	.90869	.85913	.14087	.09131	.23218	8
53	.76800	.90860	.85940	.14060	.09140	.23200	7
54	.76817	.90851	.85967	.14033	.09149	.23183	6
55	9.76835	9.90842	9.85993	10.14007	10.09158	10.23165	5
56	.76852	.90832	.86020	.13980	.09168	.23148	4
57	.76870	.90823	.86046	.13954	.09177	.23130	3
58	.76887	.90814	.86073	.13927	.09186	.23113	2
59	.76904	.90805	.86100	.13900	.09195	.23096	1
60	9.76922	9.90796	9.86126	10.13874	10.09204	10.23078	0
M	Cosine	Sine	Cotangent	Tangent	Cosecant	Secant	M

Logarithms of Trigonometrical Functions

M	Sine	Cosine	Tangent	Cotangent	Secant	Cosecant	M
0	9.76922	9.90796	9.86126	10.13874	10.09204	10.23078	60
1	.76939	.90787	.86153	.13847	.09213	.23061	59
2	.76957	.90777	.86179	.13821	.09223	.23043	58
3	.76974	.90768	.86206	.13794	.09232	.23026	57
4	.76991	.90759	.86232	.13768	.09241	.23009	56
5	9.77009	9.90750	9.86259	10.13741	10.09250	10.22991	55
6	.77026	.90741	.86285	.13715	.09259	.22974	54
7	.77043	.90731	.86312	.13688	.09269	.22957	53
8	.77061	.90722	.86338	.13662	.09278	.22939	52
9	.77078	.90713	.86365	.13635	.09287	.22922	51
10	9.77095	9.90704	9.86392	10.13608	10.09296	10.22905	50
11	.77112	.90694	.86418	.13582	.09306	.22888	49
12	.77130	.90685	.86445	.13555	.09315	.22870	48
13	.77147	.90676	.86471	.13529	.09324	.22853	47
14	.77164	.90667	.86498	.13502	.09333	.22836	46
15	9.77181	9.90657	9.86524	10.13476	10.09343	10.22819	45
16	.77199	.90648	.86551	.13449	.09352	.22801	44
17	.77216	.90639	.86577	.13423	.09361	.22784	43
18	.77233	.90630	.86603	.13397	.09370	.22767	42
19	.77250	.90620	.86630	.13370	.09380	.22750	41
20	9.77268	9.90611	9.86656	10.13344	10.09389	10.22732	40
21	.77285	.90602	.86683	.13317	.09398	.22715	39
22	.77302	.90592	.86709	.13291	.09408	.22698	38
23	.77319	.90583	.86736	.13264	.09417	.22681	37
24	.77336	.90574	.86762	.13238	.09426	.22664	36
25	9.77353	9.90565	9.86789	10.13211	10.09435	10.22647	35
26	.77370	.90555	.86815	.13185	.09445	.22630	34
27	.77387	.90546	.86842	.13158	.09454	.22613	33
28	.77405	.90537	.86868	.13132	.09463	.22595	32
29	.77422	.90527	.86894	.13106	.09473	.22578	31
30	9.77439	9.90518	9.86921	10.13079	10.09482	10.22561	30
31	.77456	.90509	.86947	.13053	.09491	.22544	29
32	.77473	.90499	.86974	.13026	.09501	.22527	28
33	.77490	.90490	.87000	.13000	.09510	.22510	27
34	.77507	.90480	.87027	.12973	.09520	.22493	26
35	9.77524	9.90471	9.87053	10.12947	10.09529	10.22476	25
36	.77541	.90462	.87079	.12921	.09538	.22459	24
37	.77558	.90452	.87106	.12894	.09548	.22442	23
38	.77575	.90443	.87132	.12868	.09557	.22425	22
39	.77592	.90434	.87158	.12842	.09566	.22408	21
40	9.77609	9.90424	9.87185	10.12815	10.09576	10.22391	20
41	.77626	.90415	.87211	.12789	.09585	.22374	19
42	.77643	.90405	.87238	.12762	.09595	.22357	18
43	.77660	.90396	.87264	.12736	.09604	.22340	17
44	.77677	.90386	.87290	.12710	.09614	.22323	16
45	9.77694	9.90377	9.87317	10.12683	10.09623	10.22306	15
46	.77711	.90368	.87343	.12657	.09632	.22289	14
47	.77728	.90358	.87369	.12631	.09642	.22272	13
48	.77744	.90349	.87396	.12604	.09651	.22256	12
49	.77761	.90339	.87422	.12578	.09661	.22239	11
50	9.77778	9.90330	9.87448	10.12552	10.09670	10.22222	10
51	.77795	.90320	.87475	.12525	.09680	.22205	9
52	.77812	.90311	.87501	.12499	.09689	.22188	8
53	.77829	.90301	.87527	.12473	.09699	.22171	7
54	.77846	.90292	.87554	.12446	.09708	.22154	6
55	9.77862	9.90282	9.87580	10.12420	10.09718	10.22138	5
56	.77879	.90273	.87606	.12394	.09727	.22121	4
57	.77896	.90263	.87633	.12367	.09737	.22104	3
58	.77913	.90254	.87659	.12341	.09746	.22087	2
59	.77930	.90244	.87685	.12315	.09756	.22070	1
60	9.77946	9.90235	9.87711	10.12289	10.09765	10.22054	0

| M | Cosine | Sine | Cotangent | Tangent | Cosecant | Secant | M |

Logarithms of Trigonometrical Functions

M	Sine	Cosine	Tangent	Cotangent	Secant	Cosecant	M
0	9.77946	9.90235	9.87711	10.12289	10.09765	10.22054	60
1	.77963	.90225	.87738	.12262	.09775	.22037	59
2	.77980	.90216	.87764	.12236	.09784	.22020	58
3	.77997	.90206	.87790	.12210	.09794	.22003	57
4	.78013	.90197	.87817	.12183	.09803	.21987	56
5	9.78030	9.90187	9.87843	10.12157	10.09813	10.21970	55
6	.78047	.90178	.87869	.12131	.09822	.21953	54
7	.78063	.90168	.87895	.12105	.09832	.21937	53
8	.78080	.90159	.87922	.12078	.09841	.21920	52
9	.78097	.90149	.87948	.12052	.09851	.21903	51
10	9.78113	9.90139	9.87974	10.12026	10.09861	10.21887	50
11	.78130	.90130	.88000	.12000	.09870	.21870	49
12	.78147	.90120	.88027	.11973	.09880	.21853	48
13	.78163	.90111	.88053	.11947	.09889	.21837	47
14	.78180	.90101	.88079	.11921	.09899	.21820	46
15	9.78197	9.90091	9.88105	10.11895	10.09909	10.21803	45
16	.78213	.90082	.88131	.11869	.09918	.21787	44
17	.78230	.90072	.88158	.11842	.09928	.21770	43
18	.78246	.90063	.88184	.11816	.09937	.21754	42
19	.78263	.90053	.88210	.11790	.09947	.21737	41
20	9.78280	9.90043	9.88236	10.11764	10.09957	10.21720	40
21	.78296	.90034	.88262	.11738	.09966	.21704	39
22	.78313	.90024	.88289	.11711	.09976	.21687	38
23	.78329	.90014	.88315	.11685	.09986	.21671	37
24	.78346	.90005	.88341	.11659	.09995	.21654	36
25	9.78362	9.89995	9.88367	10.11633	10.10005	10.21638	35
26	.78379	.89985	.88393	.11607	.10015	.21621	34
27	.78395	.89976	.88420	.11580	.10024	.21605	33
28	.78412	.89966	.88446	.11554	.10034	.21588	32
29	.78428	.89956	.88472	.11528	.10044	.21572	31
30	9.78445	9.89947	9.88498	10.11502	10.10053	10.21555	30
31	.78461	.89937	.88524	.11476	.10063	.21539	29
32	.78478	.89927	.88550	.11450	.10073	.21522	28
33	.78494	.89918	.88577	.11423	.10082	.21506	27
34	.78510	.89908	.88603	.11397	.10092	.21490	26
35	9.78527	9.89898	9.88629	10.11371	10.10102	10.21473	25
36	.78543	.89888	.88655	.11345	.10112	.21457	24
37	.78560	.89879	.88681	.11319	.10121	.21440	23
38	.78576	.89869	.88707	.11293	.10131	.21424	22
39	.78592	.89859	.88733	.11267	.10141	.21408	21
40	9.78609	9.89849	9.88759	10.11241	10.10151	10.21391	20
41	.78625	.89840	.88786	.11214	.10160	.21375	19
42	.78642	.89830	.88812	.11188	.10170	.21358	18
43	.78658	.89820	.88838	.11162	.10180	.21342	17
44	.78674	.89810	.88864	.11136	.10190	.21326	16
45	9.78691	9.89801	9.88890	10.11110	10.10199	10.21309	15
46	.78707	.89791	.88916	.11084	.10209	.21293	14
47	.78723	.89781	.88942	.11058	.10219	.21277	13
48	.78739	.89771	.88968	.11032	.10229	.21261	12
49	.78756	.89761	.88994	.11006	.10239	.21244	11
50	9.78772	9.89752	9.89020	10.10980	10.10248	10.21228	10
51	.78788	.89742	.89046	.10954	.10258	.21212	9
52	.78805	.89732	.89073	.10927	.10268	.21195	8
53	.78821	.89722	.89099	.10901	.10278	.21179	7
54	.78837	.89712	.89125	.10875	.10288	.21163	6
55	9.78853	9.89702	9.89151	10.10849	10.10298	10.21147	5
56	.78869	.89693	.89177	.10823	.10307	.21131	4
57	.78886	.89683	.89203	.10797	.10317	.21114	3
58	.78902	.89673	.89229	.10771	.10327	.21098	2
59	.78918	.89663	.89255	.10745	.10337	.21082	1
60	9.78934	9.89653	9.89281	10.10719	10.10347	10.21066	0

M	Cosine	Sine	Cotangent	Tangent	Cosecant	Secant	M

M	Sine	Cosine	Tangent	Cotangent	Secant	Cosecant	M
0	9.78934	9.89653	9.89281	10.10719	10.10347	10.21066	60
1	.78950	.89643	.89307	.10693	.10357	.21050	59
2	.78967	.89633	.89333	.10667	.10367	.21033	58
3	.78983	.89624	.89359	.10641	.10376	.21017	57
4	.78999	.89614	.89385	.10615	.10386	.21001	56
5	9.79015	9.89604	9.89411	10.10589	10.10396	10.20985	55
6	.79031	.89594	.89437	.10563	.10406	.20969	54
7	.79047	.89584	.89463	.10537	.10416	.20953	53
8	.79063	.89574	.89489	.10511	.10426	.20937	52
9	.79079	.89564	.89515	.10485	.10436	.20921	51
10	9.79095	9.89554	9.89541	10.10459	10.10446	10.20905	50
11	.79111	.89544	.89567	.10433	.10456	.20889	49
12	.79128	.89534	.89593	.10407	.10466	.20872	48
13	.79144	.89524	.89619	.10381	.10476	.20856	47
14	.79160	.89514	.89645	.10355	.10486	.20840	46
15	9.79176	9.89504	9.89671	10.10329	10.10496	10.20824	45
16	.79192	.89495	.89697	.10303	.10505	.20808	44
17	.79208	.89485	.89723	.10277	.10515	.20792	43
18	.79224	.89475	.89749	.10251	.10525	.20776	42
19	.79240	.89465	.89775	.10225	.10535	.20760	41
20	9.79256	9.89455	9.89801	10.10199	10.10545	10.20744	40
21	.79272	.89445	.89827	.10173	.10555	.20728	39
22	.79288	.89435	.89853	.10147	.10565	.20712	38
23	.79304	.89425	.89879	.10121	.10575	.20696	37
24	.79319	.89415	.89905	.10095	.10585	.20681	36
25	9.79335	9.89405	9.89931	10.10069	10.10595	10.20665	35
26	.79351	.89395	.89957	.10043	.10605	.20649	34
27	.79367	.89385	.89983	.10017	.10615	.20633	33
28	.79383	.89375	.90009	.09991	.10625	.20617	32
29	.79399	.89364	.90035	.09965	.10636	.20601	31
30	9.79415	9.89354	9.90061	10.09939	10.10646	10.20585	30
31	.79431	.89344	.90086	.09914	.10656	.20569	29
32	.79447	.89334	.90112	.09888	.10666	.20553	28
33	.79463	.89324	.90138	.09862	.10676	.20537	27
34	.79478	.89314	.90164	.09836	.10686	.20522	26
35	9.79494	9.89304	9.90190	10.09810	10.10696	10.20506	25
36	.79510	.89294	.90216	.09784	.10706	.20490	24
37	.79526	.89284	.90242	.09758	.10716	.20474	23
38	.79542	.89274	.90268	.09732	.10726	.20458	22
39	.79558	.89264	.90294	.09706	.10736	.20442	21
40	9.79573	9.89254	9.90320	10.09680	10.10746	10.20427	20
41	.79589	.89244	.90346	.09654	.10756	.20411	19
42	.79605	.89233	.90371	.09629	.10767	.20395	18
43	.79621	.89223	.90397	.09603	.10777	.20379	17
44	.79636	.89213	.90423	.09577	.10787	.20364	16
45	9.79652	9.89203	9.90449	10.09551	10.10797	10.20348	15
46	.79668	.89193	.90475	.09525	.10807	.20332	14
47	.79684	.89183	.90501	.09499	.10817	.20316	13
48	.79699	.89173	.90527	.09473	.10827	.20301	12
49	.79715	.89162	.90553	.09447	.10838	.20285	11
50	9.79731	9.89152	9.90578	10.09422	10.10848	10.20269	10
51	.79746	.89142	.90604	.09396	.10858	.20254	9
52	.79762	.89132	.90630	.09370	.10868	.20238	8
53	.79778	.89122	.90656	.09344	.10878	.20222	7
54	.79793	.89112	.90682	.09318	.10888	.20207	6
55	9.79809	9.89101	9.90708	10.09292	10.10899	10.20191	5
56	.79825	.89091	.90734	.09266	.10909	.20175	4
57	.79840	.89081	.90759	.09241	.10919	.20160	3
58	.79856	.89071	.90785	.09215	.10929	.20144	2
59	.79872	.89060	.90811	.09189	.10940	.20128	1
60	9.79887	9.89050	9.90837	10.09163	10.10950	10.20113	0
M	Cosine	Sine	Cotangent	Tangent	Cosecant	Secant	M

Logarithms of Trigonometrical Functions

M	Sine	Cosine	Tangent	Cotangent	Secant	Cosecant	M
0	9.79887	9.89050	9.90837	10.09163	10.10950	10.20113	60
1	.79903	.89040	.90863	.09137	.10960	.20097	59
2	.79918	.89030	.90889	.09111	.10970	.20082	58
3	.79934	.89020	.90914	.09086	.10980	.20066	57
4	.79950	.89009	.90940	.09060	.10991	.20050	56
5	9.79965	9.88999	9.90966	10.09034	10.11001	10.20035	55
6	.79981	.88989	.90992	.09008	.11011	.20019	54
7	.79996	.88978	.91018	.08982	.11022	.20004	53
8	.80012	.88968	.91043	.08957	.11032	.19988	52
9	.80027	.88958	.91069	.08931	.11042	.19973	51
10	9.80043	9.88948	9.91095	10.08905	10.11052	10.19957	50
11	.80058	.88937	.91121	.08879	.11063	.19942	49
12	.80074	.88927	.91147	.08853	.11073	.19926	48
13	.80089	.88917	.91172	.08828	.11083	.19911	47
14	.80105	.88906	.91198	.08802	.11094	.19895	46
15	9.80120	9.88896	9.91224	10.08776	10.11104	10.19880	45
16	.80136	.88886	.91250	.08750	.11114	.19864	44
17	.80151	.88875	.91276	.08724	.11125	.19849	43
18	.80166	.88865	.91301	.08699	.11135	.19834	42
19	.80182	.88855	.91327	.08673	.11145	.19818	41
20	9.80197	9.88844	9.91353	10.08647	10.11156	10.19803	40
21	.80213	.88834	.91379	.08621	.11166	.19787	39
22	.80228	.88824	.91404	.08596	.11176	.19772	38
23	.80244	.88813	.91430	.08570	.11187	.19756	37
24	.80259	.88803	.91456	.08544	.11197	.19741	36
25	9.80274	9.88793	9.91482	10.08518	10.11207	10.19726	35
26	.80290	.88782	.91507	.08493	.11218	.19710	34
27	.80305	.88772	.91533	.08467	.11228	.19695	33
28	.80320	.88761	.91559	.08441	.11239	.19680	32
29	.80336	.88751	.91585	.08415	.11249	.19664	31
30	9.80351	9.88741	9.91610	10.08390	10.11259	10.19649	30
31	.80366	.88730	.91636	.08364	.11270	.19634	29
32	.80382	.88720	.91662	.08338	.11280	.19618	28
33	.80397	.88709	.91688	.08312	.11291	.19603	27
34	.80412	.88699	.91713	.08287	.11301	.19588	26
35	9.80428	9.88688	9.91739	10.08261	10.11312	10.19572	25
36	.80443	.88678	.91765	.08235	.11322	.19557	24
37	.80458	.88668	.91791	.08209	.11332	.19542	23
38	.80473	.88657	.91816	.08184	.11343	.19527	22
39	.80489	.88647	.91842	.08158	.11353	.19511	21
40	9.80504	9.88636	9.91868	10.08132	10.11364	10.19496	20
41	.80519	.88626	.91893	.08107	.11374	.19481	19
42	.80534	.88615	.91919	.08081	.11385	.19466	18
43	.80550	.88605	.91945	.08055	.11395	.19450	17
44	.80565	.88594	.91971	.08029	.11406	.19435	16
45	9.80580	9.88584	9.91996	10.08004	10.11416	10.19420	15
46	.80595	.88573	.92022	.07978	.11427	.19405	14
47	.80610	.88563	.92048	.07952	.11437	.19390	13
48	.80625	.88552	.92073	.07927	.11448	.19375	12
49	.80641	.88542	.92099	.07901	.11458	.19359	11
50	9.80656	9.88531	9.92125	10.07875	10.11469	10.19344	10
51	.80671	.88521	.92150	.07850	.11479	.19329	9
52	.80686	.88510	.92176	.07824	.11490	.19314	8
53	.80701	.88499	.92202	.07798	.11501	.19299	7
54	.80716	.88489	.92227	.07773	.11511	.19284	6
55	9.80731	9.88478	9.92253	10.07747	10.11522	10.19269	5
56	.80746	.88468	.92279	.07721	.11532	.19254	4
57	.80762	.88457	.92304	.07696	.11543	.19238	3
58	.80777	.88447	.92330	.07670	.11553	.19223	2
59	.80792	.88436	.92356	.07644	.11564	.19208	1
60	9.80807	9.88425	9.92381	10.07619	10.11575	10.19193	0
M	Cosine	Sine	Cotangent	Tangent	Cosecant	Secant	M

M	Sine	Cosine	Tangent	Cotangent	Secant	Cosecant	M
0	9.80807	9.88425	9.92381	10.07619	10.11575	10.19193	60
1	.80822	.88415	.92407	.07593	.11585	.19178	59
2	.80837	.88404	.92433	.07567	.11596	.19163	58
3	.80852	.88394	.92458	.07542	.11606	.19148	57
4	.80867	.88383	.92484	.07516	.11617	.19133	56
5	9.80882	9.88372	9.92510	10.07490	10.11628	10.19118	55
6	.80897	.88362	.92535	.07465	.11638	.19103	54
7	.80912	.88351	.92561	.07439	.11649	.19088	53
8	.80927	.88340	.92587	.07413	.11660	.19073	52
9	.80942	.88330	.92612	.07388	.11670	.19058	51
10	9.80957	9.88319	9.92638	10.07362	10.11681	10.19043	50
11	.80972	.88308	.92663	.07337	.11692	.19028	49
12	.80987	.88298	.92689	.07311	.11702	.19013	48
13	.81002	.88287	.92715	.07285	.11713	.18998	47
14	.81017	.88276	.92740	.07260	.11724	.18983	46
15	9.81032	9.88266	9.92766	10.07234	10.11734	10.18968	45
16	.81047	.88255	.92792	.07208	.11745	.18953	44
17	.81061	.88244	.92817	.07183	.11756	.18939	43
18	.81076	.88234	.92843	.07157	.11766	.18924	42
19	.81091	.88223	.92868	.07132	.11777	.18909	41
20	9.81106	9.88212	9.92894	10.07106	10.11788	10.18894	40
21	.81121	.88201	.92920	.07080	.11799	.18879	39
22	.81136	.88191	.92945	.07055	.11809	.18864	38
23	.81151	.88180	.92971	.07029	.11820	.18849	37
24	.81166	.88169	.92996	.07004	.11831	.18834	36
25	9.81180	9.88158	9.93022	10.06978	10.11842	10.18820	35
26	.81195	.88148	.93048	.06952	.11852	.18805	34
27	.81210	.88137	.93073	.06927	.11863	.18790	33
28	.81225	.88126	.93099	.06901	.11874	.18775	32
29	.81240	.88115	.93124	.06876	.11885	.18760	31
30	9.81254	9.88105	9.93150	10.06850	10.11895	10.18746	30
31	.81269	.88094	.93175	.06825	.11906	.18731	29
32	.81284	.88083	.93201	.06799	.11917	.18716	28
33	.81299	.88072	.93227	.06773	.11928	.18701	27
34	.81314	.88061	.93252	.06748	.11939	.18686	26
35	9.81328	9.88051	9.93278	10.06722	10.11949	10.18672	25
36	.81343	.88040	.93303	.06697	.11960	.18657	24
37	.81358	.88029	.93329	.06671	.11971	.18642	23
38	.81372	.88018	.93354	.06646	.11982	.18628	22
39	.81387	.88007	.93380	.06620	.11993	.18613	21
40	9.81402	9.87996	9.93406	10.06594	10.12004	10.18598	20
41	.81417	.87985	.93431	.06569	.12015	.18583	19
42	.81431	.87975	.93457	.06543	.12025	.18569	18
43	.81446	.87964	.93482	.06518	.12036	.18554	17
44	.81461	.87953	.93508	.06492	.12047	.18539	16
45	9.81475	9.87942	9.93533	10.06467	10.12058	10.18525	15
46	.81490	.87931	.93559	.06441	.12069	.18510	14
47	.81505	.87920	.93584	.06416	.12080	.18495	13
48	.81519	.87909	.93610	.06390	.12091	.18481	12
49	.81534	.87898	.93636	.06364	.12102	.18466	11
50	9.81549	9.87887	9.93661	10.06339	10.12113	10.18451	10
51	.81563	.87877	.93687	.06313	.12123	.18437	9
52	.81578	.87866	.93712	.06288	.12134	.18422	8
53	.81592	.87855	.93738	.06262	.12145	.18408	7
54	.81607	.87844	.93763	.06237	.12156	.18393	6
55	9.81622	9.87833	9.93789	10.06211	10.12167	10.18378	5
56	.81636	.87822	.93814	.06186	.12178	.18364	4
57	.81651	.87811	.93840	.06160	.12189	.18349	3
58	.81665	.87800	.93865	.06135	.12200	.18335	2
59	.81680	.87789	.93891	.06109	.12211	.18320	1
60	9.81694	9.87778	9.93916	10.06084	10.12222	10.18306	0
M	Cosine	Sine	Cotangent	Tangent	Cosecant	Secant	M

M	Sine	Cosine	Tangent	Cotangent	Secant	Cosecant	M
0	9.81694	9.87778	9.93916	10.06084	10.12222	10.18306	60
1	.81709	.87767	.93942	.06058	.12233	.18291	59
2	.81723	.87756	.93967	.06033	.12244	.18277	58
3	.81738	.87745	.93993	.06007	.12255	.18262	57
4	.81752	.87734	.94018	.05982	.12266	.18248	56
5	9.81767	9.87723	9.94044	10.05956	10.12277	10.18233	55
6	.81781	.87712	.94069	.05931	.12288	.18219	54
7	.81796	.87701	.94095	.05905	.12299	.18204	53
8	.81810	.87690	.94120	.05880	.12310	.18190	52
9	.81825	.87679	.94146	.05854	.12321	.18175	51
10	9.81839	9.87668	9.94171	10.05829	10.12332	10.18161	50
11	.81854	.87657	.94197	.05803	.12343	.18146	49
12	.81868	.87646	.94222	.05778	.12354	.18132	48
13	.81882	.87635	.94248	.05752	.12365	.18118	47
14	.81897	.87624	.94273	.05727	.12376	.18103	46
15	9.81911	9.87613	9.94299	10.05701	10.12387	10.18089	45
16	.81926	.87601	.94324	.05676	.12399	.18074	44
17	.81940	.87590	.94350	.05650	.12410	.18060	43
18	.81955	.87579	.94375	.05625	.12421	.18045	42
19	.81969	.87568	.94401	.05599	.12432	.18031	41
20	9.81983	9.87557	9.94426	10.05574	10.12443	10.18017	40
21	.81998	.87546	.94452	.05548	.12454	.18002	39
22	.82012	.87535	.94477	.05523	.12465	.17988	38
23	.82026	.87524	.94503	.05497	.12476	.17974	37
24	.82041	.87513	.94528	.05472	.12487	.17959	36
25	9.82055	9.87501	9.94554	10.05446	10.12499	10.17945	35
26	.82069	.87490	.94579	.05421	.12510	.17931	34
27	.82084	.87479	.94604	.05396	.12521	.17916	33
28	.82098	.87468	.94630	.05370	.12532	.17902	32
29	.82112	.87457	.94655	.05345	.12543	.17888	31
30	9.82126	9.87446	9.94681	10.05319	10.12554	10.17874	30
31	.82141	.87434	.94706	.05294	.12566	.17859	29
32	.82155	.87423	.94732	.05268	.12577	.17845	28
33	.82169	.87412	.94757	.05243	.12588	.17831	27
34	.82184	.87401	.94783	.05217	.12599	.17816	26
35	9.82198	9.87390	9.94808	10.05192	10.12610	10.17802	25
36	.82212	.87378	.94834	.05166	.12622	.17788	24
37	.82226	.87367	.94859	.05141	.12633	.17774	23
38	.82240	.87356	.94884	.05116	.12644	.17760	22
39	.82255	.87345	.94910	.05090	.12655	.17745	21
40	9.82269	9.87334	9.94935	10.05065	10.12666	10.17731	20
41	.82283	.87322	.94961	.05039	.12678	.17717	19
42	.82297	.87311	.94986	.05014	.12689	.17703	18
43	.82311	.87300	.95012	.04988	.12700	.17689	17
44	.82326	.87288	.95037	.04963	.12712	.17674	16
45	9.82340	9.87277	9.95062	10.04938	10.12723	10.17660	15
46	.82354	.87266	.95088	.04912	.12734	.17646	14
47	.82368	.87255	.95113	.04887	.12745	.17632	13
48	.82382	.87243	.95139	.04861	.12757	.17618	12
49	.82396	.87232	.95164	.04836	.12768	.17604	11
50	9.82410	9.87221	9.95190	10.04810	10.12779	10.17590	10
51	.82424	.87209	.95215	.04785	.12791	.17576	9
52	.82439	.87198	.95240	.04760	.12802	.17561	8
53	.82453	.87187	.95266	.04734	.12813	.17547	7
54	.82467	.87175	.95291	.04709	.12825	.17533	6
55	9.82481	9.87164	9.95317	10.04683	10.12836	10.17519	5
56	.82495	.87153	.95342	.04658	.12847	.17505	4
57	.82509	.87141	.95368	.04632	.12859	.17491	3
58	.82523	.87130	.95393	.04607	.12870	.17477	2
59	.82537	.87119	.95418	.04582	.12881	.17463	1
60	9.82551	9.87107	9.95444	10.04556	10.12893	10.17449	0
M	Cosine	Sine	Cotangent	Tangent	Cosecant	Secant	M

M	Sine	Cosine	Tangent	Cotangent	Secant	Cosecant	M
0	9.82551	9.87107	9.95444	10.04556	10.12893	10.17449	60
1	.82565	.87096	.95469	.04531	.12904	.17435	59
2	.82579	.87085	.95495	.04505	.12915	.17421	58
3	.82593	.87073	.95520	.04480	.12927	.17407	57
4	.82607	.87062	.95545	.04455	.12938	.17393	56
5	9.82621	9.87050	9.95571	10.04429	10.12950	10.17379	55
6	.82635	.87039	.95596	.04404	.12961	.17365	54
7	.82649	.87028	.95622	.04378	.12972	.17351	53
8	.82663	.87016	.95647	.04353	.12984	.17337	52
9	.82677	.87005	.95672	.04328	.12995	.17323	51
10	9.82691	9.86993	9.95698	10.04302	10.13007	10.17309	50
11	.82705	.86982	.95723	.04277	.13018	.17295	49
12	.82719	.86970	.95748	.04252	.13030	.17281	48
13	.82733	.86959	.95774	.04226	.13041	.17267	47
14	.82747	.86947	.95799	.04201	.13053	.17253	46
15	9.82761	9.86936	9.95825	10.04175	10.13064	10.17239	45
16	.82775	.86924	.95850	.04150	.13076	.17225	44
17	.82788	.86913	.95875	.04125	.13087	.17212	43
18	.82802	.86902	.95901	.04099	.13098	.17198	42
19	.82816	.86890	.95926	.04074	.13110	.17184	41
20	9.82830	9.86879	9.95952	10.04048	10.13121	10.17170	40
21	.82844	.86867	.95977	.04023	.13133	.17156	39
22	.82858	.86855	.96002	.03998	.13145	.17142	38
23	.82872	.86844	.96028	.03972	.13156	.17128	37
24	.82885	.86832	.96053	.03947	.13168	.17115	36
25	9.82899	9.86821	9.96078	10.03922	10.13179	10.17101	35
26	.82913	.86809	.96104	.03896	.13191	.17087	34
27	.82927	.86798	.96129	.03871	.13202	.17073	33
28	.82941	.86786	.96155	.03845	.13214	.17059	32
29	.82955	.86775	.96180	.03820	.13225	.17045	31
30	9.82968	9.86763	9.96205	10.03795	10.13237	10.17032	30
31	.82982	.86752	.96231	.03769	.13248	.17018	29
32	.82996	.86740	.96256	.03744	.13260	.17004	28
33	.83010	.86728	.96281	.03719	.13272	.16990	27
34	.83023	.86717	.96307	.03693	.13283	.16977	26
35	9.83037	9.86705	9.96332	10.03668	10.13295	10.16963	25
36	.83051	.86694	.96357	.03643	.13306	.16949	24
37	.83065	.86682	.96383	.03617	.13318	.16935	23
38	.83078	.86670	.96408	.03592	.13330	.16922	22
39	.83092	.86659	.96433	.03567	.13341	.16908	21
40	9.83106	9.86647	9.96459	10.03541	10.13353	10.16894	20
41	.83120	.86635	.96484	.03516	.13365	.16880	19
42	.83133	.86624	.96510	.03490	.13376	.16867	18
43	.83147	.86612	.96535	.03465	.13388	.16853	17
44	.83161	.86600	.96560	.03440	.13400	.16839	16
45	9.83174	9.86589	9.96586	10.03414	10.13411	10.16826	15
46	.83188	.86577	.96611	.03389	.13423	.16812	14
47	.83202	.86565	.96636	.03364	.13435	.16798	13
48	.83215	.86554	.96662	.03338	.13446	. 16785	12
49	.83229	.86542	.96687	.03313	.13458	.16771	11
50	9.83242	9.86530	9.96712	10.03288	10.13470	10.16758	10
51	.83256	.86518	.96738	.03262	.13482	.16744	9
52	.83270	.86507	.96763	.03237	.13493	.16730	8
53	.83283	.86495	.96788	.03212	.13505	.16717	7
54	.83297	.86483	.96814	.03186	.13517	.16703	6
55	9.83310	9.86472	9.96839	10.03161	10.13528	10.16690	5
56	.83324	.86460	.96864	.03136	.13540	.16676	4
57	.83338	.86448	.96890	.03110	.13552	.16662	3
58	.83351	.86436	.96915	.03085	.13564	.16649	2
59	.83365	.86425	.96940	.03060	.13575	.16635	1
60	9.83378	9.86413	9.96966	10.03034	10.13587	10.16622	0
M	Cosine	Sine	Cotangent	Tangent	Cosecant	Secant	M

M	Sine	Cosine	Tangent	Cotangent	Secant	Cosecant	M
0	9.83378	9.86413	9.96966	10.03034	10.13587	10.16622	60
1	.83392	.86401	.96991	.03009	.13599	.16608	59
2	.83405	.86389	.97016	.02984	.13611	.16595	58
3	.83419	.86377	.97042	.02958	.13623	.16581	57
4	.83432	.86366	.97067	.02933	.13634	.16568	56
5	9.83446	9.86354	9.97092	10.02908	10.13646	10.16554	55
6	.83459	.86342	.97118	.02882	.13658	.16541	54
7	.83473	.86330	.97143	.02857	.13670	.16527	53
8	.83486	.86318	.97168	.02832	.13682	.16514	52
9	.83500	.86306	.97193	.02807	.13694	.16500	51
10	9.83513	9.86295	9.97219	10.02781	10.13705	10.16487	50
11	.83527	.86283	.97244	.02756	.13717	.16473	49
12	.83540	.86271	.97269	.02731	.13729	.16460	48
13	.83554	.86259	.97295	.02705	.13741	.16446	47
14	.83567	.86247	.97320	.02680	.13753	.16433	46
15	9.83581	9.86235	9.97345	10.02655	10.13765	10.16419	45
16	.83594	.86223	.97371	.02629	.13777	.16406	44
17	.83608	.86211	.97396	.02604	.13789	.16392	43
18	.83621	.86200	.97421	.02579	.13800	.16379	42
19	.83634	.86188	.97447	.02553	.13812	.16366	41
20	9.83648	9.86176	9.97472	10.02528	10.13824	10.16352	40
21	.83661	.86164	.97497	.02503	.13836	.16339	39
22	.83674	.86152	.97523	.02477	.13848	.16326	38
23	.83688	.86140	.97548	.02452	.13860	.16312	37
24	.83701	.86128	.97573	.02427	.13872	.16299	36
25	9.83715	9.86116	9.97598	10.02402	10.13884	10.16285	35
26	.83728	.86104	.97624	.02376	.13896	.16272	34
27	.83741	.86092	.97649	.02351	.13908	.16259	33
28	.83755	.86080	.97674	.02326	.13920	.16245	32
29	.83768	.86068	.97700	.02300	.13932	.16232	31
30	9.83781	9.86056	9.97725	10.02275	10.13944	10.16219	30
31	.83795	.86044	.97750	.02250	.13956	.16205	29
32	.83808	.86032	.97776	.02224	.13968	.16192	28
33	.83821	.86020	.97801	.02199	.13980	.16179	27
34	.83834	.86008	.97826	.02174	.13992	.16166	26
35	9.83848	9.85996	9.97851	10.02149	10.14004	10.16152	25
36	.83861	.85984	.97877	.02123	.14016	.16139	24
37	.83874	.85972	.97902	.02098	.14028	.16126	23
38	.83887	.85960	.97927	.02073	.14040	.16113	22
39	.83901	.85948	.97953	.02047	.14052	.16099	21
40	9.83914	9.85936	9.97978	10.02022	10.14064	10.16086	20
41	.83927	.85924	.98003	.01997	.14076	.16073	19
42	.83940	.85912	.98029	.01971	.14088	.16060	18
43	.83954	.85900	.98054	.01946	.14100	.16046	17
44	.83967	.85888	.98079	.01921	.14112	.16033	16
45	9.83980	9.85876	9.98104	10.01896	10.14124	10.16020	15
46	.83993	.85864	.98130	.01870	.14136	.16007	14
47	.84006	.85851	.98155	.01845	.14149	.15994	13
48	.84020	.85839	.98180	.01820	.14161	.15980	12
49	.84033	.85827	.98206	.01794	.14173	.15967	11
50	9.84046	9.85815	9.98231	10.01769	10.14185	10.15954	10
51	.84059	.85803	.98256	.01744	.14197	.15941	9
52	.84072	.85791	.98281	.01719	.14209	.15928	8
53	.84085	.85779	.98307	.01693	.14221	.15915	7
54	.84098	.85766	.98332	.01668	.14234	.15902	6
55	9.84112	9.85754	9.98357	10.01643	10.14246	10.15888	5
56	.84125	.85742	.98383	.01617	.14258	.15875	4
57	.84138	.85730	.98408	.01592	.14270	.15862	3
58	.84151	.85718	.98433	.01567	.14282	.15849	2
59	.84164	.85706	.98458	.01542	.14294	.15836	1
60	9.84177	9.85693	9.98484	10.01516	10.14307	10.15823	0
M	Cosine	Sine	Cotangent	Tangent	Cosecant	Secant	M

M	Sine	Cosine	Tangent	Cotangent	Secant	Cosecant	M
0	9.84177	9.85693	9.98484	10.01516	10.14307	10.15823	60
1	.84190	.85681	.98509	.01491	.14319	.15810	59
2	.84203	.85669	.98534	.01466	.14331	.15797	58
3	.84216	.85657	.98560	.01440	.14343	.15784	57
4	.84229	.85645	.98585	.01415	.14355	.15771	56
5	9.84242	9.85632	9.98610	10.01390	10.14368	10.15758	55
6	.84255	.85620	.98635	.01365	.14380	.15745	54
7	.84269	.85608	.98661	.01339	.14392	.15731	53
8	.84282	.85596	.98686	.01314	.14404	.15718	52
9	.84295	.85583	.98711	.01289	.14417	.15705	51
10	9.84308	9.85571	9.98737	10.01263	10.14429	10.15692	50
11	.84321	.85559	.98762	.01238	.14441	.15679	49
12	.84334	.85547	.98787	.01213	.14453	.15666	48
13	.84347	.85534	.98812	.01188	.14466	.15653	47
14	.84360	.85522	.98838	.01162	.14478	.15640	46
15	9.84373	9.85510	9.98863	10.01137	10.14490	10.15627	45
16	.84385	.85497	.98888	.01112	.14503	.15615	44
17	.84398	.85485	.98913	.01087	.14515	.15602	43
18	.84411	.85473	.98939	.01061	.14527	.15589	42
19	.84424	.85460	.98964	.01036	.14540	.15576	41
20	9.84437	9.85448	9.98989	10.01011	10.14552	10.15563	40
21	.84450	.85436	.99015	.00985	.14564	.15550	39
22	.84463	.85423	.99040	.00960	.14577	.15537	38
23	.84476	.85411	.99065	.00935	.14589	.15524	37
24	.84489	.85399	.99090	.00910	.14601	.15511	36
25	9.84502	9.85386	9.99116	10.00884	10.14614	10.15498	35
26	.84515	.85374	.99141	.00859	.14626	.15485	34
27	.84528	.85361	.99166	.00834	.14639	.15472	33
28	.84540	.85349	.99191	.00809	.14651	.15460	32
29	.84553	.85337	.99217	.00783	.14663	.15447	31
30	9.84566	9.85324	9.99242	10.00758	10.14676	10.15434	30
31	.84579	.85312	.99267	.00733	.14688	.15421	29
32	.84592	.85299	.99293	.00707	.14701	.15408	28
33	.84605	.85287	.99318	.00682	.14713	.15395	27
34	.84618	.85274	.99343	.00657	.14726	.15382	26
35	9.84630	9.85262	9.99368	10.00632	10.14738	10.15370	25
36	.84643	.85250	.99394	.00606	.14750	.15357	24
37	.84656	.85237	.99419	.00581	.14763	.15344	23
38	.84669	.85225	.99444	.00556	.14775	.15331	22
39	.84682	.85212	.99469	.00531	.14788	.15318	21
40	9.84694	9.85200	9.99495	10.00505	10.14800	10.15306	20
41	.84707	.85187	.99520	.00480	.14813	.15293	19
42	.84720	.85175	.99545	.00455	.14825	.15280	18
43	.84733	.85162	.99570	.00430	.14838	.15267	17
44	.84745	.85150	.99596	.00404	.14850	.15255	16
45	9.84758	9.85137	9.99621	10.00379	10.14863	10.15242	15
46	.84771	.85125	.99646	.00354	.14875	.15229	14
47	.84784	.85112	.99672	.00328	.14888	.15216	13
48	.84796	.85100	.99697	.00303	.14900	.15204	12
49	.84809	.85087	.99722	.00278	.14913	.15191	11
50	9.84822	9.85074	9.99747	10.00253	10.14926	10.15178	10
51	.84835	.85062	.99773	.00227	.14938	.15165	9
52	.84847	.85049	.99798	.00202	.14951	.15153	8
53	.84860	.85037	.99823	.00177	.14963	.15140	7
54	.84873	.85024	.99848	.00152	.14976	.15127	6
55	9.84885	9.85012	9.99874	10.00126	10.14988	10.15115	5
56	.84898	.84999	.99899	.00101	.15001	.15102	4
57	.84911	.84986	.99924	.00076	.15014	.15089	3
58	.84923	.84974	.99949	.00051	.15026	.15077	2
59	.84936	.84961	.99975	.00025	.15039	.15064	1
60	9.84949	9.84949	10.00000	10.00000	10.15051	10.15051	0

M	Cosine	Sine	Cotangent	Tangent	Cosecant	Secant	M

Geometrical Propositions

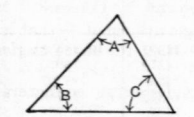

The sum of the three angles in a triangle always equals 180 degrees. Hence, if two angles are known, the third angle can always be found.

$$A + B + C = 180° \qquad A = 180° - (B + C)$$
$$B = 180° - (A + C) \qquad C = 180° - (A + B)$$

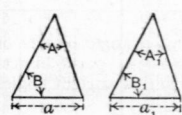

If one side and two angles in one triangle are equal to one side and similarly located angles in another triangle, then the remaining two sides and angle are also equal.

If $a = a_1$, $A = A_1$ and $B = B_1$, then the two other sides and the remaining angle are also equal.

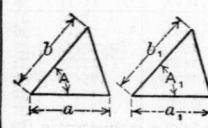

If two sides and the angle between them in one triangle are equal to two sides and a similarly located angle in another triangle, then the remaining side and angles are also equal.

If $a = a_1$, $b = b_1$ and $A = A_1$, then the remaining side and angles are also equal.

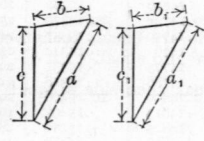

If the three sides in one triangle are equal to the three sides of another triangle, then the angles in the two triangles are also equal.

If $a = a_1$, $b = b_1$ and $c = c_1$, then the angles between the respective sides are also equal.

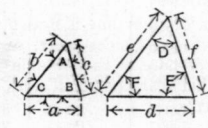

If the three sides of one triangle are proportional to corresponding sides in another triangle, then the triangles are called *similar*, and the angles in the one are equal to the angles in the other.

If $a : b : c = d : e : f$, then $A = D$, $B = E$ and $C = F$.

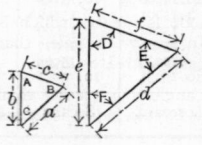

If the angles in one triangle are equal to the angles of another triangle, then the triangles are similar and their corresponding sides are proportional.

If $A = D$, $B = E$ and $C = F$, then $a : b : c = d : e : f$.

Geometrical Propositions

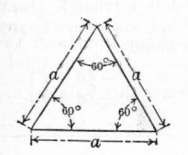

If the three sides in a triangle are equal — that is, if the triangle is *equilateral* — then the three angles are also equal.

Each of the three equal angles in an equilateral triangle is 6o degrees.

If the three angles in a triangle are equal, then the three sides are also equal.

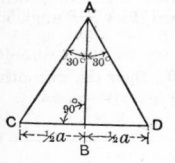

A line which in an equilateral triangle bisects or divides any of the angles into two equal parts, bisects also the side opposite the angle and is at right angles to it.

If line AB divides angle CAD into two equal parts, it also divides line CD into two equal parts and is at right angles to it.

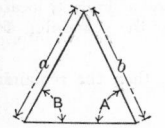

If two sides in a triangle are equal — that is, if the triangle is an *isosceles* triangle — then the angles opposite these sides are also equal.

If side a equals side b, then angle A equals angle B.

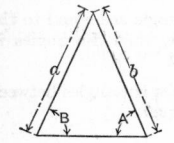

If two angles in a triangle are equal, then the sides opposite these angles are also equal.

If angles A and B are equal, then side a equals side b.

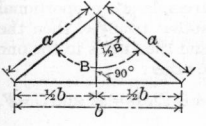

In an isosceles triangle, if a straight line is drawn from the point where the two equal sides meet, so that it bisects the third side or base of the triangle, then it also bisects the angle between the equal sides and is perpendicular to the base.

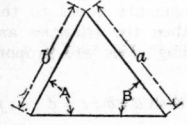

In every triangle, that angle is greater which is opposite a longer side. — In every triangle, that side is greater which is opposite a greater angle.

If a is longer than b, then angle A is greater than B. If angle A is greater than B, then side a is longer than b.

Geometrical Propositions

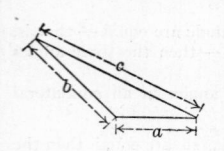

In every triangle, the sum of the lengths of two sides is always greater than the length of the third.

Side a + side b is always greater than side c.

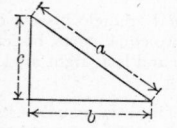

In a right-angled triangle, the square of the hypotenuse or the side opposite the right angle is equal to the sum of the squares on the two sides which form the right angle.

$$a^2 = b^2 + c^2.$$

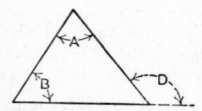

If one side of a triangle is produced, then the exterior angle is equal to the sum of the two interior opposite angles.

Angle D = angle A + angle B.

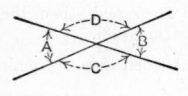

If two lines intersect, then the opposite angles formed by the intersecting lines are equal.

Angle A = angle B.
Angle C = angle D.

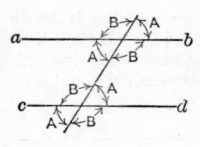

If a line intersects two parallel lines, then the corresponding angles formed by the intersecting line and the parallel lines are equal.

Lines ab and cd are parallel. Then all the angles designated A are equal, and all those designated B are equal.

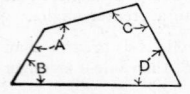

In any figure having four sides, the sum of the interior angles equals 360 degrees.

$$A + B + C + D = 360 \text{ degrees.}$$

Geometrical Propositions

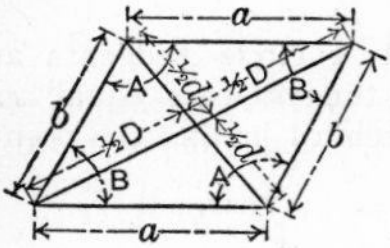

The sides which are opposite each other in a parallelogram are equal; the angles which are opposite each other are equal; the diagonal divides it into two equal parts. If two diagonals are drawn, they bisect each other.

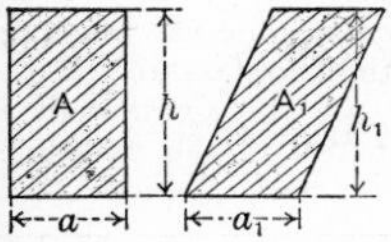

The areas of two parallelograms which have equal base and equal height, are equal.

If $a = a_1$ and $h = h_1$, then

area A = area A_1.

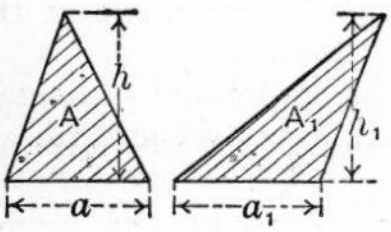

The areas of triangles having equal base and equal height are equal.

If $a = a_1$ and $h = h_1$, then

area A = area A_1.

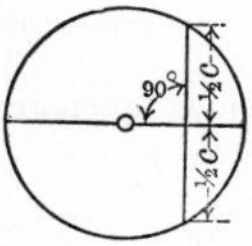

If a diameter of a circle is at right angles to a chord, then it bisects or divides the chord into two equal parts.

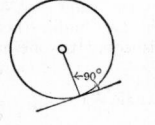

If a line is tangent to a circle, then it is also at right angles to a line drawn from the center of the circle to the point of tangency — that is, to a radial line through the point of tangency.

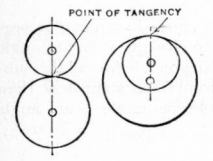

If two circles are tangent to each other, then the straight line which passes through the centers of the two circles must also pass through the point of tangency.

Geometrical Propositions

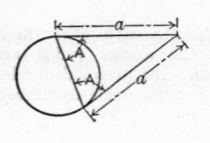

If from a point without a circle tangents are drawn to a circle, the two tangents are equal and make equal angles with the chord joining the points of tangency.

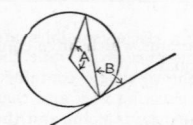

The angle between a tangent and a chord drawn from the point of tangency equals one-half the angle at the center subtended by the chord.

Angle B = ½ angle A.

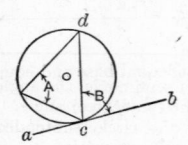

The angle between a tangent and a chord drawn from the point of tangency equals the angle at the periphery subtended by the chord.

Angle B, between tangent ab and chord cd, equals angle A subtended at the periphery by chord cd.

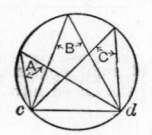

All angles having their vertex at the periphery of a circle and subtended by the same chord are equal.

Angles A, B and C, all subtended by chord cd, are equal.

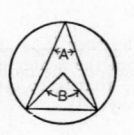

If an angle at the circumference of a circle, between two chords, is subtended by the same arc as the angle at the center, between two radii, then the angle at the circumference is equal to one-half of the angle at the center.

Angle A = ½ angle B.

A=LESS THAN 90°　B=MORE THAN 90°

 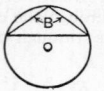

An angle subtended by a chord in a circular segment larger than one-half the circle is an acute angle — an angle less than 90 degrees. An angle subtended by a chord in a circular segment less than one-half the circle is an obtuse angle — an angle greater than 90 degrees.

Geometrical Propositions

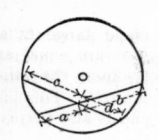

If two chords intersect each other in a circle, then the rectangle of the segments of the one equals the rectangle of the segments of the other.

$$a \times b = c \times d.$$

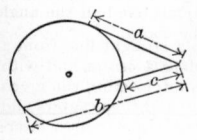

If from a point outside of a circle two lines are drawn, one of which intersects the circle while the other is tangent to it, then the rectangle contained by the total length of the intersecting line, and that part of it which is between the outside point and the periphery, equals the square of the tangent.

$$a^2 = b \times c.$$

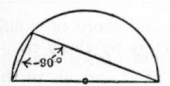

If a triangle is inscribed in a semi-circle, the angle opposite the diameter is a right (90-degree) angle.

All angles at the periphery of a circle, subtended by the diameter, are right (90-degree) angles.

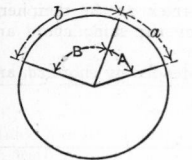

The length of circular arcs of the same circle are proportional to the corresponding angles at the center.

$$A : B = a : b.$$

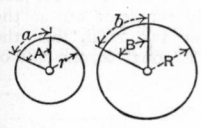

The length of circular arcs having the same center angle are proportional to the length of the radii.

If $A = B$, then $a : b = r : R$.

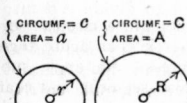

The circumferences of two circles are proportional to their radii.

The areas of two circles are proportional to the squares of their radii.

$$c : C = r : R.$$
$$a : A = r^2 : R^2.$$

Geometrical Problems

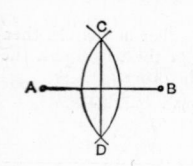

To divide a line AB into two equal parts: With the ends A and B as centers and a radius greater than one-half the line, draw circular arcs. Through the intersections C and D, draw line CD. This line divides AB into two equal parts and is also perpendicular to AB.

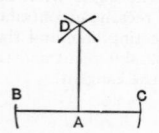

To draw a perpendicular to a straight line from a point A on that line: With A as a center and with any radius, draw circular arcs intersecting the given line at B and C. Then, with B and C as centers and a radius longer than AB, draw circular arcs intersecting at D. Line DA is perpendicular to BC at A.

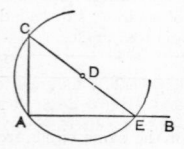

To draw a perpendicular line from a point A at the end of a line AB: With any point D, outside of the line AB, as a center, and with AD as a radius, draw a circular arc intersecting AB at E. Draw a line through E and D intersecting the arc at C; then join AC. This line is the required perpendicular.

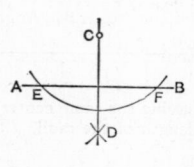

To draw a perpendicular to a line AB from a point C at a distance from it: With C as a center, draw a circular arc intersecting the given line at E and F. With E and F as centers, draw circular arcs with a radius longer than one-half the distance between E and F. These arcs intersect at D. Line CD is the required perpendicular.

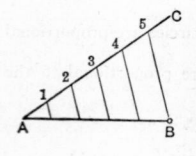

To divide a straight line AB into a number of equal parts: Let it be required to divide AB into five equal parts. Draw line AC at an angle with AB. Set off on AC five equal parts of any convenient length. Draw $B5$ and then draw lines parallel with $B5$ through the other division points on AC. The points where these lines intersect AB are the required division points.

Geometrical Problems

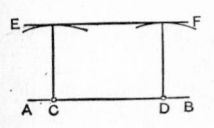

To draw a straight line parallel to a given line AB, at a given distance from it: With any points C and D on AB as centers, draw circular arcs with the given distance as radius. Line EF, drawn to touch the circular arcs, is the required parallel line.

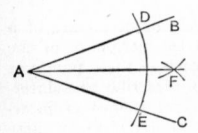

To bisect or divide an angle BAC into two equal parts: With A as a center and any radius, draw arc DE. With D and E as centers and a radius greater than one-half DE, draw circular arcs intersecting at F. Line AF divides the angle into two equal parts.

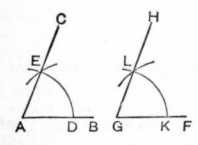

To draw an angle upon a line AB, equal to a given angle FGH: With point G as a center and with any radius, draw arc KL. With A as a center and with the same radius, draw arc DE. Make arc DE equal to KL and draw AC through E. Angle BAC then equals angle FGH.

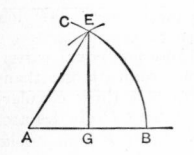

To lay out a 60-degree angle: With A as a center and any radius, draw an arc BC. With point B as a center and AB as a radius, draw an arc intersecting at E the arc just drawn. EAB is a 60-degree angle.

A 30-degree angle may be obtained either by dividing a 60-degree angle into two equal parts, or by drawing a line EG perpendicular to AB. Angle AEG is then 30 degrees.

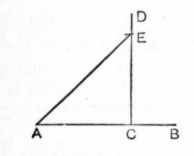

To draw a 45-degree angle: From point A on line AB set off a distance AC. Draw the perpendicular DC and set off a distance CE equal to AC. Draw AE. Angle EAC is a 45-degree angle.

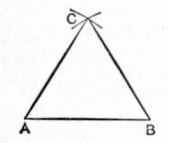

To draw an equilateral triangle, the length of the sides of which equals AB: With A and B as centers and AB as radius, draw circular arcs intersecting at C. Draw AC and BC. Then ABC is an equilateral triangle.

Geometrical Problems

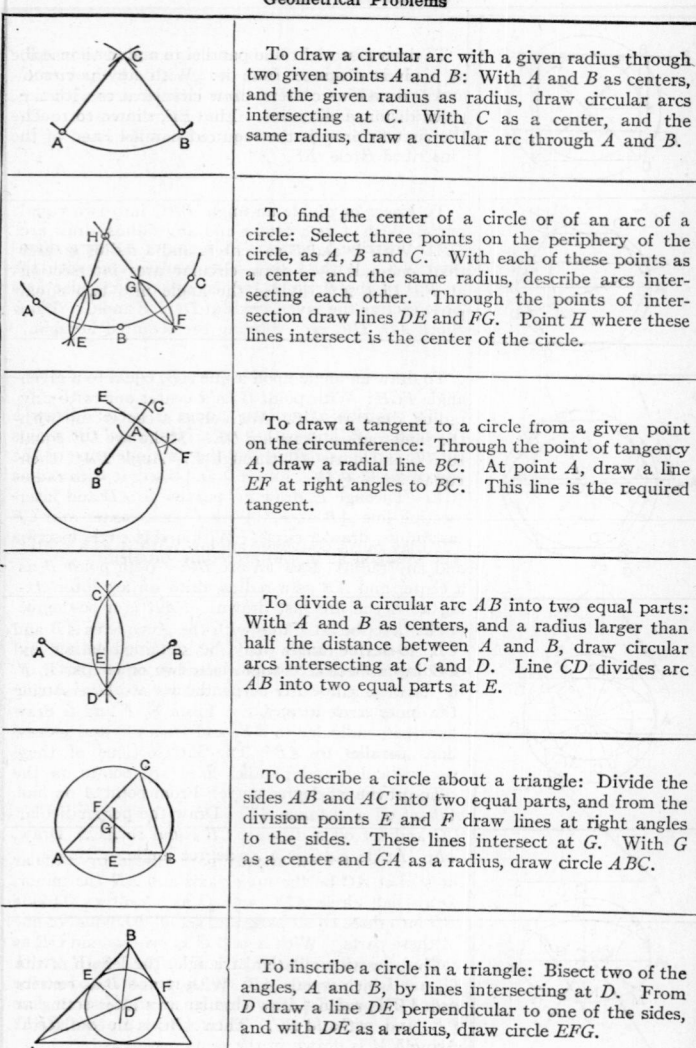

To draw a circular arc with a given radius through two given points A and B: With A and B as centers, and the given radius as radius, draw circular arcs intersecting at C. With C as a center, and the same radius, draw a circular arc through A and B.

To find the center of a circle or of an arc of a circle: Select three points on the periphery of the circle, as A, B and C. With each of these points as a center and the same radius, describe arcs intersecting each other. Through the points of intersection draw lines DE and FG. Point H where these lines intersect is the center of the circle.

To draw a tangent to a circle from a given point on the circumference: Through the point of tangency A, draw a radial line BC. At point A, draw a line EF at right angles to BC. This line is the required tangent.

To divide a circular arc AB into two equal parts: With A and B as centers, and a radius larger than half the distance between A and B, draw circular arcs intersecting at C and D. Line CD divides arc AB into two equal parts at E.

To describe a circle about a triangle: Divide the sides AB and AC into two equal parts, and from the division points E and F draw lines at right angles to the sides. These lines intersect at G. With G as a center and GA as a radius, draw circle ABC.

To inscribe a circle in a triangle: Bisect two of the angles, A and B, by lines intersecting at D. From D draw a line DE perpendicular to one of the sides, and with DE as a radius, draw circle EFG.

Geometrical Problems

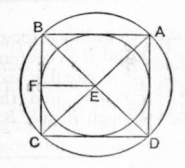

To describe a circle about a square and to inscribe a circle in a square: The center of both the circumscribed and inscribed circle is located at the point E, where the two diagonals of the square intersect. The radius of the circumscribed circle is AE, and of the inscribed circle, EF.

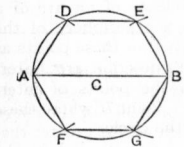

To inscribe a hexagon in a circle: Draw a diameter AB. With A and B as centers and with the radius of the circle as radius, describe circular arcs intersecting the given circle at D, E, F and G. Draw lines AD, DE, etc., forming the required hexagon.

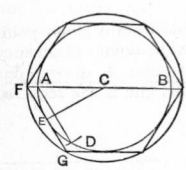

To describe a hexagon about a circle: Draw a diameter AB, and with A as a center and the radius of the circle as radius, cut the circumference of the given circle at D. Join AD and bisect it with radius CE. Through E, draw FG parallel to AD and intersecting line AB at F. With C as a center and CF as radius, draw a circle. Within this circle inscribe the hexagon as in the preceding problem.

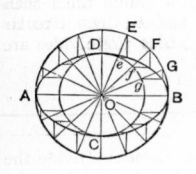

To describe an ellipse with the given axes AB and CD: Describe circles with O as a center and AB and CD as diameters. From a number of points, E, F, G, etc., on the outer circle draw radii intersecting the inner circle at e, f, g. From E, F and G draw lines perpendicular to AB, and from e, f and g draw lines parallel to AB. The intersections of these perpendicular and parallel lines are points on the curve of the ellipse.

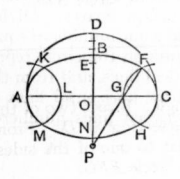

To construct an approximate ellipse by circular arcs: Let AC be the major axis and BN the minor. Draw half circle ADC with O as a center. Divide BD into three equal parts and set off BE equal to one of these parts. With A and C as centers and OE as radius, describe circular arcs KLM and FGH; with G and L as centers, and the same radius, describe arcs FCH and KAM. Through F and G draw line FP, and with P as a center draw the arc FBK. Arc HNM is drawn in the same manner.

Geometrical Problems

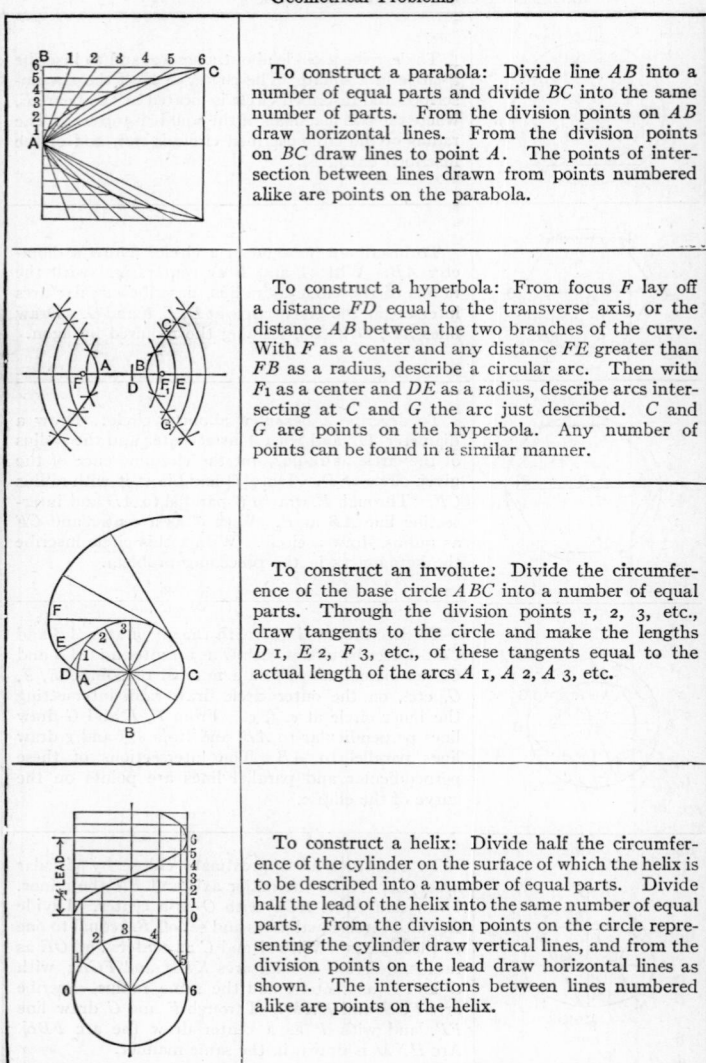

To construct a parabola: Divide line AB into a number of equal parts and divide BC into the same number of parts. From the division points on AB draw horizontal lines. From the division points on BC draw lines to point A. The points of intersection between lines drawn from points numbered alike are points on the parabola.

To construct a hyperbola: From focus F lay off a distance FD equal to the transverse axis, or the distance AB between the two branches of the curve. With F as a center and any distance FE greater than FB as a radius, describe a circular arc. Then with F_1 as a center and DE as a radius, describe arcs intersecting at C and G the arc just described. C and G are points on the hyperbola. Any number of points can be found in a similar manner.

To construct an involute: Divide the circumference of the base circle ABC into a number of equal parts. Through the division points 1, 2, 3, etc., draw tangents to the circle and make the lengths $D\,1$, $E\,2$, $F\,3$, etc., of these tangents equal to the actual length of the arcs $A\,1$, $A\,2$, $A\,3$, etc.

To construct a helix: Divide half the circumference of the cylinder on the surface of which the helix is to be described into a number of equal parts. Divide half the lead of the helix into the same number of equal parts. From the division points on the circle representing the cylinder draw vertical lines, and from the division points on the lead draw horizontal lines as shown. The intersections between lines numbered alike are points on the helix.

Mathematical Signs and Commonly Used Abbreviations

Sign	Meaning	Sign	Meaning
$+$	Plus (sign of addition)	π	Pi (3.1416)
$+$	Positive	Σ	Sigma (sign of summation)
$-$	Minus (sign of subtraction)	ω	Omega (angles measured in radians)
$-$	Negative		
$\pm$ ($\mp$)	Plus or minus (minus or plus)	g	Acceleration due to gravity (32.16 ft. per sec. per sec.)
$\times$	Multiplied by (multiplication sign)		
$\cdot$	Multiplied by (multiplication sign)	i (or j)	Imaginary quantity ($\sqrt{-1}$)
$\div$	Divided by (division sign)	sin	Sine
$:$	Divided by (division sign)	cos	Cosine
$::$	Is to (in proportion)	tan (tg) (tang)	} Tangent
$=$	Equals		
$\neq$	Is not equal to		
$\equiv$	Is identical to	cot (ctg)	} Cotangent
$::$	Equals (in proportion)		
$\approx \cong \simeq$ }	Approximately equals	sec	Secant
		cosec	Cosecant
$>$	Greater than	versin	Versed sine
$<$	Less than	covers	Coversed sine
$\geqq$	Greater than or equal to	$\sin^{-1} a$	Arc the sine of which is a
$\leqq$	Less than or equal to	arcsin a	
$\rightarrow$	Approaches as a limit	$(\sin a)^{-1}$	Reciprocal of sin a ($1 \div \sin a$)
$\propto$	Varies directly as		
$\therefore$	Therefore	sinh x	Hyperbolic sine of x
$\sqrt{}$	Square root	cosh x	Hyperbolic cosine of x
$\sqrt[3]{}$	Cube root	Δ	Delta (increment of)
$\sqrt[4]{}$	4th root	δ	Delta (variation of)
$\sqrt[n]{}$	nth root	d	Differential (in calculus)
a^2	a squared (2d power of a)	$\int$	Integral (in calculus)
a^3	a cubed (3d power of a)		
a^4	4th power of a	$\int_b^a$	Integral between the limits a and b
a^n	nth power of a		
a^{-n}	$1 \div a^n$	$!$	$5! = 1 \times 2 \times 3 \times 4 \times 5$
$\dfrac{1}{n}$	Reciprocal value of n	$\angle$	Angle
		$\llcorner$	Right angle
log	Logarithm	$\perp$	Perpendicular to
hyp. log		$\triangle$	Triangle
nat. log	Hyperbolic, natural or	$\odot$	Circle
$\log_e$	Napierian logarithm	$\square$	Parallelogram
ln		$\circ$	Degree (circular arc or temperature)
e	Base of hyp. logarithms (2.71828)	$'$	Minutes or feet
		$''$	Seconds or inches
lim.	Limit value (of an expression)	a'	a prime
∞	Infinity	a''	a double prime
α	Alpha	a_1	a sub one
β	Beta	commonly used	a_2	a sub two
γ	Gamma	to denote angles	a_n	a sub n
θ	Theta	( )	Parentheses
ϕ	Phi	[ ]	Brackets
μ	Mu (coefficient of friction)	{ }	Braces

American Standard Symbols for Mechanics, Structural Engineering and Testing Materials

Acceleration, angular	α (alpha)	Neutral axis, distance to extreme fiber	c
Acceleration, due to gravity	g	Number of revolutions per unit of time	n
Acceleration, linear	a	Period (harmonic motion)	T
Angular distance	θ (theta)	Power, horsepower	P
Angular velocity	ω (omega)	Pressure per unit of area	p
Area	A	Radius	r
Axes, through any point	$X\text{-}X$	Ratio between modulus of elasticity of steel and modulus of elasticity of concrete	n
	$Y\text{-}Y$		
	$Z\text{-}Z$		
Breadth	b	Ratio of the distance from the neutral axis to the outer fiber of a reinforced concrete beam to the distance from the outer fiber to the point of application of the resultant tensile stress	k
Center of rotation	O		
Coefficient of sliding friction	f		
Concentrated load (same as force)	F		
Constants	C		
Curvature, radius of	ρ (rho)	Ratio of the lever arm of the resisting couple in a reinforced concrete beam to the distance between the outer compressive fiber and the point of application of the resultant tensile stress	j
Deflection	y		
Deflection of a panel point of a truss	Δ (delta)		
Density	ρ (rho) or d		
Depth	d	Reactions	R
Diameter	D	Section modulus	Z or S
Distance, linear	s	Statical moment of any area about a given axis	Q
Eccentricity of application of load	e		
Efficiency (hydraulic, mechanical, volumetric)	e_h, e_m, e_v	Steel ratio, in reinforced concrete beams	p
Elasticity, modulus of	E	Stress, unit	s
Elongation, unit	δ (delta)	Stress, unit compressive	s_c
Force	F	Stress, unit tensile	s_t
Force in any bar of a framed structure due to a load of unity applied at any point in any direction	u	Stress, unit shear	s_s
		Stress, total tensile or total steel, in reinforced concrete	T
Frequency (harmonic motion)	f or n	Stress, total compressive or total concrete, in reinforced concrete	C
Gyration, radius of	k		
Head	H or h	Stress, total shear	V
Height	h	Stress, unit concrete, in reinforced concrete	f_c
Inertia, rectangular moment of	I	Stress, unit steel, in reinforced concrete	f_s
Inertia, polar moment of	J	Stress, unit shear of concrete	v
Length	L	Temperature, absolute	T
Load per unit distance	w	Temperature, ordinary	t
Load, total	W	Thickness	d or t
Mass	m	Time	t
Modulus of rupture	R	Torque	T
Moment in inch-pounds at any section of a girder due to the moment of one inch-pound applied to the girder at any point	m	Velocity, linear	V or v
		Volume	V
		Work, or energy	W
Moment of force, including bending moment	M		

Approved by American Standards Association and sponsored by the American Societ of Mechanical Engineers; American Association for the Advancement of Science; Ameri can Institute of Electrical Engineers; American Society of Civil Engineers; Society fo the Promotion of Engineering Education.

American Standard Abbreviations for Scientific and Engineering Terms — 1

Only the most commonly used terms have been included. These forms are recommended for those whose familiarity with the terms used makes possible a maximum of abbreviations. For others, less contracted combinations made up from this list may be used. For example, the list gives the abbreviation of the term "feet per second" as "fps." To some, however, ft per sec will be more easily understood.

Absolute	abs
Acre	acre
Acre-foot	acre-ft
Air horsepower	air hp
Alternating-current (as adjective)	a-c
Ampere	amp
Ampere-hour	amp-hr
Angstrom unit	A
Antilogarithm	antilog
Atomic weight	at. wt
Atmosphere	atm
Average	avg
Avoirdupois	avdp
Barometer	bar.
Barrel	bbl
Baumé	Bé
Board feet (feet board measure)	fbm
Boiler pressure	bp
Boiling point	bp
Brake horsepower	bhp
Brake horsepower-hour	bhp-hr
Brinell hardness number	Bhn
British thermal unit	Btu or B
Bushel	bu
Calory	cal
Candle	c
Candlepower	cp
Center to center	c to c
Centigram	cg
Centiliter	cl
Centimeter	cm
Centimeter-gram-second (system)	cgs
Cent	c or ¢
Chemical	chem
Chemically pure	cp
Circular	cir
Circular mils	cir mils
Coefficient	coef
Cologarithm	colog
Concentrate	conc
Conductivity	cond
Constant	const
Continental horsepower	cont hp
Cord	cd
Cosecant	csc
Cosine	cos
Cost, insurance, and freight	cif
Cotangent	ctn
Coulomb	spell out
Counter electromotive force	counter emf
Cubic	cu
Cubic centimeter	cu cm, cm³, cc (liquid, meaning milliliter, ml)
Cubic foot	cu ft
Cubic feet per second	cfs
Cubic inch	cu in.
Cubic meter	cu m or m³
Cubic micron	cu μ or cu mu or μ³
Cubic millimeter	cu mm or mm³
Cubic yard	cu yd
Current density	spell out
Cylinder	cyl
Day	spell out
Decibel	db
Degree	deg or °
Degree Centigrade	C
Degree Fahrenheit	F
Degree Kelvin	K
Degree Réaumur	R
Diameter	diam
Direct-current (as adjective)	d-c
Dozen	doz
Dram	dr
Efficiency	eff
Electric	elec
Electromotive force	emf
Elevation	el
Engine	eng
Engineer	engr
Engineering	engg
Equation	eq
External	ext
Farad	spell out
Feet board measure (board feet)	fbm
Feet per minute	fpm
Feet per second	fps
Fluid	fl
Foot	ft
Foot-candle	ft-c
Foot-Lambert	ft-L
Foot-pound	ft-lb
Foot-pound-second (system)	fps
Franc	fr
Free aboard ship	spell out
Free alongside ship	spell out
Free on board	f.o.b.
Freezing point	fp
Frequency	spell out
Furlong	fur.
Fusion point	fnp

American Standard Abbreviations for Scientific and Engineering Terms — 2

Gallon	gal
Gallons per minute	gpm
Gallons per second	gps
Grain	spell out
Gram	g
Gram-calory	g-cal
Greatest common divisor	gcd
Hectare	ha
Henry	h
High-pressure (adjective)	h-p
Horsepower	hp
Horsepower-hour	hp-hr
Hour	hr
Hundred	C
Hundredweight (112 lb.)	cwt
Hyperbolic sine	sinh
Hyperbolic cosine	cosh
Hyperbolic tangent	tanh
Inch	in,
Inch-pound	in-lb
Inches per second	ips
Indicated horsepower	ihp
Indicated horsepower-hour	ihp-hr
Intermediate-pressure (adjective)	i-p
Internal	int
Joule	j
Kilocycle	kc
Kilogram	kg
Kilogram-meter	kg-m
Kilograms per cubic meter	kg per cu m or kg/m³
Kilograms per second	kgps
Kiloliter	kl
Kilometer	km
Kilometers per second	kmps
Kilovar (reactive kilovolt-ampere)	kvar
Kilovarhour (reactive kilovolt-ampere-hour)	kvarh
Kilovolt	kv
Kilovolt-ampere	kva
Kilowatt	kw
Kilowatthour	kwhr
Lambert	L
Latitude	lat
Least common multiple	lcm
Linear foot	lin ft
Lira	spell out
Liter	l
Liquid	liq
Logarithm (common)	log
Logarithm (natural)	$\log_e$ or ln
Low-pressure (as adjective)	l-p
Lumen	l
Lumen-hour	l-hr
Lumens per watt	lpw

Magnetomotive force	mmf
Mark (German coinage)	M.
Mass	spell out
Mathematics (ical)	math
Maximum	max
Mean effective pressure	mep
Mean horizontal candlepower	mhcp
Megohm	spell out
Melting point	mp
Meter	m
Meter-kilogram	m-kg
Mho	spell out
Microampere	μa or mu a
Microfarad	μf or mu f
Micromicron	$\mu\mu$ or mu mu
Micron	μ mu
Microwatt	μw or mu w
Mile	spell out
Miles per hour	mph
Miles per hour per second	mphps
Milliampere	ma
Millifarad	mf
Milligram	mg
Millihenry	mh
Millilambert	mL
Milliliter	ml
Millimeter	mm
Millimicron	$m\mu$or m mu
Million	spell out
Million gallons per day	mgd
Millivolt	mv
Minimum	min
Minute	min
Minute (angular measure)	'
Molecular weight	mol. wt
Mol	spell out
National Electric Code	NEC
Ohm	spell out
Ohm-centimeter	ohm-cm
Ounce	oz
Ounce-foot	oz-ft
Ounce-inch	oz-in.
Parts per million	ppm
Peck	pk
Pennyweight	dwt
Peso	spell out
Pint	pt
Potential	spell out
Potential difference	spell out
Pound	lb
Pound-foot	lb-ft
Pound-inch	lb-in.
Pounds per brake horse-power-hour	lb per bhp-hr
Pounds per square foot	lb per sq ft
Pounds per square inch	lb per sq in.
Pound sterling	£
Power factor	spell out

American Standard Abbreviations for Scientific and Engineering Terms — 3

Quart	qt	Square micron	sq μ or sq mu or μ^2
Radian	spell out	Square millimeter	sq mm or mm^2
Reactive kilovolt-ampere	rkva	Square root of mean square	rms
Reactive volt-ampere	rva	Standard	std
Revolutions per minute	rpm	Stere	s
Revolutions per second	rps		
Rod	spell out	Tangent	tan
Root mean square	rms	Temperature	temp
Round	rd	Tensile strength	ts
		Thousand	M
Secant	sec	Ton	spell out
Second	sec	Ton-mile	spell out
Second (angular measure)	"	Twaddell	Twad
Second-foot (see cubic feet per second)			
Shaft horsepower	shp	Var (reactive volt-ampere)	var
Shilling	s	Versed sine	vers
Sine	sin	Volt	v
Specific gravity	sp gr	Volt-ampere	va
Specific heat	sp ht	Volt-coulomb	spell out
Spherical candle power	scp		
Square	sq	Watt	w
Square centimeter	sq cm or cm^2	Watthour	whr
Square foot	sq ft	Watts per candle	wpc
Square inch	sq in.	Week	spell out
Square kilometer	sq km or km^2	Weight	wt
Square meter	sq m or m^2	Yard	yd

Alternative abbreviations conforming to the practice of the International Electro-technical Commission.

Ampere	A	Kilowatthour	kWh	Millivolt	mV
Ampere-hour	Ah	Megawatt	MW	Ohm	Ω
Coulomb	C	Megohm	MΩ	Volt	V
Farad	F	Microampere	μA	Volt-ampere	VA
Henry	H	Microfarad	μF	Volt-coulomb	VC
Joule	J	Microwatt	μW	Watt	W
Kilovolt	kV	Milliampere	mA	Watthour	Wh
Kilovolt-ampere	kVA	Millifarad	mF		
Kilowatt	kW	Millihenry	mH		

Abbreviations should not be used where the meaning will not be clear. In case of doubt, spell out.

Abbreviations should be used sparingly in text and with regard to the context and to the training of the reader. Terms denoting units of measurement should be abbreviated in the text only when preceded by the amounts indicated in numerals; thus " several inches," " one inch," " 12 in." In tabular matter, specifications, maps, drawings, and texts for special purposes, the use of abbreviations should be governed only by the desirability of conserving space.

A sentence should not begin with a numeral followed by an abbreviation.

Short words such as ton, day, and mile should be spelled out.

The use of conventional signs for abbreviations in text is not recommended; thus " per," not /; " lb," not #; " in.," not ". Such signs may be used sparingly in tables and similar places for conserving space.

The Committee endorses the movement which was begun by the International Committee on Weights and Measures in omitting the period in abbreviations of metric units and further endorses the growing tendency toward the omission in abbreviations of other origin. In the interests of economy and the reduction of waste the elimination of the period is recommended except where such an omission results in an English word. Exceptions to this practice will be found in a few mathematical and chemical terms, such as in, tan, log, As, etc.

American Standard Drafting-Room Practice. — This standard (approved by American Standards Association) includes the lines for engineering drawings and the symbols for section lining as shown on the accompanying pages.

Dimensioning: Dimensions of parts that can be measured or that can be produced with sufficient accuracy by using an ordinary scale should be written in units and common fractions. Parts requiring greater accuracy should be dimensioned in decimal fractions. Dimensions up to and including 72 inches should preferably be expressed in inches, and those greater than this length, in feet and inches.

Where dimensions call for accurate machining with small tolerances it is recommended that the total dimension be given in inches and decimal fractions. In structural drawing all dimensions of 12 inches and over should be expressed in feet and inches. In automotive, locomotive, sheet metal and some other practices all dimensions are specified in inches.

The symbol ('') is used to indicate inches and common and decimal fractions of an inch. When all dimensions are given in inches the symbol is preferably omitted. A note may be placed on the drawing stating that all dimensions are given in inches. The symbol (') is used to indicate feet and fractions of a foot. Dimensions in feet and inches should be hyphenated, thus 4'-3''; 4'-0½''; 4'-0''.

Fractions should be written with the division in line with the dimension line.

Dimension Lines and Extension Lines: Dimension lines should be fine full lines (broken where dimension is inserted) so as to contrast with the heavier outline of the drawing, and should be placed outside the figure or drawing outline wherever possible.

Extension lines indicate the distance measured when the dimension is placed outside the figure. They are made as light full lines starting ½₂ to ¹⁄₁₆ inch away from the outline and extending about ⅛ inch beyond the dimension line.

A center line should never be used as a dimension line. A line of the piece or part illustrated or an extension of such a line should never be used as a dimension line.

Dimension Figures: A dimension line must not pass through a dimension figure. If unbroken lines are used, as is common practice in structural drawing, the dimensions are placed above the line. When fractional dimensions of less than one inch are given, the numerator should be placed above the dimension line and the denominator below.

All dimension lines and their corresponding numbers should be placed so that they may be read from the bottom or right-hand edges of the drawing. All dimensions should be placed so as to read in the direction of the dimension lines.

When there are several parallel dimension lines the figures should be staggered to avoid confusion. Dimensions should be given from a base line, a center line or a finished surface that can be readily established. Over-all dimensions should be placed outside the intermediate dimensions. In dimensioning with tolerances, if an over-all dimension is used one intermediate distance should not be dimensioned.

In dimensioning angles an arc should be drawn and the dimension placed so as to read from the horizontal position. An exception is sometimes made in the dimensioning of large areas when the dimensions are placed along the arc.

Dimensioning Circles: A dimension indicating the diameter of a circle should be followed by the abbreviation "D" except when it is obvious from the drawing that the dimension is a diameter. The dimension of a radius should always be followed by the abbreviation "R." The center should be indicated by a cross or circle and the dimension line have one arrow-head.

Dimensioning Holes: Holes which are to be drilled, reamed, punched, swaged, cored, etc., should have the diameter, given preferably on a leader, followed by the word indicating the operation, and the number of holes to be so made. Holes which are to be machined after coring or casting should have finished marks and finished dimensions specified.

If needed by the shop on account of the method of laying out, as in the button method, the chordal distances between holes on a bolt circle or the center-to-center distances between holes located by coordinates, should be calculated and dimensioned in decimals.

Dimensioning with Tolerances: Accurate dimensions which are to be established with limit gage or micrometer should be expressed in decimals to at least three places and the drawing should give the maximum and minimum limits between which the actual measurements must come. For *external* dimensions the maximum limit is placed above the line and for *internal* dimensions the minimum limit is placed above the line. This method should be used for smaller parts and where gages are extensively employed.

A second method, used for larger parts and where few gages are employed, is to give the calculated size to the required number of decimal places, followed by the tolerances plus and minus, with the plus above the minus, as $8.625D \begin{smallmatrix} +.000 \\ -.002 \end{smallmatrix}$

Changes in Dimensions: On a drawing, if a dimension must be changed, the changed figures should be underlined or otherwise marked. It is customary to note changes in dimensions in a tabulation on the drawing and to refer to them by letters or symbols placed after the altered dimensions.

Dimensioning Tapers: At least three methods of dimensioning tapers are in general use.

Standard Tapers: Give one diameter or width, the length, and insert note on drawing designating the taper by number.

Special Tapers: In dimensioning a taper when the slope is specified, the length and only one diameter should be given or the diameters at both ends of the taper should be given and length omitted.

Precision Work: In certain cases where very precise measurements are necessary the taper surface, either external or internal, is specified by giving a diameter at a certain distance from a surface and the slope of the taper.

Finish Marks: A surface to be machined or "finished" from unfinished material such as a casting or a forging should be marked with a 60 degree "V," the bottom of the "V" touching the line representing the surface to be machined or finished. A code figure or letter should then be placed in the opening of the "V" to indicate the quality of the finish desired. The meaning of these code figures or letters should then be indicated by notes at the bottom or side of the drawings.

Sizes of Drawing Paper and Cloth: The recommended standard trimmed sheet sizes of drawing paper and cloth are shown by the table.

	Size, Inches				Metric Size, mm.			
A	8½ × 11	D	22 × 34	A0	841 × 1189	A4	210 × 297
B	11 × 17	E	34 × 44	A1	594 × 841	A5	148 × 210
C	17 × 22			A2	420 × 594	A6	105 × 148
				A3	297 × 420		

The standard sizes shown by the left-hand section of the table, are based on the dimensions of the commercial letter head, 8½ × 11 inches, in general use in the United States. The use of the basic sheet size 8½ × 11 inches and its multiples permits filing of small tracings and folded blueprints in commercial standard letter files with or without correspondence. These sheet sizes also cut without unnecessary waste from the present 36 inch rolls of paper and cloth.

For drawings made in the metric system of units or for foreign correspondence it is recommended that the metric standard trimmed sheet sizes be used. (Right-hand section of table.) These sizes are based on the width to length ratio of 1 to $\sqrt{2}$.

American Standard Lines for Engineering Drawings

Use of Line	Kind of Line
Outline of Parts	HEAVY
Section lines	LIGHT
Hidden lines	MEDIUM
Center lines	LIGHT
Dimension and Extension lines	LIGHT $3\frac{1}{2}$
Cutting Plane line	HEAVY
Break lines	HEAVY / LIGHT
Adjacent Parts and Alternate Positions	MEDIUM
Ditto line	MEDIUM

The width of each type of line should be governed by the size and style of the drawing, the relative widths of different lines to be approximately as shown above. The heavy " break line " is for short breaks and is drawn free-hand. For long breaks, use the light ruled line with free-hand zigzags. The " ditto line " is an indication of repeated detail.

The standards on this and the following page have been approved by the American Standards Association and sponsored by the American Society of Mechanical Engineers and the Society for the Promotion of Engineering Education.

American Standard Symbols for Section Lining

Section Lining and Material	Section Lining and Material
Cast iron.	Electric windings, electro magnets, resistance; etc.
Steel.	Concrete.
Bronze, brass, copper and compositions.	Brick or stone masonry.
White metal, zinc, lead, babbitt and alloys.	Marble, slate, glass, porcelain, etc.
Aluminum and aluminum alloys.	Earth.
Electric insulation, Vulcanite, fibre, mica, Bakelite, etc. Show solid for narrow sections.	Rock.
Sound or heat insulation. Cork, hair-felt, wool, asbestos, magnesia, packing, etc.	Sand.
Flexible material. Fabric, felt, rubber, etc.	Water and other liquids.
Fire brick and refractory material.	Wood. Across grain With grain

Marks or Symbols Indicating Surface Finish. — The "finish marks" used on drawings may show merely what surfaces are to be finished or they may also indicate with varying degrees of exactness, the character or quality of the finish. The letter f has been used extensively to show that *some* kind of finish is required. It is common practice to so place this letter that its cross-line intersects the line on the drawing representing the surface to be finished. The desired finish is sometimes indicated approximately by the use of numbers or symbols arbitrarily selected to represent different degrees of finish or smoothness. For example, f_1 might mean a rough machined surface; f_2 ordinary machining; f_3 fine machining; f_4 ground surface; f_5 a lapped surface. While such methods are simple, they are not very definite. Whenever such symbols are used, the finish represented by each symbol should be indicated as definitely as possible by a code placed preferably right on the drawing.

Terms Relating to Finish or Surface Roughness. — The following definitions include certain terms which are commonly used in connection with modern methods of measuring or testing the degree of roughness or smoothness of a machined surface.

Surface Flaw: A defect such as a scratch, crack, ridge, or similar imperfection found in some part of a surface, or possibly at relatively infrequent intervals.

Roughness: This term relates to deviations that are typical of or inherent in any machining or finishing process, such as marks normally left by cutting tool or grinding wheel.

Waviness: This term relates to surface irregularities which are of greater magnitude or spacing than those indicated by the term roughness. Waviness might be the result of vibration or deflection of a cutting tool, of some part of the machine, or of the work itself. Waviness may be indicated by giving actual wave widths and heights in inches. Waviness may also be expressed as a percentage of contact area, especially in dealing with parts such as bearing surfaces.

Lay: This term indicates the general direction of the surface pattern or of the marks or ridges left by the tool, cutter or grinding wheel. Super finished or lapped surfaces do not have a definite lay because the pattern or grain of the surface is multi-directional. For some classes of work the lay should be designated, and symbols are used for this purpose. (See chart showing different lay symbols.)

Standard Symbols for Lay or General Direction of Surface Pattern

$=$ Parallel to boundary line of surface indicated by symbol.

$\perp$ Perpendicular to boundary line of surface indicated by symbol.

X Angular in both directions to boundary line of surface indicated by symbol.

M Multi-directional or random.

C Approximately circular relative to center of surface indicated by symbol.

R Approximately radial relative to center of surface indicated by symbol.

Microinch: The microinch (abbreviation, mu. in.) equals one millionth (0.000001) inch. This is a common unit of measurement employed in surface measurement research and in establishing standard roughness unit values.

Indicating Degrees of Roughness by Average and Dimensional Values. — The numerous irregularities which form a machined surface and determine its quality, consist of minute ridges and valleys, and the degree of roughness is determined by the magnitude, form and spacing of these irregularities; hence, it is evident that no single figure or dimensional value will represent precisely the condition or roughness quality of a surface but an average or a maximum figure may approximate this quality and be useful in specifying, checking and duplicating within practical limits, machined surfaces having finishes which have been found to meet practical requirements. There are different methods of indicating surface roughness values.

Root-Mean-Square Average. — An average value which has been used extensively in the United States is known as the root-mean-square average (abbreviation, *rms* or *RMS*). The diagram (Fig. 1), representing a very short section of a

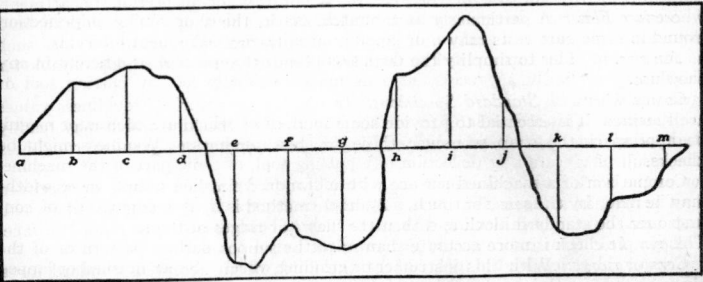

Fig. 1

surface greatly magnified, illustrates the principle involved in determining the *rms* value of a surface. Assume that the letters *a, b, c, d, e, f,* etc. represent distances in microinches above or below the mean reference line, to corresponding division points on the irregular contour of the surface; then the square root of the mean of the sum of the squares of these distances equals the *rms* value. (The mean reference line divides the irregularities so that total area of peaks above this line equals the total area of valleys below it.) Expressed as a formula

$$\text{Root-mean-square average} = \sqrt{\frac{a^2 + b^2 + c^2 + d^2 + e^2 \ldots}{n}}$$

The *rms* value gives the larger surface deviations greater "weight" than the smaller ones.

Arithmetical Average. — Referring again to the diagram, if the total sum of the heights and depths of the ridges and valleys above and below the mean reference line, is divided by the number of measurements, an arithmetical average is obtained. Thus,

$$\text{Arithmetical average} = \frac{a + b + c + d + e \ldots}{n}$$

This average is fairly close to the *rms* value, and some investigators of roughness measurements consider the arithmetical average just as effective as, or even superior to, the *rms* value. The former has been adopted in England in preference to the *rms* value.

Dimensional Specifications for Surface Irregularities. — Another general method of indicating the magnitude of surface irregularities is by specifying their maximum width and height values, in inches, as shown by the ratings which follow.

Roughness Width Rating: This term indicates the maximum permissible widths, in inches, of repetitive units of the dominant surface pattern (this may be added to the right of the lay symbol).

Waviness Width Rating: Waviness widths may also be specified directly in inches.

Height Rating: The height of roughness or waviness may be specified by giving (1) the maximum peak-to-valley height; (2) average peak-to-valley height; (3) average deviation from the mean surface (either arithmetical or root-mean-square average). The kind of height rating should, of course, be clearly specified.

Equipment for Testing Surface Quality. — Various methods have been developed for checking or measuring surface irregularities. Some of these are intended primarily for use in the research laboratory or inspection department, whereas others are particularly suitable for use in the shop. The working and even the inspection tests may only approximate theoretical roughness values such as the *rms*, in order to simplify the tests and permit the use of methods suitable for shop use.

Comparison with Standard Specimens: In plants where surface roughness values are specified, it is essential to provide some method of checking which may readily be applied in the shop wherever these finishing operations require roughness checks.

Comparison of a machined surface with a standard finished sample or specimen may be made by the sense of touch. A simple method is by dragging the finger-nail first over the standard block and then the "lay" or ridges of the machined surface. This simple check is more accurate than might be supposed.

Comparoscope: With this instrument the finish of an accepted standard for a given class of work is compared with the work itself by optical means. The more numerous and wider the surface irregularities, the brighter the surface will appear to the eye when the work is compared with the master. The images of both appear through the eye-piece of the instrument which contains a dual mircoscope and identical illumination for both master and work.

Commercial Sets of Standard Finish Specimens: A number of sets of standard surface specimens or finish samples have been placed on the market. These sets consist of blocks which have surfaces varying from the smoothest to the roughest likely to be required. Some of the more complete sets have from 18 to 25 standard surfaces with a series of nominal rms values. Some of these specimen blocks are made of stainless steel. An aluminum alloy has been employed in at least one case, and in another a hard black plastic material is used so that mere brilliance, which often is very deceptive, is eliminated in comparing the finish on the work with that of the sample.

Comparing Finishes by Projection Method: This method of inspecting and comparing surface finishes with approved standards is suitable for either shop or laboratory. A small piece of clear plastic film (Faxfilm) is softened by the use of a solvent and then is pressed into the surface, thus transferring the unevenness to the film. This film is next mounted in a 2-inch square frame which may be labeled for identification and future use. The surface pattern on the film is enlarged to 100 diameters or more if required, by means of a projector, thus permittng comparison with another film. Comparator apparatus is available for projecting simultaneously both the test specimen and a standard finish specimen.

Tracer Method of Determining Surface Quality: This method consists in tracing across the surface with a diamond or sapphire contact point which is displaced as it passes over the minute hills and valleys of the surface. These movements of the finely pointed tracer are magnified and either indicated by a meter or, with another type of instrument, are recorded graphically on a chart. The tracer point method provides a practical indication of surface roughness values and makes it possible to compare or check the values established by a tracer-type instrument, so as to maintain whatever finish standard is suitable for a given class of work.

Profilometer: In measuring surface roughness with this instrument, the surface irregularities are measured and averaged as a diamond tracer point moves slowly across the surface, and a meter shows by direct reading the average deviation in microinches. The profilometer may be applied to flat, cylindrical or curved surfaces. Different types of tracers are obtainable to permit checking various kinds of surfaces, such as small holes, narrow slots, etc. In measuring unusually smooth surfaces, odd shapes, or any place where only a short stroke can be taken, the tracer point is moved mechanically.

Brush Surface Analyzer: This instrument produces on a graduated chart a graphic ink-line record of surface irregularities showing not only the amplitude, but the form of these irregularities greatly magnified. The surface is traced or explored by a stylus having a point radius of 0.0005 inch. The displacements of this stylus by the surface irregularities are finally recorded in ink on a moving paper chart. The recorded deflections are directly proportional to those of the stylus, but are greatly magnified.

Surface Symbol for Drawings. — In specifying allowable roughness values on drawings, a V-shaped or check mark is used to designate the surface (see Fig. 2).

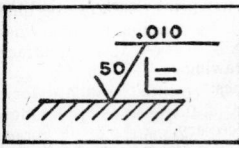

Fig. 2

The specified average or maximum height rating is placed above the vee. (This vee may have one heavy leg or flag to make it more conspicuous on the drawing.) There is a horizontal extension line at the top and the waviness value, if specified, is placed above the line. The particular example shown calls for a maximum roughness value of 50 (microinches), a maximum waviness of 0.010 inch, and a lay that is parallel to the boundary line as indicated by the symbol at the right of the vee. The lay is only specified when it is considered essential for a given class of work.

Checking Drawings. — In order that the drawings may have a high standard of excellence, a set of instructions, as given in the following, has been issued to the checkers, and also to the draftsmen and tracers, in the engineering department of a well-known machine-building company.

Inspecting a New Design: In case a new design is involved, first inspect the lay-outs carefully to see that the parts function correctly under all conditions, that they have the proper relative proportions, that the general design is correct in the matters of strength, rigidity, bearing areas, appearance, convenience of assembly, and direction of motion of the parts, and that there are no interferences. Consider the design as a whole to see if any improvements can be made. If the design appears to be unsatisfactory in any particular, or improvements appear to be possible, call the matter to the attention of the chief engineer.

Checking for Strength: Inspect the design of the part being checked for strength, rigidity and appearance by comparing it with other parts for similar service whenever possible, giving preference to the later designs in such comparison, unless the later designs are known to be unsatisfactory. If there is any question regarding the matter, compute the stresses and deformations or find out whether the chief engineer has approved the stresses or deformations that will result from the forces applied to the part in service. In checking parts that are to go on a machine of increased size, be sure that standard parts used in similar machines and proposed for use on the larger machine, have ample strength and rigidity under the new and more severe service to which they will be put.

Materials Specified. — Consider the kind of material required for the part and the various possibilities of molding, forging, welding, or otherwise forming the rough part from this material. Then consider the machining operations to see whether changes in form or design will reduce the number of operations or the cost of machining.

See that parts are designed with reference to the economical use of material, and whenever possible, utilize standard sizes of stock and material readily obtainable from local dealers. In the case of alloy steel, special bronze, and similar materials, be sure that the material can be obtained in the size required.

Method of Making Drawing. — Inspect the drawing to see that the projections and sections are made in such a way as to show most clearly the form of the piece and the work to be done on it. Make sure that any workman looking at the drawing will understand what the shape of the piece is and how it is to be molded or machined. Make sure that the delineation is correct in every particular, and that the information conveyed by the drawing as to the form of the piece is complete.

Checking Dimensions. — Check all dimensions to see that they are correct. Scale all dimensions and see that the drawing is to scale. See that the dimensions on the drawing agree with the dimensions scaled from the lay-out. Wherever any dimension is out of scale, see that the dimension is so marked. Investigate any case where the dimension, the scale of the drawing, and the scale of the lay-out do not agree. All dimensions not to scale must be underlined on the tracing. In checking dimensions, note particularly the following points:

See that all figures are correctly formed and that they will print clearly, so that the workmen can easily read them correctly.

See that the over-all dimensions are given.

See that all witness lines go to the correct part of the drawing.

See that all arrow points go to the correct witness lines.

See that proper allowance is made for all fits.

See that the tolerances are correctly given where necessary.

See that all dimensions given agree with the corresponding dimensions of adjacent parts.

Be sure that the dimensions given on a drawing are those that the machinist will use, and that the workman will not be obliged to do addition or subtraction in order to obtain the necessary measurements for machining or checking his work.

Avoid strings of dimensions where errors can accumulate. It is generally better to give a number of dimensions from the same reference surface or center line.

When holes are to be located by boring on a horizontal spindle boring machine or other similar machine, give dimensions to centers of bored holes in rectangular coordinates and from the center lines of the first hole to be bored, so that the operator will not be obliged to add measurements or transfer gages.

Checking Assembly. — See that the part can readily be assembled with the adjacent parts. If necessary, provide tapped holes for eyebolts and cored holes for tongs, lugs, or other methods of handling.

Make sure that, in being assembled, the piece will not interfere with other pieces already in place and that the assembly can be taken apart without difficulty.

Check the sum of a number of tolerances; this sum must not be great enough to permit two pieces that should not be in contact to come together.

Checking Castings. — In the case of castings, study the form of the pattern, the methods of molding, the method of supporting and venting the cores, and the effect of draft and rough molding on clearances.

Avoid undue metal thickness, and especially avoid thick and thin sections in the same casting.

Indicate all metal thicknesses, so that the molder will know what chaplets to use for supporting the cores.

See that ample fillets are provided, and that they are properly dimensioned.

See that the cores can be assembled in the mold without crushing or interference.

See that swelling, shrinkage, or misalignment of cores will not make trouble in machining.

See that the amount of finish is indicated.

See that there is sufficient finish on large castings to permit them to be "cleaned up," even though they warp. In the case of such castings, make sure that the metal thickness will be sufficient after finishing, even though the castings do warp.

Make sure that sufficient sections are shown so that the patternmakers and molders will not be compelled to make assumptions about the form of any part of the casting. This is particularly important when a number of sections of the casting are similar in form, while others differ slightly.

Checking Machined Parts. — Study the sequences of operations in machining and see that all finish marks are indicated.

See that the finish marks are placed on the lines to which dimensions are given.

See that methods of machining are indicated where necessary.

Give all drill, reamer, tap, and rose bit sizes.

See that jig and gage numbers are indicated at the proper places.

See that all necessary bosses, lugs, and openings are provided for lifting, handling, clamping, and machining the piece.

See that adequate wrench room is provided for all nuts and bolt heads.

Avoid special tools, such as taps, drills, reamers, etc., unless such tools are specially authorized.

Where parts are right- and left-hand, be sure that the hand is correctly designated. When possible, make parts symmetrical, so as to avoid having them right- and left-hand, but do not sacrifice correct design or satisfactory operation on this account.

When heat-treatment is required, the heat-treatment should be specified.

Check the title, size of machine, the scale, and the drawing number on both the drawing and the drawing record card.

Metric Dimensions on Drawings. — The length units of the metric system that are most generally used in connection with any work relating to mechanical engineering are the meter (39.37 inches) and the millimeter (0.03937 inch). One meter equals 1000 millimeters. On mechanical drawings, all dimensions are generally given in millimeters, no matter how large the dimensions may be. In fact, dimensions of such machines as locomotives and large electrical apparatus are given exclusively in millimeters. This practice is adopted to avoid mistakes due to misplacing decimal points, or mis-reading dimensions as when other units are used as well. When dimensions are given in millimeters, many of them can be given without resorting to decimal points, as a millimeter is only a little more than $\frac{1}{32}$ inch. Only dimensions of precision need be given in decimals of a millimeter; such dimensions are generally given in hundredths of a millimeter — for example, 0.02 millimeter, which is equal to 0.0008 inch. As 0.01 millimeter is equal to 0.0004 inch, it is seldom that dimensions would be given with greater accuracy than to hundredths of a millimeter.

Scales of Metric Drawings. — Drawings made to the metric system are not made to scales of $\frac{1}{2}$, $\frac{1}{4}$, $\frac{1}{8}$, etc., as in the case of drawings made to the English system. If the object cannot be drawn full size, it is generally drawn $\frac{1}{5}$ size, and, if this is too large, it is drawn $\frac{1}{10}$ size. In exceptional cases, when very large objects are to be shown on a drawing, scales of $\frac{1}{20}$, $\frac{1}{50}$, and $\frac{1}{100}$ may be used.

MECHANICS

Mechanics treats of the action of forces and their effect. A *force* is defined as any cause tending to produce or modify motion. The units by which a force is usually measured are pounds or tons. Besides force there are two other elementary quantities in mechanics from which numerous compound quantities are derived. These are *distance*, measured in linear units, as inches, feet, etc., and *time*, expressed in hours, minutes or seconds.

Work, in mechanics, is the product of force by distance, and is expressed by a combination of units of weight (force) and distance, as inch-pounds, foot-pounds, foot-tons, etc.

Power, in mechanics, is the product of force by distance divided by time, or the performance of a given amount of work in a given time, and is expressed as inch-pounds per minute, foot-pounds per minute or second, etc.

The term *power* is frequently used by writers on mechanics to designate a *force*. In connection with the so-called "mechanical powers" — the lever, wheel and axle, wedge, screw, etc. — it is usual to speak of the applied force as the power; this is, however, not strictly correct, as power should always, in mechanics, be used in accordance with the definition given above.

Horsepower (abbreviated H.P.) is the unit of power adopted for engineering work. One horsepower is equal to 33,000 foot-pounds per minute, or 550 foot-pounds per second. The metric horsepower, used in countries where the metric system is employed, is equal to 75 kilogram-meters per second, or 542.5 foot-pounds per second, or 32,550 foot-pounds per minute. The *kilowatt*, used in electrical work, equals 1.34 horsepower; or one horsepower equals 0.746 kilowatt.

Velocity is distance divided by time, and is expressed in feet per minute, miles per hour, etc.

Inertia is that property of a body which causes it to tend to continue in its present state of rest or motion, unless acted upon by some force.

Graphical Representation of Forces. — A force has three characteristics which, when known, determine it. They are direction, place of application, and magnitude. The *direction* of a force is the direction in which it tends to move the body upon which it acts. The *place of application* is generally assumed to be a point, as the center of gravity. The *magnitude* is measured in pounds, as already stated. Forces may conveniently be represented by straight lines and arrow heads. The arrow head indicates the direction of the force, and the length of the line its magnitude to any suitable scale. The point of application may be at any point on the line, but it is generally convenient to assume it to be at one end. In the accompanying

illustration, a force is supposed to act along line *AB* in a direction from left to right. The length of line *AB* shows the magnitude of the force. If point *A* is the point of application, the force is exerted as a pull, but if point *B* be assumed to be the point of application, it would indicate that the force is exerted as a push.

The single force which produces the same effect upon a body as two or more forces acting together, is called their *resultant*. The separate forces which can be so combined are called the *components*. The finding of the resultant of two or more forces is called the *composition* of forces, and the finding of two or more components of a given force, the *resolution* of forces.

On the two following pages are shown the methods used in the solution of those problems in the composition of forces that are most frequently met with. The resolution of forces is carried out in a similar manner to the composition, except that the work is carried out in a reverse order.

Composition and Resolution of Forces

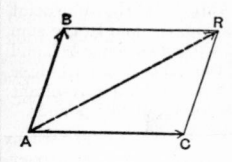

Parallelogram of Forces. — If two forces applied at a point are represented in magnitude and direction by the adjacent sides of a parallelogram (AB and AC in the accompanying illustration), their resultant will be represented in magnitude and direction by the diagonal AR drawn from the intersection of the two component forces.

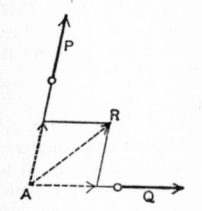

If two forces P and Q do not have the same point of application, but the lines indicating their directions intersect, the forces may be imagined as applied at the point of intersection between the lines (as at A), and the resultant of the two forces may be found by constructing the parallelogram of forces. Line AR shows the direction and magnitude of the resultant, the point of application of which may be assumed to be at any point on line AR or its extension.

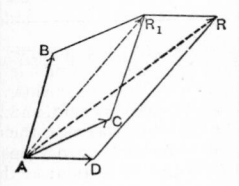

If the resultant of three or more forces having the same point of application is to be found, first find the resultant of any two of the forces (AB and AC) and then find the resultant of the resultant just found (AR_1) and the third force (AD). If there be more than three forces, continue in this manner until the resultant of all the forces has been found.

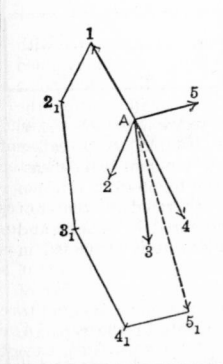

Polygon of Forces. — When several forces are applied at a point and act in a single plane, their resultant may be found more simply than by the method just described, as follows: From the extreme end of the line representing the first force, draw a line representing the second force, parallel to it and of the same length and in the direction of the second force. Then through the extreme end of this line draw a line parallel to, and of the same length and direction as the third force, and continue this until all the forces have been thus represented. Then draw a line from the point of application of the forces (as A) to the extreme point (as 5_1) of the line last drawn. This line ($A\,5_1$) is the resultant of the forces.

Composition and Resolution of Forces

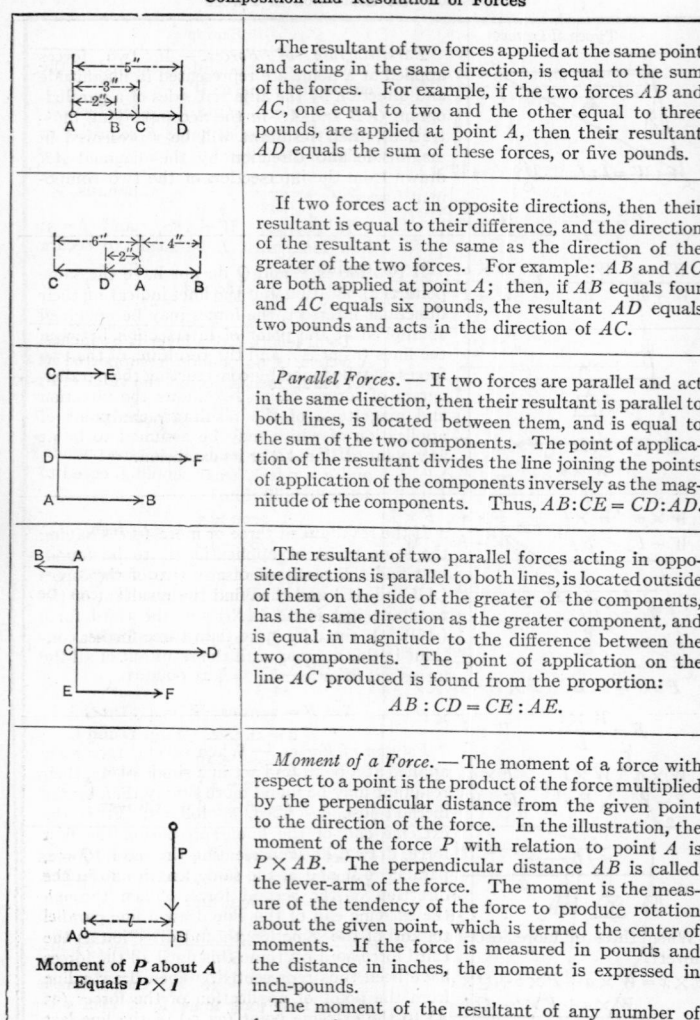

The resultant of two forces applied at the same point and acting in the same direction, is equal to the sum of the forces. For example, if the two forces AB and AC, one equal to two and the other equal to three pounds, are applied at point A, then their resultant AD equals the sum of these forces, or five pounds.

If two forces act in opposite directions, then their resultant is equal to their difference, and the direction of the resultant is the same as the direction of the greater of the two forces. For example: AB and AC are both applied at point A; then, if AB equals four and AC equals six pounds, the resultant AD equals two pounds and acts in the direction of AC.

Parallel Forces. — If two forces are parallel and act in the same direction, then their resultant is parallel to both lines, is located between them, and is equal to the sum of the two components. The point of application of the resultant divides the line joining the points of application of the components inversely as the magnitude of the components. Thus, $AB : CE = CD : AD$.

The resultant of two parallel forces acting in opposite directions is parallel to both lines, is located outside of them on the side of the greater of the components, has the same direction as the greater component, and is equal in magnitude to the difference between the two components. The point of application on the line AC produced is found from the proportion:

$$AB : CD = CE : AE.$$

Moment of a Force. — The moment of a force with respect to a point is the product of the force multiplied by the perpendicular distance from the given point to the direction of the force. In the illustration, the moment of the force P with relation to point A is $P \times AB$. The perpendicular distance AB is called the lever-arm of the force. The moment is the measure of the tendency of the force to produce rotation about the given point, which is termed the center of moments. If the force is measured in pounds and the distance in inches, the moment is expressed in inch-pounds.

The moment of the resultant of any number of forces acting together in the same plane is equal to the algebraic sum of the moments of the separate forces.

Moment of P about A
Equals $P \times I$

Levers

Types of Levers	Examples
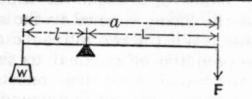 $F : W = l : L \qquad F \times L = W \times l$ $F = \dfrac{W \times l}{L} \qquad W = \dfrac{F \times L}{l}$ $L = \dfrac{W \times a}{W + F} = \dfrac{W \times l}{F}; \quad l = \dfrac{F \times a}{W + F} = \dfrac{F \times L}{W}$	A pull of 80 pounds is exerted at the end of the lever, at W; $l = 12$ inches and $L = 32$ inches. Find the value of force F required to balance the lever. $$F = \frac{80 \times 12}{32} = \frac{960}{32} = 30 \text{ pounds.}$$ If $F = 20$; $W = 180$; and $l = 3$; how long must L be made to secure equilibrium? $$L = \frac{180 \times 3}{20} = 27.$$
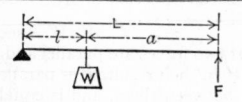 $F : W = l : L \qquad F \times L = W \times l$ $F = \dfrac{W \times l}{L} \qquad W = \dfrac{F \times L}{l}$ $L = \dfrac{W \times a}{W - F} = \dfrac{W \times l}{F}; \quad l = \dfrac{F \times a}{W - F} = \dfrac{F \times L}{W}$	Total length L of a lever is 25 inches. A weight of 90 pounds is supported at W; l is 10 inches. Find the value of F. $$F = \frac{90 \times 10}{25} = 36 \text{ pounds.}$$ If $F = 100$ pounds, $W = 2200$ pounds, and $a = 5$ feet, what should L equal to secure equilibrium? $$L = \frac{2200 \times 5}{2200 - 100} = 5.24 \text{ feet.}$$
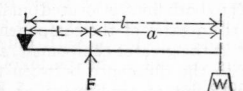 $F : W = l : L \qquad F \times L = W \times l$ $F = \dfrac{W \times l}{L} \qquad W = \dfrac{F \times L}{l}$ $L = \dfrac{W \times a}{F - W} = \dfrac{W \times l}{F}; \quad l = \dfrac{F \times a}{F - W} = \dfrac{F \times L}{W}$	$F = 28$ pounds; $L = 10$ inches; $a = 24$ inches. What weight W can be supported? $l = a + L = 24 + 10 = 34$ inches. $$W = \frac{28 \times 10}{34} = 8.23 \text{ pounds.}$$ Let $F = 12$ tons; $W = 4.5$ tons; $a = 16$ feet. Find L and l. $$L = \frac{4.5 \times 16}{12 - 4.5} = 9.6 \text{ feet;}$$ $$l = 16 + 9.6 = 25.6 \text{ feet.}$$
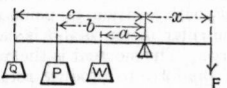 When three or more forces act on a lever: $F \times x = W \times a + P \times b + Q \times c$ $x = \dfrac{W \times a + P \times b + Q \times c}{F}$ $F = \dfrac{W \times a + P \times b + Q \times c}{x}$	Let $W = 20$, $P = 30$, and $Q = 15$ pounds; $a = 4$, $b = 7$, and $c = 10$ inches. If $x = 6$ inches, find F. $$F = \frac{20 \times 4 + 30 \times 7 + 15 \times 10}{6} = 73\tfrac{1}{3} \text{ lbs.}$$ Assuming $F = 20$ in the example above, how long must lever arm x be made? $$x = \frac{20 \times 4 + 30 \times 7 + 15 \times 10}{20} = 22 \text{ ins.}$$

Wheels and Pulleys

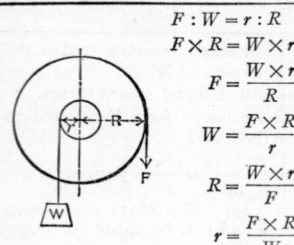

$$F : W = r : R$$
$$F \times R = W \times r$$
$$F = \frac{W \times r}{R}$$
$$W = \frac{F \times R}{r}$$
$$R = \frac{W \times r}{F}$$
$$r = \frac{F \times R}{W}$$

The radius of a drum on which is wound the lifting rope of a windlass is 2 inches. What force will be exerted at the periphery of a gear of 24 inches diameter, mounted on the same shaft as the drum and transmitting power to it, if one ton (2000 pounds) is to be lifted? Here $W = 2000$; $R = 12$; $r = 2$.

$$F = \frac{2000 \times 2}{12} = 333 \text{ pounds.}$$

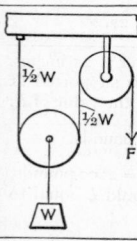

$$F = \tfrac{1}{2} W$$

The velocity with which weight W will be raised equals one-half the velocity of the force applied at F.

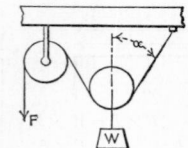

$$F : W = \sec \alpha : 2$$
$$F = \frac{W \times \sec \alpha}{2}$$
$$W = 2 F \times \cos \alpha$$

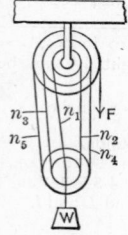

$n =$ number of strands or parts of rope (n_1, n_2, etc.).

$$F = \frac{1}{n} \times W$$

The velocity with which W will be raised equals $\frac{1}{n}$ of the velocity of the force applied at F.

In the illustration is shown a combination of a double and triple block. The pulleys each turn freely on a pin as axis, and are drawn with different diameters, to show the parts of the rope more clearly. There are 5 parts of rope. Therefore, if 200 pounds is to be lifted, the force F required at the end of the rope is:

$$F = \tfrac{1}{5} \times 200 = 40 \text{ pounds.}$$

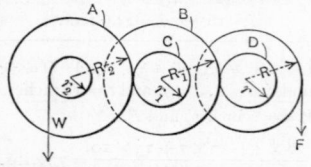

A, B, C and D are the pitch circles of gears.

$$F = \frac{W \times r \times r_1 \times r_2}{R \times R_1 \times R_2}$$
$$W = \frac{F \times R \times R_1 \times R_2}{r \times r_1 \times r_2}$$

Let the pitch diameters of gears A, B, C and D be 30, 28, 12 and 10 inches, respectively. Then $R_2 = 15$; $R_1 = 14$; $r_1 = 6$; and $r = 5$. Let $R = 12$, and $r_2 = 4$. Then the force F required to lift a weight W of 2000 pounds, friction being neglected, is:

$$F = \frac{2000 \times 5 \times 6 \times 4}{12 \times 14 \times 15} = 95 \text{ pounds.}$$

Couples. — If the forces AB and CD are equal and act in opposite directions, then the resultant equals o, or, in other words, the two forces have no resultant

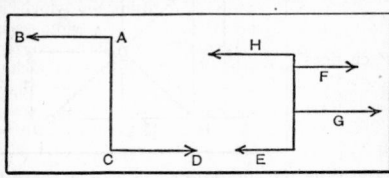

and are called a couple. A couple tends to produce rotation. The measure of this tendency is called the moment of the couple and is the product of one of the forces multiplied by the distance between the two.

As a couple has no resultant, no single force can balance or counteract the tendency to produce rotation. To prevent the rotation of a body acted upon by a couple, two other forces are therefore required, forming a second couple. In the illustration, E and F form one couple and G and H are the balancing couple. The body on which they act is in equilibrium if the moments of the two couples are equal and tend to rotate the body in opposite directions.

Differential Pulley — Screw

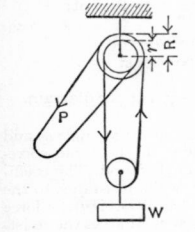

Differential Pulley. — In the differential pulley a chain must be used, engaging sprockets, so as to prevent the chain from slipping over the pulley faces.

$$P \times R = \tfrac{1}{2} W (R - r)$$

$$P = \frac{W (R - r)}{2 R}$$

$$W = \frac{2 PR}{R - r}$$

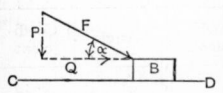

Force Moving Body on Horizontal Plane. — F tends to move B along line CD; Q is the component which actually moves B; P is the pressure, due to F, of the body on CD.

$$Q = F \times \cos \alpha; \qquad P = \sqrt{F^2 - Q^2}$$

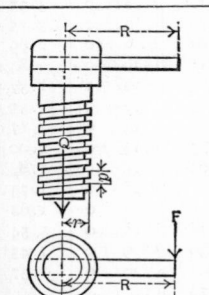

Screw. — F = force at end of handle or wrench; R = lever-arm of F; r = pitch radius of screw; p = lead of thread; Q = load. Then, neglecting friction:

$$F = Q \times \frac{p}{6.2832 R} \qquad Q = F \times \frac{6.2832 R}{p}$$

If μ is the coefficient of friction, then:

For motion in direction of load Q which *assists* it:

$$F = Q \times \frac{6.2832 \, \mu r - p}{6.2832 \, r + \mu p} \times \frac{r}{R}$$

For motion opposite load Q which *resists* it:

$$F = Q \times \frac{p + 6.2832 \, \mu r}{6.2832 \, r - \mu p} \times \frac{r}{R}$$

Toggle-joint. — If arms *ED* and *EH* are of unequal length:

$$P = \frac{Fa}{b}$$

The relation between *P* and *F* changes constantly as *F* moves downwards.

If arms *ED* and *EH* are equal:

$$P = \frac{Fa}{2h}$$

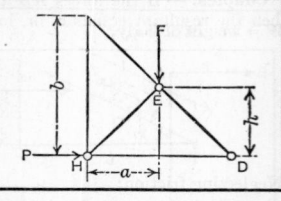

A double toggle-joint does not increase the pressure exerted so long as the relative distances moved by *F* and *P* remain the same.

Toggle-joints with Equal Arms

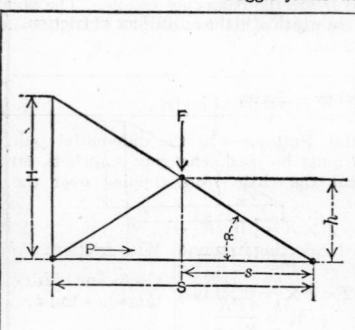

F = force applied;
P = resistance;
α = given angle.

$$2P\sin\alpha = F\cos\alpha;$$

$$\frac{P}{F} = \frac{\cos\alpha}{2\sin\alpha} = \text{coefficient};$$

or, $P = F \times \text{coefficient}.$

Equivalent expressions:

$$P = \frac{FS}{4h}; \qquad P = \frac{Fs}{H}, \text{ as per diagram.}$$

To use the table, measure angle α, and find the coefficient in the table corresponding to the angle found. The coefficient is the ratio of the resistance to the force applied, and multiplying the force applied by the coefficient gives the resistance, neglecting friction.

Angle	Coefficient	Angle	Coefficient	Angle	Coefficient	Angle	Coefficient
0° 2′	862	0° 50′	34.4	2° 45′	10.4	8° 0′	3.58
0 4	456	0 55	31.2	2 50	10.1	8 30	3.35
0 6	285	1 0	28.6	3 0	9.54	9 0	3.15
0 8	216	1 10	24.6	3 15	8.81	9 30	2.99
0 10	171	1 15	22.9	3 30	8.17	10 0	2.84
0 12	143	1 20	21.5	3 45	7.63	11 0	2.57
0 14	122	1 30	19.1	4 0	7.25	12 0	2.35
0 15	115	1 40	17.2	4 15	6.73	13 0	2.17
0 16	107	1 45	16.4	4 30	6.35	14 0	2.00
0 18	95.4	1 50	15.6	4 45	6.02	15 0	1.87
0 20	85.8	2 0	14.3	5 0	5.71	16 0	1.74
0 25	68.6	2 10	13.2	5 30	5.19	17 0	1.64
0 30	57.3	2 15	12.7	6 0	4.76	18 0	1.54
0 35	49.1	2 20	12.5	6 30	4.39	19 0	1.45
0 40	42.8	2 30	11.5	7 0	4.07	20 0	1.37
0 45	38.2	2 40	10.7	7 30	3.79	....	....

Inclined Plane — Wedge

W = weight of body.

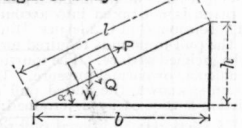

Neglecting friction:

$$P = W \times \frac{h}{l} = W \times \sin \alpha$$

$$W = P \times \frac{l}{h} = \frac{P}{\sin \alpha} = P \times \operatorname{cosec} \alpha$$

$$Q = W \times \frac{b}{l} = W \times \cos \alpha$$

If friction is taken into account, then force P to pull body up is:

$$P = W \, (\mu \cos \alpha + \sin \alpha)$$

Force P_1 to pull body down is:

$$P_1 = W \, (\mu \cos \alpha - \sin \alpha)$$

Force P_2 to hold body stationary:

$$P_2 = W \, (\sin \alpha - \mu \cos \alpha)$$

in which μ is the coefficient of friction.

W = weight of body.

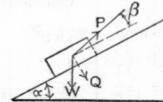

Neglecting friction:

$$P = W \times \frac{\sin \alpha}{\cos \beta}$$

$$W = P \times \frac{\cos \beta}{\sin \alpha}$$

$$Q = W \times \frac{\cos (\alpha + \beta)}{\cos \beta}$$

With friction:

Coefficient of friction $= \mu = \tan \phi$.

$$P = W \times \frac{\sin (\alpha + \phi)}{\cos (\beta - \phi)}$$

W = weight of body.

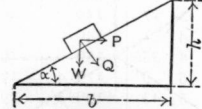

Neglecting friction:

$$P = W \times \frac{h}{b} = W \times \tan \alpha$$

$$W = P \times \frac{b}{h} = P \times \cot \alpha$$

$$Q = \frac{W}{\cos \alpha} = W \times \sec \alpha$$

With friction:

Coefficient of friction $= \mu = \tan \phi$.

$$P = W \tan (\alpha + \phi)$$

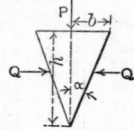

Neglecting friction:

$$P = 2 \, Q \times \frac{b}{l} = 2 \, Q \times \sin \alpha$$

$$Q = P \times \frac{l}{2 \, b} = \tfrac{1}{2} \, P \times \operatorname{cosec} \alpha$$

With friction:

Coefficient of friction $= \mu$.

$$P = 2 \, Q \, (\mu \cos \alpha + \sin \alpha)$$

Neglecting friction:

$$P = 2 \, Q \times \frac{b}{h} = 2 \, Q \times \tan \alpha$$

$$Q = P \times \frac{h}{2 \, b} = \tfrac{1}{2} \, P \times \cot \alpha$$

With friction:

Coefficient of friction $= \mu = \tan \phi$.

$$P = 2 \, Q \tan (\alpha + \phi)$$

Table of Forces on Inclined Planes

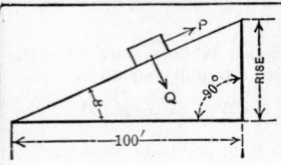

The table below makes it possible to find the force required for moving a body on an inclined plane. The friction on the plane is not taken into account. The column headed "Tension P in Cable per Ton of 2000 Pounds" gives the pull in pounds required for moving one ton along the inclined surface. The fourth column gives the perpendicular or normal pressure. If the coefficient of friction is known, the added pull required to overcome friction is thus easily determined:

$Q \times$ coefficient of friction $=$ additional pull required.

Tensions and Pressures in Pounds

Per Cent of Grade. Rise, Ft. per 100 Ft.	Angle α		Tension P in Cable per Ton of 2000 Lbs.	Perpendicular Pressure Q on Plane per Ton of 2000 Lbs.	Per Cent of Grade. Rise, Ft. Per 100 Ft.	Angle α		Tension P in Cable per Ton of 2000 Lbs.	Perpendicular Pressure Q on Plane per Ton of 2000 Lbs.
1	0°	35′	20.2	1999.8	39	21°	19′	727.0	1863.0
2	1	9	40.0	1999.4	40	21	49	743.2	1856.6
3	1	44	60.4	1999.0	41	22	18	758.8	1850.4
4	2	18	80.2	1998.2	42	22	47	774.4	1843.8
5	2	52	100.0	1997.4	43	23	17	790.4	1837.0
6	3	27	120.2	1996.2	44	23	45	805.4	1830.6
7	4	1	140.0	1995.0	45	24	14	820.8	1823.6
8	4	35	159.8	1993.6	46	24	43	836.2	1816.6
9	5	9	179.4	1991.8	47	25	11	851.0	1809.8
10	5	43	199.2	1990.0	48	25	39	865.6	1802.8
11	6	17	218.8	1987.8	49	26	7	880.4	1795.6
12	6	51	238.4	1985.6	50	26	34	894.4	1788.8
13	7	25	258.0	1983.2	51	27	2	909.0	1781.4
14	7	59	277.6	1980.6	52	27	29	922.8	1774.2
15	8	32	296.6	1977.8	53	27	56	936.8	1766.8
16	9	6	316.2	1974.8	54	28	23	950.6	1759.4
17	9	39	335.2	1971.6	55	28	49	964.0	1752.2
18	10	13	354.6	1968.2	56	29	15	977.2	1744.8
19	10	46	373.6	1964.6	57	29	41	990.4	1737.4
20	11	19	392.4	1961.0	58	30	7	1003.4	1730.0
21	11	52	411.2	1957.2	59	30	33	1016.4	1722.2
22	12	25	430.0	1953.2	60	30	58	1029.0	1714.8
23	12	58	448.6	1949.0	61	31	23	1041.4	1707.4
24	13	30	466.8	1944.6	62	31	48	1053.8	1699.6
25	14	3	485.4	1940.0	63	32	13	1066.2	1692.0
26	14	35	503.4	1935.4	64	32	38	1078.4	1684.2
27	15	7	521.4	1930.6	65	33	2	1090.2	1676.6
28	15	39	539.4	1925.8	66	33	26	1101.8	1669.0
29	16	11	557.4	1920.6	67	33	50	1113.4	1661.2
30	16	42	574.6	1915.6	68	34	13	1124.6	1653.8
31	17	14	592.4	1910.2	69	34	37	1136.0	1645.8
32	17	45	609.6	1904.6	70	35	0	1147.0	1638.2
33	18	16	626.8	1899.2	71	35	23	1158.0	1630.4
34	18	47	643.8	1893.4	72	35	46	1168.8	1622.8
35	19	18	661.0	1887.6	73	36	8	1179.2	1615.2
36	19	48	677.4	1881.6	74	36	31	1190.0	1607.2
37	20	19	694.4	1875.4	75	36	53	1200.4	1599.6
38	20	49	710.6	1869.4	..	..	..	......	......

Center of Gravity

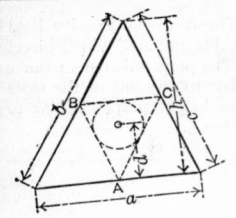

Perimeter of a Triangle. — If A, B and C are the middle points of the sides of the triangle, then the center of gravity is at the center of the circle that can be inscribed in triangle ABC. The distance d of the center of gravity from side a is:

$$d = \frac{h(b+c)}{2(a+b+c)}$$

where h is the height perpendicular to a.

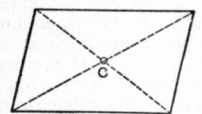

Perimeter of a Parallelogram. — The center of gravity is at the intersection of the diagonals.

Area of a Parallelogram. — The center of gravity is at the intersection of the diagonals.

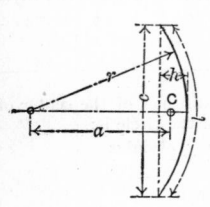

Circular Arc. — The center of gravity is on the line that bisects the arc, at a distance

$$a = \frac{r \times c}{l} = \frac{c(c^2 + 4h^2)}{8lh} \text{ from the center of the circle.}$$

For an arc equal to one-half the periphery:

$$a = 2r \div \pi = 0.6366\,r$$

For an arc equal to one-quarter of the periphery:

$$a = 2r\sqrt{2} \div \pi = 0.9003\,r$$

For an arc equal to one-sixth of the periphery:

$$a = 3r \div \pi = 0.9549\,r$$

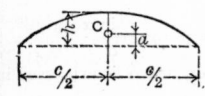

Circular Arc (approximate). —

$$a = \tfrac{2}{3}h$$

This formula is very nearly exact for all arcs less than one-quarter of the periphery. The error is only about one per cent for a quarter circle, and decreases for smaller arcs.

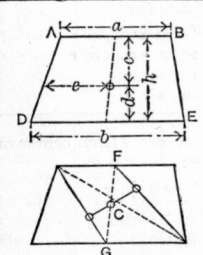

Area of Trapezoid. — The center of gravity is on the line joining the middle points of parallel lines AB and DE.

$$c = \frac{h(a+2b)}{3(a+b)} \qquad d = \frac{h(2a+b)}{3(a+b)}$$

$$e = \frac{a^2 + ab + b^2}{3(a+b)}$$

The trapezoid can also be divided into two triangles. The center of gravity is at the intersection of the line joining the centers of gravity of the triangles, and the middle line FG.

Center of Gravity

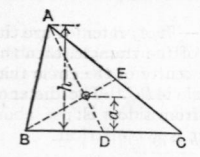

Area of Triangle. — The center of gravity is at the intersection of lines AD and BE, which bisect the sides BC and AC. The perpendicular distance from the center of gravity to any one of the sides is equal to one-third the height perpendicular to that side. Hence, $a = h \div 3$.

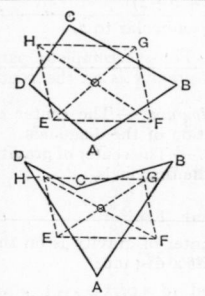

Any Four-sided Figure. — Two cases are possible, as shown in the illustration. To find the center of gravity of the four-sided figure $ABCD$, each of the sides is divided into three equal parts. A line is then drawn through each pair of division points next to the points of intersection A, B, C, and D of the sides of the figure. These lines form a parallelogram $EFGH$; the intersection of the diagonals EG and FH locates the required center of gravity.

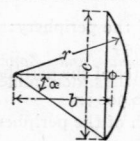

Circle Segment. — The distance of the center of gravity from the center of the circle is:

$$b = \frac{c^3}{12\,A} = \frac{2}{3} \times \frac{r^3 \sin^3 \alpha}{A}$$

in which A = area of segment.

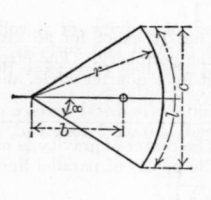

Circle Sector. — Distance b from center of gravity to center of circle is:

$$b = \frac{2\,rc}{3\,l} = \frac{r^2 c}{3\,A} = 38.197 \, \frac{r \sin \alpha}{\alpha}$$

in which A = area of sector, and α is expressed in degrees.

For the area of a half-circle:
$$b = 4\,r \div 3\,\pi = 0.4244\,r$$
For the area of a quarter circle:
$$b = 4 \, \sqrt{2} \times r \div 3\,\pi = 0.6002\,r$$
For the area of a sixth of a circle:
$$b = 2\,r \div \pi = 0.6366\,r$$

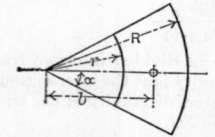

Part of Circle Ring. — Distance b from center of gravity to center of circle is:

$$b = 38.197 \, \frac{(R^3 - r^3) \sin \alpha}{(R^2 - r^2)\,\alpha}$$

Angle α is expressed in degrees.

Center of Gravity

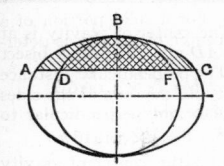

Segment of an Ellipse. — The center of gravity of an elliptic segment ABC, symmetrical about one of the axes, coincides with the center of gravity of the segment DBF of a circle, the diameter of which is equal to that axis of the ellipse about which the elliptic segment is symmetrical.

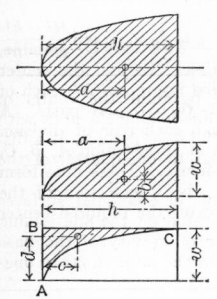

Area of a Parabola. — For the complete parabolic area, the center of gravity is on the center line or axis, and

$$a = \frac{3\,h}{5}$$

For one-half of the parabola:

$$a = \frac{3\,h}{5} \quad \text{and} \quad b = \frac{3\,w}{8}$$

For the complement area ABC:

$$c = 0.3\,h \quad \text{and} \quad d = 0.75\,w$$

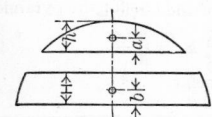

Spherical Surface of Segments and Zones of Spheres. — Distances a and b which determine the center of gravity, are:

$$a = \frac{h}{2} \qquad b = \frac{H}{2}$$

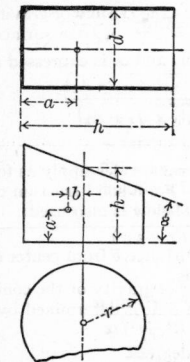

Cylinder. — The center of gravity of a solid cylinder (or prism) with parallel end surfaces, is located at the middle of the line that joins the centers of gravity of the end surfaces.

The center of gravity of a cylindrical surface or shell, with the base or end surface in one end, is found from:

$$a = \frac{2\,h^2}{4\,h + d}$$

The center of gravity of a cylinder cut off by an inclined plane is located by:

$$a = \frac{h}{2} + \frac{r^2 \tan^2 \alpha}{8\,h} \qquad b = \frac{r^2 \tan \alpha}{4\,h}$$

where α is the angle between the obliquely cut off surface and the base surface.

Center of Gravity

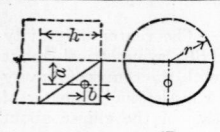

Portion of Cylinder. — For a solid portion of a cylinder, as shown, the center of gravity is determined by:

$$a = \tfrac{3}{16} \times 3.1416\, r \qquad b = \tfrac{3}{32} \times 3.1416\, h$$

For the cylindrical surface only:

$$a = \tfrac{1}{4} \times 3.1416\, r \qquad b = \tfrac{1}{8} \times 3.1416\, h$$

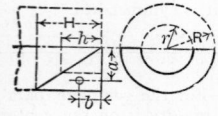

If the cylinder is hollow, the center of gravity of the solid shell is found by:

$$a = \tfrac{3}{16} \times 3.1416\, \frac{R^4 - r^4}{R^3 - r^3}; \quad b = \tfrac{3}{32} \times 3.1416\, \frac{H^4 - h^4}{H^3 - h^3}$$

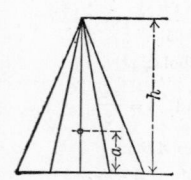

Pyramid. — In a solid pyramid the center of gravity is located on the line joining the apex with the center of gravity of the base surface, at a distance from the base equal to one-quarter of the height; or $a = \tfrac{1}{4}\, h$.

The center of gravity of the triangular surfaces forming the pyramid is located on the line joining the apex with the center of gravity of the base surface, at a distance from the base equal to one-third of the height; or $a = \tfrac{1}{3}\, h$.

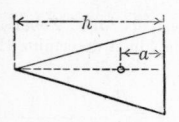

Cone. — The same rules apply as for the pyramid. For the solid cone:

$$a = \tfrac{1}{4}\, h$$

For the conical surface:

$$a = \tfrac{1}{3}\, h$$

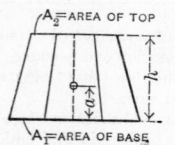

Frustum of Pyramid. — The center of gravity is located on the line that joins the centers of gravity of the end surfaces. If A_1 = area of base surface, and A_2 area of top surface,

$$a = \frac{h\left(A_1 + 2\sqrt{A_1 \times A_2} + 3\,A_2\right)}{4\left(A_1 + \sqrt{A_1 \times A_2} + A_2\right)}$$

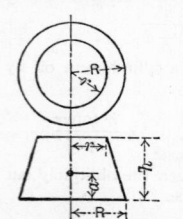

Frustum of Cone. — The same rules apply as for the frustum of a pyramid. For a solid frustum of a circular cone the formula below is also used:

$$a = \frac{h\left(R^2 + 2\,Rr + 3\,r^2\right)}{4\left(R^2 + Rr + r^2\right)}$$

The location of the center of gravity of the conical surface of a frustum of a cone is determined by:

$$a = \frac{h\left(R + 2\,r\right)}{3\left(R + r\right)}$$

Center of Gravity

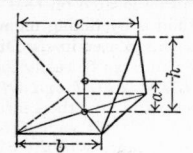

Wedge. — The center of gravity is on the line joining the center of gravity of the base with the middle point of the edge, and is located at:

$$a = \frac{h(b+c)}{2(2b+c)}$$

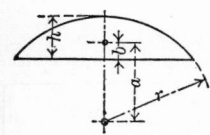

Spherical Segment. — The center of gravity of a solid segment is determined by:

$$a = \frac{3(2r-h)^2}{4(3r-h)}$$

$$b = \frac{h(4r-h)}{4(3r-h)}$$

For a half-sphere, $a = b = \frac{3}{8}r$

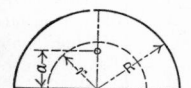

Half of a Hollow Sphere. — The center of gravity is located at:

$$a = \frac{3(R^4-r^4)}{8(R^3-r^3)}$$

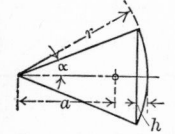

Spherical Sector. — The center of gravity of a solid sector is at:

$$a = \tfrac{3}{8}(1+\cos\alpha)r = \tfrac{3}{8}(2r-h)$$

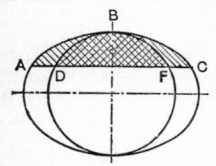

Segment of Ellipsoid or Spheroid. — The center of gravity of a solid segment ABC, symmetrical about the axis of rotation, coincides with the center of gravity of the segment DBF of a sphere, the diameter of which is equal to the axis of rotation of the spheroid.

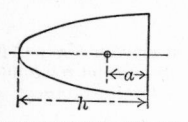

Paraboloid. — The center of gravity of a solid paraboloid of rotation is at:

$$a = \tfrac{1}{3}h$$

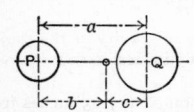

Center of Gravity of Two Bodies. — If the weights of the bodies are P and Q, and the distance between their centers of gravity is a, then:

$$b = \frac{Qa}{P+Q} \qquad c = \frac{Pa}{P+Q}$$

Center of Gravity of Figures of any Outline. — If the figure is symmetrical about a center line, as in Fig. 1, the center of gravity will be located on that line. To find the exact location on that line, the simplest method is by taking moments with reference to any convenient axis at right angles to this center line. Divide the area into geometrical figures, the centers of gravity of which can be easily found. In this case, divide the figure into three rectangles *KLMN*, *EFGH* and *OPRS*. Call the areas of these rectangles *A*, *B* and *C*, respectively, and find the center of gravity of each. Then select any convenient axis, as *XX*, at right angles to the center line *YY*, and determine distances *a*, *b* and *c*. The distance *y* of the center of gravity of the complete figure from the axis *XX* is then found from the equation:

$$y = \frac{Aa + Bb + Cc}{A + B + C}$$

As an example, assume that the area *A* is 24 square inches, *B*, 14 square inches,

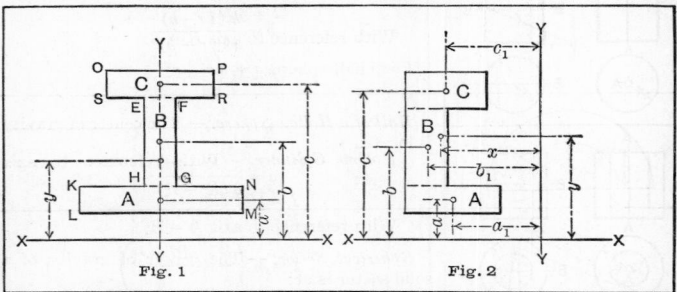

Fig. 1   Fig. 2

and *C*, 16 square inches, and that $a = 3$ inches, $b = 7.5$ inches, and $c = 12$ inches. Then:

$$y = \frac{24 \times 3 + 14 \times 7.5 + 16 \times 12}{24 + 14 + 16} = \frac{369}{54} = 6.83 \text{ inches.}$$

If the figure, the center of gravity of which is to be found, is not symmetrical about any axis, then moments must be taken with relation to two axes *XX* and *YY*, as shown in Fig. 2. The figure is divided into convenient geometrical figures, the centers of gravity of which can be easily found, the same as before. The center of gravity is determined by the equations:

$$x = \frac{Aa_1 + Bb_1 + Cc_1}{A + B + C} \qquad y = \frac{Aa + Bb + Cc}{A + B + C}$$

As an example, let $A = 14$ square inches, $B = 18$ square inches, and $C = 20$ square inches. Let $a = 3$ inches, $b = 7$ inches, and $c = 11.5$ inches. Let $a_1 = 6.5$ inches, $b_1 = 8.5$ inches, and $c_1 = 7$ inches. Then:

$$x = \frac{14 \times 6.5 + 18 \times 8.5 + 20 \times 7}{14 + 18 + 20} = \frac{384}{52} = 7.38 \text{ inches.}$$

$$y = \frac{14 \times 3 + 18 \times 7 + 20 \times 11.5}{14 + 18 + 20} = \frac{398}{52} = 7.65 \text{ inches.}$$

In other words, the center of gravity is located at a distance of 7.65 inches from the axis *XX* and 7.38 inches from the axis *YY*.

Moments of Inertia

(M = mass of body = weight ÷ 32.16)

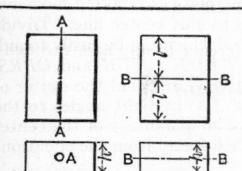	*Prism.* — With reference to axis $A-A$: $$I = \frac{M}{12}(h^2 + b^2)$$ With reference to axis $B-B$: $$I = M\left(\frac{l^2}{3} + \frac{h^2}{12}\right)$$
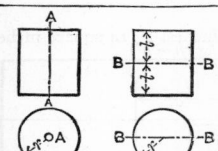	*Cylinder.* — With reference to axis $A-A$: $$I = \tfrac{1}{2} M r^2$$ With reference to axis $B-B$: $$I = M\left(\frac{l^2}{3} + \frac{r^2}{4}\right)$$
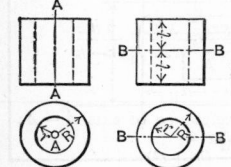	*Hollow Cylinder.* — With reference to axis $A-A$: $$I = \tfrac{1}{2} M (R^2 + r^2)$$ With reference to axis $B-B$: $$I = M\left(\frac{l^2}{3} + \frac{R^2 + r^2}{4}\right)$$
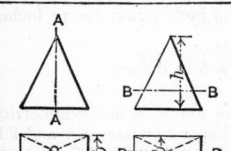	*Pyramid,* rectangular base. — With reference to axis $A-A$: $$I = \frac{M}{20}(a^2 + b^2)$$ With reference to axis $B-B$ (through the center of gravity): $$I = M\left(\frac{3}{80} h^2 + \frac{b^2}{20}\right)$$
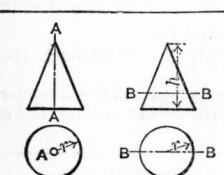	*Cone.* — With reference to axis $A-A$: $$I = \frac{3\,M}{10} r^2$$ With reference to axis $B-B$ (through the center of gravity): $$I = \frac{3\,M}{20}\left(r^2 + \frac{h^2}{4}\right)$$
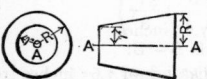	*Frustum of Cone.* — With reference to axis $A-A$: $$I = \frac{3\,M\,(R^5 - r^5)}{10\,(R^3 - r^3)}$$

Moments of Inertia

(M = mass of body = weight $\div$ 32.16)

Sphere. — With reference to any axis through the center:

$$I = \tfrac{2}{5} M r^2$$

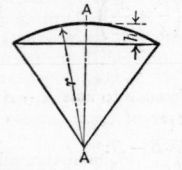

Spherical Sector. — With reference to axis $A-A$:

$$I = \frac{M}{5} (3\, rh - h^2)$$

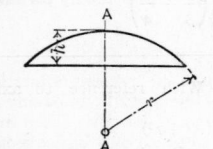

Spherical Segment. — With reference to axis $A-A$:

$$I = M \left(r^2 - \frac{3\, rh}{4} + \frac{3\, h^2}{20} \right) \frac{2\, h}{3\, r - h}$$

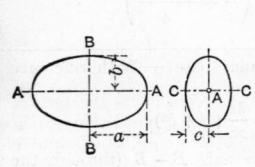

Ellipsoid. — With reference to axis $A-A$:

$$I = \frac{M}{5} (b^2 + c^2)$$

With reference to axis $B-B$:

$$I = \frac{M}{5} (a^2 + c^2)$$

With reference to axis $C-C$:

$$I = \frac{M}{5} (a^2 + b^2)$$

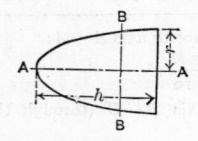

Paraboloid. — With reference to axis $A-A$:

$$I = \tfrac{1}{3} M r^2$$

With reference to axis $B-B$ (through the center of gravity):

$$I = M \left(\frac{r^2}{6} + \frac{h^2}{18} \right)$$

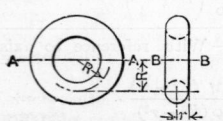

Torus. — With reference to axis $A-A$:

$$I = M \left(\frac{R^2}{2} + \frac{5\, r^2}{8} \right)$$

With reference to axis $B-B$:

$$I = M \left(R^2 + \tfrac{3}{4} r^2 \right)$$

Moment of Inertia. — The moment of inertia of a body, with respect to an axis, is the sum of the products obtained by multiplying the mass of each elementary particle by the square of its distance from the axis. Hence, the moment of inertia of the same body varies according to the position of the axis. It has its minimum value when the axis passes through the center of gravity. The moment of inertia is numerically equal to the mass of a body which, if it could be conceived of as concentrated at a distance of unity from the axis of rotation, would, if actuated by the same forces, rotate with the same angular velocity as that of the actual body. In other words, the moment of inertia bears the same relation to angular acceleration as mass does to linear acceleration. When the term moment of inertia is used in regard to areas, it is equal to the sum of the products obtained by multiplying each elementary area by the square of its distance from the axis. The moments of inertia of a number of solids are given on the two preceding pages. The moments of inertia of surfaces are especially useful in calculating the strength of beams, and the moments for a number of different cross-sections are given later in connection with the beam formulas.

If the moment of inertia I of a solid or surface, with respect to an axis through its center of gravity, is known, then the moment of inertia with respect to any parallel axis at a distance a from the axis through the center of gravity, is:

$$I_a = I + A \times a^2$$

in which A = the mass or area of the solid or figure of which the moment of inertia is to be found. For example, assume that the moment of inertia of a body having a mass of 3 is 18 with reference to an axis through the center of gravity. Find the moment of inertia with reference to a parallel axis at a distance of 5 inches from the axis through the center of gravity.

$$I_a = 18 + 3 \times 5^2 = 18 + 75 = 93.$$

Motion, Force and Work

Motion is a progressive change of position of a body. Velocity is the rate of motion. When the velocity of a body is the same at every moment during which the motion takes place, the latter is called *uniform*. When the velocity is variable and constantly increasing, the rate at which it changes is called *acceleration;* that is, acceleration is the rate at which the velocity of a body changes in a unit of time, as the change in feet per second, in one second. When the motion is decreasing instead of increasing, it is called *retarded* motion, and the rate at which the motion is retarded is frequently called the *de-acceleration*. If the acceleration is uniform, the motion is called *uniformly accelerated* motion. An example of such motion is found in that of falling bodies.

Newton's Laws of Motion. — *First Law.* Every body continues in a state of rest or in uniform motion in a straight line, except if it is compelled by a force to change its state of rest or motion.

Second Law. Change of motion is proportional to the force applied, and takes place along the straight line in which the force acts. The " force applied " represents the resultant of all the forces acting on the body. This law is sometimes worded: An unbalanced force acting on a body causes an acceleration of the body in the direction of the force of magnitude proportional to the force and inversely proportional to the mass of the body.

Third Law. To every action there is always an equal reaction, or, in other words, if a force acts to change the state of motion of a body, the body offers a resistance equal and directly opposite to the force.

Mass. — The *mass* of a body equals the weight divided by the acceleration due to gravity, or:

$$\text{Mass} = \frac{\text{weight}}{32.16}$$

General Formulas for Motion. — In the following formulas:

F = force in pounds; P = power in foot-pounds per second;
S = space in feet; K = work in foot-pounds;
T = time in seconds; H.P. = horsepower.
V = velocity in feet per second;

The relations between these various quantities are given in the following formulas:

$$F = \frac{P}{V} = \frac{K}{S} = \frac{K}{VT} = \frac{550\,\text{H.P.}}{V}$$

$$S = VT = \frac{PT}{F} = \frac{K}{F} = \frac{550\,T\,\text{H.P.}}{F}$$

$$T = \frac{S}{V} = \frac{FS}{P} = \frac{K}{FV} = \frac{FS}{550\,\text{H.P.}}$$

$$V = \frac{S}{T} = \frac{P}{F} = \frac{K}{FT} = \frac{550\,\text{H.P.}}{F}$$

$$P = FV = \frac{FS}{T} = \frac{K}{T} = 550\,\text{H.P.}$$

$$K = FS = PT = FVT = 550\,T\,\text{H.P.}$$

$$\text{H.P.} = \frac{P}{550} = \frac{FV}{550} = \frac{FS}{550\,T} = \frac{K}{550\,T}$$

Example: — A casting weighing 300 pounds is to be lifted by means of an overhead crane. The casting is lifted 10 feet in 12 seconds. What is the horsepower developed? Here $F = 300$; $S = 10$; $T = 12$.

$$\text{H.P.} = \frac{F \times S}{550\,T} = \frac{300 \times 10}{550 \times 12} = 0.45.$$

Momentum. — The momentum of a moving body is equivalent to that constant force which would bring the body to rest in one second by resisting its movement.

Momentum = mass × velocity in feet per second

$$= \frac{\text{weight}}{32.16} \times \text{velocity in feet per second.}$$

(Momentum should not be confused with the moment of a force, which is equal to the force multiplied by its lever arm.)

Falling Bodies

Under the influence of gravity alone, all bodies fall to the earth with the same velocity and with the same acceleration. The value of the acceleration is commonly denoted by the letter g. The acceleration increases with the latitude and decreases with the elevation above the level of the sea. Its value at sea level in the latitude of New York is 32.16 feet per second in one second. (In the metric system g equals 9.81 meters per second in one second at 45 degrees latitude and sea level.)

Formulas for Accelerated Motion. — In the following formulas:

V = velocity in feet per second of a falling body at the end of time T;

T = time in seconds the body is falling;

S = space in feet which the falling body passes through in time T;

u = space in feet which the body falls in the Tth second;

g = acceleration due to gravity.

$$V = gT = \frac{2S}{T} = \sqrt{2gS} = 8.02\sqrt{S}$$

$$S = \frac{1}{2}gT^2 = \frac{1}{2}VT = \frac{V^2}{2g} = \frac{V^2}{64.32}$$

$$T = \frac{V}{g} = \frac{2S}{V} = \sqrt{\frac{2S}{g}} = \frac{\sqrt{S}}{4.01} = \frac{u}{g} + \frac{1}{2}$$

$$u = g\left(T - \tfrac{1}{2}\right)$$

Examples: What velocity has a body attained after having fallen for a time of seconds?

$$V = gT = 32.16 \times 5 = 160.8 \text{ feet per second.}$$

A metal ball falls from the top of a tower 300 feet high. What length of time will be required before it reaches the ground?

$$T = \sqrt{\frac{2S}{g}} = \sqrt{\frac{2 \times 300}{32.16}} = \sqrt{18.66} = 4.32 \text{ seconds.}$$

What is the velocity of the ball in the previous example when it reaches the ground?

$$V = \sqrt{2gS} = \sqrt{2 \times 32.16 \times 300} = \sqrt{19,296} = 139 \text{ feet, nearly.}$$

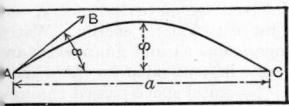

Bodies thrown at an Angle with the Vertical. — When a body is thrown in a direction other than vertical, it describes a parabolic curve. If V (represented by line AB) is the velocity at which the body is thrown from a given point, T the time it requires to pass from A to C, and the other quantities are as noted in the accompanying engraving, then:

$$a = \frac{2V^2 \sin \alpha \cos \alpha}{g}; \qquad T = \frac{2V\sin \alpha}{g}; \qquad S = \frac{V^2 \sin^2 \alpha}{2g}.$$

Example: A bullet is fired in the air at an angle of 45 degrees. The initial velocity is 600 feet per second. How far will it pass before striking the ground?

$$a = \frac{2 \times 600^2 \times 0.707 \times 0.707}{g} = 11,200 \text{ feet, approx.}$$

The distance a projectile will travel is greatest when its initial direction is at an angle of 45 degrees with the horizontal, disregarding air resistance.

Retarded Motion. — Motion of a body thrown vertically upwards (disregarding air resistance) will be retarded in the same ratio as it is accelerated when falling, the retardation or de-acceleration being 32.16 feet per second. If V = velocity at which the body begins to ascend; T = time in seconds passing before the body reaches the highest point, or the point of return; t = any time less than T ; S = height in feet to which the body will ascend before reaching its greatest height; s = space body ascends in time t ; v = velocity at the end of time t.

$$V = v + gt = \frac{s}{t} + \frac{gt}{2} = \sqrt{v^2 + 2\,gs}$$

$$v = V - gt = \frac{s}{t} - \frac{gt}{2} = \sqrt{V^2 - 2\,gs}$$

$$s = t\left(V - \frac{gt}{2}\right) = t\left(v + \frac{gt}{2}\right)$$

$$t = \frac{V - v}{g} = \frac{V}{g} - \sqrt{\frac{V^2}{g^2} - \frac{2\,S}{g}}$$

The formulas for T and S are the same as for accelerated motion.

Examples: With what velocity should a ball start to ascend in order to strike an object 30 feet above with a velocity of 20 feet per second?

$$V = \sqrt{v^2 + 2\,gs} = \sqrt{20^2 + 2 \times 32.16 \times 30} = 48.27 \text{ feet.}$$

An object is thrown vertically into the air with a velocity of 100 feet per second. When does it reach the highest point and start to return?

$$T = \frac{V}{g} = \frac{100}{32.16} = 3.11 \text{ seconds.}$$

Energy. — A body is said to possess energy when it is capable of doing work or of overcoming resistance. The energy may be either *kinetic* or *potential*. Thus, energy possessed by a body on account of its motion is kinetic or actual energy, and it is expressed in foot-pounds. Potential or latent energy is the capacity for doing work possessed by a body on account of its position or chemical composition. For example, a weight that has been lifted to some point possesses potential energy, and when the weight falls, this potential energy is changed to kinetic energy. Water stored in a reservoir and the heat or chemical energy in fuel and gunpowder are other examples of potential energy. If E = energy in foot-pounds; M = mass (weight ÷ 32.16); V = velocity in feet per second; S = total space passed through in feet; and W = weight in pounds; then:

$$E = \frac{1}{2} M V^2 = \frac{W V^2}{2\,g} = \frac{W V^2}{64.32}$$

For a falling body, acted upon by gravity alone, $E = SW$.

As an example of the use of the formulas involving velocities of falling bodies and energy, the following example is given: A projectile is fired from a 12-inch gun vertically into the air. It strikes the ground, coming down, exactly 1 minute and 40 seconds after leaving the muzzle. Disregarding air resistance, what height did the projectile reach? What was its velocity when leaving the muzzle? And what is the energy of the projectile when it strikes the ground, if its weight is assumed to be 600 pounds?

The time required for the projectile to reach its greatest height is one-half of the total time for the upward and downward journey. Thus, in 50 seconds, the projectile has reached the point where its velocity is zero, and where it begins to fall.

Hence, using the formulas given for falling bodies:

$$S = \frac{32.16 \times 50^2}{2} = \frac{32.16 \times 2500}{2} = 40,200 \text{ feet,}$$

or

$$\frac{40,200}{5,280} = 7.6 \text{ miles, approximately.}$$

The projectile's muzzle velocity would equal its velocity when it again reached the earth (if air resistance is disregarded) and it is found by the formula:

$$V = gT = 32.16 \times 50 = 1608 \text{ feet per second.}$$

The energy of the projectile when it strikes the ground equals its weight multiplied by the distance through which it has fallen. If W = weight, and E = energy, we have:

$$E = W \times S = 600 \times 40,200 = 24,120,000 \text{ foot-pounds;}$$

or by another formula for the energy:

$$E = \frac{WV^2}{2g} = \frac{600 \times 1608^2}{2 \times 32.16} = \frac{600 \times 2,585,664}{2 \times 32.16} = 24,120,000 \text{ foot-pounds.}$$

Motion on Inclined Planes. — When a body descends an inclined plane, actuated by the force of gravity, its velocity, friction being neglected, is equal to that acquired by a body falling freely the height of the plane. The formulas for uniformly accelerated motion apply to motion on inclined planes.

V = velocity of body sliding down an inclined plane,
      in feet per second, at end of time T;
S = space traversed in feet;
T = time in seconds;
α = the angle of the plane with the horizontal;
g = acceleration due to gravity = 32.16.

$$V = gT \sin \alpha = \sqrt{2 \, gS \sin \alpha}$$

$$S = \frac{gT^2 \sin \alpha}{2} = \frac{V^2}{2 \, g \sin \alpha}$$

$$T = \frac{V}{g \sin \alpha} = \sqrt{\frac{2 \, S}{g \sin \alpha}}$$

Force of a Blow. — The energy of a body raised to a given height and permitted to fall, as in the case of a drop hammer, is equal to the weight multiplied by the height through which it falls. Hence, the force of a blow cannot be expressed directly in pounds, but the energy with which a hammer will strike a piece of work can be expressed in foot-pounds. The average force of the blow, then, is equal to the number of foot-pounds, divided by the amount of the penetration. If W = weight of falling body in pounds; S = the height through which it has fallen in feet; and d = distance in feet the object struck is moved (or penetrated), then:

$$\text{average force of blow} = \frac{WS}{d}.$$

Example 1: — A pile driver weighing 200 pounds strikes the top of the pile after having fallen from a height of 20 feet. It forces the pile into the ground a distance of 6 inches. Before the ram is brought to rest, it will then have performed 200 × 20 = 4000 foot-pounds of work, and as this energy is expended in a distance of one-half foot, the average force of the blow equals 4000 ÷ ½ = 8000 pounds.

Example 2: — If, upon reaching the ground, the projectile in the example given on page 316, buries itself to a depth of 8 feet, what is the average force of the blow with which it strikes the ground?

$$F = \frac{E}{d} = \frac{24,120,000}{8} = 3,015,000 \text{ pounds.}$$

Center and Radius of Oscillation. — If a body oscillates about a horizontal axis which does not pass through its center of gravity, there will be a point on the line drawn from the center of gravity, perpendicular to the axis, the motion of which will be the same as if the whole mass were concentrated at that point. This point is called the *center of oscillation*. The *radius of oscillation* is the distance between the center of oscillation and the point of suspension. In a straight line, or in a bar of small diameter, suspended at one end and oscillating about it, the center of oscillation is at two-thirds the length of the rod from the end by which it is suspended.

When the vibrations are perpendicular to the plane of the figure, and the figure is suspended by the vertex of an angle or its uppermost point, the radius of oscillation of an isosceles triangle is equal to ¾ of the height of the triangle; of a circle, ⅝ of the diameter; of a parabola, 5/7 of the height.

If the vibrations are in the plane of the figure, then the radius of oscillation of a circle equals ¾ of the diameter; of a rectangle, suspended at the vertex of one angle, ⅔ of the diagonal.

Center of Percussion. — If a body oscillates about an axis, then the point at which, if a blow is struck by the body, the percussive action is the same as if the whole mass of the body were concentrated at that point, is called the *center of percussion*. This point is located at the same point as the center of oscillation.

Center and Radius of Gyration. — The center of gyration with reference to an axis is the point at which the entire mass of a body may be considered as concentrated, the moment of inertia, meanwhile, remaining unchanged; or, in a revolving body, the center of gyration is the point at which the whole mass of the body may be considered as concentrated, the angular velocity remaining the same. The *radius of gyration* is the distance from this point to the axis of rotation. If W is the weight of a body; I, its moment of inertia; and k, the radius of gyration, then:

$$k = \sqrt{\frac{Ig}{W}} \text{ and } I = \frac{Wk^2}{g}.$$

To find the radius of gyration of an area, as the cross-section of a beam, divide the moment of inertia of the area by the area and extract the square root.

The square of the radius of gyration of an oscillating body is equal to the product of the radius of oscillation multiplied by the distance of the center of gravity of the suspended body from the point of suspension.

When the axis, with reference to which the radius of gyration is taken, passes through the center of gravity, the radius of gyration is the least possible and is called the *principal* radius of gyration.

For a solid cylindrical body, like a disk or emery wheel, the radius of gyration is equal to the radius of the disk divided by $\sqrt{2}$ (= radius × 0.707). For a flywheel rim, it is sufficiently accurate to assume the radius of gyration to be the distance from the center to a point halfway between the outer and inner edges of the rim.

Bar of Small Diameter.
Axis at end.

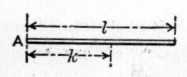

$$k = 0.5773\, l$$
$$k^2 = \tfrac{1}{3}\, l^2$$

Axis at center.

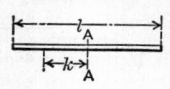

$$k = 0.2886\, l$$
$$k^2 = \tfrac{1}{12}\, l^2$$

Thin Circular Disk.
Axis through center.
Cylinder.
Axis through center.

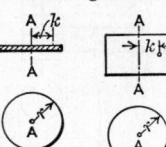

$$k = 0.7071\, r$$
$$k^2 = \tfrac{1}{2}\, r^2$$

Cylinder.
Axis, diameter at mid-length.

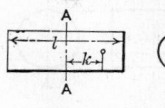
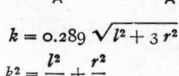

$$k = 0.289\, \sqrt{l^2 + 3\, r^2}$$
$$k^2 = \frac{l^2}{12} + \frac{r^2}{4}$$

Bar of Small Diameter,
bent to Circular Shape.
Axis, a diameter of the ring.

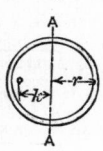

$$k = 0.7071\, r$$
$$k^2 = \tfrac{1}{2}\, r^2$$

Thin Circular Disk.
Axis its diameter.

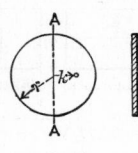

$$k = \tfrac{1}{2}\, r$$
$$k^2 = \tfrac{1}{4}\, r^2$$

Cylinder.
Axis, diameter at end.

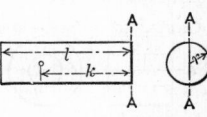

$$k = 0.289\, \sqrt{4\, l^2 + 3\, r^2}$$
$$k^2 = \frac{l^2}{3} + \frac{r^2}{4}$$

Bar of Small Diameter,
bent to Circular Shape.
Axis through center of ring.

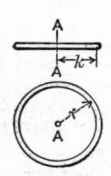

$$k = r; \qquad k^2 = r^2$$

Parallelogram (Thin flat plate).
Axis at base.

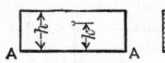

$$k = 0.5773\, h; \quad k^2 = \tfrac{1}{3}\, h^2$$

Axis at mid-height.

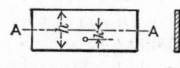

$$k = 0.2886\, h; \quad k^2 = \tfrac{1}{12}\, h^2$$

Thin, Flat, Circular Ring.
Axis its diameter.

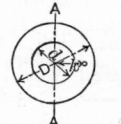

$$k = \tfrac{1}{4}\, \sqrt{D^2 + d^2}$$
$$k^2 = \frac{D^2 + d^2}{16}$$

Radius of Gyration

Thin Hollow Cylinder. Axis, diameter at midlength.

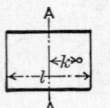

$$k = 0.289 \sqrt{l^2 + 6\,r^2}$$

$$k^2 = \frac{l^2}{12} + \frac{r^2}{2}$$

Cylinder. Axis at a distance.

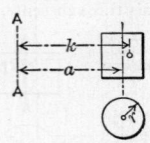

$$k = \sqrt{a^2 + \tfrac{1}{2}\,r^2}$$

$$k^2 = a^2 + \tfrac{1}{2}\,r^2$$

Parallelepiped. Axis at distance from end.

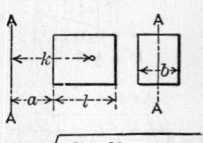

$$k = \sqrt{\frac{4\,l^2 + b^2}{12} + a^2 + al}$$

Hollow Cylinder. Longitudinal Axis.

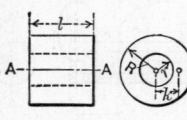

$$k = 0.7071 \sqrt{R^2 + r^2}$$

$$k^2 = \tfrac{1}{2}\,(R^2 + r^2)$$

Rectangular Prism. Axis through center.

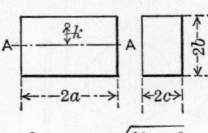

$$k = 0.577 \sqrt{b^2 + c^2}$$

$$k^2 = \tfrac{1}{3}\,(b^2 + c^2)$$

Cone. Axis at base.

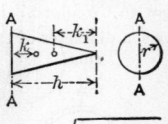

$$k = \sqrt{\frac{2\,h^2 + 3\,r^2}{20}}$$

Axis at apex.

$$k_1 = \sqrt{\frac{12\,h^2 + 3\,r^2}{20}}$$

Hollow Cylinder. Axis, diameter at midlength.

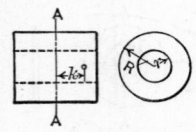

$$k = 0.289 \sqrt{l^2 + 3\,(R^2 + r^2)}$$

$$k^2 = \frac{l^2}{12} + \frac{R^2 + r^2}{4}$$

Parallelepiped. Axis at one end, central.

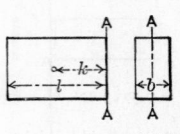

$$k = 0.289 \sqrt{4\,l^2 + b^2}$$

$$k^2 = \frac{4\,l^2 + b^2}{12}$$

Cone. Axis through its center line.

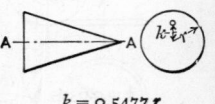

$$k = 0.5477\,r$$

$$k^2 = 0.3\,r^2$$

Radius of Gyration

Frustum of Cone.
Axis at large end.

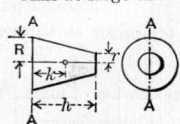

$$k = \sqrt{\frac{h^2}{10}\left(\frac{R^2 + 3\,Rr + 6\,r^2}{R^2 + Rr + r^2}\right) + \frac{3}{20}\left(\frac{R^5 - r^5}{R^3 - r^3}\right)}$$

Sphere.
Axis at a distance.

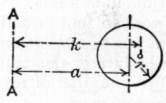

$$k = \sqrt{a^2 + \tfrac{2}{5} r^2}$$
$$k^2 = a^2 + \tfrac{2}{5} r^2$$

Sphere.
Axis its diameter.

$k = 0.6325\,r; \quad k^2 = \tfrac{2}{5}\,r^2$

Thin Spherical Shell.
$k = 0.8165\,r; \quad k^2 = \tfrac{2}{3}\,r^2$

Ellipsoid.
Axis through center.

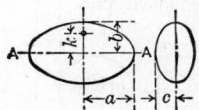

$k = 0.447\,\sqrt{b^2 + c^2}$
$k^2 = \tfrac{1}{5}\,(b^2 + c^2)$

Hollow Sphere.
Axis its diameter.

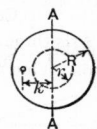

$$k = 0.6325\,\sqrt{\frac{R^5 - r^5}{R^3 - r^3}}$$

$$k^2 = \frac{2\,(R^5 - r^5)}{5\,(R^3 - r^3)}$$

Paraboloid.
Axis through center.

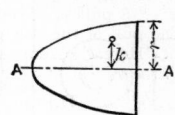

$k = 0.5773\,r$
$k^2 = \tfrac{1}{3}\,r^2$

Formulas for Rotary Motion

In the following formulas:

F = force in pounds, acting in the direction of the tangent;
P = power in foot-pounds, per second;
V = velocity in feet per second;
S = distance passed through in feet by point of application of force F;
T = time in seconds;
K = work in foot-pounds;
R = radius of revolution (radius to point of application of force F) in feet;
n = revolutions per minute;
N = total number of revolutions in time T;
H.P. = horsepower.　　　　　　　　Q = torque in pound-inches.

$$F = \frac{60\,P}{2\,\pi Rn} = \frac{9.55\,P}{Rn} = \frac{9.55\,K}{RnT} = \frac{5252\,\text{H.P.}}{Rn}$$

$$P = \frac{2\,\pi RnF}{60} = \frac{RnF}{9.55} = \frac{FRN}{0.159\,T}$$

$$V = \frac{2\,\pi Rn}{60} = 0.1047\,Rn$$

$$S = \frac{2\,\pi RnT}{60} = \frac{RnT}{9.55} = 2\,\pi RN$$

$$T = \frac{60\,S}{2\,\pi Rn} = \frac{9.55\,S}{Rn} = \frac{9.55\,K}{FRn} = \frac{FRN}{87.5\,\text{H.P.}}$$

$$K = \frac{2\,\pi FRnT}{60} = \frac{FRnT}{9.55} = 2\,\pi RNF$$

$$R = \frac{60\,V}{2\,\pi n} = \frac{9.55\,V}{n} = \frac{9.55\,P}{Fn} = \frac{5252\,\text{H.P.}}{Fn} = \frac{9.55\,K}{FnT}$$

$$n = \frac{60\,V}{2\,\pi R} = \frac{9.55\,V}{R} = \frac{5252\,\text{H.P.}}{FR}$$

$$N = \frac{87.5\,T\,\text{H.P.}}{FR} = \frac{S}{2\,\pi R} = \frac{K}{2\,\pi RF} = \frac{0.159\,PT}{FR}$$

$$\text{H.P.} = \frac{FRn}{5252} = \frac{FRN}{87.5\,T} \qquad Q = \frac{\text{H.P.} \times 33,000 \times 12}{2\pi \times n} = \frac{\text{H.P.} \times 63,000}{n}$$

Examples: — A pulley, 36 inches (3 feet) in diameter, makes 110 revolutions per minute. The pull of the belt on the pulley is 200 pounds. Find the horsepower transmitted. Here $F = 200$; $R = 1.5$; $n = 110$.

$$\text{H.P.} = \frac{FRn}{5252} = \frac{200 \times 1.5 \times 110}{5252} = 6.3.$$

What is the force exerted at the periphery of a gear 18 inches in diameter, revolving at 60 revolutions per minute and transmitting 4 horsepower? Here $R = 0.75$; $n = 60$.

$$F = \frac{5252 \times \text{H.P.}}{Rn} = \frac{5252 \times 4}{0.75 \times 60} = 467 \text{ pounds}$$

Formulas for Constantly Accelerated or Retarded Motion

In the following formulas:

F = force in pounds causing acceleration, acting on a body free to move;
T = time in seconds during which the force acts on the body;
G = constant acceleration in feet per second, due to the force F;
V = final velocity at the end of time T, or uniform velocity of a moving body;
S = distance in feet passed through while the force acts on the body;
W = weight of moving body in pounds;
P = average power exerted during time T, in foot-pounds per second;
K = work in foot-pounds (or energy) concentrated in the moving body;
g = acceleration due to gravity = 32.16.

$$F = \frac{GW}{g} = \frac{VW}{gT} = \frac{2WS}{gT^2} = \frac{WV^2}{2gS} = \frac{PT}{S} = \frac{2K}{GT^2} = \frac{K}{S} = \sqrt{\frac{2PW}{gT}}$$

$$T = \frac{V}{G} = \frac{VW}{gF} = \sqrt{\frac{2WS}{gF}} = \sqrt{\frac{2S}{G}} = \frac{K}{P} = \sqrt{\frac{2WK}{gF^2}}$$

$$G = \frac{gF}{W} = \frac{V}{T} = \frac{V^2}{2S} = \frac{2S}{T^2} = \frac{gPT}{WS} = \frac{gK}{WS} = \frac{2K}{FT^2}$$

$$V = GT = \sqrt{2GS} = \frac{2S}{T} = \frac{gFT}{W} = \sqrt{\frac{2gPT}{W}} = \sqrt{\frac{2gK}{W}} = \sqrt{\frac{2gSF}{W}}$$

$$S = \frac{VT}{2} = \frac{V^2}{2G} = \frac{PT}{F} = \frac{GT^2}{2} = \frac{K}{F} = \frac{gK}{GW} = \frac{gFT^2}{2W}$$

$$W = \frac{gF}{G} = \frac{gFT}{V} = \frac{2gK}{V^2} = \frac{2gFS}{V^2} = \frac{gFT^2}{2S} = \frac{gPT^3}{2S^2} = \frac{gT^2K}{2S^2}$$

$$P = \frac{FS}{T} = \frac{K}{T} = \frac{FV^2}{2GT} = \frac{WV^2}{2gT} = \frac{2WS^2}{gT^3} = \frac{gF^2T}{2W}$$

$$K = FS = \frac{FVT}{2} = \frac{FGT^2}{2} = PT = \frac{WV^2}{2g} = \frac{GWVT}{2g} = \frac{gF^2T^2}{2W}$$

Examples: — A body weighing 300 pounds is to be lifted. The velocity with which it is to be hoisted is 3 feet per second, and this velocity is to be reached in 5 seconds. Find the force required for hoisting during the time the motion is accelerated. Here $W = 300$; $V = 3$; $T = 5$. Then, force required for acceleration:

$$F = \frac{VW}{gT} = \frac{3 \times 300}{32.16 \times 5} = 5.6 \text{ pounds.}$$

To this is added the force required to hold the body suspended, or 300 pounds; $300 + 5.6 = 305.6$ pounds.

The force required to move a crane weighing 5000 pounds upon its runways at a uniform speed of 10 feet per second is 200 pounds. What is the force required to start the crane, if this speed is to be acquired in 6 seconds? Here $W = 5000$; $V = 10$; $T = 6$. Then:

$$F = \frac{VW}{gT} = \frac{5000 \times 10}{32.16 \times 6} = 260 \text{ pounds, approx.}$$

To this must be added the 200 pounds required to move the crane at a uniform speed of 10 feet per second, making the total force required during acceleration equal to $260 + 200 = 460$ pounds.

Formulas for Accelerated Rotary Motion

In the following formulas:

F = force in pounds, acting tangentially at end of radius R;
R = radius at end of which F is applied, in feet;
k = radius of gyration in feet;
T = time of acceleration in seconds;
n = revolutions per minute at end of time T;
N = total number of revolutions in time T;
W = weight of revolving body in pounds;
K = work in foot-pounds (or energy) concentrated in revolving body.

From the general formulas for accelerated or retarded motion on the preceding page:

$$F = \frac{VW}{gT}, \text{ from which, for rotary motion, } F = \frac{2\pi k n W}{60\, gT}$$

and

$$FR = \frac{Wk \times 2\pi k n}{60\, gT} = \frac{W \times 2\pi k^2 n}{60\, gT}$$

Assuming $g = 32.16$, we have, by substitution:

$$F = \frac{0.00326\, Wnk^2}{TR} = \frac{0.391\, WNk^2}{T^2R} = \frac{60\, K}{3.1416\, RnT} = \frac{K}{6.2832\, RN}$$

$$T = \frac{0.00326\, Wnk^2}{FR} = \sqrt{\frac{0.391\, WNk^2}{FR}} = \frac{60\, K}{3.1416\, RnF} = \frac{0.25\, k\, \sqrt{WK}}{FR}$$

$$n = \frac{120\, N}{T} = \frac{307.1\, FTR}{Wk^2} = \frac{60\, K}{3.1416\, RTF} = \frac{76.6}{k}\sqrt{\frac{K}{W}}$$

$$N = \frac{Tn}{120} = \frac{2.559\, FT^2R}{Wk^2} = \frac{K}{6.2832\, RF} = \frac{0.64\, T}{k}\sqrt{\frac{K}{W}}$$

$$k = \sqrt{\frac{307.1\, FRT}{Wn}} = \sqrt{\frac{2.559\, FRT^2}{WN}} = \frac{0.256\, KT}{N\sqrt{WNFR}} = \frac{337\, K}{n\sqrt{WnTFR}}$$

Example: — A circular disk 18 inches in diameter and weighing 12 pounds revolves about its axis. The revolving force is applied at the end of a lever of 8 inch radius. Find the force required to bring the disk to a speed of 300 revolutions per minute in 10 seconds, friction being neglected.

$$W = 12; \quad R = \tfrac{2}{3}; \quad n = 300; \quad T = 10; \quad k = 0.707 \times \tfrac{3}{4} = 0.53.$$

$$F = \frac{0.00326\, Wnk^2}{TR} = \frac{0.00326 \times 12 \times 300 \times 0.53^2}{10 \times \tfrac{2}{3}} = 0.49 \text{ pound.}$$

Example: — A flywheel, having an outside diameter of 7 feet and weighing 3000 pounds, is to be brought from a condition of rest to a speed of 200 R.P.M. A belt pull of 100 pounds is available at the periphery of the flywheel rim for this purpose; this belt pull is required entirely for acceleration. If the radius of gyration is assumed to be equal to the mean radius of the flywheel rim, which is 3 feet 3 inches, what time will be required (from rest) to obtain a speed of 200 R.P.M.?

$$F = 100; \quad R = 3.5; \quad k = 3.25; \quad n = 200; \quad W = 3000.$$

Then, time required for acceleration:

$$T = \frac{0.00326\, Wnk^2}{FR} = \frac{0.00326 \times 3000 \times 200 \times 3.25^2}{100 \times 3.5} = 59 \text{ seconds.}$$

Centrifugal Force

Centrifugal Force. — When a body rotates about any axis other than one at its center of mass, it exerts an outward radial force called centrifugal force upon the axis or any arm or cord from the axis which restrains it from moving in a straight (tangential) line. In the following formulas:

F = centrifugal force in pounds;
W = weight of revolving body in pounds;
v = velocity of revolving body in feet per second;
n = number of revolutions per minute;
g = acceleration due to gravity = 32.166 feet per second per second;
R = perpendicular distance from axis of rotation to center of mass, or
for practical use, to center of gravity of revolving body.

Note: If a body rotates about its own center of mass, R equals zero and v equals zero. This means that the *resultant* of the centrifugal forces of all the elements of the body is equal to zero or, in other words, no centrifugal force is exerted on the axis of rotation. The centrifugal force of any part or element of such a body is found by the equations given below where R is the radius to the center of gravity of the part or element. In case of a flywheel rim, the mean radius of the rim meets practical requirements, as this is the radius to center of gravity of a thin radial section.

$$F = \frac{Wv^2}{gR} = \frac{Wv^2}{32.16\,R} = \frac{4\,WR\pi^2 n^2}{60 \times 60\,g} = \frac{WRn^2}{2933} = 0.000341\,WRn^2$$

$$W = \frac{FRg}{v^2} = \frac{2933\,F}{Rn^2} \qquad v = \sqrt{\frac{FRg}{W}}$$

$$R = \frac{Wv^2}{Fg} = \frac{2933\,F}{Wn^2} \qquad n = \sqrt{\frac{2933\,F}{WR}}$$

(If n is the number of revolutions per second instead of per minute, then $F = 1.227\,WRn^2$.)

Calculating Centrifugal Force. — In the ordinary formula for centrifugal force, $F = 0.000341\,WRn^2$; the mean radius R of the flywheel or pulley rim is given in feet. For small dimensions, it is more convenient to have the formula in the form:

$$F = 0.000028416\,Wrn^2$$

in which F = centrifugal force, in pounds; W = weight of rim, in pounds; r = mean radius of rim, in inches; n = number of revolutions per minute.

In this formula let $C = 0.000028416\,n^2$. This, then, is the centrifugal force of one pound, one inch from the axis. The formula can now be written in the form,

$$F = WrC$$

C is calculated for various values of the revolutions per minute n, and the calculated values of C are tabulated in the accompanying "Table for Calculating Centrifugal Force." To find the centrifugal force in any given case, simply find the value of C in the table and multiply it by the product of W and r, the four multiplications in the original formula given thus having been reduced to two.

Table for Calculating Centrifugal Force

n	C	n	C	n	C	n	C
50	0.07104	100	0.28416	470	6.2770	5200	768.369
51	0.07391	101	0.28987	480	6.5470	5300	798.205
52	0.07684	102	0.29564	490	6.8227	5400	828.611
53	0.07982	103	0.30147	500	7.1040	5500	859.584
54	0.08286	104	0.30735	600	10.2298	5600	891.126
55	0.08596	105	0.31328	700	13.9238	5700	923.236
56	0.08911	106	0.31928	800	18.1862	5800	955.914
57	0.09232	107	0.32533	900	23.0170	5900	989.161
58	0.09559	108	0.33144	1000	28.4160	6000	1022.980
59	0.09892	109	0.33761	1100	34.3834	6100	1057.360
60	0.10230	110	0.34383	1200	40.9190	6200	1092.310
61	0.10573	115	0.37580	1300	48.0230	6300	1127.830
62	0.10923	120	0.40921	1400	55.6954	6400	1163.920
63	0.11278	125	0.44400	1500	63.9360	6500	1200.580
64	0.11639	130	0.48023	1600	72.7450	6600	1237.800
65	0.12006	135	0.51788	1700	82.1222	6700	1275.590
66	0.12378	140	0.55695	1800	92.0678	6800	1313.960
67	0.12756	145	0.59744	1900	102.5820	6900	1352.890
68	0.13140	150	0.63936	2000	113.6640	7000	1392.380
69	0.13529	160	0.72745	2100	125.3150	7100	1432.450
70	0.13924	170	0.82122	2200	137.5330	7200	1473.090
71	0.14325	180	0.92067	2300	150.3210	7300	1514.290
72	0.14731	190	1.02590	2400	163.6760	7400	1556.060
73	0.15143	200	1.1367	2500	177.6000	7500	1598.400
74	0.15561	210	1.2531	2600	192.0920	7600	1641.310
75	0.15984	220	1.3753	2700	207.1530	7700	1684.780
76	0.16413	230	1.5032	2800	222.7810	7800	1728.830
77	0.16848	240	1.6358	2900	238.9790	7900	1773.440
78	0.17288	250	1.7760	3000	255.7400	8000	1818.620
79	0.17734	260	1.9209	3100	273.0780	8100	1864.370
80	0.18186	270	2.0715	3200	290.9800	8200	1910.690
81	0.18644	280	2.2278	3300	309.4500	8300	1957.580
82	0.19107	290	2.3898	3400	328.4890	8400	2005.030
83	0.19576	300	2.5574	3500	348.0960	8500	2053.060
84	0.20050	310	2.7308	3600	368.2710	8600	2101.650
85	0.20530	320	2.9098	3700	389.0150	8700	2150.810
86	0.21016	330	3.0945	3800	410.3270	8800	2200.540
87	0.21508	340	3.2849	3900	432.2070	8900	2250.830
88	0.22005	350	3.4809	4000	454.6560	9000	2301.700
89	0.22508	360	3.6823	4100	477.6730	9100	2353.130
90	0.23017	370	3.8901	4200	501.2580	9200	2405.130
91	0.23531	380	4.1032	4300	525.4120	9300	2457.700
92	0.24051	390	4.3220	4400	550.1340	9400	2510.840
93	0.24577	400	4.5466	4500	575.4240	9500	2564.540
94	0.25108	410	4.7767	4600	601.2830	9600	2618.820
95	0.25645	420	5.0126	4700	627.7090	9700	2673.660
96	0.26188	430	5.2541	4800	654.7050	9800	2729.070
97	0.26737	440	5.5013	4900	682.2680	9900	2785.050
98	0.27291	450	5.7542	5000	710.4000	10000	2841.600
99	0.27851	460	6.0128	5100	739.1000		

FLYWHEELS

Flywheels may be classified either as *balance wheels* or as *flywheel pulleys*. The object of all flywheels is to equalize the energy exerted and the work done and thereby prevent excessive or sudden changes of speed. The permissible speed variation is an important factor in all flywheel designs. The allowable speed change varies considerably for different classes of machinery; for instance, it is about 1 or 2 per cent in modern steam engines, while in punching and shearing machinery a speed variation of 20 per cent may be allowed.

As the function of a balance wheel is to absorb and equalize energy in case the resistance to motion, or driving power, varies throughout the cycle, the rim section is generally quite heavy and is designed with reference to the energy that must be stored in it to prevent excessive speed variations and also with reference to the strength necessary to withstand safely the stresses resulting from the required speed. The rims of most balance wheels are either square or nearly square in section, but flywheel pulleys are commonly made wide to accommodate a belt and relatively thin in a radial direction, although this is not an invariable rule.

Flywheels, in general, may either be formed of a solid or one-piece section, or they may be of sectional construction. Flywheels in diameters up to about eight feet are usually cast solid, the hubs being divided in some cases to relieve cooling stresses. Flywheels ranging from, say, eight feet to fifteen feet in diameter, are commonly cast in half sections, and the larger sizes in several sections, the number of which may equal the number of arms in the wheel. The sectional flywheels may be divided into two general classes. One class includes cast wheels which are formed of sections principally because a solid casting would be too large to transport readily. The second class includes wheels of sectional construction which, by reason of the materials used and the special arrangement of the sections, enables much higher peripheral speeds to be obtained safely than would be possible with ordinary sectional wheels of the type not designed especially for high speeds. Various designs have been built to withstand the extreme stresses encountered in some classes of service. The rims in some cases are laminated, being partly or entirely formed of numerous segment-shaped steel plates. Another type of flywheel, which is superior to an ordinary sectional wheel, has a solid cast-iron rim connected to the hub by disk-shaped steel plates instead of cast spokes. Steel wheels may be divided into three distinct types, including (1) those having the center and rim built up entirely of steel plates, (2) those having a cast-iron center and steel rim, and (3) those having a cast-steel center and rim formed of steel plates. Wheels having wire-wound rims have been used to a limited extent when extremely high speeds have been necessary.

When the rim is formed of sections held together by joints it is very important to design these joints properly. The ordinary bolted and flanged rim joints located between the arms average about 20 per cent of the strength of a solid rim and about 25 per cent is the maximum strength obtainable for a joint of this kind. However, by placing the joints at the ends of the arms instead of between them, an efficiency of 50 per cent of the strength of the rim may be obtained. This is due to the fact that the joint is not subjected to the outward bending stresses between the arms but is directly supported by the arm, the end of which is secured to the rim just beneath the joint. When the rim sections of heavy balance wheels are held together by steel links shrunk into place, an efficiency of 60 per cent may be obtained; and by using a rim of box or I-section, a link type of joint connection may have an efficiency of 100 per cent.

Energy Due to Changes of Velocity. — When a flywheel absorbs energy from a variable driving force, as in the case of a steam engine, the velocity increases; and when this stored energy is given out, the velocity diminishes. When the driven member of a machine encounters a variable resistance in performing its work, as when the punch of a punching machine is passing through a steel plate, the flywheel gives up energy while the punch is at work, and, consequently, the speed of the flywheel is reduced. The total energy that a flywheel would give out if brought to a standstill is given by the formula:

$$E = \frac{Wv^2}{2\,g} = \frac{Wv^2}{64.32}$$

in which E = total energy of flywheel, in foot-pounds;

W = weight of flywheel rim, in pounds;

v = velocity at mean radius of flywheel rim, in feet per second;

g = acceleration due to gravity = 32.16.

If the velocity of a flywheel changes, the energy it will absorb or give up is proportional to the difference between the squares of its initial and final speeds, and is equal to the difference between the energy which it would give out if brought to a full stop and that which is still stored in it at the reduced velocity. Hence:

$$E_1 = \frac{Wv_1^2}{2\,g} - \frac{Wv_2^2}{2\,g} = \frac{W\,(v_1^2 - v_2^2)}{64.32}$$

in which E_1 = energy in foot-pounds which a flywheel will give out while the speed is reduced from v_1 to v_2;

W = weight of flywheel rim, in pounds;

v_1 = velocity at mean radius of flywheel rim before any energy has been given out, in feet per second;

v_2 = velocity of flywheel rim at end of period during which the energy has been given out, in feet per second.

Ordinarily, the effect of the arms and hub does not enter into flywheel calculations, and only the weight of the rim is considered. In computing the velocity, the mean radius of the rim is commonly used.

General Procedure in Flywheel Design. — The general method of designing a flywheel is to determine first the value of E_1 or the energy the flywheel must either supply or absorb for a given change in velocity, which, in turn, varies for different classes of service. The mean diameter of the flywheel may be assumed, or it may be fixed within certain limits by the general design of the machine. Ordinarily the speed of the flywheel shaft is known, at least approximately; the values of v_1 and v_2 can then be determined, the latter depending upon the allowable percentage of speed variation. When these values are known, the weight of the rim and the cross-sectional area required to obtain this weight may be computed. The general procedure will be illustrated more in detail by considering the design of flywheels for punching and shearing machinery.

Flywheels for Presses, Punches, Shears, Etc. — In these classes of machinery, the work that the machine performs is of an intermittent nature and is done during a small part of the time required for the driving shaft of the machine to make a complete revolution. In order to distribute the work of the machine over the entire period of revolution of the driving shaft, a heavy-rimmed flywheel is placed on the shaft, giving the belt an opportunity to perform an almost uniform amount of work during the whole revolution. During the greater part of the revolution of the driving shaft, the belt power is used to accelerate the speed of the flywheel. During the part of the revolution when the work is done, the energy thus stored up in the flywheel is given out at the expense of its velocity. The problem is to determine the weight and cross-sectional area of the rim when the conditions affecting the design of the flywheel are known.

Example: — A flywheel is required for a punching machine capable of punching ¾-inch holes through structural steel plates ¾ inch thick. This machine (see accompanying diagram) is of the general type having a belt-driven shaft at the rear which carries a flywheel and a pinion that meshes with a large gear on the main shaft at the top of the machine. It is assumed that the relative speeds of the pinion and large gear are 7 to 1, respectively, and that the slide is to make 30 working strokes per minute. The preliminary lay-out shows that the flywheel should have a mean diameter (see enlarged detail) of about 30 inches. Find the weight of the flywheel and the size of the rim.

Energy Supplied by Flywheel. — The energy which the flywheel must give up for a given change in velocity, and the weight of rim necessary to supply that energy, must be determined. The maximum pressure for shearing a ¾-inch hole through ¾-inch structural steel equals approximately the circumference of the hole multiplied by the thickness of the stock multiplied by the tensile strength, which is nearly the same as the shearing resistance of the steel. Thus, in this case, 3.1416 × ¾ × ¾ × 60,000 = 106,000 pounds. The average pressure will be much less than the maximum. Some designers assume that the average pressure is about

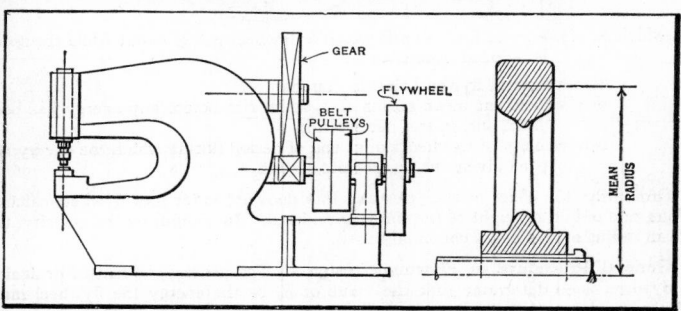

one-half the maximum, although experiments show that the material is practically sheared off when the punch has entered the sheet a distance equal to about one-third the sheet thickness. On this latter basis, the average energy E_a in foot-pounds is 2200 in this case. Thus:

$$E_a = \frac{106,000 \times \frac{1}{3} \times \frac{3}{4}}{12} = \frac{106,000}{4 \times 12} = 2200 \text{ foot-pounds.}$$

If the efficiency of the machine is taken at 85 per cent, the energy required will equal 2200 ÷ 0.85 = 2600 foot-pounds nearly. Assume that the energy supplied by the belt while the punch is at work is determined by calculation to equal 175 foot-pounds. Then the flywheel must supply 2600 − 175 = 2425 foot-pounds = E_1.

Rim Velocity at Mean Radius. — When the mean radius of the flywheel is known, the velocity of the rim at the mean radius, in feet per second, is:

$$v = \frac{2 \times 3.1416 \times R \times n}{60}$$

in which v = velocity at mean radius of flywheel, in feet per second;
R = mean radius of flywheel rim, in feet;
n = number of revolutions per minute.

Dimensions of Flywheels for Punches and Shears

(Maximum number of revolutions per minute given in table should never be exceeded
for cast-iron flywheels.)

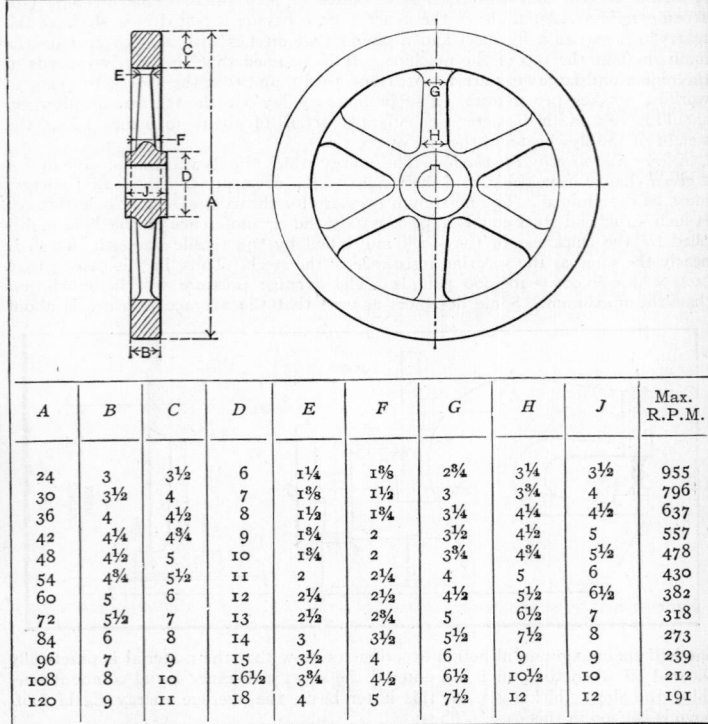

A	B	C	D	E	F	G	H	J	Max. R.P.M.
24	3	3½	6	1¼	1⅜	2¾	3¼	3½	955
30	3½	4	7	1⅜	1½	3	3¾	4	796
36	4	4½	8	1½	1¾	3¼	4¼	4½	637
42	4¼	4¾	9	1¾	2	3½	4½	5	557
48	4½	5	10	1¾	2	3¾	4¾	5½	478
54	4¾	5½	11	2	2¼	4	5	6	430
60	5	6	12	2¼	2½	4½	5½	6½	382
72	5½	7	13	2½	2¾	5	6½	7	318
84	6	8	14	3	3½	5½	7½	8	273
96	7	9	15	3½	4	6	9	9	239
108	8	10	16½	3¾	4½	6½	10½	10	212
120	9	11	18	4	5	7½	12	12	191

According to the preliminary lay-out the mean diameter in this case should be about 30 inches and the driving shaft is to make 210 R.P.M.; hence,

$$v = \frac{2 \times 3.1416 \times 1.25 \times 210}{60} = 27.5 \text{ feet per second.}$$

Weight of Flywheel Rim. — Assuming that the allowable variation in velocity when punching is about 15 per cent, and values of v_1 and v_2 are respectively 27.5 and 23.4 feet per second (27.5 × 0.85 = 23.4), the weight of a flywheel rim necessary to supply a given amount of energy in foot-pounds while the speed is reduced from v_1 to v_2 would be:

$$W = \frac{E_1 \times 64.32}{v_1^2 - v_2^2} = \frac{2425 \times 64.32}{27.5^2 - 23.4^2} = 750 \text{ pounds.}$$

Size of Rim for Given Weight. — Since 1 cubic inch of cast iron weighs 0.26 pound, a flywheel rim weighing 750 pounds contains $\frac{750}{0.26} = 2884$ cubic inches. The cross-sectional area of the rim in square inches equals the total number of cubic inches divided by the mean circumference, or $\frac{2884}{92.24} = 31$ square inches nearly, which is approximately the area of a rim $5\frac{1}{8}$ inches wide and 6 inches deep.

Simplified Flywheel Calculations. — Calculations for designing the flywheels of punches and shears are simplified by the following formulas and the accompanying table of constants applying to different percentages of speed reduction. In these formulas let:

H.P. = horsepower required;
N = number of strokes per minute;
E = total energy required per stroke, in foot-pounds;
E_1 = energy given up by flywheel, in foot-pounds;
T = time in seconds per stroke;
T_1 = time in seconds of actual cut;
W = weight of flywheel rim, in pounds;
D = mean diameter of flywheel rim, in feet;
R = maximum allowable speed of flywheel in revolutions per minute;
C and C_1 = values as given in table;
a = width of flywheel rim;
b = depth of flywheel rim;
y = ratio of depth to width of rim.

$$\text{H.P.} = \frac{EN}{33,000} = \frac{E}{T \times 550} \qquad E_1 = E\left(1 - \frac{T_1}{T}\right)$$

$$W = \frac{E_1}{CD^2R^2} \qquad a = \sqrt{\frac{1.22\,W}{12\,Dy}} \qquad b = ay$$

For cast-iron flywheels, with a maximum stress of 1000 pounds per square inch:

$$W = C_1 E_1 \qquad R = 1940 \div D$$

Values of C and C_1 in the Previous Formulas

Per Cent Reduction	C	C_1	Per Cent Reduction	C	C_1
2½	0.00000213	0.1250	10	0.00000810	0.0328
5	0.00000426	0.0625	15	0.00001180	0.0225
7½	0.00000617	0.0432	20	0.00001535	0.0173

Example 1: — A hot slab shear is required to cut a slab 4×15 inches which, at a shearing stress of 6000 pounds per square inch, gives a pressure between the knives of 360,000 pounds. The total energy required for the cut will then be $360,000 \times \frac{4}{12} = 120,000$ foot-pounds. The shear is to make 20 strokes per minute; the actual cutting time is 0.75 second, and the balance of the stroke is 2.25 seconds.

The flywheel is to have a mean diameter of 6 feet 6 inches and is to run at a speed of 200 R.P.M.; the reduction in speed to be 10 per cent per stroke when cutting.

$$\text{H.P.} = \frac{120,000 \times 20}{33,000} = 72.7 \text{ horsepower;}$$

$$E_1 = 120,000 \times \left(1 - \frac{0.75}{3}\right) = 90,000 \text{ foot-pounds;}$$

$$W = \frac{90,000}{0.0000081 \times 6.5^2 \times 200^2} = 6570 \text{ pounds.}$$

Assuming a ratio of 1.22 between depth and width of rim,

$$a = \sqrt{\frac{6570}{12 \times 6.5}} = 9.18 \text{ inches;}$$

$$b = 1.22 \times 9.18 = 11.2 \text{ inches;}$$

or size of rim, say, $9 \times 11\frac{1}{2}$ inches.

Example 2: — Suppose that the flywheel in Example 1 is to be made with a stress of 1000 pounds, due to centrifugal force, per square inch of rim section.

$$C_1 \text{ for 10 per cent} = 0.0328;$$

$$W = 0.0328 \times 90,000 = 2950 \text{ pounds.}$$

$$R = \frac{1940}{D}. \quad \text{If } D = 6 \text{ feet, } K = \frac{1940}{6} = 323 \text{ R.P.M.}$$

Assuming a ratio of 1.22 between depth and width of rim, as before:

$$a = \sqrt{\frac{2950}{12 \times 6}} = 6.4 \text{ inches;}$$

$$b = 1.22 \times 6.4 = 7.8 \text{ inches;}$$

or size of rim, say, $6\frac{1}{4} \times 8$ inches.

Stresses in Flywheel Rims. — In general, high speed is desirable for flywheels in order to avoid using wheels which are unnecessarily large and heavy. The stress which tends to rupture a flywheel rim of given area, depends solely upon the rim velocity, and is independent of the rim radius, which can be proved as follows: The sum of the centrifugal (radial) forces of the whole rim of a flywheel is:

$$F = \frac{Wv^2}{gR} = \frac{4 WR\pi^2 n^2}{60 \times 60 g} = 0.000341 WRn^2$$

where F = centrifugal force, in pounds; W = weight of rim in pounds;
R = mean radius of rim in feet, which is approximately equal to
radius of gyration; n = revolutions per minute.

The resultant of half of this force tends to disrupt one-half of the rim from the other half. The rupture is resisted by the two sections of the rim at each end of the diameter. The resultant of half the radial forces is to the sum of half of the radial forces as the diameter of the flywheel is to half its circumference, or:

$$\frac{\text{resultant}}{\text{sum of half the radial forces}} = \frac{1}{\frac{1}{2}\pi};$$

Hence,

$$\text{resultant} = \frac{2}{\pi} \times \text{sum of half the radial forces} = \frac{2}{\pi} \times \frac{0.000341 WRn^2}{2}$$

$$= 0.00010854 WRn^2.$$

As this resultant force is resisted by the section at each end of the diameter, each section must resist a force

$$S = \frac{0.00010854 \, WRn^2}{2} = 0.00005427 \, WRn^2.$$

The weight of a rim of cast iron, one square inch in section, is $2 \, \pi R \times 3.125 = 19.635 \, R$ pounds, R being in feet; hence for each square inch of rim section

$$s = 0.00005427 \times 19.635 \, R \times Rn^2 = 0.0010656 \, R^2n^2.$$

But as $v = \frac{2 \, \pi Rn}{60}$, and $v^2 = \frac{4 \, \pi^2 R^2 n^2}{3600}$, where v = velocity of rim in feet per second, it follows that

$$s = \frac{0.0010656 \, v^2 \times 3600}{4 \, \pi^2} = 0.0972 \, v^2.$$

Thus the stress in the flywheel rim is independent of the radius and depends only on the rim velocity.

Relation between Centrifugal Force and Disruptive Force in a Flywheel Rim. — When the total centrifugal force has been calculated for a flywheel rim, the result is analogous to that obtained when the total internal pressure acting on a certain length of a section of a steam boiler shell is figured. The total centrifugal force, therefore, is not equal to the disruptive force tending to tear the rim apart. For example, the total internal pressure on a 1-inch long section of a boiler shell, 50 inches in diameter (157 inches in circumference), with a pressure of 100 pounds per square inch, is 15,700 pounds. The actual bursting or tangential stress is $15,700 \div 3.1416 = 5000$ pounds. This bursting stress is resisted by two thicknesses of the shell, one on each side. In the case of the flywheel, the total centrifugal force developed in the rim must be divided by 3.1416 to get the measure of the disruptive force.

Thickness of Flywheel Rims. — A mathematical analysis of the stresses in flywheel rims is not conclusive owing to the uncertainty of shrinkage stresses in castings or the strength of the joint in the case of sectional wheels. When a flywheel of ordinary design is revolving at high speed, the tendency of the rim is to bend or bow outward between the arms, and the bending stresses may be serious, especially if the rim is wide and thin and the spokes are rather widely spaced. When the rims are thick, this tendency does not need to be considered, but in the case of a thin rim, running at a high rate of speed, the stress in the middle might become sufficiently great to cause the wheel to fail. The proper thickness of a cast-iron rim to resist this tendency is given for solid rims by the formula:

$$t = \frac{0.475 \, d}{n^2 \left(\dfrac{6000}{v^2} - \dfrac{1}{10} \right)}$$

For a jointed rim, the formula is:

$$t = \frac{0.95 \, d}{n^2 \left(\dfrac{6000}{v^2} - \dfrac{1}{10} \right)}$$

In these formulas, t = thickness of rim, in inches; d = diameter of flywheel, in inches; n = number of arms; v = peripheral speed, in feet per second.

Safe Speeds for Flywheels. — One hundred feet per second may be regarded as a safe rim speed for cast-iron wheels made in one piece, providing the design is such that there are no severe shrinkage strains in the casting. Ordinarily, there are strains, and, therefore, about 85 feet per second is as high a rim speed as should be considered good practice. If the wheel is made in halves or sections, the efficiency of the rim joint must be taken into consideration. A steel-casting flywheel made in one piece and free from shrinkage strains should run with safety at the rim speed of 200 feet per second. It should be noted that the stress in the rim increases with the square of the speed, so that even a small increase in speed causes a considerable increase in the stress.

Safe speeds for flywheels are given in the accompanying tables. The safe speeds for cast-iron flywheels with solid rims are based on a rim speed of 5280 feet per minute, or 88 feet per second. The second table of safe speeds for cast-iron flywheels with jointed rims is based on a maximum efficiency of 25 per cent for flanged joints, 50 per cent for pad joints, and 60 per cent for link joints. These speeds are recommended by the flywheel insurance department of the Fidelity & Casualty Co. of New York.

Safe Speeds for Cast-iron Flywheels with Solid Rims

Diam. of Flywheel, Feet	Max. Safe Speed, R.P.M.	Diam. of Flywheel, Feet	Max. Safe Speed, R.P.M.	Diam. of Flywheel, Feet	Max. Safe Speed, R.P.M.	Diam. of Flywheel, Feet	Max. Safe Speed, R.P.M.	Diam. of Flywheel, Feet	Max. Safe Speed, R.P.M.
1	1680	6½	258	12½	134	18½	91	24½	68
1¼	1344	7	240	13	129	19	89	25	67
1½	1120	7½	224	13½	124	19½	86	25½	66
2	840	8	210	14	120	20	84	26	65
2½	672	8½	198	14½	116	20½	82	26½	63
3	560	9	187	15	112	21	80	27	62
3½	480	9½	177	15½	108	21½	78	27½	61
4	420	10	168	16	105	22	76	28	60
4½	373	10½	160	16½	102	22½	74	28½	59
5	336	11	153	17	99	23	73	29	58
5½	305	11½	146	17½	96	23½	72	29½	57
6	280	12	140	18	93	24	70	30	56

As the stresses in the rim due to centrifugal force increase with the square of the speed, a relatively slight increase in speed may be dangerous and even cause the wheel to burst or "explode." The margin of safety on speed is the square root of the factor of safety for strength. If the speed should be tripled, the rim stress would be nine times as great as before, and in the case of a flywheel originally designed with a strength factor of safety of 27 for normal speed, this factor would be reduced to 3 if the speed were tripled. If a sectional wheel having flanged and bolted joints located between the arms had a factor of safety of 12 in the solid rim for normal speeds, the factor for the joints would be 3 or less at normal speeds, since the average strength of such joints is only about one-fifth to one-fourth the strength of the rim; therefore, in this case the flywheel would be liable to burst if the speed were increased only 73 per cent, and comparatively few flywheels have as large a margin of safety as this.

Since the material which has the greatest strength for a given weight will withstand the highest speed, wood is in this respect a better material for flywheels than cast-iron, and it has been used to some extent for large wheels.   A well-constructed maple wheel may be run safely at a rim speed of 150 feet per second, provided the wheel is not made in halves or sections with rim joints which permit taking the wheel apart.   The wooden rims are built up of segments which are sawed so as to obtain as much of the straight grain of the wood as possible.

Safe Speeds for Cast-iron Flywheels with Jointed Rims*

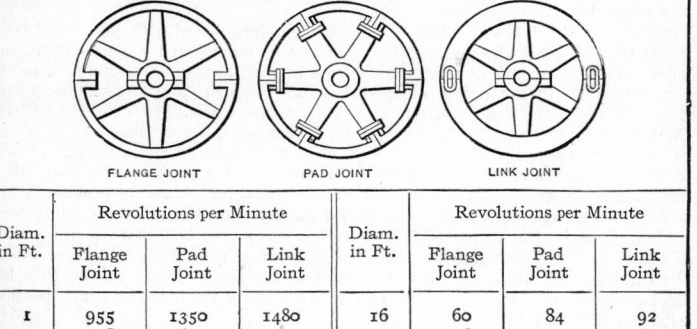

FLANGE JOINT   PAD JOINT   LINK JOINT

Diam. in Ft.	Revolutions per Minute			Diam. in Ft.	Revolutions per Minute		
	Flange Joint	Pad Joint	Link Joint		Flange Joint	Pad Joint	Link Joint
1	955	1350	1480	16	60	84	92
2	478	675	740	17	56	79	87
3	318	450	493	18	53	75	82
4	239	338	370	19	50	71	78
5	191	270	296	20	48	68	74
6	159	225	247	21	46	65	70
7	136	193	212	22	44	62	67
8	119	169	185	23	42	59	64
9	106	150	164	24	40	56	62
10	96	135	148	25	38	54	59
11	87	123	135	26	37	52	57
12	80	113	124	27	35	50	55
13	73	104	114	28	34	48	53
14	68	96	106	29	33	47	51
15	64	90	99	30	32	45	49

* If the revolutions given in the table be increased 20 per cent the margin of safety on speed will be reduced to *two and one-half;* if the revolutions be increased 50 per cent the margin of safety will be reduced to *two.*

Factors of Safety for Flywheels. — Cast-iron flywheels commonly have a factor of safety of 10.   When flywheel rims are made of wood, the full tensile strength of the wood is not obtained, and partly for this reason a factor of safety of 20 is used for wood.   In the case of a wooden rim, the real factor of safety is less than 20, because part of the tensile strength is lost in sawing, and on account of the joints between the segments.

Wheels do not often fail from torsional stress or from twisting action in pulling their load, because enough material can be put in the wheel to resist successfully any load required.   There is, however, no possible way to overcome the centrifugal force due to speed.   Increasing the thickness of the rim of the wheel does not strengthen it so far as centrifugal force is concerned, because the weight added also increases the centrifugal force, leaving the wheel no stronger than before.   There is, therefore, a definite speed at which any wheel, however sound, will explode, regardless of the amount of material it contains.

Tests to Determine Flywheel Bursting Speeds. — Tests made by Prof. C. H. Benjamin, to determine the bursting speeds of flywheels, showed the following results:

Cast-iron Wheels with Solid Rims. — Cast-iron wheels having solid rims burst at a rim speed of 395 feet per second, corresponding to a centrifugal tension of about 15,600 pounds per square inch.

Wheels with Jointed Rims. — Four wheels were tested with joints and bolts inside the rim, after the familiar design ordinarily employed for band wheels, but with the joints located at points one-fourth of the distance from one arm to the next, these being the points of least bending moment, and, consequently, the points at which the deflection due to centrifugal force would be expected to have the least effect. The tests, however, did not bear out this conclusion. The wheels burst at a rim speed of 194 feet per second, corresponding to a centrifugal tension of about 3750 pounds per square inch. These wheels, therefore, were only about one-quarter as strong as the wheels with solid rims, and burst at practically the same speed as wheels in a previous series of tests in which the rim joints were midway between the arms. This is doubtless due to the fact that the heavy mass of the flanges and bolts locates the bending moment near them. In these wheels the combined tensile strength of the bolts in the flange joints was slightly less than one-third the strength of the rim, which is about the maximum ratio possible with this style of joint.

Bursting Speed for Link Joints. — Another type of wheel with deep rim, fastened together at the joints midway between the arms by links shrunk into recesses, after the manner of flywheels for massive engines, gave much superior results. This wheel burst at a speed of 256 feet per second, indicating a centrifugal tension of about 6600 pounds per square inch.

Wheel having Tie-rods. — Tests were made on a band wheel having joints inside the rim, midway between the arms, and in all respects like others of this design previously tested, except that tie-rods were used to connect the joints with the hub. It burst at a speed of 225 feet per second, showing an increase of strength of from 30 to 40 per cent over similar wheels without the tie-rods.

Wheel Rim of I-section. — Several wheels of special design, not in common use, were also tested, the one giving the greatest strength being an English wheel, with solid rim of I-section, made of high-grade cast iron and with the rim tied to the hub by steel wire spokes. These spokes were adjusted to have a uniform tension by "tuning," and the wheel gave way at a rim speed of 424 feet per second, which is slightly higher than the speed of rupture of the solid rim wheels with ordinary style of spokes.

Bursting Speeds of Cast-iron Pulleys. — The pulley tested was of cast iron, well proportioned, and of the type used on shafting for transmitting power. It was 48 inches in diameter, had six arms and weighed 194 pounds. The rim was whole and was 8½ inches wide and about ⅜ inch thick, finished on the outside. The arms were elliptical in section, 3⅛ inches by 1¹⁄₁₆ inch at the hub, and 2 inches by ¾ inch at the rim. On the whole the wheel was well designed and showed no signs of shrinkage strains. It had, however, been balanced by riveting a cast-iron washer inside the rim at the lighter side. The pulley burst at a speed of 1100 revolutions per minute, the linear speed of the rim at rupture being 230 feet per second.

Wheel No. 2 was a cast-iron pulley of the same general style and dimensions as No. 1 but with a split hub and rim. The flanges were located midway between the arms and bolted at some little distance inside the rim; thus the joints were in the worst possible position to withstand the bending action due to centrifugal force, and their own weight only aggravated the difficulty. The flanges weighed with their bolts 7½ pounds. This wheel burst at less than 700 revolutions per minute, the tachometer not recording below this speed. It was estimated that the speed was only about 600 revolutions per minute. At 600 revolutions per minute the linear speed of the rim would be only 125 feet per second.

Tests on Flywheel of Special Construction. — The third test was on a flywheel 49 inches in diameter and weighing about 900 pounds. The rim was 6¾ inches wide and 1⅛ inches thick, and was built of ten segments, the material being steel casting. Each joint was secured by three " prisoners " of an I-section on the outside face, by link prisoners on each edge, and by a dovetailed bronze clamp on the inside, fitting over lugs on the rim. The arms were of phosphor-bronze, twenty in number, ten on each side, and were a cross in section. These arms came midway between the rim joints and were bolted to plane faces on the polygonal hub. The rim was further reinforced by a system of diagonal bracing, each section of the rim being supported at five points on each side, in such a way as to relieve it almost entirely from bending. The braces, like the arms, were of phosphor-bronze, and all bolts and connecting links of steel. This wheel was designed as a model of a proposed 30-foot flywheel. On account of the excessive air resistance the wheel was enclosed at the sides between sheet-metal disks. This wheel burst at 1775 revolutions per minute or at a linear speed of 372 feet per second. The hub and main spokes of the wheel remained nearly in place, but parts of the rim were found two hundred feet away. This sudden failure of the rim casing was unexpected, as it was thought the flange bolts were the parts to give way first. The tensile strength of the casing at the point of fracture was about four times the strength of the wheel rim at a solid section.

Stresses in Rotating Disks. — When a disk of uniform width is rotated, the max. stress S_t is tangential and at the bore of the hub, and the tangential stress is always greater than the radial stress at the same point on the disk. If S_t = maximum tangential stress in pounds per sq. in.; w = weight of material, lb. per cu. in.; N = rev. per min.; m = Poisson's ratio = 0.3 for steel; R = outer radius of disk, inches; r = inner radius of disk or radius of bore, inches.

$$S_t = 0.0000071wN^2[(3 + m)R^2 + (1 - m)r^2]$$

Steam Engine Flywheels. — The variable amount of energy during each stroke and the allowable percentage of speed variation are of especial importance in designing steam engine flywheels. The earlier the point of cut-off, the greater the variation in energy and the larger the flywheel that will be required. The weight of the reciprocating parts and the length of the connecting-rod also affect the variation. The following formula is used for computing the weight of the flywheel rim:

Let W = weight of rim in pounds;

        D = mean diameter of rim in feet;

        N = number of revolutions per minute;

        $\dfrac{1}{n}$ = allowable variation in speed (from 1/50 to 1/100);

        E = excess and deficiency of energy in foot-pounds;

        c = factor of energy excess, from the accompanying table;

    H.P. = indicated horsepower.

Then, if the indicated horsepower is given:

$$W = \frac{387,587,500 \times cn \times \text{H.P.}}{D^2 N^3} \tag{1}$$

If the work in foot-pounds is given, then:

$$W = \frac{11{,}745\, nE}{D^2N^2} \qquad (2)$$

In the second formula, E equals the average work in foot-pounds done by the engine in one revolution, multiplied by the decimal given in the accompanying

Factors for Engine Flywheel Calculations

Condensing Engines						
Fraction of stroke at which steam is cut off........	⅓	¼	⅕	⅙	⅐	⅛
Factor of energy excess...	0.163	0.173	0.178	0.184	0.189	0.191
Non-condensing Engines						
Steam cut off at........................			½	⅓	¼	⅕
Factor of energy excess..................			0.160	0.186	0.209	0.232

table, "Factors for Engine Flywheel Calculations," which covers both the condensing and non-condensing engines:

Example 1. — A non-condensing engine of 150 indicated horsepower is to make 200 revolutions per minute, with a speed variation of 2 per cent. The average cut-off is to be at one-quarter stroke, and the flywheel is to have a mean diameter of 6 feet. Required, the necessary weight of rim in pounds.

From the table $c = 0.209$, and from the data given H.P. = 150; $N = 200$; $\frac{1}{n} = \frac{1}{50}$ or $n = 50$; $D = 6$.

Substituting these values in equation (1):

$$W = \frac{387{,}587{,}500 \times 0.209 \times 50 \times 150}{6^2 \times 200^3} = 2110 \text{ pounds, nearly.}$$

Example 2. — A condensing engine, 24 × 42 inches, cuts off at one-third stroke and has a mean effective pressure of 50 pounds per square inch. The flywheel is to be 18 feet in mean diameter and make 75 revolutions per minute with a variation of 1 per cent. Required, weight of rim.

The work done on the piston in one revolution is equal to the pressure on the piston multiplied by the distance traveled or twice the stroke in feet. The area of the piston in this case is 452.4 square inches, and twice the stroke is 7 feet. The work done on the piston in one revolution is, therefore, 452.4 × 50 × 7 = 158,340 foot-pounds. From the table $c = 0.163$, and therefore:

$$E = 158{,}340 \times 0.163 = 25{,}810 \text{ foot-pounds.}$$

From the data given: $n = 100$; $D = 18$; $N = 75$. Substituting these values in equation (2):

$$W = \frac{11{,}745 \times 100 \times 25{,}810}{18^2 \times 75^2} = 16{,}650 \text{ pounds, nearly.}$$

Spokes or Arms of Flywheels. — Flywheel arms are usually of elliptical cross-section. The major axis of the ellipse is in the plane of rotation to give the arms greater resistance to bending stresses and reduce the air resistance which may be considerable at high velocity. The stresses in the arms may be severe, due to the inertia of a heavy rim when sudden load changes occur. The strength of the arms should equal three-fourths the strength of the shaft in torsion.

If W equals the width of the arm at the hub (length of major axis) and D equals the shaft diameter, then W equals 1.3 D for a wheel having 6 arms; and for an 8-arm wheel W equals 1.2 D. The thickness of the arm at the hub (length of minor axis) equals one-half the width. The arms usually taper toward the rim. The cross-sectional area at the rim should not be less than two-thirds the area at the hub.

Flywheels for Motor-driven Planers. — The primary function of a flywheel for a motor-driven planer is not so much for maintaining a constant speed as relieving the motor from excessive shocks at the points of reversal. Tests made at the Worcester Polytechnic Institute with a 36- by 36- by 10-foot planer driven by a 10-horsepower induction motor showed a current consumption of 1.85 kilowatt-hour when no flywheel was used and the length of the stroke was five feet. With a ten-foot stroke, the consumption was 1.63 kilowatt-hour without a flywheel. When a flywheel was used, the consumption was 1.3 and 1.24 kilowatt-hour, respectively, for the two lengths of stroke mentioned. Thus, with the flywheel, 29.5 per cent less power was required with the short stroke, and 24 per cent less power with the long stroke. The flywheel was also an advantage in increasing the average rate of production and preventing "slow-downs" and tardy reversals.

Critical Speed of Rotating Body. — If a body or disk mounted upon a shaft rotates about it, the center of gravity of the body or disk must be at the center of the shaft, if a perfect running balance is to be obtained. In most cases, however, the center of gravity of the disk will be slightly removed from the center of the shaft, owing to the difficulty of perfect balancing. Now, if the shaft and disk be rotated, the centrifugal force generated by the heavier side will be greater than that generated by the lighter side geometrically opposite to it, and the shaft will deflect toward the heavier side, causing the center of the disk to rotate in a small circle. These conditions hold true up to a comparatively high speed; but a point is eventually reached (at several thousand revolutions per minute) when momentarily there will be excessive vibration, and then the parts will run quietly again. The speed at which this occurs is called the *critical speed* of the wheel, and the phenomenon itself is called the *settling* of the wheel. The explanation of the settling is that at this speed the axis of rotation changes, and the wheel and shaft, instead of rotating about their geometrical center, begin to rotate about an axis through their center of gravity. The shaft itself is then deflected so that for every revolution its geometrical center traces a circle around the center of gravity of the rotating mass.

Critical speeds depend upon the magnitude or location of the load or loads carried by the shaft, the length of the shaft, its diameter and the kind of supporting bearings. The normal operating speed of a machine may or may not be higher than the critical speed. For instance, some steam turbines exceed the critical speed, although they do not run long enough at the critical speed for the vibrations to build up to an excessive amplitude. The practice of the General Electric Co. at Schenectady is to keep below the critical speeds. It is assumed that the maximum speed of a machine may be within 20 per cent of the critical speed without vibration troubles. Thus, in a design of steam turbine sets, critical speed is a factor that determines the size of the shafts, both for the generators and turbines. While a machine may run very close to the critical speed, the alignment and play of the bearings, the balance and construction generally, will require extra care, resulting in a more expensive machine; moreover, while such a machine may run smoothly for a considerable time, any looseness or play that may develop later, causing a slight unbalance, will immediately set up excessive vibrations.

Formulas for Critical Speeds. — The critical speed formulas given in the accompanying table (from the paper on Critical Speed Calculation presented

Critical Speed Formulas

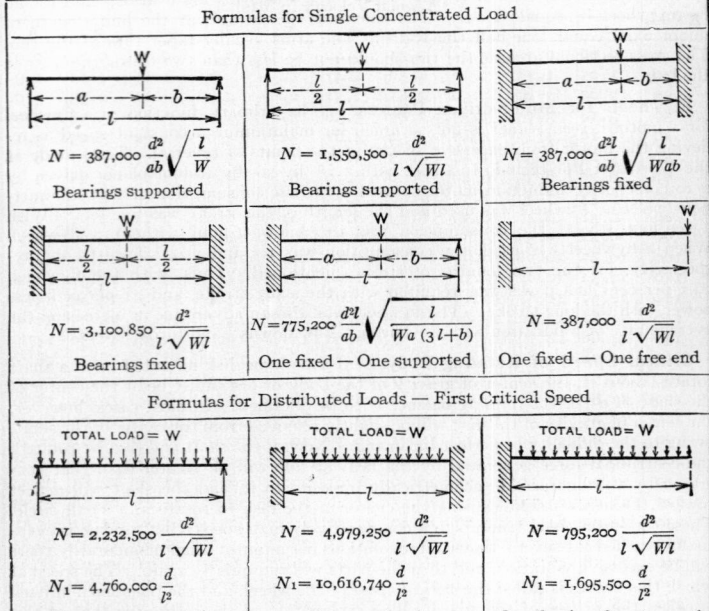

Formulas for Single Concentrated Load

$$N = 387,000 \frac{d^2}{ab} \sqrt{\frac{l}{W}}$$

Bearings supported

$$N = 1,550,500 \frac{d^2}{l\sqrt{Wl}}$$

Bearings supported

$$N = 387,000 \frac{d^2 l}{ab} \sqrt{\frac{l}{Wab}}$$

Bearings fixed

$$N = 3,100,850 \frac{d^2}{l\sqrt{Wl}}$$

Bearings fixed

$$N = 775,200 \frac{d^2 l}{ab} \sqrt{\frac{l}{Wa(3l+b)}}$$

One fixed — One supported

$$N = 387,000 \frac{d^2}{l\sqrt{Wl}}$$

One fixed — One free end

Formulas for Distributed Loads — First Critical Speed

TOTAL LOAD = W

$$N = 2,232,500 \frac{d^2}{l\sqrt{Wl}}$$

$$N_1 = 4,760,000 \frac{d}{l^2}$$

Bearings supported

TOTAL LOAD = W

$$N = 4,979,250 \frac{d^2}{l\sqrt{Wl}}$$

$$N_1 = 10,616,740 \frac{d}{l^2}$$

Bearings fixed

TOTAL LOAD = W

$$N = 795,200 \frac{d^2}{l\sqrt{Wl}}$$

$$N_1 = 1,695,500 \frac{d}{l^2}$$

One fixed — One free end

N = critical speed, R.P.M.; N_1 = critical speed of shaft alone; d = diameter of shaft, in inches; W = load applied to shaft, in pounds; l = distance between centers of bearings, in inches; a and b = distances from bearings to load.

before the A.S.M.E. by S. H. Weaver) apply to (1) shafts with single concentrated loads and (2) shafts carrying uniformly distributed loads. These formulas also cover different conditions as regards bearings. If the bearings are self-aligning or very short, the shaft is considered supported at the ends; whereas, if the bearings are long and rigid, the shaft is considered fixed. These formulas, for both concentrated and distributed loads, apply to vertical shafts as well as horizontal shafts, the critical speeds having the same value in both cases. The data required for the solution of critical speed problems are the same as for shaft deflection. As the shaft is usually of variable diameter and its stiffness is increased by a long hub, an ideal shaft of uniform diameter and equal stiffness must be assumed.

In calculating critical speeds, the weight of the shaft is either neglected or, say, one-half to two-thirds of the weight is added to the concentrated load. The formulas apply to steel shafts having a modulus of elasticity $E = 29,000,000$. While a shaft carrying a number of loads or a distributed load may have an infinite number of critical speeds, ordinarily it is the first critical speed that is of importance in engineering work, which is the speed obtained by the formulas given in the table for distributed loads.

Angular Velocity in Radians for Given Number of Revolutions per Minute

R.P.M.	Angular Velocity in Radians									
	0	1	2	3	4	5	6	7	8	9
0	0.00	0.10	0.21	0.31	0.42	0.52	0.63	0.73	0.84	0.94
10	1.05	1.15	1.26	1.36	1.47	1.57	1.67	1.78	1.88	1.99
20	2.09	2.20	2.30	2.41	2.51	2.62	2.72	2.83	2.93	3.04
30	3.14	3.25	3.35	3.46	3.56	3.66	3.77	3.87	3.98	4.08
40	4.19	4.29	4.40	4.50	4.61	4.71	4.82	4.92	5.03	5.13
50	5.24	5.34	5.44	5.55	5.65	5.76	5.86	5.97	6.07	6.18
60	6.28	6.39	6.49	6.60	6.70	6.81	6.91	7.02	7.12	7.23
70	7.33	7.43	7.54	7.64	7.75	7.85	7.96	8.06	8.17	8.27
80	8.38	8.48	8.59	8.69	8.80	8.90	9.01	9.11	9.21	9.32
90	9.42	9.53	9.63	9.74	9.84	9.95	10.05	10.16	10.26	10.37
100	10.47	10.58	10.68	10.79	10.89	11.00	11.10	11.20	11.31	11.41
110	11.52	11.62	11.73	11.83	11.94	12.04	12.15	12.25	12.36	12.46
120	12.57	12.67	12.78	12.88	12.98	13.09	13.19	13.30	13.40	13.51
130	13.61	13.72	13.82	13.93	14.03	14.14	14.24	14.35	14.45	14.56
140	14.66	14.76	14.87	14.97	15.08	15.18	15.29	15.39	15.50	15.60
150	15.71	15.81	15.92	16.02	16.13	16.23	16.34	16.44	16.55	16.65
160	16.75	16.86	16.96	17.07	17.17	17.28	17.38	17.49	17.59	17.70
170	17.80	17.91	18.01	18.12	18.22	18.33	18.43	18.53	18.64	18.74
180	18.85	18.95	19.06	19.16	19.27	19.37	19.48	19.58	19.69	19.79
190	19.90	20.00	20.11	20.21	20.32	20.42	20.52	20.63	20.73	20.84
200	20.94	21.05	21.15	21.26	21.36	21.47	21.57	21.68	21.78	21.89
210	21.99	22.10	22.20	22.30	22.41	22.51	22.62	22.72	22.83	22.93
220	23.04	23.14	23.25	23.35	23.46	23.56	23.67	23.77	23.88	23.98
230	24.09	24.19	24.29	24.40	24.50	24.61	24.71	24.82	24.92	25.03
240	25.13	25.24	25.34	25.45	25.55	25.66	25.76	25.87	25.97	26.07
250	26.18	26.28	26.39	26.49	26.60	26.70	26.81	26.91	27.02	27.12
260	27.23	27.33	27.44	27.54	27.65	27.75	27.85	27.96	28.06	28.17
270	28.27	28.38	28.48	28.59	28.69	28.80	28.90	29.01	29.11	29.22
280	29.32	29.43	29.53	29.64	29.74	29.84	29.95	30.05	30.16	30.26
290	30.37	30.47	30.58	30.68	30.79	30.89	31.00	31.10	31.21	31.31
300	31.42	31.52	31.62	31.73	31.83	31.94	32.04	32.15	32.25	32.36
310	32.46	32.57	32.67	32.78	32.88	32.99	33.09	33.20	33.30	33.41
320	33.51	33.61	33.72	33.82	33.93	34.03	34.14	34.24	34.35	34.45
330	34.56	34.66	34.77	34.87	34.98	35.08	35.19	35.29	35.39	35.50
340	35.60	35.71	35.81	35.92	36.02	36.13	36.23	36.34	36.44	36.55
350	36.65	36.76	36.86	36.97	37.07	37.18	37.28	37.38	37.49	37.59
360	37.70	37.80	37.91	38.01	38.12	38.22	38.33	38.43	38.54	38.64
370	38.75	38.85	38.96	39.06	39.16	39.27	39.37	39.48	39.58	39.69
380	39.79	39.90	40.00	40.11	40.21	40.32	40.42	40.53	40.63	40.74
390	40.84	40.94	41.05	41.15	41.26	41.36	41.47	41.57	41.68	41.78
400	41.89	41.99	42.10	42.20	42.31	42.41	42.52	42.62	42.73	42.83
410	42.93	43.04	43.14	43.25	43.35	43.46	43.56	43.67	43.77	43.88
420	43.98	44.09	44.19	44.30	44.40	44.51	44.61	44.71	44.82	44.92
430	45.03	45.13	45.24	45.34	45.45	45.55	45.66	45.76	45.87	45.97
440	46.08	46.18	46.29	46.39	46.50	46.60	46.70	46.81	46.91	47.02
450	47.12	47.23	47.33	47.44	47.54	47.65	47.75	47.86	47.96	48.07
460	48.17	48.28	48.38	48.48	48.59	48.69	48.80	48.90	49.00	49.11
470	49.22	49.32	49.43	49.53	49.64	49.74	49.85	49.95	50.06	50.16
480	50.26	50.37	50.47	50.58	50.68	50.79	50.89	51.00	51.10	51.21
490	51.31	51.42	51.52	51.63	51.73	51.84	51.94	52.05	52.15	52.26

Degrees Expressed in Radians

Deg.	Rad.	Deg.	Rad.	Deg.	Rad.	Deg.	Rad.	Deg.	Rad.	Deg.	Rad.
1	0.0175	31	0.5411	61	1.0647	91	1.5882	121	2.1118	151	2.6354
2	0.0349	32	0.5585	62	1.0821	92	1.6057	122	2.1293	152	2.6529
3	0.0524	33	0.5760	63	1.0996	93	1.6232	123	2.1468	153	2.6704
4	0.0698	34	0.5934	64	1.1170	94	1.6406	124	2.1642	154	2.6878
5	0.0873	35	0.6109	65	1.1345	95	1.6581	125	2.1817	155	2.7053
6	0.1047	36	0.6283	66	1.1519	96	1.6755	126	2.1991	156	2.7227
7	0.1222	37	0.6458	67	1.1694	97	1.6930	127	2.2166	157	2.7402
8	0.1396	38	0.6632	68	1.1868	98	1.7104	128	2.2340	158	2.7576
9	0.1571	39	0.6807	69	1.2043	99	1.7279	129	2.2515	159	2.7751
10	0.1745	40	0.6981	70	1.2217	100	1.7453	130	2.2689	160	2.7925
11	0.1920	41	0.7156	71	1.2392	101	1.7628	131	2.2864	161	2.8100
12	0.2094	42	0.7330	72	1.2566	102	1.7802	132	2.3038	162	2.8274
13	0.2269	43	0.7505	73	1.2741	103	1.7977	133	2.3213	163	2.8449
14	0.2443	44	0.7679	74	1.2915	104	1.8151	134	2.3387	164	2.8623
15	0.2618	45	0.7854	75	1.3090	105	1.8326	135	2.3562	165	2.8798
16	0.2793	46	0.8029	76	1.3265	106	1.8500	136	2.3736	166	2.8972
17	0.2967	47	0.8203	77	1.3439	107	1.8675	137	2.3911	167	2.9147
18	0.3142	48	0.8378	78	1.3614	108	1.8850	138	2.4086	168	2.9322
19	0.3316	49	0.8552	79	1.3788	109	1.9024	139	2.4260	169	2.9496
20	0.3491	50	0.8727	80	1.3963	110	1.9199	140	2.4435	170	2.9671
21	0.3665	51	0.8901	81	1.4137	111	1.9373	141	2.4609	171	2.9845
22	0.3840	52	0.9076	82	1.4312	112	1.9548	142	2.4784	172	3.0020
23	0.4014	53	0.9250	83	1.4486	113	1.9722	143	2.4958	173	3.0194
24	0.4189	54	0.9425	84	1.4661	114	1.9897	144	2.5133	174	3.0369
25	0.4363	55	0.9599	85	1.4835	115	2.0071	145	2.5307	175	3.0543
26	0.4538	56	0.9774	86	1.5010	116	2.0246	146	2.5482	176	3.0718
27	0.4712	57	0.9948	87	1.5184	117	2.0420	147	2.5656	177	3.0892
28	0.4887	58	1.0123	88	1.5359	118	2.0595	148	2.5831	178	3.1067
29	0.5061	59	1.0297	89	1.5533	119	2.0769	149	2.6005	179	3.1241
30	0.5236	60	1.0472	90	1.5708	120	2.0944	150	2.6180	180	3.1416

Minutes Expressed in Radians

Min.	Rad.	Min.	Rad.	Min.	Rad.	Min.	Rad.	Min.	Rad.	Min.	Rad.
1	0.0003	11	0.0032	21	0.0061	31	0.0090	41	0.0119	51	0.0148
2	0.0006	12	0.0035	22	0.0064	32	0.0093	42	0.0122	52	0.0151
3	0.0009	13	0.0038	23	0.0067	33	0.0096	43	0.0125	53	0.0154
4	0.0012	14	0.0041	24	0.0070	34	0.0099	44	0.0128	54	0.0157
5	0.0015	15	0.0044	25	0.0073	35	0.0102	45	0.0131	55	0.0160
6	0.0017	16	0.0047	26	0.0076	36	0.0105	46	0.0134	56	0.0163
7	0.0020	17	0.0049	27	0.0079	37	0.0108	47	0.0137	57	0.0166
8	0.0023	18	0.0052	28	0.0081	38	0.0111	48	0.0140	58	0.0169
9	0.0026	19	0.0055	29	0.0084	39	0.0113	49	0.0143	59	0.0172
10	0.0029	20	0.0058	30	0.0087	40	0.0116	50	0.0145	60	0.0175

Radians Expressed in Degrees, Minutes and Seconds

Rad.	Angle	Rad.	Angle	Rad.	Angle	Rad.	Angle	Rad.	Angle
0.001	0° 3' 26"	0.008	0° 27' 30"	0.06	3° 26' 16"	0.4	22° 55' 6"	2.0	114° 35' 30"
0.002	0 6 53	0.009	0 30 56	0.07	4 0 39	0.5	28 38 52	3.0	171 53 14
0.003	0 10 19	0.01	0 34 23	0.08	4 35 1	0.6	34 22 39	4.0	229 10 59
0.004	0 13 45	0.02	1 8 45	0.09	5 9 24	0.7	40 6 25	5.0	286 28 44
0.005	0 17 11	0.03	1 43 8	0.1	5 43 46	0.8	45 50 12	6.0	343 46 29
0.006	0 20 38	0.04	2 17 31	0.2	11 27 33	0.9	51 33 58	7.0	401 4 14
0.007	0 24 4	0.05	2 51 53	0.3	17 11 19	1.0	57 17 45	8.0	458 21 58

Angular Velocity. — The angular velocity of a rotating body is expressed in angular measure and equals the angle through which any radius of the body turns in one second. This angle is generally expressed in radians.

$$\text{One radian} = \frac{180}{\pi} = \frac{180}{3.1416} = 57.3 \text{ degrees.}$$

The angular velocity is generally denoted by the Greek letter ω. Let $\omega =$ angular velocity in radians; $r =$ radius of revolving body in feet; $n =$ number of revolutions per minute; $v =$ velocity of a point on the periphery, in feet per second; then,

$$v = \frac{2\pi r n}{60}; \qquad \omega = \frac{v}{r} = \frac{2\pi n}{60}; \qquad v = \omega r.$$

Example: — A flywheel, 12 feet in diameter, revolves at 60 revolutions per minute. Find the angular velocity ω. Here, $r = 6$; $n = 60$.

$$\omega = \frac{2 \times 3.1416 \times 60}{60} = 6.2832 \text{ radians.}$$

The table of angular velocity gives this velocity directly in radians for all numbers of revolutions per minute from 1 to 499. The method in which this table is used may be best explained by an example: Find the angular velocity in radians of a flywheel making 97 revolutions per minute. Locate 90 in the left-hand column and 7 at the top of the columns; at the intersection of the two lines, the angular velocity is read off as equal to 10.16 radians.

The Pendulum

A *simple pendulum* is a material point which is supposed to be suspended from a fixed point by a string without weight. A *compound pendulum* is a material body suspended from a fixed axis about which it oscillates by the force of gravity. The center of oscillation is the point at which, if all the matter in the compound pendulum were concentrated there, it would make a simple pendulum which would oscillate in the same periods of time. The angle included between the extreme positions of the line drawn from the point of suspension to the center of oscillation, is called the angle of oscillation. The time of vibration of a pendulum varies directly as the square root of the length and inversely as the square root of the acceleration due to gravity at the given latitude and elevation above the earth's surface. Hence, there is a definite length of a simple pendulum that vibrates seconds at any given place. At New York this length is 39.1017 inches or 3.2585 feet. In the formulas in the tables: $l =$ the length of simple pendulum or distance between point of suspension and center of oscillation, in inches; $t =$ time in seconds for n oscillations; $n =$ number of single oscillations in time t.

Simple Pendulum

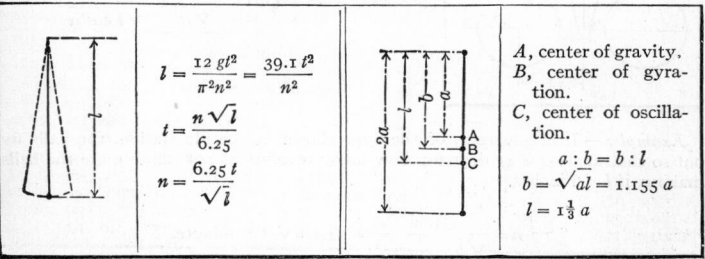

$$l = \frac{12\,gt^2}{\pi^2 n^2} = \frac{39.1\,t^2}{n^2}$$

$$t = \frac{n\sqrt{l}}{6.25}$$

$$n = \frac{6.25\,t}{\sqrt{l}}$$

A, center of gravity.
B, center of gyration.
C, center of oscillation.

$$a : b = b : l$$
$$b = \sqrt{al} = 1.155\,a$$
$$l = 1\tfrac{1}{3}\,a$$

Compound Pendulum

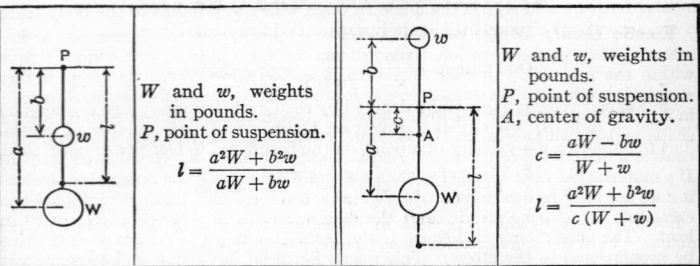

W and w, weights in pounds.
P, point of suspension.

$$l = \frac{a^2 W + b^2 w}{a W + b w}$$

W and w, weights in pounds.
P, point of suspension.
A, center of gravity.

$$c = \frac{aW - bw}{W + w}$$

$$l = \frac{a^2 W + b^2 w}{c\,(W + w)}$$

Conical Pendulum. — If a weight suspended by a cord revolves at a uniform speed along the circumference of a circle in a horizontal plane, this weight forms a conical pendulum and is held in equilibrium by three forces; the tension in the cord, the centrifugal force, and the force of gravity. Let r be the radius of the circular path in feet which the weight follows; h, the distance in feet of the plane in which the weight moves from the point of suspension; v, the velocity in feet per second of the center of gravity of the weight. Then, time t, in seconds for one revolution, is:

$$t = \frac{2\pi r}{v} = 6.283 \sqrt{\frac{h}{g}} \qquad h = \frac{g t^2}{4\pi^2} = 0.8146\, t^2$$

The principle of the conical pendulum is employed in the design of fly-ball governors for steam engines.

Application to Governors. — In the following formulas:

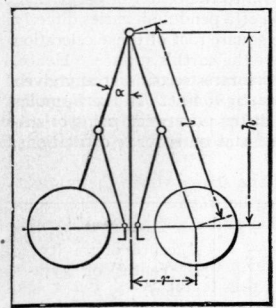

n = number of revolutions per minute;
g = acceleration due to gravity = 32.16;
α = angle made by the arm with the vertical axis;
h = vertical distance from center of ball to point of suspension, in feet;
l = length of arm, in feet.

$$n = \frac{60}{2\pi} \sqrt{\frac{g}{h}} = \frac{54.16}{\sqrt{h}} = \frac{54.16}{\sqrt{l \cos \alpha}}$$

$$h = \frac{2933}{n^2}.$$

Example: — In a governor, of the type shown in the illustration, the balls fly out so that angle $\alpha = 45$ degrees; how many revolutions per minute are the balls making, if $l = 6$ inches?

$$n = \frac{54.16}{\sqrt{\frac{1}{2} \times \cos 45^\circ}} = 91.1 \text{ rev. per minute.}$$

STRENGTH OF MATERIALS

Elastic Limit; Modulus of Elasticity. — When external forces act upon a material, they produce tension, compression, bending, shearing, or torsional stresses within the material. In most instances, a combination of two or more of these stresses is produced. All stresses to which a material is subjected cause a deformation in it. If the stress is not too great, however, the material will return to its original shape and dimensions when the external stress is removed. The property which enables a material to return to its original shape and dimensions is called its *elasticity*. If a material has been stressed to such an extent that, upon the removal of the load, it does not fully return to its original shape and dimensions, its *elastic limit* has been exceeded. Up to the elastic limit the deformation is directly proportional to the load. The elastic limit is defined as the point at which the deformation ceases to be proportional to the stress. This point, however, is difficult to determine with accuracy.

The *modulus of elasticity* of a material is the quotient obtained by dividing the stress per square inch by the elongation in one inch caused by this stress. The modulus of elasticity is generally denoted by E. If an elongation of 0.015 inch is produced in a steel bar, ten inches long, by a load of 45,000 pounds per each square inch of cross-section of the bar, then the modulus of elasticity will be:

$$E = \frac{45,000}{0.015 \div 10} = 30,000,000.$$

As the elongation is assumed to be proportional to the load up to the elastic limit, the modulus of elasticity of a material may be used for finding the elongation e produced by any load per square inch, S, or: $e = S \div E$.

For example, the modulus of elasticity of steel usually is 30,000,000. Find the elongation per inch produced by a stress of 15,000 pounds per square inch.

$$e = 15,000 \div 30,000,000 = 0.0005 \text{ inch.}$$

Factor of Safety. — The factor of safety may be considered as the product of four primary factors which may be designated as factors a, b, c and d. Designating the factor of safety by F,

$$F = a \times b \times c \times d.$$

The first of these factors a is the ratio of the ultimate strength of the material to the elastic limit, meaning, in this case, by the elastic limit, that boundary line within which the material is perfectly elastic and takes no permanent set. For ordinary materials, the factor a is 2; for nickel steel and oil tempered forgings, it is reduced to 1½.

The second factor b depends on the character of the stress within the material. This factor is 1, for a dead load; 2, for a load varying between zero and maximum; and 3, for a load which produces alternately a tension and a compression equal in amount.

The third factor c depends upon the manner in which the load is applied to the piece under stress. For a load gradually applied, this factor is 1. For a load suddenly applied, the factor is 2. If the load is applied not only suddenly but with impact, this factor must be still further increased in value. (See " Stresses in Beams Produced by Shocks.")

The last factor d may be called the factor of ignorance. The other factors provide against known conditions and this provides against the unknown. It commonly varies in value between 1½ and 3 and occasionally should be given as high a value as 10. It provides against accidental overload, against unexpectedly severe service and unreliable or imperfect materials, etc. When all the conditions are thoroughly known and there is no danger of overload, this factor may be made equal to 1½ for wrought iron and mild steel, and 2, for cast iron.

As an example of the use of the formula given for the factor of safety, find the factor of safety that ought to be used for a forged steel steam-engine piston-rod. The elastic limit will probably be slightly more than one-half the ultimate strength; hence, $a = 2$. The rod will be alternately in tension and compression; hence, $b = 3$. The steam pressure will be applied suddenly or nearly so; hence, $c = 2$. The material is of a reliable kind; hence, $d = 1½$. Then:

$$F = 2 \times 3 \times 2 \times 1½ = 18.$$

A table of factors of safety determined by the analytical method outlined, is given herewith.

Table of Factors of Safety

Class of Service	Factors				
	a	b	c	d	F
Boilers........................	2	1	1	2¼–3	4½– 6
Piston- and connecting-rods for double-acting engines	1½–2	3	2	1½	13½–18
Piston- and connecting-rod for single-acting engines	1½–2	2	2	1½	9–12
Shaft carrying bandwheel, flywheel, or armature	1½–2	3	1	1½	6¾– 9
Lathe spindles	2	2	2	1½	12
Mill shafting	2	3	2	2	24
Steel work in buildings............	2	1	1	2	4
Steel work in bridges	2	1	1	2½	5
Steel work for small work	2	1	2	1½	6
Cast-iron wheel rims	2	1	1	10	20
Steel wheel rims	2	1	1	4	8
Materials	Minimum Values				
Cast-iron and other castings	2	1	1	2	4
Wrought iron or mild steel	2	1	1	1½	3
Oil tempered or nickel steel	1½	1	1	1½	2¼
Hardened steel	1½	1	1	2	3
Bronze and brass, rolled or forged ..	2	1	1	1½	3

Strength and Properties of Tobin Bronze. — This special bronze contains from 59 to 63 per cent of copper, from ½ to 1½ per cent of tin, the remainder being zinc. It has a specific gravity of 8.4, the weight per cubic inch being 0.304 pound. On account of its tensile strength and its resistance to the corrosive action of sea water, it is used to a great extent in marine engineering. The ultimate tensile strength varies from 60,000 to 65,000 pounds per square inch, and the compressive strength from 170,000 to 180,000 pounds per square inch. The melting point is at 1600 degrees F. The non-liability of Tobin bronze to give forth sparks makes it valuable for powder plates and powder-mill tools.

Average Strength Data for Iron and Steel

For specifications of S.A.E. steels listed in this table, see section beginning page 1545

Material Letters (a) etc. Indicate Foot-notes	Ultimate Strength, Pounds per Square Inch			Yield Point, Pounds per Square Inch	Modulus of Elasticity Tension	Elongation in 2 Inches Per Cent
	Tension	Compression Footnote(m)	Shear			
Cast Iron, Soft	16,000	80,000	17,000	....	12,000,000	....
Cast Iron, Average	22,000	100,000	24,000	....	16,000,000	....
Cast Iron, Hard (a)	35,000	150,000	38,000	....	20,000,000	....
Cast Iron, High-test (b)	45,000	200,000	50,000	....	......	....
Castings, Malleable	54,000	....	48,000	36,000	25,000,000	18
Castings, Steel (c)	70,000	70,000	60,000	40,000	30,000,000	25
Carbon Steel (d)	56,000	56,000	42,000	28,000	29,000,000	30
Cold worked (e)	75,000	75,000	55,000	38,000	30,000,000	....
Casehardened (f)	80,000	80,000	60,000	50,000	30,000,000	20
Hardened, drawn (g)	120,000	120,000	90,000	90,000	30,000,000	15
Ductile Iron, *as cast* (n)	95,000	....	85,000	70,000	25,000,000	5
Annealed	70,000	....	63,000	55,000	25,000,000	20
Machinery Steel (h)	60,000	60,000	45,000	40,000	30,000,000	....
Nickel Steel (i)	130,000	130,000	98,000	100,000	30,000,000	18
S.A.E. No. 2330	145,000	145,000	110,000	120,000	30,000,000	18
S.A.E. No. 2340	165,000	165,000	125,000	150,000	30,000,000	12
Nickel-Chromium (j)	125,000	125,000	95,000	95,000	30,000,000	18
S.A.E. No. 3130	150,000	150,000	110,000	125,000	30,000,000	15
S.A.E. No. 3140	175,000	175,000	130,000	150,000	30,000,000	....
S.A.E. No. 3230	180,000	180,000	135,000	150,000	30,000,000	15
S.A.E. No. 3240	200,000	200,000	150,000	180,000	30,000,000	15
S.A.E. No. 3250	220,000	220,000	165,000	200,000	30,000,000	12
Rivet Steel	57,000	57,000	44,000	36,000	29,000,000	....
Stainless Steel (k)	225,000	225,000	....	185,000	....	9
Drawn 1290° F	120,000	120,000	....	90,000	....	22
Structural Steel	60,000	60,000	45,000	30,000	29,000,000	....
Steel Wire (l)	120,000	....	....	60,000	30,000,000	....
Annealed	80,000	....	....	40,000	29,000,000	....
Plow Steel	275,000	....	....	....	....	....
Music Wire	300,000	....	....	....	....	....
Wrought Iron	48,000	46,000	40,000	25,000	27,000,000	....

(a) Compressive strength of "white" and "high-test" irons may range from 175,000 to 250,000 lbs. per sq. in.
(b) Tensile strength may range from 40,000 to 70,000 or even higher.
(c) Heat-treated *alloy-steel* castings may have tensile strength up to 200,000 lbs. per sq. in.
(d) Soft open-hearth annealed steel.
(e) Yield-point range up to 60,000 according to amount of cold-working.
(f) Strength data for S.A.E. No. 1020 casehardened steel water-quenched and drawn to 400 deg. F.
(g) S.A.E. No. 1045, hardened in water, drawn to 800 deg. F.
(h) Some "machinery" steels have tensile strengths ranging up to 100,000.
(i) S.A.E. No. 2320. Strength data for all nickel steels listed based upon a drawing temperature of 800 deg. F. and oil-quenching.
(j) S.A.E. No. 3120. Nickel-chromium steels listed drawn to 800 deg. F.
(k) Strength data for steel drawn to 390 deg. F. Note also data for 1290 deg. F.
(l) Strength varies over wide range depending upon size and composition.
(m) For columns made of soft or medium steels, subjected to compressive and bending stresses combined, use yield point as value for ultimate compressive strength.
(n) A ductile cast iron containing magnesium.

Average Strength Data for Non-ferrous Metals — 1

Material. Letters (a) etc. Indicate Foot-notes	Elements Identifying Composition Approximate Percentages						Tensile Strength, Pounds per Square Inch	Yield Point, Pounds per Square Inch	Elongation in 2 Inches, Per Cent	Modulus of Elasticity, Tension
	Copper	Zinc	Tin	Lead	Aluminum	Iron				
Aluminum Casting(a)	7.75	0.20	....	....	90	....	19,000	....	1-2	10,300,000
S.A.E. No. 33.	7	2.5	....	....	87	1.50	21,000	....	1-2.5	
S.A.E. No. 37(b).	0.3	0.2	....	....	85	0.80	27,000	....	5-15	
S.A.E. No. 30(c).	4	....	....	....	90	1.00	36,000	....	0-2	
Aluminum Bronze Castings(d)	88	....	0.5	....	9	3.25	65,000	25,000	20	15,000,000
A.S.T.M.(e)	89.5	....	0.2	....	9.5	....	80,000	50,000	4	
S.A.E. No. 68.	86	....	....	....	8	3.50	65,000	20,000	20	
Aluminum Sheet(f)	....	....	....	....	99	....	12,000	....	15-30	10,300,000
No. 2 Half-hard.	....	....	....	....	99	....	16,000	....	3-7	
S.A.E. No. 26(g).	4	....	....	....	92	....	55,000	30,000	9-18	
Aluminum, Wrought(h)	4.5	....	....	....	92	....	60,000	....	16-22	....
S.A.E. No. 27(i).	4.5	....	....	....	92	3.50	50,000	22,000(i)	15-22	15,000,000
Aluminum Bronze, Wrought(j)	88	....	....	....	8	....	75,000	37,000	25	12,000,000
Brass Castings(k).	84	5	5	5	....	....	27,000	12,000	16	14,000,000
Yellow Brass No. 41.	63	33	1	....	....	....	25,000	12,000	20	15,000,000
Manganese Bronze(l)	57	42	....	0.15	....	....	45,000	30,000	27.5	14,000,000
Brass Sheet Quarter Hard(m)	66	33	....	0.3	....	....	52,000	....	15	
Half-hard.	66	33	....	0.3	....	....	67,000	....	5	
Hard.	66	33	....	0.3	....	....	80,000	....	5	
Extra-hard.	66	33	....	0.3	....	....	87,000	....	2	
Spring.	66	33	....	0.3	....	....	87,000	....	1	
Soft anneal.	66	33	....	0.3	....	....	40,000	....	42	

(a) Society of Automotive Engineers (S.A.E.) standard composition No. 30. Very generally used.

(b) Contains 12 to 13 per cent silicon. Resists salt water corrosion.

(c) Contains 2 per cent nickel, 1.4 magnesium, not over 0.7 silicon; heat-treated.

(d) Specification, American Society for Testing Materials (A.S.T.M.) for aluminum-bronze castings, Grade A.

(e) Castings of Grade B, heat-treated.

(f) A.S.T.M. standard. Temper No. 1 or "soft" sheet. Aluminum percentage is minimum.

(g) Same as "duralumin." Strength data for heat-treated sheets. Comp. includes 0.2–0.75% magnesium and 0.4–1.0% manganese.

(h) S.A.E. alloy No. 27, fully heat-treated. It contains 0.5–1.1 per cent manganese and 0.5–1.1 per cent silicon.

(i) Strength data applies to "solution" heat-treatment which makes alloy more workable. Yield-point range, 15,000–30,000.

(j) S.A.E. No. 69. Minimum strength data for annealed or hot-rolled bars.

(k) S.A.E. cast-brass alloy No. 40 known as "red brass."

(l) S.A.E. cast-brass alloy No. 43 commonly known as "manganese bronze."

(m) Commercial "high brass" sheet commonly used for drawing, stamping and bending. A.S.T.M. specification. Five tempers listed beginning with quarter-hard.

Average Strength Data for Non-ferrous Metals — 2

Material Letters (n) etc. Indicate Foot-notes	Elements Identifying Composition Approximate Percentages					Tensile Strength, Pounds per Square Inch	Yield Point, Pounds per Square Inch	Elongation in 2 Inches, Per Cent	Modulus of Elasticity, Tension
	Copper	Zinc	Tin	Lead	Iron				
Brass Rod(n)	60	39	0.7	0.3	...	60,000	30,000	30	15,000,000
Brass Wire	66	34	...	...	...	80,000	...	...	14,000,000
Bronze Castings(o)	87	2	10	0.2	...	30,000	15,000	14	......
Valve Bronze	88	4	6.5	1.5	...	32,000	16,000	17	......
88-8-4 Bronze	88	4	8	...	...	35,000	15,000	15	......
Phosphor-bronze(p)	80	0.75	9	9	...	25,000	12,000	8	......
Gear Bronze(q)	89	...	9	9	...	35,000	20,000	10	......
Bronze Strip(r)	94	0.2	5	0.1	0.1	55,000	...	15	15,000,000
Hard Grade A	94	0.2	5	0.1	0.1	75,000	...	5	
Extra Hard Grade A	94	0.2	5	0.1	0.1	85,000	...	2	
Half Hard Grade B	91	0.2	8	0.1	0.1	65,000	...	20	
Extra Hard Grade B	91	0.2	8	0.1	0.1	100,000	...	1	
Phosphor Bronze Wire(s)	94	0.2	5	0.1	0.1	115,000	...	...	15,900,000
Copper Sheet, Soft	99.5	...	...	...	...	36,000	...	25	15,600,000
Copper Sheet, Hard	99.5	...	...	...	...	40,000	...	8	
Copper Wire, Soft	...	...	...	...	...	37,000	...	30	
Copper Wire, Hard	...	...	...	...	...	60,000	...	...	
Lead Pipe	...	...	...	...	...	2,200	...	...	
Lead, Sheet	...	...	...	...	...	3,000	...	...	......
Magnesium Alloys(t)	...	...	...	...	...	28,000	7,000	9	6,500,000
Magnesium Alloy, Wrought(u)	...	...	...	...	...	40,000	28,000	10	
Magnesium Alloy, Cast(v)	...	...	...	...	...	35,000	18,000	2	......

(n) Naval brass or Tobin bronze rods for structural purposes and adapted to hot-forging. A.S.T.M. specification.

(o) S.A.E. No. 62 general utility bronze.

(p) S.A.E. specification No. 64. Phosphorus content, 0.05-0.25 per cent.

(q) S.A.E. specification No. 65. Phosphorus content, 0.10, 0.30 per cent.

(r) Phosphor bronze—commonly used for flat springs. S.A.E. No. 77; Grade A half-hard. Maximum-phosphorus, 0.4 per cent in Grade A; and 0.2 per cent in Grade B.

(s) S.A.E. No. 81. Primarily for springs. Contains up to 0.4 per cent phosphorus. The wire should withstand bending through an angle of 180 degrees flat back on itself without fracture on the outside of the bent portion.

(t) Downmetal -castings, not heat-treated. Magnesium, 93.7 per cent; aluminum, 6 per cent; manganese, 0.3 per cent.

(u) Same composition as (t) but in wrought condition.

(v) Heat-treated Downmetal castings for high yield point and hardness. Maximum, Magnesium, 89.9 per cent; aluminum, 10 per cent; manganese, 0.1 per cent.

Average Ultimate Strength of Common Materials other than Metals
(Pounds per square inch)

Material	Compression	Tension
Bricks, best hard..........................	12,000	400
Bricks, light red..........................	1,000	40
Brickwork, common........................	1,000	50
Brickwork, best...........................	2,000	300
Cement, Portland, one month old...........	2,000	400
Cement, Portland, one year old............	3,000	500
Concrete, Portland........................	1,000	200
Concrete, Portland, one year old...........	2,000	400
Granite...................................	19,000	700
Limestone and sandstone...................	9,000	300
Trap rock.................................	20,000	800
Slate.....................................	14,000	500
Vulcanized Fiber..........................	39,000	13,000

Influence of Temperature on the Strength of Metals

Material	Degrees Fahrenheit							
	210	400	570	750	930	1100	1300	1475
	Strength in Per Cent of Strength at 70 Degrees F.							
Wrought iron.....	104	112	116	96	76	42	25	15
Cast iron.........	....	100	99	92	76	42	....	....
Steel castings.....	109	125	121	97	57	....	....	....
Structural steel....	103	132	122	86	49	28	....	....
Copper...........	95	85	73	59	42	....	....	....
Bronze...........	101	94	57	26	18	....	....	....

Strength of Copper-zinc-tin Alloys
(U. S. Government Tests)

Percentage of			Tensile Strength, Lbs. per Sq. In.	Percentage of			Tensile Strength, Lbs. per Sq. In.	Percentage of			Tensile Strength, Lbs. per Sq. In.
Copper	Zinc	Tin		Copper	Zinc	Tin		Copper	Zinc	Tin	
45	50	5	15,000	60	20	20	10,000	75	20	5	45,000
50	45	5	50,000	65	30	5	50,000	75	15	10	45,000
50	40	10	15,000	65	25	10	42,000	75	10	15	43,000
55	43	2	65,000	65	20	15	30,000	75	5	20	41,000
55	40	5	62,000	65	15	20	18,000	80	15	5	45,000
55	35	10	32,500	65	10	25	12,000	80	10	10	45,000
55	30	15	15,000	70	25	5	45,000	80	5	15	47,500
60	37	3	60,000	70	20	10	44,000	85	10	5	43,500
60	35	5	52,500	70	15	15	37,000	85	5	10	46,500
60	30	10	40,000	70	10	20	30,000	90	5	5	42,000

General Factors of Safety

Material	Steady Load	Load Varying from Zero to Maximum in one Direction	Load Varying from Zero to Maximum in both Directions	Suddenly Varying Loads and Shocks
Cast iron............	6	10	15	20
Wrought iron........	4	6	8	12
Steel...............	5	6	8	12
Wood...............	8	10	15	20
Brick..............	15	20	25	30
Stone..............	15	20	25	30

General Formulas for the Strength of Materials.— In the following formulas:

A = area of cross-section of material in square inches;

E = modulus of elasticity;

I = moment of inertia of section about an axis passing through the center of gravity;

I_p = polar moment of inertia of section;

M_b = maximum bending moment in inch-pounds;

M_t = moment of force tending to twist (torsional moment) in inch-pounds;

P = total stress in pounds;

y = distance from center of gravity to most remote fiber;

S = permissible working stress in pounds per square inch;

Z = section modulus for bending (moment of resistance);

Z_p = section modulus for torsion;

e = elongation or shortening in inches;

l = length in inches.

For tension and compression:

$$P = A \times S; \qquad e = \frac{Pl}{AE}.$$

For shear:

$$P = A \times S.$$

Assume permissible working stress for shear to equal about four-fifths the permissible stress in tension.

For bending:

$$M_b = \frac{SI}{y} = SZ.$$

For torsion:

$$M_t = \frac{SI_p}{y} = SZ_p.$$

The rule expressed by the formula above, that the section modulus for torsion Z_p equals the polar moment of inertia I_p, divided by the distance y from the center of gravity to the most remote fiber, holds true only for circular sections, but may also be applied with fair accuracy to sections nearly circular. For other cross-sections, the section modulus of torsion does not equal the polar moment of inertia divided by the distance from the center of gravity to the most remote fiber. For-

Physical Properties of Molding Plastics

Molding Plastic Compound	Specific Gravity (Water = 1)	Tensile Strength (Pounds per square inch)	Impact Strength (Ft.-lbs. per inch of notch) (Izod)	Flexural Strength (Pounds per square inch)	Modulus of Elasticity (100,000 × Values Given)	Molding Shrinkage (Inches per Inch)	Heat Resistance Continuous (Max, Deg. F.)	Distortion Temp. (Deg. F.)	Water Absorption* (Per cent gain)
Phenolic — General Purpose	1.35–1.44	6500–8500	0.26–0.40	8800–13,000	8.8–9.5	.006–.008	302	284–302	0.5–0.6
Phenolic — Shock Resistant — 1	1.37	7500–8500	0.4–0.56	10,000	10	.0075–.009	302	275	0.49
Phenolic — Shock Resistant — 2	1.38	5300–6500	0.60–0.90	6300–11,000	10–15	.0065	250	.....	0.90
Phenolic — Shock Resistant — 3	1.37	6000–7000	1.12–1.82	9000	10	.0035–.0085	240	.....	1.00
Phenolic — Shock Resistant — 4	1.37	6300–7100	3.8–5.4	8000–11,000	10	.0035	240	.....	0.63–1.0
Phenolic — Heat Resistant — 1	1.65	4600–5500	0.26–0.32	8000	17	.0047–.0051	400	275–302	0.18
Phenolic — Heat Resistant — 2	1.89–1.93	4500–6000	0.30–1.00	8000–10,000	10–20	.0035–.0085	400–450	230–266	.046–.08
Urea	1.47–1.52	9500–12,000	0.30–0.36	10,000–14,000	11–17	.0065–.0080	212	171–176	0.25–0.35
Polystyrene (Compression molded)	1.07	5500–6500	0.40–0.70	6500–7500	4–6	.004–.005	150–170	171–176	0.05‡
Polystyrene (Injection molded)	1.07	6500–7000	0.8–1.2	14,000–19,000	3.75–4.25	.002–.008	150–170	.....	.....
Cellulose Acetate — Class I	1.26–1.40	2500–9500	1.4–4.0	5000–15,000	.....	.005–.010	.....	140–212	2.75
Cellulose Acetate — Class II	1.26–1.40	2500–9500	1.4–4.0	5000–15,000	.....	.002–.008	.....	158–250	2.00
Cellulose Acetate Butyrate	1.14–1.22	2500–7500	0.8–5.5	2800–13,000	2.0–3.5	.002–.009	140–250	136–200	0.8–2.0†
Ethyl-Cellulose	1.14	6000–9000	0.6–1.8	4000–12,000	1–4	.004–.007	140–180	130–150	0.5–1.5†
Methyl-Methacrylate	1.18–1.19	4000–6000	0.2–0.4	10,000–15,000	.....	.001–.006	120–140	125–160	0.4–0.5†
Vinyl Chloride Acetate (No filler)	1.34–1.36	8000–10,000	0.6–1.2	10,000–13,000	3.5–4.1	.001 max.	.....	140–150	0.05–0.15†

* Gain after 48 hours immersion. ‡ Gain after 318 hours immersion. † Gain after 24 hours immersion. Manufacturers should be consulted concerning the selection and application of these plastic compounds.

Note: The figures in this table are intended as a general guide only.

mulas giving the approximate section modulus for torsion for other than circular cross-sections, will be found under the head, "Polar Moment of Inertia and Polar Section Modulus." The permissible working stress for torsion may be assumed as four-fifths the permissible stress in tension.

Examples: — 1. A structural steel bar is to support (in tension) a load of 40,000 pounds. The load is gradually applied and then, after having reached its maximum value, gradually removed. Find the diameter of bar required.

From the accompanying tables: Ultimate strength of structural steel = 60,000 pounds per square inch. Factor of safety to use in present case = 6. Hence, safe working stress = 60,000 ÷ 6 = 10,000 pounds per square inch. Inserting the known values in formula $P = A \times S$:

$$40,000 = A \times 10,000; \text{ hence } A = 4 \text{ square inches.}$$

The diameter of a bar, the cross-section of which is 4 square inches, is $2\frac{1}{4}$ inches, approximately.

2. What would be the total elongation of the bar in the previous example under full load, if the bar were 5 feet long?

$$e = \frac{Pl}{AE} = \frac{40,000 \times 5 \times 12}{4 \times 30,000,000} = 0.020 \text{ inch.}$$

3. A square bar, firmly held at one end, is supporting a load of 3000 pounds at the outer free end. The length of the bar is $2\frac{1}{2}$ feet. The bar is made of structural steel, and the load is steady. Find the size of bar required for safe loading.

M_b = load × lever arm in inches = 3000 × 30 = 90,000.
S = safe stress = 60,000 ÷ 5 = 12,000.
$I = s^4 \div 12$ for a square, if s = side of square.
$y = s \div 2$ in present case.

Hence:

$$M_b = \frac{SI}{y}, \text{ or } 90,000 = \frac{12,000 \times s^4}{12 \times \frac{1}{2}s} = \frac{12,000\, s^3}{6}.$$
$$s^3 = 45, \text{ or } s = 3.56 \text{ inches.}$$

4. A square bar is subjected to a steady torsional moment of 90,000 inch-pounds. The bar is made of structural steel. Find the size of bar required for safe loading.

M_t = 90,000.
$S = (60,000 \times \frac{4}{5}) \div 5 = 9600.$
$Z_p = \frac{2}{9}s^3$ for a square, if s = side of square.

Hence:

$$M_t = SZ_p, \text{ or } 90,000 = 9600 \times \frac{2}{9}s^3;$$
$$s^3 = 42.2, \text{ approx., or } s = 3.48 \text{ inches.}$$

Formulas for Combined Bending and Torsion. — The subject of combined bending and torsion is one that has proved more confusing to machine designers than any other phase of the strength of materials that is usually encountered by the mechanical engineer engaged in ordinary machine design. Prof. A. Lewis Jenkins, in a paper presented before the annual meeting of the American Society of Mechanical Engineers in December, 1917, thoroughly analyzes the subject and gives formulas which may be directly applied by machine designers when the bending moment, the twisting moment and the permissible working stress are known. Two formulas are given, one for the design of shafts of brittle materials and one for soft ductile materials.

Grashof Formula for Brittle Materials. — The following formula, known as the Grashof formula, may be used for the design of shafts and similar machine parts constructed of brittle materials, such as cast iron, hardened or annealed tool steel, hard bronze, and other materials having a small contraction of area when tested in tension:

$$SZ = \tfrac{3}{8} M_b + \tfrac{5}{8} \sqrt{M_b^2 + M_t^2} \qquad (1)$$

in which

S = permissible or working stress in tension;

Z = rectangular (ordinary) section modulus;

M_b = bending moment to which member is subjected;

M_t = torsional moment to which member is subjected.

Formula for Soft Ductile Materials. — For the design of parts made of soft or ductile materials, such as mild (low-carbon or machine) steel, copper, soft brass and soft steel tubing, the following formulas should be used:

$$S_s Z_p = 1.3 \sqrt{M_b^2 + M_t^2} \qquad (2)$$

in which

Z_p = polar section modulus,

S_s = permissible or working stress in shear,

the notation otherwise being the same as above.

The accompanying table gives values for the unit tensile and unit shearing stresses at the yield point of a number of different materials. By using a suitable factor of safety, the permissible working stresses may be obtained from this table.

Stresses at Yield Point of Different Materials

Material	Average Stress at Yield Point, Lbs. per Sq. In.	
	Tensile	Shearing
Machine steel (mild carbon steel).........	47,000	30,000
Rivet steel.............................	39,000	24,000
High-carbon steel......................	60,000	27,000
Nickel steel...........................	70,000	37,000
Steel tubing...........................	22,000	13,000

When the preceding formulas are applicable, the Guest formula, which follows, and the use of which has been advocated often, will be found unnecessary. It would perhaps be desirable if the Guest formula were not so generally recommended, because it applies only to ductile materials of circular cross-section and if used for hard or brittle materials will result in erroneous and unsuitable dimensions.

Guest Formula. — The Guest formula for parts subjected to combined bending and torsional stresses was published in 1900 by J. J. Guest as the result of experiments made by him. It is applicable to parts of circular cross-section and when such material as mild steel (machine) steel) is used. The stress S_s in this formula may be assumed to be equal to the safe shearing or torsional stress. The formula is:

$$\text{Combined moment} = \sqrt{M_b^2 + M_t^2} = S_s Z_p \qquad (3)$$

This formula may be used in the design of shafting, etc. See also page 512. The following example illustrates the application of formula (2).

Example: — Assume a square bar of structural steel to be subjected to combined bending and torsional moments. The bending moment is 90,000 inch-pounds and the torsional moment is 90,000 inch-pounds. Find the size of a square bar required to withstand the combined moment safely. Using formula (2) for mild steel parts subjected to combined bending and torsional stresses:

$$S_s Z_p = 1.3 \sqrt{90,000^2 + 90,000^2} = 165,460 \text{ approximately.}$$

The safe unit-stress for shear is assumed as four-fifths or five-sixths of the permissible stress in tension; hence for structural steel the safe unit-stress equals $(60,000 \times \frac{4}{5} \div 5)$ or 9600 pounds per square inch; $Z_p = 0.22 s^3$ in which s equals the side of the square; therefore

$$165,460 = S_s Z_p = 9600 \times 0.22 s^3,$$
$$s^3 = 78.34 \text{ and } s = 4\tfrac{9}{32} \text{ inches.}$$

Stresses in Machine Parts

Shape of Machine Parts. — While the size of machine parts depends mainly upon the magnitude of the stresses, their shape depends to a large extent upon the manner or direction in which the load or strain is brought to bear upon them. If a part is subjected to tension only, that is, merely resists a force tending to pull it apart, then the shape is not very material, although a round rod, which is most compact and generally cheapest, is the best. Almost any other shape is satisfactory however, but it is well to avoid using thin and broad parts, as the strain might then be brought upon one edge instead of uniformly distributed over the whole area, and cause a stress in one part of the cross-section greater than that for which the material is adapted.

A machine part that is to resist compression only, should have a shape similar to that required for resisting tension, except when the proportion of its length to its diameter or thickness is such that it will be likely to buckle or bend. This will take place, in many cases, when the length exceeds five or six times the diameter and it then becomes desirable to use a hollow or cross-ribbed form of construction, with the metal as far from the axis of the piece as possible. A hollow cylindrical form is most effective, although a hollow, square or cross-ribbed form may be adopted for reasons of appearance or cheapness of production.

When a piece is designed to resist bending, it should have its greatest depth of material in the direction in which the force is applied, because the capacity of a piece to resist bending as indicated by the formula for the section modulus, increases as the square of its thickness or depth in the direction of the force, and only directly as its width. Thus, to increase the depth of a beam two or three times in the direction of the force, would increase its capacity to resist bending four or nine times; while to increase its width two or three times, would only increase its strength two or three times. The proportion of depth and width must, of course, not be carried to an extreme, as there then would be a tendency for the piece to buckle or yield sideways.

Stresses in Castings. — The stresses in castings due to shrinkage in cooling often increase, to a considerable extent, the stresses due to the load. If all parts of a casting could be made to cool equally fast, there would be little trouble from this source, but as different parts of the casting vary in thickness, the time required for cooling varies, and stressses are set up which are sometimes great enough to rupture the casting without any additional load being placed upon it. In the case of a pulley, the hub, on cooling, tends to draw the arms away from the rim. As these strains are primarily due to unequal cooling, it is evident that in order to reduce them to the lowest point, it is necessary to make the different parts of the casting as nearly uniform in thickness as possible. This, however, is not always feasible and in cases when it is not, a liberal allowance should be made for the internal stresses, by using a larger factor of safety when calculating for the external load.

Economical Sections for a Given Strength or Stiffness to Resist Bending.
— When a material such as steel is used, which has practically the same properties in tension as compression, the most economical form of beam cross-section for vertical loading only, that is, a load in a single direction, is a beam of I-section, as shown in Fig. 1. For both vertical and horizontal loading, that is, for loading in two directions at right angles to each other, a beam of hollow rectangular section,

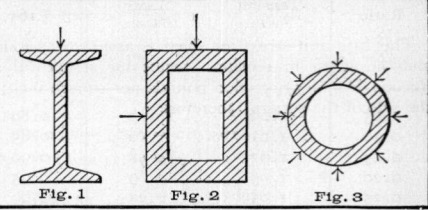

as shown in Fig. 2, will require the least amount of material for a given strength and stiffness. If the load is the same in the horizontal as in the vertical direction then the cross-section will be a hollow square. For equal loading in any direction, a hollow circular section, Fig. 3, should be used.

Stresses Due to Changes of Temperature.
— If a bar of metal is confined in a space so that it is prevented from expanding or contracting, stresses will be induced in it if it is subjected to temperature changes. These stresses are termed "temperature stresses," and their magnitude is measured by the amount of compression or elongation. If T = change in temperature in degrees F.; S = stress produced by the temperature change, per square inch; C = coefficient of linear expansion; and E = modulus of elasticity, then: $S = C \times T \times E$.

The values of the coefficient of linear expansion for one degree F. equals 0.0000074, for high-carbon steel; 0.0000065, for mild (machine) steel; 0.0000062, for cast iron; and 0.0000068, for wrought iron.

Bending Stresses Combined with Direct Tension or Compression.
— In U-shaped machine parts, such as, for example, punch or shear frames, the metal in the back of the frame resists a uniformly distributed tensile stress, due to the pressure between the jaws, and also a stress due to the bending moment set up by the same pressure. The maximum tensile stress, therefore, is composed of the sum of this uniformly distributed stress and the stress due to the bending moment. If the pressure on a machine part is in such a direction that the stresses induced are partly compression and partly bending stresses, then the stress due to direct compression is added to the compressive stress due to bending, in order to find the total compressive stress to which the machine part is subjected.

Shear Stresses Combined with Tension or Compression Stresses.
— The rather complicated calculations necessary in cases where shear stresses are combined with tension or compression stresses may be avoided by using the accompanying table which gives factors by means of which the maximum combined unit shear and the maximum combined unit tension or compression may be determined, when the forces causing shear and tension or compression are known. For example, assume that the unit shear S, as produced by the force causing shear alone, is 9000 pounds per square inch, and that the unit tension or compression T, produced by the force that causes tension or compression only, is 12,000 pounds per square inch. Then the ratio $S \div T = 0.75$, and from the table it is then found that the tension (or compression) factor $x = 1.401$ for this ratio of S to T. This means that in this case the maximum combined tension will be 1.401 times what it would have been if there had been no shear. The shear factor y is 1.20, indicating that the maximum combined shear stress is 1.20 times what it would have been if there had been no tension or compression stresses. If the separate unit stresses are known, therefore, the total combined stresses may be quickly determined by this table.

Shear Stresses Combined with Tension or Compression Stresses

Ratio $\frac{S}{T}$	Tension Factor	Shear Factor	Ratio $\frac{S}{T}$	Tension Factor	Shear Factor
	x	y		x	y
0.05	1.002	10.05	0.80	1.44	1.18
0.10	1.010	5.10	0.85	1.49	1.16
0.15	1.022	3.48	0.90	1.53	1.14
0.20	1.038	2.69	0.95	1.57	1.13
0.25	1.059	2.24	1.00	1.62	1.12
0.30	1.083	1.94	1.05	1.66	1.11
0.35	1.110	1.74	1.10	1.71	1.10
0.40	1.140	1.60	1.15	1.75	1.09
0.45	1.173	1.49	1.20	1.80	1.08
0.50	1.207	1.41	1.25	1.85	1.08
0.55	1.243	1.35	1.30	1.89	1.07
0.60	1.281	1.30	1.35	1.94	1.07
0.65	1.320	1.26	1.40	1.99	1.06
0.70	1.360	1.23	1.45	2.03	1.06
0.75	1.401	1.20	1.50	2.08	1.05

Ratio $\frac{T}{S}$	Shear Factor	Tension Factor	Ratio $\frac{T}{S}$	Shear Factor	Tension Factor
	y	x		y	x
0.05	1.0003	20.50	0.80	1.077	1.85
0.10	1.0012	10.51	0.85	1.086	1.78
0.15	1.0028	7.18	0.90	1.096	1.72
0.20	1.0050	5.52	0.95	1.107	1.67
0.25	1.0078	4.53	1.00	1.118	1.62
0.30	1.0112	3.87	1.05	1.129	1.57
0.35	1.0152	3.40	1.10	1.141	1.54
0.40	1.0198	3.04	1.15	1.153	1.50
0.45	1.0250	2.77	1.20	1.166	1.47
0.50	1.0308	2.56	1.25	1.179	1.44
0.55	1.0371	2.38	1.30	1.193	1.42
0.60	1.0440	2.24	1.35	1.206	1.39
0.65	1.0515	2.11	1.40	1.221	1.37
0.70	1.0595	2.01	1.45	1.235	1.35
0.75	1.0680	1.92	1.50	1.250	1.33

Combined Torsion and Compression. — Propeller shafts of steamers and vertical shafts carrying considerable weight, are subjected to combined torsion and compression. Let P_1 = maximum resultant compressive stress; P_2 = maximum resultant shearing stress; C = the compressive stress due to the thrust; S = the shearing stress due to the twisting moment. Then,

$$P_1 = \tfrac{1}{2}\left(C + \sqrt{C^2 + 4S^2}\right); \qquad P_2 = \tfrac{1}{2}\sqrt{C^2 + 4S^2}$$

Moments of Inertia, Section Moduli, etc., of Sections

Section A = area y = distance from axis to extreme fiber	Moment of Inertia I	Section Modulus $Z = \dfrac{I}{y}$	Radius of Gyration $r = \sqrt{\dfrac{I}{A}}$
 $A = a^2;\quad y = \tfrac{1}{2}a$	$\dfrac{a^4}{12}$	$\dfrac{a^3}{6}$	$\dfrac{a}{\sqrt{12}} = 0.289\,a$
 $A = a^2;\quad y = a$	$\dfrac{a^4}{3}$	$\dfrac{a^3}{3}$	$\dfrac{a}{\sqrt{3}} = 0.577\,a$
 $A = a^2$ $y = \dfrac{a}{\sqrt{2}} = 0.707\,a$	$\dfrac{a^4}{12}$	$\dfrac{a^3}{6\sqrt{2}} = 0.118\,a^3$	$\dfrac{a}{\sqrt{12}} = 0.289\,a$
 $A = a^2 - b^2;\ y = \tfrac{1}{2}a$	$\dfrac{a^4 - b^4}{12}$	$\dfrac{a^4 - b^4}{6a}$	$\sqrt{\dfrac{a^2 + b^2}{12}}$ $= 0.289\,\sqrt{a^2 + b^2}$
 $A = a^2 - b^2$ $y = \dfrac{a}{\sqrt{2}} = 0.707\,a$	$\dfrac{a^4 - b^4}{12}$	$\dfrac{\sqrt{2}\,(a^4 - b^4)}{12\,a}$ $= 0.118\,\dfrac{a^4 - b^4}{a}$	$\sqrt{\dfrac{a^2 + b^2}{12}}$ $= 0.289\,\sqrt{a^2 + b^2}$
 $A = bd;\quad y = \tfrac{1}{2}d$	$\dfrac{bd^3}{12}$	$\dfrac{bd^2}{6}$	$\dfrac{d}{\sqrt{12}} = 0.289\,d$

Moments of Inertia, Section Moduli, etc., of Sections

A = area y = distance from axis to extreme fiber	Moment of Inertia I	Section Modulus $Z = \dfrac{I}{y}$	Radius of Gyration $r = \sqrt{\dfrac{I}{A}}$
$A = bd; \quad y = d$	$\dfrac{bd^3}{3}$	$\dfrac{bd^2}{3}$	$\dfrac{d}{\sqrt{3}} = 0.577\,d$
$A = bd - hk$ $y = \frac{1}{2}d$	$\dfrac{bd^3 - hk^3}{12}$	$\dfrac{bd^3 - hk^3}{6\,d}$	$\sqrt{\dfrac{bd^3 - hk^3}{12\,(bd - hk)}}$ $= 0.289\sqrt{\dfrac{bd^3 - hk^3}{bd - hk}}$
$A = bd$ $y = \dfrac{bd}{\sqrt{b^2 + d^2}}$	$\dfrac{b^3d^3}{6\,(b^2 + d^2)}$	$\dfrac{b^2d^2}{6\sqrt{b^2 + d^2}}$	$\dfrac{bd}{\sqrt{6\,(b^2 + d^2)}}$ $= 0.408\dfrac{bd}{\sqrt{b^2 + d^2}}$
$A = bd$ $y = \frac{1}{2}\,(d\cos\alpha + b\sin\alpha)$	$\dfrac{bd}{12}\,(d^2\cos^2\alpha + b^2\sin^2\alpha)$	$\dfrac{bd}{6}\left(\dfrac{d^2\cos^2\alpha + b^2\sin^2\alpha}{d\cos\alpha + b\sin\alpha}\right)$	$\sqrt{\dfrac{d^2\cos^2\alpha + b^2\sin^2\alpha}{12}}$ $= 0.289 \times$ $\sqrt{d^2\cos^2\alpha + b^2\sin^2\alpha}$
$A = \frac{1}{2}bd; \quad y = \frac{2}{3}d$	$\dfrac{bd^3}{36}$	$\dfrac{bd^2}{24}$	$\dfrac{d}{\sqrt{18}} = 0.236\,d$
$A = \frac{1}{2}bd; \quad y = d$	$\dfrac{bd^3}{12}$	$\dfrac{bd^2}{12}$	$\dfrac{d}{\sqrt{6}} = 0.408\,d$

Moments of Inertia, Section Moduli, etc.

Section	Area of Section, A	Distance from Neutral Axis to Extreme Fiber, y
	$$\frac{d\,(a+b)}{2}$$	$$\frac{d\,(a+2\,b)}{3\,(a+b)}$$
	$$\frac{3\,d^2 \tan 30^\circ}{2} = 0.866\,d^2$$	$$\frac{d}{2}$$
	$$\frac{3\,d^2 \tan 30^\circ}{2} = 0.866\,d^2$$	$$\frac{d}{2 \cos 30^\circ} = 0.577\,d$$
	$2\,d^2 \tan 22\tfrac{1}{2}^\circ = 0.828\,d^2$	$$\frac{d}{2}$$
	$$\frac{\pi d^2}{4} = 0.7854\,d^2$$	$$\frac{d}{2}$$
	$$\frac{\pi\,(D^2 - d^2)}{4}$$ $$= 0.7854\,(D^2 - d^2)$$	$$\frac{D}{2}$$
	$$\frac{\pi d^2}{8} = 0.393\,d^2$$	$$\frac{(3\pi - 4)\,d}{6\pi}$$ $$= 0.288\,d$$
	$$\frac{\pi\,(R^2 - r^2)}{2}$$ $$= 1.5708\,(R^2 - r^2)$$	$$\frac{4\,(R^3 - r^3)}{3\pi\,(R^2 - r^2)}$$ $$= 0.424\,\frac{R^3 - r^3}{R^2 - r^2}$$

Moments of Inertia, Section Moduli, etc.

Moment of Inertia, I	Section Modulus. $Z = \dfrac{I}{y}$	Radius of Gyration, $r = \sqrt{\dfrac{I}{A}}$
$\dfrac{d^3\,(a^2 + 4\,ab + b^2)}{36\,(a + b)}$	$\dfrac{d^2\,(a^2 + 4\,ab + b^2)}{12\,(a + 2\,b)}$	$\sqrt{\dfrac{d^2\,(a^2 + 4\,ab + b^2)}{18\,(a + b)^2}}$
$\dfrac{A}{12}\left[\dfrac{d^2\,(1 + 2\cos^2 30°)}{4\cos^2 30°}\right]$ $= 0.06\,d^4$	$\dfrac{A}{6}\left[\dfrac{d\,(1 + 2\cos^2 30°)}{4\cos^2 30°}\right]$ $= 0.12\,d^3$	$\sqrt{\dfrac{d^2\,(1 + 2\cos^2 30°)}{48\cos^2 30°}}$ $= 0.264\,d$
$\dfrac{A}{12}\left[\dfrac{d^2\,(1 + 2\cos^2 30°)}{4\cos^2 30°}\right]$ $= 0.06\,d^4$	$\dfrac{A}{6.9}\left[\dfrac{d\,(1 + 2\cos^2 30°)}{4\cos^2 30°}\right]$ $= 0.104\,d^3$	$\sqrt{\dfrac{d^2\,(1 + 2\cos^2 30°)}{48\cos^2 30°}}$ $= 0.264\,d$
$\dfrac{A}{12}\left[\dfrac{d^2\,(1 + 2\cos^2 22\frac{1}{2}°)}{4\cos^2 22\frac{1}{2}°}\right]$ $= 0.055\,d^4$	$\dfrac{A}{6}\left[\dfrac{d\,(1 + 2\cos^2 22\frac{1}{2}°)}{4\cos^2 22\frac{1}{2}°}\right]$ $= 0.109\,d^3$	$\sqrt{\dfrac{d^2\,(1 + 2\cos^2 22\frac{1}{2}°)}{48\cos^2 22\frac{1}{2}°}}$ $= 0.257\,d$
$\dfrac{\pi d^4}{64} = 0.049\,d^4$	$\dfrac{\pi d^3}{32} = 0.098\,d^3$	$\dfrac{d}{4}$
$\dfrac{\pi\,(D^4 - d^4)}{64}$ $= 0.049\,(D^4 - d^4)$	$\dfrac{\pi\,(D^4 - d^4)}{32\,D}$ $= 0.098\,\dfrac{D^4 - d^4}{D}$	$\dfrac{\sqrt{D^2 + d^2}}{4}$
$\dfrac{(9\,\pi^2 - 64)\,d^4}{1152\,\pi}$ $= 0.007\,d^4$	$\dfrac{(9\,\pi^2 - 64)\,d^3}{192\,(3\,\pi - 4)}$ $= 0.024\,d^3$	$\dfrac{\sqrt{(9\,\pi^2 - 64)\,d^2}}{12\,\pi}$ $= 0.132\,d$
$0.1098\,(R^4 - r^4)$ $-\ \dfrac{0.283\,R^2 r^2\,(R - r)}{R + r}$	$\dfrac{I}{y}$	$\sqrt{\dfrac{I}{A}}$

Moments of Inertia, Section Moduli, etc.

Section	Area of Section, A	Distance from Neutral Axis to Extreme Fiber, y
	$\pi ab = 3.1416\, ab$	a
	$\pi (ab - cd)$ $= 3.1416\, (ab - cd)$	a
	$dt + 2\,a\,(s + n)$	$\dfrac{d}{2}$
	$dt + 2\,a\,(s + n)$	$\dfrac{b}{2}$
	$dt + a\,(s + n)$	$\dfrac{d}{2}$
	$dt + a\,(s + n)$	$b - [b^2 s + \dfrac{h t^2}{2} + \dfrac{g}{3}(b - t)^2$ $\times (b + 2\,t)] \div A$ in which g = slope of flange = $\dfrac{h - l}{2\,(b - t)}$
	$\dfrac{l\,(T + t)}{2} + Tn + a\,(s + n)$	$d - [3\,s^2\,(b - T)$ $+ 2\,am\,(m + 3\,s) + 3\,Td^2$ $- l\,(T - t)(3\,d - l)] \div 6\,A$

Moments of Inertia, Section Moduli, etc.

Moment of Inertia, I	Section Modulus, $Z = \dfrac{I}{y}$	Radius of Gyration, $r = \sqrt{\dfrac{I}{A}}$
$\dfrac{\pi a^3 b}{4} = 0.7854\,a^3 b$	$\dfrac{\pi a^2 b}{4} = 0.7854\,a^2 b$	$\dfrac{a}{2}$
$\dfrac{\pi}{4}(a^3 b - c^3 d)$ $= 0.7854\,(a^3 b - c^3 d)$	$\dfrac{\pi(a^3 b - c^3 d)}{4\,a}$ $= 0.7854\,\dfrac{a^3 b - c^3 d}{a}$	$\dfrac{1}{2}\sqrt{\dfrac{a^3 b - c^3 d}{ab - cd}}$
$\dfrac{1}{12}\left[bd^3 - \dfrac{1}{4\,g}(h^4 - l^4) \right]$ in which $g =$ slope of flange $= \dfrac{h-l}{b-t} = \dfrac{1}{6}$ for standard I-beams.	$\dfrac{1}{6\,d}\left[bd^3 - \dfrac{1}{4\,g}(h^4 - l^4) \right]$	$\sqrt{\dfrac{\dfrac{1}{12}\left[bd^3 - \dfrac{1}{4\,g}(h^4 - l^4) \right]}{dt + 2\,a\,(s+n)}}$
$\dfrac{1}{12}\left[b^3(d-h) + lt^3 \right.$ $\left. + \dfrac{g}{4}(b^4 - t^4) \right]$ in which $g =$ slope of flange (see above).	$\dfrac{1}{6\,b}\left[b^3(d-h) + lt^3 \right.$ $\left. + \dfrac{g}{4}(b^4 - t^4) \right]$	$\sqrt{\dfrac{I}{A}}$
$\dfrac{1}{12}\left[bd^3 - \dfrac{1}{8\,g}(h^4 - l^4) \right]$ in which $g =$ slope of flange $= \dfrac{h-l}{2(b-t)} = \dfrac{1}{6}$ for standard channels.	$\dfrac{1}{6\,d}\left[bd^3 - \dfrac{1}{8\,g}(h^4 - l^4) \right]$	$\sqrt{\dfrac{\dfrac{1}{12}\left[bd^3 - \dfrac{1}{8\,g}(h^4 - l^4) \right]}{dt + a\,(s+n)}}$
$\dfrac{1}{3}\left[2\,sb^3 + lt^3 + \dfrac{g}{2}(b^4 - t^4) \right]$ $- A\,(b-y)^2$ in which $g =$ slope of flange (see above).	$\dfrac{I}{y}$	$\sqrt{\dfrac{I}{A}}$
$\dfrac{1}{12}[\,l^3(T+3\,t) + 4\,bn^3$ $- 2\,am^3] - A\,(d-y-n)^2$	$\dfrac{I}{y}$	$\sqrt{\dfrac{I}{A}}$

Moments of Inertia, Section Moduli, etc.

Section	Area of Section, A	Distance from Neutral Axis to Extreme Fiber, y
	$\dfrac{l(T+t)}{2} + Tn$ $+ a(s+n)$	$\dfrac{b}{2}$
	$t(2a-t)$	$a - \dfrac{a^2 + at - t^2}{2(2a-t)}$
	$t(2a-t)$	$\dfrac{a^2 + at - t^2}{2(2a-t)\cos 45°}$
	$bd - h(b-t)$	$\dfrac{d}{2}$
	$bd - h(b-t)$	$\dfrac{b}{2}$
	$bd - h(b-t)$	$\dfrac{d}{2}$
	$bd - h(b-t)$	$b - \dfrac{2b^2 s + ht^2}{2bd - 2h(b-t)}$
	$dt + s(b-t)$	$\dfrac{d}{2}$

Moments of Inertia, Section Moduli, etc.

Moment of inertia, I	Section Modulus, $Z = \dfrac{I}{y}$	Radius of Gyration, $r = \sqrt{\dfrac{I}{A}}$
$\dfrac{sb^3 + mT^3 + lt^3}{12}$ $+ \dfrac{am\,[2\,a^2 + (2\,a + 3\,T)^2]}{36}$ $+ \dfrac{l\,(T-t)[(T-t)^2 + 2\,(T+2t)^2]}{144}$	$\dfrac{I}{y}$	$\sqrt{\dfrac{I}{A}}$
$\tfrac{1}{3}\,[ty^3 + a\,(a-y)^3$ $- (a-t)\,(a-y-t)^3]$	$\dfrac{I}{y}$	$\sqrt{\dfrac{I}{A}}$
$\tfrac{1}{3}\,[2\,x^4 - 2\,(x-t)^4$ $+ t\,[a - (2\,x - \tfrac{1}{2}\,t)]^3]$ in which $x = \dfrac{a^2 + at - t^2}{2\,(2\,a - t)}$	$\dfrac{I}{y}$	$\sqrt{\dfrac{I}{A}}$
$\dfrac{bd^3 - h^3\,(b-t)}{12}$	$\dfrac{bd^3 - h^3\,(b-t)}{6\,d}$	$\sqrt{\dfrac{bd^3 - h^3\,(b-t)}{12\,[bd - h(b-t)]}}$
$\dfrac{2\,sb^3 + ht^3}{12}$	$\dfrac{2\,sb^3 + ht^3}{6\,b}$	$\sqrt{\dfrac{2\,sb^3 + ht^3}{12\,[bd - h\,(b-t)]}}$
$\dfrac{bd^3 - h^3\,(b-t)}{12}$	$\dfrac{bd^3 - h^3\,(b-t)}{6\,d}$	$\sqrt{\dfrac{bd^3 - h^3\,(b-t)}{12\,[bd - h\,(b-t)]}}$
$\dfrac{2\,sb^3 + ht^3}{3} - A\,(b-y)^2$	$\dfrac{I}{y}$	$\sqrt{\dfrac{I}{A}}$
$\dfrac{td^3 + s^3\,(b-t)}{12}$	$\dfrac{td^2 + s^3\,(b-t)}{6\,d}$	$\sqrt{\dfrac{td^3 + s^3\,(b-t)}{12\,[td + s\,(b-t)]}}$

Moments of Inertia, Section Moduli, etc.

Section	Area of Section, A	Distance from Neutral Axis to Extreme Fiber, y
	$bs + ht + as$	$d - [td^2 + s^2(b-t)$ $+ s(a-t)(2d-s)] \div 2A$
	$bs + ht$	$d - \dfrac{d^2t + s^2(b-t)}{2(bs + ht)}$
	$bs + \dfrac{h(T+t)}{2}$	$d - [3bs^2 + 3ht(d+s)$ $+ h(T-t)(h+3s)] \div 6A$
	$t(a+b-t)$	$b - \dfrac{t(2d+a) + d^2}{2(d+a)}$
	$t(a+b-t)$	$a - \dfrac{t(2c+b) + c^2}{2(c+b)}$
	$t[b + 2(a-t)]$	$\dfrac{b}{2}$
	$t[b + 2(a-t)]$	$\dfrac{2a-t}{2}$

Moments of Inertia, Section Moduli, etc.

Moment of Inertia, I	Section Modulus, $Z = \dfrac{I}{y}$	Radius of Gyration, $r = \sqrt{\dfrac{I}{A}}$
$\frac{1}{3}[b(d-y)^3 + ay^3 - (b-t)(d-y-s)^3 - (a-t)(y-s)^3]$	$\dfrac{I}{y}$	$\sqrt{\dfrac{I}{A}}$
$\frac{1}{3}[ty^3 + b(d-y)^3 - (b-t)(d-y-s)^3]$	$\dfrac{I}{y}$	$\sqrt{\dfrac{1}{3(bs+ht)}[ty^3 + b(d-y)^3 - (b-t)(d-y-s)^3]}$
$\frac{1}{12}[4bs^3 + h^3(3t+T)] - A(d-y-s)^2$	$\dfrac{I}{y}$	$\sqrt{\dfrac{I}{A}}$
$\frac{1}{3}[ty^3 + a(b-y)^3 - (a-t)(b-y-t)^3]$	$\dfrac{I}{y}$	$\sqrt{\dfrac{1}{3t(a+b-t)}[ty^3 + a(b-y)^3 - (a-t)(b-y-t)^3]}$
$\frac{1}{3}[ty^3 + b(a-y)^3 - (b-t)(a-y-t)^3]$	$\dfrac{I}{y}$	$\sqrt{\dfrac{1}{3t(a+b-t)}[ty^3 + b(a-y)^3 - (b-t)(a-y-t)^3]}$
$\dfrac{ab^3 - c(b-2t)^3}{12}$	$\dfrac{ab^3 - c(b-2t)^3}{6b}$	$\sqrt{\dfrac{ab^3 - c(b-2t)^3}{12t[b+2(a-t)]}}$
$\dfrac{b(a+c)^3 - 2c^3d - 6a^2cd}{12}$	$\dfrac{b(a+c)^3 - 2c^3d - 6a^2cd}{6(2a-t)}$	$\sqrt{\dfrac{b(a+c)^3 - 2c^3d - 6a^2cd}{12t[b+2(a-t)]}}$

Tables of Moments of Inertia, Section Moduli, etc. — On the preceding pages are given tables of the moments of inertia and other properties of forty-two different cross-sections of such outlines as are most frequently met with in structural steel shapes or in cast-iron designs. The tables give the area of the section and the distance y from the neutral axis to the extreme fiber, in each case. In some cases, where the formulas for the section modulus and radius of gyration are very lengthy, the formula for the section modulus, for example, has been simply given as $\dfrac{I}{y}$. The radius of gyration is sometimes given as $\sqrt{\dfrac{I}{A}}$, when the complete formula would be too long to put into the space available.

Stresses in a Loaded Ring. — The load that may be safely carried by a ring loaded as indicated by the accompanying engraving is found from the formula:

$$P = \frac{2\,S\pi I}{Dy}$$

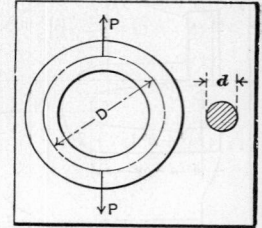

in which P = load on ring, in pounds; D = mean diameter of ring, in inches; S = allowable working stress in pounds per square inch; I = moment of inertia of section; y = distance from the center of gravity of the section to the most remote fiber, in inches.

For a ring of circular section, where d equals the diameter of the bar from which the ring is made:

$$P = 0.617\,S\,\frac{d^3}{D} \qquad S = 1.621\,P\,\frac{D}{d^3}$$

These formulas are especially applicable to loaded rings in which the diameter d is small in proportion to the mean diameter D, because it is only in such cases that the bending action becomes important. For loaded rings having an internal diameter small in proportion to the diameter of the stock, as in the case of eyebolts, the formulas would not apply, because then the metal is stressed largely in direct tension, and the formulas would give excessive dimensions.

Strength of Taper Pins. — The mean diameter of taper pin required to safely transmit a known turning moment, may be found from the formulas:

$$d = 1.13\sqrt{\frac{PR}{DS}} \quad \cdots \quad (1), \quad \text{and} \quad d = 283\sqrt{\frac{\text{H.P.}}{NDS}} \quad \cdots \quad (2)$$

in which formulas PR = turning moment in inch-pounds; S = safe unit stress = 6000 pounds per square inch; H.P. = horsepower transmitted; N = number of revolutions per minute; and d and D denote dimensions shown in the engraving.

Examples: — A lever secured to a 2-inch round shaft by a steel tapered pin (dimension d = ⅜ inch) has a pull of 50 pounds at a 30-inch radius from shaft center. Find S, the unit working stress on the pin. By transposing Formula (1):

$$S = \frac{1.27\,PR}{Dd^2} = \frac{1.27 \times 50 \times 30}{2 \times (\tfrac{3}{8})^2} = 6770$$

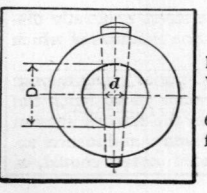

pounds per square inch (nearly), which is a safe unit working stress for machine steel in shear.

Let P = 50 pounds, R = 30 inches, D = 2 inches, and S = 6000 pounds unit working stress. Using Formula (1) to find d:

$$d = 1.13\sqrt{\frac{PR}{DS}} = 1.13\sqrt{\frac{50 \times 30}{2 \times 6000}} = 1.13\sqrt{\frac{1}{8}} = 0.4 \text{ inch.}$$

Section Modulus, Area, etc., of Sections for Punch and Shear Frames. — Machine frames cannot be standardized so as to permit tables of section modulus, area, etc., of the sections to be made up in the same way as for standard structural steel sections, but it is possible to arrange a table for punch and shear frames so as to simplify the work of selecting proper sections. A table of these quantities is, therefore, given. To illustrate the use of the table, take as an example the punch frame shown diagrammatically in Fig. 1. The distance from the center line of the punch to the back of the gap is 24 inches. Assume that the maximum pressure P, tending to force the jaws apart, is that due to punching a 1-inch circular hole in soft steel plate 1 inch thick, or say about 157,000 pounds. Consider the section at TX. The action of P is such as to produce a tensile stress on the section to the left of the neutral axis N, with a compressive stress to the right of N, both due to

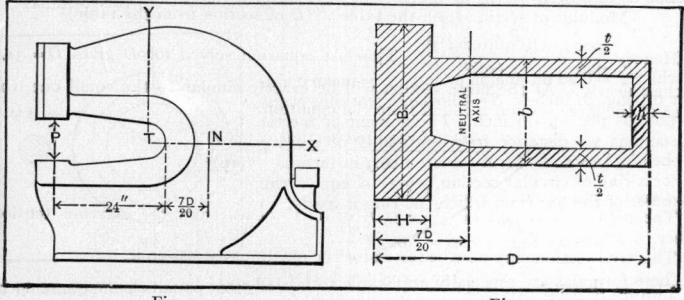

Fig. 1   Fig. 2

flexure; and, besides, there is a tensile stress distributed uniformly over the section. It is usually sufficient to determine the maximum tensile stress to the left of N.

Maximum tensile stress = flexure tensile stress + uniformly distributed tensile stress.

$$\text{Flexure tensile stress} = \frac{\text{Moment of } P \text{ about } N}{\text{Tensile section modulus of section } TX}$$

$$\text{Uniformly distributed tensile stress} = \frac{P}{\text{Area of section } TX}$$

Assume that D, in Fig. 2, is about 30 inches. Then $\frac{7 D}{20} = 10\frac{1}{2}$ inches. If 3000 pounds per square inch is the allowable fiber stress, and the stress due to flexure only is considered, the required section modulus for tension would be:

$$\frac{157,000 \times (24 + 10\frac{1}{2})}{3000} = 1800, \text{ about.}$$

As no allowance has been made for the additional tensile stress uniformly distributed over the section, a section must be selected the section modulus of which is somewhat greater than 1800, say about 2500.

The table of " Properties of Sections for Punch and Shear Frames" gives a great variety of shapes and proportions, the only dimensions common to all being the depth of section, D, and the distance of the neutral axis from the extreme tension fiber. This location of the neutral axis represents average practice and insures an economical distribution of metal. Generous fillets and rounded corners should, of course, be used on the actual section.

Suppose that a deep narrow section is desired, similar to that in Fig. 2, in which the dimensions are as follows: $D = 10$ inches; $B = 7$ inches; $b = 4$ inches; $H = 1.98$ inch; $\frac{1}{2} t = h = \frac{5}{8}$ inch; F (area) $= 26.3$ square inches; and Z_t (section modulus for tension) $= 78.6$. This section, taken from the table, is not, of course, large enough, but a similar one which is large enough may be easily found as follows:

If two sections A and B are similar in all respects, then

$$\frac{\text{Area of } A}{\text{Area of } B} = \frac{(\text{Any dimension of } A)^2}{(\text{Corresponding dimension of } B)^2},$$

and

$$\frac{\text{Section modulus of } A}{\text{Section modulus of } B} = \frac{(\text{Any dimension of } A)^3}{(\text{Corresponding dimension of } B)^3};$$

$$\frac{\text{Required section modulus}}{\text{Modulus of section from the table}} = \frac{(\text{Required } D)^3}{(D \text{ of section from the table})^3}$$

Hence, $\dfrac{2500}{78.6} = \dfrac{(\text{Required } D)^3}{(10)^3}$. This last equation solved for D gives $D = 31.7$ inches, nearly. As the large section will be exactly similar to the small one, the area of the large section is found from the equation:

$$\frac{\text{Area of required section}}{26.3} = \frac{(31.7)^2}{(10)^2}$$

and area $= 264$ square inches, about.

The neutral axis will be $\frac{7}{20} \times 31.7$, or 11.1 inches from the extreme tension fiber.

This trial section may now be tested for the maximum stress on it.

Flexure tensile stress $= \dfrac{157,000 \times (24 + 11.1)}{2500} = 2200$ pounds per square inch, about.

Uniformly distributed tensile stress $= \dfrac{157,000}{264} = 600$ pounds per square inch, about.

The total tensile stress is, therefore, 2800 pounds per square inch.

If this result had not been near enough to the 3000 pounds per square inch assumed, another section could have been selected and worked out in the same way to get a closer result. The depth D of the required section being 31.7 inches as compared with 10 inches of the similar section given in the table, each of the dimensions of the required section will be 3.17 times the corresponding one given in the table. Hence $D = 31.7$, say 32 inches; $B = 22.2$, say 22 inches; $b = 12.7$, say 13 inches; $H = 6.3$, say $6\frac{1}{2}$ inches, $\frac{1}{2} t = h = 1.98$, say 2 inches. The webs thicken gradually from the neutral axis to the tension flange so as to avoid too sudden a change in the section. For selecting the section at TY, Fig. 1, the procedure would be the same except that there would be no uniformly distributed stress to be added as in the case of section TX.

The method here given for determining the stress on the section TX is the one which is generally used in calculating the strength of shear frames and other designs of similar type. It is correct for straight beams, and formerly it was considered approximately correct for curved beams, but investigations by Bach and others showed that the maximum stresses in curved beams are very much greater than found by the methods generally used. A quick and accurate way of applying this theory, however, is impracticable; hence an approved procedure is to use the method outlined and provide an ample factor of safety. This is a safe course, because cast-iron punch frames, the sections of which have been determined by these methods, have stood up under their loads for years.

Properties of Sections for Punch and Shear Frames

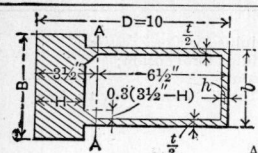

Z_c = Section Modulus for Compression;
Z_t = Section Modulus for Tension;
F = Area of Section;
I = Moment of Inertia about Gravity Axis $A - A$.

All dimensions in inches

B	b	$h = \frac{1}{2}t$	II	F	I	Z_c	Z_t
10	10	¼	0.57	15.36	228.51	35.20	65.40
		⅜	1.10	23.43	311.78	47.95	89.10
		½	1.80	31.82	397.83	61.20	113.70
	9	¼	0.51	14.66	200.77	30.89	57.36
		⅜	0.99	21.64	290.32	44.66	82.95
		½	1.61	29.56	371.95	57.22	106.27
		⅝	2.41	38.69	438.24	67.44	125.21
	8	¼	0.44	13.87	180.98	27.80	51.50
		⅜	0.88	20.41	272.07	41.90	77.70
		½	1.38	27.27	345.47	53.20	98.50
		⅝	2.04	35.20	410.37	63.10	117.00
		¾	3.50	49.63	462.98	71.20	132.00
	7	¼	0.38	13.15	172.76	26.50	49.30
		⅜	0.77	19.21	261.46	40.30	74.60
		½	1.24	25.69	320.52	49.30	91.50
		⅝	1.74	32.24	378.80	58.30	108.00
		¾	2.34	39.42	428.57	65.90	122.60
9	9	¼	0.59	14.66	204.06	31.40	58.30
		⅜	1.20	21.57	291.47	44.80	83.40
		½	2.00	30.68	363.50	55.80	103.60
	8	¼	0.50	13.83	185.91	28.60	53.65
		⅜	1.00	20.34	268.15	41.28	76.65
		½	1.70	28.07	338.66	52.15	96.81
		⅝	2.60	37.12	403.27	62.10	115.12
	7	¼	0.42	13.00	173.33	26.60	49.80
		⅜	0.89	19.25	250.41	38.40	71.60
		½	1.42	25.65	317.24	48.80	90.50
		⅝	2.11	33.03	375.00	57.70	107.10
		¾	3.06	42.13	420.36	64.60	120.10
	6	¼	0.36	12.40	161.70	24.90	46.20
		⅜	0.75	17.92	226.20	34.80	64.70
		½	1.23	23.89	290.50	44.70	83.00
		⅝	1.79	30.22	345.70	53.10	100.60
		¾	2.62	38.26	392.00	60.30	112.00
8	8	¼	0.62	14.09	187.46	28.90	53.55
		⅜	1.20	20.50	268.38	41.30	76.70
		½	2.10	28.79	336.75	51.80	96.20
	7	¼	0.55	13.69	172.25	26.50	49.20
		⅜	1.10	19.50	248.56	38.30	71.10
		½	1.90	27.07	315.01	48.50	90.00

Properties of Sections for Punch and Shear Frames

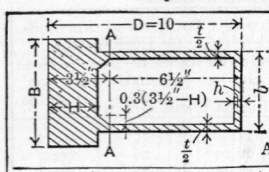

Z_c = Section Modulus for Compression;
Z_t = Section Modulus for Tension;
F = Area of Section;
I = Moment of Inertia about Gravity Axis $A - A$.

All dimensions in inches

B	b	$h = \frac{1}{2} t$	H	F	I	Z_c	Z_t
	7	⅝	3.00	36.41	377.05	58.0	108.0
		¼	0.43	12.43	155.80	23.9	44.5
	6	⅜	0.91	18.07	221.14	34.0	63.1
		½	1.50	24.20	283.77	43.5	80.8
		⅝	2.36	31.79	339.75	52.3	96.9
8		¼	0.33	11.61	139.76	21.42	39.9
		⅜	0.75	16.81	204.37	31.41	58.4
	5	½	1.25	22.27	261.65	40.25	75.2
		⅝	2.00	29.00	310.74	49.7	88.8
		¾	2.75	35.66	350.65	54.0	100.0
		¼	0.70	13.52	169.40	26.04	48.4
	7	⅜	1.40	19.99	243.80	37.5	69.6
		½	2.44	27.28	310.80	47.8	88.8
		¼	0.55	12.55	147.20	22.6	42.1
	6	⅜	1.14	18.27	220.03	33.8	62.8
		½	2.00	25.17	282.60	43.4	80.8
7		¼	0.41	12.28	136.92	20.0	39.1
		⅜	0.95	16.98	203.40	31.0	58.0
	5	½	1.65	23.03	258.64	40.0	73.8
		⅝	2.55	30.36	302.60	46.5	86.5
		¼	0.31	10.96	124.20	19.12	35.5
		⅜	0.76	15.71	183.00	28.15	52.3
	4	½	1.31	20.80	232.20	35.7	66.4
		⅝	1.98	26.30	275.00	42.3	78.6
		¼	0.68	12.56	156.25	24.0	44.6
	6	⅜	1.56	18.79	222.10	32.6	60.5
		½	3.50	30.00	275.00	42.3	78.6
		¼	0.53	11.68	180.83	29.0	51.6
6	5	⅜	1.27	17.25	214.79	33.0	61.4
		½	2.35	24.15	253.85	39.0	73.4
		¼	0.38	10.88	125.59	19.3	35.8
	4	⅜	1.00	15.84	181.36	27.9	51.8
		½	1.80	20.87	228.96	35.2	65.4
		¼	0.73	11.76	139.73	21.5	40.0
	5	⅜	1.70	17.28	196.98	30.2	56.2
		¼	0.55	10.97	125.40	19.3	35.9
5	4	⅜	1.45	16.13	181.52	28.0	52.0
		¼	0.84	10.16	110.14	17.25	32.0
	3	⅜	1.12	14.90	167.70	25.7	47.6
		½	2.10	19.99	198.57	30.5	56.8

Section Moduli for Rectangles

Section modulus values shown are for rectangles 1 inch wide. To obtain section modulus for rectangle of given length of side, multiply value in table by given width.

Length of Side	Section Modulus	Length of Side	Section Modulus	Length of Side	Section Modulus	Length of Side	Section Modulus
⅛	0.0026	2¾	1.26	12	24.00	25	104.2
3/16	0.0059	3	1.50	12½	26.04	26	112.7
¼	0.0104	3¼	1.76	13	28.17	27	121.5
5/16	0.0163	3½	2.04	13½	30.38	28	130.7
⅜	0.0234	3¾	2.34	14	32.67	29	140.2
7/16	0.032	4	2.67	14½	35.04	30	150
½	0.042	4½	3.38	15	37.5	32	171
⅝	0.065	5	4.17	15½	40.0	34	193
¾	0.094	5½	5.04	16	42.7	36	216
⅞	0.128	6	6.00	16½	45.4	38	241
1	0.167	6½	7.04	17	48.2	40	267
1⅛	0.211	7	8.17	17½	51.0	42	294
1¼	0.260	7½	9.38	18	54.0	44	323
1⅜	0.315	8	10.67	18½	57.0	46	353
1½	0.375	8½	12.04	19	60.2	48	384
1⅝	0.440	9	13.50	19½	63.4	50	417
1¾	0.510	9½	15.04	20	66.7	52	451
1⅞	0.586	10	16.67	21	73.5	54	486
2	0.67	10½	18.38	22	80.7	56	523
2¼	0.84	11	20.17	23	88.2	58	561
2½	1.04	11½	22.04	24	96.0	60	600

Section Moduli and Moments of Inertia for Round Shafts

Diam.	Section Modulus	Moment of Inertia	Diam.	Section Modulus	Moment of Inertia	Diam.	Section Modulus	Moment of Inertia
⅛	0.00019	0.00001	27/64	0.0074	0.00155	23/32	0.0364	0.01308
9/64	0.00027	0.00002	7/16	0.0082	0.00180	47/64	0.0388	0.01425
5/32	0.00037	0.00003	29/64	0.0091	0.00207	¾	0.0413	0.01550
11/64	0.00050	0.00004	15/32	0.0101	0.00237	49/64	0.0440	0.01684
3/16	0.00065	0.00006	31/64	0.0111	0.00270	25/32	0.0467	0.01825
13/64	0.00082	0.00008	½	0.0123	0.00306	51/64	0.0496	0.01976
7/32	0.00102	0.00011	33/64	0.0134	0.00346	13/16	0.0526	0.02135
15/64	0.00126	0.00015	17/32	0.0147	0.00390	53/64	0.0557	0.02305
¼	0.00153	0.00019	35/64	0.0160	0.00438	27/32	0.0588	0.02483
17/64	0.00183	0.00024	9/16	0.0174	0.00491	55/64	0.0622	0.02673
9/32	0.00218	0.00031	37/64	0.0189	0.00547	⅞	0.0656	0.02872
19/64	0.00256	0.00038	19/32	0.0205	0.00609	57/64	0.0692	0.03083
5/16	0.00299	0.00047	39/64	0.0222	0.00676	29/32	0.0728	0.03305
21/64	0.00344	0.00057	⅝	0.0239	0.00748	59/64	0.0767	0.03539
11/32	0.00398	0.00068	41/64	0.0258	0.00825	15/16	0.0807	0.03785
23/64	0.0045	0.00082	21/32	0.0277	0.00909	61/64	0.0849	0.04044
⅜	0.0052	0.00097	43/64	0.0297	0.00999	31/32	0.0891	0.04316
25/64	0.0058	0.00114	11/16	0.0318	0.01095	63/64	0.0934	0.04601
13/32	0.0066	0.00133	45/64	0.0341	0.01198	...	...	...

In this and succeeding tables, the *Polar Section Modulus* for a shaft of given diameter can be obtained by multiplying its Section Modulus by 2. Similarly its *Polar Moment of Inertia* can be obtained by multiplying its Moment of Inertia by 2.

Section Moduli and Moments of Inertia for Round Shafts

Diam.	Section Modulus	Moment of Inertia	Diam.	Section Modulus	Moment of Inertia	Diam.	Section Modulus	Moment of Inertia
1.00	0.0981	0.0490	1.50	0.3313	0.2485	2.00	0.7854	0.7854
1.01	0.1011	0.0510	1.51	0.3380	0.2552	2.01	0.7972	0.8012
1.02	0.1041	0.0531	1.52	0.3447	0.2620	2.02	0.8092	0.8172
1.03	0.1072	0.0552	1.53	0.3516	0.2689	2.03	0.8212	0.8335
1.04	0.1104	0.0574	1.54	0.3585	0.2761	2.04	0.8334	0.8501
1.05	0.1136	0.0596	1.55	0.3655	0.2833	2.05	0.8457	0.8669
1.06	0.1169	0.0619	1.56	0.3727	0.2907	2.06	0.8582	0.8839
1.07	0.1202	0.0643	1.57	0.3799	0.2982	2.07	0.8707	0.9012
1.08	0.1236	0.0667	1.58	0.3872	0.3059	2.08	0.8834	0.9188
1.09	0.1271	0.0692	1.59	0.3946	0.3137	2.09	0.8962	0.9366
1.10	0.1307	0.0718	1.60	0.4021	0.3217	2.10	0.9092	0.9547
1.11	0.1342	0.0745	1.61	0.4097	0.3298	2.11	0.9222	0.9729
1.12	0.1379	0.0772	1.62	0.4173	0.3380	2.12	0.9354	0.9915
1.13	0.1416	0.0800	1.63	0.4251	0.3465	2.13	0.9487	1.0103
1.14	0.1454	0.0829	1.64	0.4330	0.3550	2.14	0.9621	1.0295
1.15	0.1493	0.0859	1.65	0.4410	0.3638	2.15	0.9757	1.0488
1.16	0.1532	0.0888	1.66	0.4490	0.3727	2.16	0.9894	1.0685
1.17	0.1572	0.0919	1.67	0.4572	0.3818	2.17	1.0031	1.0884
1.18	0.1613	0.0951	1.68	0.4655	0.3910	2.18	1.0171	1.1086
1.19	0.1654	0.0984	1.69	0.4738	0.4004	2.19	1.0311	1.1291
1.20	0.1696	0.1018	1.70	0.4823	0.4100	2.20	1.0454	1.1499
1.21	0.1739	0.1052	1.71	0.4908	0.4197	2.21	1.0596	1.1709
1.22	0.1782	0.1087	1.72	0.4995	0.4296	2.22	1.0741	1.1923
1.23	0.1826	0.1123	1.73	0.5083	0.4397	2.23	1.0887	1.2139
1.24	0.1871	0.1160	1.74	0.5171	0.4499	2.24	1.1034	1.2358
1.25	0.1917	0.1198	1.75	0.5261	0.4603	2.25	1.1183	1.2580
1.26	0.1963	0.1237	1.76	0.5352	0.4710	2.26	1.1332	1.2806
1.27	0.2011	0.1277	1.77	0.5444	0.4818	2.27	1.1483	1.3034
1.28	0.2058	0.1317	1.78	0.5536	0.4927	2.28	1.1636	1.3265
1.29	0.2107	0.1359	1.79	0.5630	0.5039	2.29	1.1790	1.3499
1.30	0.2157	0.1402	1.80	0.5726	0.5153	2.30	1.1945	1.3737
1.31	0.2207	0.1445	1.81	0.5821	0.5268	2.31	1.2101	1.3977
1.32	0.2258	0.1490	1.82	0.5918	0.5385	2.32	1.2259	1.4234
1.33	0.2309	0.1535	1.83	0.6016	0.5505	2.33	1.2418	1.4468
1.34	0.2362	0.1582	1.84	0.6115	0.5626	2.34	1.2579	1.4718
1.35	0.2415	0.1630	1.85	0.6216	0.5749	2.35	1.2741	1.4971
1.36	0.2469	0.1679	1.86	0.6317	0.5875	2.36	1.2904	1.5227
1.37	0.2524	0.1729	1.87	0.6419	0.6002	2.37	1.3069	1.5487
1.38	0.2580	0.1780	1.88	0.6524	0.6132	2.38	1.3235	1.5750
1.39	0.2636	0.1832	1.89	0.6628	0.6263	2.39	1.3403	1.6016
1.40	0.2694	0.1886	1.90	0.6734	0.6397	2.40	1.3572	1.6286
1.41	0.2752	0.1940	1.91	0.6840	0.6532	2.41	1.3742	1.6559
1.42	0.2811	0.1995	1.92	0.6948	0.6670	2.42	1.3914	1.6836
1.43	0.2870	0.2052	1.93	0.7057	0.6810	2.43	1.4087	1.7116
1.44	0.2931	0.2110	1.94	0.7168	0.6953	2.44	1.4262	1.7399
1.45	0.2993	0.2170	1.95	0.7279	0.7097	2.45	1.4438	1.7686
1.46	0.3055	0.2230	1.96	0.7392	0.7244	2.46	1.4615	1.7977
1.47	0.3118	0.2292	1.97	0.7505	0.7393	2.47	1.4794	1.8271
1.48	0.3182	0.2355	1.98	0.7620	0.7544	2.48	1.4975	1.8526
1.49	0.3247	0.2419	1.99	0.7736	0.7698	2.49	1.5156	1.8870

Section Moduli and Moments of Inertia for Round Shafts

Diam.	Section Modulus	Moment of Inertia	Diam.	Section Modulus	Moment of Inertia	Diam.	Section Modulus	Moment of Inertia
2.50	1.5340	1.9175	3.00	2.6510	3.9761	3.50	4.2090	7.3662
2.51	1.5525	1.9483	3.01	2.6773	4.0293	3.51	4.2455	7.4507
2.52	1.5711	1.9796	3.02	2.7041	4.0831	3.52	4.2818	7.5360
2.53	1.5899	2.0112	3.03	2.7310	4.1375	3.53	4.3184	7.6220
2.54	1.6088	2.0431	3.04	2.7581	4.1924	3.54	4.3552	7.7087
2.55	1.6279	2.0755	3.05	2.7855	4.2478	3.55	4.3922	7.7962
2.56	1.6471	2.1083	3.06	2.8130	4.3038	3.56	4.4294	7.8845
2.57	1.6665	2.1414	3.07	2.8406	4.3604	3.57	4.4669	7.9734
2.58	1.6860	2.1749	3.08	2.8685	4.4175	3.58	4.5045	8.0631
2.59	1.7057	2.2088	3.09	2.8965	4.4751	3.59	4.5424	8.1536
2.60	1.7260	2.2432	3.10	2.9250	4.5333	3.60	4.5804	8.2448
2.61	1.7455	2.2779	3.11	2.9531	4.5921	3.61	4.6187	8.3367
2.62	1.7656	2.3130	3.12	2.9817	4.6514	3.62	4.6572	8.4296
2.63	1.7859	2.3485	3.13	3.0104	4.7113	3.63	4.6959	8.5231
2.64	1.8064	2.3844	3.14	3.0394	4.7718	3.64	4.7347	8.6174
2.65	1.8270	2.4208	3.15	3.0685	4.8330	3.65	4.7740	8.7125
2.66	1.8478	2.4575	3.16	3.0978	4.8946	3.66	4.8133	8.8084
2.67	1.8686	2.4947	3.17	3.1274	4.9568	3.67	4.8529	8.9050
2.68	1.8897	2.5322	3.18	3.1570	5.0197	3.68	4.8926	9.0025
2.69	1.9110	2.5702	3.19	3.1869	5.0832	3.69	4.9325	9.1007
2.70	1.9320	2.6087	3.20	3.2170	5.1472	3.70	4.9730	9.1998
2.71	1.9539	2.6476	3.21	3.2472	5.2119	3.71	5.0133	9.2996
2.72	1.9756	2.6868	3.22	3.2777	5.2771	3.72	5.0540	9.4003
2.73	1.9975	2.7266	3.23	3.3083	5.3430	3.73	5.0948	9.5018
2.74	2.0195	2.7668	3.24	3.3391	5.4094	3.74	5.1359	9.6041
2.75	2.0417	2.8074	3.25	3.3701	5.4765	3.75	5.1771	9.7072
2.76	2.0641	2.8484	3.26	3.4014	5.5442	3.76	5.2187	9.8112
2.77	2.0866	2.8899	3.27	3.4328	5.6126	3.77	5.2605	9.9160
2.78	2.1093	2.9319	3.28	3.4644	5.6815	3.78	5.3024	10.0216
2.79	2.1321	2.9743	3.29	3.4961	5.7511	3.79	5.3444	10.1286
2.80	2.1550	3.0172	3.30	3.5280	5.8214	3.80	5.3870	10.2350
2.81	2.1783	3.0605	3.31	3.5603	5.8923	3.81	5.4297	10.3436
2.82	2.2016	3.1043	3.32	3.5926	5.9638	3.82	5.4726	10.4526
2.83	2.2251	3.1486	3.33	3.6252	6.0363	3.83	5.5156	10.5624
2.84	2.2488	3.1933	3.34	3.6580	6.1088	3.84	5.5590	10.6732
2.85	2.2727	3.2385	3.35	3.6909	6.1823	3.85	5.6025	10.7848
2.86	2.2966	3.2842	3.36	3.7241	6.2564	3.86	5.6462	10.8970
2.87	2.3208	3.3304	3.37	3.7575	6.3312	3.87	5.6903	11.0110
2.88	2.3452	3.3771	3.38	3.7909	6.4067	3.88	5.7345	11.1250
2.89	2.3697	3.4242	3.39	3.8246	6.4829	3.89	5.7789	11.2400
2.90	2.3940	3.4719	3.40	3.8590	6.5597	3.90	5.8240	11.3560
2.91	2.4192	3.5200	3.41	3.8928	6.6372	3.91	5.8685	11.4730
2.92	2.4442	3.5686	3.42	3.9272	6.7154	3.92	5.9137	11.5910
2.93	2.4695	3.6178	3.43	3.9617	6.7943	3.93	5.9590	11.7100
2.94	2.4949	3.6674	3.44	3.9965	6.8739	3.94	6.0046	11.8290
2.95	2.5204	3.7175	3.45	4.0314	6.9542	3.95	6.0505	11.9500
2.96	2.5461	3.7682	3.46	4.0666	7.0352	3.96	6.0966	12.0690
2.97	2.5720	3.8196	3.47	4.1019	7.1168	3.97	6.1429	12.1930
2.98	2.5981	3.8711	3.48	4.1375	7.1976	3.98	6.1894	12.3170
2.99	2.6243	3.9233	3.49	4.1732	7.2824	3.99	6.2361	12.4410

Section Moduli and Moments of Inertia for Round Shafts

Diam.	Section Modulus	Moment of Inertia	Diam.	Section Modulus	Moment of Inertia	Diam.	Section Modulus	Moment of Inertia
4.00	6.2830	12.566	4.50	8.946	20.129	5.00	12.272	30.680
4.01	6.3304	12.692	4.51	9.006	20.308	5.01	12.345	30.926
4.02	6.3779	12.820	4.52	9.066	20.489	5.02	12.420	31.173
4.03	6.4256	12.948	4.53	9.126	20.671	5.03	12.493	31.423
4.04	6.4736	13.077	4.54	9.186	20.854	5.04	12.568	31.673
4.05	6.5217	13.207	4.55	9.247	21.039	5.05	12.644	31.925
4.06	6.5701	13.337	4.56	9.308	21.224	5.06	12.718	32.179
4.07	6.6188	13.469	4.57	9.370	21.411	5.07	12.794	32.434
4.08	6.6677	13.602	4.58	9.431	21.599	5.08	12.870	32.691
4.09	6.7169	13.736	4.59	9.493	21.788	5.09	12.946	32.949
4.10	6.7660	13.871	4.60	9.556	21.979	5.10	13.023	33.209
4.11	6.8159	14.007	4.61	9.618	22.170	5.11	13.099	33.470
4.12	6.8657	14.143	4.62	9.681	22.363	5.12	13.177	33.733
4.13	6.9164	14.281	4.63	9.744	22.557	5.13	13.254	33.997
4.14	6.9663	14.420	4.64	9.807	22.753	5.14	13.332	34.263
4.15	7.0169	14.560	4.65	9.870	22.950	5.15	13.410	34.530
4.16	7.0677	14.701	4.66	9.934	23.148	5.16	13.488	34.799
4.17	7.1188	14.843	4.67	9.998	23.347	5.17	13.567	35.070
4.18	7.1702	14.985	4.68	10.063	23.548	5.18	13.645	35.342
4.19	7.2217	15.129	4.69	10.127	23.750	5.19	13.725	35.615
4.20	7.2740	15.274	4.70	10.193	23.953	5.20	13.804	35.891
4.21	7.3256	15.420	4.71	10.258	24.157	5.21	13.884	36.168
4.22	7.3779	15.568	4.72	10.323	24.363	5.22	13.964	36.446
4.23	7.4305	15.715	4.73	10.389	24.570	5.23	14.045	36.726
4.24	7.4833	15.865	4.74	10.455	24.779	5.24	14.125	37.008
4.25	7.5364	16.015	4.75	10.522	24.989	5.25	14.206	37.291
4.26	7.5898	16.166	4.76	10.588	25.200	5.26	14.287	37.576
4.27	7.6433	16.319	4.77	10.655	25.412	5.27	14.369	37.863
4.28	7.6972	16.472	4.78	10.722	25.626	5.28	14.451	38.151
4.29	7.7513	16.626	4.79	10.790	25.841	5.29	14.534	38.440
4.30	7.8060	16.782	4.80	10.857	26.058	5.30	14.616	38.732
4.31	7.8602	16.938	4.81	10.925	26.275	5.31	14.699	39.025
4.32	7.9149	17.096	4.82	10.994	26.495	5.32	14.782	39.320
4.33	7.9701	17.255	4.83	11.062	26.715	5.33	14.866	39.617
4.34	8.0254	17.415	4.84	11.131	26.937	5.34	14.949	39.915
4.35	8.0810	17.576	4.85	11.200	27.160	5.35	15.034	40.215
4.36	8.1369	17.738	4.86	11.269	27.385	5.36	15.118	40.516
4.37	8.1930	17.902	4.87	11.339	27.611	5.37	15.202	40.819
4.38	8.2494	18.066	4.88	11.409	27.839	5.38	15.288	41.124
4.39	8.3060	18.231	4.89	11.479	28.067	5.39	15.373	41.431
4.40	8.3630	18.398	4.90	11.550	28.298	5.40	15.459	41.739
4.41	8.4200	18.566	4.91	11.621	28.530	5.41	15.545	42.049
4.42	8.4775	18.735	4.92	11.692	28.763	5.42	15.631	42.361
4.43	8.5351	18.905	4.93	11.763	28.997	5.43	15.718	42.674
4.44	8.5930	19.077	4.94	11.835	29.233	5.44	15.805	42.990
4.45	8.6513	19.249	4.95	11.907	29.471	5.45	15.893	43.307
4.46	8.7097	19.423	4.96	11.979	29.710	5.46	15.980	43.626
4.47	8.7685	19.598	4.97	12.052	29.950	5.47	16.068	43.946
4.48	8.8274	19.773	4.98	12.124	30.192	5.48	16.157	44.268
4.49	8.8867	19.950	4.99	12.198	30.435	5.49	16.245	44.592

Properties of Schedule 40, American Standard Welded and Seamless Wrought-Iron and Wrought-Steel Pipe

Diameter, Inches			Wall Thickness, Inches	Cross-Sectional Area of Metal	Weight per Foot, Pounds		Capacity per Foot of Length		Length of Pipe in Feet to Contain		Properties of Sections			
Nominal	Inside Actual	Outside Actual			Of Pipe	Of Water	In Cubic Inches	In Gallons	One Cubic Foot	One Gallon	Moment of Inertia	Radius of Gyration	Section Modulus	Torsion Section Modulus
⅛	0.269	0.405	0.068	0.072	0.25	0.028	0.67	0.003	2533.775	338.740	0.00106	0.120	0.0052	0.0104
¼	0.364	0.540	0.088	0.125	0.43	0.045	1.24	0.005	1383.789	185.000	0.00331	0.160	0.0122	0.0243
⅜	0.493	0.675	0.091	0.167	0.57	0.083	2.25	0.010	754.360	100.850	0.00729	0.210	0.0216	0.0433
½	0.622	0.840	0.109	0.250	0.86	0.132	3.63	0.016	473.906	63.356	0.01709	0.260	0.0406	0.0812
¾	0.824	1.050	0.113	0.333	1.14	0.232	6.39	0.028	270.034	36.100	0.03704	0.330	0.0704	0.1408
1	1.049	1.315	0.133	0.494	1.68	0.375	10.71	0.045	166.618	22.275	0.08734	0.420	0.1326	0.2652
1¼	1.380	1.660	0.140	0.669	2.28	0.649	17.97	0.077	96.275	12.871	0.1947	0.540	0.2342	0.4684
1½	1.610	1.900	0.145	0.799	2.72	0.882	24.36	0.106	70.733	9.456	0.3099	0.620	0.3256	0.6512
2	2.067	2.375	0.154	1.075	3.66	1.454	40.26	0.174	42.913	5.737	0.6660	0.787	0.5596	1.119
2½	2.469	2.875	0.203	1.704	5.80	2.073	57.37	0.248	30.077	4.021	1.530	0.947	1.062	2.124
3	3.068	3.500	0.216	2.228	7.58	3.201	88.82	0.383	19.479	2.604	3.017	1.164	1.721	3.442
3½	3.548	4.000	0.226	2.680	9.11	4.287	117.85	0.513	14.565	1.947	4.788	1.337	2.390	4.780
4	4.026	4.500	0.237	3.173	10.80	5.516	152.76	0.660	11.312	1.512	7.233	1.510	3.209	6.418
5	5.047	5.563	0.258	4.304	14.70	8.674	236.46	1.040	7.198	0.962	15.160	1.878	5.441	10.88
6	6.065	6.625	0.280	5.584	19.00	12.52	347.33	1.500	4.984	0.666	28.140	2.245	8.481	16.96
8	7.981	8.625	0.322	8.396	28.60	21.68	601.34	2.600	2.878	0.384	72.490	2.938	16.78	33.56
10	10.020	10.750	0.365	11.90	40.50	34.16	945.22	4.100	1.826	0.244	160.70	3.674	29.84	59.68
12	11.938	12.750	0.406	15.77	53.60	48.50	1356.48	5.870	1.273	0.170	300.30	4.370	47.00	94.00
14	13.126	14.000	0.437	18.61	63.30	58.64	1847.23	7.030	1.067	0.142	429.10	4.800	57.01	114.0
16	15.000	16.000	0.500	24.35	82.80	76.58	2405.38	9.180	0.814	0.109	731.90	5.470	91.33	182.7
18	16.876	18.000	0.562	30.79	105.0	96.93	2683.58	11.12	0.644	0.086	1172.0	6.180	129.9	259.9
20	18.814	20.000	0.593	36.15	123.0	120.46	3326.40	14.40	0.517	0.069	1703.0	6.870	170.1	340.1
24	22.626	24.000	0.687	50.31	171.0	174.23	4838.40	20.90	0.357	0.048	3424.0	8.250	284.6	569.2

Properties of Schedule 80, American Standard Welded and Seamless Wrought-Iron and Wrought-Steel Pipe

Diameter, Inches			Wall Thickness, Inches	Cross-Sectional Area of Metal	Weight per Foot, Pounds		Capacity per Foot of Length		Length of Pipe in Feet to Contain		Properties of Sections			
Nominal	Actual Inside	Actual Outside			Of Pipe	Of Water in Pipe	In Cubic Inches	In Gallons	One Cubic Foot	One Gallon	Moment of Inertia	Radius of Gyration	Section Modulus	Torsion Section Modulus
⅛	0.215	0.405	0.095	0.093	0.314	0.001	0.432	0.0019	3070.	527.0	0.00122	0.120	0.00597	0.01195
¼	0.302	0.540	0.119	0.157	0.535	0.031	0.865	0.0037	1920.	271.0	0.00377	0.159	0.01392	0.02783
⅜	0.423	0.675	0.126	0.217	0.738	0.061	1.692	0.0073	1370.	137.0	0.00862	0.177	0.01753	0.03506
½	0.546	0.840	0.147	0.320	1.087	0.102	2.808	0.0122	616.0	82.00	0.02008	0.250	0.04704	0.09408
¾	0.742	1.050	0.154	0.433	1.473	0.213	5.196	0.0225	334.0	39.20	0.04479	0.327	0.08656	0.17312
1	0.957	1.315	0.179	0.639	2.171	0.312	8.628	0.0374	200.0	26.80	0.10560	0.405	0.15730	0.31460
1¼	1.278	1.660	0.191	0.881	2.996	0.555	15.400	0.0666	114.0	15.00	0.24180	0.522	0.28830	0.57660
1½	1.500	1.900	0.200	1.068	3.631	0.765	21.200	0.0918	81.50	10.90	0.39120	0.610	0.41450	0.82900
2	1.939	2.375	0.218	1.477	5.022	1.280	35.440	0.1535	49.80	6.520	0.86790	0.760	0.71640	1.43280
2½	2.323	2.875	0.276	2.254	7.661	1.830	50.860	0.2200	34.00	4.550	1.92400	0.925	1.33590	2.67180
3	2.900	3.500	0.300	3.016	10.252	2.870	79.260	0.3440	21.70	2.910	3.89400	1.130	2.21950	4.43900
3½	3.364	4.000	0.318	3.678	12.505	3.720	106.660	0.4580	16.25	2.180	6.28000	1.310	3.13470	6.26940
4	3.826	4.500	0.337	4.407	14.983	4.970	137.960	0.5970	12.50	1.675	9.61000	1.590	4.26600	8.53200
5	4.813	5.563	0.375	6.112	20.778	7.940	218.320	0.9470	7.95	1.055	20.6700	1.840	7.42100	14.8420
6	5.761	6.625	0.432	8.405	28.573	11.30	312.800	1.3550	5.50	0.738	40.4900	2.190	12.2000	24.4000
8	7.625	8.625	0.500	12.760	43.388	19.80	547.960	2.3800	3.14	0.420	105.700	2.895	24.8800	49.7600
10	9.564	10.750	0.593	18.920	64.400	31.13	962.080	4.1650	1.80	0.244	244.380	3.590	45.4700	90.9300
12	11.376	12.750	0.687	26.030	88.600	44.04	1219.680	5.2800	1.42	0.189	474.260	4.270	74.9800	149.960
14	12.500	14.000	0.750	31.220	107.000	53.18	1472.640	6.3800	1.18	0.157	689.920	4.710	98.5600	197.120
16	14.314	16.000	0.843	40.140	137.000	69.73	1931.040	8.3600	0.895	0.119	1154.25	5.350	144.280	288.560
18	16.126	18.000	0.937	50.230	171.000	88.50	2450.880	10.6100	0.705	0.094	1830.15	6.030	203.350	406.700
20	17.938	20.000	1.031	61.440	209.000	109.51	3032.640	13.1300	0.570	0.076	2399.07	6.510	259.910	519.820
24	21.564	24.000	1.218	87.170	297.000	158.26	4382.640	19.0000	0.395	0.052	5662.00	8.350	471.830	943.670

American Standard Structural Channels

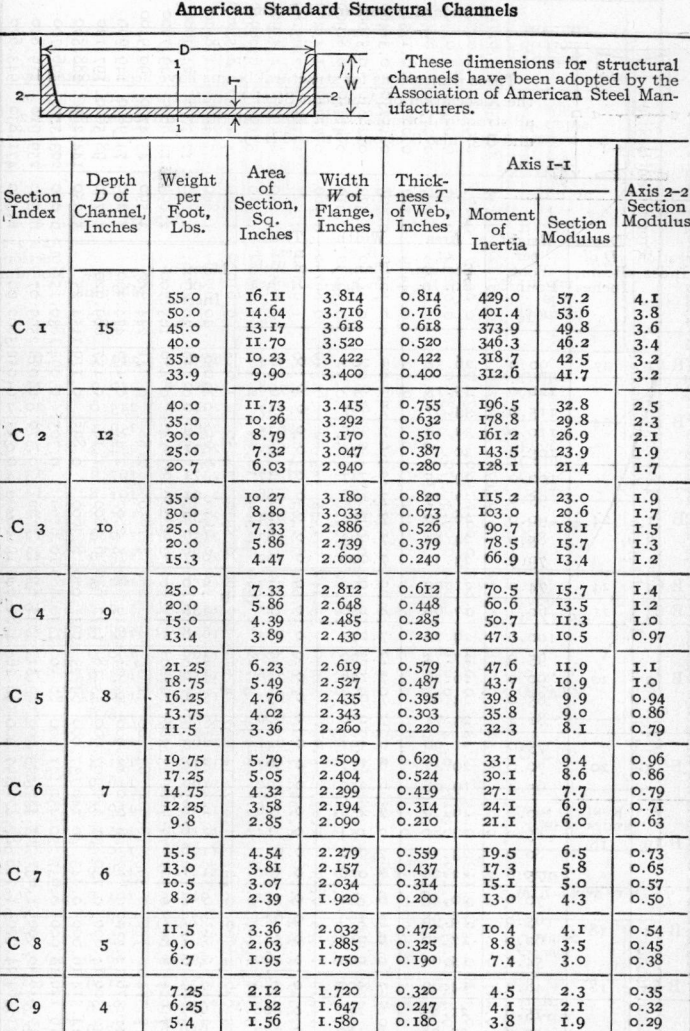

These dimensions for structural channels have been adopted by the Association of American Steel Manufacturers.

Section Index	Depth D of Channel, Inches	Weight per Foot, Lbs.	Area of Section, Sq. Inches	Width W of Flange, Inches	Thickness T of Web, Inches	Axis 1–1		Axis 2–2 Section Modulus
						Moment of Inertia	Section Modulus	
C 1	15	55.0	16.11	3.814	0.814	429.0	57.2	4.1
		50.0	14.64	3.716	0.716	401.4	53.6	3.8
		45.0	13.17	3.618	0.618	373.9	49.8	3.6
		40.0	11.70	3.520	0.520	346.3	46.2	3.4
		35.0	10.23	3.422	0.422	318.7	42.5	3.2
		33.9	9.90	3.400	0.400	312.6	41.7	3.2
C 2	12	40.0	11.73	3.415	0.755	196.5	32.8	2.5
		35.0	10.26	3.292	0.632	178.8	29.8	2.3
		30.0	8.79	3.170	0.510	161.2	26.9	2.1
		25.0	7.32	3.047	0.387	143.5	23.9	1.9
		20.7	6.03	2.940	0.280	128.1	21.4	1.7
C 3	10	35.0	10.27	3.180	0.820	115.2	23.0	1.9
		30.0	8.80	3.033	0.673	103.0	20.6	1.7
		25.0	7.33	2.886	0.526	90.7	18.1	1.5
		20.0	5.86	2.739	0.379	78.5	15.7	1.3
		15.3	4.47	2.600	0.240	66.9	13.4	1.2
C 4	9	25.0	7.33	2.812	0.612	70.5	15.7	1.4
		20.0	5.86	2.648	0.448	60.6	13.5	1.2
		15.0	4.39	2.485	0.285	50.7	11.3	1.0
		13.4	3.89	2.430	0.230	47.3	10.5	0.97
C 5	8	21.25	6.23	2.619	0.579	47.6	11.9	1.1
		18.75	5.49	2.527	0.487	43.7	10.9	1.0
		16.25	4.76	2.435	0.395	39.8	9.9	0.94
		13.75	4.02	2.343	0.303	35.8	9.0	0.86
		11.5	3.36	2.260	0.220	32.3	8.1	0.79
C 6	7	19.75	5.79	2.509	0.629	33.1	9.4	0.96
		17.25	5.05	2.404	0.524	30.1	8.6	0.86
		14.75	4.32	2.299	0.419	27.1	7.7	0.79
		12.25	3.58	2.194	0.314	24.1	6.9	0.71
		9.8	2.85	2.090	0.210	21.1	6.0	0.63
C 7	6	15.5	4.54	2.279	0.559	19.5	6.5	0.73
		13.0	3.81	2.157	0.437	17.3	5.8	0.65
		10.5	3.07	2.034	0.314	15.1	5.0	0.57
		8.2	2.39	1.920	0.200	13.0	4.3	0.50
C 8	5	11.5	3.36	2.032	0.472	10.4	4.1	0.54
		9.0	2.63	1.885	0.325	8.8	3.5	0.45
		6.7	1.95	1.750	0.190	7.4	3.0	0.38
C 9	4	7.25	2.12	1.720	0.320	4.5	2.3	0.35
		6.25	1.82	1.647	0.247	4.1	2.1	0.32
		5.4	1.56	1.580	0.180	3.8	1.9	0.29
C 10	3	6.0	1.75	1.596	0.356	2.1	1.4	0.27
		5.0	1.46	1.498	0.258	1.8	1.2	0.24
		4.1	1.19	1.410	0.170	1.6	1.1	0.21

Standard Structural I-Beams — 1

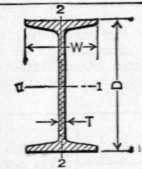

These dimensions for structural beams have been adopted by the Association of American Steel Manufacturers and apply to all structural beams, except American Standard sections B 1, B 2 and B 3; also Sections B 18 and B 19.

Section Index	Depth D of Beam, Inches	Weight per Foot, Pounds	Area of Section, Sq. In.	Width W of Flange, Inches	Thickness T of Web, Inches	Axis 1–1		Axis 2–2 Section Modulus
						Moment of Inertia	Section Modulus	
B 61	27	90.0	26.34	9.000	0.524	2958.3	219.1	16.7
B 18	24	120.0	35.13	8.048	0.798	3010.8	250.9	21.1
		115.0	33.67	7.987	0.737	2940.5	245.0	20.7
		110.0	32.18	7.925	0.675	2869.1	239.1	20.3
		105.9	30.98	7.875	0.625	2811.5	234.3	20.0
B 1	24	100.0	29.25	7.247	0.747	2371.8	197.6	13.4
		95.0	27.79	7.186	0.686	2301.5	191.8	13.0
		90.0	26.30	7.124	0.624	2230.1	185.8	12.8
		85.0	24.84	7.063	0.563	2159.8	180.0	12.5
		79.9	23.33	7.000	0.500	2087.2	173.9	12.2
B 62	24	74.2	21.70	9.000	0.476	1950.1	162.5	13.6
B 63	21	60.4	17.68	8.250	0.428	1235.5	117.7	10.6
B 2	20	100.0	29.20	7.273	0.873	1648.3	164.8	14.4
		95.0	27.74	7.200	0.800	1599.7	160.0	14.0
		90.0	26.26	7.126	0.726	1550.3	155.0	13.7
		85.0	24.80	7.053	0.653	1501.7	150.2	13.3
		81.4	23.74	7.000	0.600	1466.3	146.6	13.1
B 3	20	75.0	21.90	6.391	0.641	1263.5	126.3	9.4
		70.0	20.42	6.317	0.567	1214.2	121.4	9.2
		65.4	19.08	6.250	0.500	1169.5	116.9	8.9
B 19	18	90.0	26.29	7.236	0.796	1256.5	139.6	14.3
		85.0	24.81	7.154	0.714	1216.6	135.2	14.0
		80.0	23.34	7.072	0.632	1176.8	130.8	13.6
		75.6	22.04	7.000	0.560	1141.8	126.9	13.2
B 4	18	70.0	20.46	6.251	0.711	917.5	101.9	7.8
		65.0	18.98	6.169	0.629	877.7	97.5	7.6
		60.0	17.50	6.087	0.547	837.8	93.1	7.3
		54.7	15.94	6.000	0.460	795.5	88.4	7.1
B 64	18	48.2	14.09	7.500	0.380	737.1	81.9	8.0
B 6	15	75.0	21.85	6.278	0.868	687.2	91.6	9.8
		70.0	20.38	6.180	0.770	659.6	87.9	9.3
		65.0	18.91	6.082	0.672	632.1	84.3	8.9
		60.8	17.68	6.000	0.590	609.0	81.2	8.7

Standard Structural I-beams — 2

Section Index	Depth D of Beam, Inches	Weight per Foot, Pounds	Area of Section, Sq. In.	Width W of Flange, Inches	Thickness T of Web, Inches	Axis 1-1 Moment of Inertia	Axis 1-1 Section Modulus	Axis 2-2 Section Modulus
B 7	15	55.0	16.06	5.738	0.648	508.7	67.8	5.9
		50.0	14.59	5.640	0.550	481.1	64.2	5.7
		45.0	13.12	5.542	0.452	453.6	60.5	5.4
		42.9	12.49	5.500	0.410	441.8	58.9	5.3
B 65	15	37.3	10.91	6.750	0.332	405.5	54.1	5.9
B 8	12	55.0	16.04	5.600	0.810	319.3	53.2	6.2
		50.0	14.57	5.477	0.687	301.6	50.3	5.8
		45.0	13.10	5.355	0.565	284.1	47.3	5.5
		40.8	11.84	5.250	0.460	268.9	44.8	5.3
B 9	12	35.0	10.20	5.078	0.428	227.0	37.8	3.9
		31.8	9.26	5.000	0.350	215.8	36.0	3.8
B 66	12	27.9	8.15	6.000	0.284	199.4	33.2	4.2
B 10	10	40.0	11.69	5.091	0.741	158.0	31.6	3.7
		35.0	10.22	4.944	0.594	145.8	29.2	3.4
		30.0	8.75	4.797	0.447	133.5	26.7	3.2
		25.4	7.38	4.660	0.310	122.1	24.4	3.0
B 67	10	22.4	6.54	5.500	0.252	113.6	22.7	3.3
B 11	9	35.0	10.22	4.764	0.724	111.3	24.7	3.0
		30.0	8.76	4.601	0.561	101.4	22.5	2.8
		25.0	7.28	4.437	0.397	91.4	20.3	2.5
		21.8	6.32	4.330	0.290	84.9	18.9	2.4
B 12	8	25.5	7.43	4.262	0.532	68.1	17.0	2.2
		23.0	6.71	4.171	0.441	64.2	16.0	2.1
		20.5	5.97	4.079	0.349	60.2	15.1	2.0
		18.4	5.34	4.000	0.270	56.9	14.2	1.9
B 68	8	17.5	5.13	5.000	0.220	58.4	14.6	2.5
B 13	7	20.0	5.83	3.860	0.450	41.9	12.0	1.6
		17.5	5.09	3.755	0.345	38.9	11.1	1.6
		15.3	4.43	3.660	0.250	36.2	10.4	1.5
B 14	6	17.25	5.02	3.565	0.465	26.0	8.7	1.3
		14.75	4.29	3.443	0.343	23.8	7.9	1.2
		12.5	3.61	3.330	0.230	21.8	7.3	1.1
B 15	5	14.75	4.29	3.284	0.494	15.0	6.0	1.0
		12.25	3.56	3.137	0.347	13.5	5.4	0.91
		10.0	2.87	3.000	0.210	12.1	4.8	0.82
B 16	4	10.5	3.05	2.870	0.400	7.1	3.5	0.70
		9.5	2.76	2.796	0.326	6.7	3.3	0.65
		8.5	2.46	2.723	0.253	6.3	3.2	0.61
		7.7	2.21	2.660	0.190	6.0	3.0	0.58
B 17	3	7.5	2.17	2.509	0.349	2.9	1.9	0.47
		6.5	1.88	2.411	0.251	2.7	1.8	0.43
		5.7	1.64	2.330	0.170	2.5	1.7	0.40

Elements of Equal Angles

Size or Width W, Inches	Thickness T, Inches	Weight per Foot, Pounds	Area of Section, Sq. In.	Section Modulus Axis I-I	Radius of Gyration Axis 2-2
8 × 8	1⅛	56.9	16.73	17.5	1.55
	1¹⁄₁₆	54.0	15.87	16.7	1.56
	1	51.0	15.00	15.8	1.56
	15/16	48.1	14.12	14.9	1.56
	7/8	45.0	13.23	14.0	1.56
	13/16	42.0	12.34	13.1	1.57
	3/4	38.9	11.44	12.2	1.57
	11/16	35.8	10.53	11.2	1.58
	5/8	32.7	9.61	10.3	1.58
	9/16	29.6	8.68	9.3	1.58
	1/2	26.4	7.75	8.4	1.58
6 × 6	1	37.4	11.00	8.6	1.16
	15/16	35.3	10.37	8.1	1.16
	7/8	33.1	9.73	7.6	1.17
	13/16	31.0	9.09	7.2	1.17
	3/4	28.7	8.44	6.7	1.17
	11/16	26.5	7.78	6.2	1.17
	5/8	24.2	7.11	5.7	1.17
	9/16	21.9	6.43	5.1	1.18
	1/2	19.6	5.75	4.6	1.18
	7/16	17.2	5.06	4.1	1.19
	3/8	14.9	4.36	3.5	1.19
5 × 5	1	30.6	9.00	5.8	0.96
	15/16	28.9	8.50	5.5	0.96
	7/8	27.2	7.98	5.2	0.96
	13/16	25.4	7.47	4.9	0.97
	3/4	23.6	6.94	4.5	0.97
	11/16	21.8	6.40	4.2	0.97
	5/8	20.0	5.86	3.9	0.97
	9/16	18.1	5.31	3.5	0.98
	1/2	16.2	4.75	3.2	0.98
	7/16	14.3	4.18	2.8	0.98
	3/8	12.3	3.61	2.4	0.99
4 × 4	13/16	19.9	5.84	3.0	0.77
	3/4	18.5	5.44	2.8	0.77
	11/16	17.1	5.03	2.6	0.77
	5/8	15.7	4.61	2.4	0.77
	9/16	14.3	4.18	2.2	0.78
	1/2	12.8	3.75	2.0	0.78
	7/16	11.3	3.31	1.8	0.78
	3/8	9.8	2.86	1.5	0.79

Size or Width W, Inches	Thickness T, Inches	Weight per Foot, Pounds	Area of Section, Sq. In.	Section Modulus Axis I-I	Radius of Gyration Axis 2-2
4 × 4	5/16	8.2	2.40	1.3	0.79
	1/4	6.6	1.94	1.0	0.79
3½ × 3½	13/16	17.1	5.03	2.3	0.67
	3/4	16.0	4.69	2.1	0.67
	11/16	14.8	4.34	2.0	0.67
	5/8	13.6	3.98	1.8	0.68
	9/16	12.4	3.62	1.6	0.68
	1/2	11.1	3.25	1.5	0.68
	7/16	9.8	2.87	1.3	0.68
	3/8	8.5	2.48	1.2	0.69
	5/16	7.2	2.09	0.98	0.69
	1/4	5.8	1.69	0.79	0.69
3 × 3	5/8	11.5	3.36	1.3	0.57
	9/16	10.4	3.06	1.2	0.58
	1/2	9.4	2.75	1.1	0.58
	7/16	8.3	2.43	0.95	0.58
	3/8	7.2	2.11	0.83	0.58
	5/16	6.1	1.78	0.71	0.59
	1/4	4.9	1.44	0.58	0.59
2½ × 2½	1/2	7.7	2.25	0.73	0.47
	7/16	6.8	2.00	0.65	0.48
	3/8	5.9	1.73	0.57	0.48
	5/16	5.0	1.47	0.48	0.49
	1/4	4.1	1.19	0.39	0.49
	3/16	3.07	0.90	0.30	0.49
	1/8	2.08	0.61	0.20	0.50
2 × 2	7/16	5.3	1.56	0.40	0.39
	3/8	4.7	1.36	0.35	0.39
	5/16	3.92	1.15	0.30	0.39
	1/4	3.19	0.94	0.25	0.39
	3/16	2.44	0.71	0.19	0.40
	1/8	1.65	0.48	0.13	0.40
1¾ × 1¾	7/16	4.6	1.34	0.30	0.33
	3/8	3.99	1.17	0.26	0.34
	5/16	3.39	1.00	0.23	0.34
	1/4	2.77	0.81	0.19	0.34
	3/16	2.12	0.62	0.14	0.35
	1/8	1.44	0.42	0.10	0.35
1½ × 1½	3/8	3.35	0.98	0.19	0.29
	5/16	2.86	0.84	0.16	0.29
	1/4	2.34	0.69	0.13	0.29
	3/16	1.80	0.53	0.10	0.29
	1/8	1.23	0.36	0.07	0.30
1¼ × 1¼	5/16	2.33	0.68	0.11	0.24
	1/4	1.92	0.56	0.09	0.24
	3/16	1.48	0.43	0.07	0.24
	1/8	1.01	0.30	0.05	0.25
1 × 1	1/4	1.49	0.44	0.06	0.19
	3/16	1.16	0.34	0.04	0.19
	1/8	0.80	0.23	0.03	0.19

Length of Angles Bent to Circular Shape. — When it is required to calculate the length of an angle-iron used either inside or outside of a tank or smokestack, the following method and table of constants may be used: Assume, for example, that a stand-pipe, 20 feet inside diameter, is provided with a 3 by 3 by ⅜ inch angle-iron on the inside at the top. The circumference of a circle 20 feet in diameter is 754 inches. From the table of constants, find the constant for a 3 by 3 by ⅜ inch angle-iron, which is 4.319. The length of the angle then is 754 − 4.319 = 749.681 inches. Should the angle be on the outside, add the constant instead of subtracting it; thus, 754 + 4.319 = 758.319 inches.

Table of Constants Used for Calculating Length of Angles Bent to
Circular Shape

Size of Angle	Constant	Size of Angle	Constant
¼ × 2 × 2	2.879	½ × 3½ × 3½	5.235
⁵⁄₁₆ × 2 × 2	3.076	⅜ × 4 × 4	5.366
⅜ × 2 × 2	3.272	½ × 4 × 4	5.758
¼ × 2½ × 2½	3.403	⅜ × 5 × 5	6.414
⁵⁄₁₆ × 2½ × 2½	3.600	½ × 5 × 5	6.804
⅜ × 2½ × 2½	3.796	⅜ × 6 × 6	7.461
½ × 2½ × 2½	4.188	½ × 6 × 6	7.854
¼ × 3 × 3	3.926	¾ × 6 × 6	8.639
⁵⁄₁₆ × 3 × 3	4.123	½ × 8 × 8	9.949
⅜ × 3 × 3	4.319	¾ × 8 × 8	10.734
½ × 3 × 3	4.711	1 × 8 × 8	11.520
⅜ × 3½ × 3½	4.843	. . . .	. . . . . .

Moment of Inertia of Built-up Sections. — The usual method of calculating the moment of inertia of a built-up section involves the calculations of the moment of inertia for each element of the section about its own neutral axis, and the transferring of this moment of inertia to the previously found neutral axis of the whole built-up section. A much simpler method that can be used in the case of any section which can be divided into rectangular elements bounded by lines parallel

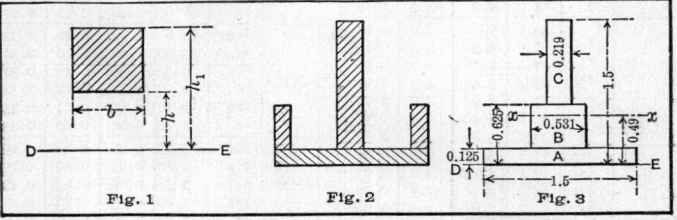

Fig. 1   Fig. 2   Fig. 3

and perpendicular to the neutral axis, is the so-called tabular method based upon the formula: $I = \dfrac{b\,(h_1{}^3 - h^3)}{3}$ in which I = the moment of inertia about axis DE, Fig. 1, and b, h and h_1 are dimensions as given in the same illustration.

The method may be illustrated by applying it to the section shown in Fig. 2, and for simplicity of calculation shown "massed" in Fig. 3. The calculation may then be tabulated as shown in the accompanying table. The distance from the axis DE to the neutral axis xx (which will be designated as d) is found by dividing the sum of the geometrical moments by the area. The moment of inertia about the neutral axis is then found in the usual way by subtracting the area multiplied by d^2 from the moment of inertia about the axis DE.

Tabulated Calculation of Moment of Inertia

Section	Breadth b	Height h_1	Area $b(h_1-h)$	h_1^2	Moment $\dfrac{b(h_1^2-h^2)}{2}$	h_1^3	I about axis DE $\dfrac{b(h_1^3-h^3)}{3}$
A	1.500	0.125	0.187	0.016	0.012	0.002	0.001
B	0.531	0.625	0.266	0.391	0.100	0.244	0.043
C	0.219	1.500	0.191	2.250	0.203	3.375	0.228
			$A = 0.644$		$M = 0.315$		$I_{DE} = 0.272$

Distance d from DE to $xx = \dfrac{M}{A} = \dfrac{0.315}{0.644} = 0.49$.

Moment of inertia of whole section with reference to its neutral axis: $I_n = I_{DE} - Ad^2 = 0.272 - 0.644 \times 0.49^2 = 0.117$.

Sections for Crane and Telpher Runways. — In the design of crane, telpher and similar runways, suitable provision should be made for the lateral strength. The three types of section most commonly used for the purposes mentioned consist of: 1. An I-beam for vertical strength with a channel riveted to the compression flange for lateral stiffness. 2. The same construction, with the addition of a smaller

Sections for Crane and Telpher Runways

Properties of Sections Consisting of One I-beam and Two Channels

Upper Channel		I-beam		Lower Channel		Section Modulus				Moment of Inertia	Distance, C
D, Inches	Weight per Foot, Pounds	H, Inches	Weight per Foot, Pounds	d, Inches	Weight per Foot, Pounds	Upper Chord, Axis A-A	Lower Chord, Axis A-A	Upper Chord, Axis B-B	Lower Chord, Axis B-B		
10	15	10	25	8	11.25	62.87	43.62	14.09	8.97	321.89	5.12
12	20.5	10	25	10	15	76.93	50.92	21.98	14.09	394.66	5.15
12	20.5	12	31.5	10	15	99.54	68.40	22.19	14.35	603.23	6.22
12	20.5	15	42	10	15	139.08	100.03	22.62	14.86	1040.34	7.80
15	33	15	42	12	20.5	185.61	119.97	42.65	22.62	1336.49	8.20
12	20.5	18	55	10	15	185.03	138.27	23.16	15.52	1652.32	9.35
15	33	18	55	12	20.5	241.06	163.01	43.11	23.16	2075.17	9.79

Sections for Crane and Telpher Runways

Properties of Sections Consisting of One I-beam and One Channel

Channel		I-beam		Section Modulus			Moment of Inertia	Distance C
D, Inches	Weight per Foot, Lbs.	H, Inches	Weight per Foot, Lbs.	Upper Chord, Axis A–A	Lower Chord, Axis A–A	Upper Chord, Axis B–B		
10	15	10	25	52.06	27.15	14.09	182.72	6.73
10	15	12	31.5	70.22	39.97	14.35	311.78	7.80
12	20.5	12	31.5	81.71	40.66	22.19	333.39	8.20
12	20.5	12	40	90.41	50.31	22.55	396.91	7.89
10	15	15	42	103.55	64.87	14.86	607.83	9.37
12	20.5	15	42	118.80	66.06	22.62	648.68	9.82
15	33	15	42	151.94	68.18	42.65	724.77	10.63
12	25	15	50	135.28	75.02	25.33	742.67	9.90
12	20.5	15	60	140.17	90.13	23.56	838.22	9.30
15	33	15	60	173.59	93.20	43.43	933.90	10.02
12	20.5	18	55	161.57	99.11	23.16	1122.90	11.33
15	33	18	55	203.18	102.50	43.11	1253.60	12.23
15	33	15	80	197.81	120.17	44.48	1151.27	9.58
12	20.5	20	65	199.98	129.60	23.72	1594.03	12.30
15	33	20	65	247.50	133.85	43.56	1772.11	13.24
15	33	20	80	278.43	164.98	44.52	2113.31	12.81
15	40	20	80	305.44	168.05	49.12	2226.62	13.25
15	33	24	80	339.17	196.13	44.46	3032.18	15.46
15	55	24	100	455.00	239.53	60.64	3894.80	16.26

Properties of Sections Consisting of Two I-beams and One Connecting Plate

Plate		I-beam		Section Modulus			Distance, D	Moment of Inertia	Distance, C
W, Inches	T, Inches	H, Inches	Weight per Foot, Lbs.	Upper Chord, Axis A–A	Lower Chord, Axis A–A	Upper Chord, Axis B–B			
12	⅜	10	25	81.01	54.18	20.27	5.75	337.02	6.22
14	½	12	31.5	131.53	81.72	36.30	7.50	630.03	7.71
14	½	12	40	147.64	100.75	40.38	7.25	748.53	7.43
14	½	15	42	192.53	131.50	40.03	7.00	1211.00	9.21
15	½	15	60	239.39	179.40	55.30	7.50	1589.54	8.86
15	½	15	70	251.22	196.35	61.22	7.50	1708.27	8.70
15	½	15	80	285.65	230.98	65.55	7.25	1979.53	8.57
16	½	18	55	279.02	197.60	60.51	8.50	2140.06	10.83
16	½	20	65	347.57	257.80	65.48	8.25	3034.28	11.77
16	½	20	80	406.10	318.45	67.99	7.50	3658.97	11.49
18	½	24	80	504.42	379.58	90.22	9.50	5306.49	13.98
18	½	24	100	545.59	435.11	106.12	9.50	5930.54	13.63

channel to the tension flange to increase the vertical strength. 3. Two I-beams side by side, with a cover plate on the top flanges only. An illustration of each of these three types is shown in the tables of "Sections for Crane and Telpher Runways," where the section modulus, moment of inertia and other properties of the three types of built-up sections are given.

Size of Rail Necessary to Carry a Given Load. — The following formulas may be employed for determining the size of rail and wheel suitable for carrying a given load. Let, A = the width of the head of the rail in inches; B = width of the tread of the rail in inches; C = the wheel-load in pounds; D = the diameter of the wheel in inches.

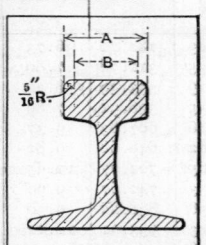

Then the width of the tread of the rail in inches is found from the formula:

$$B = \frac{C}{1250 \, D} \tag{1}$$

The width A of the head equals $B + \frac{5}{8}$ inch. The diameter D of the smallest track wheel that will safely carry the load is found from the formula:

$$D = \frac{C}{A \times K} \tag{2}$$

in which K = 600 to 800 for steel castings; K = 300 to 400 for cast iron.

As an example, assume that the wheel-load in a given case is 10,000 pounds; the diameter of the wheel is 20 inches; and the material steel casting. Determine the size of rail necessary to carry this load. From Formula (1):

$$B = \frac{10,000}{1250 \times 20} = 0.4 \text{ inch.}$$

Hence the width of the rail required equals $0.4 + \frac{5}{8}$ inch = 1.025 inch. Determine also whether a wheel 20 inches in diameter is large enough to safely carry the load. From Formula (2):

$$D = \frac{10,000}{1.025 \times 600} = 16\frac{1}{4} \text{ inches.}$$

This is the smallest diameter of track wheel that will safely carry the load; hence a 20-inch wheel is ample.

BEAMS

Reaction at the Supports. — When a beam is loaded by vertical loads or forces, the sum of the reactions at the supports equals the sum of the loads. In a simple beam, when the loads are symmetrically placed with reference to the supports, or when the load is uniformly distributed, the reaction at each end will equal one-half of the sum of the loads. When the loads are not symmetrically placed, the reaction at each support may be ascertained from the fact that the algebraic sum of the moments must equal zero. In the accompanying illustration, if moments are taken about the support to the left, then:

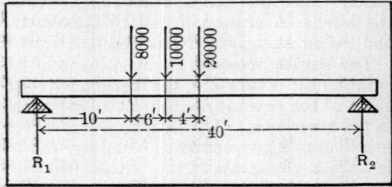

$$R_2 \times 40 - 8000 \times 10 - 10,000 \times 16 - 20,000 \times 20 = 0;$$
$$R_2 = 16,000 \text{ pounds.}$$

Moments taken about the support at the right will, in the same way, give

$$R_1 = 22,000 \text{ pounds.}$$

The sum of the reactions equals 38,000 pounds, which is also the sum of the loads. If part of the load is uniformly distributed over the beam, this part is first equally divided between the two supports, or the uniform load may be considered as concentrated at its center of gravity.

Stresses and Deflections in Beams. — On the following pages is given an extensive table of formulas for stresses and deflections in beams, shafts, etc. It is assumed that all the dimensions are in inches, all loads in pounds, and all stresses in pounds per square inch. In the tables:

E = modulus of elasticity of the material;

I = moment of inertia of the cross-section of the beam;

Z = section modulus of the cross-section of the beam = $I \div$ distance from neutral axis to extreme fiber;

W = load on beam;

s = stress in extreme fiber, or maximum stress in the cross-section considered, due to load W. A positive value of s denotes tension in the upper fibers and compression in the lower ones (as in a cantilever). A negative value of s denotes the reverse (as in a beam supported at the ends). The greatest safe load is that value of W which causes a maximum stress equal to, but not exceeding, the greatest safe value of s;

y = deflection measured from the position occupied if the load causing the deflection were removed. A positive value of y denotes deflection below this position; a negative value, deflection upward;

u, v, w, x = variable distances along the beam from a given support to any point.

If there are several kinds of loads, as, for instance, a uniform load and a load at any point, or separate loads at different points, the total stress and the total deflection at any point is found by adding together the various stresses or deflections at the point considered due to each load acting by itself. If the stress or deflection due to any one of the loads is negative, it must be subtracted instead of added.

Remarks Relative to the Use of the Tables. — In the diagrammatical illustrations of the beams and their loading, the values indicated near, but below, the supports are the "reactions" or upward forces at the supports. For Cases 1 to 12, inclusive, the reactions, as well as the formulas for the stresses, are the same whether the beam is of constant or variable cross-section. For the other cases, the reactions and the stresses given are for constant cross-section beams only.

The bending moment at any point in inch-pounds is $s \times Z$ and can be found by omitting the divisor Z in the formula for the stress given in the tables. A positive value of the bending moment denotes tension in the upper fibers and compression in the lower ones. A negative value denotes the reverse. The value of W corresponding to a given stress is found by transposition of the formula. For example, in Case 1, the stress at the critical point is $s = -Wl \div 8Z$. From this we find $W = -8Zs \div l$. Of course, the negative sign of W may be ignored.

The deflections given in the tables apply only to cases where the cross-section of the beam is constant in its entire length.

Stresses and Deflections in Beams

Type of Beam	Stresses	
	General Formula for Stress at any Point	Stresses at Critical Points
Case 1. — Supported at Both Ends, Uniform Load TOTAL LOAD W	$s = -\dfrac{W}{2Zl}x(l-x)$	Stress at center, $-\dfrac{Wl}{8Z}$ If cross-section is constant, this is the maximum stress.
Case 2. — Supported at Both Ends, Load at Center	Between each support and load, $s = -\dfrac{Wx}{2Z}$	Stress at center, $-\dfrac{Wl}{4Z}$ If cross-section is constant, this is the maximum stress.
Case 3. — Supported at Both Ends, Load at any Point $a + b = l$	For segment of length a, $s = -\dfrac{Wbx}{Zl}$ For segment of length b, $s = -\dfrac{Wav}{Zl}$	Stress at load, $-\dfrac{Wab}{Zl}$ If cross-section is constant, this is the maximum stress.
Case 4. — Supported at Both Ends, Two Symmetrical Loads	Between each support and adjacent load, $s = -\dfrac{Wx}{Z}$ Between loads, $s = -\dfrac{Wa}{Z}$	Stress at each load, and at all points between, $-\dfrac{Wa}{Z}$
Case 5. — Both Ends Overhanging Supports Symmetrically, Uniform Load TOTAL LOAD W $L = l + 2c$	Between each support and adjacent end, $s = \dfrac{W}{2ZL}(c-u)^2$ Between supports, $s = \dfrac{W}{2ZL}[c^2 - x(l-x)]$	Stress at each support, $\dfrac{Wc^2}{2ZL}$ Stress at center, $\dfrac{W}{2ZL}(c^2 - \frac{1}{4}l^2)$ If cross-section is constant, the greater of these is the maximum stress. If l is greater than $2c$, the stress is zero at points $\sqrt{\frac{1}{4}l^2 - c^2}$ on both sides of the center. If cross-section is constant and if $l = 2.828\,c$, the stresses at supports and center are equal and opposite, and are $\pm\dfrac{WL}{46.62\,Z}$

Stresses and Deflections in Beams

Deflections	
General Formula for Deflection at any Point	Deflections at Critical Points
$$y = \frac{Wx\,(l-x)}{24\,EIl}\,[l^2 + x\,(l-x)]$$	Maximum deflection, at center, $$\frac{5}{384}\,\frac{Wl^3}{EI}$$
Between each support and load, $$y = \frac{Wx}{48\,EI}\,(3\,l^2 - 4\,x^2)$$	Maximum deflection, at load, $\dfrac{Wl^3}{48\,EI}$
For segment of length a, $$y = \frac{Wbx}{6\,EIl}\,(l^2 - x^2 - b^2)$$ For segment of length b, $$y = \frac{Wav}{6\,EIl}\,(l^2 - v^2 - a^2)$$	Deflection at load, $\dfrac{Wa^2b^2}{3\,EIl}$ Let a be the length of the shorter segment and b of the longer one. The maximum deflection is in the longer segment, at $$v = b\sqrt{\frac{1}{3} + \frac{2\,a}{3\,b}} = v_1, \text{ and is } \frac{Wav_1^3}{3\,EIl}$$
Between each support and adjacent load, $$y = \frac{Wx}{6\,EI}\,[3\,a\,(l-a) - x^2]$$ Between loads, $$y = \frac{Wa}{6\,EI}\,[3\,v\,(l-v) - a^2]$$	Maximum deflection at center, $$\frac{Wa}{24\,EI}\,(3\,l^2 - 4\,a^2)$$ Deflection at loads $\dfrac{Wa^2}{6\,EI}\,(3\,l - 4\,a)$
Between each support and adjacent end, $$y = \frac{Wu}{24\,EIL}\,[6\,c^2\,(l+u) - u^2\,(4\,c - u) - l^3]$$ Between supports, $$y = \frac{Wx\,(l-x)}{24\,EIL}\,[x\,(l-x) + l^2 - 6\,c^2]$$	Deflection at ends, $$\frac{Wc}{24\,EIL}[3\,c^2\,(c+2\,l) - l^3]$$ Deflection at center, $$\frac{Wl^2}{384\,EIL}\,(5\,l^2 - 24\,c^2)$$ If l is between $2\,c$ and $2.449\,c$, there are maximum upward deflections at points $\sqrt{3\,(\tfrac{1}{4}\,l^2 - c^2)}$ on both sides of the center, which are, $-\dfrac{W}{96\,EIL}\,(6\,c^2 - l^2)^2$

Stresses and Deflections in Beams

Type of Beam	Stresses	
	General Formula for Stress at any Point	Stresses at Critical Points
Case 6. — Both Ends Overhanging Supports Unsymmetrically, Uniform Load TOTAL LOAD W $\frac{W}{2l}(l-d+c)$ $\frac{W}{2l}(l+d-c)$	For overhanging end of length c, $$s = \frac{W}{2ZL}(c-u)^2$$ Between supports, $$s = \frac{W}{2ZL}\left\{ c^2\left(\frac{l-x}{l}\right) + d^2\frac{x}{l} - x(l-x) \right\}$$ For overhanging end of length d, $$s = \frac{W}{2ZL}(d-w)^2$$	Stress at support next end of length c, $$\frac{Wc^2}{2ZL}$$ Critical stress between supports is at $$x = \frac{l^2+c^2-d^2}{2l} = x_1$$ and is $$\frac{W}{2ZL}(c^2-x_1^2)$$ Stress at support next end of length d, $$\frac{Wd^2}{2ZL}$$ If cross-section is constant, the greatest of these three is the maximum stress. If $x_1 > c$, the stress is zero at points $\sqrt{x_1^2-c^2}$ on both sides of $x=x_1$.
Case 7. — Both Ends Overhanging Supports, Load at any Point Between $\frac{Wb}{l}$ $\frac{Wa}{l}$ $(a+b=l)$	Between supports: For segment of length a, $s = -\frac{Wbx}{Zl}$ For segment of length b, $s = -\frac{Wav}{Zl}$ Beyond supports $s = 0$.	Stress at load, $$-\frac{Wab}{Zl}$$ If cross-section is constant, this is the maximum stress.
Case 8. — Both Ends Overhanging Supports, Single Overhanging Load $\frac{W(c+l)}{l}$ $-\frac{Wc}{l}$	Between load and adjacent support, $$s = \frac{W}{Z}(c-u)$$ Between supports, $$s = \frac{Wc}{Zl}(l-x)$$ Between unloaded end and adjacent support, $s = 0$.	Stress at support adjacent to load, $\frac{Wc}{Z}$ If cross-section is constant, this is the maximum stress. Stress is zero at other support.
Case 9. — Both Ends Overhanging Supports, Symmetrical Overhanging Loads 	Between each load and adjacent support, $$s = \frac{W}{Z}(c-u)$$ Between supports, $$s = \frac{Wc}{Z}$$	Stress at supports and at all points between, $\frac{Wc}{Z}$ If cross-section is constant, this is the maximum stress.

Stresses and Deflections in Beams

Deflections	
General Formula for Deflections at any Point	Deflections at Critical Points

For overhanging end of length c,

$$y = \frac{Wu}{24\,EIL}\,[2\,l\,(d^2 + 2\,c^2) + 6\,c^2 u - u^2\,(4\,c - u) - l^3]$$

Between supports,

$$y = \frac{Wx\,(l-x)}{24\,EIL}\left\{ x\,(l-x) + l^2 - 2\,(d^2 + c^2) - \frac{2}{l}\,[d^2 x + c^2\,(l-x)] \right\}$$

For overhanging end of length d,

$$y = \frac{Ww}{24\,EIL}\,[2\,l\,(c^2 + 2\,d^2) + 6\,d^2 w - w^2\,(4\,d - w) - l^3]$$

Deflection at end c,

$$\frac{Wc}{24\,EIL}\,[2\,l\,(d^2 + 2\,c^2) + 3\,c^3 - l^3]$$

Deflection at end d,

$$\frac{Wd}{24\,EIL}\,[2\,l\,(c^2 + 2\,d^2) + 3\,d^3 - l^3]$$

This case is so complicated that convenient general expressions for the critical deflections between supports cannot be obtained.

Between supports, same as Case 3.
For overhanging end of length c,

$$y = -\frac{Wabu}{6\,EIl}\,(l+b)$$

For overhanging end of length d,

$$y = -\frac{Wabw}{6\,EIl}\,(l+a)$$

Between supports, same as Case 3.

Deflection at end c, $-\dfrac{Wabc}{6\,EIl}\,(l+b)$

Deflection at end d, $-\dfrac{Wabd}{6\,EIl}\,(l+a)$

Between load and adjacent support,

$$y = \frac{Wu}{6\,EI}\,(3\,cu - u^2 + 2\,cl)$$

Between supports,

$$y = -\frac{Wcx}{6\,EIl}\,(l-x)(2\,l-x)$$

Between unloaded end and adjacent support, $y = \dfrac{Wclw}{6\,EI}$

Deflection at load, $\dfrac{Wc^2}{3\,EI}\,(c+l)$

Maximum upward deflection is at

$$x = 0.42265\,l, \text{ and is } -\frac{Wcl^2}{15.55\,EI}$$

Deflection at unloaded end, $\dfrac{Wcld}{6\,EI}$

Between each load and adjacent support, $y = \dfrac{Wu}{6\,EI}\,[3\,c\,(l+u) - u^2]$

Between supports, $y = -\dfrac{Wcx}{2\,EI}\,(l-x)$

Deflections at loads, $\dfrac{Wc^2}{6\,EI}\,(2\,c + 3\,l)$

Deflection at center, $-\dfrac{Wcl^2}{8\,EI}$

The above expressions involve the usual approximations of the theory of flexure, and hold only for small deflections. Exact expressions for deflections of any magnitude are as follows:

Between supports the curve is a circle of radius $r = \dfrac{EI}{Wc}$; $y = \sqrt{r^2 - \tfrac{1}{4}\,l^2} - \sqrt{r^2 - (\tfrac{1}{2}\,l - x)^2}$

Deflection at center, $\sqrt{r^2 - \tfrac{1}{4}\,l^2} - r$

Stresses and Deflections in Beams

Type of Beam	Stresses	
	General Formula for Stress at any Point	Stresses at Critical Points
Case 10. — Fixed at One End, Uniform Load	$s = \dfrac{W}{2\,Zl}(l-x)^2$	Stress at support, $\dfrac{Wl}{2\,Z}$ If cross-section is constant, this is the maximum stress.
Case 11. — Fixed at One End, Load at Other	$s = \dfrac{W}{Z}(l-x)$	Stress at support, $\dfrac{Wl}{Z}$ If cross-section is constant, this is the maximum stress.
Case 12. — Fixed at One End, Intermediate Load	Between support and load, $s = \dfrac{W}{Z}(l-x)$ Beyond load, $s = 0$.	Stress at support, $\dfrac{Wl}{Z}$ If cross-section is constant, this is the maximum stress.
Case 13. — Fixed at One End, Supported at the Other, Uniform Load	$s = \dfrac{W(l-x)}{2\,Zl}(\tfrac{1}{4}l - x)$	Maximum stress at point of fixture, $\dfrac{Wl}{8\,Z}$ Stress is zero at $x = \tfrac{1}{4}l$. Greatest negative stress is at $x = \tfrac{5}{8}l$ and is $-\dfrac{9}{128}\dfrac{Wl}{Z}$
Case 14. — Fixed at One End, Supported at the Other, Load at Center	Between point of fixture and load, $s = \dfrac{W}{16\,Z}(3l - 11x)$ Between support and load, $s = -\dfrac{5}{16}\dfrac{Wv}{Z}$	Maximum stress at point of fixture, $\dfrac{3}{16}\dfrac{Wl}{Z}$ Stress is zero at $x = \dfrac{3}{11}l$ Greatest negative stress at center, $-\dfrac{5}{32}\dfrac{Wl}{Z}$

Stresses and Deflections in Beams

Deflections	
General Formula for Deflection at any Point	Deflections at Critical Points
$$y = \frac{Wx^2}{24\,EIl}[2\,l^2 + (2\,l-x)^2]$$	Maximum deflection, at end, $\dfrac{Wl^3}{8\,EI}$
$$y = \frac{Wx^2}{6\,EI}(3\,l-x)$$	Maximum deflection, at end, $\dfrac{Wl^3}{3\,EI}$
Between support and load, $$y = \frac{Wx^2}{6\,EI}(3\,l-x)$$ Beyond load, $$y = \frac{Wl^2}{6\,EI}(3\,v-l)$$	Deflection at load, $\dfrac{Wl^3}{3\,EI}$ Maximum deflection, at end, $$\frac{Wl^2}{6\,EI}(2\,l+3\,b)$$
$$y = \frac{Wx^2(l-x)}{48\,EIl}(3\,l-2\,x)$$	Maximum deflection is at $x = 0.5785\,l$, and is $\dfrac{Wl^3}{185\,EI}$ Deflection at center, $\dfrac{Wl^3}{192\,EI}$ Deflection at point of greatest negative stress, at $x = \frac{5}{8}l$ is $\dfrac{Wl^3}{187\,EI}$
Between point of fixture and load, $$y = \frac{Wx^2}{96\,EI}(9\,l-11\,x)$$ Between support and load, $$y = \frac{Wv}{96\,EI}(3\,l^2-5\,v^2)$$	Maximum deflection is at $v = 0.4472\,l$, and is $\dfrac{Wl^3}{107.33\,EI}$ Deflection at load, $\dfrac{7}{768}\dfrac{Wl^3}{EI}$

Stresses and Deflections in Beams

Type of Beam	Stresses	
	General Formula for Stress at any Point	Stresses at Critical Points
Case 15. — Fixed at One End, Supported at the Other, Load at any Point $m = (l + a)(l + b) + al$ $n = al(l + b)$ $\frac{Wab(l+b)}{2l^2}$ $W\left[1 - \frac{a^2}{2l^3}(3l-a)\right]$ $\frac{Wa^2(3l-a)}{2l^3}$	Between point of fixture and load, $s = \frac{Wb}{2\,Zl^3}(n - mx)$ Between support and load, $s = -\frac{Wa^2v}{2\,Zl^3}(3l - a)$	Greatest positive stress, at point of fixture, $\dfrac{Wab}{2\,Zl^2}(l + b)$ Greatest negative stress, at load, $-\dfrac{Wa^2b}{2\,Zl^3}(3l - a)$ If $a < 0.5858\,l$, the first is the maximum stress. If $a = 0.5858\,l$, the two are equal and are $\pm \dfrac{Wl}{5.83\,Z}$. If $a > 0.5858\,l$, the second is the maximum stress. Stress is zero at $x = \dfrac{n}{m}$
Case 16. — Fixed at One End, Free but Guided at the Other, Uniform Load TOTAL LOAD W $\frac{Wl}{3}$ $\frac{Wl}{6}$ Wl	$s = \dfrac{Wl}{Z}\left\{\dfrac{1}{3} - \dfrac{x}{l} + \dfrac{1}{2}\left(\dfrac{x}{l}\right)^2\right\}$	Maximum stress, at support, $\dfrac{Wl}{3Z}$ Stress is zero for $x = 0.4227\,l$ Greatest negative stress, at free end, $-\dfrac{Wl}{6Z}$
Case 17. — Fixed at One End, Free but Guided at the Other, with Load $\frac{Wl}{2}$ $W \frac{l}{2}$ W	$s = \dfrac{W}{Z}(\tfrac{1}{2}l - x)$	Stress at support, $\dfrac{Wl}{2Z}$ Stress at free end $-\dfrac{Wl}{2Z}$ These are the maximum stresses and are equal and opposite. Stress is zero at center.
Case 18. — Fixed at Both Ends, Uniform Load TOTAL LOAD W $\frac{Wl}{12}$ $\frac{Wl}{12}$ $\frac{W}{2}$ $\frac{W}{2}$	$s = \dfrac{Wl}{2Z}\left\{\dfrac{1}{6} - \dfrac{x}{l} + \left(\dfrac{x}{l}\right)^2\right\}$	Maximum stress, at ends, $\dfrac{Wl}{12Z}$ Stress is zero at $x = 0.7887\,l$ and at $x = 0.2113\,l$ Greatest negative stress, at center, $-\dfrac{Wl}{24Z}$

Stresses and Deflections in Beams

Deflections	
General Formula for Deflections at any Point	Deflections at Critical Points
Between point of fixture and load, $$y = \frac{Wx^2b}{12\,EIl^3}\,(3\,n - mx)$$ Between support and load, $$y = \frac{Wa^2v}{12\,EIl^3}\,[3\,l^2b - v^2\,(3\,l - a)]$$	Deflection at load, $\dfrac{Wa^2b^2}{12\,EIl^3}\,(3\,l + b)$ If $a < 0.5858\,l$, maximum deflection is between load and support, at $$v = l\sqrt{\frac{b}{2\,l + b}}\ \text{and is}\ \frac{Wa^2b}{6\,EI}\sqrt{\frac{b}{2\,l + b}}$$ If $a = 0.5858\,l$, maximum deflection is at load and is $\dfrac{Wl^3}{101.9\,EI}$ If $a > 0.5858\,l$, maximum deflection is between load and point of fixture, at $$x = \frac{2\,n}{m},\ \text{and is}\ \frac{Wbn^3}{3\,EIm^2l^3}$$
$$y = \frac{Wx^2}{24\,EIl}\,(2\,l - x)^2$$	Maximum deflection, at free end, $$\frac{Wl^3}{24\,EI}$$
$$y = \frac{Wx^2}{12\,EI}\,(3\,l - 2\,x)$$	Maximum deflection, at free end, $$\frac{Wl^3}{12\,EI}$$
$$y = \frac{Wx^2}{24\,EIl}\,(l - x)^2$$	Maximum deflection, at center, $$\frac{Wl^3}{384\,EI}$$

Stresses and Deflections in Beams

Type of Beam	Stresses	
	General Formula for Stress at any Point	Stresses at Critical Points
Case 19. — Fixed at Both Ends, Load at Center	Between each end and load, $$s = \frac{W}{2Z}\left(\tfrac{1}{4}l - x\right)$$	Stress at ends $\frac{Wl}{8Z}$; at load $-\frac{Wl}{8Z}$ These are the maximum stresses and are equal and opposite. Stress is zero at $x = \tfrac{1}{4}l$
Case 20. — Fixed at Both Ends, Load at any Point	For segment of length a, $$s = \frac{Wb^2}{Zl^3}[al - x(l + 2a)]$$ For segment of length b, $$s = \frac{Wa^2}{Zl^3}[bl - v(l + 2b)]$$	Stress at end next segment of length a, $\dfrac{Wab^2}{Zl^2}$ Stress at end next segment of length b, $\dfrac{Wa^2b}{Zl^2}$ Maximum stress is at end next shorter segment. Stress is zero for $x = \dfrac{al}{l+2a}$ and $v = \dfrac{bl}{l+2b}$ Greatest negative stress, at load, $-\dfrac{2Wa^2b^2}{Zl^3}$
Case 21. — Continuous Beam, with Two Equal Spans, Uniform Load TOTAL LOAD ON EACH SPAN, W	$$s = \frac{W(l-x)}{2Zl}\left(\tfrac{1}{4}l - x\right)$$	Maximum stress at point A, $\dfrac{Wl}{8Z}$ Stress is zero at $x = \tfrac{1}{4}l$. Greatest negative stress is at $x = \tfrac{5}{8}$ and is, $-\dfrac{9}{128}\dfrac{Wl}{Z}$
Case 22. — Continuous Beam, with Two Unequal Spans, Unequal Uniform Loads TOTAL LOAD W_1 TOTAL LOAD W_2 $\dfrac{l_1 W_1(3l_1 + 4l_2) - w_1 l_2^2}{8l_1(l_1 + l_2)}$ $\dfrac{l_2 W_2(3l_2 + 4l_1) - w_1 l_1^2}{8l_2(l_1 + l_2)}$ $\left(\dfrac{W_1 + W_2}{2}\right) + \dfrac{1}{8}\left(\dfrac{W_1 l_1}{l_2} + \dfrac{W_2 l_2}{l_1}\right)$	Between R_1 and R, $$s = \frac{l_1 - x}{Z}\left\{\frac{(l_1 - x)W_1}{2l_1} - r_1\right\}$$ Between R_2 and R, $$s = \frac{l_2 - u}{Z}\left\{\frac{(l_2 - u)W_2}{2l_2} - r_2\right\}$$	Stress at support R, $\dfrac{W_1 l_1^2 + W_2 l_2^2}{8Z(l_1 + l_2)}$ Greatest stress in the first span is at $x = \dfrac{l_1}{W_1}(W_1 - r_1)$, and is, $-\dfrac{r_1^2 l_1}{2ZW_1}$ Greatest stress in the second span is at $u = \dfrac{l_2}{W_2}(W_2 - r_2)$, and is, $-\dfrac{r_2^2 l_2}{2ZW_2}$

Stresses and Deflections in Beams

Deflections	
General Formula for Deflections at any Point	Deflections at Critical Points
$$y = \frac{Wx^2}{48\,EI}(3l - 4x)$$	Maximum deflection, at load, $$\frac{Wl^3}{192\,EI}$$
For segment of length a, $$y = \frac{Wx^2b^2}{6\,EIl^3}[2a(l-x) + l(a-x)]$$ For segment of length b, $$y = \frac{Wv^2a^2}{6\,EIl^3}[2b(l-v) + l(b-v)]$$	Deflection at load, $\dfrac{Wa^3b^3}{3\,EIl^3}$ Let b be the length of the longer segment and a of the shorter one. The maximum deflection is in the longer segment, at $v = \dfrac{2bl}{l+2b}$, and is $$\frac{2\,Wa^2b^3}{3\,EI\,(l+2b)^2}$$
$$y = \frac{Wx^2(l-x)}{48\,EIl}(3l - 2x)$$	Maximum deflection is at $x = 0.5785\,l$, and is $\dfrac{Wl^3}{185\,EI}$ Deflection at center of span, $\dfrac{Wl^3}{192\,EI}$ Deflection at point of greatest negative stress, at $x = \dfrac{5}{8}l$ is $\dfrac{Wl^3}{187\,EI}$
Between R_1 and R, $$y = \frac{x(l_1 - x)}{24\,EI}\left\{ (2l_1 - x)(4r_1 - W_1) - \frac{W_1(l_1 - x)^2}{l_1} \right\}$$ Between R_2 and R, $$y = \frac{u(l_2 - u)}{24\,EI}\left\{ (2l_2 - u)(4r_2 - W_2) - \frac{W_2(l_2 - u)^2}{l_2} \right\}$$	This case is so complicated that convenient general expressions for the critical deflections cannot be obtained.

Stresses and Deflections in Beams

Type of Beam	Stresses	
	General Formula for Stress at any Point	Stresses at Critical Points
Case 23. — Continuous Beam, with Two Equal Spans, Equal Loads at Center of Each 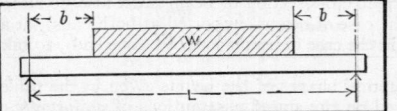	Between point A and load, $$s = \frac{W}{16\,Z}(3l - 11x)$$ Between point B and load, $$s = -\frac{5}{16}\frac{Wv}{Z}$$	Maximum stress at point A, $\dfrac{3}{16}\dfrac{Wl}{Z}$ Stress is zero at $$x = \frac{3}{11}l$$ Greatest negative stress at center of span, $$-\frac{5}{32}\frac{Wl}{Z}$$
Case 24. — Continuous Beam, with Two Unequal Spans, Unequal Loads at any Point of Each $$m = \frac{1}{2(l_1 + l_2)}\left(\frac{W_1 a_1 b_1}{l_1}(l_1 + a_1) + \frac{W_2 a_2 b_2}{l_2}(l_2 + a_2)\right)$$	Between R_1 and W_1, $$s = -\frac{wr_1}{Z}$$ Between R and W_1, $$s = \frac{I}{l_1 Z}[m(l_1 - u) - W_1 a_1 u]$$ Between R and W_2, $$s = \frac{I}{l_2 Z}[m(l_2 - x) - W_2 a_2 x]$$ Between R_2 and W_2, $$s = -\frac{vr_2}{Z}$$	Stress at load W_1, $$-\frac{a_1 r_1}{Z}$$ Stress at support R, $$\frac{m}{Z}$$ Stress at load W_2, $$-\frac{a_2 r_2}{Z}$$ The greatest of these is the maximum stress.

Deflection of Beam Uniformly Loaded for Part of Its Length. — In the following formulas, lengths are in inches, weights in pounds. W = total load; L = total length between supports; E = modulus of elasticity; I = moment of inertia of beam section; a = fraction of length of beam at each end, that is not loaded = $b \div L$; f = deflection.

$$f = \frac{WL^3}{EI\,384\,(1 - 2a)}(5 - 24a^2 + 16a^4)$$

The expression for maximum bending moment is: $M_{max.} = \frac{1}{8}WL(1 + 2a)$. These formulas apply to simple beams resting on supports at the ends.

Beams of Uniform Strength Throughout Their Length. — In nearly all cases, the bending moment in a beam is not uniform throughout its length, but varies. Therefore, a beam of uniform cross-section which is made strong enough at its most strained section, will have an excess of material at every other section. Sometimes it may be desirable to have the cross-section uniform, while in other cases the metal can be more advantageously distributed if the beam is so designed that its cross-section varies from point to point, so that it is at every point just great enough to take care of the bending stresses at that point. A table is given showing beams

Stresses and Deflections in Beams

Deflections	
General Formula for Deflections at any Point	Deflections at Critical Points
Between point A and load, $$y = \frac{Wx^2}{96\,EI}\,(9\,l - 11\,x)$$ Between point B and load, $$y = \frac{Wv}{96\,EI}\,(3\,l^2 - 5\,v^2)$$	Maximum deflection is at $v = 0.4472\,l$, and is $\dfrac{Wl^3}{107.33\,EI}$ Deflection at load, $\dfrac{7}{768}\,\dfrac{Wl^3}{EI}$
Between R_1 and W_1, $$y = \frac{w}{6\,EI}\left\{(l_1 - w)\,(l_1 + w)\,r_1 - \frac{W_1 b_1^3}{l_1}\right\}$$ Between R and W_1, $$y = \frac{u}{6\,EIl_1}\,[\,W_1 a_1 b_1\,(l_1 + a_1)$$ $$- W_1 a_1 u^2 - m\,(2\,l_1 - u)\,(l_1 - u)]$$ Between R and W_2, $$y = \frac{x}{6\,EIl_2}\,[\,W_2 a_2 b_2\,(l_2 + a_2)$$ $$- W_2 a_2 x^2 - m\,(2\,l_2 - x)\,(l_2 - x)]$$ Between R_2 and W_2, $$y = \frac{v}{6\,EI}\left\{(l_2 - v)\,(l_2 + v)\,r_2 - \frac{W_2 b_2^3}{l_2}\right\}$$	Deflection at load W_1, $$\frac{a_1 b_1}{6\,EIl_1}\,[2\,a_1 b_1 W_1 - m\,(l_1 + a_1)]$$ Deflection at load W_2, $$\frac{a_2 b_2}{6\,EIl_2}\,[2\,a_2 b_2 W_2 - m\,(l_2 + a_2)]$$ This case is so complicated that convenient general expressions for the maximum deflections cannot be obtained.

in which the load is applied in different ways and which are supported by different methods, and the shape of the beam required for uniform strength is indicated. It should be noted that the shape given is the theoretical shape required to resist bending only. It is apparent that sufficient cross-section of beam must also be added either at the points of support (in the case of beams supported at both ends), or at the point of application of the load (in the case of beams loaded at one end), to take care of the vertical shear.

It should be noted that the theoretical shapes of the beams given in the tables on the two following pages are based on the stated assumptions of uniformity of width or depth of cross-section, and unless these are observed in the design, the theoretical outlines do not apply without modifications. For example, in a cantilever with the load at one end, the outline is a parabola only when the width of the beam is uniform. It is not correct to use a strictly parabolic shape when the thickness is not uniform, as, for instance, when the beam is made of an I- or T-section. In such cases, some modification may be necessary; but it is evident that whatever the shape adopted, the correct depth of the section can be obtained by an investigation of the bending moment and the shearing load at a number of points, and then a line can be drawn through the points thus ascertained, which will provide for a beam of practically uniform strength whether the cross-section be of uniform width or not.

Beams of Uniform Strength Throughout Their Length

(All loads in pounds, all dimensions in inches.)

Type of Beam	Description	P = Carrying Capacity S = Safe Stress per Square Inch
	Load at one end. Width of beam uniform. Depth of beam decreasing towards loaded end. Outline of beam-shape, parabola with vertex at loaded end.	$P = \dfrac{Sbh^2}{6l}$
	Load at one end. Width of beam uniform. Depth of beam decreasing towards loaded end. Outline of beam, one-half of a parabola with vertex at loaded end. Beam may be reversed so that upper edge is parabolic.	$P = \dfrac{Sbh^2}{6l}$
	Load at one end. Depth of beam uniform. Width of beam decreasing towards loaded end. Outline of beam triangular, with apex at loaded end.	$P = \dfrac{Sbh^2}{6l}$
	Beam of *approximately* uniform strength. Load at one end. Width of beam uniform. Depth of beam decreasing towards loaded end, but not tapering to a sharp point.	$P = \dfrac{Sbh^2}{6l}$
	Uniformly distributed load. Width of beam uniform. Depth of beam decreasing towards outer end. Outline of beam, right-angled triangle.	$P = \dfrac{Sbh^2}{3l}$
	Uniformly distributed load. Depth of beam uniform. Width of beam gradually decreasing towards outer end. Outline of beam is formed by two parabolas which tangent each other at their vertices at the outer end of the beam.	$P = \dfrac{Sbh^2}{3l}$

Beams of Uniform Strength Throughout Their Length

Type of Beam	Description	P = Carrying Capacity S = Safe Stress per Square Inch
	Beam supported at both ends. Load concentrated at any point. Depth of beam uniform. Width of beam maximum at point of loading. Outline of beam, two triangles with apexes at points of support.	$P = \dfrac{Sbh^2l}{6\,ac}$
	Beam supported at both ends. Load concentrated at any point. Width of beam uniform. Depth of beam maximum at point of loading. Outline of beam is formed by two parabolas with their vertexes at points of support.	$P = \dfrac{Sbh^2l}{6\,ac}$
	Beam supported at both ends. Load concentrated in the middle. Depth of beam uniform. Width of beam maximum at point of loading. Outline of beam, two triangles with apexes at points of support.	$P = \dfrac{2\,Sbh^2}{3\,l}$
	Beam supported at both ends. Load concentrated at center. Width of beam uniform. Depth of beam maximum at point of loading. Outline of beam, two parabolas with vertices at points of support.	$P = \dfrac{2\,Sbh^2}{3\,l}$
	Beam supported at both ends. Load uniformly distributed. Depth of beam uniform. Width of beam maximum at center. Outline of beam, two parabolas with vertexes at middle of beam.	$P = \dfrac{4\,Sbh^2}{3\,l}$
	Beam supported at both ends. Load uniformly distributed. Width of beam uniform. Depth of beam maximum at center. Outline of beam one-half of an ellipse.	$P = \dfrac{4\,Sbh^2}{3\,l}$

Crane Girders with Curved Lower Chords. — An example of a design which makes use of the principles of beams of uniform strength is found in the ordinary fish-belly type of crane girder. When laying out crane girders, the accompanying tables will be found convenient. The engraving will explain the use of the tables. A crane girder having a span of 61 feet 3 inches has been assumed as an example. The curved part has a span of 60 feet; one-half of this distance, or 30 feet, is divided for the convenience of the templet makers into ten spaces of 3 feet each. The end ordinate, assumed here to be 1 foot, will be found at the extreme left of the tables under the heading H. The lengths of the remaining nine ordinates follow in order. The lengths of the remaining nine ordinates follow in order. For short spans, say about 30 feet, it is most convenient to divide the base of the curve into five spaces, as it is the usual practice to give ordinates about every 3 feet. In this case, we would use only every other ordinate in the tables, or, beginning with the left-hand column, the ordinates would be as found in the columns headed H, 8, 6, 4 and 2.

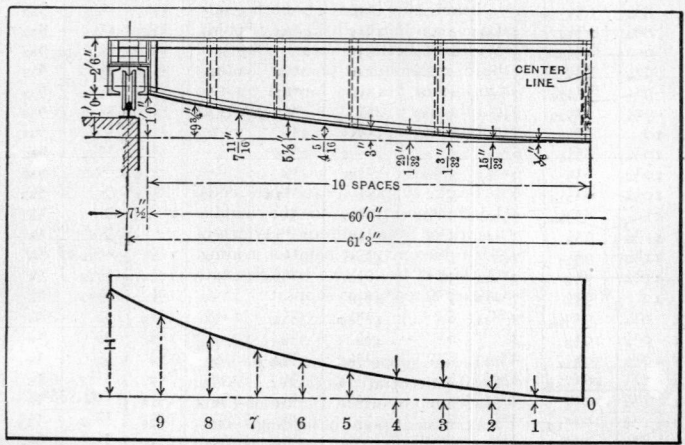

The tables are calculated from the formula:

$$X = H \times (M^2 \div N^2)$$

in which H = end ordinate; X = required ordinate; N = number of equal spaces into which the base line is divided; M = number of spaces from o to the required ordinate. When $N = 10$, as in the case for which the tables are calculated, $N^2 = 100$, and

$$X = H \times 0.01 \, M^2.$$

Hence, ordinate No. 8 equals $H \times 0.01 \times 64 = 0.64 \, H$. Ordinate No. 4 equals $H \times 0.01 \times 16 = 0.16 \, H$.

Opinions vary considerably as to the allowable working stress in crane girders. Many cranes have girders which are designed for a stress of only 8000 pounds per square inch, while in others the stress will be over 14,000 pounds. However, a general factor of safety of 5 is the most usual and desirable in crane work, and if that factor of safety is adopted, the working stress should be anywhere from 11,000 to 12,000 pounds per square inch.

Ordinates of Parabolas for Crane Girder Design — 1

H	9	8	7	6	5	4	3	2	1
Ft. Ins.	Ins.	Ins.	Ins.	Ins.	Ins.	Ins.	Ins.	Ins.	Ins.
6	4 7/8	3 27/32	2 15/16	2 5/32	1 1/2	31/32	17/32	1/4	1/16
6 1/4	5 1/16	4	3 1/16	2 1/4	1 9/16	1	9/16	1/4	1/16
6 1/2	5 1/4	4 5/32	3 3/16	2 11/32	1 5/8	1 1/32	19/32	1/4	1/16
6 3/4	5 15/32	4 5/16	3 5/16	2 7/16	1 11/16	1 3/32	19/32	9/32	1/16
7	5 11/16	4 15/32	3 7/16	2 17/32	1 3/4	1 1/8	5/8	9/32	1/16
7 1/4	5 7/8	4 21/32	3 9/16	2 5/8	1 13/16	1 5/32	21/32	9/32	1/16
7 1/2	6 1/16	4 13/16	3 11/16	2 11/16	1 7/8	1 7/32	11/16	5/16	1/16
7 3/4	6 9/32	4 31/32	3 13/16	2 25/32	1 15/16	1 1/4	11/16	5/16	1/16
8	6 15/32	5 1/8	3 15/16	2 7/8	2	1 9/32	23/32	5/16	3/32
8 1/4	6 19/32	5 9/32	4 1/32	2 31/32	2 1/16	1 5/16	3/4	11/32	3/32
8 1/2	6 7/8	5 7/16	4 5/32	3 1/16	2 1/8	1 3/8	3/4	11/32	3/32
8 3/4	7 3/32	5 19/32	4 9/32	3 5/32	2 3/16	1 13/32	25/32	11/32	3/32
9	7 9/32	5 3/4	4 13/32	3 1/4	2 1/4	1 7/16	13/16	3/8	3/32
9 1/4	7 1/2	5 15/16	4 17/32	3 3/8	2 5/16	1 15/32	27/32	3/8	3/32
9 1/2	7 11/16	6 3/32	4 21/32	3 7/16	2 3/8	1 1/2	27/32	3/8	3/32
9 3/4	7 29/32	6 1/4	4 25/32	3 1/2	2 7/16	1 9/16	7/8	13/32	3/32
10	8 3/32	6 13/32	4 29/32	3 19/32	2 1/2	1 19/32	29/32	13/32	3/32
10 1/4	8 5/16	6 9/16	5	3 11/16	2 9/16	1 5/8	15/16	13/32	3/32
10 1/2	8 1/2	6 23/32	5 5/32	3 25/32	2 5/8	1 11/16	15/16	13/32	3/32
10 3/4	8 11/16	6 7/8	5 1/4	3 7/8	2 11/16	1 23/32	31/32	7/16	3/32
11	8 29/32	7 1/32	5 13/32	3 31/32	2 3/4	1 3/4	1	7/16	1/8
11 1/4	9 1/8	7 3/16	5 1/2	4 1/16	2 13/16	1 13/16	1	7/16	1/8
11 1/2	9 5/16	7 3/8	5 5/8	4 5/32	2 7/8	1 27/32	1 1/32	15/32	1/8
11 3/4	9 1/2	7 17/32	5 3/4	4 7/32	2 15/16	1 7/8	1 1/16	15/32	1/8
12	9 3/4	7 11/16	5 7/8	4 5/16	3	1 29/32	1 3/32	15/32	1/8
1 0 1/4	9 15/16	7 27/32	6	4 13/32	3 1/16	1 31/32	1 3/32	1/2	1/8
1 0 1/2	10 1/8	8	6 1/8	4 1/2	3 1/8	2	1 1/8	1/2	1/8
1 0 3/4	10 5/16	8 5/32	6 1/4	4 19/32	3 3/16	2 3/32	1 1/8	1/2	1/8
1 1	10 17/32	8 5/16	6 3/8	4 11/16	3 1/4	2 3/32	1 5/32	17/32	1/8
1 1 1/4	10 3/4	8 15/32	6 1/2	4 25/32	3 3/8	2 1/8	1 3/16	17/32	1/8
1 1 1/2	10 15/16	8 5/8	6 5/8	4 7/8	3 3/8	2 5/32	1 7/32	17/32	1/8
1 1 3/4	11 1/8	8 3/4	6 3/4	4 15/16	3 7/16	2 3/16	1 1/4	9/16	1/8
1 2	11 11/32	8 31/32	7	5 1/32	3 1/2	2 1/4	1 1/4	9/16	5/32
1 2 1/4	11 17/32	9 1/8	7	5 1/8	3 9/16	2 9/32	1 9/32	9/16	5/32
1 2 1/2	11 3/4	9 9/32	7 3/32	5 7/32	3 5/8	2 5/16	1 5/16	19/32	5/32
1 2 3/4	11 15/16	9 7/16	7 7/32	5 5/16	3 11/16	2 3/8	1 11/32	19/32	5/32
1 3	12 5/32	9 19/32	7 11/32	5 13/32	3 3/4	2 13/32	1 11/32	19/32	5/32
1 3 1/4	12 11/32	9 3/4	7 15/32	5 1/2	3 13/16	2 7/16	1 3/8	19/32	5/32
1 3 1/2	12 9/16	9 15/16	7 19/32	5 19/32	3 7/8	2 1/2	1 13/32	5/8	5/32
1 3 3/4	12 3/4	10 3/32	7 23/32	5 21/32	3 15/16	2 17/32	1 13/32	5/8	5/32
1 4	12 31/32	10 1/4	7 27/32	5 3/4	4	2 9/16	1 7/16	5/8	5/32
1 4 1/4	13 5/32	10 13/32	7 31/32	5 27/32	4 1/16	2 19/32	1 15/32	21/32	5/32
1 4 1/2	13 3/8	10 9/16	8 3/32	5 15/16	4 1/8	2 5/8	1 15/32	21/32	5/32
1 4 3/4	13 9/16	10 23/32	8 5/32	6 1/8	4 3/16	2 11/16	1 1/2	11/16	5/32
1 5	13 25/32	10 7/8	8 11/32	6 1/4	4 1/4	2 23/32	1 17/32	11/16	5/32
1 5 1/4	13 31/32	11 1/32	8 7/16	6 9/32	4 5/16	2 3/4	1 9/16	11/16	3/16
1 5 1/2	14 3/16	11 3/16	8 9/16	6 5/16	4 3/8	2 13/16	1 9/16	11/16	3/16
1 5 3/4	14 3/8	11 3/8	8 11/16	6 13/32	4 7/16	2 27/32	1 19/32	23/32	3/16
1 6	14 19/32	11 17/32	8 13/16	6 15/32	4 1/2	2 7/8	1 5/8	23/32	3/16

Ordinates of Parabolas for Crane Girder Design — 2

		Ordinates											
H		9		8		7		6	5	4	3	2	1
Ft.	Ins.	Ft.	Ins.	Ft.	Ins.	Ft.	Ins.	Ins.	Ins.	Ins.	Ins.	Ins.	Ins.
1	6	1	2 19/32		11 17/32		8 13/16	6 15/32	4 1/2	2 7/8	1 5/8	23/32	3/16
1	6 1/4	1	2 25/32		11 11/16		8 15/16	6 9/16	4 9/16	2 15/16	1 21/32	23/32	3/16
1	6 1/2	1	3		11 27/32		9 1/16	6 21/32	4 5/8	2 31/32	1 21/32	3/4	3/16
1	6 3/4	1	3 3/16	1	0		9 3/16	6 3/4	4 11/16	3	1 11/16	3/4	3/16
1	7	1	3 13/32	1	0 5/32		9 5/16	6 27/32	4 3/4	3 1/32	1 23/32	3/4	3/16
1	7 1/4	1	3 19/32	1	0 5/16		9 7/16	6 15/16	4 13/16	3 3/32	1 23/32	3/4	3/16
1	7 1/2	1	3 25/32	1	0 15/32		9 9/16	7	4 7/8	3 1/8	1 3/4	25/32	3/16
1	7 3/4	1	4	1	0 21/32		9 11/16	7 1/8	4 15/16	3 5/32	1 25/32	25/32	3/16
1	8	1	4 3/16	1	0 13/16		9 13/16	7 3/16	5	3 3/16	1 13/16	13/16	3/16
1	8 1/4	1	4 13/32	1	0 31/32		9 15/16	7 9/32	5 1/16	3 1/4	1 13/16	13/16	3/16
1	8 1/2	1	4 19/32	1	1 1/8		10 1/32	7 3/8	5 1/8	3 9/32	1 27/32	13/16	7/32
1	8 3/4	1	4 13/16	1	1 9/32		10 5/32	7 15/32	5 3/16	3 5/16	1 7/8	27/32	7/32
1	9	1	5	1	1 7/16		10 9/32	7 9/16	5 1/4	3 3/8	1 7/8	27/32	7/32
1	9 1/4	1	5 7/32	1	1 19/32		10 13/32	7 21/32	5 5/16	3 13/32	1 29/32	27/32	7/32
1	9 1/2	1	5 13/32	1	1 3/4		10 17/32	7 3/4	5 3/8	3 7/16	1 15/16	7/8	7/32
1	9 3/4	1	5 5/8	1	1 15/16		10 21/32	7 27/32	5 7/16	3 15/32	1 31/32	7/8	7/32
1	10	1	5 13/16	1	2 3/32		10 25/32	7 15/16	5 1/2	3 17/32	1 31/32	7/8	7/32
1	10 1/4	1	6 1/32	1	2 1/4		10 29/32	8	5 9/16	3 9/16	2	29/32	7/32
1	10 1/2	1	6 7/32	1	2 7/16		11 1/32	8 3/32	5 5/8	3 19/32	2 1/32	29/32	7/32
1	10 3/4	1	6 7/16	1	2 9/16		11 5/32	8 3/16	5 11/16	3 5/8	2 1/16	29/32	7/32
1	11	1	6 5/8	1	2 23/32		11 9/32	8 9/32	5 3/4	3 11/16	2 1/16	15/16	7/32
1	11 1/4	1	6 15/16	1	2 7/8		11 13/32	8 3/8	5 13/16	3 23/32	2 3/32	15/16	7/32
1	11 1/2	1	7 1/32	1	3 1/32		11 17/32	8 15/32	5 7/8	3 3/4	2 1/8	15/16	1/4
1	11 3/4	1	7 1/4	1	3 3/16		11 5/8	8 9/16	5 15/16	3 13/16	2 1/8	31/32	1/4
2	0	1	7 7/16	1	3 3/8		11 3/4	8 21/32	6	3 27/32	2 5/32	31/32	1/4
2	0 1/4	1	7 21/32	1	3 17/32		11 7/8	8 23/32	6 1/16	3 7/8	2 3/16	31/32	1/4
2	0 1/2	1	7 27/32	1	3 11/16	1	0	8 13/16	6 1/8	3 15/16	2 7/32	31/32	1/4
2	0 3/4	1	8 1/32	1	3 27/32	1	0 1/8	8 29/32	6 3/16	3 31/32	2 7/32	1	1/4
2	1	1	8 1/4	1	4	1	0 1/4	9	6 1/4	4	2 1/4	1	1/4
2	1 1/4	1	8 15/32	1	4 5/32	1	0 3/8	9 3/32	6 5/16	4 1/32	2 9/32	1	1/4
2	1 1/2	1	8 21/32	1	4 5/16	1	0 1/2	9 3/16	6 3/8	4 3/32	2 9/32	1 1/32	1/4
2	1 3/4	1	8 27/32	1	4 15/32	1	0 5/8	9 9/32	6 7/16	4 1/8	2 5/16	1 1/32	1/4
2	2	1	9 1/16	1	4 21/32	1	0 3/4	9 3/8	6 1/2	4 5/32	2 11/32	1 1/32	1/4
2	2 1/4	1	9 1/4	1	4 13/16	1	0 7/8	9 15/32	6 9/16	4 7/32	2 3/8	1 1/16	1/4
2	2 1/2	1	9 15/32	1	4 31/32	1	1	9 17/32	6 5/8	4 1/4	2 3/8	1 1/16	1/4
2	2 3/4	1	9 21/32	1	5 1/8	1	1 3/32	9 5/8	6 11/16	4 9/32	2 13/32	1 1/16	1/4
2	3	1	9 7/8	1	5 9/32	1	1 1/4	9 23/32	6 3/4	4 5/16	2 7/16	1 3/32	9/32
2	3 1/4	1	10 1/16	1	5 7/16	1	1 11/32	9 13/16	6 13/16	4 3/8	2 15/32	1 3/32	9/32
2	3 1/2	1	10 9/32	1	5 19/32	1	1 15/32	9 29/32	6 7/8	4 13/32	2 15/32	1 3/32	9/32
2	3 3/4	1	10 15/32	1	5 3/4	1	1 19/32	10	6 15/16	4 7/16	2 1/2	1 1/8	9/32
2	4	1	10 11/16	1	5 15/16	1	1 23/32	10 3/32	7	4 15/32	2 17/32	1 1/8	9/32
2	4 1/4	1	10 7/8	1	6 3/32	1	1 27/32	10 3/16	7 1/16	4 17/32	2 17/32	1 1/8	9/32
2	4 1/2	1	11 3/32	1	6 1/4	1	1 31/32	10 1/4	7 1/8	4 9/16	2 9/16	1 5/32	9/32
2	4 3/4	1	11 9/32	1	6 13/32	1	2 3/32	10 11/32	7 3/16	4 19/32	2 19/32	1 5/32	9/32
2	5	1	11 1/2	1	6 9/16	1	2 7/32	10 7/16	7 1/4	4 21/32	2 5/8	1 5/32	9/32
2	5 1/4	1	11 11/16	1	6 23/32	1	2 11/32	10 17/32	7 5/16	4 11/16	2 5/8	1 3/16	9/32
2	5 1/2	1	11 29/32	1	6 7/8	1	2 15/32	10 5/8	7 3/8	4 23/32	2 21/32	1 3/16	5/16
2	5 3/4	2	0 3/32	1	7 1/32	1	2 19/32	10 23/32	7 7/16	4 3/4	2 11/16	1 3/16	5/16
2	6	2	0 5/16	1	7 7/32	1	2 23/32	10 13/16	7 1/2	4 13/16	2 23/32	1 7/32	5/16

Permissible Working Stresses for Structural Timbers
(U. S. Government Tests)

Kind of Timber	Bending, Pounds per Sq. In.			Compression, Pounds per Sq. In.			
	Allowable Stress in Extreme Fiber		Allowable Horizontal Shear Stress	Allowable Stress Parallel to Grain "Short Columns"		Allowable Stress Perpendicular to Grain	
	Outside Location	Dry Location	All Locations	Outside Location	Dry Location	Outside Location	Inside Location
Cedar, western red.............	800	900	80	700	700	150	200
Cedar, northern white...........	650	750	70	500	550	140	175
Chestnut......................	850	950	90	700	800	200	300
Cypress.......................	1100	1300	100	1100	1100	250	350
Douglas fir (No. 1 str'l) *........	1400	1600	100	1100	1200	250	350
Douglas fir (No. 2 str'l).........	1100	1300	90	900	1000	225	300
Fir, balsam...................	750	900	70	600	700	125	150
Gum, red.....................	900	1100	100	750	800	200	300
Hemlock, western..............	1100	1300	75	900	900	225	300
Hemlock, eastern..............	900	1000	70	700	700	225	300
Hickory......................	1500	1900	140	1200	1500	400	600
Maple, sugar or hard...........	1300	1500	150	1100	1200	375	500
Maple, silver or soft...........	900	1000	100	700	800	250	350
Oak, white or red..............	1200	1400	125	900	1000	375	500
Pine, s. yellow (dense) †........	1400	1600	125	1100	1200	250	350
Pine, s. yellow (sound).........	1100	1300	105	900	1000	225	300
Pine, eastern white............	800	900	85	750	750	150	250
Pine, western white............	800	900	85	750	750	150	250
Pine, Norway..................	1000	1100	85	800	800	175	300
Redwood......................	1000	1200	70	900	1000	150	250
Spruce, red or white...........	900	1100	85	750	800	150	250
Spruce, Englemann.............	650	750	70	550	600	140	175

* The strength of large timbers depends chiefly upon the density or weight per cubic foot of the dry wood and upon the character, size, number and location of defects. " Dense " Douglas fir of the " No. 1 structural grade " shows on one end an average of at least six annual rings per inch and at least one-third " summer wood," measured over 3 inches on a line extending from the pith to the corner farthest from the pith when the least dimension of the timber is 5 inches or more. The point where the 3-inch line begins is found by the formula $A = \frac{1}{2} D - 2$, where A = distance in inches from pith to beginning of 3-inch line and D = minimum dimension of timber in inches. The " No. 2 structural grade " for Douglas fir includes timbers not passing the No. 1 grade, because (1) there is less density than required or (2) greater defects than are permitted.

† The term " southern yellow pine " includes the species known heretofore as long-leaf pine, short-leaf pine, loblolly pine, Cuban pine and pond pine. " Dense " southern yellow pine shows on either end an average of at least six annual rings per inch and at least one-third summer wood, or else the greater number of rings shows at least one-third summer wood all as measured over the third, fourth, and fifth inches of a radial line extending from the pith. Wide-ringed material, excluded by this rule, is acceptable, provided the amount of summer wood measured as previously specified is at least one-half. " Sound " southern yellow pine includes pieces without any ring or summer wood requirement.

Rectangular Solid Beams

Style of Loading and Support	Breadth of Beam in Inches b	Height of Beam in Inches h	Stress per Sq. In. in Extreme Fibers of Beam f	Length of Beam in Inches l	Load in Pounds W
Beam fixed at one end, loaded at the other	$\dfrac{6\,lW}{fh^2}=b$	$\sqrt{\dfrac{6\,lW}{bf}}=h$	$\dfrac{6\,lW}{bh^2}=f$	$\dfrac{bfh^2}{6\,W}=l$	$\dfrac{bfh^2}{6\,l}=W$
Beam fixed at one end, uniformly loaded	$\dfrac{3\,lW}{fh^2}=b$	$\sqrt{\dfrac{3\,lW}{bf}}=h$	$\dfrac{3\,lW}{bh^2}=f$	$\dfrac{bfh^2}{3\,W}=l$	$\dfrac{bfh^2}{3\,l}=W$
Beam supported at both ends, single load in middle	$\dfrac{3\,lW}{2\,fh^2}=b$	$\sqrt{\dfrac{3\,lW}{2\,bf}}=h$	$\dfrac{3\,lW}{2\,bh^2}=f$	$\dfrac{2\,bfh^2}{3\,W}=l$	$\dfrac{2\,bfh^2}{3\,l}=W$
Beam supported at both ends, uniformly loaded	$\dfrac{3\,lW}{4\,fh^2}=b$	$\sqrt{\dfrac{3\,lW}{4\,bf}}=h$	$\dfrac{3\,lW}{4\,bh^2}=f$	$\dfrac{4\,bfh^2}{3\,W}=l$	$\dfrac{4\,bfh^2}{3\,l}=W$
Beam supported at both ends, single unsymmetrical load	$\dfrac{6\,Wac}{fh^2l}=b$	$\sqrt{\dfrac{6Wac}{bfl}}=h$	$\dfrac{6\,Wac}{bh^2l}=f$	$a+c=l$	$\dfrac{bh^2fl}{6\,ac}=W$
Beam supported at both ends, two symmetrical loads	$\dfrac{3\,Wa}{fh^2}=b$	$\sqrt{\dfrac{3\,Wa}{bf}}=h$	$\dfrac{3\,Wa}{bh^2}=f$	l, any length $\dfrac{bh^2f}{3\,W}=a$	$\dfrac{bh^2f}{3\,a}=W$

Round Solid Beams

Style of Loading and Support	Diameter of Beam in Inches	Stress per Sq. In. in Extreme Fibers of Beam	Length of Beam in Inches	Load in Pounds
	d	f	l	W

Beam fixed at one end, loaded at the other				
	$\sqrt[3]{\dfrac{10.18\,lW}{f}}=d$	$\dfrac{10.18\,lW}{d^3}=f$	$\dfrac{d^3 f}{10.18\,W}=l$	$\dfrac{d^3 f}{10.18\,l}=W$
Beam fixed at one end, uniformly loaded				
	$\sqrt[3]{\dfrac{5.092\,Wl}{f}}=d$	$\dfrac{5.092\,Wl}{d^3}=f$	$\dfrac{d^3 f}{5.092\,W}=l$	$\dfrac{d^3 f}{5.092\,l}=W$
Beam supported at both ends, single load in middle				
	$\sqrt[3]{\dfrac{2.546\,Wl}{f}}=d$	$\dfrac{2.546\,Wl}{d^3}=f$	$\dfrac{d^3 f}{2.546\,W}=l$	$\dfrac{d^3 f}{2.546\,l}=W$
Beam supported at both ends, uniformly loaded				
	$\sqrt[3]{\dfrac{1.273\,Wl}{f}}=d$	$\dfrac{1.273\,Wl}{d^3}=f$	$\dfrac{d^3 f}{1.273\,W}=l$	$\dfrac{d^3 f}{1.273\,l}=W$
Beam supported at both ends, single unsymmetrical load				
	$\sqrt[3]{\dfrac{10.18\,Wac}{fl}}=d$	$\dfrac{10.18\,Wac}{d^3 l}=f$	$a+c=l$	$\dfrac{d^3 fl}{10.18\,ac}=W$
Beam supported at both ends, two symmetrical loads				
	$\sqrt[3]{\dfrac{5.092\,Wa}{f}}=d$	$\dfrac{5.092\,Wa}{d^3}=f$	l, any length $\dfrac{d^3 f}{5.092\,W}=a$	$\dfrac{d^3 f}{5.092\,a}=W$

Strength of Channels. — Experiments on standard channels carried out by Bach (published in 1909) show that the regular bending formula for beams freely supported at their ends and loaded in the center gives too high a value for the strength of structural channels. The experiments show that the amount by which

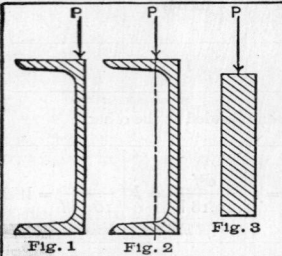

Fig. 1   Fig. 2   Fig. 3

the value obtained from the formula is greater than that obtained by experiments, is, for channels 4¾ inches high, 7 per cent; for channels 8¾ inches high, 18 per cent; and for channels 11¾ inches high, 26 per cent. These values are those found when the load is assumed to be applied in the center line of the web of the channel as shown in Fig. 1. If the load is placed along the line of the vertical neutral axis of the channel as shown in Fig. 2, the permissible load according to the beam formula is 10, 25.5 and 34 per cent greater than that shown by the experiments. These experiments, therefore, indicate that when the usual formulas employed in calculations, for channels or other structural shapes, a liberal factor of safety should be allowed in order to compensate for the difference of the results given by the formula and those of actual experiments. It should be noted that the formula for bending is fully correct whenever the section of the member is such that the load is fully distributed over the whole sectional area, as in a rectangular section, Fig. 3; but in the case of channels as well as many other structural shapes, the load is not, as a rule, properly distributed over the whole section, but stresses certain portions of the section in a higher degree than others.

Deflection as a Limiting Factor in Beam Design. — For some applications, a beam must be stronger than required by the maximum load it is to support, in order to prevent excessive deflection. Since maximum allowable deflections for such cases vary widely for different classes of service, a general formula for determining them cannot be given. When exceptionally stiff girders are required, one rule is to limit the deflection to 1 inch per 100 feet of span; hence, if l = length of span in inches, deflection = $l \div 1200$. According to another formula, deflection limit = $l \div 360$ where beams are adjacent to materials like plaster which would be broken by excessive beam deflection. Some machine parts of the beam type must be very rigid to maintain alignment under load. For example, the deflection of a locomotive guide-bar may be limited to 0.010 inch or less. These examples merely illustrate variations in practice. It is impracticable to give general formulas for determining the allowable deflection in any case, because the allowable amount depends upon the conditions governing each class of work.

Procedure in Designing for Deflection: Assume that a deflection equal to $l \div 1200$ is to be the limiting factor in selecting an I-beam having a span length of 144 inches. Supports are at both ends and load at center is 15,000 pounds. Deflection y is to be limited to $144 \div 1200 = 0.12$ inch. According to the formula on page 389 (Case 2), in which W = load on beam in pounds, l = length of span in inches, E = modulus of elasticity of material, I = moment of inertia of cross section.

$$\text{Deflection } y = \frac{Wl^3}{48EI}\text{ ; hence } I = \frac{Wl^3}{48yE} = \frac{15,000 \times 144^3}{48 \times 0.12 \times 29,000,000} = 268.1$$

A standard structural I-beam having a depth of 12 inches and weighing 40.8

pounds per foot has a moment of inertia I of 268.9 and a section modulus Z of 44.8 (see table, page 381). Checking now for maximum stress s (Case 2, page 388).

$$s = \frac{Wl}{4Z} = \frac{15,000 \times 144}{4 \times 44.8} = 12,050 \text{ lbs. per sq. in.}$$

Although deflection is the limiting factor in this case, the maximum stress is checked to make sure that it is within the allowable limit. As the limiting deflection is decreased, for a given load and length of span, the beam strength and ridigity must be increased, and, consequently, the maximum stress is decreased. Thus, in the preceding example, if the maximum deflection is 0.06 inch instead of 0.12 inch, then the calculated value for the moment of inertia I will be 536; hence, a standard 15-inch I-beam having an I value of 609 could be used (nearest value above 536). The maximum stress then would be reduced to 6650 pounds per square inch and the calculated deflection is 0.053 inch.

Strength of Columns or Struts. — Structural members which are subject to compression may be so long in proportion to the diameter or lateral dimensions that failure may be the result (1) of both compression and bending or (2) of bending or buckling to such a degree that compressive stress may be ignored. In such cases, the *slenderness ratio* is important. This ratio equals the length l of the column in inches divided by the least radius of gyration r of the cross-section. Various formulas have been used for designing columns which are too slender to be designed for compression only.

Rankine or Gordon Formula. — This formula is generally applied when slenderness ratios range between 20 and 100, and sometimes for ratios up to 120. The notation is given on page 411

$$p = \frac{S}{1 + K\left(\frac{l}{r}\right)^2} = \text{ultimate load, lbs. per sq. in.}$$

Factor K may be established by tests with a given material and end condition, and for the probable range of l/r. If determined by calculation, $K = S/C\pi^2 E$. Factor C equals 1 for either rounded or pivoted column ends, 4 for fixed ends, and 1 to 4 for square flat ends. The factors 25,000, 12,500, etc., in the Rankine formulas arranged as on page 411, equal $1/K$, and have been used extensively.

Straight-line Formula. — This general type of formula is often used in designing compression members for buildings, bridges, or similar structural work. It is convenient especially in designing a number of columns which are made of the same material but vary in size, assuming that factor B is known. This factor is determined by tests.

$$p = S_y - B\left(\frac{l}{r}\right) = \text{ultimate load, lbs. per sq. in.}$$

S_y equals yield point, lbs. per square inch, and factor B ranges from 50 to 100. Safe unit stress = p/factor of safety.

Formulas of American Railway Engineering Association. — The formulas which follow apply to structural steel having an ultimate strength of 60,000 lbs. per square inch.

For building columns with ends riveted or for a continuous column, safe unit stress = $18,000 - 60\,l/r$, with maximum unit stress limited to 15,000 lbs. per sq. in., and for slenderness ratios up to 120.

For bridge members with riveted ends, safe unit stress = 15,000 $- \frac{1}{4}\left(\frac{l}{r}\right)^2$ for slenderness ratios up to 140.

Formula of American Bridge Company. — Safe unit stress = 19,000 $-$ 100 l/r, with maximum unit stress limited to 13,000 lbs. per sq. in. and for ratios of l/r up to 120.

American Institute of Steel Construction. — For main compression members and l/r ratios up to 120, safe unit stress = 17,000 $-$ 0.485 l^2/r^2. For columns and bracing or other secondary members with l/r ratios above 120,

$$\text{Safe unit stress} = \frac{18,000}{1 + \dfrac{l^2}{18,000\, r^2}} = \text{lbs. per sq. in.}$$

Euler Formula. — This formula is for columns which are so slender that bending or buckling action predominates and compressive stresses are not taken into account.

$$P = \frac{C\pi^2 IE}{l^2} = \text{total ultimate load, in pounds}$$

For notation, see page 411. Factors C for different end conditions are included in the Euler formulas at the bottom of the table. According to a series of experiments, Euler formulas should be used and the values of l/r exceed the following ratios: Structural steel and flat ends, 195; hinged ends, 155; round ends, 120; cast iron with flat ends, 120; hinged ends, 100; round ends, 75; oak with flat ends, 130. The *critical slenderness ratio* which marks the dividing line between the shorter columns and those slender enough to warrant using the Euler formula, depends upon the column material and its end conditions. If the Euler formula is applied when the slenderness ratio is too small, the *calculated* ultimate strength will exceed the yield point of the material and, obviously, will be incorrect.

Eccentrically Loaded Columns. — In the application of the column formulas previously referred to, it is assumed that the action of the load coincides with the axis of the column. If the load is offset relative to the column axis, the column is said to be eccentrically loaded, and its strength is then calculated by using a modification of the Rankine formula, the quantity cz/r^2 being added to the denominator, as shown in the table on the next page. This modified formula is applicable to columns having a slenderness ratio varying from 20 or 30 to about 100.

Pipe Columns. — The allowable compressive stress for steel pipe columns may be determined from the formula:

$$S = 15,200 - 58\, L \div R$$

in which S = allowable compressive stress in pounds per square inch; L = length of column in inches; R = radius of gyration in inches. This formula is applicable to steel pipe columns with flat ends. No columns should be used having an unsupported length greater than 120 times its radius of gyration. The formula is based upon the requirements of the New York Building Code.

A similar formula, based upon the Chicago Building Ordinances, is:

$$S = 16,000 - 70\, L \div R$$

in which the letters denote the same quantities as in the previous formula.

Flat Stayed Surfaces. — In many cases, large flat areas are held against pressure by stays distributed at regular intervals over the surface. In boiler work, these stays are usually screwed into the plate and the projecting end riveted over to insure

Rankine's and Euler's Formulas for Columns

p = ultimate load in lbs. per square inch; P = total ultimate load in lbs.
S = ultimate compressive strength of material in pounds per square inch;
l = length of column or strut in inches;

r = least radius of gyration in inches; $r^2 = \dfrac{\text{moment of inertia}}{\text{area of section}}$;

I = least moment of inertia;
E = modulus of elasticity of material;
c = distance in inches from neutral axis of cross-section to side under compression;
z = distance in inches from axis of load to axis coinciding with center of gravity of cross-section.

Rankine's Formulas

Material	Both Ends of Column Fixed	One End Fixed and One End Rounded	Both Ends Rounded
Steel.........	$p = \dfrac{S}{1 + \dfrac{l^2}{25,000\,r^2}}$	$p = \dfrac{S}{1 + \dfrac{l^2}{12,500\,r^2}}$	$p = \dfrac{S}{1 + \dfrac{l^2}{6250\,r^2}}$
Cast Iron......	$p = \dfrac{S}{1 + \dfrac{l^2}{5000\,r^2}}$	$p = \dfrac{S}{1 + \dfrac{l^2}{2500\,r^2}}$	$p = \dfrac{S}{1 + \dfrac{l^2}{1250\,r^2}}$
Wrought Iron..	$p = \dfrac{S}{1 + \dfrac{l^2}{35,000\,r^2}}$	$p = \dfrac{S}{1 + \dfrac{l^2}{17,500\,r^2}}$	$p = \dfrac{S}{1 + \dfrac{l^2}{8750\,r^2}}$
Timber........	$p = \dfrac{S}{1 + \dfrac{l^2}{3000\,r^2}}$	$p = \dfrac{S}{1 + \dfrac{l^2}{1500\,r^2}}$	$p = \dfrac{S}{1 + \dfrac{l^2}{750\,r^2}}$

Formulas Modified for Eccentrically Loaded Columns

Material *	Both Ends of Column Fixed	One End Fixed and One End Rounded	Both Ends Rounded
Steel.........	$p = \dfrac{S}{1 + \dfrac{l^2}{25,000\,r^2} + \dfrac{cz}{r^2}}$	$p = \dfrac{S}{1 + \dfrac{l^2}{12,500\,r^2} + \dfrac{cz}{r^2}}$	$p = \dfrac{S}{1 + \dfrac{l^2}{6250\,r^2} + \dfrac{cz}{r^2}}$

* For other materials such as cast iron, etc., use the Rankine formulas given in the upper table and add to the denominator the quantity $\dfrac{cz}{r^2}$.

Euler's Formulas for Slender Columns

Both Ends of Column Fixed	One End Fixed and One End Rounded	Both Ends Rounded	One End Fixed and One End Free
$P = \dfrac{4\,\pi^2 IE}{l^2}$	$P = \dfrac{2\,\pi^2 IE}{l^2}$	$P = \dfrac{\pi^2 IE}{l^2}$	$P = \dfrac{\pi^2 IE}{4\,l^2}$

To find the total safe load for a given section, multiply the value of p (as found by any of the above formulas), by the area of the section and divide by a suitable factor of safety. (See table "General Factors of Safety.")

steam tightness. The U. S. Board of Supervising Inspectors and the American Boiler Makers Association rules give the following formula for flat stayed surfaces:

$$P = \frac{C \times t^2}{S^2}$$

in which P = pressure in pounds per square inch;

C = a constant which equals 112, for plates $\frac{7}{16}$ inch and under; 120, for plates over $\frac{7}{16}$ inch thick; 140, for plates with stays having a nut and bolt on the inside and outside; and 160, for plates with stays having washers of at least one-half the thickness of the plate, and with a diameter at least one-half of the greatest pitch.

t = thickness of plate in 16ths of an inch (thickness = $\frac{7}{16}$, $t = 7$);

S = greatest pitch of stays in inches.

Strength of Flat Plates. — Exact formulas for finding the bending moments of flat plates supported along their edges and subjected to stresses created by pressures normal to their surfaces have not been determined. The formulas given by

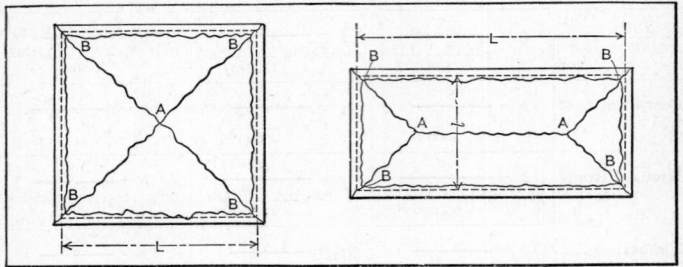

Fig. 1   Fig. 2

different authorities are founded on assumptions and should be considered as approximations only; they should be used with caution, as the results obtained are not likely to be very accurate.

A square cast-iron plate fixed or rigidly held at the edges and loaded with a uniformly distributed load, or a load concentrated at the center, would be likely to fail as shown in Fig. 1. It would first fracture along the diagonal lines from A to B and then fail at or near the fixed edges along lines BB. The plate might also shear off along the edges BB, depending upon the method of loading and the thickness of the plate. If the plate were merely supported along all the four edges, but not rigidly held, it would be likely to fail by breaking along the diagonal lines AB only.

In Fig. 2 is illustrated the probable manner of failure of a flat rectangular plate of cast iron, loaded with a uniformly distributed load. The plate, if secured along all the four edges, would probably fail by fracturing along the center line AA of the long axis of the plate and along the diagonal lines AB, and then fail at or near the edges of the support along the lines BB. If the plate were merely supported along all four edges, it would fail simply by fracturing along the center line AA and the diagonal lines AB. A plate firmly secured at the edges offers greater resistance to the stress created by the load than does a plate merely supported at the edges. While the formulas given in the following are approximate only, it is important that formulas be deduced and used for designs of this character, because they indicate, in a general way, the dimensions required, and the factor of safety assumed will always be taken large enough so that, practically, the approximate nature of the formulas does not detract from their value.

Square and Rectangular Flat Plates. — As the formulas of different authorities vary, formulas giving the higher or safer values have, as a rule, been selected. All of the flat-plate formulas given apply to cast iron, since they are usually required for this material by designers. In the following formulas: W = total load in pounds; P = load per square inch of surface, in pounds; L = span, or distance between supports, in inches; S = fiber stress in pounds per square inch; t = thickness of plate in inches. For rectangular plates, L and l are the long and short spans, or distances between the supported edges, respectively.

1. Square flat plate, supported at all four edges, with a load uniformly distributed over the unsupported surface of the plate. (Based on Grashof's formulas.)

$$W = 3.56\,St^2 \qquad S = 0.28\frac{W}{t^2} = 0.28\frac{PL^2}{t^2}$$

$$L = 1.89\,t\sqrt{\frac{S}{P}} \qquad t = 0.53\sqrt{\frac{W}{S}} = 0.53\,L\sqrt{\frac{P}{S}}$$

2. Square flat plate, firmly secured along all four edges, with a load uniformly distributed over the unsupported surface of the plate. (Based on Unwin's formulas.)

$$W = 4\,St^2 \qquad S = 0.25\frac{W}{t^2} = 0.25\frac{PL^2}{t^2}$$

$$L = 2\,t\sqrt{\frac{S}{P}} \qquad t = 0.5\sqrt{\frac{W}{S}} = 0.5\,L\sqrt{\frac{P}{S}}$$

3. Square flat plate, supported at all four edges, with a load W concentrated at the center. (Based on Grashof's formulas.)

$$W = 0.67\,St^2 \qquad S = 1.5\frac{W}{t^2} \qquad t = 1.23\sqrt{\frac{W}{S}}$$

4. Square flat plate, firmly secured along all four edges, with a load W concentrated at the center. (Based on Grashof's formulas.)

$$W = 0.76\,St^2 \qquad S = 1.31\frac{W}{t^2} \qquad t = 1.14\sqrt{\frac{W}{S}}$$

5. Flat rectangular plate, supported at all four edges, with a load uniformly distributed over the unsupported surface of the plate. (Based on Grashof's formulas.)

$$W = 1.77\frac{St^2(L^2+l^2)}{Ll} \qquad P = 1.77\frac{St^2(L^2+l^2)}{L^2l^2}$$

$$S = 0.56\frac{WLl}{t^2(L^2+l^2)} \qquad t = 0.75\sqrt{\frac{WLl}{S(L^2+l^2)}}$$

6. Flat rectangular plate, firmly secured at all four edges, with a load uniformly distributed over the unsupported area of the plate. (Based on Grashof's formulas.)

$$W = 2.67\frac{St^2(L^2+l^2)}{Ll} \qquad P = 2.67\frac{St^2(L^2+l^2)}{L^2l^2}$$

$$S = 0.375\frac{WLl}{t^2(L^2+l^2)} \qquad t = 0.62\sqrt{\frac{WLl}{S(L^2+l^2)}}$$

7. Flat rectangular plate, supported at all four edges, with a load W concentrated at the center. (Based on Grashof's formulas.)

$$W = 0.33 \frac{St^2(L^2 + l^2)}{Ll} \qquad S = \frac{3\,WLl}{t^2(L^2 + l^2)} \qquad t = 1.73 \sqrt{\frac{WLl}{S(L^2 + l^2)}}$$

8. Flat rectangular plate, firmly secured at all four edges, with a load W concentrated at the center. (Based on Grashof's formulas.)

$$W = 0.38 \frac{St^2(L^2 + l^2)}{Ll} \qquad S = 2.62 \frac{WLl}{t^2(L^2 + l^2)} \qquad t = 1.6 \sqrt{\frac{WLl}{S(L^2 + l^2)}}$$

Formulas for Circular Flat Plates. — In the following formulas:

W = total load in pounds;
P = load in pounds per square inch;
R = radius of plate, to the supporting edge, in inches;
S = fiber stress in pounds per square inch;
t = thickness of plate in inches;
d = deflection at center of plate in inches;
E = modulus of elasticity.

1. Circular flat plate, supported all around the edge, with a load uniformly distributed over the unsupported area of the plate. (Based on Reuleaux's formulas.)

$$W = 3.14\,St^2 \qquad S = \frac{PR^2}{t^2} = 0.318\,\frac{W}{t^2}$$

$$R = t\sqrt{\frac{S}{P}} \qquad t = R\sqrt{\frac{P}{S}} = 0.56\sqrt{\frac{W}{S}}$$

$$P = \frac{St^2}{R^2} \qquad d = \frac{5}{6}\frac{PR^4}{Et^3} = 0.265\,\frac{WR^2}{Et^3}$$

2. Circular flat plate, firmly secured all around the edge, with a load uniformly distributed over the unsupported area of the plate. (Based on Reuleaux's formulas.)

$$W = 4.7\,St^2 \qquad S = 0.67\,\frac{PR^2}{t^2} = 0.21\,\frac{W}{t^2}$$

$$R = 1.22\,t\sqrt{\frac{S}{P}} \qquad t = 0.81\,R\sqrt{\frac{P}{S}} = 0.46\sqrt{\frac{W}{S}}$$

$$P = 1.5\,\frac{St^2}{R^2} \qquad a = \frac{PR^4}{6\,Et^3} = 0.053\,\frac{WR^2}{Et^3}$$

3. Circular flat plate, supported all around the edge, with a load concentrated at the center of the plate upon a circular area with radius r. (Based on Bach's formulas.)

$$W = 0.7\,\frac{St^2}{1 - \dfrac{2r}{3R}} \qquad S = 1.43\,\frac{W\left(1 - \dfrac{2r}{3R}\right)}{t^2}$$

$$t = 1.2\sqrt{\frac{W\left(1 - \dfrac{2r}{3R}\right)}{S}} \qquad d = 0.5\,\frac{WR^2}{Et^3}$$

4. Circular flat plate, firmly secured all around the edge, with a load concentrated at the center of the plate upon a circular area with radius *r*. (Based on Grashof's formulas.)

$$W = 2.36 \frac{St^2}{\text{hyp. log } \frac{R}{r}} \qquad S = 0.424 \frac{W}{t^2} \text{ hyp. log } \frac{R}{r}$$

$$t = 0.65 \sqrt{\frac{W \text{ hyp. log } \frac{R}{r}}{S}} \qquad d = 0.48 \frac{WR^2}{Et^3}$$

Strength of Cylinders Subjected to Internal Pressure. — In low-pressure work, the general practice is to make the thickness of the metal equal to the internal diameter in inches times the pressure in pounds per square inch, and this product divided by twice the allowable working stress of the material. To this is added a variable quantity to allow for unsound castings and possible unknown stresses. Hence, if *t* = thickness in inches; *d* = inside diameter in inches; *P* = pressure in pounds per square inch; *S* = allowable tensile stress in pounds per square inch, then:

$$t = \frac{dP}{2S}$$

To the value of *t* thus obtained must then be added an amount to allow for variations in the material and possible excessive stresses when the cylinder is in operation.

Find the thickness required for a cast-iron cylinder, 15 inches in diameter (inside), to withstand an internal pressure of 200 pounds per square inch. Assume the allowable working stress for cast iron to be 4000 pounds per square inch. Then:

$$t = \frac{15 \times 200}{2 \times 4000} = \frac{3}{8} \text{ inch.}$$

The material being cast iron, a liberal allowance must be added to this thickness to take care of possible defects in the casting.

The formula given should be used only for low pressures. When the pressures rise, the Barlow formula is preferable. This formula is similar in form to the one already given, but it gives results quite different when applied to tubes and pipes having walls of considerable thickness in proportion to the diameter, because the Barlow formula is expressed in terms of the outside diameter, whereas the formula given above is expressed in terms of the inside diameter. The Barlow formula is:

$$t = \frac{DP}{2S}$$

in which *t* = thickness in inches; *D* = outside diameter in inches; *P* = pressure in pounds per square inch; *S* = allowable tensile stress in pounds per square inch.

This formula is based on assumptions which cannot be considered as theoretically correct, but the error is on the side of safety, and experiments have proved that of the various formulas proposed for the strength of tubes and pipes subjected to moderate pressures, the Barlow formula gives the most reliable results.

The average ultimate tensile strength of seamless steel tubes may be assumed at 55,000 pounds per square inch; that for butt-welded steel pipe at 40,000; that for lap-welded steel pipe at 50,000; and that for wrought-iron pipe (butt-welded or lap-welded) at 28,000 pounds per square inch.

If seamless steel tubes are assumed to have a strength of 100 per cent, butt-welded steel pipe has a comparative strength of 73 per cent, and lap-welded steel pipe of 92 per cent. From this it will be seen that the strength of a butt-weld is only about 80 per cent of that of a lap-weld. The relative strengths of wrought-iron and steel pipe are as follows: Butt-welded wrought-iron pipe has 70 per cent of the strength of similar butt-welded steel pipe, and lap-welded wrought-iron pipe has 57 per cent of the strength of similar lap-welded steel pipe.

Cylinders Subjected to High Internal Pressure. — For high pressures, Lamé's formula is used. This formula is in its usual form,

$$t = r\left(\sqrt{\frac{S+P}{S-P}} - 1\right)$$

sometimes inconvenient to use. The following forms of the same formula obtained by substitution are often useful:

$$S = P\frac{R^2 + r^2}{R^2 - r^2} \qquad\qquad R = r\sqrt{\frac{S+P}{S-P}}$$

$$P = S\frac{R^2 - r^2}{R^2 + r^2} \qquad\qquad r = R\sqrt{\frac{S-P}{S+P}}$$

In these formulas:

S = maximum allowable fiber stress per square inch;
R = outer radius of cylinder in inches;
r = inner radius of cylinder in inches;
P = pressure within the cylinder in pounds per square inch;
$t = R - r$ = thickness of cylinder in inches.

A table of ratios of outside radius to inside radius of thick cylinders is given for convenience in calculating the dimensions of cylinders under high internal pressure without the use of the formulas. This table is based on the Lamé formula. As an example of the use of the table, assume that a cylinder of 10 inches inside diameter is to withstand a pressure of 2500 pounds per square inch; the material is cast iron, the allowable stress in this case being 6000 pounds per square inch. To solve the problem, locate the allowable stress per square inch in the left-hand column of the table and the working pressure at the top of the columns. Then find the ratio between the outside and inside radii in the body of the table. In this case, the ratio is 1.558, and hence the outside diameter of the cylinder should be 10 × 1.558, or about 15⅝ inches.

Unless very high-grade material is used and sound castings assured, cast iron should not be used for pressures exceeding 2000 pounds per square inch. When pressures exceed 2500 pounds per square inch, the packings are likely to leak and the valves and pipe fittings give trouble. It is, therefore, advisable to keep the pressure below this point, if possible. It is well to leave more metal in the bottom of a hydraulic cylinder than is indicated by the results of calculations, because a hole of some size must be cored in the bottom to permit the entrance of a boring bar when finishing the cylinder, and when this hole is subsequently tapped and plugged it often gives trouble if the precaution mentioned is not taken.

For steady or gradually applied stresses, the maximum allowable fiber stress S in the formulas above may be assumed from 3500 to 4000 pounds per square inch for cast iron; from 6000 to 7000 pounds per square inch for brass; and as 12,000 pounds per square inch for steel castings. For intermittent stresses, such as in cylinders for steam and hydraulic work, 3000 pounds per square inch for cast iron; 5000 pounds per square inch for brass; and 10,000 pounds per square inch for steel castings, is ordinarily used. These values give ample factors of safety.

Ratio of Outside Radius to Inside Radius, Thick Cylinders

Allowable Stress in Metal per Sq. In. of Section	Working Pressure in Cylinder, Pounds per Square Inch												
	1000	1500	2000	2500	3000	3500	4000	4500	5000	5500	6000	6500	7000
2,000	1.732												
2,500	1.527	2.000											
3,000	1.414	1.732	2.236										
3,500	1.341	1.581	1.915	2.449									
4,000	1.291	1.483	1.732	2.081	2.645								
4,500	1.253	1.414	1.612	1.871	2.236	2.828							
5,000	1.224	1.362	1.527	1.732	2.000	2.380	3.000						
5,500	1.201	1.322	1.464	1.633	1.844	2.121	2.516	3.162					
6,000	1.183	1.291	1.414	1.558	1.732	1.949	2.236	2.645	3.316				
6,500		1.264	1.374	1.500	1.647	1.825	2.049	2.345	2.768	3.464			
7,000		1.243	1.341	1.453	1.581	1.732	1.914	2.144	2.449	2.886	3.605		
7,500		1.224	1.314	1.414	1.527	1.658	1.813	2.000	2.236	2.549	3.000	3.741	
8,000		1.209	1.291	1.381	1.483	1.599	1.732	1.889	2.081	2.323	2.645	3.109	3.872
8,500		1.194	1.271	1.354	1.446	1.548	1.666	1.802	1.963	2.160	2.408	2.738	3.214
9,000		1.183	1.253	1.330	1.414	1.507	1.612	1.732	1.871	2.035	2.236	2.490	2.828
9,500			1.235	1.306	1.386	1.472	1.566	1.673	1.795	1.936	2.104	2.309	2.569
10,000			1.224	1.291	1.362	1.441	1.527	1.623	1.732	1.856	2.000	2.171	2.380
10,500			1.212	1.274	1.341	1.414	1.493	1.581	1.678	1.789	1.915	2.061	2.236
11,000			1.201	1.260	1.322	1.390	1.464	1.544	1.633	1.732	1.844	1.972	2.121
11,500			1.193	1.247	1.306	1.369	1.437	1.511	1.593	1.683	1.784	1.897	2.027
12,000			1.183	1.235	1.291	1.350	1.414	1.483	1.558	1.640	1.732	1.834	1.949
12,500				1.224	1.277	1.333	1.393	1.457	1.527	1.603	1.687	1.779	1.878
13,000				1.215	1.264	1.318	1.374	1.434	1.500	1.570	1.647	1.732	1.825
13,500				1.206	1.253	1.303	1.357	1.414	1.475	1.541	1.612	1.690	1.775
14,000				1.197	1.243	1.291	1.341	1.395	1.453	1.514	1.581	1.653	1.732
14,500				1.189	1.233	1.279	1.327	1.378	1.432	1.490	1.553	1.620	1.693
15,000				1.183	1.224	1.268	1.314	1.362	1.414	1.469	1.527	1.590	1.658
16,000				1.170	1.209	1.249	1.291	1.335	1.381	1.431	1.483	1.538	1.599

Spherical Shells Subjected to Internal Pressure. — Let:

D = internal diameter of shell in inches;
P = internal pressure in pounds per square inch;
S = safe tensile stress per square inch;
t = the thickness of metal in the shell in inches.   Then:

$$P\,\frac{\pi D^2}{4} = \pi D t S, \quad \text{and} \quad t = \frac{PD}{4S}$$

This formula also applies to hemi-spherical shells, such as the hemi-spherical head of a cylindrical container subjected to internal pressure, etc.

Example: — Find the thickness of metal required in the hemi-spherical end of a cylindrical vessel, 2 feet in diameter, subjected to an internal pressure of 500 pounds per square inch. The material is mild steel and a tensile stress of 10 000 pounds per square inch is allowable.

$$t = \frac{500 \times 2 \times 12}{4 \times 10,000} = 0.3 \text{ inch.}$$

If the radius of curvature of the dome head of a boiler or container subjected to internal pressure is made equal to the diameter of the boiler, the thickness of the cylindrical shell and of the spherical head should be made the same. For example, if a boiler is 3 feet in diameter, the radius of curvature of its head should be made 3 feet, if material of the same thickness is to be used and the stresses are to be equal in both the head and cylindrical portion.

Collapsing Pressures of Cylinders and Tubes Subjected to External Pressures. — The following formulas may be used for finding the collapsing pressures of modern lap-welded Bessemer steel tubes:

$$P = 86,670\,\frac{t}{D} - 1386 \quad \dots \quad (1) \qquad P = 50,210,000\left(\frac{t}{D}\right)^3 \quad \dots \quad (2)$$

in which P = collapsing pressure in pounds per square inch; D = outside diameter of tube or cylinder in inches; t = thickness of wall in inches.

Formula (1) is for values of P greater than 580 pounds per square inch, and Formula (2) is for values of P less than 580 pounds per square inch. These formulas are substantially correct for all lengths of pipe greater than six diameters between transverse joints that tend to hold the pipe to a circular form. The pressure P found is the actual collapsing pressure, and a suitable factor of safety must be used. Ordinarily, a factor of safety of 5 is sufficient. In cases where there are repeated fluctuations of the pressure, vibration, shocks and other stresses, a factor of safety of from 6 to 12 should be used.

The table "Tubes Subjected to External Pressure" is based upon the requirements of the Steam Boat Inspection Service of the Department of Commerce and Labor and gives the permissible working pressures and corresponding minimum thickness of wall for long, plain, lap-welded and seamless steel flues subjected to external pressure only. The thicknesses in the table have been calculated from the formula:

$$T = \frac{[(F \times P) + 1386]\,D}{86,670}$$

in which D = outside diameter of flue or tube in inches; T = thickness of wall in inches; P = working pressure in pounds per square inch; F = factor of safety. The formula is applicable to working pressures greater than 100 pounds per square inch, to outside diameters from 7 to 18 inches, and to temperatures less than 650° F.

The Formulas (1) and (2) given on the preceding page were determined by Prof. R. T. Stewart, Dean of the Mechanical Engineering Department of the University of Pittsburg, in a series of experiments carried out at the plant of the National Tube Co., McKeesport, Pa. These tests occupied a period of four years. A full report of the details of these experiments will be found in a paper presented by Prof. Stewart before the American Society of Mechanical Engineers in May, 1906. The principal conclusions to be drawn from the results of this research may be briefly stated as follows:

The length of tube, between transverse joints tending to hold it to a circular form, has no practical influence upon the collapsing pressure of a commercial lap-welded steel tube, so long as this length is not less than about six times the diameter of the tube.

The apparent fiber stress under which the different tubes failed varied from about 7000 pounds per square inch for the relatively thinnest to 35,000 pounds per square inch for the relatively thickest walls. Since the average yield point of the material tested was 37,000 pounds and the tensile strength 58,000 pounds per square inch, it is evident that the strength of a tube subjected to external fluid collapsing pressure is not dependent alone upon the elastic limit or ultimate strength of the material from which it is made.

Tubes Subjected to External Pressure

Outside Diameter of Tube, Inches	Working Pressure in Pounds per Square Inch						
	100	120	140	160	180	200	220
	Thickness of Tube in Inches. Safety Factor, 5						
7	0.152	0.160	0.168	0.177	0.185	0.193	0.201
8	0.174	0.183	0.193	0.202	0.211	0.220	0.229
9	0.196	0.206	0.217	0.227	0.237	0.248	0.258
10	0.218	0.229	0.241	0.252	0.264	0.275	0.287
11	0.239	0.252	0.265	0.277	0.290	0.303	0.316
12	0.261	0.275	0.289	0.303	0.317	0.330	0.344
13	0.283	0.298	0.313	0.328	0.343	0.358	0.373
14	0.301	0.320	0.337	0.353	0.369	0.385	0.402
15	0.323	0.343	0.361	0.378	0.396	0.413	0.430
16	0.344	0.366	0.385	0.404	0.422	0.440	0.459
17	0.366	0.389	0.409	0.429	0.448	0.468	0.488
18	0.387	0.412	0.433	0.454	0.475	0.496	0.516

Dimensions and Maximum Allowable Pressure of Tubes Subjected to External Pressure

Outside Diam., Inches	Thickness of Material, Inches	Maximum Pressure Allowed, Pounds	Outside Diam., Inches	Thickness of Material, Inches	Maximum Pressure Allowed, Pounds	Outside Diam., Inches	Thickness of Material, Inches	Maximum Pressure Allowed, Pounds
2	0.095	427	3	0.109	327	4	0.134	303
2¼	0.095	380	3¼	0.120	332	4½	0.134	238
2½	0.109	392	3½	0.120	308	5	0.148	235
2¾	0.109	356	3¾	0.120	282	6	0.165	199

RIVETING AND RIVETED JOINTS

Classes of Riveted Joints. — When the plates to be joined by riveting overlap each other and are held together by one or more rows of rivets, a *lap-joint* is formed. In a *butt-joint* the plates are in the same plane and are united by a cover plate or butt strap, which is riveted to each plate. A combination lap-joint consists of a cover plate inside or outside the lap, and three rows of rivets, the central row passing through the two plates and the cover, and having twice as many rivets as the other two rows. The term *single riveting* means one row of rivets in a lap-joint or one row on each side of a butt-joint; *double riveting* means two rows of rivets in a lap-joint or two rows on each side of the joint in butt riveting. Joints are also triple and quadruple riveted.

Pitch of Rivets. — The pitch is the distance from center to center of adjacent rivets. The pitch of rivets should be as large as possible without impairing the tightness of the joint when under pressure. For single-riveted lap-joints in the circular seams of boilers which have double-riveted longitudinal lap-joints:

$$\text{pitch} = d \times 2.25 = t \times 5, \text{ approximately,}$$

in which d = the actual diameter of rivet (in parallel hole); t = thickness of plate. For double-riveted lap-joints:

$$\text{pitch} = 8\,t$$

The following formulas for determining the pitch are given by Unwin:
For single-riveted joints in single shear (mild steel):

$$\text{pitch} = 0.644\,\frac{d^2}{t} + d.$$

For single-riveted joints in double shear:

$$\text{pitch} = 1.13\,\frac{d^2}{t} + d.$$

For double-riveted joints in single shear (mild steel):

$$\text{pitch} = 1.288\,\frac{d^2}{t} + d.$$

For double-riveted joints in double shear:

$$\text{pitch} = 2.26\,\frac{d^2}{t} + d.$$

For triple-riveted joints with rivets in single shear (mild steel):

$$\text{pitch} = 1.93\,\frac{d^2}{t} + d.$$

For triple-riveted joints with rivets in double shear:

$$\text{pitch} = 3.30\,\frac{d^2}{t} + d.$$

In the foregoing formulas, d = diameter of the driven rivet.
To secure a joint of maximum strength, the breadth of lap must be such as to prevent it from breaking zigzag. Tests have demonstrated that rupture is equally probable through a diagonal as through a transverse line, unless the net diagonal

section exceeds the net section along the transverse line by 30 to 35 per cent. This corresponds to a diagonal pitch of $\frac{2}{3} P + \frac{d}{3}$, in which P is the straight pitch, and d the diameter of the rivet hole. A general rule for the pitch between rows in staggered riveting is as follows: The pitch between rows should equal one-half the pitch of the rivets in a row, plus ¼ of the diameter of the rivet holes. The distance from the edge of the rivet hole to the edge of the plate should never be less than the rivet diameter.

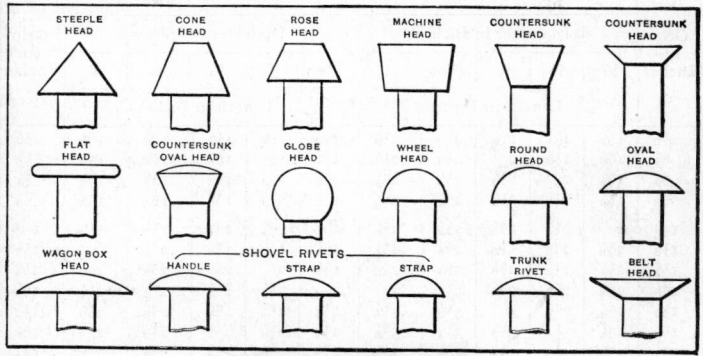

Different Types of Rivet Heads

Rivet Diameter. — Rivet diameters for plates of given thickness range in practice from $d = 1.2 \sqrt{t}$ to $d = 1.4 \sqrt{t}$, in which d = diameter of the rivet and t = thickness of plate. The larger size is preferable for steel and single-riveted joints, and the smaller for iron and multiple-riveted joints.

Length and Proportions of Rivets. — In order to form the head and fill the clearance space in the rivet hole, the rivet should have a length in excess of the thickness of the plate equal to about three-fourths the diameter for countersunk head, and from 1.3 to 1.7 times the diameter for ordinary riveting. (See table, "Rivet Lengths for Forming Round and Countersunk Heads.")

Rivet Driving. — In driving cone-head or button-head rivets, they should be "plugged" squarely into the hole, care being taken not to bend over the point of the rivet but to upset it, filling the hole its entire length. A riveting hammer should be powerful enough to form a perfect rivet head without rocking the hammer to work down the edges. The hammer should be started lightly until the rivet has settled into the hole somewhat, to prevent bending to one side. In driving any kind of rivets held or backed up by a dolly-bar or hand-hammer, the riveter should run the hammer slowly until enough head is formed to hold the rivet in the hole, as otherwise the holder-on will have difficulty in keeping the hammer or dolly-bar on the rivet. Getting the rivets into the holes hot and "getting the heads up" is a necessary preliminary to obtaining tight work. Machines for riveting may be classified according to the method of forming the rivet head, which may be either by (1) compression; (2) by a succession of rapid blows; (3) by rapid blows accompanied by rotary motion of the rivet set; (4) by combined compressive and rolling or spinning action; (5) or by the application of pressure to an electrically-heated rivet

Rivet Lengths for Forming Round and Countersunk Heads

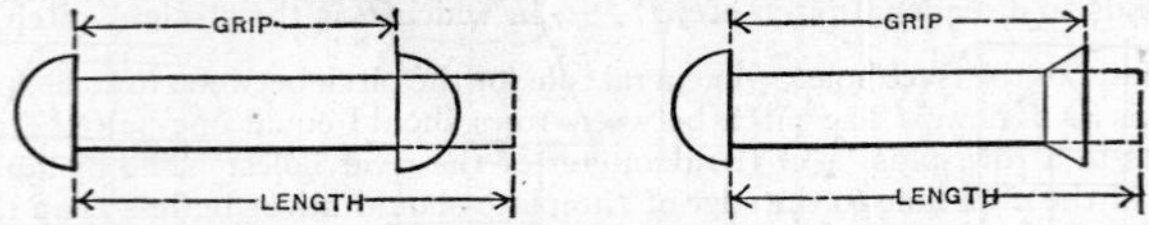

Grip in Inches	Round Head					Countersunk Head					Grip in Inches
	Diameter in Inches					Diameter in Inches					
	½	⅝	¾	⅞	1	½	⅝	¾	⅞	1	
	Length in Inches					Length in Inches					
½	1½	1¾	1⅞	2	2⅛	1⅛	1¼	1¼	1⅜	1⅜	½
⅝	1⅝	1⅞	2	2⅛	2¼	1¼	1⅜	1⅜	1½	1½	⅝
¾	1¾	2	2⅛	2¼	2⅜	1⅜	1½	1½	1⅝	1⅝	¾
⅞	1⅞	2⅛	2¼	2⅜	2½	1½	1⅝	1⅝	1¾	1¾	⅞
1	2	2¼	2⅜	2½	2⅝	1⅝	1¾	1¾	1⅞	1⅞	1
1⅛	2⅛	2⅜	2½	2⅝	2¾	1¾	1⅞	1⅞	2	2	1⅛
1¼	2¼	2½	2⅝	2¾	2⅞	1⅞	2	2	2⅛	2⅛	1¼
1⅜	2⅜	2⅝	2¾	2⅞	3	2	2⅛	2⅛	2¼	2¼	1⅜
1½	2⅝	2⅞	3	3⅛	3¼	2⅛	2¼	2⅜	2⅜	2½	1½
1⅝	2¾	3	3⅛	3¼	3⅜	2¼	2⅜	2½	2½	2⅝	1⅝
1¾	2⅞	3⅛	3¼	3⅜	3½	2⅜	2½	2⅝	2⅝	2¾	1¾
1⅞	3	3¼	3⅜	3½	3⅝	2½	2⅝	2¾	2¾	2⅞	1⅞
2	3⅛	3⅜	3½	3⅝	3¾	2⅝	2¾	2⅞	2⅞	3	2
2⅛	3¼	3½	3⅝	3¾	3⅞	2¾	2⅞	3	3	3⅛	2⅛
2¼	3⅜	3⅝	3¾	3⅞	4	2⅞	3	3⅛	3⅛	3¼	2¼
2⅜	3½	3¾	3⅞	4	4⅛	3	3⅛	3¼	3¼	3⅜	2⅜
2½	3⅝	3⅞	4	4⅛	4¼	3⅛	3¼	3⅜	3⅜	3½	2½
2⅝	3¾	4	4⅛	4¼	4⅜	3¼	3⅜	3½	3½	3⅝	2⅝
2¾	3⅞	4⅛	4¼	4⅜	4½	3⅜	3½	3⅝	3⅝	3¾	2¾
2⅞	4	4¼	4⅜	4½	4⅝	3½	3⅝	3¾	3¾	3⅞	2⅞
3	4¼	4½	4⅝	4¾	4⅞	3¾	3⅞	3⅞	4	4⅛	3
3⅛	4⅜	4⅝	4¾	4⅞	5	3⅞	4	4	4⅛	4¼	3⅛
3¼	4½	4¾	4⅞	5	5⅛	4	4⅛	4⅛	4¼	4⅜	3¼
3⅜	4⅝	4⅞	5	5⅛	5¼	4⅛	4¼	4¼	4⅜	4½	3⅜
3½	4¾	5	5⅛	5¼	5⅜	4¼	4⅜	4⅜	4½	4⅝	3½
3⅝	4⅞	5⅛	5¼	5⅜	5½	4⅜	4½	4½	4⅝	4¾	3⅝
3¾	5	5¼	5⅜	5½	5⅝	4½	4⅝	4⅝	4¾	4⅞	3¾
3⅞	5⅛	5⅜	5½	5⅝	5¾	4⅝	4¾	4¾	4⅞	5	3⅞
4	5¼	5½	5⅝	5¾	5⅞	4¾	4⅞	4⅞	5	5⅛	4
4⅛	5⅜	5⅝	5¾	5⅞	6	4⅞	5	5	5⅛	5¼	4⅛
4¼	5½	5¾	5⅞	6	6⅛	5	5⅛	5⅛	5¼	5⅜	4¼
4⅜	5⅝	5⅞	6	6⅛	6¼	5⅛	5¼	5¼	5⅜	5½	4⅜
4½	5¾	6	6¼	6⅜	6½	5¼	5⅜	5½	5½	5⅝	4½
4⅝	6	6¼	6⅜	6½	6⅝	5½	5⅝	5⅝	5⅝	5¾	4⅝
4¾	6⅛	6⅜	6½	6⅝	6¾	5⅝	5¾	5¾	5¾	5⅞	4¾
4⅞	6¼	6½	6⅝	6¾	6⅞	5¾	5⅞	5⅞	5⅞	6	4⅞
5	6⅜	6⅝	6¾	6⅞	7	5⅞	6	6	6	6⅛	5

American Standard Large Rivets — 1

BUTTON HEAD   HIGH BUTTON   CONE HEAD   PAN HEAD

Nom. Body Diam. D	Head Diam. A		Height H		Head Diam. A		Height H	
	M'f'd Note 1	Driven Note 2	M'f'd Note 1	Driven Note 2	M'f'd Note 1	Driven Note 2	M'f'd Note 1	Driven Note 2
	BUTTON HEAD				HIGH BUTTON HEAD (ACORN)			
1/2	0.875	0.922	0.375	0.344	0.781	0.875	0.500	0.375
5/8	1.094	1.141	0.469	0.438	0.969	1.063	0.594	0.453
3/4	1.313	1.375	0.563	0.516	1.156	1.250	0.688	0.531
7/8	1.531	1.594	0.656	0.609	1.344	1.438	0.781	0.609
1	1.750	1.828	0.750	0.688	1.531	1.625	0.875	0.688
1 1/8	1.969	2.063	0.844	0.781	1.719	1.813	0.969	0.766
1 1/4	2.189	2.281	0.938	0.859	1.906	2.000	1.063	0.844
1 3/8	2.406	2.516	1.031	0.953	2.094	2.188	1.156	0.938
1 1/2	2.625	2.734	1.125	1.031	2.281	2.375	1.250	1.000
1 5/8	2.844	2.969	1.219	1.125	2.469	2.563	1.344	1.094
1 3/4	3.063	3.203	1.313	1.203	2.656	2.750	1.438	1.172
	CONE HEAD				PAN HEAD			
1/2	0.875	0.922	0.438	0.406	0.875	0.922	0.350	0.328
5/8	1.094	1.141	0.547	0.516	1.094	1.141	0.438	0.406
3/4	1.313	1.375	0.656	0.625	1.313	1.375	0.525	0.484
7/8	1.531	1.594	0.766	0.719	1.531	1.594	0.613	0.578
1	1.750	1.828	0.875	0.828	1.750	1.828	0.700	0.656
1 1/8	1.969	2.063	0.984	0.938	1.969	2.063	0.788	0.734
1 1/4	2.189	2.281	1.094	1.031	2.189	2.281	0.875	0.813
1 3/8	2.406	2.516	1.203	1.141	2.406	2.516	0.963	0.906
1 1/2	2.625	2.734	1.313	1.250	2.625	2.734	1.050	0.984
1 5/8	2.844	2.969	1.422	1.344	2.844	2.969	1.138	1.063
1 3/4	3.063	3.203	1.531	1.453	3.063	3.203	1.225	1.141

Note 1. Basic dimensions of head as manufactured.
Note 2. Dimensions of manufactured head after driving and also of driven head.
The following formulas give the basic dimensions for manufactured shapes: *Button Head Rivets:* $A = 1.75D$; $H = 0.75D$; $G = 0.885D$. *High Button Head:* $A = 1.50D + 0.031$; $H = 0.75D + 0.125$; $F = 0.75D + 0.281$; $M = 0.50$; $N = 0.094$. *Cone Head:* $A = 1.75D$; $H = 0.875D$; $B = 0.938D$. *Pan Head:* $A = 1.75D$; $B = D$; $H = 0.70D$. The length (L), in all cases, is measured from the largest diameter of the bearing surface of the head, to the point in a line parallel with the axis of the rivet.

American Standard Large Rivets — 2

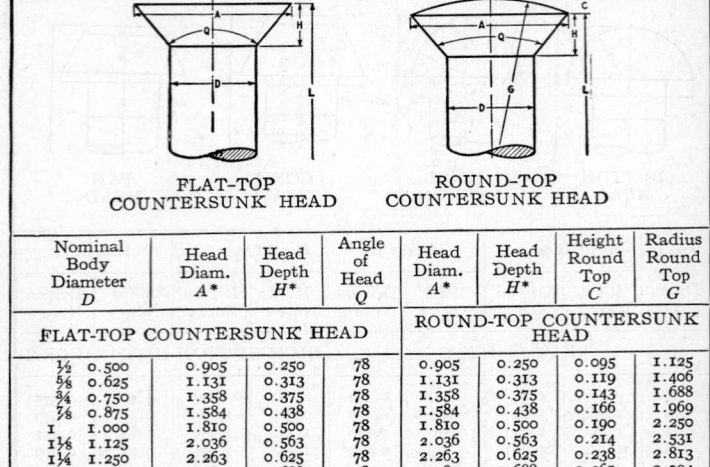

FLAT-TOP
COUNTERSUNK HEAD

ROUND-TOP
COUNTERSUNK HEAD

Nominal Body Diameter D	Head Diam. A*	Head Depth H*	Angle of Head Q	Head Diam. A*	Head Depth H*	Height Round Top C	Radius Round Top G
FLAT-TOP COUNTERSUNK HEAD				ROUND-TOP COUNTERSUNK HEAD			
½ 0.500	0.905	0.250	78	0.905	0.250	0.095	1.125
⅝ 0.625	1.131	0.313	78	1.131	0.313	0.119	1.406
¾ 0.750	1.358	0.375	78	1.358	0.375	0.143	1.688
⅞ 0.875	1.584	0.438	78	1.584	0.438	0.166	1.969
1 1.000	1.810	0.500	78	1.810	0.500	0.190	2.250
1⅛ 1.125	2.036	0.563	78	2.036	0.563	0.214	2.531
1¼ 1.250	2.263	0.625	78	2.263	0.625	0.238	2.813
1⅜ 1.375	2.489	0.688	78	2.489	0.688	0.261	3.094
1½ 1.500	2.715	0.750	78	2.715	0.750	0.285	3.375
1⅝ 1.625	2.941	0.813	78	2.941	0.813	0.309	3.656
1¾ 1.750	3.168	0.875	78	3.168	0.875	0.333	3.938

*Basic dimensions of head as manufactured.

The following formulas give the basic dimensions for manufactured shapes: *Flat-top Countersunk:* A = 1.81D; H = o.50D; included angle Q of head = 78 degrees. *Round-top Countersunk:* A = 1.81D; H = o.50D; C = o.19D; G = 2.25 D; included angle Q = 78 degrees. The length (L) is measured from the largest diameter of the bearing surface of the head to the point, in a line parallel with the axis of the rivet.

General Rules for Rivet Spacing. — The following rules for rivet spacing (given by the Cambria Steel Co.) apply to bridge and structural work. The minimum center-to-center distance or pitch should not be less than three times the rivet diameter. In bridge work, the pitch should not exceed six inches, or sixteen times the thickness of the thinnest outside plate, except in special cases. The distance between the edge of any piece and the center of the rivet hole should not be less than 1¼ inch for ¾- and ⅞-inch rivets, except in bars less than 2½ inches wide; when practicable, this distance should be at least two rivet diameters for all sizes and should not exceed eight times the plate thickness.   For flanges of girders and chords carrying floors, the pitch should not exceed four inches.   For plates in compression, the pitch in the direction of the line of tress should not exceed sixteen times the thickness of the plate, and the pitch in a direction at right angles to the line of stress should not exceed thirty-two times the thickness, except for cover plates or top chords and end posts, in which the pitch should not exceed forty times the thickness.   When rivets are adjacent to the corners of angles, etc., the space between the rivet center and the side of the adjacent leg of the angle, should not be less than one-half the diameter of the head plus ⅜ inch, for clearance.   When there is a row of rivets in the adjacent side, the ⅜-inch clearance should be measured from the rivet heads.

American Standard Small Rivets — 3

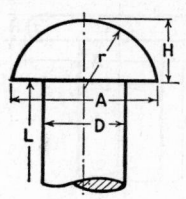 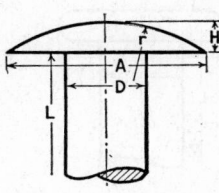

Nominal Diam. D	BUTTON HEAD			Nominal Diam. D	TRUSS OR WAGON BOX		
	A	H	r		A	H	r
3/32	0.166	0.071	0.084	3/32	0.238	0.032	0.239
1/8	0.219	0.094	0.111	1/8	0.313	0.042	0.314
5/32	0.273	0.117	0.138	5/32	0.390	0.052	0.392
3/16	0.327	0.140	0.166	3/16	0.468	0.062	0.470
7/32	0.385	0.165	0.195	7/32	0.550	0.073	0.555
1/4	0.438	0.188	0.221	1/4	0.625	0.083	0.628
9/32	0.492	0.211	0.249	9/32	0.703	0.094	0.706
5/16	0.546	0.234	0.276	5/16	0.780	0.104	0.784
11/32	0.600	0.257	0.304	11/32	0.858	0.114	0.862
3/8	0.656	0.281	0.332	3/8	0.938	0.125	0.942
7/16	0.765	0.328	0.387	7/16	1.093	0.146	1.098

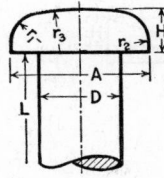 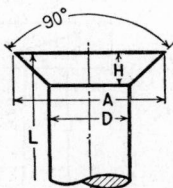

Nominal Diam. D	PAN HEAD					COUNTERSUNK	
	A	H	r_1	r_2	r_3	A	H
3/32	0.163	0.054	0.030	0.080	0.326	0.176	0.040
1/8	0.215	0.072	0.039	0.106	0.429	0.231	0.053
5/32	0.268	0.089	0.049	0.133	0.535	0.289	0.066
3/16	0.321	0.107	0.059	0.159	0.641	0.346	0.079
7/32	0.378	0.126	0.069	0.186	0.754	0.407	0.094
1/4	0.429	0.143	0.079	9.213	0.858	0.463	0.106
9/32	0.482	0.161	0.088	0.239	0.963	0.520	0.119
5/16	0.535	0.178	0.098	0.266	1.070	0.577	0.133
11/32	0.589	0.196	0.108	0.292	1.176	0.635	0.146
3/8	0.644	0.215	0.118	0.319	1.286	0.694	0.159
7/16	0.750	0.250	0.137	0.372	1.500	0.808	0.186

Length L of rivet is the ordered length and is not included in standard.

American Standard Small Rivets — 4

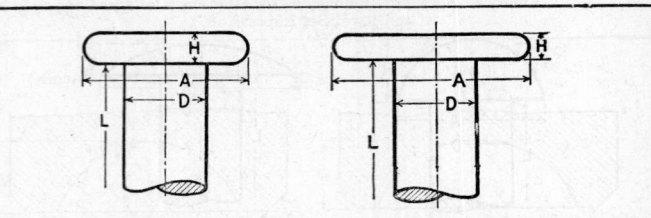

Nominal Diam. D	FLAT HEAD		Size No. (1)	TINNERS' RIVETS			
	A	H		D	A	H	L
³⁄₃₂	0.190	0.032	8 oz.	0.089	0.207	0.027	0.16
⅛	0.250	0.042	12 "	0.105	0.236	0.031	0.19
⁵⁄₃₂	0.312	0.052	1 lb.	0.111	0.249	0.033	0.20
³⁄₁₆	0.374	0.062	1½ "	0.130	0.292	0.039	0.23
⁷⁄₃₂	0.440	0.073	2 "	0.144	0.324	0.043	0.27
¼	0.500	0.083	2½ "	0.148	0.333	0.044	0.28
⁹⁄₃₂	0.562	0.094	3 "	0.160	0.360	0.048	0.31
⁵⁄₁₆	0.624	0.104	4 "	0.176	0.396	0.052	0.34
11⁄₃₂	0.686	0.114	6 "	0.203	0.456	0.060	0.39
⅜	0.750	0.125	8 "	0.224	0.504	0.067	0.44
⁷⁄₁₆	0.874	0.146	10 "	0.238	0.535	0.071	0.47
...	...	...	12 "	0.259	0.582	0.077	0.50
...	...	...	14 "	0.284	0.639	0.085	0.52
...	...	...	16 "	0.300	0.675	0.090	0.53

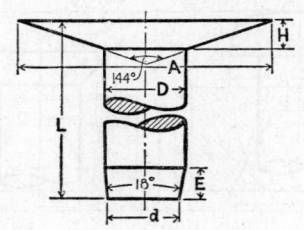

Size No. (2)	BELT RIVETS						
	D	A	H	Angle	L	E	d
7	0.180	0.504	0.054	144°	Lengths	0.072	0.162
8	0.165	0.462	0.049	144°	to be	0.066	0.148
9	0.148	0.414	0.044	144°	from	0.059	0.133
10	0.134	0.375	0.040	144°	⅜" to	0.053	0.120
11	0.120	0.336	0.036	144°	¾" by	0.048	0.108
12	0.109	0.305	0.032	144°	⅛" in-	0.043	0.098
13	0.095	0.266	0.028	144°	cre-	0.038	0.085
					ments		

(1) Size numbers refer to the "Trade Name" or weight of 1000 rivets.
(2) Size number refers to the Stubs Iron Wire Gage number of the stock used in the body of the rivet.

American Standard Dimensions for Hold-on (Dolly Bar) and Rivet Set Impression

Button Head

High Button Head (Acorn)

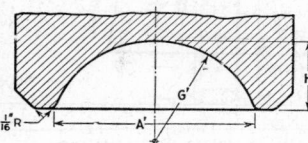
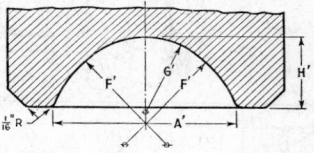

Rivet Body Diam.	BUTTON HEAD			HIGH BUTTON HEAD			
	A'	H'	G'	A'	H'	F'	G'
½	0.906	0.313	0.484	0.859	0.359	0.563	0.375
⅝	1.125	0.406	0.594	1.047	0.422	0.672	0.453
¾	1.344	0.484	0.719	1.234	0.500	0.797	0.531
⅞	1.578	0.563	0.844	1.422	0.578	0.922	0.609
1	1.813	0.641	0.953	1.609	0.656	1.031	0.688
1⅛	2.031	0.719	1.078	1.797	0.719	1.156	0.766
1¼	2.250	0.797	1.188	1.984	0.797	1.281	0.844
1⅜	2.469	0.875	1.313	2.172	0.875	1.391	0.938
1½	2.703	0.953	1.438	2.344	0.953	1.500	1.000
1⅝	2.922	1.047	1.547	2.531	1.031	1.625	1.094
1¾	3.156	1.125	1.672	2.719	1.109	1.750	1.172

Cone Head

Pan Head

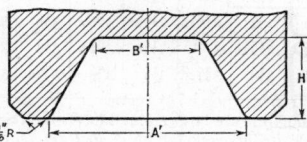
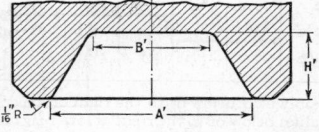

Rivet Body Diam.	CONE HEAD			Rivet Body Diam.	PAN HEAD		
	A'	B'	H'		A'	B'	H'
½	0.891	0.469	0.391	½	0.891	0.500	0.297
⅝	1.109	0.594	0.484	⅝	1.109	0.625	0.375
¾	1.328	0.703	0.578	¾	1.328	0.750	0.453
⅞	1.547	0.828	0.688	⅞	1.547	0.875	0.531
1	1.781	0.938	0.781	1	1.781	1.000	0.609
1⅛	2.016	1.063	0.875	1⅛	2.016	1.125	0.688
1¼	2.219	1.172	0.969	1¼	2.219	1.250	0.766
1⅜	2.438	1.297	1.078	1⅜	2.438	1.375	0.844
1½	2.672	1.406	1.172	1½	2.672	1.500	0.906
1⅝	2.891	1.531	1.266	1⅝	2.891	1.625	0.984
1¾	3.109	1.641	1.375	1¾	3.109	1.750	1.063

Rivet Spacing for Angles

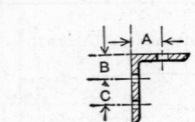

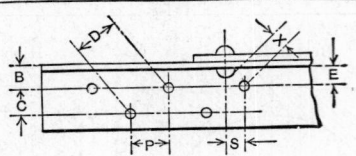

Length of Leg	A	B	C	Max. Rivet Diam.	Length of Leg	A	Max. Rivet Diam.
8	5	3	3	1	3	1 3/4	3/4
7	4 1/2	2 1/2	3	1	2 1/2	1 3/8	3/4
6	4	2 1/2	2 1/4	7/8	2 1/4	1 1/4	5/8
5	3	2	1 3/4	7/8	2	1 1/8	1/2
4	2 1/2	1 3/4	1	7/8	1 3/4	1	1/2
3 1/2	2	......	......	7/8	1 1/2	7/8	3/8

Distance *D* for Varying Values of *P* and *C*

C	Pitch of Rivets = *P*											
	1 1/8	1 1/4	1 3/8	1 1/2	1 5/8	1 3/4	1 7/8	2	2 1/8	2 1/4	2 3/8	2 1/2
1	1 1/2	1 5/8	1 11/16	1 13/16	1 7/8	2	2 1/8	2 1/4	2 5/16	2 7/16	2 9/16	2 11/16
1 1/4	1 11/16	1 3/4	1 7/8	1 15/16	2 1/16	2 1/8	2 1/4	2 3/8	2 7/16	2 9/16	2 11/16	2 13/16
1 1/2	1 7/8	1 15/16	2	2 1/8	2 3/16	2 5/16	2 3/8	2 1/2	2 5/8	2 11/16	2 13/16	2 15/16
1 3/4	2 1/16	2 1/8	2 3/16	2 5/16	2 3/8	2 7/16	2 9/16	2 5/8	2 3/4	2 7/8	2 15/16	3 1/16
2	2 5/16	2 3/8	2 7/16	2 1/2	2 9/16	2 5/8	2 3/4	2 13/16	2 15/16	3	3 1/8	3 3/16
2 1/4	2 1/2	2 9/16	2 5/8	2 11/16	2 3/4	2 7/8	2 15/16	3	3 1/16	3 3/16	3 1/4	3 3/8
2 1/2	2 3/4	2 13/16	2 7/8	2 15/16	3	3 1/16	3 1/8	3 3/16	3 1/4	3 3/8	3 7/16	3 9/16

Values of *D* below or to the right of upper zigzag line are large enough for 3/4-inch rivets. Values below or to the right of lower zigzag line are large enough for 7/8-inch rivets.

Required Clearance for Driving

E	*S*		*E*	*S*		*E*	*S*	
	3/4 Rivet	7/8 Rivet		3/4 Rivet	7/8 Rivet		3/4 Rivet	7/8 Rivet
1 1/8	1 1/8	1 3/8	1 3/8	3/4	1 1/8	1 5/8	0	11/16
1 3/16	1 1/16	1 5/16	1 7/16	5/8	1	1 11/16	0	1/2
1 1/4	15/16	1 1/4	1 1/2	7/16	15/16	1 3/4	0	0
1 5/16	7/8	1 3/16	1 9/16	0	13/16	......	.....	.....

X = 1 inch for 3/4-inch rivets; *X* = 1 3/32 inch for 7/8-inch rivets.

Proportions of Double- and Triple-riveted Butt-joints

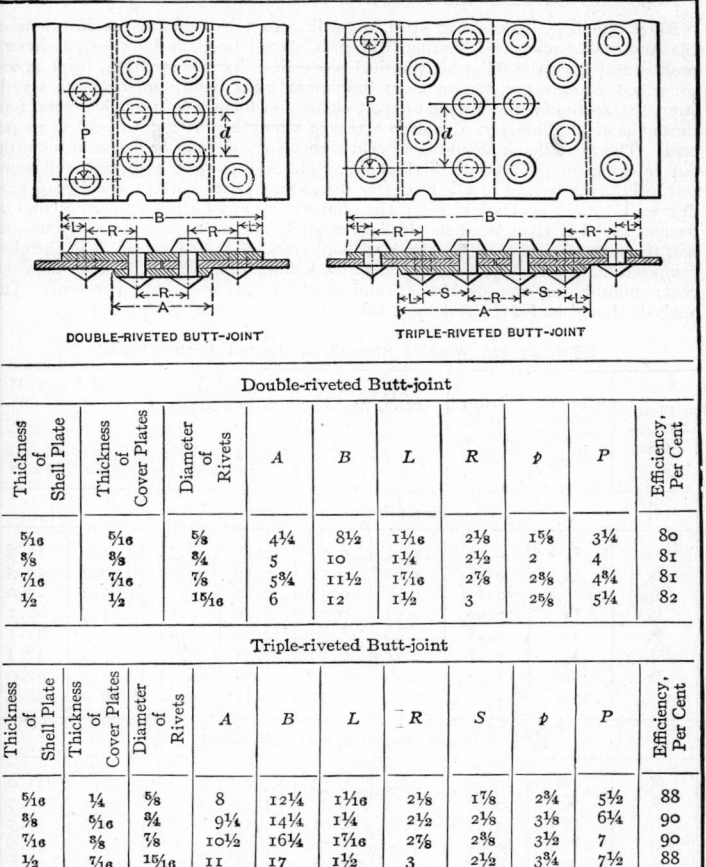

DOUBLE-RIVETED BUTT-JOINT   TRIPLE-RIVETED BUTT-JOINT

Double-riveted Butt-joint

Thickness of Shell Plate	Thickness of Cover Plates	Diameter of Rivets	A	B	L	R	p	P	Efficiency, Per Cent
⁵⁄₁₆	⁵⁄₁₆	⅝	4¼	8½	1¹⁄₁₆	2⅛	1⅝	3¼	80
⅜	⅜	¾	5	10	1¼	2½	2	4	81
⁷⁄₁₆	⁷⁄₁₆	⅞	5¾	11½	1⁷⁄₁₆	2⅞	2⅜	4¾	81
½	½	¹⁵⁄₁₆	6	12	1½	3	2⅝	5¼	82

Triple-riveted Butt-joint

Thickness of Shell Plate	Thickness of Cover Plates	Diameter of Rivets	A	B	L	R	S	p	P	Efficiency, Per Cent
⁵⁄₁₆	¼	⅝	8	12¼	1¹⁄₁₆	2⅛	1⅞	2¾	5½	88
⅜	⁵⁄₁₆	¾	9¼	14¼	1¼	2½	2⅛	3⅛	6¼	90
⁷⁄₁₆	⅜	⅞	10½	16¼	1⁷⁄₁₆	2⅞	2⅜	3½	7	90
½	⁷⁄₁₆	¹⁵⁄₁₆	11	17	1½	3	2½	3¾	7½	88

Double- and Triple-riveted Butt-joints. — The types of joints most commonly used for the longitudinal seams in boiler work are the double-riveted and triple-riveted butt-joints, with double covering strips. Quadruple-riveted joints are also used to a considerable extent for high-pressure work, these joints having a somewhat higher efficiency than triple-riveted joints. Lap-joints are no longer used in the best class of work for longitudinal seams, as experience has shown that they become weakened by continued use and are liable to fracture. Single-riveted lap-joints are sufficiently strong for the girth seams, as the pressure exerted in this direction is only one-half of that carried by the longitudinal seams. (See table "Proportions of Double- and Triple-riveted Butt-joints.")

Rivet Steel. — Boiler rivet steel, according to the standard specifications of the American Society for Testing Materials, should be made by the open-hearth process and have the following physical properties: Tensile strength, from 45,000 to 55,000 pounds per square inch; minimum yield point, one-half the tensile strength; minimum percentage of rivet elongation for a length not less than four times the rivet diameter, 1,500,000 ÷ tensile strength, but not to exceed 30 per cent. The rivet shank should bend cold through 180 degrees or flat on itself without cracking on the outside of the bend. The rivet should withstand this same test after being heated to a light cherry red as seen in the dark (not less than 1200 degrees F.) and quenched in water the temperature of which is between 80 and 90 degrees F. The rivet head should flatten, while hot, to a diameter two and one-half times the diameter of the shank without cracking at the edges. The chemical composition of the rolled bar should be as follows: Manganese, 0.30 to 0.50 per cent; phosphorus, not over 0.04; and sulphur, not over 0.045 per cent. The analysis should be from a test ingot taken during the pouring of each melt.

Efficiency and Working Strength of Riveted Joints (Unwin)

Plate Thickness	Normal Rivet Diam., Inches	Diam. Driven Rivets, Inches	Rivets in Single Shear		Rivets in Double Shear		Working Strength per Ft. of Joint, Tons	
			Pitch p, Inches	Efficiency η	Pitch p, Inches	Efficiency η	Single Shear	Double Shear
			Single-riveted Steel Joints					
5/16	11/16	0.72	1.79	0.60	2.56	0.72	14.7	17.6
3/8	3/4	0.78	1.82	0.57	2.58	0.70	16.7	20.5
7/16	13/16	0.85	1.91	0.56	2.68	0.68	19.2	23.0
1/2	7/8	0.92	2.01	0.55	2.80	0.67	21.5	26.1
5/8	15/16	0.98	2.00	0.50	2.70	0.64	24.5	31.1
3/4	1 1/8	1.17	2.35	0.50	3.24	0.64	29.3	37.4
7/8	1 3/16	1.23	2.46	0.50	3.18	0.62	34.1	42.3
1	1 5/16	1.36	2.72	0.50	3.45	0.61	39.0	47.6
			Double-riveted Joints — Mild Steel					
5/16	11/16	0.72	2.83	0.74	4.44	0.84	18.1	21.0
3/8	3/4	0.78	2.85	0.73	4.44	0.82	21.4	24.0
7/16	13/16	0.85	2.96	0.71	4.57	0.81	24.3	27.5
1/2	7/8	0.92	3.08	0.70	4.73	0.81	27.3	31.6
5/8	15/16	0.98	2.95	0.67	4.46	0.78	32.6	38.0
3/4	1 1/16	1.10	3.16	0.65	4.73	0.77	38.0	45.0
7/8	1 1/8	1.17	3.17	0.63	4.71	0.75	43.0	50.2
1	1 1/4	1.30	3.46	0.62	5.11	0.75	48.4	58.5
1 1/8	1 9/32	1.33	3.33	0.60	4.87	0.73	52.6	64.0
1 1/4	1 11/32	1.40	3.40	0.59	4.94	0.72	57.5	70.2

Let p = pitch of rivets; d = diameter of driven rivets; η = efficiency or ratio of strength of joint to strength of solid plate; then: $\eta = \dfrac{p - d}{p}$.

Riveting Pressures. — The pressures required for hot riveting ordinarily range from 75,000 to 150,000 pounds per square inch of rivet area, depending upon the class of work and the relation between the rivet diameter and the total plate thickness. The data in the table "Pressures for Hot Riveting" is from R. D. Wood & Co. It is assumed that the rivet passes through only two thicknesses of plate having a maximum total thickness not much in excess of the rivet diameter. As the total plate thickness increases beyond the rivet diameter, the riveting pressure increases approximately in proportion to the square root of the thickness. Thus, if the total thickness of the plate is four times the rivet diameter, twice the riveting pressure given in the table would be required in order to fill the rivet hole thoroughly and do good work. Double the thickness of plate would increase the necessary power about 40 per cent. Approximately four or five times as much power is required to drive rivets cold as to drive them hot. Thus a machine which will drive ¾-inch hot rivets will usually drive ⅜-inch cold rivets.

Pressures for Hot Riveting

Rivet Diameter	Class of Work and Pressure in Tons			Rivet Diameter	Class of Work and Pressure in Tons		
	Boiler	Tank	Girder		Boiler	Tank	Girder
½	20	15	9	1⅛	75	60	38
⅝	25	18	12	1¼	100	70	45
¾	33	22	15	1½	125	85	60
⅞	45	30	22	1¾	150	100	75
1	60	45	30	....	......	......	......

Loss of Strength when Holes are not Reamed. — When holes are punched in heavy steel plates there is considerable loss of strength unless the holes are reamed after punching. Annealing after punching also restores the strength. The loss in strength due to punching varies from about 10 per cent to 30 per cent for plates varying from ¼ to ¾ inch thick. The loss in case of thin plates is very slight. When holes are punched, instead of being drilled, usually the diameter should be increased from ¹⁄₁₆ to ⅛ inch by reaming, in order to remove the inferior metal around the punched hole. According to Navy Department specifications all holes in boiler plates must be drilled with the plates in place.

Loads at which Slipping Occurs in Riveted Joints. — Owing to the contraction of rivets on cooling, the plates are drawn together tightly; spaces are also left between the rivets and the holes so that it is possible for the plates to slip before shearing the rivets. The load required to overcome the frictional resistance between the plates varies (according to Bach) from 14,000 to 30,000 pounds per square inch of rivet area at each pair of surfaces in contact. It is the practice in Europe to design boiler joints with reference to the resistance to slipping, as any appreciable movement of such joints will cause leakage.

Elastic Limit of Riveted Boiler Joints. — Riveted boiler joints should cease to be steam-tight for some time before the internal pressure is equal to the elastic limit of the plate. If a boiler were stretched beyond the elastic limit of the material, the rivet holes would become stretched and the joints of the plates would be disturbed, resulting in large leakage from the rivet holes and seams. The elastic limit of riveted joints for the best quality of mild steel varies from 32,000 to 34,000 pounds per square inch and for an ordinary quality of mild steel, from 28,000 to 30,000 pounds per square inch. The elastic limit for the best quality of wrought iron varies from 24,000 to 26,000 pounds per square inch and for an ordinary quality, from 20,000 to 22,000 pounds per square inch.

Failure of Riveted Joints

A riveted joint may fail by shearing the rivets, tearing the plate between the rivets, crushing the rivets or plate, or by a combination of two or more of the foregoing causes. To determine the efficiency of a riveted joint, first calculate the breaking strength by the different ways in which it may fail. That method of failure giving the least result will show the actual strength of the joint. If this equals S_r and S equals the tensile strength of the solid plate, then the

efficiency $= \dfrac{S_r}{S}$. In the following formulas, let,

d = diameter of rivets; P = pitch of outer row of rivets;
t = thickness of plate; S = shearing strength of rivets;
t_c = thickness of cover plates; T = tensile strength of plate,
p = pitch of inner row of rivets; C = crushing strength of rivets.

(All dimensions in inches; all stresses in pounds per square inch.)

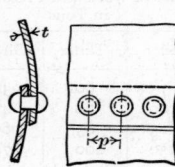

For Single-riveted Lap-joint

(1) Resistance to shearing one rivet $= \dfrac{\pi d^2}{4} S$

(2) Resistance to tearing plate between rivets
$= (p - d)\, tT$

(3) Resistance to crushing rivet or plate
$= dtC$

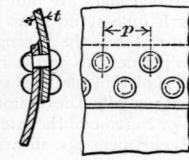

Double-riveted Lap-joint

(1) Resistance to shearing two rivets $= \dfrac{2\,\pi d^2}{4} S$

(2) Resistance to tearing between two rivets
$= (p - d)\, tT$

(3) Resistance to crushing in front of two
rivets $= 2\, dtC$

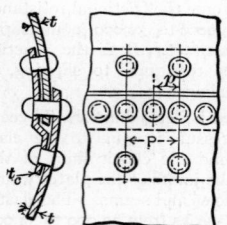

Single-riveted Lap-joint with Inside Cover Plate

(1) Resistance to tearing between outer row
of rivets $= (P - d)\, tT$

(2) Resistance to tearing between inner row
of rivets, and shearing outer row of
rivets $= (P - 2\,d)\, tT + \dfrac{\pi d^2}{4} S$

(3) Resistance to shearing three rivets $= \dfrac{3\,\pi d^2}{4} S$

(4) Resistance to crushing in front of three
rivets $= 3\, t\, dC$

(5) Resistance to tearing at inner row of
rivets, and crushing in front of one rivet
in outer row $= (P - 2\,d)\, tT + t\, dC$

Failure of Riveted Joints

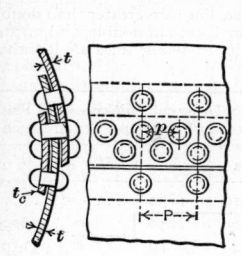

Double-riveted Lap-joint with Inside Cover Plate

(1) Resistance to tearing at outer row of rivets $= (P - d) tT$

(2) Resistance to shearing four rivets $= \dfrac{4\,\pi d^2}{4} S$

(3) Resistance to tearing at inner row and shearing outer row of rivets

$$= (P - 1\tfrac{1}{2} d) tT + \dfrac{\pi d^2}{4} S$$

(4) Resistance to crushing in front of four rivets $= 4\,t\,dC$

(5) Resistance to tearing at inner row of rivets, and crushing in front of one rivet $= (P - 1\tfrac{1}{2}d)tT + t\,dC$

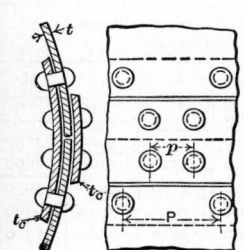

Double-riveted Butt-joint

(1) Resistance to tearing at outer row of rivets $= (P - d) tT$

(2) Resistance to shearing two rivets in double shear and one in single shear $= \dfrac{5\,\pi d^2}{4} S$

(3) Resistance to tearing at inner row of rivets and shearing one rivet of the outer row $= (P - 2\,d)\,tT + \dfrac{\pi d^2}{4} S$

(4) Resistance to crushing in front of three rivets $= 3\,t\,dC$

(5) Resistance to tearing at inner row of rivets, and crushing in front of one rivet in outer row $= (P - 2\,d)\,tT + t\,dC$

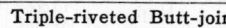

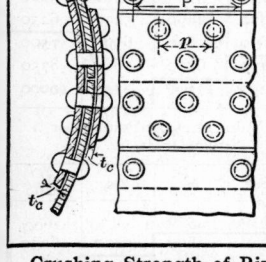

Triple-riveted Butt-joint

(1) Resistance to tearing at outer row of rivets $= (P - d) tT$

(2) Resistance to shearing four rivets in double shear and one in single shear $= \dfrac{9\,\pi d^2}{4} S$

(3) Resistance to tearing at middle row of rivets and shearing one rivet

$$= (P - 2\,d)\,tT + \dfrac{\pi d^2}{4} S$$

(4) Resistance to crushing in front of four rivets and shearing one rivet $= 4\,dtC + \dfrac{\pi d^2}{4} S$

(5) Resistance to crushing in front of five rivets $= 4\,dtC + dt_cC$

Crushing Strength of Rivets. — The crushing strength of rivets and plates, in joints that fail by crushing, is found by experiment to be high and irregular. In some cases it has amounted to 150,000 pounds per square inch; in a few tests it has been less than 85,000 pounds per square inch. A value of 95,000 pounds may be used with safety for general calculations.

Shearing Value of Rivets — Bearing Value of Riveted Plates

All bearing values above or to the right of the upper zigzag lines are greater than double shear. Values between the upper and lower zigzag lines are less than double, and greater than single, shear. Values below and to the left of the lower zigzag lines are less than single shear.

Diam. of Rivet, Inches		Area, Square Inch	Single Shear at 6000 Pounds	Bearing Value for Different Thicknesses of Plate in Inches at 12,000 Pounds per Square Inch				
Fraction	Decimal			1/4	5/16	3/8	7/16	1/2
3/8	0.375	0.1104	660	1130	1410	1690	.....	.....
1/2	0.500	0.1963	1180	1500	1880	2250	2630	3000
5/8	0.625	0.3068	1840	1880	2340	2810	3280	3750
3/4	0.750	0.4418	2650	2250	2810	3380	3940	4500
7/8	0.875	0.6013	3610	2630	3280	3940	4590	5250
1	1.000	0.7854	4710	3000	3750	4500	5250	6000

Fraction	Decimal	Area, Square Inch	Single Shear at 7500 Pounds	Bearing Value at 15,000 Pounds per Square Inch				
				1/4	5/16	3/8	7/16	1/2
3/8	0.375	0.1104	830	1410	1760	2110	.....	.....
1/2	0.500	0.1963	1470	1880	2340	2810	3280	3750
5/8	0.625	0.3068	2300	2340	2930	3520	4100	4690
3/4	0.750	0.4418	3310	2810	3520	4220	4920	5630
7/8	0.875	0.6013	4510	3280	4100	4920	5740	6560
1	1.000	0.7854	5890	3750	4690	5620	6560	7500

Fraction	Decimal	Area, Square Inch	Single Shear at 10,000 Pounds	Bearing Value at 20,000 Pounds per Square Inch				
				1/4	5/16	3/8	7/16	1/2
3/8	0.375	0.1104	1100	1880	2340	2810	.....	.....
1/2	0.500	0.1963	1960	2500	3130	3750	4380	5000
5/8	0.625	0.3068	3070	3130	3910	4690	5470	6250
3/4	0.750	0.4418	4420	3750	4690	5630	6560	7500
7/8	0.875	0.6013	6010	4380	5470	6570	7660	8750
1	1.000	0.7854	7850	5000	6250	7500	8750	10000

Fraction	Decimal	Area, Square Inch	Single Shear at 12,000 Pounds	Bearing Value at 25,000 Pounds per Square Inch				
				1/4	5/16	3/8	7/16	1/2
3/8	0.375	0.1104	1320	2350	2930	3520	.....	.....
1/2	0.500	0.1963	2360	3130	3910	4690	5470	6250
5/8	0.625	0.3068	3680	3910	4880	5860	6840	7810
3/4	0.750	0.4418	5300	4690	5860	7030	8210	9380
7/8	0.875	0.6013	7220	5470	6840	8210	9580	10940
1	1.000	0.7854	9430	6250	7820	9380	10940	12500

Shearing Value of Rivets — Bearing Value of Riveted Plates

All bearing values above or to the right of the upper zigzag lines are greater than double shear. Values between the upper and lower zigzag lines are less than double, and greater than single, shear. Values below and to the left of the lower zigzag lines are less than single shear.

Diam. of Rivet, Inches	Bearing Value for Different Thicknesses of Plate in Inches at 12,000 Pounds per Square Inch							
	9/16	5/8	11/16	3/4	13/16	7/8	15/16	1
3/8	.....	.....	.....	.....	.....	.....	.....	.....
1/2	.....	.....	.....	.....	.....	.....	.....	.....
5/8	4220	4690	.....	.....	.....	.....	.....	.....
3/4	5060	5630	6190	6750	.....	.....	.....	.....
7/8	5910	6560	7220	7880	8530	9190	9840	.....
1	6750	7500	8250	9000	9750	10500	11250	12000

Diam. of Rivet	Bearing Value at 15,000 Pounds per Square Inch							
	9/16	5/8	11/16	3/4	13/16	7/8	15/16	1
3/8	.....	.....	.....	.....	.....	.....	.....	.....
1/2	.....	.....	.....	.....	.....	.....	.....	.....
5/8	5280	5860	.....	.....	.....	.....	.....	.....
3/4	6830	7030	7720	8440	.....	.....	.....	.....
7/8	7380	8200	9030	9850	10670	11480	12300	.....
1	8440	9380	10310	11250	12190	13130	14060	15000

Diam. of Rivet	Bearing Value at 20,000 Pounds per Square Inch							
	9/16	5/8	11/16	3/4	13/16	7/8	15/16	1
3/8	.....	.....	.....	.....	.....	.....	.....	.....
1/2	.....	.....	.....	.....	.....	.....	.....	.....
5/8	7030	7810	.....	.....	.....	.....	.....	.....
3/4	8440	9380	10310	11250	.....	.....	.....	.....
7/8	9840	10940	12030	13130	14220	15310	16410	.....
1	11250	12500	13750	15000	16250	17500	18750	20000

Diam. of Rivet	Bearing Value at 25,000 Pounds per Square Inch							
	9/16	5/8	11/16	3/4	13/16	7/8	15/16	1
3/8	.....	.....	.....	.....	.....	.....	.....	.....
1/2	.....	.....	.....	.....	.....	.....	.....	.....
5/8	8790	9770	.....	.....	.....	.....	.....	.....
3/4	10550	11720	12890	14060	.....	.....	.....	.....
7/8	12310	13670	15040	16410	17770	19140	20510	.....
1	14060	15630	17190	18750	20320	21880	23440	25000

Proportions of Riveted Joints for Pressure Tanks

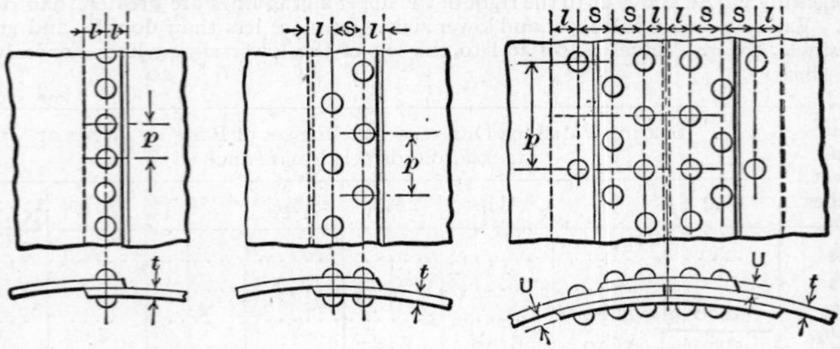

t = thickness of plate,
p = pitch of rivets, center to center,
d = diameter of rivets before driving,
D = diameter of hole,
S = distance between lines of rivets,
l = distance from edge of plate to first line of rivets,
U = thickness of strap,
E = efficiency of joint in per cent.

Thickness of Plate, t		5/16	3/8	7/16	1/2	9/16	5/8	11/16	3/4	13/16	7/8	15/16	1
Lap-joint, Single Riveted	p	2	2 1/16	2 1/8	2 1/8	2 3/16	...	...	...	...	...	...	...
	d	3/4	13/16	7/8	15/16	1	...	...	...	...	...	...	...
	D	13/16	7/8	15/16	1	1 1/16	...	...	...	...	...	...	...
	l	1 1/8	1 3/16	1 1/4	1 1/4	1 1/4	...	...	...	...	...	...	...
	E	59	56	54	53	51	...	...	...	...	...	...	...
Lap-joint, Double Riveted	p	3 3/16	3 3/16	3 3/16	3	3 1/16	3 1/8	3	2 7/8	...	...	...	...
	d	3/4	13/16	7/8	7/8	15/16	1	1	1	...	...	...	...
	D	13/16	7/8	15/16	15/16	1	1 1/16	1 1/16	1 1/16	...	...	...	...
	S	2	2	2	2	2	2	2	2	...	...	...	...
	l	1 1/8	1 3/16	1 1/4	1 1/4	1 1/4	1 1/4	1 1/4	1 1/4	...	...	...	...
	E	74	72	70	67	66	66	62	60	...	...	...	...
Double-strap Butt-joint, Triple Riveted	p	6	6	6 3/4	7	7	7	7	7	7 1/4	7	7 1/4	7
	d	5/8	3/4	7/8	7/8	7/8	7/8	15/16	15/16	1	1	1 1/8	1 1/8
	D	11/16	13/16	15/16	15/16	15/16	15/16	1	1	1 1/16	1 1/16	1 3/16	1 3/16
	l	1 1/8	1 3/16	1 1/4	1 1/4	1 1/4	1 1/4	1 1/4	1 1/4	1 1/4	1 3/8	1 3/8	1 3/8
	U	1/4	5/16	3/8	7/16	7/16	1/2	9/16	9/16	5/8	5/8	11/16	3/4
	E	88	86	86	86	86	86	85	85	85	84	83	83
	S	2 3/8 to 3 for all pitches.											

Shearing Strength of Rivets in Single Shear

Diam. of Rivet	Area of Cross-section	Shearing Strength per Square Inch				
		30,000	35,000	40,000	45,000	50,000
3/8	0.1104	3,310	3,860	4,410	4,960	5,520
1/2	0.1963	5,880	6,870	7,850	8,830	9,815
5/8	0.3068	9,200	10,730	12,270	13,800	15,340
3/4	0.4418	13,250	15,460	17,670	19,880	22,090
7/8	0.6013	18,030	21,040	24,050	27,050	30,065
1	0.7854	23,560	27,480	31,410	35,340	39,270

Shearing Strength of Rivets

Shearing resistance = NSA, in which N = number of rivets; A = cross-sectional area sheared in square inches; S = shearing strength of rivet iron = 38,000 pounds per square inch. Diameter of driven rivet equals diameter of rivet hole.

Diam. of Driven Rivet, Ins.	Area Sheared, Sq. In.	Number of Rivets Sheared = N						
		½	1	2	3	4	5	6
7/16	0.1503	2,850	5,710	11,425	17,130	22,850	28,560	34,275
½	0.1963	3,730	7,460	14,920	22,380	29,845	37,300	44,760
9/16	0.2485	4,720	9,440	18,880	28,320	37,770	47,210	56,650
5/8	0.3068	5,820	11,650	23,310	34,975	46,630	58,290	69,950
11/16	0.3712	7,050	14,100	28,210	42,310	56,425	70,530	84,630
¾	0.4418	8,390	16,780	33,570	50,360	67,150	83,940	100,720
13/16	0.5184	9,850	19,700	39,400	59,100	78,810	98,510	118,210
7/8	0.6013	11,425	22,850	45,700	68,550	91,400	114,250	137,100
15/16	0.6902	13,115	26,230	52,460	78,690	104,920	131,150	157,380
1	0.7854	14,920	29,845	59,690	89,530	119,380	149,220	179,070
1 1/16	0.8866	16,840	33,690	67,385	101,070	134,760	168,460	202,150
1 1/8	0.9940	18,880	37,770	75,540	113,310	151,090	188,860	226,630
1 3/16	1.1075	21,040	42,085	84,170	126,250	168,340	210,425	252,510

Tensile Strength of Plate per 1 Inch of Width

Thickness	Tensile Strength per Square Inch				
	50,000	55,000	60,000	65,000	70,000
1/16	3,125	3,430	3,750	4,060	4,375
⅛	6,250	6,875	7,500	8,125	8,750
3/16	9,375	10,310	11,250	12,180	13,125
¼	12,500	13,750	15,000	16,250	17,500
5/16	15,625	17,180	18,750	20,310	21,875
3/8	18,750	20,625	22,500	24,375	26,250
7/16	21,875	24,060	26,250	28,430	30,625
½	25,000	27,500	30,000	32,500	35,000
9/16	28,125	30,930	33,750	36,560	39,375
5/8	31,250	34,375	37,500	40,625	43,750
11/16	34,375	37,810	41,250	44,680	48,125
¾	37,500	41,250	45,000	48,750	52,500
13/16	40,625	44,680	48,750	52,810	56,875
7/8	43,750	48,125	52,500	56,875	61,250
15/16	46,875	51,560	56,250	60,930	65,625
1	50,000	55,000	60,000	65,000	70,000

Rivet Steel Tolerances. — According to the A.S.T.M. standard specification, permissible variations in diameters of rivet bars shall be as follows: Size of 5/16 and under, ±0.005; over 5/16 to 7/16 incl., ±0.006; over 7/16 to 5/8 incl., ±0.007; over 5/8 to 7/8 incl., ±0.008; over 7/8 to 1 incl., ±0.009; over 1 to 1⅛ incl., ±0.010; over 1⅛ to 1¼ incl., ±0.011; over 1¼ to 1⅜ inc., ±0.012.

WIRE AND SHEET-METAL GAGES

The thicknesses of sheet metals and the diameters of wires conform to various gaging systems. These gage sizes are indicated by numbers, and the following tables give the decimal equivalents of the different gage numbers. Much confusion has resulted from the use of gage numbers, and in ordering materials it is preferable to give the exact dimensions in decimal fractions of an inch. While the dimensions thus specified should conform to the gage ordinarily used for a given class of material, any error in the specification due, for example, to the use of a table having "rounded off" or approximate equivalents, will be apparent to the manufacturer at the time the order is placed. Furthermore, the decimal method of indicating wire diameters and sheet metal thicknesses has the advantage of being self-explanatory, whereas arbitrary gage numbers are not. The decimal system of indicating gage sizes is now being used quite generally, and gage numbers are gradually being discarded. Unfortunately, there is considerable variation in the use of different gages. For example, a gage ordinarily used for copper, brass and other non-ferrous materials, may at times be used for steel, and vice versa. The gages specified in the following are the ones ordinarily employed for the materials mentioned, but there are in some cases minor exceptions and variations in the different industries.

Wire Gages. — The Brown & Sharpe or American Wire Gage is generally used in the United States for all bare wire of brass, copper (except bare copper telephone wire) phosphor-bronze, German silver, aluminum, and zinc; for resistance wire of German silver and other alloys; for insulated wire of aluminum and copper. The Steel Wire Gage (also known as (1) Washburn & Moen, (2) American Steel & Wire Co, (3) Roebling, and (4) National Wire Gage) is used for bare wire of galvanized and annealed steel and iron (except telephone and telegraph), and also for spring steel wire. The American Steel & Wire Co.'s Music Wire Gage is used for music wire. The Birmingham Wire Gage sizes are very generally used for iron and steel telephone and telegraph wires, but the sizes of bare copper telephone wires, usually conform in the United States, to the Standard Wire Gage used in England. This Standard Wire Gage (also known as the Imperial Wire Gage and as the English Legal Standard) is used in England for all wires. The abbreviation S. W. G. is sometimes used for Standard Wire Gage, also the abbreviation N. B. S. for New British Standard Wire Gage. This gage was legalized in Great Britain in 1883.

Gages for Rods. — The Brown & Sharpe or American Wire Gage is used for rods of non-ferrous metals, such as brass, copper and aluminum. Stub's Steel Wire Gage is used to some extent for tool steel, drill rod and wire, and the Twist Drill and Steel Wire Gage is used for twist drills and steel drill rods.

Sheet-metal Gages. — The thicknesses of steel sheets now are based upon a weight of 41.82 pounds per square foot per inch thick. This is known as Manufacturers' Standard Gage. This gage differs from the older United States Standard which was based upon a weight of 40 pounds per square foot per inch thick. See text accompanying table on Page 440. The American or Brown & Sharpe Wire Gage is used for sheets of brass, phosphor-bronze, aluminum and German silver. The Birmingham Wire Gage is used for strip steel, steel bands, hoop steel, crucible spring sheet steel, and sheet copper. The Zinc Gage is used for sheet zinc only.

In England the Birmingham Gage legalized in 1914 is used mainly for iron and steel sheets and hoops. This 1914 Birmingham Gage differs from the older Birmingham or Stub's Iron Wire Gage. Another older gage known as the Birmingham Metal Gage is used for brass sheets. For aluminum sheets, the Imperial Wire Gage is used in England.

Wire and Sheet Metal Gages in Approximate Decimals of an Inch

No. of Wire Gage	American or Brown & Sharpe	Birmingham or Stub's Iron Wire	Washburn & Moen, Am. Steel & Wire Co., and Roebling	Stub's Steel Wire	1914 Birmingham (B.G.) Gage for Sheets, Hoops	British Imperial Wire	U.S. Standard for Steel Sheets, Inch*
0000000	......	......	0.4900	......	0.6666	0.5000	
000000	0.5800	......	0.4615	......	0.6250	0.4640	
00000	0.5165	0.500	0.4305	......	0.5883	0.4320	
0000	0.4600	0.454	0.3938	......	0.5416	0.4000	
000	0.4096	0.425	0.3625	......	0.5000	0.3720	
00	0.3648	0.380	0.3310	......	0.4452	0.3480	
0	0.3249	0.340	0.3065	......	0.3964	0.3240	
1	0.2893	0.300	0.2830	0.227	0.3532	0.3000	
2	0.2576	0.284	0.2625	0.219	0.3147	0.2760	
3	0.2294	0.259	0.2437	0.212	0.2804	0.2520	
4	0.2043	0.238	0.2253	0.207	0.2500	0.2320	
5	0.1819	0.220	0.2070	0.204	0.2225	0.2120	
6	0.1620	0.203	0.1920	0.201	0.1981	0.1920	
7	0.1443	0.180	0.1770	0.199	0.1764	0.1760	
8	0.1285	0.165	0.1620	0.197	0.1570	0.1600	
9	0.1144	0.148	0.1483	0.194	0.1398	0.1440	
10	0.1019	0.134	0.1350	0.191	0.1250	0.1280	
11	0.0907	0.120	0.1205	0.188	0.1113	0.1160	
12	0.0808	0.109	0.1055	0.185	0.0991	0.1040	
13	0.0720	0.095	0.0915	0.182	0.0882	0.0920	
14	0.0641	0.083	0.0800	0.180	0.0785	0.0800	
15	0.0571	0.072	0.0720	0.178	0.0699	0.0720	
16	0.0508	0.065	0.0625	0.175	0.0625	0.0640	
17	0.0453	0.058	0.0540	0.172	0.0556	0.0560	
18	0.0403	0.049	0.0475	0.168	0.0495	0.0480	
19	0.0359	0.042	0.0410	0.164	0.0440	0.0400	
20	0.0320	0.035	0.0348	0.161	0.0392	0.0360	
21	0.0285	0.032	0.0317	0.157	0.0349	0.0320	
22	0.0253	0.028	0.0286	0.155	0.0312	0.0280	
23	0.0226	0.025	0.0258	0.153	0.0278	0.0240	
24	0.0201	0.022	0.0230	0.151	0.0247	0.0220	
25	0.0179	0.020	0.0204	0.148	0.0220	0.0200	
26	0.0159	0.018	0.0181	0.146	0.0196	0.0180	
27	0.0142	0.016	0.0173	0.143	0.0174	0.0164	
28	0.0126	0.014	0.0162	0.139	0.0156	0.0148	
29	0.0113	0.013	0.0150	0.134	0.0139	0.0136	
30	0.0100	0.012	0.0140	0.127	0.0123	0.0124	
31	0.0089	0.010	0.0132	0.120	0.0110	0.0116	
32	0.0080	0.009	0.0128	0.115	0.0098	0.0108	
33	0.0071	0.008	0.0118	0.112	0.0087	0.0100	
34	0.0063	0.007	0.0104	0.110	0.0077	0.0092	
35	0.0056	0.005	0.0095	0.108	0.0069	0.0084	
36	0.0050	0.004	0.0090	0.106	0.0061	0.0076	
37	0.0045	......	0.0085	0.103	0.0054	0.0068	
38	0.0040	......	0.0080	0.101	0.0048	0.0060	
39	0.0035	......	0.0075	0.099	0.0043	0.0052	
40	0.0031	......	0.0070	0.097	0.0038	0.0048	
41	0.0028	......	0.0066	0.095	0.0034	0.0044	
42	0.0025	......	0.0062	0.092	0.0030	0.0040	
43	0.0022	......	0.0060	0.088	0.0027	0.0036	
44	0.00198	......	0.0058	0.085	0.0024	0.0032	
45	0.00176	......	0.0055	0.081	0.0021	0.0028	
46	0.00157	......	0.0052	0.079	0.0019	0.0024	
47	0.00140	......	0.0050	0.077	0.0017	0.0020	
48	0.00124	......	0.0048	0.075	0.0015	0.0016	
49	0.001108	......	0.0046	0.072	0.0013	0.0012	
50	0.00099	......	0.0044	0.069	0.0012	0.0010	

(Column 8, U.S. Standard for Steel Sheets: "See Manufacturers' Standard Gage for Sheet Steel; also Standard Thickness Tolerances for Sheet Steel.")

* The thicknesses equivalent to U. S. Standard Gage numbers, and applying to steel sheets as produced in modern rolling mills, are given in the table on the next page.

Manufacturers' Standard Gage for Sheet Steel

United States Standard Gage: The United States standard gage for iron and steel sheets and plates was established by Congress in 1893 and is primarily a *weight* gage rather than a thickness gage. The equivalent thicknesses were derived from the weight of wrought iron. The weight per cubic foot was taken at 480 pounds, thus making the weight of a plate 12 inches square and 1 inch thick, 40 pounds. In converting weight to equivalent thickness, gage tables formerly published contained thicknesses equivalent to the basic weights just mentioned. For example, a No. 3 U. S. gage represents a wrought-iron plate having a weight of 10 pounds per square foot; hence, if the weight per square foot per inch thick is 40 pounds, the plate thickness for a No. 3 gage = 10 ÷ 40 = 0.25 inch, which was the original thickness equivalent for this gage number. Since this and the other thickness equivalents were derived from the weight of wrought iron, they are not correct for steel. The standard below, applies to steel.

Manufacturers' Standard Gage: The basic weight for steel, as determined over a long period, has been established at 41.82 pounds per square foot per inch thick; hence, the equivalent thicknesses of steel sheets have been reduced to 40/41.82 of the original thicknesses for wrought iron. The thicknesses in the table below are based upon this weight of 41.82 pounds, and represent standard mill practice at the present time. These nominal thicknesses, however, are subject to tolerances or permissible variations as given in the table on the following page which includes both hot-rolled and cold-rolled sheets. (Note: Manufacturers of steel sheets and plates formerly used a basic weight of 40.8 pounds per square foot per inch thick, but this finally was increased to 41.82 pounds due to the increase in the density of steel following the introduction of the continuous type of rolling mill.)

Standard Gage No.	Ounces per Square Foot	Pounds per Square Foot	Equivalent Thickness, Inch	Standard Gage No.	Ounces per Square Foot	Pounds per Square Foot	Equivalent Thickness, Inch
3	160	10.0000	0.2391	21	22	1.3750	.0329
4	150	9.3750	.2242	22	20	1.2500	.0299
5	140	8.7500	.2092	23	18	1.1250	.0269
6	130	8.1250	.1943	24	16	1.0000	.0239
7	120	7.5000	.1793	25	14	0.87500	.0209
8	110	6.8750	.1644	26	12	.75000	.0179
9	100	6.2500	.1495	27	11	.68750	.0164
10	90	5.6250	.1345	28	10	.62500	.0149
11	80	5.0000	.1196	29	9	.56250	.0135
12	70	4.3750	.1046	30	8	.50000	.0120
13	60	3.7500	.0897	31	7	.43750	.0105
14	50	3.1250	.0747	32	6.5	.40625	.0097
15	45	2.8125	.0673	33	6	.37500	.0090
16	40	2.5000	.0598	34	5.5	.34375	.0082
17	36	2.2500	.0538	35	5	.31250	.0075
18	32	2.0000	.0478	36	4.5	.28125	.0067
19	28	1.7500	.0418	37	4.25	.26562	.0064
20	24	1.5000	.0359	38	4	.25000	.0060

Permissible Gage Weight Variations — All Sheets of One Gage and Size

Specified Gage Weights, Pounds per Sq. Ft.	20 Tons and Over	Under 20 to 3 Tons	Under 3 to 1 Ton	Under 1 Ton
1.875 (or 18 gage) and heavier	3½%±	5%±	7½%±	10%±
1.874 (or 19 gage) and lighter	2½%±	3%±	5%±	10%±

From "Steel Products Manual" of American Iron and Steel Institute.

Standard Thickness Tolerances for Sheet Steel
(American Iron and Steel Institute)

HOT-ROLLED SHEETS

Widths, Inches	Thickness range and plus or minus thickness tolerances						
	0.2499 0.1875	0.1874 0.1420	0.1419 0.0972	0.0971 0.0822	0.0821 0.0710	0.0709 0.0568	0.0567 0.0509
6 to 12	....	....	....	....	....	....	.005
12 to 15	.008	.007	.007	.006	.006	.006	.005
15 to 20	.008	.008	.008	.007	.007	.006	.006
20 to 32	.009	.009	.008	.007	.007	.006	.006
32 to 40	.009	.009	.009	.008	.007	.006	.006
40 to 48	.010	.010	.010	.008	.007	.006	.006
48 to 60	....	.010	.010	.008	.007	.007	.006
60 to 70	....	.011	.011	.009	.008	.007	.007
70 to 80	....	.012	.012	.009	.008	....	....
80 to 90	....	.012	.012	.010	....	....	....

Widths, Inches	Thickness range and plus or minus thickness tolerances						
	0.0508 0.0389	0.0388 0.0344	0.0343 0.0314	0.0313 0.0255	0.0254 0.0195	0.0194 0.0142	.0141 or less
To 3½ inc.	....	....	....	....	.003	.002	.002
3½ to 6	....	....	.004	.003	.003	.002	.002
6 to 12	.005	.004	.004	.003	.003	.002	.002
12 to 15	.005	.004	.004	.003	.003	.002	....
15 to 20	.005	.004	.004	.003	.003	.002	....
20 to 32	.005	.004	.004	.003	.003	.002	.002
32 to 40	.005	.004	.004	.003	.003	.002	.002
40 to 48	.005	.004	.004	.003	.003	.002	.002
48 to 60	.005	.004	.004	....	....	....	....
60 to 70	.006	.005	.005	....	....	....	....

COLD-ROLLED SHEETS

Widths, Inches	Thickness range and plus or minus tolerances						
	0.1875 up	0.1874 0.1420	0.1419 0.0972	0.0971 0.0822	0.0821 0.0710	0.0709 0.0568	0.0567 0.0509
12 to 15	.007	.006	.006	.006	.005	.005	.005
15 to 20	.007	.007	.007	.006	.005	.005	.005
20 to 24	.007	.007	.007	.006	.005	.005	.005
24 to 32	.008	.008	.008	.006	.006	.005	.005
32 to 40	.009	.009	.009	.007	.006	.005	.005
40 to 48	.010	.010	.009	007	.006	.005	.005
48 to 60	.011	.011	.010	.008	.007	.006	.005
60 to 70	.012	.011	.010	.009	.007	.006	.006
70 to 80	.013	.012	.011	.009	.007	.006	.006
80 to 90	.014	.012	.012	....	....	....	....

Widths, Inches	Thickness range and plus or minus tolerances						
	0.0508 0.0389	0.0388 0.0314	0.0313 0.0255	0.0254 0.0195	0.0194 0.0142	0.0141 0.0113	0.0112 or less
12 to 15	.004	.003	.003	.003	.002	....	....
15 to 20	.004	.003	.003	.003	.002	....	....
20 to 24	.004	.003	.003	. 003	.002	....	....
24 to 32	.004	.003	.003	.003	.002	....	....
32 to 40	.004	.0035	.003	.003	.002	.002	.0015
40 to 48	.004	.0035	.003	.003	.002	.002	....
48 to 60	.004	.0035	.0035	.003	.002	...	....
60 to 70	.005	.004	.004	....	....	....	....
70 to 80	.005	.004	.004	....	....	....	....

Thickness is measured at any point on the sheet not less than ⅜ inch from the edge.

Additional Gage Numbers and Sizes of Stub's Steel Wire

Gage No.	Stub's Steel Wire	Gage No.	Stub's Steel Wire	Gage No.	Stub's Steel Wire	Gage No.	Stub's Steel Wire	Gage No.	Stub's Steel Wire
51	0.066	57	0.042	63	0.036	69	0.029	75	0.020
52	0.063	58	0.041	64	0.035	70	0.027	76	0.018
53	0.058	59	0.040	65	0.033	71	0.026	77	0.016
54	0.055	60	0.039	66	0.032	72	0.024	78	0.015
55	0.050	61	0.038	67	0.031	73	0.023	79	0.014
56	0.045	62	0.037	68	0.030	74	0.022	80	0.013

Gages for Tubing. — The Birmingham or Stub's Iron Wire Gage is used for the following classes of tubing: Seamless brass, seamless copper, seamless steel, and aluminum. The Brown & Sharpe Wire Gage is used for brazed brass and brazed copper tubing.

Wire Drawing. — Wire drawing is the process used for producing wire of smaller diameter by drawing a wire or rod of larger diameter through a plate or die provided with a hole which reduces the size to the desired dimension. Briefly described, the machines used for wire drawing consist of a die or "draw-plate" provided with holes through which the wire is drawn, and means for pulling the wire through these dies and winding it upon a reel. The draw-plate or die for larger sizes of wire is generally made from chilled cast iron or steel, but for the finer sizes it is made from one of the less expensive or imperfect varieties of diamond, because diamond dies can be used for a longer period without losing their size. When the wire is drawn through the holes in the dies, thus reducing its diameter, the drawing action hardens the wire and makes it brittle. It must, therefore, be annealed at frequent intervals before it is further reduced to a smaller size by a subsequent drawing operation.

Strength of Piano and Plow-steel Wire. — The strength of wire is increased considerably by drawing. So-called piano wire has an ultimate tensile strength of from 300,000 to 340,000 pounds per square inch. The composition of this wire is as follows: Carbon, 0.57 per cent; silicon, 0.09 per cent; sulphur, 0.011 per cent; phosphorus, 0.018 per cent; manganese, 0.425 per cent. This wire is made in sizes ranging from 0.029 to 0.052 inch (music wire gage Nos. 12 to 22 inclusive). So-called "plow-steel" wire has an ultimate tensile strength of 345,000 pounds per square inch for wire 0.093 inch in diameter, and 200,000 pounds per square inch for wire 0.191 inch in diameter. The elongation is only about 1 per cent. The composition is about as follows: Carbon, 0.83 per cent; manganese, 0.59 per cent; silicon, 0.14 per cent; sulphur, 0.01 per cent; phosphorus, nil; copper, 0.03 per cent.

Converting Strength of Wire into Strength in Pounds per Square Inch. — The table given for this conversion has two columns, one headed "Diam. of Wire," and the other "Factor." The strength of the wire of a given diameter should be multiplied by the factor given, in order to obtain the strength per square inch. For example, it is known that a wire 0.035 inch in diameter can sustain a load of 150 pounds before breaking. Then the strength in pounds per square inch of the wire is found as below:

$$150 \times 1040 = 156,000 \text{ pounds per square inch.}$$

The factor 1040 is found opposite the diameter 0.035 in the table.

Converting Strength of Wire to Strength per Square Inch

Diam. of Wire	Factor	Diam. of Wire	Factor	Diam. of Wire	Factor	Diam. of Wire	Factor	Diam. of Wire	Factor
0.001	1,273,240	0.051	489.9	0.101	124.8	0.151	55.8	0.201	31.5
0.002	318,310	0.052	470.8	0.102	122.4	0.152	55.0	0.202	31.2
0.003	141,470	0.053	452.7	0.103	120.0	0.153	54.3	0.203	30.9
0.004	79,580	0.054	436.7	0.104	117.7	0.154	53.7	0.204	30.6
0.005	50,910	0.055	421.3	0.105	115.5	0.155	53.0	0.205	30.3
0.006	35,360	0.056	406.0	0.106	113.3	0.156	52.3	0.206	30.0
0.007	25,980	0.057	392.2	0.107	111.2	0.157	51.6	0.207	29.7
0.008	19,890	0.058	378.4	0.108	109.2	0.158	51.0	0.208	29.4
0.009	16,290	0.059	368.0	0.109	107.2	0.159	50.3	0.209	29.3
0.010	12,730	0.060	357.7	0.110	105.2	0.160	49.7	0.210	28.8
0.011	10,520	0.061	344.4	0.111	103.2	0.161	49.1	0.211	28.5
0.012	8,840	0.062	331.2	0.112	101.5	0.162	48.5	0.212	28.3
0.013	7,532	0.063	321.0	0.113	99.7	0.163	47.9	0.213	28.0
0.014	6,496	0.064	310.8	0.114	98.0	0.164	47.3	0.214	27.8
0.015	5,724	0.065	301.5	0.115	96.3	0.165	46.7	0.215	27.5
0.016	4,972	0.066	292.3	0.116	94.6	0.166	46.2	0.216	27.3
0.017	4,404	0.067	283.8	0.117	93.0	0.167	45.6	0.217	27.0
0.018	4,072	0.068	275.3	0.118	91.4	0.168	45.1	0.218	26.8
0.019	3,527	0.069	262.6	0.119	89.9	0.169	44.5	0.219	26.5
0.020	3,182	0.070	260.0	0.120	88.4	0.170	44.0	0.220	26.3
0.021	2,888	0.071	252.8	0.121	86.9	0.171	43.5	0.221	26.0
0.022	2,630	0.072	245.6	0.122	85.5	0.172	43.0	0.222	25.8
0.023	2,407	0.073	239.0	0.123	84.1	0.173	42.5	0.223	25.6
0.024	2,210	0.074	232.5	0.124	82.8	0.174	42.0	0.224	25.4
0.025	2,036	0.075	226.4	0.125	81.4	0.175	41.5	0.225	25.1
0.026	1,883	0.076	220.4	0.126	80.0	0.176	41.0	0.226	24.9
0.027	1,747	0.077	214.8	0.127	78.8	0.177	40.6	0.227	24.7
0.028	1,624	0.078	209.3	0.128	77.7	0.178	40.1	0.228	24.5
0.029	1,514	0.079	204.1	0.129	76.5	0.179	39.7	0.229	24.3
0.030	1,431	0.080	198.9	0.130	75.3	0.180	39.3	0.230	24.1
0.031	1,325	0.081	194.1	0.131	74.1	0.181	38.9	0.231	23.8
0.032	1,243	0.082	189.4	0.132	73.0	0.182	38.4	0.232	23.6
0.033	1,169	0.083	184.7	0.133	71.9	0.183	38.0	0.233	23.4
0.034	1,106	0.084	180.0	0.134	70.9	0.184	37.6	0.234	23.2
0.035	1,040	0.085	176.0	0.135	69.8	0.185	37.1	0.235	23.0
0.036	982	0.086	172.1	0.136	68.8	0.186	36.7	0.236	22.8
0.037	930	0.087	168.2	0.137	67.8	0.187	36.3	0.237	22.6
0.038	882	0.088	164.4	0.138	66.9	0.188	36.0	0.238	22.5
0.039	839	0.089	160.8	0.139	65.9	0.189	35.7	0.239	22.3
0.040	796	0.090	157.2	0.140	65.0	0.190	35.3	0.240	22.1
0.041	759	0.091	153.6	0.141	64.0	0.191	34.9	0.241	21.9
0.042	722	0.092	150.0	0.142	63.0	0.192	34.5	0.242	21.7
0.043	690	0.093	147.0	0.143	62.2	0.193	34.1	0.243	21.5
0.044	658	0.094	144.1	0.144	61.4	0.194	33.8	0.244	21.4
0.045	630	0.095	141.1	0.145	60.5	0.195	33.5	0.245	21.2
0.046	602	0.096	138.2	0.146	59.7	0.196	33.1	0.246	21.0
0.047	577	0.097	135.4	0.147	58.9	0.197	32.8	0.247	20.8
0.048	552	0.098	132.6	0.148	58.1	0.198	32.5	0.248	20.7
0.049	531	0.099	129.9	0.149	57.3	0.199	32.1	0.249	20.5
0.050	509	0.100	127.3	0.150	56.6	0.200	31.8	0.250	20.4

Comparison of Music Wire Gages

Gage Number	Am. Steel & Wire Co.*	Am. Screw & Wire Co.	Roebling, and Trenton Iron Co.	Wright Wire Co.	Poehlmann Music Wire	Felten & Guilleaume	Allhoff & Müller	W. N. Brunton Music Wire	English Music Wire
6/0	0.004	0.0095	......	......	......	......	......	......	......
5/0	0.005	0.010	......	......	......	......	......	......	......
4/0	0.006	0.011	0.007	......	0.006	0.0068	......	......	......
3/0	0.007	0.012	0.0075	......	0.007	0.0075	......	......	......
2/0	0.008	0.0133	0.0085	0.0085	0.008	0.0087	0.008	0.0085	......
0	0.009	0.0144	0.009	0.009	0.009	0.0093	0.009	0.009	......
1	0.010	0.0156	0.010	0.010	0.010	0.0098	0.010	0.010	......
2	0.011	0.0166	0.011	0.011	0.011	0.0106	0.011	0.011	0.0105
3	0.012	0.0178	0.012	0.012	0.012	0.0114	0.012	0.012	0.0115
4	0.013	0.0188	0.013	0.013	0.013	0.0122	0.013	0.013	0.0125
5	0.014	0.0202	0.014	0.014	0.014	0.0138	0.014	0.014	0.0145
6	0.016	0.0215	0.016	0.016	0.016	0.0157	0.016	0.016	0.015
7	0.018	0.023	0.018	0.018	0.018	0.0177	0.018	0.017	0.0175
8	0.020	0.0243	0.020	0.020	0.020	0.0197	0.020	0.019	0.019
9	0.022	0.0256	0.022	0.022	0.022	0.0216	0.022	0.022	0.022
10	0.024	0.027	0.024	0.024	0.024	0.0236	0.024	0.024	0.0245
11	0.026	0.0284	0.026	0.026	0.026	0.0260	0.026	0.027	0.027
12	0.029	0.0296	0.028	0.028	0.029	0.0283	0.028	0.029	0.0285
13	0.031	0.0314	0.030	0.0305	0.031	0.0303	0.030	0.031	0.0305
14	0.033	0.0326	0.032	0.0325	0.033	0.0323	0.032	0.032	0.032
15	0.035	0.0345	0.034	0.034	0.035	0.0342	0.034	0.034	0.035
16	0.037	0.036	0.036	0.036	0.037	0.0362	0.036	0.036	0.036
17	0.039	0.0377	0.038	0.038	0.039	0.0382	0.038	0.038	0.038
18	0.041	0.0395	0.040	0.0405	0.041	0.0400	0.040	0.040	0.040
19	0.043	0.0414	0.042	0.042	0.043	0.0420	0.042	0.042	0.042
20	0.045	0.0434	0.044	0.044	0.045	0.0440	0.044	0.044	0.043
21	0.047	0.046	0.046	0.046	0.047	0.0460	0.046	0.046	0.0445
22	0.049	0.0483	0.048	0.0485	0.049	0.0480	0.048	0.048	0.047
23	0.051	0.051	0.051	0.0505	0.051	0.0510	0.051	0.050	0.049
24	0.055	0.055	0.055	0.0545	0.055	0.0550	0.055	0.054	0.053
25	0.059	0.0586	0.059	0.0585	0.059	0.0590	0.059	0.058	0.056
26	0.063	0.0626	0.063	0.063	0.063	0.0630	0.063	0.062	0.0605
27	0.067	0.0675	0.067	0.067	0.067	0.0670	0.067	0.066	0.064
28	0.071	0.072	0.071	0.071	0.071	0.0710	0.071	0.069	0.0685
29	0.075	0.076	0.074	0.0745	0.075	0.0740	0.074	0.072	0.0715
30	0.080	0.080	0.078	0.078	0.080	0.0780	0.078	0.076	0.075
31	0.085	0.085	0.082	0.082	......	0.0820	0.082	0.080	......
32	0.090	0.092	0.086	0.086	......	0.0860	0.086	0.086	......
33	0.095	......	0.090	0.090	......	......	0.090	0.092	......
34	0.100	......	0.095	0.096	......	......	0.094	0.098	......
35	0.106	......	0.100	......	......	......	0.098	0.104	......
36	0.112	......	0.105	......	......	......	0.102	0.110	......
37	0.118	......	0.110	......	......	......	......	0.117	......
38	0.124	......	0.115	......	......	......	......	0.121	......
39	0.130	......	0.120	......	......	......	......	0.130	......
40	0.138	......	0.125	......	......	......	......	0.140	......
41	0.146	......	0.130	......	......	......	......	......	......

* The American Steel & Wire Co. also makes the following additional sizes: No. 42 — 0.154; No. 43 — 0.162; No. 44 — 0.170; No. 45 — 0.180.

Sizes of Wire, Drills and Sheets, arranged Progressively by Diameters or Thicknesses

Diam. or Thickness	Am. Steel & Wire Co.	Am. or B. & S. (Wire or Sheets)	Birmingham or Stub's Iron Wire (or Sheets)	Stub's Steel Wire	Trenton Iron Co.	British Imperial Wire	Music Wire (Am. Steel & Wire Co.)	U.S. St'd for Plate * See Footnote	Drill Nos. and Letters
0.00099	....	50							
0.0010	....	....	.....	.....	.....	50			
0.00111	....	49							
0.0012	....	....	.....	.....	.....	49			
0.00124	....	48							
0.00140	....	47							
0.00157	....	46							
0.0016	....	....				48			
0.00176	....	45							
0.00198	....	44							
0.0020	....	....				47			
0.00222	....	43							
0.0024	....	....				46			
0.00249	....	42							
0.0028	....	41				45			
0.00314	....	40							
0.0032	....	....				44			
0.00353	....	39							
0.0036	....	....				43			
0.0040	....	38	36			42	6/0		
0.0044	50	....	.....	.....	.....	41			
0.0045	....	37							
0.0046	49								
0.0048	48	....				40			
0.0050	47	36	35			.....	5/0		
0.0052	46	....				39			
0.0055	45								
0.0056	....	35							
0.0058	44								
0.0060	43					38	4/0		
0.0062	42								
0.0063	....	34							38
0.0066	41	....				.....	.....		37
0.0068	....	....				37			
0.0070	40	....	34		40	.....	3/0		36
0.0071	....	33							
0.0075	39	....			39				
0.0076	....	....				36			
0.0078	....	....				.....	.....		35
0.0080	38	32	33		38	.....	2/0		
0.0084	....	....				35	.....		

* The thicknesses equivalent to different gage numbers, as given in the first column, apply to wrought iron. For steel, see table on page 440.

Sizes of Wire, Drills and Sheets, arranged Progressively by Diameters or Thicknesses. *(Continued)*

Diam. or Thickness	Am. Steel & Wire Co.	Am. or B. & S. (Wire or Sheets)	Birmingham or Stub's Iron Wire (or Sheets)	Stub's Steel Wire	Trenton Iron Co.	British Imperial Wire	Music Wire (Am. Steel & Wire Co.)	U. S. St'd for Plate * See Footnote	Drill Nos. and Letters
0.0085	37	......	......	......	37				
0.0086	......	......	......	......			......	34	
0.0089	......	31							
0.0090	36	......	32	......	36	......	0		
0.0092						34			
0.0094	......						......	33	
0.0095	35				35				
0.0100	......	30	31	......	34	33	1		
0.0102							......	32	
0.0104	34								
0.0108						32			
0.0109							......	31	
0.0110					33		2		
0.0113	......	29							
0.0116						31			
0.0118	33								
0.0120	......		30	......	32	......	3		
0.0124						30			
0.0125							......	30	
0.0126	......	28							
0.0128	32								
0.0130			29	80	31	......	4		
0.0132	31								
0.0135							......		80
0.0136						29			
0.0140	30	......	28	79	30	......	5		
0.0141								29	
0.0142	......	27							
0.0145									79
0.0148						28			
0.0150	29			78	29				
0.0156								28	
0.0159	......	26							
0.0160	......		27	77	28	......	6	......	78
0.0162	28								
0.0164	......		......	......		27			
0.0170					27				
0.0172							......	27	
0.0173	27								
0.0179	......	25							
0.0180	......		26	76	26	26	7	......	77

* The thicknesses equivalent to different gage numbers, as given in the first column, apply to wrought iron. For steel, see table on page 440.

Sizes of Wire, Drills and Sheets, arranged Progressively by Diameters or Thicknesses. *(Continued)*

Diam. or Thickness	Am. Steel & Wire Co.	Am. or B. & S. (Wire or Sheets)	Birmingham or Stub's Iron Wire (or Sheets)	Stub's Steel Wire	Trenton Iron Co.	British Imperial Wire	Music Wire (Am. Steel & Wire Co.)	U. S. St'd for Plate * See Footnote	Drill Nos. and Letters
0.0181	26	......	......	......	......	......	......	......	......
0.0188	......	......	......	......	......	......	......	..26	......
0.0200	......	......	25	75	25	25	8	......	76
0.0201	......	24	......	......	......	......	......	......	......
0.0204	25	......	......	......	......	......	......	......	......
0.0210	......	......	......	......	......	......	......	......	75
0.0219	......	......	......	......	......	......	......	25	......
0.0220	......	......	24	74	......	24	9	......	......
0.0225	......	......	......	......	.24	......	......	......	74
0.0226	......	23	......	......	......	......	......	......	......
0.0230	24	......	......	73	......	......	......	......	......
0.0240	......	......	......	72	......	23	10	......	73
0.0250	......	......	23	......	.23	......	......	24	72
0.0253	......	22	......	......	......	......	......	......	......
0.0258	23	......	......	......	......	......	......	......	......
0.0260	......	......	......	71	......	......	11	......	71
0.0270	......	......	......	70	......	......	......	......	......
0.0280	......	......	22	......	22	22	......	......	70
0.0281	......	......	......	......	......	......	......	23	......
0.0285	......	21	......	......	......	......	......	......	......
0.0286	22	......	......	......	......	......	......	......	......
0.0290	......	......	......	69	......	......	12	......	......
0.02925	......	......	......	......	......	......	......	......	69
0.0300	......	......	......	68	......	......	......	......	......
0.0310	......	......	......	67	21	......	13	......	68
0.0313	......	......	......	......	......	......	......	22	......
0.0317	21	......	......	......	......	......	......	......	......
0.0320	......	20	21	66	......	21	......	......	67
0.0330	......	......	......	65	......	......	14	......	66
0.0344	......	......	......	......	......	......	......	21	......
0.0348	20	......	......	......	......	......	......	......	......
0.0350	......	......	20	64	20	......	15	......	65
0.0359	......	19	......	......	......	......	......	......	......
0.0360	......	......	......	63	......	20	......	......	64
0.0370	......	......	......	62	......	......	16	......	63
0.0375	......	......	......	......	......	......	......	20	......
0.0380	......	......	......	61	......	......	......	......	62
0.0390	......	......	......	60	......	......	17	......	61
0.0400	......	......	......	59	19	19	......	......	60
0.0403	......	18	......	......	......	......	......	......	......
0.0410	19	......	......	58	......	......	18	......	59

* The thicknesses equivalent to different gage numbers, as given in the first column, apply to wrought iron. For steel, see table on page 440.

Sizes of Wire, Drills and Sheets, arranged Progressively by Diameters or Thicknesses.   (*Continued*)

Diam. or Thickness	Am. Steel & Wire Co.	Am. or B. & S. (Wire or Sheets)	Birmingham or Stub's Iron Wire (or Sheets)	Stub's Steel Wire	Trenton Iron Co.	British Imperial Wire	Music Wire (Am. Steel & Wire Co.)	U. S. St'd for Plate * See Footnote	Drill Nos. and Letters
0.0420	......	......	19	57	......	......	......	......	58
0.0430	......	......	......	......	......	......	19	......	57
0.0438	......	......	......	......	......	......	......	19	
0.0450	......	......	......	56	18	......	20	......	
0.0453	......	17	......	......	......	......	......	......	56
0.0465	......	......	......	......	......	......	21	......	
0.0470	......	......	......	......	......	......	......	......	
0.0475	18	......	......	......	......	......	......	......	
0.0480	......	......	......	......	......	18	......	......	
0.0490	......	......	18	......	......	......	22	......	
0.0500	......	......	......	55	......	......	......	18	
0.0508	......	16	......	......	......	......	......	......	
0.0510	......	......	......	......	......	......	23	......	
0.0520	......	......	......	......	......	......	......	......	55
0.0525	......	......	......	......	17	......	......	......	
0.0540	17	......	......	......	......	......	24	......	54
0.0550	......	......	......	54	......	......	......	......	
0.0560	......	......	......	......	......	17	......	......	
0.0563	......	......	......	......	......	......	......	17	
0.0571	......	15	......	......	......	......	......	......	
0.0580	......	......	17	53	......	......	25	......	
0.0590	......	......	......	......	......	......	......	......	
0.0595	......	......	......	......	......	......	......	......	53
0.0610	......	......	......	......	16	......	......	......	
0.0625	16	......	......	......	......	......	......	16	
0.0630	......	......	......	52	......	......	26	......	
0.0635	......	......	......	......	......	......	......	......	52
0.0640	......	......	......	......	......	16	......	......	
0.0641	......	14	......	......	......	......	......	......	
0.0650	......	......	16	......	......	......	......	......	
0.0660	......	......	......	51	......	......	......	......	
0.0670	......	......	......	......	......	......	27	......	51
0.0690	......	......	......	50	......	......	......	......	
0.0700	......	......	......	......	15	......	......	......	50
0.0703	......	......	......	......	......	......	......	15	
0.0710	......	......	......	......	......	......	28	......	
0.0720	15	13	15	49	......	15	......	......	
0.0730	......	......	......	......	......	......	......	......	49
0.0750	......	......	......	48	......	......	29	......	
0.0760	......	......	......	......	......	......	......	......	48
0.0770	......	......	......	47	......	......	......	......	

* The thicknesses equivalent to different gage numbers, as given in the first column, apply to wrought iron.   For steel, see table on page 440.

Sizes of Wire, Drills and Sheets, arranged Progressively by Diameters or Thicknesses. (*Continued*)

Diam. or Thickness	Am. Steel & Wire Co.	Am. or B. & S. (Wire or Sheets)	Birmingham or Stub's Iron Wire (or Sheets)	Stub's Steel Wire	Trenton Iron Co.	British Imperial Wire	Music Wire (Am. Steel & Wire Co.)	U. S. St'd for Plate * See Footnote	Drill Nos. and Letters
0.0781								14	
0.0785									47
0.0790				46					
0.0800	14				14	14	30		
0.0808		12							
0.0810				45					46
0.0820									45
0.0830			14						
0.0850				44			31		
0.0860									44
0.0880				43					
0.0890									43
0.0900							32		
0.0907		11							
0.0915	13								
0.0920				42		13			
0.0925					13				
0.0935									42
0.0938								13	
0.0950			13	41			33		
0.0960									41
0.0970				40					
0.0980									40
0.0990				39					
0.0995									39
0.1000							34		
0.1010				38					
0.1015									38
0.1019		10							
0.1030				37					
0.1040						12			37
0.1050					12				
0.1055	12								
0.1060				36			35		
0.1065									36
0.1080				35					
0.1090			12						
0.1094								12	
0.1100				34					35
0.1110									34
0.1120				33			36		

* The thicknesses equivalent to different gage numbers, as given in the first column, apply to wrought iron. For steel, see table on page 440.

Sizes of Wire, Drills and Sheets, arranged Progressively by Diameters or Thicknesses. (Continued)

Diam. or Thickness	Am. Steel & Wire Co.	Am. or B. & S. (Wire or Sheets)	Birmingham or Stub's Iron Wire (or Sheets)	Stub's Steel Wire	Trenton Iron Co.	British Imperial Wire	Music Wire (Am. Steel & Wire Co.)	U.S. St'd for Plate * See Footnote	Drill Nos. and Letters
0.1130									33
0.1144		9							
0.1150				32					
0.1160						11			32
0.1175					11				
0.1180							37		
0.1200			11	31					31
0.1205	11								
0.1240							38		
0.1250								11	
0.1270				30					
0.1280						10			
0.1285		8							30
0.1300					10		39		
0.1340			10	29					
0.1350	10								
0.1360									29
0.1380							40		
0.1390				28					28
0.1405									
0.1406								10	
0.1430				27					
0.1440						9			27
0.1443		7							
0.1450					9				
0.1460				26			41		26
0.1470									
0.1480			9	25					
0.1483	9								25
0.1495									
0.1510				24					24
0.1520									
0.1530				23					
0.1540							42		23
0.1550				22					
0.1563								9	
0.1570				21					22
0.1590									21
0.1600					8	8			
0.1610				20					20
0.1620	8	6					43		

* The thicknesses equivalent to different gage numbers, as given in the first column, apply to wrought iron. For steel, see table on page 440.

Sizes of Wire, Drills and Sheets, arranged Progressively by Diameters or Thicknesses. *(Continued)*

Diam. or Thickness	Am. Steel & Wire Co.	Am. or B. & S. (Wire or Sheets)	Birmingham or Stub's Iron Wire (or Sheets)	Stub's Steel Wire	Trenton Iron Co.	British Imperial Wire	Music Wire (Am. Steel & Wire Co.)	U. S. St'd for Plate * See Footnote	Drill Nos. and Letters
0.1640				19					
0.1650			8						
0.1660									19
0.1680				18					
0.1695									18
0.1700							44		
0.1719								8	
0.1720				17					
0.1730									17
0.1750				16	7				
0.1760						7			
0.1770	7								16
0.1780				15					
0.1800			7	14			45		15
0.1819		5							
0.1820				13					14
0.1850				12					13
0.1875								7	
0.1880				11					
0.1890									12
0.1900					6				
0.1910				10					11
0.1920	6					6			
0.1935									10
0.1940				9					
0.1960									9
0.1970				8					
0.1990				7					8
0.2010				6					7
0.2030			6						
0.2031								6	
0.2040				5					6
0.2043		4							
0.2050					5				
0.2055									5
0.2070	5			4					
0.2090									4
0.2120				3		5			
0.2130									3
0.2188								5	
0.2190				2					
0.2200			5						

* The thicknesses equivalent to different gage numbers, as given in the first column, apply to wrought iron. For steel, see table on page 440.

Sizes of Wire, Drills and Sheets, arranged Progressively by Diameters or Thicknesses. *(Continued)*

Diam. or Thickness	Am. Steel & Wire Co.	Am. or B. & S. (Wire or Sheets)	Birmingham or Stub's Iron Wire (or Sheets)	Stub's Steel Wire	Trenton Iron Co.	British Imperial Wire	Music Wire (Am. Steel & Wire Co.)	U. S. St'd for Plate * See Footnote	Drill Nos. and Letters
0.2210									2
0.2250					4				
0.2253	4								
0.2270				1					
0.2280									1
0.2294		3							
0.2320						4			
0.2340									A
0.2344								4	
0.2380			4						B
0.2420									C
0.2437	3								
0.2450					3				
0.2460									D
0.2500								3	E
0.2520						3			
0.2570									F
0.2576		2							
0.2590			3						
0.2610									G
0.2625	2								
0.2650					2				
0.2656								2	
0.2660									H
0.2720									I
0.2760						2			
0.2770									J
0.2810									K
0.2813								1	
0.2830	1								
0.2840			2						
0.2850					1				
0.2893		1							
0.2900									L
0.2950									M
0.3000			1			1			
0.3020									N
0.3050					0				
0.3065	0								
0.3125								0	
0.3160									O
0.3230									P

* The thicknesses equivalent to different gage numbers, as given in the first column, apply to wrought iron. For steel, see table on page 440.

Diameter, Strength and Weight of Steel Wire

The breaking stress of the wire is based on a tensile strength of 100,000 pounds per square inch. For wire of greater or less strength, simply multiply the values in the table by the ratio between actual strength per square inch and 100,000. Example: A No. 15 wire is made of material having a tensile strength of 150,000 pounds per square inch. Then, breaking stress of wire = (150,000 ÷ 100,000) × 407 = 610 pounds.

No. Washburn & Moen, Am. Steel & Wire Co., and Roebling Gage	Diameter, Inches	Area, Sq. Ins.	Breaking Stress of Wire, based on 100,000 Lbs. Stress per Sq. In.	Weight in Pounds		Number of Feet in 2000 Pounds.
				Per 1000 Ft.	Per Mile	
000000	0.460	0.166191	16,620.0	558.4	2948.0	3,582
00000	0.430	0.145221	14,520.0	487.9	2576.0	4,099
0000	0.393	0.121304	12,130.0	407.6	2152.0	4,907
000	0.362	0.102922	10,290.0	345.8	1826.0	5,783
00	0.331	0.086049	8,605.0	289.1	1527.0	6,917
0	0.307	0.074023	7,400.0	248.7	1313.0	8,041
1	0.283	0.062902	6,290.0	211.4	1116.0	9,463
2	0.263	0.054325	5,430.0	182.5	964.0	10,957
3	0.244	0.046760	4,680.0	157.1	830.0	12,730
4	0.225	0.039761	3,980.0	133.6	705.0	14,970
5	0.207	0.033654	3,365.0	113.1	597.0	17,687
6	0.192	0.028953	2,895.0	97.3	514.0	20,559
7	0.177	0.024606	2,460.0	82.7	437.0	24,191
8	0.162	0.020612	2,060.0	69.3	366.0	28,878
9	0.148	0.017203	1,720.0	57.8	305.0	34,600
10	0.135	0.014314	1,430.0	48.1	254.0	41,584
11	0.120	0.011310	1,130.0	38.0	201.0	52,631
12	0.105	0.008659	866.0	29.1	154.0	68,752
13	0.092	0.006648	665.0	22.3	118.0	89,525
14	0.080	0.005027	503.0	16.9	89.2	118,413
15	0.072	0.004071	407.0	13.7	72.2	146,198
16	0.063	0.003117	312.0	10.5	55.3	191,022
17	0.054	0.002290	229.0	7.70	40.6	259,909
18	0.047	0.001735	174.0	5.83	30.8	343,112
19	0.041	0.001320	132.0	4.44	23.4	450,856
20	0.035	0.000962	96.0	3.23	17.1	618,620
21	0.032	0.000804	80.0	2.70	14.3	740,193
22	0.028	0.000616	62.0	2.07	10.9	966,651
23	0.025	0.000491	49.0	1.65	8.71	......
24	0.023	0.000415	42.0	1.40	7.37	......
25	0.020	0.000314	31.0	1.06	5.58	......
26	0.018	0.000254	25.0	0.855	4.51	......
27	0.017	0.000227	23.0	0.763	4.03	......
28	0.016	0.000201	20.0	0.676	3.57	......
29	0.015	0.000177	18.0	0.594	3.14	......
30	0.014	0.000154	15.0	0.517	2.73	......
31	0.0135	0.000143	14.0	0.481	2.54	......
32	0.013	0.000133	13.0	0.446	2.36	......
33	0.011	0.000095	9.5	0.319	1.69	......
34	0.010	0.000079	7.9	0.264	1.39	......
35	0.0095	0.000071	7.1	0.238	1.26	......
36	0.009	0.000064	6.4	0.214	1.13	......

STRENGTH AND PROPERTIES OF WIRE ROPE

Kinds of Wire Rope. — Wire rope is made with different numbers of strands and numbers of wires to the strand, according to the purpose for which it is to be used. Hoisting rope is made of 6 strands with 19 wires to the strand. This type of rope is used for elevators of all kinds, mines, conveyors, derricks, etc. A hoisting rope known as "special flexible" is made of 6 strands with 37 wires each, and one known as "extra flexible" rope is made from 8 strands with 19 wires each. These ropes are used for cranes, counterweights, dredges and similar purposes. The standard transmission or haulage rope is made from 6 strands with 7 wires to the strand. This is much stiffer than the standard hoisting rope and will not bend around as small sheaves. It is, however, better adapted for haulage and transmission purposes, because the wires are larger and do not wear through so quickly. A greater factor of safety than is used for hoisting rope is desirable. A rope made of six strands with 12 wires each, known as "running" rope, is also made.

The materials used in making wire rope are usually designated as iron, cast steel, mild plow steel, plow steel and improved plow steel. The general terms "cast steel" and "plow steel," as applied by wire rope manufacturers, designate open-hearth steel of different grades as indicated by strength data in the following tables.

Wire ropes are usually made with a hemp core or center. Sometimes the hemp center is replaced by a wire center, which adds about $7\frac{1}{2}$ per cent to the strength of the rope, but as the wear on the center is as great as on the outside strands, but little is gained. The tables of hoisting and haulage rope give the breaking stress in tons for ropes made from different grades of iron and steel. The working stress should, as a rule, not be made greater than one-fifth of the breaking stress.

In the regular type of rope, the wires of the strands are twisted in one direction and the strands laid into the rope in the opposite direction. In the Lang's lay rope, both the wires in the strands and the strands in the rope are twisted in the same direction. This rope is more easily untwisted than the regular lay rope and it is more difficult to tuck the strands securely in a splice, but it is well adapted to withstand external wear and grip action.

To preserve wire rope, linseed oil should be applied to it. The grooves of cast-iron pulleys and sheaves should be fitted with blocks of hardwood set on end, which are renewed when worn out. This will save wear and increase adhesion. When large sheaves run at high velocity, the grooves should be lined with leather set on end or with India rubber. This is done in the case of sheaves used in the transmission of power between distant points.

Stresses in Wire Ropes Due to Bending. — When wire rope is used over a pulley or sheave there is a longitudinal tension due to the weight suspended by the rope and the weight of the rope itself, and also tension and compression stresses in the part of the rope resting on the pulley due to the bending of the rope. The smaller the sheave the larger are these bending stresses. In order not to increase these stresses too much and cause undue wear in the wire rope, certain *minimum* sizes of sheaves for different sizes of ropes are recommended by the manufacturers of wire ropes, but whenever a larger diameter can be conveniently used, it is preferable. Various formulas have been deduced for calculating the stresses in wire rope due to the bending over the sheaves. The following, based on a formula used by a prominent wire rope manufacturer, gives safe results:

$$\text{Stress in pounds per square inch} = \frac{Ed}{D} \times 0.45$$

in which E = modulus of elasticity of the material from which the wire is made, about 30,000,000 for steel and 25,000,000 for iron wire;

d = diameter of component wire in inches;

D = diameter of sheave in inches.

In the formula given, the diameter of component wire is used. This diameter is approximately found as follows:

For 6 by 7 rope, $d = 0.106 \times$ diameter of rope;
For 6 by 19 rope, $d = 0.063 \times$ diameter of rope;
For 6 by 37 rope, $d = 0.045 \times$ diameter of rope;
For 8 by 19 rope, $d = 0.050 \times$ diameter of rope.

The total area in square inches of wires of different ropes is given in a following table.

Example: Find the total stress due to bending a ½-inch 6 by 7 plow steel wire rope over a sheave 24 inches in diameter.

$$\text{Stress in pounds per square inch} = \frac{30,000,000 \times 0.106 \times \frac{1}{2}}{24} \times 0.45 = 29,800$$

Area of rope (from table) = 0.0926 square inch.

Hence, total stress due to bending = 2800 pounds, approximately, or 1.4 tons. According to the table for transmission or haulage rope, the maximum safe working load for this size of rope is 1.8 tons. Hence, in this case, the total stress due to bending over the sheave is more than 75 per cent of the maximum safe working load, which leaves a very small margin of working strength for the load This illustrates the need of using as large sheaves as possible.

Total Area in Square Inches of Wires of Different Ropes

Diameter of Rope	6×7 Construction	6×19 Construction	6×37 Construction	8×19 Construction
2¾	......	2.6892	2.6704	......
2½	......	2.2224	2.2068	......
2¼	......	1.8000	1.7876	......
2	......	1.4216	1.4124	......
1¾	......	1.0888	1.0812	......
1⅝	......	0.9390	0.9324	......
1½	0.8334	0.7997	0.7929	0.6714
1⅜	0.7007	0.6723	0.6676	0.5643
1¼	0.5791	0.5556	0.5517	0.4664
1⅛	0.4691	0.4500	0.4469	0.3778
1	0.3706	0.3554	0.3531	0.2985
⅞	0.2840	0.2722	0.2703	0.2285
¾	0.2134	0.1999	0.1982	0.1678
⅝	0.1448	0.1389	0.1379	0.1166
9⁄16	0.1173	0.1125	0.1117	0.0945
½	0.0926	0.0889	0.0883	0.0746
7⁄16	0.0710	0.0681	0.0676	0.0571
⅜	0.0534	0.0500	0.0495	0.0419
5⁄16	0.0362	0.0347	0.0345	0.0291
¼	0.0231	0.0222	0.0221	0.0186

Dimensions and Strength of Transmission or Haulage Rope

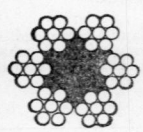

Standard transmission, haulage or standing rope is made of 6 strands and a hemp center, with 7 wires to the strand. The advantage of this rope is that the wires are coarse and resist abrasion and corrosion to the greatest possible extent, but the rope is not highly flexible.

Diameter Inches	Approx. Circumference Inches	Approx. Weight per Foot Pounds	Iron Breaking Strength Tons (2000 Lbs.)	Iron Max. Safe Working Load* Tons	Cast Steel Breaking Strength Tons (2000 Lbs.)	Cast Steel Max. Safe Working Load* Tons
1½	4¾	3.38	29.70	5.95	62.5	12.50
1⅜	4¼	2.84	25.20	5.05	53.0	10.60
1¼	4	2.34	21.00	4.20	44.5	8.90
1⅛	3½	1.90	17.20	3.45	36.4	7.30
1	3	1.50	13.70	2.75	29.0	5.80
⅞	2¾	1.15	10.50	2.10	22.4	4.50
¾	2¼	0.84	7.85	1.55	16.5	3.30
⅝	2	0.59	5.50	1.10	11.5	2.30
9⁄16	1¾	0.48	4.50	0.90	9.4	1.90
½	1½	0.38	3.55	0.70	7.5	1.50
7⁄16	1¼	0.29	2.75	0.55	5.8	1.15
⅜	1⅛	0.21	2.05	0.40	4.3	0.85
5⁄16	1	0.15	1.45	0.30	3.1	0.60
9⁄32	⅞	0.12	1.15	0.25	2.5	0.50
¼	¾	0.094	.....	....	2.0	0.40

Diameter Inches	Mild Plow Steel Breaking Strength Tons (2000 Lbs.)	Mild Plow Steel Max. Safe Working Load* Tons	Plow Steel Breaking Strength Tons (2000 Lbs.)	Plow Steel Max. Safe Working Load* Tons	Improved Plow Steel Breaking Strength Tons (2000 Lbs.)	Improved Plow Steel Max. Safe Working Load* Tons
1½	68.70	13.75	75.00	15.00	86.5	17.30
1⅜	58.20	11.65	63.50	12.70	73.5	14.70
1¼	48.70	9.75	53.00	10.60	61.0	12.20
1⅛	40.00	8.00	43.60	8.70	50.0	10.00
1	31.90	6.40	34.80	6.95	40.0	8.00
⅞	24.60	4.90	26.80	5.35	30.8	6.15
¾	18.10	3.60	19.80	3.95	22.8	4.55
⅝	12.60	2.50	13.80	2.75	16.0	3.20
9⁄16	10.30	2.05	11.30	2.25	13.0	2.60
½	8.20	1.65	9.00	1.80	10.3	2.05
7⁄16	6.30	1.25	6.90	1.40	7.9	1.60
⅜	4.70	0.95	5.15	1.05	5.9	1.20
5⁄16	3.35	0.65	3.65	0.75	4.2	0.85
9⁄32	2.70	0.55	2.95	0.60	3.4	0.70
¼	2.15	0.45	2.35	0.45	2.7	0.55

* The maximum safe working load figures are based on a safety factor of 5. For some applications a safety factor of 8 or more may be required.

Dimensions and Strength of Standard Hoisting Rope

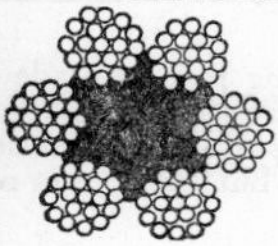

Standard hoisting rope is made of 6 strands and a hemp center, with 19 wires to the strand. The wires are comparatively small in diameter, and the wire rope, therefore, passes readily around sheaves and drums of moderate size.

Diameter Inches	Approx. Circumference Inches	Approx. Weight per Foot Pounds	Iron		Cast Steel	
			Breaking Strength Tons (2000 Lbs.)	Max. Safe Working Load* Tons	Breaking Strength Tons (2000 Lbs.)	Max. Safe Working Load* Tons
2¾	8⅝	12.10	95.00	19.00	212.0	42.40
2½	7⅞	10.00	79.10	15.80	176.0	35.20
2¼	7⅛	8.10	64.80	12.95	144.0	28.80
2⅛	6⅝	7.22	.....	.....	128.0	25.60
2	6¼	6.40	51.80	10.35	114.0	22.80
1⅞	5¾	5.63	45.80	9.15	100.0	20.00
1¾	5½	4.90	40.10	8.00	88.0	17.60
1⅝	5	4.23	34.80	6.95	76.0	15.20
1½	4¾	3.60	29.70	5.95	65.0	13.00
1⅜	4¼	3.03	25.20	5.05	55.0	11.00
1¼	4	2.50	21.00	4.20	46.0	9.20
1⅛	3½	2.03	17.20	3.45	37.0	7.40
1	3	1.60	13.70	2.75	29.5	5.90
⅞	2¾	1.23	10.60	2.10	22.8	4.55
¾	2¼	0.90	7.85	1.55	16.8	3.35
⅝	2	0.63	5.50	1.10	11.8	2.35
9/16	1¾	0.51	4.50	0.90	9.6	1.90
½	1½	0.40	3.55	0.70	7.7	1.55
7/16	1¼	0.31	2.75	0.55	6.0	1.20
⅜	1⅛	0.23	2.05	0.40	4.5	0.90
5/16	1	0.16	1.45	0.30	3.2	0.65
¼	¾	0.10	0.95	0.20	2.1	0.40

Diameter Inches	Mild Plow Steel		Plow Steel		Improved Plow Steel	
	Breaking Strength Tons (2000 Lbs.)	Max. Safe Working Load* Tons	Breaking Strength Tons (2000 Lbs.)	Max. Safe Working Load* Tons	Breaking Strength Tons (2000 Lbs.)	Max. Safe Working Load* Tons
2¾	234.0	46.80	256.0	51.20	294.0	58.80
2½	195.0	39.00	214.0	42.80	246.0	49.20
2¼	160.0	32.00	176.0	35.20	202.0	40.40
2⅛	143.0	28.60	157.0	31.40	181.0	36.20
2	127.0	25.40	140.0	28.00	161.0	32.20
1⅞	112.0	22.40	123.0	24.60	142.0	28.40
1¾	98.0	19.60	108.0	21.60	124.0	24.80
1⅝	85.0	17.00	94.0	18.80	108.0	21.60
1½	72.5	14.50	80.5	16.10	92.5	18.50
1⅜	61.5	12.30	68.0	13.60	78.5	15.70
1¼	51.0	10.20	56.5	11.30	65.0	13.00
1⅛	41.5	8.30	46.0	9.20	53.0	10.60
1	33.0	6.60	36.5	7.30	42.0	8.40
⅞	25.4	5.10	28.0	5.60	32.2	6.45
¾	18.7	3.75	20.6	4.10	23.7	4.75
⅝	13.1	2.60	14.4	2.90	16.6	3.30
9/16	10.6	2.10	11.7	2.35	13.5	2.70
½	8.5	1.70	9.4	1.90	10.8	2.15
7/16	6.6	1.30	7.3	1.45	8.4	1.70
⅜	5.0	1.00	5.5	1.10	6.3	1.23
5/16	3.5	0.70	3.9	0.80	4.5	0.90
¼	2.3	0.45	2.5	0.50	2.9	0.60

* The maximum safe working load figures are based on a safety factor of 5. For some applications a safety factor of 8 or more may be required.

Dimensions and Strength of Extra Flexible Hoisting Rope

Extra flexible hoisting rope is composed of 8 strands and a hemp center, with 19 wires to the strand. It is very flexible and can be used over comparatively small sheaves and drums.

Diam. Ins.	Approx. Wt. per Ft. Lbs.	Cast Steel		Mild Plow Steel		Plow Steel		Improved Plow Steel	
		Breaking Str'th Tons (2000 Lbs.)	Max. Safe Working Load* Tons	Breaking Str'th Tons (2000 Lbs.)	Max. Safe Working Load* Tons	Breaking Str'th Tons (2000 Lbs.)	Max. Safe Working Load* Tons	Breaking Str'th Tons (2000 Lbs.)	Max. Safe Working Load* Tons
1½	3.26	57.50	11.50	63.30	12.65	69.00	13.80	79.50	15.90
1⅜	2.74	48.60	9.70	53.40	10.70	58.30	11.65	67.00	13.40
1¼	2.27	40.40	8.10	44.40	8.90	48.40	9.70	55.70	11.15
1⅛	1.84	32.80	6.55	36.00	7.20	39.40	7.90	45.20	9.05
1	1.45	26.00	5.20	28.60	5.70	31.20	6.25	35.80	7.15
⅞	1.11	20.00	4.00	22.00	4.40	24.00	4.80	27.60	5.50
¾	0.82	14.80	2.95	16.30	3.25	17.80	3.55	20.50	4.10
⅝	0.57	10.40	2.10	11.40	2.30	12.50	2.50	14.40	2.90
9⁄16	0.46	8.50	1.70	9.40	1.90	10.30	2.05	11.80	2.35
½	0.36	6.80	1.35	7.50	1.50	8.20	1.65	9.50	1.90
7⁄16	0.28	5.30	1.05	5.80	1.15	6.30	1.25	7.30	1.45
⅜	0.20	3.95	0.80	4.35	0.85	4.70	0.95	5.45	1.10
5⁄16	0.14	2.80	0.55	3.05	0.60	3.35	0.65	3.85	0.75
¼	0.09	1.80	0.35	1.95	0.40	2.15	0.40	2.45	0.50

* The maximum safe working load figures are based on a safety factor of 5. For some applications a safety factor of 8 or more may be required.

Dimensions and Strength of Steel Clad Hoisting Rope

Steel clad hoisting rope is a regular round strand rope having 6 strands of 19 wires each. The strands of this type of rope are given an external "serving" or winding of flat strip steel which does not increase the tensile strength of the rope, but does give additional wearing service without sacrificing the flexibility in any way.

Finished Diameter over Serving Inches	Diameter of Bare Rope Inches	Approx. Weight per Foot Pounds	Plow Steel		Improved Plow Steel	
			Approx. Strength Tons (2000 Lbs.)	Max. Safe Working Load* Tons	Approx. Strength Tons (2000 Lbs.)	Max. Safe Working Load* Tons
2¼	2	7.82	140.0	28.0	161.0	32.20
2 1⁄16	1⅞	7.01	123.0	24.6	142.0	28.40
1 15⁄16	1¾	6.05	108.0	21.6	124.0	24.80
1 13⁄16	1⅝	5.39	94.0	18.8	108.0	21.60
1 11⁄16	1½	4.66	80.5	16.1	92.5	18.50
1 9⁄16	1⅜	3.99	68.0	13.6	78.5	15.70
1 7⁄16	1¼	3.35	56.5	11.3	65.0	13.00
1 5⁄16	1⅛	2.75	46.0	9.2	53.0	10.60
1 3⁄16	1	2.23	36.5	7.3	42.0	8.40
1	⅞	1.66	28.0	5.6	32.2	6.45
⅞	¾	1.40	20.6	4.1	23.7	4.75
¾	⅝	1.05	14.4	2.9	16.6	3.30
⅝	½	0.64	9.4	1.9	10.8	2.15

* The maximum safe working figures are based on a safety factor of 5. For some applications a safety factor of 8 or more may be required.

Dimensions and Strength of Special Flexible Hoisting Rope

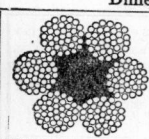 Special flexible hoisting rope is composed of 6 strands and a hemp center, with 37 wires to the strand. This is a very flexible rope and is used to a great extent on cranes and similar machinery, where the sheaves must necessarily be small in diameter. Hoisting ropes larger than 1¾ inch are usually made of 6 strands with 37 wires each, rather than of 6 strands with 19 wires.

Diam. Ins.	Approx. Wt. per Ft. Lbs.	Cast Steel		Mild Plow Steel		Plow Steel		Improved Plow Steel	
		Breaking Str'th Tons (2000 Lbs.)	Max. Safe Working Load Tons	Breaking Str'th Tons (2000 Lbs.)	Max. Safe Working Load Tons	Breaking Str'th Tons (2000 Lbs.)	Max. Safe Working Load Tons	Breaking Str'th Tons (2000 Lbs.)	Max. Safe Working Load Tons
3½	19.00	323.0	64.60	357.0	71.40	392.0	78.40	451.0	90.20
3¼	16.37	281.0	56.20	311.0	62.20	341.0	68.20	392.0	78.40
3	13.95	241.0	48.20	267.0	53.40	293.0	58.60	337.0	67.40
2¾	11.72	204.0	40.80	226.0	45.20	248.0	49.60	285.0	57.00
2½	9.69	170.0	34.00	188.0	37.60	206.0	41.20	237.0	47.40
2⅜	8.74	.....	.....	.....	.....	187.0	37.40	215.0	43.00
2¼	7.85	139.0	27.80	153.0	30.60	168.0	33.60	194.0	38.80
2⅛	7.00	125.0	25.00	138.0	27.60	151.0	30.20	174.0	34.80
2	6.20	111.0	22.20	123.0	24.60	135.0	27.00	155.0	31.00
1⅞	5.45	98.0	19.60	108.5	21.70	119.0	23.80	137.0	27.40
1¾	4.75	86.0	17.20	95.0	19.00	104.0	20.80	119.5	23.90
1⅝	4.09	74.3	14.85	82.0	16.40	89.8	17.95	103.3	20.65
1½	3.49	63.5	12.70	70.0	14.00	76.7	15.35	88.2	17.65
1⅜	2.93	53.5	10.70	59.0	11.80	64.6	12.90	74.3	14.85
1¼	2.42	44.3	8.85	48.9	9.80	53.5	10.70	61.5	12.30
1⅛	1.96	36.0	7.20	39.7	7.90	43.5	8.70	49.9	10.00
1	1.55	28.6	5.70	31.5	6.30	34.4	6.90	39.5	7.90
⅞	1.19	22.0	4.40	24.2	4.85	26.5	5.30	30.5	6.10
¾	0.87	16.4	3.30	18.1	3.60	19.8	3.95	22.8	4.55
⅝	0.61	11.6	2.30	12.8	2.55	14.0	2.80	16.1	3.20
9/16	0.49	9.5	1.90	10.5	2.10	11.5	2.30	13.2	2.65
½	0.39	7.7	1.55	8.4	1.70	9.2	1.85	10.6	2.10
7/16	0.30	6.0	1.20	6.6	1.30	7.2	1.45	8.3	1.65
⅜	0.22	4.4	0.90	4.9	1.00	5.3	1.05	6.1	1.20
5/16	0.15	3.1	0.60	3.4	0.70	3.8	0.75	4.4	0.90
¼	0.10	2.0	0.40	2.2	0.45	2.4	0.50	2.8	0.55

Dimensions and Strength of Steel Clad, Special Flexible Hoisting Rope

Steel clad, special flexible hoisting rope is a regular round strand rope having 6 strands of 37 wires each. The strands of this type of rope are given an external " serving " or winding of flat strip steel which does not increase the tensile strength of the rope but does give additional wearing service without sacrificing the flexibility in any way.

Finished Diameter over Serving Inches	Diameter of Bare Rope Inches	Approx. Weight per Foot Pounds	Plow Steel		Improved Plow Steel	
			Approx. Strength Tons (2000 Lbs.)	Max. Safe Working Load Tons	Approx. Strength Tons (2000 Lbs.)	Max. Safe Working Load Tons
2½	2¼	10.03	168.0	33.60	194.0	38.80
2¼	2	7.82	135.0	27.00	155.0	31.00
2 1/16	1⅞	7.01	119.0	23.80	137.0	27.40
1 15/16	1¾	6.05	104.0	20.80	119.5	23.90
1 13/16	1⅝	5.39	89.8	17.95	103.3	20.65
1 11/16	1½	4.66	76.7	15.35	88.2	17.65
1 9/16	1⅜	3.99	64.6	12.90	74.3	14.85
1 7/16	1¼	3.35	53.5	10.70	61.5	12.30
1 5/16	1⅛	2.75	43.5	8.70	49.9	10.00
1 3/16	1	2.23	34.4	6.90	39.5	7.90
1	⅞	1.66	26.5	5.30	30.5	6.10

Dimensions and Strength of Non-Rotating Hoisting Rope

Non-rotating hoisting rope has an inside layer of 6 strands of 7 wires each, Lang's lay laid around a hemp core and an outside layer of 12 strands of 7 wires each, regularly. This construction produces a rope that resists kinking, rotating, spinning or twisting.

Diam. Ins.	Approx. Wt. per Ft. Lbs.	Cast Steel		Mild Plow Steel		Plow Steel		Improved Plow Steel	
		Breaking Str'th Tons (2000 Lbs.)	Max. Safe Working Load* Tons	Breaking Str'th Tons (2000 Lbs.)	Max. Safe Working Load* Tons	Breaking Str'th Tons (2000 Lbs.)	Max. Safe Working Load* Tons	Breaking Str'th Tons (2000 Lbs.)	Max. Safe Working Load* Tons
1¾	5.30	....	....	....	....	....	....	115.0	23.00
1⅝	4.57	....	....	....	....	....	....	100.0	20.00
1½	3.89	....	....	....	....	....	....	85.5	17.10
1⅜	3.27	....	....	....	....	....	....	72.5	14.50
1¼	2.70	42.5	8.50	47.2	9.45	52.3	10.45	60.0	12.00
1⅛	2.19	34.2	6.85	38.4	7.70	42.5	8.50	49.0	9.80
1	1.73	27.3	5.45	30.5	6.10	33.8	6.75	38.8	7.75
⅞	1.32	21.1	4.20	23.5	4.70	25.9	5.20	29.8	5.95
¾	0.97	15.6	3.10	17.3	3.45	19.0	3.80	21.9	4.40
⅝	0.68	10.9	2.20	12.1	2.40	13.3	2.65	15.3	3.05
9⁄16	0.55	8.9	1.80	9.8	1.95	10.8	2.15	12.5	2.50
½	0.43	7.1	1.40	7.9	1.60	8.7	1.75	10.0	2.00
7⁄16	0.33	5.5	1.10	6.1	1.20	6.7	1.35	7.8	1.55
⅜	0.24	4.1	0.80	4.6	0.90	5.1	1.00	5.8	1.15

* The maximum safe working load figures are based on a safety factor of 5. For some applications a safety factor of 8 or more will be required.

Strength of Wire Rope Drums. — Usually if a drum is designed to be strong enough to resist crushing, it will be strong enough to resist bending also, except in cases of extremely long drums. To be on the safe side, however, the strength should be calculated for both crushing and bending. First consider the calculations to find the crushing stresses. Let:

T = tension in one rope, in pounds;
t = thickness of drum in inches at bottom of groove;
P = pitch of scoring, or distance between grooves in inches;
L = span in inches from center to center of bearings;
D = diameter at the bottom of the groove;
d = inside diameter of drum;
W = total load in pounds;
M_b = bending moment.

Then calculate the total crushing stresses as follows:

$$\text{Section modulus} = Z = 0.0982 \left(D^3 - \frac{d^4}{D} \right); \quad M_b = \frac{WL}{4}.$$

$$B = \frac{M_b}{Z}; \quad C = \frac{T}{Pt}.$$

Combined stress = $\sqrt{B^2 + C^2}$ \hfill (1)

The combined stresses should not exceed 6000 pounds per square inch for ordinary soft-cast iron.

To find the strength for bending, let S = safe fiber stress, which should not exceed 3000 pounds per square inch for ordinary soft-cast iron.

The diameter of the hole through the drum may then be found from the following formula:

$$d = \sqrt[4]{D^4 - \frac{D \times M_b}{0.0982\,S}} \qquad (2)$$

As an example, assume that on a five-ton crane, two $\frac{7}{16}$-inch ropes are used; that the pitch of scoring on the drum is $\frac{3}{4}$ inch; and that the distance from center to center of the bearings on the drum is 6 feet 2 inches. The inside diameter of the

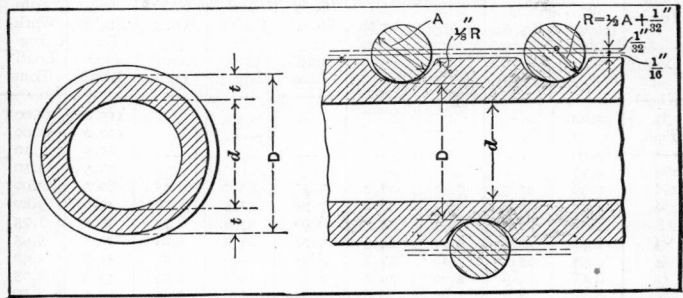

drum is 12 inches, and the diameter at the bottom of the grooves, $14\frac{11}{16}$ inches. From the formulas given:

$$Z = 0.0982 \left(14.69^3 - \frac{12^4}{14.69} \right) = 172.6;$$

$$M_b = \frac{10,000 \times 74}{4} = 185,000;$$

$$B = \frac{185,000}{172.6} = 1072; \quad C = \frac{5000}{\frac{3}{4} \times 1.34} = 5000.$$

Combined stress $= \sqrt{1072^2 + 5000^2} = 5113$ pounds per square inch.
As this is less than the allowable stress of 6000 pounds per square inch, the drum is safe from crushing.

To determine if the drum will withstand bending, use Formula (2), assuming the diameter at the bottom of the grooves to be $14\frac{11}{16}$ inches and solving for the inside diameter:

$$d = \sqrt[4]{14.69^4 - \frac{14.69 \times 185,000}{0.0982 \times 3000}} = 13.9 \text{ inches.}$$

Since the inside diameter is only 12 inches instead of 13.9 inches, it follows that the drum is strong enough for its purpose.

Sheave or Drum Diameters. — If S is the minimum recommended tread diameter of sheave or drum, S_a is the average recommended tread diameter of sheave or drum and D is the wire rope diameter, then for 6×7 rope (six strands of 7 wires each) $S = 42D$, $S_a = 72D$; for 18×7 non-spinning rope $S = 34D$, $S_a = 51D$; for 6×19 rope $S = 30D$, $S_a = 45D$; for 6×37 rope $S = 18D$, $S_a = 27D$ and for 8×19 rope $S = 21D$, $S_a = 31D$.

Life of Wire Rope. — The life of wire rope depends in the first place upon the proportions of the diameter of the pulley or sheave to the diameter of the rope.

In general, increasing the diameter of the pulleys by an amount equal to two circumferences of the rope, will double the life of the rope. When ropes are worked over a number of pulleys, the number of bends influences the length of life of the rope. It has also been shown that reverse bends, that is bending a rope in one direction over one pulley and then in the opposite direction over another pulley, has a more detrimental influence on the life of wire rope than two bends in the same direction. Ropes subjected to reverse bends have a life of only half of that of ropes

Transmission of Power by Wire Ropes

(Ropes of 6 strands with hemp core, each strand consisting of 7 wires)

Diam. of Wheel in Feet	No. of Revolutions	Trade No. of Rope	Diam. of Rope, Inches	Horsepower	Diam. of Wheel in Feet	No. of Revolutions	Trade No. of Rope	Diam. of Rope, Inches	Horsepower
3	80	23	⅜	3	9	100	20	⁹⁄₁₆	58
3	100	23	⅜	3½	9	100	19	⅝	60
3	120	23	⅜	4	9	120	20	⁹⁄₁₆	69
3	140	23	⅜	4½	9	120	19	⅝	73
4	80	23	⅜	4	9	140	20	⁹⁄₁₆	82
4	100	23	⅜	5	9	140	19	⅝	84
4	120	23	⅜	6	10	80	19	⅝	64
4	140	23	⅜	7	10	80	18	11⁄₁₆	68
5	80	22	⁷⁄₁₆	9	10	100	19	⅝	80
5	100	22	⁷⁄₁₆	11	10	100	18	11⁄₁₆	85
5	120	22	⁷⁄₁₆	13	10	120	19	⅝	96
5	140	22	⁷⁄₁₆	15	10	120	18	11⁄₁₆	102
6	80	21	½	14	10	140	19	⅝	112
6	100	21	½	17	10	140	18	11⁄₁₆	119
6	120	21	½	20	12	80	18	11⁄₁₆	93
6	140	21	½	23	12	80	17	¾	99
7	80	20	⁹⁄₁₆	20	12	100	18	11⁄₁₆	116
7	100	20	⁹⁄₁₆	25	12	100	17	¾	124
7	120	20	⁹⁄₁₆	30	12	120	18	11⁄₁₆	140
7	140	20	⁹⁄₁₆	35	12	120	17	¾	149
8	80	19	⅝	26	12	120	16	⅞	173
8	100	19	⅝	32	14	80	8	1	141
8	120	19	⅝	39	14	80	7	1⅛	148
8	140	19	⅝	45	14	100	8	1	176
9	80	20	⁹⁄₁₆	47	14	100	7	1⅛	185
9	80	19	⅝	48	.....	.....	.....	.....	.....

bent in one direction. If it be assumed that a rope making three bends in working, that is, one at the upper drum and one on each side of the lower pulley, as is the arrangement most frequently adopted in crane practice, has a life of 100, then the relative life of ropes with different bends is as follows:

1 single bend, 300; 3 bends in the same direction, 100; 3 bends of which one is a reverse bend, 75; 7 bends, 43; 7 bends of which one is a reverse bend, 37.

This indicates that it is important to increase the diameters of the pulleys when the rope is bent over more than one pulley, in order that the length of life of the rope may be approximately the same when bent over several pulleys, as when subjected to a single bend only. The effect of oiling ropes, upon the length of life, is to increase the life of a given rope by two to three times.

Dimensions of Wire-rope Pulleys for Power Transmission

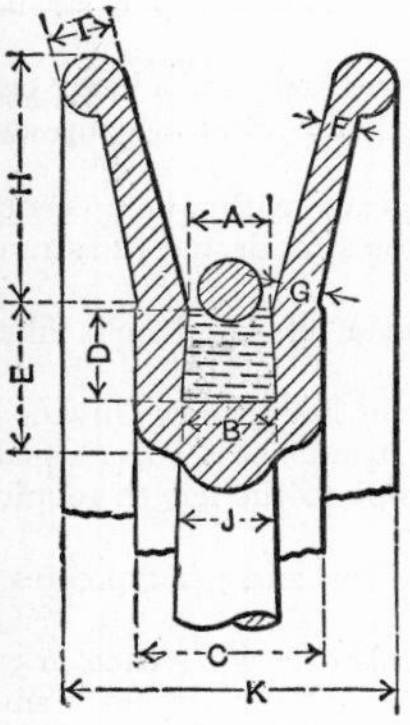

Diam. of Rope	Diam. of Pulley, Feet	Dimensions of Pulley Rim, Inches				
		A	B	C	D	E
½	3	⅝	¾	1¾	¾	1⅜
⅝	4	¾	⅞	2⅛	⅞	1½
¾	5	⅞	1	2⅜	1⅛	1¾
⅞	6	1	1⅛	2⅝	1¼	2
1	7	1⅛	1¼	2¾	1¼	2⅛
1⅛	8	1¼	1⅜	2⅞	1⅜	2¼
1¼	9	1⅜	1½	3⅛	1½	2½
1⅜	10	1½	1⅝	3¼	1⁹⁄₁₆	2⅝
1½	12	1⅝	1¾	3⅝	1¾	3

Diam. of Rope	F	G	H	I	J	K
½	¼	⅜	2	⁹⁄₁₆	⅞	3
⅝	⁵⁄₁₆	⁷⁄₁₆	2½	⅝	1	3½
¾	⅜	½	3	¾	1⅛	4
⅞	⅜	½	3½	¾	1¼	4½
1	⁷⁄₁₆	⁹⁄₁₆	3¾	⅞	1⅜	4¾
1⅛	½	⅝	4	1	1½	5
1¼	½	⅝	4¼	1	1⅝	5¼
1⅜	⁹⁄₁₆	¹¹⁄₁₆	4½	1⅛	1¾	5½
1½	⅝	¾	4¾	1¼	2	6

Arms are made with elliptic cross-section.

Definitions of Wire Rope Terms

Aeroplane Strand: A small 7- or 19-wire galvanized strand made from plow steel or crucible steel wire.

Arc Light Rope: Rope consisting of 9 strands of 4 or 7 galvanized wires and a hemp center.

Bicycle Cord: Small rope consisting of 19 strands of 3 wires each, made from crucible or plow steel.

Cable Laid Rope: A compound laid rope consisting of several ropes or several layers of strands laid together into one rope, as, for instance, 6 by 6 by 7.

Crane Rope: Wire rope consisting of 6 strands of 37 wires around a hemp center.

Crosby Clip: A grooved casting and U-shaped bolt with nuts for fastening wire ropes together.

Dragon Rope: A 6 by 25 triangular flattened strand rope with alternate regular and Lang lay strands, usually made with hemp center.

Elevator Rope: Wire rope usually made of iron and composed of 6 strands of 19 wires each, and a hemp core.

Extra Flexible Hoisting Rope: A rope consisting of 8 strands of 19 wires each with a large hemp center.

Ferry Rope: Rope consisting of 6 strands, 7 wires each, either bright or galvanized.

Flat Rope: A rope consisting of alternate right and left lay rope strands, each rope strand consisting of 4 strands of 7 wires, all sewed together with a number of soft iron sewing wires.

Flattened Strand Rope: A wire rope having non-cylindrical strands, usually of the oval or triangular type; the center wire of each strand is an oval or a triangular wire.

Galvanized Signal Strand: A 7-wire strand made up from single galvanized wire; sometimes made with 19 wires.

Guy Rope: Galvanized rope consisting of 6 strands, 7 wires each, and a hemp core.

Guy Strand: Galvanized 7-wire strand.

Hand Rope: Flexible rope consisting of 6 ropes, each composed of 6 strands, 7 wires each, and 7 hemp cores.

Haulage Rope: Rope usually composed of 6 strands, 7 wires each, and a hemp core.

Hawser: Wire rope usually consisting of 6 strands, 37 wires, and a hemp core, or 6 strands, 24 wires, and 7 hemp cores.

Hoisting Rope: Rope consisting of 6 strands of 19 wires each, with a hemp center.

Lang Lay Rope: Wire rope in which both the wires in the strands and the strands in the rope are twisted in the same direction.

Left Lay Rope: Wire rope, the strands of which form a left-hand helix like a left-hand screw thread.

Left Twist: Same as right lay, and corresponds to a right-hand screw thread.

Lay: The pitch or angle of the helix of the wires or strands of a rope, usually expressed by the ratio of the diameter of the strand or rope to the length required for one complete twist.

Lloyd's Hawser: Wire rope composed of 6 strands, 24 wires, and 7 hemp cores.

Messenger Strand: Seven-wire galvanized strand.

Non-spinning Rope: A wire rope consisting of 18 strands of 7 wires each in two layers; the inner layer consists of 6 strands Lang lay and left lay around a small hemp core, and the outer of 12 strands regular lay, right-hand lay. Will carry a load on a single end without untwisting.

Regular Lay: Strands twisted to the right and rope twisted to the left. Helix of strands takes the direction of a right-hand screw thread.

Reverse Laid Rope: A wire rope with alternate strands right and left lay.

Rheostat Rope: A small rope consisting of 8 strands of 7 wires each.

Right Lay: Known also as regular lay; strands twisted to the right and rope twisted to the left; corresponds to a right-hand screw thread.

Right Twist: Corresponds to left lay, or to a left-hand screw thread.

Running Rope: A flexible rope of 6 strands, 12 wires each, and 7 hemp cores.

Sand Line: A small rope composed of 6 strands of 7 wires each.

Sash Cord: Small rope consisting of 6 strands, 7 wires, and one hemp core; sizes ¼ inch and smaller; plain or galvanized.

Seizing Strand: Small galvanized 7-wire strand usually made in sizes ⅛ inch diameter and smaller.

Signal Strand: Usually consists of a 7-wire galvanized strand.

Special Flexible Hoisting Rope: A wire rope consisting of 6 strands, of 37 wires each, and a hemp core.

Standing Rope: Another term applied to galvanized guy rope which consists of 6 strands, 7 wires, and a hemp core.

Tiller Rope: Rope consisting of 6 ropes of 6 strands, each of 7 wires, and 7 hemp cores.

Towing Hawser: A large flexible wire rope made of galvanized wires. Usual construction, 6 strands of 37 wires each, or 6 strands of 24 wires each.

Transmission Rope: Rope composed of 6 strands, 7 wires each, and a hemp core.

Universal Lay: Another name for Lang lay.

SPRINGS

Formulas for Strength and Deflection of Springs

W = safe load, pull or pressure in pounds;
F = deflection at point of application of load, in inches;
S = safe tensile strength of the material, in pounds per square inch;
E = modulus of elasticity = 30,000,000 for steel.

Type of Spring	W, Safe Load	F, Deflection
FLAT PARALLEL SPRING	$\dfrac{Sbt^2}{6\,l}$	$\dfrac{4\,Wl^3}{Ebt^3} = \dfrac{2\,Sl^2}{3\,Et}$
FLAT TRIANGULAR SPRING	$\dfrac{Sbt^2}{6\,l}$	$\dfrac{6\,Wl^3}{Ebt^3} = \dfrac{Sl^2}{Et}$
LEAF SPRING	$\dfrac{SNbt^2}{6\,l}$ in which N = number of leaves.	$\dfrac{6\,Wl^3}{ENbt^3} = \dfrac{Sl^2}{Et}$ in which N = number of leaves.
ELLIPTIC SPRING	$\dfrac{SNbt^2}{3\,l}$ in which N = number of leaves in one-half of the spring; t = thickness of leaf.	$\dfrac{6\,Wl^3}{ENbt^3} = \dfrac{2\,Sl^2}{Et}$ in which N = number of leaves in one-half of the spring; t = thickness of leaf.
CURVED SPRING	$\dfrac{Sbt^2}{6\,p}$	$\dfrac{18\,Wp^3}{Ebt^3} = \dfrac{3\,Sp^2}{Et}$

Formulas for Strength and Deflection of Springs

W = maximum load, pull or pressure in pounds;
F = deflection at point of application of load, in inches;
S = safe tensile strength of the material in pounds per square inch (in the torsion and helical compression and extension springs, S = torsional or shearing stress); E = modulus of elasticity = 30,000,000 for steel; G = torsional modulus of elasticity = 10,000,000 to 12,000,000 for steel. See page 496.

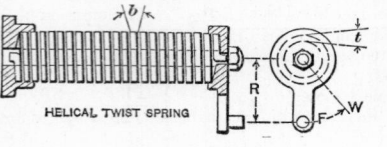 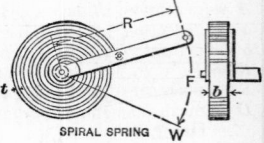

HELICAL TWIST SPRING   SPIRAL SPRING

For flat or square steel: $W = \dfrac{Sbt^2}{6R}$ For round steel (d = diam. of rod): $W = \dfrac{Sd^3}{10R}$

F = deflection.

For flat or square steel (l = length of the rod or uncoiled spring): $\quad F = \dfrac{12\,WlR^2}{Ebt^3} = \dfrac{2\,SlR}{Et}$

For round steel (d = diameter of rod; l = length, as above): $\quad F = \dfrac{20\,WlR^2}{Ed^4} = \dfrac{2\,SlR}{Ed}$

If U = deflection expressed in revolutions of the lever:

$U = \dfrac{Sl}{3El}$ for flat and square, and $\dfrac{Sl}{3Ed}$ for round steel, approx.

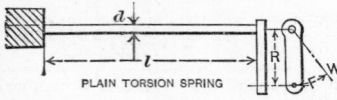

PLAIN TORSION SPRING

For square rod: $W = \dfrac{Sd^3}{4R}$ approx.

For round rod: $W = \dfrac{Sd^3}{5R}$

F = deflection.

For square rod: $F = \dfrac{6\,WR^2l}{Gd^4} = 1.5\dfrac{SlR}{Gd}$ For round rod: $F = \dfrac{10\,WR^2l}{Gd^4} = \dfrac{2\,SlR}{Gd}$

Helical Spring Design. — The design of a helical spring may be affected by various factors, such as the kind of material, whether the load is steady or fluctuating, ratio of spring diameter to wire diameter, available space as it may affect spring diameter or length, and other factors. Table 1 gives the formulas ordinarily required for different spring-designing problems. These formulas, which have been numbered for convenient reference, may be used in calculating the load capacity, deflection caused by a given load, stress when effect of spring diameter to wire diameter ratio is taken into account, and other values as indicated by the notation above the formulas. The actual deflection caused by a given load and the actual load capacity of a spring, usually vary by several per cent from the calculated deflection or load capacity, owing to unavoidable variations in dimensions of springs produced under commercial conditions; hence, if accurate deflection or load capacity is required, this should be determined by actual test whenever possible. The actual procedure in designing springs may be affected more or less by requirements of the machine or mechanism in which the spring is used. The first example which follows applies to a compression spring designed to support a given load.

Table 1. Formulas for Helical Springs Made of Round Wire or Rod

P = load, in pounds = safe working load when S is within allowable limits = load required to compress spring solid when deflection F is maximum.

p = pounds per inch of spring deflection.

F = deflection, in inches, caused by given load = total deflection from free to solid length when P = solid-height load.

f = deflection, in inches, per effective or active coil, for given load P.

A = deflection, in inches, between two loads P_1 and P_2.

a = deflection, in inches, from free length to load P_1 in case of two loads.

b = deflection, in inches, from free length to load P_2 in case of two loads.

R = $P_2 \div P_1$ in case of two loads.

S = fiber stress in pounds per square inch.

D = mean diameter of spring, in inches, = outside diameter minus wire diameter d.

d = diameter of spring wire or rod, inches.

K = Wahl factor which compensates for increase in stress as ratio of D to d decreases. (See Table 4.)

C = ratio of D to d (used in Wahl factor formula).

L = pitch or lead, in inches, of effective coil when spring is unloaded.

l = pitch of coil, in inches, when spring is supporting some load P.

N = number of active or effective coils.

H = overall length or height, in inches, of coils in free or unloaded spring. (See Table 2.)

H_w = overall length of coils, in inches, when spring is supporting some load P.

h = overall length of coils, in inches, when compressed solid.   (See Table 2.)

B = clearance space between each coil, in inches, when spring is supporting some load P.

G = torsional modulus of elasticity in pounds per square inch.

No.	Formula	No.	Formula	No.	Formula
1	$P = \dfrac{\pi S d^3}{8DK}$	8	$f = \dfrac{\pi S D^2}{GdK}$	15	$d = \dfrac{\pi S D^2}{GfK}$
2	$P = \dfrac{GFd^4}{8ND^3}$	9	$a = \dfrac{P_1 A}{P_2 - P_1}$	16	$K = \dfrac{4C-1}{4C-4} + \dfrac{0.615}{C}$
3	$p = \dfrac{Gd^4}{8ND^3}$	10	$b = \dfrac{AR}{R-1}$	17	$L = B + f + d$
4	$p = \dfrac{P}{F}$	11	$S = \dfrac{8PDK}{\pi d^3}$	18	$N = \dfrac{GFd^4}{8PD^3}$
5	$F = \dfrac{8PND^3}{Gd^4}$	12	$S = \dfrac{fGdK}{\pi D^2}$	19	$N = \dfrac{H-h}{L-d}$
6	$F = \dfrac{\pi SND^2}{GdK}$	13*	$d = \sqrt[3]{\dfrac{PD}{0.3S}}$	20	$G = \dfrac{8PND^3}{Fd^4}$
7	$f = \dfrac{8PD^3}{Gd^4}$	14	$d = \sqrt[3]{\dfrac{8PDK}{\pi S}}$	21	H and h See Table 2

* Formula No. 13 is approximate and for preliminary or trial calculations.

Table 2. Overall Lengths of Helical Springs Having Different Forms of End Coils

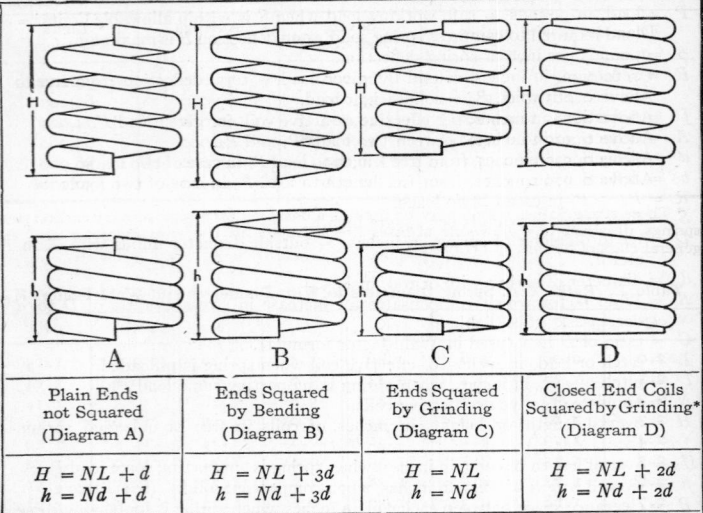

Plain Ends not Squared (Diagram A)	Ends Squared by Bending (Diagram B)	Ends Squared by Grinding (Diagram C)	Closed End Coils Squared by Grinding* (Diagram D)
$H = NL + d$ $h = Nd + d$	$H = NL + 3d$ $h = Nd + 3d$	$H = NL$ $h = Nd$	$H = NL + 2d$ $h = Nd + 2d$

H = free length overall; h = solid length overall; L = pitch or lead of free or unloaded spring; d = wire diameter; N = number of active coils.
* This form of end is often designated as "squared and ground."

Example: A steel spring is to support a load of 80 pounds. The mean diameter of the spring should be about 1.5 inches as determined by available space. Find wire diameter, deflection, pitch, number of effective coils and overall length. Assume that $G = 11,500,000$.

Effect of Wire Diameter on Allowable Stress. — Allowable or safe working stress for given kind and quality of spring wire and character of load, decreases as wire (or rod) diameter increases (see Table 3); hence, either on the basis of experience or judgment assume a trial working stress, taking into account approximate wire diameter likely to be required for the given load. In this case, an allowable working stress of 60,000 is assumed to be suitable for the kind and quality of steel and *probable* wire size. The stress will be checked later when the wire size is known.

Trial Wire Size. — A simple formula (No. 13, Table 1) will be used first to determine an approximate or trial wire size. This formula contains a constant (0.3) which results in a fairly accurate wire size when the spring is designed with reference to the Wahl factor and the ratio of D to d is somewhere near the average value.

$$\text{Trial diameter } d = \sqrt[3]{\frac{80 \times 1.5}{0.3 \times 60,000}} = 0.188 \text{ inch}$$

Nearest commercial wire size (see page 439) is No. 6, or 0.192 inch. This size will be checked.

Wahl Factor. — This factor, which is used in helical spring design, was developed by A. M. Wahl, of the Westinghouse Electric & Mfg. Co., to compensate for errors

Table 3. Allowable Working Stresses for Helical Compression or Tension Springs*

Diameter of wire, inches	Severe service	Average service	Light service
Up to 0.085	60,000	75,000	93,000
Above 0.085 to 0.185	55,000	69,000	85,000
Above 0.185 to 0.320	48,000	60,000	74,000
Above 0.320 to 0.530	42,000	52,000	65,000
Above 0.530 to 0.970	36,000	45,000	56,000
Above 0.970 to 1.5	32,000	40,000	50,000

* These stress values which may be used as a basis in designing ordinary carbon steel springs, illustrate how allowable stresses are affected by the wire diameter and the general class of service.

Table 4. Ratios C of Spring Diameters to Wire Diameters and Wahl Factors K

C	K	C	K	C	K	C	K
2.0	2.06	3.6	1.46	5.4	1.28	9.5	1.15
2.1	1.98	3.7	1.44	5.6	1.27	10.0	1.14
2.2	1.90	3.8	1.43	5.8	1.26	10.5	1.14
2.3	1.84	3.9	1.42	6.0	1.25	11.0	1.13
2.4	1.79	4.0	1.40	6.2	1.24	11.5	1.12
2.5	1.75	4.1	1.39	6.4	1.24	12.0	1.12
2.6	1.71	4.2	1.38	6.6	1.23	12.5	1.11
2.7	1.68	4.3	1.37	6.8	1.22	13.0	1.11
2.8	1.64	4.4	1.36	7.0	1.21	13.5	1.11
2.9	1.60	4.5	1.35	7.2	1.21	14.0	1.10
3.0	1.58	4.6	1.34	7.4	1.20	14.5	1.10
3.1	1.56	4.7	1.34	7.6	1.19	15.0	1.10
3.2	1.53	4.8	1.32	7.8	1.19	16.0	1.09
3.3	1.51	4.9	1.32	8.0	1.18	17.0	1.08
3.4	1.49	5.0	1.31	8.5	1.17	18.0	1.08
3.5	1.48	5.2	1.30	9.0	1.16	19.0	1.07

found to result when stresses in helical springs were computed by formulas which take into account torsional stress only. Stresses in a loaded helical spring, due to transverse shear, tension and compression are of considerable magnitude, particularly when the ratio C of mean diameter of spring to diameter of wire is low. The formula for determining the Wahl factor is given in Table 1 (see Formula No. 16). These factors are also given in Table 4 for various ratios. In this case, in using the trial wire size,

$$\text{Ratio } C = \frac{D}{d} = \frac{1.5}{0.192} = 7.8;$$

hence, Wahl factor $K = 1.19$, as shown by Table 4. This factor is used to prevent subjecting the spring to excessive stresses, especially when ratio C is small.

Check Fiber Stress. — Next insert the trial wire size in Formula No. 11. At this point it may be found necessary or desirable to use a different wire size.

$$S = \frac{8 \times 80 \times 1.5 \times 1.19}{3.1416 \times 0.192^3} = 51,500$$

This formula shows that a load of 80 pounds will cause a stress of 51,500 (in the No. 6

wire), which is within the allowable value of 60,000 pounds per square inch. If the first wire size *below* the trial size had been selected, or No. 7 (0.177 inch), then ratio $C = 8.5$; $K = 1.17$ and the working stress is 64,500. The smaller wire may safely be subjected to a somewhat higher stress as indicated by Table 3, which illustrates how the wire size affects allowable stress; hence a No. 7 wire will be used.

Deflection per Coil Due to Given Load. — Deflection caused by a given load depends upon wire diameter, spring diameter, and torsional modulus of elasticity. Using Formula No. 7,

$$f = \frac{8 \times 80 \times 1.5^3}{11,500,000 \times 0.177^4} = 0.191 \text{ inch}$$

Pitch or Lead of Unloaded Spring. — The lead or pitch of unloaded spring, for given wire diameter and deflection per coil, depends upon space required between the coils when spring is loaded. If a lathe is to be used for spring-winding, it may be possible, by slightly varying this clearance space between coils, to obtain a number of coils per inch equal to a number of threads per inch obtainable with the change-gear mechanism. Assume that clearance B between the loaded coils is to be about $\frac{1}{16}$ inch; then, using Formula No. 17,

$$L = B + f + d$$

Number of Coils per Inch. — If $B = \frac{1}{16}$ inch, the number of coils per inch in this case will equal about $2\frac{1}{4}$.

$$\text{No. coils per inch} = \frac{1}{B + f + d}$$

Assume that a lathe is to be used for coiling and that it may be geared either for $2\frac{1}{4}$ or $2\frac{1}{2}$ threads (or coils) per inch; also, that $2\frac{1}{4}$ is selected, thus increasing the clearance space. Then,

$$\text{Pitch } L = \frac{1}{2\frac{1}{4}} = 0.444 \text{ inch}$$

Now clearance $B = L - f - d = 0.444 - 0.191 - 0.177 = 0.076$ inch.

Number of Effective Coils Based Upon Solid Height of Spring. — The number of effective coils and the overall length of a spring may depend upon the available space as determined by conditions governing the design. If the spring length is excessive, the spring will buckle unless supported laterally. Assume that the solid length is not to exceed $1\frac{7}{16}$ inches and that the end coils are to be squared by grinding, as illustrated by diagram C, Table 2; then,

$$N = \frac{h}{d} = \frac{1.43}{0.177} = 8 \text{ active coils approximately}$$

If 8 is used, then: Solid length $h = 8 \times 0.177 = 1.4$ inches.
Free length $H = 8 \times 0.444 = 3.5$ inches.

Number of Effective Coils Based Upon Working Length of Spring. — The length of a spring may depend upon the available space between the spring support and the load when the latter is in the working position. The pitch l per coil of the loaded spring $= L - f$. Using the values given for the preceding example,

$$l = 0.444 - 0.191 = 0.253 \text{ inch}$$

If H_w is to be equal about $2\frac{1}{2}$ inches and the end coils are to be squared by bending as shown by diagram B, Table 2, then

$$N = \frac{H_w - 3d}{l} = \frac{2.5 - 3 \times 0.177}{0.253} = 8 \text{ coils}$$

If $N = 8$, then for the type of end coil shown by diagram B,

$$H = 8 \times 0.444 + 3 \times 0.177 = 4.1 \text{ inches}$$
$$H_w = 8 \times 0.253 + 3 \times 0.177 = 2.5 \text{ inches}$$
$$h = 8 \times 0.177 + 3 \times 0.177 = 1.95 \text{ inches}$$

Number of Effective Coils Based Upon Total Deflection. — Assume that the number of effective coils is to be based upon a total deflection from free to solid length of about $2\frac{5}{32}$ inches. Since $H - h =$ total deflection (see Formula No. 19)

$$N = \frac{2.15}{0.444 - 0.177} = 8 \text{ coils approximately}$$

Number of Active Coils when Working Deflection and Load is Known. — Formula No. 18 will be applied to the preceding example. Deflection F due to working load $= Nf = 8 \times 0.191 = 1.528$ inches.

$$N = \frac{11{,}500{,}000 \times 1.528 \times 0.177^4}{8 \times 80 \times 1.5^3} = 8 \text{ active coils}$$

Checking Load Equivalent to Working Deflection. — Deflection from free length to working position equals 1.528 inches. Applying Formula No. 2,

$$\text{Working load } P = \frac{11{,}500{,}000 \times 0.177^4 \times 1.528}{8 \times 8 \times 1.5^3} = 80 \text{ pounds}$$

Load to Compress Spring Solid. — The working load P is 80 pounds and the working deflection F is 1.528 inches. The total deflection $= N(L - d) = 8 \times (0.444 - 0.177) = 2.136$ inches. Since

working load : working deflection : : max. load : max. deflection

$$\text{Max. } P = \frac{2.136 \times 80}{1.528} = 112 \text{ pounds}$$

Formula No. 2 will also be used to check the solid height load P,

$$P = \frac{11{,}500{,}000 \times 0.177^4 \times 2.136}{8 \times 8 \times 1.5^3} = 112 \text{ pounds}$$

Check Fiber Stress for Maximum Load. — The stress increase from the working-load position to the solid-height position is proportional to the load increase and also to the increased deflection. Considering loads first,

working stress : max. stress : : working load : max. load

$$\text{Max. stress } S = \frac{64{,}500 \times 112}{80} = 90{,}000$$

working stress : max. stress : : working deflection : max. deflection

$$\text{Max. stress } S = \frac{2.136 \times 64{,}500}{1.528} = 90{,}000$$

This maximum stress must be safely within the elastic limit of the material to prevent permanent set when the spring is compressed solid.

Ratio of Mean Spring Diameter to Wire Diameter. — As a general rule, springs should be so designed that the ratio of D to d, which is often referred to as the "spring index," is somewhere between 6 and 9. This ratio should never be less than 3 or 4, and a value as low as 3 should only be used in extreme cases or where it is unavoidable owing to other conditions governing the design. As the ratio $D \div d$

is reduced, the stresses increase rapidly. A ratio of 9 is given as the ideal or optimum value by some spring designers. If F = total deflection, S = solid height stress, h_a = solid height of active coils, and other notation is as given in Table 1,

$$\frac{D}{d} = \sqrt{\frac{FGK}{\pi Sh_a}}$$

When the mean diameter, solid height and total deflection are given, this formula might be used to find the wire diameter d.

Two-load Helical Spring Design. — The procedure for designing a moving (two-load) spring varies somewhat from that for a static (single-load) spring largely because there are more requirements which must be satisfied in the final design.

Example: A compression helical spring is to have a working movement of 0.3 inch between an initial load of 6.25 pounds to be maintained at a spring length of 1.70 inches and a final load of 24.3 pounds to be maintained at a spring length of 1.40 inches. The maximum outside diameter of the spring is to be ⅝ inch. The spring is to be used for rapid reciprocating service.

Trial Wire Size. — Assume for preliminary calculations that the mean diameter of the spring will be ½ inch. This will leave 0.125 inch as a maximum allowable wire diameter. Assume that the wire diameter will fall in the second group of Table 3 (above 0.085 to 0.185 inch), then the allowable working stress for severe service will be 55,000 pounds per square inch. Using Formula No. 13, we find:

$$\text{Trial diam. } d = \sqrt[3]{\frac{24.3 \times 0.5}{0.3 \times 55,000}} = 0.0903 \text{ inch}$$

If the nearest American Steel & Wire Co. music wire size is used (No. 32 = 0.090 inch), the spring index $D \div d = 0.5 \div 0.09 = 5.55$ and the Wahl factor $K = 1.27$.

Check Fiber Stress at Final Working Load. — Using the actual wire size and the correct Wahl factor in Formula No. 11, the fiber stress S_2 at final working load is:

$$S_2 = \frac{8 \times 24.3 \times 0.5 \times 1.27}{3.1416 \times (0.09)^3} = 54,000 \text{ pounds per square inch}$$

which is within and close to the allowable limit.

Deflection per Coil Between Working Loads. — The deflection per coil is now computed for the change in load between initial and final working positions (substituting $P_2 - P_1$ in place of P in Formula No. 7). A torsional modulus of elasticity for music wire of 10,500,000 has been assumed:

$$f = \frac{8(24.3 - 6.25) \times (0.5)^3}{10,500,000 \times (0.090)^4} = 0.0262 \text{ inch per coil}$$

Number of Effective Coils. — Knowing now the deflection per coil and the required deflection between initial and final loads, the number of effective coils needed to provide this deflection can be determined:

$$N = \frac{A}{f} = \frac{0.3}{0.0262} = 11.4 \text{ active coils}$$

In this case 11½ active coils can be used.

Check Solid Length. — The solid length is now checked to make sure that it is within the allowable space limit. If squared and ground ends are used of the form shown by diagram D of Table 2, then

$$h = Nd + 2d = 11.5 \times 0.09 + 2 \times 0.09 = 1.215 \text{ inches}$$

Deflection from Free Length to Initial Load. — Using formula No. 9 the initial deflection is now computed:

$$a = \frac{6.25 \times 0.3}{24.3 - 6.25} = 0.104 \text{ inch}$$

Free Length. — The free length of the spring is now computed by adding the initial deflection a to the initial working length.

$$H = 1.70 + 0.104 = 1.804 \text{ inches}$$

Deflection to Final Working Length. — The deflection from free length to final working length is next computed by subtracting from the free length the final working length.

$$b = 1.804 - 1.40 = 0.404 \text{ inch}$$

Maximum Stress at Solid Position. — To make sure that the fiber stress resulting from compression of the spring to solid position would not be excessive, this value is computed. First compute deflection from free to solid length:

$$F = H - h = 1.804 - 1.215 = 0.589 \text{ inch}$$

Then compute stress at solid position:

$$\text{max. } S : \text{max. } F : : S_2 \text{ at load } P_2 : b$$
$$S = \frac{FS_2}{b} = \frac{0.589 \times 54,000}{0.404} = 79,000$$

which is below the yield point of the material.

Clearance Space Between Coils. — The clearance between coils at final working position is now checked to make sure that it is sufficient: Subtract from the working length at load P_2 the solid height h and divide by N.

$$B = \frac{1.40 - 1.215}{11.5} = 0.016 \text{ inch}$$

This is about 18 per cent of the wire diameter or well above the customary minimum of 10 per cent of the wire diameter or deflection per coil, whichever is larger.

Helical Round-wire Spring Tables Giving Safe Loads and Deflections. — Tables 5 to 9 inclusive give the maximum safe load in pounds and the corresponding deflection per coil for carbon steel round wire helical springs based on safe working stresses for severe service and taking into account the Wahl factor. (It should be noted that the safe working stress used in the tables varies for different ranges of wire diameter, being 60,000 pounds per square inch for the range of smallest wire sizes and only 32,000 pounds per square inch for the range of largest sizes, with intermediate values for ranges in between.) Since the values given are for severe service they should be multiplied by 1.25 for average service and by 1.55 for light service. For stainless steel and phosphor-bronze springs, apply the corresponding percentages given in Table 5 to the values given in Tables 5 to 9, inclusive.

Example: What is the maximum safe load and the corresponding deflection per coil for a carbon steel spring of ½ inch outside diameter and made of 0.020 inch diameter wire? The spring is to be used in average service.

According to the table a maximum safe load would be 0.371 pound for heavy service. For average service this would be $0.371 \times 1.25 = 0.464$ pound. The corresponding deflection is given as 0.180 inch per coil for a load of 0.371 pound in severe service. For average service this would be $0.180 \times 1.25 = 0.225$ inch per coil if the maximum safe load of 0.464 pound were used.

Other Stress or Deflection Values. — Should load and deflection values be desired for some other stress than that upon which a table is based, the table values are

Table 5. Helical Springs — Loads and Deflections

Values given are for 60,000 pounds per square inch safe working stress and a torsional modulus of elasticity equal to 11,400,000.*

Outside Diameter of Spring, Inches	Size of Wire — Roebling Music Wire Gage No.													
	5	6	7	8	9	10	11	12	13	14	15	16	17	18
	Diameter of Wire, Inches													
	0.014	0.016	0.018	0.020	0.022	0.024	0.026	0.028	0.030	0.032	0.034	0.036	0.038	0.040
1/8	0.493	0.726	1.03	1.39	1.87	2.33	2.93	3.60	4.34	5.18	6.07	6.97	8.08	8.97
	0.0123	0.0100	0.00840	0.00706	0.00612	0.00510	0.00437	0.00376	0.00323	0.00280	0.00241	0.00206	0.00179	0.00151
5/32	0.398	0.588	0.836	1.14	1.50	1.93	2.42	3.01	3.66	4.38	5.20	6.11	7.00	8.05
	0.0209	0.0174	0.0147	0.0126	0.0108	0.00940	0.00822	0.00724	0.00634	0.00560	0.00497	0.00441	0.00390	0.00348
3/16	0.334	0.494	0.700	0.957	1.27	1.63	2.07	2.55	3.11	3.76	4.47	5.26	6.14	7.12
	0.0319	0.0266	0.0227	0.0198	0.0171	0.0151	0.0134	0.0118	0.0105	0.00942	0.00850	0.00763	0.00690	0.00624
1/4	0.252	0.375	0.534	0.729	0.967	1.25	1.59	1.98	2.41	2.90	3.48	4.10	4.80	5.56
	0.0666	0.0514	0.0445	0.0390	0.0343	0.0305	0.0272	0.0247	0.0222	0.0203	0.0184	0.0169	0.0154	0.0141
5/16	0.203	0.302	0.428	0.588	0.781	1.01	1.28	1.60	1.96	2.35	2.83	3.34	3.89	4.53
	0.0990	0.0838	0.0730	0.0645	0.0572	0.0512	0.0461	0.0418	0.0381	0.0348	0.0321	0.0295	0.0271	0.0252
3/8	0.169	0.253	0.360	0.491	0.652	0.845	1.07	1.34	1.63	1.98	2.39	2.82	3.30	3.83
	0.146	0.126	0.110	0.0965	0.0857	0.0774	0.0700	0.0638	0.0581	0.0533	0.0496	0.0458	0.0426	0.0395
7/16		0.217	0.310	0.424	0.561	0.727	0.915	1.15	1.41	1.72	2.05	2.42	2.84	3.33
		0.174	0.153	0.135	0.119	0.109	0.0980	0.0903	0.0828	0.0765	0.0707	0.0654	0.0610	0.0574
1/2			0.271	0.371	0.493	0.638	0.810	1.01	1.24	1.50	1.82	2.14	2.52	2.91
			0.203	0.180	0.161	0.146	0.132	0.122	0.112	0.103	0.0957	0.0891	0.0838	0.0778
5/8					0.396	0.512	0.652	0.813	1.00	1.21	1.45	1.71	2.00	2.35
					0.259	0.236	0.215	0.198	0.182	0.168	0.157	0.146	0.136	0.129
3/4								0.679	0.834	1.02	1.22	1.44	1.70	1.96
								0.292	0.270	0.252	0.234	0.219	0.206	0.193
7/8										0.869	1.04	1.24	1.46	1.70
										0.348	0.325	0.305	0.287	0.271
1											0.906	1.08	1.27	1.48
											0.442	0.406	0.382	0.366
1 1/8													1.14	1.32
													0.490	0.463

* The values given are for severe service. For average and light service, multiply these values by 1.25 and 1.55, respectively. For stainless steel, simply multiply the load values by 0.75 and the deflection values by 0.814. For phosphor-bronze, multiply the load values by 0.50 and the deflection values by 0.95.

For full explanation of use of tables see page 473. This and the similar tables following show load and deflection values which are based upon a maximum safe working stress for severe service. It should be noted that this safe working stress is different for each table, i.e., for each range of wire diameters. Should load and deflection values be desired for some other stress than that upon which a table is based, simply multiply the table values by the ratio of the new stress value to the table stress value. Since the same torsional modulus of elasticity is used as a basis for the deflection values throughout these tables, any deflection value based on a different torsional modulus is found simply by multiplying the deflection value given in the table by the ratio of 11,400,000 to the new modulus value.

Table 6. Helical Springs — Loads and Deflections

Values given are for 60,000 pounds per square inch safe working stress and a torsional modulus of elasticity equal to 11,400,000.*

Size of Wire — Roebling Music Wire Gage No.

Upper safe-load values in each pair are (Maximum Safe Load P, in Pounds); lower values are (Deflection f, in Inches per Coil).

Outside Diameter of Spring, Inches	19	20	21	22	23	24	25	26	27	28	29	30	31
Diameter of Wire, Inches →	0.042	0.044	0.046	0.048	0.051	0.055	0.059	0.063	0.067	0.071	0.074	0.078	0.082
5/32	9.14	10.4	11.6	12.9	14.8	....	....	....	....	....	....	....	....
	0.00308	0.00273	0.00244	0.00216	0.00179	....	....	....	....	....	....	....	....
3/16	8.12	9.15	10.4	11.7	13.6	16.5	19.6	....	....	....	....	....	....
	0.00563	0.00506	0.00465	0.00418	0.00359	0.00296	0.00242	....	....	....	....	....	....
1/4	6.41	7.27	8.26	9.38	11.1	13.7	16.6	20.0	23.3	27.1	....	....	....
	0.0130	0.0119	0.0110	0.0102	0.00907	0.00780	0.00670	0.00578	0.00498	0.00430	....	....	....
5/16	5.16	5.99	6.83	7.69	9.18	11.4	13.9	16.8	19.9	23.4	26.1	30.2	34.6
	0.0231	0.0217	0.0202	0.0189	0.0171	0.0150	0.0131	0.0116	0.0103	0.00910	0.00831	0.00738	0.00658
3/8	4.45	5.06	5.76	6.54	7.81	9.73	11.9	14.4	17.2	20.1	22.7	26.4	30.3
	0.0370	0.0343	0.0321	0.0303	0.0276	0.0244	0.0218	0.0194	0.0175	0.0156	0.0146	0.0131	0.0118
7/16	3.83	4.40	5.02	5.67	6.77	8.45	10.4	12.5	15.0	17.7	20.1	23.2	26.8
	0.0536	0.0496	0.0468	0.0444	0.0405	0.0363	0.0326	0.0293	0.0266	0.0241	0.0224	0.0205	0.0187
1/2	3.37	3.86	4.40	5.02	5.96	7.45	9.16	11.1	13.3	15.7	17.7	20.7	23.8
	0.0732	0.0684	0.0646	0.0613	0.0560	0.0504	0.0456	0.0413	0.0376	0.0342	0.0331	0.0296	0.0270
5/8	2.72	3.12	3.56	4.04	4.82	6.04	7.44	9.02	11.1	12.8	14.5	16.9	19.5
	0.122	0.114	0.108	0.103	0.0947	0.0857	0.0714	0.0656	0.0601	0.0602	0.0555	0.0524	0.0486
3/4	2.28	2.61	2.98	3.39	4.05	5.06	6.24	7.57	9.09	10.8	12.2	14.2	16.5
	0.183	0.172	0.163	0.155	0.144	0.131	0.110	0.101	0.0902	0.0820	0.0766	0.0820	0.0766
7/8	1.95	2.25	2.56	2.92	3.48	4.36	5.38	6.51	7.85	9.29	10.5	12.3	14.3
	0.255	0.241	0.229	0.217	0.202	0.184	0.169	0.156	0.144	0.134	0.127	0.118	0.111
1	1.72	1.97	2.25	2.56	3.06	3.83	4.72	5.73	6.88	8.18	9.25	10.8	12.5
	0.341	0.322	0.306	0.292	0.272	0.248	0.228	0.210	0.195	0.182	0.172	0.161	0.151
1 1/8	1.53	1.75	2.01	2.27	2.72	3.42	4.21	5.12	6.13	7.29	8.25	9.67	11.2
	0.438	0.414	0.395	0.375	0.351	0.321	0.296	0.274	0.253	0.236	0.224	0.210	0.198
1 1/4	1.38	1.58	1.81	2.05	2.46	3.08	3.80	4.62	5.54	6.59	7.45	8.72	10.1
	0.548	0.520	0.494	0.472	0.440	0.405	0.372	0.345	0.319	0.298	0.284	0.266	0.250
1 3/8	....	....	1.64	1.88	2.24	2.80	3.46	4.21	5.06	6.01	6.78	7.94	9.22
	....	....	0.605	0.578	0.540	0.495	0.465	0.423	0.394	0.369	0.349	0.329	0.310
1 1/2	....	....	....	....	2.06	2.57	3.17	3.86	4.64	5.50	6.24	7.29	8.45
	....	....	....	....	0.650	0.596	0.550	0.510	0.476	0.444	0.424	0.398	0.375

* See footnote to Table 5.

Table 7. Helical Springs — Loads and Deflections

Values given are for 55,000 pounds per square inch safe working stress and a torsional modulus of elasticity equal to 11,400,000.*

Size of Wire — W. & M. Steel Wire Gage No.

Each cell gives the safe load (pounds, upper figure) and the deflection (inches, lower figure), shown here as *load / deflection*.

Outside Diameter of Spring, Inches	32† (0.086)	33† (0.090)	13 (0.0915)	(0.102)	12 (0.106)	11 (0.121)	10 (0.135)	9 (0.148)	8 (0.162)	7 (0.177)
7/16	28.1 / 0.0157	30.8 / 0.0143	33.4 / 0.0138	45.1 / 0.0110	50.0 / 0.0101	70.7 / 0.00737	93.4 / 0.00546	.....	.....	.....
1/2	25.1 / 0.0229	27.6 / 0.0210	29.9 / 0.0205	40.6 / 0.0166	45.3 / 0.0154	65.1 / 0.0116	86.9 / 0.00893	111 / 0.00705	137 / 0.00538	.....
5/8	20.6 / 0.0413	22.6 / 0.0384	24.6 / 0.0373	33.6 / 0.0312	37.5 / 0.0291	54.8 / 0.0230	74.6 / 0.0185	95.9 / 0.0152	123 / 0.0124	154 / 0.00991
3/4	17.4 / 0.0652	19.2 / 0.0610	20.8 / 0.0594	28.6 / 0.0505	31.9 / 0.0472	47.0 / 0.0382	64.2 / 0.0316	83.3 / 0.0266	107 / 0.0222	137 / 0.0184
7/8	15.0 / 0.0945	16.6 / 0.0889	18.1 / 0.0870	24.8 / 0.0743	27.8 / 0.0700	40.9 / 0.0574	56.1 / 0.0480	73.2 / 0.0410	95.2 / 0.0351	122 / 0.0295
1	13.2 / 0.130	14.6 / 0.122	15.9 / 0.119	21.9 / 0.103	24.5 / 0.0974	36.1 / 0.0804	49.6 / 0.0680	64.7 / 0.0586	84.3 / 0.0505	109 / 0.0433
1⅛	11.8 / 0.170	13.1 / 0.160	14.2 / 0.157	19.6 / 0.136	21.9 / 0.129	32.5 / 0.108	44.6 / 0.0915	58.3 / 0.0796	76.0 / 0.0690	98.3 / 0.0597
1¼	10.7 / 0.216	11.8 / 0.204	12.9 / 0.200	17.7 / 0.174	19.8 / 0.165	29.3 / 0.138	40.6 / 0.119	53.0 / 0.104	69.0 / 0.0904	89.4 / 0.0788
1⅜	9.72 / 0.267	10.8 / 0.253	11.7 / 0.248	16.2 / 0.216	18.1 / 0.206	26.8 / 0.173	37.0 / 0.149	48.6 / 0.131	63.0 / 0.115	81.9 / 0.101
1½	8.95 / 0.325	9.92 / 0.307	10.8 / 0.301	14.9 / 0.264	16.7 / 0.251	24.6 / 0.211	33.8 / 0.186	44.6 / 0.161	58.4 / 0.142	75.6 / 0.125
1⅝	8.26 / 0.387	9.16 / 0.366	9.96 / 0.360	13.7 / 0.315	15.4 / 0.300	22.8 / 0.254	31.5 / 0.221	41.3 / 0.195	54.0 / 0.172	70.1 / 0.153
1¾	7.70 / 0.456	8.52 / 0.432	9.26 / 0.423	12.8 / 0.372	14.3 / 0.353	21.2 / 0.300	29.4 / 0.261	38.5 / 0.232	50.4 / 0.205	65.4 / 0.182
1⅞	7.19 / 0.528	7.96 / 0.501	8.66 / 0.491	11.9 / 0.432	13.4 / 0.412	19.9 / 0.351	27.6 / 0.306	36.1 / 0.272	47.1 / 0.241	61.3 / 0.215
2	6.76 / 0.608	7.47 / 0.575	8.13 / 0.565	11.2 / 0.498	12.6 / 0.474	18.7 / 0.404	25.8 / 0.354	34.0 / 0.315	44.4 / 0.280	57.6 / 0.250
2¼	6.00 / 0.782	6.66 / 0.742	7.25 / 0.728	10.0 / 0.642	11.2 / 0.612	16.6 / 0.524	23.0 / 0.461	30.6 / 0.412	39.7 / 0.368	51.4 / 0.328
2½	.....	6.00 / 0.930	6.53 / 0.911	9.02 / 0.808	10.1 / 0.771	15.0 / 0.662	20.7 / 0.580	27.3 / 0.520	35.7 / 0.466	46.5 / 0.417

* See footnote to Table 5. † Roebling Music Wire Gage No.

Table 8. Helical Springs — Loads and Deflections

Values given are for a torsional modulus of elasticity equal to 11,400,000. Safe working stresses given below.

48,000 pounds per square inch*

Outside Diameter of Spring, Inches	W. & M. Steel Wire Gage No.				
	5	4	2	1	0
	Diameter of Wire, Inches				
	0.207	0.225	0.263	0.283	0.307
1¼	122	156	....	....	....
	0.0531	0.0458	....	....	....
1⅜	113	144	223	....	....
	0.0687	0.0597	0.0450	....	....
1½	104	132	207	256	....
	0.0861	0.0752	0.0576	0.0504	....
1⅝	96.8	124	194	239	306
	0.105	0.0929	0.0721	0.0632	0.0548
1¾	90.4	115	181	224	282
	0.127	0.112	0.0874	0.0774	0.0672
1⅞	84.8	108	171	211	267
	0.150	0.133	0.105	0.0930	0.0814
2	79.8	102	161	199	252
	0.176	0.156	0.124	0.110	0.0905
2¼	71.3	91.3	144	179	227
	0.232	0.208	0.166	0.149	0.131
2½	64.4	82.6	131	162	206
	0.298	0.266	0.215	0.193	0.171
2¾	58.9	75.4	119	148	188
	0.370	0.332	0.269	0.243	0.217
3	54.2	69.3	110	137	173
	0.451	0.406	0.331	0.299	0.267
3½	46.6	59.7	94.8	118	150
	0.636	0.576	0.471	0.428	0.385

42,000 pounds per square inch*

Outside Diameter of Spring, Inches	W. & M. Steel Wire Gage No.					
	2-0	3-0	4-0	5-0		½″
	Diameter of Wire, Inches					
	0.331	0.363	0.394	0.430	0.460	0.500
1⅞	289	377	....	....	....	....
	0.0623	0.0526	....	....	....	....
2	274	356	451	....	....	....
	0.0744	0.0631	0.0544	....	....	....
2¼	247	323	408	522	....	....
	0.102	0.0876	0.0759	0.0646	....	....
2½	224	294	372	478	582	734
	0.134	0.116	0.101	0.0872	0.0772	0.0660
2¾	205	269	341	440	534	677
	0.170	0.148	0.130	0.113	0.101	0.0868
3	189	249	316	406	495	629
	0.211	0.184	0.163	0.142	0.127	0.110
3½	164	215	274	353	431	548
	0.305	0.268	0.239	0.210	0.190	0.166
4	144	189	241	313	381	486
	0.416	0.368	0.329	0.292	0.265	0.234
4½	129	170	216	279	341	436
	0.546	0.484	0.434	0.386	0.352	0.313
5	116	153	195	252	308	395
	0.691	0.616	0.555	0.494	0.452	0.404
5½	106	140	178	231	282	360
	0.856	0.764	0.693	0.617	0.554	0.505
6	97.4	128	164	212	259	332
	1.04	0.927	0.838	0.752	0.690	0.619

* See footnote to Table 5.

Table 9. Helical Springs — Loads and Deflections

Values given are for a torsional modulus of elasticity equal to 11,400,000.   Safe working stresses given below.

36,000 pounds per square inch*

Outside Diam. of Spring, Inches	Diameter of Wire, Inches						
	9/16	5/8	11/16	3/4	13/16	7/8	15/16
2¾	810 / 0.0592	1080 / 0.0482	1410 / 0.0389	1678 / 0.0423	....	....	....
3	754 / 0.0769	1010 / 0.0625	1340 / 0.0519	1490 / 0.0688	1868 / 0.0583	2279 / 0.0492	....
3½	661 / 0.117	896 / 0.0985	1170 / 0.0818	1350 / 0.102	1678 / 0.0877	2059 / 0.0755	2500 / 0.0652
4	588 / 0.167	794 / 0.141	1049 / 0.119	1220 / 0.142	1530 / 0.123	1886 / 0.108	2290 / 0.0943
4½	530 / 0.226	719 / 0.193	949 / 0.164	1099 / 0.187	1390 / 0.165	1732 / 0.145	2102 / 0.128
5	478 / 0.293	653 / 0.252	863 / 0.216	1021 / 0.242	1281 / 0.212	1591 / 0.188	1930 / 0.167
5½	437 / 0.369	597 / 0.318	788 / 0.276	942 / 0.301	1179 / 0.265	1471 / 0.237	1789 / 0.211
6	402 / 0.453	548 / 0.392	727 / 0.342	873 / 0.369	1100 / 0.327	1370 / 0.291	1670 / 0.261
6½	372 / 0.546	510 / 0.475	675 / 0.417	813 / 0.440	1020 / 0.395	1269 / 0.359	1561 / 0.316
7	....	....	....	....	....	....	....
7½	....	....	....	....	....	....	....

32,000 pounds per square inch*

Outside Diam. of Spring, Inches	Diameter of Wire, Inches				
	1	1⅛	1¼	1⅜	1½
2¾	....	....	....	....	....
3	....	....	....	....	....
3½	....	....	....	....	....
4	2650 / 0.0501	....	....	....	....
4½	2429 / 0.0733	....	....	....	....
5	2240 / 0.100	3350 / 0.0564	4138 / 0.0628	....	....
5½	2067 / 0.132	3107 / 0.0787	3869 / 0.0855	5008 / 0.0690	....
6	1920 / 0.168	2880 / 0.106	3610 / 0.111	4675 / 0.0910	5974 / 0.0753
6½	1789 / 0.208	2691 / 0.136	3379 / 0.141	4419 / 0.116	5622 / 0.0966
7	1669 / 0.254	2499 / 0.170	3181 / 0.174	4170 / 0.145	5321 / 0.123
7½	....	2349 / 0.208	3002 / 0.211	3930 / 0.178	5024 / 0.150

* See footnote to Table 5.

multiplied by the ratio of the new stress value to the table stress value. Since the same torsional modulus of elasticity is used as a basis for the deflection values throughout these tables, any deflection value based on a different torsional modulus is found by multiplying the deflection values given in the tables by the ratio of 11,400,000 to the new modulus value.

Helical Spring Tables Giving Maximum Loads and Deflections. — The tables "Maximum Loads in Pounds and Corresponding Compressions per Coil in Inches of Helical Round Bar Springs," are calculated for a maximum fiber stress of 100,000 pounds per square inch, with a torsional modulus of elasticity of 11,520,000, and apply to high-grade spring wire.

Values Given in Helical Spring Tables. — The tables give in the two extreme left-hand columns the size of the wire from which the spring is made by gage number (steel wire gage) and in decimal inches, respectively. Along the top of the tables is given the mean or pitch diameter of the spring in inches. To find the values relating to any one spring, first locate in the left-hand column the size of wire from which the spring is made, and then follow the horizontal line from this size to the column headed by the mean diameter of the spring. For example, assume that the values for a spring made from No. 10 gage wire, having a mean or pitch diameter of 1⅛ inch, are to be found. Here three values are given one above the other as follows: 86, 0.255, and 330. The top value, 86, gives the load in pounds which will produce a fiber stress in the spring wire of 100,000 pounds per square inch, not taking into account any correction by introducing the Wahl factor (see next paragraph). The second value, 0.255, gives the corresponding deflection in inches per coil for this load. The third value, 330, is a constant; if this constant is divided by the number of effective coils in the entire spring, the load in pounds required to compress the spring one inch will be found.

Wahl Factor Correction for Tables. — These tables do not take into account any increase in stress which results from a decrease in the ratio of mean diameter of the spring to wire diameter as is done in the formulas given in Table 1 by the introduction of the Wahl factor previously referred to. To correct the values shown in these tables for this additional stress, in each case the first figure, or load figure, should be divided by the correct K value (see Table 4) and the second figure or deflection figure should also be divided by the correct K value. No correction is necessary for the third figure or constant.

Using Spring Tables for Stresses other than 100,000 Pounds per Square Inch. — Whenever load and deflection values are required for stresses other than 100,000 pounds per square inch the values shown should be multiplied by the ratio of the new stress value to 100,000. In each case the constant remains unchanged.

Example 1. — Taking into account Wahl factor corrections, what would be the maximum load and corresponding deflection per coil for a 1⅜ inch pitch diameter spring of No. 10 gage wire (0.135 inch diameter) at a maximum stress of 80,000 pounds per square inch.

Looking at the table we find that a load value of 70 pounds and a corresponding deflection per coil value of 0.380 inch is shown for 100,000 pounds per square inch maximum stress. First apply the Wahl factor correction. For this size of spring and wire, the spring index $D \div d = 1.375 \div 0.135 = 10.2$ and the Wahl factor is 1.14 (see Table 4). The corrected load value is $70 \div 1.14 = 61.4$ pounds and the corrected deflection value is $0.380 \div 1.14 = 0.333$ inch per coil. If these values are now revised for 80,000 pounds per square inch they will be $61.4 \times 0.80 = 49.1$ pounds and $0.333 \times 0.80 = 0.266$ inch per coil.

Example 2. — What load is required to compress a spring 1 inch if it is made from ¼-inch wire, has 1 inch mean diameter and 14 effective coils? The constant for this spring, 5625, divided by 14 gives 402 pounds required.

Maximum Loads in Pounds and Corresponding Compressions per Coil in Inches of Helical Round Bar Springs

Mean or Pitch Diameter of Spring, Inches

Size of Wire, Steel Wire Gage	Diam. of Wire, Inches	3/16	7/32	1/4	9/32	5/16	3/8	7/16	1/2	9/16	5/8	11/16	3/4	13/16	7/8	15/16	1	1 1/8
18	0.0475	22.44 0.020 1120	19.21 0.028 680	16.83 0.036 465	14.96 0.045 330	13.46 0.056 240	11.22 0.080 140	9.61 0.110 87	8.41 0.144 58	7.48 0.182 40	6.73 0.224 30	6.12 0.273 22	5.61 0.323 17	… … …	… … …	… … …	… … …	… … …
17	0.054	… … …	28.26 0.024 1180	24.73 0.031 800	21.98 0.040 500	19.80 0.049 400	16.50 0.071 230	14.13 0.096 145	12.36 0.126 95	10.99 0.158 68	9.90 0.194 50	9.00 0.238 38	8.25 0.284 29	… … …	… … …	… … …	… … …	… … …
16	0.0625	… … …	… … …	38.35 0.027 1400	34.09 0.034 1000	30.61 0.042 720	25.56 0.061 410	21.91 0.083 260	19.17 0.108 170	17.04 0.138 120	15.34 0.168 90	13.91 0.206 65	12.78 0.245 52	11.80 0.288 40	10.95 0.334 30	10.22 0.383 25	9.58 0.435 21	8.52 0.552 15
15	0.072	… … …	… … …	58.23 0.0236 2460	51.72 0.031 1630	46.58 0.037 1250	38.80 0.053 730	33.27 0.069 480	29.11 0.095 300	25.86 0.119 215	23.29 0.148 155	21.17 0.178 118	19.40 0.213 77	18.05 0.250 77	16.63 0.276 60	15.63 0.333 47	14.55 0.378 38	12.93 0.479 26
14	0.080	… … …	… … …	80.42 0.0213 3700	71.48 0.027 2610	64.34 0.033 1940	53.6 0.048 1110	46.0 0.065 700	40.2 0.085 470	35.7 0.107 330	32.17 0.133 240	29.2 0.162 180	26.8 0.191 140	24.7 0.225 110	23.0 0.261 88	21.4 0.300 70	20.1 0.341 59	17.8 0.431 40
13 1/2	0.08575	… … …	… … …	99 0.020 4950	88 0.025 3300	79 0.031 2550	66 0.046 1440	56.5 0.061 926	49.5 0.079 623	44.0 0.100 440	39.6 0.124 319	36.0 0.150 240	33.0 0.179 185	30.4 0.210 145	28.3 0.244 116	26.4 0.281 94	24.7 0.318 78	22.0 0.402 55
13	0.091	… … …	… … …	120 0.0185 6400	107 0.023 4600	92 0.029 3300	80 0.042 1900	69 0.057 1200	60 0.074 800	53.4 0.094 560	48.1 0.116 400	43.7 0.141 300	40.1 0.167 240	37.0 0.197 185	34.3 0.228 150	32.0 0.263 120	30.0 0.297 100	26.7 0.377 70
12 1/2	0.0985	… … …	… … …	150 0.017 8600	133 0.022 6000	120 0.027 4400	100 0.039 2550	85.0 0.053 1600	75.0 0.066 1080	66.7 0.087 760	60.0 0.108 555	54.6 0.131 400	50.0 0.155 320	46.0 0.182 250	42.9 0.212 200	40.0 0.243 164	37.5 0.276 135	33.3 0.350 95

Maximum Loads in Pounds and Corresponding Compressions per Coil in Inches of Helical Round Bar Springs

Each cell lists three stacked values: maximum load (pounds) / compression per coil (inches) / maximum load at next value.

Size of Wire, Steel Wire Gage	Diam. of Wire, Inches	5/16	3/8	7/16	1/2	9/16	5/8	11/16	3/4	7/8	1	1 1/8	1 1/4	1 3/8	1 1/2	1 5/8	1 3/4	1 7/8	2	2 1/8	2 1/4	2 3/8	2 1/2
							Mean or Pitch Diameter of Spring, Inches																
12	0.1055	145 / 0.025 / 5770	121 / 0.036 / 3330	104 / 0.049 / 2050	91 / 0.065 / 1400	81 / 0.082 / 980	73 / 0.101 / 720	66 / 0.122 / 540	61 / 0.146 / 410	52 / 0.198 / 260	45 / 0.260 / 170	40 / 0.328 / 120	36 / 0.406 / 89	33 / 0.488 / 67	30 / 0.584 / 50	28 / 0.686 / 40	26 / 0.795 / 32	24 / 0.913 / 26	22.7 / 1.038 / 20	...	...	...	...
11 1/2	0.113	181 / 0.023 / 7700	151 / 0.034 / 4400	129 / 0.046 / 2800	113 / 0.060 / 1850	100 / 0.076 / 1300	91 / 0.094 / 960	82 / 0.113 / 780	75 / 0.136 / 550	64.7 / 0.185 / 340	56.6 / 0.241 / 234	50.3 / 0.305 / 165	45.3 / 0.377 / 120	41.1 / 0.454 / 90	37.8 / 0.543 / 69	34.8 / 0.637 / 54	32.3 / 0.739 / 43	30.1 / 0.848 / 35	28.3 / 0.904 / 29	...	...	...	...
11	0.120	...	180 / 0.032 / 5600	155 / 0.043 / 3600	136 / 0.057 / 2380	121 / 0.072 / 1670	108 / 0.089 / 1220	99 / 0.106 / 939	90.4 / 0.128 / 700	77.5 / 0.174 / 445	67.8 / 0.227 / 300	60.3 / 0.287 / 206	54.2 / 0.355 / 150	49.3 / 0.427 / 115	45.2 / 0.511 / 88	41.7 / 0.600 / 70	38.7 / 0.696 / 55	36.2 / 0.800 / 45	33.9 / 0.909 / 37	31.9 / 1.026 / 31	30.1 / 1.150 / 27	...	...
10 1/2	0.127	...	214 / 0.029 / 7300	183 / 0.041 / 4400	161 / 0.053 / 3000	143 / 0.068 / 2000	128 / 0.084 / 1500	117 / 0.101 / 1100	107 / 0.121 / 880	92 / 0.164 / 550	80 / 0.214 / 370	71.5 / 0.271 / 266	64 / 0.335 / 190	58.5 / 0.404 / 140	53.6 / 0.483 / 110	49 / 0.567 / 85	46 / 0.657 / 70	42.9 / 0.755 / 56	40 / 0.858 / 46	38 / 0.970 / 39	36 / 1.084 / 33	...	...
10	0.135	...	...	220 / 0.039 / 5500	193 / 0.050 / 3800	172 / 0.064 / 2680	155 / 0.079 / 1960	140 / 0.095 / 1460	129 / 0.113 / 1140	110 / 0.154 / 700	96 / 0.202 / 470	86 / 0.255 / 330	77 / 0.315 / 240	70 / 0.386 / 180	64 / 0.454 / 140	59.4 / 0.533 / 110	55 / 0.618 / 88	51.5 / 0.710 / 72	48 / 0.808 / 59	45.4 / 0.912 / 49	43 / 1.020 / 42	...	...
9 1/2	0.141	...	...	252 / 0.037 / 6700	220 / 0.048 / 4500	196 / 0.061 / 3100	176 / 0.075 / 2300	160 / 0.091 / 1700	147 / 0.109 / 1300	126 / 0.148 / 840	110 / 0.193 / 550	98 / 0.244 / 400	89 / 0.302 / 290	80 / 0.364 / 200	73 / 0.435 / 165	68 / 0.510 / 130	63 / 0.594 / 105	59 / 0.680 / 85	55 / 0.772 / 70	51.8 / 0.873 / 59	49 / 0.978 / 50	...	...
9	0.148	...	...	...	254 / 0.046 / 5500	224 / 0.058 / 3860	203 / 0.072 / 2800	185 / 0.087 / 2100	170 / 0.103 / 1650	146 / 0.141 / 1000	127 / 0.184 / 690	112 / 0.233 / 480	102 / 0.287 / 355	93 / 0.350 / 265	85 / 0.412 / 206	78.3 / 0.486 / 160	73 / 0.564 / 129	68 / 0.648 / 104	63.6 / 0.736 / 86	60 / 0.832 / 72	56 / 0.932 / 60	53.7 / 1.039 / 51	52 / 1.150 / 45
8 1/2	0.1562	...	...	...	299 / 0.043 / 7000	266 / 0.055 / 4800	239 / 0.068 / 3500	218 / 0.082 / 2650	199 / 0.098 / 2000	171 / 0.134 / 1270	149 / 0.174 / 855	133 / 0.220 / 600	120 / 0.272 / 440	109 / 0.330 / 330	100 / 0.392 / 266	92 / 0.460 / 200	85.5 / 0.534 / 160	79.5 / 0.611 / 130	74.5 / 0.696 / 107	70.5 / 0.788 / 99	66.5 / 0.883 / 75	63 / 0.976 / 64	60 / 1.088 / 55

Maximum Loads in Pounds and Corresponding Compressions per Coil in Inches of Helical Round Bar Springs

Mean or Pitch Diameter of Spring, Inches

Size of Wire, Steel Wire Gage	Diam. of Wire, Inches	9/16	5/8	11/16	3/4	7/8	1	1⅛	1¼	1⅜	1½	1⅝	1¾	1⅞	2	2⅛	2¼	2⅜	2½	2⅝
8	0.162	296 / 0.053 / 5380	267 / 0.066 / 4000	243 / 0.080 / 3000	223 / 0.095 / 2300	191 / 0.129 / 1480	167 / 0.162 / 1000	148 / 0.213 / 700	133 / 0.263 / 500	121 / 0.320 / 380	111 / 0.378 / 295	102 / 0.444 / 230	95 / 0.515 / 184	89 / 0.591 / 150	83 / 0.673 / 123	78.5 / 0.766 / 103	74 / 0.851 / 86	70.3 / 0.949 / 74	66.7 / 1.052 / 63	63.6 / 1.165 / 54
7½	0.170	343 / 0.051 / 6700	309 / 0.063 / 4990	280 / 0.076 / 3680	257 / 0.090 / 2800	220 / 0.123 / 1780	193 / 0.160 / 1200	171 / 0.203 / 840	154 / 0.261 / 590	140 / 0.302 / 460	128 / 0.361 / 350	119 / 0.423 / 280	110 / 0.491 / 240	103 / 0.563 / 180	96 / 0.641 / 148	91 / 0.724 / 125	85.7 / 0.812 / 105	81 / 0.895 / 90	77 / 1.043 / 74	73.5 / 1.108 / 65
7	0.177	387 / 0.049 / 7900	348 / 0.060 / 5800	316 / 0.073 / 4300	290 / 0.087 / 3300	249 / 0.118 / 2110	217 / 0.154 / 1400	193 / 0.195 / 1000	174 / 0.240 / 725	158 / 0.289 / 540	145 / 0.346 / 418	134 / 0.407 / 329	124 / 0.472 / 262	116 / 0.541 / 214	109 / 0.616 / 175	102 / 0.696 / 146	97 / 0.780 / 124	92 / 0.870 / 105	87 / 0.962 / 90	83 / 1.064 / 78
3/16″	0.1875		414 / 0.057 / 7250	376 / 0.069 / 5440	345 / 0.081 / 4250	296 / 0.111 / 2650	259 / 0.145 / 1730	230 / 0.184 / 1250	207 / 0.227 / 900	188 / 0.276 / 680	172 / 0.327 / 520	159 / 0.384 / 410	148 / 0.445 / 330	139 / 0.511 / 270	129 / 0.582 / 220	122 / 0.657 / 185	115 / 0.736 / 156	110 / 0.800 / 135	103 / 0.908 / 110	98.6 / 1.004 / 98
6	0.192		445 / 0.055 / 8000	404 / 0.067 / 6000	370 / 0.080 / 4600	317 / 0.108 / 2900	278 / 0.142 / 1900	247 / 0.180 / 1370	222 / 0.222 / 1000	202 / 0.267 / 750	184 / 0.320 / 570	171 / 0.375 / 450	159 / 0.435 / 365	148 / 0.499 / 296	139 / 0.568 / 244	131 / 0.641 / 200	123 / 0.720 / 170	117 / 0.801 / 145	111 / 0.887 / 125	106 / 0.981 / 108
5	0.207			506 / 0.062 / 8000	464 / 0.074 / 6200	398 / 0.100 / 3900	348 / 0.131 / 2600	309 / 0.166 / 1850	278 / 0.206 / 1350	253 / 0.248 / 1000	232 / 0.296 / 780	214 / 0.347 / 610	199 / 0.403 / 490	186 / 0.462 / 400	174 / 0.526 / 330	164 / 0.595 / 275	154 / 0.666 / 230	147 / 0.743 / 200	139 / 0.824 / 168	132 / 0.910 / 145
7/32″	0.21875				553 / 0.070 / 7900	473 / 0.095 / 4960	414 / 0.125 / 3330	368 / 0.158 / 2325	331 / 0.195 / 1700	301 / 0.234 / 1280	276 / 0.280 / 985	255 / 0.329 / 775	237 / 0.381 / 620	221 / 0.438 / 500	207 / 0.498 / 415	195 / 0.563 / 345	184 / 0.631 / 290	174 / 0.703 / 245	165 / 0.779 / 210	158 / 0.861 / 183
4	0.2253				596 / 0.068 / 8700	512 / 0.093 / 5500	447 / 0.121 / 3690	397 / 0.153 / 2580	357 / 0.189 / 1850	325 / 0.228 / 1400	298 / 0.272 / 1090	275 / 0.320 / 850	256 / 0.371 / 660	238 / 0.426 / 550	223 / 0.484 / 460	210 / 0.547 / 380	199 / 0.613 / 324	188 / 0.683 / 275	178 / 0.757 / 235	170 / 0.837 / 200

Maximum Loads in Pounds and Corresponding Compressions per Coil in Inches of Helical Round Bar Springs

Size of Wire, Steel Wire Gage	Diam. of Wire, Inches	Mean or Pitch Diameter of Spring, Inches																					
		1	1⅛	1¼	1⅜	1½	1⅝	1¾	1⅞	2	2⅛	2¼	2⅜	2½	2⅝	2¾	2⅞	3	3¼	3½	3¾	4	4½
3½	0.234	503 / 0.117 / 4260	447 / 0.147 / 3000	402 / 0.182 / 2200	366 / 0.220 / 1650	335 / 0.250 / 1270	310 / 0.308 / 1000	287 / 0.357 / 800	269 / 0.410 / 650	251 / 0.467 / 530	237 / 0.526 / 440	223 / 0.590 / 375	212 / 0.657 / —	201 / 0.728 / 275	191 / 0.805 / 235	183 / 0.881 / 207	175 / 0.961 / 180	168 / 1.048 / 160	155 / 1.232 / 125	144 / 1.428 / —	134 / 1.640 / 80	126 / 1.869 / 67	....
3	0.244	570 / 0.112 / 5080	507 / 0.141 / 3590	456 / 0.175 / 2600	414 / 0.210 / 1970	380 / 0.250 / 1500	351 / 0.295 / 1185	326 / 0.342 / 950	304 / 0.392 / 775	285 / 0.447 / 637	268 / 0.504 / 530	253 / 0.565 / 447	240 / 0.630 / 380	228 / 0.698 / 326	217 / 0.771 / —	207 / 0.840 / 246	199 / — / 215	190 / 1.000 / 190	175 / 1.180 / 148	163 / 1.368 / 119	152 / 1.568 / 97	142 / 1.788 / 79	....
¼″	0.250	614 / 0.109 / 5625	545 / 0.138 / 3940	491 / 0.170 / 2880	446 / 0.205 / 2170	409 / 0.245 / 1665	378 / 0.288 / 1310	351 / 0.334 / 1050	327 / 0.383 / 850	307 / 0.436 / 637	289 / 0.492 / 587	273 / 0.552 / 494	258 / 0.615 / 419	245 / 0.680 / 360	233 / 0.753 / 310	223 / 0.820 / 270	213 / 0.901 / 236	204 / 0.983 / 205	189 / 1.152 / 164	175 / 1.336 / 130	164 / 1.533 / 106	153 / 1.744 / 87	....
2	0.263	714 / 0.103 / 7000	635 / 0.131 / 4820	571 / 0.162 / 3520	519 / 0.195 / 2660	476 / 0.233 / 2000	440 / 0.273 / 1600	408 / 0.317 / 1280	381 / 0.364 / 1045	357 / 0.414 / 860	336 / 0.468 / 720	317 / 0.524 / 600	301 / 0.585 / 510	285 / 0.648 / 440	272 / 0.716 / 380	259 / 0.782 / 330	249 / 0.857 / 290	238 / 0.933 / 255	220 / 1.095 / 193	204 / 1.270 / 160	190 / 1.468 / 128	178 / 1.656 / 107	....
1	0.283	788 / 0.122 / 6450	710 / 0.150 / 4750	646 / 0.181 / 3565	592 / 0.217 / 2725	546 / 0.254 / 2140	507 / 0.295 / 1718	474 / 0.339 / 1400	444 / 0.386 / 1150	418 / 0.435 / 960	398 / 0.487 / 817	374 / 0.543 / 688	355 / 0.602 / 590	338 / 0.665 / 510	323 / 0.724 / 446	309 / 0.797 / 387	296 / 0.868 / 341	273 / 1.017 / —	254 / 1.180 / 268	237 / 1.355 / 215	222 / 1.545 / 175	— / — / 143	....
0	0.307	1005 / 0.112 / 9000	909 / 0.139 / 6500	826 / 0.168 / 4900	757 / 0.200 / 3780	699 / 0.234 / 2990	649 / 0.272 / 2390	606 / 0.312 / 1940	568 / 0.355 / 1600	535 / 0.401 / 1300	505 / 0.450 / 1120	478 / 0.501 / 930	454 / 0.555 / 810	433 / 0.613 / 700	413 / 0.671 / 615	395 / 0.734 / 534	378 / 0.800 / 470	350 / 0.938 / —	324 / 1.090 / 370	303 / 1.249 / 304	284 / 1.421 / 240	— / — / 200	....
5/16″	0.3125	1073 / 0.110 / 9700	966 / 0.136 / 7000	880 / 0.165 / 5300	805 / 0.196 / 4090	743 / 0.230 / 3200	690 / 0.267 / 2580	644 / 0.307 / 2100	604 / 0.349 / 1860	568 / 0.394 / 1440	537 / 0.441 / 1210	509 / 0.492 / 1000	483 / 0.545 / 885	460 / 0.608 / 780	439 / 0.666 / 665	420 / 0.721 / 580	403 / 0.785 / 510	371 / 0.922 / 400	345 / 1.069 / 260	322 / 1.227 / 215	302 / 1.396 / 215	268 / 1.764 / 151	
00	0.331	1266 / 0.104 / 12,170	1146 / 0.129 / 8880	1035 / 0.156 / 6630	949 / 0.185 / 5130	876 / 0.218 / 4010	814 / 0.252 / 3230	765 / 0.289 / 2645	712 / 0.329 / 2105	670 / 0.372 / 1866	633 / 0.416 / 1520	600 / 0.465 / 1290	570 / 0.515 / 1100	542 / 0.569 / 952	518 / 0.623 / 830	495 / 0.677 / 726	474 / 0.741 / 638	438 / 0.869 / 500	407 / 1.009 / 403	382 / 1.158 / 329	356 / 1.316 / 252	317 / 1.664 / 190	
11/32″	0.34375	....	....	1276 / 0.124 / 10,200	1160 / 0.149 / 7785	1063 / 0.178 / 6970	981 / 0.209 / 5750	911 / 0.243 / 4750	851 / 0.279 / 3750	797 / 0.314 / 3048	751 / 0.358 / 2530	705 / 0.401 / 1768	672 / 0.447 / 1290	638 / 0.495 / 1100	608 / 0.548 / 970	580 / 0.597 / 846	555 / 0.634 / 760	531 / 0.712 / 586	491 / 0.837 / 469	456 / 0.971 / 380	425 / 1.116 / 317	399 / 1.259 / 220	354 / 1.604 / 220
000	0.362	....	....	1490 / 0.116 / 12,860	1355 / 0.140 / 9970	1242 / 0.168 / 7390	1146 / 0.196 / 5845	1064 / 0.231 / 4600	993 / 0.265 / 3745	931 / 0.301 / 3100	876 / 0.337 / 2600	828 / 0.377 / 2195	788 / 0.421 / 1870	745 / 0.467 / 1638	709 / 0.520 / 1363	677 / 0.562 / 1200	648 / 0.620 / 916	621 / 0.678 / 730	573 / 0.784 / 576	532 / 0.923 / 408	497 / 1.059 / 385	465 / 1.204 / 274	414 / 1.508 / 274

Formulas for Helical Rectangular Bar Springs

Notation: D, F, h, H, P, S and G represent the same quantities as for helical round bar springs; see the preceding pages; b = width of rectangular bar; t = height of rectangular bar (parallel to axis of spring). For square bar springs $b = t$ = side of square. — These formulas give approximate results, and should be used only when the difference between b and t is not very great.

To be Found	Formulas	To be Found	Formulas
P, maximum carrying capacity	$P = \dfrac{Sbt\sqrt{t^2+b^2}}{3D}$ $= \dfrac{GFbt^2(t^2+b^2)}{9.4\,hD^3}$ or, for steel springs: $P = \dfrac{26,700\,bt\sqrt{t^2+b^2}}{D}$ $= \dfrac{1,337,000\,Fbt^2(t^2+b^2)}{hD^3}$	h, solid height	$h = \dfrac{H}{1+\dfrac{3.14\,SD^2}{Gt\sqrt{t^2+b^2}}}$ or, for steel springs: $h = \dfrac{H}{1+0.02\dfrac{D^2}{t\sqrt{t^2+b^2}}}$
F, total deflection under load P	$F = \dfrac{3.14\,ShD^2}{Gt\sqrt{t^2+b^2}}$ $= \dfrac{H}{1+\dfrac{Gt\sqrt{t^2+b^2}}{3.14\,SD^2}}$ or, for steel springs: $F = 0.02\dfrac{hD^2}{t\sqrt{t^2+b^2}}$ $= \dfrac{H}{1+50.1\dfrac{t\sqrt{t^2+b^2}}{D^2}}$	L, length of bar	$L = \dfrac{3.14\,Dh}{t}$ $= \dfrac{H}{\dfrac{SD}{G\sqrt{t^2+b^2}}+0.32\dfrac{t}{D}}$ or, for steel springs: $L = \dfrac{H}{0.0063\dfrac{D}{\sqrt{t^2+b^2}}+0.32\dfrac{t}{D}}$
F_1, deflection under any load P_1 less than P	$F_1 = \dfrac{9.4\,hD^3P_1}{Gbt^2(t^2+b^2)}$ or, for steel springs: $F_1 = 0.00000075\dfrac{hD^3P_1}{bt^2(t^2+b^2)}$	H, free height	$H = h + \dfrac{3.14\,hSD^2}{Gt\sqrt{t^2+b^2}}$ or, for steel springs: $H = h + 0.02\dfrac{hD^2}{t\sqrt{t^2+b^2}}$
S, maximum fiber stress	$S = \dfrac{3DP}{bt\sqrt{t^2+b^2}}$ $= \dfrac{GFt\sqrt{t^2+b^2}}{3.14\,hD^2}$ or, for steel springs: $S = 4,000,000\dfrac{Ft\sqrt{t^2+b^2}}{hD^2}$	W, weight of spring	$W = 3.14\,bDhw$ $= \dfrac{3\,GwPF}{S^2}$ or, for steel springs: $W = 0.89\,bDh$ $= 0.0017\,PF.$

Conical Coil Springs. — All dimensions in inches, all weights in pounds. **Let:**

F = deflection or extension, under load P;
D_1 = mean diameter of largest coil;
D_2 = mean diameter of smallest coil;
p = average horizontal pitch of coils;
d = diameter of bar or wire from which coil is made;
P = capacity of spring, or weight that will compress the spring solidly;
l = length of bar in spring;
W = weight of spring;
h = solid height of spring, assumed to equal $d \times$ number of coils.

In the following formulas the allowable stress is assumed as 80,000 pounds per square inch, and the modulus of torsional elasticity as 12,600,000.

Extension conical springs:

$$F = 0.00249 \frac{D_1{}^4 - D_2{}^4}{pdD_1} \qquad P = 31,400 \frac{d^3}{D_1}$$

Compression conical springs:

$$F = 0.00332 \frac{D_1{}^3 - D_2{}^3}{pd} \qquad P = 31,400 \frac{d^3}{D_2}$$

For all conical springs:

$$l = 1.571 \frac{h}{d}(D_1 + D_2) \qquad W = 0.35 \, dh \,(D_1 + D_2)$$

If P_x is any load not exceeding P, then the corresponding deflection of a conical extension spring is:

$$F_x = \frac{P_x (D_1{}^4 - D_2{}^4)}{Gpd^4}$$

In a compression spring, the formula for the deflection under any load is the same as that just given for P_x in an extension spring, provided the load P_x is not greater than the capacity of the largest coil. If, in a compression spring, load P_x is greater than the capacity of the largest coil, but less than the capacity P of the whole spring, then some coils will be compressed down solidly, while the remainder will not be fully compressed.

Example: — Compression spring, $D_1 = 4\frac{9}{16}$ inches; $D_2 = 3\frac{9}{16}$ inches; $d = 1\frac{1}{16}$ inch; $h = 7\frac{1}{16}$ inches.

Then number of coils, $N = \dfrac{h}{d} = 6.65$; $\dfrac{D_1 - D_2}{2} = 0.5$; $p = \dfrac{D_1 - D_2}{2 N} = 0.075$.

$$F = 0.00332 \frac{(4\frac{9}{16})^3 - (3\frac{9}{16})^3}{0.075 \times 1\frac{1}{16}} = 2\frac{1}{16} \text{ inches, approximately.}$$

Free height = $7\frac{1}{16} + 2\frac{1}{16} = 9\frac{1}{8}$ inches.

Example: — Same spring in extension.

$$F = 0.00249 \frac{(4\frac{9}{16})^4 - (3\frac{9}{16})^4}{0.075 \times 1\frac{1}{16} \times 4\frac{9}{16}} = 1\frac{7}{8} \text{ inch, approximately.}$$

H (extended height) = $7\frac{1}{16} + 1\frac{7}{8} = 8\frac{15}{16}$ inches.

The free height for the compression type is greater than the possible extended length for the extension type. This is because sufficient load to fully stress the smaller or stronger coils cannot be applied without distorting the extension spring, whereas the coils may all be stressed to maximum stress in the compression type, the closing of the coils solidly together protecting the spring from over-stress.

Formulas for Elliptic Springs

S = fiber stress, assumed as 80,000 pounds per square inch for steel;

E = modulus of elasticity = 25,400,000;

P = maximum carrying capacity of spring;

F = deflection of spring under load P; the deflection under any load less than P is directly proportional to the deflection under full load;

n = number of plates or leaves in half-elliptic spring, or one-half total number of leaves in full-elliptic spring;

b = width of plates; h = thickness of plates; $L = 2l$ = effective span;

r = ratio of number of full length leaves to total number of leaves.

Type of Spring	To be Found	Formulas	Examples
Full-elliptic, with all leaves graduated	P	$P = \dfrac{2\,Snbh^2}{3\,L}$ or, for steel springs: $P = 53,000\,nbh^2 \div L$	Steel spring, number of leaves in one-half of spring = 5; Width of plates = 2 inches; Thickness of plates = $\frac{1}{4}$ inch; Effective span, L = 33 inches. Find safe load. $P = [53,000 \times 5 \times 2 \times (\frac{1}{4})^2] \div 33$ = 1000 pounds, approx.
	F	$F = \dfrac{SL^2}{2\,Eh}$ or, for steel springs: $F = 0.0016\,L^2 \div h$	
Full-elliptic, with portion of leaves graduated	P	$P = \dfrac{2\,Snbh^2}{3\,L}$ or, for steel springs: $P = 53,000\,nbh^2 \div L$	Same spring as above, with two leaves in each half extending full length of span. Find deflection. Here $r = 2 \div 5 = 0.4$. $F = 0.0031\,\dfrac{33^2}{(2 + 0.4)\frac{1}{4}}$ = 5.625 inches.
	F	$F = \dfrac{1}{2+r} \times \dfrac{SL^2}{Eh}$ or, for steel springs: $F = 0.0031\,\dfrac{L^2}{(2+r)\,h}$	
Half-elliptic, with all leaves graduated	P	$P = \dfrac{2\,Snbh^2}{3\,L}$ or, for steel springs: $P = 53,000\,nbh^2 \div L$	Same spring as above, but half-elliptic. Find deflection, if all leaves are fully graduated. $F = (0.00079 \times 33^2) \div \frac{1}{4}$ = 3.44 inches.
	F	$F = \dfrac{SL^2}{4\,Eh}$ or, for steel springs: $F = 0.00079\,L^2 \div h$	
Half-elliptic, with portion of leaves graduated	P	$P = \dfrac{2\,Snbh^2}{3\,L}$ or, for steel springs: $P = 53,000\,nbh^2 \div L$	Same spring as above, half-elliptic, with three leaves extending full length of span. Find deflection. $F = 0.0016\,\dfrac{33^2}{(2 + 0.6)\frac{1}{4}}$ = 2.68 inches.
	F	$F = \dfrac{1}{2\,(2+r)} \times \dfrac{SL^2}{Eh}$ or, for steel springs: $F = 0.0016\,\dfrac{L^2}{(2+r)\,h}$	

Elliptic Spring Tables. — The "Elliptic Spring Tables" give the maximum static load and the deflection under this load when the length or span of the spring, the number of leaves, and the width and thickness of the leaves are known. The maximum static load as given in these tables induces a fiber strain of 80,000 pounds per square inch in the leaves, and the oscillations may increase this to 100,000 pounds. The successive leaves are supposed to be regularly shortened or "graduated" in the full-elliptic spring. In the half-elliptic spring it is assumed that one-quarter of the whole number of leaves extend to the end of the spring and that the remainder are graduated. In the tables:

L = span, or length of spring in inches, not including band.
F = deflection under load P in inches for both half- and full-elliptic springs;
P = maximum static load in pounds;
N = number of leaves in the half-elliptic spring, or number of leaves in one of the halves of a full-elliptic spring;
B = width of leaves in inches.

As an example of the use of the tables, find the maximum load and deflection of a half-elliptic spring having 5 leaves made of ⅜ by 4-inch steel and having a length of 30 inches. By referring to the tables, the deflection is found to equal 1.47 inch under a maximum static load. This load is found as follows: $N \times B = 5 \times 4 = 20$. Then the maximum static load equals 10 times the value found in the column headed "2," or 10 × 500 = 5000 pounds.

The table can also be used for finding the maximum static load and the deflection if all the leaves of the spring extend the full length of the span. The maximum load in this case will be the same as when the leaves are graduated, but the deflection will be less. For full-elliptic springs it will be two-thirds of the amounts given in the column under "F" headed "Full." For half-elliptic springs it will be one-third of the amounts given in the column headed "Full." As an example, find the maximum static load and the deflection of a full-elliptic spring having 7 leaves in each half, 4 inches wide, all extending the full length of the span. The leaves are made of ⅜-inch thick steel and the span is 30 inches. From the table the deflection is found as follows: $3.20 \times \frac{2}{3} = 2.14$ inches. The value of $N \times B = 4 \times 7 = 28$. The maximum load, then, equals:

The value in column "2" × 10 = 5000
The value in column "8" = 2000

Maximum load = 7000 pounds

Elliptic Spring Tables
(For explanation see text above)

L Inches	Thickness of Steel ⅛ Inch										
	F Inches		Values of P for Varying Values of $N \times B$								
	Half	Full	1	2	3	4	5	6	7	8	9
5	0.12	0.27	167.0	334	501	668	835	1002	1169	1336	1503
6	0.18	0.39	139.0	278	417	556	695	834	973	1112	1251
7	0.24	0.52	119.0	238	357	476	595	714	833	952	1071
8	0.31	0.68	104.0	208	312	416	520	624	728	832	936
9	0.40	0.87	92.5	185	278	370	463	555	648	740	833
10	0.49	1.06	83.3	167	250	333	417	500	583	666	750
11	0.59	1.29	75.8	152	227	303	379	455	531	606	682
12	0.70	1.54	69.5	139	209	278	348	417	487	556	626

Elliptic Spring Tables

Thickness of Steel ⅛ Inch (*Continued*)

L Inches	F Inches		Values of P for Varying Values of N×B								
	Half	Full	1	2	3	4	5	6	7	8	9
13	0.83	1.80	64.2	128.0	193	257	321	385	449	514	578
14	0.96	2.10	59.6	119.0	179	238	298	358	417	477	536
15	1.10	2.40	55.6	111.0	167	222	278	334	389	445	500
16	1.25	2.73	52.2	104.0	157	209	261	314	365	418	470
17	1.41	3.08	49.1	98.2	147	196	246	295	344	393	442
18	1.59	3.46	46.4	92.8	139	186	232	278	325	371	418
19	1.77	3.85	43.9	87.8	132	176	220	263	307	351	395
20	1.96	4.26	41.6	83.2	125	166	208	250	291	333	374

Thickness of Steel 3/16 Inch

L Inches	F Inches		Values of P for Varying Values of N×B								
	Half	Full	1	2	3	4	5	6	7	8	9
8	0.21	0.46	234.0	468	702	936	1170	1404	1638	1872	2106
10	0.33	0.71	188.0	376	564	752	940	1128	1316	1504	1692
12	0.44	1.03	156.0	312	468	624	780	936	1092	1248	1404
14	0.64	1.40	134.0	268	402	536	670	804	938	1072	1206
16	0.83	1.82	117.0	234	351	468	585	702	819	936	1053
18	1.06	2.30	108.0	216	324	432	540	658	756	864	972
20	1.30	2.85	93.7	187	281	375	469	562	656	750	843
22	1.58	3.45	85.2	170	256	341	426	511	596	682	767
24	1.87	4.10	78.2	156	235	313	391	469	547	626	704
26	2.20	4.80	72.1	144	216	288	361	433	505	577	649
28	2.55	5.59	67.0	134	201	268	335	402	469	536	603
30	2.93	6.38	62.5	125	188	250	313	375	436	500	563
32	3.33	7.28	58.6	117	176	234	293	352	410	469	527
34	3.77	8.22	55.2	110	166	221	276	331	386	442	497
36	4.22	9.23	52.1	104	156	208	261	313	365	417	469
38	4.70	10.30	49.3	99	148	197	247	296	345	394	444

Thickness of Steel ¼ Inch

L Inches	F Inches		Values of P for Varying Values of N×B								
	Half	Full	1	2	3	4	5	6	7	8	9
12	0.35	0.77	278	556	834	1112	1390	1668	1946	2224	2502
14	0.48	1.04	238	476	714	952	1190	1428	1666	1904	2142
16	0.63	1.36	209	418	627	836	1045	1254	1463	1672	1881
18	0.79	1.72	185	370	555	740	925	1110	1295	1480	1665
20	0.98	2.13	167	334	501	668	835	1002	1169	1336	1503
22	1.19	2.58	152	304	456	608	760	912	1064	1216	1368
24	1.41	3.07	139	278	417	556	695	834	973	1112	1251
26	1.66	3.60	128	256	384	512	640	768	896	1024	1152
28	1.92	4.18	119	238	357	476	595	714	833	952	1071
30	2.20	4.80	111	222	333	444	555	666	777	888	999
32	2.50	5.45	104	208	312	416	520	624	728	832	936
34	2.83	6.15	98	196	294	392	490	588	686	784	882
36	3.18	6.90	93	186	279	372	465	558	651	744	837
38	3.53	7.70	88	176	264	352	440	528	616	704	792
40	3.91	8.51	83	166	249	332	415	498	581	664	747
42	4.32	9.40	79	158	237	316	395	474	553	632	711

Elliptic Spring Tables

Thickness of Steel ⁵⁄₁₆ Inch

L Inches	F Inches Half	F Inches Full	Values of P for Varying Values of N×B 1	2	3	4	5	6	7	8	9
16	0.50	1.09	325	650	975	1300	1625	1950	2275	2600	2925
18	0.63	1.38	290	580	870	1160	1450	1740	2030	2320	2610
20	0.78	1.70	260	520	780	1040	1300	1560	1820	2080	2340
22	0.95	2.07	235	470	705	940	1175	1410	1645	1880	2115
24	1.13	2.45	217	434	651	868	1085	1302	1519	1736	1953
26	1.32	2.88	200	400	600	800	1000	1200	1400	1600	1800
28	1.53	3.35	186	372	558	744	930	1116	1302	1488	1674
30	1.76	3.84	173	346	519	692	865	1038	1211	1384	1657
32	2.00	4.36	163	326	489	652	815	978	1141	1304	1467
34	2.26	4.93	153	306	459	612	765	918	1071	1224	1377
36	2.53	5.52	144	288	432	576	720	864	1008	1152	1296
38	2.82	6.15	137	274	411	548	685	822	959	1096	1233
40	3.13	6.81	130	260	390	520	650	780	910	1040	1170
42	3.45	7.51	124	248	372	496	620	744	868	992	1116
44	3.78	8.25	118	236	354	472	590	708	826	944	1062
46	4.13	9.00	113	226	339	452	565	678	791	904	1017

Thickness of Steel ¹¹⁄₃₂ Inch

L Inches	F Inches Half	F Inches Full	Values of P for Varying Values of N×B 1	2	3	4	5	6	7	8	9
20	0.71	1.55	315	630	945	1260	1575	1890	2205	2520	2835
22	0.86	1.87	286	571	859	1146	1432	1719	2005	2291	2578
24	1.02	2.21	262	524	785	1048	1310	1570	1831	2091	2358
26	1.20	2.62	242	484	725	967	1209	1450	1692	1935	2176
28	1.39	3.03	224	450	675	901	1125	1350	1576	1801	2026
30	1.60	3.49	210	420	630	840	1050	1260	1470	1680	1890
32	1.82	3.98	196	393	589	786	992	1179	1376	1571	1769
34	2.05	4.47	185	369	554	739	924	1109	1295	1478	1621
36	2.30	5.01	174	349	523	698	873	1047	1223	1398	1572
38	2.54	5.59	165	331	495	662	827	993	1158	1323	1489
40	2.84	6.20	156	315	472	630	786	945	1102	1260	1417
42	3.08	6.82	149	296	448	597	748	897	1046	1196	1346
44	3.44	7.48	143	286	429	572	715	859	1002	1145	1288
46	3.75	8.17	137	274	410	547	684	821	958	1095	1232
48	4.10	8.93	131	262	393	524	655	784	917	1048	1179
50	4.45	9.65	126	252	378	504	630	756	884	1008	1134

Thickness of Steel ⅜ Inch

L Inches	F Inches Half	F Inches Full	Values of P for Varying Values of N×B 1	2	3	4	5	6	7	8	9
20	0.65	1.42	375	750	1125	1500	1875	2250	2625	3000	3375
22	0.79	1.72	341	682	1023	1364	1705	2046	2387	2728	3069
24	0.94	2.04	312	624	936	1248	1560	1872	2184	2496	2808
26	1.10	2.40	288	576	864	1152	1440	1728	2016	2304	2592
28	1.28	2.78	268	536	804	1072	1340	1608	1876	2144	2412
30	1.47	3.20	250	500	750	1000	1250	1500	1750	2000	2250
32	1.67	3.63	234	468	702	936	1170	1404	1638	1872	2106
34	1.88	4.10	220	440	660	880	1100	1320	1540	1760	1980

Elliptic Spring Tables

	Thickness of Steel ⅜ Inch (*Continued*)										
L	F Inches		Values of P for Varying Values of N×B								
Inches	Half	Full	1	2	3	4	5	6	7	8	9
36	2.12	4.58	208	416	624	832	1040	1248	1456	1664	1872
38	2.35	5.12	197	394	591	788	985	1182	1379	1576	1773
40	2.60	5.68	187	375	562	750	937	1125	1312	1500	1687
42	2.87	6.26	178	356	534	712	890	1068	1246	1424	1602
44	3.15	6.86	170	341	511	682	852	1023	1193	1364	1534
46	3.45	7.50	163	326	489	652	815	978	1141	1304	1467
48	3.75	8.16	156	312	468	624	780	936	1092	1248	1404
50	4.07	8.87	150	300	450	600	750	900	1050	1200	1350

	Thickness of Steel ⁷⁄₁₆ Inch										
L	F Inches		Values of P for Varying Values of N×B								
Inches	Half	Full	1	2	3	4	5	6	7	8	9
24	0.81	1.76	426	852	1278	1704	2130	2556	2982	3408	3834
26	0.95	2.06	393	786	1179	1572	1965	2358	2751	3144	3537
28	1.10	2.38	365	730	1095	1460	1825	2190	2555	2920	3285
30	1.26	2.74	341	682	1023	1364	1705	2046	2387	2728	3069
32	1.43	3.12	319	638	957	1276	1595	1914	2233	2552	2871
34	1.62	3.52	301	602	903	1204	1505	1806	2107	2408	2709
36	1.81	3.95	284	568	852	1136	1420	1704	1988	2272	2556
38	2.03	4.40	269	538	807	1076	1345	1614	1883	2152	2421
40	2.24	4.88	255	510	765	1020	1275	1530	1785	2040	2295
42	2.47	5.37	243	486	729	972	1215	1458	1701	1944	2187
44	2.71	5.90	232	464	696	928	1160	1392	1624	1856	2088
46	2.96	6.45	222	444	666	888	1110	1332	1554	1776	1998
48	3.22	7.00	213	426	639	852	1065	1278	1491	1704	1917
50	3.49	7.60	204	408	612	816	1020	1224	1428	1632	1836
52	3.78	8.25	197	394	591	788	985	1182	1379	1576	1773
54	4.08	8.90	189	378	567	756	945	1134	1323	1512	1701

	Thickness of Steel ½ Inch										
L	F Inches		Values of P for Varying Values of N×B								
Inches	Half	Full	1	2	3	4	5	6	7	8	9
30	1.10	2.40	444	888	1332	1776	2220	2664	3108	3552	3996
32	1.25	2.72	416	832	1248	1664	2080	2496	2912	3328	3744
34	1.41	3.07	392	784	1176	1568	1960	2352	2744	3136	3528
36	1.58	3.45	372	744	1116	1488	1860	2232	2604	2976	3348
38	1.76	3.84	350	700	1050	1400	1750	2100	2450	2800	3150
40	1.95	4.25	333	666	999	1332	1665	1998	2331	2664	2997
42	2.16	4.68	317	634	951	1268	1585	1902	2219	2536	2853
44	2.37	5.15	303	606	909	1212	1515	1818	2121	2424	2727
46	2.58	5.62	290	580	870	1160	1450	1740	2030	2320	2610
48	2.82	6.13	277	554	831	1108	1385	1662	1939	2216	2493
50	3.06	6.65	266	532	798	1064	1330	1596	1862	2128	2394
52	3.30	7.19	256	512	768	1024	1280	1536	1792	2048	2304
54	3.57	7.75	247	494	741	988	1235	1482	1729	1976	2223
56	3.83	8.35	238	476	714	952	1190	1428	1666	1904	2142
58	4.12	8.95	230	460	690	920	1150	1380	1610	1840	2070
60	4.40	9.58	222	444	666	888	1110	1332	1554	1776	1998

Simplified Elliptic Spring Calculations. — The accompanying "Semi-elliptic Spring Table," which is based on a modulus of elasticity of 25,400,000, and a fiber stress, under maximum load, of 80,000 pounds per square inch, has been prepared to facilitate the calculation of semi- or half-elliptic springs when all the leaves are fully graduated. The safe load on one leaf, one inch wide, is found by dividing the constant given in Column "P_u" by the net length or net span L (see illustration in table on preceding page for method of measuring $L = 2 l$). The corresponding deflection is found by multiplying the constant given in the Column "F_u" by the square of the net length L.

Example: — What is the safe load on a semi- or half-elliptic fully graduated spring of five leaves, if made of ¼- by 2-inch steel; length between end bearings, 36 inches; band or seat, 3 inches?

Net length = 36 − 3 = 33 inches.

$$\text{Load on one leaf, one inch wide} = \frac{3333}{33} = \text{101.01 pounds.}$$

Load on one leaf two inches wide = 2 × 101.01 = 202.02 pounds.
Load on five two-inch leaves = 5 × 202.02 = 1010.1 pounds.
Corresponding deflection is:

$$0.00315 \times (33)^2 = 3.43 \text{ inches.}$$

Semi-Elliptic Spring Table

P_u = safe load for one leaf, 1 inch wide, having a net length of 1 inch. F_u is the corresponding deflection. Table is directly applicable only when all leaves are fully graduated.

Thickness of Leaf	P_u	F_u	Thickness of Leaf	P_u	F_u	Thickness of Leaf	P_u	F_u
¹⁄₃₂	52	0.02519	⅜	7,500	0.00210	²³⁄₃₂	27,550	0.00109
¹⁄₁₆	208	0.01260	¹³⁄₃₂	8,800	0.00194	¾	30,000	0.00105
³⁄₃₂	469	0.00840	⁷⁄₁₆	10,210	0.00180	²⁵⁄₃₂	32,550	0.00101
⅛	833	0.00630	¹⁵⁄₃₂	11,720	0.00168	¹³⁄₁₆	35,210	0.00097
⁵⁄₃₂	1302	0.00504	½	13,330	0.00157	²⁷⁄₃₂	37,960	0.00093
³⁄₁₆	1875	0.00420	¹⁷⁄₃₂	15,050	0.00148	⅞	40,830	0.00090
⁷⁄₃₂	2552	0.00360	⁹⁄₁₆	16,875	0.00140	²⁹⁄₃₂	43,800	0.00087
¼	3333	0.00315	¹⁹⁄₃₂	18,800	0.00133	¹⁵⁄₁₆	46,875	0.00084
⁹⁄₃₂	4218	0.00280	⅝	20,830	0.00126	³¹⁄₃₂	50,050	0.00081
⁵⁄₁₆	5208	0.00252	²¹⁄₃₂	22,970	0.00120	1	53,330	0.00079
¹¹⁄₃₂	6302	0.00229	¹¹⁄₁₆	25,210	0.00115	.....	.....	....

While the table is prepared for semi-elliptic springs with all leaves fully graduated, it can be used for other types of elliptic springs, if the values in the table are multiplied by certain factors.

Semi-elliptic springs with portions of the leaves graduated. — The load P remains the same as for a spring with all leaves graduated. To find the deflection, multiply the values in the table by $\dfrac{2}{2 + r} \times L^2$, where r = the ratio of the number of full length leaves to the total number of leaves.

Full-elliptic springs with all leaves graduated. — P remains the same as for a semi-elliptic spring. To find the deflection, multiply the values in the table by $2 L^2$.

Full-elliptic springs with a portion of the leaves graduated. — The load P remains the same as before, but to find the deflection, the values in the table must be multiplied by $\dfrac{4}{2+r} \times L^2$, in which r is the ratio of the number of full length leaves to the total number of leaves in one-half of the spring.

Example: — Find the load and deflection of a full-elliptic fully graduated spring having four leaves in each half; thickness of leaf = ¼ inch; effective length L = 30 inches; width of leaves, 1¾ inch. Then maximum safe load equals:

$$P = 4 \times 1\tfrac{3}{4} \times \frac{3333}{30} = 778 \text{ pounds.}$$

The deflection equals:

$$F = 2 \times 30^2 \times 0.00315 = 5.67 \text{ inches.}$$

Example: — Find the thickness and number of leaves to be used in a fully graduated full-elliptic spring which has to support 780 pounds with a deflection not exceeding 5¾ inches; the effective length L of the spring is 30 inches and the width, 1¾ inch.

The deflection equals $2 L^2 \times$ the constant F_u in the table; hence, $F = 2 F_u L^2$ or:

$$F_u = F \div 2 L^2 = 5.75 \div 1800 = 0.0032 \text{ inch.}$$

The thickness of steel which corresponds to this value F_u is ¼ inch. To find the load on one leaf, 1 inch wide, the value P_u in the table is divided by the net length of the spring. Hence, load equals 3333 ÷ 30 = 111 pounds. The load on one leaf, 1¾ inch wide, is then 111 × 1.75 = 194.25 pounds. The number of leaves required is, then, equal to the total load divided by the load on one leaf, or the required number equals 780 ÷ 194.25 = 4 leaves.

The formulas given for the calculation of elliptic springs make no allowance for variation in the thickness of different leaves in a spring. When such springs are used, the deflection of the different leaves will not be uniform, and such springs must be calculated by a general formula based upon a combination of different cantilevers, thus making allowance for the different depths of the leaves. There is nothing to be gained, however, by using leaves of different thicknesses, and springs composed of leaves of but one thickness can be designed to meet all requirements.

Results obtained from fully graduated full-elliptic springs indicate that the friction between the leaves is not great enough to seriously affect the bending action. The formulas on the preceding pages give results that agree very closely with actual conditions as determined by experiments.

Tables of Powers of Numbers for Spring Calculations. —
The third, fourth and fifth powers of numbers frequently are met with in spring calculations. Tables of cubes, fourth powers and fifth powers of fractional sizes, such as are likely to be used for springs, are, therefore, given in the following pages.

Fifth Powers of Numbers

Number	Fifth Power	Number	Fifth Power	Number	Fifth Power	Number	Fifth Power
1/16	0.0000010	9/16	0.056313	1 1/16	1.35408	1 9/16	9.3132
1/8	0.0000305	5/8	0.095367	1 1/8	1.80203	1 5/8	11.3310
3/16	0.0002317	11/16	0.153590	1 3/16	2.36139	1 11/16	13.6842
1/4	0.0009765	3/4	0.237305	1 1/4	3.05176	1 3/4	16.4131
5/16	0.0029802	13/16	0.354093	1 5/16	3.89490	1 13/16	19.5610
3/8	0.0074157	7/8	0.512909	1 3/8	4.91489	1 7/8	23.1743
7/16	0.0160284	15/16	0.724196	1 7/16	6.13818	1 15/16	27.3029
1/2	0.0312500	1	1.000000	1 1/2	7.59375	2	32.0000

Cubes of Fractional Numbers

Number	Cube	Number	Cube	Number	Cube	Number	Cube
1/16	0.00024	3 1/16	28.7229	6 1/16	222.8205	9 1/16	744.293
1/8	0.00195	3 1/8	30.5175	6 1/8	229.7832	9 1/8	759.798
3/16	0.00659	3 3/16	32.3854	6 3/16	236.8894	9 3/16	775.518
1/4	0.01562	3 1/4	34.3281	6 1/4	244.1406	9 1/4	791.453
5/16	0.03051	3 5/16	36.3469	6 5/16	251.5383	9 5/16	807.604
3/8	0.05273	3 3/8	38.4433	6 3/8	259.0839	9 3/8	823.974
7/16	0.08374	3 7/16	40.6188	6 7/16	266.7790	9 7/16	840.564
1/2	0.12500	3 1/2	42.8750	6 1/2	274.6250	9 1/2	857.375
9/16	0.17797	3 9/16	45.2131	6 9/16	282.6232	9 9/16	874.408
5/8	0.24414	3 5/8	47.6347	6 5/8	290.7753	9 5/8	891.666
11/16	0.32495	3 11/16	50.1413	6 11/16	299.0827	9 11/16	909.149
3/4	0.42187	3 3/4	52.7343	6 3/4	307.5468	9 3/4	926.859
13/16	0.53637	3 13/16	55.4152	6 13/16	316.1691	9 13/16	944.798
7/8	0.66992	3 7/8	58.1855	6 7/8	324.9511	9 7/8	962.966
15/16	0.82397	3 15/16	61.0466	6 15/16	333.8942	9 15/16	981.366
1	1.00000	4	64.0000	7	343.0000	10	1000.000
1 1/16	1.19946	4 1/16	67.0471	7 1/16	352.2697	10 1/16	1018.867
1 1/8	1.42382	4 1/8	70.1894	7 1/8	361.7050	10 1/8	1037.970
1 3/16	1.67456	4 3/16	73.4284	7 3/16	371.3073	10 3/16	1057.311
1 1/4	1.95312	4 1/4	76.7656	7 1/4	381.0781	10 1/4	1076.890
1 5/16	2.26098	4 5/16	80.2023	7 5/16	391.0187	10 5/16	1096.710
1 3/8	2.59960	4 3/8	83.7402	7 3/8	401.1308	10 3/8	1116.771
1 7/16	2.97045	4 7/16	87.3806	7 7/16	411.4157	10 7/16	1137.075
1 1/2	3.37500	4 1/2	91.1250	7 1/2	421.8750	10 1/2	1157.625
1 9/16	3.81469	4 9/16	94.9748	7 9/16	432.5100	10 9/16	1178.201
1 5/8	4.29101	4 5/8	98.9316	7 5/8	443.3222	10 5/8	1199.462
1 11/16	4.80542	4 11/16	102.9968	7 11/16	454.3132	10 11/16	1220.754
1 3/4	5.35937	4 3/4	107.1718	7 3/4	465.4843	10 3/4	1242.306
1 13/16	5.95434	4 13/16	111.4582	7 13/16	476.8371	10 13/16	1264.091
1 7/8	6.59179	4 7/8	115.8574	7 7/8	488.3730	10 7/8	1286.138
1 15/16	7.27319	4 15/16	120.3708	7 15/16	500.0935	10 15/16	1308.436
2	8.00000	5	125.0000	8	512.0000	11	1331.000
2 1/16	8.77368	5 1/16	129.7463	8 1/16	524.0939	11 1/16	1353.816
2 1/8	9.59570	5 1/8	134.6113	8 1/8	536.3769	11 1/8	1376.892
2 3/16	10.46752	5 3/16	139.5964	8 3/16	548.8503	11 3/16	1400.229
2 1/4	11.39062	5 1/4	144.7031	8 1/4	561.5156	11 1/4	1423.828
2 5/16	12.36645	5 5/16	149.9328	8 5/16	574.3742	11 5/16	1447.690
2 3/8	13.39648	5 3/8	155.2871	8 3/8	587.4277	11 3/8	1471.818
2 7/16	14.48217	5 7/16	160.7673	8 7/16	600.6774	11 7/16	1496.212
2 1/2	15.62500	5 1/2	166.3750	8 1/2	614.1250	11 1/2	1520.875
2 9/16	16.82641	5 9/16	172.1115	8 9/16	627.7717	11 9/16	1545.806
2 5/8	18.08789	5 5/8	177.9785	8 5/8	641.6191	11 5/8	1571.009
2 11/16	19.41088	5 11/16	183.9772	8 11/16	655.6687	11 11/16	1596.485
2 3/4	20.79687	5 3/4	190.1093	8 3/4	669.9218	11 3/4	1622.234
2 13/16	22.24731	5 13/16	196.3762	8 13/16	684.3801	11 13/16	1648.259
2 7/8	23.76367	5 7/8	202.7792	8 7/8	699.0449	11 7/8	1674.560
2 15/16	25.34741	5 15/16	209.3200	8 15/16	713.9177	11 15/16	1701.140
3	27.00000	6	216.0000	9	729.0000	12	1728.000

Fourth Powers of Fractional Numbers

Number	Fourth Power	Number	Fourth Power	Number	Fourth Power	Number	Fourth Power
1/16	0.000015	3 1/16	87.9853	6 1/16	1350.849	9 1/16	6745.15
1/8	0.000244	3 1/8	95.3674	6 1/8	1407.422	9 1/8	6933.16
3/16	0.001236	3 3/16	103.2287	6 3/16	1465.753	9 3/16	7125.07
1/4	0.003906	3 1/4	111.5664	6 1/4	1525.878	9 1/4	7320.94
5/16	0.009537	3 5/16	120.3991	6 5/16	1587.835	9 5/16	7520.81
3/8	0.019776	3 3/8	129.7463	6 3/8	1651.660	9 3/8	7724.76
7/16	0.036636	3 7/16	139.6274	6 7/16	1717.390	9 7/16	7932.82
1/2	0.062500	3 1/2	150.0625	6 1/2	1785.062	9 1/2	8145.06
9/16	0.100113	3 9/16	161.0717	6 9/16	1854.715	9 9/16	8361.53
5/8	0.152588	3 5/8	172.6760	6 5/8	1926.386	9 5/8	8582.28
11/16	0.223404	3 11/16	184.8962	6 11/16	2000.115	9 11/16	8807.38
3/4	0.316406	3 3/4	197.7539	6 3/4	2075.941	9 3/4	9036.87
13/16	0.435806	3 13/16	211.2707	6 13/16	2153.902	9 13/16	9270.83
7/8	0.586182	3 7/8	225.4689	6 7/8	2234.039	9 7/8	9509.29
15/16	0.772477	3 15/16	240.3711	6 15/16	2316.391	9 15/16	9752.33
1	1.000000	4	256.0000	7	2401.000	10	10000.00
1 1/16	1.274429	4 1/16	272.3789	7 1/16	2487.905	10 1/16	10252.35
1 1/8	1.601806	4 1/8	289.5314	7 1/8	2577.148	10 1/8	10509.45
1 3/16	1.988541	4 3/16	307.4817	7 3/16	2668.771	10 3/16	10771.35
1 1/4	2.441406	4 1/4	326.2539	7 1/4	2762.816	10 1/4	11038.12
1 5/16	2.967544	4 5/16	345.8728	7 5/16	2859.324	10 5/16	11309.82
1 3/8	3.574462	4 3/8	366.3635	7 3/8	2958.340	10 3/8	11586.50
1 7/16	4.270035	4 7/16	387.7514	7 7/16	3059.904	10 7/16	11868.22
1 1/2	5.062500	4 1/2	410.0625	7 1/2	3164.062	10 1/2	12155.06
1 9/16	5.960464	4 9/16	433.3227	7 9/16	3270.856	10 9/16	12444.75
1 5/8	6.972901	4 5/8	457.5588	7 5/8	3380.332	10 5/8	12744.29
1 11/16	8.109146	4 11/16	482.7976	7 11/16	3492.532	10 11/16	13046.81
1 3/4	9.378906	4 3/4	509.0664	7 3/4	3607.503	10 3/4	13355.79
1 13/16	10.792252	4 13/16	536.3928	7 13/16	3725.290	10 13/16	13667.98
1 7/8	12.359618	4 7/8	564.8049	7 7/8	3845.937	10 7/8	13986.75
1 15/16	14.091811	4 15/16	594.3310	7 15/16	3969.492	10 15/16	14311.02
2	16.000000	5	625.0000	8	4096.000	11	14641.00
2 1/16	18.095719	5 1/16	656.8408	8 1/16	4225.507	11 1/16	14976.59
2 1/8	20.390869	5 1/8	689.8830	8 1/8	4358.062	11 1/8	15317.93
2 3/16	22.897720	5 3/16	724.1565	8 3/16	4493.712	11 3/16	15665.06
2 1/4	25.628906	5 1/4	759.6914	8 1/4	4632.503	11 1/4	16018.06
2 5/16	28.597427	5 5/16	796.5183	8 5/16	4774.486	11 5/16	16377.00
2 3/8	31.816650	5 3/8	834.6682	8 3/8	4919.707	11 3/8	16741.93
2 7/16	35.300309	5 7/16	874.1723	8 7/16	5068.216	11 7/16	17112.93
2 1/2	39.062500	5 1/2	915.0625	8 1/2	5220.062	11 1/2	17490.06
2 9/16	43.117691	5 9/16	957.3706	8 9/16	5375.295	11 9/16	17873.39
2 5/8	47.480714	5 5/8	1001.1291	8 5/8	5533.965	11 5/8	18262.98
2 11/16	52.166764	5 11/16	1046.3708	8 11/16	5696.122	11 11/16	18658.91
2 3/4	57.191406	5 3/4	1093.1289	8 3/4	5861.816	11 3/4	19061.25
2 13/16	62.570571	5 13/16	1141.4367	8 13/16	6031.099	11 13/16	19470.05
2 7/8	68.320557	5 7/8	1191.3283	8 7/8	6204.023	11 7/8	19885.40
2 15/16	74.458023	5 15/16	1242.8379	8 15/16	6380.639	11 15/16	20307.36
3	81.000000	6	1296.0000	9	6561.000	12	20736.00

Squares, Cubes and Fourth Powers of Wire Diameters

American Steel & Wire Co.'s		Diameter	Section Area	Square	Cube	Fourth Power
Steel Wire Gage	Music Wire Gage	inches				
7-0	..	0.4900	0.1886	0.24010	0.11765	0.05765
6-0	..	0.4615	0.1673	0.21298	0.09829	0.04536
5-0	..	0.4300	0.1452	0.18490	0.07951	0.03419
4-0	..	0.3938	0.1218	0.15507	0.06107	0.02405
3-0	..	0.3625	0.1032	0.13141	0.04764	0.01727
2-0	..	0.331	0.0861	0.10956	0.03626	0.01201
1-0	..	0.3065	0.0738	0.09394	0.02879	0.008825
1	..	0.283	0.0629	0.08009	0.02267	0.006414
2	..	0.2625	0.0541	0.06891	0.01809	0.004748
3	..	0.2437	0.0466	0.05939	0.01482	0.003527
4	..	0.225	0.0398	0.05063	0.01139	0.002563
5	..	0.207	0.0337	0.04285	0.00887	0.001836
6	..	0.192	0.02895	0.03686	0.00708	0.001356
7	..	0.177	0.0246	0.03133	0.00555	0.000982
8	..	0.162	0.0206	0.02624	0.00425	0.000689
9	..	0.1483	0.0173	0.02199	0.00326	0.000484
10	..	0.135	0.0143	0.01823	0.00246	0.000332
11	..	0.1205	0.0114	0.01452	0.00175	0.000211
12	..	0.1055	0.0087	0.01113	0.001174	0.0001244
..	33	0.095	0.0071	0.00903	0.000857	0.0000811
13	..	0.0915	0.0066	0.00837	0.000766	0.00007c1
..	32	0.090	0.0063	0.0081	0.000729	0.0000656
..	31	0.085	0.0057	0.00723	0.000614	0.0000522
14	30	0.080	0.0050	0.0064	0.000512	0.0000410
..	29	0.075	0.0044	0.00563	0.000422	0.0000316
15	..	0.072	0.0041	0.00518	0.000373	0.0000269
..	28	0.071	0.0040	0.00504	0.000358	0.0000254
..	27	0.067	0.0036	0.00449	0.000301	0.0000202
..	26	0.063	0.0032	0.00397	0.000250	0.0000158
16	..	0.0625	0.0031	0.00391	0.000244	0.0000153
..	25	0.059	0.0027	0.00348	0.000205	0.0000121
..	24	0.055	0.0023	0.00302	0.000166	0.00000915
17	..	0.053	0.0022	0.00281	0.000149	0.00000789
..	23	0.051	0.0020	0.00260	0.000133	0.00000677
..	22	0.049	0.00188	0.00240	0.000118	0.00000577
18	..	0.0475	0.0018	0.00226	0.000107	0.00000509
..	21	0.047	0.00173	0.00221	0.000104	0.00000488
..	20	0.045	0.00159	0.00203	0.000091	0.00000410
..	19	0.043	0.00145	0.00185	0.0000795	0.00000342
19	18	0.041	0.00132	0.00168	0.0000689	0.00000283
..	17	0.039	0.00119	0.00152	0.0000593	0.00000231
..	16	0.037	0.00107	0.00137	0.0000507	0.00000188
..	15	0.035	0.00096	0.00123	0.0000429	0.00000150
20	..	0.0348	0.00095	0.00121	0.0000421	0.00000147
..	14	0.033	0.00085	0.00109	0.0000359	0.00000119
21	..	0.03175	0.00079	0.00101	0.0000320	0.00000102
..	13	0.031	0.00075	0.00096	0.0000298	0.000000924
..	12	0.029	0.00066	0.00084	0.0000244	0.000000707
22	..	0.0286	0.00064	0.00082	0.0000231	0.000000669
..	11	0.026	0.00053	0.00068	0.0000176	0.000000457
23	..	0.0258	0.00052	0.00067	0.0000172	0.000000443
..	10	0.024	0.00045	0.00058	0.0000138	0.000000332
24	..	0.023	0.00042	0.00053	0.0000122	0.000000280
..	9	0.022	0.00038	0.00048	0.0000106	0.000000234
25	..	0.0204	0.00033	0.00042	0.00000849	0.000000173
..	8	0.020	0.00031	0.0004	0.000008	0.00000016
26	..	0.0181	0.00026	0.000328	0.00000593	0.000000107
..	7	0.018	0.00025	0.000324	0.00000583	0.000000105
27	..	0.0173	0.000235	0.000299	0.00000518	0.0000000896
28	..	0.0162	0.000206	0.000262	0.00000425	0.0000000689
..	6	0.0160	0.0002	0.000256	0.00000410	0.0000000655
29	..	0.015	0.00017	0.000225	0.00000338	0.0000000506
30	5	0.014	0.00015	0.000196	0.00000274	0.0000000384
..	4	0.013	0.00013	0.000169	0.00000220	0.0000000286
..	3	0.012	0.00011	0.000144	0.00000173	0.0000000207

Modulus of Elasticity for Springs. — The torsional modulus of elasticity varies between 10,000,000 and 12,000,000 for steel, depending upon the composition and also whether the material was produced by drawing, cold-rolling, or hot-rolling. If the torsional modulus for a given material is not known, the following figures, obtained from a number of large spring manufacturers, may be used as a general guide.

Carbon steel 0.70 per cent, 10,000,000; hot-rolled bars ½ inch and larger, 10,500,000; 0.90 per cent carbon steel hot-rolled, 10,500,000; 0.90 per cent carbon steel cold-rolled, 11,000,000; oil-tempered steel, 11,500,000; hard-drawn steel, 11,500,000; soft cold-drawn alloy steel, 11,500,000; hard-drawn wire, such as "music wire," 12,000,000. (Note: One experienced user of music wire in wire diameters up to 0.100 inch, claims that a modulus of 10,500,000 gives calculated results that agree closely with actual tests as applied to very small springs. Much depends, however, upon the physical properties imparted to a particular lot of wire by the drawing process.) For brass and phosphor-bronze spring wire the range ordinarily is from 6,000,000 to 8,000,000; for monel metal, 9,000,000. The torsional modulus for a given material may be determined by inserting in the formula for *G* values for maximum load and deflection determined from actual tests.

Materials Used for Springs. — Different grades and types of steels and non-ferrous alloys are used for springs because of the different requirements, such as resistance to fatigue, corrosion, temperature, etc. While physical properties of different types of spring materials vary widely, there may also be decided variations in the same nominal grade or kind of material obtained from different sources. The information which follows is intended as a general guide only.

Hard Drawn Spring Wire. — This is a steel wire that is generally used for miscellaneous helical springs. It contains 0.50 to 0.65 carbon, 0.70 to 1.00 manganese, 0.10 to 0.20 silicon. In making this wire, hot-rolled open-hearth steel rods are annealed and then cold drawn, thus giving the wire its strength. The tensile strength for small diameters may vary from 200,000 to 300,000, and the elastic limit from 120,000 to 180,000 pounds per square inch.

Oil-Tempered Spring Wire. — This steel wire is drawn to size from basic, open hearth rods after annealing. The composition is similar to hard drawn wire, excepting the carbon content which varies from 0.60 to 0.70 per cent. The strength is obtained by heat-treatment rather than by cold working.

Music Wire. — This is a high-grade spring wire produced either in the electric furnace or by the acid open-hearth process, and it is extensively used for small springs subjected to high stresses. Music-wire gages range from 0.004 to 0.146 inch. The carbon content of music wire varies from 0.70 to 1.00, and manganese from 0.25 to 0.40 per cent. When the diameter is approximately 0.100 inch, the tensile strength is about 250,000 pounds per square inch. Music wire is more expensive than ordinary hard-drawn wire, but it can be subjected to higher stresses.

High-Carbon Annealed Wire. — This type of wire is used extensively for valve springs and scale springs. It contains from 0.85 to 1.00 carbon, 0.30 to 0.45 manganese, and from 0.10 to 0.20 silicon. It is cold drawn from annealed rods made either by the electric or open-hearth processes. The springs are heat-treated after forming. The tensile strength, after heat-treatment, varies from 250,000 to 350,000, and the elastic limit from 150,000 to 250,000 pounds per square inch, depending upon the diameter.

High-Carbon Hot-Rolled Steel. — This steel, which has a carbon content ranging from 0.90 to 1.05 per cent, is made either by the electric or open-hearth processes and is formed into springs while hot. This material is used for springs that are too large to coil cold and also for large leaf springs. Tensile strength varies from 175,000 to 195,000, and elastic limit from 120,000 to 140,000 pounds per square inch.

Silicon-Manganese Steel. — This steel is especially adapted to springs subjected to fatigue stresses. The ultimate strength ordinarily ranges from 200,000 to 250,000, and the elastic limit from 150,000 to 180,000 pounds per square inch. In the automotive industries, silicon-manganese steels are very generally used both for the coil and leaf springs. The S.A.E. silicon-manganese steel No. 9260 contains 0.55–0.65 carbon, 0.60–0.90 manganese, 1.80–2.20 silicon, 0.040 phosphorus (max.), and 0.050 sulphur (max). It is a general practice to specify manganese on the high side of the range for leaf spring sections of ⅜ inch or over and the low or medium manganese content for sections under ⅜ inch. Silicon-manganese steel S.A.E. No. 9255 is like 9260, excepting the carbon range which is 0.50–0.60 per cent. The hardening temperature for these steels is 1500 to 1650 degrees F., and oil is the quenching medium.

Chromium-Vanadium Steel. — This spring steel is superior to the straight carbon steel in toughness and when the operating temperature is too high for carbon steel. It contains from 0.45 to 0.55 carbon, 0.50 to 0.80 manganese, 0.90 to 1.20 chromium, 0.10 to 0.20 silicon, 0.15 to 0.20 vanadium. This steel is supplied either in the tempered or annealed condition. It is adapted to valve springs or wherever there are repeated stresses. The tensile strength varies from 200,000 to 300,000, and the elastic limit from 160,000 to 250,000 pounds per square inch.

Stainless Steel. — This steel not only has high resistance to corrosion, but retains its strength in temperatures up to 700 degrees F., or even higher. For hard-drawn wire, the carbon content is 0.12, with chromium ranging from 17 to 20 and nickel 8 to 10 per cent. If supplied in the annealed condition for heat-treatment after coiling, the carbon content may vary from 0.30 to 0.40 per cent. The ultimate strength ranges from 150,000 to 280,000, and the elastic limit from 75,000 to 150,000 pounds per square inch.

Phosphor Bronze. — This wire may be used where steel would corrode rapidly. It usually contains about 5 per cent tin, a trace of phosphorus (added as phosphor-tin to prevent brittleness), and the remainder copper. The tensile strength obtained by cold drawing is about 95,000 pounds per square inch and the elastic limit about 50,000 pounds per square inch for wire of No. 8 B & S gage.

S.A.E. No. 80 Brass Wire. — This cold-drawn wire is inferior in strength and corrosion resistance to phosphor bronze, but it may be used where cost of material is an important factor. Grade A, intended for severe operating conditions, contains 70 to 74 per cent copper, a maximum of 0.10 lead, a maximum of 0.06 iron, and the remainder zinc. Grade B, for ordinary requirements, has practically the same composition excepting the copper content which is 64 to 68 per cent.

Monel Metal. — This alloy has excellent corrosion-resistant properties and will withstand abnormally high temperatures. Cold-drawn wire (spring temper) has a tensile strength of 145,000 to 175,000 pounds per square inch for " K " Monel. It contains 66 per cent nickel, 29 per cent copper, 2.75 per cent aluminum, 0.9 per cent iron, 0.4 per cent manganese, and 0.25 per cent silicon.

Inconel. — This is another high-nickel alloy which is exceptionally resistant to high temperatures and corrosion. The nickel content is 79.5; chromium, 13; iron, 6.5; copper, 0.2; silicon, 0.25; manganese, 0.25. The tensile strength of cold-drawn spring wire is 165,000 to 185,000 pounds per square inch.

Beryllium-Copper Wire. — This alloy contains 2 to 2.25 per cent beryllium; 0.25 to 0.50 per cent nickel; usually less than 0.1 per cent iron; and the remainder copper. It has high resistance to fatigue and corrosion, and also high coefficient of electrical conductivity. The wire is cold drawn, and a low-temperature heat-treatment gives it a tensile strength of about 200,000 pounds per square inch.

Spring Winding or Coiling. — The methods and tools used for winding or coiling springs vary greatly in form and also in regard to productive capacity. The

method employed ordinarily depends upon the number of springs required and, to some extent, upon their form. When a comparatively small number of springs are needed in connection with repair work, etc., it is common practice to wind them in a lathe, whereas, when springs are manufactured in large quantities, special machines are employed.

Springs are often made with an "initial tension," which causes the coils to be drawn tightly together This result is secured by twisting the wire, a common example of a spring of this type being the ordinary screen-door spring. Such springs will not begin to deflect as soon as the load is applied, it being necessary to first overcome the initial tension already in the spring. With springs of this type it is possible to load to the maximum capacity without obtaining a corresponding deflection of the spring.

Tables for Spring Winding. — When springs are to be wound by using a lathe instead of a spring-coiling machine, the lathe is geared in the same manner as for screw cutting. The table "Gearing Lathe for Winding Wire Coil Springs" is given to indicate what gearing should be used. The figures in the body of the table give the number of threads per inch for which the lathe should be geared to wind coil springs of a given number of wire gage. The figures in the columns headed "A" are for close-wound tension springs, while the figures in the columns headed "B" are for compression springs. Assume, as an example, that it is required to wind a compression spring of No. 10 Brown & Sharpe gage wire. From the table, it will be seen that this spring should have four and one-half coils per inch, or in other words, that the lathe should be geared the same as for cutting four and one-half threads per inch.

The use of the table "Data for Winding Piano Wire Tension Springs" may be best explained by an example. Assume that it is required to wind three different springs: the first to be wound from 0.035-inch wire to fit in an 1 1/16-inch hole, the second to be wound from 0.040-inch wire to fit in a 3/8-inch hole, and the third to be wound from 0.060-inch wire and to be a sliding fit on a 1/2-inch shaft. The tables show the proper sizes of mandrels for winding to be as follows: For the first spring, 0.562 inch; for the second spring, 0.250 inch; and for the third spring, 0.437 inch. In the latter case, 0.011 inch is allowed for play between spring and shaft. The wire sizes given in the table conform to the English music wire gage.

In all cases when the mandrel diameter is larger than 3/8 inch, the mandrel is mounted in a lathe chuck. Mandrels less than 3/8 inch in diameter are mounted in a drill chuck. In fastening the wire in a lathe chuck, one jaw is usually loosened, and when the mandrel is driven by a drill chuck, the wire is placed between the jaws and the mandrel. If a long spring is required, a mandrel of corresponding length is used, which is ground to an angle of 60 degrees at the end to fit into a female dead center for support. The wire is placed in a bench lathe boring-tool holder or a V-holder in the toolpost. A piece of brass, about 1/8 by 1/2 by 3 inches, is placed between the wire and the toolpost screw. A V-shaped groove is filed in this brass to hold the wire in place. The groove is filed in the lengthwise direction of the brass plate and is made of the proper depth for the size of wire from which the springs are being wound. This clamping arrangement is tightened up with the toolpost wrench, just enough tension being put on the wrench to keep the wire from slipping.

Strength of Brass Wire. — The ultimate tensile strength of brass wire varies widely for different compositions and the strength per square inch increases as the diameter decreases. In general, the ultimate tensile strength of hard-drawn brass wire ranges from about 45,000 to 100,000 pounds per square inch, with higher values for some brass or bronze wires of special composition. Brass wire usually contains from 63 to 67 per cent of copper and from 33 to 37 per cent of zinc. The tensile strength increases with the zinc content within certain limits.

Gearing Lathe for Winding Wire Coil Springs. (See page 498.)

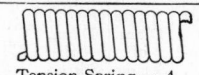
Tension Spring — A

Compression Spring — B

Number of Wire Gage	Brown & Sharpe		Birmingham or Stub's		Washburn & Moen Mfg. Co.		Trenton Iron Co.		Prentiss		Old English Brass Manufacturers'	
	A	B	A	B	A	B	A	B	A	B	A	B
000000	..	...	...	...	2	1	...	...	...	...	...	...
00000	..	...	...	1	2¼	1⅛	2	1	...	...	...	...
0000	2	1	2	1	2½	1¼	2½	1¼	...	...	...	...
000	2¼	1⅛	2¼	1⅛	2¾	1⅜	2¾	1⅜	2¾	1⅜	...	...
00	2¾	1⅜	2½	1¼	3	1½	3	1½	3	1½	...	...
0	3	1½	2⅞	1 7/16	3¼	1⅝	3	1½	3¼	1⅝	...	...
1	3¼	1⅝	3¼	1⅝	3½	1¾	3½	1¾	3¼	1⅝	...	...
2	3½	1¾	3½	1¾	3½	1¾	3½	1¾	3½	1¾	...	...
3	4	2	3½	1¾	4	2	4	2	4	2	...	...
4	4½	2¼	4	2	4	2	4	2	4	2	...	...
5	5½	2¾	4½	2¼	4½	2¼	4½	2¼	4½	2¼	...	...
6	6	3	4½	2¼	5	2½	5	2½	5	2½	...	...
7	6½	3¼	5½	2¾	5½	2¾	5½	2¾	5½	2¾	...	...
8	7	3½	6	3	6	3	6	3	6	3	...	...
9	8	4	6½	3¼	6½	3¼	6½	3¼	6½	3¼	...	...
10	9	4½	7	3½	7	3½	7	3½	7	3½	...	...
11	11	5½	8	4	8	4	8	4	8	4	...	...
12	12	6	9	4½	9	4½	9	4½	9	4½	...	...
13	14	7	10	5	10	5	10	5	10	5	...	...
14	14	7	12	6	12	6	12	6	12	6	12	6
15	16	8	13	6½	13	6½	14	7	13	6½	13	6½
16	18	9	14	7	14	7	16	8	14	7	14	7
17	22	11	16	8	16	8	18	9	16	8	16	8
18	24	12	20	10	20	10	22	11	20	10	20	10
19	28	14	23	11½	23	11½	24	12	23	11½	24	12
20	28	14	28	14	28	14	28	14	28	14	28	14
21	32	16	28	14	28	14	32	16	28	14	28	14
22	36	18	32	16	32	16	32	16	32	16	32	16
23	44	22	40	20	40	20	40	20	36	18	36	18
24	48	24	44	22	40	20	44	22	40	20	40	20
25	56	28	48	24	48	24	48	24	46	23	40	20
26	56	28	52	26	52	26	52	26	48	24	48	24
27	64	32	56	28	56	28	56	28	52	26	52	26
28	72	36	64	32	56	28	56	28	56	28	56	28
29	88	44	72	36	64	32	64	32	56	28	64	32
30	96	48	80	40	64	32	64	32	64	32	72	36
31	112	56	96	48	72	36	72	36	64	32	80	40
32	..	...	104	52	72	36	80	40	72	36	88	44
33	..	...	112	56	88	44	88	44	72	36	92	46
34	..	...	...	...	96	48	96	48	80	40	104	52
35	..	...	...	...	104	52	104	52	88	44	104	52

Data for Winding Piano Wire Tension Springs. (See page 498.)

Diam. of Mandrel, Inches	Inside Diam. of Spring, Inches	Outside Diam. of Spring, Inches	Number of Piano Wire	Diam. of Piano Wire, Inches	Diam. of Mandrel, Inches	Inside Diam. of Spring, Inches	Outside Diam. of Spring, Inches	Number of Piano Wire	Diam. of Piano Wire, Inches
0.125	0.130	0.150	1	0.0098	0.187	0.209	0.258	10	0.0245
0.187	0.192	0.212	1	0.0098	0.250	0.272	0.321	10	0.0245
0.250	0.255	0.275	1	0.0098	0.312	0.336	0.385	10	0.0245
0.312	0.318	0.338	1	0.0098	0.375	0.401	0.450	10	0.0245
0.375	0.382	0.402	1	0.0098	0.437	0.465	0.514	10	0.0245
0.125	0.130	0.151	2	0.0105	0.500	0.533	0.582	10	0.0245
0.187	0.192	0.213	2	0.0105	0.562	0.600	0.649	10	0.0245
0.250	0.255	0.276	2	0.0105	0.625	0.665	0.714	10	0.0245
0.312	0.318	0.339	2	0.0105	0.187	0.212	0.266	11	0.0270
0.375	0.382	0.403	2	0.0105	0.250	0.277	0.331	11	0.0270
0.125	0.130	0.152	3	0.0115	0.312	0.340	0.394	11	0.0270
0.187	0.193	0.215	3	0.0115	0.375	0.406	0.460	11	0.0270
0.250	0.256	0.278	3	0.0115	0.437	0.470	0.524	11	0.0270
0.312	0.320	0.342	3	0.0115	0.500	0.535	0.589	11	0.0270
0.375	0.382	0.404	3	0.0115	0.562	0.600	0.654	11	0.0270
0.125	0.135	0.160	4	0.0125	0.625	0.665	0.719	11	0.0270
0.187	0.197	0.222	4	0.0125	0.187	0.212	0.269	12	0.0285
0.250	0.260	0.285	4	0.0125	0.250	0.279	0.336	12	0.0285
0.312	0.322	0.347	4	0.0125	0.312	0.342	0.399	12	0.0285
0.375	0.385	0.410	4	0.0125	0.375	0.408	0.465	12	0.0285
0.125	0.135	0.164	5	0.0145	0.437	0.472	0.529	12	0.0285
0.187	0.198	0.227	5	0.0145	0.500	0.537	0.594	12	0.0285
0.250	0.261	0.290	5	0.0145	0.562	0.602	0.659	12	0.0285
0.312	0.324	0.353	5	0.0145	0.625	0.667	0.724	12	0.0285
0.375	0.389	0.418	5	0.0145	0.187	0.217	0.278	13	0.0305
0.125	0.135	0.165	6	0.0150	0.250	0.282	0.343	13	0.0305
0.187	0.198	0.228	6	0.0150	0.312	0.346	0.407	13	0.0305
0.250	0.262	0.292	6	0.0150	0.375	0.411	0.472	13	0.0305
0.312	0.325	0.355	6	0.0150	0.437	0.475	0.536	13	0.0305
0.375	0.390	0.420	6	0.0150	0.500	0.540	0.601	13	0.0305
0.125	0.137	0.172	7	0.0175	0.562	0.604	0.665	13	0.0305
0.187	0.201	0.236	7	0.0175	0.625	0.670	0.731	13	0.0305
0.250	0.266	0.301	7	0.0175	0.250	0.284	0.348	14	0.0320
0.312	0.330	0.365	7	0.0175	0.312	0.348	0.412	14	0.0320
0.375	0.395	0.430	7	0.0175	0.375	0.414	0.478	14	0.0320
0.125	0.138	0.176	8	0.0190	0.437	0.478	0.542	14	0.0320
0.187	0.202	0.240	8	0.0190	0.500	0.545	0.609	14	0.0320
0.250	0.266	0.304	8	0.0190	0.562	0.609	0.673	14	0.0320
0.312	0.330	0.368	8	0.0190	0.625	0.677	0.741	14	0.0320
0.375	0.396	0.434	8	0.0190	0.250	0.284	0.354	15	0.0350
0.125	0.145	0.189	9	0.0220	0.312	0.350	0.420	15	0.0350
0.187	0.209	0.253	9	0.0220	0.375	0.417	0.487	15	0.0350
0.250	0.271	0.315	9	0.0220	0.437	0.480	0.550	15	0.0350
0.312	0.335	0.379	9	0.0220	0.500	0.547	0.617	15	0.0350
0.375	0.400	0.444	9	0.0220	0.562	0.611	0.681	15	0.0350

Data for Winding Piano Wire Tension Springs

Diam. of Mandrel, Inches	Inside Diam. of Spring, Inches	Outside Diam. of Spring, Inches	Number of Piano Wire	Diam. of Piano Wire, Inches	Diam. of Mandrel, Inches	Inside Diam. of Spring, Inches	Outside Diam. of Spring, Inches	Number of Piano Wire	Diam. of Piano Wire, Inches
0.250	0.290	0.362	16	0.0360	0.312	0.369	0.467	23	0.0490
0.312	0.355	0.427	16	0.0360	0.375	0.436	0.534	23	0.0490
0.375	0.420	0.492	16	0.0360	0.437	0.500	0.598	23	0.0490
0.437	0.483	0.555	16	0.0360	0.500	0.565	0.663	23	0.0490
0.500	0.550	0.622	16	0.0360	0.562	0.628	0.726	23	0.0490
0.562	0.613	0.685	16	0.0360	0.625	0.700	0.798	23	0.0490
0.625	0.683	0.755	16	0.0360	0.312	0.371	0.477	24	0.0530
0.250	0.292	0.368	17	0.0380	0.375	0.438	0.544	24	0.0530
0.312	0.358	0.434	17	0.0380	0.437	0.504	0.610	24	0.0530
0.375	0.423	0.499	17	0.0380	0.500	0.568	0.674	24	0.0530
0.437	0.486	0.562	17	0.0380	0.562	0.630	0.736	24	0.0530
0.500	0.554	0.630	17	0.0380	0.625	0.702	0.808	24	0.0530
0.562	0.615	0.691	17	0.0380	0.312	0.374	0.486	25	0.0560
0.625	0.686	0.762	17	0.0380	0.375	0.441	0.553	25	0.0560
0.250	0.294	0.374	18	0.0400	0.437	0.508	0.620	25	0.0560
0.312	0.361	0.441	18	0.0400	0.500	0.571	0.683	25	0.0560
0.375	0.426	0.506	18	0.0400	0.562	0.634	0.746	25	0.0560
0.437	0.489	0.569	18	0.0400	0.625	0.706	0.818	25	0.0560
0.500	0.557	0.637	18	0.0400	0.312	0.375	0.495	26	0.0600
0.562	0.618	0.698	18	0.0400	0.375	0.442	0.562	26	0.0600
0.625	0.690	0.770	18	0.0400	0.437	0.511	0.631	26	0.0600
0.312	0.363	0.447	19	0.0420	0.500	0.573	0.693	26	0.0600
0.375	0.427	0.511	19	0.0420	0.562	0.635	0.755	26	0.0600
0.437	0.491	0.575	19	0.0420	0.625	0.710	0.830	26	0.0600
0.500	0.558	0.642	19	0.0420	0.375	0.445	0.573	27	0.0640
0.562	0.619	0.703	19	0.0420	0.437	0.513	0.641	27	0.0640
0.625	0.691	0.775	19	0.0420	0.500	0.575	0.703	27	0.0640
0.312	0.364	0.450	20	0.0430	0.562	0.637	0.765	27	0.0640
0.375	0.429	0.515	20	0.0430	0.625	0.713	0.841	27	0.0640
0.437	0.493	0.579	20	0.0430	0.375	0.446	0.583	28	0.0685
0.500	0.560	0.646	20	0.0430	0.437	0.514	0.651	28	0.0685
0.562	0.621	0.707	20	0.0430	0.500	0.575	0.712	28	0.0685
0.625	0.693	0.779	20	0.0430	0.562	0.638	0.775	28	0.0685
0.312	0.365	0.454	21	0.0445	0.625	0.714	0.851	28	0.0685
0.375	0.431	0.520	21	0.0445	0.375	0.448	0.591	29	0.0715
0.437	0.495	0.584	21	0.0445	0.437	0.516	0.659	29	0.0715
0.500	0.561	0.650	21	0.0445	0.500	0.577	0.720	29	0.0715
0.562	0.623	0.712	21	0.0445	0.562	0.640	0.783	29	0.0715
0.625	0.695	0.784	21	0.0445	0.625	0.714	0.857	29	0.0715
0.312	0.367	0.461	22	0.0470	0.375	0.451	0.603	30	0.0760
0.375	0.433	0.527	22	0.0470	0.437	0.518	0.670	30	0.0760
0.437	0.497	0.591	22	0.0470	0.500	0.580	0.732	30	0.0760
0.500	0.563	0.657	22	0.0470	0.562	0.643	0.795	30	0.0760
0.562	0.625	0.719	22	0.0470	0.625	0.717	0.869	30	0.0760
0.625	0.698	0.792	22	0.0470	0.375	0.455	0.617	31	0.0810

Data for Winding Piano Wire Tension Springs

Diam. of Mandrel, Inches	Inside Diam. of Spring, Inches	Outside Diam. of Spring, Inches	Number of Piano Wire	Diam. of Piano Wire, Inches	Diam. of Mandrel, Inches	Inside Diam. of Spring, Inches	Outside Diam. of Spring, Inches	Number of Piano Wire	Diam. of Piano Wire, Inches
0.437	0.522	0.684	31	0.081	0.375	0.480	0.682	34	0.101
0.500	0.585	0.747	31	0.081	0.437	0.550	0.752	34	0.101
0.562	0.647	0.809	31	0.081	0.500	0.610	0.812	34	0.101
0.625	0.722	0.884	31	0.081	0.562	0.673	0.875	34	0.101
0.375	0.461	0.633	32	0.086	0.625	0.750	0.952	34	0.101
0.437	0.527	0.699	32	0.086	0.375	0.490	0.708	35	0.109.
0.500	0.590	0.762	32	0.086	0.437	0.560	0.778	35	0.109
0.562	0.651	0.823	32	0.086	0.500	0.622	0.840	35	0.109
0.625	0.727	0.899	32	0.086	0.562	0.686	0.904	35	0.109
0.375	0.467	0.649	33	0.091	0.625	0.765	0.983	35	0.109
0.437	0.533	0.715	33	0.091	0.375	0.500	0.736	36	0.118
0.500	0.595	0.777	33	0.091	0.437	0.572	0.808	36	0.118
0.562	0.657	0.839	33	0.091	0.500	0.637	0.873	36	0.118
0.625	0.733	0.915	33	0.091	0.562	0.702	0.938	36	0.118

Stresses Produced by Shocks

Stresses in Beams Produced by Shocks. — Any elastic structure subjected to a shock will deflect until the product of the average resistance, developed by the deflection, and the distance through which it has been overcome, has reached a value equal to the energy of the shock. It follows that for a given shock, the average resisting stresses are inversely proportional to the deflection. If the structure were perfectly rigid, the deflection would be 0, and the stress infinite. The effect of a shock is, therefore, to a great extent dependent upon the elastic property (the springiness) of the structure subjected to the impact.

The energy of a body in motion, such as a falling body, may be spent in each of four ways:

1. In deforming the body struck as a whole.
2. In deforming the falling body as a whole.
3. In partial deformation of both bodies on the surface of contact (most of this energy will be transformed into heat).
4. Part of the energy will be taken up by the supports, if these be not perfectly rigid and inelastic.

How much energy is spent in the last three ways it is in most cases difficult to determine, and for this reason it is safest to figure as if the whole amount were spent as in Case 1. In cases where a reliable judgment is possible, as to what percentage of the energy is spent in other ways than the first, a corresponding fraction of the total energy can be assumed as developing stresses in the body subjected to shocks.

From an investigation into the stresses produced by shocks (see MACHINERY, October, 1909), the following conclusions may be drawn: 1. A suddenly applied load will produce the same deflection, and, therefore, the same stress as a static load twice as great. 2. The unit stress p (see formulas in the accompanying table) for a given load producing a shock, varies directly as the square root of the modulus of elasticity E, and inversely as the square root of the length L of the beam and the area of the section. Thus, for instance, if the sectional area of a beam be increased four times, the unit stress will diminish only one-half. This is entirely different from the results produced by static loads where the stress would vary inversely with the area, and within certain limits be practically independent of the modulus of elasticity.

In the table, the expression for the approximate value of p, which is applicable whenever the deflection of the beam is small as compared with the total height h through which the body producing the shock is dropped, is always the same for beams supported at both ends and subjected to shock at *any* point between the supports. In the formulas all dimensions are in inches and weights in pounds.

Stresses Produced in Beams by Shocks

Method of Support, and Point Struck by Falling Body	Fiber (Unit) Stress p produced by Weight Q Dropped Through a Distance h	Approximate Value of p
Supported at both ends; struck in center.	$p = \dfrac{QaL}{4\,I}\left(1 + \sqrt{1 + \dfrac{96\,hEI}{QL^3}}\right)$	$p = a\sqrt{\dfrac{6\,QhE}{LI}}$
Fixed at one end; struck at the other.	$p = \dfrac{QaL}{I}\left(1 + \sqrt{1 + \dfrac{6\,hEI}{QL^3}}\right)$	$p = a\sqrt{\dfrac{6\,QhE}{LI}}$
Fixed at both ends; struck in center.	$p = \dfrac{QaL}{8\,I}\left(1 + \sqrt{1 + \dfrac{384\,hEI}{QL^3}}\right)$	$p = a\sqrt{\dfrac{6\,QhE}{LI}}$

I = moment of inertia of section; a = distance of extreme fiber from neutral axis; L = length of beam; E = modulus of elasticity.

Stresses in Helical Springs Produced by Shocks. — A load suddenly applied on a spring will produce the same deflection, and, therefore, also the same unit stress, as a static load twice as great. When the load drops from a height h, the stresses are as given in the accompanying table. The approximate values are applicable

Stresses Produced in Springs by Shocks

Form of Bar from Which Spring is Made	Fiber (Unit) Stress f Produced by Weight Q Dropped a Height h on a Helical Spring	Approximate Value of f
Round	$f = \dfrac{8\,QD}{\pi d^3}\left(1 + \sqrt{1 + \dfrac{Ghd^4}{4\,QD^3 n}}\right)$	$f = 1.27\sqrt{\dfrac{QhG}{Dd^2 n}}$
Square	$f = \dfrac{9\,QD}{4\,d^3}\left(1 + \sqrt{1 + \dfrac{Ghd^4}{0.9\,\pi QD^3 n}}\right)$	$f = 1.34\sqrt{\dfrac{QhG}{Dd^2 n}}$

G = modulus of elasticity for torsion; d = diameter or side of bar; D = mean diameter of spring; n = number of coils in spring.

when the deflection is small as compared with the height h. The formulas show that the fiber stress for a given shock will be greater in a spring made from a square bar, than in one made from a round bar, if the diameter of coil be the same, and the side of the square bar equals the diameter of the round bar. It is, therefore, more economical to use round stock for springs which must withstand shocks. This is due to the fact that the deflection for the same fiber stress for a square bar spring is smaller than that for a round bar spring, the ratio being as 4 to 5. The round bar spring is therefore capable of storing more energy than a square bar spring for the same stress.

Shocks from Bodies in Motion. — The formulas given can be applied, in general, to shocks from bodies in motion. A body of the weight W moving horizontally with the velocity of v feet per second, has a stored-up energy:

$$A = \frac{1}{2} \times \frac{Wv^2}{g} \text{ foot-pounds, or } \frac{6Wv^2}{g} \text{ inch-pounds.}$$

This expression may be substituted for Qh in the tables in the equations for unit stresses containing this quantity, and the stresses produced by the energy of the moving body thereby determined.

The formulas in the tables give the maximum value of the stresses, providing the designer with something definite to guide him even in cases where he may be justified in assuming that only a part of the energy of the shock is taken up by the member under stress.

TORSIONAL STRENGTH — SHAFTING

General Formula for Torsional Strength. — In the following formulas:

P = load applied at end of lever arm R, in pounds;
R = length of lever arm in inches;
M_t = torsional or twisting moment in inch-pounds;
S = permissible working stress in pounds per square inch;
I_p = polar moment of inertia of cross-section;
y = distance from center of gravity to most remote fiber;
Z_p = section modulus for torsion, or polar section modulus.

Then, for all cross-sections:

$$P \times R = M_t = S \times Z_p.$$

For circular cross-sections:

$$P \times R = M_t = \frac{S \times I_p}{y} = S \times Z_p.$$

(Compare also page 351, "General Formulas for Strength of Materials.")

Polar Moment of Inertia and Polar Section Modulus. — The polar moment of inertia of a surface is the moment of inertia with respect to an axis through the center of gravity, at right angles to the plane of the surface. The polar moment of inertia equals the sum of two moments of inertia taken with respect to two gravity-axes in the plane of the surface at right angles to each other. Thus, for example, the polar moment of inertia of a circle or a square is equal to two times the moment of inertia with respect to an axis in the plane of the surface through the center of gravity.

The polar section modulus or section modulus of torsion for *circular* sections equals the polar moment of inertia divided by the distance from the center of gravity to the most remote fiber. This method of obtaining the polar section modulus may also be applied with fair accuracy to sections that are nearly circular. For other cross-sections, the section modulus of torsion does not equal the polar moment of inertia divided by the distance from the center of gravity to the most remote fiber. The accompanying table gives formulas for the polar section modulus for a number of sections, some of which are not circular. In the latter case, the formulas are approximate.

Polar Moment of Inertia and Polar Section Modulus

Section	Polar Moment of Inertia I_p	Polar Section Modulus Z_p
	$\dfrac{a^4}{6} = 0.1667\, a^4$	$\dfrac{2}{9}\, a^3 = 0.22\, a^3 = 0.08\, d^3$
	$\dfrac{bd\,(b^2 + d^2)}{12}$	$\dfrac{bd^2}{3 + 1.8\dfrac{d}{b}}$ (d is the shorter side)
	$\dfrac{\pi D^4}{32} = 0.098\, D^4$	$\dfrac{\pi D^3}{16} = 0.196\, D^3$
	$\dfrac{\pi}{32}\,(D^4 - d^4)$ $= 0.098\,(D^4 - d^4)$	$\dfrac{\pi}{16}\left(\dfrac{D^4 - d^4}{D}\right)$ $= 0.196\left(\dfrac{D^4 - d^4}{D}\right)$
	$\dfrac{5\sqrt{3}}{8}\, s^4 = 1.0825\, s^4$ $= 0.12\, F^4$	$= 0.20\, F^3$
	$\dfrac{\pi D^4}{32} - \dfrac{s^4}{6}$ $= 0.098\, D^4 - 0.167\, s^4$	$\dfrac{\pi D^3}{16} - \dfrac{s^4}{3\, D}$ $= 0.196\, D^3 - 0.333\,\dfrac{s^4}{D}$
	$\dfrac{\pi D^4}{32} - \dfrac{5\sqrt{3}}{8}\, s^4$ $= 0.098\, D^4 - 1.0825\, s^4$	$\dfrac{\pi D^3}{16} - \dfrac{5\sqrt{3}\, s^4}{4\, D}$ $= 0.196\, D^3 - 2.165\,\dfrac{s^4}{D}$
	$\dfrac{\sqrt{3}\, s^4}{48} = 0.036\, s^4$	$\dfrac{s^3}{20} = 0.05\, s^3$

Angle of Torsional Deflection of a Cylindrical Shaft. — Let,

L = length of shaft being twisted, in inches;
D = diameter of shaft, in inches;
T = twisting moment, in inch-pounds;
G = torsional modulus of elasticity, generally assumed as 12,000,000 for steel shafting;
α = angle of torsional deflection in degrees.

Then:

$$\alpha = \frac{583.6\,TL}{D^4 G}$$

Example: — Find the torsional deflection for a shaft 4 inches in diameter and 48 inches long, subjected to a twisting moment of 24,000 inch-pounds.

$$\alpha = \frac{583.6 \times 24,000 \times 48}{4^4 \times 12,000,000} = 0.22 \text{ degree, or 13 minutes.}$$

Strength of Shafting. — The twisting strength of a shaft is determined from the formula:

$$T = PR = \frac{3.14\,d^3 S}{16} = \frac{d^3 S}{5.1}$$

or

$$d = \sqrt[3]{\frac{5.1\,PR}{S}} = \sqrt[3]{\frac{321,000\ \text{H.P.}}{nS}}$$

in which T = twisting moment in inch-pounds; P = force acting on the shaft, producing rotation, in pounds; R = length of lever arm of force P, in inches; d = diameter of shaft in inches; S = allowable torsional shearing stress in pounds per square inch; n = number of revolutions per minute; and H.P. = horsepower to be transmitted.

The allowable stress for ordinary shafting may be assumed as 4000 pounds per square inch for main power-transmitting shafts; 6000 pounds per square inch for lineshafts carrying pulleys; and 8500 pounds per square inch for small, short shafts, countershafts, etc. The horsepower transmitted using these allowable stresses is as follows:

For main power-transmitting shafts:

$$\text{H.P.} = \frac{d^3 n}{80}; \text{ or } d = \sqrt[3]{\frac{80\ \text{H.P.}}{n}}$$

For lineshafts carrying pulleys:

$$\text{H.P.} = \frac{d^3 n}{53.5}; \text{ or } d = \sqrt[3]{\frac{53.5\ \text{H.P.}}{n}}$$

For small, short shafts:

$$\text{H.P.} = \frac{d^3 n}{38}; \text{ or } d = \sqrt[3]{\frac{38\ \text{H.P.}}{n}}$$

Shafting which is subjected to shocks, sudden starting and stopping, etc., should be given a greater factor of safety than is indicated by the allowable stresses just mentioned.

Example: — What would be the diameter of a lineshaft to transmit 10 horsepower? The shaft makes 150 revolutions per minute.

$$d = \sqrt[3]{\frac{53.5 \times 10}{150}} = 1.53, \text{ or, say, } 1\tfrac{9}{16} \text{ inch.}$$

Example: — What horsepower would a short shaft, 2 inches in diameter, carrying but two pulleys close to the bearings transmit? The shaft makes 300 revolutions per minute.

$$H.P. = \frac{2^3 \times 300}{38} = 63.$$

Torsional Deflection of Shafting. — The shafting must be proportioned not only so that it has the required strength for transmitting a given power, but so that it cannot be twisted through a greater angle than has been found satisfactory by experience. The allowable twist in degrees should, according to some authorities, not be over 5 minutes or about 0.08 degree per foot length of the shaft.

If G = the torsional modulus of elasticity of the material (= 12,000,000); L = the length of the shaft in feet; α = the angle of torsional deflection; and the other letters denote the same quantities as in the formulas just given for the strength of shafting, then the diameter, as determined from the torsional deflection, will be:

$$d = \sqrt[4]{\frac{32 \times 12 \times L \times 360 \times PR}{3.14 \times G \times \alpha \times 2 \times 3.14}}$$

For an angle of deflection equal to 0.08 degree per foot length of the shaft, or a total angle α of 0.08 L,

$$d = 0.29 \sqrt[4]{PR} = 4.6 \sqrt[4]{\frac{H.P.}{n}}$$

Example: — Find the diameter of a lineshaft to transmit 10 horsepower at 150 revolutions per minute with a torsional deflection not exceeding 0.08 degree per foot of length.

$$d = 4.6 \sqrt[4]{\frac{10}{150}} = 2.35 \text{ inches.}$$

It will be seen, by comparing with the section, "Strength of Shafting," that a larger diameter is required, in this case, to prevent excessive torsional deflection than is required by mere considerations of strength. For short shafts, it is unnecessary to calculate for the angular deflection. It is only in the case of long shafts that this is necessary, and even then only if the torsional deflection would be objectionable.

Linear Deflection of Shafting. — For lineshafting, it is considered good practice to limit the deflection to a maximum of 0.010 inch per foot of length. The maximum distance in feet between bearings, for average conditions, in order to avoid excessive linear deflection, is determined by the formulas:

$$L = 6.3 \sqrt[3]{d^2} \text{ for bare shafts;}$$
$$L = 5.2 \sqrt[3]{d^2} \text{ for shafts carrying pulleys, etc.,}$$

in which d = diameter of shaft in inches; L = maximum distance between bearings in feet. Pulleys should be placed as close to the bearings as possible.

Tables of Horsepower Transmitted by Shafting. — The accompanying table, 'Horsepower Transmitted by Shafting made from Medium Steel" gives the relation between the diameter of shaft, revolutions per minute, horsepower transmitted, and maximum distance in feet between bearings. Assume, for example, that it is required to find the diameter of a shaft for transmitting 40 horsepower at a speed of 250 revolutions per minute. The shaft is not subjected to any bending action except its own weight. From the table, it is found, by locating "40" in the column under 250 revolutions per minute, that the diameter of the shaft required is 2 inches. The maximum permissible distance between the shaft bearings is slightly more than 14 feet. When the exact horsepower cannot be found in the table, it is advisable to take the nearest larger value listed in the table and find the diameter of shafting required to transmit this horsepower. Tables are also given for the horsepower which can be safely transmitted by cold-rolled and turned steel lineshafting. The table for cold-rolled steel shafting is carried up to 5 inches only, because this diameter is the largest which is cold-rolled at the present time. These tables are used by the transmission department of the Jones & Laughlin Steel Co., and are based on the assumption that bearings are placed at intervals of from 8 to 10 feet and all

Horsepower Transmitted by Shafting made from Medium Steel

Diam. of Shaft, Inches	Transmitting Power, but Subject to No Bending Action Except Its Own Weight						Transmitting Power, and Subject to Bending Action of Pulleys, Belting, Etc.					
	Revolutions per Minute					Max. Distance in Feet Between Bearings	Revolutions per Minute					Max. Distance in Feet Between Bearings
	100 H.P.	150 H.P.	200 H.P.	250 H.P.	300 H.P.		100 H.P.	150 H.P.	200 H.P.	250 H.P.	300 H.P.	
$1\frac{1}{2}$	7	10	14	17	20	11.7	5	7	10	12	14	6.8
$1\frac{5}{8}$	9	13	17	21	26	12.4	6	9	12	15	18	7.2
$1\frac{3}{4}$	11	16	21	26	32	13.0	8	11	15	18	22	7.5
$1\frac{7}{8}$	13	20	26	33	40	13.6	9	14	19	23	28	7.9
2	16	24	32	40	48	14.2	11	17	23	28	34	8.2
$2\frac{1}{8}$	19	29	38	48	58	14.8	14	21	27	34	42	8.6
$2\frac{1}{4}$	23	34	46	57	68	15.4	16	24	33	41	48	8.9
$2\frac{3}{8}$	27	40	54	67	80	16.0	19	29	38	48	58	9.2
$2\frac{1}{2}$	31	47	63	78	94	16.5	22	33	45	55	66	9.6
$2\frac{3}{4}$	42	62	83	102	124	17.6	30	44	59	74	89	10.2
3	54	81	108	134	162	18.6	39	58	77	96	116	10.8
$3\frac{1}{4}$	69	103	137	172	206	19.7	49	74	98	123	148	11.4
$3\frac{1}{2}$	86	129	172	215	258	20.7	61	92	123	153	184	12.0
$3\frac{3}{4}$	105	158	211	264	316	21.6	75	113	151	188	226	12.5
4	128	192	256	320	384	22.6	91	137	183	228	274	13.1

pulleys are located as near to the bearings as possible. In these tables, the body part in each gives the number of horsepower to be transmitted. For example assume that a 3-inch cold-rolled steel lineshaft revolves at a speed of 400 revolutions per minute. Find the power that this shaft can safely transmit. By locating 3 inches in the left-hand column and 400 at the top of the vertical columns, and following the vertical column downward until opposite 3 inches, it is found that under the given conditions 154 horsepower may be safely transmitted.

In general, shafting up to three inches in diameter is almost always made from cold-rolled steel. This shafting is true and straight and needs no turning, but if keyways are cut in the shaft, it must, as a rule, be straightened afterwards, as the cutting of the keyways relieves the tension on the surface of the shaft due to the cold-rolling process. Sizes of shafting from three to five inches in diameter may be either cold-rolled or turned, more frequently the latter, while all larger sizes of shafting must be turned, because cold-rolled shafting is not available in diameters larger than five inches.

Horsepower Transmitted by Turned Steel Lineshafting

Diam. of Shaft	Number of Revolutions per Minute												
	100	125	150	175	200	225	250	300	350	400	450	500	600
1½	3.7	4.7	5.6	6.6	7.5	8.4	9.4	11.2	13.1	15.0	16.9	18.8	22
1⁹⁄₁₆	4.2	5.3	6.4	7.4	8.5	9.5	10.6	12.7	14.8	17.0	19.0	21	25
1⅝	4.8	5.9	7.1	8.3	9.5	10.7	11.9	14.3	16.6	19.0	21	24	28
1¹¹⁄₁₆	5.3	6.7	8.0	9.3	10.7	12.0	13.4	16.0	18.7	21	24	27	32
1¾	5.9	7.4	8.9	10.4	11.9	13.4	14.9	17.9	21	24	27	30	36
1¹³⁄₁₆	6.6	8.2	9.9	11.5	13.2	14.8	16.5	19.8	23	26	30	33	40
1⅞	7.3	9.1	11.0	12.8	14.7	16.5	18.3	22	26	29	33	37	44
1¹⁵⁄₁₆	8.1	10.0	12.1	14.1	16.1	18.2	20	24	28	32	36	40	48
2	8.9	11.1	13.3	15.6	17.8	20	22	27	31	35	40	44	53
2¹⁄₁₆	9.8	12.3	14.7	17.2	19.6	22	24	29	34	39	44	49	59
2⅛	10.6	13.3	16.0	18.6	21	24	27	32	37	43	48	53	64
2³⁄₁₆	11.6	14.6	17.5	20.0	23	26	29	35	41	47	52	58	70
2¼	12.6	15.8	19.0	22.0	25	28	32	38	44	51	57	63	76
2⁵⁄₁₆	13.7	17.2	21	24	27	31	34	41	48	55	62	69	82
2⅜	14.9	18.6	22	26	30	33	37	45	52	60	67	74	89
2⁷⁄₁₆	16.0	20	24	28	32	36	40	48	56	64	72	80	96
2½	17.4	22	26	30	35	39	43	52	61	69	78	87	104
2⁹⁄₁₆	18.7	23	28	33	37	42	47	56	66	75	84	94	112
2⅝	20	25	30	35	40	45	50	60	71	80	90	100	120
2¹¹⁄₁₆	21	27	32	38	43	48	54	65	76	86	97	108	129
2¾	23	29	35	40	46	52	58	69	81	92	104	115	138
2¹³⁄₁₆	25	31	37	43	49	56	62	74	87	99	111	124	148
2⅞	26	33	40	46	53	59	66	79	92	105	119	132	158
2¹⁵⁄₁₆	28	35	42	49	56	63	70	84	99	113	127	141	169
3	30	37	45	52	60	67	75	90	105	120	135	150	180
3⅛	34	42	51	59	68	76	85	102	119	136	152	170	203
3¼	38	48	57	67	76	86	95	114	134	153	172	191	229
3⅜	43	53	64	75	85	96	107	128	150	171	192	213	256
3½	48	60	72	83	95	107	119	143	167	190	214	238	286
3⅝	53	66	79	93	106	119	132	159	185	211	238	265	317
3¾	59	73	88	103	117	132	146	176	205	234	264	293	351
3⅞	65	81	97	113	129	145	161	194	226	258	291	322	387
4	71	89	107	125	142	160	178	213	249	284	320	356	427
4⅛	78	98	117	136	156	176	195	235	273	312	351	390	468
4¼	85	107	128	149	170	192	213	256	298	341	385	426	511
4⅜	93	116	139	163	186	210	233	279	326	372	419	466	559
4½	102	127	152	178	203	228	253	305	356	405	456	507	610
4⅝	110	138	165	193	220	247	275	330	385	440	495	550	660
4¾	119	149	179	209	238	268	298	357	416	476	537	595	714
4⅞	129	161	193	226	258	290	322	387	452	516	581	646	775
5	139	174	208	244	278	313	347	417	486	557	625	695	835

Horsepower Transmitted by Cold-rolled Steel Lineshafting

Diam. of Shaft	Number of Revolutions per Minute												
	100	125	150	175	200	225	250	300	350	400	450	500	600
1½	4.8	6.0	7.2	8.4	9.6	10.8	12.0	14.4	16.9	19.2	22	24	29
1 9/16	5.5	6.8	8.2	9.5	10.9	12.2	13.6	16.4	19.0	22	25	27	33
1 5/8	6.1	7.6	9.2	10.7	12.2	13.8	15.3	18.4	21	24	28	31	37
1 11/16	6.9	8.6	10.3	12.0	13.7	15.4	17.1	21	24	27	31	34	41
1¾	7.7	9.6	11.5	13.4	15.3	17.2	19.1	23	27	31	34	38	46
1 13/16	8.5	10.6	12.7	14.8	16.9	19.0	21	25	30	34	38	42	51
1 7/8	9.4	11.7	14.1	16.4	18.8	21	23	28	33	38	42	47	57
1 15/16	10.4	13.0	15.6	18.2	21	23	26	31	36	42	47	52	62
2	11.4	14.3	17.2	20	23	26	29	34	40	46	51	57	69
2 1/16	12.6	15.7	18.9	22	25	28	31	38	44	50	56	63	76
2 1/8	13.7	17.1	21	24	27	31	34	41	48	55	61	68	82
2 3/16	15.0	18.7	22	26	30	34	37	45	52	60	67	75	90
2¼	16.3	20	24	29	33	37	41	49	57	65	73	81	98
2 5/16	17.7	22	27	31	35	40	44	53	62	71	80	88	106
2 3/8	19.2	24	29	34	38	43	48	57	67	76	86	96	115
2 7/16	20	25	30	36	41	46	51	61	72	81	91	102	122
2½	22	28	33	39	45	50	56	67	78	89	100	112	133
2 9/16	24	30	36	42	48	54	60	72	84	96	108	120	144
2 5/8	26	32	39	45	52	58	64	77	90	104	116	129	155
2 11/16	28	35	42	48	55	62	69	83	97	111	124	138	166
2¾	30	37	44	52	59	67	74	89	104	119	133	148	178
2 13/16	32	40	47	55	63	71	79	95	111	127	143	159	190
2 7/8	34	42	51	59	68	76	85	101	119	135	152	169	203
2 15/16	36	45	54	63	72	81	90	108	127	144	162	181	217
3	39	48	58	67	77	87	96	116	135	154	173	192	231
3 1/8	44	54	65	76	87	98	109	131	152	174	196	218	261
3 1/4	49	61	73	86	98	110	122	147	172	196	221	245	294
3 3/8	55	69	83	96	110	124	137	165	192	220	247	275	330
3½	61	77	92	107	123	138	153	184	214	245	276	307	367
3 5/8	68	85	102	119	136	153	170	204	238	272	306	340	408
3¾	75	94	113	132	151	170	189	226	264	301	340	377	452
3 7/8	83	104	125	145	166	187	207	249	291	332	379	415	498
4	92	114	137	160	183	206	229	274	320	366	411	457	549
4 1/8	101	125	150	175	201	226	251	300	351	401	451	501	601
4 1/4	110	137	164	192	219	246	273	328	383	438	492	547	657
4 3/8	120	150	180	210	239	268	298	358	418	478	538	597	717
4½	130	163	195	228	261	293	326	391	455	521	586	651	781
4 5/8	141	177	212	247	283	318	354	425	495	566	636	707	848
4¾	153	191	230	268	307	344	382	459	537	613	688	765	919
4 7/8	166	207	249	290	331	372	413	496	580	662	745	827	994
5	179	224	268	313	358	402	447	537	625	715	805	895	1074

American Standard Diameters for Finished Shafting

Diameters, Inches		Minus Tolerances, Inches*	Diameters, Inches		Minus Tolerances, Inches*	Diameters, Inches		Minus Tolerances, Inches*
Transmission Shafting	Machinery Shafting		Transmission Shafting	Machinery Shafting		Transmission Shafting	Machinery Shafting	
	1/2	0.002		1 13/16	0.003		3 3/4	0.004
	9/16	0.002		1 7/8	0.003		3 7/8	0.004
	5/8	0.002	1 15/16	1 15/16	0.003	3 15/16	4	0.004
	11/16	0.002		2	0.003		4 1/4	0.005
	3/4	0.002		2 1/16	0.004	4 7/16	4 1/2	0.005
	13/16	0.002		2 1/8	0.004		4 3/4	0.005
	7/8	0.002	2 3/16	2 3/16	0.004	4 15/16	5	0.005
15/16	15/16	0.002		2 1/4	0.004		5 1/4	0.005
	1	0.002		2 5/16	0.004	5 7/16	5 1/2	0.005
	1 1/16	0.003		2 3/8	0.004		5 3/4	0.005
	1 1/8	0.003	2 7/16	2 7/16	0.004	5 15/16	6	0.005
1 3/16	1 3/16	0.003		2 1/2	0.004		6 1/4	0.005
	1 1/4	0.003		2 5/8	0.004	6 1/2	6 1/2	0.005
	1 5/16	0.003		2 3/4	0.004		6 3/4	0.005
	1 3/8	0.003	2 15/16	2 7/8	0.004	7	7	0.005
1 7/16	1 7/16	0.003		3	0.004		7 1/4	0.005
	1 1/2	0.003		3 1/8	0.004	7 1/2	7 1/2	0.005
	1 9/16	0.003		3 1/4	0.004		7 3/4	0.005
	1 5/8	0.003		3 3/8	0.004	8	8	0.005
1 11/16	1 11/16	0.003	3 7/16	3 1/2	0.004	....	....	....
	1 3/4	0.003		3 5/8	0.004			

Note: — These tolerances are *negative* or minus and represent the maximum allowable variation *below* the exact nominal size. For instance the maximum diameter of the 1 15/16 inch shaft is 1.938 inch and its minimum allowable diameter is 1.935 inch. Stock lengths of finished transmission shafting shall be: 16, 20 and 24 feet.

Shafting Diameters. — The diameter of shafting for transmitting a given amount of power may be determined by the following formulas from the American Standards Association's Code for the Design of Transmission Shafting. In these formulas:

D = outside diameter of shaft in inches;

K_m = combined shock and fatigue factor to be applied in every case to the computed bending moment (for rotating shafts, K_m = 1.5 for gradually applied or steady loads; 1.5 to 2 for suddenly applied loads and minor shocks only; 2 to 3 for suddenly applied loads and heavy shocks);

K_t = combined shock and fatigue factor to be applied in every case to the computed torsional moment (for rotating shafts and gradually applied or steady loads K_t = 1; for suddenly applied loads and minor shocks only K_t = 1 to 1.5; for suddenly applied loads and heavy shocks K_t = 1.5 to 3);

M = maximum bending moment in inch pounds;

N = revolutions per minute;

P = maximum number of horsepower to be transmitted by the shaft;

p_t = maximum shearing stress in pounds per square inch (the maximum shearing stress p_t, under combined load = 8000 pounds per square inch for "commercial steel" shafting without allowance for keyways, and 6000 pounds per square inch with allowance for keyways. p_t = 30 per cent of the elastic limit in tension, but not more than 18 per cent of the ultimate tensile strength for shafting steel purchased under definite physical specifications);

S_s = maximum permissible torsional shearing stress in pounds per square inch (the values for S_s are the same as just given for p_t).

If a solid circular shaft is subjected to a pure torsional load

$$D = \sqrt[3]{\frac{321,000 \, K_t P}{S_s N}}.$$

If a solid circular shaft is subjected to combined torsion and bending

$$D = \sqrt[3]{\frac{16}{\pi pt} \sqrt{(K_m M)^2 + \left(\frac{396,000 \, K_t P}{2 \, \pi N}\right)^2}}.$$

If B = maximum distance in feet between shaft bearings, and D = shaft diameter in inches, then under average conditions and for bare shafts B = cube root of $D^2 \times$ 6.3; for shafts carrying pulleys, etc., B = cube root of $D^2 \times 5.2$.

Formulas for Determining Combined Bending and Torsional Moments: In cases where shafts must withstand not only torsional stresses but also bending stresses which are great enough to appreciably affect the resistance of a shaft, a formula may be used to determine first the " combined moment " or " equivalent moment " resulting from the combined action of these stresses. Authorities on machine design differ in regard to the proper formula for ascertaining this equivalent moment. If M_b = bending moment in inch-pounds; M_t = torsional moment in inch-pounds; M_e = equivalent moment, then, according to the Guest formula,

$$M_e = \sqrt{M_b{}^2 + M_t{}^2} \qquad (1)$$

This Guest formula (Handbook page 354) is intended only for ductile material, such as machine steel, and for parts of *circular* cross-section, such as ordinary shafting. Another formula intended for ductile material, such as low-carbon or machine steel, is as follows:

$$M_e = 1.3 \times \sqrt{M_b{}^2 + M_t{}^2} \qquad (2)$$

A third formula which is found in many textbooks and is sometimes referred to as a formula which gives the " ideal moment," is as follows:

$$M_e = M_b + \sqrt{M_b{}^2 + M_t{}^2} \qquad (3)$$

Certain other formulas or modifications of the ones given, are sometimes used.

Use of Combined Moment in Calculating Shaft Diameter: In calculating the shaft diameter, the equivalent moment obtained by using one of the formulas above, is inserted in formula (4) in which S_s = maximum allowable torsional stress in pounds per square inch.

$$\text{Shaft diameter } D = \sqrt[3]{\frac{16 \times M_e}{S_s \times 3.1416}} = \sqrt[3]{\frac{5.1 \times M_e}{S_s}} \qquad (4)$$

Assume that a shaft is subjected to a bending moment M_b of 30,000 inch-pounds, a turning moment M_t of 60,000 inch-pounds, and S_s = 10,000 pounds per square inch. Then, if M_e is obtained by formula (1), $D = 3\frac{1}{4}$ inches; if M_e is from formula (2), $D = 3\frac{3}{16}$ inches; if M_e is from formula (3), $D = 3\frac{11}{16}$ inches, approximately in each case. In actual practice, the diameters might be changed to conform to the standard shafting sizes, as given on the preceding page. If a shaft is subjected to torsional stress only, substitute for M_e in formula (4) the turning moment in inch-pounds.

It may be necessary to make the diameter of a shaft larger than is required for strength alone in order to avoid excessive torsional deflection, especially if the shaft is quite long. One rule for deflection that has been applied quite generally in ordinary mill practice is to limit the deflection to 1 degree in a length equal to twenty times the shaft diameter. The diameter determined on this basis will equal one-tenth of the cube root of the turning moment in inch-pounds. For certain other classes of work the torsional deflection must be much less than allowed by the rule just given.

Table Giving Comparative Torsional Strength and Weight of Hollow and Solid Shafting with Same Outside Diameter

(Upper figures in each line give number of per cent decrease in strength; lower figures give per cent decrease in weight.)

Example: — A 4-inch shaft, with a 2-inch hole through it, has a weight 25 per cent less than a solid 4-inch shaft, but its strength is decreased only 6.25 per cent.

Diam. of Solid and Hollow Shaft, Inches	Diameter of Axial Hole in Hollow Shaft, Inches									
	1	1¼	1½	1¾	2	2½	3	3½	4	4½
1½	19.76 44.44	48.23 69.44	....	....	....	....	....	....	....	....
1¾	10.67 32.66	26.04 51.02	53.98 73.49	....	....	....	....	....	....	....
2	6.25 25.00	15.26 39.07	31.65 56.25	58.62 76.54	....	....	....	....	....	....
2¼	3.91 19.75	9.53 30.87	19.76 44.44	36.60 60.49	62.43 79.00	....	....	....	....	....
2½	2.56 16.00	6.25 25.00	12.96 36.00	24.01 49.00	40.96 64.00	....	....	....	....	....
2¾	1.75 13.22	4.28 20.66	8.86 29.74	16.40 40.48	27.98 52.89	68.30 82.63	....	....	....	....
3	1.24 11.11	3.01 17.36	6.25 25.00	11.58 34.01	19.76 44.44	48.23 69.44	....	....	....	....
3¼	0.87 9.46	2.19 14.80	4.54 21.30	8.41 29.00	14.35 37.87	35.02 59.17	72.61 85.22	....	....	....
3½	0.67 8.16	1.63 12.76	3.38 18.36	6.25 25.00	10.67 32.66	26.04 51.02	53.98 73.49	....	....	....
3¾	0.51 7.11	1.24 11.11	2.56 16.00	4.75 21.77	8.09 28.45	19.76 44.44	40.96 64.00	75.89 87.10	....	....
4	0.40 6.25	0.96 9.77	1.98 14.06	3.68 19.14	6.25 25.00	15.26 39.07	31.65 56.25	58.62 76.56	....	....
4¼	0.31 5.54	0.74 8.65	1.56 12.45	2.89 16.95	4.91 22.15	11.99 34.61	24.83 49.85	46.00 67.83	78.47 88.59	.....
4½	0.25 4.94	0.70 7.72	1.24 11.11	2.29 15.12	3.91 19.75	9.53 30.87	19.76 44.44	36.60 60.49	62.43 79.00	.....
4¾	0.20 4.43	0.56 6.93	1.00 9.97	1.85 13.57	3.15 17.73	7.68 27.70	15.92 39.90	29.48 54.29	50.29 70.91	80.56 89.75
5	0.16 4.00	0.40 6.25	0.81 8.10	1.51 12.25	2.56 16.00	6.25 25.00	12.96 36.00	24.01 49.00	40.96 64.00	65.61 81.00
5½	0.11 3.30	0.27 5.17	0.55 7.43	1.03 10.12	1.75 13.22	4.27 20.66	8.86 29.76	16.40 40.48	27.98 52.89	44.82 66.94
6	0.09 2.77	0.19 4.34	0.40 6.25	0.73 8.50	1.24 11.11	3.02 17.36	6.25 25.00	11.58 34.02	19.76 44.44	31.65 56.25
6½	0.06 2.36	0.14 3.70	0.29 5.32	0.59 7.24	0.90 9.47	2.19 14.79	4.54 21.30	8.41 28.99	14.35 37.87	23.98 47.93
7	0.05 2.04	0.11 3.19	0.22 4.59	0.40 6.25	0.67 8.16	1.63 12.76	3.38 18.36	6.25 25.00	10.67 32.66	17.08 41.33
7½	0.04 1.77	0.08 2.77	0.16 4.00	0.30 5.44	0.51 7.11	1.24 11.11	2.56 16.00	4.75 21.77	8.09 28.45	12.96 36.00
8	0.03 1.56	0.06 2.44	0.13 3.51	0.23 4.78	0.40 6.25	0.96 9.77	1.98 14.06	3.68 19.14	6.25 25.00	10.02 31.64

Hollow Shafts. — The following is a simple method for finding the dimensions of a hollow shaft which can be substituted for a solid shaft of equal strength to resist bending or torsion. Let D_1 = diameter of solid shaft; D = outside diameter of hollow shaft; d = inside diameter of hollow shaft; $t = \frac{1}{2}(D - d)$ = thickness of metal of hollow shaft; $k = d \div D$ = ratio of diameters of hollow shaft.

As the hollow shaft is to have the same strength to resist bending as the solid shaft, the moment of resistance of both must be equal. Hence:

$$\frac{\pi(D^4 - d^4)}{32\,D} = \frac{\pi D_1{}^3}{32}, \text{ from which } D^3 - \frac{d^4}{D} = D_1{}^3 \qquad (1)$$

If kD is substituted for d in Equation (1):

$$D^3 - D^3 k^4 = D_1{}^3, \text{ from which } \frac{D}{D_1} = \sqrt[3]{\frac{1}{1 - k^4}} \qquad (2)$$

In a similar manner, by substituting $\frac{d}{k}$ for D in Equation (1):

$$\frac{d}{D_1} = k \sqrt[3]{\frac{1}{1 - k^4}} \qquad (3)$$

Further, as $t = \frac{1}{2}(D - d)$, Formula (4) is found by substitution and simplification:

$$\frac{t}{D_1} = \frac{1 - k}{2} \sqrt[3]{\frac{1}{1 - k^4}} \qquad (4)$$

In the accompanying table the values of the factors containing k in Equations (2),

Ratio of	Ratio $d \div D$								
	0.50	0.55	0.60	0.65	0.70	0.75	0.80	0.85	0.90
$D \div D_1$ =	1.021	1.032	1.047	1.067	1.095	1.135	1.192	1.279	1.427
$d \div D_1$ =	0.510	0.567	0.628	0.694	0.767	0.851	0.951	1.087	1.284
$t \div D_1$ =	0.257	0.232	0.209	0.186	0.164	0.141	0.119	0.096	0.071
Weight of hollow shaft*...	78.3	74.35	70.2	65.8	61.3	56.4	51.6	45.4	38.7

* Weight of hollow shaft is given in per cent of weight of solid shaft.

(3), and (4) are calculated for certain values of k. The bottom line of the table gives the weight of the hollow shaft in per cent of that of the solid.

It is evident that Equation (1) would be the same, if it were derived under the assumption that the hollow shaft had the same torsional strength as the solid one, instead of having the same strength against bending, as assumed. The table will therefore hold true for shafts subjected to bending or torsion, or both.

Assume, as an example, that a solid shaft 3 inches in diameter is to be replaced by a hollow shaft, ratio k being 0.5. Then, by inserting the value found from the table in Equation (2):

$$\frac{D}{D_1} = 1.021 \text{ and } D = 3 \times 1.021 = 3.063 \text{ inches,}$$

$$d = 0.5\,D = 1.532 \text{ inch.}$$

The use of hollow shafts not only reduces the weight of a shaft for a given strength, but increases the reliability of the shafting, on account of the removal of the metal from the core of the shaft. This applies especially to shafts of large diameters, as in large steel ingots the central core is likely to be less dense than the outer portion and to show shrinkage cavities near the center.

FRICTION

Friction is the resistance to motion which takes place when one body is moved upon another, and is generally defined as "that force which acts between two bodies at their surface of contact, so as to resist their sliding on each other." The force of friction, F, bears — according to the conditions under which sliding occurs — a certain relation to the pressure between the two bodies; this pressure is called the normal pressure N. The relation between force of friction and normal pressure is given by the *coefficient of friction*, generally denoted by the Greek letter μ. Thus:

$$F = \mu \times N, \quad \text{and} \quad \mu = \frac{F}{N}$$

Example: — A body weighing 28 pounds rests on a horizontal surface. The force required to keep it in motion along the surface is 7 pounds. Find the coefficient of friction.

$$\mu = \frac{F}{N} = \frac{7}{28} = 0.25$$

If a body is placed on an inclined plane, the friction between the body and the plane will prevent it from sliding down the inclined surface, provided the angle of the plane with the horizontal is not too great. There will be a certain angle, however, at which the body will just barely be able to remain stationary, the frictional resistance being very nearly overcome by the tendency of the body to slide down. This angle is termed the angle of repose, and the tangent of this angle equals the coefficient of friction. The angle of repose is frequently denoted by the Greek letter θ. Thus, $\mu = \tan \theta$.

A greater force is required to start a body from a state of rest than to merely keep it in motion, because the *friction of rest* is greater than the *friction of motion*.

Rolling Friction. — When a body rolls on a surface, the force resisting the motion is termed *rolling friction*. This has a different value from that of the ordinary, or sliding, friction. Let W = total weight of rolling body or load on wheel, in pounds; r = radius of wheel, in feet; f = coefficient of rolling friction. Then:

$$\text{Resistance to rolling, in pounds} = \frac{W \times f}{r}$$

The coefficient of rolling friction varies with the conditions. For wood on wood it may be assumed as 0.005; for iron on iron, from 0.002 to 0.005; iron on granite, 0.007; iron on asphalt, 0.012; iron on wood, 0.018.

Laws of Friction. — The earliest experiments made on friction, which led to the establishment of definite laws, were undertaken by Morin and Rennie about 1830. The laws laid down by these early investigators, however, have been considerably modified by later investigations. The following may be considered as a correct statement of the laws of friction in their modified form, for unlubricated or dry surfaces.

1. For low pressures the friction is directly proportional to the normal pressure between the two surfaces. As the pressure increases to a high value the friction does not rise as rapidly; but when the pressure becomes abnormally high, the friction increases at a rapid rate until seizing takes place.

2. The friction both in its total amount and its coefficient is independent of the areas in contact, so long as the total pressure remains the same. This is true for moderate pressures only. For high pressures, this law is modified in the same way as in the first case.

3. At very low velocities the friction is independent of the velocity of rubbing. As the velocities increase, the friction decreases.

Lubricated Surfaces. — For well lubricated surfaces, the laws of friction are considerably different from those governing dry or poorly lubricated surfaces.

1. The frictional resistance is almost independent of the pressure per square inch, if the surfaces are flooded with oil.

2. The friction varies directly as the speed, at low pressures; but for high pressures the friction is very great at low velocities, approaching a minimum at about two feet per second linear velocity, and afterwards increasing approximately as the square root of the speed.

3. For well lubricated surfaces the frictional resistance depends, to a very great extent, on the temperature, partly because of the change in the viscosity of the oil and partly because the diameter of the bearing increases with the rise of temperature more rapidly than the diameter of the shaft, thus relieving the bearing of side pressure.

4. If the bearing surfaces are flooded with oil, the friction is almost independent of the nature of the material of the surfaces in contact. As the lubrication becomes less ample, the coefficient of friction becomes more dependent upon the material of the surfaces.

Experiments made by Tower indicate that the oil bath is very much superior to any other method of lubrication. Under conditions when with an oil bath the coefficient of friction was 0.0014, the value of this coefficient with a syphon lubricator was 0.0098, and with a pad under the journal, 0.009. This indicates that the friction when using an oil bath is only about one-seventh of the friction when using other methods of lubrication.

The comparative value of different lubricants is indicated by the same experiments. If the friction of a journal in its bearing, using a sperm oil bath, is assumed equal to 1, the friction using rape oil is 1.06; mineral oil, 1.29; lard oil, 1.35; olive oil, 1.35; and mineral grease, 2.17.

Lubricants. — The value of an oil as a lubricant depends mainly upon its film-forming capacity; that is, its capability of maintaining a film of oil between the bearing surfaces. The film-forming capacity depends to a large extent on the viscosity of the oil, but this should not be understood to mean that the oil of the highest viscosity is in every case the most suitable lubricant. On the other hand, an oil of the lowest viscosity which will retain an unbroken oil film between the bearing surfaces is the most suitable for purposes of lubrication, because a higher viscosity than that necessary to retain the oil film results in a waste of power, due to the expenditure of energy necessary to overcome the internal friction of the oil itself. For internal lubrication, only mineral oil of good quality should be used. Vegetable or animal oils are unsuitable owing to the fact that they decompose at high temperatures, forming acids which are injurious to metals. (See section on "Bearing Lubricants," page 573.) It is of importance to note that the following oils have a tendency to corrode the metals mentioned: Tallow oil, iron and copper; seal oil, copper; whale oil, lead; lard oil, lead; sperm oil, lead and zinc; rape oil, copper; cottonseed oil, tin.

Tables of Coefficients of Friction. — As the coefficient of friction depends on so many variable factors, it is impossible to give data that can be depended upon to meet all conditions, except in a very general way. The accompanying tables, however, give coefficients of friction as determined by various experimenters with different materials, conditions of loading and kinds of lubricants. The surfaces in contact, especially when poorly lubricated or dry, largely influence the coefficient of friction, which, of course, diminishes with the increasing smoothness of the surface.

Experiments by Thurston, to determine the coefficients of friction of motion and of rest of a journal, show that with a rubbing speed of 2.5 feet per second, using sperm oil as a lubricant, the coefficients at the starting were about five times the coefficients of motion, for a pressure of 50 pounds per square inch. As the pressure was increased to 500 pounds per square inch, the coefficient at starting was about thirty times greater than that of motion. With lard oil, the ratio between the two coefficients at 50 pounds pressure per square inch was about 3.5, and at 500 pounds pressure per square inch, about 20.

Coefficients of Friction

Low pressures (14 to 20 pounds per square inch). Sliding friction.

Bronze on bronze, dry................................	0.20
Bronze on cast iron, dry..............................	0.21
Bronze on wrought iron, slightly lubricated............	0.16
Cast iron on cast iron, slightly lubricated............	0.15
Cast iron on wrought iron, dry.......................	0.18
Wrought iron on wrought iron, dry....................	0.44
Cast iron on hard wood, dry..........................	0.49
Cast iron on hard wood, slightly lubricated...........	0.19
Wrought iron on hard wood, well lubricated...........	0.08
Brass on hard wood, dry..............................	0.48
Hard wood on hard wood, dry.........................	0.48
Hard wood on hard wood, well lubricated.............	0.16
Leather on hard wood, dry............................	0.33
Leather on cast iron, dry.............................	0.56

(In all cases where wood is mentioned, the motion is in the direction of the fibers of the wood.)

Coefficients of Sliding Friction

(Surfaces slightly lubricated)

Pressure, Lbs. per Sq. In.	Wrought Iron on Wrought Iron	Cast Iron on Wrought Iron	Steel on Cast Iron	Brass on Cast Iron	Pressure, Lbs. per Sq. In.	Wrought Iron on Wrought Iron	Cast Iron on Wrought Iron	Steel on Cast Iron	Brass on Cast Iron
125	0.14	0.17	0.17	0.16	485	0.40	0.37	0.36	0.22
185	0.25	0.27	0.30	0.22	525	0.41	0.37	0.36	0.22
225	0.27	0.29	0.33	0.22	565	Seized	0.37	0.36	0.23
260	0.28	0.32	0.34	0.21	600	.....	0.37	0.36	0.23
300	0.30	0.33	0.34	0.21	635	.....	0.37	0.37	0.23
335	0.31	0.33	0.35	0.21	670	.....	0.38	0.40	0.23
370	0.35	0.35	0.35	0.21	710	.....	0.43	Seized	0.23
390	0.38	0.36	0.35	0.20	780	.....	Seized	.....	0.23
450	0.39	0.36	0.35	0.21	820	.....	.....	.....	0.27

Influence of Friction on the Efficiency of Small Machine Elements. — The friction between machine parts lowers the efficiency, or the ratio of the power possible to take out of a machine element and that put into it. In the following are given average values of the efficiency, in per cent, of the most common machine elements when carefully made. Ordinary bearings, 95 to 98; roller bearings, 98; ball bearings, 99; spur gears with cast teeth, including bearings, 93; spur gears with cut teeth, including bearings, 96; bevel gears with cast teeth, including bearings, 92; bevel gears with cut teeth, including bearings, 95; belting, from 96 to 98; high-class silent power transmission chain, 97 to 99; roller chains, 95 to 97.

BEARINGS

In designing a plain or sleeve bearing for a given velocity and load, the aim is to use the highest unit pressure and oil of the lowest viscosity consistent with safe operation, assuming oil-film lubrication. If the bearing area is based upon the maximum safe unit pressure, then excessive area and unnecessary friction losses will be avoided. General formulas and data applicable to the design of all classes of plain bearings cannot be given because of the many variable factors influencing the design. These factors include the lubricant and method of applying it to the bearing, heat-radiating capacity of the bearing, finish of journal surface, properties of bearing materials, clearance, and other factors. The following notation is used:

P = bearing pressure in pounds per square inch of projected area
A = projected area in sq. in. = bearing length $\times$ diameter
V = surface or rubbing velocity of journal in feet per minute
μ = coefficient of friction
R = rate of radiation in foot-pounds per minute per square inch of projected area;
r = radiation in foot-pounds per minute per square inch of projected area per degree F. of temperature head
t = temperature head or difference between temperature of rubbing surface and atmosphere or cooling medium. (t = rise of 40 to 60 degrees F. for heavy-duty bearings, and 60 to 90 degrees F. for high-speed bearings.)

Effect of Speed Upon Allowable Pressure. — When a lubricated journal revolves, some of the lubricant will be drawn into the loaded area between the journal and bearing, thus forming a wedge-shaped oil film. This oil film will support the load on the journal within certain limits. If the velocity reaches a point where the heat is not dissipated as fast as it is generated, the viscosity of the oil may be insufficient to carry the load on the bearing; hence the maximum allowable bearing pressure per square inch depends not only upon the velocity, but also upon the viscosity of the lubricant and the rate at which heat is dissipated from the bearings either through ordinary radiation or by artificial cooling. It has been common practice to design many high-speed bearings for comparatively low unit bearing pressures; but if such bearings are rigid, have smooth accurate surfaces, and the right amount of clearance, the unit pressure (assuming perfect lubrication is maintained) may be increased as the velocity increases, up to a maximum pressure which depends upon such a complicated relationship between a number of variable factors that it can only be determined by tests with a given bearing and lubricant.

Relation Between Load and Formation of Oil Film. — For a given allowable load, a certain velocity and heat-radiating capacity is necessary to maintain an oil film that will support the load. Simple empirical formulas are sometimes used to determine the "critical" or maximum pressure, but the results can only be approximate. According to one formula, the critical pressure in pounds per square inch of projected area, *below* which a perfect oil film may be maintained at a given velocity V, and when using the more common grades of mineral engine oils, is approximately as follows: Critical pressure = $140\sqrt[3]{\dfrac{V}{T}}$. In this formula, T = temperature which is assumed to be 140 degrees (200 degrees max. at rubbing surface minus 60 degrees) for the more common grades of mineral engine oils.

Coefficient of Friction. — The coefficient of friction μ for well-lubricated journals depends largely upon the characteristics of the lubricant. The effect of bearing materials upon the coefficient of friction is important at starting or before the oil film is formed, at stopping, and also in case of lubrication failure either throughout the bearing or locally due to misalignment or journal deflection. Assuming that a perfect oil film has formed, the coefficient of friction depends upon the lubricant, the temperature, the rubbing velocity, and the load. The coefficient of friction may range from 0.0015 or 0.002 for excellent lubrication to 0.050 or higher for poor lubrication (see table).

Coefficients of Journal Friction

Method of lubrication: oil-bath

Kind of Oil	Velocity, Feet per Minute	Pressure, Pounds per Square Inch						
		100	153	205	310	415	520	625
Lard oil...... {	157	0.0042	0.0027	0.0020	0.0014	0.0012	0.0009	......
	471	0.0090	0.0052	0.0042	0.0029	0.0021	0.0017	......
Mineral grease {	157	0.0076	0.0038	0.0034	0.0022	0.0016	0.0014	0.001
	471	0.0151	0.0083	0.0066	0.0040	0.0027	0.0022	0.002
Sperm oil..... {	157	0.0030	0.0019	0.0016	0.0011	0.0015	Seized	......
	471	0.0064	0.0037	0.0027	0.0019	0.0021	......	......
Rape oil...... {	157	0.0040	0.0020	0.0014	0.0008	0.0009	0.0010	0.001*
	471	0.0070	0.0040	0.0024	0.0016	0.0016	0.0015	......
Mineral oil... {	157	0.0040	......	0.0021	0.0014	0.0012	0.0012	0.0013
	471	0.0070	......	0.0035	0.0024	0.0020	0.0018	......

* Pressure 573 pounds per square inch.

Power Loss Formulas. — A general formula for determining the amount of power lost per bearing due to friction is as follows:

$$\text{Horsepower loss} = \frac{\text{total load} \times V\mu}{33,000}.$$

An approximate formula used by the General Electric Co. for determining loss per bearing in kilowatts is: $KW \text{ loss} = \frac{0.38\,AP^{0.4}V^{1.2}}{10^6}.$

The ZN/P Value as a Basis for Designing Bearings. — If Z equals the absolute viscosity of a lubricant expressed in centipoises; N equals revolutions per minute, and P equals pressure in pounds per square inch of projected area, then the value of $\frac{ZN}{P}$ for a given design of bearing and lubricant, may be used as a guide in designing similar types of bearings assuming film lubrication. To illustrate, these ZN/P values might range from, say, 10 to 100 or more, thus indicating that the ZN/P value might lie anywhere within this range provided it was far enough from the value representing the breakdown of the oil film to provide a suitable factor of safety. Close to this film-breaking-point value is the zone of minimum friction or of thin-film lubrication; hence, the ZN/P value upon which the design is based should be as close to the danger zone and to this thin-film and low-friction value as is consistent with conditions.

The coefficient of friction is assumed to be a function of these three factors when they are combined to form a single variable ZN/P.

The range of ZN/P values, or the ideal one for a given bearing, can only be determined by actual tests (by combining maximum speeds with minimum loads and vice versa) because the allowable unit pressure for a given velocity and lubricant depends upon so many variable factors; moreover, these values for a given bearing in the zone representing the dividing line between stable and unstable lubrication, may change considerably as the bearing surfaces are worn smooth by running in. For example, tests on a bronze bearing resulted in a ZN/P value of 55 at the point of minimum friction or danger zone and a reduction in this value to about 5 after 75 hours running.

As the value of ZN/P decreases, the coefficient of friction decreases until the oil film begins to break down; then the frictional resistance increases as the contact with the journal is transferred from the oil film to the bearing material, the rate of increase depending upon the extent to which lubricant may remain and the frictional resistance of the bearing material itself. It is evident, then, that frictional losses are lowest when the ZN/P value is close to the value representing a change from stable to unstable lubrication.

Application of ZN/P Variable. — Assume that a bearing is to operate at a speed of 1850 R.P.M. The desirable bearing operating temperature is about 130° F. in this case, and pressure lubrication is to be used with a light oil having a viscosity of 150 Saybolt at 100° F. and an absolute viscosity Z of about 13.5 centipoises at the operating temperature. Assume that tests with this type of bearing operating under these general conditions have shown that a ZN/P value of 100 is a very conservative value when the bearing is new. The bearing, therefore, is to be designed on the basis of $\dfrac{ZN}{P} = 100$. Then $P = \dfrac{ZN}{100} = \dfrac{13.5 \times 1850}{100} = 250$ pounds per square inch approximately. The foregoing example is merely to illustrate the procedure. A conservative ZN/P value may not be over 20 in some cases. If the designer knows the ZN/P value at the point where the oil film breaks down, he can select a value far enough from this point to provide a suitable factor of safety. This permits using the maximum safe unit pressure and lubricant of the lowest viscosity, thus minimizing bearing losses. The load or speed combination must not exceed the safe extreme values established by the tests employed in determining the allowable range of ZN/P values for a given bearing.

Bearing Clearance. — The ratio of the clearance C (difference between journal and bearing diameters) to the diameter D is very important in connection with bearing lubrication. Accurately machined bearings with ground journals for use in steam turbines, generators, etc., usually have a clearance $C = D \times 0.001$. Clearances equal to $D \times 0.0015$ and up to $0.0035 \, D$ are often used. If it is necessary to estimate the probable journal expansion, the following coefficients of expansion can be used in the absence of more specific data from the manufacturer of the material employed: Nickel steel (10 per cent nickel), 0.0000073 inch; Bessemer rolled hard steel, 0.0000056 inch; Bessemer rolled soft steel, 0.0000063 inch.

The foregoing values represent the coefficients of expansion per inch of diameter per degree F.

Housing Design and Journal Finish. — The bearing housing should be designed as symmetrically as possible to obtain uniform expansion and retain uniform clearance over the area, to avoid local contacts with the journal. The housing should support rigidly the entire surface of the sleeve or lining. Journals which are to carry the maximum safe pressure should be finished by grinding and hardened and lapped surfaces are preferable.

Bearing Temperatures. — As a general rule, bearing temperatures should not exceed 140 to 160 degrees F. When the temperature exceeds 160 degrees F., a careful study should be made of the mechanical and lubricating conditions of the bearing.

According to the practice of the General Electric Co., bearing temperatures ordinarily are limited to a rise of about 70° F. and on large machines to 55° rise. When the bearing diameter or speed reaches a point at which, with air cooling, the temperatures would exceed these values, water cooling is adopted, the cooling coils usually being embedded in the babbitt. In measuring temperatures, place the thermometer in the lubricating oil if possible.

Heat-radiating Capacity of Bearings. — To prevent excessive heating, the heat generated must not exceed the rate of radiation after the bearing temperature is up to the maximum running temperature.

$$PV = \frac{R}{\mu}.$$

See table for values of R (based upon experiments by Lasche) both for ordinary bearings in still air and bearings ventilated by air currents.

Another equation containing a radiation factor is as follows: $PV = \frac{rt}{\mu}$. The approximate values of r for different types of bearings follow: 2 for babbitted lineshaft hanger bearings; 3 for light outboard generator bearings without oil pockets; 4 for small ring-oiler bearings with oil pockets; 5 for heavy-duty outboard generator bearings without oil pockets; 6 for heavy-duty engine main bearings without oil pockets. The normal or usual still-air allowance for rt is about 150 to 200 foot-pounds per minute, and the maximum still-air allowance about 300 to 400 foot-pounds per minute. For crankpins, use $1\frac{1}{2}$ to 2 times the still-air allowance. For liquid cooling or forced ventilation, use $1\frac{1}{2}$ to 3 times the still-air allowance depending upon the effectiveness of the cooling medium. The value of μ applies to perfect oil-film lubrication.

Heat-radiating Capacity of Bearings

Operating Condition	Bearing Temperature minus Air Temperature, Degrees F.							
	40	60	80	100	120	140	160	180
	Radiation, Ft.-lbs. per Min. per Sq. In. of Projected Area							
Well Ventilated............	180	285	405	555	740	1020	...	...
Unventilated..............	105	160	230	310	390	500	625	790
Thin Bearing..............	20	30	38	50	65	80	95	110

Diameter of Journal. — It has been assumed quite generally that the journal diameter should be held down to the minimum required for strength and stiffness in order to obtain as low a rubbing velocity V in feet per minute as possible. It has also been assumed that unit pressure P should be decreased as the velocity is increased; however, it has been demonstrated in modern practice that increasing the velocity makes it possible to increase the unit pressure on well-lubricated bearings of good design and workmanship and within limits varying for different bearings. Moreover, higher unit pressure permits reducing the bearing length in proportion to the diameter, thus avoiding deflections which, in relatively long bearings, make it much more difficult to maintain a uniform and correct amount of clearance with resulting uniformity in bearing pressure over the entire area.

Ratio of Length to Diameter. — The modern tendency is toward shorter and more rigid bearings, the lengths being less than the diameter for some types. The rigidity obtained with a short bearing is conducive to maintaining a uniform pressure film over the bearing area. Excessive length, especially if accompanied by too much deflection, results in a waste of power, whereas insufficient length for a given load, velocity, and lubricating condition may cause abrasion and seizure due to excessive unit pressures. Some ratios of length to diameter which have been used follow: Marine engine main bearings and crankpins, 1 to 1.5; stationary engine main journals, 1.5 to 2.5; stationary engine crankpins, 1; ordinary heavy shafting with fixed bearings, 2 to 3; ordinary shafting with self-adjusting bearings, 3 to 4.

Empirical Formula for Pressure and Velocity. — In the formula $PV = \dfrac{R}{\mu}$, if the value equivalent to $R \div \mu$ is determined for a given class of bearings, we have an approximate formula for checking allowable combinations of pressure and velocity for similar bearings and operating conditions; thus, PV is assumed to equal a constant. This constant, for a given bearing, may be determined for an allowable range of combined pressure-velocity values, without knowing what values of R and μ it represents. The value of μ covers a wide range, especially if imperfectly lubricated bearings are included; hence, the constant should be based upon the actual operation of a given type of bearing. The formula $PV =$ constant is quite generally used by manufacturers, but the constants for different types of bearings may vary from 10,000 to 350,000 or higher. The following formulas have been applied to ring-oiling bearings. $D =$ shaft diam. and $N =$ R.P.M.

$$P = \frac{480,000}{DN + 1200} \text{ when } DN \text{ is less than } 2000$$

$$P = 0.0065 \, DN + 135 \text{ when } DN \text{ is greater than } 2000.$$

Unit Pressure Data for Bearings. — Bearing pressures per square inch of projected area have increased considerably during recent years, especially for bearings designed to maintain perfect oil-film lubrication. These pressure increases are due to such factors as more precise knowledge of designing procedure resulting from tests and research, the use of smoother, more accurate and more rigid journals and bearing surfaces, superior bearing materials, and improved lubricants and lubricant application. (See Table.)

Oil-grooves in Bearings. — With the exception of small solid bearings subjected to light loads, it is common practice to groove bearings in order to distribute the lubricant more uniformly. Such grooves should not extend across that part of the bearing surface likely to be subjected to oil-film pressure because grooves in the pressure area permit the oil to follow the path of least resistance, thus preventing, partially, the formation of an oil film on the load-carrying side. Grooves should never be cut into the journal, but always in the surrounding bearing. A longitudinal groove along the top is often used but one inclining from the oil hole in the direction of journal rotation is preferable. This groove should not extend to the ends of the bearing, unless the bearing is ring-oiled or chain-oiled, and leakage at the ends drains to the housing well for recirculation. With two-part bearings, the longitudinal grooves may be formed along each side merely by chamfering the edges of the cap and base but not the entire length. The edges of all chamfers and grooves should be rounded to avoid sharp corners and facilitate the introduction of the oil between the journal and the bearing metal.

Location of Pressure Area and Point of Oil Entry. — The location of maximum oil-film pressure depends upon the speed, load, direction of rotation, and other factors. If the load is applied to a horizontal journal running counter-clockwise, the center of maximum pressure will be located to the right of the foot of the vertical center-line anywhere from, say, 10 to 45 degrees, depending upon the load, speed, etc. Excessive load or very low speed may shift the center of maximum pressure

Allowable Unit Bearing Pressures for Various Classes of Bearings*

Type of Bearing or Kind of Service	Pressures, Lbs. per Sq. In.
Motor and generator bearings (general)	75 to 100
Large motors and generators (journal diameters above 8 inches)	150 to 200
Turbine bearings	150 to 200
Locomotive driving axles	175 to 200
Railway car axles	300 to 325
Slow-speed stationary-engine main bearings (steam load)	200 to 400
High-speed stationary-engine main bearings (steam load)	150 to 250
Locomotive crankpins	1500 to 1700
Stationary-engine crankpins	500 to 1000
Heavy refrigerating-machinery main bearings	225 to 250
Heavy refrigerating-machinery crankpins (maximum)	900
Heavy refrigerating-machinery cross-head guides	50
Bearings for very slow speed as in turntables in bridge work	7000 to 9000
Bearings for slow speed and intermittent load as in punch presses	3000 to 4000
Heavy lineshaft, bronze or babbitt lining	100 to 150

* These pressures in pounds per square inch of area equal to length times diameter, are intended as a general guide only. The allowable unit pressure depends upon operating conditions, especially in regard to lubrication, design of bearing, workmanship, velocity, and nature of the load.

practically to the bottom of the bearing circle. The minimum pressure area for counter-clockwise rotation will be at the upper part of the bearing somewhere to the right of the vertical center-line. Reversal of rotation will shift these points of maximum and minimum pressures to the same relative positions to the left of the vertical center-line.

For gravity feed, the oil should enter on the low-pressure side; and if the journal is carrying the load, a point of entry at the top of the bearing will meet practical requirements. For pressure systems, the oil should enter adjacent to the high-pressure area on the *in-feeding* side toward which the journal surface is moving. If the point of entry is on the horizontal center-line (or below it not over 45 degrees) at the left-hand side for counter-clockwise rotation and at the right-hand side for clockwise rotation, the oil will enter on the in-feeding side.

Thrust Bearings. — Flat thrust bearings should be made of an annular form having an inside diameter one-half of the external diameter. Experiments carried out by Schiele to determine the wear in pivot bearings show that the wear is theoretically along a line called the *tractrix*, and that an end-thrust bearing made of this form will have the wear in the direction of the axis of a thrust shaft uniform at all points, but it has been shown in practice that little is to be gained by the use of bearings having this complicated shape. Experiments made on flat pivot thrust bearings, three inches in diameter, indicate that the coefficient of friction between a steel pivot and a manganese-bronze bearing, properly lubricated, using two radial oil-grooves only, varies from 0.018 at 50 revolutions per minute, to an average of 0.011 at 350 revolutions per minute. If four radial oil-grooves are used instead of two, the friction is approximately doubled, due to rupture of the oil film.

The load that may be safely carried by a thrust bearing varies with the velocity of the rubbing surfaces. The table following may be used as a guide in designing bearings in which the shaft is made from wrought iron or steel and the bearing from bronze or brass, and which have ample lubrication. In general, it is possible to use bath lubrication for thrust bearings, that is, the running surfaces are submerged constantly in a bath of oil. If the shaft is made from cast iron running on bronze or brass bearings, the values in the table for allowable pressure should be only one-half of those given.

Allowable Pressure, in Pounds per Square Inch, on Thrust Bearings

Average Velocity of Rubbing Surface, Feet per Minute	Safe Pressure, Lbs. per Sq. In.	Average Velocity of Rubbing Surface, Feet per Minute	Safe Pressure, Lbs. per Sq. In.
Slow and intermittent	1500	100 to 150	75
50	200	150 to 200	60
50 to 100	100	Over 200	50

Collar Thrust Bearings. — In collar thrust bearings, the thrust is taken by projections or shoulders on the shaft, often at some distance from its end. This type of bearing is used when a greater thrust than can be conveniently placed on a single flat or step bearing is to be taken care of. In a well-made bearing, each of the collar surfaces takes its proportionate part of the load, and it is thus possible, without using excessive diameters, to properly distribute a very great thrust on a number of collars formed solidly with the shaft, by cutting a number of grooves in the latter. One advantage of the collar bearing is that the difference between the outer and inner diameters of the bearing surface is not very great, and hence the velocities at the outer and inner edges do not vary appreciably; this, again, eliminates unequal wear on the thrust collar surfaces. The safe load that may be placed on collar thrust bearings varies between 60 to 100 pounds per square inch.

Hydraulically Supported Step Bearings. — The type of thrust bearing which is hydraulically supported has very little frictional resistance and is adapted to heavy pressures and high speeds. Bearings of this type which have been applied to Curtis vertical steam turbines are so designed that oil (water may also be used with this type of bearing), under sufficient pressure to sustain the load, is forced between recessed plates at the bottom of the shaft and then passes out radially in the form of a thin film and up through a cylindrical guide bearing located just above the bottom plates, thus floating the shaft upon the oil film.

Thrust Bearing Design Based on Principle of Wedge-shaped Oil Film. — The investigations of Professor Osborne Reynolds, following the experiments of Tower on well fitted car journals and brasses flooded with oil, showed that the oil, because of its viscosity and adhesion to the journal, is, by the journal rotation, dragged into a wedge-shaped space between the journal and brass. This action sets up pressure in the oil film which, in turn, supports the load, thus separating the bearing surfaces. The design of the Kingsbury thrust bearing is based on this principle, the bearing floating the load on wedge-shaped oil films which form automatically and without employing a high pressure oil pump. There is usually a flat, annular, revolving plate with the bearing face immersed in oil and supported on one or more shoes which are mounted to tilt as required by running conditions. These bearings are made for both horizontal and vertical shafts. The low-speed bearings may be loaded to 1000 pounds or more per square inch when using heavy oil, and high-speed bearings with light oils regularly carry loads up to 500 pounds per square inch. The friction loss in this bearing is very low. According to an approximate rule for vertical bearings having six shoes with the inside diameter one-half the outside diameter and loaded to 350 pounds per square inch of shoe area, the mean coefficient of friction is 0.00009 times the square root of the revolutions per minute and varies inversely as the square root of the unit pressure, when using dynamo oil having a temperature of about 40 degrees C. The coefficient of friction has been found by a large number of tests to vary between 0.0008 and 0.003.

Frictional Power Losses in Bearings. — In the following formulas for determining power losses due to friction, W = work expended in friction in foot-pounds per minute; μ = coefficient of friction; L = total load in pounds on bearing; D = diameter (cylindrical bearing); R = maximum radius (step or thrust bearing); r = minimum radius; N = revolutions per minute; α = one-half included angle (conical pivot bearing); M = moment of friction in inch-pounds. Then, $W = \dfrac{2\pi MN}{12}$. The values of M and W for different bearings are as follows: *Shafts and journals*: $M = \frac{1}{2}\,\mu LD$ and $W = \dfrac{2\pi\mu LDN}{24} = 0.2618\,\mu LDN$. *Flat pivot or step bearing*: $M = \frac{2}{3}\,\mu LR$ and $W = 0.349\,\mu LRN$. *Collar thrust bearing*: $M = \frac{2}{3}\,\mu L\dfrac{R^3 - r^3}{R^2 - r^2}$ and $W = 0.349\,\mu LN\dfrac{R^3 - r^3}{R^2 - r^2}$. *Conical pivot bearing*: $M = \frac{2}{3}\,\mu LR\ \mathrm{cosec}\ \alpha$ and $W = 0.349\,\mu LRN\ \mathrm{cosec}\ \alpha$. *Truncated conical pivot*: $M = \frac{2}{3}\,\mu L\dfrac{R^3 - r^3}{(R^2 - r^2)\sin \alpha}$ and $W = 0.349\,\mu LN\dfrac{R^3 - r^3}{(R^2 - r^2)\sin \alpha}$. *Hemispherical step bearing and Schiele's tractrix pivot*: $M = \mu LR$ and $W = 0.5236\,\mu LRN$. For flat bearing surfaces in general $W = \mu LS$ in which S = rate, in feet per minute, at which sliding action occurs.

Knife-edge Bearings. — The knife-edge bearings of weighing and testing apparatus should be made of steel having 0.90 to 1.00 per cent carbon. An angle of 90 degrees is recommended for knife-edge bearings. The seats for supporting the pivots should be drawn to a light straw color and the pivots slightly darker. The bearing edge may be left sharp for loads up to 1000 pounds per inch of length; for heavier loads the edge is dulled slightly with an oilstone.

Bearing Metals. — The developments which have been made in the design of plain or sleeve bearings include notable improvements in the characteristics of bearing materials. These developments in the bearing alloys are not restricted to mere changes in composition but include improvements in the physical properties due to refinement in manufacture and proper application of the alloys to shells or housings. Bearing metals are usually composed of alloys of copper, lead, tin, antimony and zinc, and are known as babbitt metal, white metal, brass, phosphor-bronze, and by various trade names. The price of these bearing metals depends largely upon the constituents. Lead and zinc are cheapest, with antimony, copper, and tin increasing progressively in price in the order named, tin being the most expensive. The more lead is used in a bearing, the cheaper it will be. Lead, however, is too soft to be used alone and must be alloyed with one of the other metals. Antimony added to lead increases the hardness and brittleness; with tin added, a tougher alloy is obtained. Nearly all the various babbitt metals are alloys of lead, tin and antimony.

Babbitt or White Metal Alloys. — Many different bearing metal compositions are referred to as babbitt metal. The accompanying table gives the compositions of five babbitt metals which have been standardized by the Society of Automotive Engineers, Inc. This table also includes general information regarding the recommended applications of these different compositions. See also the " white metal " compositions in the table "Miscellaneous Bearing Metal Compositions." These white metal alloys are known commercially as " babbitt metal."

Original Babbitt Metal: The exact composition of the original babbitt metal is not known. The ingredients were copper, tin and antimony in approximately the following proportions: 89.3 per cent tin; 3.6 per cent copper; 7.1 per cent antimony.

S.A.E. Standard Babbitt Metals (Cast)
Composition in Percentage

Spec. No.	Tin	Copper	Antimony	Lead	Iron	Arsenic	Bismuth
10	90 min.	4 to 5	4 to 5	0.35 max.	0.08 max.	0.10 max.	0.08 max.
11	86 min.	5 to 6.5	6 to 7.5	0.35 max.	0.08 max.	0.10 max.	0.08 max.
110	87.75 min.	2.25 to 3.75	7 to 8.5	0.35 max.	0.08 max.	0.10 max.	0.08 max.
13	4.5 to 5.5	0.5 max.	9.25 to 10.75	86.0 max.	....	0.6 max.	....
14	9.25 to 10.75	0.5 max.	14 to 16	76.0 max.	....	0.6 max.	....

All of these babbitt metal compositions are without zinc or aluminum.

These babbitts have non-scoring and non-wearing properties, and are resistant to corrosion from organic acid of the type normal to lubricating oil.

Babbitt No. 10: This babbitt is very fluid and may be used for bronze-backed bearings, particularly for thin linings such as are used in aircraft engines. It is also suitable for die-castings.

Babbitt No. 11: A rather hard babbitt which may be used for lining connecting-rod and shaft bearings which are subjected to heavy pressures; its "wiping" tendency is very slight. It is also suitable for die-castings.

Babbitt Nos. 13 *and* 14: Cheap babbitt metals which serve successfully where the bearings are large and the service light. They should not be used as a substitute for a babbitt with a high tin content. Nos. 13 and 14 are also suitable for die-castings.

This metal possesses great anti-frictional qualities, but the high percentage of tin makes it expensive and has led to the substitution of other metals which are marketed under the name of babbitt metal. These cheaper grades, when properly made, are for some purposes superior to the original babbitt metal.

Bronze Bearing Metals. — Plain or sleeve-type bearings made of some composition designated as "bronze" are used on many different classes of machines. The accompanying table, "Miscellaneous Bearing Metal Compositions," includes several bronze alloys conforming to S.A.E. standards. The S.A.E. composition No. 64 has been widely used. This is known as phosphor bronze. It has good anti-friction qualities and stands up very well under heavy loads and severe usage. S.A.E. standard No. 660 is another alloy which has been widely used. In the automotive industry it is used for such parts as spring bushings, torque tube bushings, steering-knuckle bushings, piston-pin bushings, thrust washers, etc. S.A.E. Specification No. 67 is known as a semi-plastic bronze. This is intended for use where a soft bronze with good anti-friction qualities is desired. The plasticity is of especial value when the shaft is soft and the speed high. S.A.E. alloy No. 63 is particularly adapted to bushings subject to heavy loads and severe working conditions or when there is vibration or shock. A hardened steel shaft should be used with this composition.

Porous Bronze Bearings. — Bearings of this type are of bronze, but are not cast in the usual way. They are composite bearings, formed initially under heavy pressure from powdered metals and graphite. The pressed composition is subjected to a temperature high enough to convert it into a true alloy resembling cast bronze, but much more porous. This porous structure forms a reservoir for oil.

Self-lubricating or Oilless Bearings. — Oilless or self-lubricating bearings are especially adapted for applications in places where oiling is undesirable, or where the bearings are difficult of access, or likely to be neglected. They are of particular value in such plants as canneries, textile mills, etc., where the product is liable to harm from dripping oil, and oilless bearings are applied in many other classes of service. A number of different types of oilless bearings have been developed, each of which doubtless has its advantages when applied under suitable conditions. One type consists of wood impregnated with wax, oil or paraffin; another is made of bronze and has graphite inserts; another type is formed of graphite impregnated with some bearing metal such as a white alloy or bronze; and still another consists of hard maple reinforced by babbitt metal, the wood shell of which is impregnated with lubricants and thus serves as an oil reservoir.

Laminated Sleeve Bearings with Bronze or Steel Backing. — This thin-shell type of bearing consists of either a tin- or lead-base white metal or babbitt fused

Miscellaneous Bearing Metal Compositions

Bearing Alloy, Nos. (1), (2), etc. indicate Footnotes	Principal Elements, Percentage					
	Copper	Tin	Lead	Zinc	Antimony	Fe. P Na*
S.A.E. No. 64 (1)	78 to 82	9 to 11	8 to 11	.75 max.	.5 max.	.25 P
S.A.E. No. 660	81 to 85	6.25 to 7.5	6 to 8	2 to 4	.25 max.	.2 Fe
S.A.E. No. 67 (2)	76.5 to 79.5	5 to 7	14.5 to 17.5	4	.4 max.	.4 Fe
S.A.E. No. 63 (3)	86 to 89	9 to 11	1 to 2.5	.75 max.		.25 P
Car Bearings (4)						
High-lead bronze	74	5	21			
Journal bronze	82 to 84	12.5 to 14.5	1	2.5 to 4.5		.06 Fe
Ajax metal	77	11.5	11.5			
Plastic bronze	65	5	30			
Camelia metal	70	4.5	15	10		.5 Fe
White brass	2	64		34		
Queen's metal	3.5	88.5		1	7	
Karmarsch metal	9.5	70.8			19.7	
Karmarsch metal	21.4	71.4			7.2	
Hoyle's metal		46	42		12	
Coleco metal	1	8	77		14	
Magnolia metal		4.75 to 6	78 to 80		15 to 16	
Tempered lead	11	.08	98.5			1.3 Na
White metal (5)	4½	91	.35	None	4½	.08 Fe
White metal	3	75	10	None	12	.08 Fe
White metal	1½	20	63.5	None	15	.08 Fe
White metal	.5 max.	5	80	None	15	
White metal	.5 max.		90	None	10	

(1) Phosphor bronze. Excellent for heavy loads and severe usage. (2) Semi-plastic bronze. Soft bronze with good anti-friction qualities. (3) Leaded gun metal. A general utility bronze, especially for bushings subjected to heavy loads.

(4) Railway journal bearings, according to standard specifications of the Association of American Railroads, have the following composition, in percentages: *Brass Back:* Lead, 15 to 22; tin, 5 to 7; max. impurities, including zinc, 3; max. impurities, excluding zinc, 1; balance, copper. *Lining:* Tin, as specified; antimony, not less than 8; tin and antimony, 10 to 14; arsenic, max., 0.2; copper, max., 0.5; sum of tin, antimony, lead and arsenic, min., 99.25; remainder, max., 0.75.

These specifications cover journal bearings for passenger and freight cars and locomotive tenders. Unless otherwise specified, the thickness of the lining is to be ¼ inch.

(5) Different grades of white metals (commercially known as babbitt metal) from the A.S.T.M. standard specifications. The cheaper grades have relatively high percentages of lead.

* Maximum percentages are given in the last column. Fe represents iron; P, phosphorus; Na, sodium.

to a reinforcing back made either of steel or bronze. The steel or bronze shell provides the necessary strength. These thin-shell bearings are not only low in cost, but
efficient and permit the use of a housing of smaller diameter, thus saving in material
and making the assembly lighter. Moreover, these bearings are inexpensive to
replace. The characteristics of both the backing material and the lining may, of
course, be selected to suit operating conditions. The strength of the backing
material is combined with the plastic qualities of the babbitt or white-metal lining,
and the degree of plasticity may be varied to suit resistance to pounding or wear.
For thin linings the S.A.E. standard babbitt composition No. 10 (see table) may be
used with bronze-backed bearings, as it is very fluid. Bronze as a backing material
is preferable to steel for certain applications. Bronze is more economical, excepting
where there is large production. If there are thrust loads, the flanges of the bronze
backing can carry such loads without lamination or lining. The heat conductivity
of bronze is higher than that of steel. Steel, however, is preferable for bearings
subjected to heavy duty as in airplane engines, steam turbines, Diesel engines, etc.

Bronze Backing Composition: The S.A.E. standard (No. 66) bronze backing for
lined bearings contains in percentage: Copper, 83 to 86; tin, 4½ to 6; lead, 8 to 10;
zinc, 2 max.; other impurities, 0.25 max.

Copper-lead, Silver and Cadmium Bearing Alloys — S.A.E. Standard

Elements	Copper-Lead Type		Silver Type		Cadmium Type	
	No. 48	No. 480	No. 17P	No. 17C	No. 18	No. 180
Copper	67 to 74	60 to 70	......	1.25 max.	0.05 max.	0.4 to 0.75
Lead	25 to 32	30 to 40	......	......	0.02 max.	0.02 max.
Tin	......	0.05	......	......	0.01	0.01
Iron	0.35 max.	0.35 max.	......	......	......	......
Zinc	0.10 max.	......	......	......	0.02 max.	0.02 max.
Nickel	......	......	......	......	1.0 to 1.5	......
Silver	1.50 max.	......	99.75 min.	98.50 min.	......	0.5 to 1.0
Phosphor.	0.025 max.	......	......	......	......	......
Cadmium	......	......	......	......	98.5 min.	98.25 min.
Other	0.15 max.	0.30 max.	......	0.25 max.	......	......

The S.A.E. tin and lead base babbitts have non-scoring and non-wearing properties
and are resistant to corrosion from organic acidity of the type normal to lubricating
oil, but they are low in resistance to fatigue. Copper-lead bearings are inferior to tin
and lead base babbits in non-scoring but they are greatly superior in resistance to
fatigue. Cadmium bearings may approach the tin or lead base babbitts in non-scoring
and the copper-lead bearings in resistance to fatigue, depending upon design and operating conditions. However, the S.A.E. copper-lead and the S.A.E. cadmium bearings
may corrode if operated at sufficiently high temperatures using lubricants containing
animal or vegetable oil additions or using mineral oils which develop acidic compounds on oxidation. Numerous satisfactory applications of these two alloys are
made in cases where such acidity is not present and does not develop in service.

S.A.E. No. 48 and No. 481 are similar to the U. S. Army Air Corps specification and
are intended primarily for airplane engine steel backed bearings. On finished sections
over ⅜ in., or sections with bronze on both sides, the iron limit shall be 0.35 per cent
maximum.

S.A.E. No. 480 is intended for general automotive bearings other than airplane
engine bearings. The tolerance on lead is purposely made broad enough to cover the
several compositions now in commercial use. A narrower lead tolerance may be
specified by the purchaser.

S.A.E. No. 17P is for plated and No. 17C for cast type steel backed bearings.

Babbitting. — Babbitt metal is extensively used as a lining for bearings, not only for its anti-frictional qualities, but because it is much cheaper than a machined box. Prior to pouring the babbitt, the bearing should be heated to prevent the molten metal from becoming chilled and sluggish. Bronze shells which are to have babbitt linings should first be tinned by immersing in a pot of molten solder. Use solder of " half and half " composition, and zinc chloride as a flux. The shell should be babbitted immediately after tinning. Babbitt should not be used for tinning, because it has a much higher melting point, which makes it difficult to maintain a molten film on the surface to be tinned. Cast-iron shells are rarely, if ever, tinned.

If much work of this kind is being done, babbitting jigs should be made. These are simply fixtures which bear against or fit into any finished surface or hole with which the mandrel must be aligned, and which hold the latter in the correct position while the babbitt is being poured. Whenever practicable, the bearing should be placed in a vertical position while pouring. The ladle should preferably have a rounded spout rather than one which is sharp or broad. A broad, thin stream or one that is intermittent tends to produce porous areas or blow-holes. Putty is preferable to clay for luting or sealing the ends of the bearings, as moisture in the clay tends to produce sputtering.

Coatings for Babbitting Mandrels. — For babbitting solid bearings, the surface of the mandrel which comes into contact with the metal, when the latter is poured into the bearing, should be coated with some substance to facilitate the removal of the mandrel from the bearing. One method of coating the mandrel is to hold it near an oil flame so that the smoke will come into contact with it and cover the surface with carbon. Instead of smoking the mandrel, the surface is sometimes covered with a coat of thin white lead. Another method is to wrap a piece of paper about the mandrel. In babbitting two-part bearings a coating or covering for the mandrel will not be necessary.

Temperature of Molten Babbitt. — Babbitt metal used for bearings is melted in iron pots or kettles, and the molten metal should be kept at a constant temperature of about 870 degrees F. A constant temperature is very important. The temperature should be increased slowly and the babbitt thoroughly stirred, especially when new babbitt is being melted, or when old babbitt which has been allowed to solidify in the pot is being re-melted. This is necessary in order to prevent certain of the constituent metals from rising to the top and becoming oxidized, as well as to prevent the heavier metals from sinking to the bottom of the pot, thus producing a non-uniform alloy. The babbitt may be melted in the pouring ladle over an open fire. The temperature is about right when a pine stick used for stirring chars but does not ignite. The mandrel temperature is right when water evaporates rapidly from its surface without spluttering.

Preheating Bearings and Mandrels. — All iron shells must be preheated to a temperature of from 200 to 300 degrees F. before pouring the babbitt. The higher temperature is preferable, as a rule, except where a lining is being poured in a very heavy shell, when it may be necessary to use the lower temperature to prevent the babbitt from cooling too slowly. The mandrels should be preheated to a temperature of from 200 to 300 degrees F. when pouring babbitt into the shells, but, for bronze shells, a somewhat lower temperature should be used. Oil-holes in the bearing shells are filled with asbestos or wood driven against the mandrel, and the joints are made tight with clay.

Pouring Babbitt Metal. — To secure good results, the babbitt must be poured at the correct temperature. If the babbitt is poured at too high a temperature, extreme shrinkage will occur, resulting in porous areas in the lining and in broken anchors; furthermore, the babbitt will be oxidized, softened, and dirty, and its anti-frictional qualities will be lowered. If the babbitt is poured at too low a temperature, a lining having a coarse granular formation is the result. If the shells and mandrels are too cold, blow-holes and similar defects will form, and the lining will shrink away from the shell in cooling. If the temperature of the shell or mandrel is too high, the babbitt will cool too slowly, and the heavier metals will have time to settle, producing a bearing which will be soft at one place and brittle at another.

Ball and Roller Bearings

Ball bearings are used in preference to sliding bearings principally for the following reasons: There is less loss of power on account of the lower coefficient of friction; the frictional resistance at starting is very much less than in a sliding bearing; ball bearings are much shorter and more compact than sliding bearings; the scraping and fitting of bearing linings is not necessary; the danger of heated bearings is practically eliminated; a bearing of proper construction can adjust itself to deflections of the shaft; the wear is practically negligible.

Steel for Balls. — In order to determine the best steel for ball bearings, one of the largest elevator companies in the United States tested, by actual use, 432 different samples of steel obtained in this country and abroad. These tests indicated that the two grades of carbon and alloy steels given herewith are especially adapted for making steel balls:

Carbon, 1.12; silicon, 0.015; phosphorus, 0.017; manganese, 0.19; sulphur, 0.019; chromium, 0.25 per cent.

Carbon, 0.95; silicon, 0.014; sulphur, 0.019; phosphorus, 0.018; manganese, 0.025; chromium, 1.25; tungsten, 0.25 per cent.

Testing Strength of Steel Balls. — The testing of a steel ball for crushing strength can be done between hardened plates by placing three balls into a rather close-fitting tube. The center ball is the one that will be tested. When the pressure is applied, the upper and lower balls will sink into the plate somewhat, which will give them a greater surface bearing than the middle ball, the latter bearing only at two points between the upper and lower balls; hence, the middle ball will ordinarily break first. If a ball is properly hardened, it will break into several pieces. Uniformity of hardness throughout the entire cross-section and a fine grain are important qualities, both of which can be determined by the appearance of the fracture. Of course, the heat-treatment must be governed by the nature of the material. The accompanying table gives the crushing loads ordinarily required by ball manufacturers for regular tool-steel balls. The figures in this table are the result of repeated tests and are considered safe for use in calculations. In selecting balls for a bearing, a factor of safety of 10 should be adopted unless the bearing is re-

Crushing Loads for Tool-steel Balls

Size of Ball, Inches	Ultimate Strength, Pounds	Size of Ball, Inches	Ultimate Strength, Pounds	Size of Ball, Inches	Ultimate Strength, Pounds	Size of Ball, Inches	Ultimate Strength, Pounds
1/16	390	1/4	6,215	5/8	39,000	1 1/8	125,000
3/32	875	5/16	9,750	3/4	56,250	1 1/4	156,000
7/64	1200	3/8	14,000	13/16	66,000	1 1/2	225,000
1/8	1560	7/16	19,100	7/8	76,000	1 5/8	263,000
9/16	3500	1/2	25,000	15/16	88,000	1 3/4	306,000
7/32	4780	9/16	31,500	1	100,000	2	400,000

quired in an extremely narrow space. The loads listed by makers for ball bearings vary considerably and when the bearings are much alike in regard to size, design and material, this difference is due to the factor of safety adopted. Alloy steel balls will usually carry from 25 to 50 per cent more load than ordinary tool-steel balls.

Test of Heat-Treatment. — In order to determine whether a ball has been properly heat-treated, enclose the finished ball in a piece of waste, place it on an anvil and break it open with a heavy blow. (The waste prevents the pieces from flying about.) If the ball has been properly heat-treated, the surface of the fracture will have a fine even grain. If it has not been properly heat-treated, the surface will appear coarse and granular. Tests have shown that the average crushing load of balls that were annealed before hardening is approximately 30 per cent greater than of balls which were not so heat-treated. The heat-treatment not only strengthens the balls but prevents them from flaking off, crumbling, etc. If during the test the ball should break in half, it would indicate that the steel had not been properly drawn after hardening, but was still subjected to internal stresses. If a ball has been properly drawn, it can be " touched " with a fine Swiss file; and under the blows of a heavy hammer, it will break into several pieces, as mentioned.

Quality of Steel Balls. — Nothing but tool or alloy steel balls should be used for high-grade work, and it is very important that they be accurate as to size and shape and be properly heat-treated to obtain a fine grain. The material of which they are made should have as high an elastic limit as possible. Case-hardened machine steel balls should not be used when heavy duty is required. While a ball can be case-hardened very deeply, the process does not remove the injurious elements, phosphorus, sulphur and silicon, which the cheaper steels contain in comparatively large percentages. Case-hardened balls have, however, proved satisfactory for many purposes, where the duty is not too severe.

Mounting Ball Bearings. — In the mounting of ball bearings, there are certain requirements which apply generally, although the exact arrangement must be governed to some extent by the conditions. If the bearing is to carry a radial load without thrust, the inner race should have a light driving fit on the shaft and be securely clamped against a shoulder by a nut or clamping device which is proof against jarring loose. The outer race of a bearing subjected to a radial load only, should fit closely in its retaining box or housing, but be free to "float" or shift in an endwise direction. When the outer race is mounted in this way, it will align itself with reference to the inner race and will tend to have a slow intermittent creeping movement, insuring a proper distribution of the load over the entire surface of the outer race. Even when it is desired to prevent end motion of the shaft, a slight lateral clearance of 0.010 or 0.015 inch should be provided, to permit the creeping movement and prevent the load from always bearing in one position on the race. When mounting for combined radial and thrust loads, the outer race of one bearing must be secured against endwise movement. If there are several radial bearings on the same shaft, the end thrust in both directions should be taken by the same bearing, and the outer races of the other bearings should be free to locate themselves. It is considered good practice when two bearings are mounted on one shaft, to prevent axial thrust by making the inner race of each bearing a light driving fit on the shaft. The outer race of one bearing has a sliding fit in its seat and is given a slight amount of axial play (say, from 0.010 to 0.020 inch); the outer race of the other bearing is also made a sliding fit, but is allowed considerable axial play. The first bearing takes the radial load and end thrust, and the second bearing, a radial load only. In selecting a bearing, it is well to remember that the rated capacity is usually for steady loads and speeds, and variations from these conditions require a reduction of the listed capacity. It is important to mount bearings so that they will be free from grit and moisture. If it is necessary to take ball bearings apart, the balls from different bearings should not be mixed, as they may vary in size more than is permissible for the individual bearing.

Thrust in Radial Bearings. — It is common practice to use the radial type of ball bearing when there is an axial thrust in addition to the normal radial load. There are three types of bearings that are combined load carriers: First, the annular ball bearing, which is primarily designed for radial loads and has no angle of contact incorporated in its design, therefore having minimum thrust capacity (approximately 20 per cent of its radial capacity). Second, the one-direction angular contact bearing, which has a thrust capacity depending upon race design and the angle incorporated, which is generally made so that the thrust capacity is 100 per cent of the radial capacity. (This bearing, however, when used for combined loads, can only be used in pairs, and must have a threaded or shim adjustment incorporated in the mounting design to allow for initial adjustment.) Third, the double angular type bearing which is really two bearings built as a self-contained unit. The functioning of this bearing is not dependent on any exterior adjustment, and the angle of contact is generally such that it will sustain approximately 150 per cent of its radial capacity as thrust.

A ball bearing of correct design has greater capacity under certain combined loads than when functioning under pure radial load. The reason for this is that the load-carrying capacity of a ball bearing is dependent on the number of balls in contact with the races under load. In general, the carrying capacity of a bearing is its ability to withstand pure radial load, and under combined loads, its capacity must be modified so that the allowable maximum load on the heaviest loaded ball under pure radial conditions is not exceeded by any load made up of thrust and radial combinations. Under pure radial load, approximately only one-third of the balls are sustaining load at any time. Under pure thrust load, all the balls are supporting load. Hence when the radial load is greater than the thrust load, a certain number of balls below the center line of the bearing opposite the applied load, will not be subjected to load, due to deformation of the parts. However, if the thrust load is greater than the radial load, all the balls will be loaded, and the maximum loaded ball will be the one subjected to maximum combined thrust and radial load.

The capacity of a ball bearing under combined loads is a function of the maximum safe ball load, the angles of contact and of load application, as measured from the plane of the balls, and also the center angle between the balls. As the pure thrust capacity of the bearing is increased by enlarging the angle of contact, there is a reduction in pure radial capacity.

Any ball bearing under combined loads becomes an angular contact bearing. This angle of contact can either be incorporated in the design or obtained by deformation of the parts under load. In other words, what is known as an annular bearing becomes an angular contact bearing when thrust is applied.

Ball Thrust Bearings. — Thrust bearings are adapted for heavy axial loads. They are made with both races flat on the bearing side; with one race flat and the other grooved; and with both races grooved. A form that is commonly used has two grooved races of circular section, and a spherical seat for one of the races or collars, so that the latter will align itself in order to distribute the load evenly over the entire number of balls. Some bearings of the thrust type have both of the outer thrust surfaces parallel. With this design, the collars should be exactly parallel, so that the load will be uniformly distributed on the balls. In fact, when two flat disks without the spherical seat are used, the capacity of the bearing depends largely upon the accuracy of the alignment, because, with even a slight distortion of the shaft, the load will not be sustained by the total number of the balls. When mounting single thrust bearings, the flat disk should properly have a tight fit on the shaft and rotate with it, the spherical seat remaining stationary, except for adjustments to compensate for changes in shaft alignment.

Capacity of Ball Thrust Bearings. — The speed at which thrust bearings are run, decidedly affects the carrying capacity, the latter rapidly diminishing as the speed increases. The centrifugal force at comparatively high speeds is the limiting feature in a bearing of this type. A general idea of the maximum loads which thrust bearings will carry at different speeds may be obtained from the accompanying tables.

Frictional Resistance. — Extensive tests for determining the coefficients of friction for various types of ball bearings show that the coefficient varies between close limits at different loads and speeds, whereas, for sliding bearings, it extends over a wide range for even small changes in speed or load. The frictional resistance of ball bearings has by actual experiment been found to vary between 0.0011 to 0.0095. These are the coefficients of friction referred to the shaft diameter, thus permitting direct comparison with coefficients of sliding friction. Ball bearings having a coefficient of friction much above 0.0015 under the greatest allowable load should not be recommended, because they are too short-lived. A coefficient of 0.0015 for a good ball bearing under its maximum load (independent of the speed, within limits) will, however, rise to approximately 0.0030, under a reduction of the load to about one-tenth of the maximum.

Loads on Ball Bearings. — The permissible load that a two-point annular ball bearing will carry can be determined approximately by the following formula (based upon the investigations of Prof. Stribeck), after a suitable value has been determined for constant K:

$$P = 0.44\,Kd^2n$$

in which K is a factor, depending upon the material in the balls, the form of the ball races and the operating speed of the bearings; n equals the number of balls; and d their diameter, taking ⅛ inch as the unit; for example, if the actual diameter is ¼ inch, d equals 2; if the diameter is ⅝ inch, d equals 5, etc. The better the material and the more careful the heat-treatment, the greater the value of factor K. When the diameter of the balls is increased, the value of K is decreased, as it is more difficult to harden a large ball uniformly, than a small one. With regard to the rotary speed, K should be diminished as the number of revolutions increases. For ball bearings made of high-grade material and accurately machined, K has the following approximate values for steady loads and uniform speeds:

Revolutions per Minute	10	150	300	500	1000	1500
Values of K	20	18	15	10	7.5	5

The preceding formula should be sufficiently accurate for bearings in which the balls vary from 10 to 20 in a set, provided the balls and races are properly proportioned. If a bearing had a comparatively large number of balls of such diameter that the strength of the races was impaired, the formula would indicate a greater load capacity than the bearing could safely carry. Even when the formula is applicable, which, as has been indicated, is only within certain limitations, it will sometimes be found that a bearing having a larger number of smaller diameter balls may be stronger than one with a less number of a larger diameter, or *vice versa*. The difference between the relative capacities may also be greater than the formula indicates, as the conditions of loading are more advantageous in a bearing having a greater number of smaller balls.

Roller Bearings. — A long series of tests with various types of roller bearings indicate that while each type has its peculiarities, there are certain principles which apply quite generally within narrow limits. The coefficient of friction of roller bearings is greater at low than at high speeds, but is much more nearly constant than in plain lubricated bearings. The coefficient of friction in bearings in which there is pure rolling is nearly constant at all speeds, but when there is end thrust, the friction decreases as the speed increases. The coefficient of friction is independent of the temperature of the bearings, unless the end thrust is excessive. The friction in a well-designed bearing is not greatly affected by lubrication. The wear of the rollers is often excessive, if the rotating parts and the casing are not hardened and well finished, especially when the bearing is subjected to end thrust. The end thrust on the rollers varies almost directly as the load on the bearing.

Loads on Roller Bearings. — The safe load diminishes as the speed of rotation of the rollers increases. If the speed is not excessive, the safe load may be determined approximately by the following formula: $P = \dfrac{Klnd^2}{ND + 2000\,d}$ in which $P =$ safe load, in pounds; $l =$ length of each roller, in inches; $n =$ number of rollers; $d =$ diameter of rollers, in inches; $N =$ revolutions per minute of shaft; $D =$ diameter of sleeve or roller path, in inches; $K =$ a constant. For first-class workmanship and solid steel rollers with hardened and ground surfaces, $K = 1,200,000$ to $2,000,000$ for rollers having a length equal to one diameter.

Load Capacities of Roller Bearings

Bore Diam., mm. *	Outside Diam., mm. *	Width, mm. *	Rollers		R.P.M. and Safe Loads in Pounds†			
			Diam., Inches	No.	100	500	1000	2000
Standard Medium Series — Partial List of Sizes								
10	35	11	3/16	10	1,050	600	500	400
15	42	13	1/4	9	1,530	900	700	565
20	52	15	1/4	12	2,040	1,200	950	750
30	72	19	3/8	12	4,200	2,450	1,950	1,550
40	90	23	7/16	12	5,500	3,220	2,550	2,020
50	110	27	9/16	12	8,500	4,980	3,950	3,130
60	130	31	5/8	12	10,260	6,000	4,760	3,780
80	170	39	3/4	15	17,600	10,300	8,170	6,500
100	215	47	1	14	27,200	15,900	12,600	....
120	260	55	1 1/8	16	38,200	22,350	17,750	....
140	300	62	1 3/8	15	50,900	29,800	23,600	....
Standard Heavy Series — Partial List of Sizes								
20	72	19	7/16	10	4,580	2,680	2,130	1,690
25	80	21	1/2	10	5,770	3,370	2,680	2,120
30	90	23	9/16	10	7,100	4,150	3,300	2,600
40	110	27	5/8	12	10,260	6,000	4,760	3,780
50	130	31	3/4	12	14,000	8,240	6,540	5,200
60	150	35	7/8	12	18,500	10,800	8,580	6,800
70	180	42	1	12	23,340	13,650	10,830	8,600
80	200	48	1 1/8	12	28,670	16,770	13,300	10,560
90	225	54	1 1/4	12	34,500	20,180	16,000	....
100	265	60	1 3/8	12	40,770	23,840	18,900	....

* For converting millimeters into inches, see table on page 1864.
† Norma-Hoffmann Bearings Corporation.

Machine Tool Roller Bearing Load Table*

Shaft Diam., Inches	Bearing Length, Inches	Roller Diam., Inches	Outside Diam. Bearing	Type of Outer Race	Speeds in R.P.M. and Load Capacities				
					25	150	300	500	1000
3/4	1	5/16	1 7/16	Split	95	83	71	61	48
3/4	1	5/16	1 5/8	Solid	380	330	284	243	190
1	2	3/8	1 15/16	Split	304	260	227	195	....
1	1	1/2	2 1/4	Solid	540	480	420	365	275
1	2	1/2	2 1/4	Solid	1,370	1220	1085	935	700
1 1/4	2	1/2	2 7/16	Split	370	314	274	232	...
1 1/4	2 1/4	5/8	2 3/4	Solid	1,940	1725	1500	1300	955
1 1/2	2	9/16	2 13/16	Split	440	370	320	266	....
1 1/2	1 1/4	3/4	3 3/8	Solid	1,100	965	835	710	525
1 1/2	2 1/2	3/4	3 3/8	Solid	2,620	2300	2000	1700	1250
1 3/4	2	9/16	3 1/16	Split	507	421	360	295	....
1 3/4	2 1/2	3/4	3 5/8	Solid	3,020	2640	2260	1925	1400
2	4	5/8	3 1/2	Split	1,285	1070	900	730	....
2	2 3/4	7/8	4 1/8	Solid	3,800	3350	2810	2400	1710
2 1/4	3	5/8	3 3/4	Split	1,030	850	710	575	....
2 1/4	2 3/4	7/8	4 3/8	Solid	4,250	3670	3120	2620	1850
2 1/2	5	11/16	4 1/8	Split	2,010	1650	1360	1090	....
2 1/2	3	15/16	4 3/4	Solid	5,150	4450	3730	3100	2170
2 3/4	3	11/16	4 3/8	Split	1,250	1000	825	650	....
2 3/4	3	15/16	5	Solid	5,600	4800	4000	3350	2280
3	3	3/4	4 3/4	Split	1,350	1080	875	700	....
3	3 1/2	1	5 3/8	Solid	7,200	6150	5100	4230	2880
3 1/2	3	1 1/8	6 1/8	Split	1,730	1450	1200	1000	....
3 1/2	4	1 1/8	6 3/8	Solid	9,050	7650	6300	5250	....
4	3	1 1/8	6 5/8	Split	1,935	1610	1320	1080	....
4	4	1 1/8	6 7/8	Solid	10,100	8450	6900	5620	....
5	4	1 1/4	7 7/8	Split	3,150	2600	2090	1690	....
5	7	1 1/4	7 7/8	Split	5,770	4750	3830	3100	....
6	4	1 1/4	8 7/8	Split	3,610	2900	2330	1810	....
6	7	1 1/4	8 7/8	Split	6,620	5300	4280	3330	....

* This table gives the load capacities of Hyatt roller bearings with rollers operating directly on shafts. The loads are based on the use of steel containing from 0.40 to 0.50 per cent carbon with a hardness of 165 Brinell or 25 scleroscope for split outer races, and 600 Brinell for solid outer races. For other degrees of hardness the loads given in the table should be multiplied by a suitable hardness factor (see table below). When the required shaft hardness cannot be obtained a bearing having a hardened solid inner race is used.

Journal Hardness Factors

Journal Material	Split Outer Race			Solid Outer Race		
	Brinell Reading	Scleroscope	Factor	Brinell Reading	Scleroscope	Factor
Steel containing about 0.10% C.......	110	16	0.66	600	88	1.00
Steel containing about 0.20% C.......	130	19	0.78	500	75	0.85
Steel containing about 0.30% C.......	150	23	0.90	400	60	0.70
Steel containing about 0.40–0.45% C...	165	25	1.00	300	45	0.50
Steel containing about 0.50–0.55% C...	175	27	1.10	....	....	....
Steel heat-treated to..................	200	30	1.20	....	....	....
Steel heat-treated to..................	250	38	1.50	....	....	....
Steel heat-treated to..................	300	45	1.80	....	....	....
Inner races and split outer races.......	....	....	1.80	....	....	....

Example: — Determine the load capacity of a 2- by 4-inch [bearing having a *split* outer race, assuming the speed is 300 R.P.M. and the shaft hardness 250 Brinell.
The load capacity given in the preceding table is 900 pounds which is based on a hardness of 165 Brinell. The hardness factor for 250 Brinell is 1.5 for a split outer race; hence the load capacity equals 900 × 1.5 = 1350 pounds.

Roller Bearings of Small-roller Type. — Bantam small-roller cageless roller bearings are compact because of the small rollers used and have high load capacities. Some rollers are only $\frac{1}{16}$ inch in diameter. If R = the safe load rating in pounds, N = total number of rollers when total circumferential clearance = 0.0001 inch per roller, minimum, and $\frac{1}{4}$ roller diameter, maximum; L = effective roller length (length minus rounded or chamfered ends); d = roller diameter inches (high limit); S = shaft speed in R.P.M., then

$$R = \frac{NLd \times 11250}{\sqrt[3]{S}}.$$

Loads may be greater or less than the rated capacity due to such factors as load distribution, distortion of supporting elements, and other factors.

Pitch and Bore Diameters. — To determine the pitch diameters, use rule and constant given in the accompanying table. The minimum total circumferential clearance of 0.0001 inch per roller should not be used if heavy lubricants are necessary. The "diametral clearance" or difference between the diameter over the rollers and the bore or inside diameter of the outer raceway, is very important. The minimum and maximum values for diametral clearance are 0.0005 to 0.0015 inch for shafts up to 2 inches; 0.0010 to 0.0020 for shafts from 2 inches to 4 inches; and 0.0015 to 0.0025 for shafts 4 inches to 6 inches diameter (not including roller tolerances).

The minimum bore diameter = pitch diameter + roller diameter + diametral clearance. The bore diameter tolerance is plus 0.0005 inch minus nothing up to 4-inch sizes. The inner raceway tolerance is plus nothing minus 0.0005 inch. For shafts over 4 inches, these tolerances are increased to 0.001 inch. Five different forms of roller ends may be used. The recommended form is a spherical section having a radius equal to one-half the roller length.

Constants for Finding Pitch Diameters of Ball and Roller Bearings

To find pitch diameter or diameter of circle intersecting centers of balls or rollers, add to roller diameter the clearance space between each pair of balls or rollers (assuming equal spacing) and multiply sum by constant given in table. If the *total* circumferential clearance is given, first divide it by total number of balls. The clearance space is measured on the chord intersecting the centers of adjacent balls.

No. of Balls	Constant	No. of Balls	Constant	No. of Balls	Constant	No. of Balls	Constant
10	3.236036	31	9.884511	52	16.561564	73	23.242782
11	3.549509	32	10.202520	53	16.879250	74	23.560273
12	3.863689	33	10.519702	54	17.199862	75	23.883449
13	4.178586	34	10.838034	55	17.517599	76	24.201045
14	4.493978	35	11.156268	56	17.835304	77	24.518626
15	4.809773	36	11.474469	57	18.152981	78	24.836174
16	5.125839	37	11.791250	58	18.470632	79	25.153708
17	5.442316	38	12.109316	59	18.788252	80	25.471218
18	5.758710	39	12.427348	60	19.105846	81	25.788702
19	6.075626	40	12.745348	61	19.427555	82	26.106171
20	6.392635	41	13.064441	62	19.744845	83	26.423612
21	6.709479	42	13.381251	63	20.062479	84	26.748188
22	7.026733	43	13.699154	64	20.380089	85	27.065753
23	7.344090	44	14.017024	65	20.697669	86	27.383306
24	7.661074	45	14.334862	66	21.015224	87	27.700831
25	7.978935	46	14.660235	67	21.336424	88	28.018339
26	8.296583	47	14.972682	68	21.654949	89	28.335836
27	8.614006	48	15.290520	69	21.972505	90	28.653295
28	8.931192	49	15.608326	70	22.290153	..	....
29	9.248982	50	15.926103	71	22.607719	..	....
30	9.566632	51	16.243850	72	22.925264	..	....

Standard Ball and Roller Bearings. — The tables which follow give the standard dimensions of ball and roller bearings as adopted by the Anti-Friction Bearing Manufacturers Association, Inc., and also by the Society of Automotive Engineers, Inc. The general types of ball and roller bearings are described and illustrated in Table 1. Table 2 lists the standard range of sizes for the different types of ball and cylindrical roller bearings and gives the number of whatever table contains the important dimensions.

Types of Ball Bearings. — The principal types of ball bearings have been standardized internationally with respect to external dimensions affecting interchangeability, such as bore diameter, outside diameter, and widths. The general characterstics of commonly used types are described below.

Radial Single-row, Non-loading Groove. — This type, which is used very extensively, takes both radial loads and also thrust loads in either direction. It contains fewer balls than the loading-groove type. This reduces the radial capacity somewhat but the uninterrupted ball race increases the thrust capacity. The non-loading groove type is used for radial and angular loads, especially if the thrust is greater than would be recommended for bearings of the loading-groove type.

Radial Single-row Loading Groove. — This type, which contains the maximum number of balls consistent with proper ring and separator proportions, is designed primarily for radial loads, although there may be moderate thrust loads from either direction when they are in combination with a radial load. After inserting the maximum number of balls with the inner ring displaced eccentrically, several additional balls are inserted through the loading groove. This ball-inserting operation may be aided by a slight spreading of the rings and possibly some heat expansion of the outer ring.

Angular Contact Single Row. — This type is designed especially for heavy combined loads where thrust may be large and axial deflection must be within close limits. A single bearing is designed for thrust in one direction only; however, opposed pairs usually are employed, thus providing secure location axially under combined loads and with thrust in either direction. Single-row angular contact bearings may be modified slightly for duplex mounting by introducing a slight offset between the inner and outer rings. This offset is taken up when the rings are clamped together, thus subjecting the bearings to an axial pressure or preload.

Double-row Bearings. — The double-row angular contact bearing is similar in effect to two single-row angular contact bearings clamped together. The width of the former, however, is less than two single bearings. Double-row bearings may be assembled with an internal preload; hence they offer considerable resistance to both radial and angular loads and are especially useful when end-play must be prevented as, for example, in thrust-producing gears.

Snap Ring Bearings. — The term "snap ring" is applied to bearings having a split ring fitted into an external groove extending around the outer ring. This snap ring, which projects beyond the outer ring surface, engages a face or shoulder on the housing, thus serving to locate the bearing axially.

Shielded Bearings. — A shielded bearing has a metal plate fixed to the outer ring. There is running clearance between the shield and the inner ring. A double-shielded bearing has shields on both sides. The function of shielding is to protect the bearing from coarse dirt, metal chips, etc. The shields are not intended to form an oil-tight enclosure, although they do tend to keep lubricant within the bearing.

Sealed Bearings. — Seals provide a contacting surface with the inner ring which is wider than the outer ring. Bearings with seals on both sides are filled with suitable lubricant by the manufacturer. If there is a seal on one side only, the bearing must be lubricated the same as the ordinary type. Sealed bearings of different makes may not be interchangeable, especially in regard to width.

Table 1.   Types of Ball and Roller Bearings Having Standard Dimensions

The symbols and dimensions found in Table 1 have been adopted as standard by the Anti-Friction Bearing Manufacturers Association, Inc., representing the principal manufacturers of ball and roller bearings and steel balls.

Type	General Description of Type	Cross-Section
	BALL BEARINGS	
BA	Angular contact single-row, singly mounted. (Bearings for duplex or multiple mountings, such as back-to-back, face-to-face, or in tandem are indicated by the suffix "F," added to the bearing code number.)	
BC	Radial single-row, non-loading groove assembly	
BL	Radial single-row, loading groove assembly Note: The addition of shields on one or both sides, or snap-ring on outer race in Types BC and BL, is indicated by the following suffixes added to the bearing code number: P (shield on one side); PP (shields on both sides); G (snap-ring on outer race); GP (shield and snap-ring on the side opposite shield).	
BD	Angular contact double-row	
BH	Radial single-row, counterbore assembly	
BM	Single-row, separable	

Table 1 (*Continued*). Types of Ball and Roller Bearings Having Standard Dimensions

Type	General Description of Type	Cross-Section
	BALL BEARINGS	
BS	Self-aligning double-row	
BIC	Radial single-row, non-loading groove assembly, inch dimensions	
BT	Thrust, single-direction, flat face	
BIT	Thrust, single-direction, flat face, inch dimensions	
BTS	Thrust, single-direction, self-aligning	
	CYLINDRICAL ROLLER BEARINGS	
RN	Cylindrical single-row, flanged inner, straight outer race	
RU	Cylindrical single-row, flanged outer, straight inner race	
RF	Cylindrical single-row, one-direction locating, outer race separable	

Table **I** (*Continued*). **Types of Ball and Roller Bearings Having Standard Dimensions**

Type	General Description of Type	Cross-Section
CYLINDRICAL ROLLER BEARINGS		
RJ	Cylindrical single-row, one-direction locating, inner race separable	
RH	Cylindrical single-row, Type RJ with shoulder ring, two-direction locating	
RK	Cylindrical single-row, self-contained, not-locating. (For designating Type RK with full roller complement, suffix "V" is added to the bearing code No.) Note: For locating shafts axially, flanges must be used. For retaining rollers and for axial location of outer rings, snap-rings or recesses may be used instead of flanges.	
RS	Self-aligning double-row with roller path of inner or outer race spherical	
TAPER ROLLER BEARINGS		
TS	Tapered rollers, single-row	
TSS	Tapered rollers, single-row, steep angle Note: Any single cone listed in the tables for Types TS and TSS can be used with flanged outer race (Type TSF) or double-row (Type TDO) in the same series.	

Table 1 (*Continued*).   **Types of Ball and Roller Bearings Having Standard Dimensions**

Type	General Description of Type	Cross-Section
	TAPER ROLLER BEARINGS	
TST	Tapered rollers, single-row, tapered bore	
TSF	Tapered rollers, single-row, flanged outer race	
TDI	Tapered rollers, double-row, single outer races	
TDO	Tapered rollers, double-row, single inner races	
TDOS	Tapered rollers, double-row, single inner races, steep angle	
TNA	Tapered rollers, double-row, single inner races, non-adjustable	
TNAS	Tapered rollers, double-row, single inner races, non-adjustable, steep angle	

The standard dimensions of the different types of ball and roller bearings listed in Table 1 are given in Tables 2 to 18.   In each case, the type of bearing is identified by means of its standard symbol.

Table 2. Standard Range of Sizes for Different Types of Bearings

Dimension Series	Types as Defined in Table 1	Range of Standard Sizes as Indicated by Nominal Bore Diameter		For Other Dimensions See —
BALL BEARINGS				
Series 10 (Extra Light)	BA BC BH	10 to 320 mm	(0.3937 inch to 12.5984 inches)	Table 3
Series 02 (Light)	BA BH BL	10 to 320 mm	(0.3937 inch to 12.5984 inches)	Table 4
	BC	4 to 320 mm	(0.1575 inch to 12.5984 inches)	Table 4
	BS	5 to 110 mm	(0.1969 inch to 4.3307 inches)	Table 4
Series 03 (Medium)	BA BC BH BL	10 to 280 mm	(0.3937 inch to 11.0236 inches)	Table 4
	BS	10 to 110 mm	(0.3937 inch to 4.3307 inches)	Table 4
Series 04 (Heavy)	BA BC BH BL BS	17 to 90 mm	(0.6693 inch to 3.5433 inches)	Table 4
Series 32 (Light)	BD	10 to 110 mm	(0.3937 inch to 4.3307 inches)	Table 5
Series 92 (Extended Light)	BD	120 to 320 mm	(4.7244 to 12.5984 inches)	Table 5
Series 33 (Medium)	BD	10 to 110 mm	(0.3937 inch to 4.3307 inches)	Table 5
Series 93 (Extended Medium)	BD	120 to 200 mm	(4.7244 to 7.8740 inches)	Table 5
Series 34 (Heavy)	BD	17 to 90 mm	(0.6693 inch to 3.5433 inches)	Table 5
....	BIC	(Sizes in inches) ⅛-inch to 1½ inches		Table 6
....	BM	5 to 17 mm	(0.1969 inch to 0.6693 inch)	Table 6
Series 22 (Light)	BS	10 to 110 mm	(0.3937 inch to 4.3307 inches)	Table 8
Series 23 (Medium)	BS	10 to 110 mm	(0.3937 inch to 4.3307 inches)	Table 8
BT (Light Series)	BTL*	10 to 125 mm	(0.3937 inch to 4.9213 inches)	Table 9
BT (Medium Series)	BTM*	10 to 140 mm	(0.3937 inch to 5.5118 inches)	Table 9

For taper roller bearings, see Tables 11 to 18.
*L indicates Light Series; M, Medium Series; X, Extra-light Series.

Table 2 *(Continued).* **Standard Range of Sizes for Different Types of Bearings**

Dimension Series	Types as Defined in Table I	Range of Standard Sizes as Indicated by Nominal Bore Diameter	For Other Dimensions See —
		BALL BEARINGS	
BTS (Medium Series)	BTSM*	10 to 140 mm (0.3937 inch to 5.5118 inches)	Table 9
BIT (Extra Light)	BITX*	(Nominal sizes in inches) ½ inch to 3½ inches	Table 10
BIT (Light)	BITL*	(Nominal sizes in inches) ¼ inch to 12 inches	Table 10
BIT (Medium)	BITM*	(Nominal sizes in inches) ½ inch to 7⅜ inches	Table 10
		CYLINDRICAL ROLLER BEARINGS	
Series 02 (Light)	RN	10 to 320 mm (0.3937 inch to 12.5984 inches)	Table 4
	RU RK	17 to 320 mm (0.6693 inch to 12.5984 inches)	Table 4
	RF RJ	17 to 150 mm (0.6693 inch to 5.9055 inches)	Table 4
Series 03 (Medium)	RN RU RK	17 to 200 mm (0.6693 inch to 7.8740 inches)	Table 4
	RF RJ	17 to 180 mm (0.6693 inch to 7.0866 inches)	Table 4
	RH	30 to 150 mm (1.1811 inch to 5.9055 inches) † Widths are 5 to 15 mm greater than given in Table 4	See Note at Left†
Series 32 (Light)	RN RU RK	17 to 110 mm (0.6693 inch to 4.3307 inches)	Table 5
Series 92 (Extended Light)	RN RU RK	120 to 320 mm (4.7244 to 12.5984 inches)	Table 5
Series 33 (Medium)	RN RU RK	17 to 110 mm (0.6693 inch to 4.3307 inches)	Table 5
Series 93 (Extended Medium)	RN RU RK	120 to 200 mm (4.7244 to 7.8740 inches)	Table 5
Series 22 (Light)	RS	80 to 320 mm (3.1496 to 12.5984 inches)	Table 8
Series 23 (Medium)	RS	40 to 280 mm (1.5748 to 11.0236 inches)	Table 8
Series 30	RS	120 to 500 mm (4.7244 to 19.6850 inches)	Table 8
Series 31	RS	110 to 500 mm (4.3307 to 19.6850 inches)	Table 8
Series 32	RS	220 to 500 mm (8.6614 to 19.6850 inches)	Table 8

For taper roller bearings, see Tables 11 to 18.
* *L* indicates Light Series; M, Medium Series; X, Extra-light Series.

Table 3.　Standard Dimensions of Ball Bearings — Types BA, BC, and BH

(The different types indicated by combinations of letters, such as BA, BC and BH, are described and illustrated in Table 1)

-Bore Diameter			Outside Diameter			Ring Width			Fillet Radius, Inch†
Mm.	Inch	Toler.	Mm.	Inch	Toler.	Mm.	Inch	Toler.	
DIMENSION SERIES 10 — EXTRA LIGHT									
10	0.3937	−.0003	26	1.0236	−.0004	8	0.3150	−.005	.016
12	0.4724	−.0003	28	1.1024	−.0004	8	0.3150	−.005	.016
15	0.5906	−.0003	32	1.2598	−.0005	9	0.3543	−.005	.016
17	0.6693	−.0003	35	1.3780	−.0005	10	0.3937	−.005	.016
20	0.7874	−.0004	42	1.6535	−.0005	12	0.4724	−.005	.025
25	0.9843	−.0004	47	1.8504	−.0005	12	0.4724	−.005	.025
30	1.1811	−.0004	55	2.1654	−.0005	13	0.5118	−.005	.04
35	1.3780	−.0005	62	2.4409	−.0005	14	0.5512	−.005	.04
40	1.5748	−.0005	68	2.6772	−.0005	15	0.5906	−.005	.04
45	1.7717	−.0005	75	2.9528	−.0005	16	0.6299	−.005	.04
50	1.9685	−.0005	80	3.1496	−.0005	16	0.6299	−.005	.04
55	2.1654	−.0006	90	3.5433	−.0006	18	0.7087	−.005	.04
60	2.3622	−.0006	95	3.7402	−.0006	18	0.7087	−.005	.04
65	2.5591	−.0006	100	3.9370	−.0006	18	0.7087	−.005	.04
70	2.7559	−.0006	110	4.3307	−.0006	20	0.7874	−.005	.04
75	2.9528	−.0006	115	4.4576	−.0006	20	0.7874	−.005	.04
80	3.1496	−.0006	125	4.9213	−.0008	22	0.8661	−.005	.04
85	3.3465	−.0008	130	5.1181	−.0008	22	0.8661	−.005	.04
90	3.5433	−.0008	140	5.5118	−.0008	24	0.9449	−.005	.06
95	3.7402	−.0008	145	5.7087	−.0008	24	0.9449	−.005	.06
100	3.9370	−.0008	150	5.9055	−.0008	24	0.9449	−.005	.06
105	4.1339	−.0008	160	6.2992	−.0010	26	1.0236	−.005	.08
110	4.3307	−.0008	170	6.6929	−.0010	28	1.1024	−.005	.08
120	4.7244	−.0008	180	7.0866	−.0010	28	1.1024	−.005	.08
130	5.1181	−.0010	200	7.8740	−.0012	33	1.2992	−.005	.08
140	5.5118	−.0010	210	8.2677	−.0012	33	1.2992	−.005	.08
150	5.9055	−.0010	225	8.8583	−.0012	35	1.3780	−.005	.08
160	6.2992	−.0010	240	9.4488	−.0012	38	1.4961	−.005	.08
170	6.6929	−.0010	260	10.2362	−.0014	42	1.6535	−.005	.08
180	7.0866	−.0010	280	11.0236	−.0014	46	1.8110	−.005	.08
190	7.4803	−.0012	290	11.4173	−.0014	46	1.8110	−.010	.08
200	7.8740	−.0012	310	12.2047	−.0014	51	2.0079	−.010	.08
220	8.6614	−.0012	340	13.3858	−.0016	56	2.2047	−.010	.10
240	9.4488	−.0012	360	14.1732	−.0016	56	2.2047	−.010	.10
260	10.2362	−.0014	400	15.7480	−.0016	65	2.5591	−.010	.12
280	11.0236	−.0014	420	16.5354	−.0018	65	2.5591	−.010	.12
300	11.8110	−.0014	460	18.1102	−.0018	74	2.9134	−.010	.12
320	12.5984	−.0016	480	18.8976	−.0018	74	2.9134	−.016	.12

† Radius of maximum fillet on shaft or in housing to be cleared by the bearing. This radius specification does not control contour of bearing corner.

Table 4. Standard Dimensions of Ball and Roller Bearings*

Bore Diameter			Outside Diameter			Ring Width			Fillet Radius, Inch†
Mm.	Inch	Toler.	Mm	Inch	Toler.	Mm.	Inch	Toler.	
DIMENSION SERIES 02 — LIGHT									
4	0.1575	— 0003	16	0.6299	—.0004	5	0.1969	—.005	.016
5	0.1969	— 0003	19	0.7480	—.0004	6	0.2362	—.005	.016
6	0.2362	—.0003	19	0.7480	—.0004	6	0.2362	—.005	.016
7	0.2756	—.0003	22	0.8661	—.0004	7	0.2756	—.005	.016
8	0.3150	—.0003	22	0.8661	—.0004	7	0.2756	—.005	.016
9	0.3543	—.0003	26	1.0236	—.0004	8	0.3150	—.005	.025
10	0.3937	—.0003	30	1.1811	—.0004	9	0.3543	—.005	.025
12	0.4724	—.0003	32	1.2598	—.0005	10	0.3937	—.005	.025
15	0.5906	—.0003	35	1.3780	—.0005	11	0.4331	—.005	.025
17	0.6693	—.0003	40	1.5748	—.0005	12	0.4724	—.005	.04
20	0.7874	—.0004	47	1.8504	—.0005	14	0.5512	—.005	.04
25	0.9843	—.0004	52	2.0472	—.0005	15	0.5906	—.005	.04
30	1.1811	—.0004	62	2.4409	—.0005	16	0.6299	—.005	.04
35	1.3780	—.0005	72	2.8346	—.0005	17	0.6693	—.005	.04
40	1.5748	—.0005	80	3.1496	—.0005	18	0.7087	—.005	.04
45	1.7717	—.0005	85	3.3465	—.0006	19	0.7480	—.005	.04
50	1.9685	—.0005	90	3.5433	—.0006	20	0.7874	—.005	.04
55	2.1654	—.0006	100	3.9370	—.0006	21	0.8268	—.005	.06
60	2.3622	—.0006	110	4.3307	—.0006	22	0.8661	—.005	.06
65	2.5591	—.0006	120	4.7244	—.0006	23	0.9055	—.005	.06
70	2.7559	—.0006	125	4.9213	—.0008	24	0.9449	—.005	.06
75	2.9528	—.0006	130	5.1181	—.0008	25	0.9843	—.005	.06
80	3.1496	—.0006	140	5.5118	—.0008	26	1.0236	—.005	.08
85	3.3465	—.0008	150	5.9055	—.0008	28	1.1024	—.005	.08
90	3.5433	—.0008	160	6.2992	—.0010	30	1.1811	—.005	.08
95	3.7402	—.0008	170	6.6929	—.0010	32	1.2598	—.005	.08
100	3.9370	—.0008	180	7.0866	—.0010	34	1.3386	—.005	.08
105	4.1339	—.0008	190	7.4803	—.0012	36	1.4173	—.005	.08
110	4.3307	—.0008	200	7.8740	—.0012	38	1.4961	—.005	.08
120	4.7244	—.0008	215	8.4646	—.0012	40	1.5748	—.005	.08
130	5.1181	—.0010	230	9.0551	—.0012	40	1.5748	—.005	.10
140	5.5118	—.0010	250	9.8425	—.0012	42	1.6535	—.005	.10
150	5.9055	—.0010	270	10.6299	—.0014	45	1.7717	—.005	.10
160	6.2992	—.0010	290	11.4173	—.0014	48	1.8898	—.005	.10
170	6.6929	—.0010	310	12.2047	—.0014	52	2.0472	—.005	.12
180	7.0866	—.0010	320	12.5984	—.0016	52	2.0472	—.005	.12
190	7.4803	—.0012	340	13.3858	—.0016	55	2.1654	—.010	.12
200	7.8740	—.0012	360	14.1732	—.0016	58	2.2835	—.010	.12
220	8.6614	—.0012	400	15.7480	—.0016	65	2.5591	—.010	.12
240	9.4488	—.0012	440	17.3228	—.0018	72	2.8346	—.010	.12
260	10.2362	—.0014	480	18.8976	—.0018	80	3.1496	—.010	.12
280	11.0236	—.0014	500	19.6850	—.0018	80	3.1496	—.010	.16
300	11.8110	—.0014	540	21.2598	—.0020	85	3.3465	—.010	.16
320	12.5984	—.0016	580	22.8346	—.0020	92	3.6220	—.016	.16
DIMENSION SERIES 03 — MEDIUM (See next page)									
10	0.3937	—.0003	35	1.3780	—.0005	11	0.4331	—.005	.025
12	0.4724	—.0003	37	1.4567	—.0005	12	0.4724	—.005	.04
15	0.5906	—.0003	42	1.6535	—.0005	13	0.5118	—.005	.04
17	0.6693	—.0003	47	1.8504	—.0005	14	0.5512	—.005	.04
20	0.7874	—.0004	52	2.0472	—.0005	15	0.5906	—.005	.04
25	0.9843	—.0004	62	2.4409	—.0005	17	0.6693	—.005	.04

* For data on types in each series and size range, see Table 2.
† Radius of maximum fillet on shaft or in housing to be cleared by the bearing. This radius specification does not control contour of bearing corner.

Table 4 *(Continued)*. Standard Dimensions of Ball and Roller Bearings

Bore Diameter			Outside Diameter			Ring Width			Fillet Radius, Inch†
Mm.	Inch	Toler.	Mm.	Inch	Toler.	Mm.	Inch	Toler.	
DIMENSION SERIES 03 — MEDIUM									
30	1.1811	—.0004	72	2.8346	—.0005	19	0.7480	—.005	.04
35	1.3780	—.0005	80	3.1496	—.0005	21	0.8268	—.005	.06
40	1.5748	—.0005	90	3.5433	—.0006	23	0.9055	—.005	.06
45	1.7717	—.0005	100	3.9370	—.0006	25	0.9843	—.005	.06
50	1.9685	—.0005	110	4.3307	—.0006	27	1.0630	—.005	.08
55	2.1654	—.0006	120	4.7244	—.0006	29	1.1417	—.005	.08
60	2.3622	—.0006	130	5.1181	—.0008	31	1.2205	—.005	.08
65	2.5591	—.0006	140	5.5118	—.0008	33	1.2992	—.005	.08
70	2.7559	—.0006	150	5.9055	—.0008	35	1.3780	—.005	.08
75	2.9528	—.0006	160	6.2992	—.0010	37	1.4567	—.005	.08
80	3.1496	—.0006	170	6.6929	—.0010	39	1.5354	—.005	.08
85	3.3465	—.0008	180	7.0866	—.0010	41	1.6142	—.005	.10
90	3.5433	—.0008	190	7.4803	—.0012	43	1.6929	—.005	.10
95	3.7402	—.0008	200	7.8740	—.0012	45	1.7717	—.005	.10
100	3.9370	—.0008	215	8.4646	—.0012	47	1.8504	—.005	.10
105	4.1339	—.0008	225	8.8583	—.0012	49	1.9291	—.005	.10
110	4.3307	—.0008	240	9.4488	—.0012	50	1.9685	—.005	.10
120	4.7244	—.0008	260	10.2362	—.0014	55	2.1654	—.005	.10
130	5.1181	—.0010	280	11.0236	—.0014	58	2.2835	—.005	.12
140	5.5118	—.0010	300	11.8110	—.0014	62	2.4409	—.005	.12
150	5.9055	—.0010	320	12.5984	—.0016	65	2.5591	—.005	.12
160	6.2992	—.0010	340	13.3858	—.0016	68	2.6772	—.005	.12
170	6.6929	—.0010	360	14.1732	—.0016	72	2.8346	—.005	.12
180	7.0866	—.0010	380	14.9606	—.0016	75	2.9528	—.005	.12
190	7.4803	—.0012	400	15.7480	—.0016	78	3.0709	—.010	.16
200	7.8740	—.0012	420	16.5454	—.0018	80	3.1496	—.010	.16
220	8.6614	—.0012	460	18.1102	—.0018	88	3.4646	—.010	.16
240	9.4488	—.0012	500	19.6850	—.0018	95	3.7402	—.010	.16
260	10.2362	—.0014	540	21.2598	—.0020	102	4.0157	—.010	.20
280	11.0236	—.0014	580	22.8346	—.0020	108	4.2520	—.010	.20
DIMENSION SERIES 04 — HEAVY									
17	0.6693	—.0003	62	2.4409	—.0005	17	0.6693	—.005	.04
20	0.7374	—.0004	72	2.8346	—.0005	19	0.7480	—.005	.04
25	0.9843	—.0004	80	3.1496	—.0005	21	0.8268	—.005	.06
30	1.1811	—.0004	90	3.5433	—.0006	23	0.9055	—.005	.06
35	1.3780	—.0005	100	3.9370	—.0006	25	0.9843	—.005	.06
40	1.5748	—.0005	110	4.3307	—.0006	27	1.0630	—.005	.08
45	1.7717	—.0005	120	4.7244	—.0006	29	1.1417	—.005	.08
50	1.9685	—.0005	130	5.1181	—.0008	31	1.2205	—.005	.08
55	2.1654	—.0006	140	5.5118	—.0008	33	1.2992	—.005	.08
60	2.3622	—.0006	150	5.9055	—.0008	35	1.3780	—.005	.08
65	2.5591	—.0006	160	6.2992	—.0010	37	1.4567	—.005	.08
70	2.7559	—.0006	180	7.0866	—.0010	42	1.6535	—.005	.10
75	2.9528	—.0006	190	7.4803	—.0012	45	1.7717	—.005	.10
80	3.1496	—.0006	200	7.8740	—.0012	48	1.8898	—.005	.10
85	3.3465	—.0008	210	8.2677	—.0012	52	2.0472	—.005	.12
90	3.5433	—.0008	225	8.8583	—.0012	54	2.1260	—.005	.12

Many cylindrical roller bearings in Types RN, RU, RF, RJ and RK have same size bore, outside diameter and width as ball bearings, according to standard specifications of the Anti-Friction Bearing Manufacturers Association, Inc. For data on types in each series and size range, see Table 2.

† Radius of maximum fillet on shaft or in housing to be cleared by the bearing. This radius specification does not control contour of bearing corner.

Table 5. Standard Dimensions of Ball and Roller Bearings*

Bore Diameter			Outside Diameter			Ring Width			Fillet Radius, Inch†
Mm.	Inch	Toler.	Mm.	Inch	Toler.	Mm.	Inch	Toler.	
DIMENSION SERIES 32 — LIGHT									
10	0.3937	—.0003	30	1.1811	—.0004	14.3	9/16	—.005	.025
12	0.4724	—.0003	32	1.2598	—.0005	15.9	5/8	—.005	.025
15	0.5906	—.0003	35	1.3780	—.0005	15.9	5/8	—.005	.025
17	0.6693	—.0003	40	1.5748	—.0005	17.5	11/16	—.005	.04
20	0.7874	—.0004	47	1.8504	—.0005	20.6	13/16	—.005	.04
25	0.9843	—.0004	52	2.0472	—.0005	20.6	13/16	—.005	.04
30	1.1811	—.0004	62	2.4409	—.0005	23.8	15/16	—.005	.04
35	1.3780	—.0005	72	2.8346	—.0005	27.0	11/16	—.005	.04
40	1.5748	—.0005	80	3.1496	—.0005	30.2	13/16	—.005	.04
45	1.7717	—.0005	85	3.3465	—.0006	30.2	13/16	—.005	.04
50	1.9685	—.0005	90	3.5433	—.0006	30.2	13/16	—.005	.04
55	2.1654	—.0006	100	3.9370	—.0006	33.3	15/16	—.005	.06
60	2.3622	—.0006	110	4.3307	—.0006	36.5	17/16	—.005	.06
65	2.5591	—.0006	120	4.7244	—.0006	38.1	1½	—.005	.06
70	2.7559	—.0006	125	4.9213	—.0008	39.7	19/16	—.005	.06
75	2.9528	—.0006	130	5.1181	—.0008	41.3	15/8	—.005	.06
80	3.1496	—.0006	140	5.5118	—.0008	44.4	13/4	—.005	.08
85	3.3465	—.0008	150	5.9055	—.0008	49.2	115/16	—.005	.08
90	3.5433	—.0008	160	6.2992	—.0010	52.4	21/16	—.005	.08
95	3.7402	—.0008	170	6.6929	—.0010	55.6	23/16	—.005	.08
100	3.9370	—.0008	180	7.0866	—.0010	60.3	23/8	—.005	.08
105	4.1339	—.0008	190	7.4803	—.0012	65.1	29/16	—.005	.08
110	4.3307	—.0008	200	7.8740	—.0012	69.8	23/4	—.005	.08
DIMENSION SERIES 92 — EXTENDED LIGHT									
120	4.7244	—.0008	215	8.4646	—.0012	...	3	—.005	.08
130	5.1181	—.0010	230	9.0551	—.0012	...	31/8	—.005	.10
140	5.5118	—.0010	250	9.8425	—.0012	...	31/4	—.005	.10
150	5.9055	—.0010	270	10.6299	—.0014	...	3½	—.005	.10
160	6.2992	—.0010	290	11.4173	—.0014	...	37/8	—.005	.10
170	6.6929	—.0010	310	12.2047	—.0014	...	41/8	—.005	.12
180	7.0866	—.0010	320	12.5984	—.0016	...	41/4	—.005	.12
190	7.4803	—.0012	340	13.3858	—.0016	...	4½	—.010	.12
200	7.8740	—.0012	360	14.1732	—.0016	...	43/4	—.010	.12
220	8.6614	—.0012	400	15.7480	—.0016	...	51/4	—.010	.12
240	9.4488	—.0012	440	17.3228	—.0018	...	53/4	—.010	.12
260	10.2362	—.0014	480	18.8976	—.0018	...	61/4	—.010	.16
280	11.0236	—.0014	500	19.6850	—.0018	...	6½	—.010	.16
300	11.8110	—.0014	540	21.2598	—.0020	...	7	—.010	.16
320	12.5984	—.0016	580	22.8346	—.0020	...	7½	—.016	.16
DIMENSION SERIES 33 — MEDIUM (See next page)									
10	0.3937	—.0003	35	1.3780	—.0005	19.0	3/4	—.005	.025
12	0.4724	—.0003	37	1.4567	—.0005	19.0	3/4	—.005	.04
15	0.5906	—.0003	42	1.6535	—.0005	19.0	3/4	—.005	.04
17	0.6693	—.0003	47	1.8504	—.0005	22.2	7/8	—.005	.04
20	0.7874	—.0004	52	2.0472	—.0005	22.2	7/8	—.005	.04
25	0.9843	—.0004	62	2.4409	—.0005	25.4	1	—.005	.04

* All sizes listed in Table 5 are standard for ball bearings of Types BD. The range of sizes for cylindrical roller bearings of Types RN, RU, and RK are given in Table 2.
† Radius of maximum fillet on shaft or in housing to be cleared by the bearing. This radius specification does not control contour of bearing corner.

Table 5 (*Continued*).　Standard Dimensions of Ball and Roller Bearings*

Bore Diameter			Outside Diameter			Ring Width			Fillet Radius, Inch†
Mm.	Inch	Toler.	Mm.	Inch	Toler.	Mm.	Inch	Toler.	

DIMENSION SERIES 33 — MEDIUM

Bore Diameter			Outside Diameter			Ring Width			Fillet Radius, Inch†
30	1.1811	−.0004	72	2.8346	−.0005	30.2	1³⁄₁₆	−.005	.04
35	1.3780	−.0005	80	3.1496	−.0005	34.9	1⅜	−.005	.06
40	1.5748	−.0005	90	3.5433	−.0006	36.5	1⁷⁄₁₆	−.005	.06
45	1.7717	−.0005	100	3.9370	−.0006	39.7	1⁹⁄₁₆	−.005	.06
50	1.9685	−.0005	110	4.3307	−.0006	44.4	1¾	−.005	.08
55	2.1654	−.0006	120	4.7244	−.0006	49.2	1¹⁵⁄₁₆	−.005	.08
60	2.3622	−.0006	130	5.1181	−.0008	54.0	2⅛	−.005	.08
65	2.5591	−.0006	140	5.5118	−.0008	58.7	2⁵⁄₁₆	−.005	.08
70	2.7559	−.0006	150	5.9055	−.0008	63.5	2½	−.005	.08
75	2.9528	−.0006	160	6.2992	−.0010	68.3	2¹¹⁄₁₆	−.005	.08
80	3.1496	−.0006	170	6.6929	−.0010	68.3	2¹¹⁄₁₆	−.005	
85	3.3465	−.0008	180	7.0866	−.0010	73.0	2⅞	−.005	.10
90	3.5433	−.0008	190	7.4803	−.0012	73.0	2⅞	−.005	.10
95	3.7402	−.0008	200	7.8740	−.0012	77.8	3¹⁄₁₆	−.005	.10
100	3.9370	−.0008	215	8.4646	−.0012	82.6	3¼	−.005	.10
105	4.1339	−.0008	225	8.8583	−.0012	87.3	3⁷⁄₁₆	−.005	.10
110	4.3307	−.0008	240	9.4488	−.0012	92.1	3⅝	−.005	.10

DIMENSION SERIES 93 — EXTENDED MEDIUM

Bore Diameter			Outside Diameter			Ring Width			Fillet Radius, Inch†
120	4.7244	−.0008	260	10.2362	−.0014	...	4⅛	−.005	.10
130	5.1181	−.0010	280	11.0236	−.0014	...	4⅜	−.005	.12
140	5.5118	−.0010	300	11.8110	−.0014	...	4½	−.005	.12
150	5.9055	−.0010	320	12.5984	−.0016	...	4⅞	−.005	.12
160	6.2992	−.0010	340	13.3858	−.0016	...	5¼	−.005	.12
170	6.6929	−.0010	360	14.1732	−.0016	...	5½	−.005	.12
180	7.0866	−.0010	380	14.9606	−.0016	...	5¾	−.005	.12
190	7.4803	−.0012	400	15.7480	−.0016	...	6	−.010	.16
200	7.8740	−.0012	420	16.5354	−.0018	...	6½	−.010	.16

DIMENSION SERIES 34 — HEAVY

Bore Diameter			Outside Diameter			Ring Width			Fillet Radius, Inch†
17	0.6693	−.0003	62	2.4409	−.0005	30.2	1³⁄₁₆	−.005	.04
20	0.7874	−.0004	72	2.8346	−.0005	34.9	1⅜	−.005	.04
25	0.9843	−.0004	80	3.1496	−.0005	34.9	1⅜	−.005	.06
30	1.1811	−.0004	90	3.5433	−.0006	39.7	1⁹⁄₁₆	−.005	.06
35	1.3780	−.0005	100	3.9370	−.0006	44.4	1¾	−.005	.06
40	1.5748	−.0005	110	4.3307	−.0006	49.2	1¹⁵⁄₁₆	−.005	.08
45	1.7717	−.0005	120	4.7244	−.0006	54.0	2⅛	−.005	.08
50	1.9685	−.0005	130	5.1181	−.0008	58.7	2⁵⁄₁₆	−.005	.08
55	2.1654	−.0006	140	5.5118	−.0008	63.5	2½	−.005	.08
60	2.3622	−.0006	150	5.9055	−.0008	66.7	2⅝	−.005	.08
65	2.5591	−.0006	160	6.2992	−.0010	71.4	2¹³⁄₁₆	−.005	.08
70	2.7559	−.0006	180	7.0866	−.0010	79.4	3⅛	−.005	.10
75	2.9528	−.0006	190	7.4803	−.0012	82.6	3¼	−.005	.10
80	3.1496	−.0006	200	7.8740	−.0012	87.3	3⁷⁄₁₆	−.005	.10
85	3.3465	−.0008	210	8.2677	−.0012	92.1	3⅝	−.005	.12
90	3.5433	−.0008	225	8.8583	−.0012	98.4	3⅞	−.005	.12

* All sizes listed in Table 5 are standard for ball bearings of Types BD. The range of sizes for cylindrical roller bearings of Types RN, RU, and RK are given in Table 2.

† Radius of maximum fillet on shaft or in housing to be cleared by the bearing. This radius specification does not control contour of bearing corner.

Table 6. Standard Dimensions of Ball Bearings —
Types BIC and BM

Type	Bore Diameter		Outside Diameter		Ring Width		Fillet Radius, Inch
	Inch	Toler.	Inch	Toler.	Inch	Toler.	
BIC	1/8	—.0003	3/8	—.0004	5/32	—.005	.012
	3/16	—.0003	1/2	—.0004	11/64	—.005	.012
	3/16	—.0003	1/2	—.0004	5/32	—.005	.012
	1/4	—.0003	5/8	—.0004	.196	—.005	.012
	1/4	—.0003	3/4	—.0004	7/32	—.005	.016
	3/8	—.0003	7/8	—.0004	7/32	—.005	.016
	1/2	—.0003	1 1/8	—.0004	1/4	—.005	.016
	5/8	—.0003	1 3/8	—.0005	9/32	—.005	.031
	3/4	—.0004	1 5/8	—.0005	5/16	—.005	.031
	7/8	—.0004	1 7/8	—.0005	3/8	—.005	.031
	1	—.0004	2	—.0005	3/8	—.005	.031
	1 1/8	—.0004	2 1/8	—.0005	3/8	—.005	.031
	1 1/4	—.0005	2 1/4	—.0005	3/8	—.005	.031
	1 3/8	—.0005	2 1/2	—.0005	7/16	—.005	.031
	1 1/2	—.0005	2 5/8	—.0005	7/16	—.005	.031

Type	Bore Diameter		Outside Diameter		Ring Width		Fillet Radius, Inch
	Mm.	Inch	Mm.	Inch	Mm.	Inch	
BM	5	.1969	16	0.6299	5	.1969	.008
	6	.2362	24	0.9449	7	.2756	.012
	7	.2756	24	0.9449	7	.2756	.012
	8	.3150	24	0.9449	7	.2756	.012
	9	.3543	28	1.1024	8	.3150	.012
	10	.3937	28	1.1024	8	.3150	.012
	11	.4331	32	1.2598	7	.2756	.016
	12	.4724	32	1.2598	7	.2756	.016
	13	.5118	30	1.1811	7	.2756	.012
	14	.5512	35	1.3780	8	.3150	.020
	15	.5906	35	1.3780	8	.3150	.020
	16	.6299	38	1.4961	10	.3937	.040
	17	.6693	44	1.7323	11	.4331	.040

Table 7. Allowable Variation Between Diameters of Largest and Smallest Balls or
Rollers in Any Assembled Bearing

Ball Bearings		Cylindrical Roller Bearings	
Range of Ball Diameters	Allowable Variation in Diameters	Range of Roller Diameters	Allowable Variation in Diameters
Up to 3/8 inch, inc.	0.00005 inch	Up to 3/8 inch, inc.	0.00010 inch
Above 3/8 to 1 inch, inc.	0.00010 inch	Above 3/8 to 1 inch, inc.	0.00015 inch
Above 1 to 2 inches, inc.	0.00015 inch	Above 1 to 2 inches, inc.	0.00020 inch
		Above 2 inches	0.00025 inch

Taper Roller Bearings
Allowable variation in diameters, 0.0001 inch for specifications No. 0 and No. 3 (Table 13)
Allowable variation in diameters, 0.00025 inch for specifications No. 2, 4B, and 4C (Table 13)

Hardness: The hardness of bearing rings, balls and rollers shall be 58 to 66 on the Rockwell C scale, dependng upon the bearing size and material. This specification does not apply to non-corrosive materials.

Table 8. Standard Dimensions of Ball and Roller Bearings*

Bore Diameter			Outside Diameter			Ring Width			Fillet Radius, Inch†
Mm.	Inch	Toler.	Mm.	Inch	Toler.	Mm.	Inch	Toler.	
DIMENSION SERIES 22 — LIGHT									
10	0.3937	—.0003	30	1.1811	—.0004	14	0.5512	—.005	.025
12	0.4724	—.0003	32	1.2598	—.0005	14	0.5512	—.005	.025
15	0.5906	—.0003	35	1.3780	—.0005	14	0.5512	—.005	.025
17	0.6693	—.0003	40	1.5748	—.0005	16	0.6299	—.005	.04
20	0.7874	—.0004	47	1.8504	—.0005	18	0.7087	—.005	.04
25	0.9843	—.0004	52	2.0472	—.0005	18	0.7087	—.005	.04
30	1.1811	—.0004	62	2.4409	—.0005	20	0.7874	—.005	.04
35	1.3780	—.0005	72	2.8346	—.0005	23	0.9055	—.005	.04
40	1.5748	—.0005	80	3.1496	—.0005	23	0 9055	—.005	.04
45	1.7717	—.0005	85	3.3465	—.0006	23	0.9055	—.005	.04
50	1.9685	—.0005	90	3.5433	—.0006	23	0.9055	—.005	.04
55	2.1654	—.0006	100	3.9370	—.0006	25	0.9843	—.005	.06
60	2.3622	—.0006	110	4.3307	—.0006	28	1.1024	—.005	.06
65	2.5591	—.0006	120	4.7244	—.0006	31	1.2205	—.005	.06
70	2.7559	—.0006	125	4.9213	—.0008	31	1.2205	—.005	.06
75	2.9528	—.0006	130	5.1181	—.0008	31	1.2205	—.005	.08
80	3.1496	—.0006	140	5.5118	—.0008	33	1.2992	—.005	.08
85	3.3465	—.0008	150	5.9055	—.0008	36	1.4173	—.005	.08
90	3.5433	—.0008	160	6.2992	—.0010	40	1.5748	—.005	.08
95	3.7402	—.0008	170	6.6929	—.0010	43	1.6929	—.005	.08
100	3.9370	—.0008	180	7.0866	—.0010	46	1.8110	—.005	.08
105	4.1339	—.0008	190	7.4803	—.0012	50	1.9685	—.005	.08
110	4.3307	—.0008	220	7.8740	—.0012	53	2.0866	—.005	.08
120	4.7244	—.0008	215	8.4646	—.0012	58	2.2835	—.005	.08
130	5.1181	—.0010	230	9.0551	—.0012	64	2.5197	—.005	.10
140	5.5118	—.0010	250	9.8425	—.0012	68	2.6772	—.005	.10
150	5.9055	—.0010	270	10.6299	—.0014	73	2.8740	—.005	.10
160	6.2992	—.0010	290	11.4173	—.0014	80	3.1496	—.005	.10
170	6.6929	—.0010	310	12.2047	—.0014	86	3.3858	—.005	.12
180	7.0866	—.0010	320	12.5984	—.0016	86	3.3858	—.005	.12
190	7.4803	—.0012	340	13.3858	—.0016	92	3.6220	—.010	.12
200	7.8740	—.0012	360	14.1732	—.0016	98	3.8583	—.010	.12
220	8.6614	—.0012	400	15.7480	—.0016	108	4.2520	—.010	.12
240	9.4488	—.0012	440	17.3228	—.0018	120	4.7244	—.010	.12
260	10.2362	—.0014	480	18.8976	—.0018	130	5.1181	—.010	.16
280	11.0236	—.0014	500	19.6850	—.0018	130	5.1181	—.010	.16
300	11.8110	—.0014	540	21.2598	—.0020	140	5.5118	—.010	.16
320	12.5984	—.0016	580	22.8346	—.0020	150	5.9055	—.016	.16
DIMENSION SERIES 23 — MEDIUM (see next page)									
10	0.3937	—.0003	35	1.3780	—.0005	17	0.6693	—.005	.025
12	0.4724	—.0003	37	1.4567	—.0005	17	0.6693	—.005	.04
15	0.5906	—.0003	42	1.6535	—.0005	17	0.6693	—.005	.04
17	0.6693	—.0003	47	1.8504	—.0005	19	0.7480	—.005	.04
20	0.7874	—.0004	52	2.0472	—.0005	21	0.8268	—.005	.04
25	0.9843	—.0004	62	2.4409	—.0005	24	0.9449	—.005	.04
30	1.1811	—.0004	72	2.8346	—.0005	27	1.0630	—.005	.04
35	1.3780	—.0005	80	3.1496	—.0005	31	1.2205	—.005	.06
40	1.5748	—.0005	90	3.5433	—.0006	33	1.2992	—.005	.06
45	1.7717	—.0005	100	3.9370	—.0006	36	1.4173	—.005	.06
50	1.9685	—.0005	110	4.3307	—.0006	40	1.5748	—.005	.08
55	2.1654	—.0006	120	4.7244	—.0006	43	1.6929	—.005	.08

*Table 8 applies to ball bearings of Type BS and to cylindrical roller bearings of Type RS. For data on the range of sizes in each series, see Table 2.

†Radius of maximum fillet on shaft or in housing to be cleared by the bearing. This radius specification does not control contour of bearing corner.

Table 8 *(Continued).* **Standard Dimensions of Ball and Roller Bearings***

Bore Diameter			Outside Diameter			Ring Width			Fillet Radius, Inch
Mm.	Inch	Toler.	Mm.	Inch	Toler.	Mm.	Inch	Toler.	

DIMENSION SERIES 23 — MEDIUM

60	2.3622	—.0006	130	5.1181	—.0008	46	1.8110	—.005	.08
65	2.5591	—.0006	140	5.5118	—.0008	48	1.8898	—.005	.08
70	2.7559	—.0006	150	5.9055	—.0008	51	2.0079	—.005	.08
75	2.9528	—.0006	160	6.2992	—.0010	55	2.1654	—.005	.08
80	3.1496	—.0006	170	6.6929	—.0010	58	2.2835	—.005	.08
85	3.3465	—.0008	180	7.0866	—.0010	60	2.3622	—.005	.10
90	3.5433	—.0008	190	7.4803	—.0012	64	2.5197	—.005	.10
95	3.7402	—.0008	200	7.8740	—.0012	67	2.6378	—.005	.10
100	3.9370	—.0008	215	8.4646	—.0012	73	2.8740	—.005	.10
105	4.1339	—.0008	225	8.8583	—.0012	77	3.0315	—.005	.10
110	4.3307	—.0008	240	9.4488	—.0012	80	3.1496	—.005	.10
120	4.7244	—.0008	260	10.2362	—.0014	86	3.3858	—.005	.10
130	5.1181	—.0010	280	11.0236	—.0014	93	3.6614	—.005	.12
140	5.5118	—.0010	300	11.8110	—.0014	102	4.0157	—.005	.12
150	5.9055	—.0010	320	12.5984	—.0016	108	4.2520	—.005	.12
160	6.2992	—.0010	340	13.3858	—.0016	114	4.4882	—.005	.12
170	6.6929	—.0010	360	14.1732	—.0016	120	4.7244	—.005	.12
180	7.0866	—.0010	380	14.9606	—.0016	126	4.9606	—.005	.12
190	7.4803	—.0012	400	15.7480	—.0016	132	5.1968	—.010	.16
200	7.8740	—.0012	420	16.5354	—.0018	138	5.4331	—.010	.16
220	8.6614	—.0012	460	18.1102	—.0018	145	5.7087	—.010	.16
240	9.4488	—.0012	500	19.6850	—.0018	155	6.1024	—.010	.16
260	10.2362	—.0014	540	21.2598	—.0020	165	6.4961	—.010	.20
280	11.0236	—.0014	580	22.8346	—.0020	175	6.8898	—.010	.20

DIMENSION SERIES 30

120	4.7244	—.0008	180	7.0866	—.0010	46	1.8110	—.005	.08
130	5.1181	—.0010	200	7.8740	—.0012	52	2.0472	—.005	.08
140	5.5118	—.0010	210	8.2677	—.0012	53	2.0866	—.005	.08
150	5.9055	—.0010	225	8.8583	—.0012	56	2.2047	—.005	.08
160	6.2992	—.0010	240	9.4488	—.0012	60	2.3622	—.005	.08
170	6.6929	—.0010	260	10.2362	—.0014	67	2.6378	—.005	.08
180	7.0866	—.0010	280	11.0236	—.0014	74	2.9134	—.005	.08
190	7.4803	—.0012	290	11.4173	—.0014	75	2.9528	—.010	.08
200	7.8740	—.0012	310	12.2047	—.0014	82	3.2283	—.010	.08
220	8.6614	—.0012	340	13.3858	—.0016	90	3.5433	—.010	.10
240	9.4488	—.0012	360	14.1732	—.0016	92	3.6220	—.010	.10
260	10.2362	—.0014	400	15.7480	—.0016	104	4.0945	—.010	.12
280	11.0236	—.0014	420	16.5354	—.0018	106	4.1732	—.010	.12
300	11.8110	—.0014	460	18.1102	—.0018	118	4.6457	—.010	.12
320	12.5984	—.0016	480	18.8976	—.0018	121	4.7638	—.016	.12
340	13.3858	—.0016	520	20.4724	—.0020	133	5.2362	—.016	.16
360	14.1732	—.0016	540	21.2598	—.0020	134	5.2756	—.016	.16
380	14.9606	—.0016	560	22.0472	—.0020	135	5.3150	—.016	.16
400	15.7480	—.0016	600	23.6220	—.0020	148	5.8268	—.016	.16
420	16.5354	—.0018	620	24.4094	—.0020	150	5.9055	—.018	.16
440	17.3228	—.0018	650	25.5906	—.0030	157	6.1811	—.018	.20
460	18.1102	—.0018	680	26.7717	—.0030	163	6.4173	—.018	.20
480	18.8976	—.0018	700	27.5591	—.0030	165	6.4961	—.018	.20
500	19.6850	—.0018	720	28.3465	—.0030	167	6.5748	—.018	.20

*Table 8 applies to ball bearings of Type BS and to cylindrical roller bearings of Type RS. For data on the range of sizes in each series, see Table 2.

Table 8 (*Continued*). **Standard Dimensions of Ball and Roller Bearings***

Bore Diameter			Outside Diameter			Ring Width			Fillet Radius, Inch†
Mm.	Inch	Toler.	Mm.	Inch	Toler.	Mm.	Inch	Toler.	
DIMENSION SERIES 31									
110	4.3307	—.0008	180	7.0866	—.0010	56	2.2047	—.005	.08
120	4.7244	—.0008	200	7.8740	—.0012	62	2.4409	—.005	.08
130	5.1181	—.0010	210	8.2677	—.0012	64	2.5197	—.005	.08
140	5.5118	—.0010	225	8.8583	—.0012	68	2.6772	—.005	.08
150	5.9055	—.0010	250	9.8425	—.0012	80	3.1496	—.005	.08
160	6.2992	—.0010	270	10.6299	—.0014	86	3.3858	—.005	.08
170	6.6929	—.0010	280	11.0236	—.0014	88	3.4646	—.005	.08
180	7.0866	—.0010	300	11.8110	—.0014	96	3.7795	—.005	.10
190	7.4803	—.0012	320	12.5984	—.0016	104	4.0945	—.010	.10
200	7.8740	—.0012	340	13.3858	—.0016	112	4.4094	—.010	.10
220	8.6614	—.0012	370	14.5669	—.0016	120	4.7244	—.010	.12
240	9.4488	—.0012	400	15.7480	—.0016	128	5.0394	—.010	.12
260	10.2362	—.0014	440	17.3228	—.0018	144	5.6693	—.010	.12
280	11.0236	—.0014	460	18.1102	—.0018	146	5.7480	—.010	.16
300	11.8110	—.0014	500	19.6850	—.0018	160	6.2992	—.010	.16
320	12.5984	—.0016	540	21.2598	—.0020	176	6.9291	—.016	.16
340	13.3858	—.0016	580	22.8346	—.0020	190	7.4803	—.016	.16
360	14.1732	—.0016	600	23.6220	—.0020	192	7.5591	—.016	.16
380	14.9606	—.0016	620	24.4094	—.0020	194	7.6378	—.016	.16
400	15.7480	—.0016	650	25.5906	—.0030	200	7.8740	—.016	.20
420	16.5354	—.0018	700	27.5591	—.0030	224	8.8189	—.018	.20
440	17.3228	—.0018	720	28.3465	—.0030	226	8.8976	—.018	.20
460	18.1102	—.0018	760	29.9213	—.0030	240	9.4488	—.018	.24
480	18.8976	—.0018	790	31.1024	—.0030	248	9.7638	—.018	.24
500	19.6850	—.0018	830	32.6772	—.0039	264	10.3937	—.018	.24
DIMENSION SERIES 32									
220	8.6614	—.0012	400	15.7480	—.0016	144	5.6693	—.010	.12
240	9.4488	—.0012	440	17.3228	—.0018	160	6.2992	—.010	.12
260	10.2362	—.0014	480	18.8976	—.0018	174	6.8504	—.010	.16
280	11.0236	—.0014	500	19.6850	—.0018	176	6.9291	—.010	.16
300	11.8110	—.0014	540	21.2598	—.0020	192	7.5591	—.010	.16
320	12.5984	—.0016	580	22.8346	—.0020	208	8.1890	—.016	.16
340	13.3858	—.0016	620	24.4094	—.0020	224	8.8189	—.016	.20
360	14.1732	—.0016	650	25.5906	—.0030	232	9.1339	—.016	.20
380	14.9606	—.0016	680	26.7717	—.0030	240	9.4488	—.016	.20
400	15.7480	—.0016	720	28.3465	—.0030	256	10.0787	—.016	.20
420	16.5354	—.0018	760	29.9213	—.0030	272	10.7087	—.018	.24
440	17.3228	—.0018	790	31.1024	—.0030	280	11.0236	—.018	.24
460	18.1102	—.0018	830	32.6772	—.0039	296	11.6535	—.018	.24
480	18.8976	—.0018	870	34.2520	—.0039	310	12.2047	—.018	.24
500	19.6850	—.0018	920	36.2205	—.0039	336	13.2283	—.018	.24

*Table 8 applies to ball bearings of Type BS and to cylindrical roller bearings of Type RS. For data on the range of ball and roller bearing sizes in each Series, see Table 2.
†Radius of maximum fillet on shaft or in housing to be cleared by the bearing. This radius specification does not control contour of bearing corner.

Table 9. Standard Dimensions of Single-direction Ball Thrust Bearings –— Type BT

Type BT	Inside Diam. B		Outside Diam. D		Height H		Shaft Fillet Radius*
	Mm.	In.	Mm.	In.	Mm.	In.	
FLAT-FACE LIGHT SERIES (LEFT DIAGRAM)							
10BTL	10	0.3937	26	1.0236	12	0.4724	0.02
12BTL	12	0.4724	28	1.1024	12	0.4724	0.02
15BTL	15	0.5906	31	1.2205	12	0.4724	0.02
18BTL	18	0.7087	35	1.3780	12	0.4724	0.02
20BTL	20	0.7874	37	1.4567	12	0.4724	0.02
25BTL	25	0.9843	45	1.7717	14	0.5512	0.02
30BTL	30	1.1811	50	1.9585	14	0.5512	0.02
35BTL	35	1.3780	55	2.1654	16	0.6299	0.02
40BTL	40	1.5748	60	2.3622	16	0.6299	0.02
45BTL	45	1.7717	68	2.6772	16	0.6299	0.02
50BTL	50	1.9685	74	2.9134	18	0.7087	0.02
55BTL	55	2.1654	78	3.0709	18	0.7087	0.02
60BTL	60	2.3622	82	3.2284	18	0.7087	0.02
65BTL	65	2.5591	90	3.5433	20	0.7874	0.02
70BTL	70	2.7559	95	3.7402	20	0.7874	0.02
75BTL	75	2.9528	100	3.9370	20	0.7874	0.02
80BTL	80	3.1496	110	4.3307	22	0.8661	0.02
85BTL	85	3.3465	115	4.5276	22	0.8661	0.02
90BTL	90	3.5433	120	4.7244	22	0.8661	0.02
95BTL	95	3.7402	130	5.1181	25	0.9843	0.02
100BTL	100	3.9370	135	5.3150	25	0.9843	0.02
105BTL	105	4.1339	140	5.5118	25	0.9843	0.02
110BTL	110	4.3307	145	5.7087	25	0.9843	0.02
115BTL	115	4.5276	150	5.9055	25	0.9843	0.02
120BTL	120	4.7244	160	6.2992	27	1.0630	0.02
125BTL	125	4.9213	165	6.4961	27	1.0630	0.02
FLAT-FACE MEDIUM SERIES (LEFT DIAGRAM)							
10BTM	10	0.3937	30	1.1811	12	0.4724	.02
15BTM	15	0.5906	35	1.3780	14	0.5512	.02
20BTM	20	0.7874	40	1.5748	14	0.5512	.02
25BTM	25	0.9843	48	1.8898	15.5	0.6103	.02
30BTM	30	1.1811	53	2.0866	15.5	0.6103	.02
35BTM	35	1.3780	62	2.4409	18	0.7087	.02
40BTM	40	1.5748	64	2.5197	18	0.7087	.02
40BTM	45	1.7717	73	2.8740	22	0.8661	.02
50BTM	50	1.9685	78	3.0709	22	0.8661	.02

* Maximum fillet radius for shaft or housing is given in this column. This fillet must be cleared by corner radius *r* (or chamfer) on bearing.

Table 9 (Continued). Standard Dimensions of Ball Thrust Bearings — Types BT and BTS

Type BT	Inside Diam. B		Outside Diam. D		Height H		Shaft Fillet Radius*
	Mm.	In.	Mm.	In.	Mm.	In.	
FLAT-FACE MEDIUM SERIES (Continued)							
55BTM	55	2.1654	88	3.4646	24.5	0.9646	.02
60BTM	60	2.3622	90	3.5433	24.5	0.9646	.02
65BTM	65	2.5591	100	3.9370	27	1.0630	.04
70BTM	70	2.7559	103	4.0551	27	1.0630	.04
75BTM	75	2.9528	110	4.3307	27	1.0630	.04
80BTM	80	3.1496	115	4.5276	29	1.1417	.04
85BTM	85	3.3465	125	4.9213	30.5	1.2008	.04
90BTM	90	3.5433	135	5.3150	30.5	1.2088	.04
95BTM	95	3.7402	140	5.5118	32.5	1.2795	.04
100BTM	100	3.9370	150	5.9055	32.5	1.2795	.04
105BTM	105	4.1339	155	6.1024	40	1.5748	.04
115BTM	115	4.5276	165	6.4961	43	1.6929	.04
125BTM	125	4.9213	175	6.8898	46.5	1.8307	.04
140BTM	140	5.5118	200	7.8740	52	2.0472	.04

SELF-ALIGNING SERIES (RIGHT DIAGRAM)

Type BTS	Diam. B		Diam. D		Diam. E		H, In.	Rad. R, In.	X, In.	Fillet, In.
	Mm.	In.	Mm.	In.	Mm.	In.				
10BTSM	10	0.3937	30	1.1811	35	1.3780	0.5906	0.9843	0.402	.02
15BTSM	15	0.5906	35	1.3750	38	1.4961	0.6693	1.1811	0.488	.02
20BTSM	20	0.7874	40	1.5748	45	1.7717	0.7087	1.3780	0.638	.02
25BTSM	25	0.9843	48	1.8898	50	1.9685	0.7480	1.5748	0.492	.02
30BTSM	30	1.1811	53	2.0866	59	2.3228	0.7874	1.7717	0.630	.02
35BTSM	35	1.3780	62	2.4409	67	2.6378	0.9055	1.9685	0.913	.02
40BTSM	40	1.5748	64	2.5197	69	2.7165	0.9055	1.9685	0.882	.02
45BTSM	45	1.7717	73	2.8740	78	3.0709	1.0630	2.3622	1.126	.02
50BTSM	50	1.9685	78	3.0709	83	3.2677	1.0630	2.5591	1.299	.02
55BTSM	55	2.1654	88	3.4646	94	3.7008	1.1811	2.7559	1.276	.02
60BTSM	60	2.3622	90	3.5433	96	3.7795	1.1811	2.9528	1.496	.02
65BTSM	65	2.5591	100	3.9370	105	4.1339	1.3386	3.1496	1.516	.04
70BTSM	70	2.7559	103	4.0551	109	4.2913	1.3386	3.3465	1.677	.04
75BTSM	75	2.9528	110	4.3307	114	4.4882	1.3386	3.5433	1.819	.04
80BTSM	80	3.1496	115	4.5276	124	4.8819	1.4567	3.7402	1.913	.04
85BTSM	85	3.3465	125	4.9213	138	5.4331	1.5748	4.1339	2.161	.04
90BTSM	90	3.5433	135	5.3150	141	5.5512	1.5748	4.3307	2.260	.04
95BTSM	95	3.7402	140	5.5118	151	5.9449	1.7126	4.5276	2.370	.04
100BTSM	100	3.9370	150	5.9055	156	6.1417	1.7323	4.9213	2.717	.04
105BTSM	105	4.1339	155	6.1024	163	6.4173	1.9291	5.1181	2.732	.04
110BTSM	110	4.3307	160	6.2992	170	6.6929	1.9291	5.3150	2.902	.04
115BTSM	115	4.5276	165	6.4961	173	6.8110	2.0472	5.5518	2.957	.04
125BTSM	125	4.9213	180	7.0866	186	7.3228	2.2047	5.9055	3.142	.04
140BTSM	140	5.5118	200	7.8740	212	8.3464	2.4409	6.6929	3.583	.04

Table 10. Standard Dimensions of Ball Thrust Bearings — Type BIT

Inside Diam., Inch	Outside Diam., Inch	Height, Inch	Fillet Radius, Inch	Inside Diam., Inch	Outside Diam., Inch	Height, Inch	Fillet Radius, Inch
BITX (Extra Light Series) Both ring bores are same diameter				BITL (Light Series) Minimum clearance bore equals small bore + 1/32"			
½	1 7/32	9/16	.030	¼	13/16	3/8	.030
9/16	1 7/32	9/16	.030	5/16	1	17/32	.030
5/8	1 11/32	9/16	.030	3/8	1	17/32	.030
11/16	1 11/32	9/16	.030	7/16	1 9/32	5/8	.030
3/4	1 15/32	9/16	.030	½	1 9/32	5/8	.030
13/16	1 15/32	9/16	.030	9/16	1 13/32	5/8	.030
7/8	1 27/32	5/8	.030	5/8	1 13/32	5/8	.030
15/16	1 27/32	5/8	.030	3/4	1 17/32	5/8	.030
1	1 31/32	5/8	.030	7/8	1 21/32	5/8	.030
1 1/16	1 31/32	5/8	.030	1	1 25/32	5/8	.030
1 1/8	2 3/32	5/8	.030	1 1/8	1 29/32	5/8	.030
1 3/16	2 3/32	5/8	.030	1 1/4	2 3/32	23/32	.030
1 1/4	2 11/32	5/8	.030	1 3/8	2 7/32	23/32	.030
1 5/16	2 11/32	5/8	.030	1 1/2	2 11/32	23/32	.040
1 3/8	2 15/32	5/8	.030	1 5/8	2 15/32	23/32	.040
1 7/16	2 15/32	5/8	.030	1 3/4	2 11/16	3/4	.040
1 1/2	2 19/32	5/8	.040	1 7/8	2 13/16	3/4	.040
1 9/16	2 19/32	5/8	.040	2	2 31/32	3/4	.040
1 5/8	2 31/32	13/16	.040	2 1/8	3 7/32	7/8	.060
1 11/16	2 31/32	13/16	.040	2 1/4	3 11/32	7/8	.060
1 3/4	3 3/32	13/16	.040	2 3/8	3 19/32	1	.060
1 13/16	3 3/32	13/16	.040	2 1/2	3 23/32	1	.060
1 7/8	3 7/32	13/16	.040	2 5/8	3 27/32	1	.060
1 15/16	3 7/32	13/16	.040	2 3/4	4 1/32	1	.060
2	3 11/32	13/16	.040	2 7/8	4 5/32	1	.060
2 1/16	3 11/32	13/16	.060	3	4 3/8	1 1/8	.080
2 1/8	3 19/32	13/16	.060	3 1/8	4 1/2	1 1/8	.080
2 3/16	3 19/32	13/16	.060	3 1/4	4 13/16	1 1/4	.080
2 1/4	3 23/32	13/16	.060	3 3/8	4 15/16	1 1/4	.080
2 5/16	3 23/32	13/16	.060	3 1/2	5 1/16	1 1/4	.080
2 3/8	3 27/32	13/16	.060	3 5/8	5 3/16	1 1/4	.080
2 7/16	3 27/32	13/16	.060	3 3/4	5 5/16	1 1/4	.080
2 1/2	3 31/32	13/16	.060	3 7/8	5 11/16	1 3/8	.080
2 9/16	3 31/32	13/16	.060	4	5 13/16	1 3/8	.080
2 5/8	4 1/32	1	.060	4 1/4	6 5/16	1 3/4	.120
2 11/16	4 1/32	1	.060	4 1/2	6 9/16	1 3/4	.120
2 3/4	4 1/32	1	.060	4 3/4	7 1/16	2	.120
2 13/16	4 15/32	1	.060	5	7 5/16	2	.120
2 7/8	4 19/32	1	.060	5 1/2	8 1/16	2 3/16	.120
2 15/16	4 19/32	1	.080	6	8 11/16	2 3/8	.120
3	4 23/32	1	.080	7	10 5/8	2 5/8	.160
3 1/4	4 31/32	1	.080	8	11 5/8	3	.160
3 1/2	5 7/32	1	.080	9	13 1/8	3 1/2	.160
...	...	...	...	10	14 5/8	4	.180
...	...	...	...	11	15 5/8	4 1/4	.180
...	...	...	...	12	17 3/8	4 1/2	.180

Table 10 (*Continued*). Standard Dimensions of Ball Thrust Bearings — Type BIT*

Inside Diam., Inch	Outside Diam., Inch	Height, Inch	Fillet Radius, Inch†	Inside Diam., Inch	Outside Diam., Inch	Height, Inch	Fillet Radius, Inch†
BITM (Medium Series) Both ring bores are of same diameter							
½	1 7/16	5/8	.030	2 7/8	4 7/16	1 1/8	.060
9/16	1 7/16	5/8	.030	2 15/16	4 7/16	1 1/8	.080
5/8	1 9/16	5/8	.030	3	4 1/2	1 1/8	.080
11/16	1 9/16	5/8	.030	3 1/8	4 5/8	1 1/8	.080
3/4	1 11/16	5/8	.030	3 1/4	4 3/4	1 1/8	.080
13/16	1 11/16	5/8	.030	3 3/8	4 7/8	1 1/8	.080
7/8	1 15/16	3/4	.030	3 1/2	5	1 1/8	.080
15/16	1 15/16	3/4	.030	3 5/8	5 5/8	1 3/8	.080
1	2 1/16	3/4	.030	3 3/4	5 3/4	1 3/8	.080
1 1/16	2 1/16	3/4	.030	3 7/8	5 7/8	1 3/8	.080
1 1/8	2 3/16	3/4	.030	4	6	1 3/8	.080
1 3/16	2 3/16	3/4	.030	4 1/8	6 1/8	1 3/8	.120
1 1/4	2 5/16	3/4	.030	4 1/4	6 1/4	1 3/8	.120
1 5/16	2 5/16	3/4	.030	4 3/8	6 3/8	1 3/8	.120
1 3/8	2 7/16	3/4	.030	4 1/2	6 3/4	1 5/8	.120
1 7/16	2 7/16	3/4	.030	4 5/8	6 7/8	1 5/8	.120
1 1/2	2 9/16	3/4	.040	4 3/4	7	1 5/8	.120
1 9/16	2 9/16	3/4	.040	4 7/8	7 1/8	1 5/8	.120
1 5/8	2 13/16	7/8	.040	5	7 1/4	1 5/8	.120
1 11/16	2 13/16	7/8	.040	5 1/8	7 3/8	1 5/8	.120
1 3/4	2 15/16	7/8	.040	5 1/4	7 1/2	1 5/8	.120
1 13/16	2 15/16	7/8	.040	5 3/8	7 5/8	1 5/8	.120
1 7/8	3 1/16	7/8	.040	5 1/2	8 1/4	1 7/8	.120
1 15/16	3 1/16	7/8	.040	5 5/8	8 3/8	1 7/8	.120
2	3 3/16	7/8	.040	5 3/4	8 1/2	1 7/8	.120
2 1/16	3 3/16	7/8	.060	5 7/8	8 5/8	1 7/8	.120
2 1/8	3 5/16	7/8	.060	6	8 3/4	1 7/8	.120
2 3/16	3 5/16	7/8	.060	6 1/8	8 7/8	1 7/8	.160
2 1/4	3 7/16	7/8	.060	6 1/4	9	1 7/8	.160
2 5/16	3 7/16	7/8	.060	6 3/8	9 1/8	1 7/8	.160
2 3/8	3 9/16	7/8	.060	6 1/2	9 1/2	2 1/4	.160
2 7/16	3 9/16	7/8	.060	6 5/8	9 5/8	2 1/4	.160
2 1/2	4	1 1/8	.060	6 3/4	9 3/4	2 1/4	.160
2 9/16	4	1 1/8	.060	6 7/8	9 7/8	2 1/4	.160
2 5/8	4 1/8	1 1/8	.060	7	10	2 1/4	.160
2 11/16	4 1/8	1 1/8	.060	7 1/8	10 1/8	2 1/4	.160
2 3/4	4 1/4	1 1/8	.060	7 1/4	10 1/4	2 1/4	.160
2 13/16	4 1/4	1 1/8	.060	7 3/8	10 3/8	2 1/4	.160
...	...	...	...	...	...	...	...

* The type letters BIT are followed by X to indicate "extra-light"; L for light, and M for medium.

† The corner radius or chamfer on bearings must clear the maximum fillet radius given in the tables. This fillet radius specification does not control the bearing corner contours.

Table 11. Standard Dimensions of Taper Roller Bearings — Type TS

Bore Diam., Inch	Outside Diam., Inch	Bearing Width, Inch	Cone Radius Inch	Cup Radius Inch	Bore Diam., Inch	Outside Diam., Inch	Bearing Width, Inch	Cone Radius Inch	Cup Radius Inch
.3750	1.2995	.3940	3/64	3/64	1.1900	2.7170	.7813	1/2	3/64
.4720	1.2995	.3940	1/32	3/64	1.2450	2.6250	.8125	1/16	1/16
.5000	1.3775	.4330	3/64	3/64	1.2500	2.3125	.5781	.040	.040
.5900	1.3775	.4330	1/32	3/64	1.2500	2.6875	.8750	9/64	1/16
.6250	1.5745	.4730	3/64	3/64	1.2500	2.7170	.7813	9/64	3/64
.6250	1.6875	.6563	1/16	1/16	1.2500	2.7500	.9375	9/64	3/64
.6250	1.8504	.5662	1/16	3/64	1.2500	2.8593	1.1875	9/64	1/8
.6250	1.9380	.9063	1/32	1/16	1.2500	2.8750	.8750	9/64	1/8
.6690	1.5745	.4730	1/32	3/64	1.2500	2.8750	.8750	9/64	1/8
.7500	1.5745	.4730	.040	3/64	1.2500	3.1250	1.1563	3/64	1/8
.7500	1.8504	.5662	3/64	3/64	1.2500	3.1496	.8268	1/32	3/64
.7500	1.9380	.9063	3/64	1/16	1.2600	2.8345	.7480	1/16	1/16
.7500	2.2400	.7625	1/16	3/64	1.3125	2.7170	.7813	9/64	3/64
.7870	1.8504	.5662	1/16	3/64	1.3125	2.7500	.9375	9/64	3/64
.7874	2.0470	.5910	1/16	3/64	1.3125	2.8750	.8750	9/64	1/8
.8125	1.9380	.7813	1/16	1/16	1.3125	3.0000	.9375	9/64	1/8
.8750	2.0470	.5910	3/64	3/64	1.3125	3.0000	1.1563	1/32	1/8
.8750	2.1250	.7625	1/16	1/16	1.3750	2.7170	.7813	1/16	3/64
.8750	2.2400	.7625	3/64	3/64	1.3750	2.8750	.8750	9/64	1/8
.8750	2.2500	.8750	1/32	1/16	1.3750	2.8750	.8750	1/32	1/8
.9375	2.2400	.7625	1/32	3/64	1.3750	2.8750	.9375	9/64	3/32
.9375	2.4375	1.1250	3/32	1/8	1.3750	3.0000	.9375	13/32	1/8
.9375	2.6150	.9375	1/32	3/64	1.3750	3.0000	1.1563	1/16	1/8
.9375	2.8345	.7480	3/32	1/16	1.3750	3.0000	1.1563	1/16	1/8
.9835	2.0470	.5910	1/16	3/64	1.3750	3.1250	1.1563	9/64	1/8
1.0000	2.0470	.5910	.040	3/64	1.3750	3.1496	.8268	1/32	3/64
1.0000	2.2500	.6875	3/64	1/16	1.3750	3.1562	1.1563	1/16	1/8
1.0000	2.3125	.7500	3/64	3/64	1.3750	3.4843	1.0625	1/32	1/32
1.0000	2.5000	.8125	9/64	3/64	1.3750	3.7500	1.0938	1/32	3/32
1.0000	2.6150	.9375	3/64	3/64	1.3770	2.8345	.6700	1/16	1/16
1.0000	2.8345	.7480	1/16	1/16	1.3779	3.1496	.8268	1/32	3/64
1.0625	2.2500	.6875	9/64	1/16	1.3779	3.1562	1.0000	1/32	1/8
1.1250	2.3125	.7500	1/32	3/64	1.4365	3.0000	.9375	9/64	1/8
1.1250	2.5000	.8125	9/64	3/64	1.4375	2.8345	.6700	1/16	1/16
1.1250	2.6150	.9375	3/64	3/64	1.4375	2.8440	.8125	9/64	1/16
1.1250	2.6875	.8750	1/32	1/16	1.4375	3.3750	1.1875	1/32	1/8
1.1250	2.7500	.9375	3/32	3/64	1.5000	2.5625	.5000	1/16	1/32
1.1250	2.8345	.7480	1/16	1/16	1.5000	2.7170	.7500	9/64	3/32
1.1250	2.8593	1.1875	3/64	1/8	1.5000	2.8345	.6700	.060	1/16
1.1250	2.8570	.8750	1/32	1/8	1.5000	2.8440	.8125	9/64	3/64
1.1562	2.6150	.9375	9/64	3/64	1.5000	3.0000	.9375	9/64	1/8
1.1805	2.4410	.6300	1/16	1/16	1.5000	3.1250	1.1563	9/64	1/8
1.1805	2.5000	.8125	3/64	3/64	1.5000	3.1495	.8270	9/64	1/16
1.1810	2.7170	.7813	9/64	3/64	1.5000	3.1496	.8268	1/32	3/64
1.1875	2.4410	.6300	1/16	1/16	1.5000	3.1562	1.1563	9/64	1/8
1.1875	2.7500	.9375	3/32	1/16	1.5000	3.3750	1.1875	9/64	1/8
1.1875	2.8593	1.1875	9/64	1/8	1.5000	3.4833	1.0625	9/64	1/32
1.1895	2.5000	.8125	9/64	3/64	1.5000	3.6875	1.2500	9/64	1/8

Table 11 (*Continued*).   Standard Dimensions of Taper Roller Bearings—
Type TS

Bore Diam., Inch	Outside Diam., Inch	Bearing Width, Inch	Cone Radius Inch	Cup Radius Inch	Bore Diam., Inch	Outside Diam., Inch	Bearing Width, Inch	Cone Radius Inch	Cup Radius Inch
1.5000	3.7500	1.0938	9/64	3/32	1.8125	3.7500	1.0938	9/64	3/32
1.5000	4.2500	1.4375	9/64	1/8	1.8750	3.5000	.8125	9/64	3/64
1.5625	3.156.	1.0000	9/64	1/8	1.8750	3.6718	1.1875	1/4	1/8
1.5625	3.1562	1.1563	9/64	1/8	1.8750	4.0000	1.3750	9/64	1/8
1.5625	3.4843	1.0625	9/64	1/32	1.8750	4.0625	1.7188	3/64	1/8
1.5748	3.1495	.8270	1/16	1/16	1.8750	4.1250	1.1875	3/16	1/8
1.5748	3.1496	.8268	9/64	3/64	1.8750	4.2500	1.4375	9/64	1/8
1.5748	3.4843	1.0625	9/64	1/32	1.8750	4.7500	1.6250	9/64	1/8
1.6250	3.0000	.8750	9/64	1/32	1.9375	4.0625	1.7188	9/64	1/8
1.6250	3.1495	.7090	1/16	1/16	1.9685	3.5000	.8125	3/32	3/64
1.6250	3.1496	.8268	9/64	3/64	1.9685	4.1250	1.1875	3/32	1/8
1.6250	3.1562	1.0000	9/64	1/8	2.0000	3.3750	.7500	.060	.060
1.6250	3.3750	1.1875	9/64	1/8	2.0000	3.5000	.8125	9/64	3/64
1.6250	3.4375	1.1875	9/64	1/8	2.0000	3.6718	1.1875	9/64	1/8
1.6250	3.4843	1.0625	9/64	1/32	2.0000	3.8125	.8750	3/32	1/16
1.6250	3.5625	1.5625	9/64	1/8	2.0000	4.0000	1.2500	9/64	1/8
1.6250	3.6875	1.2500	9/64	1/8	2.0000	4.0000	1.3750	9/64	1/8
1.6250	3.6875	1.2500	1/32	1/8	2.0000	4.1250	1.1875	1/32	1/8
1.6250	3.7500	1.0938	9/64	3/32	2.0000	4.1250	1.4375	9/64	1/8
1.6250	4.0000	1.3750	9/64	1/8	2.0000	4.1250	1.5625	9/64	1/8
1.6875	3.2650	.9375	.090	1/32	2.0000	4.2500	1.4375	9/64	1/8
1.6875	3.4375	1.1875	9/64	1/8	2.0000	4.4375	1.1875	9/64	1/8
1.6880	3.1496	.8268	9/64	3/64	2.0000	4.7500	1.6250	9/64	1/8
1.6880	3.1562	1.0000	9/64	1/8	2.0000	4.8750	1.5000	3/32	1/8
1.6880	3.2650	.9375	9/64	1/32	2.0000	5.000	2.0000	9/64	1/8
1.7500	3.0312	.6875	.060	.060	2.0625	3.6718	1.1875	3/32	1/8
1.7500	3.1875	.7500	0	1/16	2.0625	3.7500	1.0938	1/16	3/32
1.7500	3.2650	.8750	9/64	1/32	2.0625	3.8125	.8750	3/32	1/16
1.7500	3.2650	.9375	9/64	1/32	2.0625	4.2500	1.4375	9/64	1/8
1.7500	3.3464	.8125	3/32	3/64	2.1250	3.8750	.8268	1/32	1/32
1.7500	3.4375	1.1875	9/64	1/8	2.1250	4.1250	1.1875	9/64	1/8
1.7500	3.6875	1.2500	9/64	1/8	2.1250	4.1250	1.5625	9/64	1/8
1.7500	3.6875	1.2500	9/64	1/8	2.1250	4.2500	1.4375	9/64	1/8
1.7500	3.7500	1.0938	9/64	3/32	2.1250	4.7500	1.6250	9/64	1/8
1.7500	4.0000	1.3750	9/64	1/8	2.1250	4.8750	1.5000	9/64	1/8
1.7500	4.1250	1.1875	9/64	1/8	2.1250	5.0000	2.0000	9/64	1/8
1.7500	4.1250	1.4375	9/64	1/8	2.1250	5.3750	1.6250	9/64	1/8
1.7500	4.2500	1.4375	9/64	1/8	2.1653	3.8750	.8268	3/32	1/32
1.7500	4.5000	1.7500	9/64	1/8	2.1880	3.8750	.8268	3/32	1/32
1.7500	4.7500	1.6250	9/64	1/8	2.2500	3.8437	.9688	9/64	1/32
1.7710	3.2650	.9375	1/16	1/32	2.2500	3.8750	.8268	9/64	1/32
1.7710	3.6718	1.1875	9/64	1/8	2.2500	4.1250	1.1875	3/32	1/8
1.7716	3.3464	.8125	1/16	3/64	2.2500	4.3307	.8661	3/32	3/64
1.7716	3.8125	.8750	1/32	1/16	2.2500	4.4375	1.1875	9/64	1/8
1.8125	3.1250	.6875	7/64	1/16	2.2500	4.7500	1.6250	9/64	1/8
1.8125	3.1875	.7500	1/32	1/16	2.2500	4.8750	1.5000	9/64	1/8
1.8125	3.3464	.8125	3/32	3/64	2.2500	5.0000	1.7500	9/64	1/8
1.8125	3.3464	1.0000	9/64	3/64	2.2500	5.3447	2.1250	1 1/64	1/8

Table 11 (*Continued*). Standard Dimensions of Taper Roller Bearings — Type TS

Bore Diam., Inch	Outside Diam., Inch	Bearing Width, Inch	Cone Radius Inch	Cup Radius Inch	Bore Diam., Inch	Outside Diam., Inch	Bearing Width, Inch	Cone Radius Inch	Cup Radius Inch
2.3622	4.2500	1.0000	1/32	1/8	3.1875	5.2500	1.3125	9/64	1/8
2.3622	4.3307	.8661	1/32	3/64	3.1875	5.3750	1.1875	9/64	1/8
2.3750	4.0000	1.0000	9/64	1/8	3.1875	5.5115	1.4375	9/64	1/8
2.3750	4.4375	1.1875	9/64	1/8	3.1875	5.9090	1.7500	13/64	1/8
2.3750	5.3447	2.1250	9/64	1/8	3.1875	6.6250	2.1250	1/32	1/8
2.5000	4.1250	.8438	.080	.080	3.2500	5.2500	1.3125	9/64	1/8
2.5000	4.3307	.8661	9/64	3/64	3.2500	5.3750	1.1875	9/64	1/8
2.5000	4.4375	1.1875	9/64	1/8	3.2500	5.5115	1.4375	9/64	1/8
2.5000	4.6250	1.1875	1/32	1/8	3.2500	6.0000	1.6250	9/64	1/8
2.5000	4.7244	1.1418	1/32	1/8	3.2500	6.6250	2.1250	9/64	1/8
2.5000	4.8125	1.7188	9/64	1/8	3.3125	5.3750	1.1875	9/64	1/8
2.5000	4.8750	1.5000	9/64	1/8	3.3475	5.9090	1.7500	9/64	1/8
2.5000	5.0000	1.4375	9/64	1/8	3.3750	6.0000	1.5625	9/64	1/8
2.5000	5.3750	1.6250	9/64	1/8	3.3750	6.0000	1.6250	9/64	1/8
2.5625	5.3447	2.1250	9/64	1/8	3.5000	6.0000	1.5625	9/64	1/8
2.6250	4.3307	.8661	9/64	3/64	3.5000	6.3750	1.8750	9/64	1/8
2.6250	4.4375	1.1875	9/64	1/8	3.5000	7.5000	2.2500	5/16	1/8
2.6250	4.6250	1.1875	9/64	1/8	3.5430	6.3030	1.1860	3/32	1/8
2.6250	4.7244	1.1418	3/32	1/8	3.6250	6.0000	1.5625	9/64	1/8
2.6250	4.8750	1.5000	9/64	1/8	3.6250	6.7500	1.8750	9/64	1/8
2.6250	5.3750	1.6250	9/64	1/8	3.6875	5.8437	1.1250	.120	.120
2.6875	4.3307	.8661	3/32	3/64	3.7500	5.8437	1.1250	.120	.120
2.6875	4.7244	1.1418	9/64	1/8	3.7500	6.0000	1.5625	9/64	1/8
2.6875	4.8750	1.5000	9/64	1/8	3.7500	6.6250	1.6250	9/64	1/8
2.6875	5.0000	1.4375	9/64	1/8	3.7500	6.7500	1.8750	9/64	1/8
2.7500	4.6250	1.1875	9/64	1/8	3.8750	6.6250	1.6250	9/64	1/8
2.7500	4.7244	1.1418	9/64	1/8	3.8750	7.1250	1.8750	9/64	1/8
2.7500	5.0000	1.4375	9/64	1/8	4.0000	6.1875	1.4375	9/64	1/8
2.7500	5.3750	1.6250	9/64	1/8	4.0000	6.6250	1.6250	9/64	1/8
2.7500	6.0000	1.6250	9/64	1/8	4.0000	7.1250	1.8750	9/64	1/8
2.7500	6.6250	2.1250	9/64	1/8	4.0000	7.5000	2.2500	5/16	1/8
2.8125	4.6250	1.1875	9/64	1/8	4.1250	7.1250	1.8750	9/64	1/8
2.8125	5.0000	1.4375	9/64	1/8	4.2500	6.2500	.9063	9/64	1/8
2.8125	5.3750	1.6250	1/4	1/8	4.5000	7.0000	1.6250	9/64	1/8
2.8750	5.0000	1.4375	9/64	1/8	4.5000	7.5000	1.8750	9/64	1/8
2.8750	5.9090	1.7500	9/64	1/8	4.5000	8.3750	2.6250	9/32	1/8
2.8750	6.0000	1.6250	9/64	1/8	4.6250	7.1250	1.3750	9/64	1/8
2.9062	5.0000	1.4375	1/32	1/8	4.7500	8.1250	1.8750	1/8	1/8
3.0000	4.7812	.9688	.080	.080	5.0000	8.0000	1.8125	9/64	1/8
3.0000	5.2500	1.3125	1/32	1/8	5.0000	8.5000	1.8750	9/64	1/8
3.0000	5.3750	1.1875	9/64	1/8	5.0000	9.2500	2.5000	1/4	1/8
3.0000	5.5115	1.4375	9/64	1/8	5.0000	9.7500	2.5000	1/8	3/16
3.0000	5.8750	2.1250	9/64	1/8	5.0000	10.0000	3.0625	3/8	1/4
3.0000	5.9090	1.7500	9/64	1/8	5.0000	11.6250	3.2500	17/32	1/4
3.0000	6.0000	1.6250	9/64	1/8	5.0000	11.6250	3.3750	1/4	1/4
3.0000	6.3750	2.1250	9/64	1/8	5.0000	12.0000	3.1250	1/4	1/4
3.0000	6.6250	2.1250	1/4	1/8	5.0000	12.0000	2.3750	1/4	1/4
3.0625	4.7812	.9688	9/64	.080	5.0625	7.5000	1.3750	9/64	1/8

Table 11 (Continued). Standard Dimensions of Taper Roller Bearings — Type TS

Bore Diam., Inch	Outside Diam., Inch	Bearing Width, Inch	Cone Radius Inch	Cup Radius Inch	Bore Diam., Inch	Outside Diam., Inch	Bearing Width, Inch	Cone Radius Inch	Cup Radius Inch
5.0625	8.1250	1.8750	1/8	1/8	6.8750	12.2500	3.2500	1/4	1/4
5.1181	8.1250	1.8750	9/64	1/8	6.8750	14.0000	2.4375	3/16	3/16
5.2500	8.0000	1.8125	9/64	1/8	7.0000	9.7500	1.8750	9/64	1/8
5.2500	8.5000	1.8750	9/64	1/8	7.0000	11.2500	2.5000	1/4	1/8
5.2500	9.2500	2.5000	3/8	1/8	7.0000	11.3750	2.5000	9/32	1/8
5.3750	7.5000	1.5625	9/64	1/8	7.0000	12.0000	2.6250	1/4	1/8
5.3750	8.5000	1.8750	9/64	1/8	7.0000	13.2500	3.5625	1/4	1/4
5.3750	12.0000	3.1250	1/2	1/8	7.0000	14.0000	2.4375	3/16	3/16
5.5000	8.5000	1.8750	9/64	1/8	7.0000	14.3720	3.6250	1/2	1/8
5.5000	8.7500	1.3750	9/64	1/8	7.3750	11.1250	2.0000	9/64	1/8
5.5000	9.0000	2.2500	9/64	1/8	7.3750	12.5970	3.5000	7/32	3/16
5.5000	9.5000	2.2500	9/64	1/8	7.5000	10.5000	1.8750	9/64	1/8
5.5000	10.0000	2.6250	9/32	1/8	7.5000	11.1250	2.0000	9/64	1/8
5.5000	11.6250	3.2500	3/8	1/4	7.5000	12.5000	2.5000	11/64	1/8
5.5000	12.0000	2.3750	3/8	1/4	7.5000	13.0000	2.5000	9/32	1/8
5.5000	12.1250	3.5000	3/8	17/64	7.5000	14.3720	3.6250	1/4	1/8
5.6250	8.7500	1.3750	9/64	1/8	7.8750	12.5000	2.5000	11/64	1/8
5.6250	9.5000	2.2500	9/64	1/8	8.0000	12.5000	2.1250	5/32	1/8
5.7500	9.5000	2.2500	9/64	1/8	8.0000	12.5000	2.5000	11/64	1/8
5.7500	9.6250	1.8750	9/64	1/8	8.0000	12.5000	2.6250	11/64	1/8
5.7500	10.0000	2.6250	9/32	1/8	8.0000	14.3720	2.6250	1/8	1/8
5.7500	10.5625	2.9375	1/4	1/4	8.0000	16.0000	2.5000	9/32	1/4
5.7500	11.2500	3.0000	1/4	1/4	8.1250	12.5000	2.1250	5/32	1/8
5.7500	12.0000	2.3750	1/8	1/4	8.2500	12.5000	2.5000	11/64	1/8
5.7500	12.1250	3.5000	3/8	17/64	8.5000	11.4177	1.2500	9/64	1/8
5.8750	9.5000	2.2500	9/64	1/8	8.5000	14.0000	2.7500	17/64	1/16
5.8750	10.0000	2.6250	9/32	1/8	8.6602	11.4177	1.2500	9/64	1/8
5.9000	12.7500	3.0625	17/32	3/16	9.0000	11.8125	1.3125	9/64	1/8
6.0000	9.6250	1.8750	9/64	1/8	9.0000	12.8750	2.0625	1/4	1/8
6.0000	10.0000	2.6250	9/32	1/8	9.0000	14.0000	2.6875	9/32	1/8
6.0000	10.5625	2.9375	1/4	1/4	9.0000	14.0000	2.7500	17/64	1/16
6.0000	11.2500	3.0000	1/16	1/4	9.0000	15.7500	3.5000	13/32	1/4
6.0000	12.1250	3.5000	3/8	17/64	9.0000	16.0000	2.5000	9/32	1/4
6.0000	12.7500	3.0625	11/16	3/16	9.0000	16.7500	4.0000	9/32	1/4
6.2960	12.7500	3.0625	13/32	3/16	9.2500	12.8750	2.0625	1/4	1/8
6.3750	13.5000	3.1250	1/4	1/4	9.2500	12.8750	2.0625	1/4	1/8
6.5000	10.0000	1.8125	3/16	1/8	9.2500	14.0000	2.6875	9/32	1/8
6.5000	11.3750	2.5000	9/32	1/8	9.4930	14.5000	2.6875	1/4	1/8
6.5000	12.2500	3.2500	1/4	1/8	9.5000	14.0000	2.2500	1/4	1/8
6.5000	13.5000	3.1250	11/16	1/4	9.5000	14.3720	2.0000	1/4	1/8
6.5000	13.6875	2.7500	3/8	1/4	9.5000	14.5000	2.6875	1/4	1/8
6.5000	14.0000	2.4375	3/16	3/16	9.5000	17.5000	4.0000	1/4	3/16
6.5000	14.2500	4.1875	17/32	1/8	9.5000	19.2500	4.7500	1/4	1/4
6.6929	10.0000	1.8125	3/16	1/8	....	....	....	..	..
6.7500	13.5000	3.1250	1/4	1/4	....	....	....	..	..
6.7500	14.0000	2.4375	3/16	3/16	....	....	....	..	..
6.8750	9.7500	1.8750	9/64	1/8	....	....	....	..	..
6.8750	11.3750	2.5000	9/32	1/8	....	....	....	..	..

Table 12. Standard Dimensions of Taper Roller Bearings — Type TSS

The different types of bearings indicated by combinations of letters (such as TSS, etc.) are described and illustrated in Table 1.

Bore Diam., Inch	Outside Diam., Inch	Bearing Width, Inch	Cone Radius, Inch	Cup Radius, Inch	Bore Diam., Inch	Outside Diam., Inch	Bearing Width, Inch	Cone Radius, Inch	Cup Radius, Inch
0.6250	1.6875	0.5625	1⁄16	1⁄16	3.3125	6.7500	1.9375	9⁄64	1⁄8
0.7500	2.1250	0.8750	1⁄16	3⁄32	3.3465	7.8740	2.0772	9⁄64	1⁄8
1.0000	2.5625	0.8750	1⁄16	1⁄16	3.5000	7.8740	2.0772	9⁄64	1⁄8
1.0000	2.8593	0.9688	3⁄32	1⁄16	3.8125	7.4375	2.0000	9⁄64	1⁄8
1.1250	2.8593	0.9688	3⁄16	1⁄16	4.0000	7.8740	2.0772	9⁄64	1⁄8
1.1250	3.1250	1.0000	1⁄32	1⁄16	4.0000	9.8750	3.0000	1⁄4	1⁄8
1.2500	3.1250	1.0000	1⁄16	1⁄16	4.5000	9.0000	2.1250	9⁄64	1⁄8
1.5000	3.4843	1.0000	3⁄32	1⁄16	4.5000	11.0000	3.2500	1⁄4	1⁄4
1.5625	3.4843	1.0000	9⁄64	1⁄16	4.9330	9.0000	2.1250	9⁄64	1⁄8
1.6250	3.7500	1.2188	1⁄16	1⁄32	5.0000	9.0000	2.1250	9⁄64	1⁄8
1.7500	3.7500	1.2188	9⁄64	1⁄32	5.0000	12.0000	3.5000	1⁄4	1⁄4
2.0000	4.4375	1.1875	9⁄64	1⁄8	5.0312	9.0000	2.1250	9⁄64	1⁄8
2.0000	4.8750	1.4375	9⁄64	1⁄8	5.7500	12.0000	3.5000	1⁄4	1⁄4
2.1250	4.8750	1.4375	9⁄64	1⁄8	6.1250	13.5000	3.3750	1⁄4	1⁄4
2.1250	5.5130	1.4375	9⁄64	3⁄32	6.3750	14.7500	3.4375	1⁄4	1⁄16
2.3622	4.8125	1.3125	9⁄64	1⁄8	7.0000	14.0000	3.1250	1⁄4	1⁄4
2.4375	6.0000	1.8750	9⁄64	1⁄8	7.0000	16.8750	4.1875	1⁄4	1⁄4
2.5000	5.5130	1.4375	3⁄32	3⁄32	7.5000	16.8750	4.1875	1⁄4	1⁄4
2.6875	6.0000	1.8750	9⁄64	1⁄8	8.0000	19.0000	4.6250	1⁄4	1⁄4
3.0000	6.3750	1.9375	9⁄64	1⁄8	9.0000	20.0000	4.6250	1⁄4	1⁄4
3.0000	6.7500	1.9375	9⁄64	1⁄8	9.5000	20.0000	4.6250	1⁄4	1⁄4
3.1496	7.8740	2.0772	9⁄64	1⁄8	....	....	....	....	....

Any single cone listed in Table 11 (Type TS) or in Table 12 (Type TSS) can be used with a flanged outer race (Type TSF, Table 14) or double row (Type TDO, Table 16) in the same series.

Table 13. Taper Roller Bearing Tolerance Specifications

Where Tolerance is Applied	Range of Dimensions	Tolerances*				
		No. 0	No. 3	No. 2	No. 4C	No. 4B
Bore	Up to 2½	+.0005 to −.0	+.0005 to −.0	+.0005 to −.0	+.0005 to −.0	+.0005 to −.0
	2½ to 12	+.0005 to −.0	+.0005 to −.0	+.001 to −.0	+.001 to −.0	+.001 to −.0
Outside Diameter	Up to 12	+.0005 to −.0	+.0005 to −.0	+.001 to −.0	+.001 to −.0	+.001 to −.0
	12 to 24	....	+.001 to −.0	....	+.002 to −.0	+.002 to −.0
Width	All	±.008	±.008	+.008 to −.0	+.008 to −.0	+.014 to −.010
Radii	All	+1⁄64 −.0	+1⁄64 −.0	+1⁄64 −.0	+1⁄64 −.0	+1⁄64 −.0
Assembly Run-out	All	.00015	.0003	.0015	.002	.002

* For allowable variation in diameters of largest and smallest rollers in an assembled bearing, see Table 7.

Table 14. Standard Dimensions of Taper Roller Bearings — Type TSF

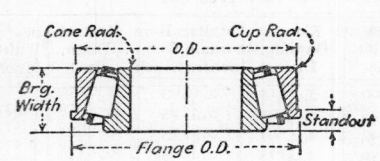

Bore Diam., Inch	Outside Diam., Inch	Flange Outside Diam.	"Standout," Inch	Bearing Width, Inch	Cone Radius, Inch	Cup Radius, Inch
0.4720	1.2595	1.3845	.1753	0.3940	1/32	3/64
0.5000	1.3775	1.5025	.1831	0.4330	3/64	3/64
0.6250	1.5745	1.6995	.1918	0.4730	3/64	3/64
0.7500	1.8504	2.0064	.2381	0.5662	3/64	1/16
0.7500	2.1250	2.2812	.4063	0.8750	1/16	3/32
0.8750	2.0625	2.2187	.3563	0.7625	1/16	1/16
0.8750	2.2400	2.3960	.2938	0.7625	3/64	1/32
0.9375	2.0470	2.2030	.2004	0.5910	1/16	1/16
1.0000	2.3750	2.5310	.3125	0.7813	3/64	1/32
1.0000	2.5625	2.7187	.4063	0.8750	1/16	1/16
1.0000	2.8593	3.0781	.5000	0.9688	3/32	1/16
1.1250	2.6150	2.7710	.3438	0.9375	3/64	1/32
1.1805	2.4410	2.5970	.2075	0.6300	1/16	1/16
1.1805	2.8345	2.9905	.2793	0.7480	1/16	1/16
1.1875	2.8593	3.0473	.4375	1.1875	9/64	1/8
1.2500	2.3125	2.4685	.2653	0.5781	.040	.040
1.2500	2.6875	2.8437	.3438	0.8750	9/64	1/16
1.2500	2.7170	2.8730	.3125	0.7813	9/64	1/32
1.2500	2.7500	2.9060	.3438	0.9375	9/64	1/16
1.3750	3.1250	3.3130	.4063	1.1563	9/64	1/8
1.3770	2.8345	2.9905	.2481	0.6700	1/16	1/16
1.4375	2.8400	3.0000	.3438	0.8125	9/64	1/32
1.5000	3.1495	3.3055	.3583	0.8270	9/64	1/16
1.5000	3.1562	3.3436	.4063	1.1563	9/64	1/8
1.5000	3.4843	3.7023	.5313	1.0000	3/32	1/16
1.5625	3.1250	3.2812	.3438	0.9375	9/64	1/32
1.5748	3.1496	3.3370	.3125	0.8268	9/64	1/32
1.6250	3.4375	3.6255	.4375	1.1875	9/64	1/8
1.6250	3.7500	3.9680	.4375	1.0938	9/64	3/32
1.7500	3.3464	3.5339	.3125	0.8125	9/64	1/16
1.7500	3.8750	4.1250	.6563	1.2188	9/64	1/32
1.8750	3.5433	3.7308	.3499	0.7874	9/64	1/32
2.0000	3.3750	3.5310	.3906	0.7500	.060	.060
2.0000	3.6718	3.8598	.4375	1.1875	9/64	1/8
2.0000	4.0000	4.2500	.5625	1.3750	9/64	1/8
2.0000	4.2500	4.4680	.4375	1.0938	9/64	1/32
2.0000	4.3750	4.6250	.5625	1.5000	9/64	1/8

Table 14 (*Continued*).   Standard Dimensions of Taper Roller Bearings —
Type TSF

Bore Diam., Inch	Outside Diam., Inch	Flange Outside, Diam.	"Stand-out," Inch	Bearing Width, Inch	Cone Radius, Inch	Cup Radius, Inch
2.0000	4.7500	5.0312	0.6563	1.6250	9⁄64	⅛
2.2500	3.8125	4.0000	0.3125	0.8268	9⁄64	1⁄32
2.2500	4.3307	4.5187	0.3125	0.8661	3⁄32	3⁄64
2.5000	4.1250	4.3125	0.4063	0.8438	.080	.080
2.5000	4.2500	4.4062	0.4063	1.0000	9⁄64	⅛
2.5000	4.4375	4.6250	0.4375	1.1875	9⁄64	⅛
2.5000	4.8750	5.1250	0.5625	1.5000	9⁄64	⅛
2.5000	5.3447	5.6567	0.6875	2.1250	11⁄64	⅛
2.5000	5.3750	5.6560	0.6563	1.6250	9⁄64	⅛
2.6875	4.7244	4.9424	0.4375	1.1730	9⁄64	1⁄32
2.7500	5.0000	5.2500	0.5625	1.4375	9⁄64	⅛
2.7500	5.8750	6.1875	0.6875	2.1250	¼	⅛
2.8750	4.4375	4.5940	0.4063	1.0000	9⁄64	⅛
3.0000	4.8125	5.0000	0.3125	0.9688	9⁄64	.080
3.0000	5.5115	5.7615	0.5625	1.4375	9⁄64	⅛
3.0000	5.9090	6.2210	0.6250	1.7500	9⁄64	⅛
3.0000	6.0000	6.2812	0.6563	1.6250	9⁄64	⅛
3.1875	5.2500	5.4690	0.5000	1.3125	9⁄64	⅛
3.1875	5.3750	5.5930	0.5313	1.1875	9⁄64	⅛
3.2500	6.3750	6.6870	0.6875	1.8750	9⁄64	⅛
3.2500	6.6250	7.0000	0.8750	2.1250	9⁄64	⅛
3.6250	6.0000	6.2500	0.6250	1.5625	9⁄64	⅛
3.7500	6.6250	6.9070	0.7188	1.6250	9⁄64	⅛
3.7500	6.7500	7.0625	0.6875	1.8750	9⁄64	⅛
3.8750	6.3750	6.6250	0.6563	1.4375	9⁄64	⅛
4.0000	7.1250	7.4370	0.6875	1.8750	9⁄64	⅛
4.0000	7.5000	7.8750	0.8750	2.2500	5⁄16	⅛
4.1875	6.5000	6.7500	0.6250	1.4375	9⁄64	⅛
4.2500	8.3750	8.8125	0.9375	2.6250	5⁄16	⅛
4.5000	7.0000	7.2812	0.7188	1.6250	9⁄64	⅛
4.5000	7.5000	7.8120	0.8125	1.8750	9⁄64	⅛
4.7500	8.1250	8.4376	0.8125	1.8750	⅛	⅛
5.0000	8.0000	8.2812	0.5938	1.8125	9⁄64	⅛
5.0000	8.5000	8.8125	0.8125	1.8750	9⁄64	⅛
5.0000	9.2500	9.6875	1.0000	2.5000	¼	⅛
5.3750	7.5000	7.7188	0.4688	1.5625	9⁄64	⅛
5.5000	9.0000	9.3750	0.8750	2.2500	9⁄64	⅛
5.6250	9.5000	9.8750	0.8750	2.2500	9⁄64	⅛
5.7500	10.0000	10.4360	1.1875	2.6250	9⁄32	⅛
6.5000	11.3750	11.8125	1.0625	2.5000	9⁄32	⅛
6.8750	9.7500	10.0312	0.6563	1.8750	9⁄64	⅛
7.0000	13.2500	13.9376	1.7500	3.5625	17⁄32	¼
7.5000	11.1250	11.5000	0.9375	2.0000	9⁄64	⅛
7.5000	12.5000	12.9380	1.1250	2.5000	11⁄64	⅛
8.1250	11.1250	11.4062	0.6563	1.8125	9⁄64	⅛
9.0000	14.0000	14.4380	1.2500	2.6875	9⁄32	⅛
9.2500	12.8750	13.2500	1.0000	2.0625	¼	⅛
9.5000	14.5000	15.0000	1.0625	2.6875	¼	⅛

Table 15. Standard Dimensions of Taper Roller Bearings — Type TDI

Bore Diam., Inch	Outside Diam., Inch	Bearing Width, Inch	Cone Radius Inch	Cup Radius Inch	Bore Diam., Inch	Outside Diam., Inch	Bearing Width. Inch	Cone Radius Inch	Cup Radius Inch
1.1875	2.4410	1.3306	1/32	1/16	5.2500	8.0000	3.6250	1/16	1/8
1.2500	2.7170	1.5625	1/16	3/64	5.2500	11.6250	6.5000	3/8	1/8
1.3125	2.7170	1.5625	1/16	3/64	5.3110	12.5000	6.3750	17/32	17/64
1.4375	2.8345	1.5392	1/32	1/16	5.3750	11.6250	6.5000	17/32	1/4
1.5000	2.8345	1.5392	1/32	1/16	5.5000	8.7500	2.3850	9/64	1/8
1.6875	3.1875	1.3750	1/32	1/16	5.5000	11.6250	6.5000	1/8	1/4
1.6875	3.3464	1.9790	1/16	3/64	5.5000	12.5000	6.3750	17/32	17/64
1.7500	3.1875	1.3750	0	1/16	5.5620	9.8750	4.3750	1/4	3/16
1.8125	3.1875	1.3750	1/32	1/16	5.6250	11.7500	4.2500	1/8	1/8
1.8750	3.8125	2.0940	1/32	1/16	5.6875	11.7500	4.2500	1/8	1/8
1.9375	3.8125	2.0940	1/32	1/16	5.7500	9.6250	3.4375	1/16	1/8
2.0000	3.8125	2.0940	1/32	1/16	5.7500	12.5000	6.3750	17/32	17/64
2.1650	5.5130	2.6020	3/32	3/32	5.8750	10.0000	4.7500	1/16	1/8
2.4375	4.3307	2.1870	1/32	3/64	6.0000	9.6250	3.4375	1/16	1/8
2.5000	5.5130	2.6020	3/32	3/32	6.0000	10.0000	6.2500	1/16	1/8
3.0000	6.3750	4.0000	9/64	1/8	6.0000	11.7500	4.2500	1/16	1/8
3.1875	5.3750	2.3750	1/16	1/8	6.0000	12.5000	6.3750	3/8	17/64
3.1875	5.5115	3.1875	1/16	1/8	6.2500	11.4375	4.9375	1/8	1/4
3.3125	5.3750	3.0000	1/32	1/8	7.0000	11.0000	4.4375	1/16	1/8
3.5000	6.3750	4.0000	1/16	1/8	7.0000	11.2500	4.1875	1/16	1/8
3.5000	7.5000	4.6250	3/8	1/8	7.0000	11.3750	6.2500	1/16	1/8
3.6250	5.8437	2.2500	1/16	.120	7.0000	12.0000	4.3086	1/8	1/8
3.7500	7.5000	4.6250	1/4	1/8	7.0000	13.0000	4.3750	1/16	1/8
3.8750	6.1875	3.1563	1/16	1/8	7.3750	12.5970	6.2500	1/8	3/16
3.8750	7.1250	4.0000	1/16	1/8	7.5000	12.5000	5.2500	1/4	1/8
4.0000	6.1875	3.1563	1/16	1/8	7.5000	13.0000	4.3750	1/4	1/8
4.0000	7.5000	4.6250	1/16	1/8	7.5000	14.5000	6.2500	1/8	1/8
4.0000	8.3750	5.6250	13/32	1/8	7.8750	12.5000	3.7500	1/8	1/8
4.1250	7.1250	4.0000	1/16	1/8	8.0000	12.5000	4.1563	1/16	1/8
4.2500	7.5000	3.8750	1/16	1/8	8.0000	12.5000	5.2500	1/4	1/8
4.2500	8.3750	5.6250	1/8	1/8	8.0000	12.5000	3.7500	1/8	1/8
4.2500	9.2500	5.5000	33/64	1/8	8.0000	14.5000	6.2500	1/8	1/8
4.5000	7.5000	3.8750	1/16	1/8	8.5000	13.0000	8.0000	1/8	1/8
4.5000	8.3750	5.6250	1/8	1/8	8.5000	14.0000	4.7500	1/16	1/16
4.5000	9.2500	5.5000	33/64	1/8	8.5000	14.0000	5.0000	1/4	1/8
4.6250	9.8750	6.0000	5/16	3/16	8.8750	14.0000	6.5000	5/16	1/16
4.7500	9.2500	5.5000	1/4	1/8	9.0000	14.0000	6.5000	5/16	1/16
4.7500	10.0000	6.3750	1/2	1/4	9.0000	15.7500	5.5000	1/8	1/8
4.8750	10.0000	6.3750	7/16	1/4	9.0000	15.7500	6.2500	1/8	1/8
5.0000	9.0000	6.3125	1/16	1/8	9.0000	16.7500	7.0000	9/64	1/4
5.0000	9.2500	5.5000	13/64	1/8	9.2500	12.8750	3.6875	1/16	1/8
5.0000	10.0000	6.3750	1/8	1/4	9.4970	14.0000	4.2500	1/16	1/8
5.0000	11.6250	5.8750	33/64	1/4	9.5000	13.5000	3.6250	1/16	1/8
5.0000	11.6250	6.5000	17/32	1/8	9.5000	14.5000	3.6500	1/16	1/8
5.1250	8.5000	4.0000	1/16	1/8	9.5000	16.5000	7.0000	1/8	1/4
5.1250	8.7500	2.3850	9/64	1/8	....	....	....	..	..

Table 16. Standard Dimensions of Taper Roller Bearings — Type TDO

Bore Diam., Inch	Outside Diam., Inch	Bearing Width, Inch	Cone Radius Inch	Cup Radius Inch	Bore Diam., Inch	Outside Diam., Inch	Bearing Width, Inch	Cone Radius Inch	Cup Radius Inch
0.7500	1.8504	1.2500	3/64	1/32	4.5000	7.0000	3.6250	9/64	1/32
1.1805	2.4410	1.5625	1/16	1/32	4.5000	7.5000	4.1875	9/64	1/16
1.1805	2.8338	1.6835	1/16	1/32	4.7500	8.1250	4.2500	1/8	1/32
1.1875	2.6150	1.7500	1/16	1/32	5.0000	7.7500	4.0000	9/64	1/32
1.1895	2.5000	1.8125	9/64	1/32	5.0000	8.5000	4.1875	9/64	1/16
1.2500	2.7500	2.6250	1/32	1/32	5.0000	9.2500	5.6250	1/4	1/16
1.3750	3.0000	1.8750	9/64	1/32	5.5000	9.3125	5.1875	9/64	11/16
1.3750	3.2500	2.6250	1/32	1/32	5.5000	12.0000	5.3438	1/8	1/16
1.5000	3.1510	1.8125	1/16	1/32	5.7500	9.6250	4.2500	9/64	1/16
1.6250	3.2500	2.4375	9/64	1/32	5.7500	10.0000	5.8750	9/32	1/16
1.6875	3.2500	1.7500	.090	1/32	6.0000	12.1250	7.8750	3/8	3/32
1.7500	3.5480	2.0000	3/32	1/32	6.5000	11.3750	5.6250	9/32	1/16
1.8750	3.5433	1.9687	9/64	1/32	6.8750	13.7500	5.5000	3/16	1/16
2.0000	3.6718	2.5625	1/32	1/32	7.0000	11.2500	5.3750	1/4	1/16
2.0000	4.2500	2.5625	1/32	1/32	7.0000	12.0000	5.8204	1/4	1/16
2.0000	4.3750	3.1250	9/64	1/16	7.5000	11.1250	4.2500	9/64	1/16
2.2500	3.9370	2.0625	3/32	1/32	7.5000	12.5000	5.7500	13/64	1/16
2.5000	4.3307	2.0625	9/64	1/32	7.5000	13.0000	5.5000	9/32	1/16
2.5000	4.8750	3.1250	9/64	1/16	7.9375	14.5000	7.6250	1/8	1/16
2.5000	5.3750	3.7500	9/64	1/16	8.0000	12.5000	5.0000	5/32	1/16
2.6875	4.7244	2.5625	9/64	1/32	8.5000	11.3125	2.7500	9/64	1/32
2.7500	5.0000	3.1875	9/64	1/16	8.5000	16.0000	7.6875	1/4	1/16
3.0000	6.1250	3.7500	9/64	1/16	8.8750	14.0000	6.0000	17/64	1/16
3.0000	6.1250	4.0000	9/64	1/16	9.0000	14.0000	6.0000	9/32	1/32
3.0000	6.3750	4.1250	9/64	1/16	9.0000	15.7500	7.3750	13/32	1/16
3.1875	5.3750	2.7500	9/64	1/32	9.0000	16.7500	8.2500	9/32	1/16
3.1875	5.5115	3.2500	9/64	1/32	9.2500	12.8750	4.5000	1/4	1/16
3.2500	6.7500	4.9375	9/64	1/32	9.5000	13.7460	5.0000	1/4	1/16
3.6250	6.0000	3.2500	9/64	1/32	9.5000	14.5000	4.7500	1/4	1/16
3.7500	6.6250	3.6250	9/64	1/32	9.5000	15.5000	6.1875	1/4	1/16
4.0000	7.1250	4.1250	9/64	1/16	9.5000	17.5000	8.2500	1/4	1/16
4.0000	7.5000	5.0000	5/16	1/16	9.5000	19.2500	10.0000	1/4	1/16
4.2500	8.3750	5.6250	5/16	1/16	....	....	....	..	..

Table 17. Standard Dimensions of Taper Roller Bearings — Type TNA

Bore Diam., Inch	Outside Diam., Inch	Bearing Width, Inch	Cone Radius Inch	Cup Radius Inch	Bore Diam., Inch	Outside Diam., Inch	Bearing Width, Inch	Cone Radius Inch	Cup Radius Inch
0.7500	1.8504	1.2500	3/64	1/32	1.9685	3.5433	1.9688	9/64	1/32
0.9835	2.4410	1.5625	1/16	1/32	2.0000	3.6718	2.5625	9/64	1/32
1.1805	2.8338	1.6835	1/16	1/32	2.0000	4.2500	2.5625	9/64	1/32
1.3770	3.1510	1.8125	1/16	1/32	2.1250	4.3750	3.1250	9/64	1/16
1.5748	3.5480	2.0000	1/16	1/32	2.1653	3.9370	2.0625	9/64	1/32
1.7188	3.2500	1.7500	.090	1/32	2.3622	4.3307	2.0625	9/64	1/32
1.7500	3.7500	2.4375	9/64	1/32	2.3622	4.7244	2.5625	9/64	1/32

Table 17 (Continued). Standard Dimensions of Taper Roller Bearings — Type TNA

Bore Diam., Inch	Outside Diam., Inch	Bearing Width, Inch	Cone Radius Inch	Cup Radius Inch	Bore Diam., Inch	Outside Diam., Inch	Bearing Width, Inch	Cone Radius Inch	Cup Radius Inch
2.3750	4.8750	3.1250	9/64	1/16	5.0000	9.2500	5.6250	9/64	1/16
2.6250	5.0000	3.1875	9/64	1/16	5.2500	8.5000	4.1875	9/64	1/16
2.7500	5.3750	3.7500	9/64	1/16	5.3750	7.5000	3.3750	9/64	1/32
2.7559	4.7244	2.5625	9/64	1/32	5.5000	9.6250	4.2500	9/64	1/16
3.0000	5.3750	2.7500	9/64	1/32	5.7500	9.3125	5.1875	9/64	1/16
3.0000	6.0000	3.7500	9/64	1/16	5.3750	9.3125	5.1875	9/64	1/16
3.2500	5.5115	3.2500	9/64	1/32	6.0000	9.6250	4.2500	9/64	1/16
3.2500	6.1250	4.0000	9/64	1/16	6.0000	10.0000	5.6250	9/64	1/16
3.2500	6.7500	4.9375	9/64	1/32	6.5000	11.3750	5.6250	9/64	1/16
3.5000	6.0000	3.2500	9/64	1/32	6.8750	9.7500	4.0625	9/64	1/32
3.5000	6.3750	4.1250	9/64	1/16	7.0000	9.7500	4.0625	9/64	1/32
3.7500	6.3750	3.2500	9/64	1/32	7.0000	11.1250	4.2500	9/64	1/16
3.7500	7.1250	4.1250	9/64	1/16	7.0000	11.3750	5.6250	7/32	1/16
4.0000	6.6250	3.6250	9/64	1/32	7.3750	12.6250	7.3125	7/32	1/16
4.0000	7.5000	5.0000	9/64	1/16	7.5000	10.2500	2.6250	9/64	1/32
4.1250	7.1250	4.1250	9/64	1/16	8.0000	12.5000	5.7500	7/32	1/16
4.5000	7.5000	4.1875	9/64	1/16	8.0000	12.5000	4.7500	1/4	1/16
4.5000	8.3750	5.6250	9/64	1/16	9.0000	14.0000	5.7500	1/4	1/16
5.0000	8.1250	4.2500	9/64	1/32	9.5000	14.5000	4.7500	1/4	1/16

Table 18. Standard Dimensions of Taper Roller Bearings — Types TNAS and TDOS

Bore Diam., Inch	Outside Diam., Inch	Bearing Width, Inch	Cone Radius Inch	Cup Radius Inch	Bore Diam., Inch	Outside Diam., Inch	Bearing Width, Inch	Cone Radius Inch	Cup Radius Inch
Type TNAS					Type TDOS				
0.7500	2.2500	1.9375	1/16	1/32	0.7500	2.2500	1.9375	1/16	1/32
1.1250	2.9375	2.1875	3/32	1/16	1.0000	2.9375	2.1875	3/32	1/16
1.3125	3.1875	2.1875	3/32	1/16	1.2500	3.1875	2.1875	1/16	1/16
1.5625	3.6250	2.1875	3/32	1/16	1.5000	3.6250	2.1875	3/32	1/16
1.6250	3.6250	2.1875	1/32	1/16	1.7500	3.7500	2.5625	9/64	1/32
1.7500	3.7500	2.5625	3/32	1/32	2.0000	4.4375	2.5625	9/64	1/16
2.0000	4.4375	2.5625	3/32	1/16	2.0000	4.8750	3.0625	9/64	1/16
2.1250	4.6250	2.8750	9/64	1/32	2.1250	4.6250	2.8750	9/64	1/32
2.1250	4.8750	3.0625	3/32	1/16	2.5000	5.5000	3.0625	3/32	1/16
2.5000	5.5000	3.0625	3/32	1/16	3.3125	7.0000	4.3125	9/64	3/32
3.0000	7.0000	4.3125	9/64	3/32	3.3465	7.8750	4.5625	9/64	3/32
3.5000	7.8750	4.5625	9/64	3/32	5.0000	9.0000	4.5625	9/64	3/32
4.5000	9.0000	4.5625	9/64	3/32	8.0000	16.0000	7.7500	1/4	1/8
....	....	....	..	..	8.9945	17.0000	7.7500	1/4	1/8

The different types of bearings indicated by combinations of letters (such as TNA, TNAS and TDOS) are described and illustrated in Table 1.

Load Capacities of Radial Ball Bearings — Single-row Light Type — 1

Bore Diameter, Millimeters *	Outside Diameter, Millimeters *	Width, Millimeters *	Ball Diameter, Inches †	No. of Balls †	Speed of Inner Ring in R.P.M. and Approximate Range of Load Ratings, in Pounds, for Different Makes			
					100	500	1000	3000
10	30	9	7/32-1/4	7-8	350-500	200-300	150-250	100-175
12	32	10	7/32-1/4	8-10	400-650	225-375	175-300	100-200
15	35	11	7/32-1/4	9-10	450-800	275-475	225-350	100-250
17	40	12	1/4-9/32	8-11	550-980	350-600	275-450	125-300
20	47	14	1/4-11/32	7-13	650-1250	400-775	325-500	150-330
25	52	15	1/4-5/16	9-14	780-1400	450-825	375-650	200-450
30	62	16	5/16-11/32	13-15	1050-2100	625-1250	480-1000	260-690
35	72	17	11/32-13/32	13-14	1450-3050	850-1800	670-1400	370-980
40	80	18	3/8-7/16	14-16	1720-3650	1000-2150	800-1700	450-1180
45	85	19	3/8-7/16	15-18	1920-3960	1120-2320	880-1840	530-1250
50	90	20	3/8-1/2	14-20	2100-4400	1220-2580	960-2040	600-1400
55	100	21	7/16-17/32	15-18	2640-5150	1550-2980	1220-2370	730-1600
60	110	22	7/16-9/16	16-21	2660-5650	1560-3300	1230-2600	850-1800
65	120	23	1/2-5/8	16-20	3250-6500	1900-3800	1500-3000	980-2080
70	125	24	1/2-9/16	16-22	3550-7050	2070-4120	1640-3770	1080-2260
75	130	25	1/2-11/16	16-22	3930-7950	2300-4450	1820-3530	1250-2400
80	140	26	5/8-3/4	15-18	4270-8700	2500-5090	1980-4040	1370-2800
85	150	28	11/16-3/4	16-20	5040-9400	2950-5550	2350-4380	....
90	160	30	11/16-13/16	16-18	5400-10500	3150-6200	2500-4900	....
95	170	32	3/4-7/8	16-18	6200-11780	3630-6900	2870-5450	....
100	180	34	13/16-15/16	16-18	7060-13000	4120-7740	3300-6000	....
105	190	36	7/8-1	16-18	7100-14200	4150-8800	3300-6800	....
110	200	38	7/8-1 1/16	16-18	7700-15500	4500-9300	3600-7300	....

Load ratings of commercial bearings vary considerably for different makes. This table is intended only as a general guide in preliminary designing. The exact rating should be obtained from the manufacturer of whatever bearing is to be used.

* For converting millimeters into inches, see table on page 1864.
† These columns give the smallest and largest ball diameters and numbers for the various commercial makes of bearings included in this table.

Load Capacities of Radial Ball Bearings — Single-row Medium Type — 2

Bore Diameter, Millimeters *	Outside Diameter, Millimeters *	Width, Millimeters *	Ball Diameter, Inches †	No. of Balls †	Speed of Inner Ring in R.P.M. and Approximate Range of Load Ratings, in Pounds, for Different Makes			
					100	500	1000	3000
10	35	11	1/4	7-8	350-630	250-350	200-280	80-190
12	37	12	1/4-9/32	7-10	450-750	320-440	240-350	100-240
15	42	13	1/4-5/16	7-11	550-890	380-520	300-400	120-280
17	47	14	5/16-11/32	7-10	780-1090	540-630	420-480	170-330
20	52	15	5/16-13/32	9-12	1000-1460	700-850	550-680	230-470
25	62	17	3/8-13/32	8-12	1300-1970	920-1140	720-900	300-630
30	72	19	7/16-15/32	8-12	1660-2600	1160-1430	900-1140	370-780
35	80	21	1/2-17/32	8-12	2170-2800	1520-1900	1180-1300	480-900
40	90	23	9/16-19/32	8-12	3000-3900	2060-2320	1460-1630	660-1100
45	100	25	5/8-11/16	8-12	3800-4650	2230-2850	1760-2200	900-1300
50	110	27	5/8-23/32	8-12	4270-4700	2500-3200	2000-2400	1000-1500
55	120	29	11/16-25/32	8-13	5050-7000	2950-4000	2350-3100	1270-1700
60	130	31	3/4-27/32	8-13	5220-8200	3050-4800	2450-3600	1500-1900
65	140	33	13/16-29/32	8-13	6750-9100	4000-5400	3140-4220	1700-2100
70	150	35	7/8-31/32	8-13	7700-10000	4500-6300	3447-4900	2000-2400
75	160	37	7/8-1	8-13	7700-10200	4500-7100	3660-5550	2250-2550
80	170	39	15/16-1 1/16	8-13	8700-11500	5100-8000	4000-6200	2500-2800
85	180	41	1-1 1/8	8-13	9500-14000	5560-9000	4400-7000	2800-3000
90	190	43	1-1 3/16	8-13	9700-14400	5700-10000	4500-7800	3100-3300
95	200	45	1 1/8-1 1/4	8-13	11900-18000	6500-11000	5220-8700	....
100	215	47	1 1/8-1 1/2	8-12	12000-20000	7000-13600	5550-10600	....
105	225	49	1 1/4-1 7/16	8-13	13350-22000	8000-14800	6300-11500	....
110	240	50	1 1/4-1 1/2	8-13	14400-23000	8400-16000	6700-12500	....

* For converting millimeters into inches, see table on page 1864.

† These columns give the smallest and largest ball diameters and numbers for the various commercial makes of bearings included in this table.

Load ratings of commercial bearings vary considerably for different makes. This table is intended only as a general guide in preliminary designing. The exact rating should be obtained from the manufacturer of whatever bearing is to be used.

Load Capacities of Radial Ball Bearings — Single-row Heavy Type — 3

Bore Diameter, Millimeters *	Outside Diameter, Millimeters *	Width, Millimeters *	Ball Diameter, Inches †	No. of Balls †	Speed of Inner Ring in R.P.M. and Approximate Range of Load Ratings, in Pounds, for Different Makes.			
					100	500	1000	3000
17	62	17	3/8-1/2	8	1550-3200	900-2000	750-1400	350-500
20	72	19	9/16	8	2000-3700	1400-2300	1100-1600	450-750
25	80	21	9/16-5/8	7-8	2150-4200	1500-2600	1200-1800	470-880
30	90	23	5/8-11/16	8-9	3350-5600	1950-3350	1550-2400	750-1050
35	100	25	11/16-13/16	9-10	3900-6400	2300-3900	1800-2600	1050-1250
40	110	27	13/16	10	4500-7200	2600-4400	2100-3000	1150-1450
45	120	29	13/16-7/8	10	5250-8100	3100-4800	2450-3250	1300-1700
50	130	31	13/16-1	8-10	6000-9000	3500-5500	2800-3700	1400-1900
55	140	33	7/8-1	10	6850-9850	4000-6000	3200-4300	1750-2200
60	150	35	15/16-1 3/16	8-10	7700-11300	4500-6350	3660-4800	1950-2500
65	160	37	1-1 1/4	8-10	8650-12700	5050-7150	4000-5300	....
70	180	42	1 1/8-1 5/16	10	10600-15700	6200-9500	4950-7400	....
75	190	45	1 3/16-1 1/2	8-10	11700-17300	6800-9600	5400-7700	....
80	200	48	1 1/4-1 7/16	11-12	12800-20300	7500-12500	5950-9750	....
85	210	52	1 5/16-1 1/2	10-11	13900-22600	8100-13600	6450-10600	....
90	225	54	1 3/8-1 5/8	10	15100-26500	8800-14900	7000-11300	....
95	250	55	1 1/4-1 13/16	10	17600-30500	10300-18000	8200-14000	....
100	265	60	1 5/8-1 15/16	10	20200-35000	11800-26000	9400-26000	....

* For converting millimeters into inches, see table on page 1864.
† These columns give the smallest and largest ball diameters and numbers for the various commercial makes of bearings included in this table.

Load ratings of commercial bearings vary considerably for different makes. This table is intended only as a general guide in preliminary designing. The exact rating should be obtained from the manufacturer of whatever bearing is to be used.

Load Capacities of Two-row Radial Ball Bearings

Bore Diam. Millimeters*	Outside Diam. Millimeters*	Width, Inches	Ball Diam., Inches	No. of Balls per Row	R.P.M. and Approximate Range of Loads, in Pounds, for Different Makes			
					100	500	1000	2000
15	42	3/4	1/4-9/32	10-11	925 / 1,900	650 / 1,100	475 / 875	300 / 700
17	47	7/8	5/16	10	1,100 / 2,100	775 / 1,200	600 / 975	400 / 775
20	52	7/8	5/16	11-12	1,275 / 2,300	900 / 1,375	700 / 1,100	475 / 875
25	62	1	3/8	12	1,775 / 3,700	1,250 / 2,175	1,000 / 1,700	600 / 1350
30	72	1 3/16	7/16	11-12	2,700 / 4,700	1,900 / 2,700	1,400 / 2,150	800 / 1700
35	80	1 3/8	1/2	12	3,400 / 5,700	2,400 / 3,300	1,850 / 2,600	1200 / 2000
40	90	1 7/16	17/32-9/16	12-13	4,200 / 6,200	2,900 / 3,700	2,300 / 2,500	1450 / 2000
45	100	1 9/16	19/32-5/8	12-13	5,100 / 7,900	3,550 / 4,600	2,750 / 3,700	1700 / 2900
50	110	1 3/4	1 1/16	12	6,000 / 9,200	4,200 / 5,300	3,300 / 4,250	2000 / 3400
55	120	1 15/16	3/4	12	7,100 / 11,000	4,950 / 6,200	3,850 / 4,850	2350 / 3800
60	130	2 1/8	13/16-27/32	12	8,200 / 13,000	4,900 / 7,700	3,900 / 5,000	2950 / 3050
65	140	2 5/16	7/8-29/32	12	9,400 / 13,700	6,600 / 8,500	5,100 / 6,300	3400 / 5000
70	150	2 1/2	15/16-31/32	12	12,000 / 16,000	8,500 / 9,600	6,300 / 7,000	3750 / 5600
75	160	2 11/16	1	12-13	11,100 / 18,300	6,500 / 10,700	5,100 / 7,400	4100 / 4900
80	170	2 11/16	1 1/16	12	15,000 / 20,000	10,300 / 11,800	7,800 / 8,200	4650 / 6500
85	180	2 7/8	1 1/8	12-13	16,700 / 22,400	11,300 / 13,100	8,600 / 9,100	6100 / 7100
90	190	2 7/8	1 3/16	12	18,500 / 24,700	12,900 / 14,400	9,300 / 10,000	....
95	200	3 1/16	1 1/4	12	20,200 / 29,400	14,100 / 15,800	10,000 / 11,000	....
100	215	3 1/4	1 5/16	12	22,000 / 32,000	15,500 / 16,800	....	....
105	225	3 7/16	1 3/8	12	24,000 / 35,000	....	....	....

* For converting millimeters into inches, see table on page 1864.

Load ratings of commercial bearings vary considerably for different makes. This table is intended only as a general guide in preliminary designing. The exact rating should be obtained from the manufacturer of whatever bearing is to be used.

Load Capacities of Thrust Ball Bearings*

Bore Diameter, Inches	Outside Diameter, Inches,	Ball Diameter, Inches	No. of Balls	R.P.M. and Approximate Range of Thrust Loads, in Pounds, for Different Makes			
				100	300	500	1000
1/2	1 9/32	1/4	8	450 750	300 450	275 350	200 240
5/8	1 13/32	1/4	8-10	500 900	330 530	300 400	200 300
3/4	1 17/32	1/4	10-12	570 900	420 530	350 400	280 290
7/8	1 21/32	1/4	11-12	630 1000	440 600	400 475	290 320
1	1 25/32	1/4	12-14	700 1000	500 600	425 475	320 335
1 1/8	1 29/32	1/4	12-15	750 1000	550 600	460 500	320 360
1 1/4	2 3/32	9/32-5/16	13-14	1150 1400	750 875	650 730	450 570
1 3/8	2 7/32	9/32-5/16	14	1200 1400	800 875	650 730	450 570
1 1/2	2 11/32	9/32-5/16	14-16	1300 1400	800 940	650 850	450 600
1 5/8	2 15/32	9/32-5/16	15-18	1300 1580	900 1000	700 950	500 675
1 3/4	2 11/16	5/16	16-17	1470 1800	970 1060	820 890	570 700
1 7/8	2 13/16	5/16	16-18	1470 1800	1030 1060	820 890	570 700
2	2 31/32	5/16	16-18	1400 1800	900 1100	825 950	570 730
2 1/4	3 11/32	3/8	16-19	2150 2400	1400 1550	1100 1400	750 1000
2 1/2	3 23/32	7/16	16-19	2700 3200	1700 2100	1400 1900	950 1400
2 3/4	4 1/32	7/16	16-20	3000 3400	1700 2200	1400 2000	950 1450
3	4 3/8	1/2	16-20	3600 4400	2100 2900	1650 2700	1200 1900
3 1/2	5 1/16	9/16	18-20	4700 5600	2800 3700	2200 3400	1500 2400
4	5 13/16	9/16-5/8	18-22	5400 7300	3300 4800	2600 4400	2400 3200

* Load ratings of commercial bearings vary considerably for different makes. This table is intended only as a general guide in preliminary designing. The exact rating should be obtained from the manufacturer of whatever bearing is to be used.

Allowable Limits for Mounting Ball Bearings on Shafts and in Housings *

Bore Diam., Inches			Shaft Diam., Inches			Fit Allowance	
Nominal	Max.	Min.	Standard	Max.	Min.	Max.	Min.
1.9685	1.9687	1.9681	1.9692	1.9695	1.9689	0.0014	0.0002
2.1654	2.1656	2.1650	2.1661	2.1664	2.1658	0.0014	0.0002
2.3622	2.3624	2.3618	2.3629	2.3632	2.3626	0.0014	0.0002
2.5591	2.5593	2.5587	2.5599	2.5603	2.5595	0.0016	0.0002
2.7559	2.7561	2.7555	2.7567	2.7571	2.7563	0.0016	0.0002
3.1496	3.1498	3.1492	3.1504	3.1508	3.1500	0.0016	0.0002
3.3465	3.3467	3.3461	3.3473	3.3477	3.3469	0.0016	0.0002
3.5433	3.5435	3.5429	3.5441	3.5445	3.5437	0.0016	0.0002
3.7402	3.7404	3.7398	3.7410	3.7414	3.7406	0.0016	0.0002
4.1339	4.1341	4.1335	4.1347	4.1351	4.1343	0.0016	0.0002
4.3307	4.3309	4.3303	4.3315	4.3319	4.3311	0.0016	0.0002
4.5276	4.5278	4.5272	4.5285	4.5290	4.5280	0.0018	0.0002
4.7244	4.7246	4.7240	4.7253	4.7258	4.7248	0.0018	0.0002
5.1181	5.1183	5.1177	5.1190	5.1195	5.1185	0.0018	0.0002
5.3150	5.3152	5.3146	5.3159	5.3164	5.3154	0.0018	0.0002
5.5118	5.5120	5.5114	5.5127	5.5132	5.5122	0.0018	0.0002
5.7087	5.7089	5.7083	5.7096	5.7101	5.7091	0.0018	0.0002
6.1024	6.1026	6.1020	6.1038	6.1044	6.1032	0.0024	0.0006
6.2992	6.2994	6.2988	6.3006	6.3012	6.3000	0.0024	0.0006
6.4961	6.4963	6.4957	6.4975	6.4981	6.4969	0.0024	0.0006
6.6929	6.6931	6.6925	6.6943	6.6949	6.6937	0.0024	0.0006

Outside Diam., Bearing			Housing Bore Diam.			Fit Allowance	
Nominal	Max.	Min.	Standard	Max.	Min.	Max.	Min.
1.5748	1.5748	1.5742	1.5756	1.5762	1.5750	0.0020	0.0002
1.8504	1.8504	1.8498	1.8512	1.8518	1.8506	0.0020	0.0002
2.4409	2.4409	2.4401	2.4421	2.4429	2.4413	0.0028	0.0004
3.1496	3.1496	3.1488	3.1508	3.1516	3.1500	0.0028	0.0004
3.5433	3.5433	3.5425	3.5445	3.5453	3.5437	0.0028	0.0004
4.3307	4.3307	4.3299	4.3327	4.3339	4.3315	0.0040	0.0008
4.9213	4.9213	4.9205	4.9233	4.9245	4.9221	0.0040	0.0008
5.5118	5.5118	5.5110	5.5138	5.5150	5.5126	0.0040	0.0008
6.2992	6.2992	6.2980	6.3016	6.3028	6.3004	0.0048	0.0012
7.0866	7.0866	7.0854	7.0890	7.0902	7.0878	0.0048	0.0012
7.8740	7.8740	7.8728	7.8764	7.8776	7.8752	0.0048	0.0012
8.4646	8.4646	8.4634	8.4670	8.4682	8.4658	0.0048	0.0012
8.8583	8.8583	8.8571	8.8607	8.8619	8.8595	0.0048	0.0012
9.4488	9.4488	9.4476	9.4512	9.4524	9.4500	0.0048	0.0012
10.2362	10.2362	10.2350	10.2386	10.2398	10.2374	0.0048	0.0012
10.6299	10.6299	10.6287	10.6327	10.6338	10.6315	0.0051	0.0016
11.4173	11.4173	11.4161	11.4201	11.4212	11.4189	0.0051	0.0016
12.2047	12.2047	12.2035	12.2075	12.2086	12.2063	0.0051	0.0016
12.9921	12.9921	12.9909	12.9949	12.9960	12.9937	0.0051	0.0016
13.7795	13.7795	13.7783	13.7823	13.7834	13.7811	0.0051	0.0016
14.5669	14.5669	14.5657	14.5697	14.5708	14.5685	0.0051	0.0016

* S K F Ball Bearing Co.

Bearing Lubricants

In selecting an oil for a definite application, determine first just what the oil has to do to provide proper lubrication. The size of the bearings, pressure, speed of the shaft, and the clearance are important. Bearings subject to high speeds and a low pressure require fairly light oil. Slow speeds and high pressures require sufficient body in the lubricant to prevent metal-to-metal contact in starting. At the same time, the lubricant should not be so viscous that undue loss of power will result from the internal friction of the lubricant itself; but too light an oil will not keep the metal surfaces apart and undue wear will result.

In order to facilitate starting machines subjected to cold weather, the oil should have a low pour-test. It is possible for bearings to wear as much during the first few minutes of a warming-up period, as in weeks under normal operating conditions. As the oil becomes warmer, the viscosity becomes lower and, in a measure, adjusts itself, assuming, of course, that it has been chosen to provide the correct body at normal operating temperatures. In this connection, attention may be called to the fact that a reduction in bearing temperatures may be obtained through the use of an oil that has the right viscosity at operating temperatures.

The accompanying tables may be helpful, as a general guide, in selecting lubricants. However, as proper lubrication is very important, it is advisable to obtain information from a specialist experienced in the selection of lubricants for different classes of service. The method of applying the lubricant is also very important.

Lubricating Oils for Miscellaneous Applications

Grade of Oil	Approximate Viscosity*	Application of Oil
Turbo oil..........	145-150	Turbo-generator bearings
Light machine oil.................	180-210	General purposes
Internal combustion engine oil...	260	Farm lighting equipment
Compressor oil...................	275	Air compressors
Pump oil.........................	300-375	Vacuum pumps
Motor oil, light, medium and heavy	200, 450, 1050	Automotive
Car oil, summer and winter......	1200, 300	Railway bearings
Crankcase oil....................	625	Steam engine crankcase
Diesel oil........................	600-900	Oil-electric locomotives
Cylinder oil.....................	2000-3500	Steam cylinders and wherever heavy oil is needed

* Lubricating oils with Saybolt universal viscosity readings from 145 to 3500 seconds at 100 degrees F.

Naphthene- or Paraffin-Base Oils. — The question is often asked as to whether naphthene- or paraffin-base oils are the better lubricants. This depends upon the application. The so-called naphthene and paraffin crude oils are, in all cases, mixtures; that is, the naphthene oils contain paraffin hydrocarbons and the paraffin oils contain naphthene hydrocarbons, so that these hydrocarbons are intermingled in the crude oils of both kinds. The ratio of these hydrocarbons determines the nomenclature. Paraffin oils seem to provide a more firmly adhering film, but they are also more subject to carbonization. The naphthene oils resist heat fairly well and have greater fluidity at reduced temperatures. Therefore, in selecting an oil, say for use in combustion engines, a blend that minimizes the defects in each kind may be desirable.

Most oils offered for industrial lubrication are straight refined petroleum products. However, in some instances, it is desirable to blend mineral oils with animal or vegetable oils. Cylinder oils, for instance, are often compounded with from 4 to 6 per cent of acidless tallow to make them adhere to metal surfaces.

Selection of Lubricant to Suit Operating Conditions. — Bearing pressures, speeds, temperatures, clearances, areas of contact, gear tooth pressure, or the necessity of operating in the presence of dust, dirt, water, or other contaminating foreign matter, all impose lubricating requirements that must be taken into consideration. It is erroneous to assume that any grade of oil or grease that has proved satisfactory on certain types of equipment will serve equally well on any other, especially where the operating conditions are different. In many plants perhaps a single grade of steam-cylinder oil, a medium-viscosity machine oil, and a medium- or light-consistency cup grease may suffice. Normally, however, in the modern industrial plant, the equipment involved is so designed as to include a considerable number of wearing elements of widely differing construction. Just as this construction differs, so may it be expected that the lubricating requirements will differ. In many cases, similar lubricants can be used; on the other hand, every case should receive individual attention in selecting a suitable lubricant.

Viscosity of a Lubricant and its Load-carrying Capacity. — Viscosity is to some extent indicative of load-carrying capacity. In fact, before the advent of " extreme pressure lubricants," it used to be regarded as the predominating characteristic of an oil for such service, on the assumption that the heavier-bodied products would better resist the squeezing-out effect of heavy journal or gear-tooth loads. Later, however, resistance to shear and film strength were proved to be more related to the chemical nature of the lubricant, a definite chemical reaction between the lubricant and the metallic surfaces under load being required. Theoretically, the smoother the bearing surfaces, the better; however, tests indicate that some degree of finish only *approaching* the ideal has practical advantages, evidently because microscopic scratches or depressions form reservoirs for the lubricant without appreciable interference with the maintenance of an adequate oil film. Thus, while bearings do require an excellent quality of finish, the highest degree obtainable by superfinishing methods may not be desirable.

Grease Lubricants. — The term " grease " is applied to a mixture of mineral oil with fats that have been saponified with an alkali. To this mixture, fillers may or may not be added. Grease lubricant is available in three general classes known as hard grease, soft grease, and non-fluid oil. Suppliers usually classify greases as hard, medium-hard, medium, soft, and semi-fluid. The consistency may be indicated by numbers as, for example, No. 1, No. 2, and No. 3.

In comparison with oil, grease occupies a minor yet important place in the field of lubrication. It provides a solid lubricant for use where a fluid is not practicable, or at least not economical, as in certain types of vertical and horizontal motors having ball or roller bearings; in cases where the motor operates at an angle; in instances where the moving parts are so worn that oil will run away and be wasted; and in other places where oil will not "stay put."

Three General Methods of Grease Lubrication. — Three general types of grease devices can usually be made to cover the needs — namely, small compression cups loaded by means of a pressure gun; a one-shot system piped to the bearings from a reservoir operated intermittently by pressure; and a pressure system in which the grease is forced constantly to the various parts of the machine.

Compression cups having standard Zerk or Alemite fittings are primarily suited for relatively small machines or machines that cannot easily or economically be greased under pressure. One-shot and constant-pressure systems can be used to advantage on large machines. Grease feeds should be carefully regulated to avoid waste and excess grease about the machine. Since the room temperature of the shop varies seasonably, grease feeds should be adjusted at least twice a year in order to get the best results.

Compression grease cups are especially suitable for the bearings of mixing or screening machines, sand conveyors, etc., that are subjected to dust, dirt, and fine abrasive materials. On such equipment, grease has the advantage over oil in that it forces the old lubricant out of the bearing and thereby prevents the introduction of abrasive particles into the bearing surfaces. There are other applications for grease, of course, such as the lubrication of ball and roller bearings and worn bearings that would permit oil to flow through between the bearing and shaft without adequately lubricating them. Grease is adaptable for the lubrication of many machine tool parts. Grease lubrication is generally applied only to the individual servicing of bearings. The compression grease cup, the pin type lubricator, or the pressure grease-gun fitting constitutes the usual equipment. However, a multiple-fitting lubricator has been developed to make the application of grease to each lubricated part more automatic.

Properties Desirable in Oils for Electric Motors. — If motor bearings are lubricated by oil, it is of the utmost importance that the oil should not be too high in viscosity, in order to avoid internal friction in the molecules, with subsequent loss of power. On the other hand, oil too low in viscosity will not "stay put" and will not provide an adequate film to prevent bearing wear and "seizure." Sealed-sleeve or other ring-oiling bearings should be used when the shafts are horizontal or only slightly inclined. Grease-lubricated bearings are used in motors that operate at an angle. Naturally the clearances for bearings lubricated with grease are larger than when oil is used. For outdoor service, low temperatures may prevail and compression grease cups may have to be used.

For the lubrication of industrial motors, satisfactory service will be obtained from a well-refined pure petroleum oil, free from acid, sediment, dirt, or other foreign material. It should have a Saybolt universal viscosity of from 180 to 210 seconds at 100 degrees F., and a pour-test of 35 degrees F., if the motor is to operate at normal temperatures; o degrees F. if the motor is subjected to periodic freezing temperatures; and minus 40 degrees F. if the motor is to operate continuously under freezing temperatures. Under the latter condition, a viscosity of 80 to 110 seconds at 100 degrees F. is satisfactory.

Lubrication of Ball and Roller Bearings. — To obtain the full measure of efficiency and service from ball and roller bearing equipment, the kind and quality of the lubricant, as well as the system of applying it, must be adapted to the design of the bearing, the design of the machine, and the operating conditions. The SKF Industries, Inc., have conducted extensive tests to determine the most efficient lubricants for ball and roller bearings operating under different conditions. A brief summary of the results of these tests follows.

Operating Temperatures: Under ordinary conditions the temperature of a bearing while running will be from 10 to 60 degrees F. above that of the room. If it exceeds 125 degrees F., ordinary greases will frequently prove unsatisfactory. They will tend to soften and flow continuously into the path of the rolling elements, causing a rise in the normal operating temperature due to the increased frictional resistance introduced. This may eventually result in the separation of the oil and soap base, with a complete loss of lubricating qualities. In some cases, greases developed for use at high temperatures may be employed. Care should be taken, however, to see that they meet all the requirements for adequate lubrication.

Mineral oil of proper physical and chemical properties is an ideal lubricant for ball and roller bearings when the housing is designed to control the quantity entering the bearing and to prevent leakage and protect the bearing from the entrance of foreign matter. A ball or roller bearing should not be subjected to temperatures in excess of 300 degrees F., because there will be danger of drawing the temper of the hardened steel races and balls.

Classification of Oils: Viscosity is the governing physical property of oil, and "consistency," or stiffness, is the governing physical property of grease. Both of these properties vary with the temperature, so that it is extremely important to consider the actual temperature developed in a bearing during operation in order to select a suitable oil or grease.

The classification of the oils here referred to (including the accompanying tables), arranged according to their viscosities as determined by a Saybolt standard universal viscosimeter at 100 degrees F., is as follows:

Extra Light.	135 to 165 seconds
Light.	180 to 220 seconds
Medium.	270 to 330 seconds
Heavy.	360 to 440 seconds
Extra Heavy.	450 to 550 seconds
Steam Cylinder and Valve Oils.	2000 to 2500 seconds

Lubricating Oils for Ball and Roller Bearings

Oils for Ball and Cylindrical Roller Bearings					
Radial Load on Bearing, Pounds*	Revolutions per Minute				
	300	600	1200	1800	3600
50	Light	Light	Light	Medium	Medium
100	Light	Light	Medium	Medium	Medium
500	Light	Medium	Medium	Medium	Heavy
1,000	Medium	Medium	Heavy	Heavy	Heavy
2,000	Medium	Heavy	Heavy	Ex. heavy	. . . .
5,000	Heavy	Heavy	Ex. heavy	. . . .	. . . .
7,500	Heavy	Ex. heavy	. . . .	. . . .	. . . .
10,000	Ex. heavy	. . . .	. . . .	. . . .	. . . .
15,000	Ex. heavy	. . . .	. . . .	. . . .	. . . .

Greases are also used under these conditions. It is suggested that generally a No. 2 grease can be used when a light or medium oil is specified, and a stiffer or high-temperature grease when heavy and extra heavy oil is called for.

Oils for Ball Bearings Operated at High Speeds					
Radial Load on Bearing, Pounds*	Revolutions per Minute and Permissible Shaft Sizes				
	5000 60 mm.	7200 50 mm.	10,000 40 mm.	15,000 30 mm.	20,000 25 mm.
10	Spindle oil	Spindle oil	Spindle oil	Spindle oil	Extra light
25	Spindle oil	Spindle oil	Spindle oil	Extra light	Light
50	Spindle oil	Extra light	Extra light	Light	. . . .
100	Extra light	Light	Light	Medium	. . . .
200	Medium	Medium	Heavy	. . . .	. . . .
300	Medium	Heavy	. . . .	. . . .	. . . .

Greases are also used under these conditions, the suitability of any grease being best determined by actual trial.

* For thrust loads, multiply the actual load by 4, and enter the table with this value of load.

Quantity of Lubricant Required: In no case does a ball or roller bearing require a large quantity of lubricant. On the contrary, a few drops of oil, or a corresponding amount of grease, properly distributed over the running surfaces of the bearing, will provide satisfactory lubrication for a considerable period of time. A large volume of lubricant within a bearing will usually result in high operating temperatures, due to the working or churning of the lubricant by the rolling elements and retainer. This may seriously impair the useful life of the lubricant through oxidation or sludging of the oil or actual disintegration of greases.

Satisfactory lubrication of horizontal shafts operating at speeds below 3600 revolutions per minute will usually be attained if the oil level is kept at about the center of the lowermost ball or roller in the bearing. The oil can be kept at this level by a tell-tale level plug, a sight gage, or an overflow pipe. On vertical shafts, some form of flinger is usually employed to raise the oil from a reservoir in the bottom of the housing to the surfaces of the bearing.

Use of Grease: If grease is used, the housing should not be kept more than one-fourth to one-half full of the lubricant. Unlike oil, there is no way of controlling with any degree of exactness the quantity of grease in a housing, and greater care must therefore be taken to avoid overloading. A bearing that runs at too high a temperature will often return to normal temperature if some of the lubricating grease is removed.

Grease is being used successfully for the lubrication of ball bearings at high speeds, but great care is necessary, both from the standpoint of housing design and selection of the lubricant, in order to obtain satisfactory results. Any system employed must be designed to feed only a limited amount of grease to the bearing. For the average application at operating speeds up to 3600 revolutions per minute, a grease of soft consistency, such as a No. 2 grease, will usually be found satisfactory, provided it is suitable in other respects. Hard greases, such as No. 3, may be used if the grease is to serve as a packing medium around the shaft to prevent the entrance of dirt, water, or other corrosive substances.

Splash System of Lubrication for Gears. — There are two methods for supplying and distributing lubrication in gear drives — the splash and the pressure systems. The splash system depends on the action of the teeth in the gear as they pass through a reservoir of lubricant in the base of the housing. To avoid excessive churning and foaming, the gear should dip only a comparatively small amount into the reservoir. Just how deep depends on the tooth velocity, the pitch, the design of the gear, and the type of lubricant. Usually the teeth dip in a little more than their own depth. There should be a large amount of lubricant in the reservoir. This requires a large trough, which should be of almost rectangular section and at no point close to the rotating gear teeth. Special gages are available to show the depth of lubricant.

Where the splash from the gear teeth is to lubricate the bearings, often the lubricant which is splashed on the inside of the cover is collected in troughs which are cast as a part of the housing or cover, from which it flows to the bearings through passages or ducts. The return to the reservoir is through draining canals. Suitable seals are provided to prevent leakage along the shafts. Sometimes baffle plates and drip fins are used to further direct the lubricant.

Pressure System of Lubrication for Gears. — The positive circulating or pressure system supplies the lubricant under pump or gravity pressure, through feed pipes, directly to the point of tooth engagement and to the individual bearings. It is used where the tooth velocities and bearing speeds are so high that the lubricant churns and heats excessively from the action of the gear teeth if they are allowed to dip into it. Also, at very high speeds the lubricants are thrown off from the gear teeth by centrifugal force and must be applied to the point of tooth engagement through specially designed spray nozzles. Positive circulation is also used in slower speed gear sets because it eliminates the "human element," and in special designs which cannot be lubricated conveniently by splash.

A pump is required, usually of the gear or rotary type, driven directly from the gear unit itself through gears or chains, or by a separate motor. It is customary as a safeguard to include "tell-tales" or relays in the electrical hook-up, to insure a warning or shutdown if the pressure in the feed pipes becomes too low.

Centralized Lubrication Systems. — Various forms of centralized lubrication systems are used to simplify and render more efficient the task of lubricating machines. In general, a central reservoir provides the supply of oil, which is conveyed to each bearing either through individual lines of tubing or through a single line of tubing that has branches extending to each of the different bearings. Oil is pumped into the lines either manually by a single movement of a lever or handle, or automatically by mechanical drive from some revolving shaft or other part of the machine. In either case, all bearings in the central system are lubricated simultaneously.

Centralized force-feed lubrication is adaptable to various classes of machine tools such as lathes, planers, and milling machines and to many other types of machines. In modern machine tools used to their full capacity, the pressures on certain bearings are relatively high and under such conditions, pressure lubrication is most advantageous. Furthermore, it permits the use of a lighter grade of oil, especially when the pressure on the lubricating system is sufficient to assure complete coverage of the moving parts.

The planning of a centralized lubricating system must be done in accordance with the character of the work, the prevailing pressures, and the type of machinery to be lubricated. On milling machines, the installation of oil reservoirs of sufficient capacity or of independent force-feed lubricators simplifies the problem of design and construction. There are other types of machines, however, for which flood lubrication is regarded as a practical necessity. These machines are equipped with self-contained oiling systems, the lubricant being pumped to the bearings, gears, and slides by means of a pump, placed either in the oil reservoir itself or at some convenient external point.

Gravity Lubrication Systems. — Gravity systems of lubrication usually consist of a small number of distributing centers or manifolds from which oil is taken by piping as directly as possible to the various surfaces to be lubricated, each bearing point having its own independent pipe and set of connections. The aim of the gravity system, as of all lubrication systems, is to provide a reliable means of supplying the bearing surfaces with the proper amount of lubricating oil. The means employed to maintain this steady supply of oil include drip feeds, wick feeds, and the wiping type of oiler. Most manifolds are adapted to use either or both drip and wick feeds.

Drip-feed Lubricators: A drip feed consists of a simple cup or manifold mounted in a convenient position for filling and connected by a pipe or duct to each bearing to be oiled. The rate of feed in each pipe is regulated by a needle or conical valve. A loose-fitting cover is usually fitted to the manifold in order to prevent cinders or other foreign matter from becoming mixed with the oil. When a cylinder or other chamber operating under pressure is to be lubricated, the oil-cup takes the form of a lubricator having a tight-fitting screw cover and a valve in the oil line. To fill a lubricator of this kind, it is only necessary to close the valve and unscrew the cover.

Operation of Wick Feeds: For a wick feed, the siphoning effect of strands of worsted yarn is employed. The worsted wicks give a regular and reliable supply of oil and at the same time act as filters and strainers. A wick composed of the proper number of strands is fitted into each oil-tube. In order to insure using the proper sizes of wicks, a study should be made of the oil requirements of each installation, and the number of strands necessary to meet the demands of bearings at different rates of speed should be determined. When the necessary data have been obtained, a table should be prepared showing the size of wick or the number of strands to be used for each bearing of the machine.

Oil-conducting Capacity of Wicks: With the oil level maintained at a point ⅜ to ¾ inch below the top of an oil-tube, each strand of a clean worsted yarn will carry slightly more than one drop of oil a minute. A twenty-four-strand wick will feed approximately thirty drops a minute, which is ordinarily sufficient for operating a large bearing at high speed. The wicks should be removed from the oil-tubes when the machinery is idle. If left in place, they will continue to deliver oil to the bearings until the supply in the cup is exhausted, thus wasting a considerable quantity of oil, as well as flooding the bearing. When bearings require an extra supply of oil temporarily, it may be supplied by dipping the wicks or by pouring oil down the tubes from an oil-can or, in the case of drip feeds, by opening the needle valves. When equipment that has remained idle for some time is to be started up, the wicks should be dipped and the moving parts oiled by hand to insure an ample initial supply of oil. The oil should be kept at about the same level in the cup, as otherwise the rate of flow will be affected. Wicks should be lifted periodically to prevent dirt accumulations at the ends from obstructing the flow of oil.

How Lubricating Wicks are Made: Wicks for lubricating purposes are made by cutting worsted yarn into lengths about twice the height of the top of the oil-tube above the bottom of the oil-cup, plus 4 inches. Half the required number of strands are then assembled and doubled over a piece of soft copper wire, laid across the middle of the strands. The free ends are then caught together by a small piece of folded sheet lead, and the copper wire twisted together throughout its length. The lead serves to hold the lower end of the wick in place, and the wire assists in forcing the other end of the wick several inches into the tube. When the wicks are removed, the free end of the copper wire may be hooked over the tube end to indicate which tube the wick belongs to. Dirt from the oil causes the wick to become gummy and to lose its filtering effect. Wicks that have thus become clogged with dirt should be cleaned or replaced by new ones. The cleaning is done by boiling the wicks in soda water and then rinsing them thoroughly to remove all traces of the soda. Oil-pipes are sometimes fitted with openings through which the flow of oil can be observed. In some installations, a short glass tube is substituted for such an opening.

Wiper-type Lubricating Systems: Wiper-type lubricators are used for out-of-the-way oscillating parts. A wiper consists of an oil-cup with a central blade or plate extending above the cup, and is attached to a moving part. A strip of fibrous material fed with oil from a source of supply is placed on a stationary part in such a position that the cup in its motion scrapes along the fibrous material and wipes off the oil, which then passes to the bearing surfaces.

Oil manifolds, cups, and pipes should be cleaned occasionally with steam conducted through a hose or with boiling soda water. When soda water is used, the pipes should be disconnected, so that no soda water can reach the bearings.

When Bearings Must Operate Long Periods without Relubrication. — Bearings for certain classes of service must operate over long periods without relubrication, as, for example, a motor installation on an airplane beacon; hence the efforts of ball-bearing manufacturers to produce bearings so completely sealed as to enable them to retain their original charge of grease for many months. In appreciation of this requirement, the petroleum industry has developed lubricants that will maintain lubrication for a long period without change in structure, homogeneity, lubricating properties, or leakage.

On the other hand, to attempt to use completely sealed bearings in the cement mill, for example, might lead to serious bearing failure. Here the grease must serve to prevent entry of abrasive foreign matter. A bearing that permits some leakage, so that a collar of grease develops and frequent relubrication is necessary, is often the safest installation in such service, especially in view of the variety of load and temperature conditions involved.

Over-heated Bearings. — An over-heated bearing may be due to a number of different causes, such as incorrect design of bearing, use of an unsuitable lubricant, or improper method of applying the lubricant. When a bearing suddenly becomes heated, it is advisable to immediately apply a fatty oil of good quality, as the viscosity of an oil of this kind does not diminish with the rise of temperature to the same extent as with a mineral oil; moreover, the fixed oils are more "oily." Rape or olive oils are good for such emergencies. Sometimes a bearing runs hot because it has been without oil for a short time. When it is not feasible to stop the rotating part (as in the case of marine engine bearings) it is common to turn a stream of clear or soapy water upon the heated part. Sometimes serious damage can be prevented by throwing plumbago upon the journal or by applying the plumbago mixed with oil. When a bearing which has run cool (thus showing that the design is not at fault) repeatedly becomes heated, it should be taken apart and be examined carefully. The boxes may be adjusted too closely, the journal may be out of true, or the bearing surfaces be scored or grooved. Sometimes a surface crack in a bearing will cause heating, because it intercepts the oil film and allows the lubricant to escape. If the bearing is apparently in good order, the lubricant may be the cause of the trouble. If the viscosity is too low, the oil film does not form properly and there is direct contact between the rubbing surfaces. A bearing also tends to become heated if the viscosity of the oil is too high.

Lubricants for Lathe Centers. — The following lubricants are recommended for lathe centers to prevent cutting or abrasion: 1. Dry or powdered red lead mixed with a good grade of mineral oil to the consistency of cream. 2. White lead mixed with sperm oil with enough graphite added to give the mixture a dark lead color (when necessary, thin by adding more oil). 3. Graphite one part and tallow four parts, the two ingredients being thoroughly mixed.

Petroleum-Base Rust Preventive Materials. — There are many kinds of materials used to prevent the corrosion of metal parts, including plastics, which form a continuous film that can be stripped off; waxes that adhere tenaciously to metal surfaces; metallic soaps; paint, lacquers, and primers; and petroleum-base compounds. This last group constitutes the largest percentage of rust preventive materials.

Four types of petroleum-base rust preventive materials are used: (1) straight petroleum oils; (2) specially prepared rustproofing oils; (3) heavy non-drying compounds; and (4) hard-drying coatings.

Straight mineral oils are suitable only when the steel is stored in a place where the conditions conducive to rusting are not severe and where the steel is protected against atmospheric condensation due to temperature changes. It is usually true that the heavier the oil, the better the protection; but no straight mineral oil will give long-time rust prevention.

Straight Petroleum Oils: These are usually well refined lubricating oils containing no fatty oils or other added materials. Either a paraffin- or naphthene-base oil can be used with good results. Light oils having a viscosity of from 85 to 250 seconds Saybolt universal at 100 degrees F. are used, chiefly for the temporary protection of sheet steel. They furnish good rust protection and lubrication between the sheets in a stack, although they do not give complete protection to the steel against rusting in the presence of moisture. Water will tend to penetrate a straight mineral oil film and cause rusting to the steel beneath, sometimes within a few hours.

Special Rustproofing Oils: Many rust-proofing oils are composed chiefly of petroleum lubricating oils with or without volatile thinners, to which have been added small amounts of other protective materials. The thinner acts merely as a solvent to reduce the viscosity and aid in uniformly spreading a thin layer of the rust preventing material. These oils range from a very low viscosity of around 35 seconds Saybolt universal at 100 degrees F. up to very heavy grades of cylinder oils. They are particularly useful when storage conditions are such that steel surfaces are exposed to atmospheric changes but they are not intended for protection under outdoor atmospheric conditions, although the better grades will provide such protection to a limited extent. They will give long-time protection to steel that is not exposed directly to the elements and they will give much better service in this respect than a straight mineral oil.

Heavy Non-Drying Rustproof Compounds: These include petroleum compounds that are relatively viscous and non-hardening but that can be applied with a brush or heated for a dipping operation to produce a waterproof film. Some of these materials penetrate beneath existing rust and prevent further deterioration of the metal underneath. Most of them can be readily removed with some solvent such as kerosene. They are especially suitable for the protection of steel surfaces during storage or shipment under unfavorable weather conditions. When such a compound is applied over existing rust without chipping, filing, or grinding to obtain a clean surface, a thicker application is necessary to permit the penetration of the compound beneath the rust layer in order to prevent further rusting. Where possible, however, heavy rust should be removed thoroughly before the metal is treated. Whenever heating is necessary to obtain the fluidity required to permit dipping, swabbing, or spraying, the flash point should be well above the maximum temperature to which the compound is heated. In the case of materials applied cold and containing solvents, the flash point should be above 100 degrees F.

Hard Drying Coatings: Hard drying coatings are usually employed for semipermanent coverage of outside steel surfaces. Normally, such materials are either paints or non-oxidizing asphaltic materials. These contain thinners to facilitate application. Upon evaporation of the thinner, a hard, tough surface results which is reasonably resistant to wear and weather. The length of protection afforded by these materials varies widely according to their character and the kind of weather to which the protected surfaces are exposed.

Application of Rust Preventive Materials. — Permanent structures are usually coated with either hard-drying paint or a petroleum-base material. Sheet steel in storage or in transit is most often protected by some type of oil. Machined steel parts are generally coated with heavy petroleum compounds that can be removed without much difficulty when necessary. If the surfaces of iron and steel can be kept absolutely dry, no rust will ever develop, because moisture must be present to complete the oxidizing reaction; hence drying is desirable prior to the application of any rust-preventive material. Moisture is especially likely to be present when any drying operation is carried out by direct contact with live steam. Under such conditions, the final treatment should be drying with hot dry air to remove any traces of moisture.

The application of rust-preventive oils is simple. In steel mills, these oils are frequently applied with felt rollers after the last rolling and cleaning operation. In machine shops, steel parts are usually dipped into rust-preventive oils at the completion of each machining operation. Parts too large for this procedure can be coated by brushing or spraying. Heavier types of compounds are applied according to their consistency. They may require heating before application, however, and are particularly suitable for use in connection with a dipping operation when relatively permanent protection is desired. The lighter grades of rust-prevention compounds are generally brushed or sprayed on the steel surfaces.

Rust Resisting Grease for Nuts. — When nuts, wash-out plugs, etc., are lubricated to prevent corrosion and facilitate their removal after a long period, a lubricant should be used which does not evaporate, and which does not corrode or otherwise injure the metallic surfaces. Use a lubricant consisting of thick mineral cylinder oil, or petroleum jelly mixed with black lead. Do not use tallow or any fat oil or grease, as fat soon undergoes a change and allows the thread surfaces to corrode. A thin mineral oil is also unsuitable as it soon flows out of the joint and evaporates. Sometimes there should be no lubricant, especially if the nuts are subjected to vibration which tends to loosen them, as the nuts of rail fish-plates, etc.

Rust or Corrosion Removal from Non-Machined Surfaces. — The method used for removing rust or corrosion will depend on the depth of the corrosion and the type of surface needed after the corrosion has been removed. Scratch-brushing is probably the simplest method, but may leave the surface quite rough. Sand-blasting is effective in cleaning metal surfaces preparatory to the application of most protective coatings under conditions where pickling or other methods of cleaning are impractical or inadequate; sometimes chilled steel shot is used instead of sand. But this method does not remove tightly adhering mill scale nor clean the crevices as well as pickling. It may leave the metal with a rather smooth and less desirable finish.

Corrosion in the form of scale can be removed by pickling, using a 5 per cent solution of hydrochloric acid or a 5 to 10 per cent sulphuric acid solution. The bath is kept at about 180 degrees F. by the injection of steam. The disadvantage of pickling is that a large per cent of the scale comes off first, and while the remainder is being removed, the bare metal exposed to attack is eaten away more rapidly.

It is possible also to cause brittleness of the metal, due to the absorption of hydrogen. If this occurs, the ductility of the metal may be largely restored by heating it in water at the boiling point for several hours in an open tank. Some organic compounds, such as sizing, off-grade flour, or bran, added to the pickle solution, help to keep down acid fumes and to protect the exposed metal from overpickling without reducing the rate of scale removal. Continued agitation and aeration of the pickling bath save time and the amount of acid used.

Electrolytic pickling may be used for special work. The surface of the metal may be cleaned by making it the anode or the cathode (with an insoluble anode) in an electrolyte through which a current is passed. When used as the anode, the rapid solution of the metal and oxygen liberated on the surface loosens the scale. When used as the cathode, the hydrogen deposited on the surface reduces the oxide scale and aids in removing it. This hydrogen may make the metal more brittle than when cleaned at the anode, but the metal is cleaned this way without loss of weight.

Rust Removal from Machined Surfaces. — Slight amounts of rust may be removed by the use of oil and crocus cloth. Various solutions available on the market are quite effective for removing a very light coating of rust. In no instance can it be expected that a smooth, polished surface will be left after any of the above treatments, as the rust coating is never eaten away evenly; and there will be deep pits in some spots. However, as a general rule, surface corrosion should be removed before attempting to cover with any preservative coating, to safeguard against the corrosion continuing under the coating, causing it finally to peel off.

KEYS AND KEYWAYS

Dimensions of Sunk Keys. — Keys are generally proportioned with relation to the shaft diameter, instead of considering the torsional load in each case, because of practical reasons, such as standardization and interchangeability. The following rules, which apply to sunk keys, have been used widely; it is preferable, however, to proportion keys according to an adopted standard.

Rule 1. The key width equals $\frac{1}{4}$ of the shaft diameter; the thickness, $\frac{1}{6}$ of the shaft diameter; the minimum length, $1\frac{1}{2}$ times the shaft diameter. Expressing these rules as formulas:

$$W = \frac{D}{4} \qquad T = \frac{1}{6} D \qquad L = 1.5\,D$$

in which W = key width; T = key thickness; L = key length; and D = shaft diameter. This notation is also used in the following formulas:

Rule 2. $W = \frac{3}{16} D + \frac{1}{16}$ inch; $\qquad T = \frac{1}{8} D + \frac{1}{8}$ inch; $\qquad L = \frac{3}{10} D^2 \div T$.

For splines or feather keys, interchange the dimensions for width and thickness.

Rule 3. (Unwin.) $W = \frac{1}{4} D + \frac{1}{8}$ inch; $\qquad T = \frac{1}{8} D + \frac{1}{8}$ inch.

When gears or pulleys transmitting only a small amount of power are keyed to large shafts, these dimensions are excessive.

The taper of sunk keys is usually about $\frac{1}{8}$ or $\frac{3}{16}$ inch per foot. The depth of a taper keyseat at the deep end should be $\frac{3}{5}$ of the key thickness.

Proportions of Sunk Keys (U. S. Navy Standard)

Diam. of Shaft	Width of Key	Thickness of Key	Diam. of Shaft	Width of Key	Thickness of Key	Diam. of Shaft	Width of Key	Thickness of Key	Diam. of Shaft	Width of Key	Thickness of Key
1/2	7/32	3/16	2 1/4	9/16	5/16	5	1 1/16	5/8	7 3/4	1 9/16	7/8
5/8	1/4	3/16	2 1/2	5/8	3/8	5 1/4	1 1/8	5/8	8	1 5/8	7/8
3/4	9/32	3/16	2 3/4	5/8	3/8	5 1/2	1 3/16	5/8	8 1/4	1 5/8	15/16
7/8	9/32	7/32	3	11/16	7/16	5 3/4	1 3/16	11/16	8 1/2	1 3/4	15/16
1	5/16	7/32	3 1/4	3/4	7/16	6	1 1/4	11/16	8 3/4	1 3/4	15/16
1 1/8	11/32	1/4	3 1/2	13/16	7/16	6 1/4	1 5/16	3/4	9	1 3/4	1
1 1/4	3/8	1/4	3 3/4	13/16	1/2	6 1/2	1 3/8	3/4	9 1/4	1 7/8	1
1 3/8	3/8	1/4	4	7/8	1/2	6 3/4	1 3/8	3/4	9 1/2	1 7/8	1 1/16
1 1/2	13/32	1/4	4 1/4	15/16	9/16	7	1 7/16	13/16	9 3/4	2	1 1/16
1 3/4	7/16	5/16	4 1/2	1	9/16	7 1/4	1 1/2	13/16	10	2	1 1/16
2	1/2	5/16	4 3/4	1	9/16	7 1/2	1 9/16	7/8	...	...	....

Propeller Keys. — The practice of the U. S. Navy in proportioning keys for propellers is to make the width of the key about $1\frac{1}{2}$ times its thickness. The thickness, in turn, is so determined that the side pressure on the propeller hub, calculated from the maximum turning moment on the shaft, does not exceed 25,000 pounds per square inch. Ordinarily, the key is so proportioned that the pressure on the keyway will not exceed 22,000 pounds per square inch. With this pressure, if the key thickness is over $\frac{1}{8}$ of the shaft diameter, two keys set opposite are preferred. The hub of the propeller is bored, tapered and fitted to a corresponding taper on the shaft, which is provided with a retaining nut.

Gib-Head Taper Stock Keys

American Standard

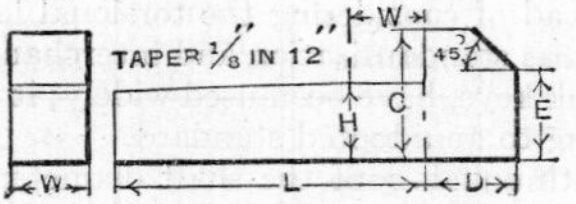

All Dimensions in Inches

Type of Key	Shaft Diameters (Inclusive)	Key		Gib Head			Tolerances	
		W	H*	C	D	E	Width (Minus)	Height (Plus)
Square Type	½–9/16	⅛	⅛	¼	7/32	5/32	0.0020	0.0020
	⅝–⅞	3/16	3/16	5/16	9/32	7/32	0.0020	0.0020
	15/16–1¼	¼	¼	7/16	11/32	11/32	0.0020	0.0020
	1 5/16–1⅜	5/16	5/16	9/16	13/32	13/32	0.0020	0.0020
	1 7/16–1¾	⅜	⅜	11/16	15/32	15/32	0.0020	0.0020
	1 13/16–2¼	½	½	⅞	19/32	⅝	0.0025	0.0025
	2 5/16–2¾	⅝	⅝	1 1/16	23/32	¾	0.0025	0.0025
	2⅞–3¼	¾	¾	1¼	⅞	⅞	0.0025	0.0025
	3⅜–3¾	⅞	⅞	1½	1	1	0.0030	0.0030
	3⅞–4½	1	1	1¾	1 3/16	1 3/16	0.0030	0.0030
	4¾–5½	1¼	1¼	2	1 7/16	1 7/16	0.0030	0.0030
	5¾–6	1½	1½	2½	1¾	1¾	0.0030	0.0030
Flat Type	½–9/16	⅛	3/32	3/16	⅛	⅛	0.0020	0.0020
	⅝–⅞	3/16	⅛	¼	3/16	5/32	0.0020	0.0020
	15/16–1¼	¼	3/16	5/16	¼	3/16	0.0020	0.0020
	1 5/16–1⅜	5/16	¼	⅜	5/16	¼	0.0020	0.0020
	1 7/16–1¾	⅜	¼	7/16	⅜	5/16	0.0020	0.0020
	1 13/16–2¼	½	⅜	⅝	½	7/16	0.0025	0.0025
	2 5/16–2¾	⅝	7/16	¾	⅝	½	0.0025	0.0025
	2⅞–3¼	¾	½	⅞	¾	⅝	0.0025	0.0025
	3⅜–3¾	⅞	⅝	1 1/16	⅞	¾	0.0030	0.0030
	3⅞–4½	1	¾	1¼	1	13/16	0.0030	0.0030
	4¾–5½	1¼	⅞	1½	1¼	1	0.0030	0.0030
	5¾–6	1½	1	1¾	1½	1¼	0.0030	0.0030

* This height of the key is measured at a distance *W* from the gib head.

Diameters of Shafts	Stock Length (L) of Key						
½–9/16	½	¾	1	1¼	1½	1¾	2
⅝–⅞	¾	1⅛	1½	1⅞	2¼	2⅝	3
15/16–1¼	1	1½	2	2½	3	3½	4
1 5/16–1⅜	1¼	1⅞	2½	3⅛	3¾	4⅜	5½
1 7/16–1¾	1½	2¼	3	3¾	4½	5¼	6
1 13/16–2¼	2	3	4	5	6	7	8
2 5/16–2¾	2½	3¾	5	6¼	7½	8¾	10
2⅞–3¼	3	4½	6	7½	9	10½	12
3⅜–3¾	3½	5¼	7	8¾	10½	12¼	14
3⅞–4½	4	6	8	10	12	14	16
4¾–5½	5	7½	10	12½	15	17½	20
5¾–6	6	9	12	15	18	21	24

American Standard Square and Flat Stock Keys

Shaft Diam., Inches	Square Key Sizes, Inches	Flat Key Sizes, Inches	Minus Tolerances,* Inches	Shaft Diam., Inches	Square Key Sizes, Inches	Flat Key Sizes, Inches	Minus Tolerances,* Inches
1/2	1/8	1/8×3/32	0.0020	2 3/8	5/8	5/8×7/16	0.0025
9/16	1/8	1/8×3/32	0.0020	2 7/16	5/8	5/8×7/16	0.0025
5/8	3/16	3/16×1/8	0.0020	2 1/2	5/8	5/8×7/16	0.0025
11/16	3/16	3/16×1/8	0.0020	2 5/8	5/8	5/8×7/16	0.0025
3/4	3/16	3/16×1/8	0.0020	2 3/4	5/8	5/8×7/16	0.0025
13/16	3/16	3/16×1/8	0.0020	2 7/8	3/4	3/4×1/2	0.0025
7/8	3/16	3/16×1/8	0.0020	2 15/16	3/4	3/4×1/2	0.0025
15/16	1/4	1/4×3/16	0.0020	3	3/4	3/4×1/2	0.0025
1	1/4	1/4×3/16	0.0020	3 1/8	3/4	3/4×1/2	0.0025
1 1/16	1/4	1/4×3/16	0.0020	3 1/4	3/4	3/4×1/2	0.0025
1 1/8	1/4	1/4×3/16	0.0020	3 3/8	7/8	7/8×5/8	0.0030
1 3/16	1/4	1/4×3/16	0.0020	3 7/16	7/8	7/8×5/8	0.0030
1 1/4	1/4	1/4×3/16	0.0020	3 1/2	7/8	7/8×5/8	0.0030
1 5/16	5/16	5/16×1/4	0.0020	3 5/8	7/8	7/8×5/8	0.0030
1 3/8	5/16	5/16×1/4	0.0020	3 3/4	7/8	7/8×5/8	0.0030
1 7/16	3/8	3/8×1/4	0.0020	3 7/8	1	1 ×3/4	0.0030
1 1/2	3/8	3/8×1/4	0.0020	3 15/16	1	1 ×3/4	0.0030
1 9/16	3/8	3/8×1/4	0.0020	4	1	1 ×3/4	0.0030
1 5/8	3/8	3/8×1/4	0.0020	4 1/4	1	1 ×3/4	0.0030
1 11/16	3/8	3/8×1/4	0.0020	4 7/16	1	1 ×3/4	0.0030
1 3/4	3/8	3/8×1/4	0.0020	4 1/2	1	1 ×3/4	0.0030
1 13/16	1/2	1/2×3/8	0.0025	4 3/4	1 1/4	1 1/4×7/8	0.0030
1 7/8	1/2	1/2×3/8	0.0025	4 15/16	1 1/4	1 1/4×7/8	0.0030
1 15/16	1/2	1/2×3/8	0.0025	5	1 1/4	1 1/4×7/8	0.0030
2	1/2	1/2×3/8	0.0025	5 1/4	1 1/4	1 1/4×7/8	0.0030
2 1/16	1/2	1/2×3/8	0.0025	5 7/16	1 1/4	1 1/4×7/8	0.0030
2 1/8	1/2	1/2×3/8	0.0025	5 1/2	1 1/4	1 1/4×7/8	0.0030
2 3/16	1/2	1/2×3/8	0.0025	5 3/4	1 1/2	1 1/2×1	0.0030
2 1/4	1/2	1/2×3/8	0.0025	5 15/16	1 1/2	1 1/2×1	0.0030
2 5/16	5/8	5/8×7/16	0.0025	6	1 1/2	1 1/2×1	0.0030

* *Note:* — These tolerances are *negative* or minus and represent the maximum allowable variation *below* the exact nominal size. For instance, the standard stock square key for a 2-inch shaft has a maximum size of 0.500 × 0.500 inches and a minimum size of 0.4975 × 0.4975 inches.

It is understood that these keys are to be cut from cold-finished stock and are to be used without machining.

Woodruff Key Sizes for Different Shaft Diameters

Shaft Diam.	Key* Numbers	Shaft Diam.	Key Numbers	Shaft Diam.	Key Numbers
5/16-3/8	1	7/8 -15/16	6, 8, 10	1 3/8 -1 7/16	13, 16, 21
7/16-1/2	2, 4	1	9, 11, 13	1 1/2 -1 5/8	15, 18, 21, 24
9/16-5/8	3, 5	1 1/16-1 1/8	9, 11, 13, 16	1 11/16-1 3/4	18, 21, 24
11/16-3/4	3, 5, 7	1 3/16	11, 13, 16	1 13/16-2	23, 25
13/16	6, 8	1 1/4 -1 5/16	11, 13, 16, 21	2 1/16 -2 1/2	25

* See manufacturers' numbers, page 587, col. two and nominal sizes, col. three.

Square and Flat, Plain Taper Stock Keys

| American Standard | TAPER $\frac{1}{8}$ IN 12″ —W— | All Dimensions in Inches |

Diameters of Shafts (Inclusive)	Square Type		Flat Type		Tolerances on Keys	
	Max. Width W	Height at H*	Max. Width W	Height at H*	Width (Minus)	Height (Plus)
$\frac{1}{2}$–$\frac{9}{16}$	$\frac{1}{8}$	$\frac{1}{8}$	$\frac{1}{8}$	$\frac{3}{32}$	0.0020	0.0020
$\frac{5}{8}$–$\frac{7}{8}$	$\frac{3}{16}$	$\frac{3}{16}$	$\frac{3}{16}$	$\frac{1}{8}$	0.0020	0.0020
$\frac{15}{16}$–$1\frac{1}{4}$	$\frac{1}{4}$	$\frac{1}{4}$	$\frac{1}{4}$	$\frac{3}{16}$	0.0020	0.0020
$1\frac{5}{16}$–$1\frac{3}{8}$	$\frac{5}{16}$	$\frac{5}{16}$	$\frac{5}{16}$	$\frac{1}{4}$	0.0020	0.0020
$1\frac{7}{16}$–$1\frac{3}{4}$	$\frac{3}{8}$	$\frac{3}{8}$	$\frac{3}{8}$	$\frac{1}{4}$	0.0020	0.0020
$1\frac{13}{16}$–$2\frac{1}{4}$	$\frac{1}{2}$	$\frac{1}{2}$	$\frac{1}{2}$	$\frac{3}{8}$	0.0025	0.0025
$2\frac{5}{16}$–$2\frac{3}{4}$	$\frac{5}{8}$	$\frac{5}{8}$	$\frac{5}{8}$	$\frac{7}{16}$	0.0025	0.0025
$2\frac{7}{8}$–$3\frac{1}{4}$	$\frac{3}{4}$	$\frac{3}{4}$	$\frac{3}{4}$	$\frac{1}{2}$	0.0025	0.0025
$3\frac{3}{8}$–$3\frac{3}{4}$	$\frac{7}{8}$	$\frac{7}{8}$	$\frac{7}{8}$	$\frac{5}{8}$	0.0030	0.0030
$3\frac{7}{8}$–$4\frac{1}{2}$	1	1	1	$\frac{3}{4}$	0.0030	0.0030
$4\frac{3}{4}$–$5\frac{1}{2}$	$1\frac{1}{4}$	$1\frac{1}{4}$	$1\frac{1}{4}$	$\frac{7}{8}$	0.0030	0.0030
$5\frac{3}{4}$–6	$1\frac{1}{2}$	$1\frac{1}{2}$	$1\frac{1}{2}$	1	0.0030	0.0030

Diameters	Stock Length (L) of Key†						
$\frac{1}{2}$–$\frac{9}{16}$	$\frac{1}{2}$	$\frac{3}{4}$	1	$1\frac{1}{4}$	$1\frac{1}{2}$	$1\frac{3}{4}$	2
$\frac{5}{8}$–$\frac{7}{8}$	$\frac{3}{4}$	$1\frac{1}{8}$	$1\frac{1}{2}$	$1\frac{7}{8}$	$2\frac{1}{4}$	$2\frac{5}{8}$	3
$\frac{15}{16}$–$1\frac{1}{4}$	1	$1\frac{1}{2}$	2	$2\frac{1}{2}$	3	$3\frac{1}{2}$	4
$1\frac{5}{16}$–$1\frac{3}{8}$	$1\frac{1}{4}$	$1\frac{7}{8}$	$2\frac{1}{2}$	$3\frac{1}{8}$	$3\frac{3}{4}$	$4\frac{1}{2}$	$5\frac{1}{4}$
$1\frac{7}{16}$–$1\frac{3}{4}$	$1\frac{1}{2}$	$2\frac{1}{4}$	3	$3\frac{3}{4}$	$4\frac{1}{2}$	$5\frac{1}{4}$	6
$1\frac{13}{16}$–$2\frac{1}{4}$	2	3	4	5	6	7	8
$2\frac{5}{16}$–$2\frac{3}{4}$	$2\frac{1}{2}$	$3\frac{3}{4}$	5	$6\frac{1}{4}$	$7\frac{1}{2}$	$8\frac{3}{4}$	10
$2\frac{7}{8}$–$3\frac{1}{4}$	3	$4\frac{1}{2}$	6	$7\frac{1}{2}$	9	$10\frac{1}{2}$	12
$3\frac{3}{8}$–$3\frac{3}{4}$	$3\frac{1}{2}$	$5\frac{1}{4}$	7	$8\frac{3}{4}$	$10\frac{1}{2}$	$12\frac{1}{4}$	14
$3\frac{7}{8}$–$4\frac{1}{2}$	4	6	8	10	12	14	16
$4\frac{3}{4}$–$5\frac{1}{2}$	5	$7\frac{1}{2}$	10	$12\frac{1}{2}$	15	$17\frac{1}{2}$	20
$5\frac{3}{4}$–6	6	9	12	15	18	21	24

* The height of the key is measured at the distance W from the large end.

† The minimum stock length of keys is equal to four times the key width, and the maximum stock length of keys is equal to sixteen times the key width. The increments of increase of length are equal to twice the width.

Cotters. — A cotter is a form of key that is used to connect rods, etc., that are subjected either to tension or compression or both, the cotter being subjected to shearing stresses at two transverse cross-sections. When taper cotters are used for drawing and holding parts together, if the cotter is held in place by the friction between the bearing surfaces, the taper should not be too great. Ordinarily a taper varying from $\frac{1}{4}$ to $\frac{1}{2}$ inch per foot is used for plain cotters. When a set-screw or other device is used to prevent the cotter from backing out of its slot, the taper may vary from $1\frac{1}{2}$ to 2 inches per foot.

Table 1. Woodruff Keys, Key-slots, and Keyways* — S.A.E. Standard

American Standard Key Number[1]	Manufacturers' Number[2]	Nominal Size A and B	Key			Key-Slot			Key Above Shaft	Keyway	
			Width	Diam.	Depth	Depth	Width	Width		Width[1]	Depth
			A	B	C[3]	D	E	E	F	G	H
			+.001 −.000	+.000 −.010	+.000 −.005	+.005 −.000	(Min.)	(Max.)	±.005	+.002 −.000	+.005 −.000
....	201	1/16x1/4	.0625	.250	.109	.0728	.0615	.0630	.0312	.0635	.0372
....	206	1/16x5/16	.0625	.312	.140	.1038	.0615	.0630	.0312	.0635	.0372
....	207	3/32x5/16	.0938	.312	.140	.0882	.0928	.0943	.0469	.0948	.0529
....	211	1/16x3/8	.0625	.375	.172	.1358	.0615	.0630	.0312	.0635	.0372
....	212	3/32x3/8	.0938	.375	.172	.1202	.0928	.0943	.0469	.0948	.0529
....	213	1/8x3/8	.1250	.375	.172	.1045	.1240	.1255	.0625	.1260	.0685
204	1	1/16x1/2	.0625	.500	.203	.1668	.0615	.0630	.0312	.0635	.0372
304	2	3/32x1/2	.0938	.500	.203	.1511	.0928	.0943	.0469	.0948	.0529
404	3	1/8x1/2	.1250	.500	.203	.1355	.1240	.1255	.0625	.1260	.0685
305	4	3/32x5/8	.0938	.625	.250	.1981	.0928	.0943	.0469	.0948	.0529
405	5	1/8x5/8	.1250	.625	.250	.1825	.1240	.1255	.0625	.1260	.0685
505	6	5/32x5/8	.1563	.625	.250	.1669	.1553	.1568	.0781	.1573	.0841
....	61	3/16x5/8	.1875	.625	.250	.1513	.1863	.1880	.0937	.1885	.0997
406	7	1/8x3/4	.1250	.750	.313	.2455	.1240	.1255	.0625	.1260	.0685
506	8	5/32x3/4	.1563	.750	.313	.2299	.1553	.1568	.0781	.1573	.0841
606	9	3/16x3/4	.1875	.750	.313	.2143	.1863	.1880	.0937	.1885	.0997
....	91	1/4x3/4	.2500	.750	.313	.1830	.2487	.2505	.1250	.2510	.1310
507	10	5/32x7/8	.1563	.875	.375	.2919	.1553	.1568	.0781	.1573	.0841
607	11	3/16x7/8	.1875	.875	.375	.2763	.1863	.1880	.0937	.1885	.0997
....	12	7/32x7/8	.2188	.875	.375	.2607	.2175	.2193	.1093	.2198	.1153
807	A	1/4x7/8	.2500	.875	.375	.2450	.2487	.2505	.1250	.2510	.1310
608	13	3/16x1	.1875	1.000	.438	.3393	.1863	.1880	.0937	.1885	.0997
....	14	7/32x1	.2188	1.000	.438	.3237	.2175	.2193	.1093	.2198	.1153
808	15	1/4x1	.2500	1.000	.438	.3080	.2487	.2505	.1250	.2510	.1310
1008	B	5/16x1	.3125	1.000	.438	.2768	.3111	.3130	.1562	.3135	.1622
609	16	3/16x1 1/8	.1875	1.125	.484	.3853	.1863	.1880	.0937	.1885	.0997
....	17	7/32x1 1/8	.2188	1.125	.484	.3697	.2175	.2193	.1093	.2198	.1153
809	18	1/4x1 1/8	.2500	1.125	.484	.3540	.2487	.2505	.1250	.2510	.1310
1009	C	5/16x1 1/8	.3125	1.125	.484	.3228	.3111	.3130	.1562	.3135	.1622
....	19	3/16x1 1/4	.1875	1.250	.547	.4483	.1863	.1880	.0937	.1885	.0997
....	20	7/32x1 1/4	.2188	1.250	.547	.4327	.2175	.2193	.1093	.2198	.1153
810	21	1/4x1 1/4	.2500	1.250	.547	.4170	.2487	.2505	.1250	.2510	.1310
1010	D	5/16x1 1/4	.3125	1.250	.547	.3858	.3111	.3130	.1562	.3135	.1622
1210	E	3/8x1 1/4	.3750	1.250	.547	.3545	.3735	.3755	.1875	.3760	.1935
811	22	1/4x1 3/8	.2500	1.375	.594	.4640	.2487	.2505	.1250	.2510	.1310
1011	23	5/16x1 3/8	.3125	1.375	.594	.4328	.3111	.3130	.1562	.3135	.1622
1211	F	3/8x1 3/8	.3750	1.375	.594	.4015	.3735	.3755	.1875	.3760	.1935
812	24	1/4x1 1/2	.2500	1.500	.641	.5110	.2487	.2505	.1250	.2510	.1310
1012	25	5/16x1 1/2	.3125	1.500	.641	.4798	.3111	.3130	.1562	.3135	.1622
1212	G	3/8x1 1/2	.3750	1.500	.641	.4485	.3735	.3755	.1875	.3760	.1935

* 1, 2, 3, See footnotes under Table 2.
All dimensions in inches.

Table 2. Woodruff Keys, Key-slots, and Keyways* — S.A.E. Standard

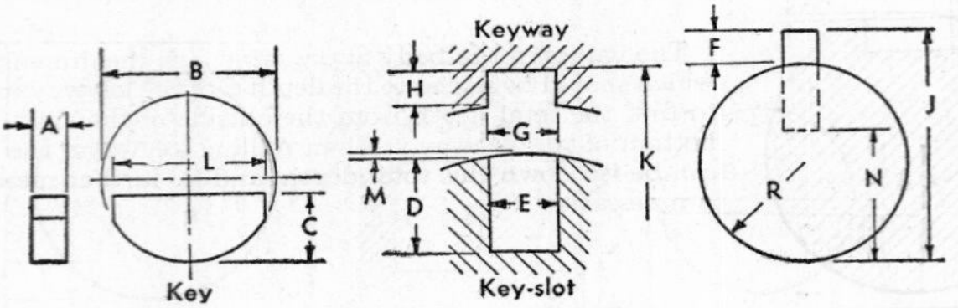

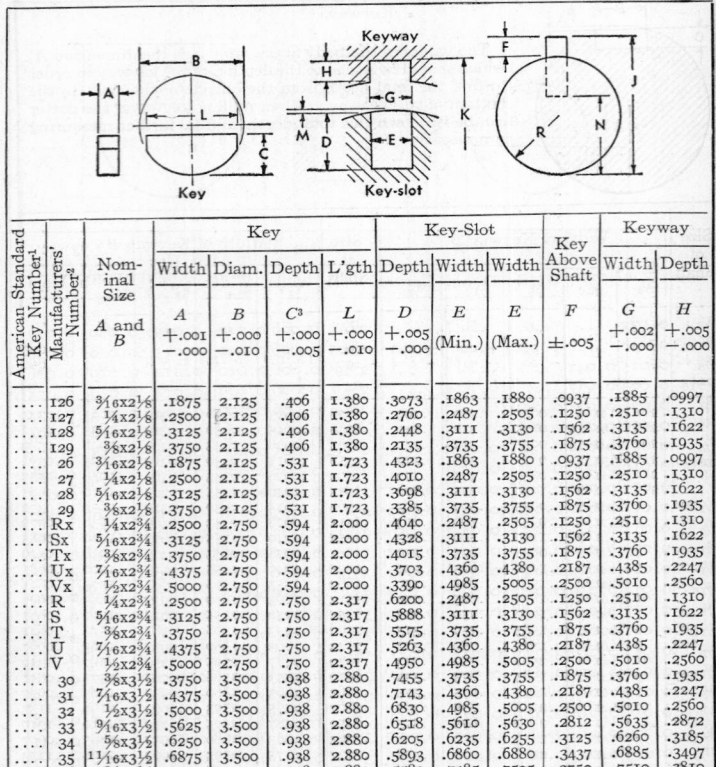

American Standard Key Number[1]	Manufacturers' Number[2]	Nominal Size A and B	Key Width A +.001 −.000	Key Diam. B +.000 −.010	Key Depth C[3] +.000 −.005	Key L'gth L +.000 −.010	Key-Slot Depth D +.005 −.000	Key-Slot Width E (Min.)	Key-Slot Width E (Max.)	Key Above Shaft F ±.005	Keyway Width G +.002 −.000	Keyway Depth H +.005 −.000
....	126	3/16x2 1/8	.1875	2.125	.406	1.380	.3073	.1863	.1880	.0937	.1885	.0997
....	127	1/4x2 1/8	.2500	2.125	.406	1.380	.2760	.2487	.2505	.1250	.2510	.1310
....	128	5/16x2 1/8	.3125	2.125	.406	1.380	.2448	.3111	.3130	.1562	.3135	.1622
....	129	3/8x2 1/8	.3750	2.125	.406	1.380	.2135	.3735	.3755	.1875	.3760	.1935
....	26	3/16x2 1/8	.1875	2.125	.531	1.723	.4323	.1863	.1880	.0937	.1885	.0997
....	27	1/4x2 1/8	.2500	2.125	.531	1.723	.4010	.2487	.2505	.1250	.2510	.1310
....	28	5/16x2 1/8	.3125	2.125	.531	1.723	.3698	.3111	.3130	.1562	.3135	.1622
....	29	3/8x2 1/8	.3750	2.125	.531	1.723	.3385	.3735	.3755	.1875	.3760	.1935
....	Rx	1/4x2 3/4	.2500	2.750	.594	2.000	.4640	.2487	.2505	.1250	.2510	.1310
....	Sx	5/16x2 3/4	.3125	2.750	.594	2.000	.4328	.3111	.3130	.1562	.3135	.1622
....	Tx	3/8x2 3/4	.3750	2.750	.594	2.000	.4015	.3735	.3755	.1875	.3760	.1935
....	Ux	7/16x2 3/4	.4375	2.750	.594	2.000	.3703	.4360	.4380	.2187	.4385	.2247
....	Vx	1/2x2 3/4	.5000	2.750	.594	2.000	.3390	.4985	.5005	.2500	.5010	.2560
....	R	1/4x2 3/4	.2500	2.750	.750	2.317	.6200	.2487	.2505	.1250	.2510	.1310
....	S	5/16x2 3/4	.3125	2.750	.750	2.317	.5888	.3111	.3130	.1562	.3135	.1622
....	T	3/8x2 3/4	.3750	2.750	.750	2.317	.5575	.3735	.3755	.1875	.3760	.1935
....	U	7/16x2 3/4	.4375	2.750	.750	2.317	.5263	.4360	.4380	.2187	.4385	.2247
....	V	1/2x2 3/4	.5000	2.750	.750	2.317	.4950	.4985	.5005	.2500	.5010	.2560
....	30	3/8x3 1/2	.3750	3.500	.938	2.880	.7455	.3735	.3755	.1875	.3760	.1935
....	31	7/16x3 1/2	.4375	3.500	.938	2.880	.7143	.4360	.4380	.2187	.4385	.2247
....	32	1/2x3 1/2	.5000	3.500	.938	2.880	.6830	.4985	.5005	.2500	.5010	.2560
....	33	9/16x3 1/2	.5625	3.500	.938	2.880	.6518	.5610	.5630	.2812	.5635	.2872
....	34	5/8x3 1/2	.6250	3.500	.938	2.880	.6205	.6235	.6255	.3125	.6260	.3185
....	35	11/16x3 1/2	.6875	3.500	.938	2.880	.5893	.6860	.6880	.3437	.6885	.3497
....	36	3/4x3 1/2	.7500	3.500	.938	2.880	.5580	.7485	.7505	.3750	.7510	.3810

All dimensions in inches.

* *Material:* Carbon steel of 0.30 carbon minimum having a minimum hardness of Rockwell C10; S.A.E. 2330 or 8630 alloy steel heat treated to a hardness of Rockwell C40–50; or other alloy steels having equal physical properties at the same hardness. Alloy heat treated keys are marked with depressions on the top to distinguish them from carbon steel keys.

[1] American Standard key numbers (ASA B17f) indicate nominal dimensions given in column 3. Last two digits give diameter B in eighths of an inch; the digits preceding last two give width A in thirty-seconds. Thus, 204 indicates a key 2/32x4/8 or 1/16 by 1/2 inch.

[2] Manufacturers' numbers for nominal key sizes in column 3.

[3] To obtain a flat at bottom of key, height C may be reduced about 0.010 inch (the standard reduction ranges from 0.009 to 0.011 inch).

Top of key to opposite side of shaft: $J = N + C$

Bottom of key-slot to opposite side of shaft: $N = 2R - (M + D)$ and $M = R - \sqrt{R^2 - (\frac{1}{2}E)^2}$

Bottom of keyway to opposite side of bore: $K = 2R - M + H$

Dimensions for Obtaining Depths of Keyseats

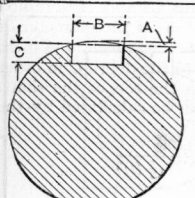

The values in the body of the table give the dimension A, which should be added to the depth C of the keyway in order to find the total depth from the outside of the shaft to the bottom of the keyway. When milling keyways, the cutter can be fed down this total depth, and no further measuring is necessary.

Size of Shaft	Width of Keyway B					Size of Shaft	Width of Keyway B				
	1/4	5/16	3/8	7/16	1/2		1/4	5/16	3/8	7/16	1/2
1/2	0.032	...	...	....	....	2 5/16	0.006	0.010	0.015	0.020	0.027
9/16	0.028	...	...	....	....	2 3/8	0.006	0.010	0.015	0.020	0.026
5/8	0.025	0.041	...	....	....	2 7/16	0.006	0.010	0.014	0.019	0.026
11/16	0.023	0.037	...	....	....	2 1/2	0.006	0.009	0.014	0.019	0.025
3/4	0.022	0.034	0.051	....	....	2 9/16	0.006	0.009	0.014	0.018	0.024
13/16	0.019	0.031	0.046	....	....	2 5/8	0.006	0.009	0.013	0.018	0.024
7/8	0.017	0.028	0.042	0.058	....	2 11/16	0.005	0.008	0.013	0.018	0.023
15/16	0.016	0.026	0.039	0.054	....	2 3/4	0.005	0.008	0.013	0.017	0.023
1	0.015	0.024	0.036	0.050	0.067	2 13/16	0.005	0.008	0.012	0.017	0.022
1 1/16	0.014	0.022	0.034	0.047	0.062	2 7/8	0.005	0.008	0.012	0.016	0.022
1 1/8	0.013	0.021	0.032	0.044	0.058	2 15/16	0.005	0.008	0.012	0.016	0.021
1 3/16	0.013	0.020	0.030	0.042	0.055	3	0.005	0.008	0.011	0.016	0.021
1 1/4	0.012	0.019	0.029	0.039	0.052	3 1/16	0.005	0.008	0.011	0.015	0.020
1 5/16	0.012	0.019	0.027	0.038	0.049	3 1/8	0.005	0.007	0.011	0.015	0.020
1 3/8	0.012	0.018	0.026	0.036	0.047	3 3/16	0.005	0.007	0.011	0.015	0.019
1 7/16	0.011	0.017	0.025	0.034	0.045	3 1/4	0.004	0.007	0.011	0.014	0.019
1 1/2	0.011	0.016	0.024	0.032	0.042	3 5/16	0.004	0.007	0.010	0.014	0.019
1 9/16	0.010	0.015	0.023	0.030	0.041	3 3/8	0.004	0.007	0.010	0.014	0.018
1 5/8	0.010	0.015	0.022	0.029	0.039	3 7/16	0.004	0.007	0.010	0.014	0.018
1 11/16	0.010	0.014	0.021	0.028	0.038	3 1/2	0.004	0.007	0.010	0.013	0.018
1 3/4	0.009	0.014	0.020	0.027	0.037	3 9/16	0.004	0.006	0.010	0.013	0.017
1 13/16	0.009	0.013	0.019	0.026	0.035	3 5/8	0.004	0.006	0.010	0.013	0.017
1 7/8	0.009	0.013	0.019	0.025	0.033	3 11/16	0.004	0.006	0.009	0.013	0.017
1 15/16	0.009	0.012	0.018	0.025	0.032	3 3/4	0.004	0.006	0.009	0.012	0.016
2	0.008	0.012	0.017	0.024	0.031	3 13/16	0.004	0.006	0.009	0.012	0.016
2 1/16	0.008	0.011	0.017	0.023	0.030	3 7/8	0.004	0.006	0.009	0.012	0.016
2 1/8	0.007	0.011	0.016	0.022	0.029	3 15/16	0.004	0.006	0.009	0.012	0.016
2 3/16	0.007	0.010	0.016	0.022	0.029	4	0.004	0.006	0.009	0.012	0.016
2 1/4	0.007	0.010	0.015	0.021	0.028	...	...	...	...	....	....

Gaging Depths of Keyseats. — The table, "Dimensions for Obtaining Depths of Keyseats" was compiled to facilitate the accurate milling of keyseats. This table gives the distance A (see illustration accompanying table) between the top of the shaft and a line passing through the upper corners or edges of the keyseat. Dimension A is added to the side depth of the keyseat to get the total depth from the outside of the shaft. To mill a keyseat, adjust the cutter until it just touches.

the top of the shaft, and set the dial of the elevating screw to zero; then sink the cutter to the total depth, which equals depth C at the side, plus distance A obtained

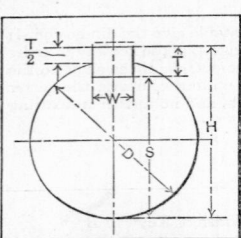

from the table. For example, if the diameter of the shaft is 3 inches and the key width is ½ inch, 0.021 inch should be added to the depth C in order to get the total depth from the top of the shaft. The height A of the arc can be calculated by the following formula:

$$A = R - \sqrt{R^2 - (\tfrac{1}{2} B)^2}$$

in which A = height of arc; R = radius of shaft; B = width of keyseat.

Example: — If the shaft radius is 5 inches and the width of the keyseat, 2 inches, then:

$$A = 5 - \sqrt{5^2 - 1^2} = 5 - \sqrt{24} = 0.101 \text{ inch.}$$

A method of measuring keyseats, which reduces the amount of fitting to a minimum, is indicated by the accompanying illustration. The keyway in the shaft is measured for depth as indicated by S, and the keyseat in the hub is measured across the bore, as at H. The advantage of this method is that the space T between the shaft and the hub does not vary (provided the keyseats are accurately cut and gaged) even though there be slight variations between the shaft diameter and the bore of the hub. The dimensions H and S for various diameters of shafts are given in the table, "Dimensions for Measuring Keyseats Across Shaft and Bore of Hub." In compiling this table, the following rules were used: The key width equals the fractional size nearest ¼ of the shaft diameter, the fractions varying by $\frac{1}{16}$ inch increments up to ¾ inch widths, then by ⅛ inch up to 1¼ inch, after which the advance is made by ¼ inch increments. The key thickness at the thin end equals ¾ of the width, and the taper is ⅛ inch per foot. Keys 1 inch wide and wider are made thinner than the foregoing rule calls for. The keyway depth in the hub and shaft are made approximately equal at the thin end of the key, and the depth in the hub is measured at the shallow end of the keyway. With this system, there is no necessity of varying the standard for an extra long hub, as the depth simply increases with the length.

Key Fitting. — The proper method of fitting keys depends somewhat upon the type of key used. The tapered sunk key not only acts as a driver for the keyed part, but holds it against axial or endwise movement, and should have a bearing on all sides. The straight sunk key should have a good bearing on the sides, and ordinarily there is either a slight clearance at the top or a light bearing. When a straight key is to resist endwise, as well as rotary, movement, it is made to bear all over, but, in any case, the principal bearing should be on the sides. The saddle key, which is simply concaved on one side to fit the shaft and is tapered on the top should be so fitted that it bears lightly on the sides and heavily between the shaft and hub throughout its entire length. As the drive with this type of key is not positive, it is only used when there is little power to transmit. The flat key, which is of rectangular section and bears a flat surface on the shaft, is fitted practically in the same manner as the saddle key. The corners of all keys should be filed off slightly before driving, to prevent a heavy bearing at these points. When fitting Woodruff keys, it is good practice to bevel the circular edges somewhat to insure the key entering easily.

Dimensions for Measuring Keyseats Across Shaft and Bore of Hub

Diam. of Shaft, Inches	Width of Key, Inches	Thickness of Key, Inches	Hub Dimension for Keyway at Thin End, Inches	Shaft Dimension for Keyway, Inches	Diam. of Shaft, Inches	Width of Key, Inches	Thickness of Key, Inches	Hub Dimension for Keyway at Thin End, Inches	Shaft Dimension for Keyway, Inches
D	W	T	H^*	S^*	D	W	T	H^*	S^*
3/4	3/16	9/64	13/16	43/64	3 1/2	7/8	21/32	3 25/32	3 1/8
13/16	3/16	9/64	7/8	47/64	3 9/16	7/8	21/32	3 27/32	3 3/16
7/8	3/16	9/64	15/16	51/64	3 5/8	7/8	21/32	3 29/32	3 1/4
15/16	1/4	3/16	1 1/64	53/64	3 11/16	7/8	21/32	3 31/32	3 5/16
1	1/4	3/16	1 5/64	57/64	3 3/4	7/8	21/32	4 1/32	3 3/8
1 1/16	1/4	3/16	1 9/64	61/64	3 13/16	7/8	21/32	4 3/32	3 7/16
1 1/8	1/4	3/16	1 13/64	1 1/64	3 7/8	1	11/16	4 5/32	3 15/32
1 3/16	5/16	15/64	1 9/32	1 3/64	3 15/16	1	11/16	4 7/32	3 17/32
1 1/4	5/16	15/64	1 11/32	1 7/64	4	1	11/16	4 9/32	3 19/32
1 5/16	5/16	15/64	1 13/32	1 11/64	4 1/16	1	11/16	4 11/32	3 21/32
1 3/8	5/16	15/64	1 15/32	1 15/64	4 1/8	1	11/16	4 13/32	3 23/32
1 7/16	3/8	9/32	1 9/16	1 9/32	4 3/16	1	11/16	4 15/32	3 25/32
1 1/2	3/8	9/32	1 5/8	1 11/32	4 1/4	1	11/16	4 17/32	3 27/32
1 9/16	3/8	9/32	1 11/16	1 13/32	4 5/16	1	11/16	4 19/32	3 29/32
1 5/8	3/8	9/32	1 3/4	1 15/32	4 3/8	1 1/8	3/4	4 11/16	3 15/16
1 11/16	7/16	21/64	1 53/64	1 1/2	4 7/16	1 1/8	3/4	4 3/4	4
1 3/4	7/16	21/64	1 57/64	1 9/16	4 1/2	1 1/8	3/4	4 13/16	4 1/16
1 13/16	7/16	21/64	1 61/64	1 5/8	4 9/16	1 1/8	3/4	4 7/8	4 1/8
1 7/8	7/16	21/64	2 1/64	1 11/16	4 5/8	1 1/8	3/4	4 15/16	4 3/16
1 15/16	1/2	3/8	2 3/32	1 23/32	4 11/16	1 1/8	3/4	5	4 1/4
2	1/2	3/8	2 5/32	1 25/32	4 3/4	1 1/8	3/4	5 1/16	4 5/16
2 1/16	1/2	3/8	2 7/32	1 27/32	4 7/8	1 1/4	13/16	5 1/4	4 7/16
2 1/8	1/2	3/8	2 9/32	1 29/32	4 15/16	1 1/4	13/16	5 5/16	4 1/2
2 3/16	9/16	27/64	2 23/64	1 15/16	5	1 1/4	13/16	5 3/8	4 9/16
2 1/4	9/16	27/64	2 27/64	2	5 1/8	1 1/4	13/16	5 1/2	4 11/16
2 5/16	9/16	27/64	2 31/64	2 1/16	5 3/16	1 1/4	13/16	5 9/16	4 3/4
2 3/8	9/16	27/64	2 35/64	2 1/8	5 1/4	1 1/4	13/16	5 5/8	4 13/16
2 7/16	5/8	15/32	2 5/8	2 5/32	5 3/8	1 1/4	13/16	5 3/4	4 15/16
2 1/2	5/8	15/32	2 11/16	2 7/32	5 7/16	1 1/4	13/16	5 13/16	5
2 9/16	5/8	15/32	2 3/4	2 9/32	5 1/2	1 1/4	13/16	5 7/8	5 1/16
2 5/8	5/8	15/32	2 13/16	2 11/32	5 5/8	1 1/4	13/16	6	5 3/16
2 11/16	11/16	33/64	2 59/64	2 13/32	5 11/16	1 1/4	13/16	6 1/16	5 1/4
2 3/4	11/16	33/64	2 63/64	2 15/32	5 3/4	1 1/4	13/16	6 1/8	5 5/16
2 13/16	11/16	33/64	3 3/64	2 17/32	5 7/8	1 1/2	7/8	6 1/4	5 3/8
2 7/8	11/16	33/64	3 7/64	2 19/32	6	1 1/2	7/8	6 3/8	5 1/2
2 15/16	3/4	9/16	3 11/64	2 39/64	6 1/8	1 1/2	7/8	6 1/2	5 5/8
3	3/4	9/16	3 15/64	2 43/64	6 1/4	1 1/2	7/8	6 5/8	5 3/4
3 1/16	3/4	9/16	3 19/64	2 47/64	6 3/8	1 1/2	7/8	6 3/4	5 7/8
3 1/8	3/4	9/16	3 23/64	2 51/64	6 1/2	1 1/2	7/8	6 7/8	6
3 3/16	3/4	9/16	3 27/64	2 55/64	6 5/8	1 1/2	7/8	7	6 1/8
3 1/4	3/4	9/16	3 31/64	2 59/64	6 3/4	1 3/4	1	7 1/4	6 1/4
3 5/16	3/4	9/16	3 35/64	2 63/64	7 1/8	1 3/4	1	7 1/2	6 1/2
3 3/8	7/8	21/32	3 21/32	3	7 3/8	1 3/4	1	7 3/4	6 3/4
3 7/16	7/8	21/32	3 23/32	3 1/16	7 5/8	1 3/4	1	8	7

* For notation see illustration accompanying paragraph, " Gaging Depths of Keyseats."

Table 1. British Standard Rectangular Parallel Keys and Keyways

All dimensions are in inches

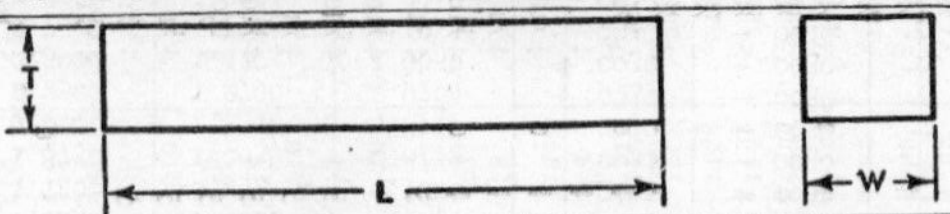

Designation of key size and type
Example: ¾- by ½-inch size
B.S.K. ¾ R.

Shaft Diameters		Key		Keyway			Tolerances			Standard Lengths		
					Minimum Depth on Center Line*		On Key	On Keyway				
Over	To and Including	Nominal and Min. Width, W	Nominal and Min. Thickness, T	Max. Width in Shaft and Hub	In Shaft	In Hub	Width and Thickness −.0000	Width +.0000	Depth −.0000	Min., L	Increasing by	Max., L
3/16	1/4	3/32	3/32	0.0938	0.0584	0.0374	+.0010	−.0010	+.0010	3/8	1/8	3/4
1/4	3/8	1/8	1/8	0.1250	0.0766	0.0504	+.0010	−.0010	+.0010	1/2	1/8	1
3/8	1/2	5/32	5/32	0.1563	0.0935	0.0648	+.0010	−.0010	+.0010	5/8	1/8	1¼
1/2	3/4	3/16	5/32	0.1875	0.0935	0.0648	+.0010	−.0010	+.0010	3/4	1/4	1½
3/4	1	1/4	3/16	0.2500	0.1130	0.0765	+.0010	−.0010	+.0010	1	1/4	2
1	1¼	5/16	7/32	0.3125	0.1325	0.0883	+.0010	−.0010	+.0010	1¼	1/4	2½
1¼	1½	3/8	1/4	0.3750	0.1521	0.0999	+.0010	−.0010	+.0010	1½	1/4	3
1½	1¾	7/16	9/32	0.4375	0.1721	0.1122	+.0015	−.0015	+.0010	1¾	1/4	3½
1¾	2	1/2	11/32	0.5000	0.2073	0.1395	+.0015	−.0015	+.0010	2	1/2	4
2	2¼	9/16	3/8	0.5625	0.2269	0.1511	+.0015	−.0015	+.0010	2½	1/2	5
2¼	2½	5/8	13/32	0.6250	0.2465	0.1628	+.0015	−.0015	+.0010	2½	1/2	5
2½	2¾	11/16	15/32	0.6875	0.2822	0.1906	+.0020	−.0020	+.0015	3	1/2	6
2¾	3	3/4	1/2	0.7500	0.3018	0.2022	+.0020	−.0020	+.0015	3	1/2	6
3	3½	7/8	5/8	0.8750	0.3746	0.2544	+.0020	−.0020	+.0015	3½	1/2	7
3½	4	1	11/16	1.0000	0.4137	0.2778	+.0020	−.0020	+.0015	4	1	8
4	4½	1⅛	3/4	1.1250	0.4528	0.3012	+.0020	−.0020	+.0015	5	1	10
4½	5	1¼	13/16	1.2500	0.4920	0.3245	+.0020	−.0020	+.0015	5	1	10
5	5½	1⅜	15/16	1.3750	0.5629	0.3796	+.0025	−.0025	+.0015	6	1	12
5½	6	1½	1	1.5000	0.6021	0.4029	+.0025	−.0025	+.0015	6	1	12
6	6½	1⅝	1 1/16	1.6250	0.6413	0.4262	+.0025	−.0025	+.0015	7	1	14
6½	7	1¾	1 3/16	1.7500	0.7117	0.4808	+.0025	−.0025	+.0015	7	1	14
7	7½	1⅞	1¼	1.8750	0.7513	0.5047	+.0030	−.0030	+.0020	8	1	16
7½	8	2	1⅜	2.0000	0.8217	0.5593	+.0030	−.0030	+.0020	8	2	16
8	9	2¼	1½	2.2500	0.9046	0.6014	+.0030	−.0030	+.0020	10	2	20
9	10	2½	1⅝	2.5000	0.9829	0.6481	+.0030	−.0030	+.0020	10	2	20
10	11	2¾	1⅞	2.7500	1.1248	0.7582	+.0040	−.0040	+.0020	12	2	24
11	12	3	2	3.0000	1.2031	0.8049	+.0040	−.0040	+.0020	12	2	24

* [illegible] make depth at sides of keyway equal approximately one-half key thickness.

Table 2. British Standard Square Parallel Keys and Keyways

All dimensions are in inches

Designation of key size and type
Example: ¾-inch size
B.S.K. ¾ S.

Shaft Diameters		Key	Keyway			Tolerances				Standard Lengths		
		Nominal and Min. Width and Thickness, W and T	Max. Width in Shaft and Hub	Min. Depth on Center Line*		On Key	On Keyway					
Over	To and Including			In Shaft	In Hub	Width and Thickness +.0000 −.0000	Width +.0000	Depth −.0000		Min., L	Increasing by	Max., L
3/16	1/4	3/32	0.0938	0.0584	0.0374	+.0010	−.0010	+.0010		3/8	1/8	3/4
1/4	3/8	1/8	0.1250	0.0766	0.0504	+.0010	−.0010	+.0010		1/2	1/8	1
3/8	1/2	5/32	0.1563	0.0935	0.0648	+.0010	−.0010	+.0010		5/8	1/8	1 1/4
1/2	3/4	3/16	0.1875	0.1091	0.0804	+.0010	−.0010	+.0010		3/4	1/4	1 1/2
3/4	1	1/4	0.2500	0.1443	0.1077	+.0010	−.0010	+.0010		1	1/4	2
1	1 1/4	5/16	0.3125	0.1794	0.1351	+.0010	−.0010	+.0010		1 1/4	1/4	2 1/2
1 1/4	1 1/2	3/8	0.3750	0.2146	0.1624	+.0015	−.0015	+.0010		1 1/2	1/4	3
1 1/2	1 3/4	7/16	0.4375	0.2502	0.1903	+.0015	−.0015	+.0010		1 3/4	1/4	3 1/2
1 3/4	2	1/2	0.5000	0.2853	0.2177	+.0015	−.0015	+.0010		2	1/4	4
2	2 1/4	9/16	0.5625	0.3207	0.2448	+.0015	−.0015	+.0010		2 1/2	1/2	5
2 1/4	2 1/2	5/8	0.6250	0.3559	0.2721	+.0015	−.0015	+.0010		2 1/2	1/2	5
2 1/2	2 3/4	11/16	0.6875	0.3916	0.2999	+.0020	−.0020	+.0010		3	1/2	6
2 3/4	3	3/4	0.7500	0.4268	0.3272	+.0020	−.0020	+.0015		3	1/2	6
3	3 1/2	7/8	0.8750	0.4996	0.3794	+.0020	−.0020	+.0015		3 1/2	1/2	7
3 1/2	4	1	1.0000	0.5700	0.4340	+.0020	−.0020	+.0015		4	1	8
4	4 1/2	1 1/8	1.1250	0.6403	0.4887	+.0020	−.0025	+.0015		5	1	10
4 1/2	5	1 1/4	1.2500	0.7108	0.5432	+.0020	−.0025	+.0015		5	1	10
5	5 1/2	1 3/8	1.3750	0.7817	0.5983	+.0025	−.0025	+.0015		6	1	12
5 1/2	6	1 1/2	1.5000	0.8521	0.6529	+.0025	−.0025	+.0015		6	1	12
6	6 1/2	1 5/8	1.6250	0.9226	0.7074	+.0025	−.0025	+.0015		7	1	14
6 1/2	7	1 3/4	1.7500	0.9930	0.7620	+.0025	−.0025	+.0015		7	1	14
7	7 1/2	1 7/8	1.8750	1.0638	0.8172	+.0025	−.0030	+.0020		8	2	16
7 1/2	8	2	2.0000	1.1342	0.8718	+.0030	−.0030	+.0020		8	2	16
8	9	2 1/4	2.2500	1.2796	0.9764	+.0030	−.0030	+.0020		10	2	20
9	10	2 1/2	2.5000	1.4204	1.0856	+.0030	−.0030	+.0020		10	2	20
10	11	2 3/4	2.7500	1.5623	1.1957	+.0040	−.0040	+.0020		12	2	24
11	12	3	3.0000	1.7031	1.3049	+.0040	−.0040	+.0020		12	2	24

* These depths, on center line or at top of shaft arc, make depth at sides of keyway equal approximately one-half key thickness.

Table 3. British Standard Plain Rectangular Taper Keys and Keyways

All dimensions are in inches
Taper of key, 1 in 100

Designation of key size and type
Example: 3/4 by 1/2-inch size
P.R.T.
B.S.K. 3/4

Shaft Diam.		Key			Keyway			Tolerances				Standard Lengths		
						Minimum Depth on Center Line*		Key		Keyway				
Over	To and Including	Nominal and Min. Width, W	Nominal Thickness	Min. Thickness Large End, T	Max. Width in Shaft and Hub	In Shaft	Deep End of Hub	Width −.0000	Thickness −.0000	Width +.0000	Depth −.0000	Min., L	Increasing by	Max., L
3/16	1/4	3/32	3/32	0.097	0.0938	0.0584	0.0354	+.0010	+.0020	−.0010	+.0010	3/8	1/8	3/4
1/4	3/8	1/8	1/8	0.129	0.1250	0.0766	0.0474	+.0010	+.0020	−.0010	+.0010	1/2	1/8	1
3/8	1/2	5/32	5/32	0.160	0.1563	0.0935	0.0618	+.0010	+.0020	−.0010	+.0010	5/8	1/8	1 1/4
1/2	3/4	3/16	5/32	0.160	0.1875	0.0935	0.0618	+.0010	+.0020	−.0010	+.0010	3/4	1/4	1 1/2
3/4	1	1/4	3/16	0.191	0.2500	0.1130	0.0725	+.0010	+.0020	−.0010	+.0010	1	1/4	2
1	1 1/4	5/16	7/32	0.222	0.3125	0.1325	0.0843	+.0010	+.0020	−.0010	+.0010	1 1/4	1/4	2 1/2
1 1/4	1 1/2	3/8	1/4	0.254	0.3750	0.1521	0.0959	+.0010	+.0020	−.0010	+.0010	1 1/2	1/4	3
1 1/2	1 3/4	7/16	9/32	0.286	0.4375	0.1721	0.1082	+.0015	+.0020	−.0015	+.0010	1 3/4	1/4	3 1/2
1 3/4	2	1/2	3/8	0.348	0.5000	0.2073	0.1355	+.0015	+.0040	−.0015	+.0010	2	1/4	4
2	2 1/4	9/16	3/8	0.380	0.5625	0.2269	0.1471	+.0015	+.0040	−.0015	+.0010	2 1/2	1/4	4 1/2
2 1/4	2 1/2	5/8	13/32	0.411	0.6250	0.2465	0.1588	+.0015	+.0040	−.0015	+.0010	2 1/2	1/4	5
2 1/2	2 3/4	11/16	15/32	0.475	0.6875	0.2822	0.1866	+.0015	+.0040	−.0015	+.0015	3	1/2	5 1/2
2 3/4	3	3/4	1/2	0.507	0.7500	0.3018	0.1982	+.0020	+.0040	−.0020	+.0015	3	1/2	6
3	3 1/2	7/8	5/8	0.632	0.8750	0.3746	0.2504	+.0020	+.0040	−.0020	+.0015	3 1/2	1/2	7
3 1/2	4	1	11/16	0.694	1.0000	0.4137	0.2738	+.0020	+.0040	−.0020	+.0015	4	1/2	8
4	4 1/2	1 1/8	3/4	0.757	1.1250	0.4528	0.2962	+.0020	+.0040	−.0020	+.0015	5	1/2	9
4 1/2	5	1 1/4	13/16	0.819	1.2500	0.4920	0.3195	+.0020	+.0040	−.0020	+.0015	5	1	10
5	5 1/2	1 3/8	15/16	0.945	1.3750	0.5629	0.3746	+.0020	+.0040	−.0020	+.0015	6	1	11
5 1/2	6	1 1/2	1	1.008	1.5000	0.6021	0.3979	+.0020	+.0050	−.0020	+.0015	6	1	12
6	6 1/2	1 5/8	1 1/16	1.070	1.6250	0.6413	0.4212	+.0025	+.0050	−.0025	+.0015	7	1	13
6 1/2	7	1 3/4	1 3/16	1.195	1.7500	0.7117	0.4758	+.0025	+.0050	−.0025	+.0015	7	1	14
7	7 1/2	1 7/8	1 1/4	1.260	1.8750	0.7513	0.4997	+.0025	+.0050	−.0025	+.0020	8	1	15
7 1/2	8	2	1 3/8	1.385	2.0000	0.8217	0.5543	+.0025	+.0050	−.0025	+.0020	10	2	16
8	9	2 1/4	1 1/2	1.510	2.2500	0.9046	0.5964	+.0030	+.0050	−.0030	+.0020	10	2	18
9	10	2 1/2	1 5/8	1.635	2.5000	0.9829	0.6431	+.0030	+.0050	−.0030	+.0020	12	2	20
10	11	2 3/4	1 7/8	1.887	2.7500	1.1248	0.7532	+.0030	+.0050	−.0040	+.0020	12	2	22
11	12	3	2	2.012	3.0000	1.2031	0.7999	+.0040	+.0050	−.0040	+.0020	12	2	24

* These depths, on center line or at top of shaft arc, make depth at sides of keyway equal approximately one-half key thickness.

Table 4. British Standard Plain Square Taper Keys and Keyways

All dimensions are in inches
Taper of key, 1 in 100

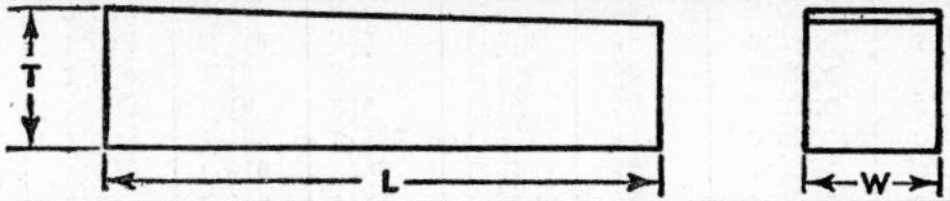

Designation of key size and type
Example: ¾-inch size
B.S.K. ¾ P.S.T.

Shaft Diams.		Key		Keyway			Tolerances				Standard Lengths		
					Minimum Depth on Center Line*		Key		Keyway				
Over	To and Including	Nominal and Min. Size, *W*	Min. Thickness Large End, *T*	Max. Width in Shaft and Hub	In Shaft	Deep End of Hub	Width −.0000	Thickness −.0000	Width +.0000	Depth −.0000	Min., *L*	Increasing by	Max., *L*
3/16	1/4	3/32	0.097	0.0938	0.0584	0.0354	+.0010	+.0020	−.0010	+.0010	3/8	1/8	3/4
1/4	3/8	1/8	0.129	0.1250	0.0766	0.0474	+.0010	+.0020	−.0010	+.0010	1/2	1/8	1
3/8	1/2	5/32	0.160	0.1563	0.0935	0.0618	+.0010	+.0020	−.0010	+.0010	5/8	1/8	1¼
1/2	3/4	3/16	0.191	0.1875	0.1091	0.0774	+.0010	+.0020	−.0010	+.0010	3/4	1/4	1½
3/4	1	1/4	0.254	0.2500	0.1443	0.1037	+.0010	+.0020	−.0010	+.0010	1	1/4	2
1	1¼	5/16	0.316	0.3125	0.1794	0.1311	+.0010	+.0020	−.0010	+.0010	1¼	1/4	2½
1¼	1½	3/8	0.379	0.3750	0.2146	0.1584	+.0010	+.0020	−.0010	+.0010	1½	1/4	3
1½	1¾	7/16	0.442	0.4375	0.2502	0.1863	+.0015	+.0020	−.0015	+.0010	1¾	1/4	3½
1¾	2	1/2	0.505	0.5000	0.2853	0.2137	+.0015	+.0040	−.0015	+.0010	2	1/2	4
2	2¼	9/16	0.567	0.5625	0.3207	0.2408	+.0015	+.0040	−.0015	+.0010	2½	1/2	4½
2¼	2½	5/8	0.630	0.6250	0.3559	0.2681	+.0015	+.0040	−.0015	+.0010	2½	1/2	5
2½	2¾	11/16	0.694	0.6875	0.3916	0.2959	+.0020	+.0040	−.0020	+.0015	3	1/2	5½
2¾	3	3/4	0.756	0.7500	0.4268	0.3232	+.0020	+.0040	−.0020	+.0015	3	1/2	6
3	3½	7/8	0.882	0.8750	0.4996	0.3754	+.0020	+.0040	−.0020	+.0015	3½	1/2	7
3½	4	1	1.007	1.0000	0.5700	0.4300	+.0020	+.0040	−.0020	+.0015	4	1	8
4	4½	1⅛	1.132	1.1250	0.6403	0.4837	+.0020	+.0040	−.0020	+.0015	5	1	9
4½	5	1¼	1.257	1.2500	0.7108	0.5382	+.0020	+.0040	−.0020	+.0015	5	1	10
5	5½	1⅜	1.383	1.3750	0.7817	0.5933	+.0025	+.0050	−.0025	+.0015	6	1	11
5½	6	1½	1.508	1.5000	0.8521	0.6479	+.0025	+.0050	−.0025	+.0015	6	1	12
6	6½	1⅝	1.633	1.6250	0.9226	0.7024	+.0025	+.0050	−.0025	+.0015	7	1	13
6½	7	1¾	1.758	1.7500	0.9930	0.7570	+.0025	+.0050	−.0025	+.0015	7	1	14
7	7½	1⅞	1.885	1.8750	1.0638	0.8122	+.0030	+.0050	−.0030	+.0020	8	1	15
7½	8	2	2.010	2.0000	1.1342	0.8668	+.0030	+.0050	−.0030	+.0020	8	2	16
8	9	2¼	2.260	2.2500	1.2796	0.9714	+.0030	+.0050	−.0030	+.0020	10	2	18
9	10	2½	2.510	2.5000	1.4204	1.0806	+.0030	+.0050	−.0030	+.0020	10	2	20
10	11	2¾	2.762	2.7500	1.5623	1.1907	+.0040	+.0050	−.0040	+.0020	12	2	22
11	12	3	3.012	3.0000	1.7031	1.2999	+.0040	+.0050	−.0040	+.0020	12	2	24

* These depths, on center line or at top of shaft arc, make depth at sides of keyway equal approximately one-half key thickness.

Table 5. British Standard Gib-Head Rectangular Taper Keys and Keyways

All dimensions are in inches
For key and keyway tolerances, see Table 4

Designation of key size and type
Example: ¾- by ½-inch size
B.S.K.   ¾   G.R.T.

Shaft Diameters		Key			Gib-Head				Keyway			Standard Lengths		
Over	To and Including	Nominal and Min. Width, W	Nominal Thickness	Min. Thickness Large End, T	A	B	C	Radius, R	Max. Width in Shaft and Hub	Minimum Depth on Center Line* — In Shaft	Minimum Depth on Center Line* — Deep End of Hub	Min. L	Increasing by	Max. L
3/16	1/4	3/32	3/32	0.099	5/32	7/32	1/8	1/32	0.0938	0.0584	0.0354	1/2	1/8	7/8
1/4	3/8	1/8	1/8	0.130	3/16	9/32	5/32	1/32	0.1250	0.0766	0.0474	5/8	1/8	1 1/8
3/8	1/2	5/32	5/32	0.162	7/32	5/16	3/16	1/32	0.1563	0.0935	0.0618	3/4	1/8	1 1/2
1/2	3/4	3/16	5/32	0.162	1/4	11/32	3/16	1/32	0.1875	0.0935	0.0618	1	1/4	1 3/4
3/4	1	1/4	3/16	0.194	5/16	13/32	7/32	1/16	0.2500	0.1130	0.0725	1 1/4	1/4	2 1/4
1	1 1/4	5/16	7/32	0.226	3/8	15/32	1/4	1/16	0.3125	0.1325	0.0843	1 1/2	1/4	2 3/4
1 1/4	1 1/2	3/8	1/4	0.258	7/16	17/32	9/32	1/16	0.3750	0.1521	0.0959	1 3/4	1/4	3
1 1/2	1 3/4	7/16	9/32	0.291	1/2	19/32	5/16	1/16	0.4375	0.1721	0.1082	2	1/4	3 1/2
1 3/4	2	1/2	11/32	0.354	9/16	11/16	3/8	1/16	0.5000	0.2073	0.1355	2 1/4	1/4	4
2	2 1/4	9/16	3/8	0.386	5/8	3/4	7/16	1/8	0.5625	0.2269	0.1471	2 1/2	1/4	4 1/2
2 1/4	2 1/2	5/8	13/32	0.418	11/16	13/16	7/16	1/8	0.6250	0.2465	0.1588	3	1/2	5
2 1/2	2 3/4	11/16	15/32	0.483	3/4	29/32	1/2	1/8	0.6875	0.2822	0.1866	3	1/2	5 1/2
2 3/4	3	3/4	1/2	0.515	13/16	31/32	17/32	1/8	0.7500	0.3018	0.1982	3 1/2	1/2	6
3	3 1/2	7/8	5/8	0.641	15/16	1 5/32	21/32	1/8	0.8750	0.3746	0.2504	4	1/2	7
3 1/2	4	1	11/16	0.705	1 1/16	1 9/32	23/32	1/4	1.0000	0.4137	0.2738	4 1/2	1/2	8
4	4 1/2	1 1/8	3/4	0.768	1 3/16	1 13/32	25/32	1/4	1.1250	0.4528	0.2962	5	1	9
4 1/2	5	1 1/4	13/16	0.832	1 5/16	1 17/32	27/32	1/4	1.2500	0.4920	0.3195	6	1	10
5	5 1/2	1 3/8	15/16	0.959	1 7/16	1 23/32	31/32	1/4	1.3750	0.5629	0.3746	6	1	11
5 1/2	6	1 1/2	1	1.023	1 9/16	1 27/32	1 3/32	1/4	1.5000	0.6021	0.3979	7	1	12
6	6 1/2	1 5/8	1 1/16	1.087	1 11/16	2 1/32	1 5/32	1/4	1.6250	0.6413	0.4212	8	1	14
6 1/2	7	1 3/4	1 3/16	1.213	1 13/16	2 5/32	1 9/32	1/4	1.7500	0.7117	0.4758	8	1	15
7	7 1/2	1 7/8	1 1/4	1.279	1 15/16	2 9/32	1 7/16	1/4	1.8750	0.7513	0.4997	9	1	16
7 1/2	8	2	1 3/8	1.405	2 1/16	2 5/8	1 9/16	3/8	2.0000	0.8217	0.5543	10	2	17
8	9	2 1/4	1 1/2	1.533	2 5/16	2 3/4	1 11/16	3/8	2.2500	0.9046	0.5904	11	2	18
9	10	2 1/2	1 5/8	1.660	2 9/16	3	1 15/16	3/8	2.5000	0.9829	0.6431	12	2	21
10	11	2 3/4	1 7/8	1.915	2 13/16	3 3/8	2 1/16	3/8	2.7500	1.1248	0.7532	14	2	24
11	12	3	2	2.042	3 1/16	3 5/8	2 3/16	3/8	3.0000	1.2031	0.7999	15	2	27

* These depths, on center line or at top of shaft arc, make depth at sides of keyway equal approximately one-half key thickness.

Table 6. British Standard Gib-Head Square Taper Keys and Keyways

All dimensions are in inches
For key and keyway tolerances, see Table 4

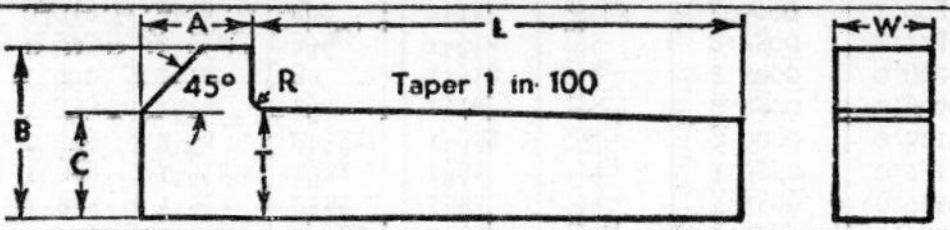

Designation of key size and type
Example: 3/4-inch size
B.S.K. 3/4 G.S.T.

Shaft Diameters		Key		Gib-Head				Keyway			Standard Lengths		
									Minimum Depth on Center Line*				
Over	To and Including	Nominal and Min. Size, *W*	Min. Thickness Large End, *T*	*A*	*B*	*C*	Radius, *R*	Max. Width in Shaft and Hub	In Shaft	Deep End of Hub	Min., *L*	Increasing by	Max., *L*
3/16	1/4	3/32	0.099	5/32	7/32	1/8	1/32	0.0938	0.0584	0.0354	1/2	1/8	7/8
1/4	3/8	1/8	0.130	3/16	9/32	5/32	1/32	0.1250	0.0766	0.0474	5/8	1/8	1 1/8
3/8	1/2	5/32	0.162	7/32	5/16	3/16	1/32	0.1563	0.0935	0.0618	3/4	1/8	1 1/2
1/2	3/4	3/16	0.193	1/4	3/8	7/32	1/32	0.1875	0.1091	0.0774	1	1/4	1 3/4
3/4	1	1/4	0.257	5/16	15/32	9/32	1/16	0.2500	0.1443	0.1037	1 1/4	1/4	2 1/4
1	1 1/4	5/16	0.320	3/8	9/16	11/32	1/16	0.3125	0.1794	0.1311	1 1/2	1/4	2 3/4
1 1/4	1 1/2	3/8	0.383	7/16	21/32	13/32	1/16	0.3750	0.2146	0.1584	2	1/4	3 1/2
1 1/2	1 3/4	7/16	0.447	1/2	3/4	15/32	1/16	0.4375	0.2502	0.1863	2 1/4	1/4	4
1 3/4	2	1/2	0.510	9/16	27/32	17/32	1/16	0.5000	0.2853	0.2137	2 1/2	1/2	4 1/2
2	2 1/4	9/16	0.573	5/8	15/16	19/32	1/8	0.5625	0.3207	0.2408	3	1/2	5
2 1/4	2 1/2	5/8	0.636	11/16	1 1/32	21/32	1/8	0.6250	0.3559	0.2681	3	1/2	5 1/2
2 1/2	2 3/4	11/16	0.701	3/4	1 1/8	23/32	1/8	0.6875	0.3916	0.2959	3 1/2	1/2	6
2 3/4	3	3/4	0.765	13/16	1 7/32	25/32	1/8	0.7500	0.4268	0.3232	4	1/2	7
3	3 1/2	7/8	0.891	15/16	1 13/32	29/32	1/8	0.8750	0.4996	0.3754	4 1/2	1/2	8
3 1/2	4	1	1.017	1 1/16	1 19/32	1 1/32	1/8	1.0000	0.5700	0.4300	5	1	9
4	4 1/2	1 1/8	1.143	1 3/16	1 25/32	1 5/32	1/4	1.1250	0.6403	0.4837	6	1	10
4 1/2	5	1 1/4	1.270	1 5/16	1 31/32	1 9/32	1/4	1.2500	0.7108	0.5382	6	1	11
5	5 1/2	1 3/8	1.397	1 7/16	2 5/32	1 13/32	1/4	1.3750	0.7817	0.5933	7	1	12
5 1/2	6	1 1/2	1.523	1 9/16	2 11/32	1 17/32	1/4	1.5000	0.8521	0.6479	8	1	14
6	6 1/2	1 5/8	1.649	1 11/16	2 17/32	1 21/32	1/4	1.6250	0.9226	0.7024	8	1	15
6 1/2	7	1 3/4	1.776	1 13/16	2 23/32	1 25/32	1/4	1.7500	0.9930	0.7570	9	1	16
7	7 1/2	1 7/8	1.904	1 15/16	2 29/32	1 29/32	1/4	1.8750	1.0638	0.8122	9	1	17
7 1/2	8	2	2.030	2 1/16	3 3/32	2 1/32	1/4	2.0000	1.1342	0.8668	10	2	18
8	9	2 1/4	2.283	2 5/16	3 1/2	2 5/16	3/8	2.2500	1.2796	0.9714	11	2	21
9	10	2 1/2	2.535	2 9/16	3 7/8	2 9/16	3/8	2.5000	1.4204	1.0806	12	2	22
10	11	2 3/4	2.790	2 13/16	4 1/4	2 13/16	3/8	2.7500	1.5623	1.1907	14	2	24
11	12	3	3.042	3 1/16	4 5/8	3 1/16	3/8	3.0000	1.7031	1.2999	15	2	27

* These depths, on center line or at top of shaft arc, make depth at sides of keyway equal approximately one-half key thickness.

Kennedy Double and Single Keys

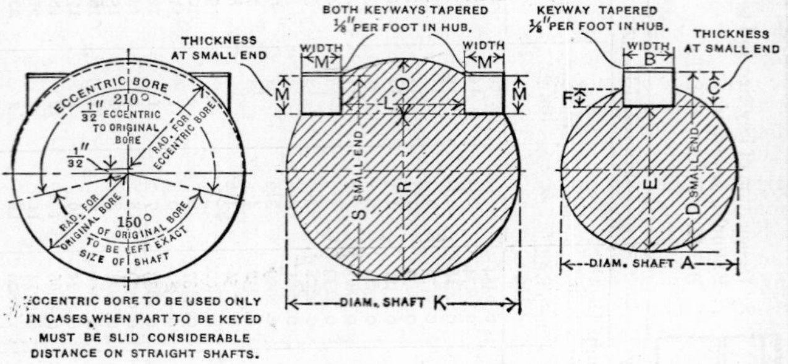

For shafts above 6 inches in diameter, double keys should be used. If the torque is intermittent and power is transmitted alternately in opposite directions, double keys should be used for diameters down to and including 4 inches. Single keys may be used for sizes up to and including 6 inches, provided the torque is quite constant and the power transmission is always in one direction.

The sides and bottom of the keyway in a shaft should be straight and parallel. In the hub, the sides should be straight and parallel and the bottom tapered ⅛ inch per foot.

Double Keys

K	*L*	*M*	*O*	*R*	*S*	*K*	*L*	*M*	*O*	*R*	*S*
4	2⅛	11/16	1	3	3 11/16	16	8	3	4⅛	11⅞	14⅞
4½	2⅜	¾	1⅛	3⅜	4⅛	18	9	3⅜	4⅝	13⅜	16¾
5	2 9/16	⅞	1¼	3¾	4⅝	20	10	3¾	5⅛	14⅞	18⅝
6	3 1/16	1 1/16	1½	4½	5 9/16	22	11	4⅛	5⅝	16⅜	20½
7	3 9/16	1¼	1¾	5¼	6½	24	12	4½	6⅛	17⅞	22⅜
8	4 1/16	1 7/16	2	6	7 7/16	26	13	4⅞	6⅝	19⅜	24¼
9	4 9/16	1⅝	2¼	6¾	8⅜	28	14	5¼	7⅛	20⅞	26⅛
10	5 1/16	1 13/16	2½	7½	9 5/16	30	15	5⅝	7⅝	22⅜	28
11	5½	2	2¾	8¼	10¼	32	16	6	8⅛	23⅞	29⅞
12	6	2¼	3⅛	8⅞	11⅛	34	17	6⅜	8⅝	25⅜	31¾
14	7	2⅝	3⅝	10⅜	13	36	18	6¾	9⅛	26⅞	33⅝

Single Keys

A	*B*	*C*	*D*	*E*	*F*	*A*	*B*	*C*	*D*	*E*	*F*
1	⅜	7/32	1 3/32	⅞	0.088	3	⅞	⅝	3¼	2⅝	0.309
1¼	7/16	5/16	1⅜	1 1/16	0.148	3½	1	11/16	3 13/16	3⅛	0.302
1½	½	11/32	1 21/32	1 5/16	0.144	4	1¼	13/16	4 5/16	3½	0.399
1¾	9/16	7/16	1 15/16	1½	0.203	4½	1⅜	⅞	4 13/16	3 15/16	0.454
2	⅝	½	2 3/16	1 11/16	0.262	5	1½	1	5⅜	4⅜	0.509
2½	¾	9/16	2¾	2 3/16	0.254	6	1¾	1¼	6½	5¼	0.619

American Standard Involute Splines. — These splines or multiple keys are similar in form to internal and external involute gears having a pressure angle (see diagram) of 30 degrees. The general practice is to form the external splines either by hobbing or on a gear shaper, and internal splines either by broaching or on a gear shaper. The internal spline is held to basic dimensions and the external spline is varied to control the fit. Involute splines have maximum strength at the base, they can be accurately spaced and are self-centering, thus equalizing the bearing and stresses, and they can be measured and fitted accurately.

Terms Applied to Involute Splines. — The accompanying diagram shows the meaning of terms used in the tables of dimensions. The splines are of involute form between the fillets at the base and the chamfers at the tips or corners. The TIF or True Involute Form diameter is measured from the point of intersection of the fillet and the true involute form. Modifications in the true involute form are discussed under "Types of Fit."

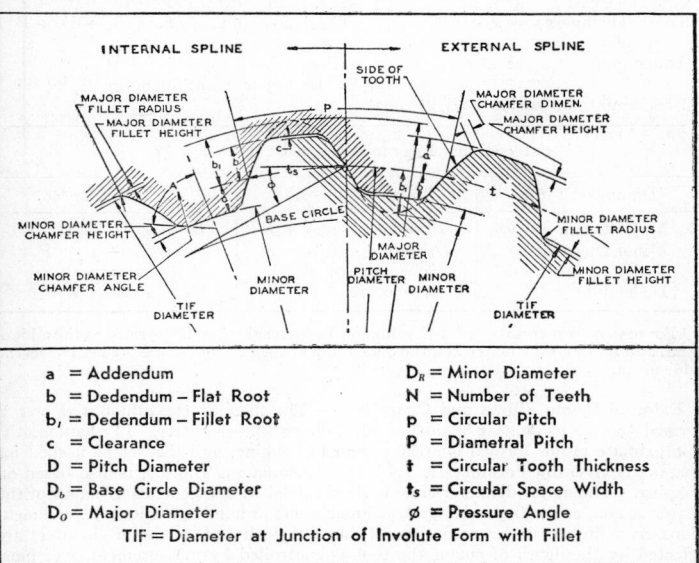

a = Addendum
b = Dedendum – Flat Root
b_f = Dedendum – Fillet Root
c = Clearance
D = Pitch Diameter
D_b = Base Circle Diameter
D_o = Major Diameter

D_R = Minor Diameter
N = Number of Teeth
p = Circular Pitch
P = Diametral Pitch
t = Circular Tooth Thickness
t_s = Circular Space Width
$\varnothing$ = Pressure Angle

TIF = Diameter at Junction of Involute Form with Fillet

Tooth Proportions. — The spline teeth are one-half the depth of standard gear teeth. There are 15 diametral pitches, 1/2, 2.5/5, 3/6, 4/8, 5/10, 6/12, 8/16, 10/20, 12/24, 16/32, 20/40, 24/48, 32/64, 40/80, and 48/96. The numerator in this fractional designation of diametral pitch controls the pitch diameter, and the denominator, which is always double the numerator, controls the tooth depth. For convenience in calculation, only the numerator is used in the formulas given and is designated as P. Diametral pitch, as in gears, means the number of teeth per inch of pitch diameter.

Spline teeth may have either a flat root or a rounded fillet root. The former is shown in solid and the latter in dashed outline in the accompanying diagram.

Formulas for the basic dimensions of both internal and external splines are given in Table 1. Formulas for the dimensions required in making and checking involute splines are given in Table 2. Table 3 gives the dimensions of fillets and chamfers of splines of 1/2 (one/two) diametral pitch. Dimensions for other pitches are found by using the formulas in Table 2 and data from Table 3. Tables 4 through 7 and the text on page 607 give the data and formulas for checking involute spline sizes by the pin method.

Table 1.   Basic Formulas for Dimensions of American Standard Involute Splines

(See page 599 for meaning of symbols.)

External and Internal Flat and Fillet Root Splines	
Pitch Diameter $D = N \div P$	Major Diam. (ext.) $D_o = (N + 1) \div P$
Circular Pitch $p = \pi \div P$	TIF Diam. (ext.) $TIF = (N - 1) \div P$
Tooth Thickness $t = \pi \div 2P$ (circular)	TIF Diam. (int.) $TIF = (N + 1) \div P$
Addendum $a = 0.500 \div P$	Minor Diam. $D_R = (N - 1) \div P$ (for minor diam. fits only)
Dedendum[1] $b = (0.600 \div P) + .002$	

External and Internal Fillet Root Splines Only		
Diametral Pitch	½ through 12⁄24	16⁄32 through 48⁄96
Major Diam. (int.)	$D_o = (N + 1.8) \div P$	$D_o = (N + 1.8) \div P$
Minor Diam. (ext.)	$D_R = (N - 1.8) \div P$	$D_R = (N - 2) \div P$
Dedendum (int.)	$b_1 = 0.900 \div P$	$b_1 = 0.900 \div P$
Dedendum (ext.)	$b_1 = 0.900 \div P$	$b_1 = 1.000 \div P$

[1] For major diameter fits, the dedendum of the internal spline is the same as the addendum, and for minor diameter fits, the dedendum of the external spline is the same as the addendum.

External Spline Fillets and Chamfers. — The fillet at the minor diameter is formed by the generating action of the hob or shaper cutter. In shaping, the approximate radius formed is greater than in hobbing, and the height needed for shaping is given by Formula 24, Table 2. Formula 23, Table 2, is also based on shaping. The major diameter chamfer is obtained by the generating action of the cutter or hob, or can be made by special machining or hand operation. The dimensions given by Formulas 20 and 21, Table 2 (length and height of chamfer) are affected by the depth of cut of the tool as controlled by measurement over pins. The fillet radius given by Formula 23 is based on a 20-tooth shaper cutter design.

Internal Spline Fillets and Chamfers. — The fillet at the major diameter may be constant for broached parts, but if cut with a shaper cutter, the generating action forms a fillet, having a height as given by Formula 7, Table 2. The minor diameter chamfer may be cut flat by a broach, but will be slightly curved if produced by a shaper cutter. Formula 16, Table 2, provides sufficient height for shaper cutting, which is greater than needed for any other method. In the case of a minor diameter fit, Formula 15, Table 2 gives in degrees the angle between the tooth center-line and the flat of the chamfer produced by a special chamfer cutter. The fillet radius given by Formula 6, Table 2 is based on a 4-tooth shaper cutter design.

Table 2. Formulas for Dimensions of American Standard Involute Splines — Internal

N = Number of teeth in spline; D = Numerator of given diametral pitch such as 8 in 8/16.

No.	Fit Type[1]	Fit Class	Formulas for Internal Splines (The Column numbers in these formulas refer to Table 3)	Machining Tolerance Limits	Diametral Pitch*
I	All	All	Pitch Diam., $D = N \div P$		All
2	All	All	Base Circle Diam., $D_b = D \cos 30° = (N \div P) \cos 30°$		All
3	Mj	All	Major Diam., $D_o = (N + 1) \div P$		All
4	Mj	All	TIF Diam., Min. $= 1.0001 [(N+1) \div P] + .0007 - 2(\text{Col. } 2 \div P)$	$+(.0007 + .0001 D_o) - .0000$	All
5	Mj, Fl, Fi	All	Minor Diam., $D_R = (N - 1) \div P$ except that for 6 & 7 teeth $1\frac{1}{2}$ to $20\!\!\!/40$, $D_R = D_b + .010$; 6 & 7 teeth ($2\frac{3}{8}$ to $4\!\!\!/96$), $D_R = D_b + .25(D - D_b)$, 8 teeth ($2\frac{3}{8}$ to $12\!\!\!/24$), Arbitrary correction	$\left\{\begin{array}{l}+.0050 - .0000\\+.0035 - .0000\\+.0025 - .0000\\+.0015 - .0000\end{array}\right.$	$3\frac{1}{2}$ to $\frac{4}{8}$; $5\!\!\!/10$ to $8\!\!\!/16$; $10\!\!\!/40$ to $20\!\!\!/40$; $24\!\!\!/48$ to $48\!\!\!/96$
6	Mj, Fl, Mn	All	Major Diam. Fillet Radius, App. $=$ Column $1 \div P$		All
7	Mj, Fl, Mn	All	Major Diam. Fillet Height, Max. $=$ Column $2 \div P$		All
8a	Fl, Mn	All	Major Diam., $D_o = [(N + 1.2) \div P] + .0040$ (for full dedendum)[2] clearance, $c = (0.1 \div P) + .002$	$+[(0.1 \div P) + .05] - 0$	All
8b	Fl	All	(for short dedendum)[3] Major Diam., $D_o = (N + 1.8) \div P$	$+(.0007 + .0001 D_o)$ $-(.0007 + .0001 D_o)$	All
9	Fl, Fi, Mn	All	TIF Diam., Min. $= (N + 1) \div P$	$+[(0.1 \div P) + .05] - 0$	All
10	Fi	All	Major Diam., $D_o = (N + 1.8) \div P$		All
11	All	All	Space Width, t_s (Basic) $= 1.570796 \div P$ Minimum (Effective) Maximum (Dimensional) $t_s(\text{min}) = t_s(\text{Basic})$ $t_s(\text{max}) = t_s(\text{Basic}) + .0001(.396N + 45)$ $t_s(\text{min}) = t_s(\text{Basic})$ $t_s(\text{max}) = t_s(\text{Basic}) + .0001(.156N + 42)$ $t_s(\text{min}) = t_s(\text{Basic})$ $t_s(\text{max}) = t_s(\text{Basic}) + .0001(.132N + 40)$ $t_s(\text{min}) = t_s(\text{Basic})$ $t_s(\text{max}) = t_s(\text{Basic}) + .0001(.096N + 37)$ $t_s(\text{min}) = t_s(\text{Basic})$ $t_s(\text{max}) = t_s(\text{Basic}) + .0001(.072N + 30)$ $t_s(\text{min}) = t_s(\text{Basic})$ $t_s(\text{max}) = t_s(\text{Basic}) + .0001(.072N + 24)$	The following tolerances are for reference only and are included in maximums. $+.0020 - .0000$ $+.0020 - .0000$ $+.0020 - .0000$ $+.0020 - .0000$ $+.0015 - .0000$ $+.0010 - .0000$	$1\frac{1}{2}$ $2.5\!\!\!/6$ 36 $4\!\!\!/8$ and $5\!\!\!/10$ $6\!\!\!/12$ and $9\!\!\!/16$ $19\!\!\!/20$ and $48\!\!\!/96$
12	Mn	X	Minor Diam., $D_R = [(N - 1) \div P] + .0015$	$+(.0019 + .0001 D_R) - .0000$	$5\!\!\!/10$ to $19\!\!\!/32$
13	Mn	Y	Minor Diam., $D_R = [(N - 1) \div P] + .0001$	$+(.0006 + .0001 D_R) - .0000$	$5\!\!\!/10$ to $19\!\!\!/32$
14	Mn	Z	Minor Diam., $D_R = [(N - 1) \div P] - (.0007 + .0002 D_R)$	$+.0000 - (.0009 + .0001 D_R)$	$5\!\!\!/10$ to $19\!\!\!/32$
15	Mn		Minor Diam. Chamfer Angle $= 53.5°$ for $N = 6$ to 37; $54°$ for $N = 38$ to 50		
16	Mn	All	Minor Diam. Chamfer Height $=$ Column $7 \div P$		$5\!\!\!/10$ to $19\!\!\!/32$

For footnotes, see end of table on page 603.

Table 2 (*Continued*). Formulas for Dimensions of American Standard Involute Splines — External

No.	Fit Type[1]	Fit Class	Formulas for External Splines (The Column numbers in these formulas refer to Table 3)	Machining Tolerance Limits	Diametral Pitch*
I	All	All	Pitch Diam., $D = N ÷ P$		All
2	All	All	Base Circle Diam., $D_b = D \cos 30° = (N ÷ P) \cos 30°$		All
17	Mj	I	Major Diam., $D_o = [(N+1) ÷ P] - .0015$	$+.0000 - (.0019 + .0002D_o)$	All
18	Mj	II	Major Diam., $D_o = [(N+1) ÷ P] - .0001$	$+.0000 - (.0006 + .0002D_o)$	All
19	Mj	III	Major Diam., $D_o = 1.0001[(N+1) ÷ P] + .0008$	$+(.0009 + .0002D_o) - .0000$	All
20	Mj	All	Major Diameter Chamfer Length, App. = Column 5 ÷ P		All
21	Mj	All	Major Diameter Chamfer Height, Min. = Column 6 ÷ P		All
22	Mj, Fl	All	Minor Diam., $D_R = [(N-1.2) ÷ P] - .0040$ (See Formula 26)	$+0 - [(0.1 ÷ P) + .005]$	All
23	Mj, Fl, Mn	All	Minor Diameter Fillet Radius, App. = Column 3 ÷ P		All
24	Mj, Fl, Mn	All	Minor Diameter Fillet Height, Max. = Column 4 ÷ P		All
25	Fl, Fi, Mn	All	Major Diam., $D_o = (N+1) ÷ P$ (See Note[3])	$+.0000 - .0100$ $+.0000 - .0070$ $+.0000 - .0050$ $+.0000 - .0030$	½ to ⅞ 5⁄10 to 9⁄16 19⁄50 to 20⁄40 24⁄48 to 48⁄96
26	Fi, Mj[4]	All	Minor Diam., $D_R = (N-1.8) ÷ P$ $D_R = (N-2.0) ÷ P$	$+0 - [(0.1 ÷ P) + .005]$	½ to 12⁄24 16⁄32 to 48⁄96
27	Mj, Fl, Fi	All	TIF Diameter, Max. = Same as Minor Diam. (Formula 5)		All
28	Fl, Fi, Fi, Mj, Mn	A I, II, III X, Y, Z	Tooth Thickness, t (Basic) = 1.570796 ÷ P Maximum (Effective) · · · Minimum (Dimensional) $t(\text{max}) = t(\text{Basic}) - .0005$ $t(\text{min}) = t(\text{Basic}) - .0001(.360N ÷ 52)$ $t(\text{max}) = t(\text{Basic}) - .0005$ $t(\text{min}) = t(\text{Basic}) - .0001(.120N ÷ 48)$ $t(\text{max}) = t(\text{Basic}) - .0005$ $t(\text{min}) = t(\text{Basic}) - .0001(.090N ÷ 47)$ $t(\text{max}) = t(\text{Basic}) - .0005$ $t(\text{min}) = t(\text{Basic}) - .0001(.072N ÷ 43)$ $t(\text{max}) = t(\text{Basic}) - .0005$ $t(\text{min}) = t(\text{Basic}) - .0001(.054N ÷ 36)$ $t(\text{max}) = t(\text{Basic}) - .0005$ $t(\text{min}) = t(\text{Basic}) - .0001(.054N ÷ 35)$ $t(\text{max}) = t(\text{Basic}) - .0005$ $t(\text{min}) = t(\text{Basic}) - .0001(.054N ÷ 30)$	The following tolerances are for reference only and are included in minimums. $+.0000 - .0020$ $+.0000 - .0020$ $+.0000 - .0020$ $+.0000 - .0020$ $+.0000 - .0015$ $+.0000 - .0015$ $+.0000 - .0010$	½ 2.5⁄6 36 4⁄8 to 5⁄10 9⁄12 to 8⁄16 19⁄20 to 20⁄40 24⁄48 to 48⁄96

Table 2 (*Continued*). **Formulas for Dimensions of American Standard Involute Splines — External**

No.	Fit Type[1]	Fit Class	Formulas for External Splines (The Column numbers in these formulas refer to Table 3)	Machining Tolerance Limits	Diametral Pitch*
29	Fl, Fi	B	Tooth Thickness, t(Basic) $= 1.570796 \div P$ **Maximum (Effective)** — **Minimum (Dimensional)** t(max) $= t$(Basic) $+ .0015$ — t(min) $= t$(Basic) $- .0001(.360N + 27)$ t(max) $= t$(Basic) $+ .0015$ — t(min) $= t$(Basic) $- .0001(.120N + 23)$ t(max) $= t$(Basic) $+ .0015$ — t(min) $= t$(Basic) $- .0001(.090N + 22)$ t(max) $= t$(Basic) $+ .0015$ — t(min) $= t$(Basic) $- .0001(.072N + 18)$ t(max) $= t$(Basic) $+ .0013$ — t(min) $= t$(Basic) $- .0001(.054N + 18)$ t(max) $= t$(Basic) $+ .0011$ — t(min) $= t$(Basic) $- .0001(.054N + 19)$ t(max) $= t$(Basic) $+ .0009$ — t(min) $= t$(Basic) $- .0001(.054N + 16)$	The following tolerances are for reference only and are included in minimums. $+.0000 - .0015$ $+.0000 - .0015$ $+.0000 - .0015$ $+.0000 - .0015$ $+.0000 - .0015$ $+.0000 - .0015$ $+.0000 - .0010$	½ 2.5⁄5 3⁄6 3⁄8 to 5⁄10 6⁄12 to 8⁄16 10⁄20 to 20⁄40 24⁄48 to 48⁄96
30	Fl, Fi	C	Tooth Thickness, t(Basic) $= 1.570796 \div P$ **Maximum (Effective)** — **Minimum (Dimensional)** t(max) $= t$(Basic) $+ .0045$ — t(min) $= t$(Basic) $- .0001(.360N - 3)$ t(max) $= t$(Basic) $+ .0042$ — t(min) $= t$(Basic) $- .0001(.120N - 4)$ t(max) $= t$(Basic) $+ .0042$ — t(min) $= t$(Basic) $- .0001(.090N - 5)$ t(max) $= t$(Basic) $+ .0036$ — t(min) $= t$(Basic) $- .0001(.072N - 3)$ t(max) $= t$(Basic) $+ .0030$ — t(min) $= t$(Basic) $- .0001(.054N + 1)$ t(max) $= t$(Basic) $+ .0030$ — t(min) $= t$(Basic) $- .0001(.054N)$ t(max) $= t$(Basic) $+ .0030$ — t(min) $= t$(Basic) $- .0001(.054N - 5)$	The following tolerances are for reference only and are included in minimums. $+.0000 - .0015$ $+.0000 - .0015$ $+.0000 - .0015$ $+.0000 - .0015$ $+.0000 - .0015$ $+.0000 - .0015$ $+.0000 - .0010$	½ 2.5⁄5 3⁄6 3⁄8 to 5⁄10 6⁄12 to 8⁄16 10⁄20 to 20⁄40 24⁄48 to 48⁄96
31	Mn	All	Minor Diam., $D_R = (N - 1) \div P$	$+.0000 - (.0006 + .0002 D_R)$	5⁄10 to 16⁄32
32	Mn	All	TIF Diameter, Maximum $= [(N - 1) \div P] + 2(\text{Col. } 4 \div P)$		5⁄10 to 16⁄32

[1] Mj = Major Diameter Fit; Fl = Flat Root Tooth Side Fit; Fi = Fillet Root Tooth Side Fit; Mn = Minor Diameter Fit.

[2] Major Diameter intended to be used when cutting by a generating process.

[3] When Major Diameter (Formula 8b) is used for internal spline, subtract from Major Diameter (Formula 25) of external spline twice the maximum dimensional clearance (2 [Formula 11 − Formula 28, 29, or 30]), and apply chamfer.

[4] May be used for major diameter fits in place of Formula 22. If this is done, Formulas 23 and 24 are not used. American Standard ASA B5.15-1950 gives the required fillet dimensions (see footnote, Table 3).

* For minor diameter fits, only 5⁄10, 6⁄12, 8⁄16, 10⁄20, 12⁄24, and 16⁄32 diametral pitches are used.

Types and Classes of Fit. — There are three methods of fitting splined members together:

Major Diameter: On the major diameter, where fit is controlled by varying the major diameter of the external spline.

Sides of Teeth: On the sides of the teeth, where fit is controlled by varying the tooth thickness. It is customary to use this type fit for the fillet root type spline but it may also be used for the flat root type spline.

Minor Diameter: On the minor diameter, where fit is controlled by varying the minor diameter of the internal spline.

These three types of fits are each divided into three classes:

Sliding Fits which must have clearance at all points.

Close Fits which must be close on either the major diameter, sides of tooth or minor diameter.

Press Fits which must have interference on either the major diameter, sides of teeth or minor diameter.

For the major diameter type of fit these classes are called respectively I, II, and III. For the sides of teeth fit these classes are designated respectively as A, B and C. For the minor diameter type of fit these classes are designated respectively X, Y and Z.

Allowable Errors. — Four types of allowable (unavoidable) errors are recognized.

Accumulated Pitch Error (Spacing) is the greatest difference in any two teeth between the actual and theoretical tooth spacing on the same circle. Measurements are taken from one pitch point selected as reference, to the corresponding points on all other teeth, and will be affected by involute profile error and out-of-roundness.

Profile Error is the difference between the highest and lowest readings of a dial indicator moving along the true involute curve in the plane of rotation and having a finger contacting the actual active tooth profile.

Out of Roundness is the difference between the maximum and minimum measurements over or between pins.

Lead Error is a deviation of the teeth from the dimensional lead of the spline per unit of face width. Lead error is usually measured by traversing a dial indicator along the tooth face normal to the pitch line and parallel to the axis of the spline.

Only the first three types of allowable errors are usually taken into account in the case of straight splines. Experience has shown that not all of the possible extreme errors will occur at one time so that instead of using the total of these three classes of errors (or in some cases all four classes), 60 per cent of whichever total is taken has been adopted as a fair maximum for computing effective fits. In the formulas in Table 2 which take account of the first three allowable errors, the values used have been based upon 60 per cent of established tabulated allowable error values for different diametral pitches, numbers of teeth, and length of spline.

Space Width and Tooth Thickness Dimensions. — Insofar as the fit between an internal spline and an external spline is concerned, the effect of any errors present is the same as if the space width of the internal spline were *less* than it actually measured and the tooth thickness of the external spline were *more* than it actually measured. The *effective space width* of an internal spline is, then, equal to the actual (called dimensional) space width minus an amount which represents the effect of the errors present. These errors are allowable (unavoidable) errors such as have been listed in the preceding paragraph and errors arising from machine tool adjustments which vary the depth of cut. These latter errors are taken care of by machining tolerances as indicated in Table 2.

Table 3. Dimensions of Fillets and Chamfers for Involute Splines

(See Table 2 for use of these data.)

N	Fillet*				Chamfer			N	Fillet*				Chamfer		
	Rad.	Ht.	Rad.	Ht.	Dim.	Ht.	Ht.		Rad.	Ht.	Rad.	Ht.	Dim.	Ht.	Ht.
	1	2	3	4	5	6	7		1	2	3	4	5	6	7
6	.145	.052	.170	.168	.228	.091	.200	29	.217	.101	.100	.075	.239	.106	.090
7	.160	.060	.150	.150	.230	.094	.180	30	.217	.102	.100	.074	.239	.106	.090
8	.170	.066	.140	.137	.230	.095	.165	31	.218	.102	.100	.074	.239	.106	.090
9	.178	.071	.130	.127	.232	.097	.150	32	.218	.103	.100	.073	.239	.106	.090
10	.184	.075	.120	.119	.233	.098	.145	33	.219	.103	.100	.072	.239	.106	.085
11	.189	.079	.116	.113	.234	.099	.135	34	.219	.103	.100	.072	.239	.106	.085
12	.193	.081	.110	.107	.234	.100	.130	35	.219	.104	.100	.071	.239	.106	.085
13	.196	.084	.108	.103	.235	.100	.125	36	.220	.104	.100	.071	.240	.106	.085
14	.199	.086	.105	.099	.235	.101	.120	37	.220	.104	.100	.070	.240	.107	.085
15	.201	.088	.102	.096	.236	.102	.115	38	.220	.105	.100	.070	.240	.107	.085
16	.203	.090	.100	.093	.236	.102	.110	39	.221	.105	.100	.069	.240	.107	.085
17	.205	.091	.100	.091	.236	.103	.110	40	.221	.105	.100	.069	.240	.107	.085
18	.207	.093	.100	.089	.237	.103	.105	41	.221	.106	.100	.069	.240	.107	.085
19	.208	.094	.100	.087	.237	.103	.105	42	.222	.106	.100	.068	.240	.107	.080
20	.209	.095	.100	.085	.237	.104	.100	43	.222	.106	.100	.068	.240	.107	.080
21	.210	.096	.100	.083	.237	.104	.100	44	.222	.106	.100	.068	.240	.107	.080
22	.212	.097	.100	.082	.237	.104	.100	45	.222	.106	.100	.067	.240	.107	.080
23	.212	.097	.100	.081	.238	.104	.095	46	.222	.107	.100	.067	.240	.107	.080
24	.213	.098	.100	.080	.238	.105	.095	47	.223	.107	.100	.067	.240	.107	.080
25	.214	.099	.100	.079	.238	.105	.095	48	.223	.107	.100	.066	.240	.107	.080
26	.215	.100	.100	.078	.238	.105	.095	49	.223	.107	.100	.066	.240	.107	.080
27	.215	.100	.100	.077	.239	.105	.090	50	.223	.107	.100	.066	.240	.107	.080
28	.216	.101	.100	.076	.239	.105	.090								

* The fillet radii of fillet root type teeth of internal and external splines are determined by layout. For actual dimensions for given diametral pitch and tooth number refer to American Standard ASA B5.15-1950.

In checking the space width of an internal spline against the established limits, which are found by the formulas given in Table 2, the *minimum* is checked by an effective measurement that is made with gages which take into account the effect of the various errors present. If gages are not available, a pin measurement may be taken as explained in the next section, " Measurement of Space Width and Tooth Thickness." The *maximum* space width is checked as a dimensional measurement between pins; Table 6 gives the necessary formulas.

The *effective tooth thickness* of an external spline is equal to the actual or dimensional tooth thickness plus an amount which represents the allowable errors and machining tolerances. In checking the tooth thickness of an external spline against the established limits which are found by formulas given in Table 2, the *maximum* is checked by an effective measurement that is made with gages which take into account the effect of any errors present. Should gages not be available, a pin measurement may be made as explained in the following section. The *minimum* is checked as a dimensional measurement over pins; Table 7 gives the necessary formulas.

The *effective clearance* (positive or negative) between two splined parts is equal to the effective space width of the internal spline minus the effective tooth thickness of the external spline. Negative clearance indicates interference.

Measurement of Space Width and Tooth Thickness. — The tooth thickness of an external spline is determined by measuring over pins and the space width of an internal spline is determined by measuring between pins. The diameter of the measuring pin is optional within a narrow range but for the sake of uniformity, and to follow a satisfactory practice, the basic pin measurements given in Table 5 are based on a pin size (see Table 4) of 1.4400 divided by P for internal and 1.9200 divided by P for external splines where P is the diametral pitch as used in all formulas in Table 2.

Table 4.　Recommended Measuring Pin Sizes for Involute Splines

Recommended Pin Diameters

For Internal Splines* $\quad d_n = 1.4400 \div P$

For External Splines $\quad d_x = 1.9200 \div P$

* These pins should be flatted as shown if they are used to measured *flat root* internal splines.

Table 5.　Basic Pin Measurements for 1/2 Diametral Pitch Internal and External Splines

(These data to be used with formulas in Tables 6 and 7)

No. of Teeth	Internal Splines Between Pins M_i	F	External Splines Over Pins M_e	E	No. of Teeth	Internal Splines Between Pins M_i	F	External Splines Over Pins M_e	E
1	2	3	4	5	1	2	3	4	5
6	4.3933	1.91	8.8660	1.305	29	27.3571	1.76	31.9405	1.573
7	5.2232	1.83	9.6819	1.302	30	28.3994	1.76	32.9862	1.580
8	6.3954	1.86	10.8944	1.362	31	29.3599	1.76	33.9465	1.581
9	7.2618	1.81	11.7535	1.364	32	30.3995	1.76	34.9890	1.587
10	8.3966	1.83	12.9144	1.406	33	31.3623	1.76	35.9517	1.589
11	9.2867	1.80	13.8003	1.409	34	32.3995	1.76	36.9916	1.594
12	10.3973	1.81	14.9295	1.440	35	33.3645	1.76	37.9565	1.596
13	11.3040	1.79	15.8335	1.443	36	34.3996	1.76	38.9939	1.600
14	12.3978	1.80	16.9412	1.467	37	35.3665	1.76	39.9607	1.602
15	13.3167	1.78	17.8584	1.471	38	36.3996	1.75	40.9960	1.606
16	14.3982	1.79	18.9507	1.490	39	37.3682	1.75	41.9645	1.608
17	15.3265	1.78	19.8934	1.493	40	38.3997	1.75	42.9980	1.611
18	16.3985	1.78	20.9584	1.509	41	39.3698	1.75	43.9680	1.613
19	17.3343	1.78	21.8934	1.512	42	40.3997	1.75	44.9996	1.616
20	18.3987	1.78	22.9649	1.525	43	41.3712	1.75	45.9711	1.617
21	19.3405	1.77	23.9062	1.528	44	42.3998	1.75	47.0013	1.621
22	20.3989	1.77	24.9704	1.539	45	43.3725	1.75	47.9740	1.622
23	21.3457	1.77	25.9168	1.541	46	44.3998	1.75	49.0028	1.625
24	22.3991	1.77	26.9752	1.551	47	45.3737	1.75	49.9766	1.626
25	23.3501	1.77	27.9259	1.553	48	46.3999	1.75	51.0041	1.629
26	24.3992	1.76	28.9793	1.562	49	47.3748	1.75	51.9790	1.630
27	25.3528	1.76	29.9337	1.564	50	48.3999	1.75	53.0055	1.632
28	26.3993	1.76	30.9829	1.571	..	....	....	....	.....

Table 6.　Formulas for Maximum Measurement Between Pins for Internal Splines

(Column references are to Table 5.)

Class Fit	Range of Pitches	Formula for M_i (Max) Measurement Between Pins
All	½	(Col. 2 ÷ P) + .0001F (.396N + 45)
	2.5⁄5	(Col. 2 ÷ P) + .0001F (.156N + 42)
	3⁄6	(Col. 2 ÷ P) + .0001F (.132N + 40)
	4⁄8 & 5⁄10	(Col. 2 ÷ P) + .0001F (.096N + 37)
	6⁄12 & 8⁄16	(Col. 2 ÷ P) + .0001F (.072N + 30)
	10⁄20 to 48⁄96	(Col. 2 ÷ P) + .0001F (.072N + 24)

Table 7.   Formulas for Minimum Measurement Over Pins for External Splines

(Column references are to Table 5.)

Class Fit	Range of Pitches	Formula for M_e (Min) Measurement Over Pins
A (I, II, III)* (X, Y, Z,)†	½	(Col. 4 ÷ P) — .0001E (.360N + 52)
	2.⁵⁄₅	(Col. 4 ÷ P) — .0001E (.120N + 48)
	³⁄₆	(Col. 4 ÷ P) — .0001E (.090N + 47)
	⁴⁄₈ & ⁵⁄₁₀	(Col. 4 ÷ P) — .0001E (.072N + 43)
	⁹⁄₁₂ & ⁸⁄₁₆	(Col. 4 ÷ P) — .0001E (.054N + 36)
	¹⁹⁄₂₀ to ²⁹⁄₄₀	(Col. 4 ÷ P) — .0001E (.054N + 35)
	²⁴⁄₄₈ to ⁴⁸⁄₉₆	(Col. 4 ÷ P) — .0001E (.054N + 30)
B	½	(Col. 4 ÷ P) — .0001E (.360N + 27)
	2.⁵⁄₅	(Col. 4 ÷ P) — .0001E (.120N + 23)
	³⁄₆	(Col. 4 ÷ P) — .0001E (.090N + 22)
	⁴⁄₈ & ⁵⁄₁₀	(Col. 4 ÷ P) — .0001E (.072N + 18)
	⁹⁄₁₂ & ⁸⁄₁₆	(Col. 4 ÷ P) — .0001E (.054N + 18)
	¹⁹⁄₂₀ to ²⁹⁄₄₀	(Col. 4 ÷ P) — .0001E (.054N + 19)
	²⁴⁄₄₈ to ⁴⁸⁄₉₆	(Col. 4 ÷ P) — .0001E (.054N + 16)
C	½	(Col. 4 ÷ P) — .0001E (.360N − 3)
	2.⁵⁄₅	(Col. 4 ÷ P) — .0001E (.120N − 4)
	³⁄₆	(Col. 4 ÷ P) — .0001E (.090N − 5)
	⁴⁄₈ & ⁵⁄₁₀	(Col. 4 ÷ P) — .0001E (.072N − 3)
	⁹⁄₁₂ & ⁸⁄₁₆	(Col. 4 − P) — .0001E (.054N + 1)
	¹⁹⁄₂₀ to ²⁹⁄₄₀	(Col. 4 ÷ P) — .0001E (.054N)
	²⁴⁄₄₈ to ⁴⁸⁄₉₆	(Col. 4 ÷ P) — .0001E (.054N − 5)

* For a tighter major diameter fit, formulas given for Class B fits may be used.

† For tighter minor diameter fits, formulas given for Class B or Class C fits may be used.

These measurements with pins will not check spacing errors and hence cannot measure *effective* tooth thickness or *effective* space width. For this reason, minimum pin measurements for internal splines and maximum pin measurements for external splines are not specified in Tables 6 and 7. Instead of pin measurements, gages should be used where possible to control maximum *effective* tooth thickness and minimum *effective* space width. Where this is not feasible, the maximum (*effective*) tooth thickness for an external spline may be checked by a pin measurement based upon the following formula: —

$$M_e \text{ (max)} = M_e \text{ (min)} + T_m \times E$$

where M_e (max) = maximum measurement over pins
M_e (min) = minimum measurement over pins (see Table 7)
T_m = tolerance for tooth thickness machining errors (see Table 2)
E = factor taken from Table 5

Similarly when it is not feasible to check the minimum (effective) space width, the minimum limit of space width for an internal spline may be checked by pin measurement based upon the following formula:

$$M_i \text{ (min)} = M_i \text{ (max)} − T_m \times F$$

where M_i (min) = minimum measurement between pins
M_i (max) = maximum measurement between pins (see Table 6)
T_m = tolerance for space width machining errors (see Table 2)
F = factor taken from Table 5

Table 1.　S.A.E. Standard Splined Fittings

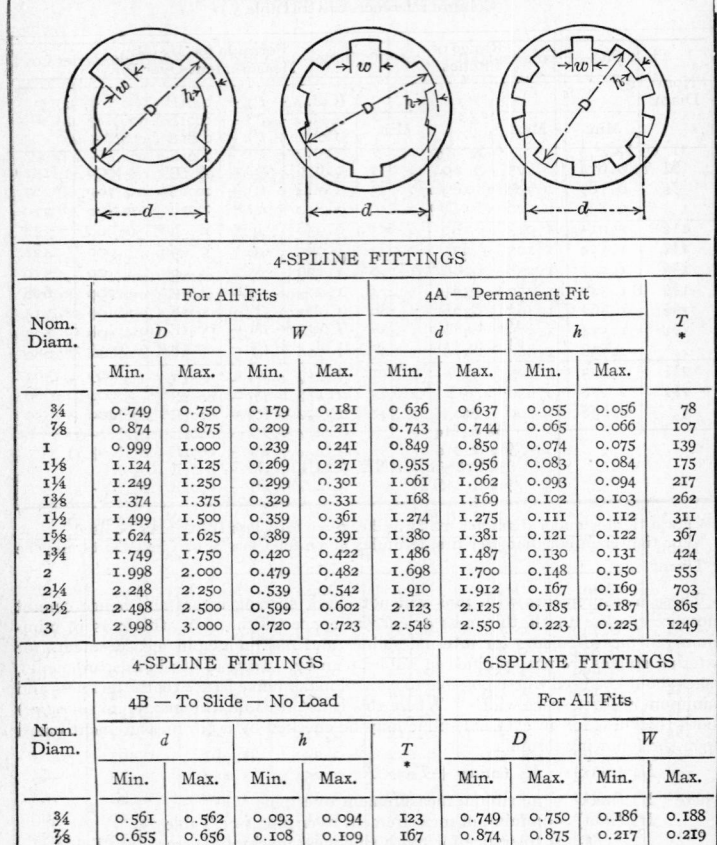

4-SPLINE FITTINGS

Nom. Diam.	For All Fits				4A — Permanent Fit				T *
	D		W		d		h		
	Min.	Max.	Min.	Max.	Min.	Max.	Min.	Max.	
3/4	0.749	0.750	0.179	0.181	0.636	0.637	0.055	0.056	78
7/8	0.874	0.875	0.209	0.211	0.743	0.744	0.065	0.066	107
1	0.999	1.000	0.239	0.241	0.849	0.850	0.074	0.075	139
1 1/8	1.124	1.125	0.269	0.271	0.955	0.956	0.083	0.084	175
1 1/4	1.249	1.250	0.299	0.301	1.061	1.062	0.093	0.094	217
1 3/8	1.374	1.375	0.329	0.331	1.168	1.169	0.102	0.103	262
1 1/2	1.499	1.500	0.359	0.361	1.274	1.275	0.111	0.112	311
1 5/8	1.624	1.625	0.389	0.391	1.380	1.381	0.121	0.122	367
1 3/4	1.749	1.750	0.420	0.422	1.486	1.487	0.130	0.131	424
2	1.998	2.000	0.479	0.482	1.698	1.700	0.148	0.150	555
2 1/4	2.248	2.250	0.539	0.542	1.910	1.912	0.167	0.169	703
2 1/2	2.498	2.500	0.599	0.602	2.123	2.125	0.185	0.187	865
3	2.998	3.000	0.720	0.723	2.548	2.550	0.223	0.225	1249

4-SPLINE FITTINGS　　　6-SPLINE FITTINGS

Nom. Diam.	4B — To Slide — No Load				T *	For All Fits			
	d		h			D		W	
	Min.	Max.	Min.	Max.		Min.	Max.	Min.	Max.
3/4	0.561	0.562	0.093	0.094	123	0.749	0.750	0.186	0.188
7/8	0.655	0.656	0.108	0.109	167	0.874	0.875	0.217	0.219
1	0.749	0.750	0.124	0.125	219	0.999	1.000	0.248	0.250
1 1/8	0.843	0.844	0.140	0.141	277	1.124	1.125	0.279	0.281
1 1/4	0.936	0.937	0.155	0.156	341	1.249	1.250	0.311	0.313
1 3/8	1.030	1.031	0.171	0.172	414	1.374	1.375	0.342	0.344
1 1/2	1.124	1.125	0.186	0.187	491	1.499	1.500	0.373	0.375
1 5/8	1.218	1.219	0.202	0.203	577	1.624	1.625	0.404	0.406
1 3/4	1.311	1.312	0.218	0.219	670	1.749	1.750	0.436	0.438
2	1.498	1.500	0.248	0.250	875	1.998	2.000	0.497	0.500
2 1/4	1.685	1.687	0.279	0.281	1106	2.248	2.250	0.560	0.563
2 1/2	1.873	1.875	0.310	0.312	1365	2.498	2.500	0.622	0.625
3	2.248	2.250	0.373	0.375	1969	2.998	3.000	0.747	0.750

* See note at end of Table 4.

Table 2. S.A.E. Standard Splined Fittings

6 – SPLINE FITTINGS

Nom. Diam.	6A—Permanent Fit			6B—To Slide—No Load			6C—To Slide Under Load		
	d		T *	d		T *	d		T *
	Min.	Max.		Min.	Max.		Min.	Max.	
¾	0.674	0.675	80	0.637	0.638	117	0.599	0.600	152
⅞	0.787	0.788	109	0.743	0.744	159	0.699	0.700	207
1	0.899	0.900	143	0.849	0.850	208	0.799	0.800	270
1⅛	1.012	1.013	180	0.955	0.956	263	0.899	0.900	342
1¼	1.124	1.125	223	1.062	1.063	325	0.999	1.000	421
1⅜	1.237	1.238	269	1.168	1.169	393	1.099	1.100	510
1½	1.349	1.350	321	1.274	1.275	468	1.199	1.200	608
1⅝	1.462	1.463	376	1.380	1.381	550	1.299	1.300	713
1¾	1.574	1.575	436	1.487	1.488	637	1.399	1.400	827
2	1.798	1.800	570	1.698	1.700	833	1.598	1.600	1080
2¼	2.023	2.025	721	1.911	1.913	1052	1.798	1.800	1367
2½	2.248	2.250	891	2.123	2.125	1300	1.998	2.000	1688
3	2.698	2.700	1283	2.548	2.550	1873	2.398	2.400	2430

10 – SPLINE FITTINGS

Nom. Diam.	For All Fits				10A—Permanent Fit		
	D		W		d		T *
	Min.	Max.	Min.	Max.	Min.	Max.	
¾	0.749	0.750	0.115	0.117	0.682	0.683	120
⅞	0.874	0.875	0.135	0.137	0.795	0.796	165
1	0.999	1.000	0.154	0.156	0.909	0.910	215
1⅛	1.124	1.125	0.174	0.176	1.023	1.024	271
1¼	1.249	1.250	0.193	0.195	1.137	1.138	336
1⅜	1.374	1.375	0.213	0.215	1.250	1.251	406
1½	1.499	1.500	0.232	0.234	1.364	1.365	483
1⅝	1.624	1.625	0.252	0.254	1.478	1.479	566
1¾	1.749	1.750	0.271	0.273	1.592	1.593	658
2	1.998	2.000	0.309	0.312	1.818	1.820	860
2¼	2.248	2.250	0.348	0.351	2.046	2.048	1088
2½	2.498	2.500	0.387	0.390	2.273	2.275	1343
3	2.998	3.000	0.465	0.468	2.728	2.730	1934
3½	3.497	3.500	0.543	0.546	3.182	3.185	2632
4	3.997	4.000	0.621	0.624	3.637	3.640	3438
4½	4.497	4.500	0.699	0.702	4.092	4.095	4351
5	4.997	5.000	0.777	0.780	4.547	4.550	5371
5½	5.497	5.500	0.855	0.858	5.002	5.005	6500
6	5.997	6.000	0.933	0.936	5.457	5.460	7735

* See note at end of Table 4.

Table 3. S.A.E. Standard Splined Fittings

	10-SPLINE FITTINGS						
	10B — To Slide — No Load			10C — To Slide Under Load			
Nom. Diam.	*d*		*T* *	*d*		*T* *
	Min.	Max.		Min.	Max.	
¾	0.644	0.645	183	0.607	0.608	241
⅞	0.752	0.753	248	0.708	0.709	329
1	0.859	0.860	326	0.809	0.810	430
1⅛	0.967	0.968	412	0.910	0.911	545
1¼	1.074	1.075	508	1.012	1.013	672
1⅜	1.182	1.183	614	1.113	1.114	813
1½	1.289	1.290	732	1.214	1.215	967
1⅝	1.397	1.398	860	1.315	1.316	1135
1¾	1.504	1.505	997	1.417	1.418	1316
2	1.718	1.720	1302	1.618	1.620	1720
2¼	1.933	1.935	1647	1.821	1.823	2176
2½	2.148	2.150	2034	2.023	2.025	2688
3	2.578	2.580	2929	2.428	2.430	3869
3½	3.007	3.010	3987	2.832	2.835	5266
4	3.437	3.440	5208	3.237	3.240	6878
4½	3.867	3.870	6591	3.642	3.645	8705
5	4.297	4.300	8137	4.047	4.050	10746
5½	4.727	4.730	9846	4.452	4.455	13003
6	5.157	5.160	11718	4.857	4.860	15475

	16-SPLINE FITTINGS						
	For All Fits				16A — Permanent Fit		
Nom. Diam.	*D*		*W*		*d*		*T* *
	Min.	Max.	Min.	Max.	Min.	Max.	
2	1.997	2.000	0.193	0.196	1.817	1.820	1375
2½	2.497	2.500	0.242	0.245	2.273	2.275	2149
3	2.997	3.000	0.291	0.294	2.727	2.730	3094
3½	3.497	3.500	0.340	0.343	3.182	3.185	4212
4	3.997	4.000	0.389	0.392	3.637	3.640	5501
4½	4.497	4.500	0.438	0.441	4.092	4.095	6962
5	4.997	5.000	0.487	0.490	4.547	4.550	8595
5½	5.497	5.500	0.536	0.539	5.002	5.005	10395
6	5.997	6.000	0.585	0.588	5.457	5.460	12377

* See note at end of Table 4.

Table 4.   S.A.E. Standard Splined Fittings

Nom. Diam.	16-SPLINE FITTINGS					
	16B — To Slide — No Load			16C — To Slide Under Load		
	d		T *	d		T *
	Min.	Max.		Min.	Max.	
2	1.717	1.720	2083	1.617	1.620	2751
2½	2.147	2.150	3255	2.022	2.025	4299
3	2.577	2.580	4687	2.427	2.430	6190
3½	3.007	3.010	6378	2.832	2.835	8426
4	3.437	3.440	8333	3.237	3.240	11005
4½	3.867	3.870	10546	3.642	3.645	13928
5	4.297	4.300	13020	4.047	4.050	17195
5½	4.727	4.730	15754	4.452	4.455	20806
6	5.157	5.160	18749	4.857	4.860	24760

* *Torque Capacity of Spline Fittings:* The torque capacities of the different spline fittings
are given in the columns headed "T". The torque capacity, per inch of bearing length
at 1000 pounds pressure per square inch on the sides of the spline, may be determined by
the following formula, in which T = torque capacity in inch-pounds per inch of length,
N = number of splines, R = mean radius or radial distance from center of hole to center
of spline, h = depth of spline:

$$T = 1000\ NRh$$

Table 5.   Formulas for Determining Dimensions of S.A.E. Standard Splines

No. of Splines	W, For All Fits	A Permanent Fit		B To Slide Without Load		C To Slide Under Load	
		h	d	h	d	h	d
Four	0.241D[1]	0.075D	0.850D	0.125D	0.750D	....	....
Six	0.250D	0.050D	0.900D	0.075D	0.850D	0.100D	0.800D
Ten	0.156D	0.045D	0.910D	0.070D	0.860D	0.095D	0.810D
Sixteen	0.098D	0.045D	0.910D	0.070D	0.860D	0.095D	0.810D

These formulas give the maximum dimensions for W, h and d, as listed in Tables 1 to 4
inclusive. (1) Four splines for fits A and B only.

S.A.E. Standard Spline Fittings. — The S.A.E. spline fittings (Tables 1 to 4
inclusive) have become an established standard for many applications in the
automotive, machine tool, and other industries. The dimensions given, in inches,
apply only to soft broached holes. The tolerances given may be readily maintained by usual broaching methods. The tolerances selected for the large and
small diameters may depend upon whether the fit between the mating part, as
finally made, is on the large or the small diameter. The other diameter, which
is designed for clearance, may have a larger manufactured tolerance. If the
final fit between the parts is on the sides of the spline only, larger tolerances are
permissible for both the large and small diameters. The spline should not be
more than 0.006 inch per foot out of parallel with respect to the shaft axis. No
allowance is made for corner radii to obtain clearance. Radii at the corners of
the spline should not exceed 0.015 inch.

Proportions of Square Shafts and Fit Allowances

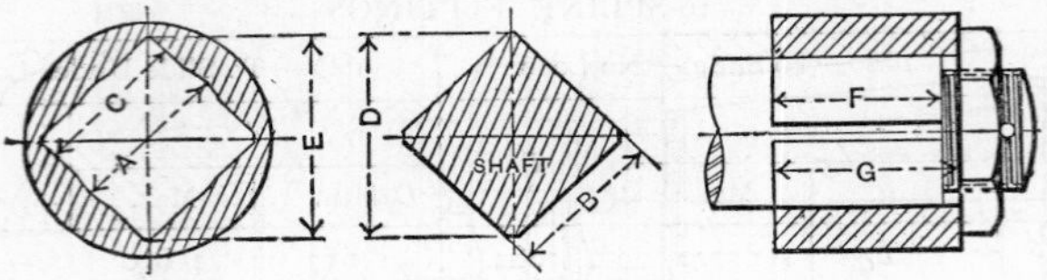

Nominal Diam.	Permanent Fit $\frac{B}{D} = 0.80$							Sliding Fit $\frac{B}{D} = 0.73$				
	A	*B*	*C*	*D*	*E*	*F*	*G*	*A*	*B*	*C*	*D*	*E*
1/4	0.193	0.189 0.188	0.187 0.186	0.250 0.245	0.260 0.252	5/16	3/8	0.257	0.248 0.247	0.250 0.249	0.344 0.339	0.354 0.346
3/8	0.290	0.283 0.282	0.281 0.280	0.375 0.370	0.385 0.377	7/16	1/2	0.386	0.373 0.372	0.375 0.374	0.516 0.511	0.526 0.518
1/2	0.386	0.377 0.376	0.375 0.374	0.500 0.495	0.510 0.502	11/16	3/4	33/64	0.498 0.497	0.500 0.499	0.687 0.682	0.697 0.689
5/8	33/64	0.502 0.501	0.500 0.499	0.625 0.620	0.635 0.627	11/16	3/4	41/64	0.623 0.622	0.625 0.624	0.844 0.839	0.854 0.846
3/4	37/64	0.564 0.563	0.562 0.561	0.750 0.745	0.760 0.752	15/16	1	49/64	0.748 0.747	0.750 0.749	1.031 1.026	1.051 1.036
7/8	45/64	0.689 0.688	0.687 0.686	0.875 0.870	0.885 0.877	1 1/8	1 1/4	29/32	0.873 0.872	0.875 0.874	1.187 1.182	1.207 1.192
1	27/32	0.815 0.814	0.812 0.811	1.000 0.995	1.020 1.005	1 3/8	1 1/2	1 1/32	0.998 0.997	1.000 0.999	1.375 1.370	1.395 1.380
1 1/8	29/32	0.878 0.877	0.875 0.874	1.125 1.120	1.145 1.130	1 3/8	1 1/2	1 5/32	1.123 1.122	1.125 1.124	1.562 1.557	1.582 1.567
1 1/4	1 1/32	1.103 1.102	1.000 0.999	1.250 1.245	1.270 1.255	1 3/8	1 1/2	1 9/32	1.248 1.247	1.250 1.249	1.687 1.682	1.707 1.692
1 3/8	1 5/32	1.128 1.127	1.125 1.124	1.375 1.370	1.395 1.380	1 7/8	2	1 27/64	1.373 1.372	1.375 1.374	1.875 1.870	1.895 1.880
1 1/2	1 5/32	1.128 1.127	1.125 1.124	1.500 1.495	1.520 1.505	1 7/8	2	1 35/64	1.498 1.497	1.500 1.499	2.062 2.057	2.082 2.067
1 3/4	1 27/64	1.378 1.377	1.375 1.374	1.750 1.745	1.770 1.755	2 1/8	2 1/4	1 13/16	1.748 1.747	1.750 1.749	2.375 2.370	2.395 2.380
2	1 35/64	1.504 1.503	1.500 1.498	2.000 1.995	2.020 2.005	2 7/8	3	2 1/16	1.997 1.996	2.000 1.998	2.750 2.745	2.770 2.755
2 1/4	1 13/16	1.754 1.753	1.750 1.748	2.250 2.245	2.270 2.255	2 7/8	3	2 5/16	2.247 2.246	2.250 2.248	3.062 3.057	3.082 3.067
2 1/2	2 1/16	2.004 2.003	2.000 1.998	2.500 2.495	2.520 2.505	3 3/8	3 1/2	2 37/64	2.497 2.496	2.500 2.498	3.437 3.432	3.457 3.442
2 3/4	2 5/16	2.254 2.253	2.250 2.248	2.750 2.745	2.770 2.755	3 3/8	3 1/2	2 55/64	2.747 2.746	2.750 2.748	3.750 3.745	3.770 3.755
3	2 37/64	2.504 2.503	2.500 2.498	3.000 2.995	3.020 3.005	3 7/8	4	3 3/32	2.997 2.996	3.000 2.998	4.125 4.120	4.145 4.130
3 1/2	2 55/64	2.754 2.753	2.750 2.748	3.500 3.495	3.520 3.505	4 3/8	4 1/2	3 39/64	3.497 3.496	3.500 3.498	4.750 4.745	4.770 4.755
4	3 23/64	3.254 3.253	3.250 3.248	4.000 3.995	4.020 4.005	5 3/8	5 1/2	4 1/8	3.997 3.996	4.000 3.998	5.500 5.495	5.520 5.505

Taper Shaft Ends or Fittings with Plain or Slotted Nuts — S.A.E. Standard

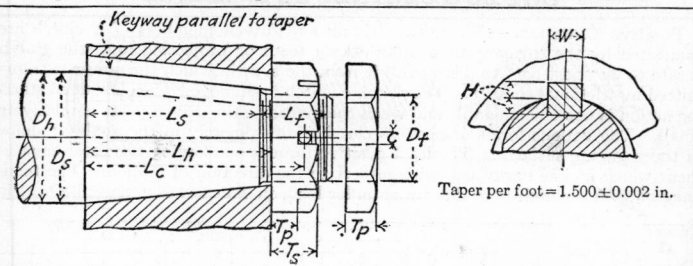

Taper per foot = 1.500±0.002 in.

Nom. Diam.	Diam. of Shaft, D_s		Diam. of Hole, D_h		L_c	L_s	L_h	L_t	D_t	Th'ds per Inch
	max.	min.	max.	min.						
3/8	0.375	0.374	0.373	0.372	47/64	7/16	1/2	23/64	5/16	32
1/2	0.500	0.499	0.498	0.497	63/64	11/16	3/4	23/64	5/16	32
5/8	0.625	0.624	0.623	0.622	1 3/32	11/16	3/4	17/32	1/2	28
3/4	0.750	0.749	0.748	0.747	1 11/32	15/16	1	17/32	1/2	28
7/8	0.875	0.874	0.873	0.872	1 11/16	1 1/8	1 1/4	1 1/16	5/8	24
1	1.001	0.999	0.997	0.995	1 15/16	1 3/8	1 1/2	1 1/16	3/4	20
1 1/8	1.126	1.124	1.122	1.120	1 15/16	1 3/8	1 1/2	1 1/16	7/8	20
1 1/4	1.251	1.249	1.247	1.245	1 15/16	1 3/8	1 1/2	1 1/16	1	20
1 3/8	1.376	1.374	1.372	1.370	2 7/16	1 7/8	2	1 1/16	1	20
1 1/2	1.501	1.499	1.497	1.495	2 7/16	1 7/8	2	1 1/16	1	20
1 5/8	1.626	1.624	1.622	1.620	2 13/16	2 1/8	2 1/4	1 3/16	1 1/4	18
1 3/4	1.751	1.749	1.747	1.745	2 13/16	2 1/8	2 1/4	1 3/16	1 1/4	18
1 7/8	1.876	1.874	1.872	1.870	3 1/16	2 3/8	2 1/2	1 3/16	1 1/4	18
2	2.001	1.999	1.997	1.995	3 9/16	2 7/8	3	1 3/16	1 1/4	18
2 1/4	2.252	2.248	2.245	2.242	3 9/16	2 7/8	3	1 3/16	1 1/2	18
2 1/2	2.502	2.498	2.495	2.492	4 9/32	3 3/8	3 1/2	1 1/4	2	16
2 3/4	2.752	2.748	2.745	2.742	4 9/32	3 3/8	3 1/2	1 1/4	2	16
3	3.002	2.998	2.995	2.992	4 25/32	3 7/8	4	1 1/4	2	16
3 1/4	3.252	3.248	3.245	3.242	5 1/32	4 1/8	4 1/4	1 1/4	2	16
3 1/2	3.502	3.498	3.495	3.492	5 7/16	4 3/8	4 1/2	1 3/8	2 1/2	16
4	4.002	3.998	3.995	3.992	6 7/16	5 3/8	5 1/2	1 3/8	2 1/2	16

Nom. Diam.	T_s	T_p	Width of Nut, Flats	Keyway*				Square Key		C †
				W max.	W min.	H max.	H min.	max.	min.	
3/8	17/64	3/16	1/2	0.0937	0.0927	0.0499	0.0484	0.0947	0.0942	5/64
1/2	17/64	3/16	1/2	0.1250	0.1240	0.0655	0.0640	0.1260	0.1255	5/64
5/8	7/16	1/4	3/4	0.1562	0.1552	0.0811	0.0796	0.1572	0.1567	1/8
3/4	7/16	1/4	3/4	0.1875	0.1865	0.0968	0.0953	0.1885	0.1880	1/8
7/8	1/2	5/16	15/16	0.2500	0.2490	0.1280	0.1265	0.2510	0.2505	5/32
1	1/2	5/16	1 1/16	0.2500	0.2490	0.1280	0.1265	0.2510	0.2505	5/32
1 1/8	1/2	5/16	1 1/4	0.3125	0.3115	0.1615	0.1590	0.3140	0.3130	5/32
1 1/4	1/2	5/16	1 7/16	0.3125	0.3115	0.1615	0.1590	0.3140	0.3130	5/32
1 3/8	1/2	5/16	1 7/16	0.3750	0.3740	0.1930	0.1905	0.3765	0.3755	5/32
1 1/2	1/2	5/16	1 7/16	0.3750	0.3740	0.1930	0.1905	0.3765	0.3755	5/32
1 5/8	5/8	7/16	2 3/16	0.4375	0.4365	0.2242	0.2217	0.4390	0.4380	5/32
1 3/4	5/8	7/16	2 3/16	0.4375	0.4365	0.2242	0.2217	0.4390	0.4380	5/32
1 7/8	5/8	7/16	2 3/16	0.4375	0.4365	0.2242	0.2217	0.4390	0.4380	5/32
2	5/8	7/16	2 3/16	0.5000	0.4990	0.2555	0.2530	0.5015	0.5005	5/32
2 1/4	5/8	7/16	2 3/8	0.5625	0.5610	0.2962	0.2912	0.5645	0.5630	7/32
2 1/2	1	5/8	3 1/8	0.6250	0.6235	0.3275	0.3225	0.6270	0.6255	7/32
2 3/4	1	5/8	3 1/8	0.6875	0.6860	0.3587	0.3537	0.6895	0.6880	7/32
3	1	5/8	3 1/8	0.7500	0.7485	0.3900	0.3850	0.7520	0.7505	7/32
3 1/4	1	5/8	3 1/8	0.7500	0.7485	0.3900	0.3850	0.7520	0.7505	7/32
3 1/2	1 1/8	3/4	3 7/8	0.8750	0.8735	0.4525	0.4475	0.8770	0.8755	9/32
4	1 1/8	3/4	3 7/8	1.0000	0.9985	0.5150	0.5100	1.0020	1.0005	9/32

* Dimensions H of keyway measured normal or perpendicular to key.
† Center-line of cotter-pin hole is 90 degrees from position of keyway as shown on drawing.

CLUTCHES AND COUPLINGS

Positive Clutches. — When the driving and driven members of a clutch are connected by the engagement of interlocking teeth or projecting lugs, the clutch is said to be "positive" to distinguish it from the type in which the power is transmitted by frictional contact. The positive clutch is employed when a sudden starting action is not objectionable and when the inertia of the driven parts is relatively small. The various forms of positive clutches differ merely in the angle or shape of the engaging surfaces. The least positive form is one having planes of engagement which incline backward, with respect to the direction of motion. The tendency of such a clutch is to disengage under load, in which case it must be held in

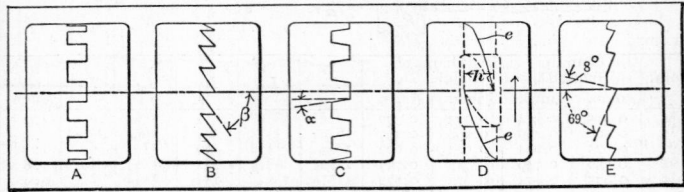

Fig. 1.—Types of Clutch Teeth

position by axial pressure. This pressure may be regulated to perform normal duty, permitting the clutch to slip and disengage when over-loaded. Positive clutches, with the engaging planes parallel to the axis of rotation, are held together to obviate the tendency to jar out of engagement, but they provide no safety feature against over-load. So-called "under-cut" clutches engage more tightly the heavier the load, and are designed to be disengaged only when free from load. The teeth of positive clutches are made in a variety of forms, a few of the more common styles being shown in Fig. 1. Clutch *A* is a straight-toothed type, and *B* has angular

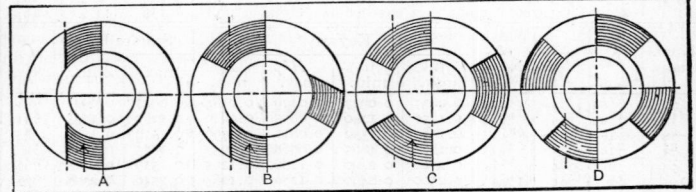

Fig. 2.—Diagrammatical View Showing Method of Cutting Clutch Teeth

or saw-shaped teeth. The driving member of the former can be rotated in either direction; the latter is adapted to the transmission of motion in one direction only, but is more readily engaged. The angle β of the cutter for a saw-tooth clutch *B* is ordinarily 60 degrees. Clutch *C* is similar to *A*, except that the sides of the teeth are inclined to facilitate engagement and disengagement. Teeth of this shape are sometimes used when a clutch is required to run in either direction without backlash. Angle α is varied to suit requirements and should not exceed 8 or 9 degrees. The straight-tooth clutch *A* is also modified to make the teeth engage more readily, by rounding the corners of the teeth at the top and bottom. Clutch *D* (commonly called a "spiral-jaw" clutch) differs from *B* in that the surfaces *e* are helicoidal. The driving member of this clutch can only transmit motion in one direction.

Clutches of this type are known as right- and left-hand, the former driving when turning to the right, as indicated by the arrow in the illustration. Clutch E is the form used on the back-shaft of the Brown & Sharpe automatic screw machines. The faces of the teeth are radial and incline at an angle of 8 degrees with the axis, so that the clutch can readily be disengaged. This type of clutch is easily operated, with little jar or noise. The 2-inch diameter size has 10 teeth. Height of working face, ⅛ inch.

Cutting Clutch Teeth. — A common method of cutting a straight-tooth clutch is indicated by the diagrams A, B and C, Fig. 2, which show the first, second and third cuts required for forming the three teeth. The work is held in the chuck of a dividing-head, the latter being set at right angles to the table. A plain milling

Fig. 3

cutter may be used (unless the corners of the teeth are rounded), the side of the cutter being set to exactly coincide with the center-line. When the number of teeth in the clutch is odd, the cut can be taken clear across the blank as shown, thus finishing the sides of two teeth with one passage of the cutter. When the number of teeth is even, as at D, it is necessary to mill all the teeth on one side and then set the cutter for finishing the opposite side. Therefore, clutches of this type commonly have an odd number of teeth. The maximum width of the cutter depends upon the width of the space at the narrow ends of the teeth If the cutter must be quite narrow in order to pass the narrow ends, some stock may be left in the tooth spaces, which must be removed by a separate cut. If the tooth is of the modified form shown at C, Fig. 1, the cutter should be set as indicated in Fig. 3; that is, so that a point a on

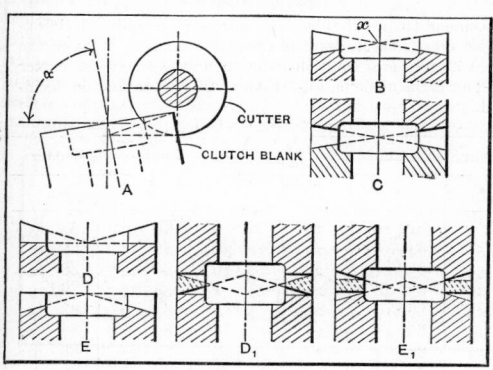

Fig. 4

the cutter at a radial distance d equal to one-half the depth of the clutch teeth lies in a radial plane. When it is important to eliminate all backlash, point a is sometimes located at a radial distance d equal to six-tenths of the depth of the tooth, in order to leave clearance spaces at the bottoms of the teeth; the two clutch members will then fit together tightly. Clutches of this type must be held in mesh.

Cutting Saw-tooth Clutches. — When milling clutches having angular teeth as shown at B, Fig. 1, the axis of the clutch blank should be inclined a certain angle α from the vertical, as shown at A in Fig. 4. If the teeth were milled with the blank vertical, the tops of the teeth would incline towards the center as at D, whereas, if the blank were set to such an angle that the tops of the teeth were square with the axis, the bottoms would incline upwards as at E. In either case, the two clutch members would not mesh completely; the engagement of the teeth cut as shown at D and E would be as indicated at D_1 and E_1 respectively. As will be seen, when the outer points of the teeth at D_1 are at the bottom of the grooves in the opposite member, the inner ends are not together, the contact area being represented by the dotted lines. At E_1 the inner ends of the teeth strike first and spaces are left between the teeth around the outside of the clutch. To overcome this objectionable feature, the clutch teeth should be cut as indicated at B, or so that the bottoms and tops of the teeth have the same inclination, converging at a central point x. The teeth of both members will then engage across the entire width as shown at C. The angle α required for cutting a clutch as at B can be determined by the following formula in which α equals the required angle, and N, the number of teeth;

$$\cos \alpha = \tan \frac{180 \text{ deg.}}{N} \times \cot \text{ cutter angle.}$$

Expressing this formula as a rule: To determine the cosine of angle α (see diagram A, Fig. 4) find the tangent of the angle obtained by dividing 180 degrees by the number of teeth, and multiply this tangent by the cotangent of the cutter angle.

These angles for various numbers of teeth and for either a 60-, 70- or 80-degree single-angle cutter are given in the following table:

Angle of Dividing-head for Milling Clutches with Single-angle Cutter

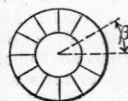

The cosine of the angle to which the milling machine dividing-head is set equals the tangent of one-half of angle β between the teeth (see illustration) multiplied by the cotangent of the cutter angle. This is the angle (a, Fig. 4) shown by graduations on dividing-head.

No. of Teeth	Angle of Single-angle Cutter			No. of Teeth	Angle of Single-angle Cutter		
	60°	70°	80°		60°	70°	80°
5	....	....	82° 12′	18	84° 9′	86° 19′	88° 13′
6	....	77° 52′	84. 9	19	84 30	86 31	88 19
7	73° 50′	79 54	85 10	20	84 46	86 42	88 24
8	76 10	81 20	85 48	21	85 1	86 51	88 29
9	77 52	82 23	86 19	22	85 13	87 0	88 33
10	79 12	83 13	86 43	23	85 27	87 8	88 37
11	80 14	83 54	87 4	24	85 38	87 15	88 40
12	81 6	84 24	87 18	25	85 49	87 22	88 43
13	81 49	84 51	87 30	26	85 59	87 28	88 46
14	82 26	85 12	87 42	27	86 8	87 34	88 50
15	82 57	85 34	87 51	28	86 16	87 39	88 52
16	83 24	85 51	87 59	29	86 24	87 44	88 54
17	83 48	86 6	88 7	30	86 31	87 48	88 56

Friction Clutches. — Clutches which transmit motion from the driving to the driven member by the friction between the engaging surfaces are built in many different designs, although practically all of them can be classified under four general types, namely, conical clutches; radially-expanding clutches; contracting-

Angle of Dividing-head for Milling V-shaped Teeth with Double-angle Cutter

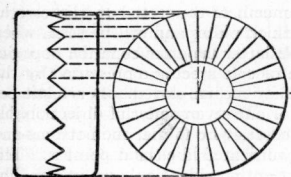

The cosine of the angle to which to set the dividing-head equals the tangent of 90 degrees divided by number of teeth, multiplied by the cotangent of one-half the cutter angle. Thus:

$$\cos \text{ index-head angle} = \tan \frac{90}{N} \times \cot \frac{\text{cutter angle}}{2}$$

This is the angle (*a*, Fig. 4) shown by graduations on the dividing-head.

No. of Teeth	Included Angle of Cutter		No. of Teeth	Included Angle of Cutter	
	60°	90°		60°	90°
10	74° 5′	80° 53′	31	84° 57′	87° 5′
11	75 35	81 53	32	85 6	87 11
12	76 50	82 26	33	85 16	87 16
13	77 52	83 2	34	85 25	87 21
14	78 45	83 32	35	85 32	87 26
15	79 31	83 58	36	85 40	87 30
16	80 11	84 21	37	85 47	87 34
17	80 46	84 41	38	85 54	87 38
18	81 17	84 59	39	86 0	87 42
19	81 45	85 15	40	86 6	87 45
20	82 10	85 29	41	86 12	87 48
21	82 34	85 42	42	86 17	87 51
22	82 53	85 54	43	86 22	87 54
23	83 12	86 5	44	86 27	87 57
24	83 29	86 15	45	86 32	88 0
25	83 45	86 24	46	86 37	88 3
26	84 1	86 32	47	86 41	88 5
27	84 13	86 39	48	86 45	88 8
28	84 25	86 46	49	86 49	88 10
29	84 37	86 53	50	86 53	88 12
30	84 47	86 59	..	.. ..	.. ..

The angles given in the table above are applicable to the milling of V-shaped grooves in brackets, etc., which must have toothed surfaces to prevent the two members from turning relative to each other, except when unclamped for angular adjustment.

band clutches; and friction disk clutches in single and multiple types. There are many modifications of these general classes, some of which combine the features of different types. The proportions of various sizes of cone clutches are given in the table " Cast-iron Friction Clutches." The multi-cone friction clutch is a further development of the cone clutch. Instead of having a single cone-shaped surface, there is a series of concentric conical rings which engage annular grooves formed by corresponding rings on the opposite clutch member. The internal-expanding type is provided with shoes which are forced outward against an enclosing drum by the action of levers connecting with a collar free to slide along the shaft. The engaging shoes are commonly lined with wood to increase the coefficient of friction. The well-known Weston disk clutch is based on the principle of multiple-plane friction. It consists of a series of alternating plates or disks so arranged that one set engages with an outside cylindrical case and the other set with the shaft. When these plates are pressed together by spring pressure, or by other means, motion is transmitted from the driving to the driven members connected to the clutch. Some disk clutches have a few rather heavy or thick plates and others a relatively large number of thinner plates. Clutches of the latter type are common in automobile construction. One set of disks may be of soft steel and the other set of phosphor-bronze, or some other combination may be employed. For instance, disks are sometimes provided with cork inserts, or one set or series of disks may be faced with a special friction material such as asbestos-wire fabric, as in the case of "dry plate" clutches, the disks of which are not lubricated like the disks of a clutch having, for example, the steel and phosphor-bronze combination. It is common practice to hold the driving and driven members of friction clutches into engagement by means of spring pressure, although pneumatic and hydraulic pressure is sometimes employed.

Cast-iron Friction Clutches

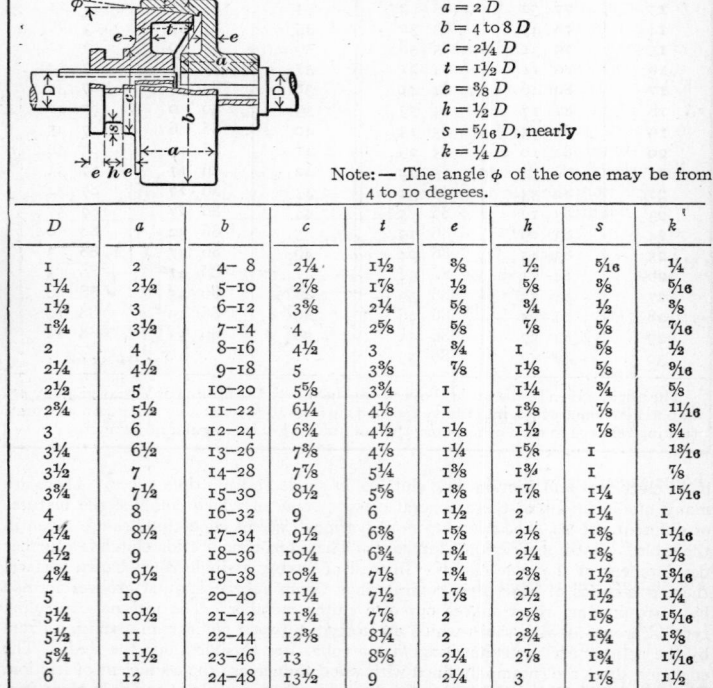

For sizes not given below:

$a = 2 D$
$b = 4$ to $8 D$
$c = 2\frac{1}{4} D$
$t = 1\frac{1}{2} D$
$e = \frac{3}{8} D$
$h = \frac{1}{2} D$
$s = \frac{5}{16} D$, nearly
$k = \frac{1}{4} D$

Note: — The angle ϕ of the cone may be from 4 to 10 degrees.

D	a	b	c	t	e	h	s	k
1	2	4– 8	2¼	1½	⅜	½	⁵⁄₁₆	¼
1¼	2½	5–10	2⅞	1⅞	½	⅝	⅜	⁵⁄₁₆
1½	3	6–12	3⅜	2¼	⅝	¾	½	⅜
1¾	3½	7–14	4	2⅝	⅝	⅞	⅝	⁷⁄₁₆
2	4	8–16	4½	3	¾	1	⅝	½
2¼	4½	9–18	5	3⅜	⅞	1⅛	⅝	⁹⁄₁₆
2½	5	10–20	5⅝	3¾	1	1¼	¾	⅝
2¾	5½	11–22	6¼	4⅛	1	1⅜	⅞	¹¹⁄₁₆
3	6	12–24	6¾	4½	1⅛	1½	⅞	¾
3¼	6½	13–26	7⅜	4⅞	1¼	1⅝	1	¹³⁄₁₆
3½	7	14–28	7⅞	5¼	1⅜	1¾	1	⅞
3¾	7½	15–30	8½	5⅝	1⅜	1⅞	1¼	¹⁵⁄₁₆
4	8	16–32	9	6	1½	2	1¼	1
4¼	8½	17–34	9½	6⅜	1⅝	2⅛	1⅜	1¹⁄₁₆
4½	9	18–36	10¼	6¾	1¾	2¼	1⅜	1⅛
4¾	9½	19–38	10¾	7⅛	1¾	2⅜	1½	1³⁄₁₆
5	10	20–40	11¼	7½	1⅞	2½	1½	1¼
5¼	10½	21–42	11¾	7⅞	2	2⅝	1⅝	1⁵⁄₁₆
5½	11	22–44	12⅜	8¼	2	2¾	1¾	1⅜
5¾	11½	23–46	13	8⅝	2¼	2⅞	1¾	1⁷⁄₁₆
6	12	24–48	13½	9	2¼	3	1⅞	1½

Power Transmitting Capacity of Friction Clutches. — When selecting a clutch for a given class of service, it is advisable to consider any overloads that may be encountered and base the power transmitting capacity of the clutch upon such overloads. When the load varies or is subject to frequent release or engagement, the clutch capacity should be greater than the actual amount of power transmitted. If the power is derived from a gas or gasoline engine, the horse-power rating of the clutch should be 75 or 100 per cent greater than that of the engine.

Formulas for Cone Clutches. — In cone clutch design, different formulas have been developed for determining the horsepower transmitted. These formulas, at first sight, do not seem to agree, there being a variation due to the fact that in some of the formulas the friction clutch surfaces are assumed to engage without slip, whereas, in others, some allowance is made for slip. The following formulas include both of these conditions:

H.P. = horsepower transmitted;
N = revolutions per minute;
r = mean radius of friction cone, in inches;
r_1 = large radius of friction cone, in inches;
r_2 = small radius of friction cone, in inches;
R_1 = outside radius of leather band, in inches;
R_2 = inside radius of leather band, in inches;
V = velocity of a point at distance r from the center, in feet per minute;

F = tangential force acting at radius r, in pounds;
P_n = total normal pressure between cone surfaces, in pounds;
P_s = spring pressure, in pounds;
α = angle of clutch surface with axis of shaft = 7 to 13 degrees;
β = included angle of clutch leather, when developed, in degrees;
f = coefficient of friction = 0.20 to 0.25 for greasy leather on iron;
p = allowable pressure per square inch of leather band = 7 to 8 pounds;
W = width of clutch leather, in inches.

$$R_1 = \frac{r_1}{\sin \alpha} \qquad R_2 = \frac{r_2}{\sin \alpha}$$

$$\beta = \sin \alpha \times 360 \qquad r = \frac{r_1 + r_2}{2}$$

$$V = \frac{2\pi r N}{12}$$

$$F = \frac{\text{H.P.} \times 33{,}000}{V} \qquad W = \frac{P_n}{2\pi r p} \qquad \text{H.P.} = \frac{P_n f r N}{63{,}025}$$

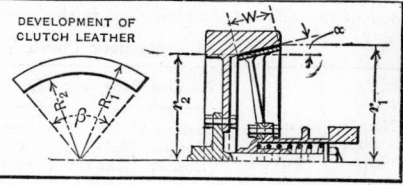

DEVELOPMENT OF CLUTCH LEATHER

For engagement with some slip:

$$P_n = \frac{P_s}{\sin \alpha} \qquad P_s = \frac{\text{H.P.} \times 63{,}025 \sin \alpha}{f r N}$$

For engagement without slip:

$$P_n = \frac{P_s}{\sin \alpha + f \cos \alpha} \qquad P_s = \frac{\text{H.P.} \times 63{,}025 \,(\sin \alpha + f \cos \alpha)}{f r N}$$

Angle of Cone. — If the angle of the conical surface of the cone type of clutch is too small, it may be difficult to release the clutch on account of the wedging effect, whereas, if the angle is too large, excessive spring pressure will be required to prevent slipping. The minimum angle for a leather-faced cone is about 8 or 9 degrees and the maximum angle about 13 degrees. An angle of 12½ degrees appears to be the most common and is generally considered good practice. These angles are given with relation to the clutch axis and are one-half the included angle.

Power Transmitted by Disk Clutches. — The approximate amount of power that a disk clutch will transmit may be determined from the following formula, in which H = horsepower transmitted by the clutch: μ = coefficient of friction; r = mean radius of engaging surfaces; F = axial force in pounds (spring pressure) holding disks in contact; N = number of frictional surfaces; S = speed of shaft in revolutions per minute:

$$H = \frac{\mu r F N S}{63,000}$$

Frictional Coefficients for Clutch Calculations. — While the frictional coefficients used by designers of clutches differ somewhat and depend upon variable factors, the following values may be used in clutch calculations: For greasy leather on cast iron about 0.20 or 0.25; leather on metal that is quite oily 0.15; metal and cork on oily metal 0.32; the same on dry metal 0.35; metal on dry metal 0.15; disk clutches having lubricated surfaces 0.10.

Magnetic Clutches. — Clutches of the magnetic type, like other electrical apparatus, are adapted to remote and automatic control. They are especially applicable for high-speed drives; for heavy duty; for use with motors that cannot start heavy loads; and for stopping machinery quickly, in which case a brake is used in combination with the clutch. The Cutler-Hammer magnetic clutch has a field or driving member and an armature or driven member. Each of these parts is carried by a flexible spring steel plate so that when current passes through the winding of the field, the armature is attracted to it and the friction surfaces come into engagement. The turning power of the clutch depends entirely upon the friction surfaces which are held together by magnetic attraction. Current is conducted to the magnetizing winding of the field through two collector rings and graphite brushes. These clutches are operated by direct current. The ratings of some of the different sizes are given in the accompanying table.

Magnetic Clutch Ratings *

Nominal Size, Inches	Maximum Speed, R.P.M.	Ratings Type H-30 Clutches			Ratings Type H-60 Clutches		
		Maximum Torque, Lbs. at 1 Ft. Radius	Safe H.P. at 100 R.P.M.	Current Consumption, Watts	Maximum Torque, Lbs. at 1 Ft. Radius	Safe H.P. at 100 R.P.M.	Current Consumption, Watts
10	2000	89	1.1	78	....	....	......
12	1680	154	2.0	93	....	....	......
14	1440	245	3.0	115	490	6	130
16	1260	366	4.5	133	732	9	160
20	1000	714	9.0	177	1,428	18	200
24	840	1233	15.5	260	2,466	31	247
28	725	1960	25.0	280	3,920	49	253
32	635	2920	37.0	315	5,840	74	250
40	500	5710	72.0	380	10,420	132	341
48	420	9860	124.0	460	19,720	250	400
60	340	....	......	......	38,600	485	645

* Cutler-Hammer Mfg. Co.

Safety Flange Couplings

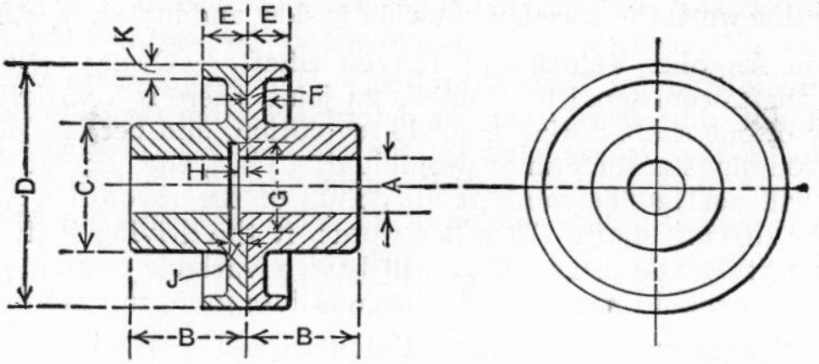

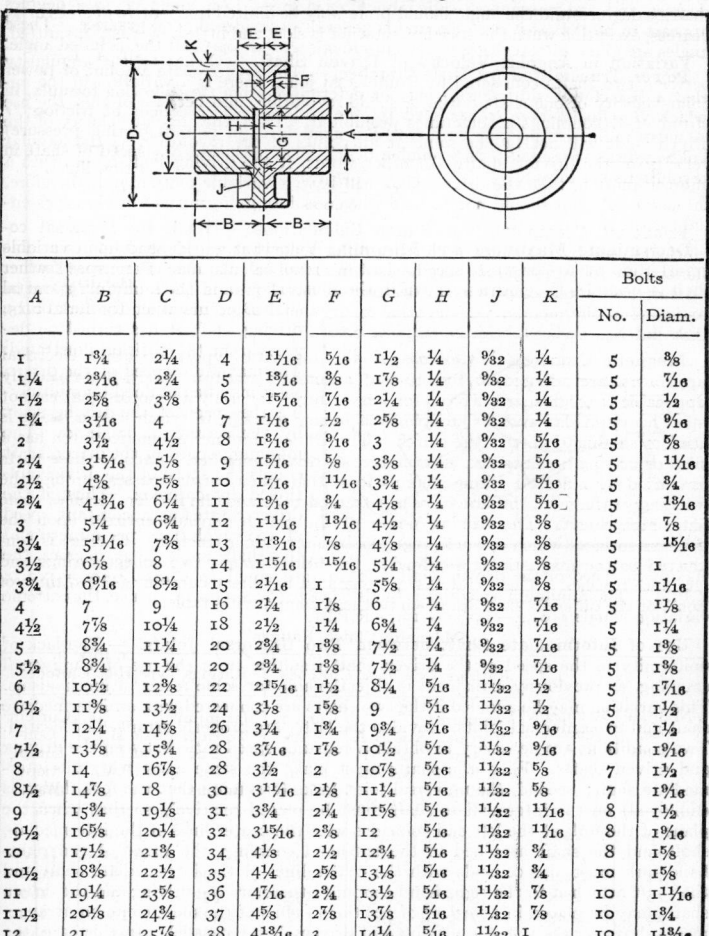

A	*B*	*C*	*D*	*E*	*F*	*G*	*H*	*J*	*K*	Bolts	
										No.	Diam.
1	1 3/4	2 1/4	4	11/16	5/16	1 1/2	1/4	9/32	1/4	5	3/8
1 1/4	2 3/16	2 3/4	5	13/16	3/8	1 7/8	1/4	9/32	1/4	5	7/16
1 1/2	2 5/8	3 3/8	6	15/16	7/16	2 1/4	1/4	9/32	1/4	5	1/2
1 3/4	3 1/16	4	7	1 1/16	1/2	2 5/8	1/4	9/32	1/4	5	9/16
2	3 1/2	4 1/2	8	1 3/16	9/16	3	1/4	9/32	5/16	5	5/8
2 1/4	3 15/16	5 1/8	9	1 5/16	5/8	3 3/8	1/4	9/32	5/16	5	11/16
2 1/2	4 3/8	5 5/8	10	1 7/16	11/16	3 3/4	1/4	9/32	5/16	5	3/4
2 3/4	4 13/16	6 1/4	11	1 9/16	3/4	4 1/8	1/4	9/32	5/16	5	13/16
3	5 1/4	6 3/4	12	1 11/16	13/16	4 1/2	1/4	9/32	3/8	5	7/8
3 1/4	5 11/16	7 3/8	13	1 13/16	7/8	4 7/8	1/4	9/32	3/8	5	15/16
3 1/2	6 1/8	8	14	1 15/16	15/16	5 1/4	1/4	9/32	3/8	5	1
3 3/4	6 9/16	8 1/2	15	2 1/16	1	5 5/8	1/4	9/32	3/8	5	1 1/16
4	7	9	16	2 1/4	1 1/8	6	1/4	9/32	7/16	5	1 1/8
4 1/2	7 7/8	10 1/4	18	2 1/2	1 1/4	6 3/4	1/4	9/32	7/16	5	1 1/4
5	8 3/4	11 1/4	20	2 3/4	1 3/8	7 1/2	1/4	9/32	7/16	5	1 3/8
5 1/2	8 3/4	11 1/4	20	2 3/4	1 3/8	7 1/2	1/4	9/32	7/16	5	1 3/8
6	10 1/2	12 3/8	22	2 15/16	1 1/2	8 1/4	5/16	11/32	1/2	5	1 7/16
6 1/2	11 3/8	13 1/2	24	3 1/8	1 5/8	9	5/16	11/32	1/2	5	1 1/2
7	12 1/4	14 5/8	26	3 1/4	1 3/4	9 3/4	5/16	11/32	9/16	6	1 1/2
7 1/2	13 1/8	15 3/4	28	3 7/16	1 7/8	10 1/2	5/16	11/32	9/16	6	1 9/16
8	14	16 7/8	28	3 1/2	2	10 7/8	5/16	11/32	5/8	7	1 1/2
8 1/2	14 7/8	18	30	3 11/16	2 1/8	11 1/4	5/16	11/32	5/8	7	1 9/16
9	15 3/4	19 1/8	31	3 3/4	2 1/4	11 5/8	5/16	11/32	11/16	8	1 1/2
9 1/2	16 5/8	20 1/4	32	3 15/16	2 3/8	12	5/16	11/32	11/16	8	1 9/16
10	17 1/2	21 3/8	34	4 1/8	2 1/2	12 3/4	5/16	11/32	3/4	8	1 5/8
10 1/2	18 3/8	22 1/2	35	4 1/4	2 5/8	13 1/8	5/16	11/32	3/4	10	1 5/8
11	19 1/4	23 5/8	36	4 7/16	2 3/4	13 1/2	5/16	11/32	7/8	10	1 11/16
11 1/2	20 1/8	24 3/4	37	4 5/8	2 7/8	13 7/8	5/16	11/32	7/8	10	1 3/4
12	21	25 7/8	38	4 13/16	3	14 1/4	5/16	11/32	1	10	1 13/16

The Universal Joint. — This form of coupling, originally known as Hooke's coupling, is used for connecting two shafts the axes of which are not in line with each other, but which merely intersect at a point. There are many different designs of universal joints or couplings, which are based on the principle embodied in the original design. One well-known type is shown by the accompanying diagram.

As a rule, a universal joint does not work well if the angle α (see illustration) is more than 45 degrees, and the angle should preferably be limited to about 20 degrees or 25 degrees, excepting when the speed of rotation is slow and little power is transmitted.

Variation in Angular Velocity of Driven Shaft. — Owing to the angularity between two shafts connected by a universal joint, there is a variation in the angular velocity of one shaft during a single revolution, and because of this, the use of universal couplings is sometimes prohibited. Thus, the angular velocity of the driven shaft will not be the same at all points of the revolution as the angular velocity of the driving shaft. In other words, if the driving shaft moves with a uniform motion, then the driven shaft will have a variable motion and, therefore, the universal joint should not be used when absolute uniformity of motion is essential for the driven shaft.

Determining Maximum and Minimum Velocities. — If shaft A (see diagram) runs at a constant speed, shaft B revolves at maximum speed when shaft A occupies the position shown in the illustration, and the minimum speed of shaft B occurs when the fork of the

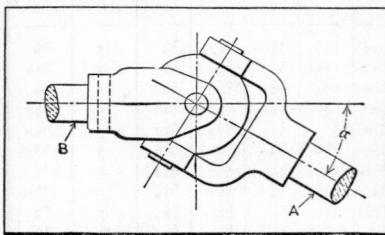

driving shaft A has turned 90 degrees from the position illustrated. The maximum speed of the driven shaft may be obtained by multiplying the speed of the driving shaft by the secant of angle α. The minimum speed of the driven shaft equals the speed of the driver multiplied by cosine α. Thus, if the driver rotates at a constant speed of 100 revolutions per minute and the shaft angle is 25 degrees, the maximum speed of the driven shaft is at a rate equal to $1.1034 \times 100 = 110.34$ R.P.M. The minimum speed rate equals $0.9063 \times 100 = 90.63$; hence, the extreme variation equals $110.34 - 90.63 = 19.71$ R.P.M.

Use of Intermediate Shaft between Two Universal Joints. — The lack of uniformity in the speed of the driven shaft resulting from the use of a universal coupling, as previously explained, is objectionable for some forms of mechanisms. This variation may be avoided if the two shafts are connected with an intermediate shaft and two universal joints, provided the latter are properly arranged or located. Two conditions are necessary to obtain a constant speed ratio between the driving and driven shafts. First, the shafts must make the same angle with the intermediate shaft; second, the universal joint forks (assuming that the fork design is employed) on the intermediate shaft must be placed relatively so that when the plane of the fork at the left end coincides with the center lines of the intermediate shaft and the shaft attached to the left-hand coupling, the plane of the right-hand fork must also coincide with the center lines of the intermediate shaft and the shaft attached to the right-hand coupling; therefore the driving and the driven shafts may be placed in a variety of positions. One of the most common arrangements, however, is with the driving and driven shafts parallel. In this case, the forks on the intermediate shafts should be placed in the same plane.

This intermediate connecting shaft is frequently made telescoping, and then the driving and driven shafts can be moved independently of each other within certain limits in longitudinal and lateral directions. The telescoping intermediate shaft consists of a rod which enters a sleeve and is provided with a suitable spline, to prevent rotation between the rod and sleeve and permit a sliding movement. This arrangement is applied to various machine tools.

Proportions of Knuckle Joints

For sizes not given below:

$a = 1.2 D$	$h = 2 D$
$b = 1.1 D$	$i = 0.5 D$
$c = 1.2 D$	$j = 0.25 D$
$e = 0.75 D$	$k = 0.5 D$
$f = 0.6 D$	$l = 1.5 D$
$g = 1.5 D$	

D	a	b	c	e	f	g	h	i	j	k	l
1/2	5/8	9/16	5/8	3/8	5/16	3/4	1	1/4	1/8	1/4	3/4
3/4	7/8	3/4	7/8	9/16	7/16	1 1/8	1 1/2	3/8	3/16	3/8	1 1/8
1	1 1/4	1 1/8	1 1/4	3/4	5/8	1 1/2	2	1/2	1/4	1/2	1 1/2
1 1/4	1 1/2	1 3/8	1 1/2	15/16	3/4	1 7/8	2 1/2	5/8	5/16	5/8	1 7/8
1 1/2	1 3/4	1 5/8	1 3/4	1 1/8	7/8	2 1/4	3	3/4	3/8	3/4	2 1/4
1 3/4	2 1/8	2	2 1/8	1 5/16	1 1/16	2 5/8	3 1/2	7/8	7/16	7/8	2 5/8
2	2 3/8	2 1/4	2 3/8	1 1/2	1 3/16	3	4	1	1/2	1	3
2 1/4	2 3/4	2 1/2	2 3/4	1 11/16	1 3/8	3 3/8	4 1/2	1 1/8	9/16	1 1/8	3 3/8
2 1/2	3	2 3/4	3	1 7/8	1 1/2	3 3/4	5	1 1/4	5/8	1 1/4	3 3/4
2 3/4	3 1/4	3	3 1/4	2 1/16	1 5/8	4 1/8	5 1/2	1 3/8	11/16	1 3/8	4 1/8
3	3 5/8	3 1/4	3 5/8	2 1/4	1 13/16	4 1/2	6	1 1/2	3/4	1 1/2	4 1/2
3 1/4	4	3 5/8	4	2 7/16	2	4 7/8	6 1/2	1 5/8	13/16	1 5/8	4 7/8
3 1/2	4 1/4	3 7/8	4 1/4	2 5/8	2 1/8	5 1/4	7	1 3/4	7/8	1 3/4	5 1/4
3 3/4	4 1/2	4 1/8	4 1/2	2 13/16	2 1/4	5 5/8	7 1/2	1 7/8	15/16	1 7/8	5 5/8
4	4 3/4	4 3/8	4 3/4	3	2 3/8	6	8	2	1	2	6
4 1/4	5 1/8	4 3/4	5 1/8	3 3/16	2 9/16	6 3/8	8 1/2	2 1/8	1 1/16	2 1/8	6 3/8
4 1/2	5 1/2	5	5 1/2	3 3/8	2 3/4	6 3/4	9	2 1/4	1 1/8	2 1/4	6 3/4
4 3/4	5 3/4	5 1/4	5 3/4	3 9/16	2 7/8	7 1/8	9 1/2	2 3/8	1 3/16	2 3/8	7 1/8
5	6	5 1/2	6	3 3/4	3	7 1/2	10	2 1/2	1 1/4	2 1/2	7 1/2

Flexible Couplings. — Flexible couplings are used mostly for coupling together electrical machinery or for coupling electrical to other machinery. The general types of flexible couplings include the leather link coupling, the endless belt coupling, and the rubber buffer coupling. The leather link coupling consists of two iron castings with flanges which are connected by leather links and bolts. The bolts are generally six in number and each alternate bolt is tightly fitted in the flange of one casting, but has considerable play in the other. The leather links are placed around pairs of adjacent bolts and provide a slight flexibility for the drive. This coupling is adapted for shafts up to 3½ inches in diameter. The endless belt flexible coupling is adapted for shafts of larger diameter. It consists of two steel rings, one outer and one inner, in which slots are formed and through which two endless leather belts are interwoven. The rubber buffer coupling is formed of two disks; the driving side transmits motion to the driven side by means of studs, bolts or interlocking arms surrounded by heavy rubber bushings which give the necessary flexibility. The "mill type" flexible coupling, which is used chiefly in steel mills, is formed of three steel castings and is adapted to severe service.

American Standard Shaft Couplings*

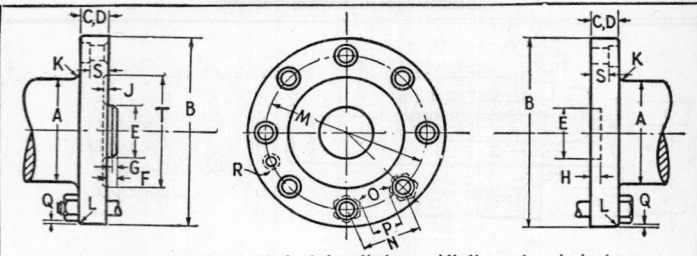

J = 1/32 inch and *G* = 1/16 inch for all sizes.   All dimensions in inches.

Diam. Shaft A	Diam. Flange B	Thickness of Flange		Diam. E*	Height Above Face F	Depth Below Face H	Diam. Relief T	Radius Fillet K	Radius Corner L*
		C*	D						
3½	7½	⅞	⅞	2⅛	3/16	¼	.....	3/16	1/16
4	8½	1	1	2⅜	3/16	¼	.....	3/16	1/16
4½	9	1⅛	1⅛	2¾	3/16	¼	.....	3/16	1/16
5	10¼	1¼	1¼	3	3/16	¼	.....	3/16	1/16
5½	10⅞	1⅜	1⅜	3¼	3/16	¼	.....	¼	1/16
6	11½	1½	1½	3⅝	3/16	¼	6⅝	¼	1/16
6½	12¾	1⅝	1⅝	3⅞	3/16	¼	7⅛	¼	1/16
7	13½	1¾	1¾	4¼	¼	5/16	7¾	⅜	3/32
7½	14	1⅞	1¾	4½	¼	5/16	8¼	⅜	3/32
8	15	2	1⅞	4¾	¼	5/16	8¾	½	3/32
8½	15½	2⅛	1⅞	5⅛	¼	5/16	9⅜	½	3/32
9	16¼	2¼	2	5⅜	¼	5/16	9⅞	⅝	3/32
10	18	2½	2¼	6	¼	5/16	11	¾	3/32

Diam. Shaft A	Diam. Bolt Circle M	Center Distance, Bolts N	Coupling Bolts O		Size of Nuts	Min. Distance Between Nuts P	Clearance for Nut Guard Q	Jack Bolts R	
			Number Bolts	Body Diam.				Number	Size
3½	5⅝	2.81	6	⅞	⅞	1.16	0.107	.....	.....
4	6¼	3.12	6	⅞	⅞	1.47	0.107	.....	.....
4½	6⅞	3.43	6	1	1	1.56	0.124	.....	.....
5	7¾	3.87	6	1¼	1¼	1.56	0.095	.....	.....
5½	8⅜	4.18	6	1¼	1¼	1.87	0.095	.....	.....
6	9	3.44	8	1¼	1¼	1.13	0.095	.....	.....
6½	9¾	4.87	6	1½	1½	2.13	0.128	.....	.....
7	10½	4.02	8	1½	1½	1.28	0.129	2	¾
7½	11	4.21	8	1½	1½	1.50	0.13	2	¾
8	12	4.59	8	1¾	1½	1.84	0.13	2	¾
8½	12½	4.78	8	1¾	1½	2.04	0.13	2	¾
9	13¼	4.10	10	1¾	1½	1.36	0.13	2	¾
10	14½	4.48	10	2	1¾	1.29	0.16	2	¾

*Integrally forged flange type for hydro-electric units.   Complete standard includes sizes up to 40 inches shaft diameter.   Flange thicknesses C are for shafts subject to bending.
Fitting allowance on dimension E for male half-coupling shall be −0.001 inch.   Radius L omitted when a nut guard is furnished.   When outside diameter of nut guard is equal to flange diameter B a recess is provided in place of radius L.   For bolt sizes under 1 inch, use American National Standard, Fine-Thread Series; for sizes 1 inch to 2 inches inclusive, 8 threads per inch; for sizes over 2 inches, 6 threads per inch.   Jack bolts furnished with horizontal shafts only and provided in the male half-coupling.

Double-cone Clamping Coupling

A	B	C	D	E	F	G	H	J	K	L	M	No. of Bolts	No. of Keys
$1\frac{7}{16}$	$5\frac{1}{4}$	$2\frac{3}{4}$	$2\frac{1}{8}$	$1\frac{5}{8}$	$\frac{5}{8}$	$2\frac{1}{8}$	$4\frac{3}{4}$	$1\frac{1}{8}$	1	5	$\frac{1}{2}$	3	1
$1\frac{15}{16}$	7	$3\frac{1}{2}$	$2\frac{7}{8}$	$2\frac{1}{8}$	$\frac{5}{8}$	$2\frac{3}{4}$	$6\frac{1}{4}$	$1\frac{1}{8}$	$1\frac{3}{8}$	$6\frac{1}{4}$	$\frac{1}{2}$	3	1
$2\frac{7}{16}$	$8\frac{3}{4}$	$4\frac{5}{16}$	$3\frac{5}{8}$	3	$\frac{3}{4}$	$3\frac{1}{2}$	$7\frac{13}{16}$	$1\frac{7}{8}$	$1\frac{3}{4}$	$7\frac{7}{8}$	$\frac{5}{8}$	3	1
3	$10\frac{1}{2}$	$5\frac{1}{2}$	$4\frac{3}{32}$	$3\frac{1}{2}$	$\frac{3}{4}$	$4\frac{3}{16}$	9	$2\frac{1}{4}$	2	$9\frac{1}{2}$	$\frac{5}{8}$	3	1
$3\frac{1}{2}$	$12\frac{1}{4}$	7	$5\frac{3}{8}$	$4\frac{3}{8}$	$\frac{7}{8}$	$5\frac{1}{16}$	$11\frac{1}{4}$	$2\frac{5}{8}$	$2\frac{1}{8}$	$11\frac{1}{4}$	$\frac{3}{4}$	4	1
4	14	7	$5\frac{1}{2}$	$4\frac{3}{4}$	$\frac{7}{8}$	$5\frac{1}{2}$	12	$3\frac{3}{4}$	$2\frac{1}{2}$	12	$\frac{3}{4}$	4	1
$4\frac{1}{2}$	$15\frac{1}{2}$	8	$6\frac{7}{8}$	$5\frac{1}{4}$	$\frac{7}{8}$	$6\frac{3}{4}$	$13\frac{1}{2}$	$3\frac{3}{4}$	$2\frac{3}{4}$	$14\frac{1}{2}$	$\frac{3}{4}$	4	1
5	17	9	$7\frac{1}{4}$	$5\frac{3}{4}$	$\frac{7}{8}$	7	15	$3\frac{3}{4}$	3	$15\frac{1}{4}$	$\frac{3}{4}$	4	1
$5\frac{1}{2}$	$17\frac{1}{2}$	$9\frac{1}{2}$	$7\frac{3}{4}$	$6\frac{1}{4}$	1	7	$15\frac{1}{2}$	$3\frac{3}{4}$	3	$15\frac{1}{4}$	$\frac{7}{8}$	4	1
6	18	10	$8\frac{1}{4}$	$6\frac{3}{4}$	1	7	16	$3\frac{3}{4}$	3	$15\frac{1}{4}$	$\frac{7}{8}$	4	2

FRICTION BRAKES

Formulas for Band Brakes. — In any band brake, such as shown in **Fig. 1,** in the tabulation of the formulas, where the brake wheel rotates in a **clockwise** direction, the tension in that part of the band marked x equals $P\,\dfrac{1}{e^{\mu\theta}-1}$

The tension in that part marked y equals $P\,\dfrac{e^{\mu\theta}}{e^{\mu\theta}-1}$

> P = tangential force in pounds at rim of brake wheel;
> e = base of natural logarithms = 2.71828;
> μ = coefficient of friction between the brake band and the **brake wheel;**
> θ = angle of contact of the brake band with the brake wheel **expressed in**
>   radians (one radian = $\dfrac{180 \text{ deg.}}{\pi}$ = 57.296 degrees).

For simplicity in the formulas presented, the tensions at x and y (Fig. 1) **are** denoted by T_1 and T_2 respectively, for clockwise rotation. When the direction of the rotation is reversed, the tension in x equals T_2, and the tension in y equals T_1, which is the reverse of the tension in the clockwise direction.

The value of the expression $e^{\mu\theta}$ in these formulas may be most easily solved **by** means of logarithms. The value of $e^{\mu\theta}$ is found by multiplying the logarithm of e by the product of the numerical values of μ and θ, and finding the number whose logarithm is equal to the result of this multiplication. The procedure may be best illustrated by an example.

Formulas for Simple and Differential Band Brakes

F = force in pounds at end of brake handle; P = tangential force in pounds at rim of brake wheel; e = base of natural logarithms = 2.71828; μ = coefficient of friction between the brake band and the brake wheel; θ = angle of contact of the brake band with the brake wheel, expressed in radians (one radian = $\frac{180°}{\pi}$ = 57.296 degrees).

$$T_1 = P\frac{1}{e^{\mu\theta} - 1} \qquad\qquad T_2 = P\frac{e^{\mu\theta}}{e^{\mu\theta} - 1}$$

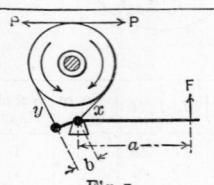

Fig. 1

Simple band brake.
For clockwise rotation:
$$F = \frac{bT_2}{a} = \frac{Pb}{a}\left(\frac{e^{\mu\theta}}{e^{\mu\theta} - 1}\right)$$
For counter clockwise rotation:
$$F = \frac{bT_1}{a} = \frac{Pb}{a}\left(\frac{1}{e^{\mu\theta} - 1}\right)$$

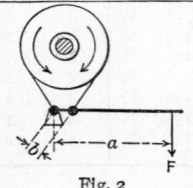

Fig. 2

Simple band brake.
For clockwise rotation:
$$F = \frac{bT_1}{a} = \frac{Pb}{a}\left(\frac{1}{e^{\mu\theta} - 1}\right)$$
For counter clockwise rotation:
$$F = \frac{bT_2}{a} = \frac{Pb}{a}\left(\frac{e^{\mu\theta}}{e^{\mu\theta} - 1}\right)$$

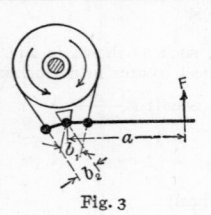

Fig. 3

Differential band brake.
For clockwise rotation:
$$F = \frac{b_2T_2 - b_1T_1}{a} = \frac{P}{a}\left(\frac{b_2e^{\mu\theta} - b_1}{e^{\mu\theta} - 1}\right)$$
For counter clockwise rotation:
$$F = \frac{b_2T_1 - b_1T_2}{a} = \frac{P}{a}\left(\frac{b_2 - b_1e^{\mu\theta}}{e^{\mu\theta} - 1}\right)$$
In this case, if b_2 is equal to, or less than, $b_1e^{\mu\theta}$, the force F will be 0 or negative and the band brake works automatically.

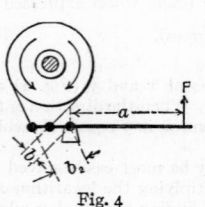

Fig. 4

Differential band brake.
For clockwise rotation:
$$F = \frac{b_2T_2 + b_1T_1}{a} = \frac{P}{a}\left(\frac{b_2e^{\mu\theta} + b_1}{e^{\mu\theta} - 1}\right)$$
For counter clockwise rotation:
$$F = \frac{b_1T_2 + b_2T_1}{a} = \frac{P}{a}\left(\frac{b_1e^{\mu\theta} + b_2}{e^{\mu\theta} - 1}\right)$$
If $b_2 = b_1$, both of the above formulas reduce to
$$F = \frac{Pb_1}{a}\left(\frac{e^{\mu\theta} + 1}{e^{\mu\theta} - 1}\right).$$ In this case, the same force F is required for rotation in either direction.

In a band brake of the type in Fig. 1, dimension $a = 24$ inches, and $b = 4$ inches; force $P = 100$ pounds; coefficient $\mu = 0.2$, and angle of contact = 240 degrees, or

$$\theta = \frac{240}{180} \times \pi = 4.18.$$

The rotation is clockwise. Find force F required.

$$F = \frac{Pb}{a}\left(\frac{e^{\mu\theta}}{e^{\mu\theta}-1}\right) = \frac{100 \times 4}{24}\left(\frac{2.71828^{0.2\times4.18}}{2.71828^{0.2\times4.18}-1}\right)$$

$$= \frac{400}{24} \times \frac{2.71828^{0.836}}{2.71828^{0.836}-1} = 16.66 \times \frac{2.31}{2.31-1} = 29.4.$$

The calculations for determining the value of $e^{\mu\theta}$ are rather cumbersome, and the accompanying table will save calculations.

Table of Values of $e^{\mu\theta}$

Proportion of Contact to Whole Circumference, $\dfrac{\theta}{2\pi}$	Steel Band on Cast Iron, $\mu = 0.18$	Leather Belt on			
		Wood	Cast Iron		
		Slightly Greasy; $\mu = 0.47$	Very Greasy; $\mu = 0.12$	Slightly Greasy; $\mu = 0.28$	Damp; $\mu = 0.38$
0.1	1.12	1.34	1.08	1.19	1.27
0.2	1.25	1.81	1.16	1.42	1.61
0.3	1.40	2.43	1.25	1.69	2.05
0.4	1.57	3.26	1.35	2.02	2.60
0.425	1.62	3.51	1.38	2.11	2.76
0.45	1.66	3.78	1.40	2.21	2.93
0.475	1.71	4.07	1.43	2.31	3.11
0.5	1.76	4.38	1.46	2.41	3.30
0.525	1.81	4.71	1.49	2.52	3.50
0.55	1.86	5.07	1.51	2.63	3.72
0.6	1.97	5.88	1.57	2.81	4.19
0.7	2.21	7.90	1.66	3.43	5.32
0.8	2.47	10.60	1.83	4.09	6.75
0.9	2.77	14.30	1.97	4.87	8.57
1.0	3.10	19.20	2.12	5.81	10.90

Coefficient of Friction in Brakes. — The coefficients of friction that may be assumed for friction brake calculations are as follows: Iron on iron, 0.25 to 0.3; leather on iron, 0.3; cork on iron, 0.35. Values somewhat lower than these should be assumed when the velocities exceed 400 feet per minute at the beginning of the braking operation.

For brakes where wooden brake blocks are used on iron drums, poplar has proved the best brake-block material. The best material for the brake drum is wrought iron. Poplar gives a high coefficient of friction, and is little affected by oil. The average coefficient of friction for poplar brake blocks and wrought-iron drums is

0.6; for poplar on cast iron, 0.35; for oak on wrought iron, 0.5; for oak on cast iron, 0.3; for beech on wrought iron, 0.5; for beech on cast iron, 0.3; for elm on wrought iron, 0.6; and for elm on cast iron, 0.35. The objection to elm is that the friction decreases rapidly if the friction surfaces are oily. The coefficient of friction for elm and wrought iron, if oily, is less than 0.4.

Formulas for Block Brakes

F = force in pounds at end of brake handle;
P = tangential force in pounds at rim of brake wheel;
μ = coefficient of friction between the brake block and brake wheel.

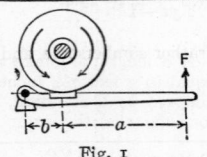

Fig. 1

Block brake.
For rotation in either direction:

$$F = P\,\frac{b}{a+b} \times \frac{1}{\mu} = \frac{Pb}{a+b}\left(\frac{1}{\mu}\right)$$

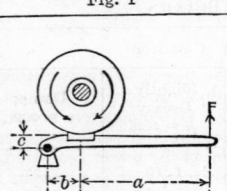

Fig. 2

Block brake.
For clockwise rotation:

$$F = \frac{\dfrac{Pb}{\mu} - Pc}{a+b} = \frac{Pb}{a+b}\left(\frac{1}{\mu} - \frac{c}{b}\right)$$

For counter clockwise rotation:

$$F = \frac{\dfrac{Pb}{\mu} + Pc}{a+b} = \frac{Pb}{a+b}\left(\frac{1}{\mu} + \frac{c}{b}\right)$$

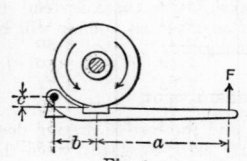

Fig. 3

Block brake.
For clockwise rotation:

$$F = \frac{\dfrac{Pb}{\mu} + Pc}{a+b} = \frac{Pb}{a+b}\left(\frac{1}{\mu} + \frac{c}{b}\right)$$

For counter clockwise rotation:

$$F = \frac{\dfrac{Pb}{\mu} - Pc}{a+b} = \frac{Pb}{a+b}\left(\frac{1}{\mu} - \frac{c}{b}\right)$$

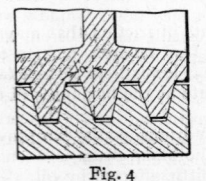

Fig. 4

The brake wheel and friction block of the block brake are often grooved as shown in Fig. 4. In this case, substitute for μ in the above equations the value $\dfrac{\mu}{\sin\alpha + \mu\cos\alpha}$ where α is one-half the angle included by the faces of the grooves.

Calculating Horsepower from Dynamometer Tests. — When a dynamometer is arranged for obtaining the horsepower transmitted by a shaft, as indicated by the diagrammatic view in the accompanying illustration, the horsepower may be obtained by the formula:

$$\text{H.P.} = \frac{2\pi LPN}{33,000}$$

in which H.P. = horsepower transmitted; N = number of revolutions per minute; L = distance (as shown in illustration) from center of pulley to point of action of weight P, in feet; P = weight hung on brake arm or read on scale.

By adopting a length of brake arm equal to 5 feet 3 inches, the formula may be reduced to the simple form:

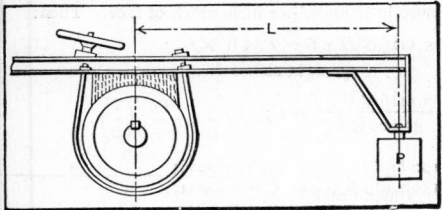

$$\text{H.P.} = \frac{NP}{1000}$$

If a length of brake arm equal to 2 feet 7½ inches is adopted as a standard, the formula takes the form:

$$\text{H.P.} = \frac{NP}{2000}$$

The *transmission* type of dynamometer measures the power by transmitting it through the mechanism of the dynamometer from the apparatus in which it is generated, or to the apparatus in which it is to be utilized. Dynamometers known as *indicators* operate by simultaneously measuring the pressure and volume of a confined fluid. This type may be used for the measurement of the power generated by steam or gas engines or absorbed by refrigerating machinery, air compressors, or pumps. An electrical dynamometer is for measuring the power of an electric current, based on the mutual action of currents flowing in two coils. It consists principally of one fixed and one movable coil, which, in the normal position, are at right angles to each other. Both coils are connected in series, and, when a current traverses the coils, the fields produced are at right angles; hence, the coils tend to take up a parallel position. The movable coil with an attached pointer will be deflected, the deflection measuring directly the electric current.

Friction Wheels for Power Transmission

When a rotating member is driven intermittently and the rate of driving does not need to be positive, friction wheels are frequently used, especially when the amount of power to be transmitted is comparatively small. The driven wheels in a pair of friction disks should always be made of a harder material than the driving wheels, so that if the driven wheel should be held stationary by the load, while driving wheel revolves under its own pressure, a flat spot may not be rapidly worn on the driven wheel. The driven wheels, therefore, are usually made of iron, while the driving wheels are made of or covered with, rubber, paper, leather, wood or fiber. The safe working pressures per inch of contact for various materials are as follows: Straw fiber, 150; leather fiber, 240; tarred fiber, 240; leather, 150; wood, 100 to 150; paper, 150. Coefficients of friction for different combinations of materials are given in the following table. Smaller values should be used for exceptionally high speeds, or when the transmission must be started while under load.

Horsepower of Friction Wheels. — Let D = diameter of friction wheel in inches; N = Number of revolutions per minute; W = width of face in inches; f =

Working Values of Coefficient of Friction

Materials	Coefficient of Friction	Materials	Coefficient of Friction
Straw fiber and cast iron......	0.26	Tarred fiber and aluminum...	0.18
Straw fiber and aluminum....	0.27	Leather and cast iron.........	0.14
Leather fiber and cast iron....	0.31	Leather and aluminum........	0.22
Leather fiber and aluminum...	0.30	Leather and typemetal........	0.25
Tarred fiber and cast iron.....	0.15	Wood and metal..............	0.25
Paper and cast iron	0.20		

coefficient of friction; P = pressure in pounds, per inch width of face. Then:

$$\text{H.P.} = \frac{3.1416 \times D \times N \times P \times W \times f}{33,000 \times 12}$$

Assume

$$\frac{3.1416 \times P \times f}{33,000 \times 12} = C;$$

then,

for $P = 100$ and $f = 0.20$, $C = 0.00016$;

for $P = 150$ and $f = 0.20$, $C = 0.00024$;

for $P = 200$ and $f = 0.20$, $C = 0.00032$.

The horsepower transmitted is then:

$$\text{H.P.} = D \times N \times W \times C.$$

Example: — Find the horsepower transmitted by a pair of friction wheels; the diameter of the driving wheel is 10 inches, and it revolves at 200 revolutions per minute. The width of the wheel is 2 inches. The pressure per inch width of face is 150 pounds, and the coefficient of friction 0.20.

$$\text{H.P.} = 10 \times 200 \times 2 \times 0.00024 = 0.96 \text{ horsepower.}$$

Horsepower Which May be Transmitted by Means of a Clean Paper Friction Wheel of One-inch Face when Run Under a Pressure of 150 Pounds

(Rockwood Mfg. Co.)

Diameter of Friction	Revolutions per Minute										
	25	50	75	100	150	200	300	400	600	800	1000
4	0.023	0.047	0.071	0.095	0.142	0.190	0.285	0.380	0.571	0.76	0.95
6	0.035	0.071	0.107	0.142	0.214	0.285	0.428	0.571	0.856	1.14	1.42
8	0.047	0.095	0.142	0.190	0.285	0.380	0.571	0.761	1.142	1.52	1.90
10	0.059	0.119	0.178	0.238	0.357	0.476	0.714	0.952	1.428	1.90	2.38
14	0.083	0.166	0.249	0.333	0.499	0.666	0.999	1.332	1.999	2.66	3.33
16	0.095	0.190	0.285	0.380	0.571	0.761	1.142	1.523	2.284	3.04	3.80
18	0.107	0.214	0.321	0.428	0.642	0.856	1.285	1.713	2.570	3.42	4.28
24	0.142	0.285	0.428	0.571	0.856	1.142	1.713	2.284	3.427	4.56	5.71
30	0.178	0.357	0.535	0.714	1.071	1.428	2.142	2.856	4.284	5.71	7.14
36	0.214	0.428	0.642	0.856	1.285	1.713	2.570	3.427	5.140	6.85	8.56
42	0.249	0.499	0.749	0.999	1.499	1.999	2.998	3.998	5.997	7.99	9.99
48	0.285	0.571	0.856	1.142	1.713	2.284	3.427	4.569	6.854	9.13	11.42
50	0.297	0.595	0.892	1.190	1.785	2.380	3.570	4.760	7.140	9.52	11.90

CAMS AND CAM DESIGN

Classes of Cams. — Cams may, in general, be divided into two classes: uniform motion cams and uniformly accelerated motion cams. The uniform motion cam moves the follower at the same rate of speed from the beginning to the end of the stroke; but as the movement is started from zero to the full speed of the uniform motion and stops in the same abrupt way, there is a distinct shock at the beginning and end of the stroke, if the movement is at all rapid. In machinery working at a high rate of speed, therefore, it is important that cams are so constructed that sudden shocks are avoided when starting the motion or when reversing the direction of motion of the follower. The cam best suited for high speeds is one where the speed at first is slow and then accelerated at a uniform rate until the maximum speed is reached. The speed is then again uniformly retarded until the rate of motion of the follower is zero or nearly zero when the reversal takes place. A cam constructed along these lines is called a uniformly accelerated motion cam. The distances

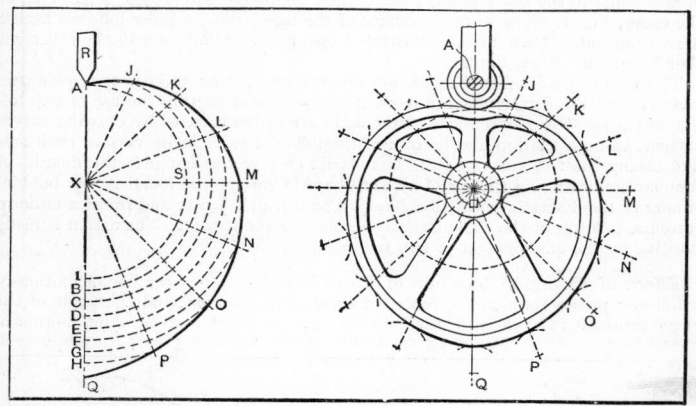

Fig 1   Fig. 2

which the follower passes through during equal periods of time increase in the same ratio as the distances passed through in consecutive seconds by a freely falling body acted upon by gravity alone. A cam constructed on these lines, therefore, is often called a gravity-curve cam.

Laying-out a Uniform Motion Cam. — The laying-out of a heart-shaped cam will serve as an illustration of the general method. In Fig. 1, the pointed follower R is to be given a reciprocating motion. The throw is assumed to be $1\frac{1}{2}$ inch. Let X be the center of the cam. Let A be the point at which the follower is at the lower end of the stroke. Draw semi-circle ASI, and extend the diameter at the side opposite A, a distance IQ, equal to the required throw. Divide IQ into any number of equal parts, as at B, C, D, etc., and divide the semi-circle by the same number of radii, equally distributed. With X as a center and a radius equal to XB, describe an arc intersecting XJ at J. With the same center and a radius equal to XC, describe an arc intersecting XK at K. Continue this process through the points D, E, F, etc., thus obtaining the points L, M, N, etc. The latter are points on the required curve. The other half of the cam is laid out in the same manner.

The excessive friction of a pointed follower such as that shown at R necessitates the use of a follower that will reduce the amount of friction to a minimum. A small roller meets this requirement. If a roller is employed as a follower, the problem of laying out the cam curve becomes modified. A roller traveling along the curve shown in Fig. 1 would not impart to the follower-rod the desired uniform rise and fall. The variation would be but slight, yet sufficient to merit consideration where accuracy is desired.

Cams with Roller Followers. — Fig. 2 represents a heart-shaped cam that is, designed for the same movement as the cam, Fig. 1, but it has a roller follower. The curve may be laid out as described in connection with the diagram, Fig. 1, because the curve of Fig. 1 represents the path followed by the center of the roller, Fig. 2. To locate the working surface of a cam having a roller type of follower, draw a series of arcs equal to the roller radius from various points or centers A, J, K, L, etc., on the curve, Fig. 1. The working surface of the cam having a roller follower is then drawn tangent to these arcs as illustrated by Fig. 2. The center of the roller will then follow the curve, Fig. 1.

This cam depends upon the action of gravity, or a spring, to keep the follower in contact with the driver. It can be made positive in action by the use of two followers placed at the extremities of the diameter of the cam, or by drawing curves tangent to both the top and bottom of the follower roller in its various positions, and taking the two curves as the boundaries of a groove cut into the metal. A familiar application of the use of a heart-shaped cam may be found in the bobbin-winder of the domestic sewing machine. The thread is fed to and fro at a uniform rate, the follower of the cam acting as a guide for the thread. The action is made positive by the employment of two follower rollers.

Effect of Changing Location of Cam Roller. — When the line of motion of a follower passes through the center of rotation of the cam, and the angle of the curve causes it to work hard, the curve may be modified, and the same motion of

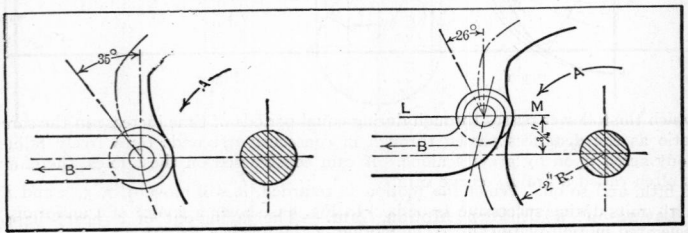

Fig. 3   Fig. 4

follower obtained by placing the follower with its line of action parallel to its original position and not passing through the center of the cam. A condition may be assumed, as shown in Fig. 3. Here the cam rotates in the direction indicated by arrow A. It moves the follower ¾ inch in the direction indicated by arrow B, during a 30-degree angle of motion of the cam-shaft. The angle of the cam presented to the follower at the beginning of the stroke would be 35 degrees, as determined by the tangent to the curve. Should the cam curve work hard at the required speed, the cam would be made of greater diameter, if possible, which would reduce the angle of the cam. The design of the machine, however, might make this change impossible. Another way consists in changing the location of the cam roller. In Fig. 4 all conditions are the same as in Fig. 3, except that the roller has been placed ¾ inch above the line passing through the center of the cam. The center of the roller will now pass along the line *LM*, or parallel to the line of motion in Fig. 3. The angle of the curve presented to the roller in this case is 26 degrees — much less than the angle in Fig. 3 — and the angle decreases as the roller moves away from the center of rotation. There is, of course, a limit to the distance the roller may be changed, for if placed too far away from the center line, the thrust in the direction at right angles to the direction of motion of the follower would be so great as to offset the advantage gained. Even without the aid of an illustration it may be seen that to place the cam roller on the other side of the center would cause the angle of the cam curve to increase, thus making conditions worse. The offset of the roller should be in the direction opposed to the direction of motion of the cam.

Laying-out a Uniformly Accelerated Motion Cam. — When a uniformly accelerated motion is used, the distances passed through by the follower during equal periods of time increase uniformly, so that if, for instance, the follower moves a distance equal to 1 length unit during the first second, and 3 during the second, it will move 5 length units during the third second, 7 during the fourth, 9 during

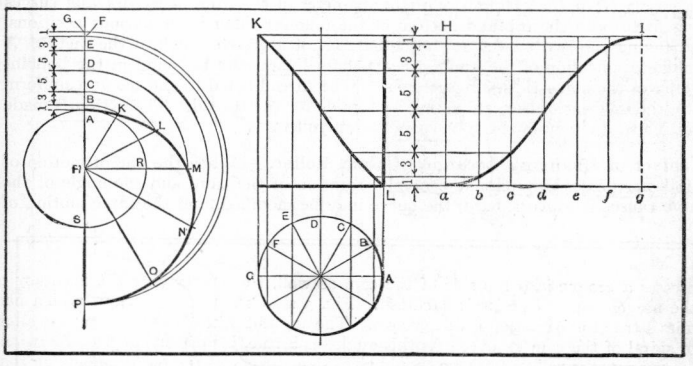

Fig. 5   Fig. 6

the fifth, and so on. When the motion is retarded, it will move 9, 7, 5, 3 and 1 length units during successive seconds. In Fig. 5 is shown a layout of a uniformly accelerated motion plate cam. The motion of the follower is back and forth from *A* to *G*. The rise takes place during 180 degrees and the fall during an equal period, the two halves of the cam being alike. To construct the cam, divide the half circle *ARS* into six equal parts, and draw radii *HK*, *HL*, etc. Divide *AG* into two equal parts, *AD* and *DG*, and then divide each of these parts into three divisions, the lengths of which are to each other as 1 : 3 : 5. With *H* as a center, draw circular arcs from *B*, *C*, *D*, etc., to *K*, *L*, *M*, etc. The intersections between the circles and the radii are points on the cam curve. If the half circle *ARS* should be divided into eight equal parts instead of six, line *AG* would also have to be divided into eight parts in the proportions 1 : 3 : 5 : 7 : 7 : 5 : 3 : 1. With a cam constructed in this manner, the follower starts at A with a velocity of zero; it reaches its maximum velocity at D, and at G, where the motion is reversed, the velocity is again zero.

Development and Layout of a Uniformly Accelerated Motion Cylindrical Cam. — To the right in Fig. 6 is shown the development of a uniformly accelerated motion cam curve laid out on the surface of a cylindrical cam. This development is necessary for finding the projection on the cylindrical surface, as shown at KL. To construct the developed curve, first divide the base circle of the cylinder into, say, twelve equal parts. Set off these parts along line ag. Only one-half of the layout has been shown, as the other half is constructed in the same manner, except that the curve is here falling instead of rising. Divide line aH into the same number of divisions as the half circle, the divisions being in the proportion $1:3:5:5:3:1$. Draw horizontal lines from these division points and vertical lines from a, b, c, etc. The intersections between the two sets of lines are points on the developed cam curve. These points are transferred to the cylindrical surface at the left by projection in the usual manner.

Shape of Rolls for Cylinder Cams. — The rolls for cylindrical cams working in a groove in the cam should be conical rather than cylindrical in shape, in order that they may rotate freely and without excessive friction. Fig. 1 shows a straight roll and groove, the action of which is faulty because of the varying surface speed at the top and bottom of the groove. Fig. 2 shows a roll with curved surface. For heavy work, however, the small bearing area is quickly worn down and the roll

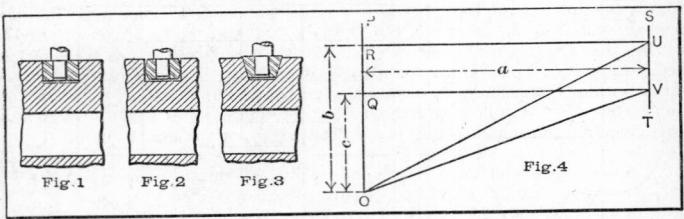

Fig. 1   Fig. 2   Fig. 3   Fig. 4

presses a groove into the side of the cam as well, thus destroying the accuracy of the movement and creating backlash. Fig. 3 shows the conical shape which permits a true rolling action in the groove. The amount of taper depends on the angle of spiral of the cam groove. As this angle, as a rule, is not constant for the whole movement, the roll and groove should be designed to meet the requirements on that section of the cam where the heaviest duty is performed. Frequently the cam groove is of a nearly even spiral angle for a considerable length. The method for determining the angle of the roll and groove to work correctly during the important part of the cycle is as follows:

In Fig. 4, b is the circumferential distance on the surface of the cam that includes the section of the groove for which correct rolling action is required. The throw of the cam for this circumferential movement is a. Line OU is the development of the movement of the cam roll during the given part of the cycle, and c is the movement corresponding to b, but on a circle the diameter of which is equal to that of the cam at the bottom of the groove. With the same throw a as before, the line OV will be the development of the cam at the bottom of the groove. OU then is the length of the helix traveled by the top of the roll, while OV is the travel at the bottom of the groove. If then the top width and bottom width of the groove be made proportional to OU and OV, the groove will be properly proportioned.

Cam Rolls and Roll Studs. — It is important that the cam roll and roll stud be ground all over after hardening. The end of the roller should be cut back or recessed $\frac{1}{64}$ of an inch or thereabouts on the sides for some distance, beginning at the periphery, so as to avoid undue friction against the collar of the stud or the part in which it is mounted. On account of the warping that takes place in hardening, rolls that are not ground both on the inside and on the outside often will stop under heavy load, until in time flat spots are worn on the face, and then the working surface of the cam will begin to wear or is roughed up. Roll studs that are out of parallel with the working surface of the cam, even to a very small degree, also cause trouble. The same difficulty is met with on cylinder or barrel cams if the milling cutter is set below or above the center of the cam when cutting it. The roll will then bear at one end only at the most important time — when the throw takes place.

There is a great deal of end pressure on the conical rolls used in barrel cams, and this must be taken care of by thrust collars on the studs on which the rolls are mounted, or, better still, by a ball race scored in the collar and the large end of the roll, so as to provide for a ball thrust bearing. The end pressure on a conical roll, however, reduces the side pressure on the stud to a considerable extent, so that the stud may be made shorter or smaller in diameter than when a roll with parallel sides is used.

Cam Milling. — Plate cams having a constant rise, such as are used on automatic screw machines, can be cut in a universal milling machine, with the spiral head either in a vertical position or set at an angle α, as shown by the illustration. When the spiral head is set vertical, the "lead" of the cam (or its rise for one complete revolution) is the same as the lead for which the machine is geared; but when the spiral head and cutter are inclined, any lead or rise of the cam can be obtained, provided it is less than the lead for which the machine is geared, that is, less than the forward feed of the table for one turn of the spiral-head spindle. The cam lead, then, can be varied within certain limits by simply changing the inclination α of the spiral head and cutter. In the following formulas for determining this angle of inclination, for a given rise of cam and with the machine geared for a certain lead, let

α = angle to which index head and milling attachment are set;
r = rise of cam in given part of circumference;
R = "lead" of cam, or rise if latter were continued at given rate for one complete revolution;
L = spiral lead for which milling machine is geared;
N = part of circumference in which rise is required, expressed as a decimal in hundredths of cam circumference.

$$\sin \alpha = \frac{R}{L}, \text{ and } R = \frac{r}{N} ; \text{ hence, } \sin \alpha = \frac{r}{N \times L}$$

For example, suppose a cam is to be milled having a rise of 0.125 inch in 300 degrees or in 0.83 of the circumference, and that the machine is geared for the smallest possible lead, or 0.67 inch; then:

$$\sin \alpha = \frac{r}{N \times L} = \frac{0.125}{0.83 \times 0.67} = 0.2247,$$

which is approximately the sine of 13 degrees. Therefore, to secure a rise of 0.125 inch with the machine geared for 0.67 inch lead, the spiral head is elevated to an angle of 13 degrees and the vertical milling attachment is also swiveled around to locate the cutter in line with the spiral-head spindle, so that the edge of the finished cam will be parallel to its axis of rotation. When there are several lobes on a cam, having different leads, the machine can be geared for a lead somewhat in excess of the greatest lead on the cam, and then all the lobes can be milled without changing the spiral head gearing, by simply varying the angle of the spiral head and cutter to suit the different cam leads. Whenever possible, it is advisable to mill on the under side of the cam, as there is less interference from chips; moreover, it is easier to see any lines that may be laid out on the cam face. To set the cam for a new cut, it is first

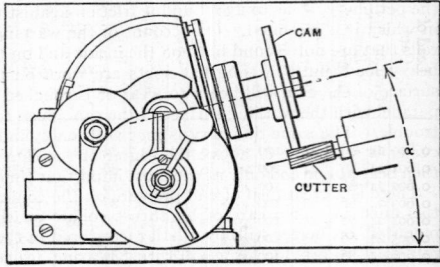

turned back by operating the handle of the table feed screw, after which the index crank is disengaged from the plate and turned the required amount.

The accompanying tables give the combinations of change gears and the angular setting required for cutting a cam of any lead likely to be met with in practice. The figures in the column headed "Lead of Cam," represent the rise for one complete revolution. Set the vertical attachment to the angle given in the table. For the dividing head, subtract the angle in the table from 90 degrees; the difference is the angle to which the spindle must be raised from the horizontal position.

Example: — If the angle is 39½ degrees, set the spindle of the vertical attachment 39½ degrees from the vertical. Set the dividing head 50½ degrees from the horizontal position (90 — 39½ = 50½). These tables were compiled by the Cincinnati Milling Machine Co.

Simple Method for Cutting Uniform Motion Cams. — Cams are generally laid out with dividers, machined and filed to the line; but for a cam that must

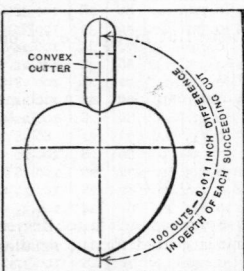

advance a certain number of thousandths per revolution of spindle this method is not accurate. Cams are easily and accurately cut in the following manner. Let it be required to make the heart cam shown in the illustration. The throw of this cam is 1.1 inch. Now, by setting the index on the milling machine to cut 200 teeth and also dividing 1.1 inch by 100, we find that we have 0.011 inch to recede from or advance towards the cam center for each cut across the cam. Placing the cam securely on an arbor, and the latter between the centers of the milling machine, and using a convex cutter set the proper distance from the center of the arbor, make the first cut across the cam. Then, by lowering the milling machine knee 0.011 inch and

turning the index pin the proper number of holes on the index plate, take the next cut and so on. Each cut should be marked on paper so that there will be no mistake as to the number of cuts taken; when 100 cuts have been made, the knee must be raised in order to complete the opposite side of the cam.

This method can also be used to advantage for milling uniform motion cam lobes extending only over a portion of the cam circumference. After the milling has been completed, the surface of the cam must be smoothed off by means of filing

Change Gears and Angles for Cam Milling — 1

Lead of Cam	Gear on Worm	First Intermediate	Second Intermediate	Gear on Screw	Angle	Lead of Cam	Gear on Worm	First Intermediate	Second Intermediate	Gear on Screw	Angle	Lead of Cam	Gear on Worm	First Intermediate	Second Intermediate	Gear on Screw	Angle
0.600	24	86	24	100	26½	0.650	24	86	24	100	14	0.700	24	72	24	100	29
0.601	24	86	24	100	26	0.651	24	86	28	100	33½	0.701	24	72	24	86	41
0.602	24	86	24	100	26	0.652	24	86	24	100	13½	0.702	24	86	28	100	26
0.603	24	86	28	100	39½	0.653	24	86	32	100	43	0.703	24	72	24	100	28½
0.604	24	72	24	100	41	0.654	24	86	24	100	12½	0.704	24	86	32	100	38
0.605	24	86	24	100	25½	0.655	24	86	24	100	12	0.705	24	86	28	100	25½
0.606	24	86	28	100	39	0.656	24	86	24	100	11½	0.706	24	72	24	100	28
0.607	24	86	24	100	25	0.657	24	86	24	100	11	0.707	24	72	24	86	40½
0.608	24	72	24	100	40½	0.658	24	86	32	100	42½	0.708	24	86	28	100	25
0.609	24	86	24	100	24½	0.659	24	72	24	100	34½	0.709	24	72	28	100	40½
0.610	24	86	24	100	24½	0.660	24	86	24	100	10	0.710	24	72	24	100	27½
0.611	24	86	28	100	38½	0.661	24	86	28	100	32	0.711	24	86	28	100	24½
0.612	24	86	24	100	24	0.662	24	86	28	100	32	0.712	24	72	24	86	40
0.613	24	72	24	100	40	0.663	24	72	24	100	34	0.713	24	72	24	100	27
0.614	24	86	24	100	23½	0.664	24	86	32	100	42	0.714	24	64	24	100	39½
0.615	24	86	28	100	38	0.665	24	72	24	100	44½	0.715	24	72	24	100	40
0.616	24	86	24	100	23	0.666	24	86	28	100	31½	0.716	24	86	28	100	23½
0.617	24	72	24	100	39½	0.667	24	72	24	100	33½	0.717	24	72	24	86	39½
0.618	24	72	24	100	39½	0.668	24	64	24	100	42	0.718	24	86	32	100	36½
0.619	24	86	24	100	22½	0.669	24	72	24	86	44	0.719	24	86	28	100	23
0.620	24	86	28	100	37½	0.670	24	86	28	100	31	0.720	24	72	28	100	39½
0.621	24	86	24	100	22	0.671	24	72	24	100	33	0.721	24	86	28	100	22½
0.622	24	72	24	100	39	0.672	24	36	28	100	30½	0.722	24	72	24	100	25½
0.623	24	86	24	100	21½	0.673	24	86	24	100	30½	0.723	24	64	24	100	36½
0.624	24	86	28	100	37	0.674	24	64	24	100	41½	0.724	24	86	28	100	22
0.625	24	86	24	100	21	0.675	24	72	24	100	32½	0.725	24	72	24	100	25
0.626	24	86	32	100	45½	0.676	24	86	28	100	30	0.726	24	86	28	100	21½
0.627	24	86	24	100	20½	0.677	24	72	28	100	43½	0.727	24	86	32	100	35½
0.628	24	86	28	100	36½	0.678	24	72	24	100	32	0.728	24	72	24	100	24½
0.629	24	86	24	100	20	0.679	24	86	32	100	40½	0.729	24	86	28	100	21
0.630	24	72	24	100	38	0.680	24	72	24	86	43	0.730	24	72	28	100	38½
0.631	24	86	32	100	45	0.681	24	72	24	100	31½	0.731	24	72	24	100	24
0.632	24	86	24	100	36	0.682	24	72	28	100	43	0.732	24	86	28	100	20½
0.633	24	86	24	100	19	0.683	24	86	28	100	29	0.733	24	72	24	86	38
0.634	24	72	24	100	37½	0.684	24	86	32	100	40	0.734	24	86	28	100	20
0.635	24	86	24	100	18½	0.685	24	72	24	86	42½	0.735	24	72	28	100	38
0.636	24	86	28	100	35½	0.686	24	86	28	100	28½	0.736	24	86	28	100	19½
0.637	24	86	32	100	44½	0.687	24	72	28	100	42½	0.737	24	64	24	100	35
0.638	24	72	24	100	37	0.688	24	72	28	100	42½	0.738	24	72	24	86	37½
0.639	24	86	24	100	17½	0.689	24	86	32	100	39½	0.739	24	72	24	100	22½
0.640	24	86	24	100	35	0.690	24	86	28	100	28	0.740	24	72	24	100	37½
0.641	24	86	24	100	17	0.691	24	72	24	86	42	0.741	24	86	28	100	18½
0.642	24	86	32	100	44	0.692	24	86	28	100	27½	0.742	24	72	24	100	22
0.643	24	86	24	100	34½	0.693	24	72	28	100	42	0.743	24	86	28	100	18
0.644	24	86	24	100	16	0.694	24	86	32	100	39	0.744	24	72	24	100	21½
0.645	24	86	24	100	15½	0.695	24	64	24	100	39½	0.745	24	72	28	100	37
0.646	24	86	24	100	15½	0.696	24	86	28	100	27	0.746	24	64	24	100	34
0.647	24	86	24	100	15	0.697	24	72	24	86	41½	0.747	24	86	28	100	17
0.648	24	86	32	100	43½	0.698	24	72	28	100	41½	0.748	24	72	24	86	36½
0.649	24	86	24	100	14½	0.699	24	86	32	100	38½	0.749	24	86	28	100	16½

Change Gears and Angles for Cam Milling — 2

Lead of Cam	Gear on Worm	First Intermediate	Second Intermediate	Gear on Screw	Angle
0.750	24	72	28	100	36½
0.751	24	86	28	100	16
0.752	24	72	24	100	20
0.753	24	86	32	100	32½
0.754	24	72	24	100	19½
0.755	24	72	28	100	36
0.756	24	86	28	100	14½
0.757	24	72	24	86	35½
0.758	24	86	28	100	14
0.759	24	64	24	100	32½
0.760	24	72	28	100	35½
0.761	24	86	28	100	13
0.762	24	72	24	86	35
0.763	24	72	24	100	17½
0.764	24	86	28	100	12
0.765	24	72	24	100	17
0.766	24	72	24	86	34½
0.767	24	72	24	100	16½
0.768	24	86	28	100	10½
0.769	24	86	28	100	10
0.770	24	86	32	100	30½
0.771	24	72	24	86	34
0.772	24	72	24	100	15
0.773	24	86	32	100	30
0.774	24	72	24	100	14½
0.775	24	64	24	100	30½
0.776	24	72	24	100	14
0.777	24	86	32	100	29½
0.778	24	72	28	100	33½
0.779	24	72	24	100	13
0.780	24	72	24	86	33
0.781	24	72	24	100	12½
0.782	24	72	28	100	33
0.783	24	64	24	100	29½
0.784	24	72	24	100	11½
0.785	24	86	32	100	28½
0.786	28	86	32	100	41
0.787	24	64	24	100	29
0.788	24	72	24	100	10
0.789	24	72	24	86	32
0.790	24	64	24	86	41
0.791	24	64	24	100	28½
0.792	24	86	32	100	27½
0.793	24	72	24	86	31½
0.794	24	72	24	86	43
0.795	24	72	28	100	31½
0.796	24	64	24	86	40½
0.797	24	72	24	86	31
0.798	28	86	32	100	40
0.799	24	72	32	100	41½
0.800	24	72	28	100	31
0.801	24	72	24	86	30½
0.802	24	64	24	86	40
0.803	24	86	32	100	26
0.804	28	86	32	100	39½
0.805	24	72	32	100	41
0.806	24	86	32	100	25½
0.807	24	64	24	86	39½
0.808	24	72	28	100	30
0.809	24	64	24	100	26
0.810	28	86	32	100	39
0.811	24	72	32	100	40½
0.812	24	72	28	100	29½
0.813	24	72	24	86	29
0.814	24	64	24	86	39
0.815	28	86	32	100	38½
0.816	24	72	28	100	29
0.817	24	72	24	86	28½
0.818	24	72	24	86	41
0.819	24	86	32	100	23½
0.820	24	72	28	100	28½
0.821	24	72	24	86	28
0.822	24	86	32	100	23
0.823	24	72	32	100	39½
0.824	24	72	28	100	28
0.825	24	72	24	86	27½
0.826	28	86	32	100	37½
0.827	24	72	23	100	27½
0.828	24	86	32	100	22
0.829	24	86	40	100	42
0.830	24	64	24	86	37½
0.831	24	72	28	86	40
0.832	24	72	24	86	26½
0.833	24	56	24	100	36
0.834	24	86	32	100	21
0.835	24	72	24	100	38½
0.836	24	72	24	86	26
0.837	24	72	28	86	39½
0.838	24	56	24	100	35½
0.839	24	86	32	100	20
0.840	24	64	24	100	21
0.841	24	72	32	100	38
0.842	24	86	32	100	19½
0.843	24	72	28	86	39
0.844	24	86	32	100	19
0.845	24	72	28	100	25
0.846	24	64	24	100	20
0.847	24	86	32	100	18½
0.848	24	64	24	100	19½
0.849	24	86	32	100	18
0.850	24	72	24	86	24
0.851	24	64	24	100	19
0.852	24	72	28	100	24
0.853	24	72	24	86	23½
0.854	24	86	32	100	17
0.855	24	64	28	100	35½
0.856	24	86	32	100	16½
0.857	24	64	24	86	35
0.858	24	64	24	100	17½
0.859	24	72	24	86	22½
0.860	24	64	28	100	35
0.861	24	72	28	86	37½
0.862	24	72	28	100	22½
0.863	24	64	24	100	16½
0.864	28	86	32	100	34
0.865	24	64	24	100	16
0.866	24	86	32	100	14
0.867	24	64	24	100	15½
0.868	24	72	28	100	21½
0.869	24	64	24	100	15
0.870	24	86	32	100	13
0.871	24	64	24	100	14½
0.872	24	86	24	100	12½
0.873	24	64	24	100	14
0.874	24	72	24	86	20
0.875	24	86	32	100	11½
0.876	24	64	28	100	33½
0.877	24	64	24	100	13
0.878	24	86	32	100	10½
0.879	24	64	24	100	12½
0.880	24	64	24	100	12
0.881	24	64	28	100	33
0.882	24	64	24	86	32½
0.883	24	64	24	100	32
0.884	28	86	32	100	32
0.885	24	64	24	100	10½
0.886	24	64	24	100	10
0.887	24	72	24	86	17½
0.888	24	64	24	86	32
0.889	24	72	28	100	17
0.890	24	72	24	100	17½
0.891	24	56	24	100	30
0.892	24	72	24	86	16½
0.893	28	86	32	100	31
0.894	24	72	24	86	16
0.895	24	64	28	86	31½
0.896	24	72	24	86	15½
0.897	24	72	28	100	16
0.898	24	72	24	86	15
0.899	24	72	28	100	15½

Change Gears and Angles for Cam Milling—3

Lead of Cam	Gear on Worm	First Intermediate	Second Intermediate	Gear on Screw	Angle	Lead of Cam	Gear on Worm	First Intermediate	Second Intermediate	Gear on Screw	Angle	Lead of Cam	Gear on Worm	First Intermediate	Second Intermediate	Gear on Screw	Angle
0.900	24	56	24	100	29	0.950	24	72	32	86	40	1.000	24	86	44	100	35½
0.901	24	72	28	100	15	0.951	24	56	24	100	22½	1.001	24	56	24	100	13½
0.902	24	72	24	86	14	0.952	28	86	32	100	24	1.002	28	86	32	100	16
0.903	24	72	28	100	14½	0.953	24	64	24	86	24½	1.003	24	56	24	100	13
0.904	24	72	24	86	13½	0.954	24	56	24	100	22	1.004	28	86	32	100	15½
0.905	24	72	28	100	14	0.955	24	72	32	100	26½	1.005	24	56	24	100	12½
0.906	24	72	24	86	13	0.956	24	64	28	86	38½	1.006	24	56	24	100	12
0.907	24	72	28	100	13½	0.957	24	56	24	100	21½	1.007	24	64	24	86	16
0.908	24	72	24	86	12½	0.958	24	72	28	86	28	1.008	24	56	24	100	11½
0.909	24	72	28	100	13	0.959	24	72	32	100	26	1.009	28	86	32	100	14½
0.910	24	72	32	100	31½	0.960	24	64	24	86	23½	1.010	24	56	24	100	11
0.911	24	72	28	100	12½	0.961	24	86	44	100	38½	1.011	28	86	32	100	14
0.912	24	72	28	100	12	0.962	24	72	28	86	27½	1.012	24	56	24	100	10½
0.913	24	72	24	86	11	0.963	28	86	32	100	22½	1.013	24	56	24	100	10
0.914	24	72	28	100	11½	0.964	24	56	24	100	20½	1.014	24	64	24	86	14½
0.915	24	72	32	100	31	0.965	24	64	32	100	36½	1.015	28	86	32	100	13
0.916	24	72	24	85	10	0.966	28	86	32	100	22	1.016	24	64	24	86	14
0.917	24	72	28	100	10½	0.967	24	56	24	100	20	1.017	28	86	32	100	12½
0.918	24	64	28	100	29	0.968	24	56	24	86	36	1.018	24	64	24	86	13½
0.919	24	72	28	100	10	0.969	24	64	28	86	37½	1.019	28	86	32	100	12
0.920	28	86	32	100	28	0.970	24	56	24	100	19½	1.020	24	64	24	86	13
0.921	24	56	24	100	26½	0.971	24	72	28	86	26½	1.021	28	86	32	100	11½
0.922	24	64	28	86	41	0.972	86	44	32	64	6	1.022	24	64	24	86	12½
0.923	24	64	28	100	28½	0.973	24	55	24	100	19	1.023	28	86	32	100	11
0.924	28	86	32	100	27½	0.974	24	64	24	86	21½	1.024	24	64	24	86	12
0.925	24	56	24	100	26	0.975	24	72	32	100	24	1.025	24	64	28	100	12½
0.926	24	64	32	100	39½	0.976	28	85	32	100	20½	1.026	24	64	24	86	11½
0.927	24	64	28	100	28	0.977	24	64	28	100	21½	1.027	24	64	28	100	12
0.928	24	64	24	86	40½	0.978	24	56	24	100	18	1.028	24	64	24	86	11
0.929	24	56	24	100	25½	0.979	28	86	32	100	20	1.029	24	64	28	100	11½
0.930	24	72	28	86	31	0.980	24	64	28	100	21	1.030	24	64	24	86	10½
0.931	24	64	28	100	27½	0.981	24	64	24	86	20½	1.031	24	64	28	100	11
0.932	28	72	32	100	41½	0.982	28	86	32	100	19½	1.032	24	64	24	86	10½
0.933	24	64	24	86	27	0.983	24	72	28	86	25	1.033	24	72	32	100	14½
0.934	24	86	44	100	40½	0.984	24	56	24	100	17	1.034	24	64	28	100	10
0.935	24	72	28	86	30½	0.985	28	86	32	100	19	1.035	24	72	32	100	14
0.936	24	56	24	100	24½	0.986	24	72	32	100	22½	1.036	24	56	24	86	30
0.937	24	64	24	86	26½	0.987	24	64	24	86	19½	1.037	24	72	32	100	13½
0.938	24	72	32	100	28½	0.988	28	86	32	100	18½	1.038	24	72	28	86	17
0.939	24	64	32	100	38½	0.989	24	56	24	86	16	1.039	24	64	32	100	30
0.940	24	56	24	100	24	0.990	24	64	24	86	19	1.040	24	72	32	100	13
0.941	24	64	24	100	26	0.991	28	86	32	100	18	1.041	24	56	24	86	29½
0.942	24	72	32	100	28	0.992	24	56	24	100	15½	1.042	24	72	32	100	12½
0.943	24	72	32	86	40½	0.993	24	64	24	86	18½	1.043	24	72	28	86	16
0.944	24	56	24	100	23½	0.994	24	56	24	100	15	1.044	24	72	32	100	12
0.945	24	64	24	86	25½	0.995	24	72	28	86	23½	1.045	24	86	40	100	20½
0.946	24	72	32	100	27½	0.996	24	56	24	100	14½	1.046	24	72	32	100	11½
0.947	24	56	24	100	23	0.997	24	56	24	86	33½	1.047	24	72	32	100	11
0.948	28	86	32	100	24½	0.998	24	56	24	100	14	1.048	24	72	28	86	15
0.949	24	64	24	86	25	0.999	28	86	32	100	16½	1.049	24	72	32	100	10½

Change Gears and Angles for Cam Milling — 4

Lead of Cam	Gear on Worm	First Intermediate	Second Intermediate	Gear on Screw	Angle
1.050	24	72	28	86	14½
1.051	24	72	32	100	10
1.052	24	86	40	100	19½
1.053	24	72	28	86	14
1.054	24	72	28	86	14
1.055	24	72	28	86	13½
1.056	24	56	24	86	28
1.057	24	72	28	86	13
1.058	24	86	40	100	18½
1.059	24	72	28	86	12½
1.060	28	86	40	100	35½
1.061	24	72	28	86	12
1.062	24	72	28	86	12
1.063	24	72	28	86	11½
1.064	24	86	40	100	17½
1.065	24	72	28	86	11
1.066	24	56	24	86	27
1.067	24	72	28	86	10½
1.068	24	64	28	86	29
1.069	24	72	28	86	10
1.070	24	86	40	100	16½
1.071	32	56	24	100	38½
1.072	28	72	32	100	30½
1.073	24	86	40	100	16
1.074	24	64	32	100	26½
1.075	24	86	40	100	15½
1.076	24	64	32	86	39½
1.077	28	72	32	100	30
1.078	24	86	40	100	15
1.079	24	56	24	86	25½
1.080	24	86	40	100	14½
1.081	28	64	32	100	39½
1.082	28	86	44	100	41
1.083	24	86	40	100	14
1.084	24	56	24	86	25
1.085	24	86	40	100	13½
1.086	28	86	40	100	33½
1.087	24	86	40	100	13
1.088	24	56	24	86	24½
1.089	24	86	40	100	12½
1.090	24	72	32	86	28½
1.091	24	86	48	100	35½
1.092	24	86	40	100	12
1.093	24	56	24	86	24
1.094	24	86	40	100	11½
1.095	24	72	32	86	28
1.096	24	86	40	100	11
1.097	24	86	40	100	10½
1.098	28	72	32	100	28
1.099	24	86	40	100	10
1.100	28	72	32	86	40½
1.101	24	56	24	86	23
1.102	24	64	28	86	25½
1.103	28	72	32	100	27½
1.104	24	86	44	100	26
1.105	24	56	24	86	22½
1.106	40	64	24	100	42½
1.107	24	64	28	86	25
1.108	24	86	44	100	25½
1.109	24	56	24	86	22
1.110	24	72	32	86	26½
1.111	24	64	28	86	24½
1.112	24	72	40	100	33½
1.113	24	56	24	86	21½
1.114	24	64	32	86	37
1.115	24	64	28	86	24
1.116	24	56	24	86	21
1.117	24	86	44	100	24½
1.118	28	72	32	100	26
1.119	24	72	32	86	25½
1.120	24	56	24	86	20½
1.121	24	64	32	86	36½
1.122	24	86	44	100	24
1.123	28	72	32	100	25½
1.124	24	56	24	86	20
1.125	28	64	32	100	36½
1.126	24	86	44	100	23½
1.127	24	56	24	86	19½
1.128	24	64	32	86	20
1.129	24	64	32	86	36
1.130	24	72	40	100	32
1.131	24	56	24	86	19
1.132	24	64	28	86	22
1.133	24	72	32	86	24
1.134	24	56	24	86	18½
1.135	24	64	32	100	19
1.136	24	64	28	86	21½
1.137	24	56	24	86	18
1.138	24	64	32	100	18½
1.139	28	86	40	100	29
1.140	24	64	28	86	21
1.141	24	56	24	86	17½
1.142	24	64	32	86	35
1.143	24	86	44	100	21½
1.144	24	56	24	86	17
1.145	28	72	32	100	23
1.146	24	86	44	100	21
1.147	24	56	24	86	16½
1.148	24	64	32	100	17
1.149	28	72	32	100	22½
1.150	24	56	24	86	16
1.151	24	64	32	100	16½
1.152	28	86	44	100	36½
1.153	24	56	24	86	15½
1.154	24	64	28	86	19
1.155	24	56	24	86	15
1.156	24	64	32	100	15½
1.157	28	72	32	100	21½
1.158	24	56	24	86	14½
1.159	24	64	32	100	15
1.160	24	56	24	86	14
1.161	24	64	28	86	18
1.162	24	64	32	100	14½
1.163	24	56	24	86	13½
1.164	24	64	32	100	14
1.165	24	56	24	86	13
1.166	24	72	40	100	29
1.167	24	64	32	100	13½
1.168	24	56	24	86	12½
1.169	24	64	32	100	13
1.170	24	56	24	86	12
1.171	24	64	28	86	16½
1.172	24	56	24	86	11½
1.173	28	72	32	100	19½
1.174	24	56	24	86	11
1.175	28	86	40	100	25½
1.176	24	56	24	86	10½
1.177	24	64	28	86	15½
1.178	24	56	24	86	10
1.179	24	64	32	86	15
1.180	24	64	32	100	15½
1.181	32	56	24	100	30½
1.182	24	64	32	100	10
1.183	24	86	44	100	15½
1.184	24	64	32	86	9½
1.185	24	64	28	86	14
1.186	24	86	44	100	15
1.187	24	64	28	86	13½
1.188	24	72	40	100	27
1.189	24	86	44	100	14½
1.190	24	64	28	86	13
1.191	24	86	44	100	14
1.192	24	64	28	86	12½
1.193	28	72	32	100	16½
1.194	24	64	28	86	12
1.195	24	72	32	86	15½
1.196	28	72	32	100	16
1.197	24	64	28	86	11½
1.198	24	72	32	86	15
1.199	24	64	28	86	11

Change Gears and Angles for Cam Milling — 5

Lead of Cam	Gear on Worm	First Intermediate	Second Intermediate	Gear on Screw	Angle	Lead of Cam	Gear on Worm	First Intermediate	Second Intermediate	Gear on Screw	Angle	Lead of Cam	Gear on Worm	First Intermediate	Second Intermediate	Gear on Screw	Angle
1.200	24	72	32	86	14½	1.250	24	64	28	72	31	1.300	24	86	48	100	14
1.201	24	64	28	86	10½	1.251	24	86	48	100	21	1.301	24	72	40	100	12½
1.202	24	64	28	86	10	1.252	28	86	40	100	16	1.302	24	64	32	86	21
1.203	24	86	44	100	11½	1.253	24	72	40	100	20	1.303	24	86	48	100	13½
1.204	28	72	32	100	14½	1.254	24	64	32	86	26	1.304	24	72	40	100	12
1.205	24	86	44	100	11	1.255	28	86	40	100	15½	1.305	24	64	28	72	26½
1.206	24	72	32	86	13½	1.256	24	64	28	72	30½	1.306	24	72	40	100	11½
1.207	24	86	44	100	10½	1.257	24	72	40	100	19½	1.307	32	56	24	100	17½
1.208	24	72	32	86	13	1.258	28	86	40	100	15	1.308	24	72	40	100	11
1.209	24	86	44	100	10	1.259	24	86	48	100	20	1.309	28	86	44	100	24
1.210	28	72	32	100	13½	1.260	28	86	40	100	14½	1.310	24	64	28	72	26
1.211	24	72	32	86	12½	1.261	28	86	40	100	14½	1.311	24	72	40	100	10½
1.212	28	72	32	100	13	1.262	32	56	24	100	23	1.312	40	64	24	100	29
1.213	24	72	32	86	12	1.263	28	86	40	100	14	1.313	24	72	40	100	10
1.214	24	86	48	100	25	1.264	24	72	40	100	18½	1.314	28	86	44	100	23½
1.215	24	72	32	86	11½	1.265	28	86	44	100	28	1.315	24	86	48	100	11
1.216	32	56	24	100	27½	1.266	28	86	40	100	13½	1.316	28	64	32	100	20
1.217	24	72	32	86	11	1.267	24	86	48	100	19	1.317	28	72	32	86	24½
1.218	24	72	40	100	24	1.268	24	72	40	100	18	1.318	24	86	48	100	10½
1.219	24	72	32	86	10½	1.269	28	86	40	100	13	1.319	24	64	32	86	19
1.220	28	86	40	100	20½	1.270	24	72	44	100	30	1.320	24	86	48	100	10
1.221	24	72	32	86	10	1.271	28	86	40	100	12½	1.321	32	56	24	100	15½
1.222	24	72	40	100	23½	1.272	28	72	32	86	28½	1.322	28	72	32	86	24
1.223	28	72	32	100	10½	1.273	28	86	40	100	12	1.323	24	64	32	86	18½
1.224	28	86	40	100	20	1.274	28	86	40	100	12	1.324	32	56	24	100	15
1.225	28	72	32	100	10	1.275	24	72	40	100	17	1.325	28	86	48	100	32
1.226	24	72	48	100	40	1.276	28	86	40	100	11½	1.326	32	86	40	100	27
1.227	28	86	40	100	19½	1.277	28	86	44	100	27	1.327	32	56	24	100	14½
1.228	28	86	44	100	31	1.278	28	86	40	100	11	1.328	28	64	32	100	18½
1.229	24	86	48	100	23½	1.279	24	64	32	86	23½	1.329	28	86	44	100	22
1.230	28	64	32	100	28½	1.280	28	86	40	100	10½	1.330	32	56	24	100	14
1.231	28	86	40	100	19	1.281	24	72	40	100	16	1.331	28	64	32	100	18
1.232	24	72	40	100	22½	1.282	28	86	40	100	10	1.332	28	64	32	100	18
1.233	32	86	40	100	34	1.283	28	72	32	86	27½	1.333	32	56	24	100	13½
1.234	24	86	48	100	23	1.284	24	72	40	100	15½	1.334	24	64	32	86	17
1.235	28	86	40	100	18½	1.285	24	72	40	100	15½	1.335	28	64	32	100	17½
1.236	24	72	40	100	22	1.286	40	64	24	100	31	1.336	32	56	24	100	13
1.237	32	56	24	100	25½	1.287	24	72	40	100	15	1.337	28	72	32	86	22½
1.238	28	86	40	100	18	1.288	24	72	40	100	15	1.338	32	56	24	100	12½
1.239	24	64	32	72	42	1.289	24	64	32	86	22½	1.339	32	56	24	100	12½
1.240	24	72	40	100	21½	1.290	24	72	40	100	14½	1.340	24	72	44	100	24
1.241	28	86	44	100	30	1.291	24	72	40	100	14½	1.341	32	56	24	100	12
1.242	28	86	40	100	17½	1.292	32	56	24	100	19½	1.342	28	64	32	100	16½
1.243	32	56	24	100	25	1.293	24	72	40	100	14	1.343	32	56	24	100	11½
1.244	24	72	40	100	21	1.294	24	86	48	100	15	1.344	24	64	32	86	15½
1.245	28	86	40	100	17	1.295	28	72	32	86	26½	1.345	24	72	44	100	23½
1.246	32	72	40	100	45½	1.296	24	72	40	100	13½	1.346	32	56	24	100	11
1.247	24	86	48	100	21½	1.297	24	86	48	100	14½	1.347	24	64	32	86	15
1.248	28	86	40	100	16½	1.298	24	64	32	86	21½	1.348	32	56	24	100	10½
1.249	24	72	40	100	20½	1.299	24	72	40	100	13	1.349	28	64	32	100	15½

Change Gears and Angles for Cam Milling — 6

Lead of Cam	Gear on Worm	First Intermediate	Second Intermediate	Gear on Screw	Angle	Lead of Cam	Gear on Worm	First Intermediate	Second Intermediate	Gear on Screw	Angle	Lead of Cam	Gear on Worm	First Intermediate	Second Intermediate	Gear on Screw	Angle
1.350	32	56	24	100	10	1.400	40	64	24	100	21	1.450	32	86	40	100	13
1.351	24	64	32	86	14½	1.401	28	72	32	86	14½	1.451	28	64	32	86	27
1.352	28	64	32	100	15	1.402	28	86	44	100	12	1.452	40	64	24	100	14½
1.353	24	72	44	86	37½	1.403	24	72	44	100	17	1.453	32	86	40	100	12½
1.354	24	64	32	86	14	1.404	28	72	32	86	14	1.454	28	86	48	100	21½
1.355	28	64	32	100	14½	1.405	24	64	28	72	15½	1.455	32	86	40	100	12
1.356	24	64	32	86	13½	1.406	28	86	44	100	11	1.456	24	72	40	86	20
1.357	24	64	28	72	21½	1.407	28	72	32	86	13½	1.457	24	72	40	86	20
1.358	28	64	32	100	14	1.408	24	64	28	72	15	1.458	32	86	40	100	11½
1.359	24	64	32	86	13	1.409	28	86	44	100	10½	1.459	40	64	24	100	13½
1.360	28	72	32	86	20	1.410	28	72	32	86	13	1.460	24	44	32	86	44
1.361	28	64	32	100	13½	1.411	28	86	48	100	25½	1.461	32	86	40	100	11
1.362	24	64	32	86	12½	1.412	24	64	28	72	14½	1.462	40	64	24	100	13
1.363	28	86	44	100	18	1.413	28	72	32	86	12½	1.463	32	86	40	100	10½
1.364	24	64	32	86	12	1.414	24	72	44	100	15½	1.464	40	64	24	100	12½
1.365	24	64	32	86	12	1.415	28	72	32	86	12	1.465	32	86	40	100	10
1.366	24	64	28	72	20½	1.416	24	64	44	86	42½	1.466	24	72	40	86	19
1.367	24	64	32	86	11½	1.417	24	72	44	100	15	1.467	40	64	24	100	12
1.368	28	72	32	86	19	1.418	28	72	32	86	11½	1.468	28	64	40	100	33
1.369	24	64	32	86	11	1.419	32	86	40	100	17½	1.469	28	86	48	100	20
1.370	28	86	44	100	17	1.420	28	72	32	86	11	1.470	40	64	24	100	11½
1.371	24	64	32	86	10½	1.421	24	64	28	72	13	1.471	28	72	40	100	19
1.372	24	64	32	86	10½	1.422	40	64	24	100	18½	1.472	40	64	24	100	11
1.373	28	64	44	100	44½	1.423	28	72	32	86	10½	1.473	40	64	24	100	11
1.374	24	64	32	86	10	1.424	28	64	32	86	29	1.474	24	72	40	86	18
1.375	32	86	40	100	22½	1.425	28	72	32	86	10	1.475	40	64	24	100	10½
1.376	28	72	32	86	18	1.426	24	64	28	72	12	1.476	28	72	40	100	18½
1.377	28	64	32	100	10½	1.427	32	86	40	100	16½	1.477	40	64	24	100	10
1.378	28	86	44	100	16	1.428	28	86	48	100	24	1.478	24	72	40	86	17½
1.379	28	64	32	100	10	1.429	24	64	28	72	11½	1.479	24	64	32	72	27½
1.380	28	72	32	86	17½	1.430	32	86	40	100	16	1.480	28	72	40	100	18
1.381	28	86	44	100	15½	1.431	24	64	28	72	11	1.481	28	64	32	86	24½
1.382	24	64	32	72	34	1.432	24	72	44	100	12½	1.482	24	72	40	86	17
1.383	24	64	28	72	18½	1.433	28	86	48	100	23½	1.483	44	64	24	100	26
1.384	28	86	44	100	15	1.434	24	64	28	72	10½	1.484	28	72	40	100	17½
1.385	28	64	44	100	44	1.435	24	72	44	100	12	1.485	24	64	32	72	27
1.386	40	64	24	100	22½	1.436	24	64	28	72	10	1.486	24	72	40	86	16½
1.387	28	86	44	100	14½	1.437	32	86	40	100	15	1.487	28	86	48	100	18
1.388	28	64	32	86	31½	1.438	24	72	44	100	11½	1.488	28	72	40	100	17
1.389	32	86	40	100	21	1.439	28	86	48	100	23	1.489	24	72	48	100	21½
1.390	28	86	44	100	14	1.440	24	72	44	100	11	1.490	24	72	40	86	16
1.391	28	72	32	86	16	1.441	32	86	40	100	14½	1.491	28	86	48	100	17½
1.392	44	64	24	100	32½	1.442	24	72	44	100	10½	1.492	28	72	40	100	16½
1.393	28	86	44	100	13½	1.443	24	72	44	100	10½	1.493	28	64	32	86	23½
1.394	28	72	32	86	15½	1.444	32	86	40	100	14	1.494	24	72	40	86	15½
1.395	24	72	44	100	18	1.445	24	72	44	100	10	1.495	28	86	48	100	17
1.396	28	86	44	100	13	1.446	24	72	44	86	32	1.496	28	72	40	100	16
1.397	24	72	44	86	35	1.447	32	56	40	100	13½	1.497	24	72	40	86	15
1.398	28	72	32	86	15	1.448	28	72	40	100	21½	1.498	32	64	40	100	41½
1.399	28	86	44	100	12½	1.449	40	64	24	100	15	1.499	28	72	40	100	15½

Change Gears and Angles for Cam Milling — 7

Lead of Cam	Gear on Worm	First Intermediate	Second Intermediate	Gear on Screw	Angle	Lead of Cam	Gear on Worm	First Intermediate	Second Intermediate	Gear on Screw	Angle	Lead of Cam	Gear on Worm	First Intermediate	Second Intermediate	Gear on Screw	Angle
1.500	28	64	40	100	31	1.550	44	64	24	100	20	1.600	44	56	24	100	21
1.501	32	86	44	100	23½	1.551	44	64	24	100	20	1.601	28	64	32	86	10½
1.502	28	86	48	100	16	1.552	24	72	48	100	14	1.602	24	64	32	72	16
1.503	28	72	40	100	15	1.553	28	64	32	72	37	1.603	28	64	32	86	10
1.504	24	72	40	86	14	1.554	24	64	40	86	27	1.604	32	86	44	100	11½
1.505	24	64	32	72	25½	1.555	44	64	24	100	19½	1.605	40	56	24	100	20½
1.506	28	72	40	100	14½	1.556	24	64	32	72	21	1.606	24	64	32	72	15½
1.507	24	72	40	86	13½	1.557	28	64	32	86	17	1.607	32	86	44	100	11
1.508	24	72	48	100	19½	1.558	24	72	48	86	24	1.608	44	64	24	100	13
1.509	28	64	32	86	22	1.559	24	72	48	100	13	1.609	28	72	48	100	30½
1.510	24	72	40	86	13	1.560	44	64	24	100	19	1.610	32	86	44	100	10½
1.511	24	64	32	72	25	1.561	28	64	32	86	16½	1.611	24	64	44	100	12½
1.512	24	64	44	86	38	1.562	24	72	48	100	12½	1.612	32	86	44	100	10
1.513	24	72	40	86	12½	1.563	28	72	44	100	24	1.613	28	72	44	100	19½
1.514	24	72	48	86	35½	1.564	24	72	44	86	23½	1.614	24	64	44	100	12
1.515	28	64	32	86	21½	1.565	24	72	48	100	12	1.615	24	64	48	86	39½
1.516	24	72	40	86	12	1.566	32	86	44	100	17	1.616	40	56	24	100	19½
1.517	24	72	48	100	18½	1.567	28	64	44	100	35½	1.617	24	64	44	100	11½
1.518	32	86	44	100	22	1.568	24	72	48	100	11½	1.618	24	64	32	72	14
1.519	24	72	40	86	11½	1.569	28	64	32	86	15½	1.619	32	86	48	100	25
1.520	28	86	48	100	13½	1.570	32	72	40	100	28	1.620	44	64	24	100	11
1.521	24	72	40	86	11	1.571	24	72	48	100	11	1.621	24	64	32	72	13½
1.522	24	72	40	86	11	1.572	28	64	32	86	15	1.622	44	64	24	100	10½
1.523	28	86	48	100	13	1.573	24	72	48	100	10½	1.623	28	72	44	100	18½
1.524	24	72	40	86	10½	1.574	32	86	44	100	16	1.624	24	64	32	72	13
1.525	24	72	40	100	14½	1.575	24	72	44	86	22½	1.625	24	64	24	100	10
1.526	24	72	40	86	10	1.576	24	72	48	100	10	1.626	24	72	44	86	17½
1.527	28	72	40	100	11	1.577	32	86	44	100	15½	1.627	24	64	32	72	12½
1.528	32	86	44	100	24	1.578	44	64	24	100	17	1.628	24	64	32	72	12½
1.529	28	86	48	100	12	1.579	28	100	56	86	30	1.629	32	72	40	86	38
1.530	28	72	40	100	10½	1.580	28	64	32	86	14	1.630	24	64	32	72	12
1.531	28	72	44	100	26½	1.581	32	86	44	100	15	1.631	24	64	32	72	12
1.532	28	72	40	100	10	1.582	44	64	24	100	16½	1.632	28	72	44	100	17½
1.533	32	86	44	100	20½	1.583	28	64	32	86	13½	1.633	28	72	40	86	25½
1.534	28	86	48	100	11	1.584	40	56	24	100	22½	1.634	24	72	40	72	11½
1.535	28	64	32	86	19½	1.585	32	86	44	100	14½	1.635	24	72	44	86	16½
1.536	32	72	40	86	42	1.586	28	64	32	86	13	1.636	24	64	32	72	11
1.537	28	86	48	100	10½	1.587	24	64	40	100	24½	1.637	32	72	40	100	23
1.538	24	72	48	100	16	1.588	32	86	44	100	14	1.638	32	86	48	100	23½
1.539	28	86	48	100	10	1.589	28	64	32	85	12½	1.639	24	64	32	72	10½
1.540	28	100	56	72	45	1.590	44	64	24	100	15½	1.640	28	72	40	86	25
1.541	40	56	24	100	26	1.591	32	72	40	100	26½	1.641	28	72	44	100	16½
1.542	24	72	48	100	15½	1.592	28	64	32	86	12	1.642	24	64	32	72	10
1.543	32	86	44	100	19½	1.593	24	64	40	100	24	1.643	24	64	40	86	15½
1.544	28	64	32	86	18½	1.594	44	64	24	100	15	1.644	24	64	40	86	19½
1.545	24	72	48	100	15	1.595	28	64	32	86	11½	1.645	28	72	40	100	16
1.546	24	72	48	100	15	1.596	24	64	44	100	34	1.646	28	72	40	86	24½
1.547	40	56	24	100	25½	1.597	44	64	24	100	14½	1.647	24	72	44	86	15
1.548	28	64	32	86	18	1.598	28	64	32	86	11	1.648	40	56	24	100	16
1.549	24	72	48	100	14½	1.599	24	64	40	86	23½	1.649	28	72	44	100	15½

Change Gears and Angles for Cam Milling — 8

Lead of Cam	Gear on Worm	First Intermediate	Second Intermediate	Gear on Screw	Angle	Lead of Cam	Gear on Worm	First Intermediate	Second Intermediate	Gear on Screw	Angle	Lead of Cam	Gear on Worm	First Intermediate	Second Intermediate	Gear on Screw	Angle
1.650	28	64	40	100	19½	1.700	32	72	40	100	17	1.750	32	86	48	100	11½
1.651	24	72	44	86	14½	1.701	32	64	40	86	43	1.751	32	72	40	100	10
1.652	40	56	24	100	15½	1.702	28	64	40	100	13½	1.752	28	100	56	86	16
1.653	28	72	44	100	15	1.703	24	64	40	86	12½	1.753	32	86	48	100	11
1.654	24	72	44	86	14	1.704	28	64	40	72	45½	1.754	28	72	48	100	20
1.655	28	64	40	100	19	1.705	28	64	40	100	13	1.755	28	72	40	86	14
1.656	28	72	44	100	14½	1.706	24	64	40	86	12	1.756	32	86	48	100	10½
1.657	28	72	44	100	14½	1.707	40	86	44	100	33½	1.757	28	100	56	86	15½
1.658	24	72	44	86	13½	1.708	28	64	40	100	12½	1.758	32	72	44	100	26
1.659	24	64	40	86	18	1.709	24	64	40	86	11½	1.759	32	86	48	100	10
1.660	28	72	44	100	14	1.710	28	72	40	86	19	1.760	28	72	48	100	19½
1.661	24	72	44	86	13	1.711	32	72	44	100	29	1.761	28	100	56	86	15
1.662	32	86	48	100	21½	1.712	24	64	40	86	11	1.762	28	64	32	72	25
1.663	40	56	24	100	14	1.713	32	72	40	100	15½	1.763	28	72	40	86	13
1.664	28	72	44	100	13½	1.714	32	64	40	100	31	1.764	24	72	48	86	18½
1.665	28	72	44	86	12½	1.715	24	64	40	86	10½	1.765	28	100	56	86	14½
1.666	28	64	32	72	31	1.716	28	72	40	86	18½	1.766	28	72	40	86	12½
1.667	28	72	44	100	13	1.717	32	72	40	100	15	1.767	44	56	24	100	20½
1.668	28	72	44	86	12	1.718	24	64	40	86	10	1.768	32	72	48	100	34
1.669	28	64	40	100	17½	1.719	28	72	48	100	23	1.769	28	72	40	86	12
1.670	28	72	44	100	12½	1.720	28	72	40	86	18	1.770	28	72	48	100	18½
1.671	24	72	44	86	11½	1.721	28	64	40	100	10½	1.771	28	72	40	86	18½
1.672	24	64	40	86	16½	1.722	24	44	32	86	32	1.772	44	56	24	100	20
1.673	40	56	24	100	12½	1.723	28	64	40	100	10	1.773	28	72	40	86	11½
1.674	24	72	44	86	11	1.724	28	100	56	86	19	1.774	24	72	48	86	17½
1.675	28	64	44	100	29½	1.725	32	72	40	100	14	1.775	24	44	32	86	29
1.676	24	72	44	86	10½	1.726	24	56	40	86	30	1.776	28	72	40	86	11
1.677	28	72	44	100	11½	1.727	32	72	44	100	28	1.777	32	56	40	100	39
1.678	28	64	40	100	16½	1.728	32	72	40	100	13½	1.778	44	56	24	100	19½
1.679	24	72	44	86	10	1.729	32	72	40	100	13½	1.779	28	72	40	86	10½
1.680	28	72	44	100	11	1.730	28	72	40	86	17	1.780	28	100	56	86	12½
1.681	24	64	40	86	15½	1.731	24	72	48	86	21½	1.781	28	72	40	86	10
1.682	28	72	44	100	10½	1.732	32	72	40	100	13	1.782	32	64	40	100	27
1.683	40	56	24	100	11	1.733	32	86	48	100	14	1.783	28	100	56	86	12
1.684	32	86	48	100	19½	1.734	28	72	40	86	16½	1.784	24	56	40	86	26½
1.685	28	72	44	100	10	1.735	28	72	40	86	16½	1.785	28	72	48	100	17
1.686	28	64	40	100	15½	1.736	32	72	40	100	12½	1.786	28	100	56	86	11½
1.687	32	64	40	100	32½	1.737	32	86	48	100	13½	1.787	32	72	44	100	24
1.688	40	56	24	100	10	1.738	32	56	40	100	40½	1.788	24	72	48	86	16
1.689	32	86	48	100	19	1.739	32	72	40	100	12	1.789	28	100	56	86	11
1.690	28	64	40	100	15	1.740	32	86	48	100	13	1.790	28	100	56	86	11
1.691	32	72	40	100	18	1.741	28	72	44	86	29	1.791	24	64	44	86	21
1.692	24	64	40	86	14	1.742	32	72	40	100	11½	1.792	28	100	56	86	10½
1.693	24	72	48	86	24½	1.743	28	72	40	86	15½	1.793	28	100	56	86	10½
1.694	32	72	44	100	30	1.744	32	86	48	100	12½	1.794	44	56	24	100	18
1.695	44	56	24	100	26	1.745	32	72	40	100	11	1.795	28	100	56	86	10
1.696	24	64	40	86	13½	1.746	24	64	44	86	24½	1.796	28	64	32	72	22½
1.697	28	72	44	86	31½	1.747	32	86	48	100	12	1.797	24	72	48	86	15
1.698	28	64	40	100	14	1.748	32	72	40	100	10½	1.798	28	64	40	86	20½
1.699	24	64	40	86	13	1.749	28	72	48	100	20½	1.799	28	72	48	100	15½

Change Gears and Angles for Cam Milling — 9

Lead of Cam	Gear on Worm	First Intermediate	Second Intermediate	Gear on Screw	Angle	Lead of Cam	Gear on Worm	First Intermediate	Second Intermediate	Gear on Screw	Angle	Lead of Cam	Gear on Worm	First Intermediate	Second Intermediate	Gear on Screw	Angle
1.800	32	72	44	100	23	1.850	28	64	44	100	16	1.900	28	64	40	86	21
1.801	24	72	48	86	14½	1.851	44	56	24	100	11	1.901	28	64	32	72	12
1.802	28	64	32	72	22	1.852	28	72	44	86	21½	1.902	28	64	32	72	12
1.803	28	72	48	100	15	1.853	28	56	32	72	33½	1.903	28	72	44	86	17
1.804	32	72	44	86	37½	1.854	44	56	24	100	10½	1.904	24	64	48	86	24½
1.805	24	72	48	86	14	1.855	28	64	44	100	15½	1.905	28	64	32	72	11½
1.806	24	56	40	86	25	1.856	24	64	40	72	27	1.906	32	72	44	100	13
1.807	28	72	48	100	14½	1.857	44	56	24	100	10	1.907	32	64	40	100	17½
1.808	28	72	48	100	14½	1.858	24	64	44	86	14½	1.908	28	64	32	72	11
1.809	24	72	48	86	13½	1.859	28	64	44	100	15	1.909	32	72	48	100	26½
1.810	28	72	48	86	33½	1.860	32	72	44	100	18	1.910	32	72	44	100	12½
1.811	28	72	48	100	14	1.861	24	56	40	86	21	1.911	24	56	40	86	16½
1.812	24	72	48	86	13	1.862	24	64	44	86	14	1.912	28	64	32	72	10½
1.813	44	56	24	100	16	1.863	24	56	40	86	20½	1.913	32	72	44	100	12
1.814	24	64	44	86	19	1.864	28	64	44	100	14½	1.914	28	64	32	72	10
1.815	28	72	48	100	13½	1.865	32	72	44	100	17½	1.915	28	64	32	72	10
1.816	24	72	48	86	12½	1.866	24	64	44	86	13½	1.916	24	56	40	86	16
1.817	44	56	24	100	15½	1.867	32	64	40	100	21	1.917	32	72	44	100	11½
1.818	28	72	44	86	24	1.868	28	64	44	100	14	1.918	28	72	44	86	15½
1.819	24	72	48	86	12	1.869	28	64	32	72	16	1.919	24	44	32	86	19
1.820	24	64	44	86	18½	1.870	24	64	44	86	13	1.920	32	72	44	100	11
1.821	28	64	32	72	20½	1.871	32	72	44	100	17	1.921	24	56	40	86	15½
1.822	44	56	24	100	15	1.872	28	64	44	100	13½	1.922	28	72	44	86	15
1.823	24	72	48	86	11½	1.873	24	64	44	86	12½	1.923	32	72	44	100	10½
1.824	40	86	44	100	27	1.874	24	64	44	86	12½	1.924	28	64	40	86	19
1.825	24	64	44	86	18	1.875	32	72	44	100	16½	1.925	24	56	40	86	15
1.826	24	72	48	86	11	1.876	28	64	44	100	13	1.926	32	72	44	100	10
1.827	28	64	32	72	20	1.877	24	64	44	86	12	1.927	28	72	44	86	14½
1.828	24	56	40	86	23½	1.878	28	64	32	72	15	1.928	28	64	44	86	30½
1.829	24	72	48	86	10½	1.879	28	64	44	100	12½	1.929	24	56	40	86	14½
1.830	28	72	48	100	11½	1.880	24	64	44	86	11½	1.930	24	56	40	86	14½
1.831	28	64	44	100	18	1.881	32	72	40	86	24½	1.931	28	72	44	86	14
1.832	24	72	48	86	10	1.882	28	64	32	72	14½	1.932	32	64	40	100	15
1.833	28	72	48	100	11	1.883	28	64	44	100	12	1.933	48	56	24	100	20
1.834	44	56	24	100	13½	1.884	24	64	44	86	11	1.934	24	56	40	86	14
1.835	24	64	44	86	17	1.885	32	72	44	100	15½	1.935	28	72	44	86	13½
1.836	28	72	48	100	10½	1.886	28	64	44	100	11½	1.936	32	64	40	100	14½
1.837	28	64	40	86	25½	1.887	24	64	44	86	10½	1.937	28	64	48	86	37½
1.838	44	56	24	100	13	1.888	28	72	44	86	18½	1.938	24	56	40	86	13½
1.839	28	72	48	100	10	1.889	32	72	44	100	15	1.939	28	72	44	86	13
1.840	24	64	44	86	16½	1.890	24	64	44	86	10	1.940	28	64	48	100	22½
1.841	44	56	24	100	12½	1.891	32	64	40	100	19	1.941	32	64	40	100	14
1.842	32	72	40	86	27	1.892	32	72	48	100	27½	1.942	24	56	40	86	13
1.843	28	64	48	86	41	1.893	28	64	44	100	10½	1.943	28	72	44	86	12½
1.844	28	64	32	72	18½	1.894	28	64	32	72	13	1.944	32	56	40	86	43
1.845	44	56	24	100	12	1.895	24	56	40	86	18	1.945	48	56	24	100	19
1.846	28	64	44	100	16½	1.896	28	64	44	100	10	1.946	28	72	44	86	12
1.847	24	44	32	86	24½	1.897	32	64	40	100	18½	1.947	28	72	44	86	12
1.848	44	56	24	100	11½	1.898	28	64	32	72	12½	1.948	32	72	40	86	19½
1.849	24	64	44	86	15½	1.899	28	72	48	86	29	1.949	24	56	40	86	12

Change Gears and Angles for Cam Milling — 10

Lead of Cam	Gear on Worm	First Intermediate	Second Intermediate	Gear on Screw	Angle	Lead of Cam	Gear on Worm	First Intermediate	Second Intermediate	Gear on Screw	Angle	Lead of Cam	Gear on Worm	First Intermediate	Second Intermediate	Gear on Screw	Angle
1.950	28	72	44	86	11½	2.200	24	56	40	72	22½	2.450	24	64	48	72	11½
1.955	32	72	48	86	38	2.205	48	56	32	100	36½	2.455	40	72	48	100	23
1.960	28	72	44	86	10	2.210	48	100	56	86	45	2.460	28	64	48	72	32½
1.965	24	44	32	86	14½	2.215	24	56	40	72	21½	2.465	32	64	44	86	15½
1.970	32	64	40	100	10	2.220	32	72	44	86	12½	2.470	28	40	32	86	18½
1.975	28	64	40	86	14	2.225	28	44	32	86	20	2.475	32	64	40	72	27
1.980	28	64	48	100	19½	2.230	32	64	40	86	16½	2.480	44	48	28	100	15
1.985	24	64	48	86	18½	2.235	44	86	40	100	24½	2.485	28	72	56	86	11
1.990	28	64	40	86	12	2.240	32	56	40	86	11½	2.490	28	72	56	86	10½
1.995	40	86	44	100	13	2.245	28	64	56	86	38	2.495	24	44	40	86	10½
2.000	48	56	24	72	13½	2.250	24	64	44	72	11	2.500	28	64	48	72	31
2.005	28	100	56	72	23	2.255	32	64	48	100	20	2.505	24	56	44	72	17
2.010	32	72	40	100	13½	2.260	44	56	32	100	26	2.510	28	40	44	86	45½
2.015	40	86	48	100	25½	2.265	28	44	32	86	17	2.515	32	64	44	86	10½
2.020	28	72	48	86	21½	2.270	28	44	32	86	16½	2.520	44	48	28	100	11
2.025	32	72	40	86	11½	2.275	32	64	40	86	12	2.525	48	56	32	100	23
2.030	24	64	40	72	13	2.280	28	64	40	72	31½	2.530	24	56	44	72	15
2.035	24	64	48	86	13½	2.285	44	86	48	100	12½	2.535	32	56	40	86	17½
2.040	32	72	48	100	17	2.290	24	44	40	86	25½	2.540	32	64	48	86	24½
2.045	24	64	40	72	11	2.295	32	64	48	100	17	2.545	32	56	40	86	29½
2.050	28	64	48	100	12½	2.300	24	56	40	72	15	2.550	28	64	44	72	17½
2.055	28	64	48	86	11	2.305	24	56	40	72	14½	2.555	32	56	40	86	16
2.060	32	72	48	100	15	2.310	24	56	40	72	14	2.560	32	64	48	86	23½
2.065	28	64	48	100	10½	2.315	24	56	40	72	13½	2.565	28	40	32	86	10
2.070	32	72	48	100	14	2.320	28	44	32	86	11½	2.570	44	48	40	100	45½
2.075	40	44	24	100	18	2.325	28	44	32	86	11	2.575	24	56	44	72	10½
2.080	32	64	44	100	19	2.330	40	100	56	72	41½	2.580	40	72	56	86	44½
2.085	24	64	48	72	33½	2.335	28	64	48	86	17	2.585	32	56	40	86	13½
2.090	32	72	48	100	11½	2.340	24	56	48	72	35	2.590	32	56	40	86	13
2.095	28	56	32	72	19½	2.345	24	56	40	72	10	2.595	44	40	32	72	42½
2.100	28	44	32	86	27½	2.350	28	64	44	72	28½	2.600	32	56	40	86	12
2.105	40	86	48	100	19½	2.355	44	86	48	100	16½	2.605	32	56	40	86	11½
2.110	28	64	44	86	19½	2.360	32	64	44	100	10½	2.610	32	64	40	72	20
2.115	28	72	48	86	13	2.365	24	56	48	86	8½	2.615	24	56	48	100	44½
2.120	28	72	48	86	12½	2.370	24	44	32	72	19½	2.620	28	64	44	72	11½
2.125	32	64	44	100	15	2.375	28	64	48	86	13½	2.625	44	56	24	64	27
2.130	28	100	56	72	12	2.380	32	100	56	72	17	2.630	28	56	32	100	16½
2.135	28	72	48	86	10½	2.385	32	72	56	86	34½	2.635	40	72	48	86	22
2.140	24	56	40	72	26	2.390	28	64	40	72	10½	2.640	48	100	56	72	45
2.145	28	100	56	72	10	2.395	40	72	44	100	11½	2.645	24	40	44	86	30½
2.150	32	72	44	86	19	2.400	56	64	32	100	31	2.650	40	56	44	86	43½
2.155	44	56	32	100	31	2.405	28	64	48	86	10	2.655	56	64	32	100	18½
2.160	32	64	44	100	11	2.410	32	100	56	72	14½	2.660	44	48	40	100	43½
2.165	28	56	32	72	13	2.415	44	86	48	100	10½	2.665	28	64	48	72	24
2.170	32	72	48	86	29	2.420	32	100	56	72	13½	2.670	28	48	44	72	41½
2.175	32	72	44	86	17	2.425	32	100	56	72	13	2.675	48	64	28	56	44½
2.180	40	86	48	100	12½	2.430	32	100	56	72	12½	2.680	28	44	48	86	41
2.185	28	56	32	72	10½	2.435	32	72	48	86	11	2.685	40	100	56	72	44
2.190	32	56	40	86	34½	2.440	32	72	48	86	10½	2.690	40	64	44	100	12
2.195	28	64	48	86	26	2.445	44	56	32	100	13½	2.695	40	64	44	100	11½

Change Gears and Angles for Cam Milling — 11

Lead of Cam	Gear on Worm	First Intermediate	Second Intermediate	Gear on Screw	Angle	Lead of Cam	Gear on Worm	First Intermediate	Second Intermediate	Gear on Screw	Angle	Lead of Cam	Gear on Worm	First Intermediate	Second Intermediate	Gear on Screw	Angle
2.700	28	44	48	86	40½	2.950	40	64	48	100	10½	3.200	48	100	56	72	31
2.705	56	64	32	100	15	2.955	48	64	28	56	38	3.205	28	40	44	86	26½
2.710	40	72	56	86	41½	2.960	24	44	48	72	35½	3.210	24	44	48	72	28
2.715	40	56	44	86	42	2.965	32	64	44	72	14	3.215	40	64	48	72	39½
2.720	48	64	28	56	43½	2.970	32	64	48	72	27	3.220	56	44	28	86	39
2.725	44	48	40	100	42	2.975	40	56	44	86	35½	3.225	24	44	48	72	27½
2.730	48	100	56	72	43	2.980	48	40	28	100	27½	3.230	48	40	28	100	16
2.735	44	40	32	100	39	2.985	44	48	40	100	35½	3.235	32	72	64	86	12
2.740	28	44	48	86	39½	2.990	28	48	44	72	33	3.240	24	44	48	72	27
2.745	40	72	44	86	15	2.995	48	64	28	56	37	3.245	28	40	44	86	25
2.750	28	64	48	72	19½	3.000	40	100	56	64	31	3.250	44	64	48	100	10
2.755	44	40	32	100	38½	3.005	40	64	48	86	30½	3.255	32	48	40	72	28½
2.760	28	44	48	86	39	3.010	28	56	64	86	36	3.260	32	56	44	72	21
2.765	48	64	28	56	42½	3.015	48	64	28	56	36½	3.265	48	100	56	72	29
2.770	28	48	44	72	39	3.020	48	100	56	72	36	3.270	40	56	44	86	26½
2.775	40	72	44	86	12½	3.025	40	100	56	72	13½	3.275	44	40	32	100	21½
2.780	40	72	44	86	12	3.030	40	64	44	72	37½	3.280	48	64	28	56	29
2.785	24	44	48	72	40	3.035	24	40	48	86	25	3.285	32	48	40	72	27½
2.790	28	48	44	72	38½	3.040	44	48	40	100	34	3.290	32	44	40	86	13½
2.795	32	48	40	72	41	3.045	32	64	48	72	24	3.295	24	44	48	72	25
2.800	24	56	48	72	11½	3.050	40	56	44	100	14	3.300	32	48	40	72	27
2.805	24	56	48	72	11	3.055	56	44	28	86	42½	3.305	40	72	56	86	24
2.810	44	56	24	64	17½	3.060	28	44	48	86	30½	3.310	44	48	40	100	25½
2.815	28	44	40	86	18	3.065	40	56	44	86	33	3.315	32	48	40	72	26½
2.820	40	56	44	86	39½	3.070	28	40	44	86	31	3.320	28	40	44	86	22
2.825	32	56	44	72	36	3.075	44	48	40	100	33	3.325	40	56	44	86	24½
2.830	48	64	28	56	41	3.080	40	64	48	86	28	3.330	28	56	64	72	26½
2.835	28	48	40	72	29	3.085	28	56	64	86	34	3.335	28	64	56	72	11½
2.840	40	56	44	86	39	3.090	48	64	28	64	34½	3.340	40	64	44	86	29
2.845	28	44	40	86	16	3.095	48	100	56	72	34	3.345	32	44	48	86	34½
2.850	28	56	64	86	40	3.100	24	44	48	72	31½	3.350	44	48	40	100	24
2.855	28	44	48	86	36½	3.105	40	100	56	64	27½	3.355	48	100	56	72	26
2.860	40	56	44	86	38½	3.110	44	48	40	100	32	3.360	40	56	48	100	11½
2.865	24	44	48	72	38	3.115	28	48	40	72	16	3.365	28	40	44	86	20
2.870	44	48	40	100	38½	3.120	44	64	48	100	19	3.370	40	64	28	56	26
2.875	40	64	48	86	34½	3.125	32	56	44	72	26½	3.375	44	48	40	100	23
2.880	48	100	56	72	39½	3.130	32	56	48	86	11	3.380	32	56	48	86	27½
2.885	24	44	48	72	37½	3.135	28	44	48	86	28	3.385	28	64	56	86	25½
2.890	44	48	40	100	38	3.140	32	56	48	86	10	3.390	48	40	32	100	28
2.895	32	56	44	72	34	3.145	48	64	28	56	33	3.395	32	56	44	72	13½
2.900	28	44	40	86	11½	3.150	28	44	48	86	27½	3.400	40	56	44	86	21½
2.905	40	72	48	86	20½	3.155	28	64	56	72	22	3.405	28	44	48	86	16½
2.910	28	44	40	86	10½	3.160	44	48	40	100	30½	3.410	32	48	40	72	23
2.915	28	40	44	86	35½	3.165	24	44	48	72	29½	3.415	28	40	44	86	17½
2.920	28	48	44	72	35	3.170	28	48	40	72	12	3.420	32	40	48	86	40
2.925	40	64	48	86	33	3.175	32	48	40	72	31	3.425	28	56	64	86	23
2.930	32	64	44	72	16½	3.180	40	56	44	86	29½	3.430	28	44	48	86	15
2.935	48	64	28	56	38½	3.185	40	100	56	64	24½	3.435	40	100	56	64	20½
2.940	40	64	48	86	11½	3.190	28	56	64	86	31	3.440	48	100	56	64	35
2.945	40	72	56	86	35½	3.195	44	72	48	86	20½	3.445	28	44	48	86	14

GEARING

Spur Gearing

Definitions of Gear Terms. — The terms which follow are commonly applied to various classes of gearing.

Addendum: Height of tooth above pitch circle or the radial distance between the pitch circle and the top of the tooth (see illustration).

Arc of action: Arc of the pitch circle through which a tooth travels from the first point of contact with the mating tooth to the point where contact ceases.

Arc of approach: Arc of the pitch circle through which a tooth travels from the first point of contact with the mating tooth to the pitch point.

Arc of recession: Arc of the pitch circle through which a tooth travels from its contact with the mating tooth at the pitch point to the point where its contact ceases.

Backlash: The play between mating teeth or the shortest distance between the non-driving surfaces of adjacent teeth.

Base circle: The circle from which an involute tooth curve is generated or developed.

Chordal addendum: The radial distance from a line representing the chordal thickness at the pitch circle to the top of the tooth.

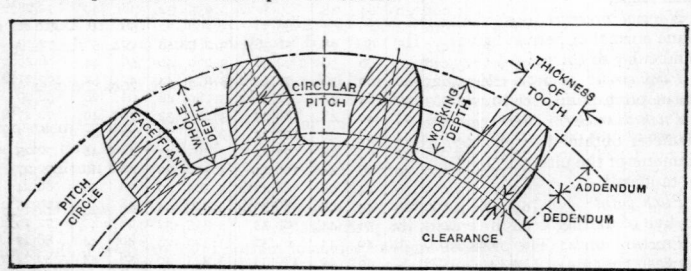

[Gear Tooth Parts

Chordal thickness: Length of the chord subtended by the circular thickness arc (the dimension obtained when a gear-tooth caliper is used to measure the thickness at the pitch circle).

Circular pitch: Length of the arc of the pitch circle between the centers or other corresponding points of adjacent teeth (see illustration).

Circular thickness: The thickness of the tooth on the pitch circle — also known as arc thickness.

Clearance: Radial distance between the top of a tooth and the bottom of the mating tooth space.

Contact ratio: Ratio of the arc of action to the circular pitch.

Dedendum: Depth of tooth space below pitch circle or radial dimension between the pitch circle and the bottom of a tooth space (see illustration).

Diametral pitch: Ratio of the number of teeth to the number of inches of pitch diameter — equals number of gear teeth to each inch of pitch diameter. (See also normal diametral pitch.)

Face of tooth: That surface of the tooth which is between the pitch circle and the top of the tooth.

Face width: Width of the pitch surface. The *active face width* is the width which actually makes contact with a mating gear. When herringbone gears have a central clearance groove, the width of this groove is not included in the active face width.

Flank of tooth: That surface which is between the pitch circle and the bottom land. The flank includes the fillet.

Internal diameter: The diameter of a circle coinciding with the tops of the teeth of an internal gear.

Land: The *top land* is the top surface of a tooth, and the *bottom land* is the surface of the gear between the flanks of adjacent teeth.

Line of action: That portion of the common tangent to the base circles along which contact between mating involute gear teeth occurs.

Module: Ratio of the pitch diameter to the number of teeth. Ordinarily, module is understood to mean ratio of pitch diameter *in millimeters* to the number of teeth. The English module is a ratio of the pitch diameter in inches to the number of teeth.

Normal circular pitch: The shortest distance on the pitch surface between the centers or any other corresponding points of adjacent teeth — applied to helical gearing.

Normal diametral pitch: The diametral pitch corresponding to the normal circular pitch and equal to number of teeth divided by the product of the pitch diameter and the cosine of the helix angle; also equals diametral pitch divided by cosine of the helix angle.

Normal pressure angle: Applied to helical gears to indicate pressure angle in a plane normal or perpendicular to the teeth as distinguished from a plane that is perpendicular to the axis of the gear.

Pitch circle: A circle the radius of which is equal to the distance from the gear axis to the pitch point (see illustration).

Pitch diameter: Diameter of the pitch circle (generally understood to mean the diameter obtained by dividing the number of teeth by the diametral pitch or the diameter of the pitch circle when the center-to-center distance between mating gears is standard).

Pitch point: The point of tangency of the pitch circles or the point where the center-line of mating gears intersects the pitch circles.

Pressure angle: The pressure angle of a pair of mating involute gears is the angle between the line of action and a line perpendicular to the center-line of these gears. (See also normal pressure angle.)

Ratio of gearing: Ratio of the numbers of teeth on mating gears. Ordinarily the ratio is found by dividing the number of teeth on the larger gear by the number of teeth on the smaller gear or pinion. For example, if the ratio is 2 or "2 to 1," this usually means that the smaller gear or pinion makes two revolutions to one revolution of the larger mating gear.

Root circle: A circle coinciding with the bottoms of the tooth spaces.

Root diameter: Diameter of the root circle.

Whole depth: Radial dimension between top of tooth and root circle — also known as total depth (see illustration).

Working depth: Depth to which a tooth extends into the tooth space of a mating gear when the center distance is standard — equals twice the addendum (see illustration).

Diametral and Circular Pitch Systems. — The diametral pitch system is applied to most of the cut gearing produced in the United States. If gear teeth are larger than about one diametral pitch, it is common practice to use the circular pitch system. The latter is also applied to smaller gears, particularly if the required center-to-center distance cannot be obtained by standard diametral pitch. In such cases a special circular pitch might be necessary. The circular pitch system is also applied to cast gearing and it is commonly used in connection with worm gearing, although such gearing may also be designed for diametral pitch.

Pitch Diameters Obtained with Diametral Pitch System. — The diametral pitch system is arranged to provide a series of standard tooth sizes, the principle being similar to the standardization of screw thread pitches. Inasmuch as there must be a whole number of teeth on each gear, the increase in pitch diameter per tooth varies according to the pitch. For example, the pitch diameter of a gear having, say, 20 teeth of 4 diametral pitch, will be 5 inches; 21 teeth, 5¼ inches, and so on, the increase in diameter for each additional tooth being equal to ¼ inch for 4 diametral pitch. Similarly, for 2 diametral pitch the variations for successive numbers of teeth would equal ½ inch, and for 10 diametral pitch the variations would equal ⅒ inch, etc. If a center distance cannot be obtained exactly with a given diametral pitch, ordinarily the designer can alter the center distance the amount required. (See Circular Pitch for Given Center Distance.)

American Standard Spur Gear Tooth Forms. — There are four American standard spur-gear tooth forms, and these basic tooth standards are also applied to some extent in designing certain other types of gears. In establishing a gear-tooth standard, it is only necessary to give the proportions of the rack teeth because the rack is the basis or foundation of a standard system of interchangeable spur gears.

American Standard 14½-Degree Full-Depth Tooth. — Standard tooth forms differ in regard to tooth depth for a given pitch and the angle or form of the basic rack tooth. The upper diagram, page 652, shows the rack of a standard 14½-degree full-depth involute tooth. The total depth equals 2.157 divided by the diametral pitch and the other proportions are indicated by the formulas for full-depth teeth (upper half of table, page 653). This total depth is termed " full depth." The " stub tooth," referred to later, is somewhat shorter for a given pitch.

This 14½-degree full-depth standard tooth form is very satisfactory, assuming that the tooth numbers are large enough to avoid excessive undercutting of the teeth. Undercutting will begin when the number of teeth is less than 32 and it may be excessive if the number is less than 22.

American Standard 20-Degree Full-Depth Tooth. — Practically the only difference between this 20-degree standard and the 14½-degree standard just referred to is in the pressure angle. (See second diagram, page 652.) The addendum, dedendum, and total depth are the same as for the 14½-degree full-depth tooth. This 20-degree rack tooth and gear teeth generated from it are wider at the base and consequently stronger than the 14½-degree standard as indicated by a comparison of the two basic rack diagrams. The larger pressure angle also reduces undercutting which begins when the number of teeth is less than 18 and may be excessive when the number is less than 14. The formulas for the 14½-degree and the 20-degree full-depth tooth standards are identical excepting the radius of the fillet at the base of the tooth.

American Standard 14½-Degree Composite System. — This standard differs from the 14½-degree full-depth involute system in regard to the form of the basic rack teeth. The nominal pressure angle is the same and also the various formulas for determining tooth depth, addendum, dedendum, etc. The straight-sided or involute form of rack, however, is modified by introducing a cycloidal curve below the pitch line, and also one above it to make the tooth symmetrical as required for interchangeable gearing. Since it would be impracticable to produce in the shop a rack with cycloidal curves, or a cutter of this exact form, the approximate form of rack shown by the third diagram, page 652, is used and meets practical requirements. The curves of this approximate rack are arcs having a radius equal to 3.750 divided by the diametral pitch. These curves are close approximations of the cycloidal curves on the theoretical rack.

The 14½-degree composite tooth form was developed originally for use with the form milling process and gear teeth conforming to this standard generally are cut by form milling. They can, however, be produced readily on hobbing or other generating machines by making a hob or cutter of the basic rack form. If a hob is used, the relieving tool can be made to the form of the basic rack tooth. The line of tooth action is longer with the composite system than with the pure involute tooth form.

American Standard 20-Degree Stub-Tooth Involute System. — This standard (see fourth diagram, page 652) differs from the 20-degree standard represented by the second diagram, in regard to the tooth depth, which equals 1.8 divided by the diametral pitch. The 20-degree pressure angle, in combination with a shorter tooth, strengthens the stub form and pinions with 12 and 13 teeth are only slightly undercut. The length of contact between mating gears, however, is shortened, which tends to offset the increase in individual tooth strength and also tends toward greater noise when the gears are running, unless this tendency is offset by greater accuracy in cutting and mounting. Whether this noise tendency constitutes an objectionable feature may, for a given grade of gearing, depend upon the class of service. For example, noise which might be excessive in an automotive transmission, would not be a factor in gearing applied to some other classes of machinery.

The 20-degree stub tooth is extensively used for automotive transmissions because relatively small gears are required and the maximum power-transmitting capacity for a given pitch or material is essential. For this class of service, however, very accurate gears are necessary and the mountings are designed to minimize noise. Helical forms of teeth are also utilized because they are conducive to smooth continuous action. The American Standard 20-degree stub tooth system is recommended by the American Gear Manufacturers' Association. Gears having this stub tooth may be used interchangeably with other stub-tooth systems and only the amount of clearance will be affected as the result of variations in tooth heights.

Fellows Stub-Tooth System. — The system of stub gear teeth introduced by the Fellows Gear Shaper Co. is based upon the use of two diametral pitches. One diametral pitch, say, 8, is used as the basis for obtaining the dimensions for the addendum and dedendum, while another diametral pitch, say, 6, is used for obtaining the dimensions of the thickness of the tooth, the number of teeth, and the pitch diameter. Teeth made according to this system are designated as $\frac{6}{8}$ pitch, $12\frac{1}{4}$ pitch, etc., the numerator in this fraction indicating the pitch determining the thickness of the tooth and the number of teeth, and the denominator, the pitch determining the depth of the tooth. The clearance is made greater than in the ordinary gear-tooth system and equals 0.25 ÷ denominator of the diametral pitch. The pressure angle is 20 degrees.

Nuttall Stub-Tooth System. — In a system of stub gear teeth originated by the R. D. Nuttall Co., the tooth dimensions are based directly upon the circular pitch. The addendum is made equal to 0.250 × the circular pitch, and the dedendum equal to 0.300 × the circular pitch. The pressure angle is 20 degrees.

Notation. — In formulas which follow and in the table of "Rules and Formulas for Dimensions of Spur Gears," the notation below is used:

P = diametral pitch;	C = center distance;
P' = circular pitch;	S = addendum;
N = number of teeth; (if the number of teeth in both gear and pinion are referred to, N_g = number of teeth in gear, and N_p = number of teeth in pinion);	F = face width;
	W = whole depth of tooth;
	T = thickness of tooth of **pitch circle**;
	O = outside diameter of gear;
D = pitch diameter;	V = velocity in feet per **minute at** pitch diameter.

American Standard Spur Gear Tooth Forms
(Formulas on next page)

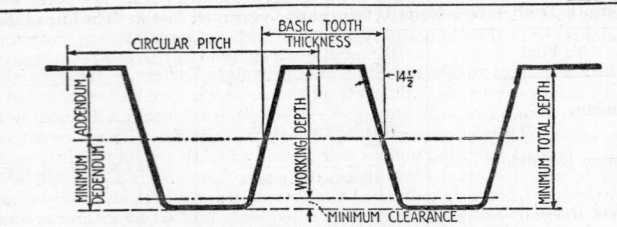

Basic Rack of the 14 1/2-Degree Full-Depth Involute System

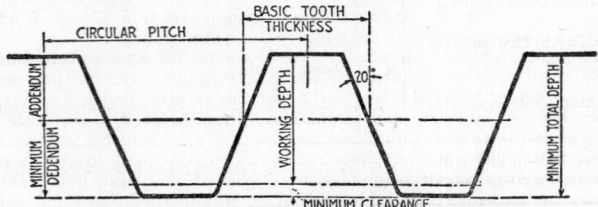

Basic Rack of the 20-Degree Full-Depth Involute System

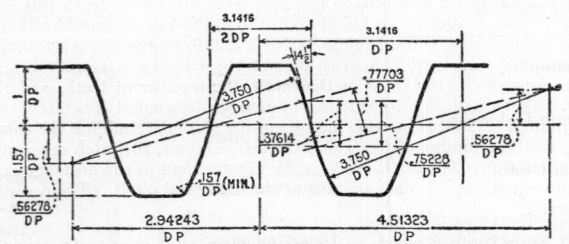

Approximation of Basic Rack for the 14 1/2-Degree Composite System

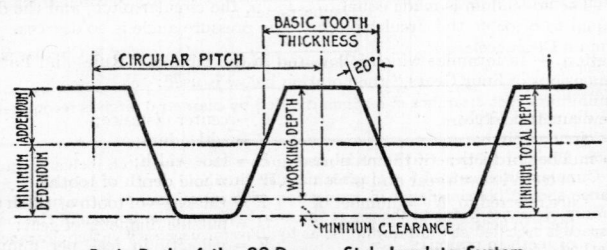

Basic Rack of the 20-Degree Stub Involute System

American Standard Spur Gear Tooth Forms

Full-depth Teeth — 14½-degree Involute and Composite; also 20-degree Involute

To Find	Diametral Pitch Known	Circular Pitch Known
Addendum.................	$\dfrac{1}{\text{Diametral pitch}}$	0.3183 × Circular pitch
Minimum Dedendum.....	$\dfrac{1.157}{\text{Diametral pitch}}$	0.3683 × Circular pitch
Working Depth..........	$\dfrac{2}{\text{Diametral pitch}}$	0.6366 × Circular pitch
Minimum Total Depth....	$\dfrac{2.157}{\text{Diametral pitch}}$	0.6866 × Circular pitch
Basic Tooth Thickness on Pitch Line.............	$\dfrac{1.5708}{\text{Diametral pitch}}$	0.5 × Circular pitch
Minimum Clearance.......	$\dfrac{0.157}{\text{Diametral pitch}}$	0.05 × Circular pitch

Note: Radius of Fillet = 1⅓ × Clearance for 14½-degree full-depth tooth and 1½ × Clearance for 20-degree full-depth tooth.

Stub Teeth — Involute System

To Find	Diametral Pitch Known	Circular Pitch Known
Addendum.................	$\dfrac{0.8}{\text{Diametral pitch}}$	0.2546 × Circular pitch
Minimum Dedendum.....	$\dfrac{1}{\text{Diametral pitch}}$	0.3183 × Circular pitch
Working Depth..........	$\dfrac{1.6}{\text{Diametral pitch}}$	0.5092 × Circular pitch
Minimum Total Depth....	$\dfrac{1.8}{\text{Diametral pitch}}$	0.5729 × Circular pitch
Basic Tooth Thickness on Pitch Line.............	$\dfrac{1.5708}{\text{Diametral pitch}}$	0.5 × Circular pitch
Minimum Clearance.......	$\dfrac{0.2}{\text{Diametral pitch}}$	0.0637 × Circular pitch

A minimum root clearance of 0.2 inch divided by diametral pitch is recommended for new cutters and gears.

Note: The term Diametral Pitch is used up to 1 diametral pitch inclusive and the term Circular Pitch is used for 3 inches circular pitch and over. A suitable working tolerance should be considered in connection with all minimum recommendations. Minimum clearance between the top of the gear tooth and the bottom of the mating gear space is specified as "minimum" so as to allow for necessary cutter clearance for all methods of producing gears.

Rules and Formulas for Dimensions of Spur Gears*

No. of Rule	To Find	Rule	Formula
1	Diametral Pitch	Divide 3.1416 by circular pitch.	$P = \dfrac{3.1416}{P'}$
2	Circular Pitch	Divide 3.1416 by diametral pitch.	$P' = \dfrac{3.1416}{P}$
3	Pitch Diameter	Divide number of teeth by diametral pitch.	$D = \dfrac{N}{P}$
4	Pitch Diameter	Multiply number of teeth by circular pitch and divide the product by 3.1416.	$D = \dfrac{NP'}{3.1416}$
5	Center Distance	Add the number of teeth in both gears and divide the sum by two times the diametral pitch.	$C = \dfrac{N_g + N_p}{2\,P}$
6	Center Distance	Multiply the sum of the number of teeth in both gears by circular pitch and divide the product by 6.2832.	$C = \dfrac{(N_g + N_p)\,P'}{6.2832}$
7	Addendum	Divide 1 by diametral pitch.	$S = \dfrac{1}{P}$
8	Addendum	Divide circular pitch by 3.1416.	$S = \dfrac{P'}{3.1416}$
9	Clearance	Divide 0.157 by diametral pitch.	$\dfrac{0.157}{P}$
10	Clearance	Divide circular pitch by 20.	$\dfrac{P'}{20}$
11	Whole Depth of Tooth	Divide 2.157 by diametral pitch.	$W = \dfrac{2.157}{P}$
12	Whole Depth of Tooth	Multiply 0.6866 by circular pitch.	$W = 0.6866\,P'$
13	Thickness of Tooth	Divide 1.5708 by diametral pitch.	$T = \dfrac{1.5708}{P}$
14	Thickness of Tooth	Divide circular pitch by 2.	$T = \dfrac{P'}{2}$
15	Outside Diameter	Add 2 to the number of teeth and divide the sum by diametral pitch.	$O = \dfrac{N+2}{P}$
16	Outside Diameter	Multiply the sum of the number of teeth plus 2 by circular pitch and divide the product by 3.1416.	$O = \dfrac{(N+2)\,P'}{3.1416}$
17	Diametral Pitch	Divide number of teeth by pitch diameter.	$P = \dfrac{N}{D}$
18	Circular Pitch	Multiply pitch diameter by 3.1416 and divide by number of teeth.	$P' = \dfrac{3.1416\,D}{N}$
19	Pitch Diameter	Subtract two times the addendum from outside diameter.	$D = O - 2S$
20	Number of Teeth	Multiply pitch diameter by diametral pitch.	$N = P \times D$
21	Number of Teeth	Multiply pitch diameter by 3.1416 and divide the product by circular pitch.	$N = \dfrac{3.1416\,D}{P'}$
22	Outside Diameter	Add two times the addendum to the pitch diameter.	$O = D + 2S$
23	Base Circle Diameter	Multiply pitch diam. by cosine pressure angle; use same rule for internal gears	$D_b = D \cos A$
24	Length of Rack	Multiply number of rack teeth by 3.1416 and divide by diametral pitch	$L = \dfrac{3.1416\,N}{P}$

* Rules and formulas relating to tooth depth and outside diam. apply to full-depth teeth.

Gear Tooth Parts

(Diametral Pitch Gears)

Diametral Pitch	Circular Pitch	Thickness of Tooth on Pitch Line	Addendum	Working Depth of Tooth	Depth of Space below Pitch Line	Whole Depth of Tooth
P	P'	T	S	W'	$S+F$	W
½	6.2832	3.1416	2.0000	4.0000	2.3142	4.3142
¾	4.1888	2.0944	1.3333	2.6666	1.5428	2.8761
1	3.1416	1.5708	1.0000	2.0000	1.1571	2.1571
1¼	2.5133	1.2566	0.8000	1.6000	0.9257	1.7257
1½	2.0944	1.0472	0.6666	1.3333	0.7714	1.4381
1¾	1.7952	0.8976	0.5714	1.1429	0.6612	1.2326
2	1.5708	0.7854	0.5000	1.0000	0.5785	1.0785
2¼	1.3963	0.6981	0.4444	0.8888	0.5143	0.9587
2½	1.2566	0.6283	0.4000	0.8000	0.4628	0.8628
2¾	1.1424	0.5712	0.3636	0.7273	0.4208	0.7844
3	1.0472	0.5236	0.3333	0.6666	0.3857	0.7190
3½	0.8976	0.4488	0.2857	0.5714	0.3306	0.6163
4	0.7854	0.3927	0.2500	0.5000	0.2893	0.5393
5	0.6283	0.3142	0.2000	0.4000	0.2314	0.4314
6	0.5236	0.2618	0.1666	0.3333	0.1928	0.3595
7	0.4488	0.2244	0.1429	0.2857	0.1653	0.3081
8	0.3927	0.1963	0.1250	0.2500	0.1446	0.2696
9	0.3491	0.1745	0.1111	0.2222	0.1286	0.2397
10	0.3142	0.1571	0.1000	0.2000	0.1157	0.2157
11	0.2856	0.1428	0.0909	0.1818	0.1052	0.1961
12	0.2618	0.1309	0.0833	0.1666	0.0964	0.1798
13	0.2417	0.1208	0.0769	0.1538	0.0890	0.1659
14	0.2244	0.1122	0.0714	0.1429	0.0826	0.1541
15	0.2094	0.1047	0.0666	0.1333	0.0771	0.1438
16	0.1963	0.0982	0.0625	0.1250	0.0723	0.1348
17	0.1848	0.0924	0.0588	0.1176	0.0681	0.1269
18	0.1745	0.0873	0.0555	0.1111	0.0643	0.1198
19	0.1653	0.0827	0.0526	0.1053	0.0609	0.1135
20	0.1571	0.0785	0.0500	0.1000	0.0579	0.1079
22	0.1428	0.0714	0.0455	0.0909	0.0526	0.0980
24	0.1309	0.0654	0.0417	0.0833	0.0482	0.0898
26	0.1208	0.0604	0.0385	0.0769	0.0445	0.0829
28	0.1122	0.0561	0.0357	0.0714	0.0413	0.0770
30	0.1047	0.0524	0.0333	0.0666	0.0386	0.0719
32	0.0982	0.0491	0.0312	0.0625	0.0362	0.0674
34	0.0924	0.0462	0.0294	0.0588	0.0340	0.0634
36	0.0873	0.0436	0.0278	0.0555	0.0321	0.0599
38	0.0827	0.0413	0.0263	0.0526	0.0304	0.0568
40	0.0785	0.0393	0.0250	0.0500	0.0289	0.0539
42	0.0748	0.0374	0.0238	0.0476	0.0275	0.0514
44	0.0714	0.0357	0.0227	0.0455	0.0263	0.0490
46	0.0683	0.0341	0.0217	0.0435	0.0252	0.0469
48	0.0654	0.0327	0.0208	0.0417	0.0241	0.0449
50	0.0628	0.0314	0.0200	0.0400	0.0231	0.0431

Gear Tooth Parts

(Circular Pitch Gears)

Circular Pitch	Diametral Pitch	Thickness of Tooth on Pitch Line	Addendum	Working Depth of Tooth	Depth of Space below Pitch Line	Whole Depth of Tooth
P'	P	T	S	W'	$S + F$	W
4	0.7854	2.0000	1.2732	2.5464	1.4732	2.7464
3½	0.8976	1.7500	1.1140	2.2281	1.2890	2.4031
3	1.0472	1.5000	0.9549	1.9098	1.1049	2.0598
2¾	1.1424	1.3750	0.8753	1.7506	1.0128	1.8881
2½	1.2566	1.2500	0.7957	1.5915	0.9207	1.7165
2¼	1.3963	1.1250	0.7162	1.4323	0.8287	1.5448
2	1.5708	1.0000	0.6366	1.2732	0.7366	1.3732
1⅞	1.6755	0.9375	0.5968	1.1937	0.6906	1.2874
1¾	1.7952	0.8750	0.5570	1.1141	0.6445	1.2016
1⅝	1.9333	0.8125	0.5173	1.0345	0.5985	1.1158
1½	2.0944	0.7500	0.4775	0.9549	0.5525	1.0299
1⁷⁄₁₆	2.1855	0.7187	0.4576	0.9151	0.5294	0.9870
1⅜	2.2848	0.6875	0.4377	0.8754	0.5064	0.9441
1⁵⁄₁₆	2.3936	0.6562	0.4178	0.8356	0.4834	0.9012
1¼	2.5133	0.6250	0.3979	0.7958	0.4604	0.8583
1³⁄₁₆	2.6456	0.5937	0.3780	0.7560	0.4374	0.8154
1⅛	2.7925	0.5625	0.3581	0.7162	0.4143	0.7724
1¹⁄₁₆	2.9568	0.5312	0.3382	0.6764	0.3913	0.7295
1	3.1416	0.5000	0.3183	0.6366	0.3683	0.6866
¹⁵⁄₁₆	3.3510	0.4687	0.2984	0.5968	0.3453	0.6437
⅞	3.5904	0.4375	0.2785	0.5570	0.3223	0.6007
¹³⁄₁₆	3.8666	0.4062	0.2586	0.5173	0.2993	0.5579
¾	4.1888	0.3750	0.2387	0.4775	0.2762	0.5150
¹¹⁄₁₆	4.5696	0.3437	0.2189	0.4377	0.2532	0.4720
⅔	4.7124	0.3333	0.2122	0.4244	0.2455	0.4577
⅝	5.0265	0.3125	0.1989	0.3979	0.2301	0.4291
⁹⁄₁₆	5.5851	0.2812	0.1790	0.3581	0.2071	0.3862
½	6.2832	0.2500	0.1592	0.3183	0.1842	0.3433
⁷⁄₁₆	7.1808	0.2187	0.1393	0.2785	0.1611	0.3003
⅖	7.8540	0.2000	0.1273	0.2546	0.1473	0.2746
⅜	8.3776	0.1875	0.1194	0.2387	0.1381	0.2575
⅓	9.4248	0.1666	0.1061	0.2122	0.1228	0.2289
⁵⁄₁₆	10.0531	0.1562	0.0995	0.1989	0.1151	0.2146
²⁄₇	10.9956	0.1429	0.0909	0.1819	0.1052	0.1962
¼	12.5664	0.1250	0.0796	0.1591	0.0921	0.1716
²⁄₉	14.1372	0.1111	0.0707	0.1415	0.0818	0.1526
⅕	15.7080	0.1000	0.0637	0.1273	0.0737	0.1373
³⁄₁₆	16.7552	0.0937	0.0597	0.1194	0.0690	0.1287
⅙	18.8496	0.0833	0.0531	0.1061	0.0614	0.1144
⅐	21.9911	0.0714	0.0455	0.0910	0.0526	0.0981
⅛	25.1327	0.0625	0.0398	0.0796	0.0460	0.0858
⅑	28.2743	0.0555	0.0354	0.0707	0.0409	0.0763
⅒	31.4159	0.0500	0.0318	0.0637	0.0368	0.0687
¹⁄₁₆	50.2655	0.0312	0.0199	0.0398	0.0230	0.0429

Standard 20-Degree Stub Teeth

Dimensions Based Upon Formulas of the American Standard

Diametral Pitch	Circular Pitch	Thickness of Tooth on Pitch Line	Addendum	Working Depth of Tooth	Dedendum or Depth of Space Below Pitch Line	Whole Depth of Tooth
½	6.2832	3.1416	1.6000	3.2000	2.0000	3.6000
¾	4.1888	2.0944	1.0667	2.1334	1.3333	2.4000
1	3.1416	1.5708	.8000	1.6000	1.0000	1.8000
1¼	2.5133	1.2566	0.6400	1.2800	0.8000	1.4400
1½	2.0944	1.0472	0.5333	1.0666	0.6667	1.2000
1¾	1.7952	0.8976	0.4571	0.9142	0.5714	1.0285
2	1.5708	0.7854	0.4000	0.8000	0.5000	0.9000
2¼	1.3963	0.6981	0.3556	0.7112	0.4444	0.8000
2½	1.2566	0.6283	0.3200	0.6400	0.4000	0.7200
2¾	1.1424	0.5712	0.2909	0.5818	0.3636	0.6545
3	1.0472	0.5236	0.2667	0.5334	0.3333	0.6000
3½	0.8976	0.4488	0.2286	0.4572	0.2857	0.5143
4	0.7854	0.3927	0.2000	0.4000	0.2500	0.4500
5	0.6283	0.3142	0.1600	0.3200	0.2000	0.3600
6	0.5236	0.2618	0.1333	0.2666	0.1667	0.3000
7	0.4488	0.2244	0.1143	0.2286	0.1428	0.2571
8	0.3927	0.1963	0.1000	0.2000	0.1250	0.2250
9	0.3491	0.1745	0.0889	0.1778	0.1111	0.2000
10	0.3142	0.1571	0.0800	0.1600	0.1000	0.1800
11	0.2856	0.1428	0.0727	0.1454	0.0909	0.1636
12	0.2618	0.1309	0.0667	0.1334	0.0833	0.1500
13	0.2417	0.1208	0.0615	0.1230	0.0769	0.1384
14	0.2244	0.1122	0.0571	0.1142	0.0714	0.1285
15	0.2094	0.1047	0.0533	0.1066	0.0667	0.1200
16	0.1963	0.0982	0.0500	0.1000	0.0625	0.1125
17	0.1848	0.0924	0.0470	0.0940	0.0588	0.1058
18	0.1745	0.0873	0.0444	0.0888	0.0556	0.1000
19	0.1653	0.0827	0.0421	0.0842	0.0526	0.0947
20	0.1571	0.0785	0.0400	0.0800	0.0500	0.0900
22	0.1428	0.0714	0.0364	0.0728	0.0454	0.0818
24	0.1309	0.0654	0.0333	0.0666	0.0417	0.0750
26	0.1208	0.0604	0.0308	0.0616	0.0384	0.0692
28	0.1122	0.0561	0.0286	0.0572	0.0357	0.0643
30	0.1047	0.0524	0.0267	0.0534	0.0333	0.0600
32	0.0982	0.0491	0.0250	0.0500	0.0312	0.0562
34	0.0924	0.0462	0.0236	0.0472	0.0294	0.0530
36	0.0873	0.0436	0.0222	0.0444	0.0278	0.0500
38	0.0827	0.0413	0.0210	0.0420	0.0263	0.0473
40	0.0785	0.0393	0.0200	0.0400	0.0250	0.0450

Dimensions of Stub Gear Teeth (Fellows Gear Shaper Co.'s System)

Diametral Pitch	Thickness of Tooth	Addendum	Working Depth	Depth of Space below Pitch Line	Clearance	Whole Depth of Tooth
4/5	0.3927	0.2000	0.4000	0.2500	0.0500	0.4500
5/7	0.3142	0.1429	0.2858	0.1786	0.0357	0.3214
6/8	0.2618	0.1250	0.2500	0.1562	0.0312	0.2812
7/9	0.2244	0.1111	0.2222	0.1389	0.0278	0.2500
8/10	0.1963	0.1000	0.2000	0.1250	0.0250	0.2250
9/11	0.1745	0.0909	0.1818	0.1136	0.0227	0.2045
10/12	0.1571	0.0833	0.1667	0.1041	0.0208	0.1875
12/14	0.1309	0.0714	0.1429	0.0893	0.0179	0.1607

Diametral Pitch Gear Tooth Parts for Stub Teeth (Nuttall System)

(Based on: addendum = 0.250 × circular pitch; dedendum = 0.300 × circular pitch.)

Diametral Pitch	Equivalent Circular Pitch	Thickness of Tooth on Pitch Line	Addendum	Working Depth	Depth of Space below Pitch Line	Whole Depth
½	6.2832	3.1416	1.5708	3.1416	1.8849	3.4557
¾	4.1888	2.0944	1.0472	2.0944	1.2566	2.3038
1	3.1416	1.5708	0.7854	1.5708	0.9424	1.7278
1¼	2.5133	1.2566	0.6283	1.2566	0.7539	1.3822
1½	2.0944	1.0472	0.5236	1.0472	0.6283	1.1519
1¾	1.7952	0.8976	0.4488	0.8976	0.5385	0.9873
2	1.5708	0.7854	0.3927	0.7854	0.4712	0.8639
2¼	1.3963	0.6981	0.3490	0.6981	0.4188	0.7678
2½	1.2566	0.6283	0.3141	0.6283	0.3769	0.6910
2¾	1.1424	0.5712	0.2856	0.5712	0.3427	0.6283
3	1.0472	0.5236	0.2618	0.5236	0.3141	0.5759
3½	0.8976	0.4488	0.2244	0.4488	0.2692	0.4936
4	0.7854	0.3927	0.1963	0.3927	0.2355	0.4318
5	0.6283	0.3141	0.1570	0.3142	0.1884	0.3454
6	0.5236	0.2618	0.1309	0.2618	0.1571	0.2880
7	0.4488	0.2244	0.1122	0.2244	0.1346	0.2468
8	0.3927	0.1963	0.0981	0.1963	0.1177	0.2158
9	0.3491	0.1745	0.0872	0.1745	0.1046	0.1918
10	0.3142	0.1571	0.0785	0.1571	0.0942	0.1727
11	0.2856	0.1428	0.0714	0.1428	0.0857	0.1571
12	0.2618	0.1309	0.0654	0.1309	0.0785	0.1439
13	0.2417	0.1208	0.0604	0.1208	0.0725	0.1329
14	0.2244	0.1122	0.0561	0.1122	0.0673	0.1234
15	0.2094	0.1047	0.0523	0.1047	0.0627	0.1150
16	0.1963	0.0982	0.0491	0.0982	0.0589	0.1080
17	0.1848	0.0924	0.0462	0.0924	0.0554	0.1016
18	0.1745	0.0873	0.0436	0.0873	0.0523	0.0959
19	0.1653	0.0827	0.0413	0.0827	0.0495	0.0908
20	0.1571	0.0785	0.0392	0.0785	0.0470	0.0862
22	0.1428	0.0714	0.0357	0.0714	0.0423	0.0785

Circular Pitch Gear Tooth Parts for Stub Teeth (Nuttall System)

(Based on: addendum = 0.250 × circular pitch; dedendum = 0.300 × circular pitch.)

Circular Pitch	Circular Pitch (Decimal Equivalent)	Diametral Pitch	Thickness of Tooth on Pitch Line	Addendum	Working Depth	Depth of Space below Pitch Line	Whole Depth
2	2.0000	1.5708	1.0000	0.5000	1.0000	0.6000	1.1000
1⅞	1.8750	1.6755	0.9375	0.4687	0.9375	0.5624	1.0311
1¾	1.7500	1.7952	0.8750	0.4375	0.8750	0.5250	0.9625
1⅝	1.6250	1.9333	0.8125	0.4062	0.8125	0.4874	0.8936
1½	1.5000	2.0944	0.7500	0.3750	0.7500	0.4500	0.8250
1⁷⁄₁₆	1.4375	2.1855	0.7187	0.3593	0.7187	0.4311	0.7904
1⅜	1.3750	2.2848	0.6875	0.3437	0.6875	0.4124	0.7561
1⅓	1.3333	2.3562	0.6666	0.3333	0.6666	0.3999	0.7332
1⁵⁄₁₆	1.3125	2.3936	0.6562	0.3281	0.6562	0.3937	0.7218
1¼	1.2500	2.5133	0.6250	0.3125	0.6250	0.3750	0.6875
1³⁄₁₆	1.1875	2.6456	0.5937	0.2968	0.5937	0.3561	0.6529
1⅛	1.1250	2.7925	0.5625	0.2812	0.5625	0.3374	0.6186
1¹⁄₁₆	1.0625	2.9568	0.5312	0.2656	0.5312	0.3187	0.5843
1	1.0000	3.1416	0.5000	0.2500	0.5000	0.3000	0.5500
15⁄16	0.9375	3.3510	0.4687	0.2343	0.4687	0.2811	0.5154
⅞	0.8750	3.5904	0.4375	0.2187	0.4375	0.2624	0.4811
13⁄16	0.8125	3.8666	0.4062	0.2031	0.4062	0.2437	0.4468
¾	0.7500	4.1888	0.3750	0.1875	0.3750	0.2250	0.4125
11⁄16	0.6875	4.5696	0.3437	0.1718	0.3437	0.2061	0.3779
⅔	0.6666	4.7124	0.3333	0.1666	0.3333	0.1999	0.3666
⅝	0.6250	5.0265	0.3125	0.1562	0.3125	0.1874	0.3436
9⁄16	0.5625	5.5851	0.2812	0.1400	0.2812	0.1687	0.3093
½	0.5000	6.2832	0.2500	0.1250	0.2500	0.1500	0.2750
7⁄16	0.4375	7.1808	0.2187	0.1093	0.2187	0.1311	0.2404
⅜	0.3750	8.3776	0.1875	0.0937	0.1875	0.1124	0.2061
⅓	0.3333	9.4248	0.1666	0.0833	0.1666	0.0999	0.1832
5⁄16	0.3125	10.0531	0.1562	0.0781	0.1562	0.0937	0.1718
¼	0.2500	12.5664	0.1250	0.0625	0.1250	0.0750	0.1375
⅕	0.2000	15.7080	0.1000	0.0500	0.1000	0.0600	0.1100
3⁄16	0.1875	16.7552	0.0937	0.0468	0.0937	0.0561	0.1029
⅙	0.1666	18.8496	0.0833	0.0416	0.0833	0.0499	0.0915
⅛	0.1250	25.1327	0.0625	0.0312	0.0625	0.0374	0.0686
⅑	0.1111	28.2743	0.0555	0.0277	0.0555	0.0332	0.0609
⅒	0.1000	31.4159	0.0500	0.0250	0.0500	0.0300	0.0550
1⁄16	0.0625	50.2655	0.0312	0.0156	0.0312	0.0187	0.0343
1⁄20	0.0500	62.8318	0.0250	0.0125	0.0250	0.0150	0.0275

Clearance of Gears Cut on the Gear Shaper. — When gears are cut on the gear shaper, the clearance is made equal to 0.25 ÷ diametral pitch. Hence the root diameter of these gears is smaller than the root diameter of ordinary milled gears. A table is given (page 694) of root diameters of gears cut on the gear shaper. The pitch and outside (blank) diameters are the same as for diametral pitch gears, and the tables, "Pitch Diameters of Diametral Pitch Gears," and "Outside Diameters of Diametral Pitch Gears," apply to gears cut on the gear shaper also.

Rules for Spur Gears Having Stub Teeth

To Find	Rule
Pitch Diameter	*Rule:* For American Standard 20-Degree Stub-Tooth Gear divide the number of teeth N by the diametral pitch P, the same as for full-depth teeth. *Rule:* For Fellows Stub-Tooth Gear divide the number of teeth by the pitch given in the numerator of the pitch fraction (by 6 if the pitch is 6/8) to find pitch diameter. *Example:* What is the pitch diameter of a Fellows stub-tooth gear of 6/8 pitch and 24 teeth? $$D = \frac{24}{6} = 4 \text{ inches}$$
Outside Diameter	*Rule:* For American Standard 20-Degree Stub-Tooth Gear add 1.6 to the number of teeth and divide the sum by the diametral pitch. *Rule:* For Fellows Stub-Tooth Gear divide number of teeth by pitch in numerator of pitch fraction (by 6 if pitch is 6/8); then add 2 divided by denominator pitch (2 divided by 8 if pitch is 6/8). *Example:* The pitch diameter of a gear is 4 inches, there being 24 teeth of 6/8 pitch; find the outside diameter. $$\text{Outside diam.} = \frac{24}{6} + \frac{2}{8} = 4\tfrac{1}{4} \text{ inches}$$
Addendum	*Rule:* For American Standard 20-Degree Stub Tooth divide 0.8 by the diametral pitch. The addendum of a tooth of, say, 4 diametral pitch, is the same as that of a Fellows stub tooth of 4/5 pitch. *Rule:* For Fellows Stub Tooth divide 1 by the diametral pitch in the denominator of the fraction (by 10 if the pitch is 8/10). *Example:* Determine the addendum or radial distance from pitch circle to top of tooth of 4/5 pitch. $$\text{Addendum} = \frac{1}{5} = 0.200 \text{ inch}$$
Whole Depth or Depth of Cut	*Rule:* For American Standard 20-Degree Stub Tooth divide 1.8 by the diametral pitch P. *Rule:* For Fellows Stub-Tooth Gear divide 2.25 by the denominator of the pitch fraction (by 8 if pitch is 6/8). *Example:* If pitch of gear is 8/10, what is whole depth of tooth? $$W = \frac{2.25}{10} = 0.225 \text{ inch}$$

Note: The shorter and stronger 20-degree stub tooth is especially adapted to small tooth numbers and high-power transmissions as in automobile transmission gears, mill gears, etc. For large tooth numbers either the 14½-degree or the 20-degree full-depth tooth form generally is recommended.

Chordal Thicknesses of Gear Teeth at Pitch Line

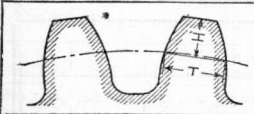

T = chordal thickness of tooth at pitch line;
H = perpendicular distance from chord to outside circumference of gear (corrected addendum).

Diametral Pitch	Dimension	No. 1 135 Teeth	No. 2 55 Teeth	No. 3 35 Teeth	No. 4 26 Teeth	No. 5 21 Teeth	No. 6 17 Teeth	No. 7 14 Teeth	No. 8 12 Teeth
		\multicolumn{8}{c}{Number of Gear Cutter, and Corresponding Number of Teeth}							
1	T	1.5707	1.5706	1.5702	1.5698	1.5694	1.5686	1.5675	1.5663
	H	1.0047	1.0112	1.0176	1.0237	1.0294	1.0362	1.0440	1.0514
1½	T	1.0471	1.0470	1.0468	1.0465	1.0462	1.0457	1.0450	1.0442
	H	0.6698	0.6741	0.6784	0.6824	0.6862	0.6908	0.6960	0.7009
2	T	0.7853	0.7853	0.7851	0.7849	0.7847	0.7843	0.7837	0.7831
	H	0.5023	0.5056	0.5088	0.5118	0.5147	0.5181	0.5220	0.5257
2½	T	0.6283	0.6282	0.6281	0.6279	0.6277	0.6274	0.6270	0.6265
	H	0.4018	0.4044	0.4070	0.4094	0.4117	0.4144	0.4176	0.4205
3	T	0.5235	0.5235	0.5234	0.5232	0.5231	0.5228	0.5225	0.5221
	H	0.3349	0.3370	0.3392	0.3412	0.3431	0.3454	0.3480	0.3504
3½	T	0.4487	0.4487	0.4486	0.4485	0.4484	0.4481	0.4478	0.4475
	H	0.2870	0.2889	0.2907	0.2919	0.2935	0.2954	0.2977	0.3004
4	T	0.3926	0.3926	0.3926	0.3924	0.3923	0.3921	0.3919	0.3915
	H	0.2511	0.2528	0.2544	0.2559	0.2573	0.2590	0.2610	0.2628
5	T	0.3141	0.3141	0.3140	0.3139	0.3138	0.3137	0.3135	0.3132
	H	0.2009	0.2022	0.2035	0.2047	0.2058	0.2072	0.2088	0.2102
6	T	0.2618	0.2617	0.2617	0.2616	0.2615	0.2614	0.2612	0.2610
	H	0.1674	0.1685	0.1696	0.1706	0.1715	0.1727	0.1740	0.1752
7	T	0.2244	0.2243	0.2243	0.2242	0.2242	0.2240	0.2239	0.2237
	H	0.1435	0.1444	0.1453	0.1462	0.1470	0.1480	0.1491	0.1502
8	T	0.1963	0.1963	0.1962	0.1962	0.1961	0.1960	0.1959	0.1958
	H	0.1255	0.1264	0.1272	0.1279	0.1286	0.1295	0.1305	0.1314
9	T	0.1745	0.1745	0.1744	0.1744	0.1743	0.1743	0.1741	0.1740
	H	0.1116	0.1123	0.1130	0.1137	0.1143	0.1151	0.1160	0.1168
10	T	0.1570	0.1570	0.1570	0.1569	0.1569	0.1568	0.1567	0.1566
	H	0.1004	0.1011	0.1017	0.1023	0.1029	0.1036	0.1044	0.1051
11	T	0.1428	0.1428	0.1427	0.1427	0.1426	0.1426	0.1425	0.1424
	H	0.0913	0.0919	0.0925	0.0930	0.0935	0.0942	0.0949	0.0955
12	T	0.1309	0.1309	0.1308	0.1308	0.1308	0.1307	0.1306	0.1305
	H	0.0837	0.0842	0.0848	0.0853	0.0857	0.0863	0.0870	0.0876
14	T	0.1122	0.1122	0.1121	0.1121	0.1121	0.1120	0.1119	0.1118
	H	0.0717	0.0722	0.0726	0.0731	0.0735	0.0740	0.0745	0.0751
16	T	0.0981	0.0981	0.0981	0.0981	0.0980	0.0980	0.0979	0.0979
	H	0.0628	0.0632	0.0636	0.0639	0.0643	0.0647	0.0652	0.0657
18	T	0.0872	0.0872	0.0872	0.0872	0.0872	0.0871	0.0870	0.0870
	H	0.0558	0.0561	0.0565	0.0568	0.0571	0.0575	0.0580	0.0584
20	T	0.0785	0.0785	0.0785	0.0785	0.0784	0.0784	0.0783	0.0783
	H	0.0502	0.0505	0.0508	0.0511	0.0514	0.0518	0.0522	0.0525

Chordal Thicknesses of Gear Teeth at Pitch Line

Circular Pitch	Dimension	Number of Gear Cutter, and Corresponding Number of Teeth							
		No. 1 135 Teeth	No. 2 55 Teeth	No. 3 35 Teeth	No. 4 26 Teeth	No. 5 21 Teeth	No. 6 17 Teeth	No. 7 14 Teeth	No. 8 12 Teeth
¼	T	0.1250	0.1250	0.1249	0.1249	0.1249	0.1248	0.1247	0.1246
	H	0.0799	0.0804	0.0809	0.0814	0.0819	0.0824	0.0830	0.0836
⁵⁄₁₆	T	0.1562	0.1562	0.1562	0.1561	0.1561	0.1560	0.1559	0.1558
	H	0.0999	0.1006	0.1012	0.1018	0.1023	0.1030	0.1038	0.1045
⅜	T	0.1875	0.1875	0.1874	0.1873	0.1873	0.1872	0.1871	0.1870
	H	0.1199	0.1207	0.1214	0.1221	0.1228	0.1236	0.1245	0.1254
⁷⁄₁₆	T	0.2187	0.2187	0.2186	0.2186	0.2185	0.2184	0.2183	0.2181
	H	0.1399	0.1408	0.1416	0.1425	0.1433	0.1443	0.1453	0.1464
½	T	0.2500	0.2500	0.2499	0.2498	0.2498	0.2496	0.2495	0.2493
	H	0.1599	0.1609	0.1619	0.1629	0.1638	0.1649	0.1661	0.1673
⁹⁄₁₆	T	0.2812	0.2812	0.2811	0.2810	0.2810	0.2808	0.2806	0.2804
	H	0.1799	0.1810	0.1821	0.1832	0.1842	0.1855	0.1868	0.1882
⅝	T	0.3125	0.3125	0.3123	0.3123	0.3122	0.3120	0.3118	0.3116
	H	0.1998	0.2012	0.2023	0.2036	0.2047	0.2061	0.2076	0.2091
11⁄16	T	0.3437	0.3437	0.3436	0.3435	0.3434	0.3432	0.3430	0.3427
	H	0.2198	0.2213	0.2226	0.2239	0.2252	0.2267	0.2283	0.2300
¾	T	0.3750	0.3750	0.3748	0.3747	0.3747	0.3744	0.3742	0.3740
	H	0.2398	0.2414	0.2428	0.2443	0.2457	0.2473	0.2491	0.2509
13⁄16	T	0.4062	0.4062	0.4060	0.4059	0.4059	0.4056	0.4054	0.4050
	H	0.2598	0.2615	0.2631	0.2647	0.2661	0.2679	0.2699	0.2718
⅞	T	0.4375	0.4375	0.4373	0.4372	0.4371	0.4368	0.4366	0.4362
	H	0.2798	0.2816	0.2833	0.2850	0.2866	0.2885	0.2906	0.2927
15⁄16	T	0.4687	0.4687	0.4685	0.4684	0.4683	0.4680	0.4678	0.4674
	H	0.2998	0.3018	0.3035	0.3054	0.3071	0.3092	0.3114	0.3137
I	T	0.5000	0.5000	0.4998	0.4997	0.4996	0.4993	0.4990	0.4986
	H	0.3198	0.3219	0.3238	0.3258	0.3276	0.3298	0.3322	0.3346
1⅛	T	0.5625	0.5625	0.5623	0.5621	0.5620	0.5617	0.5613	0.5610
	H	0.3597	0.3621	0.3642	0.3665	0.3685	0.3710	0.3737	0.3764
1¼	T	0.6250	0.6250	0.6247	0.6246	0.6245	0.6241	0.6237	0.6232
	H	0.3997	0.4023	0.4047	0.4072	0.4095	0.4122	0.4152	0.4182
1⅜	T	0.6875	0.6875	0.6872	0.6870	0.6869	0.6865	0.6861	0.6856
	H	0.4397	0.4426	0.4452	0.4479	0.4504	0.4534	0.4567	0.4600
1½	T	0.7500	0.7500	0.7497	0.7495	0.7494	0.7489	0.7485	0.7480
	H	0.4797	0.4828	0.4857	0.4887	0.4914	0.4947	0.4983	0.5019
1¾	T	0.8750	0.8750	0.8746	0.8744	0.8743	0.8737	0.8732	0.8726
	H	0.5596	0.5633	0.5666	0.5701	0.5733	0.5771	0.5813	0.5855
2	T	1.0000	1.0000	0.9996	0.9994	0.9992	0.9986	0.9980	0.9972
	H	0.6396	0.6438	0.6476	0.6516	0.6552	0.6596	0.6644	0.6692
2¼	T	1.1250	1.1250	1.1246	1.1242	1.1240	1.1234	1.1226	1.1220
	H	0.7195	0.7242	0.7285	0.7330	0.7371	0.7420	0.7474	0.7528
2½	T	1.2500	1.2500	1.2494	1.2492	1.2490	1.2482	1.2474	1.2464
	H	0.7995	0.8047	0.8095	0.8145	0.8190	0.8245	0.8305	0.8365
3	T	1.5000	1.5000	1.4994	1.4990	1.4990	1.4978	1.4970	1.4960
	H	0.9594	0.9657	0.9714	0.9774	0.9828	0.9894	0.9966	1.0038

Chordal Thicknesses and Addenda for Gear Cutters

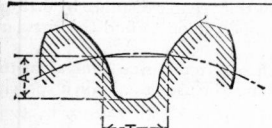

T = chordal thickness of cutter at pitch line;
A = perpendicular distance from chord to outside circumference of cutter (corrected addendum).

Diametral Pitch	Dimension	No. 1 135 Teeth	No. 2 55 Teeth	No. 3 35 Teeth	No. 4 26 Teeth	No. 5 21 Teeth	No. 6 17 Teeth	No. 7 14 Teeth	No. 8 12 Teeth
					Number of Gear Cutter				
1	T	1.5707	1.5706	1.5702	1.5698	1.5694	1.5686	1.5675	1.5663
	A	1.1525	1.1459	1.1395	1.1334	1.1277	1.1209	1.1131	1.1057
1½	T	1.0471	1.0470	1.0468	1.0465	1.0462	1.0457	1.0450	1.0442
	A	0.7683	0.7639	0.7596	0.7556	0.7518	0.7472	0.7420	0.7371
2	T	0.7853	0.7853	0.7851	0.7849	0.7847	0.7843	0.7837	0.7831
	A	0.5762	0.5729	0.5697	0.5667	0.5638	0.5604	0.5565	0.5528
2½	T	0.6283	0.6282	0.6281	0.6279	0.6277	0.6274	0.6270	0.6265
	A	0.4610	0.4583	0.4558	0.4533	0.4511	0.4483	0.4452	0.4423
3	T	0.5235	0.5235	0.5234	0.5232	0.5231	0.5228	0.5225	0.5221
	A	0.3841	0.3819	0.3798	0.3778	0.3759	0.3736	0.3710	0.3685
3½	T	0.4487	0.4487	0.4486	0.4485	0.4484	0.4481	0.4478	0.4475
	A	0.3292	0.3274	0.3255	0.3238	0.3222	0.3202	0.3180	0.3159
4	T	0.3926	0.3926	0.3925	0.3924	0.3923	0.3921	0.3919	0.3915
	A	0.2881	0.2864	0.2848	0.2833	0.2819	0.2802	0.2783	0.2764
5	T	0.3141	0.3141	0.3140	0.3139	0.3138	0.3137	0.3135	0.3132
	A	0.2305	0.2291	0.2279	0.2266	0.2255	0.2242	0.2226	0.2211
6	T	0.2617	0.2617	0.2617	0.2616	0.2615	0.2614	0.2612	0.2610
	A	0.1921	0.1910	0.1899	0.1889	0.1879	0.1868	0.1855	0.1842
7	T	0.2243	0.2243	0.2243	0.2242	0.2242	0.2240	0.2239	0.2237
	A	0.1646	0.1637	0.1627	0.1619	0.1611	0.1601	0.1590	0.1579
8	T	0.1963	0.1963	0.1962	0.1962	0.1961	0.1960	0.1959	0.1957
	A	0.1440	0.1432	0.1424	0.1416	0.1409	0.1401	0.1391	0.1382
9	T	0.1745	0.1745	0.1744	0.1744	0.1743	0.1742	0.1741	0.1740
	A	0.1280	0.1273	0.1266	0.1259	0.1253	0.1245	0.1236	0.1228
10	T	0.1570	0.1570	0.1570	0.1569	0.1569	0.1568	0.1567	0.1566
	A	0.1152	0.1144	0.1139	0.1133	0.1127	0.1120	0.1113	0.1105
11	T	0.1427	0.1427	0.1427	0.1427	0.1426	0.1426	0.1425	0.1423
	A	0.1047	0.1041	0.1035	0.1030	0.1025	0.1019	0.1012	0.1005
12	T	0.1308	0.1308	0.1308	0.1308	0.1308	0.1307	0.1306	0.1305
	A	0.0960	0.0954	0.0949	0.0944	0.0939	0.0934	0.0927	0.0921
14	T	0.1122	0.1122	0.1121	0.1121	0.1121	0.1120	0.1119	0.1118
	A	0.0823	0.0818	0.0814	0.0809	0.0805	0.0800	0.0795	0.0789
16	T	0.0981	0.0981	0.0981	0.0981	0.0981	0.0980	0.0979	0.0979
	A	0.0720	0.0716	0.0712	0.0708	0.0705	0.0700	0.0695	0.0691
18	T	0.0872	0.0872	0.0872	0.0872	0.0872	0.0871	0.0871	0.0870
	A	0.0640	0.0636	0.0633	0.0629	0.0626	0.0622	0.0618	0.0614
20	T	0.0785	0.0785	0.0785	0.0785	0.0784	0.0784	0.0783	0.0783
	A	0.0576	0.0573	0.0569	0.0566	0.0564	0.0560	0.0556	0.0553

Circular Pitch for Given Center Distance. — *Rule:* When a special circular pitch is required to obtain a given center distance, multiply center distance by 6.2832 and divide product by total number of teeth on gear and pinion to find the circular pitch.

Example: Gear has 60 teeth and pinion 20 teeth. A tooth size equivalent to about 4 diametral pitch is desired but circular pitch must be used to obtain a special center distance of 10.230 inches. Then

$$\text{Circular pitch} = \frac{10.230 \times 6.2832}{60 + 20} = 0.8035 \text{ inch}$$

This circular pitch of 0.8035 inch is 0 0181 inch greater than the circular pitch equivalent to 4 diametral pitch.

Number of Gear and Pinion Teeth for Given Center Distance and Diametral Pitch. — *Rule:* Divide the speed of the driving gear in revolutions per minute by the speed of the driven gear and add one to the quotient. Next divide the total number of teeth in both gears by the sum previously obtained, and the quotient will equal the number of teeth n in the driving gear. This number subtracted from the total number of teeth will equal the number of teeth N required in the driven gear. The total number of teeth equals twice the product of the center distance multiplied by the diametral pitch.

Example: The center-to-center distance is 6 inches and the diametral pitch is 10. The speeds of the driving and the driven gears are to be 100 and 60 revolutions per minute, respectively; find the number of teeth for each gear.

$$\text{Total No. of teeth} = 2 \times 6 \times 10 = 120$$

$$\text{For driver, } n = \frac{120}{\frac{100}{60} + 1} = 45$$

$$\text{For driven gear, } N = 120 - 45 = 75$$

Face Width Proportioned Relative to Pitch. — The minimum face width of a spur gear is usually about three times the circular pitch. The maximum face width ordinarily does not exceed four times the circular pitch. (The width of some gears equals five times the circular pitch but such a width is not recommended as a general rule.)

Example: The diametral pitch of a gear is 2; determine the face width, making the width equal to 3.5 times the circular pitch.

Diametral pitch of 2 equals 1.57 inch circular pitch approximately.

$$\text{Face width} = 1.57 \times 3.5 = 5.5 \text{ inches}$$

Tooth Thickness on Pitch Circle. — When the outside diameter is standard, use Rule 1 to obtain the arc thickness or thickness along the pitch circle.

Rule 1: Divide 1.5708 by the diametral pitch to obtain the arc thickness measured along the pitch circle; or multiply circular pitch by 0.5.

When the outside diameter of a small pinion is not standard but is enlarged to avoid undercut and improve the tooth action, the teeth are located farther out radially relative to the pitch circle; consequently the tooth thickness on the pitch circle (arc thickness) is increased. Then use Rule 2.

Rule 2: Find the difference between standard addendum and the long addendum, and multiply difference by tangent of pressure angle; multiply this product by 2 and *add* result to one-half of circular pitch, thus obtaining arc thickness on pitch circle.

Example: The outside diameter of a pinion having 10 teeth of 5 diametral pitch and a pressure angle of 14½ degrees is to be increased 0.2746 inch. Determine arc tooth thickness on pitch circle. The standard addendum is 0.2 inch. This is to be increased 0.2746 ÷ 2 = 0.1373 inch = difference between standard and long addendum. The circular pitch equivalent to 5 diametral pitch = 0.6283.

$$\text{Arc thickness} = \frac{0.6283}{2} + (2 \times 0.1373 \times 0.25862) = 0.3852 \text{ inch}$$

This arc thickness or thickness of tooth along the pitch circle cannot be measured when cutting a gear but is used in determining the chordal thickness which is the dimension measured with a gear tooth caliper

Tooth Thickness on Pitch Circle when Outside Diameter of Gear is Reduced. — If the outside diameter of a gear is reduced an amount equal to the increase in the outside diameter of the pinion to maintain a standard center distance, the gear-tooth thickness on the pitch circle will be decreased.

Rule: Find difference between standard and short addendum and multiply difference by tangent of pressure angle; multiply this product by 2 and *subtract* the result from one-half the circular pitch.

Example: The outside diameter of a gear is to be reduced 0.2746 inch or an amount equal to the increase in outside diameter of its mating pinion. Circular pitch equals 0.6283 inch. Determine tooth thickness on pitch circle. The addendum is to be decreased 0.2746 ÷ 2 = 0.1373 inch; hence

$$\text{Arc thickness} = \frac{0.6283}{2} - (2 \times 0.1373 \times 0.25862) = 0.2432 \text{ inch}$$

Thickness of Stub Tooth on Pitch Circle. — *Rule:* For an American Standard 20-Degree stub tooth, or a Nuttall stub tooth, divide 1.5708 by the diametral pitch.

Rule: For Fellows stub tooth, divide 1.5708 by the diametral pitch in the numerator of the fraction (by 6 if the pitch is ⁶⁄₈).

Example: What is the pitch-line thickness of a Fellows stub tooth of ⁸⁄₁₀ pitch?

$$\text{Thickness} = \frac{1.5708}{8} = 0.1963 \text{ inch}$$

Chordal Thickness of Tooth when Outside Diameter is Standard. — In checking the thickness of a gear tooth, the chordal or straight-line thickness is measured.

Rule: To find the chordal thickness, divide 90 by the number of teeth; find the sine of angle thus obtained and multiply it by the pitch diameter.

Example: A pinion has 15 teeth of 3 diametral pitch; the pitch diameter = 15 ÷ 3 = 5 inches; hence

$$\text{Chordal thickness} = 5 \times \sin\frac{90}{15} = 5 \times \sin 6° = 0.5226 \text{ inch}$$

Thickness on pitch circle is 0.5236 inch.

Chordal Thickness of Tooth when Outside Diameter is Special. — *Rule:* First find the arc tooth thickness (thickness on pitch circle) of enlarged pinion or reduced gear (see preceding rules and formulas); multiply arc thickness by 90 and divide product by 3.1416 times radius of pitch circle; find sine of angle thus obtained and multiply it by pitch diameter D.

$$\text{Chordal thickness} = D \times \sin\frac{90 \times \text{arc thickness}}{\text{Pitch radius} \times 3.1416}$$

Example 1: The outside diameter of a pinion having 12 teeth of 2 diametral pitch and a pressure angle of 14½ degrees, has been enlarged an amount equal to 1.2477 ÷ 2 = 0.624 inch. This enlargement has increased the addendum from 0.5000 to 0.812 inch (see table on page 670); hence, the arc thickness at the pitch circle (as determined by rule previously given) has been increased to 0.94678 inch.

$$\text{Chordal thickness (pinion)} = \frac{12}{2} \times \sin \frac{90 \times 0.94678}{3 \times 3.1416} = 0.9428 \text{ inch.}$$

Example 2: Gear having 30 teeth is to mesh with pinion of Example 1 and is reduced so that arc thickness at the pitch circle is 0.6240; then

$$\text{Chordal thickness (gear)} = \frac{30}{2} \times \sin \frac{90 \times 0.6240}{7.5 \times 3.1416} = 0.6236 \text{ inch.}$$

In many cases the chordal thickness of a gear tooth, especially if the number of teeth is large, is practically the same as the arc thickness.

Chordal Addendum. — In measuring the chordal thickness, the vertical scale of a gear tooth caliper is set to the chordal or " corrected " addendum to locate the caliper jaws at the pitch line (see accompanying illustration). The simplified formula which follows may be used in determining the chordal addendum either when the addendum is standard for full-depth or stub teeth or when the addendum is either longer or shorter than standard as in case of an enlarged pinion or a gear which is to mesh with an enlarged pinion and has a reduced addendum to maintain the standard center-to-center distance. The arc thickness in the formula is along the pitch circle.

$$\text{Chordal addendum} = \text{addendum} + \frac{\text{arc thickness}^2}{4 \times \text{pitch diameter}}.$$

Example 1: A pinion has 12 teeth of 2 diametral pitch; the addendum = 0.5000 inch (standard for full-depth teeth); and tooth thickness on pitch line = 0.7854 inch, as shown by table of " Gear Tooth Parts," page 655. Then,

$$\text{Chordal addendum} = 0.5000 + \frac{0.7854^2}{4 \times (12 \div 2)} = 0.5257 \text{ inch.}$$

Example 2: The outside diameter of a pinion having 12 teeth of 2 diametral pitch is to be enlarged 0.624 inch to avoid undercut (see table on page 670), thus increasing the addendum from 0.500 to 0.812 inch and the arc thickness at the pitch line from 0.7854 to 0.9468. Then,

$$\text{Chordal addendum of pinion} = 0.8120 + \frac{0.9468^2}{4 \times (12 \div 2)} = 0.8494$$

Example 3: The outside diameter of a gear having 60 teeth is to mesh with pinion of Example 2 and is to have the addendum reduced from 0.500 to 0.188 inch (to maintain the standard center distance), thus reducing the arc thickness to 0.6240.

$$\text{Chordal addendum of gear} = 0.188 + \frac{0.6240^2}{4 \times (60 \div 2)} = 0.1912$$

When a gear addendum is reduced as much as the mating pinion addendum is increased, the minimum number of gear teeth required to prevent undercutting, depends upon the enlargement of the mating pinion. To illustrate, if a 14½-degree pinion with 13 teeth is enlarged 1.185 inch, then the reduced mating gear should have 51 teeth to avoid undercut (see table, page 670).

Measuring Thickness of Gear Tooth. — In cutting gear teeth, the general practice is to adjust the cutter or hob until it grazes the outside diameter of the blank; the cutter is then sunk to the total depth of the tooth space plus whatever slight additional amount may be required to provide the necessary play or backlash between the teeth. (Information on the amount of backlash and the excess depth of cut required will be given later.) If the outside diameter of the gear blank is correct, the tooth thickness should also be correct after the cutter has been sunk to the depth required for a given pitch and backlash. However, it is advisable to check the tooth thickness by measuring it, and the vernier gear-tooth caliper (see accompanying illustration) is commonly used in measuring the thickness.

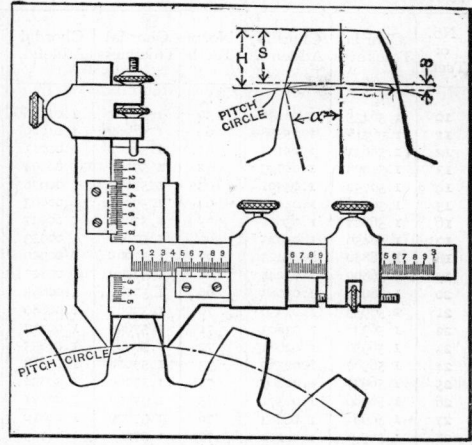

The vertical scale of this caliper is set so that when it rests upon the top of the tooth as shown, the lower ends of the caliper jaws will be at the height of the pitch circle; the horizontal scale then shows the chordal thickness of the tooth at this point. If the gear is being cut on a milling machine or with the type of gear-cutting machine employing a formed milling cutter, the tooth thickness is checked by first taking a trial cut for a short distance at one side of the blank; then the gear blank is indexed for the next space and another cut is taken far enough to mill the full outline of the tooth. The tooth thickness is then measured.

Before the gear-tooth caliper can be used, it is necessary to determine the correct chordal thickness and also the chordal addendum (or "corrected addendum" as it is sometimes called). The vertical scale is set to the chordal addendum, thus locating

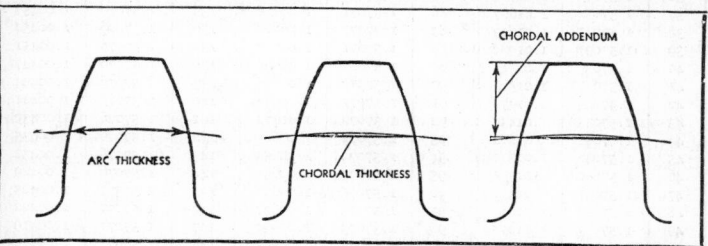

the ends of the jaws at the height of the pitch circle. The rules or formulas to use in determining the chordal thickness and chordal addendum will depend upon the outside diameter of the gear; for example, if the outside diameter of a small pinion is enlarged to avoid undercut and improve the tooth action, this must be taken into account in figuring the chordal thickness and chordal addendum as shown by the accompanying rules. The detail of a gear tooth included with the gear-tooth caliper illustration, represents the chordal thickness T, the addendum S, and the chordal addendum H.

Chordal Thickness and Chordal Addendum of Gear Teeth

This table is for spur gears of one diametral pitch. For any other diametral pitch, divide the given value by the required pitch. Table gives the chordal thickness and chordal addendum at the pitch circle when addendum is standard for full-depth teeth. Table is applicable to helical gears as explained on next page.

No. of Teeth	Chordal Thickness	Chordal Addend.	No. of Teeth	Chordal Thickness	Chordal Addend.	No. of Teeth	Chordal Thickness	Chordal Addend.
10	1.56435	1.06156	59	1.57061	1.01046	108	1.57074	1.00570
11	1.56546	1.05598	60	1.57062	1.01029	109	1.57075	1.00565
12	1.56631	1.05133	61	1.57062	1.01011	110	1.57075	1.00560
13	1.56698	1.04739	62	1.57063	1.00994	111	1.57075	1.00556
14	1.56752	1.04401	63	1.57063	1.00978	112	1.57075	1.00551
15	1.56794	1.04109	64	1.57064	1.00963	113	1.57075	1.00546
16	1.56827	1.03852	65	1.57064	1.00947	114	1.57075	1.00541
17	1.56856	1.03625	66	1.57065	1.00933	115	1.57075	1.00537
18	1.56880	1.03425	67	1.57065	1.00920	116	1.57075	1.00533
19	1.56899	1.03244	68	1.57066	1.00907	117	1.57075	1.00529
20	1.56918	1.03083	69	1.57066	1.00893	118	1.57075	1.00524
21	1.56933	1.02936	70	1.57067	1.00880	119	1.57075	1.00519
22	1.56948	1.02803	71	1.57067	1.00867	120	1.57075	1.00515
23	1.56956	1.02681	72	1.57067	1.00855	121	1.57075	1.00511
24	1.56967	1.02569	73	1.57068	1.00843	122	1.57075	1.00507
25	1.56977	1.02466	74	1.57068	1.00832	123	1.57076	1.00503
26	1.56986	1.02371	75	1.57068	1.00821	124	1.57076	1.00499
27	1.56991	1.02284	76	1.57069	1.00810	125	1.57076	1.00495
28	1.56998	1.02202	77	1.57069	1.00799	126	1.57076	1.00491
29	1.57003	1.02127	78	1.57069	1.00789	127	1.57076	1.00487
30	1.57008	1.02055	79	1.57069	1.00780	128	1.57076	1.00483
31	1.57012	1.01990	80	1.57070	1.00772	129	1.57076	1.00479
32	1.57016	1.01926	81	1.57070	1.00762	130	1.57076	1.00475
33	1.57019	1.01869	82	1.57070	1.00752	131	1.57076	1.00472
34	1.57021	1.01813	83	1.57070	1.00743	132	1.57076	1.00469
35	1.57025	1.01762	84	1.57071	1.00734	133	1.57076	1.00466
36	1.57028	1.01714	85	1.57071	1.00725	134	1.57076	1.00462
37	1.57032	1.01667	86	1.57071	1.00716	135	1.57076	1.00457
38	1.57035	1.01623	87	1.57071	1.00708	136	1.57076	1.00454
39	1.57037	1.01582	88	1.57071	1.00700	137	1.57076	1.00451
40	1.57039	1.01542	89	1.57072	1.00693	138	1.57076	1.00447
41	1.57041	1.01504	90	1.57072	1.00686	139	1.57076	1.00444
42	1.57043	1.01471	91	1.57072	1.00679	140	1.57076	1.00441
43	1.57045	1.01434	92	1.57072	1.00672	141	1.57076	1.00439
44	1.57047	1.01404	93	1.57072	1.00665	142	1.57076	1.00435
45	1.57048	1.01370	94	1.57072	1.00658	143	1.57076	1.00432
46	1.57050	1.01341	95	1.57073	1.00651	144	1.57076	1.00429
47	1.57051	1.01311	96	1.57073	1.00644	145	1.57077	1.00425
48	1.57052	1.01285	97	1.57073	1.00637	146	1.57077	1.00422
49	1.57053	1.01258	98	1.57073	1.00630	147	1.57077	1.00419
50	1.57054	1.01233	99	1.57073	1.00623	148	1.57077	1.00416
51	1.57055	1.01209	100	1.57073	1.00617	149	1.57077	1.00413
52	1.57056	1.01187	101	1.57074	1.00611	150	1.57077	1.00411
53	1.57057	1.01165	102	1.57074	1.00605	151	1.57077	1.00409
54	1.57058	1.01143	103	1.57074	1.00599	152	1.57077	1.00407
55	1.57058	1.01121	104	1.57074	1.00593	153	1.57077	1.00405
56	1.57059	1.01102	105	1.57074	1.00587	154	1.57077	1.00402
57	1.57060	1.01083	106	1.57074	1.00581	155	1.57077	1.00400
58	1.57061	1.01064	107	1.57074	1.00575	156	1.57077	1.00397

Helical Gears: In applying the table on page 668 to helical gears, especially when the number of teeth is small and the helix angle large, divide the actual number of helical gear teeth by the cube of the cosine of the helix angle; then use the quotient as the number of teeth in entering the table, instead of the actual number; finally, divide the table values by the *normal* diametral pitch to get the normal chordal thickness and the normal chordal addendum. Example: Helical gear has 18 teeth of 1 normal diametral pitch and helix angle of 45 degrees. Then, $18 \div \cos^3 45° = 51$ = number of teeth used in entering table.

Average Backlash for General Purpose Gearing

Spur, Helical and Bevel Gears				Worm Gears			
D. P.	Backlash	D. P.	Backlash	C. P.	Backlash	C. P.	Backlash
1	.025–.040	8	.004–.006	4	.032–.050	½	.005–.007
2	.014–.020	16	.002–.004	2	.017–.025	¼	.003–.005
4	.007–.011	32	.002–.004	1	.009–.014	⅛	.002–.004

Excess Depth of Cut to Obtain Backlash. — The backlash may be obtained by cutting the tooth spaces slightly deeper than standard, thus making the teeth thinner than the theoretical standard thickness.

Rule 1: If the teeth of *both* mating gears are cut deeper, the excess depth of cut is equal to the amount of backlash wanted if pressure angle of hob or generating tool is 14½ degrees.

Rule 2: If the gear is driven by a small pinion, cut the pinion teeth to standard depth and the gear teeth to an excess depth equal to twice the amount of backlash (if pressure angle is 14½ degrees).

Rule 3: For a pressure angle of 20 degrees, the excess depth of cut, if applied to both gears, equals the backlash multiplied by 0.73.

Rule 4: If excess depth of cut is applied to large gear only and pressure angle is 20 degrees, multiply backlash by 1.46.

Example: A backlash of 0.008 inch is to be obtained by cutting the teeth of both mating gears deeper than standard. The pressure angle is 20 degrees; then

$$\text{Excess depth of cut} = 0.008 \times 0.73 = 0.0058 \text{ inch}$$

Increasing Pinion Diameter to Avoid Undercut. — Excessive interference or undercutting of the teeth of the smaller gears or pinions may be avoided either by enlarging the outside diameter, increasing the pressure angle, or by increasing both the outside diameter and pressure angle. This increase in outside diameter does not change the velocity ratio or the procedure in cutting the teeth on a hobbing machine or generating type of shaper or planer.

Rule: Multiply square of cosine of pressure angle by pitch diameter D and add to product twice the working depth w.

$$o = (\cos^2 \text{ pressure angle} \times D) + (2 \times w)$$

in which o = outside diameter of enlarged blank.

Example: A pinion having 10 teeth of 5 diametral pitch is to mesh with a gear having 54 teeth. Determine the increase in pinion diameter (to improve tooth action and avoid interference or undercut). The pressure angle is 14½ degrees.

Solution: Cosine of 14½ degrees is 0.96815; pitch diameter = $10 \div 5 = 2$ inches; working depth for 5 diametral pitch is 0.400 inch; hence

$$\text{Outside diam.} = (0.96815^2 \times 2) + (2 \times 0.4) = 2.6746''$$

Increasing Pinion Diameter to avoid Undercut and Obtain Full Involute Tooth Action

Number of Pinion Teeth	Changes in Pinion and Gear Diameters	Circular Tooth Thickness		Min. No. of Teeth in Mating Gear	
		Pinion	Mating Gear	To avoid Undercut	For full involute Action
14½-degree Full-depth Involute					
10	1.3731	1.9259	1.2157	54	27
11	1.3104	1.9097	1.2319	53	27
12	1.2477	1.8935	1.2481	52	28
13	1.1850	1.8773	1.2643	51	28
14	1.1223	1.8611	1.2805	50	28
15	1.0597	1.8449	1.2967	49	28
16	0.9970	1.8286	1.3130	48	28
17	0.9343	1.8124	1.3292	47	28
18	0.8716	1.7962	1.3454	46	28
19	0.8089	1.7800	1.3616	45	28
20	0.7462	1.7638	1.3778	44	28
21	0.6835	1.7476	1.3940	43	28
22	0.6208	1.7314	1.4102	42	27
23	0.5581	1.7151	1.4265	41	27
24	0.4954	1.6989	1.4427	40	27
25	0.4328	1.6827	1.4589	39	26
26	0.3701	1.6665	1.4751	38	26
27	0.3074	1.6503	1.4913	37	26
28	0.2447	1.6341	1.5075	36	25
29	0.1820	1.6179	1.5237	35	25
30	0.1193	1.6017	1.5399	34	24
31	0.0566	1.5854	1.5562	33	24
20-degree Full-depth Involute					
8	1.0642	1.9581	1.1835	26	16
9	0.9472	1.9156	1.2260	25	16
10	0.8302	1.8730	1.2686	24	16
11	0.7132	1.8304	1.3112	23	16
12	0.5963	1.7878	1.3538	22	15
13	0.4793	1.7453	1.3963	21	14
14	0.3623	1.7027	1.4389	20	14
15	0.2453	1.6601	1.4815	19	14
16	0.1284	1.6175	1.5241	18	13
17	0.0114	1.5749	1.5667	17	13

Dimensions (inches) in table are based upon one diametral pitch. For other pitches divide dimensions given by the diametral pitch desired.

Add to the standard outside diameter of the pinion amount given in second column of table divided by diametral pitch, and (to maintain center distance) subtract the same amount from outside diameter of mating gear.

If T = chordal thickness at pitch circle; D = pitch diameter; C = circular thickness of tooth on pitch circle (see table); R = pitch radius; and H = amount to add to long or short addendum to obtain corrected addendum required in using gear-tooth caliper, then

$$T = D \times \sin \frac{90\,C}{R \times 3.1416} \qquad H = R\left(1 - \cos \frac{90\,C}{R \times 3.1416}\right).$$

Long addendum pinions in mesh with standard gears will run with full involute action, but the center distance will be greater than standard.

Standard outside diameter of pinion = $(10 + 2) \div 5 = 2.4$ inches; hence diameter as been increased $2.6746 - 2.4000 = 0.2746$ inch. The standard outside diameter f the gear must be reduced 0.2746 inch, in this case, to avoid changing the standard enter distance, but the enlarged pinion will run with a standard gear.

The accompanying table shows the amount that the pinion diameter must be acreased to avoid undercut. In this table the number of pinion teeth ranges from o to 31 for a pressure angle of $14\frac{1}{2}$ degrees because undercutting begins when the inion has less than 32 teeth. When the pressure angle is 20 degrees, undercutting oes not begin until the number of teeth is less than 18 as indicated by the lower art of the table. Enlargement of a pinion is similar in its effect to moving the eeth outward radially relative to the pitch circle; consequently, the circular tooth hickness at the pitch circle is increased and the amount depends upon the enlarge- nent as shown by column 3. If the mating gear diameter is reduced, the circular ooth thickness *at the pitch circle* will be reduced also as shown by column 4.

Minimum Number of Teeth to Avoid Undercut. — The minimum number of xternal spur gear teeth N which can be generated without undercut when using a traight-sided unmodified hob or a rack type of cutter, may be found by the follow- ag formula in which A = pressure angle and S = addendum for 1 diametral itch = 1 for American Standard full-depth teeth = 0.8 for American Standard tub teeth

$$N = 2S \times \operatorname{cosec}^2 A$$

Full-Depth Teeth: If addendum $S = 1$ and pressure angle $A = 14\frac{1}{2}$ degrees, $= 32$; if $S = 1$ and $A = 20$ degrees, $N = 18$ (Note: in using formula, frac- onal values of N are rounded upward to obtain a whole number.)

Stub Teeth: If addendum $S = 0.8$ for 1 diametral pitch and pressure angle = 20 degrees, $N = 14$.

Gear to Mesh with Enlarged Pinion: The fifth column in the accompanying table aows the minimum number of teeth in a mating gear which can be cut with a hob : rack type cutter without undercut, when the outside diameter of the gear has een reduced an amount equal to the pinion enlargement to retain the standard enter distance. In using the preceding formula to find N for the gear, insert ddendum S of enlarged mating pinion.

Example: A gear is to mesh with a 24-tooth pinion of 1 diametral pitch which as been enlarged 0.4954 inch, as shown by the table. The pressure angle is $14\frac{1}{2}$ egrees. Find minimum number of teeth N for reduced gear.

Pinion addendum = $1 + (0.4954 \div 2) = 1.2477$; hence

$$N = 2 \times 1.2477 \times 15.95 = 39.8 \text{ (use 40)}$$

Contact Ratio. — When gears intermesh, one pair of teeth must remain in en- gement until the following pair are in position to carry the load. This overlap- ag of tooth action is indicated by the *contact ratio*. The contact ratio of involute ur gears may be determined by the following formula in which R = pitch radius first gear; r = pitch radius of second gear; R_o = outside radius of first gear; = outside radius of second gear; R_b = base circle radius of first gear; r_b = base rcle radius of second gear ($R_b = R \cos A$ and $r_b = r \cos A$); A = pressure angle; = center distance; P' = circular pitch:

$$\text{Contact ratio} = \frac{\sqrt{R_o^2 - R_b^2} + \sqrt{r_o^2 - r_b^2} - C \sin A}{P' \cos A}$$

As a general rule, the contact ratio of gears for power transmission should not less than 1.40. A ratio as low as 1.20 may be used in extreme cases, although e gearing must be very accurate to avoid excessive noise.

SPUR GEARING

Pitch Diameters of Diametral Pitch Gears

No. of Teeth	Diametral Pitch								
	3 P	4 P	5 P	6 P	8 P	10 P	12 P	14 P	16 P
10	3.333	2.500	2.000	1.667	1.250	1.000	0.833	0.714	0.625
11	3.667	2.750	2.200	1.833	1.375	1.100	0.917	0.786	0.687
12	4.000	3.000	2.400	2.000	1.500	1.200	1.000	0.857	0.750
13	4.333	3.250	2.600	2.167	1.625	1.300	1.083	0.929	0.812
14	4.667	3.500	2.800	2.333	1.750	1.400	1.167	1.000	0.875
15	5.000	3.750	3.000	2.500	1.875	1.500	1.250	1.071	0.937
16	5.333	4.000	3.200	2.667	2.000	1.600	1.333	1.143	1.000
17	5.667	4.250	3.400	2.833	2.125	1.700	1.417	1.214	1.062
18	6.000	4.500	3.600	3.000	2.250	1.800	1.500	1.286	1.125
19	6.333	4.750	3.800	3.167	2.375	1.900	1.583	1.357	1.187
20	6.667	5.000	4.000	3.333	2.500	2.000	1.667	1.429	1.250
21	7.000	5.250	4.200	3.500	2.625	2.100	1.750	1.500	1.312
22	7.333	5.500	4.400	3.667	2.750	2.200	1.833	1.571	1.375
23	7.667	5.750	4.600	3.833	2.875	2.300	1.917	1.643	1.437
24	8.000	6.000	4.800	4.000	3.000	2.400	2.000	1.714	1.500
25	8.333	6.250	5.000	4.167	3.125	2.500	2.083	1.786	1.562
26	8.667	6.500	5.200	4.333	3.250	2.600	2.167	1.857	1.625
27	9.000	6.750	5.400	4.500	3.375	2.700	2.250	1.929	1.687
28	9.333	7.000	5.600	4.667	3.500	2.800	2.333	2.000	1.750
29	9.667	7.250	5.800	4.833	3.625	2.900	2.417	2.071	1.812
30	10.000	7.500	6.000	5.000	3.750	3.000	2.500	2.143	1.875
31	10.333	7.750	6.200	5.167	3.875	3.100	2.583	2.214	1.937
32	10.667	8.000	6.400	5.333	4.000	3.200	2.667	2.286	2.000
33	11.000	8.250	6.600	5.500	4.125	3.300	2.750	2.357	2.062
34	11.333	8.500	6.800	5.667	4.250	3.400	2.833	2.429	2.125
35	11.667	8.750	7.000	5.833	4.375	3.500	2.917	2.500	2.187
36	12.000	9.000	7.200	6.000	4.500	3.600	3.000	2.571	2.250
37	12.333	9.250	7.400	6.167	4.625	3.700	3.083	2.643	2.312
38	12.667	9.500	7.600	6.333	4.750	3.800	3.167	2.714	2.375
39	13.000	9.750	7.800	6.500	4.875	3.900	3.250	2.786	2.437
40	13.333	10.000	8.000	6.667	5.000	4.000	3.333	2.857	2.500
41	13.667	10.250	8.200	6.833	5.125	4.100	3.417	2.929	2.562
42	14.000	10.500	8.400	7.000	5.250	4.200	3.500	3.000	2.625
43	14.333	10.750	8.600	7.167	5.375	4.300	3.583	3.071	2.687
44	14.667	11.000	8.800	7.333	5.500	4.400	3.667	3.143	2.750
45	15.000	11.250	9.000	7.500	5.625	4.500	3.750	3.214	2.812
46	15.333	11.500	9.200	7.667	5.750	4.600	3.833	3.286	2.875
47	15.667	11.750	9.400	7.833	5.875	4.700	3.917	3.357	2.937
48	16.000	12.000	9.600	8.000	6.000	4.800	4.000	3.429	3.000
49	16.333	12.250	9.800	8.167	6.125	4.900	4.083	3.500	3.062
50	16.667	12.500	10.000	8.333	6.250	5.000	4.167	3.571	3.125
51	17.000	12.750	10.200	8.500	6.375	5.100	4.250	3.643	3.187
52	17.333	13.000	10.400	8.667	6.500	5.200	4.333	3.714	3.250
53	17.667	13.250	10.600	8.833	6.625	5.300	4.417	3.786	3.312
54	18.000	13.500	10.800	9.000	6.750	5.400	4.500	3.857	3.375
55	18.333	13.750	11.000	9.167	6.875	5.500	4.583	3.929	3.437

Pitch Diameters of Diametral Pitch Gears

No. of Teeth	Diametral Pitch								
	3 P	4 P	5 P	6 P	8 P	10 P	12 P	14 P	16 P
56	18.667	14.000	11.200	9.333	7.000	5.600	4.667	4.000	3.500
57	19.000	14.250	11.400	9.500	7.125	5.700	4.750	4.071	3.562
58	19.333	14.500	11.600	9.667	7.250	5.800	4.833	4.143	3.625
59	19.667	14.750	11.800	9.833	7.375	5.900	4.917	4.214	3.687
60	20.000	15.000	12.000	10.000	7.500	6.000	5.000	4.286	3.750
61	20.333	15.250	12.200	10.167	7.625	6.100	5.083	4.357	3.812
62	20.667	15.500	12.400	10.333	7.750	6.200	5.167	4.429	3.875
63	21.000	15.750	12.600	10.500	7.875	6.300	5.250	4.500	3.937
64	21.333	16.000	12.800	10.667	8.000	6.400	5.333	4.571	4.000
65	21.667	16.250	13.000	10.833	8.125	6.500	5.417	4.643	4.062
66	22.000	16.500	13.200	11.000	8.250	6.600	5.500	4.714	4.125
67	22.333	16.750	13.400	11.167	8.375	6.700	5.583	4.786	4.187
68	22.667	17.000	13.600	11.333	8.500	6.800	5.667	4.857	4.250
69	23.000	17.250	13.800	11.500	8.625	6.900	5.750	4.929	4.312
70	23.333	17.500	14.000	11.667	8.750	7.000	5.833	5.000	4.375
71	23.667	17.750	14.200	11.833	8.875	7.100	5.917	5.071	4.437
72	24.000	18.000	14.400	12.000	9.000	7.200	6.000	5.143	4.500
73	24.333	18.250	14.600	12.167	9.125	7.300	6.083	5.214	4.562
74	24.667	18.500	14.800	12.333	9.250	7.400	6.167	5.286	4.625
75	25.000	18.750	15.000	12.500	9.375	7.500	6.250	5.357	4.687
76	25.333	19.000	15.200	12.667	9.500	7.600	6.333	5.429	4.750
77	25.667	19.250	15.400	12.833	9.625	7.700	6.417	5.500	4.812
78	26.000	19.500	15.600	13.000	9.750	7.800	6.500	5.571	4.875
79	26.333	19.750	15.800	13.167	9.875	7.900	6.583	5.643	4.937
80	26.667	20.000	16.000	13.333	10.000	8.000	6.667	5.714	5.000
81	27.000	20.250	16.200	13.500	10.125	8.100	6.750	5.786	5.062
82	27.333	20.500	16.400	13.667	10.250	8.200	6.833	5.857	5.125
83	27.667	20.750	16.600	13.833	10.375	8.300	6.917	5.929	5.187
84	28.000	21.000	16.800	14.000	10.500	8.400	7.000	6.000	5.250
85	28.333	21.250	17.000	14.167	10.625	8.500	7.083	6.071	5.312
86	28.667	21.500	17.200	14.333	10.750	8.600	7.167	6.143	5.375
87	29.000	21.750	17.400	14.500	10.875	8.700	7.250	6.214	5.437
88	29.333	22.000	17.600	14.667	11.000	8.800	7.333	6.286	5.500
89	29.667	22.250	17.800	14.833	11.125	8.900	7.417	6.357	5.562
90	30.000	22.500	18.000	15.000	11.250	9.000	7.500	6.429	5.625
91	30.333	22.750	18.200	15.167	11.375	9.100	7.583	6.500	5.687
92	30.667	23.000	18.400	15.333	11.500	9.200	7.667	6.571	5.750
93	31.000	23.250	18.600	15.500	11.625	9.300	7.750	6.643	5.812
94	31.333	23.500	18.800	15.667	11.750	9.400	7.833	6.714	5.875
95	31.667	23.750	19.000	15.833	11.875	9.500	7.917	6.786	5.937
96	32.000	24.000	19.200	16.000	12.000	9.600	8.000	6.857	6.000
97	32.333	24.250	19.400	16.167	12.125	9.700	8.083	6.929	6.062
98	32.667	24.500	19.600	16.333	12.250	9.800	8.167	7.000	6.125
99	33.000	24.750	19.800	16.500	12.375	9.900	8.250	7.071	6.187
100	33.333	25.000	20.000	16.667	12.500	10.000	8.333	7.143	6.250

Outside Diameters of Diametral Pitch Gears

No. of Teeth	Diametral Pitch								
	3 P	4 P	5 P	6 P	8 P	10 P	12 P	14 P	16 P
10	4.000	3.000	2.400	2.000	1.500	1.200	1.000	0.857	0.750
11	4.333	3.250	2.600	2.167	1.625	1.300	1.083	0.929	0.812
12	4.667	3.500	2.800	2.333	1.750	1.400	1.167	1.000	0.875
13	5.000	3.750	3.000	2.500	1.875	1.500	1.250	1.071	0.937
14	5.333	4.000	3.200	2.667	2.000	1.600	1.333	1.143	1.000
15	5.667	4.250	3.400	2.833	2.125	1.700	1.417	1 214	1.062
16	6.000	4.500	3.600	3.000	2.250	1.800	1.500	1.286	1.125
17	6.333	4.750	3.800	3.167	2.375	1.900	1.583	1.357	1.187
18	6.667	5.000	4.000	3.333	2.500	2.000	1.667	1.429	1.250
19	7.000	5.250	4.200	3.500	2.625	2.100	1.750	1.500	1.312
20	7.333	5.500	4.400	3.667	2.750	2.200	1.833	1.571	1.375
21	7.667	5.750	4.600	3.833	2.875	2.300	1.917	1.643	1.437
22	8.000	6.000	4.800	4.000	3.000	2.400	2.000	1.714	1.500
23	8.333	6.250	5.000	4.167	3.125	2.500	2.083	1.786	1.562
24	8.667	6.500	5.200	4.333	3.250	2.600	2.167	1.857	1.625
25	9.000	6.750	5.400	4.500	3.375	2.700	2.250	1.929	1.687
26	9.333	7.000	5.600	4.667	3.500	2.800	2.333	2.000	1.750
27	9.667	7.250	5.800	4.833	3.625	2.900	2.417	2.071	1.812
28	10.000	7.500	6.000	5.000	3.750	3.000	2.500	2.143	1.875
29	10.333	7.750	6.200	5.167	3.875	3.100	2.583	2.214	1.937
30	10.667	8.000	6.400	5.333	4.000	3.200	2.667	2.286	2.000
31	11.000	8.250	6.600	5.500	4.125	3.300	2.750	2.357	2.062
32	11.333	8.500	6.800	5.667	4.250	3.400	2.833	2.429	2.125
33	11.667	8.750	7.000	5.833	4.375	3.500	2.917	2.500	2.187
34	12.000	9.000	7.200	6.000	4.500	3.600	3.000	2.571	2.250
35	12.333	9.250	7.400	6.167	4.625	3.700	3.083	2.643	2.312
36	12.667	9.500	7.600	6.333	4.750	3.800	3.167	2.714	2.375
37	13.000	9.750	7.800	6.500	4.875	3.900	3.250	2.786	2.437
38	13.333	10.000	8.000	6.667	5.000	4.000	3.333	2.857	2.500
39	13.667	10.250	8.200	6.833	5.125	4.100	3.417	2.929	2.562
40	14.000	10.500	8.400	7.000	5.250	4.200	3.500	3.000	2.625
41	14.333	10.750	8.600	7.167	5.375	4.300	3.583	3.071	2.687
42	14.667	11.000	8.800	7.333	5.500	4.400	3.667	3.143	2.750
43	15.000	11.250	9.000	7.500	5.625	4.500	3.750	3.214	2.812
44	15.333	11.500	9.200	7.667	5.750	4.600	3.833	3.286	2.875
45	15.667	11.750	9.400	7.833	5.875	4.700	3.917	3.357	2.937
46	16.000	12.000	9.600	8.000	6.000	4.800	4.000	3.429	3.000
47	16.333	12.250	9.800	8.167	6.125	4.900	4.083	3.500	3.062
48	16.667	12.500	10.000	8.333	6.250	5.000	4.167	3.571	3.125
49	17.000	12.750	10.200	8.500	6.375	5.100	4.250	3.643	3.187
50	17.333	13.000	10.400	8.667	6.500	5.200	4.333	3.714	3.250
51	17.667	13.250	10.600	8.833	6.625	5.300	4.417	3.786	3.312
52	18.000	13.500	10.800	9.000	6.750	5.400	4.500	3.857	3.375
53	18.333	13.750	11.000	9.167	6.875	5.500	4.583	3.929	3.437
54	18.667	14.000	11.200	9.333	7.000	5.600	4.667	4.000	3.500
55	19.000	14.250	11.400	9.500	7.125	5.700	4.750	4.071	3.562

Outside Diameters of Diametral Pitch Gears

No. of Teeth	Diametral Pitch								
	3 P	4 P	5 P	6 P	8 P	10 P	12 P	14 P	16 P
56	19.333	14.500	11.600	9.667	7.250	5.800	4.833	4.143	3.625
57	19.667	14.750	11.800	9.833	7.375	5.900	4.917	4.214	3.687
58	20.000	15.000	12.000	10.000	7.500	6.000	5.000	4.286	3.750
59	20.333	15.250	12.200	10.167	7.625	6.100	5.083	4.357	3.812
60	20.667	15.500	12.400	10.333	7.750	6.200	5.167	4.429	3.875
61	21.000	15.750	12.600	10.500	7.875	6.300	5.250	4.500	3.937
62	21.333	16.000	12.800	10.667	8.000	6.400	5.333	4.571	4.000
63	21.667	16.250	13.000	10.833	8.125	6.500	5.417	4.643	4.062
64	22.000	16.500	13.200	11.000	8.250	6.600	5.500	4.714	4.125
65	22.333	16.750	13.400	11.167	8.375	6.700	5.583	4.786	4.187
66	22.667	17.000	13.600	11.333	8.500	6.800	5.667	4.857	4.250
67	23.000	17.250	13.800	11.500	8.625	6.900	5.750	4.929	4.312
68	23.333	17.500	14.000	11.667	8.750	7.000	5.833	5.000	4.375
69	23.667	17.750	14.200	11.833	8.875	7.100	5.917	5.071	4.437
70	24.000	18.000	14.400	12.000	9.000	7.200	6.000	5.143	4.500
71	24.333	18.250	14.600	12.167	9.125	7.300	6.083	5.214	4.562
72	24.667	18.500	14.800	12.333	9.250	7.400	6.167	5.286	4.625
73	25.000	18.750	15.000	12.500	9.375	7.500	6.250	5.357	4.687
74	25.333	19.000	15.200	12.667	9.500	7.600	6.333	5.429	4.750
75	25.667	19.250	15.400	12.833	9.625	7.700	6.417	5.500	4.812
76	26.000	19.500	15.600	13.000	9.750	7.800	6.500	5.571	4.875
77	26.333	19.750	15.800	13.167	9.875	7.900	6.583	5.643	4.937
78	26.667	20.000	16.000	13.333	10.000	8.000	6.667	5.714	5.000
79	27.000	20.250	16.200	13.500	10.125	8.100	6.750	5.786	5.062
80	27.333	20.500	16.400	13.667	10.250	8.200	6.833	5.857	5.125
81	27.667	20.750	16.600	13.833	10.375	8.300	6.917	5.929	5.187
82	28.000	21.000	16.800	14.000	10.500	8.400	7.000	6.000	5.250
83	28.333	21.250	17.000	14.167	10.625	8.500	7.083	6.071	5.312
84	28.667	21.500	17.200	14.333	10.750	8.600	7.167	6.143	5.375
85	29.000	21.750	17.400	14.500	10.875	8.700	7.250	6.214	5.437
86	29.333	22.000	17.600	14.667	11.000	8.800	7.333	6.286	5.500
87	29.667	22.250	17.800	14.833	11.125	8.900	7.417	6.357	5.562
88	30.000	22.500	18.000	15.000	11.250	9.000	7.500	6.429	5.625
89	30.333	22.750	18.200	15.167	11.375	9.100	7.583	6.500	5.687
90	30.667	23.000	18.400	15.333	11.500	9.200	7.667	6.571	5.750
91	31.000	23.250	18.600	15.500	11.625	9.300	7.750	6.643	5.812
92	31.333	23.500	18.800	15.667	11.750	9.400	7.833	6.714	5.875
93	31.667	23.750	19.000	15.833	11.875	9.500	7.917	6.786	5.937
94	32.000	24.000	19.200	16.000	12.000	9.600	8.000	6.857	6.000
95	32.333	24.250	19.400	16.167	12.125	9.700	8.083	6.929	6.062
96	32.667	24.500	19.600	16.333	12.250	9.800	8.167	7.000	6.125
97	33.000	24.750	19.800	16.500	12.375	9.900	8.250	7.071	6.187
98	33.333	25.000	20.000	16.667	12.500	10.000	8.333	7.143	6.250
99	33.667	25.250	20.200	16.833	12.625	10.100	8.417	7.214	6.312
100	34.000	25.500	20.400	17.000	12.750	10.200	8.500	7.286	6.375

Root Diameters of Diametral Pitch Gears

No. of Teeth	Diametral Pitch								
	3 P	4 P	5 P	6 P	8 P	10 P	12 P	14 P	16 P
10	2.562	1.921	1.537	1.281	0.961	0.769	0.640	0.549	0.480
11	2.895	2.171	1.737	1.448	1.086	0.869	0.724	0.621	0.543
12	3.229	2.421	1.937	1.614	1.211	0.969	0.807	0.692	0.605
13	3.562	2.671	2.137	1.781	1.336	1.069	0.890	0.763	0.668
14	3.895	2.921	2.337	1.948	1.461	1.169	0.974	0.835	0.730
15	4.229	3.171	2.537	2.114	1.586	1.269	1.057	0.906	0.793
16	4.562	3.421	2.737	2.281	1.711	1.369	1.140	0.978	0.855
17	4.895	3.671	2.937	2.448	1.836	1.469	1.224	1.049	0.918
18	5.229	3.921	3.137	2.614	1.961	1.569	1.307	1.121	0.980
19	5.562	4.171	3.337	2.781	2.086	1.669	1.390	1.192	1.043
20	5.895	4.421	3.537	2.948	2.211	1.769	1.474	1.263	1.105
21	6.229	4.671	3.737	3.114	2.336	1.869	1.557	1.335	1.168
22	6.562	4.921	3.937	3.281	2.461	1.969	1.640	1.406	1.230
23	6.895	5.171	4.137	3.448	2.586	2.069	1.724	1.478	1.293
24	7.229	5.421	4.337	3.614	2.711	2.169	1.807	1.549	1.355
25	7.562	5.671	4.537	3.781	2.836	2.269	1.890	1.621	1.418
26	7.895	5.921	4.737	3.948	2.961	2.369	1.974	1.692	1.480
27	8.229	6.171	4.937	4.114	3.086	2.469	2.057	1.763	1.543
28	8.562	6.421	5.137	4.281	3.211	2.569	2.140	1.835	1.605
29	8.895	6.671	5.337	4.448	3.336	2.669	2.224	1.906	1.668
30	9.229	6.921	5.537	4.614	3.461	2.769	2.307	1.978	1.730
31	9.562	7.171	5.737	4.781	3.586	2.869	2.390	2.049	1.793
32	9.895	7.421	5.937	4.948	3.711	2.969	2.474	2.121	1.855
33	10.229	7.671	6.137	5.114	3.836	3.069	2.557	2.192	1.918
34	10.562	7.921	6.337	5.281	3.961	3.169	2.640	2.263	1.980
35	10.895	8.171	6.537	5.448	4.086	3.269	2.724	2.335	2.043
36	11.229	8.421	6.737	5.614	4.211	3.369	2.807	2.406	2.105
37	11.562	8.671	6.937	5.781	4.336	3.469	2.890	2.478	2.168
38	11.895	8.921	7.137	5.948	4.461	3.569	2.974	2.549	2.230
39	12.229	9.171	7.337	6.114	4.586	3.669	3.057	2.621	2.293
40	12.562	9.421	7.537	6.281	4.711	3.769	3.140	2.692	2.355
41	12.895	9.671	7.737	6.448	4.836	3.869	3.224	2.763	2.418
42	13.229	9.921	7.937	6.614	4.961	3.969	3.307	2.835	2.480
43	13.562	10.171	8.137	6.781	5.086	4.069	3.390	2.906	2.543
44	13.895	10.421	8.337	6.948	5.211	4.169	3.474	2.978	2.605
45	14.229	10.671	8.537	7.114	5.336	4.269	3.557	3.049	2.668
46	14.562	10.921	8.737	7.281	5.461	4.369	3.640	3.121	2.730
47	14.895	11.171	8.937	7.448	5.586	4.469	3.724	3.192	2.793
48	15.229	11.421	9.137	7.614	5.711	4.569	3.807	3.263	2.855
49	15.562	11.671	9.337	7.781	5.836	4.669	3.890	3.335	2.918
50	15.895	11.921	9.537	7.948	5.961	4.769	3.974	3.406	2.980
51	16.229	12.171	9.737	8.114	6.086	4.869	4.057	3.478	3.043
52	16.562	12.421	9.937	8.281	6.211	4.969	4.140	3.549	3.105
53	16.895	12.671	10.137	8.448	6.336	5.069	4.224	3.621	3.168
54	17.229	12.921	10.337	8.614	6.461	5.169	4.307	3.692	3.230
55	17.562	13.171	10.537	8.781	6.586	5.269	4.390	3.763	3.293

Root Diameters of Diametral Pitch Gears

No. of Teeth	Diametral Pitch								
	3 P	4 P	5 P	6 P	8 P	10 P	12 P	14 P	16 P
56	17.895	13.421	10.737	8.948	6.711	5.369	4.474	3.835	3.355
57	18.229	13.671	10.937	9.114	6.836	5.469	4.557	3.906	3.418
58	18.562	13.921	11.137	9.281	6.961	5.569	4.640	3.978	3.480
59	18.895	14.171	11.337	9.448	7.086	5.669	4.724	4.049	3.543
60	19.229	14.421	11.537	9.614	7.211	5.769	4.807	4.121	3.605
61	19.562	14.671	11.737	9.781	7.336	5.869	4.890	4.192	3.668
62	19.895	14.921	11.937	9.948	7.461	5.969	4.974	4.263	3.730
63	20.229	15.171	12.137	10.114	7.586	6.069	5.057	4.335	3.793
64	20.562	15.421	12.337	10.281	7.711	6.169	5.140	4.406	3.855
65	20.895	15.671	12.537	10.448	7.836	6.269	5.224	4.478	3.918
66	21.229	15.921	12.737	10.614	7.961	6.369	5.307	4.549	3.980
67	21.562	16.171	12.937	10.781	8.086	6.469	5.390	4.621	4.043
68	21.895	16.421	13.137	10.948	8.211	6.569	5.474	4.692	4.105
69	22.229	16.671	13.337	11.114	8.336	6.669	5.557	4.763	4.168
70	22.562	16.921	13.537	11.281	8.461	6.769	5.640	4.835	4.230
71	22.895	17.171	13.737	11.448	8.586	6.869	5.724	4.906	4.293
72	23.229	17.421	13.937	11.614	8.711	6.969	5.807	4.978	4.355
73	23.562	17.671	14.137	11.781	8.836	7.069	5.890	5.049	4.418
74	23.895	17.921	14.337	11.948	8.961	7.169	5.974	5.121	4.480
75	24.229	18.171	14.537	12.114	9.086	7.269	6.057	5.192	4.543
76	24.562	18.421	14.737	12.281	9.211	7.369	6.140	5.263	4.605
77	24.895	18.671	14.937	12.448	9.336	7.469	6.224	5.335	4.668
78	25.229	18.921	15.137	12.614	9.461	7.569	6.307	5.406	4.730
79	25.562	19.171	15.337	12.781	9.586	7.669	6.390	5.478	4.793
80	25.895	19.421	15.537	12.948	9.711	7.769	6.474	5.549	4.855
81	26.229	19.671	15.737	13.114	9.836	7.869	6.557	5.621	4.918
82	26.562	19.921	15.937	13.281	9.961	7.969	6.640	5.692	4.980
83	26.895	20.171	16.137	13.448	10.086	8.069	6.724	5.763	5.043
84	27.229	20.421	16.337	13.614	10.211	8.169	6.807	5.835	5.105
85	27.562	20.671	16.537	13.781	10.336	8.269	6.890	5.906	5.168
86	27.895	20.921	16.737	13.948	10.461	8.369	6.974	5.978	5.230
87	28.229	21.171	16.937	14.114	10.586	8.469	7.057	6.049	5.293
88	28.562	21.421	17.137	14.281	10.711	8.569	7.140	6.121	5.355
89	28.895	21.671	17.337	14.448	10.836	8.669	7.224	6.192	5.418
90	29.229	21.921	17.537	14.614	10.961	8.769	7.307	6.263	5.480
91	29.562	22.171	17.737	14.781	11.086	8.869	7.390	6.335	5.543
92	29.895	22.421	17.937	14.948	11.211	8.969	7.474	6.406	5.605
93	30.229	22.671	18.137	15.114	11.336	9.069	7.557	6.478	5.668
94	30.562	22.921	18.337	15.281	11.461	9.169	7.640	6.549	5.730
95	30.895	23.171	18.537	15.448	11.586	9.269	7.724	6.621	5.793
96	31.229	23.421	18.737	15.614	11.711	9.369	7.807	6.692	5.855
97	31.562	23.671	18.937	15.781	11.836	9.469	7.890	6.763	5.918
98	31.895	23.921	19.137	15.948	11.961	9.569	7.974	6.835	5.980
99	32.229	24.171	19.337	16.114	12.086	9.669	8.057	6.906	6.043
100	32.562	24.421	19.537	16.281	12.211	9.769	8.140	6.978	6.105

SPUR GEARING

Pitch Diameters for Circular Pitch Gears

No. of Teeth	Circular Pitch in Inches								
	½	⅝	¾	⅞	1	1⅛	1¼	1⅜	1½
12	1.910	2.387	2.865	3.342	3.820	4.297	4.775	5.252	5.730
13	2.069	2.586	3.104	3.621	4.138	4.655	5.173	5.689	6.207
14	2.228	2.785	3.342	3.900	4.456	5.013	5.570	6.127	6.684
15	2.387	2.984	3.581	4.178	4.775	5.371	5.968	6.565	7.162
16	2.546	3.183	3.820	4.456	5.093	5.730	6.366	7.003	7.639
17	2.705	3.382	4.059	4.735	5.411	6.088	6.764	7.440	8.117
18	2.865	3.581	4.297	5.013	5.730	6.446	7.162	7.878	8.594
19	3.024	3.780	4.536	5.292	6.048	6.804	7.560	8.316	9.072
20	3.183	3.979	4.775	5.570	6.366	7.162	7.958	8.753	9.549
21	3.342	4.178	5.014	5.849	6.684	7.520	8.356	9.191	10.027
22	3.501	4.377	5.252	6.128	7.003	7.878	8.754	9.629	10.504
23	3.660	4.576	5.491	6.406	7.321	8.236	9.152	10.067	10.981
24	3.820	4.775	5.730	6.684	7.639	8.594	9.550	10.504	11.459
25	3.979	4.974	5.969	6.962	7.958	8.953	9.948	10.941	11.936
26	4.138	5.173	6.207	7.241	8.276	9.311	10.345	11.379	12.414
27	4.297	5.372	6.446	7.520	8.594	9.669	10.743	11.817	12.891
28	4.456	5.571	6.684	7.798	8.913	10.027	11.141	12.255	13.369
29	4.615	5.770	6.923	8.077	9.231	10.385	11.539	12.692	13.846
30	4.775	5.969	7.162	8.356	9.549	10.743	11.937	13.130	14.324
31	4.934	6.168	7.401	8.634	9.868	11.101	12.335	13.568	14.801
32	5.093	6.366	7.639	8.913	10.186	11.459	12.733	14.006	15.279
33	5.252	6.565	7.878	9.191	10.504	11.817	13.131	14.443	15.756
34	5.411	6.764	8.117	9.470	10.822	12.175	13.528	14.881	16.234
35	5.570	6.963	8.356	9.748	11.141	12.533	13.926	15.319	16.711
36	5.730	7.162	8.594	10.026	11.459	12.891	14.324	15.756	17.189
37	5.889	7.361	8.833	10.305	11.778	13.250	14.722	16.193	17.666
38	6.048	7.560	9.072	10.584	12.096	13.608	15.120	16.631	18.144
39	6.207	7.759	9.311	10.862	12.414	13.966	15.518	17.069	18.621
40	6.366	7.958	9.549	11.141	12.732	14.324	15.916	17.507	19.099
41	6.525	8.157	9.788	11.419	13.051	14.682	16.314	17.944	19.576
42	6.684	8.356	10.027	11.698	13.369	15.040	16.711	18.382	20.053
43	6.844	8.554	10.266	11.976	13.687	15.398	17.109	18.820	20.531
44	7.003	8.753	10.504	12.255	14.006	15.756	17.507	19.258	21.008
45	7.162	8.952	10.743	12.533	14.324	16.114	17.905	19.695	21.486
46	7.321	9.151	10.981	12.812	14.642	16.472	18.303	20.133	21.963
47	7.480	9.350	11.220	13.091	14.961	16.830	18.701	20.571	22.441
48	7.639	9.549	11.459	13.369	15.279	17.189	19.099	21.008	22.918
49	7.798	9.748	11.698	13.647	15.597	17.547	19.497	21.446	23.396
50	7.958	9.947	11.936	13.926	15.916	17.905	19.894	21.884	23.873
51	8.117	10.146	12.175	14.205	16.234	18.263	20.292	22.322	24.351
52	8.276	10.345	12.414	14.483	16.552	18.621	20.690	22.759	24.828
53	8.435	10.544	12.653	14.761	16.870	18.979	21.088	23.196	25.305
54	8.594	10.743	12.891	15.040	17.189	19.337	21.486	23.634	25.783
55	8.753	10.942	13.130	15.319	17.507	19.695	21.884	24.072	26.260
56	8.913	11,141	13.369	15.597	17.825	20.053	22.282	24.510	26.738

Pitch Diameters for Circular Pitch Gears

No. of Teeth	Circular Pitch in Inches								
	½	⅝	¾	⅞	1	1⅛	1¼	1⅜	1½
57	9.072	11.340	13.608	15.875	18.144	20.412	22.680	24.947	27.215
58	9.231	11.539	13.847	16.154	18.462	20.770	23.078	25.385	27.693
59	9.390	11.738	14.086	16.433	18.780	21.128	23.476	25.823	28.170
60	9.549	11.937	14.324	16.711	19.099	21.486	23.873	26.260	28.648
61	9.708	12.136	14.563	16.989	19.417	21.844	24.271	26.698	29.125
62	9.868	12.335	14.802	17.268	19.735	22.202	24.669	27.136	29.603
63	10.027	12.533	15.041	17.547	20.054	22.560	25.067	27.574	30.080
64	10.186	12.732	15.279	17.825	20.372	22.918	25.465	28.011	30.558
65	10.345	12.931	15.518	18.103	20.690	23.277	25.863	28.449	31.035
66	10.504	13.130	15.756	18.382	21.008	23.635	26.260	28.887	31.513
67	10.663	13.329	15.995	18.661	21.327	23.993	26.658	29.324	31.991
68	10.822	13.528	16.234	18.939	21.645	24.351	27.056	29.762	32.468
69	10.981	13.727	16.473	19.218	21.963	24.709	27.454	30.199	32.945
70	11.141	13.926	16.711	19.497	22.282	25.067	27.852	30.637	33.422
71	11.300	14.125	16.950	19.775	22.600	25.425	28.250	31.075	33.900
72	11.459	14.324	17.189	20.053	22.918	25.783	28.648	31.513	34.377
73	11.618	14.523	17.428	20.331	23.237	26.141	29.046	31.950	34.855
74	11.777	14.722	17.666	20.610	23.555	26.499	29.443	32.388	35.332
75	11.936	14.921	17.905	20.889	23.873	26.857	29.841	32.826	35.810
76	12.096	15.120	18.144	21.167	24.192	27.215	30.239	33.263	36.287
77	12.255	15.319	18.383	21.446	24.510	27.574	30.637	33.701	36.765
78	12.414	15.518	18.621	21.725	24.828	27.932	31.035	34.139	37.242
79	12.573	15.716	18.860	22.003	25.146	28.290	31.433	34.576	37.720
80	12.732	15.915	19.099	22.282	25.465	28.648	31.831	35.014	38.197
81	12.891	16.114	19.338	22.560	25.783	29.006	32.229	35.452	38.674
82	13.051	16.313	19.576	22.839	26.101	29.364	32.627	35.890	39.152
83	13.210	16.512	19.815	23.117	26.420	29.722	33.025	36.327	39.629
84	13.369	16.711	20.053	23.396	26.738	30.080	33.423	36.765	40.107
85	13.528	16.910	20.292	23.674	27.056	30.438	33.821	37.202	40.584
86	13.687	17.109	20.531	23.953	27.375	30.796	34.218	37.640	41.062
87	13.846	17.308	20.770	24.232	27.693	31.154	34.616	38.078	41.539
88	14.006	17.507	21.008	24.510	28.011	31.513	35.014	38.515	42.017
89	14.165	17.706	21.247	24.788	28.330	31.871	35.412	38.953	42.494
90	14.324	17.905	21.486	25.067	28.648	32.229	35.810	39.391	42.972
91	14.483	18.104	21.725	25.345	28.966	32.587	36.208	39.829	43.449
92	14.642	18.303	21.963	25.624	29.284	32.945	36.606	40.266	43.927
93	14.801	18.502	22.202	25.902	29.603	33.303	37.004	40.704	44.404
94	14.961	18.701	22.441	26.181	29.921	33.661	37.402	41.142	44.882
95	15.120	18.900	22.680	26.460	30.239	34.019	37.800	41.579	45.359
96	15.279	19.099	22.918	26.738	30.558	34.377	38.197	42.017	45.837
97	15.438	19.298	23.157	27.016	30.876	34.736	38.595	42.454	46.314
98	15.597	19.497	23.396	27.295	31.194	35.094	38.993	42.892	46.792
99	15.756	19.695	23.635	27.574	31.513	35.452	39.391	43.330	47.269
100	15.915	19.894	23.873	27.852	31.831	35.810	39.789	43.767	47.746

Pitch Diameters for Circular Pitch Gears

No. of Teeth	Circular Pitch in Inches									
	1⅝	1¾	1⅞	2	2⅛	2¼	2⅜	2½	2¾	3
12	6.20	6.68	7.16	7.64	8.12	8.59	9.07	9.55	10.50	11.46
13	6.72	7.24	7.76	8.28	8.79	9.31	9.83	10.34	11.38	12.41
14	7.24	7.80	8.35	8.91	9.47	10.03	10.59	11.14	12.25	13.36
15	7.76	8.35	8.95	9.54	10.15	10.74	11.34	11.93	13.13	14.32
16	8.27	8.91	9.55	10.18	10.82	11.46	12.10	12.73	14.00	15.28
17	8.79	9.47	10.14	10.82	11.50	12.17	12.85	13.53	14.88	16.23
18	9.31	10.03	10.74	11.46	12.17	12.89	13.61	14.32	15.76	17.19
19	9.83	10.58	11.34	12.10	12.85	13.61	14.36	15.12	16.63	18.14
20	10.34	11.14	11.93	12.73	13.53	14.32	15.12	15.92	17.51	19.10
21	10.86	11.70	12.53	13.37	14.20	15.04	15.87	16.71	18.38	20.05
22	11.38	12.25	13.13	14.00	14.88	15.76	16.63	17.50	19.26	21.01
23	11.90	12.81	13.73	14.64	15.56	16.47	17.39	18.30	20.13	21.96
24	12.41	13.37	14.32	15.27	16.23	17.19	18.14	19.10	21.01	22.92
25	12.93	13.93	14.92	15.91	16.91	17.90	18.90	19.89	21.88	23.87
26	13.45	14.48	15.52	16.55	17.59	18.62	19.65	20.69	22.76	24.83
27	13.96	15.04	16.11	17.19	18.26	19.34	20.41	21.48	23.63	25.78
28	14.48	15.60	16.71	17.82	18.94	20.05	21.17	22.28	24.51	26.74
29	15.00	16.15	17.31	18.46	19.61	20.77	21.93	23.07	25.38	27.69
30	15.52	16.70	17.90	19.10	20.29	21.48	22.69	23.87	26.26	28.64
31	16.03	17.26	18.50	19.73	20.96	22.20	23.44	24.66	27.14	29.60
32	16.55	17.82	19.10	20.37	21.64	22.92	24.19	25.46	28.01	30.55
33	17.07	18.38	19.69	21.00	22.32	23.63	24.94	26.25	28.88	31.50
34	17.59	18.94	20.29	21.64	23.00	24.34	25.70	27.05	29.76	32.46
35	18.10	19.49	20.89	22.27	23.67	25.06	26.46	27.85	30.64	33.42
36	18.61	20.05	21.48	22.91	24.35	25.78	27.21	28.65	31.51	34.38
37	19.13	20.61	22.08	23.55	25.03	26.50	27.97	29.44	32.39	35.33
38	19.65	21.17	22.68	24.19	25.70	27.21	28.73	30.24	33.26	36.29
39	20.17	21.73	23.28	24.83	26.38	27.93	29.48	31.03	34.13	37.24
40	20.69	22.28	23.87	25.46	27.06	28.65	30.24	31.83	35.01	38.19
41	21.21	22.84	24.47	26.09	27.73	29.36	30.99	32.62	35.89	39.15
42	21.72	23.39	25.07	26.73	28.41	30.08	31.75	33.42	36.76	40.11
43	22.24	23.95	25.66	27.37	29.09	30.80	32.50	34.21	37.64	41.06
44	22.76	24.51	26.26	28.01	29.77	31.51	33.26	35.01	38.51	42.01
45	23.28	25.07	26.86	28.65	30.44	32.23	34.02	35.81	39.39	42.97
46	23.79	25.62	27.45	29.28	31.11	32.94	34.77	36.60	40.26	43.93
47	24.31	26.18	28.05	29.92	31.79	33.66	35.53	37.40	41.14	44.88
48	24.82	26.74	28.64	30.55	32.47	34.38	36.28	38.19	42.02	45.84
49	25.34	27.29	29.24	31.19	33.14	35.09	37.04	38.99	42.89	46.79
50	25.86	27.85	29.84	31.83	33.82	35.81	37.80	39.79	43.77	47.75
51	26.38	28.41	30.44	32.47	34.49	36.52	38.55	40.58	44.64	48.70
52	26.90	28.97	31.04	33.10	35.17	37.24	39.31	41.38	45.51	49.65
53	27.41	29.52	31.63	33.74	35.85	37.96	40.07	42.18	46.39	50.61
54	27.93	30.08	32.23	34.38	36.53	38.68	40.83	42.97	47.27	51.56
55	28.45	30.64	32.82	35.01	37.20	39.39	41.58	43.76	48.14	52.52
56	28.96	31.19	33.42	35.65	37.88	40.11	42.33	44.56	49.02	53.47

Pitch Diameters for Circular Pitch Gears

No. of Teeth	Circular Pitch in Inches									
	1⅝	1¾	1⅞	2	2⅛	2¼	2⅜	2½	2¾	3
57	29.48	31.75	34.02	36.28	38.55	40.82	43.09	45.36	49.89	54.43
58	30.00	32.31	34.62	36.92	39.23	41.54	43.85	46.15	50.77	55.38
59	30.52	32.87	35.21	37.56	39.91	42.25	44.60	46.95	51.64	56.34
60	31.03	33.42	35.80	38.20	40.58	42.97	45.36	47.74	52.52	57.30
61	31.55	33.98	36.40	38.83	41.26	43.69	46.11	48.54	53.39	58.25
62	32.07	34.54	37.00	39.47	41.93	44.40	46.87	49.34	54.27	59.20
63	32.58	35.09	37.60	40.10	42.61	45.12	47.62	50.13	55.14	60.16
64	33.10	35.65	38.19	40.74	43.29	45.84	48.38	50.93	56.02	61.12
65	33.62	36.21	38.79	41.38	43.97	46.55	49.14	51.72	56.90	62.07
66	34.14	36.76	39.39	42.02	44.64	47.27	49.89	52.52	57.77	63.02
67	34.66	37.32	39.99	42.65	45.32	47.98	50.65	53.32	58.65	63.98
68	35.17	37.88	40.58	43.29	45.99	48.70	51.41	54.11	59.52	64.94
69	35.69	38.44	41.18	43.92	46.67	49.42	52.16	54.91	60.40	65.89
70	36.21	38.99	41.78	44.56	47.35	50.13	52.92	55.70	61.27	66.84
71	36.72	39.55	42.37	45.20	48.02	50.85	53.67	56.50	62.15	67.80
72	37.24	40.11	42.97	45.84	48.70	51.56	54.43	57.30	63.02	68.76
73	37.76	40.66	43.57	46.47	49.38	52.28	55.19	58.09	63.90	69.71
74	38.28	41.22	44.16	47.11	50.05	53.00	55.94	58.89	64.77	70.66
75	38.79	41.78	44.76	47.74	50.73	53.71	56.70	59.68	65.65	71.62
76	39.31	42.33	45.36	48.38	51.41	54.43	57.45	60.48	66.52	72.57
77	39.83	42.89	45.95	49.02	52.08	55.14	58.21	61.27	67.40	73.53
78	40.34	43.45	46.55	49.66	52.76	55.86	58.96	62.07	68.28	74.48
79	40.86	44.01	47.15	50.29	53.43	56.58	59.72	62.86	69.15	75.44
80	41.38	44.56	47.74	50.93	54.11	57.29	60.48	63.66	70.03	76.39
81	41.90	45.12	48.34	51.56	54.79	58.01	61.23	64.46	70.90	77.35
82	42.41	45.68	48.94	52.20	55.46	58.73	61.99	65.25	71.78	78.30
83	42.93	46.23	49.54	52.84	56.14	59.44	62.75	66.05	72.65	79.26
84	43.45	46.79	50.14	53.47	56.81	60.16	63.50	66.84	73.52	80.21
85	43.97	47.35	50.73	54.11	57.49	60.88	64.26	67.64	74.40	81.17
86	44.48	47.90	51.33	54.75	58.17	61.59	65.01	68.44	75.28	82.12
87	45.00	48.46	51.92	55.38	58.85	62.31	65.77	69.23	76.15	83.08
88	45.52	49.02	52.52	56.02	59.52	63.02	66.53	70.03	77.03	84.03
89	46.03	49.58	53.12	56.66	60.20	63.74	67.28	70.82	77.91	84.99
90	46.55	50.13	53.71	57.30	60.88	64.46	68.04	71.62	78.78	85.94
91	47.07	50.69	54.31	57.93	61.55	65.17	68.79	72.41	79.65	86.90
92	47.59	51.25	54.91	58.57	62.23	65.89	69.55	73.21	80.53	87.85
93	48.10	51.80	55.50	59.20	62.90	66.60	70.30	74.00	81.41	88.81
94	48.62	52.36	56.10	59.84	63.58	67.32	71.06	74.80	82.28	89.76
95	49.14	52.92	56.70	60.48	64.26	68.04	71.81	75.60	83.16	90.72
96	49.65	53.47	57.29	61.11	64.93	68.75	72.57	76.39	84.03	91.67
97	50.17	54.03	57.89	61.75	65.61	69.47	73.33	77.19	84.91	92.62
98	50.69	54.59	58.49	62.39	66.29	70.19	74.08	77.98	85.78	93.58
99	51.21	55.15	59.08	63.02	66.96	70.90	74.84	78.78	86.56	94.54
100	51.72	55.70	59.68	63.66	67.64	71.62	75.59	79.57	87.53	95.49

Outside Diameters of Circular Pitch Gears

No. of Teeth	Circular Pitch in Inches								
	½	⅝	¾	⅞	1	1⅛	1¼	1⅜	1½
12	2.228	2.785	3.342	3.900	4.456	5.013	5.570	6.127	6.684
13	2.387	2.984	3.581	4.178	4.775	5.371	5.968	6.565	7.162
14	2.546	3.183	3.820	4.456	5.093	5.730	6.366	7.003	7.639
15	2.705	3.382	4.059	4.735	5.411	6.088	6.764	7.440	8.117
16	2.865	3.581	4.297	5.013	5.730	6.446	7.162	7.878	8.594
17	3.024	3.780	4.536	5.292	6.048	6.804	7.560	8.316	9.072
18	3.183	3.979	4.775	5.570	6.366	7.162	7.958	8.753	9.549
19	3.342	4.178	5.014	5.849	6.684	7.520	8.356	9.191	10.027
20	3.501	4.377	5.252	6.128	7.003	7.878	8.754	9.629	10.504
21	3.660	4.576	5.491	6.406	7.321	8.236	9.152	10.067	10.981
22	3.820	4.775	5.730	6.684	7.639	8.594	9.550	10.504	11.459
23	3.979	4.974	5.969	6.962	7.958	8.953	9.948	10.941	11.936
24	4.138	5.173	6.207	7.241	8.276	9.311	10.345	11.379	12.414
25	4.297	5.372	6.446	7.520	8.594	9.669	10.743	11.817	12.891
26	4.456	5.571	6.684	7.798	8.913	10.027	11.141	12.255	13.369
27	4.615	5.770	6.923	8.077	9.231	10.385	11.539	12.692	13.846
28	4.775	5.969	7.162	8.356	9.549	10.743	11.937	13.130	14.324
29	4.934	6.168	7.401	8.634	9.868	11.101	12.335	13.568	14.801
30	5.093	6.366	7.639	8.913	10.186	11.459	12.733	14.006	15.279
31	5.252	6.565	7.878	9.191	10.504	11.817	13.131	14.443	15.756
32	5.411	6.764	8.117	9.470	10.822	12.175	13.528	14.881	16.234
33	5.570	6.963	8.356	9.748	11.141	12.533	13.926	15.319	16.711
34	5.730	7.162	8.594	10.026	11.459	12.891	14.324	15.756	17.189
35	5.889	7.361	8.833	10.305	11.778	13.250	14.722	16.193	17.666
36	6.048	7.560	9.072	10.584	12.096	13.608	15.120	16.631	18.144
37	6.207	7.759	9.311	10.862	12.414	13.966	15.518	17.069	18.621
38	6.366	7.958	9.549	11.141	12.732	14.324	15.916	17.507	19.099
39	6.525	8.157	9.788	11.419	13.051	14.682	16.314	17.944	19.576
40	6.684	8.356	10.027	11.698	13.369	15.040	16.711	18.382	20.053
41	6.844	8.554	10.266	11.976	13.687	15.398	17.109	18.820	20.531
42	7.003	8.753	10.504	12.255	14.006	15.756	17.507	19.258	21.008
43	7.162	8.952	10.743	12.533	14.324	16.114	17.905	19.695	21.486
44	7.321	9.151	10.981	12.812	14.642	16.472	18.303	20.133	21.963
45	7.480	9.350	11.220	13.091	14.961	16.830	18.701	20.571	22.441
46	7.639	9.549	11.459	13.369	15.279	17.189	19.099	21.008	22.918
47	7.798	9.748	11.698	13.647	15.597	17.547	19.497	21.446	23.396
48	7.958	9.947	11.936	13.926	15.916	17.905	19.894	21.884	23.873
49	8.117	10.146	12.175	14.205	16.234	18.263	20.292	22.322	24.351
50	8.276	10.345	12.414	14.483	16.552	18.621	20.690	22.759	24.828
51	8.435	10.544	12.653	14.761	16.870	18.979	21.088	23.196	25.305
52	8.594	10.743	12.891	15.040	17.189	19.337	21.486	23.634	25.783
53	8.753	10.942	13.130	15.319	17.507	19.695	21.884	24.072	26.260
54	8.913	11.141	13.369	15.597	17.825	20.053	22.281	24.510	26.738
55	9.072	11.340	13.608	15.875	18.144	20.412	22.680	24.947	27.215
56	9.231	11.539	13.847	16.154	18.462	20.770	23.078	25.385	27.693

Outside Diameters of Circular Pitch Gears

No. of Teeth	Circular Pitch in Inches								
	½	⅝	¾	⅞	1	1⅛	1¼	1⅜	1½
57	9.390	11.738	14.086	16.433	18.780	21.128	23.476	25.823	28.170
58	9.549	11.937	14.324	16.711	19.099	21.486	23.873	26.260	28.648
59	9.708	12.136	14.563	16.989	19.417	21.844	24.271	26.698	29.125
60	9.868	12.335	14.802	17.268	19.735	22.202	24.669	27.136	29.603
61	10.027	12.533	15.041	17.547	20.054	22.560	25.067	27.574	30.080
62	10.186	12.732	15.279	17.825	20.372	22.918	25.465	28.011	30.558
63	10.345	12.931	15.518	18.103	20.690	23.277	25.863	28.449	31.035
64	10.504	13.130	15.756	18.382	21.008	23.635	26.260	28.887	31.513
65	10.663	13.329	15.995	18.661	21.327	23.993	26.658	29.324	31.991
66	10.822	13.528	16.234	18.939	21.645	24.351	27.056	29.762	32.468
67	10.981	13.727	16.473	19.218	21.963	24.709	27.454	30.199	32.945
68	11.141	13.926	16.711	19.497	22.282	25.067	27.852	30.637	33.422
69	11.300	14.125	16.950	19.775	22.600	25.425	28.250	31.075	33.900
70	11.459	14.324	17.189	20.053	22.918	25.783	28.648	31.513	34.377
71	11.618	14.523	17.428	20.331	23.237	26.141	29.046	31.950	34.855
72	11.777	14.722	17.666	20.610	23.555	26.499	29.443	32.388	35.332
73	11.936	14.921	17.905	20.889	23.873	26.857	29.841	32.826	35.810
74	12.096	15.120	18.144	21.167	24.192	27.215	30.239	33.263	36.287
75	12.255	15.319	18.383	21.446	24.510	27.574	30.637	33.701	36.765
76	12.414	15.518	18.621	21.725	24.828	27.932	31.035	34.139	37.242
77	12.573	15.716	18.860	22.003	25.146	28.290	31.433	34.576	37.720
78	12.732	15.915	19.099	22.282	25.465	28.648	31.831	35.014	38.197
79	12.891	16.114	19.338	22.560	25.783	29.006	32.229	35.452	38.674
80	13.051	16.313	19.576	22.839	26.101	29.364	32.627	35.890	39.152
81	13.210	16.512	19.815	23.117	26.420	29.722	33.025	36.327	39.629
82	13.369	16.711	20.053	23.396	26.738	30.080	33.423	36.765	40.107
83	13.528	16.910	20.292	23.674	27.056	30.438	33.821	37.202	40.584
84	13.687	17.109	20.531	23.953	27.375	30.796	34.218	37.640	41.062
85	13.846	17.308	20.770	24.232	27.693	31.154	34.616	38.078	41.539
86	14.006	17.507	21.008	24.510	28.011	31.513	35.014	38.515	42.017
87	14.165	17.706	21.247	24.788	28.330	31.871	35.412	38.953	42.494
88	14.324	17.905	21.486	25.067	28.648	32.229	35.810	39.391	42.972
89	14.483	18.104	21.725	25.345	28.966	32.587	36.208	39.829	43.449
90	14.642	18.303	21.963	25.624	29.284	32.945	36.606	40.266	43.927
91	14.801	18.502	22.202	25.902	29.603	33.303	37.004	40.704	44.404
92	14.961	18.701	22.441	26.181	29.921	33.661	37.402	41.142	44.882
93	15.120	18.900	22.680	26.460	30.239	34.019	37.800	41.579	45.359
94	15.279	19.099	22.918	26.738	30.558	34.377	38.197	42.017	45.837
95	15.438	19.298	23.157	27.016	30.876	34.736	38.595	42.454	46.314
96	15.597	19.497	23.396	27.295	31.194	35.094	38.993	42.892	46.792
97	15.756	19.695	23.635	27.574	31.513	35.452	39.391	43.330	47.269
98	15.915	19.894	23.873	27.852	31.831	35.810	39.789	43.767	47.746
99	16.074	20.093	24.112	28.131	32.149	36.168	40.187	44.205	48.224
100	16.233	20.292	24.350	28.409	32.467	36.526	40.585	44.643	48.701

Outside Diameters of Circular Pitch Gears

No. of Teeth	Circular Pitch in Inches									
	1⅝	1¾	1⅞	2	2⅛	2¼	2⅜	2½	2¾	3
12	7.24	7.80	8.35	8.91	9.47	10.03	10.59	11.14	12.25	13.36
13	7.76	8.35	8.95	9.54	10.15	10.74	11.35	11.93	13.13	14.32
14	8.27	8.91	9.55	10.18	10.82	11.46	12.10	12.73	14.00	15.28
15	8.79	9.47	10.14	10.82	11.50	12.17	12.85	13.53	14.88	16.23
16	9.31	10.03	10.74	11.46	12.17	12.89	13.61	14.32	15.76	17.19
17	9.83	10.58	11.34	12.10	12.85	13.61	14.36	15.12	16.63	18.14
18	10.34	11.14	11.93	12.73	13.53	14.32	15.12	15.92	17.51	19.10
19	10.86	11.70	12.53	13.37	14.20	15.04	15.87	16.71	18.38	20.05
20	11.38	12.25	13.13	14.00	14.88	15.76	16.63	17.50	19.26	21.01
21	11.90	12.81	13.73	14.64	15.56	16.47	17.39	18.30	20.13	21.96
22	12.41	13.37	14.32	15.27	16.23	17.19	18.14	19.10	21.01	22.92
23	12.93	13.93	14.92	15.91	16.91	17.90	18.90	19.89	21.88	23.87
24	13.45	14.48	15.52	16.55	17.59	18.62	19.65	20.69	22.76	24.83
25	13.96	15.04	16.11	17.19	18.26	19.34	20.41	21.48	23.63	25.78
26	14.48	15.60	16.71	17.82	18.94	20.05	21.17	22.28	24.51	26.74
27	15.00	16.15	17.31	18.46	19.61	20.77	21.93	23.07	25.38	27.69
28	15.52	16.70	17.90	19.10	20.29	21.48	22.69	23.87	26.26	28.64
29	16.03	17.26	18.50	19.73	20.96	22.20	23.44	24.66	27.14	29.60
30	16.55	17.82	19.10	20.37	21.64	22.92	24.19	25.46	28.01	30.55
31	17.07	18.38	19.69	21.00	22.32	23.63	24.94	26.25	28.88	31.50
32	17.59	18.94	20.29	21.64	23.00	24.34	25.70	27.05	29.76	32.46
33	18.10	19.49	20.89	22.27	23.67	25.06	26.46	27.85	30.64	33.42
34	18.61	20.05	21.48	22.91	24.35	25.78	27.21	28.65	31.51	34.38
35	19.13	20.61	22.08	23.55	25.03	26.50	27.97	29.44	32.39	35.33
36	19.65	21.17	22.68	24.19	25.70	27.21	28.73	30.24	33.26	36.29
37	20.17	21.73	23.28	24.83	26.38	27.93	29.48	31.03	34.13	37.24
38	20.69	22.28	23.87	25.46	27.06	28.65	30.24	31.83	35.01	38.19
39	21.21	22.84	24.47	26.09	27.73	29.36	30.99	32.62	35.89	39.15
40	21.72	23.39	25.07	26.73	28.41	30.08	31.75	33.42	36.76	40.11
41	22.24	23.95	25.66	27.37	29.09	30.80	32.50	34.21	37.64	41.06
42	22.76	24.51	26.26	28.01	29.77	31.51	33.26	35.01	38.51	42.01
43	23.28	25.07	26.86	28.65	30.44	32.23	34.02	35.81	39.39	42.97
44	23.79	25.62	27.45	29.28	31.11	32.94	34.77	36.60	40.26	43.93
45	24.31	26.18	28.05	29.92	31.79	33.66	35.53	37.40	41.14	44.88
46	24.82	26.74	28.64	30.55	32.47	34.38	36.28	38.19	42.02	45.84
47	25.34	27.29	29.24	31.19	33.14	35.09	37.04	38.99	42.89	46.79
48	25.86	27.85	29.84	31.83	33.82	35.81	37.80	39.79	43.77	47.75
49	26.38	28.41	30.44	32.47	34.49	36.52	38.55	40.58	44.64	48.70
50	26.90	28.97	31.04	33.10	35.17	37.24	39.31	41.38	45.51	49.65
51	27.41	29.52	31.63	33.74	35.85	37.96	40.07	42.18	46.39	50.61
52	27.93	30.08	32.23	34.38	36.53	38.68	40.83	42.97	47.27	51.56
53	28.45	30.64	32.82	35.01	37.20	39.39	41.58	43.76	48.14	52.52
54	28.96	31.19	33.42	35.65	37.88	40.11	42.33	44.56	49.02	53.47
55	29.48	31.75	34.02	36.28	38.55	40.82	43.09	45.36	49.89	54.43
56	30.00	32.31	34.62	36.92	39.23	41.54	43.85	46.15	50.77	55.38

Outside Diameters of Circular Pitch Gears

No. of Teeth	Circular Pitch in Inches									
	1⅝	1¾	1⅞	2	2⅛	2¼	2⅜	2½	2¾	3
57	30.52	32.87	35.21	37.56	39.91	42.25	44.60	46.95	51.64	56.34
58	31.03	33.42	35.80	38.20	40.58	42.97	45.36	47.74	52.52	57.30
59	31.55	33.98	36.40	38.83	41.26	43.69	46.11	48.54	53.39	58.25
60	32.07	34.54	37.00	39.47	41.93	44.40	46.87	49.34	54.27	59.20
61	32.58	35.09	37.60	40.10	42.61	45.12	47.62	50.13	55.14	60.16
62	33.10	35.65	38.19	40.74	43.29	45.84	48.38	50.93	56.02	61.12
63	33.62	36.21	38.79	41.38	43.97	46.55	49.14	51.72	56.90	62.07
64	34.14	36.76	39.39	42.02	44.64	47.27	49.89	52.52	57.77	63.02
65	34.66	37.32	39.99	42.65	45.32	47.98	50.65	53.32	58.65	63.98
66	35.17	37.88	40.58	43.29	45.99	48.70	51.41	54.11	59.52	64.94
67	35.69	38.44	41.18	43.92	46.67	49.42	52.16	54.91	60.40	65.89
68	36.21	38.99	41.78	44.56	47.35	50.13	52.92	55.70	61.27	66.84
69	36.72	39.55	42.37	45.20	48.02	50.85	53.67	56.50	62.15	67.80
70	37.24	40.11	42.97	45.84	48.70	51.56	54.43	57.30	63.02	68.76
71	37.76	40.66	43.57	46.47	49.38	52.28	55.19	58.09	63.90	69.71
72	38.28	41.22	44.16	47.11	50.05	53.00	55.94	58.89	64.77	70.66
73	38.79	41.78	44.76	47.74	50.73	53.71	56.70	59.68	65.65	71.62
74	39.31	42.33	45.36	48.38	51.41	54.43	57.45	60.48	66.52	72.57
75	39.83	42.89	45.95	49.02	52.08	55.14	58.21	61.27	67.40	73.53
76	40.34	43.45	46.55	49.66	52.76	55.86	58.96	62.07	68.28	74.48
77	40.86	44.01	47.15	50.29	53.43	56.58	59.72	62.86	69.15	75.44
78	41.38	44.56	47.74	50.93	54.11	57.29	60.48	63.66	70.03	76.39
79	41.90	45.12	48.34	51.56	54.79	58.01	61.23	64.46	70.90	77.35
80	42.41	45.68	48.94	52.20	55.46	58.73	61.99	65.25	71.78	78.30
81	42.93	46.23	49.54	52.84	56.14	59.44	62.75	66.05	72.65	79.26
82	43.45	46.79	50.14	53.47	56.81	60.16	63.50	66.84	73.52	80.21
83	43.97	47.35	50.73	54.11	57.49	60.88	64.26	67.64	74.40	81.17
84	44.48	47.90	51.33	54.75	58.17	61.59	65.01	68.44	75.28	82.12
85	45.00	48.46	51.92	55.38	58.85	62.31	65.77	69.23	76.15	83.08
86	45.52	49.02	52.52	56.02	59.52	63.02	66.53	70.03	77.03	84.03
87	46.03	49.58	53.12	56.66	60.20	63.74	67.28	70.82	77.91	84.99
88	46.55	50.13	53.71	57.30	60.88	64.46	68.04	71.62	78.78	85.94
89	47.07	50.69	54.31	57.93	61.55	65.17	68.79	72.41	79.65	86.90
90	47.59	51.25	54.91	58.57	62.23	65.89	69.55	73.21	80.53	87.85
91	48.10	51.80	55.50	59.20	62.90	66.60	70.30	74.00	81.41	88.81
92	48.62	52.36	56.10	59.84	63.58	67.32	71.06	74.80	82.28	89.76
93	49.14	52.92	56.70	60.48	64.26	68.04	71.81	75.60	83.16	90.72
94	49.65	53.47	57.29	61.11	64.93	68.75	72.57	76.39	84.03	91.67
95	50.17	54.03	57.89	61.75	65.61	69.47	73.33	77.19	84.91	92.62
96	50.69	54.59	58.49	62.39	66.29	70.19	74.08	77.98	85.78	93.58
97	51.21	55.15	59.08	63.02	66.96	70.90	74.84	78.78	86.66	94.54
98	51.72	55.70	59.68	63.66	67.64	71.62	75.59	79.57	87.53	95.49
99	52.24	56.25	60.28	64.30	68.32	72.34	76.35	80.37	88.41	96.45
100	52.76	56.81	60.88	64.94	68.99	73.05	77.11	81.16	89.28	97.40

Root Diameters of Circular Pitch Gears

No. of Teeth	Circular Pitch in Inches								
	½	⅝	¾	⅞	1	1⅛	1¼	1⅜	1½
12	1.542	1.927	2.313	2.698	3.083	3.468	3.855	4.240	4.626
13	1.701	2.126	2.552	2.977	3.401	3.826	4.253	4.677	5.103
14	1.860	2.325	2.790	3.256	3.719	4.184	4.650	5.115	5.580
15	2.019	2.524	3.029	3.534	4.038	4.542	5.048	5.553	6.058
16	2.178	2.723	3.268	3.812	4.356	4.901	5.446	5.991	6.535
17	2.337	2.922	3.507	4.091	4.674	5.259	5.844	6.428	7.013
18	2.497	3.121	3.745	4.369	4.993	5.617	6.242	6.866	7.490
19	2.656	3.320	3.984	4.648	5.311	5.975	6.640	7.304	7.968
20	2.815	3.519	4.223	4.926	5.629	6.333	7.038	7.741	8.445
21	2.974	3.718	4.462	5.205	5.947	6.691	7.436	8.179	8.923
22	3.133	3.917	4.700	5.484	6.266	7.049	7.834	8.617	9.400
23	3.292	4.116	4.939	5.762	6.584	7.407	8.232	9.055	9.877
24	3.452	4.315	5.178	6.040	6.902	7.765	8.630	9.492	10.355
25	3.611	4.514	5.417	6.318	7.221	8.124	9.028	9.929	10.832
26	3.770	4.713	5.655	6.597	7.539	8.482	9.425	10.367	11.310
27	3.929	4.912	5.894	6.876	7.857	8.840	9.823	10.805	11.787
28	4.088	5.111	6.132	7.154	8.176	9.198	10.221	11.243	12.265
29	4.247	5.310	6.371	7.433	8.494	9.556	10.619	11.680	12.742
30	4.407	5.509	6.610	7.712	8.812	9.914	11.017	12.118	13.220
31	4.566	5.708	6.849	7.990	9.131	10.272	11.415	12.556	13.697
32	4.725	5.906	7.087	8.269	9.449	10.630	11.813	12.994	14.175
33	4.884	6.105	7.326	8.547	9.767	10.988	12.211	13.431	14.652
34	5.043	6.304	7.565	8.826	10.085	11.346	12.608	13.869	15.130
35	5.202	6.503	7.804	9.104	10.404	11.704	13.006	14.307	15.607
36	5.362	6.702	8.042	9.382	10.722	12.062	13.404	14.744	16.085
37	5.521	6.901	8.281	9.661	11.041	12.421	13.802	15.181	16.562
38	5.680	7.100	8.520	9.940	11.359	12.779	14.200	15.619	17.040
39	5.839	7.299	8.759	10.218	11.677	13.137	14.598	16.057	17.517
40	5.998	7.498	8.997	10.497	11.995	13.495	14.996	16.495	17.995
41	6.157	7.697	9.236	10.775	12.314	13.853	15.394	16.932	18.472
42	6.316	7.896	9.475	11.054	12.632	14.211	15.791	17.370	18.949
43	6.476	8.094	9.714	11.332	12.950	14.569	16.189	17.808	19.427
44	6.635	8.293	9.952	11.611	13.269	14.927	16.587	18.246	19.904
45	6.794	8.492	10.191	11.889	13.587	15.285	16.985	18.683	20.382
46	6.953	8.691	10.429	12.168	13.905	15.643	17.383	19.121	20.859
47	7.112	8.890	10.668	12.447	14.224	16.001	17.781	19.559	21.337
48	7.271	9.089	10.907	12.725	14.542	16.360	18.179	19.996	21.814
49	7.430	9.288	11.146	13.003	14.860	16.718	18.577	20.434	22.292
50	7.590	9.487	11.384	13.282	15.179	17.076	18.974	20.872	22.769
51	7.749	9.686	11.623	13.561	15.497	17.434	19.372	21.310	23.247
52	7.908	9.885	11.862	13.839	15.815	17.792	19.770	21.747	23.724
53	8.067	10.084	12.101	14.117	16.133	18.150	20.168	22.184	24.201
54	8.226	10.283	12.339	14.396	16.452	18.508	20.566	22.622	24.679
55	8.385	10.482	12.578	14.675	16.770	18.866	20.964	23.060	25.156
56	8.545	10.681	12.817	14.952	17.088	19.224	21.362	23.498	25.634

Root Diameters of Circular Pitch Gears

No. of Teeth	Circular Pitch in Inches								
	½	⅝	¾	⅞	1	1⅛	1¼	1⅜	1½
57	8.704	10.880	13.056	15.231	17.407	19.583	21.760	23.935	26.111
58	8.863	11.079	13.295	15.510	17.725	19.941	22.158	24.373	26.589
59	9.022	11.278	13.534	15.789	18.043	20.299	22.556	24.811	27.066
60	9.181	11.477	13.772	16.067	18.362	20.657	22.953	25.248	27.544
61	9.340	11.676	14.011	16.345	18.680	21.015	23.351	25.686	28.021
62	9.500	11.875	14.250	16.624	18.998	21.373	23.749	26.124	28.499
63	9.659	12.073	14.489	16.903	19.317	21.731	24.147	26.562	28.976
64	9.818	12.272	14.727	17.181	19.635	22.089	24.545	26.999	29.454
65	9.977	12.471	14.966	17.459	19.953	22.448	24.943	27.437	29.931
66	10.136	12.670	15.204	17.738	20.271	22.806	25.340	27.875	30.409
67	10.295	12.869	15.443	18.017	20.590	23.164	25.738	28.312	30.886
68	10.454	13.068	15.682	18.295	20.908	23.522	26.136	28.750	31.364
69	10.613	13.267	15.921	18.574	21.226	23.880	26.534	29.187	31.841
70	10.773	13.466	16.159	18.853	21.545	24.238	26.932	29.625	32.318
71	10.932	13.665	16.398	19.131	21.863	24.596	27.330	30.063	32.796
72	11.091	13.864	16.637	19.409	22.181	24.954	27.728	30.501	33.273
73	11.250	14.063	16.876	19.687	22.500	25.312	28.126	30.938	33.751
74	11.409	14.262	17.114	19.966	22.818	25.670	28.523	31.376	34.228
75	11.568	14.461	17.353	20.245	23.136	26.028	28.921	31.814	34.706
76	11.728	14.660	17.592	20.523	23.455	26.386	29.319	32.251	35.183
77	11.887	14.859	17.831	20.802	23.773	26.745	29.717	32.689	35.661
78	12.046	15.058	18.069	21.081	24.091	27.103	30.115	33.127	36.138
79	12.205	15.256	18.308	21.359	24.409	27.461	30.513	33.564	36.616
80	12.364	15.455	18.547	21.638	24.728	27.819	30.911	34.002	37.093
81	12.523	15.654	18.786	21.916	25.046	28.177	31.309	34.440	37.570
82	12.683	15.853	19.024	22.195	25.364	28.535	31.707	34.878	38.048
83	12.842	16.052	19.263	22.473	25.683	28.893	32.105	35.315	38.525
84	13.001	16.251	19.501	22.752	26.001	29.251	32.503	35.753	39.003
85	13.160	16.450	19.740	23.030	26.319	29.609	32.901	36.190	39.480
86	13.319	16.649	19.979	23.309	26.638	29.967	33.298	36.628	39.958
87	13.478	16.848	20.218	23.588	26.956	30.325	33.696	37.066	40.435
88	13.638	17.047	20.456	23.866	27.274	30.684	34.094	37.503	40.913
89	13.797	17.246	20.695	24.144	27.593	31.042	34.492	37.941	41.390
90	13.956	17.445	20.934	24.423	27.911	31.400	34.890	38.379	41.868
91	14.115	17.644	21.173	24.701	28.229	31.758	35.288	38.817	42.345
92	14.274	17.843	21.411	24.980	28.547	32.116	35.686	39.254	42.823
93	14.433	18.042	21.650	25.258	28.866	32.474	36.084	39.692	43.300
94	14.593	18.241	21.889	25.537	29.184	32.832	36.482	40.130	43.778
95	14.752	18.440	22.128	25.816	29.502	33.190	36.880	40.567	44.255
96	14.911	18.639	22.366	26.094	29.821	33.548	37.277	41.005	44.733
97	15.070	18.838	22.605	26.372	30.139	33.907	37.675	41.442	45.210
98	15.229	19.037	22.844	26.651	30.457	34.265	38.073	41.880	45.688
99	15.388	19.235	23.083	26.930	30.776	34.623	38.471	42.318	46.165
100	15.547	19.434	23.321	27.208	31.094	34.981	38.869	42.755	46.642

Root Diameters of Circular Pitch Gears

No. of Teeth	Circular Pitch in Inches									
	1⅝	1¾	1⅞	2	2⅛	2¼	2⅜	2½	2¾	3
12	5.00	5.39	5.78	6.16	6.55	6.93	7.32	7.70	8.47	9.24
13	5.52	5.95	6.38	6.80	7.22	7 65	8.08	8.50	9.35	10.20
14	6.04	6.51	6.97	7.43	7.90	8 37	8.84	9.30	10.22	11.15
15	6.56	7.06	7.57	8.06	8.58	9.08	9.60	10.09	11.10	12.11
16	7.07	7.62	8.17	8.70	9.25	9.80	10.35	10.89	11.97	13.07
17	7.59	8.18	8.76	9.34	9.93	10.51	11.10	11.69	12.85	14.02
18	8.11	8.74	9.36	9.98	10.60	11.23	11.86	12.48	13.73	14.98
19	8.63	9.29	9.96	10.62	11.28	11.95	12.61	13.28	14.60	15.93
20	9.14	9.85	10.55	11.25	11.96	12.66	13.37	14.08	15.48	16.89
21	9.66	10.41	11.15	11.89	12.63	13.38	14.12	14.87	16.35	17.84
22	10.18	10.96	11.75	12.52	13.31	14.10	14.88	15.66	17.23	18.80
23	10.70	11.52	12.35	13.16	13.99	14.81	15.64	16.46	18.10	19.75
24	11.21	12.08	12.94	13.79	14.66	15.53	16.39	17.26	18.98	20.71
25	11.73	12.64	13.54	14.43	15.34	16.24	17.15	18.05	19.85	21.66
26	12.25	13.19	14.14	15.07	16.02	16.96	17.90	18.85	20.73	22.62
27	12.76	13.75	14.73	15.71	16.69	17.68	18.66	19.64	21.60	23.57
28	13.28	14.31	15.33	16.34	17.37	18.39	19.42	20.44	22.48	24.53
29	13.80	14.86	15.93	16.98	18.04	19.11	20.18	21.23	23.35	25.48
30	14.32	15.41	16.52	17.62	18.72	19.82	20.94	22.03	24.23	26.43
31	14.83	15.97	17.12	18.25	19.39	20.54	21.69	22.82	25.11	27.39
32	15.35	16.53	17.72	18.89	20.07	21.26	22.44	23.62	25.98	28.34
33	15.87	17.09	18.31	19.52	20.75	21.97	23.19	24.41	26.85	29.29
34	16.39	17.65	18.91	20.16	21.43	22.68	23.95	25.21	27.73	30.25
35	16.90	18.20	19.51	20.79	22.10	23.40	24.71	26.01	28.61	31.21
36	17.41	18.76	20.10	21.43	22.78	24.12	25.46	26.81	29.48	32.17
37	17.93	19.32	20.70	22.07	23.46	24.84	26.22	27.60	30.36	33.12
38	18.45	19.88	21.30	22.71	24.13	25.55	26.98	28.40	31.23	34.08
39	18.97	20.44	21.90	23.35	24.81	26.27	27.73	29.19	32.10	35.03
40	19.49	20.99	22.49	23.98	25.49	26.99	28.49	29.99	32.98	35.98
41	20.01	21.55	23.09	24.61	26.16	27.70	29.24	30.78	33.86	36.94
42	20.52	22.10	23.69	25.26	26.84	28.42	30.00	31.58	34.73	37.90
43	21.04	22.66	24.28	25.89	27.52	29.14	30.75	32.37	35.61	38.85
44	21.56	23.22	24.88	26.53	28.20	29.85	31.51	33.17	36.48	39.80
45	22.08	23.78	25.48	27.17	28.87	30.57	32.27	33.97	37.36	40.76
46	22.59	24.33	26.07	27.80	29.54	31.28	33.02	34.76	38.23	41.72
47	23.11	24.89	26.67	28.44	30.22	32.00	33.78	35.56	39.11	42.67
48	23.62	25.45	27.26	29.07	30.90	32.72	34.53	36.35	39.99	43.63
49	24.14	26.00	27.86	29.71	31.57	33.43	35.29	37.15	40.86	44.58
50	24.66	26.56	28.46	30.35	32.25	34.15	36.04	37.95	41.74	45.54
51	25.18	27.12	29.06	30.99	32.92	34.86	36.80	38.74	42.61	46.49
52	25.70	27.68	29.66	31.62	33.60	35.58	37.56	39.54	43.48	47.44
53	26.21	28.23	30.25	32.26	34.28	36.30	38.32	40.34	44.36	48.40
54	26.73	28.79	30.85	32.90	34.96	37.02	39.08	41.13	45.24	49.35
55	27.25	29.35	31.44	33.53	35.63	37.73	39.83	41.92	46.11	50.31
56	27.76	29.90	32.04	34.17	36.31	38.45	40.58	42.72	46.99	51.26

Root Diameters of Circular Pitch Gears

No. of Teeth	Circular Pitch in Inches									
	1⅝	1¾	1⅞	2	2⅛	2¼	2⅜	2½	2¾	3
57	28.28	30.46	32.64	34.81	36.98	39.16	41.34	43.52	47.86	52.22
58	28.80	31.02	33.24	35.45	37.66	39.88	42.10	44.31	48.74	53.17
59	29.32	31.58	33.83	36.09	38.34	40.59	42.85	45.11	49.61	54.13
60	29.83	32.13	34.42	36.73	39.01	41.31	43.61	45.90	50.49	55.09
61	30.35	32.69	35.02	37.36	39.69	42.03	44.36	46.70	51.36	56.04
62	30.87	33.25	35.62	38.00	40.36	42.74	45.12	47.50	52.24	56.99
63	31.38	33.80	36.22	38.63	41.04	43.46	45.87	48.29	53.11	57.95
64	31.90	34.36	36.81	39.27	41.72	44.18	46.63	49.09	53.99	58.91
65	32.42	34.92	37.41	39.91	42.40	44.89	47.39	49.88	54.87	59.86
66	32.94	35.47	38.01	40.55	43.07	45.61	48.14	50.68	55.74	60.81
67	33.46	36.03	38.61	41.18	43.75	46.32	48.90	51.48	56.62	61.77
68	33.97	36.59	39.20	41.82	44.42	47.04	49.66	52.27	57.49	62.73
69	34.49	37.15	39.80	42.45	45.10	47.76	50.41	53.07	58.37	63.68
70	35.01	37.70	40.40	43.09	45.78	48.47	51.17	53.86	59.24	64.63
71	35.52	38.26	40.99	43.73	46.45	49.18	51.92	54.66	60.12	65.59
72	36.04	38.82	41.59	44.37	47.13	49.90	52.68	55.46	60.99	66.55
73	36.56	39.37	42.19	45.00	47.81	50.62	53.44	56.25	61.87	67.50
74	37.08	39.93	42.78	45.64	48.48	51.34	54.19	57.05	62.74	68.45
75	37.59	40.49	43.38	46.27	49.16	52.05	54.95	57.84	63.62	69.41
76	38.11	41.04	43.98	46.91	49.84	52.77	55.70	58.64	64.49	70.36
77	38.63	41.60	44.57	47.55	50.51	53.48	56.46	59.43	65.37	71.32
78	39.14	42.16	45.17	48.19	51.19	54.20	57.21	60.23	66.25	72.27
79	39.66	42.72	45.77	48.82	51.86	54.92	57.97	61.02	67.12	73.23
80	40.18	43.27	46.36	49.46	52.54	55.63	58.73	61.82	68.00	74.18
81	40.70	43.83	46.96	50.09	53.22	56.35	59.48	62.62	68.87	75.14
82	41.21	44.39	47.56	50.73	53.89	57.07	60.24	63.41	69.75	76.09
83	41.73	44.94	48.16	51.37	54.57	57.78	61.00	64.21	70.62	77.05
84	42.25	45.50	48.76	52.00	55.24	58.50	61.75	65.00	71.49	78.00
85	42.77	46.06	49.35	52.64	55.92	59.22	62.51	65.80	72.37	78.96
86	43.28	46.61	49.95	53.28	56.60	59.93	63.26	66.60	73.25	79.91
87	43.80	47.17	50.54	53.91	57.28	60.65	64.02	67.39	74.12	80.87
88	44.32	47.73	51.14	54.55	57.95	61.36	64.78	68.19	75.00	81.82
89	44.83	48.29	51.74	55.19	58.63	62.08	65.53	68.98	75.88	82.78
90	45.35	48.84	52.33	55.83	59.31	62.80	66.29	69.78	76.75	83.73
91	45.87	49.40	52.93	56.46	59.98	63.51	67.04	70.57	77.62	84.69
92	46.39	49.96	53.53	57.10	60.66	64.23	67.80	71.37	78.50	85.64
93	46.90	50.51	54.12	57.73	61.33	64.94	68.55	72.16	79.38	86.60
94	47.42	51.07	54.72	58.37	62.01	65.66	69.31	72.96	80.25	87.55
95	47.94	51.63	55.32	59.01	62.69	66.38	70.06	73.76	81.13	88.51
96	48.45	52.18	55.91	59.64	63.36	67.09	70.82	74.55	82.00	89.46
97	48.97	52.74	56.51	60.28	64.04	67.81	71.58	75.35	82.88	90.41
98	49.49	53.30	57.11	60.92	64.72	68.53	72.33	76.14	83.75	91.37
99	50.01	53.86	57.70	61.55	65.39	69.24	73.09	76.94	84.63	92.33
100	50.52	54.41	58.30	62.19	66.07	69.96	73.84	77.73	85.50	93.28

Outside Diameters of Stub-tooth Gears

(Fellows Gear Shaper Co.'s System)

No. of Teeth	Diametral Pitch					
	4/5	5/7	6/8	8/10	10/12	12/14
10	2.900	2.286	1.917	1.450	1.167	0.976
11	3.150	2.486	2.083	1.575	1.267	1.060
12	3.400	2.686	2.250	1.700	1.367	1.143
13	3.650	2.886	2.417	1.82_	1.467	1.226
14	3.900	3.086	2.583	1.950	1.567	1.310
15	4.150	3.286	2.750	2.075	1.667	1.393
16	4.400	3.486	2.917	2.200	1.767	1.476
17	4.650	3.686	3.083	2.325	1.867	1.560
18	4.900	3.886	3.250	2.450	1.967	1.643
19	5.150	4.086	3.417	2.575	2.067	1.726
20	5.400	4.286	3.583	2.700	2.167	1.810
21	5.650	4.486	3.750	2.825	2.267	1.893
22	5.900	4.686	3.917	2.950	2.367	1.976
23	6.150	4.886	4.083	3.075	2.467	2.060
24	6.400	5.086	4.250	3.200	2.567	2.143
25	6.650	5.286	4.417	3.325	2.667	2.226
26	6.900	5.486	4.583	3.450	2.767	2.310
27	7.150	5.686	4.750	3.575	2.867	2.393
28	7.400	5.886	4.917	3.700	2.967	2.476
29	7.650	6.086	5.083	3.825	3.067	2.560
30	7.900	6.286	5.250	3.950	3.167	2.643
31	8.150	6.486	5.417	4.075	3.267	2.726
32	8.400	6.686	5.583	4.200	3.367	2.810
33	8.650	6.886	5.750	4.325	3.467	2.893
34	8.900	7.086	5.917	4.450	3.567	2.976
35	9.150	7.286	6.083	4.575	3.667	3.060
36	9.400	7.486	6.250	4.700	3.767	3.143
37	9.650	7.686	6.417	4.825	3.867	3.226
38	9.900	7.886	6.583	4.950	3.967	3.310
39	10.150	8.086	6.750	5.075	4.067	3.393
40	10.400	8.286	6.917	5.200	4.167	3.476
41	10.650	8.486	7.083	5.325	4.267	3.560
42	10.900	8.686	7.250	5.450	4.367	3.643
43	11.150	8.886	7.417	5.575	4.467	3.726
44	11.400	9.086	7.583	5.700	4.567	3.810
45	11.650	9.286	7.750	5.825	4.667	3.893
46	11.900	9.486	7.917	5.950	4.767	3.976
47	12.150	9.686	8.083	6.075	4.867	4.060
48	12.400	9.886	8.250	6.200	4.967	4.143
49	12.650	10.086	8.417	6.325	5.067	4.226
50	12.900	10.286	8.583	6.450	5.167	4.310
51	13.150	10.486	8.750	6.575	5.267	4.393
52	13.400	10.686	8.917	6.700	5.367	4.476
53	13.650	10.886	9.083	6.825	5.467	4.560
54	13.900	11.086	9.250	6.950	5.567	4.643
55	14.150	11.286	9.417	7.075	5.667	4.726

Outside Diameters of Stub-tooth Gears

(Fellows Gear Shaper Co.'s System)

No. of Teeth	Diametral Pitch					
	4/5	5/7	6/8	8/10	10/12	12/14
56	14.400	11.486	9.583	7.200	5.767	4.810
57	14.650	11.686	9.750	7.325	5.867	4.893
58	14.900	11.886	9.917	7.450	5.967	4.976
59	15.150	12.086	10.083	7.575	6.067	5.060
60	15.400	12.286	10.250	7.700	6.167	5.143
61	15.650	12.486	10.417	7.825	6.267	5.226
62	15.900	12.686	10.583	7.950	6.367	5.310
63	16.150	12.886	10.750	8.075	6.467	5.393
64	16.400	13.086	10.917	8.200	6.567	5.476
65	16.650	13.286	11.083	8.325	6.667	5.560
66	16.900	13.486	11.250	8.450	6.767	5.643
67	17.150	13.686	11.417	8.575	6.867	5.726
68	17.400	13.886	11.583	8.700	6.967	5.810
69	17.650	14.086	11.750	8.825	7.067	5.893
70	17.900	14.286	11.917	8.950	7.167	5.976
71	18.150	14.486	12.083	9.075	7.267	6.060
72	18.400	14.686	12.250	9.200	7.367	6.143
73	18.650	14.886	12.417	9.325	7.467	6.226
74	18.900	15.086	12.583	9.450	7.567	6.310
75	19.150	15.286	12.750	9.575	7.667	6.393
76	19.400	15.486	12.917	9.700	7.767	6.476
77	19.650	15.686	13.083	9.825	7.867	6.560
78	19.900	15.886	13.250	9.950	7.967	6.643
79	20.150	16.086	13.417	10.075	8.067	6.726
80	20.400	16.286	13.583	10.200	8.167	6.810
81	20.650	16.486	13.750	10.325	8.267	6.893
82	20.900	16.686	13.917	10.450	8.367	6.976
83	21.150	16.886	14.083	10.575	8.467	7.060
84	21.400	17.086	14.250	10.700	8.567	7.143
85	21.650	17.286	14.417	10.825	8.667	7.226
86	21.900	17.486	14.583	10.950	8.767	7.310
87	22.150	17.686	14.750	11.075	8.867	7.393
88	22.400	17.886	14.917	11.200	8.967	7.476
89	22.650	18.086	15.083	11.325	9.067	7.560
90	22.900	18.286	15.250	11.450	9.167	7.643
91	23.150	18.486	15.417	11.575	9.267	7.726
92	23.400	18.686	15.583	11.700	9.367	7.810
93	23.650	18.886	15.750	11.825	9.467	7.893
94	23.900	19.086	15.917	11.950	9.567	7.976
95	24.150	19.286	16.083	12.075	9.667	8.060
96	24.400	19.486	16.250	12.200	9.767	8.143
97	24.650	19.686	16.417	12.325	9.867	8.226
98	24.900	19.886	16.583	12.450	9.967	8.310
99	25.150	20.086	16.750	12.575	10.067	8.393
100	25.400	20.286	16.917	12.700	10.167	8.476

Root Diameters of Stub-tooth Gears)

(Fellows Gear Shaper Co.'s System)

No. of Teeth	Diametral Pitch					
	4/6	5/7	6/8	8/10	10/12	12/14
10	2.000	1.643	1.355	1.000	0.792	0.655
11	2.250	1.843	1.521	1.125	0.892	0.739
12	2.500	2.043	1.688	1.250	0.992	0.822
13	2.750	2.243	1.855	1.375	1.092	0.905
14	3.000	2.443	2.021	1.500	1.192	0.989
15	3.250	2.643	2.188	1.625	1.292	1.072
16	3.500	2.843	2.355	1.750	1.392	1.155
17	3.750	3.043	2.521	1.875	1.492	1.239
18	4.000	3.243	2.688	2.000	1.592	1.322
19	4.250	3.443	2.855	2.125	1.692	1.405
20	4.500	3.643	3.021	2.250	1.792	1.489
21	4.750	3.843	3.188	2.375	1.892	1.572
22	5.000	4.043	3.355	2.500	1.992	1.655
23	5.250	4.243	3.521	2.625	2.092	1.739
24	5.500	4.443	3.688	2.750	2.192	1.822
25	5.750	4.643	3.855	2.875	2.292	1.905
26	6.000	4.843	4.021	3.000	2.392	1.989
27	6.250	5.043	4.188	3.125	2.492	2.072
28	6.500	5.243	4.355	3.250	2.592	2.155
29	6.750	5.443	4.521	3.375	2.692	2.239
30	7.000	5.643	4.688	3.500	2.792	2.322
31	7.250	5.843	4.855	3.625	2.892	2.405
32	7.500	6.043	5.021	3.750	2.992	2.489
33	7.750	6.243	5.188	3.875	3.092	2.572
34	8.000	6.443	5.355	4.000	3.192	2.655
35	8.250	6.643	5.521	4.125	3.292	2.739
36	8.500	6.843	5.688	4.250	3.392	2.822
37	8.750	7.043	5.855	4.375	3.492	2.905
38	9.000	7.243	6.021	4.500	3.592	2.989
39	9.250	7.443	6.188	4.625	3.692	3.072
40	9.500	7.643	6.355	4.750	3.792	3.155
41	9.750	7.843	6.521	4.875	3.892	3.239
42	10.000	8.043	6.688	5.000	3.992	3.322
43	10.250	8.243	6.855	5.125	4.092	3.405
44	10.500	8.443	7.021	5.250	4.192	3.489
45	10.750	8.643	7.188	5.375	4.292	3.572
46	11.000	8.843	7.355	5.500	4.392	3.655
47	11.250	9.043	7.521	5.625	4.492	3.739
48	11.500	9.243	7.688	5.750	4.592	3.822
49	11.750	9.443	7.855	5.875	4.692	3.905
50	12.000	9.643	8.021	6.000	4.792	3.989
51	12.250	9.843	8.188	6.125	4.892	4.072
52	12.500	10.043	8.355	6.250	4.992	4.155
53	12.750	10.243	8.521	6.375	5.092	4.239
54	13.000	10.443	8.688	6.500	5.192	4.322
55	13.250	10.643	8.855	6.625	5.292	4.405

Root Diameters of Stub-tooth Gears

(Fellows Gear Shaper Co.'s System)

No. of Teeth	Diametral Pitch					
	⁴⁄₆	⁵⁄₇	⁶⁄₈	⁸⁄₁₀	¹⁰⁄₁₂	¹²⁄₁₄
56	13.500	10.843	9.021	6.750	5.392	4.489
57	13.750	11.043	9.188	6.875	5.492	4.572
58	14.000	11.243	9.355	7.000	5.592	4.655
59	14.250	11.443	9.521	7.125	5.692	4.739
60	14.500	11.643	9.688	7.250	5.792	4.822
61	14.750	11.843	9.855	7.375	5.892	4.905
62	15.000	12.043	10.021	7.500	5.992	4.989
63	15.250	12.243	10.188	7.625	6.092	5.072
64	15.500	12.443	10.355	7.750	6.192	5.155
65	15.750	12.643	10.521	7.875	6.292	5.239
66	16.000	12.843	10.688	8.000	6.392	5.322
67	16.250	13.043	10.855	8.125	6.492	5.405
68	16.500	13.243	11.021	8.250	6.592	5.489
69	16.750	13.443	11.188	8.375	6.692	5.572
70	17.000	13.643	11.355	8.500	6.792	5.655
71	17.250	13.843	11.521	8.625	6.892	5.739
72	17.500	14.043	11.688	8.750	6.992	5.822
73	17.750	14.243	11.855	8.875	7.092	5.905
74	18.000	14.443	12.021	9.000	7.192	5.989
75	18.250	14.643	12.188	9.125	7.292	6.072
76	18.500	14.843	12.355	9.250	7.392	6.155
77	18.750	15.043	12.521	9.375	7.492	6.239
78	19.000	15.243	12.688	9.500	7.592	6.322
79	19.250	15.443	12.855	9.625	7.692	6.405
80	19.500	15.643	13.021	9.750	7.792	6.489
81	19.750	15.843	13.188	9.875	7.892	6.572
82	20.000	16.043	13.355	10.000	7.992	6.655
83	20.250	16.243	13.521	10.125	8.092	6.739
84	20.500	16.443	13.688	10.250	8.192	6.822
85	20.750	16.643	13.855	10.375	8.292	6.905
86	21.000	16.843	14.021	10.500	8.392	6.989
87	21.250	17.043	14.188	10.625	8.492	7.072
88	21.500	17.243	14.355	10.750	8.592	7.155
89	21.750	17.443	14.521	10.875	8.692	7.239
90	22.000	17.643	14.688	11.000	8.792	7.322
91	22.250	17.843	14.855	11.125	8.892	7.405
92	22.500	18.043	15.021	11.250	8.992	7.489
93	22.750	18.243	15.188	11.375	9.092	7.572
94	23.000	18.443	15.355	11.500	9.192	7.655
95	23.250	18.643	15.521	11.625	9.292	7.739
96	23.500	18.843	15.688	11.750	9.392	7.822
97	23.750	19.043	15.855	11.875	9.492	7.905
98	24.000	19.243	16.021	12.000	9.592	7.989
99	24.250	19.443	16.188	12.125	9.692	8.072
100	24.500	19.643	16.355	12.250	9.792	8.155

Root Diameters of Gears Cut on Gear Shapers

No. of Teeth	Diametral Pitch								
	3 P	4 P	5 P	6 P	8 P	10 P	12 P	14 P	16 P
10	2.500	1.875	1.500	1.250	0.938	0.750	0.625	0.536	0.469
11	2.833	2.125	1.700	1.417	1.063	0.850	0.708	0.607	0.531
12	3.167	2.375	1.900	1.583	1.188	0.950	0.792	0.679	0.594
13	3.500	2.625	2.100	1.750	1.313	1.050	0.875	0.750	0.656
14	3.833	2.875	2.300	1.917	1.438	1.150	0.958	0.822	0.719
15	4.167	3.125	2.500	2.083	1.563	1.250	1.042	0.893	0.781
16	4.500	3.375	2.700	2.250	1.688	1.350	1.125	0.965	0.844
17	4.833	3.625	2.900	2.417	1.813	1.450	1.208	1.036	0.906
18	5.167	3.875	3.100	2.583	1.938	1.550	1.292	1.107	0.969
19	5.500	4.125	3.300	2.750	2.063	1.650	1.375	1.179	1.031
20	5.833	4.375	3.500	2.917	2.188	1.750	1.458	1.250	1.094
21	6.167	4.625	3.700	3.083	2.313	1.850	1.542	1.322	1.156
22	6.500	4.875	3.900	3.250	2.438	1.950	1.625	1.393	1.219
23	6.833	5.125	4.100	3.417	2.563	2.050	1.708	1.465	1.281
24	7.167	5.375	4.300	3.583	2.688	2.150	1.792	1.536	1.344
25	7.500	5.625	4.500	3.750	2.813	2.250	1.875	1.607	1.406
26	7.833	5.875	4.700	3.917	2.938	2.350	1.958	1.679	1.469
27	8.167	6.125	4.900	4.083	3.063	2.450	2.042	1.750	1.531
28	8.500	6.375	5.100	4.250	3.188	2.550	2.125	1.822	1.594
29	8.833	6.625	5.300	4.417	3.313	2.650	2.208	1.893	1.656
30	9.167	6.875	5.500	4.583	3.438	2.750	2.292	1.965	1.719
31	9.500	7.125	5.700	4.750	3.563	2.850	2.375	2.036	1.781
32	9.833	7.375	5.900	4.917	3.688	2.950	2.458	2.107	1.844
33	10.167	7.625	6.100	5.083	3.813	3.050	2.542	2.179	1.906
34	10.500	7.875	6.300	5.250	3.938	3.150	2.625	2.250	1.969
35	10.833	8.125	6.500	5.417	4.063	3.250	2.708	2.322	2.031
36	11.167	8.375	6.700	5.583	4.188	3.350	2.792	2.393	2.094
37	11.500	8.625	6.900	5.750	4.313	3.450	2.875	2.465	2.156
38	11.833	8.875	7.100	5.917	4.438	3.550	2.958	2.536	2.219
39	12.167	9.125	7.300	6.083	4.563	3.650	3.042	2.607	2.281
40	12.500	9.375	7.500	6.250	4.688	3.750	3.125	2.679	2.344
41	12.833	9.625	7.700	6.417	4.813	3.850	3.208	2.750	2.406
42	13.167	9.875	7.900	6.583	4.938	3.950	3.292	2.822	2.469
43	13.500	10.125	8.100	6.750	5.063	4.050	3.375	2.893	2.531
44	13.833	10.375	8.300	6.917	5.188	4.150	3.458	2.965	2.594
45	14.167	10.625	8.500	7.083	5.313	4.250	3.542	3.036	2.656
46	14.500	10.875	8.700	7.250	5.438	4.350	3.625	3.107	2.719
47	14.833	11.125	8.900	7.417	5.563	4.450	3.708	3.179	2.781
48	15.167	11.375	9.100	7.583	5.688	4.550	3.792	3.250	2.844
49	15.500	11.625	9.300	7.750	5.813	4.650	3.875	3.322	2.906
50	15.833	11.875	9.500	7.917	5.938	4.750	3.958	3.393	2.969
51	16.167	12.125	9.700	8.083	6.063	4.850	4.042	3.465	3.031
52	16.500	12.375	9.900	8.250	6.188	4.950	4.125	3.536	3.094
53	16.833	12.625	10.100	8.417	6.313	5.050	4.208	3.607	3.156
54	17.167	12.875	10.300	8.583	6.438	5.150	4.292	3.679	3.219
55	17.500	13.125	10.500	8.750	6.563	5.250	4.375	3.750	3.281

Root Diameters of Gears Cut on Gear Shapers

No. of Teeth	Diametral Pitch								
	3 P	4 P	5 P	6 P	8 P	10 P	12 P	14 P	16 P
56	17.833	13.375	10.700	8.917	6.688	5.350	4.458	3.822	3.344
57	18.167	13.625	10.900	9.083	6.813	5.450	4.542	3.893	3.406
58	18.500	13.875	11.100	9.250	6.938	5.550	4.625	3.965	3.469
59	18.833	14.125	11.300	9.417	7.063	5.650	4.708	4.036	3.531
60	19.167	14.375	11.500	9.583	7.188	5.750	4.792	4.107	3.594
61	19.500	14.625	11.700	9.750	7.313	5.850	4.875	4.179	3.656
62	19.833	14.875	11.900	9.917	7.438	5.950	4.958	4.250	3.719
63	20.167	15.125	12.100	10.083	7.563	6.050	5.042	4.322	3.781
64	20.500	15.375	12.300	10.250	7.688	6.150	5.125	4.393	3.844
65	20.833	15.625	12.500	10.417	7.813	6.250	5.208	4.465	3.906
66	21.167	15.875	12.700	10.583	7.938	6.350	5.292	4.536	3.969
67	21.500	16.125	12.900	10.750	8.063	6.450	5.375	4.607	4.031
68	21.833	16.375	13.100	10.917	8.188	6.550	5.458	4.679	4.094
69	22.167	16.625	13.300	11.083	8.313	6.650	5.542	4.750	4.156
70	22.500	16.875	13.500	11.250	8.438	6.750	5.625	4.822	4.219
71	22.833	17.125	13.700	11.417	8.563	6.850	5.708	4.893	4.281
72	23.167	17.375	13.900	11.583	8.688	6.950	5.792	4.965	4.344
73	23.500	17.625	14.100	11.750	8.813	7.050	5.875	5.036	4.406
74	23.833	17.875	14.300	11.917	8.938	7.150	5.958	5.107	4.469
75	24.167	18.125	14.500	12.083	9.063	7.250	6.042	5.179	4.531
76	24.500	18.375	14.700	12.250	9.188	7.350	6.125	5.250	4.594
77	24.833	18.625	14.900	12.417	9.313	7.450	6.208	5.322	4.656
78	25.167	18.875	15.100	12.583	9.438	7.550	6.292	5.393	4.719
79	25.500	19.125	15.300	12.750	9.563	7.650	6.375	5.465	4.781
80	25.833	19.375	15.500	12.917	9.688	7.750	6.458	5.536	4.844
81	26.167	19.625	15.700	13.083	9.813	7.850	6.542	5.607	4.906
82	26.500	19.875	15.900	13.250	9.938	7.950	6.625	5.679	4.969
83	26.833	20.125	16.100	13.417	10.063	8.050	6.708	5.750	5.031
84	27.167	20.375	16.300	13.583	10.188	8.150	6.792	5.822	5.094
85	27.500	20.625	16.500	13.750	10.313	8.250	6.875	5.893	5.156
86	27.833	20.875	16.700	13.917	10.438	8.350	6.958	5.965	5.219
87	28.167	21.125	16.900	14.083	10.563	8.450	7.042	6.036	5.281
88	28.500	21.375	17.100	14.250	10.688	8.550	7.125	6.107	5.344
89	28.833	21.625	17.300	14.417	10.813	8.650	7.208	6.179	5.406
90	29.167	21.875	17.500	14.583	10.938	8.750	7.292	6.250	5.469
91	29.500	22.125	17.700	14.750	11.063	8.850	7.375	6.322	5.531
92	29.833	22.375	17.900	14.917	11.188	8.950	7.458	6.393	5.594
93	30.167	22.625	18.100	15.083	11.313	9.050	7.542	6.465	5.656
94	30.500	22.875	18.300	15.250	11.438	9.150	7.625	6.536	5.719
95	30.833	23.125	18.500	15.417	11.563	9.250	7.708	6.607	5.781
96	31.167	23.375	18.700	15.583	11.688	9.350	7.792	6.679	5.844
97	31.500	23.625	18.900	15.750	11.813	9.450	7.875	6.750	5.906
98	31.833	23.875	19.100	15.917	11.938	9.550	7.958	6.822	5.969
99	32.167	24.125	19.300	16.083	12.063	9.650	8.042	6.893	6.031
100	32.500	24.375	19.500	16.250	12.188	9.750	8.125	6.965	6.094

Selection of Cutter for Given Pitch. — When gears are to be cut on a generating type of gear-cutting machine such as a gear hobber or gear shaper, a hob or cutter of, say, 3 diametral pitch may be used for any gear of that diametral pitch, regardless of the number of gear teeth. When gear teeth are cut by using formed milling cutters, the cutter must be selected to suit both the pitch and the number of teeth because the shapes of the tooth spaces vary according to the number of teeth. For instance, the tooth spaces of a small pinion are not of the same shape as the spaces of a large gear of equal pitch. Theoretically, there should be a different formed cutter for every tooth number, but such refinement is unnecessary in practice. An involute formed cutters commonly used are made in series of eight cutters for each diametral pitch (see accompanying table). The shape of each cutter in this series is correct for a certain number of teeth only, but it can be used for other numbers within the limits given. For instance, a No. 6 cutter may be used for gears having from 17 to 20 teeth, but the tooth outline is correct only for 17 teeth or the lowest number in the range, which is also true of the other cutters listed. When this cutter is used for a gear having, say, 19 teeth, too much material is removed from the upper surfaces of the teeth, although the gear meets ordinary requirements. When greater accuracy of tooth shape is desired to insure smoother or quieter operation, an intermediate series of cutters having half-numbers may be used provided the number of gear teeth is between the number listed for the regular cutters (see table).

Gear teeth cut by the generating process are given the required shape or curvature by a generating action resulting from the rotation of the gear blank relative to the cutter; consequently, a hob or any generating type of cutter of a given pitch may be used for any number of teeth. In the practical application of the generating principle to gear-hobbing machines, the hob used has cutting edges of the same shape as teeth of a rack of corresponding pitch, except for minor variations such as, for example, as increasing the length of the hob teeth to provide for clearance at the bottom of the tooth spaces. The tooth shape should conform to the basic rack. See "American Standard Spur Gear Tooth Forms."

Series of Involute Gear Cutters for Each Pitch

Number of Cutter	Will cut Gears from	Number of Cutter	Will cut Gears from
1	135 teeth to a rack	5	21 to 25 teeth
2	55 to 134 teeth	6	17 to 20 teeth
3	35 to 54 teeth	7	14 to 16 teeth
4	26 to 34 teeth	8	12 to 13 teeth

The regular cutters listed above are used ordinarily. The cutters listed below (an intermediate series having half numbers) may be used when greater accuracy of tooth shape is essential in cases where the number of teeth is between the numbers for which the regular cutters are intended.

Number of Cutter	Will cut Gears from	Number of Cutter	Will cut Gears from
$1\frac{1}{2}$	80 to 134 teeth	$5\frac{1}{2}$	19 to 20 teeth
$2\frac{1}{2}$	42 to 54 teeth	$6\frac{1}{2}$	15 to 16 teeth
$3\frac{1}{2}$	30 to 34 teeth	$7\frac{1}{2}$	13 teeth
$4\frac{1}{2}$	23 to 25 teeth	...	....

Internal Spur Gears. — An internal gear may be proportioned like a standard spur gear turned "outside in" or with addendum and dedendum in reverse positions; however, to avoid interference or improve the tooth form and action, the internal diameter of the gear should be increased and the outside diameter of the mating pinion is also made larger than the size based upon standard or conventional tooth proportions. The extent of these enlargements will be illustrated by means of examples given in connection with the Rules for Internal Gears. The 20-degree involute full-depth tooth form is recommended for internal gears; the 20-degree stub tooth and the 14½-degree full-depth tooth are also used.

Methods of Cutting Internal Gears. — Internal spur gears are cut by methods similar in principle to those employed for external spur gears. They may be cut by one of the following methods: (1) By a generating process, as when using a Fellows gear shaper; (2) by using a formed cutter and milling the teeth; (3) by planing, using a machine of the templet or form-copying type (especially applicable to gears of large pitch); and (4) by using a formed tool which reproduces its shape and is given a planing action either on a slotting or a planing type of machine. Internal gears frequently have a web at one side which limits the amount of clearance space at the ends of the teeth. Such gears may be cut readily on a gear shaper. The most practical method of cutting very large internal gears is on a planer of the form-copying type. A regular spur gear planer is equipped with a special tool-holder for locating the tool in the position required for cutting internal teeth.

Formed Cutters for Internal Gears. — When formed cutters are used, a special cutter usually is desirable, because the tooth spaces of an internal gear are not the same shape as the tooth spaces of external gearing having the same pitch and number of teeth. This is due to the fact that an internal gear is a spur gear "turned outside in." According to one rule, the standard No. 1 cutter for external gearing may be used for internal gears of 4 diametral pitch and finer, when there are sixty teeth or more. This No. 1 cutter, as applied to external gearing, is intended for all gears having from 135 teeth to a rack. The finer the pitch and the larger the number of teeth, the better the results obtained with a No. 1 cutter. The standard No. 1 cutter is considered satisfactory for jobbing work, and usually when the number of gears to be cut does not warrant obtaining a special cutter, although the use of the No. 1 cutter is not practicable when the number of teeth in the pinion is large in proportion to the number of teeth in the internal gear.

Arc Thickness of Internal Gear Tooth. — *Rule:* If internal diameter of internal gear is enlarged as determined by Rules 1 and 2 for Internal Diameters (see Rules for Internal Gears), the arc tooth thickness at the pitch circle equals 1.3888 divided by the diametral pitch, assuming a pressure angle of 20 degrees.

Arc Thickness of Pinion Tooth. — *Rule:* If pinion for internal gear is larger than conventional size (see Outside Diameter of Pinion for Internal Gear, under Rules for Internal Gears), then the arc tooth thickness on pitch circle equals 1.7528 divided by the diametral pitch, assuming a pressure angle of 20 degrees.

Note: For chordal thickness and chordal addendum, see rules and formulas for spur gears.

Relative Sizes of Internal Gear and Pinion. — If a pinion is too large or too near the size of its mating internal gear, serious interference or modification of the tooth shape may occur.

Rule: For internal gears having a 20-degree pressure angle and full-depth teeth, the difference between number of teeth in gear and pinion should not be less than 12. For teeth of stub form, the smallest difference should be 7 or 8 teeth. For a pressure angle of 14½ degrees, the difference in tooth numbers should not be less than 15

Rules for Internal Gears — 20-degree Full-depth Teeth

To Find	Rule
Pitch Diameter	*Rule:* To find the pitch diameter of an internal gear, divide number of internal gear teeth by the diametral pitch. The pitch diameter of mating pinion also equals number of pinion teeth divided by diametral pitch, the same as for external spur gears.
Internal Diameter (Enlarged to avoid Interference)	*Rule 1:* For internal gears to mesh with pinions having 16 teeth or more, subtract 1.2 from the number of teeth and divide remainder by diametral pitch. *Example:* An internal gear has 72 teeth of 6 diametral pitch and the mating pinion has 18 teeth; then $$\text{Internal diameter} = \frac{72 - 1.2}{6} = 11.8 \text{ inches}$$ *Rule 2:* If circular pitch is used, subtract 1.2 from the number of internal gear teeth, multiply remainder by the circular pitch, and divide the product by 3.1416.
Internal Diameter (Based upon Spur Gear Reversed)	*Rule:* If the internal gear is to be designed to conform to a spur gear turned outside in, then subtract 2 from the number of teeth and divide remainder by the diametral pitch to find internal diameter. *Example:* (Same as Example above.) $$\text{Internal diameter} = \frac{72 - 2}{6} = 11.666 \text{ inches}$$
Outside Diameter of Pinion for Internal Gear	*Note:* If the internal gearing is to be proportioned like standard spur gearing, use the rule or formula previously given for spur gears in determining the outside diameter. The rule and formula following apply to a pinion that is enlarged and intended to mesh with an internal gear enlarged as determined by the preceding Rules 1 and 2 above. *Rule:* For pinions having 16 teeth or more, add 2.5 to the number of pinion teeth and divide by the diametral pitch. *Example 1:* A pinion for driving an internal gear is to have 18 teeth (full depth) of 6 diametral pitch; then $$\text{Outside diameter} = \frac{18 + 2.5}{6} = 3.416 \text{ inches}$$ Using the rule for external spur gears, the outside diameter = 3.333 inches.
Center Distance	*Rule 1:* Subtract the number of pinion teeth from the number of internal gear teeth and divide remainder by two times the diametral pitch. *Rule 2:* If the circular-pitch system is used, multiply the difference between the number of gear and pinion teeth by the circular pitch and divide product by 6.2832.

British Standard for Spur and Helical Gears. — This revised standard (No. 436–1940) applies to machine cut or ground spur gears and to single or double helical gears connecting parallel shafts. Internal as well as external gears are included. The pressure angle is 20 degrees and the working depth equals twice the module (whether English or metric should be stated). The tooth form represents a well-balanced compromise between strength, wear resistance, and quietness of operation. Gears are divided into five general classes.

Class A1, Precision Ground Gears (nominal proportions of basic rack tooth for this class are the same as shown by accompanying diagram for circular pitch of 1, except that fillet radius at the root is 0.0938 instead of 0.124 and the dedendum is 0.4583 instead of 0.3979).

Class A2, Precision Cut Gears for peripheral speeds above 2000 feet per minute.

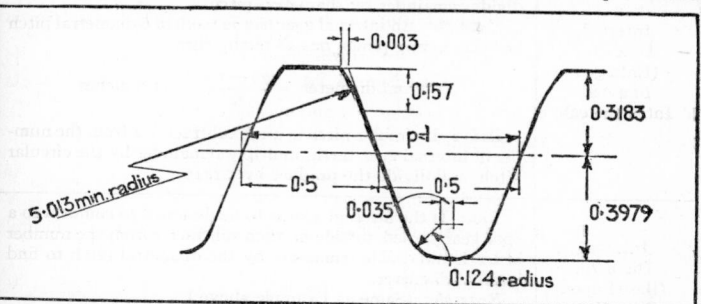

Class B, High-class Cut Gears for peripheral speeds between 750 and 3000 feet per minute (nominal proportions of basic rack for Classes A2 and B are shown by accompanying diagram).

Class C, Commercial Cut Gears for peripheral speeds below 1200 feet per minute; *Class D,* Large Internal Gears (basic rack for Classes C and D same as diagram excepting tip radius is 4.098, easing 0.006 and its depth, 0.200.

The range of speeds specified for gears of Classes A2, B and C permits considerable overlap between the classes. The notation follows:

A = Gear addendum	p_n = Normal pitch
a = Pinion addendum	T = Number of gear teeth
k_p = Pinion correction factor	t = Number of pinion teeth
k_w = Gear correction factor	Δ = Center distance extension factor
P_n = Normal diametral pitch	σ = Helix angle
p = Circular pitch	

Easing or Tip Relief. — The form is involute excepting for a slight easing at the point. The maximum amount of this easing or tip relief is as follows:

For Classes A1, A2, and B (Precision Ground, Precision Cut and High-class Cut Gears)

$$e = 0.003p \text{ extending } 0.157p \text{ in depth}$$

For Classes C and D (Commercial Cut and Large Internal Gears)

$$e = 0.006p \text{ extending } 0.20p \text{ in depth.}$$

Helical Gear Teeth. — The shape and proportions of helical gear teeth in the normal section, corresponds to the basic rack tooth forms, normal pitch being substituted for circular pitch. (Note that $p_n = p \cos \sigma$; also $P_n = \pi \div p_n$.)

Addendum — Gear and Pinion. — The *recommended* addendum values vary according to pitch and numbers of teeth in mating gears, in order to obtain full involution action, avoid undercutting in some cases, and obtain better zone and strength factors (factors used in calculating the horsepower rating).

$$\text{Pinion addendum } a = \frac{p_n}{\pi}(1 + k_p) = \frac{1 + k_p}{P_n} \tag{1}$$

$$\text{Gear addendum } A = \frac{p_n}{\pi}(1 + k_w) = \frac{1 + k_w}{P_n} \tag{2}$$

The correction factors k_p and k_w for pinion and gear, are determined as follows: *When $(t + T) \sec^3 \sigma$ is 60 or greater:*

$$\text{Pinion factor } k_p = 0.4\left(1 - \frac{t}{T}\right) \tag{3}$$

$$\text{or } 0.02(30 - t \sec^3 \sigma) \text{ whichever is greater} \tag{4}$$

$$\text{Gear factor } k_w = -k_p \tag{5}$$

Note: In the case of spur gears, $\sec^3 \sigma = 1$ and may be omitted.

When $(t + T) \sec^3 \sigma$ is less than 60:

$$\text{Pinion factor } k_p = 0.02(30 - t \sec^3 \sigma) \tag{6}$$

$$\text{Gear factor } k_w = 0.02(30 - T \sec^3 \sigma) \tag{7}$$

The center distance also is extended an amount indicated by the following formula when $(t + T) \sec^3 \sigma$ is less than 60.

$$\text{Extension of center distance} = \frac{\Delta p_n}{\pi} = \frac{\Delta}{P_n} \tag{8}$$

Factors used in Center Distance Extension Formula No. 8

Sum of Correction Factors $k_p + k_w$	Factor Δ	Sum of Correction Factors $k_p + k_w$	Factor Δ	Sum of Correction Factors $k_p + k_w$	Factor Δ	Sum of Correction Factors $k_p + k_w$	Factor Δ
0.025	0.025	0.225	0.218	0.425	0.400	0.625	0.555
0.050	0.050	0.250	0.243	0.450	0.420	0.650	0.575
0.075	0.075	0.275	0.267	0.475	0.444	0.675	0.588
0.100	0.100	0.300	0.288	0.500	0.462	0.700	0.606
0.125	0.122	0.325	0.313	0.525	0.480	0.725	0.623
0.150	0.146	0.350	0.332	0.550	0.500	0.750	0.636
0.175	0.170	0.375	0.356	0.575	0.516	0.775	0.650
0.200	0.196	0.400	0.376	0.600	0.536	0.800	0.663

After finding the sum of k_p and k_w, the value of Δ is obtained either directly, or by interpolation, from the accompanying table (based upon chart in the British standard).

For internal gears (irrespective of numbers of teeth)

$$k_p = 0.4 \quad \text{and} \quad k_w = -k_p \tag{9}$$

Outside Diameter of Pinion. — If number of pinion teeth is such that $t \sec^3 \sigma$ is less than 17, outside diameter is reduced but the pitch diameter and root diameter are not changed.

$$\text{Pinion diam. reduction} = \frac{p_n}{\pi} \times 0.04(17 - t \sec^3 \sigma) = \frac{0.04(17 - t \sec^3 \sigma)}{P_n} \tag{10}$$

Example 1. — Find the addendum values for a pair of spur gears. The pinion has 26 teeth, the gear 73 teeth, and the circular pitch is 0.5 inch. In this case, $t + T = 26 + 73 = 99$. Since this sum is larger than 60, pinion correction factor k_p is determined either by formula (3) or (4), whichever yields the greater value.

Applying formula (3), $k_p = 0.4 \left(1 - \dfrac{26}{73} \right) = 0.258$.

Applying formula (4), $k_p = 0.02(30 - 26) = 0.08$.

Hence, pinion correction factor $k_p = 0.258$ and gear correction factor $k_w = -0.258$.

Applying formula (1), pinion addendum $a = \dfrac{0.5}{\pi} \times 1.258 = 0.200$ inch.

Applying formula (2), gear addendum $A = \dfrac{0.5}{\pi} \times 0.742 = 0.118$ inch.

Note: The regular unmodified addendum in this case would equal $0.3183 \times 0.5 = 0.159$ inch for pinion and gear.

Example 2. — Find the addendum values for a pair of helical gears. The pinion has 11 teeth, the gear 22 teeth. The normal diametral pitch is 4 and the helix angle is $22°30'$ ($\sec^3 22.5° = 1.268$).

First determine whether Formulas (3), (4) and (5) or Formulas (6) and (7) are to be used for finding the pinion and gear correction factors k_p and k_w.

$$(t + T) \sec^3 \sigma = (11 + 22) \times 1.268 = 41.8$$

Since 41.8 is less than 60, Formulas (6) and (7) should be used.

$$k_p = 0.02(30 - 11 \times 1.268) = 0.321$$
$$k_w = 0.02(30 - 22 \times 1.268) = 0.042$$

Next, determine the extension of the center distance using Formula (8).

$$k_p + k_w = 0.321 + 0.042 = 0.363$$

Factor Δ obtained from the accompanying table by interpolation is about 0.345; hence, using Formula (8)

$$\text{Extension of center distance} = \frac{0.345}{4} = 0.086 \text{ inch}$$

$$\text{Center distance} = \frac{11 + 22}{2 \times 4} + 0.086 = 4.211 \text{ inches}$$

$$\text{Gear addendum} = \frac{1 + 0.042}{4} = 0.260 \text{ inch}$$

Finally, check to see if the outside diameter of the pinion should be reduced. In this example, $t \sec^3 \sigma = 11 \times 1.268 = 13.948$. Since this is less than 17, the pinion addendum is first obtained by Formula (1) and then it is reduced.

By Formula (1), $a = \dfrac{1 + 0.321}{4} = 0.330$ inch.

By Formula (10), diam. reduction $= \dfrac{0.04(17 - 13.948)}{4} = 0.030$ inch.

$$\text{Actual pinion addendum} = 0.330 - \frac{0.030}{2} = 0.315 \text{ inch}$$

British Standard Pitches and Equivalent Diametral, Circular and Metric Pitches

Standard Pitches in Bold Type

Diametral Pitch	Circular Pitch, Inches	Module Millimeters	Diametral Pitch	Circular Pitch, Inches	Module Millimeters	Diametral Pitch	Circular Pitch, Inches	Module Millimeters
½	6.2832	50.7991	2.2848	**1⅜**	11.1168	10.0531	**5⁄16**	2.5265
.5080	6.1844	**50**	2.3090	1.3606	**11**	10.1598	.3092	**2½**
.5236	**6**	48.5095	**2½**	1.2560	10.1598	**11**	.2856	2.3090
.5644	5.5659	**45**	2.5133	**1¼**	10.1062	**12**	.2618	2.1166
.5712	**5½**	44.4671	2.5400	1.2369	**10**	12.5664	**¼**	2.0212
.6283	**5**	40.4246	**2¾**	1.1424	9.2362	12.6998	.2474	**2**
.6350	4.9475	**40**	2.7925	**1⅛**	9.0955	**13**	.2417	1.9538
.6981	**4½**	36.3822	2.8222	1.1132	**9**	**14**	.2244	1.8143
.7257	4.3290	**35**	**3**	1.0472	8.4665	**15**	.2094	1.6933
¾	4.1888	33.8661	3.1416	**1**	8.0849	**16**	.1963	1.5875
.7854	**4**	32.3397	3.1749	.9895	**8**	16.7562	**3⁄16**	1.5159
.8378	**3¾**	30.3185	3.3510	**15⁄16**	7.5796	16.9330	.1855	**1½**
.8467	3.7106	**30**	**3½**	.8976	7.2571	**17**	.1848	1.4941
.8976	**3½**	28.2972	3.5904	**⅞**	7.0743	**18**	.1745	1.4111
.9666	**3¼**	26.2760	3.6285	.8658	**7**	**19**	.1653	1.3368
1	3.1416	25.3995	3.8666	**13⁄16**	6.5690	**20**	.1571	1.2700
1.0160	3.0922	**25**	3.9076	.8040	**6½**	**22**	.1428	1.1545
1.0472	**3**	24.2548	**4**	.7854	6.3499	**24**	.1309	1.0583
1.1424	**2¾**	22.2335	4.1888	**¾**	6.0637	**25**	.1257	1.0160
1¼	2.5133	20.3196	4.2333	.7421	**6**	25.1327	**⅛**	1.0106
1.2566	**2½**	20.2123	4.5696	**11⁄16**	5.5584	25.3995	.1237	**1**
1.2700	2.4737	**20**	4.6181	.6803	**5½**	**26**	.1208	.9769
1.3963	**2¼**	18.1911	**5**	.6283	5.0799	**28**	.1122	.9071
1.4111	2.2264	**18**	5.0265	**⅝**	5.0531	**30**	.1047	.8467
1½	2.0944	16.9330	5.0799	.6184	**5**	**32**	.0982	.7847
1.5708	**2**	16.1698	5.5851	**9⁄16**	4.5478	**34**	.0924	.7470
1.5875	1.9790	**16**	5.6443	.5566	**4½**	**36**	.0873	.7055
1.6755	**1⅞**	15.1592	**6**	.5236	4.2333	**38**	.0827	.6684
1.6933	1.8553	**15**	6.2832	**½**	4.0425	**40**	.0785	.6350
1¾	1.7952	14.5140	6.3499	.4947	**4**	**42**	.0748	.6048
1.7952	**1¾**	14.1486	**7**	.4488	3.6285	**44**	.0714	.5773
1.8143	1.7316	**14**	7.1808	**7⁄16**	3.5372	**46**	.0683	.5522
1.9333	**1⅝**	13.1380	7.2571	.4329	**3½**	**48**	.0654	.5292
1.9538	1.6079	**13**	**8**	.3927	3.1749	**50**	.0628	.5080
2	1.5708	12.6998	8.3776	**⅜**	3.0318	50.2655	**1⁄16**	.5053
2.0944	**1½**	12.1274	8.4665	.3711	**3**	50.7991	.0618	**½**
2.1166	1.4842	**12**	**9**	.3491	2.8222	**56**	.0561	.4536
2¼	1.3963	11.2887	**10**	.3142	2.5400	**60**	.0524	.4233

The module of a gear is the pitch diameter divided by the number of teeth; hence it is the reciprocal of diametral pitch. The module may be expressed in any units; but when no units are stated, it is understood to be in millimeters. The metric module, therefore, equals the pitch diameter in millimeters divided by the number of teeth. To find the metric module equivalent to a given diametral pitch, divide 25.4 by the diametral pitch. To find the diametral pitch equivalent to a given module, divide 25.4 by the module. (25.4 = number of millimeters per inch.)

Gear Design Based upon Module System. — The *module* of a gear equals the pitch diameter divided by the number of teeth, whereas *diametral pitch* equals the number of teeth divided by the pitch diameter. The module system is in general use in countries which have adopted the metric system; hence the term module is usually understood to mean the pitch diameter *in millimeters* divided by the number of teeth. The module system may, however, also be based upon inch measurements and then it is known as English module, to avoid confusion with the metric module. Module is an actual dimension, whereas diametral pitch is only a ratio. Thus, if the pitch diameter of a gear is 50 millimeters and the number of teeth 25, the module is 2 which means that there are 2 millimeters of pitch diameter for each tooth. The table "Tooth Dimensions Based Upon Module System" shows the relation between module, diametral pitch, and circular pitch.

German Standard Tooth Form for Spur and Bevel Gears (DIN — 867)

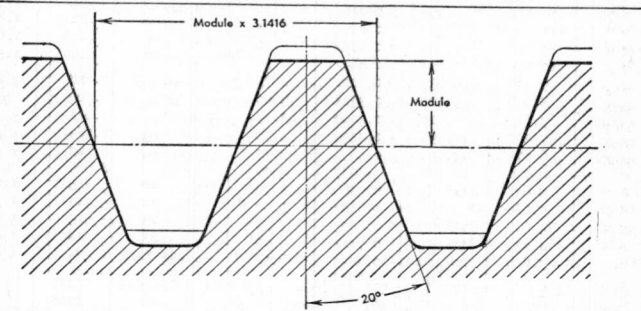

The flanks or sides are straight (involute system) and the pressure angle is 20 degrees. The shape of the root clearance space and the amount of clearance depend upon the method of cutting and special requirements. The amount of clearance may vary from 0.1 × module to 0.3 × module.

To Find	Module Known	Circular Pitch Known
Addendum..........	Equals module	0.3183 × Circular pitch
Dedendum..........	1.157 × module* 1.167 × module**	0.3683 × Circular pitch* 0.3714 × Circular pitch**
Working Depth......	2 × module	0.6366 × Circular pitch
Total Depth.........	2.157 × module* 2.167 × module**	0.6866 × Circular pitch* 0.6898 × Circular pitch**
Tooth Thickness on Pitch Line..........	1.5708 × module	0.5 × Circular pitch

Formulas for dedendum and total depth, marked (*) are used when clearance equals 0.157 × module. Formulas marked (**) are used when clearance equals one-sixth module. It is the common practice among American cutter manufacturers to make the clearance of metric or module cutters equal to 0.157 × module.

Tooth Dimensions Based Upon Module System

Module, DIN Standard Series	Equivalent Diametral Pitch	Circular Pitch		Addendum, Millimeters	Dedendum, Millimeters*	Whole Depth,* Millimeters	Whole Depth,† Millimeters
		Millimeters	Inches				
0.3	84.667	0.943	0.0371	0.30	0.35	0.650	0.647
0.4	63.500	1.257	0.0495	0.40	0.467	0.867	0.863
0.5	50.800	1.571	0.0618	0.50	0.583	1.083	1.079
0.6	42.333	1.885	0.0742	0.60	0.700	1.300	1.294
0.7	36.286	2.199	0.0865	0.70	0.817	1.517	1.510
0.8	31.750	2.513	0.0989	0.80	0.933	1.733	1.726
0.9	28.222	2.827	0.1113	0.90	1.050	1.950	1.941
1	25.400	3.142	0.1237	1.00	1.167	2.167	2.157
1.25	20.320	3.927	0.1546	1.25	1.458	2.708	2.697
1.5	16.933	4.712	0.1855	1.50	1.750	3.250	3.236
1.75	14.514	5.498	0.2164	1.75	2.042	3.792	3.774
2	12.700	6.283	0.2474	2.00	2.333	4.333	4.314
2.25	11.289	7.069	0.2783	2.25	2.625	4.875	4.853
2.5	10.160	7.854	0.3092	2.50	2.917	5.417	5.392
2.75	9.236	8.639	0.3401	2.75	3.208	5.958	5.932
3	8.466	9.425	0.3711	3.00	3.500	6.500	6.471
3.25	7.815	10.210	0.4020	3.25	3.791	7.041	7.010
3.5	7.257	10.996	0.4329	3.50	4.083	7.583	7.550
3.75	6.773	11.781	0.4638	3.75	4.375	8.125	8.089
4	6.350	12.566	0.4947	4.00	4.666	8.666	8.628
4.5	5.644	14.137	0.5566	4.50	5.25	9.750	9.707
5	5.080	15.708	0.6184	5.00	5.833	10.833	10.785
5.5	4.618	17.279	0.6803	5.50	6.416	11.916	11.864
6	4.233	18.850	0.7421	6.00	7.000	13.000	12.942
6.5	3.908	20.420	0.8035	6.50	7.583	14.083	14.021
7	3.628	21.991	0.8658	7.	8.166	15.166	15.099
8	3.175	25.132	0.9895	8.	9.333	17.333	17.256
9	2.822	28.274	1.1132	9.	10.499	19.499	19.413
10	2.540	31.416	1.2368	10.	11.666	21.666	21.571
11	2.309	34.558	1.3606	11.	12.833	23.833	23.728
12	2.117	37.699	1.4843	12.	14.000	26.000	25.884
13	1.954	40.841	1.6079	13.	15.166	28.166	28.041
14	1.814	43.982	1.7317	14.	16.332	30.332	30.198
15	1.693	47.124	1.8541	15.	17.499	32.499	32.355
16	1.587	50.266	1.9790	16.	18.666	34.666	34.512
18	1.411	56.549	2.2263	18.	21.000	39.000	38.826
20	1.270	62.832	2.4737	20.	23.332	43.332	43.142
22	1.155	69.115	2.7210	22.	25.665	47.665	47.454
24	1.058	75.398	2.9685	24.	28.000	52.000	51.768
27	0.941	84.823	3.339	27.	31.498	58.498	58.239
30	0.847	94.248	3.711	30.	35.000	65.000	64.713
33	0.770	103.673	4.082	33.	38.498	71.498	71.181
36	0.706	113.097	4.453	36.	41.998	77.998	77.652
39	0.651	122.522	4.824	39.	45.497	84.497	84.123
42	0.605	131.947	5.195	42.	48.997	90.997	90.594
45	0.564	141.372	5.566	45.	52.497	97.497	97.065
50	0.508	157.080	6.184	50.	58.330	108.330	107.855
55	0.462	172.788	6.803	55.	64.163	119.163	118.635
60	0.423	188.496	7.421	60.	69.996	129.996	129.426
65	0.391	204.204	8.040	65.	75.829	140.829	140.205
70	0.363	219.911	8.658	70.	81.662	151.662	150.997
75	0.339	235.619	9.276	75.	87.495	162.495	161.775

* Dedendum and total depth when clearance = 0.1666 × module, or one-sixth module.
† Total depth equivalent to American standard full-depth teeth. (Clearance = 0.157 × module.)

Rules for Module System of Gearing

To Find	Rule
Metric Module	*Rule* 1: To find the metric module, divide the pitch diameter in millimeters by the number of teeth. *Example* 1: The pitch diameter of a gear is 200 millimeters and the number of teeth, 40; then $$\text{module} = \frac{200}{40} = 5$$ *Rule* 2: Multiply circular pitch in millimeters by 0.3183. *Example* 2: (Same as Example 1. Circular pitch of this gear equals 15.708 millimeters). $$\text{module} = 15.708 \times 0.3183 = 5$$ *Rule* 3: Divide outside diameter in millimeters by the number of teeth plus 2.
English Module	*Note:* The module system is usually applied when gear dimensions are expressed in millimeters, but module may also be based upon inch measurements. *Rule:* To find the English module, divide pitch diameter in inches by number of teeth. *Example:* A gear has 48 teeth and a pitch diameter of 12 inches. $$\text{module} = \frac{12}{48} = \frac{1}{4} \text{ module or 4 diametral pitch}$$
Metric Module Equivalent to Diametral Pitch	*Rule:* To find the metric module equivalent to a given diametral pitch, divide 25.4 by the diametral pitch. *Example:* Determine metric module equivalent to 10 diametral pitch. $$\text{Equivalent module} = \frac{25.4}{10} = 2.54$$ *Note:* The nearest standard module is 2.5.
Diametral Pitch Equivalent to Metric Module	*Rule:* To find the diametral pitch equivalent to a given module, divide 25.4 by the module. (25.4 = number of millimeters per inch.) *Example:* The module is 12; determine equivalent diametral pitch. $$\text{Equivalent diametral pitch} = \frac{25.4}{12} = 2.117$$ *Note:* A diametral pitch of 2 is the nearest *standard* equivalent.
Pitch Diameter	*Rule:* Multiply number of teeth by module. *Example:* The metric module is 8 and gear has 40 teeth; then $$D = 40 \times 8 = 320 \text{ millimeters} = 12.598 \text{ inches}$$
Outside Diameter	*Rule:* Add 2 to the number of teeth and multiply sum by the module. *Example:* A gear has 40 teeth and module is 6. Find outside or blank diameter. $$\text{Outside diameter} = (40 + 2) \times 6 = 252 \text{ millimeters}$$

For tooth dimensions, see table Tooth Dimensions Based Upon Module System; also formulas below German Standard Tooth Form.

Dimensions of Spur Gears. (See page 707.)

Dimensions of Spur Gears with Oval Arms

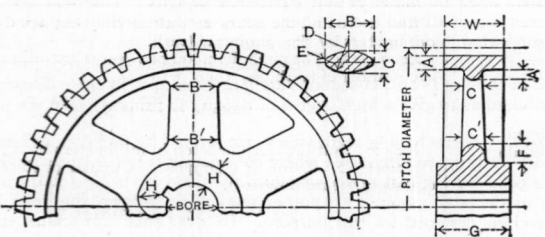

P = diametral pitch, P' = circular pitch.

$A = 1.57 \div P = 0.5\,P'$;
$B = 6.28 \div P = 2.0\,P'$;
$C = 3.14 \div P = P'$;
$D = 4.71 \div P = 1.5\,P'$;
$E = 0.79 \div P = 0.25\,P'$;

$F = 2.00 \div P = 0.65\,P'$;
$G = W + 0.025$ pitch diameter;
$H = 0.44 \times$ bore;
$B' = B + \tfrac{3}{4}$ inch per foot;
$C' = C + \tfrac{3}{4}$ inch per foot.

Dimensions of Spur Gears with Ribbed Arms or Arms of H-section

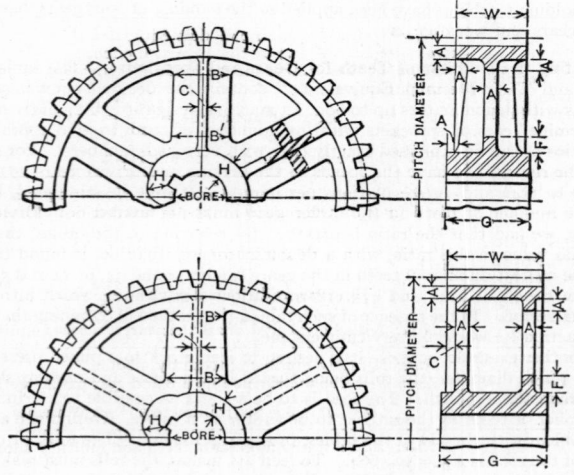

P = diametral pitch, P' = circular pitch.

$A = 1.57 \div P = 0.5\,P'$;
$B = 7.85 \div P = 2.5\,P'$;
$C = 0.94 \div P = 0.3\,P'$;
$F = 2.20 \div P = 0.7\,P'$;

$G = W + 0.025$ pitch diameter;
$H = 0.44 \times$ bore;
$B' = B + \tfrac{3}{4}$ inch per foot;

Proportions of Cast Spur Gears. — The table " Dimensions of Spur Gears " gives the formulas for proportioning cast gears with arms of different cross-sections. This table will prove satisfactory for general conditions, but in individual cases modifications must be made to suit particular designs. The oval arm is the one best adapted for small and medium size gears and gives the best appearance. It requires somewhat more metal for the same strength than the designs shown in the lower part of the table, but it is very easily molded. For large size gears, however, arms of the +, T- and H-sections are largely used. In these designs the metal is so distributed as to give a high degree of rigidity in proportion to the weight.

Cast Teeth. — Gears having teeth which are formed by molding and casting so as to eliminate cutting are often used where cut gearing is not required. One method of making gears having cast teeth is to form the mold by using a pattern which is a duplicate of the gear required. Another method is to form the mold by using a special machine designed for this purpose. In using such a machine, the molding may be done either by employing a single-tooth hard-wood pattern or a segment-shaped pattern having two or three teeth. The pattern is located radially to suit the gear radius and the teeth impressions are formed around the mold by progressively indexing either the arm which carries the tooth pattern or by indexing the mold itself. The ring of sand inside of the flask is first formed by means of a sweep, and a core box is used for forming the arms of the gear. Molding machines produce accurate molds but the cast gear may be distorted by uneven shrinkage of the arms. In such cases, the rim may be cast separately and then attached to the gear center or spider. Some cast gears are strengthened by shrouding the teeth. Cast teeth are often used where speeds are low and precision gearing is not required. Gear-tooth molding machines have been applied to the molding of spur gears, bevel gears, helical gears and worm gears.

Selecting the Number of Teeth for Gears and Sprockets. — The tables "Gear Ratios and Their Decimal Equivalents " contain the decimal equivalents of all fractions with denominators up to 60. In machine design it is frequently necessary to determine gears or sprockets with low numbers of teeth to give approximately such ratios as can be expressed exactly only with very high numbers. For example, it may be required to have the speeds of the driving and driven gears as nearly as possible to 1149 and 473 revolutions per minute. It may be stipulated, however, that the number of teeth in the larger gear must not exceed 60. Dividing 473 by 1149, we find that the ratio is 0.4117. By referring to the tables, the nearest fractional value to this ratio, with a denominator less than 60, is found to be $\frac{7}{17}$; thus, the nearest number of teeth in the gears can be 14 and 34, or 21 and 51. This will give speeds of 1149 and 473.118 revolutions per minute, which introduces a very small error. In the absence of such tables, the method of obtaining the approximate fraction $\frac{7}{17}$ would be very cumbersome.

As another example, suppose it is desired to feed stock to a punch press through rolls of 4-inch diameter, the rolls being turned by a ratchet and pawl at the end of each stroke of the punch. The feed is to be as near as possible to 2¼ inches, and the number of teeth in the ratchet to be as low as possible. To find the answer to this problem with the aid of the tables, proceed as follows: The feed for one revolution of the rolls is $4\pi = 12.5664$. To feed 2¼ inches, the rolls must make $2.25 \div 12.5664 = 0.1790$ of a revolution. Referring to the table, the nearest fraction to this ratio is $\frac{5}{28}$; hence we choose a ratchet gear of 28 teeth, feeding five teeth at a stroke. The feed will be 2.244 inches instead of 2.25 inches, an error of only 0.006 inch. If we should choose the next higher fraction to the ratio 0.1790, which is $\frac{7}{39}$, the ratchet would have 39 teeth, and a feed of seven teeth in this ratchet would be equivalent to a feed of 2.256 inches — an error of only 0.006 inch.

Gear Ratios and Their Decimal Equivalents

Decimal Equivalent	Gear Ratio	Decimal Equivalent	Gear Ratio	Decimal Equivalent	Gear Ratio	Decimal Equivalent	Gear Ratio	Decimal Equivalent	Gear Ratio	Decimal Equivalent	Gear Ratio
0.0167	1/60	0.0455	1/22	0.0862	5/58	0.1277	9/47	0.1698	9/53	0.2105	4/19
0.0169	1/59	0.0465	2/43	0.0870	2/23	0.1282	5/39	0.1702	8/47	0.2115	11/52
0.0172	1/58	0.0476	1/21	0.0877	5/57	0.1290	4/31	0.1707	7/41	0.2121	7/33
0.0175	1/57	0.0488	2/41	0.0882	3/34	0.1296	7/54	0.1714	6/35	0.2128	10/47
0.0178	1/56	0.0500	1/20	0.0889	4/45	0.1304	3/23	0.1724	5/29	0.2143	3/14
0.0182	1/55	0.0508	3/59	0.0893	5/56	0.1316	5/38	0.1731	9/52	0.2157	11/51
0.0185	1/54	0.0513	2/39	0.0909	1/11	0.1321	7/53	0.1739	4/23	0.2162	8/37
0.0189	1/53	0.0517	3/58	0.0926	5/54	0.1333	2/15	0.1750	7/40	0.2167	13/60
0.0192	1/52	0.0526	1/19	0.0930	4/43	0.1346	7/52	0.1754	10/57	0.2174	5/23
0.0196	1/51	0.0536	3/56	0.0937	3/32	0.1351	5/37	0.1765	3/17	0.2182	12/55
0.0200	1/50	0.0541	2/37	0.0943	5/53	0.1356	8/59	0.1778	8/45	0.2187	7/32
0.0204	1/49	0.0545	3/55	0.0952	2/21	0.1364	3/22	0.1786	5/28	0.2195	9/41
0.0208	1/48	0.0555	1/18	0.0962	5/52	0.1373	7/51	0.1795	7/39	0.2200	11/50
0.0213	1/47	0.0566	3/53	0.0968	3/31	0.1379	4/29	0.1800	9/50	0.2203	13/59
0.0217	1/46	0.0571	2/35	0.0976	4/41	0.1389	5/36	0.1818	2/11	0.2222	2/9
0.0222	1/45	0.0577	3/52	0.0980	5/51	0.1395	6/43	0.1833	11/60	0.2241	13/58
0.0227	1/44	0.0588	1/17	0.1000	1/10	0.1400	7/50	0.1837	9/49	0.2245	11/49
0.0233	1/43	0.0600	3/50	0.1017	6/59	0.1404	8/57	0.1842	7/38	0.2250	9/40
0.0238	1/42	0.0606	2/33	0.1020	5/49	0.1429	1/7	0.1852	5/27	0.2258	7/31
0.0244	1/41	0.0612	3/49	0.1026	4/39	0.1455	8/55	0.1860	8/43	0.2264	12/53
0.0250	1/40	0.0625	1/16	0.1034	3/29	0.1458	7/48	0.1864	11/59	0.2273	5/22
0.0256	1/39	0.0638	3/47	0.1042	5/48	0.1463	6/41	0.1875	3/16	0.2281	13/57
0.0263	1/38	0.0645	2/31	0.1053	2/19	0.1471	5/34	0.1887	10/53	0.2286	8/35
0.0270	1/37	0.0652	3/46	0.1064	5/47	0.1481	4/27	0.1892	7/37	0.2292	11/48
0.0278	1/36	0.0667	1/15	0.1071	3/28	0.1489	7/47	0.1897	11/58	0.2308	3/13
0.0286	1/35	0.0678	4/59	0.1081	4/37	0.1500	3/20	0.1904	4/21	0.2321	13/56
0.0294	1/34	0.0682	3/44	0.1087	5/46	0.1509	8/53	0.1915	9/47	0.2326	10/43
0.0303	1/33	0.0690	2/29	0.1091	6/55	0.1515	5/33	0.1923	5/26	0.2333	7/30
0.0312	1/32	0.0698	3/43	0.1111	1/9	0.1522	7/46	0.1930	11/57	0.2340	11/47
0.0323	1/31	0.0702	4/57	0.1132	6/53	0.1525	9/59	0.1935	6/31	0.2353	4/17
0.0333	1/30	0.0714	1/14	0.1136	5/44	0.1538	2/13	0.1944	7/36	0.2364	13/55
0.0339	2/59	0.0727	4/55	0.1143	4/35	0.1552	9/58	0.1951	8/41	0.2368	9/38
0.0345	1/29	0.0732	3/41	0.1154	3/26	0.1556	7/45	0.1956	9/46	0.2373	14/59
0.0351	2/57	0.0741	2/27	0.1163	5/43	0.1562	5/32	0.1961	10/51	0.2381	5/21
0.0357	1/28	0.0750	3/40	0.1167	7/60	0.1569	8/51	0.1964	11/56	0.2391	11/46
0.0364	2/55	0.0755	4/53	0.1176	2/17	0.1579	3/19	0.2000	1/5	0.2400	6/25
0.0370	1/27	0.0769	1/13	0.1186	7/59	0.1591	7/44	0.2034	12/59	0.2407	13/54
0.0377	2/53	0.0784	4/51	0.1190	5/42	0.1600	4/25	0.2037	11/54	0.2414	7/29
0.0385	1/26	0.0789	3/38	0.1200	3/25	0.1607	9/56	0.2040	10/49	0.2424	8/33
0.0392	2/51	0.0800	2/25	0.1207	7/58	0.1613	5/31	0.2045	9/44	0.2432	9/37
0.0400	1/25	0.0811	3/37	0.1212	4/33	0.1622	6/37	0.2051	8/39	0.2439	10/41
0.0408	2/49	0.0816	4/49	0.1220	5/41	0.1628	7/43	0.2059	7/34	0.2444	11/45
0.0417	1/24	0.0833	1/12	0.1224	6/49	0.1633	8/49	0.2069	6/29	0.2449	12/49
0.0426	2/47	0.0847	5/59	0.1228	7/57	0.1636	9/55	0.2075	11/53	0.2453	13/53
0.0435	1/23	0.0851	4/47	0.1250	1/8	0.1667	1/6	0.2083	5/24	0.2456	14/57
0.0444	2/45	0.0857	3/35	0.1273	7/55	0.1695	10/59	0.2093	9/43	0.2500	1/4

Gear Ratios and Their Decimal Equivalents (*Continued*)

Decimal Equivalent	Gear Ratio	Decimal Equivalent	Gear Ratio	Decimal Equivalent	Gear Ratio	Decimal Equivalent	Gear Ratio	Decimal Equivalent	Gear Ratio	Decimal Equivalent	Gear Ratio
0.2542	15/59	0.2927	12/41	0.3390	20/59	0.3778	17/45	0.4186	18/43	0.4596	17/37
0.2545	14/55	0.2931	17/58	0.3393	19/56	0.3784	14/37	0.4194	13/31	0.4600	23/50
0.2549	13/51	0.2941	5/17	0.3396	18/53	0.3793	11/29	0.4200	21/50	0.4615	9/13
0.2553	12/47	0.2955	13/44	0.3400	17/50	0.3800	19/50	0.4211	8/19	0.4630	25/54
0.2558	11/43	0.2963	8/27	0.3404	16/47	0.3810	8/21	0.4222	19/45	0.4634	19/41
0.2564	10/39	0.2973	11/37	0.3409	15/44	0.3818	21/55	0.4231	11/26	0.4643	13/28
0.2571	9/35	0.2979	14/47	0.3415	14/41	0.3824	13/34	0.4237	25/59	0.4651	20/43
0.2581	8/31	0.2982	17/57	0.3421	13/38	0.3830	18/47	0.4242	14/33	0.4655	27/58
0.2586	15/58	0.3000	3/10	0.3429	12/35	0.3833	23/60	0.4250	17/40	0.4667	7/15
0.2593	7/27	0.3019	16/53	0.3437	11/32	0.3846	5/13	0.4255	20/47	0.4681	22/47
0.2600	13/50	0.3023	13/43	0.3448	10/29	0.3860	22/57	0.4259	23/54	0.4687	15/32
0.2609	6/23	0.3030	10/33	0.3455	19/55	0.3864	17/44	0.4286	3/7	0.4694	23/49
0.2619	11/42	0.3036	17/56	0.3462	9/26	0.3871	12/31	0.4310	25/58	0.4706	8/17
0.2632	5/19	0.3043	7/23	0.3469	17/49	0.3878	19/49	0.4314	22/51	0.4717	25/53
0.2642	14/53	0.3051	18/59	0.3478	8/23	0.3889	7/18	0.4318	19/44	0.4722	17/36
0.2647	9/34	0.3056	11/36	0.3488	15/43	0.3898	23/59	0.4324	16/37	0.4727	26/55
0.2653	13/49	0.3061	15/49	0.3500	7/20	0.3902	16/41	0.4333	13/30	0.4737	9/19
0.2667	4/15	0.3077	4/13	0.3509	20/57	0.3913	9/23	0.4340	23/53	0.4746	28/59
0.2679	15/56	0.3091	17/55	0.3514	13/37	0.3922	20/51	0.4348	10/23	0.4750	19/40
0.2683	11/41	0.3095	13/42	0.3519	19/54	0.3929	11/28	0.4359	17/39	0.4762	10/21
0.2692	7/26	0.3103	9/29	0.3529	6/17	0.3939	13/33	0.4364	24/55	0.4773	21/44
0.2703	10/37	0.3111	14/45	0.3542	17/48	0.3947	15/38	0.4375	7/16	0.4783	11/23
0.2708	13/48	0.3125	5/16	0.3548	11/31	0.3953	17/43	0.4386	25/57	0.4792	23/48
0.2712	16/59	0.3137	16/51	0.3556	16/45	0.3958	19/48	0.4390	18/41	0.4800	12/25
0.2727	3/11	0.3143	11/35	0.3559	21/59	0.3962	21/53	0.4400	11/25	0.4808	25/52
0.2745	14/51	0.3148	17/54	0.3571	5/14	0.3966	23/58	0.4407	26/59	0.4815	13/27
0.2750	11/40	0.3158	6/19	0.3585	19/53	0.4000	2/5	0.4412	15/34	0.4821	27/56
0.2759	8/29	0.3166	19/60	0.3590	14/39	0.4035	23/57	0.4419	19/43	0.4827	14/29
0.2766	13/47	0.3171	13/41	0.3600	9/25	0.4038	21/52	0.4423	23/52	0.4833	29/60
0.2778	5/18	0.3182	7/22	0.3611	13/36	0.4043	19/47	0.4444	4/9	0.4839	15/31
0.2791	12/43	0.3191	15/47	0.3617	17/47	0.4048	17/42	0.4464	25/56	0.4848	16/33
0.2800	7/25	0.3200	8/25	0.3621	21/58	0.4054	15/37	0.4468	21/47	0.4857	17/35
0.2807	16/57	0.3208	17/53	0.3636	4/11	0.4062	13/32	0.4474	17/38	0.4865	18/37
0.2812	9/32	0.3214	9/28	0.3654	19/52	0.4068	24/59	0.4483	13/29	0.4872	19/39
0.2821	11/39	0.3220	19/59	0.3659	15/41	0.4074	11/27	0.4490	22/49	0.4878	20/41
0.2826	13/46	0.3226	10/31	0.3667	11/30	0.4082	20/49	0.4500	9/20	0.4884	21/43
0.2830	15/53	0.3235	11/34	0.3673	18/49	0.4091	9/22	0.4510	23/51	0.4889	22/45
0.2833	17/60	0.3243	12/37	0.3684	7/19	0.4103	16/39	0.4516	14/31	0.4894	23/47
0.2857	2/7	0.3250	13/40	0.3696	17/46	0.4107	23/56	0.4524	19/42	0.4898	24/49
0.2881	17/59	0.3256	14/43	0.3703	10/27	0.4118	7/17	0.4528	24/53	0.4902	25/51
0.2885	15/52	0.3261	15/46	0.3714	13/35	0.4130	19/46	0.4545	5/11	0.4906	26/53
0.2889	13/45	0.3265	16/49	0.3721	16/43	0.4138	12/29	0.4561	26/57	0.4909	27/55
0.2895	11/38	0.3269	17/52	0.3725	19/51	0.4146	17/41	0.4565	21/46	0.4912	28/57
0.2903	9/31	0.3273	18/55	0.3729	22/59	0.4151	22/53	0.4571	16/35	0.4915	29/59
0.2909	16/55	0.3276	19/58	0.3750	3/8	0.4167	5/12	0.4576	27/59	0.5000	1/2
0.2917	7/24	0.3333	1/3	0.3774	20/53	0.4182	23/55	0.4583	11/24	0.5085	30/59

Gear Ratios and Their Decimal Equivalents (Continued)

Decimal Equivalent	Gear Ratio	Decimal Equivalent	Gear Ratio	Decimal Equivalent	Gear Ratio	Decimal Equivalent	Gear Ratio	Decimal Equivalent	Gear Ratio	Decimal Equivalent	Gear Ratio
0.5088	29/57	0.5435	25/46	0.5854	24/41	0.6275	32/51	0.6731	35/52	0.7111	32/45
0.5091	28/55	0.5439	31/57	0.5862	17/29	0.6279	27/43	0.6735	33/49	0.7115	37/52
0.5094	27/53	0.5455	6/11	0.5870	27/46	0.6286	22/35	0.6739	31/46	0.7119	42/59
0.5098	26/51	0.5472	29/53	0.5882	10/17	0.6296	17/27	0.6744	29/43	0.7143	5/7
0.5102	25/49	0.5476	23/42	0.5893	33/56	0.6304	29/46	0.6750	27/40	0.7167	43/60
0.5106	24/47	0.5484	17/31	0.5897	23/39	0.6316	12/19	0.6757	25/37	0.7170	38/53
0.5111	23/45	0.5490	28/51	0.5909	13/22	0.6326	31/49	0.6765	23/34	0.7174	33/46
0.5116	22/43	0.5500	11/20	0.5918	29/49	0.6333	19/30	0.6774	21/31	0.7179	28/39
0.5122	21/41	0.5510	27/49	0.5926	16/27	0.6341	26/41	0.6780	40/59	0.7187	23/32
0.5128	20/39	0.5517	16/29	0.5932	35/59	0.6346	33/52	0.6786	19/28	0.7193	41/57
0.5135	19/37	0.5526	21/38	0.5937	19/32	0.6364	7/11	0.6792	36/53	0.7200	18/25
0.5142	18/35	0.5532	26/47	0.5946	22/37	0.6379	37/58	0.6800	17/25	0.7209	31/43
0.5151	17/33	0.5536	31/56	0.5952	25/42	0.6383	30/47	0.6809	32/47	0.7222	13/18
0.5161	16/31	0.5556	5/9	0.5957	28/47	0.6389	23/36	0.6818	15/22	0.7234	34/47
0.5167	31/60	0.5577	29/52	0.5962	31/52	0.6400	16/25	0.6829	28/41	0.7241	21/29
0.5172	15/29	0.5581	24/43	0.5965	34/57	0.6410	25/39	0.6833	41/60	0.7250	29/40
0.5179	29/56	0.5588	19/34	0.6000	3/5	0.6415	34/53	0.6842	13/19	0.7255	37/51
0.5185	14/27	0.5593	33/59	0.6034	35/58	0.6429	9/14	0.6852	37/54	0.7273	8/11
0.5192	27/52	0.5600	14/25	0.6038	32/53	0.6441	38/59	0.6857	24/35	0.7288	43/59
0.5200	18/25	0.5610	23/41	0.6042	29/48	0.6444	29/45	0.6863	35/51	0.7292	35/48
0.5208	25/48	0.5614	32/57	0.6047	26/43	0.6452	20/31	0.6875	11/16	0.7297	27/37
0.5217	12/23	0.5625	9/16	0.6053	23/38	0.6458	31/48	0.6889	31/45	0.7308	19/26
0.5227	23/44	0.5636	31/55	0.6060	20/33	0.6471	11/17	0.6897	20/29	0.7317	30/41
0.5238	11/21	0.5641	22/39	0.6071	17/28	0.6481	35/54	0.6905	29/42	0.7321	41/56
0.5250	21/40	0.5652	13/23	0.6078	31/51	0.6486	24/37	0.6909	38/55	0.7333	11/15
0.5254	31/59	0.5660	30/53	0.6087	14/23	0.6491	37/57	0.6923	9/13	0.7347	36/49
0.5263	10/19	0.5667	17/30	0.6098	25/41	0.6500	13/20	0.6939	34/49	0.7353	25/34
0.5273	29/55	0.5676	21/37	0.6102	36/59	0.6512	28/43	0.6949	41/59	0.7358	39/53
0.5278	19/36	0.5682	25/44	0.6111	11/18	0.6522	15/23	0.6957	16/23	0.7368	14/19
0.5283	28/53	0.5686	29/51	0.6122	30/49	0.6531	32/49	0.6964	39/56	0.7381	31/42
0.5294	9/17	0.5690	33/58	0.6129	19/31	0.6538	17/26	0.6970	23/33	0.7391	17/23
0.5306	26/49	0.5714	4/7	0.6136	27/44	0.6545	36/55	0.6977	30/43	0.7400	37/50
0.5312	17/32	0.5741	31/54	0.6140	35/57	0.6552	19/29	0.6981	37/53	0.7407	20/27
0.5319	25/47	0.5745	27/47	0.6154	8/13	0.6562	21/32	0.7000	7/10	0.7414	43/58
0.5333	8/15	0.5750	23/40	0.6167	37/60	0.6571	23/35	0.7018	40/57	0.7419	23/31
0.5345	31/58	0.5757	19/33	0.6170	29/47	0.6579	25/38	0.7021	33/47	0.7429	26/35
0.5349	23/43	0.5763	34/59	0.6176	21/34	0.6585	27/41	0.7027	26/37	0.7436	29/39
0.5357	15/28	0.5769	15/26	0.6182	34/55	0.6591	29/44	0.7037	19/27	0.7442	32/43
0.5366	22/41	0.5778	26/45	0.6190	13/21	0.6596	31/47	0.7045	31/44	0.7447	35/47
0.5370	29/54	0.5789	11/19	0.6200	31/50	0.6600	33/50	0.7059	12/17	0.7451	38/51
0.5385	7/13	0.5800	29/50	0.6207	18/29	0.6604	35/53	0.7069	41/58	0.7455	41/55
0.5400	27/50	0.5806	18/31	0.6216	23/37	0.6607	37/56	0.7073	29/41	0.7458	44/59
0.5405	20/37	0.5814	25/43	0.6222	28/45	0.6610	39/59	0.7083	17/24	0.7500	3/4
0.5417	13/24	0.5818	32/55	0.6226	33/53	0.6666	2/3	0.7091	39/55	0.7544	43/57
0.5424	32/59	0.5833	7/12	0.6250	5/8	0.6724	39/58	0.7097	22/31	0.7547	40/53
0.5429	19/35	0.5849	31/53	0.6271	37/59	0.6727	37/55	0.7105	27/38	0.7551	37/49

Gear Ratios and Their Decimal Equivalents (*Continued*)

Decimal Equivalent	Gear Ratio	Decimal Equivalent	Gear Ratio	Decimal Equivalent	Gear Ratio	Decimal Equivalent	Gear Ratio	Decimal Equivalent	Gear Ratio	Decimal Equivalent	Gear Ratio
0.7561	31/41	0.7949	31/39	0.8378	31/37	0.8788	29/33	0.9189	34/37	0.9600	24/25
0.7568	28/37	0.7955	35/44	0.8387	26/31	0.8793	51/58	0.9200	23/25	0.9608	49/51
0.7576	25/33	0.7959	39/49	0.8393	47/56	0.8800	22/25	0.9211	35/38	0.9615	25/26
0.7586	22/29	0.7963	43/54	0.8400	21/25	0.8810	37/42	0.9216	47/51	0.9623	51/53
0.7593	41/54	0.7966	47/59	0.8409	37/44	0.8814	52/59	0.9231	12/13	0.9630	26/27
0.7600	19/25	0.8000	4/5	0.8421	16/19	0.8824	15/17	0.9245	49/53	0.9636	53/55
0.7609	35/46	0.8036	45/56	0.8431	43/51	0.8833	53/60	0.9250	37/40	0.9643	27/28
0.7619	16/21	0.8039	41/51	0.8437	27/32	0.8837	38/43	0.9259	25/27	0.9649	55/57
0.7627	45/59	0.8043	37/46	0.8444	38/45	0.8846	23/26	0.9268	38/41	0.9655	28/29
0.7632	29/38	0.8049	33/41	0.8448	49/58	0.8857	31/35	0.9273	51/55	0.9661	57/59
0.7636	42/55	0.8056	29/36	0.8462	11/13	0.8864	39/44	0.9286	13/14	0.9667	29/30
0.7647	13/17	0.8065	25/31	0.8475	50/59	0.8868	47/53	0.9298	53/57	0.9677	30/31
0.7660	36/47	0.8070	46/57	0.8478	39/46	0.8889	8/9	0.9302	40/43	0.9687	31/32
0.7667	23/30	0.8077	21/26	0.8485	28/33	0.8909	49/55	0.9310	27/29	0.9697	32/33
0.7674	33/43	0.8085	38/47	0.8491	45/53	0.8913	41/46	0.9318	41/44	0.9706	33/34
0.7679	43/56	0.8095	17/21	0.8500	17/20	0.8919	33/37	0.9322	55/59	0.9714	34/35
0.7692	10/13	0.8103	47/58	0.8511	40/47	0.8929	25/28	0.9333	14/15	0.9722	35/36
0.7708	37/48	0.8108	30/37	0.8519	23/27	0.8936	42/47	0.9348	43/46	0.9730	36/37
0.7714	27/35	0.8113	43/53	0.8529	29/34	0.8947	17/19	0.9355	29/31	0.9737	37/38
0.7719	44/57	0.8125	13/16	0.8537	35/41	0.8958	43/48	0.9362	44/47	0.9743	38/39
0.7727	17/22	0.8136	48/59	0.8542	41/48	0.8966	26/29	0.9375	15/16	0.9750	39/40
0.7736	41/53	0.8140	35/43	0.8545	47/55	0.8974	35/39	0.9388	46/49	0.9756	40/41
0.7742	24/31	0.8148	22/27	0.8571	6/7	0.8980	44/49	0.9394	31/33	0.9762	41/42
0.7750	31/40	0.8158	31/38	0.8596	49/57	0.8983	53/59	0.9400	47/50	0.9767	42/43
0.7755	38/49	0.8163	40/49	0.8600	43/50	0.9000	9/10	0.9412	16/17	0.9773	43/44
0.7759	45/58	0.8167	49/60	0.8604	37/43	0.9020	46/51	0.9423	49/52	0.9778	44/45
0.7778	7/9	0.8182	9/11	0.8611	31/36	0.9024	37/41	0.9429	33/35	0.9783	45/46
0.7797	46/59	0.8200	41/50	0.8621	25/29	0.9032	28/31	0.9434	50/53	0.9787	46/47
0.7800	39/50	0.8205	32/39	0.8627	44/51	0.9038	47/52	0.9444	17/18	0.9792	47/48
0.7805	32/41	0.8214	23/28	0.8636	19/22	0.9048	19/21	0.9455	52/55	0.9796	48/49
0.7812	25/32	0.8222	37/45	0.8644	51/59	0.9057	48/53	0.9459	35/37	0.9800	49/50
0.7818	43/55	0.8235	14/17	0.8649	32/37	0.9062	29/32	0.9464	53/56	0.9804	50/51
0.7826	18/23	0.8246	47/57	0.8654	45/52	0.9070	39/43	0.9474	18/19	0.9808	51/52
0.7833	47/60	0.8250	33/40	0.8667	13/15	0.9074	49/54	0.9483	55/58	0.9811	52/53
0.7838	29/37	0.8261	19/23	0.8679	46/53	0.9091	10/11	0.9487	37/39	0.9815	53/54
0.7843	40/51	0.8269	43/52	0.8684	33/38	0.9107	51/56	0.9492	56/59	0.9818	54/55
0.7857	11/14	0.8276	24/29	0.8696	20/23	0.9111	41/45	0.9500	19/20	0.9821	55/56
0.7872	37/47	0.8286	29/35	0.8704	47/54	0.9118	31/34	0.9512	39/41	0.9825	56/57
0.7879	26/33	0.8293	34/41	0.8710	27/31	0.9123	52/57	0.9524	20/21	0.9828	57/58
0.7885	41/52	0.8298	39/47	0.8718	34/39	0.9130	21/23	0.9535	41/43	0.9831	58/59
0.7895	15/19	0.8302	44/53	0.8723	41/47	0.9138	53/58	0.9545	21/22	0.9833	59/60
0.7907	34/43	0.8305	49/59	0.8727	48/55	0.9143	32/35	0.9555	43/45	....	...
0.7917	19/24	0.8333	5/6	0.8750	7/8	0.9149	43/47	0.9565	22/23	....	...
0.7926	42/53	0.8364	46/55	0.8772	50/57	0.9153	54/59	0.9574	45/47	....	...
0.7931	23/29	0.8367	41/49	0.8775	43/49	0.9167	11/12	0.9583	23/24	....	...
0.7941	27/34	0.8372	36/43	0.8780	36/41	0.9184	45/49	0.9592	47/49	....	...

Grant's Odontograph. — The table entitled "Grant's Odontograph" provides a simple means for laying out accurately shaped gear teeth by means of circular arcs which very closely approximate the exact tooth curves. The method was devised by Mr. George B. Grant, and differs for cycloidal and involute teeth.

Odontograph for Cycloidal System. — First draw the pitch, addendum, root and clearance circles and space off the pitch of the teeth on the pitch circle in the

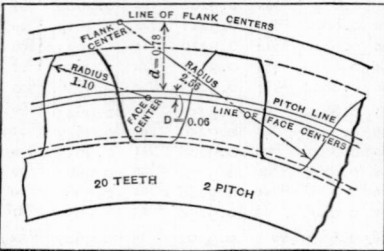

usual way. Then draw the circle marked "line of flank centers" at the distance d, as given in the table outside of the pitch line and draw the "line of face centers" at the distance D inside of it. With the face radius R in the dividers, draw in all the face curves from centers on the "line of face centers"; then with the flank radius r draw all the flank curves from centers on the "line of flank centers."

Fig. 1

The table gives the distances D and d and radii R and r, for pitches either exactly 1 diametral or 1 inch circular pitch. For any other pitch, divide or multiply as directed in the table. The illustration, Fig. 1, shows the method applied to laying out a two diametral pitch gear. The odontograph may also be applied to laying out teeth for internal gears.

Odontograph Table for Involute System. — Lay off the pitch, addendum, root and clearance circles and space off the teeth on the pitch line, as indicated in Fig. 2. Draw the "base line" 1/60 of the pitch diameter inside the pitch line. Use the face radius as given in the table for involute teeth for drawing all the faces from the pitch line to the addendum line, the centers being on the "base line." If the pitch is any other than 1 diametral or 1-inch circular pitch, divide or multiply the values given in the table as directed. To draw the flanks of the teeth from the pitch line to the "base line," use the flank radius given, with the center on the "base line." Then draw straight radial flanks from the "base line" to the root line, and round them into the clearance line. The illustration, Fig. 2, shows the method applied to laying out a two diametral pitch gear. The odontograph table for involute teeth can be used

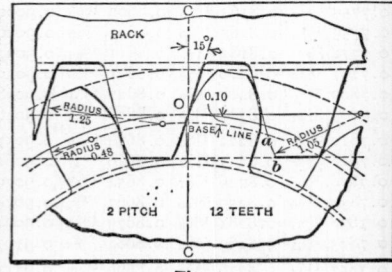

Fig. 2

for internal gears in the same way as for external gears, but care must be taken that the point of the tooth of the gear is cut off to avoid interference. No correction for interference, however, is needed on the points of the pinion teeth or on the flanks of the gear teeth.

Special Rule for Involute Rack. — Draw the sides of the rack teeth as straight lines inclined 15 degrees to the center line COC. Draw the outer half ab of the face by means of a circular arc having a radii of 2.10 inches divided by the diametral pitch, or 0.67 inch multiplied by the circular pitch, the center for this arc being on the pitch line of the rack.

Grant's Odontograph

	Table for Cycloidal Teeth							
Number of Teeth in the Gear		R, r, D and d for One Diametral Pitch; for any other Pitch divide Values given by that Pitch				R, r, D and d for One Inch Circular Pitch; for any other Pitch multiply Values given by that Pitch		
		Faces		Flanks		Faces		Flanks	
Exact	Also Used for	R	D	r	d	R	D	r	d
10	10	1.99	0.02	−8.00	4.00	0.62	0.01	−2.55	1.27
11	11	2.00	0.04	−11.05	6.50	0.63	0.01	−3.34	2.07
12	12	2.01	0.06	∞	∞	0.64	0.02	∞	∞
13½	13– 14	2.04	0.07	15.10	9.43	0.65	0.02	4.80	3.00
15½	15– 16	2.10	0.09	7.86	3.46	0.67	0.03	2.50	1.10
17½	17– 18	2.14	0.11	6.13	2.20	0.68	0.04	1.95	0.70
20	19– 21	2.20	0.13	5.12	1.57	0.70	0.04	1.63	0.50
23	22– 24	2.26	0.15	4.50	1.13	0.72	0.05	1.43	0.36
27	25– 29	2.33	0.16	4.10	0.96	0.74	0.05	1.30	0.29
33	30– 36	2.40	0.19	3.80	0.72	0.76	0.06	1.20	0.23
42	37– 48	2.48	0.22	3.52	0.63	0.79	0.07	1.12	0.20
58	49– 72	2.60	0.25	3.33	0.54	0.83	0.08	1.06	0.17
97	73–144	2.83	0.28	3.14	0.44	0.90	0.09	1.00	0.14
290	145–300	2.92	0.31	3.00	0.38	0.93	0.10	0.95	0.12
∞	Rack	2.96	0.34	2.96	0.34	0.94	0.11	0.94	0.11

	Table for Involute Teeth								
No. of Teeth in the Gear	Radii for One Diametral Pitch; for any other Pitch divide Values given by that Pitch		Radii for One Inch Circular Pitch; for any other Pitch multiply Values given by that Pitch		No. of Teeth in the Gear	Radii for One Diametral Pitch; for any other Pitch divide Values given by that Pitch		Radii for One Inch Circular Pitch; for any other Pitch multiply Values given by that Pitch	
	Face Radius	Flank Radius	Face Radius	Flank Radius		Face Radius	Flank Radius	Face Radius	Flank Radius
10	2.28	0.69	0.73	0.22	28	3.92	2.59	1.25	0.82
11	2.40	0.83	0.76	0.27	29	3.99	2.67	1.27	0.85
12	2.51	0.96	0.80	0.31	30	4.06	2.76	1.29	0.88
13	2.62	1.09	0.83	0.34	31	4.13	2.85	1.31	0.91
14	2.72	1.22	0.87	0.39	32	4.20	2.93	1.34	0.93
15	2.82	1.34	0.90	0.43	33	4.27	3.01	1.36	0.96
16	2.92	1.46	0.93	0.47	34	4.33	3.09	1.38	0.99
17	3.02	1.58	0.96	0.50	35	4.39	3.16	1.39	1.01
18	3.12	1.69	0.99	0.54	36	4.45	3.23	1.41	1.03
19	3.22	1.79	1.03	0.57	37– 40	4.20		1.34	
20	3.32	1.89	1.06	0.60	41– 45	4.63		1.48	
21	3.41	1.98	1.09	0.63	46– 51	5.06		1.61	
22	3.49	2.06	1.11	0.66	52– 60	5.74		1.83	
23	3.57	2.15	1.13	0.69	61– 70	6.52		2.07	
24	3.64	2.24	1.16	0.71	71– 90	7.72		2.46	
25	3.71	2.33	1.18	0.74	91–120	9.78		3.11	
26	3.78	2.42	1.20	0.77	121–180	13.38		4.26	
27	3.85	2.50	1.23	0.80	181–360	21.62		6.88	

Power Transmitting Capacity of Spur Gears. — The amount of power which can safely be transmitted by a pair of gears running at a given speed depends upon the allowable tooth load. This allowable load may be determined with reference to the strength of the teeth or it may be established with reference to tooth wear. If gearing is used only intermittently and for short periods, the allowable load may be based upon tooth strength. If tooth wear is an important consideration, the power transmitting capacity both with reference to wear and tooth strength should be determined; then the smaller of the two values is used. In case the pinion and gear are made of different materials, the power capacity is based either upon the pinion or gear, depending upon which has the lower allowable tooth load.

The Lewis Formula. — The Lewis formula (introduced by Wilfred Lewis in 1892) has been used extensively for determining the power transmitting capacity of gearing. This formula is based upon the beam strength of the teeth. The formulas under "Rules and Formulas for the Strength of Gear Teeth" are based upon the original Lewis formula but have been rearranged somewhat. Formula No. 3, for example, is arranged for diametral pitch (instead of circular pitch as originally) which accounts for the fact that the strength factors Y in Table 2 are 3.1416 times the factors in the original table. The factors for Fellows stub-tooth gears, as given in Table 2a, are based upon circular pitch.

Safe Load at Pitch Line: Before applying Rule and Formula 3 to find the allowable load L, the value of the strength factor Y must be determined by referring to Table 2 or 2a. The shape of a tooth of given pitch and pressure angle varies with the number of teeth. The smaller the number, the weaker the tooth of a given pitch and material; hence select factor Y in the table opposite the number of teeth and beneath the required pressure angle.

Formulas Containing Different Velocity Factors. — The power-transmitting capacity as determined by the Lewis formula usually is less than the actual amount which could be transmitted safely, and in many cases it is considerably below the actual capacity. This is particularly true of accurate high-speed gearing. In the formulas which follow, there is a factor G. This factor serves to reduce the allowable pitch-line load as the velocity increases, the same as in the Lewis formula. $G = 55 \times (600 + V)$ for cut gears of ordinary accuracy. $G = 27 \times (1200 + V)$ for cut gears of the better grades. $G = 423 \times (78 + \sqrt{V})$ for very accurate gears and pitch-line velocities of 4000 ft. per min. or higher (A.G.M.A. recommendation). The first factor G is the equivalent of the velocity factor $600 \div (600 + V)$ in the Lewis formula. The other factors G allow larger loads at a given velocity, thus increasing the computed horsepower capacity.

The face width of a spur gear usually equals three to five times the circular pitch with about four times circular pitch as an average value. Theoretically, the power-transmitting capacity increases in proportion to the face width, but this only holds true within certain practical limits because very wide gearing may not have proper contact throughout the length of the teeth, possibly because of deflections or imperfect mounting. Formula (6) shows the diametral pitch required when the face width equals k times the circular pitch, with the value of k ranging from 3 to 5.

$$\text{H.P.} = \frac{S_s F V Y}{P G} \quad (5); \qquad P = \sqrt{\frac{3.1416 \times S_s V Y k}{(\text{H.P.}) \times G}} \qquad (6)$$

Spur Gear Power-transmitting Capacity Based Either Upon Tooth Strength or Wear Load Limit. — The allowable pitch-line load and power-transmitting capacity of metal spur gears may be limited either by the beam strength of the teeth

Rules and Formulas for the Strength of Gear Teeth
(Based on the Lewis Formula)

D = pitch diameter of gear in ins.;	F = width of face in inches;
R = revolutions per minute;	Y = outline factor (see Table 2);
V = velocity in ft. per min. at pitch diameter;	P = diametral pitch (if circular pitch is given, divide 3.1416 by circular pitch to obtain diametral pitch);
S_s = allowable static unit stress for material;	L = maximum safe tangential load in pounds at pitch diameter;
S = allowable unit stress for material at given velocity;	H.P. = maximum safe horsepower.

Use rules and Formulas (1) to (4) in the order given.

No.	To Find	Rule	Formula
1	Velocity in feet per min. at the pitch diameter.	Multiply the product of the diameter in inches and the number of revolutions per minute, by 0.262.	$V = 0.262\ DR$
2	Allowable unit stress at given velocity.	Multiply the allowable static stress by 600 and divide the result by the velocity in feet per minute plus 600.	$S = S_s \times \dfrac{600}{600 + V}$
3	Maximum safe tangential load at pitch diameter.	Multiply together the allowable stress for the given velocity, the width of face, and the tooth outline factor; divide the result by the diametral pitch.	$L = \dfrac{SFY}{P}$
4	Maximum safe horsepower.	Multiply the safe load at the pitch line by the velocity in feet per minute, and divide the result by 33,000.	H.P. $= \dfrac{LV}{33,000}$

(as determined by the Lewis type of formula) or by the surface endurance limit of the material, the lower of these values being used. The designing procedure which follows is based upon two assumptions. (1) The service or operating conditions of the transmission are such that the dynamic or maximum momentary load on the gear teeth should be determined to insure the proper relationship between this dynamic load and the beam strength and limiting wear loads. (2) The class of service is such that tooth wear rather than beam strength may be the important factor in determining the limiting load and power-transmitting capacity. (For some applications as, for example, where gears are used infrequently, wear may be of no practical importance and tooth proportions should be based upon beam strength only.)

Buckingham's Dynamic Load Formula. — Assume that L_t = total applied load at pitch line, in pounds, equivalent to the given horsepower (H.P.); L_d = total dynamic load, in pounds; B = deformation factor (see Table 4); V = velocity at pitch line, feet per minute; F = face width, inches.

$$L_d = \frac{0.05\ V\ (FB + L_t)}{0.05\ V + \sqrt{FB + L_t}} + L_t \text{ where } L_t = \frac{\text{H.P.} \times 33,000}{V} \tag{7}$$

For values not included in Table 4, the value of B may be determined by one of the following formulas in which e = error in action, inch, and E_1 and E_2 = modulus of elasticity (see formulas at bottom of next page).

Table 1. Safe Static Stresses for Different Gear Materials

The allowable average stresses for the materials listed below are intended as a general guide only and should be replaced wherever possible by strength data applying to whatever gear material is actually used.   The allowable stresses may vary over a much wider range than here given due to variations in the properties of different materials and the varying effects of heat-treatments, if any, on the physical properties.

Material	Safe Stress, S_S Lbs. per Sq. In.	Material	Safe Stress, S_S Lbs. per Sq. In.
Plain cast iron (Note 1)	7,000–10,000	Molybdenum steel,	
Alloy cast iron (Note 2)	12,000–15,000	S.A.E. 4340 (Note 5)	60,000–70,000
Semi-steel	8,000–12,000	S.A.E. 4640 (Note 5)	50,000–60,000
Carbon steel,			
S.A.E. 1020 (Note 3)	20,000–25,000	Chromium steel,	
S.A.E. 1045 (Note 4)	35,000–40,000	S.A.E. 5140 (Note 7)	50,000–60,000
Nickel steel,		Chromium-vanadium,	
S.A.E. 2320 (Note 3)	40,000–45,000	S.A.E. 6145 (Note 5)	50,000–60,000
S.A.E. 2345 (Note 5)	45,000–55,000	Phosphor gear bronze,	
		S.A.E. No. 63	
Nickel-chromium,		(Note 8)	8,000–10,000
S.A.E. 3115 (Note 3)	35,000–40,000	S.A.E. No. 65	
		(Note 9)	10,000–12,000
S.A.E. 3145 (Note 6)	45,000–60,000	Non-metallic materials (Note 10)	

Note 1. Safe stress values for plain cast irons ranging in tensile strength from 20,000 to 30,000 pounds per square inch and in hardness from about 160 to 200 Brinell.

Note 2. Safe stress values for alloy cast irons varying in tensile strength from 35,000 to 45,000 pounds per square inch and in hardness from about 180 to 240 Brinell.

Note 3. Strength data applies to gears which have been casehardened and tempered or drawn.

Note 4. Hardened by quenching in water or oil (depending upon section and relative importance of hardness and toughness) and tempered as required.

Note 5. Hardened by quenching in oil and tempering; water quenching not recommended.

Note 6. Quench in oil and temper to 375 to 425 degrees F. for gears.

Note 7. This steel is used extensively for gears and shafts hardened by direct cyaniding.

Note 8. Preferred for use with worm gears driven by unhardened worms.

Note 9. Preferred for use with gears driven by hardened and ground worms.

Note 10. Definite information regarding the allowable stresses for non-metallic gear materials should be obtained directly from the manufacturer of whatever material is to be used.

For 14½ degree Pressure Angle	For 20-degree Full-depth Form	For 20-degree Stub-tooth Form
$B = \dfrac{0.107\,e}{\left(\dfrac{1}{E_1} + \dfrac{1}{E_2}\right)}$	$B = \dfrac{0.111\,e}{\left(\dfrac{1}{E_1} + \dfrac{1}{E_2}\right)}$	$B = \dfrac{0.115\,e}{\left(\dfrac{1}{E_1} + \dfrac{1}{E_2}\right)}$

Table 2. Strength Factors Used in Calculating the Power Capacity of Spur Gears

	American Standard Tooth Forms						
Number of Teeth	14½ Deg. Composite and Involute	20 Deg. Full-Depth Involute System	20 Deg. Stub-Tooth System	Number of Teeth	14½ Deg. Composite and Involute	20 Deg. Full-Depth Involute System	20 Deg. Stub-Tooth System
	Strength Factors Y for Use with Diametral Pitch						
12	0.210	0.245	0.311	28	0.314	0.352	0.430
13	0.220	0.261	0.324	30	0.320	0.358	0.437
14	0.226	0.276	0.339	34	0.327	0.371	0.446
15	0.236	0.289	0.348	38	0.336	0.383	0.456
16	0.242	0.295	0.361	43	0.346	0.396	0.462
17	0.251	0.302	0.367	50	0.352	0.408	0.474
18	0.261	0.308	0.377	60	0.358	0.421	0.484
19	0.273	0.314	0.386	75	0.364	0.434	0.496
20	0.283	0.320	0.393	100	0.371	0.446	0.506
21	0.289	0.327	0.399	150	0.377	0.459	0.518
22	0.292	0.330	0.405	300	0.383	0.471	0.534
24	0.298	0.336	0.415	Rack	0.390	0.484	0.550
26	0.307	0.346	0.424				

The strength factors above are for use in formulas containing diametral pitch. These factors are 3.1416 times those used in formulas based upon circular pitch.

Table 2a. Strength Factors Y for Stub Tooth Gears — For Use with Circular Pitch

No. of Teeth	Fellows System — See Formulas page 723 and 726								Nuttall System
	$\frac{4}{5}$	$\frac{5}{7}$	$\frac{9}{8}$	$\frac{7}{6}$	$\frac{8}{10}$	$\frac{9}{11}$	$\frac{10}{12}$	$\frac{12}{14}$	
12	0.096	0.111	0.102	0.100	0.096	0.100	0.093	0.092	0.099
13	0.101	0.115	0.107	0.106	0.101	0.104	0.098	0.096	0.103
14	0.105	0.119	0.112	0.111	0.106	0.108	0.102	0.100	0.108
15	0.108	0.123	0.115	0.115	0.110	0.111	0.105	0.103	0.111
16	0.111	0.126	0.119	0.118	0.113	0.114	0.109	0.106	0.115
17	0.114	0.129	0.122	0.121	0.116	0.116	0.111	0.109	0.117
18	0.117	0.131	0.124	0.124	0.119	0.119	0.114	0.111	0.120
19	0.119	0.133	0.127	0.127	0.122	0.121	0.116	0.113	0.123
20	0.121	0.135	0.129	0.129	0.124	0.123	0.118	0.115	0.125
21	0.123	0.137	0.131	0.131	0.126	0.125	0.120	0.117	0.127
22	0.125	0.139	0.133	0.133	0.128	0.126	0.122	0.118	0.128
23	0.126	0.141	0.134	0.135	0.129	0.128	0.123	0.120	0.130
24	0.128	0.142	0.136	0.136	0.131	0.129	0.125	0.121	0.131
25	0.129	0.143	0.137	0.138	0.133	0.130	0.126	0.123	0.133
26	0.130	0.145	0.139	0.139	0.134	0.132	0.128	0.124	0.134
27	0.132	0.146	0.140	0.140	0.135	0.133	0.129	0.125	0.136
28	0.133	0.147	0.141	0.141	0.136	0.134	0.130	0.126	0.137
29	0.134	0.148	0.142	0.143	0.137	0.135	0.131	0.127	0.138
30	0.135	0.149	0.143	0.144	0.138	0.136	0.132	0.128	0.139
32	0.137	0.150	0.145	0.146	0.140	0.137	0.134	0.130	0.141
35	0.139	0.153	0.147	0.148	0.143	0.139	0.136	0.132	0.143
37	0.140	0.154	0.149	0.149	0.144	0.141	0.138	0.133	0.145
40	0.142	0.156	0.151	0.151	0.146	0.142	0.140	0.135	0.146
45	0.145	0.159	0.154	0.154	0.149	0.145	0.142	0.138	0.149
50	0.147	0.161	0.156	0.156	0.151	0.147	0.144	0.140	0.151
55	0.149	0.162	0.157	0.158	0.152	0.149	0.146	0.141	0.153
60	0.150	0.164	0.159	0.159	0.154	0.150	0.148	0.143	0.154
70	0.153	0.166	0.161	0.161	0.156	0.152	0.150	0.145	0.157
80	0.155	0.168	0.163	0.163	0.158	0.154	0.152	0.147	0.159
100	0.158	0.171	0.166	0.166	0.160	0.156	0.154	0.150	0.161
150	0.162	0.174	0.170	0.169	0.164	0.160	0.158	0.154	0.165
200	0.164	0.176	0.172	0.171	0.166	0.162	0.160	0.156	0.167
Rack	0.173	0.184	0.179	0.176	0.172	0.170	0.168	0.166	0.175

Error in Action. — The maximum error in action between gears is given in Table 3. The left-hand section of this table includes three classes of gears and a range of diametral pitches. The right-hand section indicates accuracy required at different pitch-line velocities. The errors shown are intended to keep the noise of operation and intensity of dynamic load within reasonable limits. Where extreme quietness of operation is required, a greater degree of accuracy is necessary.

Static Beam Strength of Teeth. — The safe static beam strength is based upon the Lewis equation. In the following formula, L_b = safe static beam load on teeth, in pounds or load, when $V = 0$; G = factor based upon velocity and grade of gearing (see values given in connection with Formula 5). Other notation is the same as given on page 715:

$$L_b = \frac{S_s FY}{P} \quad (8); \quad \text{H.P.} = \frac{L_b V}{G} \quad (9)$$

Buckingham's Formula for Wear Load Limit. — The limit load for wear depends upon the surface endurance limits of the materials, the radii of curvature of the mating profiles, and the relative hardnesses of the mating surfaces. L_w = limiting static load for wear, pounds; D_p = pitch diameter of pinion, inches; N_p = number of pinion teeth; N_g = number of gear teeth; A = pressure angle; K = load stress

Table 3. Maximum Error in Action Between Gears

D.P.	Class 1	Class 2	Class 3	V	Error	V	Error	V	Error
1	.0048	.0024	.0012	250	.0037	1750	.0017	3250	.0008
2	.0040	.0020	.0010	500	.0032	2000	.0015	3500	.0007
3	.0032	.0016	.0008	750	.0028	2250	.0013	4000	.0006
4	.0026	.0013	.0007	1000	.0024	2500	.0012	4500	.0006
5	.0022	.0011	.0006	1250	.0021	2750	.0010	5000	.0005
6 & finer	.0020	.0010	.0005	1500	.0019	3000	.0009	& over	

Table 4. Deformation Factors B for Dynamic Load Formula

Material, Gear and Pinion (See Footnote)	Tooth Form	.0005	.001	.002	.003	.004	.005
C.I. & C.I.	14½ Deg.	400	800	1600	2400	3200	4000
C.I. & S.		550	1100	2200	3300	4400	5500
S. & S.		800	1600	3200	4800	6400	8000
C.I. & C.I.	20 Deg. Full Depth	415	830	1660	2490	3320	4150
C.I. & S.		570	1140	2280	3420	4560	5700
S. & S.		830	1660	3320	4980	6640	8300
C.I. & C.I.	20 Deg. Stub	430	860	1720	2580	3440	4300
C.I. & S.		590	1180	2360	3540	4720	5900
S. & S.		860	1720	3440	5160	6880	8600

Note: Abbreviation "C.I." is for cast iron, and "S" for steel.

factor, Table 5; Q = ratio factor; E_1 and E_2 = moduli of elasticity of material in each mating gear; S_c = surface endurance limit of materials, in pounds per square inch (Table 5).

$$K = \frac{S_c^2 \sin A}{1.4}\left(\frac{1}{E_1} + \frac{1}{E_2}\right); \qquad L_w = D_p F K Q \qquad (10)$$

$Q = \dfrac{2N_g}{N_g + N_p}$ for external spur gears; $\quad Q = \dfrac{2N_g}{N_g - N_p}$ for internal spur gears.

Relation Between Dynamic Load, Beam Strength, and Wear Load Limit. — The load-carrying capacity should be based either upon the beam strength or wear load limit, the lower of these two values being used.

Beam Strength. — The static beam strength of the gear tooth should always be greater than the dynamic load. $L_b = 1.25 \times L_d$ for steady loads; $L_b = 1.35 \times L_d$ for pulsating loads; $L_b = 1.50 \times L_d$ for shock loads. These values are given as a general guide, and experience may indicate desirable modifications.

Example: Determine the diametral pitch and face width of two mating spur gears which are to transmit 40 H.P. Driver speed = 500 R.P.M.; ratio of driven to driving gear size = 5; approximate center distance = 15 inches; teeth are to

Table 5. Values of K used in Formula for Wear Load Limit

Material in Pinion	Brinell Number	Material in Gear	Brinell Number	S_c	K $14\frac{1}{2}°$	K $20°$
Steel	150	Steel	150	50,000	30	41
Steel	200	Steel	150	60,000	43	58
Steel	250	Steel	150	70,000	58	79
Steel	200	Steel	200	70,000	58	79
Steel	250	Steel	200	80,000	76	103
Steel	300	Steel	200	90,000	96	131
Steel	250	Steel	250	90,000	96	131
Steel	300	Steel	250	100,000	119	162
Steel	350	Steel	250	110,000	144	196
Steel	300	Steel	300	110,000	144	196
Steel	350	Steel	300	120,000	171	233
Steel	400	Steel	300	125,000	186	254
Steel	350	Steel	350	130,000	201	275
Steel	400	Steel	350	140,000	233	318
Steel	400	Steel	400	150,000	268	366
Steel	150	Cast Iron		50,000	44	60
Steel	200	Cast Iron		70,000	87	119
Steel	250	Cast Iron		90,000	144	196
Steel	150	Ph. Bronze		50,000	46	62
Steel	200	Ph. Bronze		70,000	91	124
Steel	250	Ph. Bronze		85,000	135	204
Cast Iron		Cast Iron		90,000	193	284

be 20-degree full-depth form; gear is to be made of cast iron, and pinion of steel with a hardness of 250 Brinell.

Select a trial value for diametral pitch based either upon judgment or previous experience with similar transmissions. Assume that $P = 3$. According to Formula 5, page 654, $N_g + N_p = 2 PC$; hence, in this trial equation, $N_g + N_p = 2 \times 3 \times 15 = 90$ teeth. As the ratio is 5, the number of pinion teeth = $90 \div (5 + 1) = 15$; hence, gear size = $90 - 15 = 75$. If the face width equals about four times the circular pitch (an approved proportion), then $F = \dfrac{\pi 4}{P} = 4$ inches approximately. Now determine the pitch-line velocity V by applying Formula 1, page 715. Gear pitch diameter = $75 \div 3 = 25$ inches; hence, $V = 0.262 \times 25 \times 100 = 655$ feet per minute.

Dynamic Load. — The load $L_t = 33,000 \times \text{H.P.} \div V = 33,000 \times 40 \div 655 = 2000$ pounds approximately. Assuming an error in action of 0.002 inch (see Table 3), the deformation factor B for a cast-iron gear and steel pinion, and 20-degree full depth teeth = 2280 (Table 4). Applying Formula (7)

$$L_d = \frac{0.05 \times 655 \,(4 \times 2280 + 2000)}{0.05 \times 655 + \sqrt{4 \times 2280 + 2000}} + 2000 = 4635 \text{ pounds}$$

Beam Strength. — In this case, the cast-iron gear teeth have a lower beam strength than the steel pinion teeth; hence, the beam strength of the gear teeth will be determined. Assume an allowable static stress of 10,000 pounds per square inch. Inserting the known values in Formula (8)

$$L_b = \frac{S_s FY}{P} = \frac{10,000 \times 4 \times 0.434}{3} = 5790 \text{ pounds approximately}$$

Thus, $L_b = 1.25 \, L_d$ approximately and is satisfactory for a steady load.

Wear Load Limit. — The wear load limit L_w (Formula 10) ordinarily is computed for the pinion, even when the pinion is of steel and is harder than the gear, because the larger number of pinion revolutions and resulting tooth wear more than offsets the increase in endurance limit of the material; moreover, the harder pinion will cold work the gear-tooth surfaces, thus increasing their surface endurance limit. Table 5 gives a K value of 196 for a steel pinion of 250 Brinell and a cast-iron gear. The pinion diameter = $15 \div 3 = 5$ inches.

$$Q = \frac{2 \times 75}{75 + 15} = 1.66; \quad L_w = 5 \times 4 \times 196 \times 1.66 = 6500 \text{ pounds}$$

British Standard Horsepower Formulas. — The horsepower formulas which follow are included in the revised British standard specifications (No. 436–1940) for machine cut spur gears and also for helical gears used in driving parallel shafts. Two formulas are given. One indicates the horsepower with reference to tooth strength; the other, the horsepower as limited by tooth wear. In deciding upon the horsepower capacity formula, the Committee gave special consideration to the question whether the speed factor should be based on revolutions per minute or pitch-line speed in feet per minute, and the former was adopted. The power capacity of both gear and pinion should be checked (1) for tooth wear, and (2) for tooth strength. The smallest of the four power ratings thus obtained should be used.

In the following formulas S_c = surface stress factor (Table 6); X_c = speed factor for wear (Table 7); Z = zone factor (see chart, page 724); F = face width, inches; N = revolutions per minute; T = number of teeth; K = pitch factor = $P^{0.8}$; P = diametral pitch; S_b = bending stress (Table 6); X_b = speed factor for

Table 6. Basic Surface and Bending-Stress Factors of Spur and Helical Gears

Factors for use in British Standard Horsepower Formula

Type of Material (Numbers in Parentheses Indicate Footnotes)	Minimum Tensile Strength Tons per Sq. In.	Minimum Brinell Hardness Number	Surface Stress Factor S_c	Bending Stress Lb. per Sq. In. S_b
Fabric..............................	..	..	560	4,500
Cast Iron, Ordinary Grade...........	12	165	1,000	5,800
" " , Medium Grade............	16	210	1,350	7,600
" " , High Grade, as Cast.......	22	220	1,450	10,400
Castings, Malleable.................	20	140	850	11,000
Phosphor Bronze, Sand Cast.........	12	69	700	7,000
" " , Chill Cast.........	15	82	850	8,500
" " , Centrifugally Cast..	17	90	1,000	10,000
Cast Steel, 0.35% to 0.45% Carbon...	35	145	1,400	19,000
" " , 0.50% to 0.55% Carbon (1)	38	160 (3)	3,100	13,000
Forged Carbon Steel, 0.15% Carbon (2)	32	140 (4)	9,000	28,000
" " " , 0.40% Carbon (6)	35	145	1,400	17,000
" " " , 0.40% Carbon (7)	35	145	1,600	19,000
" " " , 0.40% Carbon (1)	35	145 (8)	2,800	12,000
" " " , 0.40% Carbon (9)	40	175	1,800	20,000
" " " , 0.40% Carbon(10)	40	175	2,000	22,000
" " " , 0.55% Carbon (6)	45	200	2,000	21,600
" " " , 0.55% Carbon (7)	45	200	2,300	24,000
" " " , 0.55% Carbon (1)	45	200 (11)	4,000	15,000
Nickel Steel, 1% nickel..........(12)	40	175	2,000	22,000
" " , 3% nickel..........(12)	45	200	2,300	24,000
" " , 3% nickel.......... (2)	45	200 (13)	10,200	40,000
" " , 3½% nickel........ (1)	55	250 (14)	5,100	18,500
" " , 3½% nickel........(12)	55	250	3,000	30,000
" " , 3½% nickel........ (2)	45	200 (15)	10,200	40,000
" " , 5% nickel.......... (2)	55	250 (16)	11,200	47,000
Nickel-chromium, 1½% Ni, 1% Cr(17)	55	250	3,000	30,000
" " , 1½% Ni, 1% Cr (1)	55	250 (13)	5,100	18,500
" " , 1½%..........(17)	100	440	5,500	40,000
" " , 3½%..........(17)	55	250	3,000	30,000
" " , 3½%.......... (1)	55	250 (14)	5,100	18,500
" " , 3½%.......... (2)	55	250 (16)	11,200	47,000
Carbon-chromium, 0.55% carbon..(18)	55	250	3,000	30,000
" " , 0.55% carbon..(18)	65	290	3,500	36,000
" " , 0.55% carbon.. (1)	55	250 (14)	5,100	18,500

(1) Surface Hardened; (2) Casehardened; (3) Core, 160; case, 530; (4) Hardness of core; (5) Core, 140; case, 640; (6) normalized; for sections thicker than 5 inches; (7) normalized; for sections less than 5 inches thick; (8) Core, 145; case, 460; (9) Heat-treated; for sections thicker than 5 inches; (10) Heat-treated; for sections less 5 inches thick; (11) Core, 200; case, 520; (12) Heat-treated; (13) Core; (14) Core, 250; case, 500; (15) Core, 200; case, 620; (16) Core, 250; case, 600; (17) Oil hardened and tempered to strength given in second col.; (18) Heat-treated to strength given in second column.

Table 7. Speed Factors X_c for Wear

Rev. per Minute	Running Time — Hours per Day							
	1	2	4	6	8	12	18	24
	Speed Factors X_c for Wear							
100	0.935	0.735	0.585	0.515	0.470	0.410	0.350	0.320
150	0.865	0.685	0.540	0.475	0.435	0.370	0.330	0.300
200	0.825	0.650	0.520	0.460	0.415	0.360	0.310	0.280
300	0.775	0.615	0.485	0.425	0.380	0.330	0.290	0.270
400	0.730	0.580	0.460	0.400	0.360	0.320	0.270	0.250
500	0.700	0.550	0.440	0.380	0.350	0.305	0.260	0.240
600	0.680	0.530	0.425	0.370	0.340	0.290	0.250	0.230
800	0.635	0.500	0.400	0.350	0.320	0.270	0.240	0.220
1,000	0.610	0.480	0.380	0.335	0.305	0.260	0.230	0.210
1,500	0.550	0.440	0.345	0.310	0.275	0.240	0.210	0.190
2,000	0.520	0.415	0.325	0.290	0.260	0.220	0.200	0.180
2,500	0.480	0.380	0.305	0.265	0.240	0.210	0.185	0.165
3,000	0.450	0.355	0.280	0.250	0.225	0.195	0.170	0.155
4,000	0.415	0.325	0.260	0.225	0.207	0.180	0.155	0.145
5,000	0.380	0.305	0.240	0.210	0.190	0.165	0.145	0.132
6,000	0.355	0.285	0.225	0.200	0.180	0.155	0.135	0.125
7,000	0.340	0.270	0.215	0.190	0.170	0.150	0.130	0.118
8,000	0.325	0.260	0.205	0.180	0.165	0.142	0.125	0.113
9,000	0.315	0.250	0.200	0.175	0.157	0.135	0.120	0.108
10,000	0.305	0.240	0.190	0.165	0.152	0.130	0.115	0.105

Table 8. Speed Factors X_b for Strength

Running Time, Hours per Day	Revolutions per Minute									
	100	150	200	300	400	500	600	800	1000	1500
	Speed Factors X_b for Strength									
1	0.600	0.550	0.525	0.445	0.435	0.420	0.415	0.410	0.385	0.350
3	0.510	0.435	0.425	0.410	0.400	0.380	0.370	0.345	0.330	0.300
6	0.430	0.415	0.405	0.380	0.360	0.345	0.330	0.310	0.295	0.275
12	0.410	0.380	0.360	0.340	0.320	0.310	0.300	0.285	0.270	0.245
24	0.375	0.350	0.330	0.310	0.295	0.285	0.275	0.255	0.245	0.225

Running Time, Hours per Day	Revolutions per Minute									
	2000	2500	3000	4000	5000	6000	7000	8000	9000	10,000
	Speed Factors X_b for Strength									
1	0.325	0.305	0.285	0.260	0.240	0.225	0.215	0.208	0.200	0.192
3	0.285	0.260	0.245	0.225	0.208	0.195	0.185	0.178	0.170	0.165
6	0.255	0.235	0.220	0.200	0.185	0.175	0.165	0.160	0.153	0.148
12	0.230	0.215	0.200	0.182	0.168	0.158	0.150	0.145	0.140	0.135
24	0.210	0.195	0.180	0.165	0.152	0.143	0.138	0.130	0.126	0.120

Table 9. Pitch Factors K

Diametral Pitch	Factor K	Diametral Pitch	Factor K	Diametral Pitch	Factor K	Diametral Pitch	Factor K
1	1.00	2¼	1.90	4	3.05	9	5.80
1¼	1.20	2½	2.10	5	3.65	10	6.40
1½	1.40	2¾	2.25	6	4.25	12	7.40
1¾	1.55	3	2.40	7	4.80	14	8.30
2	1.75	3½	2.70	8	5.40	16	9.25

strength (Table 8); Y = strength factor (see chart, page 725). The wear and strength formulas follow:

$$\text{Horsepower for wear} = \frac{S_c X_c Z F N T}{126,000 K P}$$

$$\text{Horsepower for strength} = \frac{S_b X_b Y F N T}{126,000 P^2}$$

Example: Find the allowable horsepower for spur gears. The pinion and gear speeds are 500 and 100 revolutions per minute; continuous operation 12 hours per day; diametral pitch, 3; face width, 4 inches; pressure angle 20 degrees; pinion, 20 teeth; pinion material, 0.40% carbon steel normalized; gear, 100 teeth; gear material, cast iron of ordinary grade.

Horsepower formulas for wear and for strength are applied to both gear and pinion as shown below and the smallest horsepower rating (approximately 40 in this case) is used.

$$\text{Pinion H.P. for wear} = \frac{1600 \times 0.305 \times 2.20 \times 4 \times 500 \times 20}{126,000 \times 2.40 \times 3} = 47$$

$$\text{Gear H.P. for wear} = \frac{1000 \times 0.410 \times 2.20 \times 4 \times 100 \times 100}{126,000 \times 2.40 \times 3} = 40$$

$$\text{Pinion H.P. for strength} = \frac{19,000 \times 0.305 \times 0.72 \times 4 \times 500 \times 20}{126,000 \times 3 \times 3} = 147$$

$$\text{Gear H.P. for strength} = \frac{5800 \times 0.410 \times 0.61 \times 4 \times 100 \times 100}{126,000 \times 3 \times 3} = 51$$

This gear horsepower rating based upon tooth wear is somewhat lower than that of the pinion for wear and also lower than the gear and pinion power capacity based upon tooth strength; hence the power rating would be about 40 horsepower, assuming, of course, that the gearing is to be used sufficiently to warrant establishing a power rating upon tooth wear rather than tooth strength.

Horsepower Capacity of Stub-tooth Gearing. — The horsepower capacity of stub-tooth gears of the American standard form may be determined by using the formulas previously given for full-depth teeth. The strength factor Y must, of course, be selected for American standard stub teeth (see Table 2).

Power Capacity of Fellows Stub-tooth Gears. — If the stub teeth are based on the Fellows system, the circular pitch is equivalent to the diametral pitch in the numerator of the fraction. For example, if a stub-tooth gear is of 4/5 pitch, the circular pitch is equivalent to 4 diametral pitch, or 0.7854. Stub-tooth gears of the Nuttall system are based directly upon the circular pitch. Table 2a gives strength factors for both Fellows and Nuttall stub-tooth gears. These factors are based upon circular pitch. The number of horsepower according to a conservative rating, is found by the formula:

$$\text{H.P.} = \frac{S_s \times F \times P' \times Y \times V}{55 \times (600 + V)} \quad \text{and} \quad P' = \frac{\text{H.P.} \times 55 \times (600 + V)}{S_s \times F \times Y \times V}$$

In applying the formula for P' to the Fellows system, the object is to determine what circular pitch is equivalent to a diametral pitch in the numerator of one of the series of pitches seen at the top of the table of factors Y for the Fellows system; hence the formula may be written as follows:

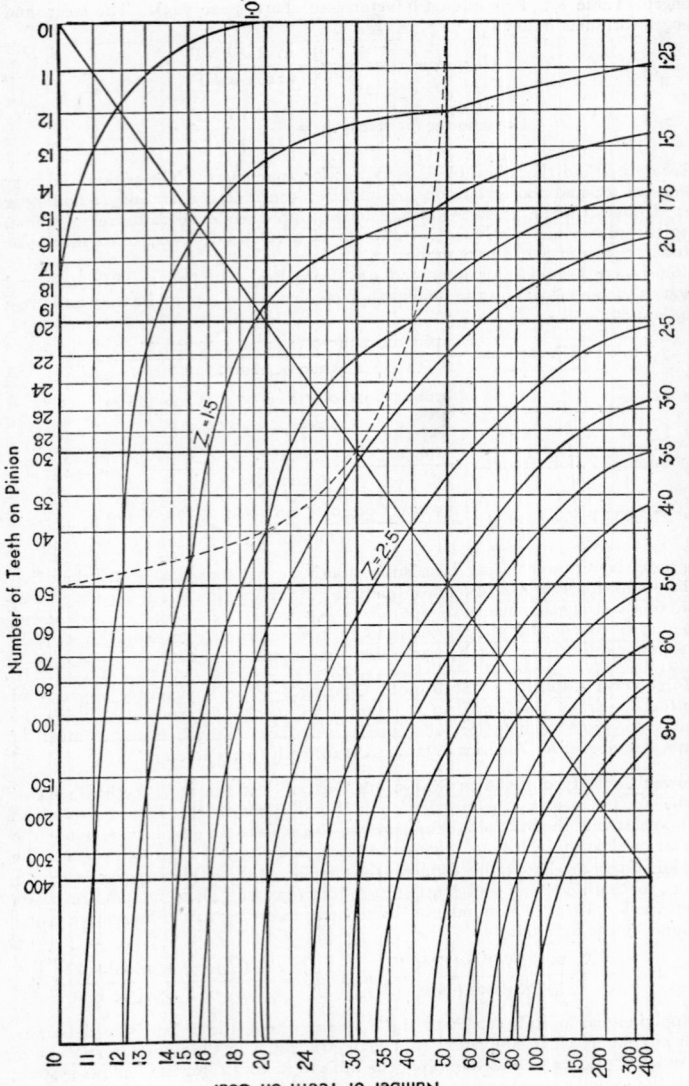

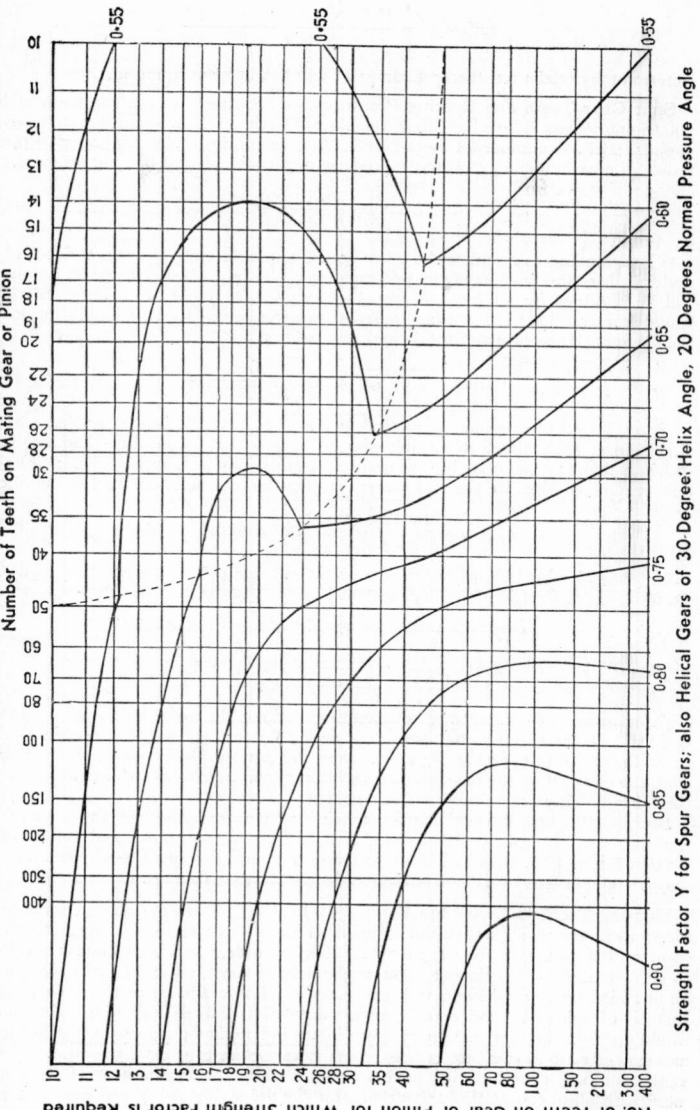

Number of Teeth on Mating Gear or Pinion

No. of Teeth on Gear or Pinion for Which Strength Factor is Required

Strength Factor Y for Spur Gears; also Helical Gears of 30-Degree Helix Angle, 20 Degrees Normal Pressure Angle

$$P' \times Y = \frac{\text{H.P.} \times 55 \times (600 + V)}{S_s \times F \times V}$$

Determine by trial what factor Y times P' will balance the equation.

Spur Gear Tooth and Bearing Pressures. — Pressure between the teeth of involute spur gears is exerted along the line of action. If L = tangential load in pounds, H.P. = number of horsepower, R = revolutions per minute, r = pitch radius of gear in inches, P = tooth pressure in pounds = total bearing pressure.

$$L = \frac{\text{H.P.} \times 63,000}{R \times r}$$

The load tending to separate the gears equals approximately the tangential load L multiplied by the tangent of the pressure angle. A more accurate result, however, will be obtained by adding 3 degrees to the pressure angle to allow for friction. This separating load is less than the total bearing load. If L_s = separating load, then the tooth pressure and total bearing pressure

$$P = \sqrt{L^2 + L_s^2} = \frac{L}{\cos \text{ pressure angle}}$$

Example — A spur pinion supported on each side by ball bearings rotates 2175 R.P.M. and transmits to a mating gear 20 horsepower. The pitch diameter is 2 inches and the pressure angle, 20 degrees. Determine (1) tangential load; (2) the load tending to separate the two gears; and (3) the total load on the two bearings.

$$L = \frac{20 \times 63,000}{2175 \times 2} = 290 \text{ pounds}$$

This tangential load L will now be used in determining the separating load L_s. To compensate for friction, 3 degrees will be added to the pressure angle.

$$L_s = L \times \tan 23° = 290 \times 0.424 = 123 \text{ pounds}$$

$$P = \sqrt{290^2 + 123^2} = \frac{290}{\cos 23°} = 315 \text{ pounds}$$

If the gears are located midway between the bearings, the radial load will be equally divided. If the distance between the bearing centers is, say, 8 inches, and the central plane of the gearing is 3 inches from the center of one bearing and 5 inches from the other, then the nearest bearing will carry five-eighths of the total load and the other bearing the remaining three-eighths.

Bearing pressures are not affected much by changes in the pressure angle. In the preceding example, if the pressure angle is 14½ degrees plus an allowance of 3 degrees for friction, then the total load would equal 304 pounds — a reduction of only 11 pounds due to a change from 20 degrees to 14½ degrees.

Hunting Tooth to Distribute Wear. — When one of two meshing gears is provided with one more tooth than is required for a given ratio, this extra tooth is commonly known as a "hunting tooth." For example, if a driven shaft is required to revolve about three times as fast as the driving shaft, an exact ratio of 3 could be obtained by using driving and driven gears with 72 and 24 teeth, respectively. Instead of using this exact ratio, many millwrights, when installing cast gears, would use a driving gear having 73 teeth instead of 72, and a driven gear of 24 teeth making the ratio in this case, 3.0417 which is very close to the desired ratio. Now, as the number of teeth do not have a common divisor, each tooth of one gear will mesh with all of the mating teeth one after the other, instead of meshing with the same teeth continually. The theory is that when the teeth mesh progressively in this manner, thus distributing the wear, all of the teeth will eventually be worn to some indefinite, but comparatively true, shape. To illustrate the action, any two teeth which happen to meet during the first revolution will be separated by one tooth space at the completion of the second revolution, by two tooth spaces at the end of the third revolution, and so on; hence the name "hunting tooth."

Maag Gearing. — In the design of the Maag system of gearing, a 15-degree pressure angle is maintained for large gears, but for relatively small gears the angles and also the blank diameters or positions of the teeth relative to the pitch circles, are varied with the idea of obtaining the most satisfactory operation for gearing of a given ratio. This is a departure from standardization and the use of gears which are interchangeable at standard center distances. Those advocating this system, however, believe that what is lost in this respect is more than gained by so forming the teeth of a gear and pinion of given ratio as to obtain more rolling and less sliding action combined with stronger teeth without under-cutting, even when the gears are very small. When necessary or desirable to use gears having possibly not more than five or six teeth, a practical tooth form may be obtained by changing the pressure angle and the relation of the tooth to its pitch circle, to suit the conditions. It has long been the practice to obtain an improvement of tooth shape, by the enlargement of small spur and bevel pinions but with the Maag system, the plan is to so modify the relations between addenda, dedenda, and pressure angle as to secure what is considered the best tooth form for each particular ratio.

Properties of the Involute Curve. — The involute curve is used almost exclusively for gear-tooth profiles, because of certain important properties which are here summarized.

1. The form or shape of an involute curve depends upon the diameter of the base circle from which it is derived. (If a taut line were unwound from the circumference of a circle — the *base circle* of the involute — the end of that line or any point on the unwound portion, would describe an involute curve.)

2. It a gear tooth of involute curvature acts against the involute tooth of a mating gear while rotating at a uniform rate, the angular motion of the driven gear will also be uniform, even though the center-to-center distance is varied.

3. The relative rate of motion between driving and driven gears having involute tooth curves, is established by the diameters of their base circles.

4. Contact between intermeshing involute teeth on a driving and driven gear is along a straight line that is tangent to the two base circles of these gears. This is the *line of action.*

5. The point where the line of action intersects the common center-line of the mating involute gears, establishes the radii of the pitch circles of these gears; hence true pitch circle diameters are affected by a change in the center distance. (Pitch diameters obtained by dividing the number of teeth by the diametral pitch, applies when the center distance equals the total number of teeth on both gears divided by twice the diametral pitch.)

6. The pitch diameters of mating involute gears are directly proportional to the diameters of their respective base circles; thus, if the base circle of one mating gear is three times as large as the other, the pitch circle diameters will be in the same ratio.

7. The angle between the line of action and a line perpendicular to the common center-line of mating gears, is the *pressure angle;* hence the pressure angle is affected by any change in the center distance.

8. When an involute curve acts against a straight line (as in the case of an involute pinion acting against straight-sided rack teeth), the straight line is tangent to the involute and perpendicular to its line of action.

Different Classes of Steels for Industrial Gearing

Casehardening Steels for Gears	
Kind of Steel	Characteristics and Uses
S.A.E. 1020	For parts that must be wear-resisting. The core is very ductile. No great core strength.
S.A.E. 2315	For parts where a tough core and a hard case are necessary for strength and wear resistance. Distortion is low. A good all around case-hardening steel.
S.A.E. 3115	Particularly suited for selective casehardening where the non-case-hardened parts must be strong. Also suitable for large parts. An extremely strong and tough steel.
S.A.E. 2512	For parts where extreme strength, toughness, and resistance to wear are desired. Distortion after quenching much less than for any of the previous steels.
S.A.E. 4615 S.A.E. 4620	Extensively used for carburized gears where high fatigue resistance and tensile properties are required. No. 4620 should be used for the heavier sections.

Full-Hardening Steels for Gears	
Kind of Steel	Characteristics, Treatment, and Uses
S.A.E. 1045 (Forgings) S.A.E. 1240 (Castings)	Quench in brine or circulating water to obtain desired hardness. Used for medium and large sized parts where strength, toughness, and resistance to wear are desired. An excellent "tough hard" material for parts subjected to shock. Cannot be used for parts having thin sections.
S.A.E. 1045 (Forgings) S.A.E. 1240 (Castings)	Oil-quench. Used for parts where toughness, medium hardness, and minimum distortion are required. Especially suitable for shafts and large gears.
S.A.E. 3145	Oil-quench. A strong, tough steel with great capacity for resisting shock loads. A good all around, inexpensive alloy steel.
S.A.E. 6145	Oil-quench. Used for gears where hardness combined with strength and toughness is required. Somewhat difficult to machine. A sensitive heat-treating steel.
S.A.E. 4150	Oil-quench. Toughness and shock resistance with no sacrifice in hardness are obtainable with this steel. Hardness penetration is deep and distortion low.

Steels for Gears Machined After Heat-Treatment	
Kind of Steel	Characteristics and Treatment
S.A.E. 1045 (Forgings) S.A.E. 1240 (Castings)	Water-quench and draw. Strength, toughness, and wear resistance are good. Ductile and therefore highly resistant to shock.
S.A.E. 3140	Oil-treat and draw. Greater strength and toughness obtainable than with S.A.E. 1045. A good all around steel. Very resistant to fatigue failures.
S.A.E. 4130	Oil- or water-quench and draw. At the same hardness, the toughness and ductility are greater than for the previous steels. Easily machineable at high hardnesses. Great impact strength.

9. The pressure angle, in the case of an involute pinion acting against straight-sided rack teeth, is the angle between the line of action and the line of the rack's motion. If the involute pinion rotates at a uniform rate, movement of the rack will also be uniform.

Classification of Gear Steels. — Gear steels may be divided into two general classes — the plain carbon and the alloy steels. Alloy steels are used to some extent in the industrial field, but heat-treated plain carbon steels are far more common. The use of untreated alloy steels for gears is seldom, if ever, justified, and then, only when heat-treating facilities are lacking. The points to be considered in determining whether to use heat-treated plain carbon steels or heat-treated alloy steels are: Does the service condition or design require the superior characteristics of the alloy steels, or, if alloy steels are not required, will the advantages to be derived offset the additional cost? For most applications, plain carbon steels, heat-treated to obtain the best of their qualities for the service intended, are satisfactory and quite economical. The advantages obtained from using heat-treated alloy steels in place of heat-treated plain carbon steels are as follows:

1. Increased surface hardness and depth of hardness penetration for the same carbon content and quench.

2. Ability to obtain the same surface hardness with a less drastic quench and, in the case of some of the alloys, a lower quenching temperature, thus giving less distortion.

3. Increased toughness, as indicated by the higher values of yield point, elongation, and reduction of area.

4. Finer grain size, with the resulting higher impact toughness and increased wear resistance.

5. In the case of some of the alloys, better machining qualities or the possibility of machining at higher hardnesses.

Use of Casehardening Steels. — Each of the two general classes of gear steels may be further subdivided as follows: (1) Casehardening steels; (2) full-hardening steels; and (3) steels that are heat-treated and drawn to a hardness that will permit machining. The first two — casehardening and full-hardening steels — are interchangeable for some kinds of service, and the choice is often a matter of personal opinion. Casehardening steels with their extremely hard, fine-grained (when properly treated) case and comparatively soft and ductile core are generally used when resistance to wear is desired. Casehardening alloy steels have a fairly tough core, but not as tough as that of the full-hardening steels. In order to realize the greatest benefits from the core properties, casehardened steels should be double-quenched. This is particularly true of the alloy steels, because the benefits derived from their use seldom justify the additional expense, unless the core is refined and toughened by a second quench. The penalty that must be paid for the additional refinement is increased distortion, which may be excessive if the shape or design is not all that it might be.

Use of "Full-Hardening" Steels. — Full-hardening steels are used when great strength, high endurance limit, toughness, and resistance to shock are required. These qualities are governed by the kind of steel and treatment used. Fairly high surface hardnesses are obtainable in this group, though not so high as those of the casehardening steels. For that reason, the resistance to wear is not so great as might be obtained, but when wear resistance combined with great strength and toughness is required, this type of steel is superior to the others. Full-hardening steels become distorted to some extent when hardened, the amount depending upon the steel and quenching medium used. For that reason, full-hardening steels are not suitable for high-speed gearing where noise is a factor, or for gearing where

accuracy is of paramount importance, except, of course, in cases where grinding of
the teeth is practicable. The medium and high-carbon percentages require an oil
quench, but a water quench may be necessary for the lower carbon contents, in order
to obtain the highest physical properties and hardness. The distortion, however,
will be greater with the water quench.

Heat-Treatment that Permits Machining. — When the grinding of gear teeth
is not practicable and a high degree of accuracy is required, hardened steels may be
drawn or tempered to a hardness that will permit the cutting of the teeth. This
treatment gives a highly refined structure, great toughness, and, in spite of the low
hardness, excellent wearing qualities. The lower strength is somewhat compensated for by the elimination of the increment loads due to the impacts which are
caused by inaccuracies. When steels that have a low degree of hardness penetration from surface to core are treated in this manner, the design cannot be based on
the physical properties corresponding to the hardness at the surface. Since the
physical properties are determined by the hardness, the drop in hardness from surface to core will give lower physical properties at the root of the tooth, where the
stress is greatest. The quenching medium may be either oil, water, or brine, depending on the steel used and hardness penetration desired. The amount of distortion, of course, is immaterial, because the machining is done after heat-treating.

Making Pinion Harder than Gear to Equalize Wear. — Beneficial results from
a wear standpoint are obtained by making the pinion harder than the gear. The
pinion, having a lesser number of teeth than the gear, naturally does more work
per tooth, and the differential in hardness between the pinion and the gear (the
amount being dependent on the ratio) serves to equalize the rate of wear. The
harder pinion teeth correct the errors in the gear teeth to some extent by the initial
wear and then seem to burnish the teeth of the gear and increase its ability to withstand wear by the greater hardness due to the cold-working of the surface. In
applications where the gear ratio is high and there are no severe shock loads, a
casehardened pinion running with an oil-treated gear, treated to a Brinell hardness
at which the teeth may be cut after treating, is an excellent combination. The
pinion, being relatively small, is distorted but little, and distortion in the gear is
circumvented by cutting the teeth after treatment.

Recommended Gear Materials. — The following recommended practice re-
lating to the selection of gear materials has been approved by the American
Standards Association, the American Gear Manufacturer's Association, and the
American Society of Mechanical Engineers.

Forged and Rolled Carbon Steels for Gears. — This specification covers steel
for gears in three groups, according to heat treatment, as follows: (a) case-hardened
gears, (b) unhardened gears, not heat treated after machining, and (c) hardened and
tempered gears.

Forged and rolled carbon gear steels shall be purchased on the basis of the requirements as to chemical composition specified in Table 1. Class N steel will
normally be ordered in ten point carbon ranges within these limits. Requirements as
to physical properties have been omitted, but when they are called for the requirements as to carbon shall be omitted. The steels may be made by either or
both the open hearth and electric furnace processes.

Forged and Rolled Alloy Steels for Gears. — This specification covers alloy
steel for gears, in two classes according to heat treatment, as follows: (a) case-
hardened gears, and (b) hardened and tempered gears. Forged and rolled alloy
gear steels shall be purchased on the basis of the requirements as to chemical composition specified in Table 2. Requirements as to physical properties have been

omitted. The steel shall be made by either or both the open hearth and electric furnace process.

Steel Castings for Gears. — It is recommended that steel castings for cut gears be purchased on the basis of chemical analysis and that only two types of analysis be used, one for case-hardened gears and the other for both untreated gears and those which are to be hardened and tempered. The steel is to be made by the open hearth, crucible or electric furnace processes. The converter process is not recognized. Sufficient risers shall be provided to secure soundness and freedom from undue segregation. Risers shall not be broken off the unannealed castings by force. Where risers are cut off with a torch the cut shall be at least one-half inch above the surface of the castings, and the remaining metal removed by chipping, grinding, or other non-injurious method.

Steel for use in gears shall conform to the requirements, as to chemical composition as indicated in Table 3. All steel castings for gears must be thoroughly normalized or annealed, using such temperature and time as will entirely eliminate the characteristic structure of unannealed castings.

Effect of Alloying Metals on Gear Steels. — The effect of the various alloying elements on steel will be summarized in order to assist engineers in deciding upon the particular kind of alloy steel to use for specific purposes. The characteristics, outlined apply only to heat-treated steels. When the effect of the addition of an alloying element is stated, it is understood that reference is made to alloy steels of a given carbon content, compared with a plain carbon steel of the same carbon content.

Nickel — The addition of nickel tends to increase the hardness and strength, with but little sacrifice of ductility. The hardness penetration is somewhat greater than that of plain carbon steels. Its use as an alloying element lowers the critical points and produces less distortion, due to the lower quenching temperature. The nickel steels of the case-hardening group carburize more slowly, but the grain growth is less.

Chromium — Chromium increases the hardness and strength over that obtained by the use of nickel, though the loss of ductility is greater. Chromium refines the grain and imparts a greater depth of hardness. Chromium steels have a high degree of wear resistance and are easily machined in spite of the fine grain.

Manganese — When present in sufficient amounts to warrant the use of the term alloy, the addition of manganese is very effective. It gives greater strength than nickel, and a higher degree of toughness than chromium. Owing to its susceptibility to cold-working, it is likely to flow under severe unit pressures. Up to the present time, it has never been used to any great extent for heat-treated gears, but is now receiving an increasing amount of attention.

Vanadium — Vanadium has a similar effect to that of manganese — increasing the hardness, strength, and toughness. The loss of ductility is somewhat more than that due to manganese, but the hardness penetration is greater than for any of the other alloying elements. Owing to the extremely fine-grained structure, the impact strength is high; but vanadium tends to make machining difficult.

Molybdenum — Molybdenum has the property of increasing the strength without affecting the ductility. For the same hardness, steels containing molybdenum are more ductile than any other alloy steels, and having nearly the same strength, are tougher; in spite of the increased toughness, the presence of molybdenum does not make machining more difficult. In fact, such steels can be machined at a higher hardness than any of the other alloy steels. The impact strength is nearly as great as that of the vanadium steels.

Chrome-Nickel Steels — The combination of the two alloying elements chromium and nickel adds the beneficial qualities of both. The high degree of ductility

Table 1. Compositions of Forged and Rolled Carbon Steels for Gears

Heat-treatment	Class	Carbon	Manganese	Phosphorus	Sulphur
Case-hardened........	C	0.15-0.25	0.40-0.70	0.045 max	0.055 max
Untreated............	N	0.25-0.50	0.50-0.80	0.045 max	0.055 max
Hardened............ (or untreated)	H	0.40-0.50	0.40-0.70	0.045 max	0.055 max

Table 2. Forged and Rolled Alloy Steels for Gears

No.*	Carbon	Manganese	Sulph Max.	Nickel	Chrome	Vanadium	
						Min.	Desired
2315	0.10-0.20	0.30-0.60	0.05	3.25-3.75	....	....	....
2350	0.45-0.55	0.50-0.80	0.05	3.25-3.75	....	....	....
2512	0.17 max	0.30-0.60	0.05	4.75-5.25	....	....	....
3115	0.10-0.20	0.30-0.60	0.05	1.00-1.50	0.45-0.75	....	....
3215	0.10-0.20	0.30-0.60	0.045	1.50-2.00	0.90-1.25	....	....
3250	0.45-0.55	0.30-0.60	0.045	1.50-2.00	0.90-1.25	....	....
3312	0.17 max	0.30-0.60	0.045	3.25-3.75	1.25-1.75	....	....
3340	0.35-0.45	0.30-0.60	0.045	3.25-3.75	1.25-1.75	....	....
6120	0.15-0.25	0.30-0.60	0.045	....	0.80-1.10	0.15	0.18
6150	0.45-0.55	0.50-0 80	0.045	....	0.80-1.10	0.15	0.18
4615	0.10-0.20	0.30-0.60	0.05	1.50-2.00	....	....	....

* S.A.E. steel numbers are given in Column 1. Steel No. 4615 contains 0.20-0.30 per cent molybdenum. The maximum phosphorus content for all steels is 0.04 per cent.

Table 3. Compositions of Steel Castings for Gears

Heat-treatment	Class	Carbon	Manganese	Phosphorus		Sulphur
				Acid	Basic	
Case-hardened ...	C	0.15-0.25	0.40-0.60	0.06 max	0.05 max	0.06 max
Untreated or Hardened........	H	0.30-0.40	0.40-0.60	0.06 max	0.05 max	0.06 max

present in nickel steels is complemented by the high strength, finer grain size, deep hardening and wear-resistant properties imparted by the addition of chromium. The increased toughness makes these steels more difficult to machine than the plain carbon steels, and they are more difficult to heat-treat. The distortion increases with the amount of chromium and nickel.

Chrome-Vanadium Steels — Chrome-vanadium steels have practically the same tensile properties as the chrome-nickel steels, but the hardening power, impact strength, and wear resistance are increased by the finer grain size. They are difficult to machine and become distorted more easily than the other alloy steels.

Chrome-Molybdenum Steels — This group has the same qualities as the straight molybdenum steels, but the hardening depth and wear resistance are increased by the addition of chromium. This steel is very easily heat-treated and machined.

Nickel-Molybdenum Steels — Nickel-molybdenum steels have qualities similar to chrome-molybdenum steel. The toughness is said to be greater, but the steel is somewhat more difficult to machine.

Bronze and Brass Gear Castings. — These specifications cover non-ferrous metals for spur, bevel, and worm gears, bushings and flanges for composition gears. This material shall be purchased on the basis of chemical composition. The alloys may be made by any approved method.

Spur and Bevel Gears: For spur and bevel gears, hard cast bronze is recommended (A.S.T.M. B–10–18; S.A.E. No. 62; and the well-known 88–10–2 mixture) with the following limits as to composition: Copper, 86 to 89; tin, 9 to 11; zinc, 1 to 3; lead (max), 0.20; iron (max), 0.06 per cent. Good castings made from this bronze should have the following minimum physical characteristics: Ultimate strength, 30,000 pounds per square inch; yield point, 15,000 pounds per square inch; elongation in 2 inches, 14 per cent.

Worm Gears: For bronze worm gears, two alternative analyses of phosphor bronze are recommended, S.A.E. No. 65 and No. 63.

S.A.E. No. 65 (called phosphor gear bronze) has the following composition: Copper, 88 to 90; tin, 10 to 12; phosphorus, 0.1 to 0.3; lead, zinc and impurities (max), 0.5 per cent. Good castings made of this alloy should have the following minimum physical characteristics: Ultimate strength, 35,000 pounds per square inch; yield point, 20,000 pounds per square inch; elongation in 2 inches, 10 per cent.

The composition of S.A.E. No. 63 (called leaded gun metal) follows: Copper, 86 to 89; tin, 9 to 11; lead, 1 to 2.5; phosphorus (max), 0.25; zinc and impurities (max), 0.50 per cent.

Good castings made of this alloy should have the following minimum physical characteristics: Ultimate strength, 30,000 pounds per square inch; yield point, 12,000 pounds per square inch; elongation in 2 inches, 10 per cent.

These alloys, especially No. 65, are adapted to chilling for hardness and refinement of grain. No. 65 is to be preferred for use with worms of great hardness and fine accuracy. No. 63 is to be preferred for use with unhardened worms.

Gear Bushings: For bronze bushings for gears, S.A.E. No. 64 is recommended of the following analysis: Copper, 78.5 to 81.5; tin, 9 to 11; lead, 9 to 11; phosphorus, 0.05 to 0.25; zinc (max), 0.75; other impurities (max), 0.25 per cent. Good castings of this alloy should have the following minimum physical characteristics: Ultimate strength, 25,000 pounds per square inch; yield point, 12,000 pounds per square inch; elongation in 2 inches, 8 per cent.

Flanges for Composition Pinions: For brass flanges for composition pinions A.S.T.M. B-30-32T, and S.A.E. No. 40 are recommended. This is a good cast red brass of sufficient strength and hardness to take its share of load and wear when the design is such that the flanges mesh with the mating gear. The composition is as follows: Copper, 83 to 86; tin, 4.5 to 5.5; lead, 4.5 to 5.5; zinc, 4.5 to 5.5 iron (max) 0.35; antimony (max), 0.25 per cent; aluminum, none. Good castings made from this alloy should have the following minimum physical characteristics: Ultimate strength, 27,000 pounds per square inch; yield point, 12,000 pounds per square inch; elongation in 2 inches, 16 per cent.

Materials for Worm Gearing. — The Hamilton Gear & Machine Co. conducted an extensive series of tests on a variety of materials that might be used for worm gears, to ascertain which material is the most suitable. According to these tests chill-cast nickel-phosphor-bronze ranks first in resistance to wear and deformation. This bronze is composed of approximately 87.5 per cent copper, 11 per cent tin, 1.5 per cent nickel, with from 0.1 to 0.2 per cent phosphorus. The worms used in these tests were made from S.A.E.-2315, 3½ per cent nickel steel, casehardened, ground, and polished. The Shore scleroscope hardness of the worms was between 80 and 90. This nickel alloy steel was adopted after numerous tests of a variety of steels, because it provided the necessary strength, together with the degree of hardness required.

The material that showed up second best in these tests was a No. 65 S.A.E. bronze. Navy bronze (88-10-2) containing 2 per cent of zinc, with no phosphorus, and not chilled, performed satisfactorily at speeds of 600 revolutions per minute, but was not sufficiently strong at lower speeds. Red brass (85-5-5) proved slightly better at from 1500 to 1800 revolutions per minute, but would bend at lower speeds, before it would show actual wear.

Non-metallic Gearing. — Non-metallic or composition gearing is used primarily where quietness of operation at high speed is the first consideration. Non-metallic materials are also applied very generally to timing gears and numerous other classes of gearing. Rawhide was used originally for non-metallic gears, but other materials have been introduced which have important advantages. These later materials are sold by different firms under various trade names, such as Micarta, Textolite, Formica, Dilecto, Spauldite, Phenolite, Fibroc, Fabroil, Synthane, Celoron, etc. Most of these gear materials consist of layers of canvas which is impregnated with bakelite and forced together under hydraulic pressure, which, in conjunction with the application of heat, forms a dense rigid mass.

Although bakelite gears in general are resilient, they are self-supporting and require no side plates or shrouds unless subjected to a heavy starting torque. The phenol resinoid element makes these gears proof against vermin and rodents.

The non-metallic gear materials referred to are generally assumed to have the power-transmitting capacity of cast iron. While the tensile strength may be considerably less than that of cast iron, the resiliency of these materials enables them to withstand impact and abrasion to a degree that might result in excessive wear of cast-iron teeth. Thus in many cases, composition gearing of impregnated canvas has proved to be more durable than cast iron and much more durable than rawhide.

Application of Non-metallic Gears. — The most effective field of use for these non-metallic materials is for high-speed duty. At low speeds, where the starting torque may be high, or where the load may fluctuate widely, or when high shock loads may be encountered, these non-metallic materials do not always prove satisfactory. In general, non-metallic materials should not be used for pitch-line velocities below 600 feet per minute.

Tooth Form: The best tooth form for non-metallic materials is the 20-degree stub-tooth system. When only a single pair of gears is involved and the center distance can be varied, the best results will be obtained by making the non-metallic driving pinion of all-addendum form, while the driven metal gear is made with standard tooth proportions. Such a drive will carry from 50 to 75 per cent greater loads than one of standard tooth proportions.

Material for Mating Gear: For durability under load, the use of hardened steel (over 400 Brinell) for the mating metal gear appears to give the best results. A good second choice for the material of the mating member is cast iron. The use of brass, bronze, or soft steel (under 400 Brinell) as a material for the mating member of phenolic laminated gears leads to excessive abrasive wear.

Power-transmitting Capacity of Non-metallic Gears. — The characteristics of gears made of phenolic laminated materials are so different from those of metal gears that they should be considered in a class by themselves. Because of the low modulus of elasticity, most of the effects of small errors in tooth form and spacing are absorbed at the tooth surfaces by the elastic deformation, and have but little effect on the strength of the gears.

If

S = safe working stress for a given velocity

S_s = allowable static stress

V = pitch-line velocity in feet per minute

then, according to the recommended practice of the American Gear Manufacturers' Association,

$$S = S_s \times \left(\frac{150}{200 + V} + 0.25 \right)$$

The value of S_s for phenolic laminated materials is given as 6000 pounds per square inch. The accompanying table gives the safe working stresses S for different pitch-line velocities. When the value of S is known, the horsepower capacity is determined by using the regular Lewis formula for spur gears. (See Formulas 3 and 4 in the table " Rules and Formulas for the Strength of Gear Teeth.")

Safe Working Stresses for Non-metallic Gears

Pitch-line Velocity Feet per Minute V	Safe Working Stresses	Pitch-line Velocity Feet per Minute V	Safe Working Stresses	Pitch-line Velocity Feet per Minute V	Safe Working Stresses
600	2625	1800	1950	4000	1714
700	2500	2000	1909	4500	1691
800	2400	2200	1875	5000	1673
900	2318	2400	1846	5500	1653
1000	2250	2600	1821	6000	1645
1200	2143	2800	1800	6500	1634
1400	2063	3000	1781	7000	1622
1600	2000	3500	1743	7500	1617

The tensile strength of the phenolic laminated materials used for gears, is slightly less than that of cast iron. These materials are far softer than any metal, and the modulus of elasticity is about one-thirtieth that of steel. In other words, if the tooth load on a steel gear which causes a deformation of 0.001 inch were applied to the tooth of a similar gear made of phenolic laminated material, the tooth of the non-metallic gear would be deformed about ½₀ inch. Under these conditions, several things will happen. With all gears, regardless of the theoretical duration of contact, one tooth only will carry the load until the load is sufficient to deform the tooth the amount of the error that may be present. On metal gears, when the tooth has been deformed the amount of the error, the stresses set up in the materials may approach or exceed the elastic limit of the material. Hence for standard tooth forms and those generated from standard basic racks, it is dangerous to calculate their strength as very much greater than that which can safely be carried on a single tooth. On gears made of phenolic laminated materials, on the other hand, the teeth will be deformed the amount of this normal error without setting up any appreciable stresses in the material, so that the load is actually supported by several teeth.

All materials have their own peculiar and distinct characteristics, so that under certain specific conditions, each material has a field of its own where it is superior to any other. Such fields may overlap to some extent, and only in such overlapping fields are different materials directly competitive. For example, steel is more or less ductile, has a high tensile strength, and a high modulus of elasticity. Cast iron, on the other hand, is not ductile, has a low tensile strength, but a high compressive strength, and a low modulus of elasticity. Hence when stiffness and high tensile strength are essential, steel is far superior to cast iron. On the other hand, when these two characteristics are unimportant, but high compressive strength and a moderate amount of elasticity are essential, cast iron is superior to steel.

Preferred Pitch for Non-metallic Gears. — The pitch of the gear or pinion should bear a reasonable relation either to the horsepower or speed or to the applied torque, as shown by the accompanying table which conforms to recommended practice of the American Gear Manufacturers' Association. The upper half of this table is based upon horsepower transmitted at a given pitch-line velocity. The lower half gives the torque in pounds-feet or the torque at a 1-foot radius. This torque T for any given horsepower and speed can be obtained from the following formula:

$$T = \frac{5252 \times \text{H.P.}}{\text{R.P.M.}}$$

Bore Sizes for Non-metallic Gears. — For plain phenolic laminated pinions, that is, pinions without metal end plates, a drive fit of 0.001 inch per inch of shaft diameter should be used. For shafts above 2.5 inches in diameter, the fit should be constant at 0.0025 to 0.003 inch. When metal reinforcing end plates are used, the drive fit should conform to the same standards as used for metal.

Preferred Pitches for Non-metallic Gears*

Diametral Pitch for Given Horsepower and Pitch Line Velocities			
Horsepower Transmitted	Pitch Line Velocity up to 1000 Feet per Minute	Pitch Line Velocity from 1000 to 2000 Feet per Minute	Pitch Line Velocity over 2000 Feet per Minute
¼–1	8–10	10–12	12–16
1–2	7–8	8–10	10–12
2–3	6–7	7–8	8–10
3–7½	5–6	6–7	7–8
7½–10	4–5	5–6	6–7
10–15	3–4	4–5	5–6
15–25	2½–3	3–4	4–5
25–60	2–2½	2½–3	3–4
60–100	1¾–2	2–2½	2½–3
100–150	1½–1¾	1¾–2	2–2½

Torque in Pounds-feet for Given Diametral Pitch					
Diametral Pitch	Torque in Pounds-feet		Diametral Pitch	Torque in Pounds-feet	
	Minimum	Maximum		Minimum	Maximum
16	1	2	4	50	100
12	2	4	3	100	200
10	4	8	2½	200	450
8	8	15	2	450	900
6	15	30	1½	900	1800
5	30	50	1	1800	3500

* These preferred pitches are applicable both to rawhide and the phenolic laminated types of materials.

The root diameter of a pinion of phenolic laminated type should be such that the minimum distance from the edge of the keyway to the root diameter will be at least equal to the depth of tooth.

Keyway Stresses for Non-metallic Gears. — The keyway stress should not exceed 3000 pounds per square inch on a plain phenolic laminated gear or pinion. The keyway stress is calculated by the formula:

$$S = \frac{33,000 \times \text{H.P.}}{V \times A}$$

in which

S = unit stress in pounds per square inch;

H.P. = horsepower transmitted;

V = peripheral speed of shaft in feet per minute; and

A = square inch area of keyway in pinion (length × height).

If the keyway stress formula is expressed in terms of shaft radius r and revolutions per minute, it will read:

$$S = \frac{63,000 \times \text{H.P.}}{\text{R.P.M.} \times r \times A}$$

When the design is such that the keyway stresses exceed 3000 pounds, metal reinforcing end plates may be used. Such end plates should not extend beyond the root diameter of the teeth. The distance from the outer edge of the retaining bolt to the root diameter of the teeth shall not be less than a full tooth depth. The use of drive keys should be avoided, but if required, metal end plates should be used on the pinion to take the wedging action of the key.

For phenolic laminated pinions, the face of the mating gear should be the same or slightly greater than the pinion face.

Invention of Gear Teeth. — The invention of gear teeth represents a gradual evolution from gearing of primitive form. The earliest evidence we have of an investigation of the problem of *uniform motion* from toothed gearing and the successful solution of that problem, dates from the time of Olaf Roemer, the celebrated Danish astronomer, who, in the year 1674, proposed the epicycloidal form to obtain uniform motion. Evidently Robert Willis, professor in the University of Cambridge, was the first to make a practical application of the epicycloidal curve so as to provide for an interchangeable series of gears. Willis gives credit to Camus for conceiving the idea of interchangeable gears, but claims for himself its first application. The involute tooth was suggested as a theory by early scientists and mathematicians, but it remained for Willis to present it in a practical form. Perhaps the earliest conception of the application of this form of teeth to gears was by Philippe de Lahire, a Frenchman, who considered it, in theory, equally suitable with the epicycloidal for tooth outlines. This was about 1695 and not long after Roemer had first demonstrated the epicycloidal form. The applicability of the involute had been further elucidated by Leonard Euler, a Swiss mathematician, born at Basel, 1707, who is credited by Willis with being the first to suggest it. Willis devised the Willis odontograph for laying out involute teeth.

A pressure angle of 14½ degrees was selected for three different reasons. First, because the sine of 14½ degrees is nearly ¼, making it convenient in calculation; second, because this angle coincided closely with the pressure angle resulting from the usual construction of epicycloidal gear teeth; third, because the angle of the straight-sided involute rack is the same as the 29-degree worm thread.

Gear Teeth of Different Diametral Pitch, Full Size

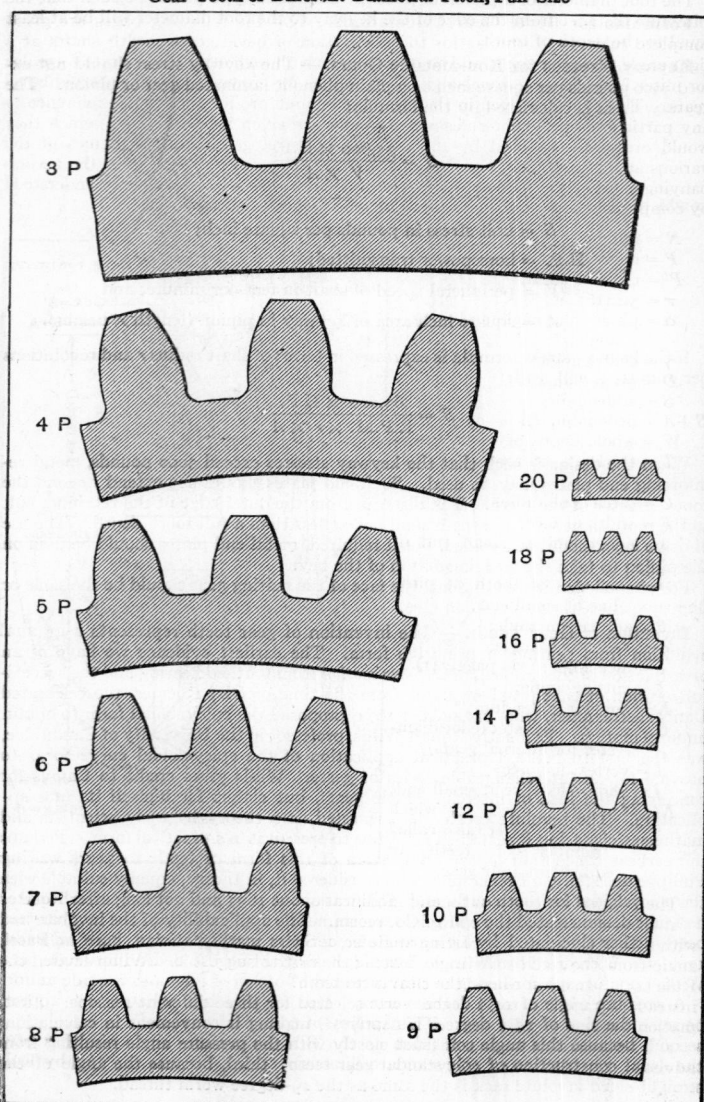

Bevel Gearing

Formulas for Bevel Gear Calculations. — On the following pages are given complete rules and formulas for the calculation of bevel gearing with shafts at a right angle, an acute angle, and an obtuse angle with each other. Separate formulas for miter bevel gearing are also given, as well as for crown gears and internal bevel gears. The numbers given in the left-hand column are for convenient reference to any particular rule. The rules and formulas are given in the order in which they would ordinarily be used by the designer of bevel gearing. The names of the various angles and dimensions referred to in bevel gearing are given in the accompanying engraving. The notation used in the formulas, which is easily understood by comparing the formula with the corresponding rule, is as follows:

N = number of teeth;
P = diametral pitch;
P' = circular pitch;
π = 3.1416;
α = pitch cone angle and edge angle;
γ = center angle;
D = pitch diameter;
S = addendum;
$S+A$ = dedendum (A = clearance);
W = whole depth of tooth space;
T = thickness of tooth at pitch line;
C = pitch cone radius;
F = width of face;
s = addendum at small end of tooth;
t = thickness of tooth at pitch line at small end;
θ = addendum angle;
ϕ = dedendum angle;
δ = face angle; (see page 741)
ζ = cutting angle;
K = angular addendum;
O = outside diameter (edge diameter for internal gears);
J = vertex distance;
j = vertex distance at small end;
N' = number of teeth for which to select cutter, also called "number of teeth in equivalent spur gear."

The following exceptions to, and modifications of, the rules given should be noted:

1. The Brown & Sharpe Mfg. Co. recommends that for shaping bevel gear teeth with a formed cutter, the cutting angle be determined by subtracting the *addendum* angle from the pitch cone angle, instead of subtracting the dedendum angle, as in Rule (15). In other words, the clearance at the bottom of the tooth is made uniform instead of tapering toward the vertex. This gives a somewhat closer approximation to the desired shape. This applies, of course, also to Rule (25).

2. In generating machines (such as the Bilgram and the Gleason) it is often advisable to depart from the standard dimensions of gear teeth as given by Rules

Rules and Formulas for Calculating Bevel Gears with Shafts at Right Angles

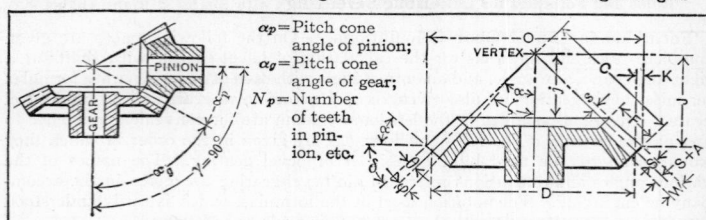

α_p = Pitch cone angle of pinion;
α_g = Pitch cone angle of gear;
N_p = Number of teeth in pinion, etc.

Use Rules and Formulas Nos. 1 to 21 in the order given.

No.	To Find	Rule	Formula
1	Pitch Cone Angle (or Edge Angle) of Pinion.	Divide the number of teeth in the pinion by the number of teeth in the gear to get the tangent.	$\tan \alpha_p = \dfrac{N_p}{N_g}$
2	Pitch Cone Angle (or Edge Angle) of Gear.	Divide the number of teeth in the gear by the number of teeth in the pinion to get the tangent.	$\tan \alpha_g = \dfrac{N_g}{N_p}$
3	Proof of Calculations for Pitch Cone Angles.	The sum of the pitch cone angles of the pinion and gear equals 90 degrees.	$\alpha_p + \alpha_g = 90°$
4	Pitch Diameter.	Divide the number of teeth by the diametral pitch; or multiply the number of teeth by the circular pitch and divide by 3.1416.	$D = \dfrac{N}{P} = \dfrac{NP'}{\pi}$
5	Addendum.	Divide 1.0 by the diametral pitch; or multiply the circular pitch by 0.318.	$S = \dfrac{1.0}{P}$ $= 0.318\,P'$
6	Dedendum.	Divide 1.157 by the diametral pitch; or multiply the circular pitch by 0.368.	$S + A = \dfrac{1.157}{P}$ $= 0.368\,P'$
7	Whole Depth of Tooth Space.	Divide 2.157 by the diametral pitch; or multiply the circular pitch by 0.687.	$W = \dfrac{2.157}{P}$ $= 0.687\,P'$
8	Thickness of Tooth at Pitch Line.	Divide 1.571 by the diametral pitch; or divide the circular pitch by 2.	$T = \dfrac{1.571}{P} = \dfrac{P'}{2}$
9	Pitch Cone Radius.	Divide the pitch diameter by twice the sine of the pitch cone angle.	$C = \dfrac{D}{2 \times \sin \alpha}$
10	Addendum of Small End of Tooth.	Subtract the width of face from the pitch cone radius, divide the remainder by the pitch cone radius and multiply by the addendum.	$s = S \times \dfrac{C - F}{C}$
11	Thickness of Tooth at Pitch Line at Small End.	Subtract the width of face from the pitch cone radius, divide the remainder by the pitch cone radius and multiply by the thickness of the tooth at the pitch line.	$t = T \times \dfrac{C - F}{C}$
12	Addendum Angle.	Divide the addendum by the pitch cone radius to get the tangent.	$\tan \theta = \dfrac{S}{C}$
13	Dedendum Angle.	Divide the dedendum by the pitch cone radius to get the tangent.	$\tan \phi = \dfrac{S + A}{C}$

Note: Rows 5 through 13 carry the left-margin label "These dimensions are the same for both gear and pinion."

Rules and Formulas for Calculating Bevel Gears with Shafts at Right Angles

No.	To Find	Rule	Formula
14	Face Angle Note: There are two methods of designating as indicated by Rules 1 and 2.	*Rule 1:* Subtract sum of pitch cone and addendum angles from 90 degrees. (Face angle obtained by Rule 1, indicates directly angular position of compound rest in turning blank — See drawing, page 739). *Rule 2:* Add addendum angle to pitch cone angle.	$\delta = 90° - (\alpha + \theta)$
15	Cutting Angle.*	Subtract the dedendum angle from the pitch cone angle	$\zeta = \alpha - \phi$
16	Angular Addendum.	Multiply the addendum by the cosine of the pitch cone angle.	$K = S \times \cos \alpha$
17	Outside Diameter.	Add twice the angular addendum to the pitch diameter.	$O = D + 2K$
18	Vertex or Apex Distance.	Multiply one-half the outside diameter by the tangent of the face angle.	$J = \dfrac{O}{2} \times \tan \delta$
19	Vertex or Apex Distance at Small End of Tooth.	Subtract the width of face from the pitch cone radius; divide the remainder by the pitch cone radius and multiply by the apex distance.	$j = J \times \dfrac{C - F}{C}$
20	Number of Teeth for which to Select Cutter.	Divide the number of teeth by the cosine of the pitch cone angle.	$N' = \dfrac{N}{\cos \alpha}$
21	Proof of Calculations by Rules Nos. 9, 12, 14, 16 and 17.	The outside diameter equals twice the pitch cone radius multiplied by the cosine of the face angle and divided by the cosine of the addendum angle.	$O = \dfrac{2C \times \cos \delta}{\cos \theta}$

* See paragraph " Formulas for Bevel Gear Calculations."

and Formulas (1) to (44). For instance, where the pinion is made of bronze and the gear of steel, the teeth of the former can be made wider and those of the latter correspondingly thinner, so as to nearly equalize the strength of the two. Again, where the pinion has few teeth and the gear many, it may be advisable to make the addendum on the pinion larger and the dedendum correspondingly smaller, reversing this on the gear, making the addendum smaller and the dedendum larger. This is done to avoid interference and undercut on the flanks of small pinions.

Internal bevel gearing should be avoided except in cases where cast gears would be satisfactory, because it is practically impossible to cut internal bevel gearing. It may be possible to produce internal bevel gears on some forms of templet planing machines, if the pitch cone angle is not too great, but it is impossible on any form of generating machine. Internal bevel gearing can usually be avoided.

Examples of Bevel Gear Calculations. — In the following are given a number of examples of the use of the formulas for bevel gear calculations. While it is not necessary in practice to have the dimensions accurate within 0.0001 inch, it is well to carry out the calculations to four decimal places. This permits accurate checking of the results by Formulas (3) and (21).

Shafts at Right Angles. — Let it be required to make the necessary calculations for a pair of bevel gears in which the shafts are at right angles; diametral pitch = 3, number of teeth in gear = 60, number of teeth in pinion = 15, and width of face = 4 inches.

$$\tan \alpha_p = 15 \div 60 = 0.25000 = \tan 14° 2' \tag{1}$$

$$\tan \alpha_g = 60 \div 15 = 4.00000 = \tan 75° 58' \tag{2}$$

$$\gamma = 14° 2' + 75° 58' = 90° \tag{3}$$

$$D_p = 15 \div 3 = 5.000'' \tag{4}$$

$$S = 1 \div 3 = 0.3333'' \tag{5}$$

$$S + A = \frac{1.157}{3} = 0.3856'' \tag{6}$$

$$W = \frac{2.157}{3} = 0.7190'' \tag{7}$$

$$T = \frac{1.571}{3} = 0.5236'' \tag{8}$$

$$C = \frac{5}{2 \times 0.24249} = 10.3097'' \tag{9}$$

$$s = 0.3333 \times \frac{6.31}{10.31} = 0.2040'' \tag{10}$$

$$t = 0.5236 \times \frac{6.31}{10.31} = 0.3204'' \tag{11}$$

$$\tan \theta = \frac{0.3333}{10.3097} = 0.03233 = \tan 1° 51' \tag{12}$$

$$\tan \phi = \frac{0.3856}{10.3097} = 0.03740 = \tan 2° 9' \tag{13}$$

$$\delta = 90° - (14° 2' + 1° 51') = 74° 7' \tag{14}$$

$$\zeta = 14° 2' - 2° 9' = 11° 53' \tag{15}$$

$$K = 0.3333 \times 0.97015 = 0.3234'' \tag{16}$$

$$O = 5.000 + 2 \times 0.3234 = 5.6468'' \tag{17}$$

$$J = \frac{5.6468}{2} \times 3.51441 = 9.9225'' \tag{18}$$

$$j = 9.9225 \times \frac{6.31}{10.31} = 6.0726'' \tag{19}$$

$$N' = \frac{15}{0.97015} = 15.4 \tag{20}$$

$$5.6468'' = \frac{20.6194 \times 0.27368}{0.99948} = 5.6461'' \tag{21}$$

This gives all the data required for the pinion. Rules (5) to (13), inclusive, apply equally to the gear and the pinion, so that only calculations by Rules and Formulas (4) and (14) to (21) need be made for the gear, although it is well to calculate Formula (9) a second time as a check for the same calculation for the pinion.

$$D = \frac{60}{3} = 20.000'' \tag{4}$$

$$C = \frac{20}{2 \times 0.97015} = 10.3077'' \tag{9}$$

Rules and Formulas for Calculating Miter Bevel Gearing

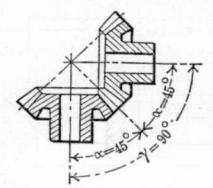 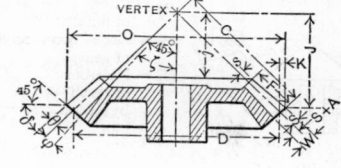

Use Rules and Formulas Nos. 22, 4–8, 23, 10–13, 24–26, 17–19, 27 and 21 in the order given. All dimensions thus obtained are the same for both gears of a pair.

No.	To Find	Rule	Formula
22	Pitch Cone Angle.	Pitch cone angle equals 45 degrees.	$\alpha = 45^\circ$
23	Pitch Cone Radius.	Multiply the pitch diameter by 0.707.	$C = 0.707\,D$
24	Face Angle.	Subtract the addendum angle from 45°.	$\delta = 45^\circ - \theta$
25	Cutting Angle.*	Subtract the dedendum angle from 45°.	$\zeta = 45^\circ - \phi$
26	Angular Addendum.	Multiply the addendum by 0.707.	$K = 0.707\,S$
27	Number of Teeth for which to Select Cutter.	Multiply the number of teeth by 1.41.	$N' = 1.41\,N$

* See paragraph " Formulas for Bevel Gear Calculations."

$$\delta = 90 - (75^\circ\ 58' + 1^\circ\ 51') = 12^\circ\ 11' \tag{14}$$

$$\zeta = 75^\circ\ 58' - 2^\circ\ 9' = 73^\circ\ 49' \tag{15}$$

$$K = 0.3333 \times 0.24249 = 0.0808'' \tag{16}$$

$$O = 20 + 2 \times 0.0808 = 20.1616'' \tag{17}$$

$$J = \frac{20.1616}{2} \times 0.2159 = 2.1764'' \tag{18}$$

$$j = 2.1764 \times \frac{6.31}{10.31} = 1.3320'' \tag{19}$$

$$N' = \frac{60}{0.24249} = 247 \tag{20}$$

$$20.1616'' \cong \frac{20.6154 \times 0.97748}{0.99948} = 20.1615'' \tag{21}$$

This gives the calculations necessary for this pair of gears.

Acute Angle Bevel Gearing. — Let it next be required to calculate the dimensions of a pair of bevel gears the center angle of which is 75 degrees, the number of teeth in the pinion 15, the number of teeth in the gear 60, the diametral pitch 3, and the width of face 4 inches. Following the directions given in the tables of rules and formulas for bevel gear calculations:

$$\tan \alpha_p = \frac{0.96593}{\frac{60}{15} + 0.25882} = 0.22681 = \tan 12^\circ\ 47' \tag{28}$$

Rules and Formulas for Calculating Bevel Gears with Shafts at an Acute Angle

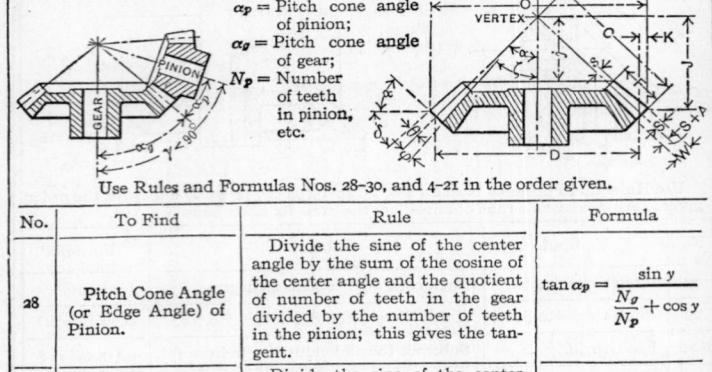

α_p = Pitch cone angle of pinion;
α_g = Pitch cone angle of gear;
N_p = Number of teeth in pinion, etc.

Use Rules and Formulas Nos. 28–30, and 4–21 in the order given.

No.	To Find	Rule	Formula
28	Pitch Cone Angle (or Edge Angle) of Pinion.	Divide the sine of the center angle by the sum of the cosine of the center angle and the quotient of number of teeth in the gear divided by the number of teeth in the pinion; this gives the tangent.	$\tan \alpha_p = \dfrac{\sin y}{\dfrac{N_g}{N_p} + \cos y}$
29	Pitch Cone Angle (or Edge Angle) of Gear.	Divide the sine of the center angle by the sum of the cosine of the center angle and the quotient of the number of teeth in the pinion divided by the number of teeth in the gear; this gives the tangent.	$\tan \alpha_g = \dfrac{\sin y}{\dfrac{N_p}{N_g} + \cos y}$
30	Proof of Calculations for Pitch Cone Angles.	The sum of the pitch cone angles of the pinion and gear equals the center angle.	$\alpha_p + \alpha_g = y$

$$\tan \alpha_g = \frac{0.96593}{\frac{15}{60} + 0.25882} = 1.89837 = \tan 62°\ 13' \tag{29}$$

$$\gamma = 12°\ 47' + 62°\ 13' = 75° \tag{30}$$

Formulas (4) to (8) as in first example; also, $C = 11.2989''$, $s = 0.2154''$, $t = 0.3382''$, $\theta = 1°\ 41'$, $\phi = 1°\ 57'$, $\delta = 75°\ 32'$, $\zeta = 10°\ 50'$, $K = 0.3251''$, $O = 5.6502''$, $J = 10.9501''$, $j = 7.0748''$, and $N' = 15.3$, also,

$$5.6502'' \simeq \frac{22.598 \times 0.24982}{0.99957} = 5.6483'' \tag{21}$$

For the gear, the additional calculations give: $C = 11.303''$, $\delta = 26°\ 6'$, $\zeta = 60°\ 16'$, $K = 0.1553''$, $O = 20.3106''$, $J = 4.9748''$, $j = 3.2142''$, $N' = 129$.

$$20.3106'' \simeq \frac{22.606 \times 0.89803}{0.99957} = 20.3096'' \tag{21}$$

The above calculations are not all given in full, as most of them are merely duplications of formulas previously used.

Obtuse Angle Bevel Gearing. — Let it be required to calculate the dimensions of the same set of gears with a center angle of 100 degrees. This being an example of obtuse angle gearing, apply Formula (31) as follows:

$$\tan \alpha_p = \frac{0.98481}{\frac{60}{15} - 0.17365} = 0.25738 = \tan 14°\ 26' \tag{31}$$

Rules and Formulas for Calculating Bevel Gears with Shafts at an Obtuse Angle

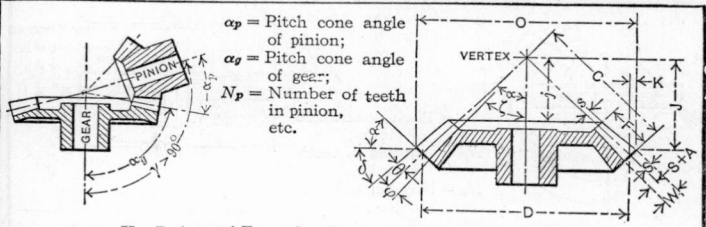

α_p = Pitch cone angle of pinion;
α_g = Pitch cone angle of gear;
N_p = Number of teeth in pinion, etc.

Use Rules and Formulas Nos. 31 and 32 as directed below.

No.	To Find	Rule	Formula
31	Pitch Cone Angle (or Edge Angle) of Pinion.	Divide the sine of 180 degrees minus the center angle by the difference between the quotient of the number of teeth in the gear divided by the number of teeth in the pinion and the cosine of 180 degrees minus the center angle; this gives the tangent.	$\tan \alpha_p = \dfrac{\sin (180° - y)}{\dfrac{N_g}{N_p} - \cos (180° - y)}$
32	Whether Gear is a Regular Bevel Gear, a Crown Gear, or an Internal Bevel Gear.	Add 90 degrees to the pitch cone angle of the pinion. If the sum is greater than the center angle use Rules and Formulas Nos. 33, 30 and 4-21 in the order given. If the sum equals the center angle see rules and formulas for crown gear. If the sum is less than the center angle see rules and formulas for internal bevel gear.	
33	Pitch Cone Angle (or Edge Angle) of Gear.	Divide the sine of 180 degrees minus the center angle by the difference between the quotient of the number of teeth in the pinion divided by the number of teeth in the gear and the cosine of 180 degrees minus the center angle; this gives the tangent.	$\tan \alpha_g = \dfrac{\sin (180° - y)}{\dfrac{N_p}{N_g} - \cos (180° - y)}$

and thus discover that it is an example of regular obtuse angle gearing, since

$$14° \ 26' + 90° = 104° \ 26' > 100° \tag{32}$$

The remaining calculations for the angles are as follows:

$$\tan \alpha = \frac{0.98481}{\frac{15}{60} - 0.17365} = 12.8986 = \tan 85° \ 34' \tag{33}$$

$$\gamma = 14° \ 26' + 85° \ 34' = 100° \tag{30}$$

and the calculations for the other dimensions as per the table.

Crown Gear. — Suppose it is required to make a crown gear and a pinion for the same number of teeth, pitch and face as in the previous examples. What are

Rules and Formulas for Calculating Crown Gears

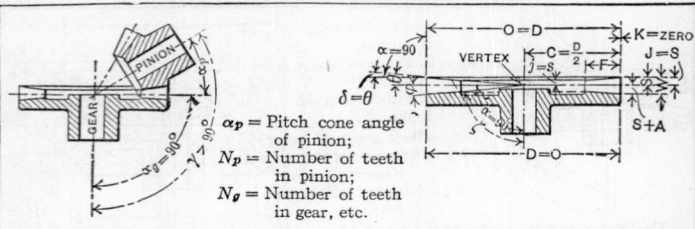

α_p = Pitch cone angle of pinion;
N_p = Number of teeth in pinion;
N_g = Number of teeth in gear, etc.

Use Rules Nos. 31 and 4–21 in the order given, for the pinion; use Rules Nos. 30, 4–8, 36, 10–13, 37, 15 and 38 in the order given for the crown gear; if dimensions for crown gear are known, to find center angle and dimensions of pinion, use Rules and Formulas Nos. 34, 35 and 4–21 in the order given.

No.	To Find	Rule	Formula
34	Pitch Cone Angle (or Edge Angle) of Pinion.	Divide the number of teeth in the pinion by the number of teeth in the gear, to get the sine.	$\sin \alpha_p = \dfrac{N_p}{N_g}$
35	Center Angle.	Add 90 degrees to the pitch cone angle of the pinion.	$y = 90° + \alpha_p$
36	Pitch Cone Radius.	Divide the pitch diameter by 2.	$C = \dfrac{D}{2}$
37	Face Angle of Gear.	The face cone angle of the gear equals the addendum angle.	$\delta_g = \theta$
38	Number of Teeth for which to Select Cutter.	The teeth are equivalent in form to rack teeth.	$N_g' = \text{infinity}$

the additional calculations necessary? Following the proper formulas in the order given:

$$\sin \alpha_p = \frac{15}{60} = 0.25000 = \sin 14° 29' \tag{34}$$

$$\gamma = 90° + 14° 29' = 104° 29' \tag{35}$$

The other calculations are similar to those already given.

Internal Bevel Gear. — Let it be required to design a pair of bevel gears of the same number of teeth, pitch and face, in which the center angle is 115 degrees. This being an example of obtuse angle gearing, use Formula (31).

$$\tan \alpha_p = \frac{0.90631}{\frac{60}{15} - 0.42262} = 0.25334 = \tan 14° 13' \tag{31}$$

Then, according to Rule (32):

$$14° 13' + 90° = 104° 13' < 115° \tag{32}$$

showing that the gear is an internal bevel gear. Applying the rules and formulas for internal bevel gearing:

$$\tan \alpha_a = \frac{0.90631}{0.42262 - \frac{15}{60}} = 5.25032 = \tan 79° 13'$$

$$180° - 79° 13' = 100° 47' \tag{39}$$

Rules and Formulas for Calculating Internal Bevel Gears

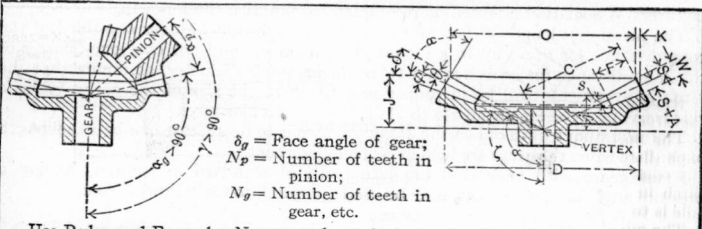

δ_g = Face angle of gear;
N_p = Number of teeth in pinion;
N_g = Number of teeth in gear, etc.

Use Rules and Formulas Nos. 31 and 4–21 inclusive for the pinion; use Rules and Formulas Nos. 39, 30, 40, 41, 15, 42, 43, 18, 19, 44 and 21 in the order given for the gear.

No.	To Find	Rule	Formula
39	Pitch Cone Angle (or Edge Angle) of Gear.	Divide the sine of 180 degrees minus the center angle by the difference between the cosine of 180 degrees minus the center angle and the quotient of the number of teeth in the pinion divided by the number of teeth in the gear; subtract the angle whose tangent is thus found from 180 degrees.	$\tan \alpha_a = \dfrac{\sin(180 - y)}{\cos(180 - y) - \dfrac{N_p}{N_g}}$ $\alpha_g = 180 - \alpha_a$
40	Pitch Cone Radius.	Divide the pitch diameter by twice the sine of 180 degrees minus the pitch cone angle.	$C = \dfrac{D_g}{2\sin(180 - \alpha_g)}$
41	Face Angle of Gear.	Subtract 90 degrees from the sum of the pitch cone angle and the addendum angle.	$\delta_g = \alpha_g + \theta - 90°$
42	Angular Addendum of Gear.	Multiply the addendum by the cosine of 180 degrees minus the pitch cone angle.	$K_g = S \times \cos(180 - \alpha_g)$
43	Outside (or Edge) Diameter of Gear.	Subtract twice the angular addendum from the pitch diameter.	$O_g = D_g - 2 K_g$
44	Number of Teeth for which to Select Cutter.	Divide the number of teeth by the cosine of 180 degrees minus the pitch cone angle.	$N_g' = \dfrac{N_g}{\cos(180 - \alpha_g)}$

$$\gamma = 100° \, 47' + 14° \, 13' = 115° \tag{30}$$

$$C = \frac{20}{2 \times 0.98234} = 10.1797'' \tag{40}$$

$$\delta = 100° \, 47' + 1° \, 53' - 90° = 12° \, 40' \tag{41}$$
$$\zeta = 98° \, 37', \text{ and } K = 0.0624''$$

$$O = 20 - 2 \times 0.0624 = 19.8752'' \tag{43}$$

$$N' = \frac{60}{0.1871} = 320 \text{ (internal)} \tag{44}$$

The calculations for the pinion and the other calculations for the gear are similar to those already given.

Recommended Practice for Bevel Gearing. — The American Gear Manufacturers' Association adopted as recommended practice the following rules:

The maximum length of face of bevel gears should not be over one-third of the cone distance for gears up to 3 inches pitch diameter and not over one-quarter of the cone distance for gears from 3 to 20 inches pitch diameter, assuming that the pitch in every case will be in proper proportion to the size of the gears. A safe rule is to make the face from $1\frac{1}{2}$ to $2\frac{1}{2}$ times the circular pitch.

The minimum length of bearing along the face is to be at least one-half the length of the face when the gears are held in correct alignment.

Bevel gears with generated involute teeth of standard addendum, having a pressure angle of $14\frac{1}{2}$ degrees, may be used according to the following rule:

Ratio	Number of Teeth
1 to 1	14 and over
$1\frac{1}{2}$ to 1	18 and over
2 to 1	19 and over
3 to 1 and over	21 and over

The rules as given apply mainly to gears up to 20 inches pitch diameter and to average machine design as distinguished from gears for automobiles.

Tables for Determining the Outside Diameter of Bevel Gears. — These tables are used for finding the outside diameter of bevel gears when the pitch diameter is known, and apply only to bevel gears with axes at right angles. The figures given in the table (in the column giving the number of teeth in the gear and opposite the number of teeth in the pinion) are for 1 diametral pitch; they are, therefore, to be divided by the diametral pitch of the gears, and the quotient thus obtained is added to the pitch diameter. For each combination of teeth, two figures are given. The upper value is for the gear and the lower for the pinion.

Example. — Find the outside diameter of a pair of bevel gears, 10 diametral pitch, with 35 and 23 teeth.

In the tables the diameter increments are found to be 1.10 for the gear and 1.67 for the pinion, for 1 diametral pitch. For 10 diametral pitch, then, $1.10 \div 10 = 0.110$, and $1.67 \div 10 = 0.167$. The pitch diameter of the gear is 3.5 inches; thus, $3.5 + 0.110 = 3.610$ inches is the outside diameter of the gear. The pitch diameter of the pinion is 2.3 inches; hence, $2.3 + 0.167 = 2.467$ inches is the outside diameter of the pinion.

The table "Diameter Increments for Bevel Gears" can be used in cases where the required number of teeth is not given in the tables just referred to. The object of the table is the same — that of obtaining the outside diameter when the pitch diameter is known. In these tables the column headed "Ratio" gives the ratio of the number of teeth in a pair of gears, and the two columns headed "Gear" and "Pinion" give the amount to add to the pitch diameter to obtain the outside diameter for 1 diametral pitch. Thus, to find the diameter increments, first divide the number of teeth in the gear by the number of teeth in the pinion, and find this ratio in the table. Then divide the values given in the table opposite this ratio by the given pitch. The table is applicable to bevel gears with axes at right angles only.

Example. — Find the outside diameter of a pair of bevel gears, 75 and 20 teeth, 6 diametral pitch.

Dividing the number of teeth in the gear by the number of teeth in the pinion gives a ratio of 3.75. From the table the diameter increment is then found to be 0.515 for the gear, and 1.933 for the pinion. Dividing each by 6 gives 0.086 and 0.322. The pitch diameter of the gear is 12.5 inches and of the pinion 3.333 inches. Adding the diameter increments just found gives 12.586 inches for the outside diameter of the gear, and 3.655 inches for the outside diameter of the pinion.

Diameter Increments for Bevel Gears

Ratio	Gear	Pinion	Ratio	Gear	Pinion	Ratio	Gear	Pinion
1.000	1.414	1.414	2.250	0.812	1.827	4.70	0.416	1.956
1.025	1.396	1.431	2.275	0.805	1.831	4.75	0.411	1.957
1.050	1.380	1.448	2.30	0.797	1.834	4.80	0.407	1.958
1.075	1.362	1.464	2.35	0.783	1.840	4.85	0.404	1.959
1.100	1.345	1.480	2.40	0.770	1.846	4.90	0.400	1.960
1.125	1.328	1.494	2.45	0.755	1.851	5.00	0.392	1.961
1.150	1.312	1.509	2.50	0.743	1.857	5.10	0.385	1.962
1.175	1.296	1.523	2.55	0.730	1.862	5.20	0.377	1.964
1.200	1.280	1.536	2.60	0.718	1.867	5.30	0.370	1.965
1.225	1.264	1.549	2.65	0.706	1.871	5.40	0.364	1.966
1.250	1.249	1.561	2.70	0.694	1.875	5.50	0.357	1.967
1.275	1.234	1.573	2.75	0.683	1.880	5.60	0.351	1.968
1.300	1.219	1.585	2.80	0.672	1.883	5.70	0.345	1.970
1.325	1.204	1.596	2.85	0.662	1.887	5.80	0.340	1.971
1.350	1.190	1.607	2.90	0.652	1.890	5.90	0.334	1.972
1.375	1.176	1.617	2.95	0.642	1.894	6.00	0.329	1.973
1.400	1.162	1.627	3.00	0.632	1.897	6.10	0.323	1.974
1.425	1.149	1.636	3.05	0.623	1.900	6.20	0.318	1.975
1.450	1.135	1.646	3.10	0.614	1.903	6.30	0.313	1.975
1.475	1.122	1.655	3.15	0.605	1.906	6.40	0.309	1.976
1.500	1.109	1.664	3.20	0.596	1.909	6.50	0.304	1.977
1.525	1.096	1.672	3.25	0.588	1.911	6.60	0.299	1.977
1.550	1.084	1.680	3.30	0.580	1.914	6.70	0.295	1.978
1.575	1.072	1.688	3.35	0.571	1.916	6.80	0.291	1.979
1.600	1.060	1.696	3.40	0.564	1.918	6.90	0.287	1.979
1.625	1.047	1.703	3.45	0.557	1.921	7.00	0.283	1.980
1.650	1.036	1.710	3.50	0.550	1.923	7.10	0.279	1.980
1.675	1.025	1.717	3.55	0.542	1.925	7.20	0.275	1.981
1.700	1.014	1.723	3.60	0.535	1.927	7.30	0.271	1.981
1.725	1.003	1.730	3.65	0.528	1.929	7.40	0.268	1.982
1.750	0.992	1.736	3.70	0.521	1.931	7.50	0.264	1.982
1.775	0.982	1.742	3.75	0.515	1.933	7.60	0.261	1.983
1.800	0.971	1.748	3.80	0.509	1.934	7.70	0.257	1.983
1.825	0.961	1.754	3.85	0.503	1.936	7.80	0.254	1.983
1.850	0.951	1.760	3.90	0.497	1.937	7.90	0.251	1.984
1.875	0.941	1.765	3.95	0.491	1.939	8.00	0.248	1.984
1.900	0.931	1.770	4.00	0.485	1.940	8.10	0.245	1.985
1.925	0.922	1.775	4.05	0.479	1.941	8.20	0.242	1.985
1.950	0.912	1.780	4.10	0.473	1.943	8.30	0.239	1.985
1.975	0.903	1.784	4.15	0.468	1.944	8.40	0.236	1.986
2.000	0.894	1.790	4.20	0.463	1.945	8.50	0.234	1.986
2.025	0.885	1.793	4.25	0.458	1.947	8.60	0.231	1.986
2.050	0.876	1.797	4.30	0.453	1.948	8.70	0.228	1.986
2.075	0.868	1.801	4.35	0.448	1.949	8.80	0.225	1.987
2.100	0.860	1.805	4.40	0.443	1.950	8.90	0.223	1.987
2.125	0.851	1.809	4.45	0.438	1.951	9.00	0.220	1.987
2.150	0.843	1.813	4.50	0.434	1.952	9.20	0.216	1.988
2.175	0.835	1.817	4.55	0.429	1.953	9.40	0.211	1.988
2.200	0.828	1.821	4.60	0.425	1.954	9.50	0.209	1.989
2.225	0.820	1.824	4.65	0.420	1.955	10.00	0.198	1.990

Amount to Add to Pitch Diameter to Obtain Outside Diameter of Bevel Gears

Number of Teeth in Gear (top values = gear, bottom values = pinion). Rows indexed by Number of Teeth in Pinion.

Teeth in Pinion	72	71	70	69	68	67	66	65	64	63	62	61	60	59	58
12	0.33 / 1.97	0.33 / 1.97	0.34 / 1.97	0.34 / 1.97	0.35 / 1.97	0.35 / 1.97	0.36 / 1.97	0.36 / 1.97	0.37 / 1.97	0.37 / 1.96	0.38 / 1.96	0.39 / 1.96	0.39 / 1.96	0.40 / 1.96	0.41 / 1.96
13	0.36 / 1.97	0.36 / 1.97	0.37 / 1.97	0.37 / 1.97	0.38 / 1.96	0.38 / 1.96	0.39 / 1.96	0.39 / 1.96	0.40 / 1.96	0.40 / 1.96	0.41 / 1.96	0.42 / 1.96	0.42 / 1.95	0.43 / 1.95	0.44 / 1.95
14	0.38 / 1.96	0.39 / 1.96	0.39 / 1.96	0.40 / 1.96	0.40 / 1.96	0.41 / 1.96	0.42 / 1.96	0.42 / 1.95	0.43 / 1.95	0.43 / 1.95	0.44 / 1.95	0.45 / 1.95	0.45 / 1.95	0.46 / 1.95	0.47 / 1.94
15	0.41 / 1.96	0.41 / 1.96	0.42 / 1.96	0.42 / 1.95	0.43 / 1.95	0.44 / 1.95	0.44 / 1.95	0.45 / 1.95	0.46 / 1.95	0.46 / 1.95	0.47 / 1.94	0.48 / 1.94	0.48 / 1.94	0.49 / 1.94	0.50 / 1.94
16	0.43 / 1.95	0.44 / 1.95	0.45 / 1.95	0.45 / 1.95	0.46 / 1.95	0.46 / 1.95	0.47 / 1.94	0.48 / 1.94	0.48 / 1.94	0.49 / 1.94	0.50 / 1.94	0.51 / 1.93	0.52 / 1.93	0.52 / 1.93	0.53 / 1.93
17	0.46 / 1.95	0.47 / 1.95	0.47 / 1.94	0.48 / 1.94	0.48 / 1.94	0.49 / 1.94	0.50 / 1.94	0.51 / 1.93	0.51 / 1.93	0.52 / 1.93	0.53 / 1.93	0.54 / 1.93	0.55 / 1.92	0.55 / 1.92	0.56 / 1.92
18	0.48 / 1.94	0.49 / 1.94	0.50 / 1.94	0.50 / 1.94	0.51 / 1.93	0.52 / 1.93	0.53 / 1.93	0.53 / 1.93	0.54 / 1.93	0.55 / 1.92	0.56 / 1.92	0.57 / 1.92	0.57 / 1.92	0.58 / 1.91	0.59 / 1.91
19	0.51 / 1.93	0.52 / 1.93	0.52 / 1.93	0.53 / 1.93	0.54 / 1.93	0.55 / 1.92	0.55 / 1.92	0.56 / 1.92	0.57 / 1.92	0.58 / 1.91	0.59 / 1.91	0.59 / 1.91	0.60 / 1.91	0.61 / 1.90	0.62 / 1.90
20	0.54 / 1.93	0.54 / 1.92	0.55 / 1.92	0.56 / 1.92	0.56 / 1.92	0.57 / 1.92	0.58 / 1.91	0.59 / 1.91	0.60 / 1.91	0.61 / 1.91	0.61 / 1.90	0.62 / 1.90	0.63 / 1.90	0.64 / 1.89	0.65 / 1.89
21	0.56 / 1.92	0.57 / 1.92	0.57 / 1.92	0.58 / 1.91	0.59 / 1.91	0.60 / 1.91	0.61 / 1.90	0.61 / 1.90	0.62 / 1.90	0.63 / 1.90	0.64 / 1.89	0.65 / 1.89	0.66 / 1.88	0.67 / 1.88	0.68 / 1.88
22	0.58 / 1.91	0.59 / 1.91	0.60 / 1.91	0.61 / 1.91	0.62 / 1.90	0.62 / 1.90	0.63 / 1.90	0.64 / 1.89	0.65 / 1.89	0.66 / 1.89	0.67 / 1.88	0.68 / 1.88	0.69 / 1.88	0.70 / 1.87	0.71 / 1.87
23	0.61 / 1.91	0.62 / 1.90	0.62 / 1.90	0.64 / 1.90	0.64 / 1.89	0.65 / 1.89	0.66 / 1.89	0.67 / 1.89	0.68 / 1.88	0.69 / 1.88	0.70 / 1.88	0.71 / 1.87	0.72 / 1.87	0.73 / 1.86	0.74 / 1.86
24	0.63 / 1.90	0.64 / 1.89	0.65 / 1.89	0.66 / 1.89	0.67 / 1.89	0.67 / 1.88	0.68 / 1.88	0.69 / 1.88	0.70 / 1.87	0.71 / 1.87	0.72 / 1.87	0.73 / 1.86	0.74 / 1.86	0.75 / 1.85	0.76 / 1.85
25	0.66 / 1.89	0.67 / 1.88	0.67 / 1.88	0.68 / 1.88	0.69 / 1.87	0.70 / 1.87	0.71 / 1.87	0.72 / 1.87	0.73 / 1.86	0.74 / 1.86	0.75 / 1.86	0.76 / 1.85	0.77 / 1.85	0.78 / 1.84	0.79 / 1.84
26	0.68 / 1.88	0.69 / 1.88	0.70 / 1.87	0.71 / 1.87	0.71 / 1.87	0.72 / 1.86	0.73 / 1.86	0.74 / 1.86	0.75 / 1.85	0.76 / 1.85	0.77 / 1.84	0.78 / 1.84	0.80 / 1.84	0.81 / 1.83	0.82 / 1.82
27	0.70 / 1.87	0.71 / 1.87	0.72 / 1.87	0.73 / 1.86	0.74 / 1.86	0.75 / 1.86	0.76 / 1.85	0.77 / 1.85	0.78 / 1.84	0.79 / 1.84	0.80 / 1.83	0.81 / 1.83	0.82 / 1.82	0.83 / 1.82	0.84 / 1.81
28	0.72 / 1.86	0.73 / 1.86	0.74 / 1.85	0.75 / 1.85	0.76 / 1.85	0.77 / 1.85	0.78 / 1.84	0.79 / 1.84	0.80 / 1.83	0.81 / 1.83	0.82 / 1.82	0.83 / 1.82	0.85 / 1.81	0.86 / 1.81	0.87 / 1.80
29	0.75 / 1.86	0.76 / 1.85	0.77 / 1.85	0.78 / 1.84	0.78 / 1.84	0.79 / 1.84	0.80 / 1.83	0.82 / 1.83	0.83 / 1.82	0.84 / 1.82	0.85 / 1.81	0.86 / 1.81	0.87 / 1.80	0.88 / 1.80	0.89 / 1.79
30	0.77 / 1.85	0.78 / 1.84	0.79 / 1.84	0.80 / 1.83	0.81 / 1.83	0.82 / 1.83	0.83 / 1.82	0.84 / 1.81	0.85 / 1.81	0.86 / 1.81	0.87 / 1.80	0.88 / 1.79	0.89 / 1.79	0.91 / 1.78	0.92 / 1.78
31	0.79 / 1.84	0.80 / 1.83	0.81 / 1.83	0.82 / 1.82	0.83 / 1.82	0.84 / 1.82	0.85 / 1.81	0.86 / 1.81	0.87 / 1.80	0.88 / 1.79	0.89 / 1.79	0.91 / 1.78	0.92 / 1.78	0.93 / 1.77	0.94 / 1.77
32	0.81 / 1.83	0.82 / 1.82	0.83 / 1.82	0.84 / 1.81	0.85 / 1.81	0.86 / 1.80	0.87 / 1.80	0.88 / 1.79	0.89 / 1.79	0.91 / 1.78	0.92 / 1.77	0.93 / 1.77	0.94 / 1.76	0.95 / 1.76	0.97 / 1.75
33	0.83 / 1.82	0.84 / 1.81	0.85 / 1.81	0.86 / 1.80	0.87 / 1.80	0.88 / 1.79	0.89 / 1.79	0.91 / 1.78	0.92 / 1.78	0.93 / 1.77	0.94 / 1.77	0.95 / 1.76	0.96 / 1.75	0.98 / 1.75	0.99 / 1.74
34	0.85 / 1.81	0.86 / 1.80	0.87 / 1.80	0.88 / 1.79	0.89 / 1.79	0.91 / 1.78	0.92 / 1.78	0.93 / 1.77	0.94 / 1.77	0.95 / 1.76	0.96 / 1.75	0.97 / 1.75	0.99 / 1.74	1.00 / 1.73	1.01 / 1.73
35	0.87 / 1.80	0.88 / 1.79	0.89 / 1.79	0.90 / 1.78	0.92 / 1.78	0.93 / 1.77	0.94 / 1.77	0.95 / 1.76	0.96 / 1.75	0.97 / 1.75	0.98 / 1.74	1.00 / 1.73	1.01 / 1.73	1.02 / 1.72	1.03 / 1.71
36	0.89 / 1.79	0.90 / 1.78	0.91 / 1.78	0.93 / 1.77	0.94 / 1.77	0.95 / 1.76	0.96 / 1.76	0.98 / 1.75	0.99 / 1.74	1.00 / 1.74	1.02 / 1.73	1.03 / 1.72	1.04 / 1.71	1.05 / 1.71	1.05 / 1.70
37	0.91 / 1.78	0.92 / 1.77	0.93 / 1.77	0.95 / 1.76	0.96 / 1.76	0.97 / 1.75	0.98 / 1.74	0.99 / 1.74	1.00 / 1.73	1.01 / 1.72	1.03 / 1.72	1.04 / 1.71	1.05 / 1.70	1.06 / 1.69	1.08 / 1.69
38	0.93 / 1.77	0.94 / 1.76	0.95 / 1.76	0.97 / 1.75	0.98 / 1.75	0.99 / 1.74	1.00 / 1.73	1.01 / 1.73	1.02 / 1.72	1.03 / 1.71	1.05 / 1.71	1.06 / 1.70	1.07 / 1.69	1.08 / 1.68	1.10 / 1.67

Of the two values given, the upper is for the gear, the lower for the pinion.

Amount to Add to Pitch Diameter to Obtain Outside Diameter of Bevel Gears (*Continued*)

Number of Teeth in Pinion		Number of Teeth in Gear														
		57	56	55	54	53	52	51	50	49	48	47	46	45	44	43
	12	0.41 / 1.96	0.42 / 1.96	0.43 / 1.95	0.43 / 1.95	0.44 / 1.95	0.45 / 1.95	0.46 / 1.95	0.47 / 1.94	0.48 / 1.94	0.48 / 1.94	0.49 / 1.94	0.50 / 1.94	0.52 / 1.93	0.53 / 1.93	0.54 / 1.93
	13	0.44 / 1.95	0.45 / 1.95	0.46 / 1.95	0.47 / 1.94	0.48 / 1.94	0.48 / 1.94	0.49 / 1.94	0.50 / 1.94	0.51 / 1.93	0.52 / 1.93	0.53 / 1.93	0.54 / 1.92	0.56 / 1.92	0.57 / 1.92	0.58 / 1.91
	14	0.48 / 1.94	0.48 / 1.94	0.49 / 1.94	0.50 / 1.94	0.51 / 1.93	0.52 / 1.93	0.53 / 1.93	0.54 / 1.93	0.55 / 1.92	0.56 / 1.92	0.57 / 1.91	0.58 / 1.91	0.59 / 1.91	0.61 / 1.91	0.62 / 1.90
	15	0.51 / 1.94	0.52 / 1.93	0.53 / 1.93	0.54 / 1.93	0.54 / 1.92	0.55 / 1.92	0.56 / 1.92	0.57 / 1.92	0.59 / 1.91	0.60 / 1.91	0.61 / 1.91	0.62 / 1.90	0.63 / 1.90	0.65 / 1.89	0.66 / 1.89
	16	0.54 / 1.93	0.55 / 1.92	0.56 / 1.92	0.57 / 1.92	0.58 / 1.91	0.59 / 1.91	0.60 / 1.91	0.61 / 1.90	0.62 / 1.90	0.63 / 1.90	0.64 / 1.89	0.66 / 1.89	0.67 / 1.88	0.68 / 1.88	0.70 / 1.87
	17	0.57 / 1.92	0.58 / 1.91	0.59 / 1.91	0.60 / 1.91	0.61 / 1.90	0.62 / 1.90	0.63 / 1.90	0.64 / 1.89	0.66 / 1.89	0.67 / 1.89	0.68 / 1.88	0.69 / 1.88	0.71 / 1.87	0.72 / 1.87	0.74 / 1.86
	18	0.60 / 1.91	0.61 / 1.90	0.62 / 1.90	0.63 / 1.90	0.64 / 1.89	0.65 / 1.89	0.67 / 1.89	0.68 / 1.88	0.69 / 1.88	0.70 / 1.87	0.72 / 1.87	0.73 / 1.86	0.74 / 1.86	0.76 / 1.85	0.77 / 1.84
	19	0.63 / 1.90	0.64 / 1.89	0.65 / 1.89	0.66 / 1.89	0.67 / 1.88	0.69 / 1.88	0.70 / 1.87	0.71 / 1.87	0.72 / 1.86	0.74 / 1.86	0.75 / 1.85	0.76 / 1.85	0.78 / 1.84	0.79 / 1.84	0.81 / 1.83
	20	0.66 / 1.89	0.67 / 1.88	0.68 / 1.88	0.69 / 1.88	0.71 / 1.87	0.72 / 1.87	0.73 / 1.86	0.74 / 1.86	0.76 / 1.85	0.77 / 1.85	0.78 / 1.84	0.80 / 1.83	0.81 / 1.83	0.83 / 1.82	0.84 / 1.81
	21	0.70 / 1.87	0.70 / 1.87	0.71 / 1.87	0.72 / 1.86	0.74 / 1.86	0.75 / 1.85	0.76 / 1.85	0.77 / 1.84	0.79 / 1.84	0.80 / 1.83	0.82 / 1.83	0.83 / 1.82	0.85 / 1.81	0.86 / 1.80	0.88 / 1.80
	22	0.72 / 1.87	0.73 / 1.86	0.74 / 1.86	0.75 / 1.85	0.77 / 1.85	0.78 / 1.84	0.79 / 1.84	0.81 / 1.83	0.82 / 1.82	0.83 / 1.82	0.85 / 1.81	0.86 / 1.80	0.88 / 1.80	0.89 / 1.79	0.91 / 1.78
	23	0.75 / 1.85	0.76 / 1.85	0.77 / 1.85	0.78 / 1.84	0.80 / 1.83	0.81 / 1.83	0.82 / 1.82	0.84 / 1.82	0.85 / 1.81	0.86 / 1.80	0.88 / 1.80	0.89 / 1.79	0.91 / 1.78	0.93 / 1.77	0.94 / 1.76
	24	0.78 / 1.84	0.79 / 1.84	0.80 / 1.83	0.81 / 1.83	0.83 / 1.82	0.84 / 1.82	0.85 / 1.81	0.87 / 1.80	0.88 / 1.80	0.89 / 1.79	0.91 / 1.78	0.93 / 1.77	0.94 / 1.76	0.96 / 1.76	0.97 / 1.75
	25	0.80 / 1.83	0.82 / 1.83	0.83 / 1.82	0.84 / 1.81	0.85 / 1.81	0.87 / 1.80	0.88 / 1.80	0.89 / 1.79	0.91 / 1.78	0.92 / 1.77	0.94 / 1.77	0.95 / 1.76	0.97 / 1.75	0.99 / 1.74	1.01 / 1.73
	26	0.83 / 1.82	0.84 / 1.81	0.85 / 1.81	0.87 / 1.80	0.88 / 1.80	0.89 / 1.79	0.91 / 1.78	0.92 / 1.77	0.94 / 1.77	0.95 / 1.76	0.97 / 1.75	0.98 / 1.74	1.00 / 1.73	1.02 / 1.72	1.04 / 1.71
	27	0.86 / 1.81	0.87 / 1.80	0.88 / 1.80	0.89 / 1.79	0.91 / 1.78	0.92 / 1.78	0.94 / 1.77	0.95 / 1.76	0.97 / 1.75	0.98 / 1.74	1.00 / 1.73	1.01 / 1.72	1.03 / 1.71	1.05 / 1.70	1.06 / 1.69
	28	0.88 / 1.80	0.89 / 1.79	0.91 / 1.78	0.92 / 1.78	0.93 / 1.77	0.95 / 1.76	0.96 / 1.75	0.98 / 1.75	0.99 / 1.74	1.01 / 1.73	1.02 / 1.72	1.04 / 1.71	1.06 / 1.70	1.07 / 1.69	1.09 / 1.68
	29	0.91 / 1.78	0.92 / 1.78	0.93 / 1.77	0.95 / 1.76	0.96 / 1.75	0.97 / 1.75	0.99 / 1.74	1.00 / 1.73	1.02 / 1.72	1.03 / 1.71	1.05 / 1.70	1.07 / 1.68	1.08 / 1.68	1.10 / 1.67	1.12 / 1.66
	30	0.93 / 1.77	0.94 / 1.76	0.96 / 1.76	0.98 / 1.74	0.99 / 1.74	1.00 / 1.73	1.01 / 1.72	1.03 / 1.71	1.04 / 1.71	1.06 / 1.70	1.08 / 1.69	1.09 / 1.68	1.11 / 1.66	1.13 / 1.65	1.14 / 1.64
	31	0.96 / 1.76	0.97 / 1.75	0.98 / 1.74	1.00 / 1.73	1.01 / 1.73	1.02 / 1.72	1.04 / 1.71	1.05 / 1.70	1.07 / 1.69	1.09 / 1.68	1.10 / 1.67	1.12 / 1.66	1.13 / 1.65	1.15 / 1.63	1.17 / 1.62
	32	0.98 / 1.74	0.99 / 1.74	1.01 / 1.73	1.02 / 1.72	1.03 / 1.71	1.04 / 1.71	1.06 / 1.69	1.08 / 1.68	1.09 / 1.67	1.11 / 1.66	1.13 / 1.65	1.14 / 1.64	1.16 / 1.63	1.18 / 1.62	1.19 / 1.60
	33	1.00 / 1.73	1.02 / 1.72	1.03 / 1.71	1.04 / 1.71	1.06 / 1.70	1.08 / 1.69	1.09 / 1.68	1.10 / 1.67	1.12 / 1.66	1.13 / 1.65	1.15 / 1.64	1.17 / 1.63	1.18 / 1.61	1.20 / 1.60	1.22 / 1.59
	34	1.02 / 1.72	1.04 / 1.71	1.05 / 1.70	1.07 / 1.69	1.08 / 1.68	1.09 / 1.67	1.11 / 1.66	1.12 / 1.65	1.14 / 1.64	1.16 / 1.63	1.17 / 1.62	1.19 / 1.61	1.21 / 1.59	1.22 / 1.58	1.24 / 1.57
	35	1.05 / 1.70	1.06 / 1.70	1.07 / 1.69	1.09 / 1.68	1.10 / 1.67	1.12 / 1.66	1.13 / 1.65	1.15 / 1.64	1.17 / 1.63	1.18 / 1.62	1.19 / 1.60	1.21 / 1.59	1.23 / 1.58	1.25 / 1.57	1.26 / 1.55
	36	1.07 / 1.69	1.08 / 1.68	1.10 / 1.67	1.11 / 1.66	1.12 / 1.65	1.14 / 1.64	1.15 / 1.63	1.17 / 1.62	1.18 / 1.61	1.19 / 1.60	1.21 / 1.59	1.23 / 1.57	1.25 / 1.56	1.27 / 1.55	1.28 / 1.53
	37	1.09 / 1.68	1.10 / 1.67	1.12 / 1.66	1.13 / 1.65	1.14 / 1.64	1.16 / 1.63	1.17 / 1.62	1.19 / 1.61	1.21 / 1.60	1.22 / 1.58	1.24 / 1.57	1.25 / 1.56	1.27 / 1.55	1.29 / 1.53	1.30 / 1.52

Of the two values given, the upper is for the gear, the lower for the pinion.

Amount to Add to Pitch Diameter to Obtain Outside Diameter of Bevel Gears (Continued)

Number of Teeth in Gear

Values given as upper / lower (upper for the gear, lower for the pinion).

Teeth in Pinion	42	41	40	39	38	37	36	35	34	33	32	31	30	29	28
12	0.55/1.92	0.56/1.92	0.58/1.92	0.59/1.91	0.61/1.91	0.63/1.90	0.63/1.90	0.65/1.89	0.67/1.88	0.68/1.88	0.70/1.87	0.72/1.87	0.74/1.86	0.76/1.85	0.79/1.84
13	0.59/1.91	0.60/1.91	0.61/1.90	0.63/1.90	0.65/1.89	0.66/1.89	0.68/1.88	0.70/1.87	0.71/1.87	0.73/1.86	0.75/1.85	0.77/1.84	0.80/1.83	0.82/1.82	0.84/1.81
14	0.63/1.90	0.65/1.89	0.66/1.89	0.67/1.88	0.69/1.88	0.71/1.86	0.72/1.86	0.74/1.85	0.76/1.84	0.78/1.83	0.80/1.83	0.82/1.82	0.85/1.81	0.87/1.80	0.89/1.79
15	0.67/1.88	0.69/1.88	0.70/1.87	0.72/1.87	0.74/1.86	0.75/1.85	0.77/1.85	0.79/1.84	0.81/1.83	0.83/1.82	0.85/1.81	0.87/1.80	0.89/1.79	0.92/1.78	0.94/1.76
16	0.71/1.87	0.73/1.86	0.74/1.86	0.76/1.85	0.77/1.85	0.79/1.84	0.81/1.83	0.83/1.82	0.85/1.81	0.88/1.80	0.89/1.79	0.91/1.77	0.94/1.75	0.97/1.75	0.99/1.74
17	0.75/1.85	0.77/1.85	0.78/1.84	0.79/1.83	0.81/1.83	0.83/1.82	0.86/1.81	0.88/1.80	0.89/1.79	0.91/1.77	0.94/1.76	0.96/1.75	0.99/1.74	1.01/1.73	1.04/1.71
18	0.79/1.84	0.80/1.83	0.82/1.82	0.84/1.81	0.86/1.81	0.88/1.80	0.89/1.79	0.91/1.78	0.93/1.77	0.94/1.76	0.98/1.74	1.01/1.73	1.03/1.72	1.06/1.70	1.08/1.68
19	0.82/1.82	0.84/1.81	0.86/1.81	0.88/1.80	0.89/1.79	0.91/1.78	0.93/1.77	0.95/1.76	0.97/1.75	0.99/1.73	1.02/1.72	1.04/1.70	1.07/1.69	1.10/1.67	1.12/1.66
20	0.86/1.81	0.88/1.80	0.89/1.79	0.91/1.78	0.93/1.77	0.95/1.76	0.97/1.75	0.99/1.74	1.01/1.72	1.04/1.71	1.06/1.70	1.08/1.68	1.11/1.66	1.14/1.64	1.16/1.63
21	0.89/1.79	0.91/1.78	0.93/1.77	0.94/1.76	0.97/1.75	0.99/1.74	1.01/1.73	1.03/1.72	1.05/1.70	1.07/1.69	1.10/1.67	1.12/1.65	1.14/1.64	1.17/1.62	1.20/1.60
22	0.93/1.77	0.95/1.76	0.96/1.75	0.98/1.74	1.00/1.73	1.02/1.72	1.04/1.71	1.06/1.69	1.09/1.68	1.11/1.66	1.13/1.65	1.16/1.63	1.18/1.61	1.21/1.59	1.24/1.57
23	0.96/1.75	0.98/1.74	1.00/1.73	1.01/1.72	1.04/1.71	1.06/1.70	1.08/1.68	1.10/1.67	1.12/1.66	1.14/1.64	1.17/1.62	1.19/1.61	1.21/1.59	1.24/1.57	1.27/1.55
24	0.99/1.74	1.01/1.72	1.03/1.71	1.05/1.70	1.07/1.69	1.08/1.68	1.11/1.66	1.13/1.65	1.15/1.63	1.17/1.62	1.20/1.60	1.23/1.58	1.25/1.56	1.28/1.54	1.30/1.52
25	1.02/1.72	1.04/1.71	1.06/1.70	1.08/1.68	1.10/1.67	1.12/1.65	1.14/1.64	1.16/1.63	1.18/1.61	1.20/1.59	1.23/1.58	1.26/1.56	1.28/1.54	1.31/1.52	1.33/1.49
26	1.05/1.70	1.07/1.69	1.09/1.68	1.11/1.66	1.13/1.65	1.15/1.64	1.17/1.62	1.19/1.61	1.21/1.59	1.24/1.57	1.26/1.55	1.28/1.53	1.31/1.51	1.34/1.49	1.36/1.47
27	1.08/1.68	1.10/1.67	1.12/1.66	1.14/1.64	1.15/1.63	1.18/1.62	1.20/1.60	1.22/1.58	1.24/1.57	1.27/1.54	1.29/1.53	1.31/1.51	1.34/1.49	1.36/1.46	1.39/1.44
28	1.11/1.66	1.13/1.65	1.14/1.64	1.16/1.62	1.19/1.61	1.21/1.59	1.23/1.58	1.25/1.56	1.27/1.54	1.29/1.53	1.32/1.51	1.34/1.48	1.36/1.46	1.39/1.41	1.41/1.41
29	1.14/1.65	1.15/1.63	1.17/1.62	1.19/1.60	1.21/1.59	1.23/1.57	1.26/1.56	1.28/1.54	1.30/1.52	1.32/1.50	1.34/1.48	1.37/1.46	1.39/1.44	1.41/1.41	....
30	1.16/1.63	1.18/1.61	1.20/1.59	1.22/1.59	1.24/1.57	1.26/1.55	1.28/1.54	1.30/1.52	1.32/1.50	1.35/1.48	1.37/1.46	1.39/1.44	1.41/1.41	....	....
31	1.19/1.61	1.21/1.59	1.23/1.58	1.25/1.57	1.26/1.55	1.28/1.53	1.31/1.51	1.33/1.51	1.35/1.48	1.37/1.46	1.39/1.44	1.41/1.41	....		
32	1.21/1.59	1.23/1.58	1.25/1.56	1.27/1.54	1.29/1.53	1.31/1.51	1.33/1.50	1.35/1.48	1.37/1.46	1.39/1.44	1.41/1.41	....			
33	1.24/1.57	1.25/1.56	1.27/1.54	1.29/1.53	1.31/1.51	1.33/1.49	1.35/1.48	1.37/1.45	1.39/1.43	1.41/1.41	....				
34	1.26/1.55	1.28/1.54	1.30/1.52	1.31/1.51	1.33/1.49	1.35/1.48	1.37/1.45	1.39/1.43	1.41/1.41	....					
35	1.28/1.54	1.30/1.52	1.32/1.50	1.34/1.49	1.35/1.48	1.38/1.45	1.39/1.43	1.41/1.41	....						
36	1.30/1.52	1.32/1.50	1.34/1.49	1.36/1.47	1.38/1.45	1.40/1.43	1.41/1.41	....							
37	1.32/1.50	1.34/1.49	1.36/1.47	1.38/1.45	1.40/1.43	1.41/1.41	....								

Of the two values given, the upper is for the gear, the lower for the pinion.

Amount to Add to Pitch Diameter to Obtain Outside Diameter of Bevel Gears (*Continued*)

No. Teeth in Pinion		27	26	25	24	23	22	21	20	19	18	17	16	15	14	13
12	gear	0.81	0.84	0.87	0.89	0.93	0.96	0.99	1.03	1.07	1.11	1.15	1.20	1.25	1.30	1.36
	pin	1.83	1.82	1.80	1.79	1.77	1.76	1.74	1.71	1.69	1.66	1.63	1.60	1.56	1.52	1.47
13	gear	0.87	0.89	0.92	0.95	0.98	1.02	1.05	1.09	1.13	1.17	1.21	1.26	1.31	1.36	1.41
	pin	1.80	1.79	1.77	1.76	1.74	1.72	1.70	1.68	1.65	1.62	1.59	1.55	1.51	1.47	1.41
14	gear	0.92	0.95	0.98	1.01	1.04	1.07	1.11	1.15	1.19	1.23	1.27	1.32	1.36	1.41	....
	pin	1.78	1.76	1.75	1.73	1.71	1.69	1.66	1.64	1.61	1.58	1.54	1.50	1.46	1.41	....
15	gear	0.97	1.00	1.03	1.06	1.09	1.13	1.16	1.20	1.24	1.28	1.32	1.37	1.41	....	....
	pin	1.75	1.73	1.71	1.70	1.68	1.65	1.63	1.60	1.57	1.54	1.50	1.46	1.41	....	....
16	gear	1.02	1.05	1.08	1.11	1.14	1.18	1.21	1.25	1.29	1.33	1.37	1.41	....	....	....
	pin	1.72	1.70	1.68	1.66	1.64	1.62	1.59	1.56	1.53	1.49	1.46	1.41	....	....	....
17	gear	1.07	1.09	1.12	1.16	1.19	1.22	1.26	1.30	1.33	1.37	1.41	....	....		
	pin	1.69	1.67	1.65	1.63	1.61	1.58	1.55	1.52	1.49	1.45	1.41	....	....		
18	gear	1.11	1.14	1.17	1.20	1.23	1.27	1.30	1.34	1.38	1.41	....				
	pin	1.66	1.64	1.62	1.60	1.57	1.55	1.52	1.49	1.45	1.41	....				
19	gear	1.15	1.18	1.21	1.24	1.27	1.31	1.34	1.38	1.41	....					
	pin	1.64	1.61	1.59	1.57	1.54	1.51	1.48	1.45	1.41	....					
20	gear	1.19	1.22	1.25	1.28	1.31	1.35	1.38	1.41	....						
	pin	1.61	1.59	1.56	1.54	1.51	1.48	1.45	1.41	....						
21	gear	1.23	1.26	1.29	1.32	1.35	1.38	1.41	....							
	pin	1.58	1.56	1.53	1.50	1.48	1.45	1.41	....							
22	gear	1.26	1.29	1.32	1.35	1.38	1.41	...								
	pin	1.55	1.53	1.50	1.47	1.45	1.41	...								
23	gear	1.30	1.33	1.35	1.38	1.41	....									
	pin	1.52	1.50	1.47	1.44	1.41	....									
24	gear	1.33	1.36	1.39	1.41	....										
	pin	1.49	1.47	1.44	1.41	....										
25	gear	1.36	1.39	1.41	....											
	pin	1.47	1.44	1.41	....											
26	gear	1.39	1.41	....												
	pin	1.44	1.41	....												
27	gear	1.41	....													
	pin	1.41	....													

Of the two values given, the upper is for the gear, the lower for the pinion.

Edge or Pitch Cone Angles, Face Angles and Cutting Angles of Bevel Gears. — These tables have been computed by the Brown & Sharpe Mfg. Co. for convenience in calculating the data for bevel gears with axes at right angles. They do not apply to bevel gears with axes at any other angle. To use the tables, the number of teeth in the gear and pinion must be known. Locate the number of teeth in the gear on the horizontal line at the top of the table and the number of teeth in the pinion in the vertical column on the left-hand side. At the intersection of the lines or columns for these numbers of teeth, two angles are given. The angle applying to the gear is always placed above the angle applying to the pinion.

The tables "Face Angles of Bevel Gears" are arranged in the same manner as the tables for "Edge or Pitch Cone Angles." Of the two angles that are given for each combination of number of teeth, the upper is for the gear, and the lower for the pinion. The cutting angle for a gear or pinion, when cut by rotary milling cutters, is equal to the angle of face of its mate.

As an example of the use of the tables, find the cutting angles for a pair of bevel gears with 15 and 60 teeth. From the table on page 760, these angles are found to be 12 deg. 11 min., and 74 deg. 7 min., if the gears are cut with rotary milling cutters.

Edge or Pitch Cone Angles of Bevel Gears

		72	71	70	69	68	67	66	65	64	63	62	61
		Number of Teeth in Gear											
Number of Teeth in Pinion	12	80°33' / 9°27'	80°25' / 9°35'	80°16' / 9°44'	80°8' / 9°52'	79°59' / 10°1'	79°51' / 10°9'	79°42' / 10°18'	79°32' / 10°28'	79°23' / 10°37'	79°13' / 10°47'	79°3' / 10°57'	78°52' / 11°8'
	13	79°46' / 10°14'	79°37' / 10°23'	79°29' / 10°31'	79°20' / 10°40'	79°11' / 10°49'	79°1' / 10°59'	78°51' / 11°9'	78°41' / 11°19'	78°31' / 11°29'	78°20' / 11°40'	78°9' / 11°51'	77°58' / 12°2'
	14	79°0' / 11°0'	78°51' / 11°9'	78°41' / 11°19'	78°32' / 11°28'	78°22' / 11°38'	78°11' / 11°49'	78°1' / 11°59'	77°51' / 12°9'	77°40' / 12°20'	77°28' / 12°32'	77°17' / 12°43'	77°5' / 12°55'
	15	78°14' / 11°46'	78°4' / 11°56'	77°54' / 12°6'	77°44' / 12°16'	77°34' / 12°26'	77°23' / 12°37'	77°12' / 12°48'	77°0' / 13°0'	76°48' / 13°12'	76°36' / 13°24'	76°24' / 13°36'	76°11' / 13°49'
	16	77°28' / 12°32'	77°18' / 12°42'	77°7' / 12°53'	76°57' / 13°3'	76°45' / 13°15'	76°34' / 13°26'	76°22' / 13°38'	76°10' / 13°50'	75°58' / 14°2'	75°45' / 14°15'	75°32' / 14°28'	75°18' / 14°42'
	17	76°43' / 13°17'	76°32' / 13°28'	76°21' / 13°39'	76°10' / 13°50'	75°58' / 14°2'	75°45' / 14°15'	75°33' / 14°27'	75°21' / 14°39'	75°8' / 14°52'	74°54' / 15°6'	74°40' / 15°20'	74°25' / 15°35'
	18	75°58' / 14°2'	75°46' / 14°14'	75°35' / 14°25'	75°23' / 14°37'	75°10' / 14°50'	74°58' / 15°2'	74°45' / 15°15'	74°31' / 15°29'	74°17' / 15°43'	74°3' / 15°57'	73°49' / 16°11'	73°33' / 16°27'
	19	75°13' / 14°47'	75°1' / 14°59'	74°49' / 15°11'	74°36' / 15°24'	74°23' / 15°37'	74°10' / 15°50'	73°56' / 16°4'	73°42' / 16°18'	73°28' / 16°32'	73°13' / 16°47'	72°58' / 17°2'	72°42' / 17°18'
	20	74°29' / 15°31'	74°16' / 15°44'	74°3' / 15°57'	73°50' / 16°10'	73°37' / 16°23'	73°23' / 16°37'	73°9' / 16°51'	72°54' / 17°6'	72°39' / 17°21'	72°23' / 17°37'	72°7' / 17°53'	71°51' / 18°9'
	21	73°45' / 16°15'	73°32' / 16°28'	73°18' / 16°42'	73°4' / 16°56'	72°50' / 17°10'	72°36' / 17°24'	72°21' / 17°39'	72°6' / 17°54'	71°50' / 18°10'	71°34' / 18°26'	71°17' / 18°43'	71°0' / 19°0'
	22	73°1' / 16°59'	72°47' / 17°13'	72°33' / 17°27'	72°19' / 17°41'	72°4' / 17°56'	71°49' / 18°11'	71°34' / 18°26'	71°18' / 18°42'	71°2' / 18°58'	70°45' / 19°15'	70°28' / 19°34'	70°10' / 19°50'
	23	72°17' / 17°43'	72°3' / 17°57'	71°49' / 18°11'	71°34' / 18°26'	71°19' / 18°41'	71°3' / 18°57'	70°47' / 19°13'	70°30' / 19°30'	70°14' / 19°46'	69°57' / 20°3'	69°39' / 20°21'	69°20' / 20°40'
	24	71°34' / 18°26'	71°19' / 18°41'	71°5' / 18°55'	70°49' / 19°11'	70°34' / 19°26'	70°17' / 19°43'	70°1' / 19°59'	69°44' / 20°16'	69°26' / 20°34'	69°9' / 20°51'	68°50' / 21°10'	68°31' / 21°29'
	25	70°51' / 19°9'	70°36' / 19°24'	70°21' / 19°39'	70°5' / 19°55'	69°49' / 20°11'	69°32' / 20°28'	69°15' / 20°45'	68°57' / 21°3'	68°40' / 21°20'	68°21' / 21°39'	68°3' / 21°57'	67°43' / 22°17'
	26	70°9' / 19°51'	69°53' / 20°7'	69°37' / 20°23'	69°21' / 20°39'	69°4' / 20°56'	68°48' / 21°12'	68°30' / 21°30'	68°12' / 21°48'	67°54' / 22°6'	67°34' / 22°26'	67°15' / 22°45'	66°55' / 23°5'
	27	69°27' / 20°33'	69°10' / 20°50'	68°54' / 21°6'	68°38' / 21°22'	68°20' / 21°40'	68°3' / 21°57'	67°45' / 22°15'	67°26' / 22°34'	67°8' / 22°52'	66°48' / 23°12'	66°28' / 23°32'	66°7' / 23°53'
	28	68°45' / 21°15'	68°29' / 21°31'	68°12' / 21°48'	67°55' / 22°5'	67°37' / 22°23'	67°19' / 22°41'	67°1' / 22°59'	66°42' / 23°18'	66°22' / 23°38'	66°2' / 23°58'	65°42' / 24°18'	65°21' / 24°39'
	29	68°4' / 21°56'	67°47' / 22°13'	67°30' / 22°30'	67°12' / 22°48'	66°54' / 23°6'	66°36' / 23°24'	66°17' / 23°43'	65°57' / 24°3'	65°37' / 24°23'	65°16' / 24°44'	64°55' / 25°5'	64°34' / 25°26'
	30	67°23' / 22°37'	67°6' / 22°54'	66°48' / 23°12'	66°30' / 23°30'	66°12' / 23°48'	65°52' / 24°8'	65°33' / 24°27'	65°14' / 24°46'	64°53' / 25°7'	64°32' / 25°28'	64°10' / 25°50'	63°49' / 26°11'
	31	66°42' / 23°18'	66°25' / 23°35'	66°6' / 23°54'	65°48' / 24°12'	65°29' / 24°31'	65°10' / 24°50'	64°50' / 25°10'	64°30' / 25°30'	64°9' / 25°51'	63°48' / 26°12'	63°26' / 26°34'	63°3' / 26°57'
	32	66°2' / 23°58'	65°44' / 24°16'	65°26' / 24°34'	65°7' / 24°53'	64°48' / 25°12'	64°28' / 25°32'	64°8' / 25°52'	63°47' / 26°13'	63°26' / 26°34'	63°4' / 26°56'	62°42' / 27°18'	62°19' / 27°41'
	33	65°23' / 24°37'	65°4' / 24°56'	64°45' / 25°15'	64°26' / 25°34'	64°7' / 25°53'	63°47' / 26°13'	63°26' / 26°34'	63°5' / 26°55'	62°43' / 27°17'	62°21' / 27°39'	61°58' / 28°2'	61°35' / 28°25'
	34	64°43' / 25°17'	64°25' / 25°35'	64°5' / 25°55'	63°46' / 26°14'	63°26' / 26°34'	63°5' / 26°55'	62°45' / 27°15'	62°23' / 27°37'	62°1' / 27°59'	61°38' / 28°22'	61°15' / 28°45'	60°52' / 29°8'
	35	64°5' / 25°55'	63°45' / 26°15'	63°26' / 26°34'	63°6' / 26°54'	62°46' / 27°14'	62°25' / 27°35'	62°4' / 27°56'	61°42' / 28°18'	61°19' / 28°41'	60°57' / 29°3'	60°33' / 29°27'	60°9' / 29°51'
	36	63°26' / 26°34'	63°7' / 26°53'	62°47' / 27°13'	62°27' / 27°33'	62°6' / 27°54'	61°45' / 28°15'	61°23' / 28°37'	61°1' / 28°59'	60°38' / 29°22'	60°15' / 29°45'	59°51' / 30°9'	59°27' / 30°33'
	37	62°48' / 27°12'	62°28' / 27°32'	62°8' / 27°52'	61°48' / 28°12'	61°27' / 28°33'	61°5' / 28°55'	60°44' / 29°16'	60°21' / 29°39'	59°58' / 30°2'	59°35' / 30°25'	59°10' / 30°50'	58°46' / 31°14'
	38	62°11' / 27°49'	61°51' / 28°9'	61°30' / 28°30'	61°9' / 28°51'	60°48' / 29°12'	60°26' / 29°34'	60°4' / 29°56'	59°41' / 30°19'	59°18' / 30°42'	58°54' / 31°6'	58°30' / 31°30'	58°5' / 31°55'

Of the two angles given, the upper is for the gear, the lower for the pinion.

Edge or Pitch Cone Angles of Bevel Gears (*Continued*)

Number of Teeth in Gear — angles given as gear (upper) / pinion (lower).

Teeth in Pinion	60	59	58	57	56	55	54	53	52	51	50	49
12	78°41'/11°19'	78°30'/11°30'	78°19'/11°41'	78°7'/11°53'	77°54'/12°6'	77°42'/12°18'	77°28'/12°32'	77°15'/12°45'	77°0'/13°0'	76°46'/13°14'	76°30'/13°30'	76°14'/13°46'
13	77°46'/12°14'	77°34'/12°26'	77°22'/12°38'	77°9'/12°51'	76°56'/13°4'	76°42'/13°18'	76°28'/13°32'	76°13'/13°47'	75°58'/14°2'	75°42'/14°18'	75°26'/14°34'	75°8'/14°52'
14	76°52'/13°8'	76°39'/13°21'	76°26'/13°34'	76°12'/13°48'	75°58'/14°2'	75°43'/14°17'	75°28'/14°32'	75°12'/14°48'	74°56'/15°4'	74°39'/15°21'	74°21'/15°39'	74°3'/15°57'
15	75°58'/14°2'	75°44'/14°16'	75°30'/14°30'	75°15'/14°45'	75°0'/15°0'	74°44'/15°16'	74°29'/15°31'	74°12'/15°48'	73°55'/16°5'	73°37'/16°23'	73°18'/16°42'	72°59'/17°1'
16	75°4'/14°56'	74°49'/15°11'	74°35'/15°25'	74°19'/15°41'	74°3'/15°57'	73°47'/16°13'	73°30'/16°30'	73°12'/16°48'	72°54'/17°6'	72°35'/17°25'	72°15'/17°45'	71°55'/18°5'
17	74°11'/15°49'	73°56'/16°4'	73°40'/16°20'	73°24'/16°36'	73°7'/16°53'	72°49'/17°11'	72°31'/17°29'	72°13'/17°47'	71°54'/18°6'	71°34'/18°26'	71°13'/18°47'	70°52'/19°8'
18	73°18'/16°42'	73°2'/16°58'	72°45'/17°15'	72°29'/17°31'	72°11'/17°49'	71°53'/18°7'	71°34'/18°26'	71°15'/18°45'	70°54'/19°6'	70°33'/19°27'	70°12'/19°48'	69°50'/20°10'
19	72°26'/17°34'	72°9'/17°51'	71°52'/18°8'	71°34'/18°26'	71°15'/18°45'	70°57'/19°3'	70°37'/19°23'	70°17'/19°43'	69°56'/20°4'	69°34'/20°26'	69°12'/20°48'	68°48'/21°12'
20	71°34'/18°26'	71°16'/18°44'	70°59'/19°1'	70°40'/19°20'	70°21'/19°39'	70°1'/19°59'	69°41'/20°19'	69°19'/20°41'	68°57'/21°3'	68°35'/21°25'	68°12'/21°48'	67°48'/22°12'
21	70°43'/19°17'	70°24'/19°36'	70°6'/19°54'	69°46'/20°14'	69°26'/20°34'	69°6'/20°54'	68°45'/21°15'	68°23'/21°37'	68°0'/22°0'	67°37'/22°23'	67°13'/22°47'	66°48'/23°12'
22	69°52'/20°8'	69°33'/20°27'	69°13'/20°47'	68°54'/21°6'	68°33'/21°27'	68°12'/21°48'	67°50'/22°10'	67°27'/22°33'	67°4'/22°56'	66°40'/23°20'	66°15'/23°45'	65°49'/24°11'
23	69°2'/20°58'	68°42'/21°18'	68°22'/21°38'	68°2'/21°58'	67°41'/22°19'	67°18'/22°42'	66°55'/23°5'	66°32'/23°28'	66°8'/23°52'	65°44'/24°16'	65°18'/24°42'	64°51'/25°9'
24	68°12'/21°48'	67°52'/22°8'	67°31'/22°29'	67°10'/22°50'	66°48'/23°12'	66°26'/23°34'	66°2'/23°58'	65°38'/24°22'	65°14'/24°46'	64°48'/25°12'	64°22'/25°38'	63°54'/26°6'
25	67°23'/22°37'	67°2'/22°58'	66°41'/23°19'	66°19'/23°41'	65°57'/24°3'	65°33'/24°27'	65°9'/24°51'	64°45'/25°15'	64°20'/25°40'	63°53'/26°7'	63°26'/26°34'	62°58'/27°2'
26	66°34'/23°26'	66°13'/23°47'	65°51'/24°9'	65°29'/24°31'	65°6'/24°54'	64°42'/25°18'	64°18'/25°42'	63°52'/26°8'	63°26'/26°34'	62°59'/27°1'	62°31'/27°29'	62°3'/27°57'
27	65°46'/24°14'	65°25'/24°35'	65°2'/24°58'	64°39'/25°21'	64°16'/25°44'	63°51'/26°9'	63°26'/26°34'	63°0'/27°0'	62°34'/27°26'	62°6'/27°54'	61°38'/28°22'	61°8'/28°52'
28	64°59'/25°1'	64°37'/25°23'	64°14'/25°46'	63°50'/26°10'	63°26'/26°34'	63°1'/26°59'	62°36'/27°24'	62°9'/27°51'	61°42'/28°18'	61°14'/28°46'	60°45'/29°15'	60°15'/29°45'
29	64°12'/25°48'	63°50'/26°10'	63°26'/26°34'	63°2'/26°58'	62°37'/27°23'	62°12'/27°48'	61°45'/28°15'	61°19'/28°41'	60°51'/29°9'	60°23'/29°37'	59°53'/30°7'	59°23'/30°37'
30	63°26'/26°34'	63°3'/26°57'	62°39'/27°21'	62°14'/27°46'	61°49'/28°11'	61°23'/28°37'	60°57'/29°3'	60°29'/29°31'	60°1'/29°59'	59°32'/30°28'	59°2'/30°58'	58°32'/31°28'
31	62°40'/27°20'	62°18'/27°42'	61°53'/28°7'	61°28'/28°32'	61°2'/28°58'	60°36'/29°24'	60°9'/29°51'	59°41'/30°19'	59°12'/30°48'	58°42'/31°18'	58°12'/31°48'	57°41'/32°19'
32	61°56'/28°4'	61°32'/28°28'	61°7'/28°53'	60°41'/29°19'	60°15'/29°45'	59°48'/30°12'	59°21'/30°39'	58°52'/31°8'	58°34'/31°26'	57°54'/32°6'	57°23'/32°37'	56°52'/33°8'
33	61°11'/28°49'	60°47'/29°13'	60°21'/29°39'	59°56'/30°4'	59°29'/30°31'	59°2'/30°58'	58°34'/31°26'	58°5'/31°55'	57°36'/32°24'	57°6'/32°54'	56°34'/33°26'	56°2'/33°58'
34	60°28'/29°32'	60°3'/29°57'	59°37'/30°23'	59°11'/30°49'	58°44'/31°16'	58°16'/31°44'	57°48'/32°12'	57°19'/32°41'	56°49'/33°11'	56°19'/33°41'	55°47'/34°13'	55°15'/34°45'
35	59°45'/30°15'	59°19'/30°41'	58°53'/31°7'	58°27'/31°33'	58°0'/32°0'	57°32'/32°28'	57°3'/32°57'	56°33'/33°27'	56°3'/33°57'	55°32'/34°28'	55°0'/35°0'	54°28'/35°32'
36	59°2'/30°58'	58°37'/31°23'	58°10'/31°50'	57°43'/32°17'	57°16'/32°44'	56°48'/33°12'	56°19'/33°41'	55°49'/34°11'	55°18'/34°42'	54°47'/35°13'	54°15'/35°45'	53°42'/36°18'
37	58°20'/31°40'	57°54'/32°6'	57°28'/32°32'	57°1'/32°59'	56°32'/33°28'	56°4'/33°56'	55°35'/34°25'	55°5'/34°55'	54°34'/35°26'	54°2'/35°58'	53°30'/36°30'	52°56'/37°4'
38	57°39'/32°21'	57°13'/32°47'	56°46'/33°14'	56°19'/33°41'	55°51'/34°9'	55°21'/34°39'	54°52'/35°8'	54°23'/35°37'	53°51'/36°9'	53°18'/36°42'	52°46'/37°14'	52°12'/37°48'

Number of Teeth in Pinion

Of the two angles given, the upper is for the gear, the lower for the pinion.

Edge or Pitch Cone Angles of Bevel Gears (*Continued*)

Number of Teeth in Pinion		48	47	46	45	44	43	42	41	40	39	38	37
		Number of Teeth in Gear											
	12	75°58'/14°2'	75°41'/14°19'	75°23'/14°37'	75°4'/14°56'	74°45'/15°15'	74°25'/15°35'	74°3'/15°57'	73°41'/16°19'	73°18'/16°42'	72°54'/17°6'	72°28'/17°32'	72°2'/17°58'
	13	74°51'/15°9'	74°32'/15°28'	74°13'/15°47'	73°53'/16°7'	73°32'/16°28'	73°11'/16°49'	72°48'/17°12'	72°25'/17°35'	71°59'/18°1'	71°34'/18°26'	71°7'/18°53'	70°39'/19°21'
	14	73°44'/16°16'	73°25'/16°35'	73°4'/16°56'	72°43'/17°17'	72°21'/17°39'	71°58'/18°2'	71°34'/18°26'	71°9'/18°51'	70°43'/19°17'	70°15'/19°45'	69°46'/20°14'	69°16'/20°44'
	15	72°39'/17°21'	72°18'/17°42'	71°56'/18°4'	71°34'/18°26'	71°10'/18°50'	70°46'/19°14'	70°21'/19°39'	69°54'/20°6'	69°26'/20°34'	68°58'/21°2'	68°28'/21°32'	67°56'/22°4'
	16	71°34'/18°26'	71°12'/18°48'	70°49'/19°11'	70°26'/19°34'	70°1'/19°59'	69°35'/20°25'	69°9'/20°51'	68°41'/21°19'	68°12'/21°48'	67°42'/22°18'	67°10'/22°50'	66°37'/23°23'
	17	70°30'/19°30'	70°7'/19°53'	69°43'/20°17'	69°17'/20°43'	68°52'/21°8'	68°26'/21°34'	67°58'/22°2'	67°29'/22°31'	66°58'/23°2'	66°27'/23°33'	65°54'/24°6'	65°19'/24°41'
	18	69°26'/20°34'	69°3'/20°57'	68°38'/21°22'	68°12'/21°48'	67°45'/22°15'	67°17'/22°43'	66°48'/23°12'	66°18'/23°42'	65°46'/24°14'	65°14'/24°46'	64°39'/25°21'	64°4'/25°56'
	19	68°25'/21°35'	67°59'/22°1'	67°34'/22°26'	67°6'/22°54'	66°38'/23°22'	66°10'/23°50'	65°39'/24°21'	65°8'/24°52'	64°36'/25°24'	64°2'/25°58'	63°26'/26°34'	62°49'/27°11'
	20	67°23'/22°37'	66°57'/23°3'	66°30'/23°30'	66°2'/23°58'	65°33'/24°27'	65°3'/24°57'	64°32'/25°28'	64°0'/26°0'	63°26'/26°34'	62°51'/27°9'	62°14'/27°46'	61°37'/28°23'
	21	66°22'/23°38'	65°55'/24°5'	65°28'/24°32'	64°59'/25°1'	64°29'/25°31'	63°58'/26°2'	63°26'/26°34'	62°53'/27°7'	62°18'/27°42'	61°42'/28°18'	61°4'/28°56'	60°25'/29°35'
	22	65°23'/24°37'	64°55'/25°5'	64°26'/25°34'	63°57'/26°3'	63°26'/26°34'	62°54'/27°6'	62°21'/27°39'	61°47'/28°13'	61°11'/28°49'	60°34'/29°26'	59°56'/30°4'	59°15'/30°45'
	23	64°24'/25°36'	63°55'/26°5'	63°26'/26°34'	62°56'/27°4'	62°24'/27°36'	61°52'/28°8'	61°18'/28°42'	60°42'/29°18'	60°6'/29°54'	59°28'/30°32'	58°49'/31°11'	58°8'/31°52'
	24	63°26'/26°34'	62°57'/27°3'	62°27'/27°33'	61°56'/28°4'	61°23'/28°37'	60°50'/29°10'	60°15'/29°45'	59°39'/30°21'	59°2'/30°58'	58°23'/31°37'	57°44'/32°16'	57°2'/32°58'
	25	62°29'/27°31'	61°59'/28°1'	61°29'/28°31'	60°57'/29°3'	60°24'/29°36'	59°50'/30°10'	59°14'/30°46'	58°38'/31°22'	58°0'/32°0'	57°20'/32°40'	56°40'/33°20'	55°57'/34°3'
	26	61°33'/28°27'	61°3'/28°57'	60°31'/29°29'	59°59'/30°1'	59°25'/30°35'	58°50'/31°10'	58°14'/31°46'	57°37'/32°23'	56°58'/33°2'	56°19'/33°41'	55°37'/34°23'	54°54'/35°6'
	27	60°38'/29°22'	60°7'/29°53'	59°35'/30°25'	59°2'/30°58'	58°28'/31°32'	57°53'/32°7'	57°16'/32°44'	56°38'/33°22'	55°59'/34°1'	55°18'/34°42'	54°36'/35°24'	53°53'/36°7'
	28	59°45'/30°15'	59°13'/30°47'	58°40'/31°20'	58°7'/31°53'	57°32'/32°28'	56°56'/33°4'	56°19'/33°41'	55°40'/34°20'	55°0'/35°0'	54°19'/35°41'	53°37'/36°23'	52°53'/37°7'
	29	58°52'/31°8'	58°19'/31°41'	57°46'/32°14'	57°12'/32°48'	56°37'/33°23'	56°0'/34°0'	55°23'/34°37'	54°44'/35°16'	54°3'/35°57'	53°22'/36°38'	52°39'/37°21'	51°55'/38°5'
	30	58°0'/32°0'	57°27'/32°33'	56°53'/33°7'	56°19'/33°41'	55°43'/34°17'	55°5'/34°55'	54°28'/35°32'	53°48'/36°12'	53°7'/36°53'	52°26'/37°34'	51°42'/38°18'	50°58'/39°2'
	31	57°8'/32°52'	56°36'/33°24'	56°1'/33°59'	55°26'/34°34'	54°50'/35°10'	54°12'/35°48'	53°34'/36°26'	52°54'/37°6'	52°13'/37°47'	51°31'/38°29'	50°48'/39°12'	50°2'/39°58'
	32	56°19'/33°41'	55°45'/34°15'	55°11'/34°49'	54°35'/35°25'	53°58'/36°2'	53°21'/36°39'	52°42'/37°18'	52°2'/37°58'	51°20'/38°40'	50°38'/39°22'	49°54'/40°6'	49°9'/40°51'
	33	55°30'/34°30'	54°56'/35°4'	54°21'/35°39'	53°45'/36°15'	53°8'/36°52'	52°29'/37°31'	51°50'/38°9'	51°10'/38°50'	50°29'/39°31'	49°46'/40°14'	49°2'/40°58'	48°16'/41°44'
	34	54°41'/35°19'	54°7'/35°53'	53°32'/36°28'	52°56'/37°4'	52°18'/37°42'	51°40'/38°20'	51°0'/39°0'	50°20'/39°40'	49°38'/40°22'	48°55'/41°5'	48°11'/41°49'	47°25'/42°35'
	35	53°54'/36°6'	53°20'/36°40'	52°44'/37°16'	52°8'/37°52'	51°30'/38°30'	50°51'/39°9'	50°12'/39°48'	49°31'/40°29'	48°48'/41°12'	48°5'/41°55'	47°21'/42°39'	46°35'/43°25'
	36	53°8'/36°52'	52°33'/37°27'	51°57'/38°3'	51°20'/38°40'	50°43'/39°17'	50°4'/39°56'	49°24'/40°36'	48°43'/41°17'	48°0'/42°0'	47°17'/42°43'	46°33'/43°27'	45°47'/44°13'
	37	52°23'/37°37'	51°47'/38°13'	51°12'/38°48'	50°35'/39°25'	49°56'/40°4'	49°17'/40°43'	48°37'/41°23'	47°56'/42°4'	47°14'/42°46'	46°30'/43°30'	45°46'/44°14'	45°
	38	51°38'/38°22'	51°3'/38°57'	50°27'/39°33'	49°49'/40°11'	49°11'/40°49'	48°32'/41°28'	47°52'/42°8'	47°10'/42°50'	46°28'/43°32'	45°45'/44°15'	45°	......

Of the two angles given, the upper is for the gear, the lower for the pinion.

Edge or Pitch Cone Angles of Bevel Gears (Continued)

Upper value is for the gear, lower value is for the pinion.

Teeth in Pinion	\	Number of Teeth in Gear											
		36	**35**	**34**	**33**	**32**	**31**	**30**	**29**	**28**	**27**	**26**	**25**
12		71°34' 18°26'	71°5' 18°55'	70°34' 19°26'	70°1' 19°59'	69°26' 20°34'	68°50' 21°10'	68°12' 21°48'	67°31' 22°29'	66°48' 23°12'	66°2' 23°58'	65°14' 24°46'	64°22' 25°38'
13		70°9' 19°51'	69°37' 20°23'	69°5' 20°55'	68°30' 21°30'	67°53' 22°7'	67°15' 22°45'	66°34' 23°26'	65°51' 24°9'	65°6' 24°54'	64°17' 25°43'	63°26' 26°34'	62°31' 27°29'
14		68°45' 21°15'	68°12' 21°48'	67°37' 22°23'	67°0' 23°0'	66°23' 23°37'	65°42' 24°18'	64°59' 25°1'	64°14' 25°46'	63°26' 26°34'	62°36' 27°24'	61°42' 28°18'	60°45' 29°15'
15		67°23' 22°37'	66°48' 23°12'	66°12' 23°48'	65°33' 24°27'	64°53' 25°7'	64°10' 25°50'	63°26' 26°34'	62°39' 27°21'	61°49' 28°11'	60°57' 29°3'	60°1' 29°59'	59°2' 30°58'
16		66°2' 23°58'	65°26' 24°34'	64°48' 25°12'	64°8' 25°52'	63°26' 26°34'	62°42' 27°18'	61°56' 28°4'	61°7' 28°53'	60°15' 29°45'	59°21' 30°39'	58°23' 31°37'	57°23' 32°37'
17		64°43' 25°17'	64°6' 25°54'	63°26' 26°34'	62°45' 27°15'	62°1' 27°59'	61°15' 28°45'	60°28' 29°32'	59°37' 30°23'	58°44' 31°16'	57°48' 32°12'	56°49' 33°11'	55°47' 34°13'
18		63°26' 26°34'	62°47' 27°13'	62°6' 27°54'	61°23' 28°37'	60°38' 29°22'	59°51' 30°9'	59°2' 30°58'	58°10' 31°50'	57°16' 32°44'	56°19' 33°41'	55°18' 34°42'	54°15' 35°45'
19		62°10' 27°50'	61°30' 28°30'	60°48' 29°12'	60°4' 29°56'	59°18' 30°42'	58°30' 31°30'	57°39' 32°21'	56°46' 33°14'	55°51' 34°9'	54°52' 35°8'	53°51' 36°9'	52°46' 37°14'
20		60°57' 29°3'	60°15' 29°45'	59°32' 30°28'	58°47' 31°13'	58°0' 32°0'	57°10' 32°50'	56°19' 33°41'	55°24' 34°36'	54°28' 35°32'	53°28' 36°32'	52°26' 37°34'	51°20' 38°40'
21		59°45' 30°15'	59°2' 30°58'	58°18' 31°42'	57°32' 32°28'	56°43' 33°17'	55°53' 34°7'	55°0' 35°0'	54°5' 35°55'	53°7' 36°53'	52°8' 37°52'	51°4' 38°56'	49°58' 40°2'
22		58°34' 31°26'	57°51' 32°9'	57°6' 32°54'	56°19' 33°41'	55°29' 34°31'	54°38' 35°22'	53°45' 36°15'	52°49' 37°11'	51°50' 38°10'	50°49' 39°11'	49°46' 40°14'	48°39' 41°21'
23		57°25' 32°35'	56°41' 33°19'	55°55' 34°5'	55°7' 34°53'	54°18' 35°42'	53°26' 36°34'	52°31' 37°29'	51°35' 38°25'	50°36' 39°24'	49°34' 40°26'	48°30' 41°30'	47°23' 42°37'
24		56°19' 33°41'	55°33' 34°27'	54°47' 35°13'	53°58' 36°2'	53°8' 36°52'	52°15' 37°45'	51°20' 38°40'	50°23' 39°37'	49°24' 40°36'	48°22' 41°38'	47°17' 42°43'	46°10' 43°50'
25		55°13' 34°47'	54°28' 35°32'	53°40' 36°20'	52°51' 37°9'	52°0' 38°0'	51°7' 38°53'	50°12' 39°48'	49°14' 40°46'	48°14' 41°46'	47°12' 42°48'	46°7' 43°53'	45°
26		54°10' 35°50'	53°24' 36°36'	52°36' 37°24'	51°46' 38°14'	50°54' 39°6'	50°1' 39°59'	49°5' 40°55'	48°7' 41°53'	47°7' 42°53'	46°5' 43°55'	45°	......
27		53°7' 36°53'	52°21' 37°39'	51°33' 38°27'	50°43' 39°17'	49°51' 40°9'	48°57' 41°3'	48°0' 42°0'	47°3' 42°57'	46°2' 43°58'	45°	......	......
28		52°8' 37°52'	51°20' 38°40'	50°32' 39°28'	49°41' 40°19'	48°49' 41°11'	47°55' 42°5'	46°58' 43°2'	46°0' 44°0'	45°	......		
29		51°9' 38°51'	50°21' 39°39'	49°32' 40°28'	48°41' 41°19'	47°49' 42°11'	46°54' 43°6'	45°58' 44°2'	45°	......			
30		50°12' 39°48'	49°24' 40°36'	48°35' 41°25'	47°43' 42°17'	46°51' 43°9'	45°56' 44°4'	45°	......				
31		49°16' 40°44'	48°28' 41°32'	47°39' 42°21'	46°47' 43°13'	45°54' 44°6'	45°	......					
32		48°22' 41°38'	47°34' 42°26'	46°44' 43°16'	45°53' 44°7'	45°	......						
33		47°29' 42°31'	46°41' 43°19'	45°51' 44°9'	45°	......							
34		46°38' 43°22'	45°50' 44°10'	45°	......								
35		45°48' 44°12'	45°	......									
36		45°	......										

Of the two angles given, the upper is for the gear, the lower for the pinion.

Edge or Pitch Cone Angles of Bevel Gears (Continued)

		Number of Teeth in Gear											
		24	23	22	21	20	19	18	17	16	15	14	13
Number of Teeth in Pinion	12	63°26' 26°34'	62°27' 27°33'	61°23' 28°37'	60°15' 29°45'	59°2' 30°58'	57°44' 32°16'	56°19' 33°41'	54°47' 35°13'	53°7' 36°53'	51°20' 38°40'	49°24' 40°36'	47°17' 42°43'
	13	61°33' 28°27'	60°31' 29°29'	59°25' 30°35'	58°14' 31°46'	56°58' 33°2'	55°37' 34°23'	54°10' 35°50'	52°36' 37°24'	50°54' 39°6'	49°5' 40°55'	47°7' 42°53'	45°
	14	59°45' 30°15'	58°40' 31°20'	57°32' 32°28'	56°19' 33°41'	55°0' 35°0'	53°37' 36°23'	52°8' 37°52'	50°32' 39°28'	48°48' 41°12'	46°58' 43°2'	45°	.....
	15	58°0' 32°0'	56°53' 33°7'	55°43' 34°17'	54°28' 35°32'	53°7' 36°53'	51°42' 38°18'	50°12' 39°48'	48°35' 41°25'	46°51' 43°9'	45°	.....	.....
	16	56°19' 33°41'	55°11' 34°49'	53°58' 36°2'	52°42' 37°18'	51°20' 38°40'	49°54' 40°6'	48°22' 41°38'	46°44' 43°16'	45°	.....	.....	.....
	17	54°41' 35°19'	53°32' 36°28'	52°18' 37°42'	51°0' 39°0'	49°38' 40°22'	48°11' 41°49'	46°38' 43°22'	45°	.....	.....	.....	.....
	18	53°7' 36°53'	51°57' 38°3'	50°43' 39°17'	49°24' 40°36'	48°0' 42°0'	46°33' 43°27'	45°	.....	.....	.....	.....	.....
	19	51°38' 38°22'	50°26' 39°34'	49°11' 40°49'	47°52' 42°8'	46°28' 43°32'	45°	.....	.....	.....	.....	.....	.....
	20	50°12' 39°48'	48°59' 41°1'	47°43' 42°17'	46°24' 43°36'	45°	.....	.....	.....	.....	.....	.....	.....
	21	48°48' 41°12'	47°36' 42°24'	46°20' 43°40'	45°	.....	.....	.....	.....	.....	.....	.....	.....
	22	47°29' 42°31'	46°16' 43°44'	45°	.....	.....	.....	.....	.....	.....	.....	.....	.....
	23	46°13' 43°47'	45°	.....	.....	.....	.....	.....	.....	.....	.....	.....	.....
	24	45°	.....	.....	.....	.....	.....	.....	.....	.....	.....	.....	.....

Of the two angles given, the upper is for the gear, the lower for the pinion.

Materials Used for Making Bevel Gears. — Cast iron is used for the largest work, and for smaller work which is not to be subjected to heavy duty. In cases where great working stress or a sudden shock is liable to come on the teeth, steel is ordinarily used. Such gears are made from bar stock for the smallest work, from drop forgings for intermediate sizes made on a manufacturing basis and from steel castings for heavy work. The softer grades of steel are not suitable for high-speed service, as this material abrades more rapidly than cast iron. This objection does not apply to hardened steel, such as is used in automobile transmission gears.

It is quite common to make the gear and pinion of different materials. This is advantageous from the standpoint of both efficiency and durability. Cast iron and steel, and steel and bronze are common combinations. In general, the pinion should be made of the stronger material, since it is of weak form; and it should be made of the more durable material, as it revolves more rapidly and each tooth comes into working contact more times per minute than do those of the larger mating gear. In a steel and cast iron combination, then, the pinion should be of steel, while the gear is of cast iron.

Non-metallic materials are used for many pinions, especially in cases where it is desired to run gearing at a very high speed and with as little noise as possible. If the speeds are comparatively low and especially if high shock loads are likely to occur, these non-metallic materials may not prove satisfactory. In the section on spur gearing, additional information will be found on various commercial non-metallic materials and their practical application.

Face Angles of Bevel Gears

Table gives face angles measured as shown by diagram on page 739. To find *cutting angle* when *milling cutter* is used, see text, page 753.

		Number of Teeth in Gear											
		72	71	70	69	68	67	66	65	64	63	62	61
Number of Teeth in Pinion	12	7°53' / 78°59'	8° / 78°50'	8°7' / 78°39'	8°14' / 78°30'	8°21' / 78°19'	8°28' / 78°10'	8°35' / 77°59'	8°43' / 77°47'	8°51' / 77°37'	8°59' / 77°25'	9°7' / 77°13'	9°17' / 77°1'
	13	8°40' / 78°12'	8°48' / 78°2'	8°54' / 77°52'	9°2' / 77°42'	9°9' / 77°31'	9°18' / 77°20'	9°26' / 77°8'	9°35' / 76°56'	9°43' / 76°45'	9°52' / 76°32'	10°1' / 76°19'	10°11' / 76°7'
	14	9°26' / 77°26'	9°34' / 77°16'	9°42' / 77°4'	9°50' / 76°54'	9°59' / 76°43'	10°8' / 76°30'	10°16' / 76°18'	10°25' / 76°7'	10°35' / 75°55'	10°45' / 75°41'	10°54' / 75°28'	11°5' / 75°15'
	15	10°12' / 76°40'	10°21' / 76°29'	10°30' / 76°18'	10°38' / 76°6'	10°47' / 75°55'	10°57' / 75°43'	11°6' / 75°30'	11°16' / 75°16'	11°27' / 75°3'	11°37' / 74°49'	11°47' / 74°35'	11°59' / 74°21'
	16	10°59' / 75°55'	11°7' / 75°43'	11°17' / 75°31'	11°26' / 75°20'	11°37' / 75°7'	11°46' / 74°54'	11°56' / 74°40'	12°7' / 74°27'	12°17' / 74°13'	12°29' / 73°59'	12°40' / 73°44'	12°52' / 73°28'
	17	11°44' / 75°10'	11°54' / 74°58'	12°4' / 74°46'	12°13' / 74°33'	12°24' / 74°20'	12°34' / 74°5'	12°46' / 73°52'	12°56' / 73°38'	13°7' / 73°23'	13°21' / 73°9'	13°32' / 72°52'	13°45' / 72°36'
	18	12°29' / 74°25'	12°40' / 74°12'	12°50' / 74°0'	13° / 73°46'	13°12' / 73°32'	13°23' / 73°19'	13°34' / 73°4'	13°47' / 72°49'	13°59' / 72°33'	14°12' / 72°18'	14°24' / 72°2'	14°38' / 71°44'
	19	13°14' / 73°40'	13°25' / 73°27'	13°36' / 73°14'	13°48' / 73°	14° / 72°46'	14°11' / 72°31'	14°24' / 72°16'	14°36' / 72°	14°49' / 71°45'	15°2' / 71°28'	15°15' / 71°11'	15°30' / 70°54'
	20	13°59' / 72°57'	14°11' / 72°43'	14°23' / 72°29'	14°34' / 72°14'	14°46' / 72°	15°4' / 71°45'	15°11' / 71°29'	15°25' / 71°13'	15°39' / 70°56'	15°52' / 70°38'	16°7' / 70°21'	16°21' / 70°3'
	21	14°43' / 72°13'	14°55' / 71°59'	15°8' / 71°44'	15°21' / 71°29'	15°33' / 71°13'	15°46' / 70°58'	15°59' / 70°41'	16°13' / 70°25'	16°28' / 70°8'	16°42' / 69°50'	16°58' / 69°32'	17°13' / 69°13'
	22	15°27' / 71°29'	15°40' / 71°14'	15°53' / 70°59'	16°6' / 70°44'	16°20' / 70°28'	16°33' / 70°11'	16°47' / 69°55'	17°2' / 69°38'	17°16' / 69°20'	17°31' / 69°1'	17°49' / 68°43'	18°3' / 68°23'
	23	16°12' / 70°46'	16°24' / 70°30'	16°38' / 70°16'	16°51' / 69°59'	17°5' / 69°43'	17°20' / 69°26'	17°34' / 69°8'	17°50' / 68°50'	18°5' / 68°33'	18°20' / 68°14'	18°36' / 67°54'	18°54' / 67°34'
	24	16°55' / 70°3'	17°9' / 69°47'	17°22' / 69°32'	17°37' / 69°15'	17°51' / 68°58'	18°6' / 68°40'	18°21' / 68°23'	18°37' / 68°5'	18°53' / 67°45'	19°9' / 67°27'	19°26' / 67°6'	19°44' / 66°46'
	25	17°39' / 69°21'	17°52' / 69°4'	18°6' / 68°48'	18°21' / 68°31'	18°36' / 68°14'	18°52' / 67°56'	19°7' / 67°37'	19°24' / 67°18'	19°40' / 67°	19°57' / 66°39'	20°14' / 66°20'	20°32' / 65°58'
	26	18°21' / 68°39'	18°36' / 68°22'	18°51' / 68°5'	19°6' / 67°48'	19°22' / 67°30'	19°37' / 67°13'	19°53' / 66°53'	20°10' / 66°34'	20°26' / 66°14'	20°45' / 65°53'	21°2' / 65°32'	21°21' / 65°11'
	27	19°3' / 67°57'	19°19' / 67°39'	19°34' / 67°22'	19°49' / 67°5'	20°6' / 66°46'	20°22' / 66°28'	20°38' / 66°8'	20°56' / 65°48'	21°13' / 65°29'	21°32' / 65°8'	21°50' / 64°46'	22°10' / 64°24'
	28	19°46' / 67°16'	20°1' / 66°59'	20°17' / 66°41'	20°32' / 66°22'	20°50' / 66°4'	21°6' / 65°44'	21°23' / 65°25'	21°41' / 65°5'	22° / 64°44'	22°18' / 64°22'	22°37' / 64°1'	22°56' / 63°38'
	29	20°27' / 66°35'	20°43' / 66°17'	20°59' / 65°59'	21°16' / 65°40'	21°33' / 65°21'	21°50' / 65°2'	22°8' / 64°42'	22°27' / 64°21'	22°45' / 63°59'	23°5' / 63°37'	23°25' / 63°15'	23°44' / 62°52'
	30	21°9' / 65°55'	21°25' / 65°37'	21°42' / 65°18'	21°58' / 64°58'	22°15' / 64°39'	22°34' / 64°18'	22°52' / 63°58'	23°10' / 63°38'	23°30' / 63°16'	23°50' / 62°54'	24°10' / 62°30'	24°30' / 62°7'
	31	21°50' / 65°14'	22°6' / 64°56'	22°24' / 64°36'	22°41' / 64°17'	22°59' / 63°57'	23°17' / 63°37'	23°35' / 63°15'	23°55' / 62°55'	24°14' / 62°32'	24°34' / 62°10'	24°54' / 61°46'	25°17' / 61°23'
	32	22°31' / 64°35'	22°48' / 64°16'	23°4' / 63°56'	23°23' / 63°37'	23°40' / 63°16'	23°59' / 62°55'	24°18' / 62°34'	24°38' / 62°12'	24°58' / 61°50'	25°18' / 61°26'	25°39' / 61°3'	26°1' / 60°39'
	33	23°10' / 63°56'	23°28' / 63°36'	23°46' / 63°16'	24°4' / 62°56'	24°22' / 62°36'	24°41' / 62°15'	25°1' / 61°53'	25°21' / 61°31'	25°42' / 61°8'	26°2' / 60°44'	26°24' / 60°20'	26°45' / 59°55'
	34	23°51' / 63°17'	24°8' / 62°58'	24°27' / 62°37'	24°44' / 62°16'	25°4' / 61°56'	25°23' / 61°33'	25°42' / 61°12'	26°3' / 60°49'	26°24' / 60°26'	26°46' / 60°2'	27°7' / 59°37'	27°29' / 59°13'
	35	24°29' / 62°39'	24°48' / 62°18'	25°6' / 61°58'	25°25' / 61°37'	25°44' / 61°16'	26°4' / 60°54'	26°24' / 60°32'	26°45' / 60°9'	27°6' / 59°44'	27°28' / 59°22'	27°50' / 58°56'	28°13' / 58°31'
	36	25°9' / 62°1'	25°27' / 61°41'	25°45' / 61°20'	26°5' / 60°59'	26°24' / 60°36'	26°45' / 60°15'	27°5' / 59°51'	27°26' / 59°28'	27°48' / 59°4'	28°10' / 58°40'	28°33' / 58°15'	28°56' / 57°50'
	37	25°47' / 61°23'	26°6' / 61°2'	26°25' / 60°41'	26°44' / 60°20'	27°4' / 59°58'	27°25' / 59°35'	27°45' / 59°13'	28°7' / 58°49'	28°29' / 58°25'	28°51' / 58°1'	29°15' / 57°35'	29°38' / 57°10'

Of the two angles given, the upper is for the gear, the lower for the pinion.

Face Angles of Bevel Gears (Continued)

Values shown as gear angle (upper) / pinion angle (lower).

Number of Teeth in Pinion	\ Number of Teeth in Gear → 60	59	58	57	56	55	54	53	52	51	50	49
12	9°26' / 76°48'	9°35' / 76°35'	9°45' / 76°23'	9°55' / 76°8'	10°6' / 75°54'	10°16' / 75°40'	10°28' / 75°24'	10°39' / 75°9'	10°52' / 74°52'	11°3' / 74°37'	11°15' / 74°15'	11°30' / 73°58'
13	10°21' / 75°53'	10°31' / 75°39'	10°42' / 75°26'	10°53' / 75°11'	11°4' / 74°56'	11°16' / 74°40'	11°28' / 74°24'	11°42' / 74°8'	11°54' / 73°50'	12°8' / 73°32'	12°20' / 73°12'	12°37' / 72°53'
14	11°16' / 75°	11°27' / 74°45'	11°39' / 74°31'	11°50' / 74°14'	12°2' / 73°58'	12°16' / 73°42'	12°29' / 73°25'	12°43' / 73°7'	12°57' / 72°49'	13°11' / 72°29'	13°26' / 72°8'	13°42' / 71°48'
15	12°11' / 74°7'	12°22' / 73°50'	12°35' / 73°35'	12°48' / 73°18'	13°1' / 73°1'	13°16' / 72°44'	13°28' / 72°26'	13°43' / 72°7'	13°59' / 71°49'	14°14' / 71°28'	14°30' / 71°6'	14°47' / 70°45'
16	13°5' / 73°13'	13°18' / 72°56'	13°30' / 72°40'	13°45' / 72°23'	13°59' / 72°5'	14°13' / 71°47'	14°28' / 71°28'	14°44' / 71°8'	15°1' / 70°49'	15°17' / 70°27'	15°35' / 70°5'	15°52' / 69°42'
17	13°59' / 72°21'	14°11' / 72°3'	14°26' / 71°45'	14°40' / 71°28'	14°57' / 71°9'	15°11' / 70°49'	15°28' / 70°30'	15°44' / 70°10'	16°1' / 69°49'	16°18' / 69°26'	16°37' / 69°3'	16°55' / 68°39'
18	14°52' / 71°28'	15°6' / 71°10'	15°21' / 70°51'	15°36' / 70°34'	15°52' / 70°14'	16°7' / 69°53'	16°26' / 69°34'	16°42' / 69°12'	17°1' / 68°49'	17°20' / 68°26'	17°39' / 68°3'	17°58' / 67°39'
19	15°44' / 70°30'	15°59' / 70°17'	16°15' / 69°59'	16°31' / 69°39'	16°49' / 69°19'	17°2' / 68°58'	17°23' / 68°37'	17°41' / 68°15'	18° / 67°52'	18°21' / 67°29'	18°40' / 67°4'	19°1' / 66°37'
20	16°37' / 69°45'	16°53' / 69°25'	17°8' / 69°6'	17°26' / 68°46'	17°44' / 68°26'	18°1' / 68°3'	18°19' / 67°41'	18°40' / 67°18'	19° / 66°54'	19°20' / 66°30'	19°41' / 66°5'	20°2' / 65°38'
21	17°28' / 68°54'	17°46' / 68°34'	18°2' / 68°14'	18°20' / 67°54'	18°39' / 67°31'	18°57' / 67°9'	19°16' / 66°46'	19°37' / 66°23'	19°58' / 65°58'	20°19' / 65°33'	20°41' / 65°7'	21°3' / 64°39'
22	18°20' / 68°4'	18°37' / 67°43'	18°56' / 67°22'	19°13' / 67°1'	19°32' / 66°38'	19°52' / 66°16'	20°12' / 65°52'	20°33' / 65°27'	20°55' / 65°3'	21°17' / 64°37'	21°40' / 64°10'	22°3' / 63°41'
23	19°10' / 67°14'	19°28' / 66°52'	19°48' / 66°32'	20°5' / 66°9'	20°25' / 65°47'	20°47' / 65°23'	21°8' / 64°58'	21°29' / 64°33'	21°52' / 64°8'	22°13' / 63°41'	22°37' / 63°13'	23°2' / 62°44'
24	20°1' / 66°25'	20°19' / 66°3'	20°39' / 65°41'	20°58' / 65°18'	21°19' / 64°55'	21°39' / 64°31'	22°1' / 64°5'	22°24' / 63°40'	22°46' / 63°14'	23°10' / 62°46'	23°36' / 62°19'	24° / 61°48'
25	20°51' / 65°37'	21°10' / 65°14'	21°29' / 64°51'	21°50' / 64°28'	22°11' / 64°5'	22°33' / 63°39'	22°55' / 63°14'	23°18' / 62°48'	23°41' / 62°21'	24°7' / 61°53'	24°32' / 61°24'	24°57' / 60°53'
26	21°41' / 64°49'	22° / 64°26'	22°20' / 64°2'	22°41' / 63°39'	23°3' / 63°15'	23°25' / 62°49'	23°47' / 62°23'	24°13' / 61°56'	24°36' / 61°28'	25°1' / 60°59'	25°28' / 60°30'	25°53' / 59°59'
27	22°29' / 64°1'	22°49' / 63°39'	23°10' / 63°14'	23°31' / 62°49'	23°53' / 62°25'	24°16' / 61°58'	24°40' / 61°32'	25°2' / 61°5'	25°29' / 60°37'	25°55' / 60°7'	26°22' / 59°38'	26°48' / 59°5'
28	23°17' / 63°15'	23°38' / 62°52'	23°59' / 62°27'	24°21' / 62°1'	24°44' / 61°36'	25°7' / 61°9'	25°31' / 60°43'	25°56' / 60°14'	26°22' / 59°46'	26°48' / 59°16'	27°15' / 58°45'	27°43' / 58°13'
29	24°4' / 62°28'	24°25' / 62°5'	24°48' / 61°40'	25°10' / 61°14'	25°33' / 60°47'	25°57' / 60°21'	26°22' / 59°52'	26°47' / 59°25'	27°14' / 58°56'	27°40' / 58°26'	28°8' / 57°54'	28°36' / 57°22'
30	24°51' / 61°43'	25°12' / 61°18'	25°36' / 60°54'	25°59' / 60°27'	26°22' / 60°	26°47' / 59°33'	27°12' / 59°6'	27°38' / 58°36'	28°4' / 58°6'	28°32' / 57°36'	29° / 57°4'	29°28' / 56°32'
31	25°38' / 60°58'	25°58' / 60°34'	26°22' / 60°8'	26°46' / 59°42'	27°10' / 59°14'	27°34' / 58°46'	28°3' / 58°15'	28°27' / 57°49'	28°54' / 57°18'	29°23' / 56°47'	29°51' / 56°15'	30°20' / 55°42'
32	26°23' / 60°15'	26°45' / 59°49'	27°9' / 59°23'	27°34' / 58°56'	27°58' / 58°28'	28°23' / 57°59'	28°49' / 57°31'	29°17' / 57°1'	29°44' / 56°41'	30°12' / 56°	30°42' / 55°28'	31°10' / 54°54'
33	27°9' / 59°37'	27°31' / 59°5'	27°56' / 58°38'	28°19' / 58°11'	28°45' / 57°43'	29°10' / 57°14'	29°37' / 56°45'	30°5' / 56°15'	30°32' / 55°49'	31°1' / 55°13'	31°31' / 54°39'	32°1' / 54°5'
34	27°52' / 58°58'	28°16' / 58°22'	28°40' / 57°54'	29°5' / 57°27'	29°31' / 56°59'	29°57' / 56°29'	30°24' / 56°	30°52' / 55°29'	31°20' / 54°58'	31°49' / 54°27'	32°19' / 53°53'	32°50' / 53°20'
35	28°36' / 58°6'	29°1' / 57°39'	29°25' / 57°11'	29°50' / 56°44'	30°15' / 56°14'	30°42' / 55°45'	31°10' / 55°16'	31°38' / 54°44'	32°7' / 54°13'	32°36' / 53°40'	33°7' / 53°7'	33°38' / 52°34'
36	29°20' / 57°24'	29°43' / 56°57'	30°9' / 56°29'	30°35' / 56°1'	31° / 55°32'	31°27' / 55°3'	31°55' / 54°33'	32°23' / 54°1'	32°53' / 53°28'	33°23' / 52°57'	33°53' / 52°23'	34°25' / 51°40'
37	30°2' / 56°42'	30°27' / 56°15'	30°52' / 55°48'	31°18' / 55°20'	31°45' / 54°49'	32°12' / 54°20'	32°40' / 53°50'	33°8' / 53°18'	33°38' / 52°46'	34°9' / 52°13'	34°40' / 51°40'	35°12' / 51°4'
38	30°44' / 56°2'	31°9' / 55°35'	31°35' / 55°7'	32°1' / 54°39'	32°27' / 54°9'	32°56' / 53°38'	33°24' / 53°8'	33°52' / 52°38'	34°22' / 52°4'	34°54' / 51°30'	35°24' / 50°56'	35°57' / 50°21'

Of the two angles given, the upper is for the gear, the lower for the pinion.

Face Angles of Bevel Gears (Continued)

Of the two angles given, the upper is for the gear, the lower for the pinion.

Left axis: **Number of Teeth in Pinion** (rows). Top axis: **Number of Teeth in Gear** (columns).

Pinion	48	47	46	45	44	43	42	41	40	39	38	37
12	11°43' / 73°39'	11°58' / 73°20'	12°13' / 72°59'	12°29' / 72°37'	12°45' / 72°15'	13°1' / 71°51'	13°19' / 71°25'	13°37' / 70°59'	13°57' / 70°33'	14°18' / 70°6'	14°39' / 69°35'	15°1' / 69°5'
13	12°51' / 72°33'	13°7' / 72°11'	13°23' / 71°49'	13°40' / 71°26'	13°58' / 71°2'	14°16' / 70°38'	14°35' / 70°11'	14°55' / 69°45'	15°17' / 69°15'	15°39' / 68°47'	16°1' / 68°15'	16°25' / 67°43'
14	13°59' / 71°27'	14°15' / 71°5'	14°33' / 70°41'	14°51' / 70°17'	15°10' / 69°52'	15°30' / 69°26'	15°51' / 68°59'	16°13' / 68°31'	16°34' / 68°0'	16°59' / 67°29'	17°24' / 66°56'	17°50' / 66°22'
15	15°5' / 70°23'	15°23' / 69°59'	15°42' / 69°34'	16°1' / 69°9'	16°22' / 68°42'	16°43' / 68°15'	17°5' / 67°47'	17°28' / 67°16'	17°53' / 66°45'	18°18' / 66°14'	18°44' / 65°40'	19°11' / 65°3'
16	16°11' / 69°19'	16°30' / 68°54'	16°50' / 68°28'	17°10' / 68°2'	17°32' / 67°34'	17°56' / 67°6'	18°18' / 66°36'	18°42' / 66°4'	19°9' / 65°33'	19°35' / 64°59'	20°3' / 64°23'	20°32' / 63°46'
17	17°15' / 68°15'	17°36' / 67°50'	17°57' / 67°23'	18°20' / 66°54'	18°43' / 66°27'	19°6' / 65°58'	19°31' / 65°27'	19°57' / 64°54'	20°24' / 64°20'	20°51' / 63°45'	21°21' / 63°9'	21°53' / 62°31'
18	18°20' / 67°12'	18°41' / 66°47'	19°3' / 66°19'	19°27' / 65°51'	19°50' / 65°20'	20°18' / 64°48'	20°42' / 64°18'	21°9' / 63°45'	21°37' / 63°9'	22°6' / 62°34'	22°38' / 61°56'	23°9' / 61°17'
19	19°22' / 66°12'	19°46' / 65°44'	20°8' / 65°16'	20°34' / 64°46'	20°59' / 64°15'	21°24' / 63°44'	21°52' / 63°10'	22°20' / 62°36'	22°49' / 62°1'	23°20' / 61°24'	23°52' / 60°44'	24°26' / 60°4'
20	20°25' / 65°11'	20°49' / 64°43'	21°13' / 64°13'	21°39' / 63°43'	22°5' / 63°11'	22°32' / 62°38'	23°0' / 62°4'	23°30' / 61°30'	24°1' / 60°53'	24°32' / 60°14'	25°6' / 59°34'	25°40' / 58°54'
21	21°27' / 64°11'	21°52' / 63°42'	22°17' / 63°13'	22°43' / 62°41'	23°10' / 62°8'	23°38' / 61°34'	24°8' / 61°0'	24°39' / 60°25'	25°10' / 59°46'	25°43' / 59°7'	26°18' / 58°26'	26°53' / 57°43'
22	22°27' / 63°13'	22°53' / 62°43'	23°19' / 62°11'	23°46' / 61°40'	24°15' / 61°7'	24°44' / 60°32'	25°14' / 59°56'	25°46' / 59°20'	26°19' / 58°41'	26°53' / 58°1'	27°27' / 57°19'	28°5' / 56°35'
23	23°27' / 62°15'	23°54' / 61°44'	24°21' / 61°13'	24°49' / 60°41'	25°18' / 60°6'	25°47' / 59°31'	26°18' / 58°54'	26°52' / 58°16'	27°26' / 57°38'	28°0' / 56°56'	28°36' / 56°14'	29°14' / 55°30'
24	24°26' / 61°18'	24°53' / 60°47'	25°21' / 60°15'	25°49' / 59°41'	26°20' / 59°6'	26°51' / 58°31'	27°23' / 57°53'	27°57' / 57°15'	28°31' / 56°35'	29°7' / 55°53'	29°43' / 55°11'	30°22' / 54°26'
25	25°24' / 60°22'	25°52' / 59°51'	26°20' / 59°18'	26°50' / 58°44'	27°21' / 58°9'	27°52' / 57°32'	28°26' / 56°54'	28°59' / 56°15'	29°34' / 55°34'	30°12' / 54°52'	30°49' / 54°9'	31°29' / 53°23'
26	26°21' / 59°27'	26°49' / 58°55'	27°19' / 58°21'	27°47' / 57°47'	28°21' / 57°11'	28°54' / 56°34'	29°27' / 55°55'	30°1' / 55°15'	30°38' / 54°34'	31°14' / 53°52'	31°54' / 53°8'	32°34' / 52°22'
27	27°17' / 58°33'	27°46' / 58°0'	28°16' / 57°26'	28°47' / 56°51'	29°19' / 56°15'	29°52' / 55°38'	30°27' / 54°59'	31°3' / 54°19'	31°39' / 53°37'	32°18' / 52°54'	32°57' / 52°9'	33°37' / 51°23'
28	28°12' / 57°42'	28°42' / 57°8'	29°12' / 56°32'	29°43' / 55°57'	30°16' / 55°20'	30°50' / 54°42'	31°25' / 54°3'	32°2' / 53°22'	32°39' / 52°39'	33°18' / 51°56'	33°57' / 51°11'	34°39' / 50°25'
29	29°5' / 56°49'	29°37' / 56°15'	30°8' / 55°40'	30°40' / 55°4'	31°13' / 54°27'	31°48' / 53°48'	32°23' / 53°9'	32°59' / 52°27'	33°38' / 51°44'	34°17' / 51°1'	34°58' / 50°16'	35°39' / 49°29'
30	29°58' / 55°58'	30°30' / 55°24'	31°2' / 54°48'	31°34' / 54°12'	32°8' / 53°34'	32°44' / 52°54'	33°19' / 52°15'	33°57' / 51°33'	34°36' / 50°50'	35°15' / 50°7'	35°56' / 49°20'	36°38' / 48°34'
31	30°52' / 55°8'	31°22' / 54°34'	31°55' / 53°57'	32°29' / 53°21'	33°2' / 52°42'	33°39' / 52°2'	34°15' / 51°23'	34°53' / 50°41'	35°31' / 49°57'	36°11' / 49°13'	36°52' / 48°28'	37°35' / 47°39'
32	31°42' / 54°20'	32°14' / 53°44'	32°46' / 53°8'	33°21' / 52°31'	33°56' / 51°52'	34°31' / 51°12'	35°8' / 50°32'	35°46' / 49°50'	36°27' / 49°7'	37°6' / 48°22'	37°48' / 47°36'	38°31' / 46°49'
33	32°32' / 53°13'	33°4' / 52°56'	33°38' / 52°20'	34°12' / 51°42'	34°47' / 51°3'	35°24' / 50°22'	36°0' / 49°41'	36°39' / 48°59'	37°19' / 48°17'	38°0' / 47°32'	38°42' / 46°46'	39°26' / 45°58'
34	33°22' / 52°44'	33°54' / 52°8'	34°28' / 51°32'	35°3' / 50°50'	35°38' / 50°14'	36°15' / 49°33'	36°53' / 48°52'	37°32' / 48°12'	38°11' / 47°27'	38°53' / 46°43'	39°35' / 45°57'	40°18' / 45°8'
35	34°10' / 51°58'	34°42' / 51°22'	35°17' / 50°45'	35°51' / 50°7'	36°27' / 49°27'	37°5' / 48°47'	37°42' / 48°6'	38°22' / 47°24'	39°3' / 46°39'	39°44' / 45°54'	40°26' / 45°8'	41°10' / 44°20'
36	34°57' / 51°13'	35°31' / 50°37'	36°5' / 49°59'	36°41' / 49°21'	37°16' / 48°42'	37°53' / 48°1'	38°32' / 47°20'	39°11' / 46°37'	39°52' / 45°52'	40°34' / 45°8'	41°15' / 44°21'	42°0' / 43°34'
37	35°43' / 50°29'	36°18' / 49°52'	36°51' / 49°15'	37°27' / 48°37'	38°4' / 47°56'	38°42' / 47°16'	39°20' / 46°34'	40°0' / 45°52'	40°41' / 45°8'	41°22' / 44°22'	42°5' / 43°37'	42°48' /
38	36°29' / 49°45'	37°3' / 49°9'	37°38' / 48°32'	38°14' / 47°52'	38°51' / 47°13'	39°28' / 46°32'	40°7' / 45°51'	40°47' / 45°7'	41°28' / 44°24'	42°0' / 43°39'	42°52' /	

Of the two angles given, the upper is for the gear, the lower for the pinion.

Face Angles of Bevel Gears (Continued)

Number of Teeth in Pinion	Number of Teeth in Gear											
	36	35	34	33	32	31	30	29	28	27	26	25
12	15°24' / 68°32'	15°49' / 67°59'	16°15' / 67°23'	16°43' / 66°45'	17°13' / 66°5'	17°43' / 65°23'	18°15' / 64°39'	18°51' / 63°53'	19°27' / 63°3'	20°5' / 62°9'	20°46' / 61°14'	21°31' / 60°15'
13	16°51' / 67°9'	17°19' / 66°33'	17°46' / 65°56'	18°16' / 65°16'	18°48' / 64°34'	19°21' / 63°51'	19°57' / 63°5'	20°32' / 62°14'	21°11' / 61°23'	21°54' / 60°28'	22°37' / 59°29'	23°26' / 58°28'
14	18°17' / 65°47'	18°45' / 65°9'	19°16' / 64°30'	19°48' / 63°48'	20°20' / 63°6'	20°56' / 62°20'	21°34' / 61°32'	22°13' / 60°41'	22°55' / 59°47'	23°38' / 58°50'	24°25' / 57°49'	25°16' / 56°46'
15	19°40' / 64°26'	20°11' / 63°49'	20°44' / 63°8'	21°18' / 62°24'	21°53' / 61°39'	22°31' / 60°51'	23°10' / 60°2'	23°51' / 59°9'	24°35' / 58°13'	25°20' / 57°14'	26°11' / 56°13'	27°3' / 55°7'
16	21°3' / 63°7'	21°36' / 62°28'	22°9' / 61°45'	22°45' / 61°1'	23°22' / 60°14'	24°1' / 59°25'	24°42' / 58°34'	25°26' / 57°40'	26°12' / 56°42'	27°1' / 55°43'	27°52' / 54°38'	28°45' / 53°31'
17	22°24' / 61°50'	22°57' / 61°9'	23°33' / 60°25'	24°10' / 59°40'	24°50' / 58°52'	25°31' / 58°1'	26°14' / 57°10'	26°59' / 56°13'	27°47' / 55°15'	28°37' / 54°13'	29°30' / 53°8'	30°26' / 52°0'
18	23°43' / 60°35'	24°18' / 59°52'	24°56' / 59°8'	25°34' / 58°20'	26°15' / 57°31'	26°57' / 56°39'	27°42' / 55°46'	28°30' / 54°49'	29°18' / 53°50'	30°9' / 52°47'	31°5' / 51°41'	32°2' / 50°32'
19	25°1' / 59°21'	25°37' / 58°37'	26°15' / 57°51'	26°56' / 57°4'	27°38' / 56°14'	28°22' / 55°22'	29°8' / 54°26'	29°56' / 53°28'	30°43' / 52°28'	31°40' / 51°24'	32°36' / 50°18'	33°36' / 49°8'
20	26°16' / 58°10'	26°55' / 57°25'	27°34' / 56°38'	28°15' / 55°49'	28°58' / 54°58'	29°44' / 54°4'	30°31' / 53°9'	31°21' / 52°9'	32°13' / 51°9'	33°8' / 50°4'	34°5' / 48°57'	35°6' / 47°46'
21	27°30' / 57°0'	28°10' / 56°14'	28°50' / 55°26'	29°32' / 54°36'	30°17' / 53°43'	31°4' / 52°50'	31°52' / 51°52'	32°43' / 50°53'	33°36' / 49°50'	34°31' / 48°47'	35°31' / 47°39'	36°32' / 46°28'
22	28°43' / 55°51'	29°22' / 55°4'	30°5' / 54°17'	30°48' / 53°26'	31°34' / 52°32'	32°22' / 51°38'	33°11' / 50°41'	34°3' / 49°41'	34°57' / 48°37'	35°54' / 47°32'	36°52' / 46°24'	37°55' / 45°13'
23	29°53' / 54°43'	30°35' / 53°57'	31°18' / 53°8'	32°1' / 52°15'	32°48' / 51°24'	33°36' / 50°28'	34°27' / 49°29'	35°20' / 48°30'	36°15' / 47°27'	37°12' / 46°20'	38°12' / 45°12'	39°15' / 44°1'
24	31°2' / 53°40'	31°45' / 52°51'	32°28' / 52°2'	33°14' / 51°10'	34°1' / 50°17'	34°50' / 49°20'	35°42' / 48°22'	36°35' / 47°21'	37°30' / 46°18'	38°28' / 45°9'	39°29' / 44°3'	40°32' / 42°52'
25	32°10' / 52°36'	32°52' / 51°48'	33°37' / 50°57'	34°23' / 50°5'	35°11' / 49°11'	36°0' / 48°14'	36°52' / 47°16'	37°47' / 46°15'	38°43' / 45°11'	39°41' / 44°5'	40°43' / 42°57'	41°46'
26	33°15' / 51°35'	33°58' / 50°46'	34°45' / 49°55'	35°31' / 49°3'	36°19' / 48°7'	37°10' / 47°12'	38°2' / 46°12'	38°56' / 45°10'	39°53' / 44°7'	40°52' / 43°2'	41°53'	
27	34°20' / 50°34'	35°3' / 49°45'	35°49' / 48°55'	36°36' / 48°2'	37°25' / 47°7'	38°16' / 46°10'	39°10' / 45°10'	40°4' / 44°10'	41°1' / 43°5'	42°		
28	35°21' / 49°37'	36°7' / 48°47'	36°52' / 47°56'	37°40' / 47°2'	38°29' / 46°7'	39°21' / 45°11'	40°15' / 44°11'	41°9' / 43°9'	42°7'			
29	36°23' / 48°41'	37°8' / 47°50'	37°54' / 46°58'	38°42' / 46°4'	39°32' / 45°10'	40°24' / 44°12'	41°18' / 43°14'	42°13'				
30	37°21' / 47°45'	38°7' / 46°55'	38°53' / 46°3'	39°43' / 45°9'	40°32' / 44°14'	41°25' / 43°17'	42°18'					
31	38°20' / 46°52'	39°5' / 46°1'	39°52' / 45°10'	40°41' / 44°15'	41°32' / 43°20'	42°23'						
32	39°15' / 45°59'	40°1' / 45°9'	40°49' / 44°17'	41°38' / 43°24'	42°28'							
33	40°10' / 45°8'	40°56' / 44°18'	41°44' / 43°26'	42°33'								
34	41°4' / 44°20'	41°49' / 43°29'	42°37'									
35	41°55' / 43°31'	42°41'										
36	42°45'											

Of the two angles given, the upper is for the gear, the lower for the pinion.

Face Angles of Bevel Gears *(Continued)*

		Number of Teeth in Gear											
		24	23	22	21	20	19	18	17	16	15	14	13
	12	22°18' 59°10'	23°8' 58°2'	24°3' 56°49'	25°2' 55°32'	26°3' 54°7'	27°11' 52°39'	28°25' 51°3'	29°43' 49°17'	31°11' 47°25'	32°44' 45°24'	34°26' 43°14'	36°16' 40°50'
	13	24°15' 57°21'	25°9' 56°11'	26°6' 54°56'	27°8' 53°36'	28°14' 52°10'	29°25' 50°39'	30°42' 49°2'	32°4' 47°16'	33°34' 45°22'	35°10' 43°20'	36°55' 41°9'	38°48'
	14	26°8' 55°38'	27°5' 54°25'	28°4' 53°8'	29°9' 51°47'	30°20' 50°20'	31°33' 48°47'	32°52' 47°8'	34°17' 45°21'	35°50' 43°26'	37°28' 41°24'	39°15'	.....
	15	27°58' 53°58'	28°58' 52°44'	30°0' 51°26'	31°6' 50°2'	32°19' 48°33'	33°36' 47°0'	34°56' 45°20'	36°23' 43°33'	37°57' 41°39'	39°38'	.....	.....
Number of Teeth in Pinion	16	29°43' 52°21'	30°44' 51°6'	31°50' 49°46'	32°58' 48°22'	34°12' 46°52'	35°31' 45°19'	36°54' 43°38'	38°23' 41°51'	39°57'	.....		
	17	31°26' 50°48'	32°28' 49°32'	33°35' 48°11'	34°47' 46°47'	36°0' 45°16'	37°21' 43°43'	38°45' 42°1'	40°15'	.....			
	18	33°4' 49°18'	34°8' 48°2'	35°15' 46°41'	36°28' 45°16'	37°45' 43°45'	39°5' 42°11'	40°31'	.....				
	19	34°38' 47°54'	35°44' 46°36'	36°53' 45°15'	38°6' 43°50'	39°24' 42°20'	40°45'	.....					
	20	36°8' 46°32'	37°16' 45°14'	38°26' 43°52'	39°39' 42°27'	40°57'	.....						
	21	37°37' 45°13'	38°44' 43°56'	39°54' 42°34'	41°8'	.....							
	22	39°0' 43°58'	40°8' 42°40'	41°19'	.....								
	23	40°20' 42°46'	41°28'	.....									
	24	41°38'	.....										

Of the two angles given, the upper is for the gear, the lower for the pinion.

Dedendum Angles for Different Addendum Angles. — When the shafts of bevel gears are not at right angles or when the depth of the tooth is greater or smaller than the standard depth for the thickness of tooth used, the table "Dedendum Angles for Different Addendum Angles" may be employed. The addendum angle is first calculated from the formula:

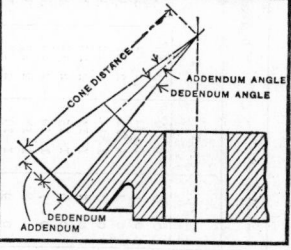

$$\text{Addendum} \div \text{cone distance} = \text{tangent of addendum angle}.$$

Then the dedendum angle may be found directly from the table. When the table is used for teeth that are not of standard depth, the *ratio* of the dedendum to the addendum must still remain the same as for standard involute teeth.

As an example of the use of the table, find the dedendum angle for an addendum angle of 3 degrees 43 minutes. At the intersection of the vertical column under 3 degrees and the horizontal line opposite 43 minutes, the answer, 4 degrees 18 minutes, is found. This difference between addendum and dedendum angles does not apply to gears cut by rotary cutters (see page 739).

Dedendum Angles for Different Addendum Angles*

Degrees (Minutes 0–29)

Minutes	0	1	2	3	4	5
0	0° 0′	1° 9′	2° 19′	3° 28′	4° 38′	5° 47′
1	0 1	1 11	2 20	3 29	4 39	5 48
2	0 2	1 12	2 21	3 31	4 40	5 49
3	0 3	1 13	2 22	3 32	4 41	5 51
4	0 4	1 14	2 23	3 33	4 42	5 52
5	0 5	1 15	2 25	3 34	4 44	5 53
6	0 6	1 16	2 26	3 35	4 45	5 54
7	0 7	1 18	2 27	3 36	4 46	5 55
8	0 8	1 19	2 28	3 38	4 47	5 56
9	0 9	1 20	2 29	3 39	4 48	5 58
10	0 10	1 21	2 30	3 40	4 49	5 59
11	0 12	1 22	2 32	3 41	4 50	6 0
12	0 13	1 23	2 33	3 42	4 52	6 1
13	0 14	1 24	2 34	3 43	4 53	6 2
14	0 15	1 26	2 35	3 44	4 54	6 3
15	0 16	1 27	2 36	3 46	4 55	6 5
16	0 17	1 28	2 37	3 47	4 56	6 6
17	0 19	1 29	2 39	3 48	4 57	6 7
18	0 20	1 30	2 40	3 49	4 59	6 8
19	0 21	1 31	2 41	3 50	5 0	6 9
20	0 22	1 33	2 42	3 51	5 1	6 10
21	0 23	1 34	2 43	3 53	5 2	6 11
22	0 24	1 35	2 44	3 54	5 3	6 13
23	0 25	1 36	2 45	3 55	5 4	6 14
24	0 27	1 37	2 47	3 56	5 6	6 15
25	0 28	1 38	2 48	3 57	5 7	6 16
26	0 29	1 40	2 49	3 58	5 8	6 17
27	0 30	1 41	2 50	4 0	5 9	6 18
28	0 31	1 42	2 51	4 1	5 10	6 20
29	0 33	1 43	2 52	4 2	5 11	6 21

Degrees (Minutes 30–59)

Minutes	0	1	2	3	4	5
30	0° 35′	1° 44′	2° 54′	4° 3′	5° 12′	6° 22′
31	0 36	1 45	2 55	4 4	5 14	6 23
32	0 37	1 46	2 56	4 5	5 15	6 24
33	0 38	1 48	2 57	4 6	5 16	6 25
34	0 39	1 49	2 58	4 8	5 17	6 26
35	0 41	1 50	2 59	4 9	5 18	6 28
36	0 42	1 51	3 1	4 10	5 19	6 29
37	0 43	1 52	3 2	4 11	5 21	6 30
38	0 44	1 53	3 3	4 12	5 22	6 31
39	0 45	1 55	3 4	4 13	5 23	6 32
40	0 46	1 56	3 5	4 15	5 24	6 33
41	0 47	1 57	3 6	4 16	5 25	6 35
42	0 49	1 58	3 7	4 17	5 26	6 36
43	0 50	1 59	3 9	4 18	5 27	6 37
44	0 51	2 0	3 10	4 19	5 29	6 38
45	0 52	2 2	3 11	4 20	5 30	6 39
46	0 53	2 3	3 12	4 22	5 31	6 40
47	0 54	2 4	3 13	4 23	5 32	6 42
48	0 56	2 5	3 14	4 24	5 33	6 43
49	0 57	2 6	3 16	4 25	5 34	6 44
50	0 58	2 7	3 17	4 26	5 36	6 45
51	0 59	2 8	3 18	4 27	5 37	6 46
52	1 0	2 10	3 19	4 28	5 38	6 47
53	1 1	2 11	3 20	4 30	5 39	6 48
54	1 2	2 12	3 21	4 31	5 40	6 50
55	1 4	2 13	3 23	4 32	5 41	6 51
56	1 5	2 14	3 24	4 33	5 43	6 52
57	1 6	2 15	3 25	4 34	5 44	6 53
58	1 7	2 17	3 26	4 35	5 45	6 54
59	1 8	2 18	3 27	4 37	5 46	6 55

BEVEL GEARING

General Considerations Relating to Design of Bevel Gears. — The performance of the most carefully designed and made bevel gears depends to a considerable extent on the design of the machine in which they are used. When the shafts on which a pair of bevel gears are mounted are poorly supported or poorly fitted in their bearings, the pressure of the driving gear on the driven causes it to climb upon the latter, throwing the shafts out of alignment. This in turn causes the teeth to bear with a greater pressure at one end of the face (usually at the outer end) than at the other, thus making the tooth more liable to break than is the case when the pressure is more evenly distributed. It is important, therefore, to provide rigid shafts and bearings and careful workmanship for bevel gearing.

Proportions of Bevel Gears. — Various forms may be given to the blanks or wheels on which bevel gear teeth are cut, depending on the size, material, service, etc., to be provided for. The pinion type of blank is mostly used for gears of a small number of teeth and small pitch cone angle. When the diameter of the bore comes too near to the bottoms of the teeth at the small end, it is customary to omit the usual recess in the front face. For gears of a larger number of teeth, the web type is appropriate. This does not require to be finished all over, as the sides of the web, the outside of the hub, and the under side of the rim may be rough.

A gear suitable for very heavy work should have the web reinforced by ribs. The web may be cut out so that the rim is supported by T-shaped arms. This makes a very stiff wheel and at the same time a very light one, in proportion to its strength.

The question of alignment of the shafts should be considered in deciding upon the width of face of the gear. Making the width of the face more than one-third of the pitch cone radius adds practically nothing to the strength of the gear, since the added portion is progressively weaker as the tooth is lengthened. In addition to this, there is the danger that through springing of the shafts or poor workmanship, the load will be thrown onto the weak end of the tooth, thus fracturing it. For this reason it may be laid down as a definite rule that there is nothing to be gained by making the face of the bevel gear more than one-third of the pitch cone radius.

The Brown & Sharpe Mfg. Co., in one of its publications, gives a rule for the maximum width of face allowable for a given pitch. The width of face should not exceed 2½ times the circular pitch, or 8 divided by the diametral pitch. This rule is rational, since the danger to the teeth from the misalignment of the shafts increases both with the width of face and with the decrease of the size of the tooth, so that both of these should be reckoned with. In designing gearing it is well to check the width of face from the rule relating to the pitch cone radius and that relating to the pitch as well, to see that it does not exceed the maximum allowed by either.

Table for Selecting Cutters for Bevel Gears. — This table gives the number of cutter to use for various numbers of teeth in the gear and pinion. It applies to bevel gears with axes at right angles only. The number of the cutter for the gear is given first, followed by the number for the pinion.

Example. — Required the cutters for a pair of bevel gears where the gear has 24 teeth and the pinion, 12 teeth. The table shows that the numbers of the cutters to be used are Nos. 3 and 8, No. 3 being for the gear, and No. 8 for the pinion.

For 14½-degree involute teeth, the standard cutter series furnished by the makers of formed gear cutters is commonly used. There are 8 cutters in the series, to cover the full range from the 12-tooth pinion to a crown gear. The standard bevel gear cutter is made thinner than the standard spur gear cutter, as it must pass through the narrow tooth space at the inner end of the face. As usually kept in stock, these cutters are thin enough for bevel gears in which the width of face is not more than one-third the pitch cone radius.

Number of Cutters for Cutting Bevel Gears

		Number of Teeth in Pinion															
		12	13	14	15	16	17	18	19	20	21	22	23	24	25	26	27	28
Number of Teeth in Gear	12	7-7																
	13	6-7	6-6															
	14	5-7	6-6	6-6														
	15	5-7	5-6	5-6	5-5													
	16	4-7	5-7	5-6	5-6	5-5												
	17	4-7	4-7	4-6	5-6	5-5	5-5											
	18	4-7	4-7	4-6	4-6	4-5	4-5	5-5										
	19	3-7	4-7	4-6	4-6	4-6	4-5	4-5	4-4									
	20	3-7	3-7	4-6	4-6	4-6	4-5	4-5	4-4	4-4								
	21	3-8	3-7	3-7	3-6	4-6	4-6	4-5	4-5	4-4	4-4							
	22	3-8	3-7	3-7	3-6	3-6	3-5	4-5	4-5	4-4	4-4	4-4						
	23	3-8	3-7	3-7	3-6	3-6	3-5	3-5	3-5	3-4	4-4	4-4	4-4					
	24	3-8	3-7	3-7	3-6	3-6	3-6	3-5	3-5	3-4	3-4	3-4	4-4	4-4				
	25	2-8	2-7	3-7	3-7	3-6	3-6	3-6	3-5	3-5	3-5	3-4	3-4	3-4	4-4			
	26	2-8	2-7	3-7	3-7	3-6	3-6	3-6	3-5	3-5	3-5	3-4	3-4	3-4	3-4	3-3		
	27	2-8	2-7	2-7	2-6	3-6	3-6	3-5	3-5	3-5	3-4	3-4	3-4	3-4	3-4	3-3	3-3	
	28	2-8	2-7	2-7	2-6	2-6	3-6	3-5	3-5	3-5	3-4	3-4	3-4	3-4	3-4	3-3	3-3	3-3
	29	2-8	2-7	2-7	2-7	2-6	2-6	3-5	3-5	3-5	3-4	3-4	3-4	3-4	3-4	3-3	3-3	3-3
	30	2-8	2-7	2-7	2-7	2-6	2-6	2-5	2-5	3-5	3-5	3-4	3-4	3-4	3-4	3-4	3-3	3-3
	31	2-8	2-7	2-7	2-7	2-6	2-6	2-5	2-5	2-5	3-4	3-4	3-4	3-4	3-4	3-4	3-3	3-3
	32	2-8	2-7	2-7	2-7	2-6	2-6	2-5	2-5	2-5	2-4	2-4	3-4	3-4	3-4	3-4	3-3	3-3
	33	2-8	2-8	2-7	2-7	2-6	2-6	2-6	2-5	2-5	2-4	2-4	2-4	3-4	3-4	3-4	3-4	3-3
	34	2-8	2-8	2-7	2-7	2-6	2-6	2-6	2-5	2-5	2-5	2-4	2-4	2-4	2-4	2-4	3-4	3-3
	35	2-8	2-8	2-7	2-7	2-6	2-6	2-6	2-5	2-5	2-5	2-4	2-4	2-4	2-4	2-4	2-4	2-3
	36	2-8	2-8	2-7	2-7	2-6	2-6	2-6	2-5	2-5	2-5	2-4	2-4	2-4	2-4	2-4	2-4	2-3
	37	2-8	2-8	2-7	2-7	2-6	2-6	2-6	2-5	2-5	2-5	2-5	2-4	2-4	2-4	2-4	2-4	2-3
	38	2-8	2-8	2-7	2-7	2-6	2-6	2-6	2-5	2-5	2-5	2-5	2-4	2-4	2-4	2-4	2-4	2-4
	39	2-8	2-8	2-7	2-7	2-6	2-6	2-6	2-5	2-5	2-5	2-5	2-4	2-4	2-4	2-4	2-4	2-4
	40	1-8	2-8	2-7	2-7	2-6	2-6	2-6	2-5	2-5	2-5	2-5	2-4	2-4	2-4	2-4	2-4	2-4
	41	1-8	1-8	2-7	2-7	2-6	2-6	2-6	2-6	2-5	2-5	2-5	2-4	2-4	2-4	2-4	2-4	2-4
	42	1-8	1-8	2-7	2-7	2-6	2-6	2-6	2-6	2-5	2-5	2-5	2-5	2-4	2-4	2-4	2-4	2-4
	43	1-8	1-8	1-7	2-7	2-6	2-6	2-6	2-6	2-5	2-5	2-5	2-5	2-4	2-4	2-4	2-4	2-4
	44	1-8	1-8	1-7	1-7	2-6	2-6	2-6	2-6	2-5	2-5	2-5	2-5	2-5	2-4	2-4	2-4	2-4
	45	1-8	1-8	1-7	1-7	1-6	2-6	2-6	2-6	2-5	2-5	2-5	2-5	2-5	2-4	2-4	2-4	2-4
	46	1-8	1-8	1-7	1-7	1-7	2-6	2-6	2-6	2-5	2-5	2-5	2-5	2-5	2-4	2-4	2-4	2-4
	47	1-8	1-8	1-7	1-7	1-7	1-6	2-6	2-6	2-5	2-5	2-5	2-5	2-5	2-4	2-4	2-4	2-4
	48	1-8	1-8	1-7	1-7	1-7	1-6	1-6	2-6	2-6	2-5	2-5	2-5	2-5	2-4	2-4	2-4	2-4
	49	1-8	1-8	1-7	1-7	1-7	1-6	1-6	1-6	2-5	2-5	2-5	2-5	2-4	2-4	2-4	2-4	2-4
	50	1-8	1-8	1-7	1-7	1-7	1-6	1-6	1-6	2-5	2-5	2-5	2-5	2-4	2-4	2-4	2-4	2-4
	51	1-8	1-8	1-7	1-7	1-7	1-6	1-6	1-6	1-5	1-5	2-5	2-5	2-4	2-4	2-4	2-4	2-4
	52	1-8	1-8	1-7	1-7	1-7	1-6	1-6	1-6	1-5	1-5	2-5	2-5	2-4	2-4	2-4	2-4	2-4
	53	1-8	1-8	1-7	1-7	1-7	1-6	1-6	1-6	1-5	1-5	1-5	2-5	2-4	2-4	2-4	2-4	2-4
	54	1-8	1-8	1-7	1-7	1-7	1-6	1-6	1-6	1-5	1-5	1-5	1-5	2-4	2-4	2-4	2-4	2-4
	55	1-8	1-8	1-7	1-7	1-7	1-6	1-6	1-6	1-5	1-5	1-5	1-5	1-4	2-4	2-4	2-4	2-4

For bevel gears with axes at right angles.

Number of cutter for gear given first, followed by number for pinion.

Number of Cutters for Cutting Bevel Gears

		Number of Teeth in Pinion																
		12	13	14	15	16	17	18	19	20	21	22	23	24	25	26	27	28
Number of Teeth in Gear	56	1–8	1–8	1–7	1–7	1–6	1–6	1–6	1–6	1–5	1–5	1–5	1–5	1–4	1–4	2–4	2–4	2–4
	57	1–8	1–8	1–7	1–7	1–6	1–6	1–6	1–6	1–5	1–5	1–5	1–5	1–4	1–4	2–4	2–4	2–4
	58	1–8	1–8	1–7	1–7	1–6	1–6	1–6	1–6	1–5	1–5	1–5	1–5	1–4	1–4	1–4	1–4	2–4
	59	1–8	1–8	1–7	1–7	1–6	1–6	1–6	1–6	1–5	1–5	1–5	1–5	1–5	1–4	1–4	1–4	2–4
	60	1–8	1–8	1–7	1–7	1–6	1–6	1–6	1–6	1–5	1–5	1–5	1–5	1–5	1–4	1–4	1–4	1–4
	61	1–8	1–8	1–7	1–7	1–6	1–6	1–6	1–6	1–5	1–5	1–5	1–5	1–4	1–4	1–4	1–4	1–4
	62	1–8	1–8	1–7	1–7	1–6	1–6	1–6	1–6	1–5	1–5	1–5	1–5	1–4	1–4	1–4	1–4	1–4
	63	1–8	1–8	1–7	1–7	1–6	1–6	1–6	1–6	1–5	1–5	1–5	1–5	1–5	1–4	1–4	1–4	1–4
	64	1–8	1–8	1–7	1–7	1–6	1–6	1–6	1–6	1–6	1–5	1–5	1–5	1–5	1–4	1–4	1–4	1–4
	65	1–8	1–8	1–7	1–7	1–7	1–6	1–6	1–6	1–6	1–5	1–5	1–5	1–5	1–4	1–4	1–4	1–4
	66	1–8	1–8	1–7	1–7	1–7	1–6	1–6	1–6	1–6	1–5	1–5	1–5	1–5	1–4	1–4	1–4	1–4
	67	1–8	1–8	1–7	1–7	1–7	1–6	1–6	1–6	1–6	1–5	1–5	1–5	1–5	1–4	1–4	1–4	1–4
	68	1–8	1–8	1–7	1–7	1–7	1–6	1–6	1–6	1–6	1–5	1–5	1–5	1–5	1–4	1–4	1–4	1–4
	69	1–8	1–8	1–7	1–7	1–7	1–6	1–6	1–6	1–6	1–5	1–5	1–5	1–5	1–4	1–4	1–4	1–4
	70	1–8	1–8	1–7	1–7	1–7	1–6	1–6	1–6	1–6	1–5	1–5	1–5	1–5	1–4	1–4	1–4	1–4
	71	1–8	1–8	1–7	1–7	1–7	1–6	1–6	1–6	1–6	1–5	1–5	1–5	1–5	1–4	1–4	1–4	1–4
	72	1–8	1–8	1–7	1–7	1–7	1–6	1–6	1–6	1–6	1–5	1–5	1–5	1–5	1–4	1–4	1–4	1–4
	73	1–8	1–8	1–7	1–7	1–7	1–6	1–6	1–6	1–6	1–5	1–5	1–5	1–5	1–4	1–4	1–4	1–4
	74	1–8	1–8	1–7	1–7	1–7	1–6	1–6	1–6	1–6	1–5	1–5	1–5	1–5	1–4	1–4	1–4	1–4
	75	1–8	1–8	1–7	1–7	1–7	1–6	1–6	1–6	1–6	1–5	1–5	1–5	1–5	1–4	1–4	1–4	1–4
	76	1–8	1–8	1–7	1–7	1–7	1–6	1–6	1–6	1–6	1–5	1–5	1–5	1–5	1–4	1–4	1–4	1–4
	77	1–8	1–8	1–7	1–7	1–7	1–6	1–6	1–6	1–6	1–5	1–5	1–5	1–5	1–4	1–4	1–4	1–4
	78	1–8	1–8	1–7	1–7	1–7	1–6	1–6	1–6	1–6	1–5	1–5	1–5	1–5	1–4	1–4	1–4	1–4
	79	1–8	1–8	1–7	1–7	1–7	1–6	1–6	1–6	1–6	1–5	1–5	1–5	1–5	1–4	1–4	1–4	1–4
	80	1–8	1–8	1–7	1–7	1–7	1–6	1–6	1–6	1–6	1–5	1–5	1–5	1–5	1–4	1–4	1–4	1–4
	81	1–8	1–8	1–7	1–7	1–7	1–6	1–6	1–6	1–6	1–5	1–5	1–5	1–5	1–4	1–4	1–4	1–4
	82	1–8	1–8	1–7	1–7	1–7	1–6	1–6	1–6	1–6	1–5	1–5	1–5	1–5	1–4	1–4	1–4	1–4
	83	1–8	1–8	1–7	1–7	1–7	1–6	1–6	1–6	1–6	1–5	1–5	1–5	1–5	1–4	1–4	1–4	1–4
	84	1–8	1–8	1–7	1–7	1–7	1–6	1–6	1–6	1–6	1–5	1–5	1–5	1–5	1–4	1–4	1–4	1–4
	85	1–8	1–8	1–7	1–7	1–7	1–6	1–6	1–6	1–6	1–5	1–5	1–5	1–5	1–4	1–4	1–4	1–4
	86	1–8	1–8	1–7	1–7	1–7	1–5	1–6	1–6	1–6	1–5	1–5	1–5	1–5	1–4	1–4	1–4	1–4
	87	1–8	1–8	1–7	1–7	1–7	1–6	1–6	1–6	1–6	1–5	1–5	1–5	1–5	1–4	1–4	1–4	1–4
	88	1–8	1–8	1–7	1–7	1–7	1–6	1–6	1–6	1–6	1–5	1–5	1–5	1–5	1–4	1–4	1–4	1–4
	89	1–8	1–8	1–7	1–7	1–7	1–6	1–6	1–6	1–6	1–5	1–5	1–5	1–5	1–4	1–4	1–4	1–4
	90	1–8	1–8	1–7	1–7	1–7	1–6	1–6	1–6	1–6	1–5	1–5	1–5	1–5	1–4	1–4	1–4	1–4
	91	1–8	1–8	1–7	1–7	1–7	1–6	1–6	1–6	1–6	1–5	1–5	1–5	1–5	1–4	1–4	1–4	1–4
	92	1–8	1–8	1–7	1–7	1–7	1–6	1–6	1–6	1–6	1–5	1–5	1–5	1–5	1–4	1–4	1–4	1–4
	93	1–8	1–8	1–7	1–7	1–7	1–6	1–6	1–6	1–6	1–5	1–5	1–5	1–5	1–4	1–4	1–4	1–4
	94	1–8	1–8	1–7	1–7	1–7	1–6	1–6	1–6	1–6	1–5	1–5	1–5	1–5	1–4	1–4	1–4	1–4
	95	1–8	1–8	1–7	1–7	1–7	1–6	1–6	1–6	1–6	1–5	1–5	1–5	1–5	1–4	1–4	1–4	1–4
	96	1–8	1–8	1–7	1–7	1–7	1–6	1–6	1–6	1–6	1–5	1–5	1–5	1–5	1–4	1–4	1–4	1–4
	97	1–8	1–8	1–7	1–7	1–7	1–6	1–6	1–6	1–6	1–5	1–5	1–5	1–5	1–4	1–4	1–4	1–4
	98	1–8	1–8	1–7	1–7	1–7	1–6	1–6	1–6	1–6	1–5	1–5	1–5	1–5	1–4	1–4	1–4	1–4
	99	1–8	1–8	1–7	1–7	1–7	1–6	1–6	1–6	1–6	1–5	1–5	1–5	1–5	1–4	1–4	1–4	1–4
	100	1–8	1–8	1–7	1–7	1–7	1–6	1–6	1–6	1–6	1–5	1–5	1–5	1–5	1–4	1–4	1–4	1–4

For bevel gears with axes at right angles.
Number of cutter for gear given first, followed by number for pinion.

Offset of Cutter for Milling Bevel Gears. — When milling bevel gears with a rotary formed cutter, it is necessary to take two cuts through each tooth space with the gear blank slightly off center, first on one side and then on the other, to obtain a tooth of approximately the correct form. The gear blank is also rotated proportionately to obtain the proper tooth thickness at the large and small ends. The amount that the gear blank or cutter should be offset from the central position can be determined quite accurately by the use of the table "Factors for Obtaining Offset for Cutting Bevel Gears," in conjunction with the following rule: Find the factor in the table corresponding to the number of cutter used and to the ratio of the pitch cone radius to the face width; then divide this factor by the diametral pitch and subtract the result from half the thickness of the cutter at the pitch line.

Factors for Obtaining Offset for Cutting Bevel Gears

No. of Cutter	Ratio of Pitch Cone Radius to Width of Face $\left(\dfrac{C}{F}\right)$												
	$\dfrac{3}{1}$	$\dfrac{3\frac{1}{4}}{1}$	$\dfrac{3\frac{1}{2}}{1}$	$\dfrac{3\frac{3}{4}}{1}$	$\dfrac{4}{1}$	$\dfrac{4\frac{1}{4}}{1}$	$\dfrac{4\frac{1}{2}}{1}$	$\dfrac{4\frac{3}{4}}{1}$	$\dfrac{5}{1}$	$\dfrac{5\frac{1}{2}}{1}$	$\dfrac{6}{1}$	$\dfrac{7}{1}$	$\dfrac{8}{1}$
1	0.254	0.254	0.255	0.256	0.257	0.257	0.257	0.258	0.258	0.259	0.260	0.262	0.264
2	0.266	0.268	0.271	0.272	0.273	0.274	0.274	0.275	0.277	0.279	0.280	0.283	0.284
3	0.266	0.268	0.271	0.273	0.275	0.278	0.280	0.282	0.283	0.286	0.287	0.290	0.292
4	0.275	0.280	0.285	0.287	0.291	0.293	0.296	0.298	0.298	0.302	0.305	0.308	0.311
5	0.280	0.285	0.290	0.293	0.295	0.296	0.298	0.300	0.302	0.307	0.309	0.313	0.315
6	0.311	0.318	0.323	0.328	0.330	0.334	0.337	0.340	0.343	0.348	0.352	0.356	0.362
7	0.289	0.298	0.308	0.316	0.324	0.329	0.334	0.338	0.343	0.350	0.360	0.370	0.376
8	0.275	0.286	0.296	0.309	0.319	0.331	0.338	0.344	0.352	0.361	0.368	0.380	0.386

Note. — For obtaining offset by above table, use formula:

$$\text{Offset} = \frac{T}{2} - \frac{\text{factor from table}}{P}$$

P = diametral pitch of gear to be cut;
T = thickness of cutter used, measured at pitch line.

Expressing this rule as a formula, in which O = amount of offset; T = thickness of cutter at pitch line; P = diametral pitch of gear; F = factor from table, we have

$$O = \frac{T}{2} - \frac{F}{P}$$

To illustrate, what would be the amount of offset for a bevel gear having 24 teeth, 6 pitch, 30-degree pitch cone angle and 1¼ inch face or tooth length? In order to obtain a factor from the table, the ratio of the pitch cone radius to the face width must be determined. The pitch cone radius equals the pitch diameter divided by twice the sine of the pitch cone angle = $\dfrac{4}{2 \times 0.5}$ = 4 inches. As the face width is 1.25, the ratio is $\dfrac{4}{1.25} = \dfrac{3.2}{1}$ or about 3¼. The factor in the table for this ratio is 0.280 with a No. 4 cutter, which would be the cutter number for this particular gear. The thickness of the cutter at the pitch line is measured by using a vernier gear tooth caliper. The depth $S + A$ (see illustration; S = addendum; A = clearance) at which to take the measurement equals 1.157 divided by the diametral pitch; thus, $1.157 \div 6 = 0.1928$ inch. The cutter thickness at this depth will vary with different cutters and even with the same cutter as it is ground away, because formed bevel gear cutters are commonly provided with side relief. Assuming that the thickness is 0.1745 inch, and substituting the values in the formula given, we have:

$$\text{Offset} = \frac{0.1745}{2} - \frac{0.280}{6} = 0.0406.$$

Adjusting the Gear Blank for Milling. — After the offset is determined, the blank is adjusted laterally this amount, and the tooth spaces are milled around the blank. After having milled one side of each tooth to the proper dimensions, the blank is set over in the opposite direction the same amount from a position central with the cutter, and is rotated to line up the cutter with a tooth space at the small end. A trial cut is then taken, which will leave the tooth being milled a little too thick, provided the cutter is thin enough — as it should be — to pass through the small end of the tooth space of the finished gear. This trial tooth is made the proper thickness by rotating the blank toward the cutter. To test the amount of offset measure the tooth thickness (with a vernier caliper) at the large and small ends. The caliper should be set so that the addendum at the small end is in proper proportion to the addendum at the large end; that is, in the ratio, $\frac{C-F}{C}$ (see illustration). In taking these measurements, if the thicknesses at both ends (which should be in this same ratio) are too great, rotate the tooth toward the cutter and take trial cuts until the proper thickness at either the large or small end is obtained.

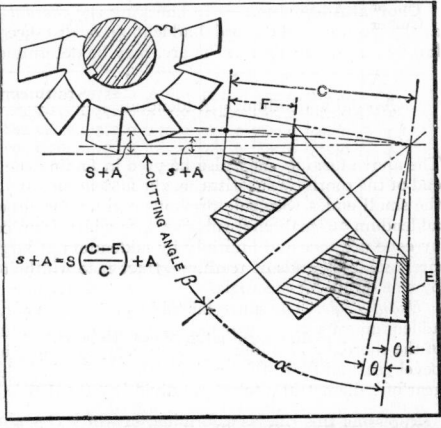

If the large end of the tooth is the right thickness and the small end too thick, the blank was offset too much; inversely, if the small end is correct and the large end too thick, the blank was not set enough off center, and, in either case, its position should be changed accordingly. The formula and table previously referred to will enable a properly turned blank to be set accurate enough for general work. The dividing head should be set to the cutting angle β (see illustration), which is found by subtracting the addendum angle θ from the pitch cone angle α. After cutting a bevel gear by the method described, the sides of the teeth at the small end should be filed as indicated by the shade lines at E; that is, by filing off a triangular area from the point of the tooth at the large end to the point at the small end, thence down to the pitch line and back diagonally to a point at the large end.

Circular or Arc Thickness of Tooth. — The rules which follow are for determining the circular or arc thickness at both the large and small ends of a bevel gear tooth having a standard addendum. *Rule* 1: The arc or circular thickness at the large end of tooth and on the pitch circle, equals 1.5708 divided by the diametral pitch. It also equals the circular pitch divided by 2

Rule 2: To find arc thickness at small end of tooth, subtract face width from cone distance; divide remainder by cone distance and multiply by tooth thickness at large end.

Chordal Thickness at Large End of Tooth. — The following rule applies to a bevel gear tooth having a standard addendum.

Rule: To find chordal thickness at large end, and on the pitch circle, divide 90 degrees by number of teeth, find sine of angle thus obtained, and multiply it by pitch diameter. (Formulas based upon the " back cone distance " have been used for determining the chordal thickness of bevel gears, but the same results are obtained with the comparatively simple rule here given.)

The spur gear table on page 668 may also be used for finding the chordal thickness of a bevel gear having standard addendum. This thickness is the same as that of a spur gear having the same pitch and number of teeth. Merely divide chordal thickness in table by diametral pitch of bevel gear.

Chordal Addendum. — In checking the *chordal* thickness of a bevel gear tooth at the pitch line, the chordal addendum or distance from the top of the tooth at the large end to the chord of the arc, may be determined by the following formula:

$$\text{Chordal addendum} = \text{Addendum} + \frac{\text{Arc thickness}^2 \times \cos \text{pitch-cone angle}}{4 \times \text{Pitch diameter}}$$

The above formula may also be used in finding the chordal addendum at the small end of the tooth by substituting the addendum, arc thickness, and pitch diameter at the small end. (See rule previously given for circular or arc thickness.) To find addendum at small end, subtract face width from cone distance; divide remainder by cone distance and multiply by addendum at large end. To find radius of pitch circle at small ends of teeth, subtract face width from cone distance and multiply by sine of pitch-cone angle.

Use of Table: The spur gear table on page 668 may be used for finding the chordal addendum of a bevel gear having standard addendum. Multiply the decimal part of the chordal addendum for a spur gear, by the cosine of the pitch-cone angle of the bevel gear, add 1 to the product (thus obtaining the chordal addendum for a bevel gear of 1 diametral pitch), and divide by the diametral pitch of the bevel gear.

Forms of Bevel Gear Tooth. — A correctly formed bevel gear tooth has the same sectional shape throughout its length but on a uniformly diminishing scale from the large to the small end. The only way to obtain this correct form is by using a generating type of bevel gear cutting machine. The tooth curvature is generated from a straight-sided cutter or tool having an angle equal to the required pressure angle. This tool represents the side of a crown gear. The teeth of a true involute crown gear, however, have sides which are very slightly curved. If the curvature of the cutting tool conforms to that of the involute crown gear, an involute form of bevel gear tooth will be obtained. The use of a straight-sided tool is more practical and results in a very slight change of tooth shape to what is known as the "octoid" form. Both the octoid and involute forms give theoretically correct action.

Bevel gear teeth, like those for spur gears, differ as to pressure angle and tooth proportions. For example, the whole depth and the addendum (at large end of tooth) may be the same as for a spur gear of equal pitch. Many bevel gears, however, both of the straight tooth and spiral-bevel types, have lengthened pinion addenda and shortened gear addenda as in the case of spur gears. See the Gleason Works System; also the British standard.

Straight-tooth Bevel Gears — Gleason Works System

Pitch Diameter Pitch-cone Angle Pitch-cone Radius Dedendum Angle Root or Cutting Angle	See rules and formulas on pages 740 and 741 for ordinary bevel gears

Note: The rules which follow apply to right-angle, general industrial drives (both speed-decreasing and speed-increasing) with 13 or more pinion teeth.

To Find	Rule
Whole Depth	For teeth coarser than 20 diametral pitch, divide 2.188 by diametral pitch. For teeth of 20 diametral pitch and finer, divide 2.200 by diametral pitch and add 0.002 inch.
Addendum, Gear	Divide number of teeth on gear by number on pinion to get ratio; find in Table A the addendum opposite this ratio and divide it by diametral pitch.
Addendum, Pinion	Divide 2.00 by diametral pitch and subtract from quotient the gear addendum.
Dedendum, Gear	Subtract from whole depth, the gear addendum.
Dedendum, Pinion	Subtract from whole depth, the pinion addendum.
Outside Diameter	Multiply addendum (of gear or pinion, as the case may be) by the cosine of the pitch-cone angle; double the product and add it to the pitch diameter.
Circular Thickness of Gear Tooth at Large End	*Pressure angle 14½ degrees.* Divide 1.071 by the diametral pitch; add quotient to 0.5 times gear addendum; subtract from this sum an amount x (Table B) divided by diametral pitch. (x is selected according to gearing ratio and number of pinion teeth.) *Pressure angle 17½ degrees.* Divide 0.971 by diametral pitch; add quotient to 0.6 times gear addendum; subtract from this sum an amount x (Table B) divided by diametral pitch. *Pressure angle 20 degrees.* Divide 0.871 by diametral pitch; add quotient to 0.7 times gear addendum; subtract from this sum an amount x (Table B) divided by the diametral pitch.
Circular Thickness, Pinion Tooth	Divide 3.1416 by the diametral pitch and subtract from quotient the circular thickness of gear tooth. Note: This rule applies to pressure angles of 14½, 17½, and 20 degrees.
Chordal Thickness, Gear and Pinion	To find chordal thickness at large end of the tooth, divide the cube of the circular thickness, by 6 times the square of the pitch diameter; subtract quotient from circular thickness; then subtract one-half total backlash.
Chordal Addendum, Gear and Pinion	Multiply square of circular thickness by cosine of pitch-cone angle; divide product by 4 times pitch diameter and add quotient to addendum.
Face Angle for Uniform Clearance	Face angle of blank, measured from axis, equals 90 degrees minus root angle or cutting angle of mating gear.

Straight-tooth Bevel Gears — Gleason Works System

TABLE A. GEAR ADDENDA FOR 1 DIAMETRAL PITCH AND VARIOUS GEAR AND PINION RATIOS

Ratio = Number of teeth in gear ÷ Number of teeth in pinion

From	To	Add., Inch	From	To	Add., Inch	From	To	Add., Inch	From	To	Add., Inch
1.00	1.00	1.000	1.15	1.17	0.880	1.42	1.45	0.760	2.06	2.16	0.640
1.00	1.02	0.990	1.17	1.19	0.870	1.45	1.48	0.750	2.16	2.27	0.630
1.02	1.03	0.980	1.19	1.21	0.860	1.48	1.52	0.740	2.27	2.41	0.620
1.03	1.04	0.970	1.21	1.23	0.850	1.52	1.56	0.730	2.41	2.58	0.610
1.04	1.05	0.960	1.23	1.25	0.840	1.56	1.60	0.720	2.58	2.78	0.600
1.05	1.06	0.950	1.25	1.27	0.830	1.60	1.65	0.710	2.78	3.05	0.590
1.06	1.08	0.940	1.27	1.29	0.820	1.65	1.70	0.700	3.05	3.41	0.580
1.08	1.09	0.930	1.29	1.31	0.810	1.70	1.76	0.690	3.41	3.94	0.570
1.09	1.11	0.920	1.31	1.33	0.800	1.76	1.82	0.680	3.94	4.82	0.560
1.11	1.12	0.910	1.33	1.36	0.790	1.82	1.89	0.670	4.82	6.81	0.550
1.12	1.14	0.900	1.36	1.39	0.780	1.89	1.97	0.660	6.81	∞	0.540
1.14	1.15	0.890	1.39	1.42	0.770	1.97	2.06	0.650	....	....	....

As in the original system, long and short addenda have been adopted for all ratios except those with equal numbers of teeth. A long-addendum pinion and a short-addendum gear have more action in recess than in approach (with pinion driving), have stronger pinion teeth, and can have a lower pressure angle without undercut.

TABLE B. VALUES OF X FOR CIRCULAR OR ARC THICKNESS FORMULA

Number of Teeth in Pinion	Ratio = Number of gear teeth ÷ Number of pinion teeth							
	1.00 to 1.25	1.25 to 1.50	1.50 to 1.75	1.75 to 2.00	2.00 to 2.25	2.25 to 2.50	2.50 to 2.75	2.75 to 3.00
	Values of x (in Inches) for Different Ratios							
13	0.000	0.015	0.040	0.045	0.050	0.060	0.070	0.080
14	0.000	0.015	0.030	0.050	0.065	0.080	0.090	0.100
15 to 17	0.000	0.000	0.010	0.020	0.030	0.045	0.060	0.070
18 to 21	0.000	0.000	0.000	0.000	0.010	0.030	0.045	0.060
22 to 29	0.000	0.000	0.000	0.000	0.010	0.030	0.040	0.050
30 and up	0.000	0.000	0.000	0.000	0.010	0.025	0.035	0.040

Number of Teeth in Pinion	Ratios						
	3.00 to 3.25	3.25 to 3.50	3.50 to 3.75	3.75 to 4.00	4.00 to 4.50	4.50 to 5.00	5.00 and higher
	Values of x (in Inches) for Different Ratios						
13	0.090	0.100	0.110	0.120	0.135	0.150	0.165
14	0.110	0.120	0.125	0.130	0.140	0.150	0.160
15 to 17	0.080	0.090	0.095	0.100	0.110	0.115	0.120
18 to 21	0.070	0.080	0.085	0.090	0.095	0.100	0.100
22 to 29	0.060	0.065	0.070	0.070	0.080	0.085	0.085
30 and up	0.045	0.050	0.055	0.060	0.065	0.070	0.070

Spiral Bevel Gears—Gleason Works System

| Pitch Diameter Pitch-cone Angle Pitch-cone Radius Dedendum Angle Root or Cutting Angle | See rules and formulas on pages 740 and 741 for ordinary bevel gears |

Note: The rules which follow apply to right-angle general industrial drives (both speed-decreasing and speed-increasing) with 12 or more pinion teeth.

To Find	Rule
Whole Depth	For diametral pitches up to 20, divide 1.888 by diametral pitch. For pitches of 20 and finer, divide 1.950 by diametral pitch.
Addendum, Gear	Divide number of teeth on gear by number of teeth on pinion to find ratio of gearing. Find, in Table C, addendum opposite this ratio. Divide addendum value from table by diametral pitch.
Addendum, Pinion	Divide 1.7 by diametral pitch and subtract from quotient the gear addendum.
Dedendum, Gear and Pinion	Subtract from whole depth, addendum of gear or pinion, as case may be.
Outside Diameter	Multiply addendum (of gear or pinion, as the case may be) by the cosine of the pitch-cone angle, double the product and add to the pitch diameter.
Circular Thickness T of Gear Tooth for Pressure Angles of $14\frac{1}{2}°$, $16°$, $17\frac{1}{2}°$, $20°$, (P = diametral pitch)	For pressure angle of $14\frac{1}{2}°$ $$T = \frac{1.061}{P} + (0.60 \times \text{gear addendum}) - \frac{X \text{ (Table D)}}{P}$$ For pressure angle of $16°$ $$T = \frac{1.019}{P} + (0.65 \times \text{gear addendum}) - \frac{X \text{ (Table D)}}{P}$$ For pressure angle of $17\frac{1}{2}°$ $$T = \frac{0.976}{P} + (0.70 \times \text{gear addendum}) - \frac{X \text{ (Table D)}}{P}$$ For pressure angle of $20°$ $$T = \frac{0.856}{P} + (0.84 \times \text{gear addendum}) - \frac{X \text{ (Table D)}}{P}$$
Circular Thickness, Pinion Tooth	To find circular tooth thickness on the pitch circle, divide 3.1416 by the diametral pitch and from this quotient subtract the circular thickness of the gear tooth.
Root Angle or Cutting Angle	Root angle or cutting angle equals pitch-cone angle minus dedendum angle.
Face Angle of Blank for Uniform Clearance	Face angle of blank, measured from axis, equals 90 degrees minus root angle of mating gear or pinion.
Vertex Distance or Cone Center to Crown	Multiply addendum (of gear or pinion, as case may be) by sine of pitch-cone angle and subtract product from pitch radius.

Spiral Bevel Gears — Gleason Works System

TABLE C. GEAR ADDENDA FOR 1 DIAMETRAL PITCH AND VARIOUS GEAR AND PINION RATIOS

Gearing ratio = Number of gear teeth ÷ Number of pinion teeth											
Ratios		Add.,	Ratios		Add.,	Ratios		Add.,	Ratios		Add.,
From	To	Inch	From	To	Inch	From	To	Inch	From	To	Inch
1.00	1.00	0.850	1.15	1.17	0.750	1.41	1.44	0.650	1.99	2.10	0.550
1.00	1.02	0.840	1.17	1.19	0.740	1.44	1.48	0.640	2.10	2.23	0.540
1.02	1.03	0.830	1.19	1.21	0.730	1.48	1.52	0.630	2.23	2.38	0.530
1.03	1.05	0.820	1.21	1.23	0.720	1.52	1.57	0.620	2.38	2.58	0.520
1.05	1.06	0.810	1.23	1.26	0.710	1.57	1.63	0.610	2.58	2.82	0.510
1.06	1.08	0.800	1.26	1.28	0.700	1.63	1.68	0.600	2.82	3.17	0.500
1.08	1.09	0.790	1.28	1.31	0.690	1.68	1.75	0.590	3.17	3.67	0.490
1.09	1.11	0.780	1.31	1.34	0.680	1.75	1.82	0.580	3.67	4.56	0.480
1.11	1.13	0.770	1.34	1.37	0.670	1.82	1.90	0.570	4.56	7.00	0.470
1.13	1.15	0.760	1.37	1.41	0.660	1.90	1.99	0.560	7.00	∞	0.460

TABLE D. VALUES OF X FOR CIRCULAR OR ARC THICKNESS FORMULA

	Gearing ratio = Number of gear teeth ÷ Number of pinion teeth							
	Ratios							
Number of Teeth in Pinion	1.00 to 1.25	1.25 to 1.50	1.50 to 1.75	1.75 to 2.00	2.00 to 2.25	2.25 to 2.50	2.50 to 2.75	2.75 to 3.00
	Values of x (in Inches) for Different Ratios							
12 to 13	0.005	0.015	0.025	0.035	0.045	0.055	0.065	0.075
14 to 16	0.000	0.005	0.015	0.025	0.035	0.050	0.060	0.075
17 to 19	0.000	0.000	0.005	0.015	0.025	0.035	0.050	0.065
20 and up	0.000	0.000	0.000	0.005	0.015	0.025	0.040	0.050
	Ratios							
Number of Teeth in Pinion	3.00 to 3.25	3.25 to 3.50	3.50 to 3.75	3.75 to 4.00	4.00 to 4.50	4.50 to 5.00	5.00 and higher	
	Values of x (in Inches) for Different Ratios							
12 to 13	0.085	0.095	0.105	0.115	0.125	0.135	0.135	
14 to 16	0.085	0.095	0.100	0.105	0.105	0.105	0.105	
17 to 19	0.075	0.085	0.090	0.090	0.090	0.090	0.090	
20 and up	0.055	0.060	0.060	0.060	0.060	0.060	0.060	

The method followed in proportioning the addendum (Table C) and dedendum was to adjust them until the amount of sliding during approach was about the same or slightly less than the sliding action during recess. This also had the effect of making the arc of recess greater than the arc of approach, which is very desirable, since recess action is quieter than approach. To obtain these conditions, it was necessary to decrease the gear addendum and increase the pinion addendum as the ratios of the numbers of teeth in the gear and pinion became greater. These values of addendum for gear and pinion were originally worked out for each ratio and number of teeth, and from an examination of them it was found possible to make an arrangement in a tabular form according to ratios without sacrifice of practical qualities.

Gleason Works System of Bevel Gears. — The system of bevel gears introduced by the Gleason Works, Rochester, N. Y., is designed to give the quietest form of tooth consistent with strength and wearing qualities. With this system the gear addendum is decreased and the pinion addendum is increased as the ratio of gear teeth to pinion teeth becomes greater. The basis of the system is in using the lowest pressure angle that can be employed without introducing undercut. This system provides a basis for designing both straight- and spiral-bevel gears with the most desirable tooth forms for practical operating conditions. The calculations employed in obtaining essential dimensions and angles are indicated by the accompanying tables or charts. The original system has been revised so that undercut is eliminated in all cases. Face angles for both straight- and spiral-bevel gears have also been changed to make the clearance uniform between the top of a tooth and the root of its mating tooth. The system is designed to include all of the ratios in common use and to provide gear and pinion teeth of approximately equal strength. It is intended for generated teeth and for general industrial drives of both speed-decreasing and speed-increasing types. The axes are assumed to be at right angles and the pinion in straight-tooth gearing is to have 13 or more teeth and in spiral-bevel gearing 12 or more teeth.

Addendums: — As in the original system long and short addendums have been adopted for all ratios except those with equal numbers of teeth. A long addendum pinion and a short addendum gear have more action in recess than in approach (with pinion driving), have stronger pinion teeth, and can have a lower pressure angle without undercut.

Face Width: — The face width should preferably be limited to from 0.25 to 0.30 times the cone distance or pitch-cone radius. Longer face widths may increase the strength theoretically, but they may introduce manufacturing difficulties by requiring tools of less point width and decrease the possible fillet radius.

Backlash: — The recommended backlash for both straight- and spiral-bevel gearing, is as follows: For 1 diametral pitch (D.P.) — 0.020 to 0.030; for 2 D.P. — 0.012 to 0.016; for 3 D.P. — 0.008 to 0.011; for 4 D.P. — 0.006 to 0.008; for 6 D.P. — 0.004 to 0.006; for 10 D. P. — 0.002 to 0.004; and for 20 D.P., and finer — 0.001 to 0.003 inch. When the gear member of a spiral-bevel gear is cut "spread-blade," all the backlash is taken from the pinion thickness. When both members are cut "single-side" the thickness of each member is reduced by one half the backlash. Because of manufacturing tolerances and changes resulting from heat-treatment, it frequently is necessary to increase these figures to obtain correct backlash in assembly.

Tooth Thickness: — The transverse tooth thickness for spiral-bevel gears, obtained by the accompanying formulas and data, is recommended when the "single-side" method of cutting is employed. The spiral angle in this case is the same on both sides of the tooth. In order to balance the strengths of gear and pinion teeth, the tooth thickness is based upon the worst conditions of loading or the condition existing when one tooth carries the entire load.

Basic Pressure Angle: — In the Gleason system, the basic pressure angle is 14½ degrees. Certain advantages are generally associated with low pressure angle, such as, (1) larger contact ratio or greater arc of action; (2) less effect of eccentricity; (3) smaller radial and axial thrust loads. These advantages are obtained in ratios with sufficiently large numbers of teeth. In certain ratios with small numbers of teeth in the pinion, however, a low pressure angle, together with standard depths, is accompanied by undercut, which decreases the tooth contact and the strength. In the original system, a slight amount of undercut was allowed. In the revised systems undercut has been eliminated in all cases by extending the range of ratios. Because of the extensive application to industrial gear drives of the Gleason Jobbing Systems having 16-degree and 20-degree pressure angles, the use of 14½ degree and 17½ degree angles is gradually decreasing. It may therefore be preferred to adopt only 16-degree and 20-degree angles for general use, but in no case should a smaller pressure angle be used than indicated by the following list

Pressure Angles for Straight-bevel Gear Systems: — In the straight system, pressure angles of 14½, 17½, and 20 degrees are utilized in conjunction with the following ratios:

14½-degree Pressure Angle: Ratios with 27 or more teeth on pinion; $2\frac{9}{30}$ and higher; $2\frac{5}{45}$ and higher; $2\frac{4}{48}$ and higher.

17½-degree Pressure Angle: Ratios, $2\frac{9}{26}$ to $2\frac{9}{29}$; $2\frac{5}{25}$ to $2\frac{5}{34}$; $2\frac{4}{24}$ to $2\frac{4}{47}$; $2\frac{3}{23}$ to $2\frac{3}{100}$; $2\frac{2}{22}$ to $2\frac{2}{100}$; $2\frac{1}{21}$ to $2\frac{1}{100}$; $2\frac{9}{20}$ to $2\frac{9}{100}$; $1\frac{9}{19}$ to $1\frac{9}{100}$; $1\frac{5}{21}$ to $1\frac{5}{100}$; $1\frac{7}{26}$ to $1\frac{7}{100}$.

20-degree Pressure Angle: Ratios, $1\frac{5}{18}$ to $1\frac{5}{20}$; $1\frac{7}{17}$ to $1\frac{7}{25}$; $1\frac{9}{16}$ to $1\frac{9}{100}$; $1\frac{5}{15}$ to $1\frac{5}{100}$; $1\frac{4}{16}$ to $1\frac{4}{100}$; $1\frac{3}{23}$ to $1\frac{3}{100}$. The 20-degree group includes all ratios for aircraft and instrument gears.

Pressure Angles for Spiral-bevel Gear Systems: — In the revised spiral-bevel gear system there are four pressure angles for application to the following ratios:

14½-degree Pressure Angle: Ratios with 28 or more teeth in pinion; $2\frac{7}{29}$ and higher; $2\frac{9}{30}$ and higher; $2\frac{5}{42}$ and higher; $2\frac{4}{33}$ and higher; $2\frac{3}{36}$ and higher; $2\frac{3}{40}$ and higher; $2\frac{1}{42}$ and higher; $2\frac{9}{60}$ and higher; $1\frac{9}{70}$ and higher.

16-degree Pressure Angle: Ratios $2\frac{7}{27}$ to $2\frac{7}{28}$; $2\frac{9}{26}$ to $2\frac{9}{29}$; $2\frac{5}{25}$ to $2\frac{5}{31}$; $2\frac{4}{24}$ to $2\frac{4}{32}$; $2\frac{3}{25}$ to $2\frac{3}{35}$; $2\frac{3}{36}$ to $2\frac{3}{39}$; $2\frac{1}{27}$ to $2\frac{1}{41}$; $2\frac{9}{29}$ to $2\frac{9}{49}$; $1\frac{9}{31}$ to $1\frac{9}{69}$; $1\frac{5}{36}$ to $1\frac{5}{100}$; $1\frac{7}{45}$ to $1\frac{7}{100}$; $1\frac{9}{59}$ to $1\frac{9}{100}$.

17½-degree Pressure Angle: Ratios $2\frac{3}{23}$ to $2\frac{3}{24}$; $2\frac{3}{22}$ to $2\frac{3}{25}$; $2\frac{1}{21}$ to $2\frac{1}{26}$; $2\frac{9}{22}$ to $2\frac{9}{28}$; $1\frac{9}{22}$ to $1\frac{9}{30}$; $1\frac{3}{23}$ to $1\frac{3}{35}$; $1\frac{7}{25}$ to $1\frac{7}{44}$; $1\frac{9}{27}$ to $1\frac{9}{63}$; $1\frac{5}{30}$ to $1\frac{5}{100}$; $1\frac{4}{37}$ to $1\frac{4}{100}$; $1\frac{3}{61}$ to $1\frac{3}{100}$.

20-degree Pressure Angle: Ratios $2\frac{9}{20}$ to $2\frac{9}{21}$; $1\frac{9}{19}$ to $1\frac{9}{21}$; $1\frac{5}{18}$ to $1\frac{5}{22}$; $1\frac{7}{17}$ to $1\frac{7}{24}$; $1\frac{9}{18}$ to $1\frac{9}{26}$; $1\frac{5}{19}$ to $1\frac{5}{29}$; $1\frac{4}{20}$ to $1\frac{4}{26}$; $1\frac{3}{22}$ to $1\frac{3}{60}$; $1\frac{3}{26}$ to $1\frac{3}{100}$. This group includes *all* ratios for aircraft and instrument gears.

British Standard for Bevel Gears. — The British standard specifications for machine cut bevel gearing applies to all bevel gears connecting intersecting shafts and includes either straight, curved, helical or spiraloid teeth having a pressure angle of 20 degrees. These gears are divided into two general classes:

Class B — High-class cut gears suitable for peripheral speeds above 750 feet per minute.

Class C — Commercial cut gears suitable for peripheral speeds below 1200 feet per minute.

This specification does not apply to aviation gearing. The range of speeds specified for the two classes of gears in this specification have been so fixed as to permit of considerable overlap between the classes. Where at any particular speed a gear may fall in either of the two classes, it is implied that the lower class is suitable for the duty; but where it is desired to have special high-grade work for a particular duty, or to meet exceptionally severe conditions, the higher class may be selected.

Form of Tooth. — The British standard form of tooth for straight bevel gears and as proportioned for a unit circular pitch of one inch, is the same as shown by the lower basic rack tooth shape on page 699, excepting for the following minor changes. The flat at the bottom of the tooth space is 0.095 instead of 0.035 (for the unit circular pitch of one inch) and the radius of the fillet is 0.082 instead of 0.124 inch. In all other respects, the basic tooth shape for bevel gears is the same as for high-class or commercial cut spur gears. This tooth form is generated from a tool having an angle of 20 degrees and a straight side, excepting that a slight easing of the tip of the tooth is permissible. The amount of this easing or tip relief shall not exceed the following values measured on the basic rack:

Class B — High-class cut gears. — 0.004 × circular pitch extending
0.125 × circular pitch in depth.
Class C — Commercial cut gears. — 0.008 × circular pitch extending
0.125 × circular pitch in depth.

The shape and proportions of teeth for helical and spiraloid bevel gears on a section at right angles to the tooth spiral conforms to the shape for straight teeth, normal pitch being substituted for circular pitch.

Clearance Space. — The bottom clearance space at the small end of the tooth shall be a smooth continuous curve and shall be as nearly semi-circular in form as the tooth form and system of cutting will permit. This requirement shall not preclude the provision of slight "flats" at the bottom of the clearance spaces, as shown.

Face Width. — The specification recommends a face width limited to one-third of the cone distance (pitch-cone radius) and a pitch that is not less than one-third of the face width.

Addendum Correction. — In order to avoid undercutting of pinion teeth, or to secure conjugate tooth action, the pinion addendum is increased and the mating gear addendum decreased by the same amount for certain combinations of gearing. The "virtual number" of pinion teeth is first determined. This is defined as the number on a complete gear having a pitch radius equal to that on the developed back cone and it is equal to the actual number of teeth multiplied by the secant of the pitch-cone angle. Columns 2 and 3 of the accompanying table give the corrected pinion and wheel (or gear) addenda suitable for virtual tooth numbers ranging from 10 to 19. Under the heading "Caliper Settings," the measuring height and the chordal tooth thickness when measured at that height are given. All of these values are for 1 D. P. and must be divided by the required diametral pitch. If the sum of the virtual numbers of teeth is less than 40, the design should have special consideration as correction of the pinion may introduce undercutting in the wheel.

Corrected Addenda and Caliper Settings Included in British Standard for Bevel Gears

Virtual Number of Teeth in Pinion = $n \sec \alpha$	Corrected Addenda		Caliper Settings			
			Pinion		Wheel	
	Pinion	Wheel	Height	Thickness	Height	Thickness
20 or above	1.00	1.00	0.747	1.387	0.747	1.387
19	1.04	0.96	0.783	1.413	0.712	1.361
18	1.08	0.92	0.818	1.438	0.677	1.336
17	1.12	0.88	0.854	1.464	0.641	1.310
16	1.16	0.84	0.889	1.490	0.606	1.284
15	1.20	0.80	0.924	1.515	0.571	1.258
14	1.24	0.76	0.960	1.541	0.535	1.233
13	1.28	0.72	0.995	1.567	0.500	1.207
12	1.32	0.68	1.030	1.593	0.465	1.181
11	1.36	0.64	1.065	1.618	0.429	1.156
10	1.40	0.60	1.101	1.644	0.394	1.130

The figures are for 20-degree full-depth teeth of 1 diametral pitch. The corresponding settings for other pitches are obtained by dividing the above values by the diametral pitch.

Spiral Bevel Gearing. — Spiral bevel gears having curved teeth, a normal pressure angle of 14½ degrees and a spiral angle of not less than 30 degrees may be corrected according to the following formula for correction coefficient:

$$\text{Correction coefficient} = 0.4 \times \left[1 - \left(\frac{n}{N}\right)^2 \right]$$

In this formula n and N are the actual numbers of teeth on the wheel or gear.

Example: To find the correction for a pair of spiral bevel gears, 30 degrees spiral angle, 14½ degrees normal pressure angle, 10 and 45 teeth, 5 diametral pitch:

$$\text{Correction coefficient} = 0.4 \times \left[1 - \left(\frac{10}{45}\right)^2 \right] = 0.38$$

Amount of correction = 0.38 × ⅕ = 0.076 inch; that is, addendum of pinion is increased, and that of the wheel reduced by 0.076 inch.

Common Causes of Gear Failures. — Gear failures may be due to the kind or to the quality of the material used, the kind of heat-treatment, improper mounting, incorrect design, and other factors. The following outline of common causes applies to various types of heat-treated steel gears. Some of the causes are non-uniformity of the physical structure or grain size of the steel as it comes from the mill; irregularity in the chemical composition; and improper design of successful foundry or heat-treating methods.

Causes of Rapid Wear or Breakage. — When the teeth wear rapidly, it is often because they are not hard enough. This would indicate insufficient time allowed for heating prior to quenching, or poor quenching due to the use of a quenching medium that was too hot. When the teeth are broken off with a sharp break at the root, this usually indicates a low impact value in the steel, which is caused by too deep hardening or too low a drawing temperature. Dirty steel, either from inclusions or impurities, will also cause low ductility and impact values. This condition can generally be easily recognized under the microscope.

If the material is free from inclusions and the heat-treatment has been properly done, then fatigue failure is purely a case of overloading; and if the load cannot be reduced, an alloy steel must be used to raise the fatigue limit high enough to take care of the service conditions.

When gears crack through the web, rim, hub, bore, or junction of the arm with the rim or hub, the cause is usually a defect in the material. If the gear is made from a casting, the fractured surface may show shrinkage, slag inclusion, or a chemical segregation. In forgings, there may be rolling seams or laps in the web of the gear or there may be a pipe or segregation in the hub, due to insufficient cropping of the ingot. Each of these defects may cause shrinkage strains from quenching beyond the elastic limit of the steel, so that an internal crack starts. This crack may cause failure in the heat-treating department or in service under comparatively low loads or vibrations.

Too sharp corners of keyways are responsible for most of the cracks that occur in hubs. All machined corners should be well rounded to remove the danger of starting a crack.

Quenching Strains. — Since fully 75 per cent of gear failures are directly or indirectly the result of quenching strains, it would appear that this factor in the heat-treating process should be given particular care. The fact that a 0.15 to 0.25 per cent carbon steel gear, carburized and water quenched, having a tensile strength of 35,000 to 40,000 pounds per square inch will make a satisfactory gear for many installations, indicates that the teeth only need be hardened, while the rest of the gear may be left soft. The setting up within the gear of quenching stresses that would cause its failure by cracking would thus be eliminated.

Lack of Surface Hardness. — Occasionally pinions of from 0.40 to 0.50 per cent carbon steel will register a Brinell hardness of only from 300 to 350 after water quenching, whereas it should be around 445 to 510. The pinions may be low in hardness on the outside diameter, but register the proper hardness in the center of the teeth at their roots. In such a case, it may be assumed that the blanks were made from rolled or forged bar material and that insufficient stock was allowed on the original outside diameter for the complete removal of the decarburized surface metal. If the pinion is soft all over, then the blank or bar of steel from which the pinion was made has been overheated at some time and cannot be recovered by any heat-treating process other than remelting it into new steel.

In castings for gears, an excess of a poor grade of foundry scrap used in making up the charge is often the cause of trouble. The charge should be so balanced that a maximum of 55 per cent of old foundry scrap is never exceeded, and a sufficient amount of good scrap and pig iron should be used. Like overheated forged steel, a poor casting must be remelted, as no form of heat-treatment will restore it.

Strength of Bevel Gears. — The strength of bevel gears having straight teeth may be calculated by using a slight modification of the Lewis formula for spur gears. First use formulas 1 and 2 on page 715. Then, to determine the value of Y, divide the number of bevel-gear teeth by the cosine of the pitch-cone angle to obtain the number of teeth in an *equivalent* spur gear. (Formula for pitch-cone angle a is on page 740.) Next use this equivalent spur-gear tooth number in selecting factor Y from the table on page 717. For straight bevel gears

$$L = \frac{SFY\ (C - F)}{PC}$$

In this formula F = face width (see recommended practice, page 748) and C = pitch-cone radius (formula, page 740). The factor $(C - F) \div C$ approximately expresses the ratio of the strength of a bevel gear to that of a spur gear of the same pitch and number of teeth.

Spiral Type Bevel Gears. — This type of gearing is similar to ordinary bevel gearing except that the teeth are curved and are at an angle to the pitch-cone radius of the gear. The shape of the tooth which is actually produced is not a spiral or curve in one plane, but, when projected on a plane, is close to a true spiral; hence the name "spiral type bevel gear." The tooth curve, if continued, would intersect the cone center of the gear, which distinguishes the spiral type bevel gear from the "skew bevel gear" in which the tooth elements are straight and do not intersect the cone center, if extended. The spiral type bevel gear is adapted for high-ratio drives; 10-, 11-, and 12-tooth pinions are used in ratios up to 6 to 1 with satisfactory results.

Designing Spiral Bevel and Hypoid Gears. — The strength of spiral bevel and hypoid gears exceeds that of corresponding straight bevels because the former have a greater number of teeth in contact. Hypoid gears are given the same wear-load rating as spiral bevel gears provided the lubrication is suitable for hypoid service. The allowable loads for straight bevel gears are about 80 per cent of the loads for spiral bevel and hypoid gears. The following formulas, data, and information are based upon the practice of the Gleason Works.

The empirical formula (3) for industrial installations (not automotive) is based upon the wear load, rather than strength, since wear is the determining factor in the majority of gear installations. The rating of spiral bevel and hypoid gears is based upon the safe transmission of the full-rated capacity under continuous operation, 50 per cent overload at starting, and 50 per cent momentary overload during operation. Proper assembly in a rigid mounting and good lubrication are assumed.

H.P. = horsepower to be transmitted
L = total tangential load, in pounds, at pitch diameter
L_w = total allowable pitch-line load, in pounds, as limited by pinion-tooth wear
V = pitch-line velocity in feet per minute
D = pitch diameter of pinion in inches
R = revolutions per minute of pinion
P = diametral pitch
S_s = static stress, in pounds per square inch, produced by L if the latter were a static load
S = actual operating stress, in pounds per square inch (maximum value should not exceed two-thirds ultimate strength of material)
F = face length, inches (preferably about $\frac{1}{4}$ C and not over $\frac{1}{3}$ C)
C = pitch-cone distance or radius
N = number of pinion teeth
M = material factor (see table 1)
Z = nature of load or service factor (see table 2)
Y = outline factor (see table 3)
T = velocity factor for wear. For speeds V under 300 ft. per min. = 1.4; 300–600 = 1.2; 600–1000 = 1.1; 1000–1500 = 1.0; 1500–2500 = 0.9; 2500–3500 = 0.8; over 3000 = 0.7

$$V = 0.262\, DR \quad (1) \qquad L = \frac{\text{H.P.} \times 33{,}000}{V} \quad (2) \qquad L_w = 470 \sqrt{\frac{N}{P}}\, MZFT \quad (3)$$

$$S_s = \frac{LCP}{(C - F)\, FY} \quad (4) \qquad S = S_s \times \frac{1200 + V}{1200} \quad (5)$$

Application of Formulas. — Formula (2) gives the tangential load at the pitch line resulting from the transmission of a given horsepower at velocity V. This load L should not exceed L_w which is the wear load. The relation between L and L_w for a given horsepower will depend upon the pitch-line velocity which, for a given value of R, depends upon the values of N and P which must be assumed until the right values are determined by trial as shown later. Table 1 gives the material factors for use in formula (3), and Table 2 the service factors. The latter are based upon average conditions, and for some installations experience may show that other factors are applicable.

Example of Spiral Bevel Gear Design. — Assume that H.P. = 30; $R = 1400$; gear and pinion ratio = 4. Materials: Oil-hardened steel pinion and cast-iron gear. Load: intermittent with light shocks. Determine the size and face width of the pinion and gear consistent with the allowable wear load.

By way of trial, assume that $N = 20$ and $P = 5$; then $D = 4$ inches. The cone distance C for this diameter and a 4-to-1 ratio = 8.25 inches approximately. Since F should preferably = about $\frac{1}{4}$ C, assume that $F = 2\frac{1}{4}$ inches.

Table 1 shows that $M = 0.4$ for these materials; and according to Table 2, $Z = 1$ for an intermittent service with light shocks; $V = 0.262 \times 4 \times 1400 = 1467$ and $T = 1$. Inserting all of these values in formula (3),

$$L_w = 470 \sqrt{\frac{20}{5}} \times 0.4 \times 1 \times 2\frac{1}{4} \times 1.0 = 846 \text{ pounds} = \text{allowable wear load.}$$

Next determine load L for a 4-inch pinion rotating at 1400 revolutions per minute.

$$L = \frac{30 \times 33{,}000}{1467} = 675$$

This tangential load of 675 pounds is within the allowable wear-load limit of 846 pounds; however, if in the trial calculation, N had been given a smaller value of, say, 15, with the other values remaining the same, V would = 1100 and L_w 900; but the value of L_w would only be 487 provided $F = \frac{1}{4}$ C ($C = 6$ inches approximately for a 3-inch pinion and 12-inch gear), thus indicating that a larger pinion with a higher pitch-line speed and greater face width is required.

Table 1. Material Factors (M) Used in Wear Load Formula

Pinion	Gear	M				
Cast Iron or Soft Steel	Cast Iron	0.30	The material factors (M) are based upon the hardness factors listed below.			
Heat-treated Steel	Heat-treated Steel	0.35				
Casehardened Steel	Cast Iron	0.40	Condition of Steel	Brinell	Sclero-scope	S.A.E. Steels Commonly Used
Oil-hardened Steel	Cast Iron	0.40				
Casehardened Steel	Unhardened Steel	0.45	Unhardened Steel	160–190	25–28	1035
Oil-hardened Steel	Unhardened Steel	0.45	Heat-treated Steel	200–260	30–36	2335 3140
Casehardened Steel	Heat-treated Steel	0.50	Oil-hardened Steel	....	70–80	3245
Oil-hardened Steel	Heat-treated Steel	0.50	Casehardened (Heavy Sections)		75–85	2317
Oil-hardened Steel	Oil-hardened Steel	0.65				
Casehardened Steel	Oil-hardened Steel	0.70	Surface-hardened		70–80	3140 or cast steel 0.35 C; 1.25 Mn.
Casehardened or Surface h'd.	Casehardened or Surface h'd.	1.00				

Table 2. Nature of Load and Service Factors

Intermittent Service	$Z = 1.3$ for non-pulsating load; 1.0 for light shock; 0.65 for heavy shock.
Continuous Service	$Z = 1.0$ for non-pulsating load; 0.75 for light shock; 0.50 for heavy shock.
Starting	$Z = 1.5$ for infrequent loads of short duration.

Checking Beam Strength of Teeth. — Although the wear load is the determining factor usually, for exceptionally heavy loads or high peripheral speeds, gears should be checked to make sure that the actual operating stress does not exceed two-thirds of the ultimate strength of the material. The maximum allowable stresses in pounds per square inch for different materials are as follows: Cast iron, 8000 to 10,000; nickel iron, 12,000; cast steel, 15,000 to 20,000; steel No. 1035 (S.A.E.), 30,000; oil-hardened steel Nos. 2335 and 3140 — 50,000 (1200° draw temp.), and 120,000 (400° draw temp.); oil-hardened steel 3245 — 130,000; casehardened steels Nos. 2315 and 4615 — 65,000; casehardened steel No. 2512 — 75,000; casehardened steel No. 3312 X — 80,000.

To illustrate the procedure in checking the strength, the values in the foregoing example will be used. Formula (4) gives the static stress S_s resulting from a load equal to L.

$$S_s = \frac{675 \times 8.25 \times 5}{(8.25-2.25)\ 2.25 \times 0.412} = 5000$$

The actual operating stress S is greater than S_s due to impact stresses, and formula (5) is arranged to determine this increased value of S to ascertain if it is within

Table 3. — Strength or Y Factors for Gleason Works System of Bevel Gears*

Number of Pinion Teeth	Ratios = Number of Gear Teeth ÷ Number of Pinion Teeth							
	1.00 to 1.25	1.25 to 1.50	1.50 to 1.75	1.75 to 2.00	2.00 to 2.25	2.25 to 2.50	2.50 to 2.75	2.75 to 3.00
	Strength Factors Y							
5	0.297	0.322	0.343	0.361	0.376	0.388	0.398	0.406
6	0.310	0.332	0.353	0.372	0.386	0.398	0.406	0.414
7	0.318	0.333	0.347	0.360	0.373	0.384	0.392	0.398
8	0.298	0.320	0.336	0.348	0.357	0.366	0.373	0.379
9	0.292	0.313	0.327	0.338	0.346	0.352	0.357	0.363
10	0.315	0.338	0.353	0.363	0.371	0.345	0.326	0.342
11	0.316	0.335	0.343	0.325	0.327	0.333	0.338	0.344
12	0.298	0.318	0.333	0.343	0.351	0.357	0.363	0.368
13	0.302	0.320	0.334	0.343	0.351	0.358	0.365	0.371
14	0.306	0.322	0.334	0.345	0.354	0.362	0.369	0.374
15	0.314	0.330	0.342	0.352	0.360	0.368	0.374	0.380
16	0.322	0.335	0.347	0.358	0.367	0.374	0.381	0.386
17–18	0.329	0.343	0.354	0.364	0.373	0.382	0.389	0.394
19–21	0.339	0.351	0.362	0.373	0.382	0.389	0.396	0.401
22–25	0.351	0.363	0.373	0.382	0.391	0.398	0.403	0.407
26–30	0.364	0.374	0.384	0.393	0.399	0.404	0.407	0.410

No. of Teeth	3.00 to 3.25	3.25 to 3.50	3.50 to 3.75	3.75 to 4.00	4.00 to 4.50	4.50 to 5.00	5.00 to ∞
5	0.411	0.416	0.420	0.424	0.431	0.438	0.450
6	0.419	0.424	0.428	0.431	0.436	0.443	0.452
7	0.405	0.410	0.415	0.419	0.426	0.432	0.439
8	0.384	0.388	0.392	0.394	0.397	0.400	0.405
9	0.367	0.370	0.373	0.376	0.380	0.384	0.388
10	0.351	0.357	0.363	0.367	0.371	0.374	0.377
11	0.350	0.356	0.361	0.367	0.375	0.384	0.390
12	0.372	0.377	0.379	0.381	0.384	0.386	0.388
13	0.376	0.381	0.384	0.386	0.388	0.391	0.393
14	0.378	0.382	0.386	0.389	0.391	0.393	0.395
15	0.385	0.389	0.392	0.394	0.397	0.399	0.402
16	0.390	0.394	0.397	0.400	0.402	0.404	0.406
17–18	0.398	0.400	0.403	0.406	0.407	0.409	0.410
19–21	0.405	0.407	0.410	0.411	0.412	0.414	0.415
22–25	0.410	0.412	0.413	0.414	0.415	0.417	0.418
26–30	0.412	0.414	0.415	0.416	0.417	0.418	0.419

* These Y factors are only approximate for bypoid gears.

the safe limit of two-thirds of the ultimate strength of the material. Thus, in this example

$$S = S_s \times \frac{1200 + V}{1200} = 5000 \times \frac{1200 + 1467}{1200} = 11,000$$

The empirical formula (3) is based upon the pinion only but the strength of the weaker member, or gear in this case, should be considered. A value for S of 11,000 is above the maximum given for cast iron but within the limit for nickel iron.

The velocity factor in formula (5) (as used by the Gleason Works) is inverted as compared with the common arrangement for the Lewis formula. This inverted factor is designed to give the actual increase in stress due to increased shocks or impact stresses as V increases, rather than the amount S should be reduced below the static unit stress S_s of the material (as in the usual arrangement of the Lewis formula) in order to provide a safe value for determining the power capacity. While either arrangement may be employed, the Gleason formula is considered more direct as it is designed to indicate the true stress and its relation to the ultimate strength of the material.

Axial Thrust of Spiral-type Bevel Gears. — If W = tooth load tangential to pitch circle, pounds; O = pressure angle; H = spiral angle and a = pitch-cone angle; T = axial thrust load, pounds, then for *clockwise rotation* (as seen from large end) of the *driving member* with right-hand spiral

$$T = W \left[(\tan H \cos a) - \left(\frac{\tan O \sin a}{\cos H} \right) \right]$$

The formula above also applies to a *driven member rotating clockwise* if the hand of the spiral is left.

For *counter-clockwise rotation* of the *driving member* with right-hand spiral

$$T = W \left[(\tan H \cos a) + \left(\frac{\tan O \sin a}{\cos H} \right) \right]$$

This second formula also applies to a *driven member rotating counter-clockwise* if the hand of the spiral is left.

A right-hand spiral pinion driving clockwise tends to move toward the cone center while a left-hand pinion tends to move away because of the oblique direction of the curved teeth. If there is any end play in the pinion shaft, the movement of a right-hand spiral pinion driving clockwise will take up the backlash under heavy load and the teeth of gear and pinion may wedge together; while a left-hand spiral pinion under the same conditions would back away and merely introduce additional backlash between the teeth. The hand of spiral should be selected, so as to make the member having the greater axial thrust tend to move out of mesh under load. In a reversible drive, there is no choice unless the pair performs a heavier duty in one direction the greater part of the time. With the improved ball and roller bearings now obtainable, spiral bevel gears are regularly used in reversible drives.

If a hypoid pinion is below center and to the right when facing the gear, it should always be left-hand. With the pinion above center and to the right, it should always be right-hand. Hypoid gears may be used in reversible drives with proper thrust provision.

Cutting Spiral Type Bevel Gears. — The cutter used on the Gleason spiral-type bevel gear generator is in the form of a face mill, which holds quite a number of blades or cutters which pass through the blank along a curved path. The same cutter is used for both sides of the tooth and for both pinion and gear. The gear and the cutter roll together, giving correctly generated teeth of involute form.

Advantages of Spiral Type Bevel Gears. — Spiral type bevel gears are quiet when running, as the engagement is gradual. The teeth, instead of striking a full-line contact at once, engage each other with an action which suggests the smoothness of a worm and worm-wheel. There is a continuous pitch-line contact so that a number of teeth are bearing the load simultaneously and there is a gradual engagement that reduces wear. Another point of advantage is the range of endwise adjustment of the pinion, which is possible without causing noise or spoiling the bearing of the teeth.

Hypoid Gears. — Hypoid gears resemble, in general appearance, spiral bevel gears except that the axis of the pinion is offset relative to the gear axis. Hypoid gears have two important advantages: The small amount of lengthwise sliding of the teeth resulting from the offset, tends to make hypoid gears even smoother running than spiral bevel gears. The offset between the gear axes also makes it possible for both gear and pinion shafts to continue past each other. The axis of the pinion is offset from the axis of the gear by an amount that varies with the diameter and the ratio. The direction of offset determines the hand of the spiral. In rear-axle design, a pinion below center will have a left-hand spiral, while a pinion above center will have a right-hand spiral. The position below center is preferable for two reasons: First, the axial thrust resulting on the pinion on a forward drive is directed away from the gear, and heavy loads tend to move the pinion out of mesh rather than draw it in; Second, the contact between mating tooth surfaces is more intimate on the drive side. The total tooth load of hypoid gears, or load normal to the tooth surface, is only slightly larger than the effective circumferential or tangential tooth load of the gear. In spiral bevel gears, the normal load is considerably larger.

Worm Gearing

Formulas for Worm Gearing. — Worm gearing may be employed (1) as an efficient, steady transmitter of power; (2) when a large reduction in velocity is desired; (3) when considerable increase in "mechanical advantage" is required, or, in other words, when a given applied force must overcome a comparatively high resistance to motion. The notation below is used in the formulas on the following pages.

a = addendum, worm thread

A = addendum, worm-wheel tooth

B = dedendum, worm-wheel tooth

b = dedendum, worm thread

C = center distance (Fig. 1)

c = clearance

D = pitch diameter of worm-wheel

d = pitch diameter of worm

d_o = outside diameter of worm

D_o = outside or over-all diameter of worm-wheel

D_t = throat diameter of worm-wheel

E = efficiency of worm gearing, per cent

F = nominal face width of wheel rim

F_e = effective face width (Fig. 1)

f = coefficient of friction

G = length of worm threaded section

H = horsepower rating

L = lead of worm thread = pitch × number of threads or " starts "

L_a = lead angle of worm = helix angle measured from a plane perpendicular to worm axis

M = torque applied to worm-wheel, pound-inches

m = module = 0.3183 × axial pitch

N = revolutions per minute of worm-wheel

n = revolutions per minute of worm

P = axial pitch of worm and circular pitch of wheel

P_n = normal pitch of worm

Q = arc length of worm-wheel tooth measured along root

R = ratio of worm gearing = No. of wheel teeth ÷ No. of worm threads

S = surface stress factor (Table 4)

S_b = bending stress factor, lbs. per sq. in. (Table 4)

T = number of teeth on worm-wheel

t = number of threads or "starts" on worm — 2 for double thread, 3 for triple thread, 4 for quadruple thread, etc.

U = radius of worm-wheel throat (Fig. 1)

V = rubbing speed of worm in feet per minute

W = whole tooth depth (worm and worm-wheel)

X_w = speed factor when load rating is limited by *wear* (Fig. 2)

X_s = speed factor when load rating is limited by *strength* (Table 5)

ϕ = angle of friction (tan ϕ = coefficient of friction)

Materials for Worm Gearing. — Worm gears, especially for power transmission, should have steel worms and phosphor bronze wheels. This combination is used extensively. The worms should be hardened and ground to obtain accuracy and a smooth finish.

The phosphor bronze wheels should contain from 10 to 12 per cent of tin. The S.A.E. phosphor gear bronze (No. 65) contains 88–90% copper, 10–12% tin, 0.50% lead, 0.50% zinc (but with a maximum total lead, zinc and nickel content of 1.0 per cent), phosphorous 0.10–0.30%, aluminum 0.005%. The S.A.E. nickel phosphor gear bronze (No. 65 + Ni) contains 87% copper, 11% tin, 2% nickel and 0.2% phosphorous. Table 4 shows the British Standard wheel and worm materials.

Single-thread Worms. — The ratio of the worm speed to the worm-wheel speed may range from 1.5 or even less up to 100 or more. Worm gears having high ratios are not very efficient as transmitters of power; nevertheless high as well as low ratios often are required. Since the ratio equals the number of worm-wheel teeth divided by the number of threads or "starts" on the worm, single-thread worms are used to obtain a high ratio. As a general rule, a ratio of 50 is about the maximum recommended for a single worm and gear combination, although ratios up to 100 or higher are possible. When a high ratio is required, it may be preferable to use, in combination, two sets of worm gears of the multi-thread type in preference to one set of the single-thread type in order to obtain the same total reduction and a higher combined efficiency.

Single-thread worms are comparatively inefficient because of the effect of the low lead angle (see Efficiency of Worm Gearing); consequently, single-thread worms are not used when the primary purpose is to transmit power as efficiently as possible but they may be employed either when a large speed reduction with one set of gearing is necessary, or possibly as a means of adjustment, especially if "mechanical advantage", or self-locking are important factors.

Multi-thread Worms. — When worm gearing is designed primarily for transmitting power efficiently, the lead angle of the worm should be as high as is consistent with other requirements and preferably between, say, 25 or 30 and 45 degrees, as indicated by Tables 1 and 2. This means that the worm must be multi-threaded. To obtain a given ratio, some number of worm-wheel teeth divided by some number of worm threads must equal the ratio. Thus, if the ratio is 6, combinations such as the following might be used:

$$\frac{24}{4}, \frac{30}{5}, \frac{36}{6}, \frac{42}{7}$$

The numerators represent the number of worm-wheel teeth and the denominators, the number of worm threads or "starts." The number of worm-wheel teeth may

Rules and Formulas for Worm Gearing — 1

No.	To Find	Rule	Formula
1	Addendum	Addendum may be affected by lead angle. See paragraph, Addendum and Dedendum.	
2	Center Distance	Add pitch diameter of worm-wheel to pitch diameter of worm, and divide sum by 2.	$C = \dfrac{(D + d)}{2}$
3		Divide number of worm threads by tangent lead angle, add number of wheel teeth and multiply sum by quotient obtained by dividing pitch by 6.2832.	$C = \dfrac{P}{6.2832}\left(\dfrac{t}{\tan L_a} + T\right)$
4	Dedendum	Dedendum may be affected by lead angle. See paragraph, Addendum and Dedendum.	
5	Clearance	British Standard — multiply cosine lead angle by 0.2 times module.	$c = 0.2\, m \cos L_a$
6	Face Width, Worm-wheel	For single and double thread worms, multiply pitch by 2.38 and add 0.25. (Shell type worm.)	$F = 2.38\, P + 0.25$
7		For triple and quadruple thread worm, multiply pitch by 2.15 and add 0.2. (Shell type.)	$F = 2.15\, P + 0.2$
8		When worm threads are integral with shaft, face width of worm-wheel may equal $C^{0.875}$ divided by 3.	$F = \dfrac{C^{0.875}}{3}$
9	Lead of Worm Thread	Multiply pitch by number of worm threads or "starts."	$L = tP$
10		Multiply pitch circumference of worm by tangent of lead angle.	$L = \pi d \times \tan L_a$
11		Divide pitch circumference of worm-wheel by ratio.	$L = \pi D \div R$
12	Lead Angle, Worm	Divide lead by pitch circumference of worm; quotient is tangent of lead angle.	$\tan L_a = \dfrac{L}{3.1416\, d}$
13	Outside Diam., Worm	Add to pitch diameter twice the addendum. See paragraph, Pitch Diameter of Worm; also Addendum and Dedendum.	$d_0 = d + 2a$
14	Outside Diam., Worm-wheel	For outside or over-all diameter of worm-wheel, see paragraph, Outside Diameter of Worm-wheel.	
15	Pitch of Worm and Wheel	Divide lead by number of threads or "starts" on worm = axial pitch of worm and circular pitch of worm-wheel.	$P = \dfrac{L}{t}$
16		Subtract the worm pitch diameter from twice the center distance. Multiply by 3.1416 and divide by number of wheel teeth.	$P = \dfrac{(2C - d) \times 3.1416}{T}$

Rules and Formulas for Worm Gearing — 2

No.	To Find	Rule	Formula
17	Pitch of Worm, Normal	Multiply axial pitch by cosine of lead angle to find normal pitch.	$P_n = P \times \cos L_a$
18	Pitch Diam., Worm	Subtract pitch diameter of worm-wheel from twice the center distance.	$d = 2C - D$
19		Subtract twice the addendum from outside diameter. See Addendum and Dedendum.	$d = d_0 - 2a$
20		Multiply lead by cotangent lead angle and divide product by 3.1416.	$d = \dfrac{L \times \cot L_a}{3.1416}$
21	Pitch Diam., Worm-wheel	Subtract pitch diameter of worm from twice the center distance.	$D = 2C - d$
22		Multiply number of wheel teeth by axial pitch of worm and divide product by 3.1416.	$D = \dfrac{TP}{3.1416}$
23	Radius of Rim Corner, Wheel	Multiply pitch by 0.25	$\text{Rad.} = 0.25\,P$
24		British Standard: Radius = 0.5 module.	$\text{Rad.} = 0.5\,m$
25	Ratio	Divide number of wheel teeth by number of worm threads.	$R = T \div t$
26	Rubbing Speed, Ft. per Minute	Divide wheel pitch diameter by ratio; square quotient and add to square of worm pitch diameter; multiply square root of this sum by 0.262 × R.P.M. of worm.	$V = 0.262\,n\sqrt{d^2 + \left(\dfrac{D}{R}\right)^2}$
27		Multiply 0.262 × pitch diameter of worm by R.P.M. of worm; then multiply product by secant of lead angle.	$V = 0.262\,dn \times \sec L_a$
28	Throat Diam., Worm-wheel	Add twice the addendum to pitch diameter — see paragraph, Addendum and Dedendum.	$D_t = D + 2A$
29	Throat Radius, Worm-wheel	Subtract twice worm addendum from outside radius of worm.	$U = \dfrac{d_0}{2} - 2a$
30	Tooth Depth	Whole depth equals addendum + dedendum. See paragraph, Addendum and Dedendum.	$W = a + b$ or $A + B$
31	Worm Thread Length	Multiply the number of wheel teeth by 0.02, add 4.5 and multiply sum by pitch.	$G = P(4.5 + 0.02\,T)$
32		British Standard — Subtract square of worm-wheel pitch diameter from square of outside diameter and extract square root of remainder.	$G = \sqrt{D_0^2 - D^2}$

not be an exact multiple of the number of threads on a multi-thread worm (as explained later) in order to obtain a " hunting tooth " action.

Number of Threads or " Starts " on Worm: The number of threads on the worm ordinarily varies from one to six or eight, depending upon the ratio of the gearing. As the ratio is increased, the number of worm threads is reduced, as a general rule. In some cases, however, the higher of two ratios may also have a larger number of threads. For example, a ratio of $6\frac{1}{5}$ would have 5 threads whereas a ratio of $6\frac{5}{6}$ would have 6 threads. Whenever the ratio is fractional, the number of threads on the worm equals the denominator of the fractional part of the ratio.

Ratio for Obtaining " Hunting Tooth " Action.

In designing worm gears having multi-thread worms, it is common practice to select a number of wheel teeth that is not an exact multiple of the number of worm threads. To illustrate, if the desired ratio is about 5 or 6, the actual ratio might be $5\frac{1}{6}$, $5\frac{5}{6}$, $5\frac{2}{7}$, $6\frac{1}{6}$, etc., so that combinations such as $3\frac{1}{6}$, $3\frac{5}{6}$, $3\frac{7}{7}$ or $3\frac{1}{5}$ would be obtained. Since the number of wheel teeth and number of worm threads do not have a common divisor, the threads of the worm will mesh with all of the wheel teeth in succession, thus obtaining a "hunting tooth" or self-indexing action. This progressive change will also occur during the worm wheel hobbing operation, and its primary purpose is to produce more accurate worm wheels by uniformly distributing among all of the teeth, any slight errors which might exist in the hob teeth. Another object is to improve the "running-in" action between the hardened and ground worm and the phosphor bronze wheel, but in order to obtain this advantage, the threads on the worm must be accurately or uniformly spaced by precise indexing. With a "hunting tooth ratio," if the thread spacing of a multi-thread worm is inaccurate, load distribution on the threads will be unequal and some threads might not even make contact with the wheel teeth. For this reason, if the indexing is

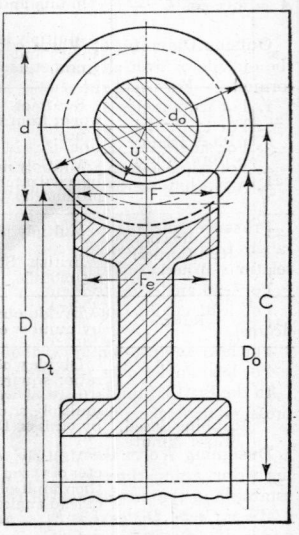

Fig. 1

inaccurate, it is preferable to avoid a hunting tooth ratio, but in that case, if the gearing is disassembled, the same worm and gear teeth should be mated when reassembled.

Pitch Diameter of Worm.

The worm must be strong enough to transmit its maximum load without excessive deflection but the diameter should be as small as is consistent with the necessary strength in order to minimize the rubbing speed. It is impracticable to give a rule or formula that is generally applicable, but the following empirical rules are based upon actual practice and may prove useful as a general guide. They apply to casehardened alloy steel worms which are integral with the shaft.

For ratios of 5, 6, or 7, the pitch diameter ranges approximately from 0.38 C when center distance C is 4 inches to 0.33 C when C is 20 inches.

For ratios of 8, 9, 10, the pitch diameter ranges approximately from 0.38 C when center distance C is 4 inches to 0.25 C when C is 30 inches.

For ratios of 10 to 20, the pitch diameter ranges approximately from 0.37 C when center distance C is 4 inches to 0.24 C when C is 30 inches.

For ratios of 20 to 40, the pitch diameter ranges approximately from 0.36 C when center distance C is 4 inches to 0.23 C when C is 30 inches.

According to another empirical formula pitch diameter $d = C^{0.875} \div 2.2$.

Addendum and Dedendum. — The following A.G.M.A. formulas are applicable to industrial worm gearing. For single- and double-thread worms, addendum $a = 0.318 P$ and whole depth $W = 0.686 P$; for triple and quadruple threads, addendum $a = 0.286 P$ and whole depth $W = 0.623 P$.

According to the British standard, $a = $ module $m = 0.3183 P$; $b = m(2.2 \cos L_a - 1)$; $A = m(2 \cos L_a - 1)$; $B = m(1 + 0.2 \cos L_a)$.

Outside Diameter of Worm-wheel. — Practice varies somewhat in determining the outside or over-all diameter of the worm-wheel, as indicated by the following formulas. For usual rim shape, see Fig. 1.

1. For lead angles up to about 15 or 20 degrees, $D_o = D + (3 \times 0.3183 P)$
2. For lead angles over 20 degrees, $D_o = D + (3 \times 0.3183 P \times \cos L_a)$
3. For single and double thread, $D_o = D_t + 0.4775 P$
4. For triple and quadruple thread, $D_o = D_t + 0.3183 P$
5. According to British standard, $D_o = D + 2 A + m$

Pressure Angles. — The pressure angle (one-half the included thread angle) ranges from $14\frac{1}{2}$ to 30 degrees. While the practice varies somewhat, the following relationship between lead angle and pressure angle may be used as a general guide.

For lead angles up to about 10 or 12 degrees, pressure angle = $14\frac{1}{2}$ degrees.

For lead angles from 10 to 12 to about 20 or 25 degrees, pressure angle = 20 degrees.

For lead angles from 25 to about 35 degrees, pressure angle = 25 degrees.

For lead angles over 35 degrees, pressure angle = 30 degrees.

In the British Standard specifications, the recommended thread form has a normal pressure angle of 20 degrees.

Designing Worm Gearing Relative to Center Distance and Ratio. — In designing worm gears, three general cases or types of problems may be encountered in establishing the proportions of the worm and worm-wheel.

When Center Distance is Fixed and Ratio may be Varied: The ratio in this case is nominal and may be varied somewhat to meet other conditions. Assume that the required center distance is 6 inches, the desired ratio is about 7, and the pitch of the worm and wheel is to be approximately 1 inch. Combinations of worm-wheels and worms such as the following might be used in this case:

$$\frac{28}{4}, \quad \frac{35}{5}, \quad \frac{42}{6}, \quad \frac{56}{8}, \text{ etc.}$$

Suppose we select the $\frac{28}{4}$ combination for trial but change the number of wheel teeth from 28 to 29 to obtain a self-indexing or " hunting tooth " action. The ratio now equals $\frac{29}{4}$ or 7.25. Then, for trial purposes

$$\text{Pitch diameter } D \text{ of wheel} = \frac{T \times P}{\pi} = \frac{29 \times 1}{3.1416} = 9.231 \text{ inches}$$

$$\text{Pitch diameter } d \text{ of worm} = 2C - D = 2 \times 6 - 9.231 = 2.769 \text{ inches}$$

Assume that experience, tests, or calculations show that a worm of smaller diameter will have the necessary bending and torsional strength and that a pitch of 1.0625 will be satisfactory. Then the pitch diameter of the worm will be decreased to 2.192 inches and the pitch diameter of the wheel will be increased to 9.808 inches. A check of the lead-angle will show that it equals $31°41'$ which is conducive to high efficiency.

When Ratio is Fixed and Center Distance may be Varied: Assume that the required ratio is 7¼ and that the center distance may be any value consistent with approved designing practice. This ratio may be obtained with a number of different worm and worm-wheel sizes. For example, in a series of commercial worm gears, the following combinations are employed for gearing having a ratio of 7¼ with center distances varying from 4 to 8.25 inches. The number of worm threads is 4 and the number of teeth on the worm-wheel 29 in all cases.

When $C = 4$ inches, $d = 1.654$; $D = 6.346$; $P = 0.6875$; $L_a = 27°54'$
When $C = 5$ inches, $d = 1.923$; $D = 8.077$; $P = 0.875$; $L_a = 30°5'$
When $C = 6$ inches, $d = 2.192$; $D = 9.808$; $P = 1.0625$; $L_a = 31°41'$
When $C = 7$ inches, $d = 2.461$; $D = 11.539$; $P = 1.25$; $L_a = 32°53'$
When $C = 8.25$ inches, $d = 2.942$; $D = 13.558$; $P = 1.4687$, $L_a = 32°27'$

The horsepower rating increases considerably as the proportions of the worm gearing increase; hence if the gears are intended primarily for power transmission, the general proportions must be selected with reference to the power-transmitting capacity, and, usually the smallest and most compact design that will give satisfactory performance should be selected. The power capacity of the transmission, however, does not depend solely upon the proportions of the worm and worm-wheel. For example, the quality and viscosity of the lubricant is an important factor. The load transmitting capacity of the lubricant may also be increased decidedly when excessive temperature rises are prevented by special means such as forced air cooling. (See "Water and Forced-Air Cooling.")

When Both Ratio and Center Distance are Fixed: When both ratio and center distance are fixed, the problem usually is to obtain the *best proportions* of worm and wheel conforming to these fixed values.

Example: The required ratio is 6 (6 to 1) and the center distance is fixed at 3.600 inches. Assume that experience or tests show that an axial pitch of 0.50 inch will meet strength requirements. (If normal pitch P_n is given, change to axial pitch $(P = P_n \div \cos L_a)$. With a ratio of 6, some of the combinations for trial are:

$$\frac{30}{5}; \quad \frac{36}{6}; \quad \frac{42}{7}.$$

Trial calculations will show that the 36/6 combination gives the best proportions of worm and wheel for the center distance and pitch specified. Thus

$$D = \frac{TP}{\pi} = \frac{36 \times 0.5}{3.1416} = 5.729; \quad d = 2C - D = 2 \times 3.6 - 5.729 = 1.471$$

The lead angle is about 33 degrees. The effect of lead angle on efficiency is dealt with in a following paragraph. The total obtained by adding the number of worm-wheel teeth to the number of worm threads, equals $36 + 6 = 42$ (a total of 40 is a desirable minimum). With the 42/7 combination of the same pitch, the worm would be too small (0.516 inch); and with the 30/5 combination it would be too large (2.426 inches). The present trend in gear designing practice is to use finer pitches than in the past. In the case of worm gears, the pitch may, in certain instances, be changed somewhat either to permit cutting with available equipment or to improve the proportions of worm and wheel.

When Ratio, Pitch and Lead Angle are Fixed. Assume that $R = 10$, axial pitch $P = 0.16$ inch, $L_a = 30$ degrees and $C = 3$ inches, approximately.

The first step is to determine for the given ratio, pitch and lead angle, the number of worm threads t which will give a center distance nearest 3 inches.

$$t = \frac{C \times 2\pi \times \tan L_a}{P \times (1 + R \tan L_a)} = \frac{3 \times 6.2832 \times 0.57735}{0.16 \times (1 + 10 \times 0.57735)} = 10.04$$

The whole number nearest 10.04, or 10, is the required number of worm threads; hence number of teeth on worm-wheel equals $R \times 10 = 100$

$$d = (L \cot L_a) \div \pi = (10 \times 0.16 \times 1.732) \div \pi = 0.8821 \text{ inches}$$

$$D = (TP) \div \pi = (100 \times 0.16) \div \pi = 5.0929 \text{ inches}$$

$$C = (D + d) \div 2 = (5.0929 + 0.8821) \div 2 = 2.9875 \text{ inches}$$

Efficiency of Worm Gearing. — The efficiency at a given speed, depends upon the worm lead angle, the workmanship, lubrication, and the general design of the transmission. When worm gearing consists of a hardened and ground worm running with an accurately hobbed wheel properly lubricated, the efficiency depends chiefly upon the lead angle and coefficient of friction between the worm and wheel. In the lower range of lead angles, the efficiency increases considerably as the lead angle increases, as shown by Tables 1 and 2. This increase in efficiency remains practically constant for lead angles between 30 and 45 degrees. Several formulas for obtaining efficiency percentage follow:

With worm driving:

$$E = 100 - \frac{R}{2} \text{ (empirical rule)}; \quad E = \frac{\tan L_a}{\tan (L_a + \phi)}; \quad E = \frac{L}{L + f\pi d}$$

With wheel driving:

$$E = 100 - 2R \text{ (empirical rule)}; \quad E = \frac{\tan (L_a - \phi)}{\tan L_a}$$

Table 1. Efficiency of Worm Gearing for Different Lead Angles and Frictional Coefficients

Coefficient of Friction	Lead Angle of Worm								
	5 Deg.	10 Deg.	15 Deg.	20 Deg.	25 Deg.	30 Deg.	35 Deg.	40 Deg.	45 Deg.
0.01	89.7	94.5	96.1	97.0	97.4	97.7	97.9	98.0	98.0
0.02	81.3	89.5	92.6	94.1	95.0	95.5	95.9	96.0	96.1
0.03	74.3	85.0	89.2	91.4	92.7	93.4	93.9	94.1	94.2
0.04	68.4	80.9	86.1	88.8	90.4	91.4	92.0	92.2	92.3
0.05	63.4	77.2	83.1	86.3	88.2	89.4	90.1	90.4	90.5
0.06	59.0	73.8	80.4	84.0	86.1	87.5	88.2	88.6	88.7
0.07	55.2	70.7	77.8	81.7	84.1	85.6	86.4	86.9	86.9
0.08	51.9	67.8	75.4	79.6	82.2	83.8	84.7	85.2	85.2
0.09	48.9	65.2	73.1	77.6	80.3	82.0	83.0	83.5	83.5
0.10	46.3	62.7	70.9	75.6	78.5	80.3	81.4	81.9	81.8

The efficiencies obtained by these formulas and other modifications of them, differ somewhat and do not take into account bearing and oil-churning losses. The efficiency may be improved somewhat after the " running in " period.

Self-locking or Irreversible Worm Gearing. — Neglecting friction in the bearings, worm gearing is irreversible when the efficiency is zero or negative, the lead angle being equal to or less than the angle ϕ of friction (tan ϕ = coefficient of friction). When worm gearing is self-locking or irreversible, this means that the wheel

Table 2.   Efficiency of Worm Gearing for Different Lead Angles and Pitch-line Velocities

Velocity at Pitch Line, Feet per Minute	Lead or Helix Angle, Degrees					
	5	10	20	30	40	45
	Efficiency, Per Cent					
5	40	56	69	76	79	80
10	47	62	74	79	82	82
20	52	67	78	83	85	86
30	56	71	81	85	87	87
40	60	74	83	87	88	88
50	63	76	85	88	89	89
75	67	80	87	90	90	90
100	70	82	88	91	91	91
150	74	84	90	92	92	92
200	76	85	91	92	92	92

Table 3.   Coefficients of Friction (f) for Worm Gearing*

Rubbing Speed, Ft. per Min.	Coefficients of Friction	Rubbing Speed, Ft. per Min.	Coefficients of Friction	Rubbing Speed, Ft. per Min.	Coefficients of Friction	Rubbing Speed, Ft. per Min.	Coefficients of Friction
30	0.073	180	0.045	550	0.028	1600	0.0175
40	0.070	190	0.044	600	0.027	1700	0.0170
50	0.066	200	0.043	650	0.026	1800	0.0165
60	0.062	225	0.041	700	0.026	1900	0.0165
70	0.060	250	0.040	750	0.025	2000	0.0160
80	0.058	275	0.038	800	0.024	2100	0.0160
90	0.056	300	0.036	850	0.023	2200	0.0155
100	0.054	325	0.035	900	0.023	2300	0.0150
110	0.052	350	0.034	950	0.022	2400	0.0150
120	0.051	375	0.033	1000	0.022	2500	0.0150
130	0.050	400	0.033	1100	0.021	2600	0.0145
140	0.049	425	0.032	1200	0.020	2700	0.0145
150	0.048	450	0.031	1300	0.019	2800	0.0140
160	0.047	475	0.030	1400	0.019	2900	0.0140
170	0.046	500	0.030	1500	0.018	3000	0.0140

* These values for different rubbing speeds, are based upon the use of phosphor bronze wheels with case-hardened ground and polished steel worms lubricated with mineral oil.

cannot drive the worm. Since the angle of friction changes rapidly with the rubbing speed, and the static angle of friction may be reduced by external vibration, it is usually impracticable to design irreversible worm gears with any security. If irreversibility is desired it is recommended that some form of brake be employed.

Worm Gear Operating Temperatures. — The load capacity of a worm gear lubricant at operating temperature is an important factor in establishing the continuous power-transmitting capacity of the gearing. If the churning or turbulence of the oil generates excessive heat, the viscosity of the lubricant may be reduced below its load-supporting capacity. The temperature measured in the oil sump should not, as a rule, exceed 180 to 200 degrees F. or rise more than 120 to 140 degrees F. above a surrounding air temperature of 60 degrees F. In rear axle motor vehicle transmissions, the maximum operating temperature may be somewhat higher than the figures given and usually is limited to about 220 degrees F.

Thermal Rating. — In some cases, especially when the worm speed is comparatively high, the horsepower capacity of worm gearing should be based upon its thermal rating instead of the mechanical rating. To illustrate, worm gearing may have a thermal rating of, say, 60 H.P., and mechanical ratings which are considerably higher than 60 for the higher speed ranges. This means that the gearing is capable of transmitting more than 60 H.P. so far as wear and strength are concerned but not without overheating; hence, in this case a rating of 60 should be considered maximum. Of course, if the power to be transmitted is less than the thermal rating for a given ratio, then the thermal rating may be ignored.

Water and Forced-Air Cooling. — One method of increasing the thermal rating of a speed-reducing unit of the worm gear type, is by installing a water-cooling coil through which water is circulated to prevent an excessive rise of the oil temperature. According to one manufacturer, the thermal rating may be increased as much as 35 per cent in this manner. Much larger increases have been obtained by means of a forced air cooling system incorporated in the design of the speed-reducing unit. A fan which is mounted on the worm shaft draws air through a double walled housing, thus maintaining a comparatively low oil bath temperature. A fan cooling system makes it possible to transmit a given amount of power through a worm-gear unit that is much smaller than one not equipped with a fan.

Horsepower Rating for Worm Gearing. — According to the British Standard for determining the power-transmitting capacity, the permissible load as limited by wear, is determined for both worm and wheel; then the permissible load as limited by strength is determined for both worm and wheel and the lowest of the four load values in pound-inches of torque is used in the horsepower formula, as shown later by an example. The formulas which follow are for determining the " normal rating " which is the safe loading for operating periods of 12 hours per day. The permissible torque in pound-inches as limited by wear is the lower of the two values obtained by Formula (1) when it is applied to both wheel and worm.

$$\text{Limiting } \textit{wear} \text{ load (torque), pound-inches} = 0.18SX_wF_eD^{1.8} \qquad (1)$$

The permissible torque in pound-inches as limited by strength is the lower of the two values obtained by Formula (2) when it is applied to both wheel and worm.

$$\text{Limiting } \textit{strength} \text{ load (torque), pound-inches} = 0.625S_bX_sQmD \cos L_a \qquad (2)$$

Horsepower rating $= \dfrac{MN}{63{,}000}$ where M is the smallest of the four values obtained

Table 4. Bending Stress and Surface Stress Factors for Worm Gears

Example: Wheel is Phosphor Bronze, Centrifugally Cast (Material in Classification A.) Worm is 3½ per cent Nickel Casehardening Steel (In Classification E.)

Find Factor S for wheel under worm material E (upper section of table) and opposite " Phosphor Bronze, Centrifugally Cast." (*S* equals 2000.)

Find Factor S for worm under wheel material A (lower section of table) and opposite " 3½ per cent Nickel Casehardening Steel." (*S* equals 6500.)

Find Factor S_b for wheel in column " Bending Stress Factor " and opposite " Phosphor Bronze, Centrifugally Cast." (*S_b* equals 10,000.)

Find Factor S_b for worm in column " Bending Stress Factor " and opposite " 3½ per cent Nickel Casehardening Steel." (*S_b* equals 40,000.)

Wheel Materials		Bending Stress Factor S_b Pounds per Sq. In.	Find surface stress factor S for wheel, under worm material classification letter				
			A	B	C	D	E
A	Phosphor Bronze, Sand Cast	7,000	..	600*	600	700	1400
	Phosphor Bronze, Chill Cast	8,500	..	800*	800	900	1600
	Phosphor Bronze, Centrifugally Cast	10,000	..	1000*	1000	1100	2000
B	Cast Iron (Gray)	6,000	900*	600*	600†	600†	750†

Worm Materials		Bending Stress Factor S_b Pounds per Sq. In.	Find surface stress factor S for worm, under wheel material classification letter				
			A	B	C	D	E
C	0.4 Per Cent Carbon Steel, Normalized	20,000	1400	900†	..	..	..
D	0.55 Per Cent Carbon Steel, Normalized	22,000	2000	1100†	..	..	..
E	Low-carbon Casehardening Steel	27,000	6000	4000†	..	..	..
	3½ Per Cent Nickel Casehardening Steel	40,000	6500	4000†	..	..	2000†
	5 Per Cent Nickel Casehardening Steel	47,000	7000	4000†	..	..	2000†
	3½ Per Cent Nickel-chromium Casehardening Steel	47,000	7000	4000†	..	..	2000†
	High Nickel-chrom. Casehardening Steel	47,000	8000	4000†	..	..	2000†

* Maximum permissable rubbing speeds, 500 feet per minute.
† Should not be used except for hand operated gearing.

by applying Formula (1) to wheel and worm and Formula (2) to wheel and worm. While modern practice is to design gears for power transmission on the basis of wear or durability, it is necessary in many cases to check for strength.

Example: Find the normal horsepower rating for worm gearing having a ratio of 15⅓ (or 15⅓ to 1); a center distance of 10¼ inches; worm speed of 680 R.P.M.; wheel speed of about 44.35 R.P.M. The worm has three threads and the wheel, 46 teeth. The worm is made of 3½ per cent nickel steel casehardened and the wheel of phosphor bronze, chill cast. Pitch diameter of worm = 3.112 inches; pitch diameter of wheel = 17.388 inches; lead angle = 20°1′; pitch = 1.1875 inch; and module = $1.1875 \times 0.3183 = 0.378$; outside diameter of worm = 3.868 inches.

Effective face width F_e (see Fig. 1) which is used in determining wear load, may be obtained readily by measurement of full scale drawing. Assume that $F_e = 2.3$.

Rubbing Speed. — Rubbing speed = $0.262dn$ sec $L_a = 0.262 \times 3.112 \times 680 \times 1.0643 = 590$ feet per minute, approximately.

Wear Load, Wheel. — Find S in Table 4 opposite " Phosphor Bronze, Chill Cast " and under worm material E. S for wheel = 1600.

Find X_w for wheel. Rubbing speed is 590 feet per minute and speed of wheel about 44 R.P.M. Referring to the chart, Fig. 2, the intersection of the vertical line from the rubbing speed and the horizontal line from the wheel speed, is close to the 0.3 curve; hence we may assume that $X_w = 0.30$, approximately.

Wear load, wheel = $0.18 \times 1600 \times 0.30 \times 2.3 \times 17.388^{1.8} = 33{,}937$ pound-inches.

Wear Load, Worm. — Find S in Table 4 opposite " 3½ Per Cent Nickel Case-hardened Steel " and under wheel material A. S for worm = 6500. Find X_w for worm. Rubbing speed is 590 feet per minute and R.P.M. of worm is 680. The point of intersection on chart (Fig. 2) indicates that $X_w = 0.155$, approximately.

Wear load, worm = $0.18 \times 6500 \times 0.155 \times 2.3 \times 17.388^{1.8} = 71{,}233$ pound-inches.

Strength Load, Wheel. — Find S_b in Table 4 opposite " Phosphor Bronze, Chill Cast." $S_b = 8500$. Find speed factor X_s for wheel in Table 5. This factor for 44.35 R.P.M. is approximately 0.47. The value of Q or arc length of tooth at root, may be determined accurately enough for practical requirements by measuring full scale drawing. Assume in this case that $Q = 2.5$ inches approximately.

Strength Load, Wheel = $0.625 \times 8500 \times 0.47 \times 2.5 \times 0.378 \times 17.388 \times 0.93959 = 38{,}550$ pound-inches.

Strength Load, Worm. — Value of S_b for worm for 3½ per cent nickel casehardened steel is 40,000 as shown by Table 4. Speed factor X_s for worm speed of 680 R.P.M. (see Table 5) is 0.29 approximately.

Table 5. Speed Factors X_s for Worm Gearing (Strength)

R.P.M.	Speed Factor X_s	R.P.M.	Speed Factor X_s	R.P.M.	Speed Factor X_s	R.P.M.	Speed Factor X_s
10	0.560	90	0.420	500	0.310	3000	0.200
15	0.540	100	0.415	600	0.300	3500	0.190
20	0.520	150	0.385	700	0.290	4000	0.180
30	0.500	200	0.365	800	0.280	4500	0.175
40	0.480	250	0.350	900	0.270	5000	0.170
50	0.460	300	0.340	1000	0.260	6000	0.160
60	0.450	350	0.335	1500	0.240	7000	0.150
70	0.440	400	0.330	2000	0.225	8000	0.140
80	0.430	450	0.320	2500	0.210	9000	0.135

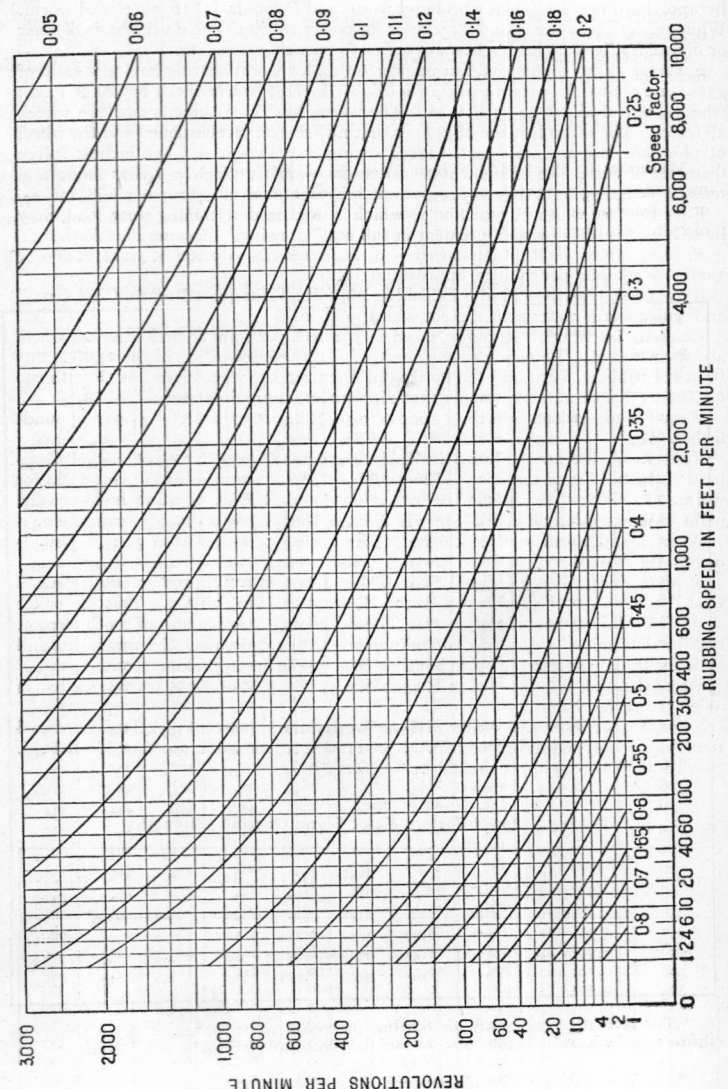

Strength load, worm = 0.625 × 40,000 × 0.29 × 2.5 × 0.378 × 17.388 × 0.93959 = 111,930 pound-inches.

Horsepower Rating. — In the foregoing example, the wear load of 33,937 pound-inches of torque for the wheel is the lowest of the four values; hence

$$\text{Horsepower rating} = \frac{33{,}937 \times 44.35}{63{,}000} = 24 \text{ approximately}$$

Methods of Machining Worm Threads. — In producing worm threads, the method employed may depend upon quantity required, number of threads on worm or its lead angle, and equipment available. Methods of cutting threads on worms of cylindrical form are described on page 800.

Table 6. Change Gears for Cutting Diametral Pitch Worms*

Diametral Pitch to be Cut	Width of Tool Point	Threads per Inch on Lead Screw							
		2	3	4	5	6	7	8	10
2	0.487	22/7	33/7	44/7	55/7	66/7	77/7	88/7	110/7
2¼	0.433	176/63	88/21	352/63	440/63	176/21	88/9	704/63	880/63
2½	0.390	88/35	132/35	176/35	44/7	264/35	308/35	352/35	440/35
2¾	0.354	16/7	24/7	32/7	40/7	48/7	56/7	64/7	80/7
3	0.325	44/21	22/7	88/21	110/21	44/7	22/3	176/21	220/21
3½	0.278	88/49	132/49	176/49	220/49	264/49	44/7	352/49	440/49
4	0.243	11/7	33/14	22/7	55/14	33/7	11/2	44/7	55/7
4½	0.217	88/63	44/21	176/63	220/63	88/21	44/9	352/63	440/63
5	0.195	44/35	66/35	88/35	22/7	132/35	22/5	176/35	44/7
6	0.162	22/21	11/7	44/21	55/21	22/7	11/3	88/21	110/21
7	0.139	44/49	66/49	88/49	110/49	132/49	22/7	176/49	220/49
8	0.122	11/14	33/28	11/7	55/28	33/14	11/4	22/7	55/14
9	0.108	44/63	22/21	88/63	110/63	44/21	22/9	176/63	220/63
10	0.097	22/35	33/35	44/35	11/7	66/35	11/5	88/35	22/7
11	0.088	4/7	6/7	8/7	10/7	12/7	14/7	16/7	20/7
12	0.081	11/21	11/14	22/21	55/42	11/7	11/6	44/21	55/21
14	0.069	22/49	33/49	44/49	55/49	66/49	11/7	88/49	110/49
16	0.061	11/28	33/56	22/28	55/56	33/28	11/8	11/7	55/28
18	0.054	22/63	11/21	44/63	55/63	22/21	11/9	88/63	110/63
20	0.049	11/35	33/70	22/35	11/14	33/35	11/10	44/35	11/7
22	0.044	2/7	3/7	4/7	5/7	6/7	7/7	8/7	10/7
24	0.040	11/42	33/84	11/21	55/84	11/14	11/12	22/21	55/42
26	0.037	22/91	33/91	44/91	55/91	66/91	11/13	88/91	110/91
28	0.035	11/49	33/98	22/49	55/98	33/49	11/14	44/49	55/49
30	0.032	22/105	11/35	44/105	11/21	22/35	11/15	88/105	22/21
32	0.030	11/56	33/112	11/28	55/112	33/56	11/16	11/14	55/56
40	0.024	11/70	33/140	11/35	11/28	33/70	11/20	22/35	11/14
48	0.020	11/84	33/168	11/42	55/168	33/84	11/24	11/21	55/84

* The ratio of change gears for cutting diametral pitch worms is as 22 times the threads per inch on lead-screw is to 7 times the diametral pitch to be cut. Thus,

$$\frac{22 \times \text{Threads per Inch}}{7 \times \text{Diametral Pitch}} = \text{Ratio of Change Gears}$$

Table 7. Approximate Worm-thread Lead Angle, in Degrees, for Given Lead and Pitch Diameter

Lead of Worm, Inches	Pitch-line Diameter of Worm, Inches																				
	1	1⅛	1¼	1⅜	1½	1⅝	1¾	1⅞	2	2⅛	2¼	2⅜	2½	2⅝	2¾	2⅞	3	3⅛	3¼	3⅜	3½
¼	4½	4	3½	3¼	3	2¾	2½	2½	2¼	2¼	2	2	2	1¾	1¾	1½	1½	1½	1½	1½	1½
⅜	6¾	6	5½	5	4½	4¼	4	3¾	3½	3¼	3	3	2¾	2½	2½	2½	2¼	2¼	2¼	2	2
½	9	8	7¼	6¾	6	5½	5¼	5	4½	4¼	4¼	4	3¾	3½	3¼	3¼	3	3	2¾	2¾	2½
⅝	11¼	10	9	8¼	7½	7	6½	6	5¾	5¼	5	4¾	4½	4½	4¼	4	3¾	3¾	3½	3½	3¼
¾	13½	12	10¾	10	9	8½	7¾	7¼	6¾	6½	6	5¾	5½	5¼	5	4¾	4½	4½	4¼	4¼	4
⅞	15½	14	12½	11½	10½	9¾	9	8½	8	7½	7	6¾	6½	6	5¾	5½	5¼	5	5	4¾	4½
1	17¾	16	14¼	13	12	11¼	10¼	9¾	9	8½	8	7¾	7¼	7	6¾	6¼	6	5¾	5½	5½	5¼
1⅛	19¾	18	16	14¾	13½	12½	11½	11	10¼	9½	9	8½	8	7¾	7½	7¼	6¾	6½	6¼	6	6
1¼	21¾	19½	17¾	16¼	15	13¾	12¾	12	11¼	10¾	10	9½	9	8¾	8¼	8	7¾	7½	7	6¾	6½
1⅜	23¾	21¼	19¼	17¾	16¼	15	14	13	12½	11¾	11	10½	10	9½	9	8¾	8¼	8	7¾	7½	7
1½	25½	23	21	19¼	17½	16½	15¼	14¼	13½	12¾	12	11½	11	10¼	10	9½	9	8¾	8½	8	7¾
1⅝	27½	24¾	22½	20¾	19	17¾	16½	15½	14½	13¾	13	12¼	11¾	11¼	10¾	10¼	9¾	9½	9	8¾	8½
1¾	29¼	26½	24	22	20½	19	17¾	16½	15½	14¾	14	13¼	12½	12	11½	11	10½	10	9¾	9½	9
1⅞	30¾	28	25½	23½	21¾	20¼	19	17½	16¾	15¾	15	14¼	13½	13	12¼	11¾	11¼	11	10½	10	9¾
2	32½	29¾	27	25	23	21½	20	19	17¾	16¾	15¾	15	14¼	13¾	13¼	12½	12	11½	11	10¾	10½
2¼	35¾	32¾	30	27½	25½	24	22¼	21	19¾	18¾	17¾	17	16	15¼	14¾	14	13½	13	12½	12	11½
2½	38½	35½	32½	30	28	26¼	24½	23	21¾	20¾	19½	18½	17¾	17	16¼	15½	15	14¼	13¾	13½	12¾
2¾	41¼	38	35	32½	30¼	28½	26½	25	23¾	22½	21¼	20¼	19¼	18½	17¾	17	16¼	15¾	15	14¾	14
3	43¾	40½	37½	35	32½	30½	28¾	27	25½	24¼	23	22	21	20	19¼	18½	17¾	17	16½	16	15¼
3¼	46	42¾	39¾	37	34½	32½	30¾	29	27½	26	24¼	23½	22½	21½	20¾	19¾	19	18½	17¾	17	16½
3½	48¼	45	41¾	39¼	36¾	34½	32½	30¾	29¼	27¾	26¼	25¼	24	23	22	21¼	20½	19½	19	18¼	17¾
3¾	50¼	47	43¾	41	38¾	36½	34¼	32½	31	29½	28	26¾	25½	24½	23½	22½	21¾	21	20¼	19½	19
4	51¾	48½	45¾	43	40½	38¼	36	34¼	32¾	31	29½	28¼	27	26	25	24	23	22	21½	20¾	20
4¼	53½	50½	47½	44¾	42¼	39¾	37¾	36	34¼	32½	31	29¾	28½	27¼	26¼	25¼	24¼	23½	22½	22	21¼
4½	55	42	49	46½	43¾	41½	39½	37½	35¾	34	32½	31¼	30	28¾	27½	26½	25½	24½	23¾	23	22½
4¾	56½	53½	50½	48	45¼	43	40¾	39	37¼	35½	34	32½	31¼	30	29	27¾	26¾	25¾	25	24	23½
5	57¾	54¾	51¾	49¼	46¾	44½	42¼	40½	38¾	37	35¼	34	32½	31¼	30¼	29	28	27	26	25¼	24½
5¼	59¼	56¼	53¼	50¾	48	46	43¾	41¾	40	38¼	36½	35¼	34	32½	31½	30¼	29	28¼	27	26½	25½
5½	60¼	57¼	54¾	52	49½	47¼	45	43	41¼	39½	38	36½	35	33¾	32¾	31½	30¼	29¼	28¼	27½	26½
5¾	61¼	58½	55¾	53	50¾	48½	46¼	44¼	42½	40¾	39¼	37¾	36¼	35	33¾	32½	31½	30¼	29½	28½	27¾
6	62¼	59¾	57	54¼	52	49½	47½	45¾	43¾	42	40¼	39	37½	36¼	35	33¾	32½	31½	30½	29½	28¾

Table 7. (*Continued*). **Approximate Worm-thread Lead Angle, in Degrees, for Given Lead and Pitch Diameter**

Lead of Worm, Inches	Pitch-line Diameter of Worm, Inches																			
	3⅝	3¾	3⅞	4	4⅛	4¼	4⅜	4½	4⅝	4¾	4⅞	5	5⅛	5¼	5⅜	5½	5⅝	5¾	5⅞	6
¼	1¼	1¼	1¼	1¼	1¼	1¼	1	1	1	1	1	1	1	1	1	1	1	1	1	1
⅜	2	2	2	1¾	1¾	1¾	1½	1½	1½	1½	1½	1½	1½	1½	1¼	1¼	1¼	1¼	1¼	1¼
½	2½	2½	2½	2¼	2¼	2¼	2	2	2	2	2	2	2	2	1¾	1¾	1¾	1¾	1¾	1½
⅝	3¼	3	3	2¾	2¾	2¾	2½	2½	2½	2½	2½	2¼	2¼	2¼	2¼	2¼	2¼	2	2	2
¾	3¾	3¾	3½	3¼	3¼	3¼	3¼	3	3	3	3	2¾	2¾	2¾	2¾	2½	2½	2¼	2¼	2¼
⅞	4½	4¼	4¼	4	4	4	3¾	3½	3½	3½	3¼	3¼	3¼	3	3	3	2¾	2¾	2¾	2¾
1	5	5	4¾	4½	4½	4½	4¼	4	4	3¾	3¾	3¾	3½	3½	3½	3¼	3¼	3¼	3¼	3
1⅛	5¾	5½	5½	5¼	5	5	4¾	4½	4½	4¼	4¼	4¼	4	4	3¾	3¾	3¾	3¾	3½	3½
1¼	6¼	6	6	5¾	5½	5½	5¼	5	5	4¾	4¾	4½	4½	4½	4¼	4¼	4¼	4	4	3¾
1⅜	7	6¾	6½	6¼	6	6	5¾	5½	5½	5¼	5¼	5	5	4¾	4¾	4½	4½	4½	4¼	4¼
1½	7½	7¼	7	6¾	6¾	6½	6¼	6	6	5¾	5½	5½	5¼	5¼	5	5	4¾	4¾	4¾	4½
1⅝	8¼	8	7¾	7½	7¼	7	6¾	6½	6½	6¼	6	6	5¾	5¾	5½	5½	5¼	5¼	5	5
1¾	8¾	8½	8¼	8	7¾	7½	7¼	7	7	6¾	6½	6½	6¼	6	6	5¾	5¾	5½	5½	5½
1⅞	9½	9	8¾	8½	8¼	8	7¾	7½	7½	7¼	7	7	6¾	6½	6½	6¼	6	6	5¾	5¾
2	10	9¾	9½	9	8¾	8½	8½	8¼	8	7¾	7½	7¼	7¼	7	6¾	6¾	6½	6½	6¼	6
2¼	11¼	11	10½	10¼	10	9½	9½	9	9	8¾	8½	8¼	8	8	7¾	7½	7½	7¼	7	7
2½	12½	12	11¾	11¼	11	10¾	10½	10	10	9½	9¼	9¼	9	8¾	8½	8¼	8¼	8	7¾	7½
2¾	13¾	13¼	12¾	12¼	12	11¾	11½	11	10¾	10½	10¼	10	9¾	9½	9¼	9¼	9	8¾	8½	8½
3	15	14½	14	13½	13	13	12¼	12	11½	11½	11	11	10¾	10½	10¼	10	9¾	9½	9½	9¼
3¼	16	15½	15	14½	14¼	14	13¼	13	12½	12¼	12	11¾	11½	11	11	10¾	10½	10¼	10¼	10
3½	17¼	16¾	16	15½	15½	15	14¼	14	13½	13¼	13	12½	12¼	12	11¾	11½	11¼	11	10¾	10½
3¾	18½	18	17¼	16½	16¼	15¾	15¼	15	14½	14¼	13¾	13½	13	13	12½	12¼	12	11¾	11½	11¼
4	19½	19	18½	17½	17¼	16¾	16¼	16	15½	15	14½	14¼	14	13¾	13¼	13	13	12½	12¼	12
4¼	20½	20	19½	18½	18½	17¾	17¼	16¾	16½	16	15½	15¼	15	14½	14	14	13¾	13½	13	12¾
4½	21½	21	20½	19¾	19½	18½	18¼	17½	17¼	17	16½	16	15¾	15¼	15	14¾	14½	14¼	13¾	13½
4¾	22¾	22	21½	20¾	20½	19½	19¼	18½	18¼	18	17¼	17	16½	16	16	15½	15¼	15	14½	14¼
5	23¾	23	22½	21¾	21¼	20½	20	19½	19	18½	18¼	18	17¼	17	16½	16¼	16	15½	15¼	15
5¼	24¾	24	23½	22½	22	21½	21	20½	20	19½	19	18½	18¼	17¾	17½	17	16¾	16¼	16	15¾
5½	25¾	25¼	24½	23½	23	22½	22	21½	21	20½	20	19½	19	18½	18¼	18	17½	17	16¾	16½
5¾	27	26¼	25½	24½	24	23½	23	22	21¾	21	20½	20¼	19¾	19½	19	18½	18¼	17¾	17½	17
6	27¾	27	26½	25½	25	24¼	23¾	23	22½	22	21½	21	20½	20	19½	19¼	19	18½	18	17¾

1. *Milling with a Disk-shaped Cutter.* The cutter has straight sides or edges and it is inclined an amount equal to the lead angle to locate the cutting side in alignment with the thread groove. There is a traversing movement per work revolution equal to the required lead. If the worm has two or more threads or starts, these are, of course, milled one at a time and should be uniformly spaced by indexing. *Precise indexing is very important.* A worm- or thread-milling machine is used.

2. *Hobbing.* A regular gear-hobbing machine is very efficient, especially for multi-thread worms, because all of the threads are finished simultaneously instead of taking separate cuts and indexing. The hobbing machine is geared with reference to the number of threads on the worm, the procedure being similar to that followed in cutting a helical gear.

3. *Generating by using a Worm Thread Generator.* The machine is equipped with a helical type gear shaper cutter, the axis of which is at right angles to the axis of the worm. The cutter generates the thread or threads as it rolls in mesh with the rotating work.

4. *Cutting in a Lathe.* One method is to locate the top cutting face of the tool normal or perpendicular to the worm thread. A second method is to locate the top cutting face in the same plane as the axis of the worm. With this method, cutting difficulties are encountered when the lead angles are comparatively large, due to the negative rake on the following side of the tool. As a general rule, the first method is preferable when a lathe must be used.

Grinding Worm Threads and Hobs. — A common method of producing worm threads is by milling with a disk-shaped cutter and then grinding after the hardening operation. The milling cutter has straight edges and the grinding wheel straight sides, because of the practical advantage in producing and maintaining these straight edges and sides.

In finishing hardened steel worms by grinding, the straight-sided grinding wheel produces a thread having convex sides and this curvature should be duplicated on the worm-wheel hob. This can be accomplished by finishing both worm and hob with grinding wheels which are maintained within diameter limits established by experience. In the case of multi-thread worms, accuracy of the indexing is essential when grinding both the worm and hob and accurate uniform lead is also important.

Hindley Worm Gearing. — The Hindley type of worm gear was used in first the Hindley dividing engine. In the Hindley worm gear the worm, instead of being cylindrical in outline, and the projection of the pitch line being a straight line, has a curved outline, the projection of the pitch line of the worm being a circular arc corresponding to the pitch line of the gear. The following claims are made for the contact of the Hindley worm and gear: — 1. The contact is purely sliding contact. 2. The nature of the contact is linear, closely resembling surface contact. 3. Linear contact extends from the top to the root of the teeth. 4. The contact is on the axial section. 5. The thread section fills the tooth space on the axial section only. 6. The mid-portion of the hob has little or no effect in shaping the teeth of the gear. 7. Surface contact exists on opposite sides of the axial plane at the end of the worm thread, and is intermittent in nature, because the end of the thread passes out of contact with the tooth in the revolving of the worm. This contact is on a plane normal with the thread angle.

There is, however, considerable difference of opinion as to the actual contact between the worm and wheel in the Hindley worm gear. In practice, it is usual to allow considerable back-lash between the thread and the teeth of the worm gear. This play tends to counteract faults in the workmanship, either in construction or erection. The worm of Hindley gearing must be centered in both planes, with relation to the wheel, and be carefully secured axially, as endwise movement would seriously affect the bearing of the teeth and greatly increase the friction. The length of the worm should not exceed one-third of the wheel diameter. The face of the wheel at the root of the tooth should not exceed, in width, one-half of the worm diameter at the center.

Cone-drive Worm Gearing. — Contact between the worm and wheel of the conventional type of worm gearing is theoretically a line contact; however, due to deflection of the materials under load, the line is increased to a narrow band or contact zone. In attempting to produce a double-enveloping type of worm gear (with the worm curved longitudinally to fit the curvature of the wheel as shown by illustration), the problem primarily was that of generating the worm and worm

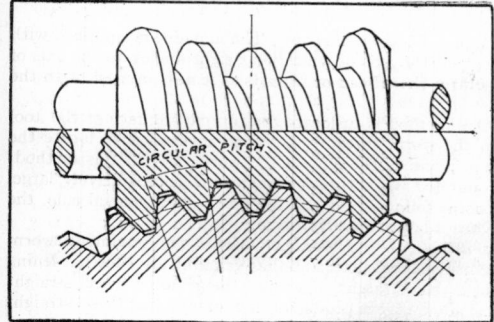

wheel in such a manner as to obtain *area contact* between the engaging teeth. A practical method of obtaining such contact was developed by Samuel I. Cone at the Norfolk Navy Yard, and this is known as "Cone-drive" worm gearing. The Cone generating method make it possible to cut the worm and gear without any interference which would alter the required tooth form. The larger tooth bearing area and multiple tooth contact obtained with this type of worm gearing, increases the load-carrying or horsepower capacity. The accompanying table, which is intended as a general guide only, gives the horsepower ratings of Cone-drive worm gearing, for various center distances, ratios, and worm speeds. These ratings were obtained from data compiled by the Michigan Tool Co. The mechanical horsepower ratings take into account (1) a pressure constant which varies for different center distances,

Horsepower Rating of Cone-drive Worm Gearing — 1

Center Distance, Inches	Ratio	Worm Speeds — R.P.M.							Thermal H.P. Ratings
		100	300	580	870	1150	1750	2400	
		Mechanical Horsepower Ratings							
2	6¼ : 1	0.19	0.47	0.80	1.07	1.29	1.66	1.97	2.21
2	10 : 1	0.21	0.57	0.97	1.34	1.60	2.14	2.53	2.02
2	16 : 1	0.14	0.37	0.63	0.84	1.00	1.32	1.57	1.64
2	20 : 1	0.12	0.30	0.48	0.65	0.79	1.00	1.21	1.53
2⅛	15 : 1	0.12	0.30	0.51	0.68	0.83	1.05	1.27	1.62
2¼	3⅙ : 1	0.37	0.89	1.39	1.79	2.10	2.58	2.92	4.68
2¼	7¾ : 1	0.38	0.97	1.60	2.11	2.53	3.21	3.76	3.62
2½	8⅔ : 1	0.49	1.26	2.14	2.75	3.30	4.14	4.88	3.85
2½	14 : 1	0.23	0.51	0.84	1.10	1.32	1.72	2.03	2.26
2½	30 : 1	0.12	0.32	0.54	0.72	0.87	1.12	1.32	1.27
2¾	6¼ : 1	0.85	2.14	3.44	4.65	5.47	6.75	8.06	5.31
2¾	32 : 1	0.19	0.51	0.84	1.11	1.33	1.71	2.00	1.84
2¾	64 : 1	0.08	0.22	0.36	0.49	0.58	0.75	0.88	0.77
3	4¼ : 1	1.23	2.83	4.73	6.24	7.28	9.09	1.07	9.80
3	17 : 1	0.48	1.21	1.98	2.64	3.06	4.04	4.85	4.12

Horsepower Rating of Cone-drive Worm Gearing — 2

Center Distance, Inches	Ratio	Worm Speeds — R.P.M. 100	300	580	870	1150	1750	2400	Thermal H.P. Ratings
		Mechanical Horsepower Ratings							
3	24 : 1	0.35	0.89	1.46	1.94	2.28	2.97	3.49	3.13
3	42 : 1	0.20	0.52	0.84	1.10	1.36	1.77	2.00	1.80
3¼	18 : 1	0.56	1.45	2.32	3.10	3.61	4.75	5.79	4.56
3⅜	30 : 1	0.39	1.00	1.64	2.15	2.56	3.20	3.75	3.40
3½	4 : 1	1.93	4.60	7.41	9.79	11.4	14.3	16.8	13.2
3½	15 : 1	0.67	1.68	2.76	3.59	5.10	5.25	6.12	5.80
3½	24 : 1	0.56	1.41	2.32	3.06	3.62	4.53	5.19	4.90
3½	49 : 1	0.33	0.87	1.52	2.00	2.38	2.92	3.25	2.52
4	5⅕ : 1	2.93	6.77	10.5	13.2	15.3	18.8	20.9	19.4
4	13 : 1	1.42	3.60	5.82	7.42	8.78	10.7	12.4	11.2
4	17 : 1	1.13	2.86	4.50	5.95	6.82	8.70	9.90	8.50
4¼	3 : 1	4.50	10.2	15.2	18.9	22.0	26.1	29.0	24.5
4¼	12½ : 1	1.83	4.54	7.30	9.30	11.1	13.6	14.1	9.52
4¼	30 : 1	0.91	2.31	3.74	4.84	5.64	7,12	8.07	6.29
4½	3⅐ : 1	4.70	10.3	15.2	18.9	21.9	26.3	29.9	25.1
4½	15 : 1	1.83	4.70	6.70	8.75	10.7	14.1	15.5	11.7
4½	24 : 1	1.19	2.97	4.71	6.11	7.13	8.78	10.2	8.30
5	12½ : 1	3.40	8.40	13.0	16.7	19.3	23.8	26.9	16.8
5½	4⅚ : 1	7.03	16.8	25.2	32.2	35.8	42.5	46.5	32.0
5½	9⅔ : 1	4.82	11.4	17.7	22.5	26.1	33.0	36.3	21.0
5½	12 : 1	4.15	9.96	15.9	19.5	22.5	27.3	31.1	15.0
6	4⅛ : 1	10.8	24.2	35.4	43.6	49.6	58.4	64.2	34.0
6	9 : 1	6.91	16.5	25.2	31.7	36.2	44.1	49.7	21.4
6	15 : 1	4.52	11.3	16.6	21.3	24.4	27.8	32.9	14.6
6	30 : 1	2.20	5.50	8.80	11.2	12.9	15.8	17.8	9.38
7	5⅐ : 1	16.6	36.7	54.3	66.7	75.7	88.6	96.2	37.0
7	25 : 1	4.9	11.7	18.8	22.9	26.2	33.1	35.3	13.0
7	70 : 1	1.84	4.38	7.03	8.57	9.85	12.4	13.4	5.2
8	5⅗ : 1	23.4	51.8	76.3	91.5	105	123	136	48
8	50 : 1	4.05	9.36	13.9	17.8	20.4	24.5	27.6	8.8
8	72 : 1	2.29	5.72	8.44	10.7	12.2	13.7	16.2	6.6
9	67 : 1	4.18	9.70	14.5	19.3	20.7	24.1	26.9	8.5
9¾	25 : 1	11.5	25.7	38.3	47.1	53.3	63.1	69.3	23.3
9¾	50 : 1	6.00	13.3	20.0	24.8	28.5	32.8	36.0	12.4
10	11½ : 1	25.1	55.4	81.1	98.5	111	130	143	42.6
10	23 : 1	13.4	30.2	45.0	55.0	62.8	73.7	81.0	25.5
10	40 : 1	9.25	21.0	31.2	38.5	43.7	51.6	56.9	16.5
10	69 : 1	5.51	11.4	17.0	20.8	23.3	27.4	30.2	10.2
11	50 : 1	8.00	18.0	26.2	32.2	36.2	42.2	45.3	15.4
11¼	60 : 1	8.61	19.2	28.0	34.3	39.9	45.0	49.7	13.4
12	6⅕ : 1	68.4	144	20.6	248	275	311	341	87.0
12	10⅓ : 1	47.0	101	143	176	197	222	243	61.5
12	20 : 1	27.4	57.2	84.7	100	116	134	150	39.0
12	32 : 1	18.7	41.0	60.5	74.6	82.8	96.4	104	26.5
13	10¼ : 1	60.0	128	181	217	241	276	303	71.0
15	7⅘ : 1	111	229	344	392	431	514	525	112
16½	120 : 1	12.1	25.5	36.4	43.7	48.3	54.5	58.2	13.5
18	11 : 1	138	272	395	454	496	555	593	120
18	70 : 1	25.0	51.4	71.8	85.5	94.3	107	119	25.5
22	180 : 1	11.5	24.8	35.0	43.1	47.3	54.0	57.8	13.4
23½	15 : 1	237	467	644	740	809	907	977	155
24	50 : 1	77.5	150	208	239	261	292	326	57.5

(2) a ratio correction factor, and (3) a velocity factor. The ratings thus obtained apply when the operation does not exceed 8 to 10 hours out of 24 and is free from recurring shock loads. For 8- to 10-hour service with recurring shock loads, or for 24-hour service without shock loads, the mechanical ratings should be reduced by dividing by 1.2. For 24-hour shock service, the ratings should be divided by 1⅛. For intermittent service, where the maximum operating cycle in a 2-hour period does not exceed 15 minutes, the mechanical rating may be divided by 0.7. Cone-drive worm gears have been used for many different applications and for a wide range of ratios, including reductions up to 180 to 1 and speed increases up to 1 to 6. Speed variations have ranged from 30,000 R.P.M. down to ⅟₁₅ revolution per minute, and sizes from 1 inch to many feet in diameter for gear wheels.

Worm Gear Hobs. — An ideal hob would have exactly the same pitch diameter and lead angle as the worm; repeated sharpening, however, would reduce the hob size because of the form-relieved teeth. Hence, the general practice is to make hobs (especially the radial or in-feed type) "over-size" to provide a grinding allowance and increase the hob life. An over-size hob has a larger pitch diameter and smaller lead angle than the worm, but repeated sharpenings gradually reduce these differences. To compensate for the smaller lead angle of an over-size hob, the hob axis may be set 90-degrees relative to the wheel axis plus the difference between the *lead* angle of the worm at the pitch line, and the *lead* angle of the over-size hob at its pitch line. This angular adjustment is in the direction required to increase the inclination of the worm wheel teeth so that the axis of the assembled worm will be 90 degrees from the wheel axis. ("Lead angle" is measured from a plane perpendicular to worm or hob axis.)

A second method is to make the worm diameter equal to the hob diameter as the latter is changed by sharpening. The worm wheel diameter may also be changed to maintain a given center distance. When this second method is employed, the hob's spindle remains in the 90-degree position.

Hob Diameter Formulas: If D = pitch diameter of worm; D_h = pitch diameter of hob; A = addendum of worm and worm wheel; C = clearance between worm and worm wheel; and S = increase in hob diameter or "over-size" allowance for sharpening.

$$\text{Outside diameter } O \text{ of hob} = D + 2A + 2C + S$$
$$\text{Root diameter of hob} = D - 2A$$
$$\text{Pitch diameter } D_h \text{ of hob} = O - (2A + 2C)$$

Sharpening Allowance: The "over-size" varies for different classes of hobs. In making tangential hobs, the general practice is to provide a very small sharpening allowance; the hob then can be set in the 90-degree position without introducing excessive errors. Finishing hobs, which are sometimes used after a rough hobbing operation, also have small sharpening allowances and little relief in order to minimize size changes resulting from sharpening. Hobs for ordinary commercial work are given the following sharpening allowance, according to the recommended practice of the American Gear Manufacturers Association: In this formula, h = helix angle of hob at outside diameter measured from axis; H = helix angle of hob at pitch diameter measured from axis.

$$\text{Sharpening allowance} = 0.075 \times \text{normal pitch} \times \left[\frac{16 - (h - H)}{16} \right] + 0.010$$

Number of Flutes or Gashes in Hobs. For finding the approximate number of flutes in a hob, the following rule may be used: Multiply the diameter of the hob by 3, and divide this product by twice the linear pitch. This rule gives suitable results for hobs for general purposes. Certain modifications, however, are necessary as explained in the following paragraph.

It is important that the number of flutes or gashes in hobs bear a certain relation to the number of threads in the hob and the number of teeth in the worm-wheel to be hobbed. In the first place, avoid having a common factor between the number of threads in the hob and the number of flutes; that is, if the worm is double-threaded, the number of gashes should be, say, 7 or 9, rather than 8. If it is triple-threaded, the number of gashes should be 7 or 11, rather than 6 or 9. The second requirement is to avoid having a common factor between the number of threads in the hob and the number of teeth in the worm-wheel. For example, if the number of teeth in the wheel is 28, it would be best to have the hob triple-threaded, as 3 is not a factor of 28. Again, if there were to be 36 threads in the worm-gear, it would be preferable to have 5 threads in the hob.

The cutter used in gashing hobs should be from ⅛ to ¼ inch thick at the periphery, according to the pitch of the thread of the hob. The width of the gash at the periphery of the hob should be about 0.4 times the pitch of the flutes. The cutter should be sunk into the hob blank so that it reaches from 3⁄16 to ¼ inch below the root of the thread.

Helical Fluted Hobs. — Hobs are generally fluted parallel with the axis, but it is obvious that the cutting action will be better if they are fluted on a helix at right angles with the thread helix. The difficulty of relieving the teeth with the ordinary backing-off attachment is the cause for using a flute parallel with the axis. Flutes cut at right angles to the direction of the thread can, however, also be relieved, if the angle of the flutes is slightly modified. In order to relieve hobs with a regular relieving attachment, it is necessary that the number of teeth in one revolution along the thread helix be such that the relieving attachment can be geared to suit it. The following method makes it possible to select an angle of flute that will make the flute come *approximately* at right angles to the thread, and at the same time the angle is so selected that the relieving attachment can be properly geared for relieving the hob.

Let $\qquad$ C = pitch circumference;

$\qquad\qquad$ T = developed length of thread in one turn;

$\qquad\qquad$ N = number of teeth in one turn along thread helix;

$\qquad\qquad$ F = number of flutes;

$\qquad\qquad$ α = angle of thread helix.

Then (see illustration on the following page):

$\qquad$ $C \div F$ = length of each small division on pitch circumference;

$(C \div F) \times \cos \alpha$ = length of division on developed thread;

$\qquad$ $C \div \cos \alpha = T$.

Hence
$$\frac{T}{(C \div F) \cos \alpha} = N = \frac{F}{\cos^2 \alpha}$$

Now, if $\qquad\qquad$ α = 30 degrees, $N = 1\tfrac{1}{3} F$;

$\qquad\qquad\qquad$ α = 45 degrees, $N = 2 F$;

$\qquad\qquad\qquad$ α = 60 degrees, $N = 4 F$.

In most cases, however, such simple relations are not obtained. Suppose for example that $F = 7$, and $\alpha = 35$ degrees. Then $N = 10.432$, and no gears could be selected that would relieve this hob. By a very slight change in the helix angle of the flute, however, we can change N to 10 or 10½; in either case we can find suitable gears for the relieving attachment.

The rule for finding the modified helical lead of the flute is: Multiply the lead of the hob by F, and divide the product by the difference between the desired values of N and F.

Hence, the lead of flute required to make $N = 10$ is:

Lead of hob $\times$ $(7 \div 3)$.

To make $N = 10\frac{1}{2}$, we have:

Lead of flute = lead of hob $\times$ $(7 \div 3.5)$.

From this the angle of the flute can easily be found.

That the rule given is correct will be understood from the following consideration. Change the angle of the flute helix β so that AG contains the required number of parts N desired. Then EG contains $N - F$ parts. But $\cot \beta = BD \div ED$ and by the law of similar triangles,

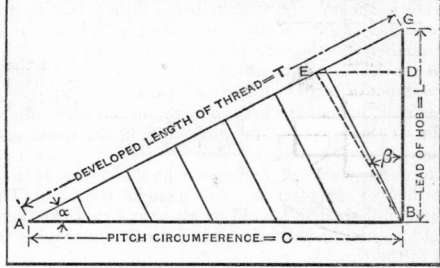

$$BD = \frac{F}{N} \times BG, \text{ and } ED = \frac{N - F}{N} C$$

The lead of the helix of the flute, however, is $C \times \cot \beta$.

Hence, the required lead of the helix of the flute:

$$C \times \cot \beta = \frac{F}{N - F} L$$

This formula makes it possible always to flute hobs so that they can be conveniently relieved, and at the same time have the flutes at approximately right angles to the thread.

Helical Gearing

Basic Rules and Formulas for Helical Gear Calculations. — The ten rules and formulas in the accompanying table may be called the basic rules for helical gear calculations. The following definitions should be clearly understood in order to avoid misunderstandings. The *center angle* of a pair of helical gears is the angle made by the two center lines or axes of the gears. The *tooth angle* is the angle which the direction of the tooth makes with the axis of the gear. The *normal diametral pitch* is the diametral pitch of the cutter used for cutting the teeth in helical gears. In the formulas in the table of "Basic Rules and Formulas for Helical Gear Calculations" the following notation is used:

P_n = normal diametral pitch (pitch of cutter);
D = pitch diameter;
N = number of teeth;
α = helix angle;
γ = center angle, or angle between shafts;
C = center distance;

N' = number of teeth for which to select a formed cutter;
L = lead of tooth helix;
S = addendum;
W = whole depth of tooth;
T_n = normal tooth thickness at pitch line;
O = outside diameter.

The rules and formulas are given in the same order as they would ordinarily be used by the designer when calculating a pair of helical gears. The formulas, how-

Basic Rules and Formulas for Helical Gear Calculations

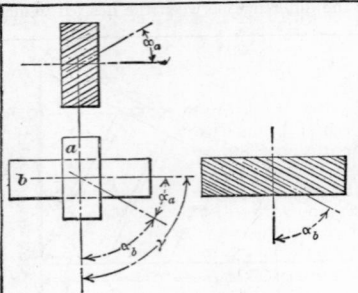

In the formulas, N, α, etc., are the numbers of teeth, helix angle, etc., for *either* gear or pinion; the notations N_a, N_b, α_a, α_b, etc., refer to the teeth or angles in the pinion or gear, respectively, in a pair of gears a and b.

No.	To Find	Rule	Formula
I	Relation between Shaft and Tooth Angles.	See rules at bottom of page 809.	
2	Pitch Diameter.	Divide the number of teeth by the product of the normal pitch and the cosine of the tooth angle.	$D = \dfrac{N}{P_n \cos \alpha}$
3	Center Distance.	Add together the pitch diameters of the two gears and divide by 2.	$C = \dfrac{D_a + D_b}{2}$
4	Checking Calculations in (2) and (3); for use when angle between shafts is 90 degrees.	To prove the calculations for pitch diameters and center distance, multiply the number of teeth in the first gear by the tangent of the tooth angle of that gear, and add the number of teeth in the second gear to the product; the sum should equal twice the product of the center distance multiplied by the normal diametral pitch, multiplied by the sine of the tooth angle of the first gear.	$N_b + (N_a \times \tan \alpha_a) = 2CP_n \times \sin \alpha_a$
5	Number of Teeth for which to Select Formed Cutter.	Divide the number of teeth in the gear by the cube of the cosine of the tooth angle.	$N' = \dfrac{N}{(\cos \alpha)^3}$
6	Lead of Tooth Helix.	Multiply the pitch diameter by 3.1416 times the cotangent of the tooth angle.	$L = \pi D \times \cot \alpha$
7	Addendum.	Divide 1 by the normal diametral pitch.	$S = \dfrac{1}{P_n}$
8	Whole Depth of Tooth.	Divide 2.157 by the normal diametral pitch.	$W = \dfrac{2.157}{P_n}$
9	Normal Tooth Thickness at Pitch Line.	Divide 1.571 by the normal diametral pitch.	$T_n = \dfrac{1.571}{P_n}$
10	Outside Diameter.	Add twice the addendum to the pitch diameter.	$O = D + 2S$

ever, cannot be directly applied to all cases of helical gear problems, and a complete set of formulas for each of the sixteen different cases which are frequently met with is, therefore, given in the following, together with an example for each case. These sixteen cases are:

1. Shafts parallel, ratio 1 ("1 to 1"), center distance approximate.
2. Shafts parallel, ratio 1, center distance exact.
3. Shafts parallel, ratio other than 1, center distance approximate.
4. Shafts parallel, ratio other than 1, center distance exact.
5. Shafts at right angles, ratio 1, center distance approximate.
6. Shafts at right angles, ratio 1, center distance exact.
7. Shafts at right angles, ratio other than 1, center distance approximate.
8. Shafts at right angles, ratio other than 1, center distance exact.
9. Shafts at 45-degree angle, ratio 1, center distance approximate.
10. Shafts at 45-degree angle, ratio 1, center distance exact.
11. Shafts at 45-degree angle, ratio other than 1, center distance approximate.
12. Shafts at 45-degree angle, ratio other than 1, center distance exact.
13. Shafts at any angle, ratio 1, center distance approximate.
14. Shafts at any angle, ratio 1, center distance exact.
15. Shafts at any angle, ratio other than 1, center distance approximate.
16. Shafts at any angle, ratio other than 1, center distance exact.

Pitch of Cutter for Helical Gears. — The thickness of the cutter at the pitch line for cutting helical gears should equal one-half the normal circular pitch n (see illustration). If a cutter were used having a thickness, at the pitch line, equal to one-half the circular pitch P, as for spur gearing, the spaces between the teeth would be cut too wide, thus producing thin teeth. The normal pitch varies with the angle α of the helix; hence, the helix angle must be considered when selecting a cutter. The cutter should be of the same pitch as the *normal* diametral pitch of the gear and this normal pitch is found by dividing the "real" diametral pitch by the cosine of the helix angle. To illustrate, if the pitch diameter of a helical gear is 6.718 and there are 38 teeth having a helix angle of 45 degrees, the "real" diametral pitch equals 38 ÷ 6.718 = 5.656; then, the normal diametral pitch equals 5.656 divided by the cosine of 45 degrees or 5.656 ÷ 0.707 = 8. A cutter, then, of 8 diametral pitch is the one to use for this particular gear. This same result could also be

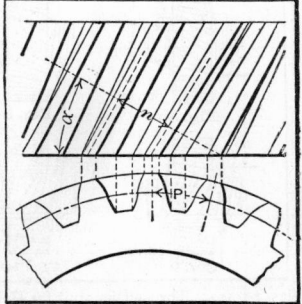

obtained as follows: If the circular pitch P is 0.5554, the normal circular pitch n can be found by multiplying the circular pitch P by the cosine of the helix angle. For example, 0.5554 × 0.707 = 0.3927. The normal diametral pitch is then found by dividing 3.1416 by the normal circular pitch. Thus 3.1416 ÷ 0.3927 = 8, which is the diametral pitch of the cutter.

Helical gears should preferably be cut on some type of gear-cutting machine such as a "hobber," or on a shaper or planer of the generating type. Milling machines are used in some shops, especially when a gear-cutting machine is not available, The pitch of the formed cutter used in milling a helical gear, must not only conform to the normal diametral pitch of the gear, but the cutter number must also be determined. See page 829, under "Number of Cutter for Helical Gears." See also page 833.

Procedure in Calculating Helical Gears. — One of the first steps necessary in helical gear design is to determine the direction of the thrust, if the thrust is to be taken in one direction only. When the direction of the thrust has been determined and the relative position of the driver and driven gear is known, the direction of helix (right- or left-hand) may be found. The thrust diagrams, Figs. 1 to 28, are used for finding the direction of helix. The arrows at the end bearings of the gears indicate the direction of the reaction against the thrust caused by the tooth pressure. The direction of the thrust depends on the direction of helix, the relative positions of driver and driven gear, and the direction of rotation. If the exact

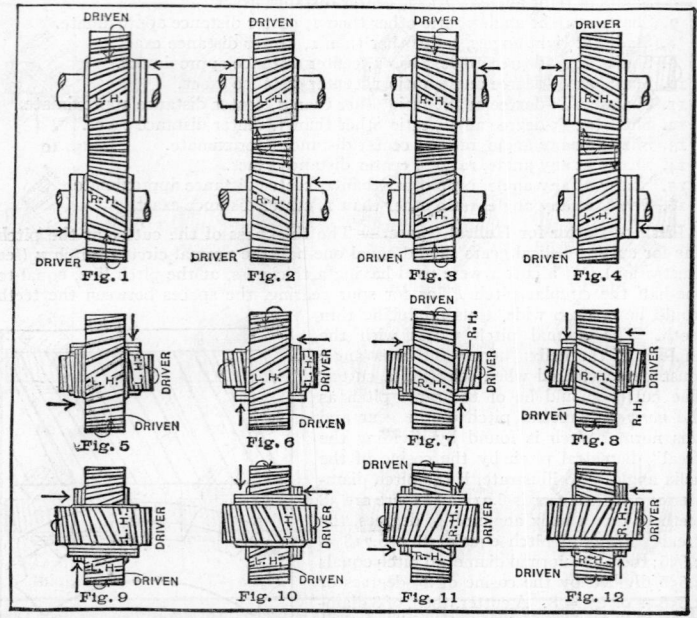

Figs. 1 to 12. Thrust Diagrams for Helical Gears — Direction of Thrust depends upon Direction of Rotation, Relative Position of Driver and Driven Gear, and Direction of Helix

condition with regard to thrust is not found in the diagrams, it may be obtained by changing any one of these three conditions; that is, in Fig. 1 the thrust may be changed to the opposite direction by interchanging driver or driven gear, by reversing the direction of rotation or by changing the direction of helix. Any one of these alterations will produce a thrust in the opposite direction.

The conditions of the design determine the nature of the center distance, whether it must be exact or approximate. The number of teeth in each gear is, of course, determined by the required speed ratios of the shafts. The angle of helix depends upon the conditions of the design and the relative position of the shafts. For parallel shafts the helix angle should not exceed 20 degrees in order to avoid excessive end thrust. In order to obtain smooth running gears, the helix angle should be such that one end of the tooth remains in contact until the opposite end of the following tooth has found a bearing.

As far as the calculations are concerned, the formulas are the same for a 135-degree shaft angle as for an angle of 45 degrees. The following general rule relative to gears having a shaft angle of 45 degrees should be observed: When the helix angle of each gear is less than 45 degrees, then the helix angles are of the same hand and one helix angle is 45 degrees minus the other. When the helix angle of either gear is greater than 45 degrees, then the helix angles are of opposite hand, and the helix angle of one gear is 45 degrees plus the helix angle of the other.

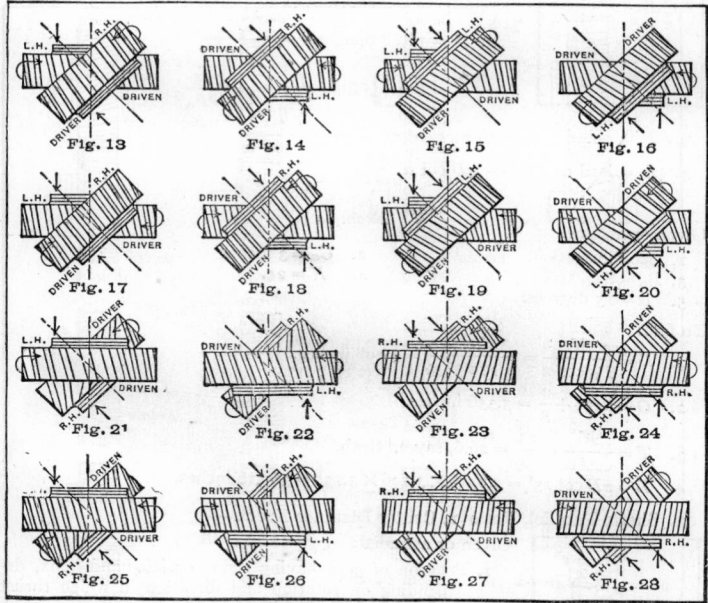

Figs. 13 to 28. Thrust Diagrams for Helical Gears — Direction of Thrust depends upon Direction of Rotation, Relative Position of Driver and Driven Gear, and Direction of Helix

When designing helical gears with shafts at an angle other than 90 degrees to each other, it is of considerable advantage to draw the outline of one gear on a piece of drawing paper tacked to the drawing board, and the outline of the other on a piece of tracing paper. In this way the gear drawn on the tracing paper can be moved about to the correct angle with relation to the gear beneath, and the conditions of thrust, direction of rotation and hand of helix can be more easily determined. The following rules should be observed for helical gears with shafts at any given angle. If each helix angle is less than the shaft angle, then the sum of the helix angles of the two gears will equal the angle between the shafts, and the helix is of the same hand in both gears; if the helix angle of one of the gears is greater than the shaft angle, then the difference between the helix angles of the two gears will be equal to the shaft angle, and the gears will be of opposite hand.

1. Shafts Parallel, Ratio 1 (or "1 to 1"), Center Distance Approximate. —

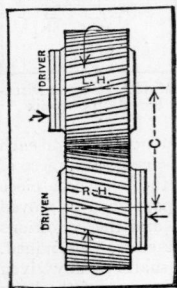

Given or assumed:

1. Hand of helix on driver or driven gear depending on rotation and direction in which thrust is to be received.
2. C_a = approximate center distance.
3. P_n = normal diametral pitch (pitch of cutter).
4. N = number of teeth.
5. α = angle of helix (usually less than 20 degrees for single gears to avoid excessive end thrust).

To find:

1. D = pitch diameter = $\dfrac{N}{P_n \cos \alpha}$

2. O = outside diameter = $D + \dfrac{2}{P_n}$

3. T = number of teeth marked on cutter = $\dfrac{N}{\cos^3 \alpha}$

4. L = lead of helix = $\pi D \cot \alpha$.

Given or assumed:

Example

1. See illustration.
3. $P_n = 8$.
5. $\alpha = 15$ degrees.

2. $C_a = 3$ inches
4. $N = 24$.

To find:

1. $D = \dfrac{N}{P_n \cos \alpha} = \dfrac{24}{8 \times 0.9659} = 3.106$ inches.

2. $O = 3.106 + \dfrac{2}{8} = 3.356$ inches.

3. $T = \dfrac{N}{\cos^3 \alpha} = \dfrac{24}{0.9} = 26.6$, say 27 teeth.

4. $L = \pi D \cot 15° = 3.1416 \times 3.106 \times 3.732 = 36.416$ inches.

2. Shafts Parallel, Ratio 1, Center Distance Exact. —

Given or assumed:

1. Position of gear having right- or left-hand helix, depending on rotation and direction in which thrust is to be received.
2. C = exact center distance = pitch diameter D.
3. P_n = normal diametral pitch (pitch of cutter).
4. N = number of teeth in each gear.

To find:

1. $\cos \alpha = \dfrac{N}{P_n D}$

2. O = outside diameter = $D + \dfrac{2}{P_n}$

3. T = number of teeth marked on formed milling cutter = $\dfrac{N}{\cos^3 \alpha}$

4. L = lead of helix = $\pi D \cot \alpha$.

α is usually less than 20 degrees to avoid excessive end thrust.

Example

Given or assumed:

1. See illustration.   2. $C = 3$ inches.
3. $P_n = 8$.   4. $N = 22$.

To find:

1. $\cos \alpha = \dfrac{N}{P_n D} = \dfrac{22}{8 \times 3} = 0.9166$, or $\alpha = 23° \, 34'$.

2. $O = D + \dfrac{2}{P_n} = 3 + \dfrac{2}{8} = 3\frac{1}{4}$ inches.

3. $T = \dfrac{N}{\cos^3 \alpha} = \dfrac{22}{(0.92)^3} = 28.2$, say 28 teeth.

4. $L = \pi D \cot \alpha = 3.1416 \times 3 \times 2.29 = 21.58$ inches.

3. Shafts Parallel, Ratio Other Than 1, Center Distance Approximate. —

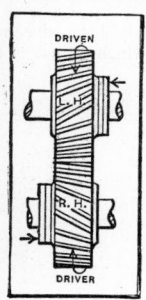

Given or assumed:

1. Position of gear having right- or left-hand helix, depending upon rotation and direction in which thrust is to be received.
2. C_a = approximate center distance.
3. P_n = normal diametral pitch.
4. N = number of teeth in large gear.
5. n = number of teeth in small gear.
6. α = angle of helix.

To find:

1. D = pitch diameter of large gear $= \dfrac{N}{P_n \cos \alpha}$

2. d = pitch diameter of small gear $= \dfrac{n}{P_n \cos \alpha}$

3. O = outside diameter of large gear $= D + \dfrac{2}{P_n}$

4. o = outside diameter of small gear $= d + \dfrac{2}{P_n}$

5. T = number of teeth marked on formed cutter (large gear) $= \dfrac{N}{\cos^3 \alpha}$

6. t = number of teeth marked on formed cutter (small gear) $= \dfrac{n}{\cos^3 \alpha}$

7. L = lead of helix on large gear $= \pi D \cot \alpha$.
8. l = lead of helix on small gear $= \pi d \cot \alpha$.
9. C = center distance (if not right vary α) $= \frac{1}{2}(D + d)$.

Example

Given or assumed:

1. See illustration.   2. $C_a = 17$ inches.   3. $P_n = 2$.   4. $N = 48$.
5. $n = 20$.   6. $\alpha = 20$ degrees.

To find:

1. $D = \dfrac{N}{P_n \cos \alpha} = \dfrac{48}{2 \times 0.9397} = 25.541$ inches.

2. $d = \dfrac{n}{P_n \cos \alpha} = \dfrac{20}{2 \times 0.9397} = 10.642$ inches.

3. $O = D + \dfrac{2}{P_n} = 25.541 + \dfrac{2}{2} = 26.541$ inches.

4. $o = d + \dfrac{2}{P_n} = 10.642 + \dfrac{2}{2} = 11.642$ inches.

5. $T = \dfrac{N}{\cos^3 \alpha} = \dfrac{48}{(0.9397)^3} = 57.8$, say 58 teeth.

6. $t = \dfrac{n}{\cos^3 \alpha} = \dfrac{20}{(0.9397)^3} = 24.1$, say 24 teeth.

7. $L = \pi D \cot \alpha = 3.1416 \times 25.541 \times 2.747 = 220.42$ inches.

8. $l = \pi d \cot \alpha = 3.1416 \times 10.642 \times 2.747 = 91.84$ inches.

9. $C = \tfrac{1}{2}(D + d) = \tfrac{1}{2}(25.541 + 10.642) = 18.091$ inches.

4. Shafts Parallel, Ratio Other Than 1, Center Distance Exact. —

Given or assumed:

1. Position of gear having right- or left-hand helix, depending upon rotation and direction in which thrust is to be received.
2. C = exact center distance.
3. P_n = normal diametral pitch (pitch of cutter).
4. N = number of teeth in large gear.
5. n = number of teeth in small gear.

To find:

1. $\cos \alpha = \dfrac{N + n}{2 P_n C}$

2. D = pitch diameter of large gear = $\dfrac{N}{P_n \cos \alpha}$

3. d = pitch diameter of small gear = $\dfrac{n}{P_n \cos \alpha}$

4. O = outside diameter of large gear = $D + \dfrac{2}{P_n}$

5. o = outside diameter of small gear = $d + \dfrac{2}{P_n}$

6. T = number of teeth marked on formed milling cutter (large gear) = $\dfrac{N}{\cos^3 \alpha}$

7. t = number of teeth marked on formed milling cutter (small gear) = $\dfrac{n}{\cos^3 \alpha}$

8. L = lead of helix (large gear) = $\pi D \cot \alpha$

9. l = lead of helix (small gear) = $\pi d \cot \alpha$

Example

Given or assumed:

1. See illustration. 2. $C = 18.75$ inches. 3. $P_n = 4$. 4. $N = 96$. 5. $n = 48$.

To find:

1. $\cos \alpha = \dfrac{N + n}{2 P_n C} = \dfrac{96 + 48}{2 \times 4 \times 18.75} = 0.96$, or $\alpha = 16°\ 16'$.

2. $D = \dfrac{N}{P_n \cos \alpha} = \dfrac{96}{4 \times 0.96} = 25$ inches.

3. $d = \dfrac{n}{P_n \cos \alpha} = \dfrac{48}{4 \times 0.96} = 12.5$ inches.

4. $O = D + \dfrac{2}{P_n} = 25 + \dfrac{2}{4} = 25.5$ inches.

5. $o = d + \dfrac{2}{P_n} = 12.5 + \dfrac{2}{4} = 13$ inches.

6. $T = \dfrac{N}{\cos^3 \alpha} = \dfrac{96}{(0.96)^3} = 108$ teeth.

7. $t = \dfrac{n}{\cos^3 \alpha} = \dfrac{48}{(0.96)^3} = 54$ teeth.

8. $L = \pi D \cot \alpha = 3.1416 \times 25 \times 3.427 = 269.15$ inches.

9. $l = \pi d \cot \alpha = 3.1416 \times 12.5 \times 3.427 = 134.57$ inches.

5. Shafts at Right Angles, Ratio 1, Center Distance Approximate. —

When the helix angles are 45 degrees, the gears are exactly alike; when other than 45 degrees, the sum of the helix angles must equal 90 degrees.

Given or assumed:

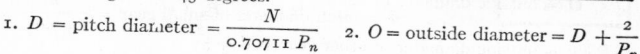

1. Position of gear having right- or left-hand helix, depending on the rotation and direction in which the thrust is to be received.
2. C_a = approximate center distance.
3. P_n = normal diametral pitch (pitch of cutter).
4. N = number of teeth.
5. α = angle of helix.

To find:

(a) When helix angles are 45 degrees.

    1. D = pitch diameter = $\dfrac{N}{0.70711 P_n}$ 2. O = outside diameter = $D + \dfrac{2}{P_n}$

    3. T = number of teeth marked on formed milling cutter = $\dfrac{N}{0.353}$

    4. L = lead of helix = πD.   5. C = center distance = D.

(b) When helix angles are other than 45 degrees.

    1. D = pitch diameter = $\dfrac{N}{P_n \cos \alpha}$

    2. T = number of teeth marked on formed milling cutter = $\dfrac{N}{\cos^3 \alpha}$

    3. C = center distance = sum of pitch radii.

    4. L = lead of helix = $\pi D \cot \alpha$.

Example

Given or assumed:

1. See illustration.   2. C_a = 2.5 inches.   3. P_n = 10.

    4. N = 18 teeth.   5. α = 45 degrees.

To find:

1. $D = \dfrac{N}{0.70711 P_n} = \dfrac{18}{0.70711 \times 10} = 2.546$ inches.

2. $O = D + \dfrac{2}{P_n} = 2.546 + \dfrac{2}{10} = 2.746$ inches.

3. $T = \dfrac{N}{\cos^3 \alpha} = \dfrac{18}{0.353} = 51$ teeth.

4. $L = \pi D \times 1 = 3.1416 \times 2.546 = 7.999$ inches.

6. Shafts at Right Angles, Ratio 1, Center Distance Exact. —

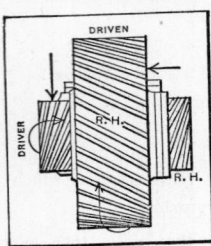

Gears have same direction of helix but probably different pitch diameters and helix angles; the sum of the latter must be 90 degrees. Given or assumed:

1. Position of gear having right- or left-hand helix depending on rotation and direction of thrust.

2. P_n = normal diametral pitch (pitch of cutter).

3. ϕ = approximate helix angle of one gear.

4. C = center distance.

5. N = number of teeth = nearest whole number to
   $CP_n \times \cos \phi$ for approximately 45°; and

   $CP_n \times \dfrac{\sin 2\phi}{\sqrt{1 + \sin 2\phi}}$ for any angle.

To find:

1. α = helix angle of one gear

$$\sin 2\alpha = \frac{N^2}{2\,C^2 P_n{}^2} \pm \sqrt{\frac{N^2}{C^2 P_n{}^2} + \left(\frac{N^2}{2\,C^2 P_n{}^2}\right)^2}$$

2. β = helix angle of other gear = $90° - \alpha$.

3. D = pitch diameter of one gear = $\dfrac{N}{P_n \cos \alpha}$

4. d = pitch diameter of other gear = $\dfrac{N}{P_n \cos \beta}$

5. O = outside diameter of one gear = $D + \dfrac{2}{P_n}$

6. o = outside diameter of other gear = $d + \dfrac{2}{P_n}$

7. T = number of teeth marked on formed cutter for one gear = $\dfrac{N}{\cos^3 \alpha}$

8. t = number of teeth marked on formed cutter for other gear = $\dfrac{N}{\cos^3 \beta}$

9. L = lead of helix for one gear = $\pi D \cot \alpha$.

10. l = lead of helix for other gear = $\pi d \cot \beta$.

Example

Given or assumed:

1. See illustration.   2. $P_n = 10$.   3. $\phi = 45$ degrees.   4. $C = 4$ inches.

5. $N = CP_n \cos \phi = 4 \times 10 \times 0.70711 = 28.28$, say 28 teeth.

To find:

1. $\sin 2\alpha = 0.98664$, or $\alpha = 40° \ 19'$. 2. $\beta = 90° - \alpha = 49° \ 41'$.

3. $D = \dfrac{N}{P_n \cos \alpha} = \dfrac{28}{10 \times 0.76248} = 3.672$ inches.

4. $d = \dfrac{N}{P_n \cos \beta} = \dfrac{28}{10 \times 0\ 64701} = 4.328$ inches

5. $O = 3.672 + 0.2 = 3.872$ inches.

6. $o = 4.328 + 0.2 = 4.528$ inches.

7. $T = \dfrac{N}{\cos^3 \alpha} = \dfrac{28}{(0.762)^3} = 63.6$, say 64 teeth.

8. $t = \dfrac{N}{\cos^3 \beta} = \dfrac{28}{(0.647)^3} = 103.8$, say 104 teeth.

9. $L = \pi D \cot \alpha = 3.1416 \times 3.672 \times 1.1787 = 13.597$ inches.

10. $l = \pi d \cot \beta = 3.1416 \times 4.328 \times 0.84841 = 11.536$ inches.

7. Shafts at Right Angles, Ratio Other Than 1, Center Distance Approx. — Sum of helix angles of gear and pinion must equal 90 degrees.

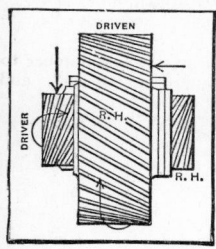

Given or assumed:

   1. Position of gear having right- or left-hand helix, depending on rotation and direction in which thrust is to be received.
   2. C_a = approximate center distance.
   3. P_n = normal diametral pitch (pitch of cutter).
   4. R = ratio of gear to pinion size.
   5. n = number of teeth in pinion = $\dfrac{1.41\, C_a P_n}{R + 1}$ for 45 degrees; and $\dfrac{2\, C_a P_n \cos \alpha \cos \beta}{R \cos \beta + \cos \alpha}$ for any angle.

   6. N = number of teeth in gear = nR.
   7. α = angle of helix of gear.
   8. β = angle of helix of pinion.

To find:

(a) When helix angles are 45 degrees.

   1. D = pitch diameter of gear = $\dfrac{N}{0.70711\, P_n}$

   2. d = pitch diameter of pinion = $\dfrac{n}{0.70711\, P_n}$

   3. O = outside diameter of gear = $D + \dfrac{2}{P_n}$

   4. o = outside diameter of pinion = $d + \dfrac{2}{P_n}$

   5. T = number of formed cutter (gear) = $\dfrac{N}{0.353}$

   6. t = number of formed cutter (pinion) = $\dfrac{n}{0.353}$

   7. L = lead of helix of gear = πD.

   8. l = lead of helix of pinion = πd.

   9. C = center distance (exact) = $\dfrac{D + d}{2}$

(b) When helix angles are other than 45 degrees.

1. $D = \dfrac{N}{P_n \cos \alpha}$ 2. $d = \dfrac{n}{P_n \cos \beta}$ 3. $T = \dfrac{N}{\cos^3 \alpha}$

4. $t = \dfrac{n}{\cos^3 \beta}$ 5. $L = \pi D \cot \alpha$ 6. $l = \pi d \cot \beta$

Example

Given or assumed:

1. See illustration.   2. $C_a = 3.2$ inches.   3. $P_n = 10.$ 4. $R = 1.5.$

5. $n = \dfrac{1.41\, C_a P_n}{R+1} = \dfrac{1.41 \times 3.2 \times 10}{1.5+1} =$ say 18 teeth.

6. $N = nR = 18 \times 1.5 = 27$ teeth.

7. $\alpha = 45$ degrees.   8. $\beta = 45$ degrees.

To find:

1. $D = \dfrac{N}{0.70711\, P_n} = \dfrac{27}{0.70711 \times 10} = 3.818$ inches.

2. $d = \dfrac{n}{0.70711\, P_n} = \dfrac{18}{0.70711 \times 10} = 2.545$ inches.

3. $O = D + \dfrac{2}{P_n} = 3.818 + \dfrac{2}{10} = 4.018$ inches.

4. $o = d + \dfrac{2}{P_n} = 2.545 + \dfrac{2}{10} = 2.745$ inches.

5. $T = \dfrac{N}{0.353} = \dfrac{27}{0.353} = 76.5,$ say 76 teeth.

6. $t = \dfrac{n}{0.353} = \dfrac{18}{0.353} = 51$ teeth.

7. $L = \pi D = 3.1416 \times 3.818 = 12$ inches.
8. $l = \pi d = 3.1416 \times 2.545 = 8$ inches.

9. $C = \dfrac{D+d}{2} = \dfrac{3.818 + 2.545}{2} = 3.182$ inches.

8. Shaft at Right Angles, Ratios Other Than 1, Center Distance Exact. —

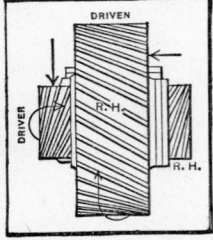

Gears have same direction of helix. The sum of the helix angles will equal 90 degrees.

Given or assumed:

1. Position of gear having right- or left-hand helix depending on rotation and direction in which thrust is to be received.
2. P_n = normal diametral pitch (pitch of cutter).
3. R = ratio of number of teeth in large gear to number of teeth in small gear.
4. α_a = approximate helix angle of large gear.
5. C = exact center distance.

To find:

1. n = number of teeth in small gear nearest

$$\dfrac{2\, C P_n \sin \alpha_a}{1 + R \tan \alpha_a}$$

2. N = number of teeth in large gear = $Rn.$

3. α = exact helix angle of large gear, found by trial from

$$R \sec \alpha + \operatorname{cosec} \alpha = \dfrac{2\, C P_n}{n}$$

4. β = exact helix angle of small gear $= 90° - \alpha$.

5. D = pitch diameter of large gear $= \dfrac{N}{P_n \cos \alpha}$

6. d = pitch diameter of small gear $= \dfrac{n}{P_n \cos \beta}$

7. O = outside diameter of large gear $= D + \dfrac{2}{P_n}$

8. o = outside diameter of small gear $= d + \dfrac{2}{P_n}$

9. T = number of teeth marked on cutter for large gear $= \dfrac{N}{\cos^3 \alpha}$

10. t = number of teeth marked on cutter for small gear $= \dfrac{n}{\cos^3 \beta}$

11. L = lead of helix on large gear $= \pi D \cot \alpha$.

12. l = lead of helix on small gear $= \pi d \cot \beta$.

Example

Given or assumed:

   1. See illustration.   **2.** $P_n = 8$.   **3.** $R = 3$.   **4.** $\alpha_a = 45$ degrees.

   5. $C = 10$ inches.

To find:

1. $n = \dfrac{2\,CP_n \sin \alpha_a}{1 + R \tan \alpha_a} = \dfrac{2 \times 10 \times 8 \times 0.70711}{1 + 3} = 28.25$, say 28 teeth.

2. $N = Rn = 3 \times 28 = 84$ teeth.

3. $R \sec \alpha + \operatorname{cosec} \alpha = \dfrac{2\,CP_n}{n} = \dfrac{2 \times 10 \times 8}{28} = 5.714$, or $\alpha = 46° 6'$.

4. $\beta = 90° - \alpha = 90° - 46° 6' = 43° 54'$.

5. $D = \dfrac{N}{P_n \cos \alpha} = \dfrac{84}{8 \times 0.6934} = 15.143$ inches.

6. $d = \dfrac{n}{P_n \cos \beta} = \dfrac{28}{8 \times 0.72055} = 4.857$ inches.

7. $O = D + \dfrac{2}{P_n} = 15.143 + 0.25 = 15.393$ inches.

8. $o = d + \dfrac{2}{P_n} = 4.857 + 0.25 = 5.107$ inches.

9. $T = \dfrac{N}{\cos^3 \alpha} = \dfrac{84}{0.333}$, say 252 teeth.

10. $t = \dfrac{n}{\cos^3 \beta} = \dfrac{28}{0.374}$, say 75 teeth.

11. $L = \pi D \cot \alpha = 3.1416 \times 15.143 \times 0.96232 = 45.78$ inches.

12. $l = \pi d \cot \beta = 3.1416 \times 4.857 \times 1.0392 = 15.857$ inches.

9. Shafts at 45-Degree Angle, Ratio 1, Center Distance Approximate. —

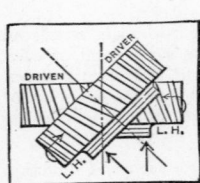

The sum of the helix angles of the two gears equals 45 degrees, and the gears are of the same hand, if each angle is less than 45 degrees. The difference between the helix angles equals 45 degrees, and the gears are of opposite hand, if either angle is greater than 45 degrees.

Given or assumed:

1. Hand of helix, depending on rotation and direction in which thrust is to be received.
2. C_a = approximate center distance.
3. P_n = normal diametral pitch (pitch of cutter).
4. α = angle of helix of driving gear.
5. β = angle of helix of driven gear.
6. N = number of teeth nearest $\dfrac{2\,C_a P_n \cos\alpha \cos\beta}{\cos\alpha + \cos\beta}$

To find:

(a) When helix angles are 22½ degrees.

1. D = pitch diameter = $\dfrac{N}{0.9239\,P_n}$ 2. O = outside diameter = $D + \dfrac{2}{P_n}$
3. T = number of teeth marked on formed cutter = $N \div 0.788$.
4. L = lead of helix = $7.584\,D$.
5. C = center distance = D.

(b) When helix angles are other than 22½ degrees.

1. D = pitch diameter of driver = $\dfrac{N}{P_n \cos\alpha}$

2. d = pitch diameter of driven gear = $\dfrac{N}{P_n \cos\beta}$

3. O = outside diameter of driver = $D + \dfrac{2}{P_n}$

4. o = outside diameter of driven gear = $d + \dfrac{2}{P_n}$

5. T = number of teeth marked on cutter for driver = $N \div \cos^3\alpha$.
6. t = number of teeth marked on cutter for driven gear = $N \div \cos^3\beta$.
7. L = lead of helix for driver = $\pi D \cot\alpha$.
8. l = lead of helix for driven gear = $\pi d \cot\beta$.
9. C = actual center distance = sum of pitch radii.

Example

Given or assumed:

1. See illustration.   2. C_a = 4 inches.   3. P_n = 10.
4 and 5. $\alpha = \beta$ = 22½ deg.   6. N = 37.

To find:

1. $D = \dfrac{N}{0.9239\,P_n} = \dfrac{37}{0.9239 \times 10} = 4.005$ inches.

2. $O = D + \dfrac{2}{P_n} = 4.005 + \dfrac{2}{10} = 4.205$ inches.

4. o = outside diameter of pinion = $d + \dfrac{2}{P_n}$

5. T = number of teeth marked on formed cutter for gear = $N \div \cos^3 \alpha$.

6. t = number of teeth marked on formed cutter for pinion = $n \div \cos^3 \beta$.

7. L = lead of helix on gear = $\pi D \cot \alpha$.

8. l = lead of helix on pinion = $\pi d \cot \beta$.

9. C = actual center distance = $\dfrac{D + d}{2}$

Example

Given or assumed:

1. See illustration.   2. $C = 12$ inches.   3. $P_n = 6$.   4. $R = 3$.

5. $\alpha = 20$ deg.   6. $\beta = 25$ deg.

7. $n = \dfrac{2CP_n \cos\alpha \cos\beta}{R\cos\beta + \cos\alpha} = \dfrac{2 \times 12 \times 6 \times 0.93969 \times 0.90631}{(3 \times 0.90631) + 0.93969} = 34$ teeth, approx.

8. $N = Rn = 3 \times 34 = 102$ teeth.

To find:

1. $D = \dfrac{N}{P_n \cos\alpha} = \dfrac{102}{6 \times 0.93969} = 18.091$ inches.

2. $d = \dfrac{n}{P_n \cos\beta} = \dfrac{34}{6 \times 0.90631} = 6.252$ inches.

3. $O = D + \dfrac{2}{P_n} = 18.091 + \dfrac{2}{6} = 18.424$ inches.

4. $o = d + \dfrac{2}{P_n} = 6.252 + \dfrac{2}{6} = 6.585$ inches.

5. $T = N \div \cos^3 \alpha = 102 \div 0.83 = 123$ teeth.

6. $t = n \div \cos^3 \beta = 34 \div 0.744 = 46$ teeth.

7. $L = \pi D \cot\alpha = \pi \times 18.091 \times 2.747 = 156.12$ inches.

8. $l = \pi d \cot\beta = \pi \times 6.252 \times 2.145 = 42.13$ inches.

9. $C = \dfrac{D + d}{2} = \dfrac{18.091 + 6.252}{2} = 12.1715$ inches.

12. Shafts at 45-Degree Angle, Ratio Other Than 1, Center Distance Exact.—

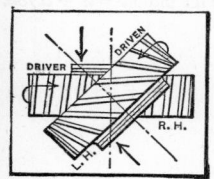

The sum of the helix angles of the two gears equals 45 degrees, and the gears are of the same hand, if each angle is less than 45 degrees. The difference between the helix angles equals 45 degrees, and the gears are of opposite hand, if either angle is greater than 45 degrees.

Given or assumed:

1. Hand of helix, depending on rotation and direction in which thrust is to be received.

2. P_n = normal diametral pitch (pitch of cutter).

3. R = ratio of large to small gear size = $N \div n$.

4. α_a = approximate helix angle of large gear.

5. β_a = approximate helix angle of small gear.

6. C = center distance.

7. n = number of teeth in small gear nearest $\dfrac{2\,CP_n \cos \alpha_a \cos \beta_a}{R \cos \beta_a + \cos \alpha_a}$

8. N = number of teeth, large gear = Rn.

To find:

1. α and β. exact helix angles, by trial from $R \sec \alpha + \sec \beta = \dfrac{2\,CP_n}{n}$

2. D = pitch diameter of large gear = $\dfrac{N}{P_n \cos \alpha}$

3. d = pitch diameter of small gear = $\dfrac{n}{P_n \cos \beta}$

4. O = outside diameter of large gear = $D + \dfrac{2}{P_n}$

5. o = outside diameter of small gear = $d + \dfrac{2}{P_n}$

6. T = number of teeth marked on formed cutter for large gear = $N \div \cos^3 \alpha$.

7. t = number of teeth marked on formed cutter for small gear = $n \div \cos^3 \beta$.

8. L = lead of helix for large gear = $\pi D \cot \alpha$.

9. l = lead of helix for small gear = $\pi d \cot \beta$.

Example

Given or assumed:

1. See illustration. 2. $P_n = 4$. 3. $R = 4$.
4. $\alpha_a = 50$ degrees. 5. $\beta_a = 5$ degrees. 6. $C = 30$ inches.

7. $n = \dfrac{2\,CP_n \cos \alpha_a \cos \beta_a}{R \cos \beta_a + \cos \alpha_a} = \dfrac{2 \times 30 \times 4 \times 0.643 \times 0.996}{(4 \times 0.996) + 0.643} = 33$ teeth.

8. $N = Rn = 4 \times 33 = 132$ teeth.

To find:

1. α and β from $R \sec \alpha + \sec \beta = \dfrac{2\,CP_n}{n} = \dfrac{2 \times 30 \times 4}{33} = 7.273$. By trial $\alpha = 50°\,21'$, and $\beta = 5°\,21'$.

2. $D = \dfrac{N}{P_n \cos \alpha} = \dfrac{132}{4 \times 0.63810} = 51.716$ inches.

3. $d = \dfrac{n}{P_n \cos \beta} = \dfrac{33}{4 \times 0.99564} = 8.286$ inches.

4. $O = D + \dfrac{2}{P_n} = 51.716 + \dfrac{2}{4} = 52.216$ inches.

5. $o = d + \dfrac{2}{P_n} = 8.286 + \dfrac{2}{4} = 8.786$ inches.

6. $T = N \div \cos^3 \alpha = 132 \div 0.26 = 508$ teeth.

7. $t = n \div \cos^3 \beta = 33 \div 0.987 = 33$ teeth.

8. $L = \pi D \cot \alpha = \pi \times 51.716 \times 0.82874 = 134.6$ inches.

9. $l = \pi d \cot \beta = \pi \times 8.286 \times 10.678 = 278$ inches.

13. Shafts at any Angle, Ratio 1, Center Distance Approximate. —

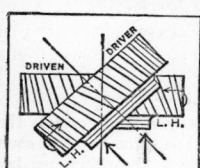

The sum of the helix angles of the two gears equals the shaft angle, and the gears are of the same hand, if each angle is less than the shaft angle. The difference between the helix angles equals the shaft angle, and the gears are of opposite hand, if either angle is greater than the shaft angle.

Given or assumed:

  1. Hand of helix, depending on rotation and direction in which thrust is to be received.

2. C_a = approximate center distance.

3. P_n = normal diametral pitch (pitch of cutter).

4. α = angle of helix of one gear.

5. β = angle of helix of other gear.

6. N = number of teeth nearest $\dfrac{2\,C_a P_n \cos\alpha \cos\beta}{\cos\alpha + \cos\beta}$

To find:

1. D = pitch diameter of one gear = $\dfrac{N}{P_n \cos\alpha}$

2. d = pitch diameter of other gear = $\dfrac{N}{P_n \cos\beta}$

3. O = outside diameter of one gear = $D + \dfrac{2}{P_n}$

4. o = outside diameter of other gear = $d + \dfrac{2}{P_n}$

5. T = number of teeth marked on formed cutter for one gear = $N \div \cos^3\alpha$.

6. t = number of teeth marked on formed cutter for other gear = $N \div \cos^3\beta$.

7. L = lead of helix for one gear = $\pi D \cot\alpha$.

8. l = lead of helix for other gear = $\pi d \cot\beta$.

9. C = actual center distance = $\dfrac{D + d}{2}$

Example

Given or assumed (angle of shafts, 30 degrees):

  1. See illustration.   2. C_a = 5 inches.   3. P_n = 10.

  4. α = 20 degrees.   5. β = 10 degrees.   6. N = 48.

To find:

1. $D = \dfrac{N}{P_n \cos\alpha} = \dfrac{48}{10 \times 0.9397} = 5.108$ inches.

2. $d = \dfrac{N}{P_n \cos\beta} = \dfrac{48}{10 \times 0.9848} = 4.874$ inches.

3. $O = D + \dfrac{2}{P_n} = 5.108 + \dfrac{2}{10} = 5.308$ inches.

4. $o = d + \dfrac{2}{P_n} = 4.874 + \dfrac{2}{10} = 5.074$ inches.

5. $T = N \div \cos^3\alpha = 48 \div 0.83 = 58$ teeth.

6. $t = N \div \cos^3\beta = 48 \div 0.96 = 50$ teeth.

7. $L = \pi D \cot \alpha = \pi \times 5.108 \times 2.747 = 44.08$ inches.

8. $l = \pi d \cot \beta = \pi \times 4.874 \times 5.671 = 86.84$ inches.

9. $C = \dfrac{D + d}{2} = \dfrac{5.108 + 4.874}{2} = 4.991$ inches.

14. Shafts at Any Angle, Ratio 1, Center Distance Exact. —

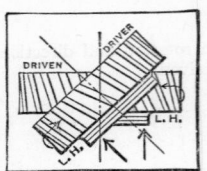

The sum of the helix angles of the two gears equals the shaft angle, and the gears are of the same hand, if each angle is less than the shaft angle. The difference between the helix angles equals the shaft angle, and the gears are of opposite hand, if either angle is greater than the shaft angle.

Given or assumed:

   1. Hand of helix, depending on rotation and direction in which thrust is to be received.

2. C = center distance.

3. P_n = normal diametral pitch (pitch of cutter).

4. α_a = approximate helix angle of one gear.

5. β_a = approximate helix angle of other gear.

6. N = number of teeth nearest $\dfrac{2\,CP_n \cos \alpha_a \cos \beta_a}{\cos \alpha_a + \cos \beta_a}$

To find:

1. α and β = exact helix angles, found by trial from $\sec \alpha + \sec \beta = \dfrac{2\,CP_n}{N}$

2. D = pitch diameter of one gear = $\dfrac{N}{P_n \cos \alpha}$

3. d = pitch diameter of other gear = $\dfrac{N}{P_n \cos \beta}$

4. O = outside diameter of one gear = $D + \dfrac{2}{P_n}$

5. o = outside diameter of other gear = $d + \dfrac{2}{P_n}$

6. T = number of teeth marked on formed cutter for one gear = $N \div \cos^3 \alpha$.

7. t = number of teeth marked on formed cutter for other gear = $N \div \cos^3 \beta$.

8. L = lead of helix for one gear = $\pi D \cot \alpha$.

9. l = lead of helix for other gear = $\pi d \cot \beta$.

Example

Given or assumed (angle of shafts, 50 degrees):

   1. See illustration. 2. $C = 10$ inches. 3. $P_n = 10$. 4. $\alpha_a = 20$ deg.

   5. $\beta_a = 30$ deg.

   6. $N = \dfrac{2\,CP_n \cos \alpha_a \cos \beta_a}{\cos \alpha_a + \cos \beta_a} = \dfrac{2 \times 10 \times 10 \times 0.93969 \times 0.86603}{0.93969 + 0.86603} = 90$ teeth.

To find:

   1. α and β from $\sec \alpha + \sec \beta = \dfrac{2\,CP_n}{N} = \dfrac{2 \times 10 \times 10}{90} = 2.222$. By trial α and β,

       respectively, $= 19° \, 20'$ and $30° \, 40'$.

2. $D = \dfrac{N}{P_n \cos \alpha} = \dfrac{90}{10 \times 0.94361} = 9.537$ inches.

3. $d = \dfrac{N}{P_n \cos \beta} = \dfrac{90}{10 \times 0.86015} = 10.463$ inches.

4. $O = D + \dfrac{2}{P_n} = 9.537 + \dfrac{2}{10} = 9.737$ inches.

5. $o = d + \dfrac{2}{P_n} = 10.463 + \dfrac{2}{10} = 10.663$ inches.

6. $T = N \div \cos^3 \alpha = 90 \div 0.84 = 107$ teeth.

7. $t = N \div \cos^3 \beta = 90 \div 0.64 = 141$ teeth.

8. $L = \pi D \cot \alpha = \pi \times 9.537 \times 2.85 = 85.39$ inches.

9. $l = \pi d \cot \beta = \pi \times 10.463 \times 1.686 = 55.42$ inches.

15. Shafts at Any Angle, Ratio Other Than 1, Center Distance Approx. —

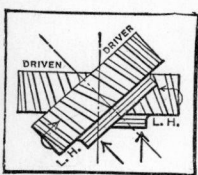

The sum of the helix angles of the two gears equals the shaft angle, and the gears are of the same hand, if each angle is less than the shaft angle. The difference between the helix angles equals the shaft angle, and the gears are of opposite hand, if either angle is greater than the shaft angle.

Given or assumed:

1. Hand of helix, depending on rotation and direction in which thrust is to be received.

2. C_a = center distance.

3. P_n = normal diametral pitch (pitch of cutter).

4. R = ratio of gear to pinion = $N \div n$.

5. α = angle of helix, gear.

6. β = angle of helix, pinion.

7. n = number of teeth in pinion nearest $\dfrac{2 C_a P_n \cos \alpha \cos \beta}{R \cos \beta + \cos \alpha}$ for any angle,

and $\dfrac{2 C_a P_n \cos \alpha}{R + 1}$ when both angles are equal.

8. N = number of teeth in gear = Rn.

To find:

1. D = pitch diameter of gear = $\dfrac{N}{P_n \cos \alpha}$

2. d = pitch diameter of pinion = $\dfrac{n}{P_n \cos \beta}$

3. O = outside diameter of gear = $D + \dfrac{2}{P_n}$

4. o = outside diameter of pinion = $d + \dfrac{2}{P_n}$

5. T = number of teeth marked on cutter for gear = $N \div \cos^3 \alpha$.

6. t = number of teeth marked on cutter for pinion = $n \div \cos^3 \beta$.

7. L = lead of helix on gear = $\pi D \cot \alpha$.

8. l = lead of helix on pinion = $\pi d \cot \beta$.

9. C = actual center distance = $\dfrac{D + d}{2}$

Example

Given or assumed (angle of shafts, 60 degrees):

   1. See illustration.   **2.** $C_a = 12$ inches.   **3.** $P_n = 8$.
   4. $R = 4$.   **5.** $\alpha = 30$ degrees.   **6.** $\beta = 30$ degrees.

   7. $n = \dfrac{2\,C_a P_n \cos \alpha}{R+1} = \dfrac{2 \times 12 \times 8 \times 0.86603}{4+1} = 33$ teeth.

   8. $N = 4 \times 33 = 132$ teeth.

To find:

   1. $D = \dfrac{N}{P_n \cos \alpha} = \dfrac{132}{8 \times 0.86603} = 19.052$ inches.

   2. $d = \dfrac{n}{P_n \cos \beta} = \dfrac{33}{8 \times 0.86603} = 4.763$ inches.

   3. $O = D + \dfrac{2}{P_n} = 19.052 + \dfrac{2}{8} = 19.302$ inches.

   4. $o = d + \dfrac{2}{P_n} = 4.763 + \dfrac{2}{8} = 5.013$ inches.

   5. $T = N \div \cos^3 \alpha = 132 \div 0.65 = 203$ teeth.
   6. $t = n \div \cos^3 \beta = 33 \div 0.65 = 51$ teeth.
   7. $L = \pi D \cot \alpha = \pi \times 19.052 \times 1.732 = 103.66$ inches.
   8. $l = \pi d \cot \beta = \pi \times 4.763 \times 1.732 = 25.92$ inches.

   9. $C = \dfrac{D+d}{2} = \dfrac{19.052 + 4.763}{2} = 11.9075$ inches.

16. Shafts at Any Angle, Ratio Other Than 1, Center Distance Exact. —

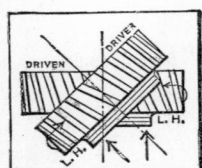

The sum of the helix angles of the two gears equals the shaft angle, and the gears are of the same hand, if each angle is less than the shaft angle. The difference between the helix angles equals the shaft angle, and the gears are of opposite hand, if either angle is greater than the shaft angle.

Given or assumed:

   1. Hand of helix, depending on rotation and direction in which thrust is to be received.

   2. C = center distance.

   3. P_n = normal diametral pitch (pitch of cutter).
   4. α_a = approximate helix angle of gear.
   5. β_a = approximate helix angle of pinion.
   6. R = ratio of gear to pinion size = $N \div n$.

   7. n = number of pinion teeth nearest $\dfrac{2\,CP_n \cos \alpha_a \cos \beta_a}{R \cos \beta_a + \cos \alpha_a}$

   8. N = number of gear teeth = Rn.

To find:

   1. α and β, exact helix angles, found by trial from $R \sec \alpha + \sec \beta = \dfrac{2\,CP_n}{n}$

   2. D = pitch diameter of gear = $\dfrac{N}{P_n \cos \alpha}$

   3. d = pitch diameter of pinion = $\dfrac{n}{P_n \cos \beta}$

4. O = outside diameter of gear = $D + \dfrac{2}{P_n}$

5. o = outside diameter of pinion = $d + \dfrac{2}{P_n}$

6. T = number of teeth marked on formed cutter for gear = $N \div \cos^3 \alpha$.
7. t = number of teeth marked on formed cutter for pinion = $n \div \cos^3 \beta$.
8. L = lead of helix on gear = $\pi D \cot \alpha$.
9. l = lead of helix on pinion = $\pi d \cot \beta$.

Example

Given or assumed (angle of shafts, 60 degrees):

1. See illustration. 2. $C = 40$ inches. 3. $P_n = 4$.
4. $\alpha_a = 20$ degrees. 5. $\beta_a = 40$ degrees. 6. $R = 3$.

7. $n = \dfrac{2 CP_n \cos \alpha_a \cos \beta_a}{R \cos \beta_a + \cos \alpha_a} = \dfrac{2 \times 40 \times 4 \times 0.9397 \times 0.766}{(3 \times 0.766) + 0.9397} = 71$ teeth.

8. $N = Rn = 3 \times 71 = 213$ teeth.

To find:

1. α and β from $R \sec \alpha + \sec \beta = \dfrac{2 CP_n}{n} = \dfrac{2 \times 40 \times 4}{71} = 4.507$.

By trial $\alpha = 22° 24' 30''$ and $\beta = 37° 35' 30''$.

2. $D = \dfrac{N}{P_n \cos \alpha} = \dfrac{213}{4 \times 0.92449} = 57.599$ inches.

3. $d = \dfrac{n}{P_n \cos \beta} = \dfrac{71}{4 \times 0.79238} = 22.401$ inches.

4. $O = D + \dfrac{2}{P_n} = 57.599 + \dfrac{2}{4} = 58.099$ inches.

5. $o = d + \dfrac{2}{P_n} = 22.401 + \dfrac{2}{4} = 22.901$ inches.

6. $T = N \div \cos^3 \alpha = 213 \div 0.79 = 270$ teeth.
7. $t = n \div \cos^3 \beta = 71 \div 0.497 = 143$ teeth.
8. $L = \pi D \cot \alpha = \pi \times 57.599 \times 2.4252 = 438.8$ inches.
9. $l = \pi d \cot \beta = \pi \times 22.401 \times 1.2989 = 91.41$ inches.

Special Case of Helical Gear Design. — The following method is used when the distance between the centers of the shafts, the speed ratio and an approximate ratio of the pitch diameters of the gears are given. (Shafts at 90 degrees angle.) In the formulas, let:

D = diameter of driver; α = angle of teeth in driver with its
d = diameter of driven gear;   axis;
S = speed of driver; N = number of teeth in driver;
s = speed of driven gear; n = number of teeth in driven gear;
P_n = normal diametral pitch; C = center distance.

Assume trial values for D and d; then an approximate angle α is derived from the formula:

$$\frac{ds}{DS} = \cot \alpha \qquad\qquad (1)$$

Then find by trial the number of teeth for each of the gears which, with the given speed ratio, will most nearly satisfy the equation:

$$2 C = \frac{N}{P_n \cos \alpha} + \frac{n}{P_n \sin \alpha} \tag{2}$$

Then make corrections of the angle α until a value is found which exactly satisfies the last equation. This being done, the pitch diameters are:

$$D = \frac{N}{P_n \cos \alpha} \qquad d = \frac{n}{P_n \sin \alpha}$$

Example: — Find the diameters and angles of teeth of two helical gears with shafts at right angles; the distance between the centers is $4\frac{1}{8}$ inches, the speed ratio of the driver to the follower is 2 to 1, and the ratio of D to d is about 9 to 8. Following the method outlined:

$$\frac{ds}{DS} = \frac{8 \times 1}{9 \times 2} = 0.444 = \cot 66°, \text{ approx.}$$

By trial, it will be found that 14 and 28 teeth will nearly satisfy Equation (2), making $2 C = 8.134$.

Subtracting, $8.250 - 8.134 = 0.116$; thus an angle of 66 degrees introduces an error of 0.116 inch for twice the distance between the centers of the shafts. By repeated trials it is found that 66 degrees 48 minutes gives:

$$\frac{14}{8 \times 0.3939} + \frac{28}{8 \times 9191} = 8.25 \text{ inches.}$$

Hence this angle is the tooth angle of the driver, and:

$$D = \frac{14}{8 \times 0.3939} = 4.442 \text{ inches.} \qquad d = \frac{28}{8 \times 0.9191} = 3.808 \text{ inches.}$$

Constants for Calculating Helical Gears. — The tables entitled " Constants for Calculating Helical Gears " give factors which can frequently be employed in helical gear calculations to reduce the time necessary for the computation of the angles and dimensions. The body of the table gives constants C_t (= center distance of shafts per tooth of pinion) for each speed ratio given, for *shafts at right angles only;* factors U, F and L are applicable to gears with shafts at any angle. The constants for unit diameter of gear per tooth, U, and for unit center distance per tooth of fastest running gear, C_t, are calculated for gears cut with spur gear cutters of one diametral pitch. For any other pitch, divide the constant by the diametral pitch of the cutter used. The tables are calculated for each degree from 21 to 69 degrees helix angle. For fractional parts of degrees sufficient accuracy for practical purposes is obtained by simply proportioning the value between those given. The notation used in the tables and in the following examples is as follows:

U = unit diameter per tooth, for 1 diametral pitch;

F = cutter factor;

L = lead of helix per inch pitch diameter;

P_n = normal diametral pitch;

α = helix angle;

D = pitch diameter;

N = number of teeth (N_a = number of teeth in pinion);

C = center distance;

C_t = center distance per tooth of pinion for 1 diametral pitch.

For finding the pitch diameter, center distance, lead of helix and number of teeth for which to select a formed cutter, the following formulas are used:

$$D = \frac{U \times N}{P_n} \qquad C = \frac{C_t}{P_n} \times N_a$$

Lead of helix = $L \times D$.

Number of teeth for which to select cutter = $F \times N$.

Example: — Find the number of teeth, diameters and center distances for a pair of gears where the helix angle of the pinion is 60 degrees; of the gear, 30 degrees; speed ratio, 2 to 5; diametral pitch, 6.

From the table, $C_t = 2.4435$; then:

$$C = \frac{2.4435}{6} \times N_a = 0.40725 \, N_a$$

Assume a required center distance of approximately 5 inches, and make $N_a = 12$, then:

$$C = 0.40725 \times 12 = 4.887 \text{ inches.}$$

Number of teeth in gear: $12 \times 5\frac{1}{2} = 30$.

Pitch diameter of pinion: $D = \dfrac{U \times N}{P_n} = \dfrac{2 \times 12}{6} = 4$ inches.

Lead of helix of pinion: $L \times D = 1.814 \times 4 = 7.256$ inches.
Number of teeth for which to select cutter = $F \times N = 8 \times 12 = 96$.
The formulas are used in the same manner for finding the pitch diameter, lead and cutter for the gear.

Example: — Shaft angle, 65 degrees; speed ratio, 1 to 4; 8 diametral pitch.
In this case, factors C_t do not apply, because the shafts are not at right angles. Assume pinion to have 8 teeth, 30-degree helix angle; the gear, 32 teeth, 35-degree helix angle, then:

Diameter of pinion: $D = \dfrac{1.1547 \times 8}{8} = 1.155$ inch.

Diameter of gear: $D = \dfrac{1.2208 \times 32}{8} = 4.883$ inches.

Center distance: $C = \dfrac{1.155 + 4.883}{2} = 3.019$ inches.

In this case the constants for both gear and pinion are found at the top of the tables, in the section designated "Gear."

Number of Cutter for Milling Helical Gears. — The proper cutter to use for *spur* gears depends upon the pitch of the teeth and also upon the number of teeth, but a cutter for milling *helical* gears is not selected with reference to the actual number of teeth in the gear, as in spur gearing. If the actual number of teeth in a helical gear is divided by the cube of the cosine of the tooth angle, the quotient will represent the number of teeth for which the cutter should be selected, according to the system for spur gear cutters. Suppose a helical gear is to have 38 teeth cut at an angle of 45 degrees; then the cutter to use would be determined as follows: The cosine of 45 degrees is 0.7071, and $38 \div 0.7071^3 = \dfrac{38}{0.3535} = 107$. The table in the section on Spur Gearing, "Series of Involute Gear Cutters for Each Pitch," calls for a No. 2 cutter for spur gears having any number of teeth between 55 and 134; hence, that is the cutter to use for a helical gear having 38 teeth and a tooth angle of 45 degrees. It will be understood that this "No. 2" has nothing to do with the pitch of the cutter, which is determined as explained on page 807.

Constants for Calculating Helical Gears

Gear										
	L	8.1841	7.7757	7.4011	7.0561	6.7372	6.4412	6.1657	5.9085	5.6676
	F	1.23	1.25	1.28	1.31	1.34	1.37	1.41	1.45	1.49
	U	1.0711	1.0785	1.0864	1.0946	1.1034	1.1126	1.1223	1.1326	1.1433
	α	21	22	23	24	25	26	27	28	29

Speed Ratio	C_t = Center Distance per Tooth of Pinion. Shaft Angle, 90°								
1 to 10	6.7511	6.7275	6.7115	6.7025	6.6999	6.7036	6.7130	6.7278	6.7481
1 to 9	6.2155	6.1882	6.1683	6.1552	6.1482	6.1473	6.1518	6.1616	6.1764
1 to 8	5.6799	5.6490	5.6251	5.6078	5.5965	5.5910	5.5907	5.5953	5.6048
1 to 7	5.1443	5.1097	5.0819	5.0605	5.0449	5.0347	5.0295	5.0290	5.0331
1 to 6	4.6087	4.5704	4.5388	4.5132	4.4932	4.4784	4.4683	4.4627	4.4614
1 to 5	4.0731	4.0311	3.9956	3.9659	3.9415	3.9221	3.9072	3.8964	3.8897
2 to 9	3.8054	3.7615	3.7240	3.6922	3.6657	3.6440	3.6266	3.6133	3.6039
1 to 4	3.5376	3.4919	3.4524	3.4186	3.3898	3.3658	3.3460	3.3302	3.3181
2 to 7	3.2698	3.2222	3.1808	3.1449	3.1140	3.0877	3.0654	3.0470	3.0322
3 to 10	3.1805	3.1324	3.0903	3.0537	3.0220	2.9949	2.9719	2.9526	2.9370
1 to 3	3.0020	2.9526	2.9092	2.8713	2.8382	2.8095	2.7849	2.7639	2.7464
3 to 8	2.8234	2.7728	2.7282	2.6888	2.6543	2.6241	2.5978	2.5751	2.5558
2 to 5	2.7342	2.6830	2.6376	2.5976	2.5623	2.5314	2.5043	2.4807	2.4606
3 to 7	2.6449	2.5931	2.5471	2.5064	2.4707	2.4387	2.4108	2.3864	2.3653
4 to 9	2.6003	2.5481	2.5018	2.4608	2.4244	2.3923	2.3640	2.3392	2.3176
1 to 2	2.4664	2.4133	2.3660	2.3239	2.2865	2.2532	2.2237	2.1976	2.1747
5 to 9	2.3593	2.3055	2.2574	2.2145	2.1762	2.1420	2.1115	2.0843	2.0604
4 to 7	2.3325	2.2785	2.2302	2.1871	2.1486	2.1142	2.0834	2.0560	2.0318
3 to 5	2.2879	2.2336	2.1850	2.1415	2.1026	2.0678	2.0367	2.0088	1.9842
5 to 8	2.2522	2.1976	2.1488	2.1050	2.0658	2.0307	1.9992	1.9711	1.9461
2 to 3	2.1986	2.1437	2.0945	2.0502	2.0107	1.9751	1.9431	1.9145	1.8889
7 to 10	2.1603	2.1052	2.0556	2.0112	1.9712	1.9353	1.9030	1.8740	1.8481
5 to 7	2.1450	2.0898	2.0401	1.9956	1.9555	1.9195	1.8870	1.8578	1.8317
3 to 4	2.1093	2.0538	2.0039	1.9591	1.9187	1.8824	1.8496	1.8201	1.7936
7 to 9	2.0838	2.0281	1.9781	1.9330	1.8924	1.8559	1.8229	1.7931	1.7664
4 to 5	2.0647	2.0089	1.9587	1.9135	1.8727	1.8360	1.8028	1.7729	1.7460
5 to 6	2.0379	1.9819	1.9315	1.8861	1.8451	1.8082	1.7748	1.7446	1.7174
6 to 7	2.0201	1.9639	1.9134	1.8679	1.8268	1.7897	1.7561	1.7257	1.6983
7 to 8	2.0073	1.9511	1.9004	1.8548	1.8136	1.7764	1.7427	1.7122	1.6847
8 to 9	1.9978	1.9415	1.8908	1.8451	1.8038	1.7665	1.7327	1.7021	1.6745
9 to 10	1.9903	1.9340	1.8832	1.8375	1.7961	1.7587	1.7249	1.6942	1.6666
1 to 1	1.9308	1.8740	1.8229	1.7766	1.7348	1.6969	1.6625	1.6313	1.6031

Pinion									
	α	69	68	67	66	65	64	63	62	61
	U	2.7904	2.6695	2.5593	2.4586	2.3662	2.2812	2.2027	2.1300	2.0627
	F	21.7	19.1	16.8	14.9	13.3	11.9	10.7	9.71	8.79
	L	1.2059	1.2693	1.3335	1.3987	1.4649	1.5322	1.6007	1.6704	1.7414

Constants for Calculating Helical Gears

Gear								
L	5.4414	5.2282	5.0276	4.8376	4.6576	4.4867	4.3240	4.1690
F	1.54	1.59	1.64	1.69	1.75	1.81	1.88	1.96
U	1.1547	1.1666	1.1792	1.1924	1.2062	1.2208	1.2361	1.2521
α	30	31	32	33	34	35	36	37

Speed Ratio	C_t = Center Distance per Tooth of Pinion. Shaft Angle, 90°							
1 to 10	6.7738	6.8040	6.8395	6.8799	6.9252	6.9755	7.0311	7.0916
1 to 9	6.1964	6.2207	6.2499	6.2837	6.3221	6.3651	6.4131	6.4655
1 to 8	5.6190	5.6373	5.6603	5.6875	5.7190	5.7547	5.7950	5.8394
1 to 7	5.0416	5.0540	5.0707	5.0914	5.1159	5.1444	5.1770	5.2133
1 to 6	4.4643	4.4707	4.4811	4.4952	4.5128	4.5340	4.5589	4.5873
1 to 5	3.8869	3.8874	3.8915	3.8990	3.9097	3.9236	3.9409	3.9612
2 to 9	3.5982	3.5958	3.5967	3.6009	3.6081	3.6184	3.6319	3.6482
1 to 4	3.3095	3.3041	3.3019	3.3028	3.3066	3.3132	3.3228	3.3351
2 to 7	3.0208	3.0124	3.0071	3.0047	3.0050	3.0081	3.0138	3.0221
3 to 10	2.9246	2.9152	2.9089	2.9054	2.9045	2.9063	2.9108	2.9177
1 to 3	2.7321	2.7208	2.7123	2.7066	2.7035	2.7029	2.7048	2.7090
3 to 8	2.5397	2.5263	2.5158	2.5079	2.5024	2.4994	2.4988	2.5004
2 to 5	2.4435	2.4291	2.4176	2.4085	2.4019	2.3977	2.3958	2.3960
3 to 7	2.3472	2.3319	2.3193	2.3092	2.3014	2.2959	2.2928	2.2917
4 to 9	2.2991	2.2833	2.2702	2.2595	2.2512	2.2451	2.2413	2.2395
1 to 2	2.1548	2.1374	2.1227	2.1104	2.1004	2.0925	2.0868	2.0830
5 to 9	2.0393	2.0208	2.0048	1.9912	1.9798	1.9704	1.9632	1.9578
4 to 7	2.0104	1.9916	1.9754	1.9614	1.9496	1.9399	1.9322	1.9265
3 to 5	1.9623	1.9430	1.9262	1.9117	1.8993	1.8890	1.8807	1.8743
5 to 8	1.9238	1.9041	1.8869	1.8720	1.8591	1.8483	1.8396	1.8326
2 to 3	1.8661	1.8458	1.8280	1.8124	1.7988	1.7873	1.7778	1.7699
7 to 10	1.8249	1.8041	1.7859	1.7698	1.7557	1.7437	1.7336	1.7252
5 to 7	1.8084	1.7875	1.7690	1.7527	1.7385	1.7263	1.7159	1.7073
3 to 4	1.7699	1.7486	1.7297	1.7130	1.6983	1.6856	1.6747	1.6656
7 to 9	1.7424	1.7208	1.7016	1.6846	1.6696	1.6565	1.6453	1.6358
4 to 5	1.7217	1.6999	1.6806	1.6633	1.6481	1.6347	1.6232	1.6134
5 to 6	1.6929	1.6708	1.6511	1.6335	1.6179	1.6042	1.5923	1.5821
6 to 7	1.6736	1.6514	1.6314	1.6136	1.5978	1.5838	1.5717	1.5612
7 to 8	1.6599	1.6375	1.6174	1.5994	1.5834	1.5693	1.5570	1.5463
8 to 9	1.6496	1.6271	1.6069	1.5888	1.5727	1.5584	1.5460	1.5352
9 to 10	1.6416	1.6190	1.5987	1.5805	1.5643	1.5499	1.5374	1.5265
1 to 1	1.5774	1.5541	1.5332	1.5143	1.4973	1.4821	1.4687	1.4569

Pinion								
α	60	59	58	57	56	55	54	53
U	2.0000	1.9416	1.8871	1.8361	1.7883	1.7434	1.7013	1.6616
F	8.00	7.31	6.72	6.18	5.72	5.30	4.93	4.59
L	1.8138	1.8877	1.9631	2.0402	2.1190	2.1997	2.2825	2.3673

Constants for Calculating Helical Gears

Gear									
	L	4.0211	3.8795	3.7439	3.6139	3.4891	3.3689	3.2532	3.1416
	F	2.04	2.13	2.23	2.33	2.44	2.56	2.69	2.83
	U	1.2690	1.2868	1.3054	1.3250	1.3456	1.3673	1.3902	1.4142
	α	38	39	40	41	42	43	44	45

Speed Ratio	C_t = Center Distance per Tooth of Pinion. Shaft Angle, 90°							
I to 10	7.1573	7.2283	7.3050	7.3872	7.4755	7.5699	7.6706	7.7782
I to 9	6.5228	6.5849	6.6522	6.7247	6.8027	6.8862	6.9755	7.0711
I to 8	5.8882	5.9415	5.9995	6.0622	6.1298	6.2025	6.2805	6.3640
I to 7	5.2537	5.2981	5.3468	5.3997	5.4570	5.5189	5.5854	5.6569
I to 6	4.6192	4.6548	4.6941	4.7372	4.7842	4.8352	4.8903	4.9497
I to 5	3.9847	4.0114	4.0414	4.0747	4.1114	4.1515	4.1952	4.2426
2 to 9	3.6675	3.6897	3.7151	3.7434	3.7750	3.8097	3.8477	3.8891
I to 4	3.3502	3.3680	3.3887	3.4121	3.4385	3.4678	3.5001	3.5355
2 to 7	3.0330	3.0463	3.0624	3.0809	3.1022	3.1260	3.1526	3.1820
3 to 10	2.9272	2.9391	2.9536	2.9705	2.9900	3.0121	3.0368	3.0641
I to 3	2.7157	2.7246	2.7360	2.7496	2.7657	2.7842	2.8051	2.8284
3 to 8	2.5042	2.5102	2.5184	2.5288	2.5415	2.5563	2.5734	2.5927
2 to 5	2.3985	2.4030	2.4097	2.4184	2.4293	2.4424	2.4575	2.4749
3 to 7	2.2927	2.2957	2.3009	2.3080	2.3172	2.3284	2.3417	2.3570
4 to 9	2.2398	2.2421	2.2465	2.2528	2.2611	2.2714	2.2838	2.2981
I to 2	2.0812	2.0813	2.0833	2.0871	2.0929	2.1005	2.1100	2.1213
5 to 9	1.9543	1.9526	1.9528	1.9546	1.9584	1.9638	1.9710	1.9799
4 to 7	1.9226	1.9204	1.9201	1.9215	1.9247	1.9296	1.9362	1.9446
3 to 5	1.8697	1.8668	1.8657	1.8662	1.8687	1.8726	1.8783	1.8856
5 to 8	1.8274	1.8239	1.8222	1.8221	1.8238	1.8271	1.8320	1.8385
2 to 3	1.7639	1.7596	1.7569	1.7559	1.7565	1.7587	1.7625	1.7678
7 to 10	1.7186	1.7136	1.7103	1.7086	1.7085	1.7099	1.7128	1.7173
5 to 7	1.7005	1.6953	1.6917	1.6896	1.6892	1.6903	1.6929	1.6971
3 to 4	1.6582	1.6524	1.6482	1.6455	1.6444	1.6447	1.6466	1.6499
7 to 9	1.6280	1.6217	1.6171	1.6139	1.6123	1.6122	1.6135	1.6163
4 to 5	1.6053	1.5987	1.5938	1.5903	1.5883	1.5878	1.5887	1.5910
5 to 6	1.5736	1.5666	1.5611	1.5571	1.5547	1.5536	1.5539	1.5556
6 to 7	1.5524	1.5451	1.5394	1.5351	1.5322	1.5308	1.5308	1.5321
7 to 8	1.5373	1.5298	1.5238	1.5193	1.5162	1.5145	1.5142	1.5153
8 to 9	1.5260	1.5183	1.5122	1.5075	1.5042	1.5023	1.5018	1.5026
9 to 10	1.5172	1.5094	1.5031	1.4983	1.4949	1.4928	1.4921	1.4928
I to I	1.4467	1.4379	1.4306	1.4246	1.4201	1.4168	1.4149	1.4142

Pinion									
	α	52	51	50	49	48	47	46	45
	U	1.6243	1.5890	1.5557	1.5242	1.4945	1.4663	1.4396	1.4142
	F	4.29	4.01	3.77	3.54	3.34	3.15	2.98	2.83
	L	2.4545	2.5440	2.6361	2.7302	2.8287	2.9296	3.0338	3.1416

Table for Selecting Cutter for Milling Helical Gears

Angle of Helix, α	K	Angle of Helix, α	K	Angle of Helix, α	K	Angle of Helix, α	K
0° 0′	1.000	21° 0′	1.228	42° 0′	2.436	63° 0′	10.69
0° 30′	1.000	21° 30′	1.241	42° 30′	2.495	63° 30′	11.27
1° 0′	1.001	22° 0′	1.254	43° 0′	2.557	64° 0′	11.87
1° 30′	1.001	22° 30′	1.268	43° 30′	2.621	64° 30′	12.55
2° 0′	1.002	23° 0′	1.282	44° 0′	2.687	65° 0′	13.25
2° 30′	1.003	23° 30′	1.297	44° 30′	2.756	65° 30′	14.03
3° 0′	1.004	24° 0′	1.312	45° 0′	2.828	66° 0′	14.86
3° 30′	1.005	24° 30′	1.328	45° 30′	2.902	66° 30′	15.80
4° 0′	1.007	25° 0′	1.344	46° 0′	2.983	67° 0′	16.76
4° 30′	1.009	25° 30′	1.360	46° 30′	3.066	67° 30′	17.85
5° 0′	1.011	26° 0′	1.377	47° 0′	3.152	68° 0′	18.98
5° 30′	1.013	26° 30′	1.395	47° 30′	3.242	68° 30′	20.33
6° 0′	1.016	27° 0′	1.414	48° 0′	3.336	69° 0′	21.72
6° 30′	1.019	27° 30′	1.434	48° 30′	3.436	69° 30′	23.33
7° 0′	1.022	28° 0′	1.454	49° 0′	3.540	70° 0′	25.00
7° 30′	1.026	28° 30′	1.474	49° 30′	3.650	70° 30′	26.97
8° 0′	1.030	29° 0′	1.495	50° 0′	3.767	71° 0′	28.97
8° 30′	1.034	29° 30′	1.517	50° 30′	3.887	71° 30′	31.40
9° 0′	1.038	30° 0′	1.540	51° 0′	4.012	72° 0′	33.88
9° 30′	1.042	30° 30′	1.563	51° 30′	4.144	72° 30′	36.92
10° 0′	1.047	31° 0′	1.588	52° 0′	4.284	73° 0′	40.00
10° 30′	1.052	31° 30′	1.613	52° 30′	4.433	73° 30′	43.88
11° 0′	1.057	32° 0′	1.640	53° 0′	4.586	74° 0′	47.79
11° 30′	1.062	32° 30′	1.667	53° 30′	4.752	74° 30′	54.72
12° 0′	1.068	33° 0′	1.695	54° 0′	4.925	75° 0′	57.68
12° 30′	1.074	33° 30′	1.724	54° 30′	5.101	75° 30′	64.15
13° 0′	1.080	34° 0′	1.755	55° 0′	5.295	76° 0′	70.65
13° 30′	1.087	34° 30′	1.787	55° 30′	5.497	76° 30′	79.20
14° 0′	1.094	35° 0′	1.819	56° 0′	5.710	77° 0′	87.78
14° 30′	1.102	35° 30′	1.853	56° 30′	5.940	77° 30′	99.50
15° 0′	1.110	36° 0′	1.889	57° 0′	6.190	78° 0′	111.3
15° 30′	1.118	36° 30′	1.926	57° 30′	6.435	79° 0′	144.0
16° 0′	1.127	37° 0′	1.963	58° 0′	6.720	80° 0′	191.2
16° 30′	1.136	37° 30′	2.003	58° 30′	7.010	81° 0′	261.4
17° 0′	1.145	38° 0′	2.044	59° 0′	7.321	82° 0′	370.6
17° 30′	1.154	38° 30′	2.086	59° 30′	7.650	83° 0′	552.1
18° 0′	1.163	39° 0′	2.130	60° 0′	8.000	84° 0′	876.4
18° 30′	1.172	39° 30′	2.176	60° 30′	8.380	85° 0′	1509.0
19° 0′	1.182	40° 0′	2.225	61° 0′	8.780	86° 0′	2940.0
19° 30′	1.193	40° 30′	2.275	61° 30′	9.209	87° 0′	6990.0
20° 0′	1.204	41° 0′	2.326	62° 0′	9.658	......	....
20° 30′	1.216	41° 30′	2.380	62° 30′	10.160	......	....

Table for Selecting Cutter for Milling Helical Gears. — The "Table for Selecting Cutter for Milling Helical Gears" gives the value of the factor $K = \dfrac{1}{\cos^3 \alpha}$ which enters in the formula for finding the number of teeth for which to select the cutter for milling helical gears. The table is used as follows: Multiply the actual number of teeth in the helical gear to be cut by the factor K, as given in the table opposite the angle of helix. The product gives the number of teeth for which to select the cutter.

Example: — Angle of helix = 30 degrees; number of teeth in helical gear = 18. Factor K for 30 degrees, as found from the table, equals 1.540. Then, number of teeth for which to select the cutter = 18 × 1.540 = 28, approximately. Hence, use spur gear cutter for 28 teeth, or cutter No. 4.

Angular Position of Table. — When cutting helical gears in a milling machine it is common practice to set the table to the angle of the teeth at the pitch line, although some contend that if the angle is taken at some point below the pitch line, milled teeth of a better shape will be obtained. The angle is determined by first getting the tangent of the angle, and then finding the corresponding angle from a table of tangents. Assume that the angle is to be based upon a pitch diameter of 4.46 inches, and a lead of 20 inches; then the tangent equals $\dfrac{4.46 \times 3.1416}{20} = 0.700$, which is the tangent of 35 degrees; therefore the table should be swiveled 35 degrees from its position at right angles to the spindle.

Milling the Helical Teeth. — The teeth of a helical gear are proportioned from the normal pitch and not the circular pitch. The whole depth of the tooth can be found by dividing 2.157 by the normal diametral pitch of the gear, which corresponds to the pitch of the cutter. The thickness of the tooth at the pitch line equals 1.571 divided by the normal diametral pitch. After a tooth space has been milled, the cutter should be prevented from dragging through it when being returned for another cut. This can be done by lowering the blank slightly, or by stopping the machine and turning the cutter to such a position that the teeth will not touch the work. If the gear has teeth coarser than 10 or 12 diametral pitch, it is well to take a roughing and a finishing cut. When pressing a helical gear blank on the arbor, it should be remembered that it is more likely to slip when being milled than a spur gear, because the pressure of the cut, being at an angle, tends to rotate the blank on the arbor.

Change-gears for Helical Gear Hobbing. — If a gear-hobbing machine is not equipped with a differential, there is a fixed relation between the index and feed gears and it is necessary to compensate for even slight errors in the index gear ratio, to avoid excessive lead errors. This may be done readily (as shown by the example to follow) by modifying the ratio of the feed gears slightly, thus offsetting the index gear error and making very accurate leads possible.

Machine Without Differential: The formulas which follow may be applied in computing the index gear ratio.

R = index-gear ratio	N = number of teeth on gear
L = lead of gear, inches	P_n = normal diametral pitch
F = feed per gear revolution, inch	P_{nc} = normal circular pitch
K = machine constant	A = helix angle, relative to axis
T = number of threads on hob	M = feed gear constant

$$R = \frac{L \div F}{(L \div F) \pm 1} \times \frac{KT}{N} = \frac{L}{L \pm F} \times \frac{KT}{N} = \frac{\text{Driving gear sizes}}{\text{Driven gear sizes}} \quad (\mathrm{I})$$

Use minus (−) sign in formulas (1) and (2) when gear and hob are the same " hand " and plus (+) sign when they are of opposite hand.

$$R = \cfrac{KT}{N \pm \cfrac{P_n \times \sin A \times F}{\pi}} = \cfrac{KT}{N \pm \cfrac{\sin A \times F}{P_{nc}}} \qquad (2)$$

$$\text{Ratio of feed gears} = \frac{F}{M}; \quad F = \frac{L(NR - KT)}{NR} \qquad (3)$$

$$L = \frac{FNR}{NR - KT} = \text{lead obtained with available index and feed gears} \qquad (4)$$

Note: If gear and hob are of opposite hand, then in Formula (3) change $L(NR - KT)$ to $L(KT - NR)$; also in Formula (4) change $NR - KT$ to $KT - NR$.

Example: A right-hand helical gear with 48 teeth of 10 normal diametral pitch, has a lead of 44.0894 inches. The feed is to be 0.035 inch, with whatever slight adjustment may be necessary to compensate for the error in available index gears. $K = 30$ and $M = 0.075$. A single-thread right-hand hob is to be used

$$R = \frac{44.0894}{44.0894 - 0.035} \times \frac{30 \times 1}{48} = 0.62549654;$$

Log $0.62549654 = \bar{1}.7962249$ (seven-place table)

Since the ratio is less than 1 in this case, eliminate the minus characteristic ($\bar{1}$) by subtracting log of desired ratio, from log of 1 which is 0.00000, thus obtaining log of reciprocal of ratio. Later, the fractions representing gear sizes will be inverted to obtain the actual ratio. If ratio is greater than 1, use log of desired ratio.

$$
\begin{array}{ll}
0.000000 & = \text{Log of 1} \\
-\bar{1}.796225 & = \text{Log of ratio desired (rounded to six places)} \\
\hline
0.203775 & = \text{Log of reciprocal of ratio}
\end{array}
$$

Note that $0.000000 - \bar{1}.796225 = 0.000000 - (-1 + .796225) = 0.000000 + 1 - .796225 = 0.203775$.
Select trial log (from table beginning on page 1171) equal approximately to one-half log of reciprocal. Then proceed as follows:

    1. Subtract from log of reciprocal, trial log selected from table.
    2. Compare difference between logs in step 1, with nearest log in table.
        Repeat step 1 until difference is restricted to at least the fifth place.

Assume that 0.101873 is selected as trial log.

$$
\begin{array}{ll}
0.203775 & = \text{log of reciprocal} \\
-0.101873 & = \text{trial log} \\
\hline
0.101902 & = \text{difference (not close to any table log)}
\end{array}
$$

$$
\begin{array}{ll}
0.203775 & = \text{log of reciprocal} \\
-0.101990 & = \text{second trial log} \\
\hline
0.101785 & = \text{difference (0.101799 nearest log in table)}
\end{array}
$$

Second trial log $0.101990 = \log \dfrac{43}{34}$; log nearest final difference or $0.101799 = \log \dfrac{67}{53}$. Inverting, obtainable index ratio $= \dfrac{34}{43} \times \dfrac{53}{67} = 0.62547726$.

    (If desired index ratio is greater than 1 and log of index ratio is used instead of log of reciprocal of this ratio, the fractions obtained are *not* inverted. The procedure otherwise is the same as here outlined.)

Index ratio error $= 0.62549654 - 0.62547726 = 0.00001928$.

Now use formula (3) to find slight change required in rate of feed. This change compensates sufficiently for the error in available index gears.

Change in Feed Rate: Insert in formula (3) obtainable index ratio.

$$F = \frac{44.0894 \times (48 \times 0.62547726 - 30)}{48 \times 0.62547726} = 0.0336417$$

$$\text{Modified feed gear ratio} = \frac{F}{M} = \frac{0.0336417}{0.075} = 0.448556$$

$$\text{Log } 0.44853 = \bar{1}.6517915; \text{ log of reciprocal} = 0.3482085$$

To find close approximation to modified feed gear ratio, proceed as in finding suitable gears for index ratio, thus obtaining $\frac{106}{71} \times \frac{112}{75}$. Inverting, modified feed gear ratio $= \frac{71}{106} \times \frac{75}{112} = 0.448534$.

Modified feed $F =$ obtainable modified feed ratio $\times M = 0.448534 \times 0.075 = 0.03364$ inch. If the feed rate is not modified, even a small error in the index gear ratio may result in an excessive lead error.

Checking Accuracy of Lead: The modified feed and obtainable index ratio are inserted in formula (4). Desired lead $= 44.0894$ inches. Lead obtained $= 44.087196$ inches; hence the computed error $= 44.0894 - 44.087196 = 0.002204$ inch or about 0.00005 inch per inch of lead.

Machine with Differential: If a machine is equipped with a differential, the *lead gears* are computed in order to obtain the required helix angle and lead. The instructions of the hobbing machine manufacturer should be followed in computing the lead gears, because the ratio formula is affected by the location of the differential gears. If these gears are *ahead* of the index gears, the lead gear ratio is not affected by a change in the number of teeth to be cut (see formula 5); hence, the same lead gears are used when, for example, a gear and pinion are cut on the same machine. In the formulas which follow, the notation is the same as previously given, with these exceptions: $R_d =$ lead gear ratio for machine with differential; $P_a =$ axial or linear pitch of helical gear $=$ distance from center of one tooth to center of next tooth measured parallel to gear axis $=$ total lead $L \div$ number of teeth N.

$$R_d = \frac{P_a \times T}{K} = \frac{L \times T}{N \times K} = \frac{\pi \times \text{cosec } A \times T}{P_n \times K} = \frac{\text{Driven gear sizes}}{\text{Driving gear sizes}} \qquad (5)$$

The number of hob threads T is included in the formula because double-thread hobs are used sometimes, especially for roughing in order to reduce the hobbing time. Lead gears having a ratio sufficiently close to the required ratio, may be determined by using the table of gear ratio logarithms as previously described in connection with the non-differential type of machine. When using a machine equipped with a differential, the effect of a lead-gear ratio error upon the lead of the gear, is small in comparison with the effect of an index gear error when using a non-differential type of machine. The lead obtained with a given or obtainable lead gear ratio may be determined by the following formula: $L = (R_d N K) \div T$. In this formula, R_d represents the ratio obtained with available gears. If the given lead is 44.0894 inches, as in the preceding example, then the desired ratio as obtained with formula (5) would be 0.9185292 if $K = 1$. Assume that the lead gears (selected by using logs. of ratios as on page 835) have a ratio of 0.9184704; then this ratio error of 0.0000588 would result in a computed lead error of only 0.000065 inch per inch.

Formula (5), as mentioned, applies to machines having the differential located *ahead* of the index gears. If the differential is located after the index gears, it is necessary to change lead gears whenever the index gears are changed for hobbing a different number of teeth, as indicated by the following formula which gives the lead gear ratio. In this formula, D = pitch diameter.

$$R_d = \frac{L \times T}{K} = \frac{D \times \pi \times T}{K \times \tan A} = \frac{\text{Driven gear sizes}}{\text{Driving gear sizes}} \qquad (6)$$

General Remarks on Helical Gear Hobbing. — In cutting teeth having large angles, it is desirable to have the direction of helix of the hob the same as the direction of helix of the gear, or in other words, the gear and the hob of the same " hand." Then the direction of the cut will come against the movement of the blank. At ordinary angles, however, one hob will cut both right- and left-hand gears. In setting up the hobbing machine for helical gears, care should be taken to see that the vertical feed does not trip until the machine has been stopped or the hob has fed down past the finished gear.

Herringbone Gears

Double helical or herringbone gears are commonly used in parallel-shaft transmissions, especially when a smooth, continuous action (due to the gradual overlapping engagement of the teeth) is essential, as in high-speed drives where the pitchline velocity may range from about 1000 to 3000 feet per minute in commercial gearing and up to 12,000 feet per minute or higher in more specialized installations. These relatively high speeds are encountered in marine reduction gears, in certain speed-reducing and speed-increasing units, and in various other transmissions, particularly in connection with steam turbine and electric motor drives.

Causes of Herringbone Gear Failures. — Where failure occurs in a herringbone gear transmission, it is rarely due to tooth breakage but usually to excessive wear or sub-surface failures, such as pitting and spalling; hence, it is common practice to base the design of such gears upon durability, or upon tooth pressures which are within the allowable limits for wear. In this connection, it seems to have been well established by tests of both spur gears and herringbone gears, that there is a critical surface pressure value for teeth having given physical properties and coefficient of friction. According to these tests, pressures above the critical value result in rapid wear and a short gear life, whereas when pressures are below the critical, wear is negligible. The yield point or endurance limit of the material marks the critical loading point, and in practical designing a reasonable factor of safety would, of course, be employed.

General Classes of Helical Gear Problems. — There are two general classes of problems. In one case, the problem is to design gears capable of transmitting a given amount of power at a given speed, safely and without excessive wear; hence, in this case the required proportions must be determined. In the second case, the proportions and speed are known and the power-transmitting capacity is required. The first case is the more difficult and also the more common. In establishing the proportions of the gearing, there are numerous possible combinations of pinion diameter and face width which, theoretically at least, will meet the requirements. The speed of the driver and the ratio of the gearing ordinarily are known.

A.G.M.A. Horsepower Rating Formula. — Equation (1) which follows is the standard of the American Gear Manufacturers Association for determining the horsepower ratings of helical and herringbone gears. These ratings for wear or surface durability normally represent tooth loads that are well within the allowable limits for strength. In the equations which follow:

Table 1. F_i Factor for Given Face Width

			Face Width (W) in Inches				
2	4	6	8	10	12	14	16	18
F_i factors for high-speed pinions of single, double and triple reduction units (See Note 1)							
1.25	2.45	3.55	4.50	5.35	6.05	6.70	7.20	7.65
F_i factors for low-speed pinions of double, and intermediate gears of triple reduction units (See Note 2)							
1.70	3.25	4.70	6.00	7.10	8.10	8.95	9.65	10.20
F_i factors for low-speed pinions of triple reduction units (See Note 3)							
1.85	3.50	4.95	6.30	7.50	8.50	9.45	10.20	10.80

For face widths greater than 18 inches:
$$\begin{cases} \text{Note 1.} & F_i = 0.425 \times W \\ \text{Note 2.} & F_i = 0.570 \times W \\ \text{Note 3.} & F_i = 0.600 \times W \end{cases}$$

P_w = horsepower rating based upon wear or surface durability;

F_i = combined factor relating to face width and pinion location in gearing designed for either single, double, or triple speed reduction (see Table 1);

K_r = combined factor for hardness of pinion and gear, and ratio of gear to pinion size (K_r also takes into account tooth form) — see Table 2;

D_s = combined factor relating to pitch diameter and speed of pinion;

d = pitch diameter of pinion, inches; n = revolutions per minute of pinion; W = face width in inches; V = pitch line velocity in feet per minute; C_v = velocity factor. (In equation (3) for trial calculations, the constant 1.5 is an assumed mean value of the reciprocal of C_v.)

$$\text{Horsepower rating } P_w = F_i \times K_r \times D_s \tag{1}$$

$$D_s = \frac{d^2 \times C_v \times n}{126,000} \text{ where } C_v = \frac{78}{78 + \sqrt{V}} \tag{2}$$

Load Capacity of Gearing is Based Upon Size of Pinion. — In designing herringbone gears it is the general practice except with low ratios, to base the load or power-transmitting capacity upon the pinion size which is assumed to be weaker than the gear and subject to greater wear. In preliminary calculations, one plan which has been applied quite extensively is to assume that the load-carrying capacity of the transmission is directly proportional to the product of the face width and the square of the pinion pitch diameter. The product of the face width and the square of the center distance has also been used as a power capacity factor. A third method which may be utilized in conjunction with the A.G.M.A. horsepower Equation (1) is to use the cube of the pinion diameter in connection with the preliminary calculations for establishing the proportions of gears having a given power capacity. Regardless of the method, the ratio of face width to pinion diameter should agree with established practice.

Ratio of Face Width to Pinion Diameter. — The face width is generally established with reference to the pinion diameter. The pinion width must be kept within certain limits to prevent excessive deflection between the supporting bearings. According to some authorities, the face width for ordinary applications should be limited to from one 1½ to 2 times the pinion diameter. According to another source, 2 to 2½ times the pinion diameter represents approved practice. In some cases, the ratio of face width to pinion diameter may be as high as 3; hence, it is evident that quite a number of different combinations of pinion width and diameter might be employed in transmitting a given amount of power.

Table 2. K_r Factor for Given Ratio of Gear to Pinion — External Gears

Ratio of Gear to Pinion Size	Brinell Hardness of Gear (G) and Pinion (P) (Note: Both gear and pinion are cut after hardening)							
	(G)180 (P)210	(G)210 (P)245	(G)225 (P)265	(G)245 (P)285	(G)255 (P)300	(G)270 (P)315	(G)285 (P)335	(G)300 (P)350
	K_r Factor							
1	204	240	261	294	311	339	369	403
1.2	221	262	284	319	338	367	399	436
1.4	236	280	304	341	361	391	425	465
1.6	250	296	322	360	382	413	450	490
1.8	262	310	338	378	400	432	471	513
2	272	321	350	391	415	450	490	533
2.25	283	334	364	407	431	469	509	555
2.5	291	345	376	420	445	484	526	575
3	306	361	393	440	467	509	553	604
3.5	318	375	408	457	483	529	575	628
4	326	385	420	470	497	545	590	644
4.5	333	394	430	481	509	558	603	658
5	340	401	437	490	518	568	614	669
6	350	414	449	503	530	581	630	685
8	361	429	465	521	550	601	654	710
10	370	439	477	533	563	615	670	727
15	382	452	492	550	584	635	690	751
20	388	460	500	559	591	645	700	762

Formula for Preliminary Calculations Based upon Cube of Pinion Diameter. — The following equation will be found convenient to use in preliminary or trial calculations for determining the size of a pinion having a given power-transmitting capacity (constant 1.5 is assumed mean value of C_v reciprocal):

$$d^3 = \frac{1.5 \times P_w \times 126{,}000}{n \times K_r} \qquad (3)$$

The procedure in using this equation in conjunction with the A.G.M.A. Formula (1) for horsepower rating will be demonstrated by an example.

Example: Herringbone gears are to be designed for transmitting about 900 H.P. at 2400 R.P.M. Ratio of gear to pinion size is 4 to 1. Diametral pitch (to be selected) is pitch in transverse plane or plane of rotation. Determine the pinion diameter and face width. Assume for trial purposes that pinion hardness is 265 Brinell.

Find Factor K_r. — Table 2 shows that $K_r = 420$ for a pinion and gear hardness of 265 and 225 Brinell, respectively, and a ratio of gear to pinion size of 4. A trial pinion pitch diameter will now be determined.

$$d^3 = \frac{1.5 \times 900 \times 126{,}000}{2400 \times 420} = 169; \quad d = \sqrt[3]{169} = 5.53 \text{ inches}$$

Selecting Pitch Diameter Corresponding to Standard Diametral Pitch. — This approximate or trial pitch diameter of 5.53 is next changed to some near value corresponding to a standard diametral pitch and a number of teeth within the usual range for herringbone pinions (ordinarily from 14 to 34 teeth). Since diametral pitch is in the plane of rotation, pitch diameter = number of teeth ÷ diametral pitch; hence spur gear table on page 672 may be used in selecting a suitable diametral pitch and number of teeth. The following combinations have pitch diameters which are close to the trial value of 5.53: for 22 teeth of 4 D.P., pitch diameter = 5.5; for 28 teeth of 5 D.P., pitch diameter = 5.6; for 33 teeth of 6 D.P., pitch diameter = 5.5. Assume that we select for trial 28 teeth of 5 D.P. or a pitch diameter of 5.6 inches. (Note: Since pitch is in plane of rotation, hob or cutter must conform to desired helix angle.)

Find Trial Factor F_i from Table 1. — Assume by way of trial that F_i is equal to the pinion diameter, or 5.6 in this case. Table 1 shows that this value lies between F_i

Table 3. Additional K_r Factors — External Gears

Note: In the following formulas for K_r

$$C_r = \frac{\text{gear ratio}}{\text{gear ratio} + 1} \quad \text{where gear ratio} = \frac{\text{No. teeth in gear}}{\text{No. teeth in pinion}}$$

Gear and Pinion Hardened after Cutting: — Case-hardened or through-hardened steel: Gear and pinion 575 Brinell, $K_r = 1530 \times 0.9 \times C_r$; gear and pinion 500 Brinell, $K_r = 1350 \times 0.9 \times C_r$; gear 350 Brinell, pinion 450 Brinell, $K_r = 1060 \times 0.9 \times C_r$. Surface-hardened steel: gear and pinion 440 Brinell, $K_r = 0.890 \times 0.9 \times C_r$.

Gear Cut after Hardening, Pinion Hardened after Cutting: — Case-hardened or through-hardened steel: Gear 335 Brinell, pinion 380 Brinell, $K_r = 973 \times 0.95 \times C_r$; gear 315 Brinell, pinion 360 Brinell, $K_r = 870 \times 0.95 \times C_r$; gear 225 Brinell, pinion 450 Brinell, $K_r = 608 \times 0.95 \times C_r$.

Cast Iron: — Gear 200 Brinell, pinion 210 Brinell, $K_r = 344 \times C_r$.

Bronze: — Gear 40,000 pounds per square inch tensile strength, pinion 180 Brinell, $K_r = 274 \times C_r$.

factors for face widths of 10 and 12 inches. By interpolation, the face width W corresponding to a F_i value of 5.6 is found to be 10.7 inches.

Find Factor D_s. — This factor relating to pitch diameter and speed of pinion is found by Formula (2). First calculate V and C_v.

$$V = \frac{\pi \times d \times n}{12} = \frac{3.1416 \times 5.6 \times 2400}{12} = 3518 \text{ ft. per min.}$$

$$C_v = \frac{78}{78 + \sqrt{3518}} = 0.568; \quad D_s = \frac{5.6^2 \times 0.568 \times 2400}{126,000} = 0.34$$

Inserting these factors F_i, K_r, and D_s in Equation (1)

$$P_w = 5.6 \times 420 \times 0.34 = 800 \text{ horsepower}$$

Changing Trial Values to Obtain Given Power Capacity. — Since the horsepower capacity specified in this case is 900, or 100 more than shown by trial solution, we may either (1) increase face width and factor F_i; (2) increase pinion hardness and factor K_r; or (3) increase pinion diameter and factor D_s. Assume that face width is increased. Then,

$$F_i = 5.6 \times \frac{900}{800} = 6.3$$

If $F_i = 6.3$, then by interpolating in Table 1, we obtain a corresponding face width of 12.8. The ratio of this increased face width to pinion diameter = 12.8 ÷ 5.6 = 2.28, which is within the range of approved practice. When these revised figures are inserted in Equation (1), it will be seen that the capacity has been increased to 900 H.P. Thus,

$$P_w = 6.3 \times 420 \times 0.340 = 900 \text{ horsepower approximately.}$$

Gear Ratios. — A single gear train generally is used if the ratio of gear to pinion size is not over 10 or 12. Double or triple reductions would be used for higher ratios.

Helix Angles. — For herringbone gears, helix angles usually range from 20 to 45 degrees. Angles of 23 and 30 degrees have been used extensively. The higher angles are for precision gears and comparatively low tooth pressures.

Pitch of Pinion Teeth. — Comparatively fine pitches are used for herringbone gears in turbine-driven or other high-speed transmissions. Coarse pitches would not be satisfactory for such applications because of the reduction in contact in the axial plane. Where heavy shock loads are encountered, as in rolling mill drives, for example, large pitches are commonly employed. The number of teeth in a herringbone pinion of given size, does not affect materially the load-carrying capacity, provided the number is somewhere between 14 and 34. According to Farrel-Birmingham Co., the number of teeth should be related to the peripheral velocity as indicated by the following figures which are intended as a general guide. For velocities below 500 feet per minute, 14 to 25 teeth; for velocities between 500 and 1000 feet per minute, 17 to 27 teeth; for velocities higher than 1000 feet per minute, 19 to 33 teeth. Although the number of teeth selected for a given pitch diameter also fixes the pitch, any one of several combinations may meet the requirements.

Formula for Checking Diametral Pitch. — According to Buckingham, the pitch should not be finer than indicated by the following equation in which K varies according to pinion hardness as follows: $K = .036$ for 225 Brinell, $.040$ for 245 Brinell; $.045$ for 280 Brinell; $.050$ for 315 Brinell, and $.054$ for 350 Brinell.

Minimum tooth size (diametral pitch) $= (WdnK) \div$ horsepower capacity.

According to this formula, the diametral pitch of the herringbone gear referred to in the preceding example may be as fine as 8.

Replacement of Spur Gears by Helical Gears. — If spur gears are to be replaced either by single helical or herringbone gears without changing the center distance the procedure is as follows:

Rule: Select a spur gear hob (or cutter) for generating slightly smaller teeth on the helical gearing. For example, if diametral pitch of spur gearing is 6, make normal diametral pitch of herringbone gearing 7. Then, $6 \div 7 =$ cosine of herringbone gear helix angle required to obtain 6 diametral pitch *in plane of rotation*, thus retaining spur gear center distance.

Note: If special hob is available having the same diametral pitch *in plane of rotation* as spur gearing to be replaced, merely cut helical or herringbone to whatever helix angle the hob (or other cutter) is intended for.

Planetary Gearing

Planetary or epicyclic gearing provides means of obtaining a compact design of transmission, with driving and driven shafts in line, and a large speed reduction when required. Typical arrangements of planetary gearing are shown by the following diagrams which are accompanied by speed ratio formulas. When planetary gears are arranged as shown by Figs. 5, 6, 9 and 12, the speed of the follower relative to the driver is increased, whereas Figs. 7, 8, 10 and 11 illustrate speed-reducing mechanisms.

Direction of Rotation. — In using the following formulas, if the final result is preceded by a minus sign (negative), this indicates that the driver and follower will rotate in opposite directions. In all other cases, rotation is in the same direction.

Compound Drive. — The formulas accompanying Figs. 19 to 22, inclusive, are for obtaining the speed ratios when there are *two* driving members rotating at different speeds. For example, in Fig. 19, the central shaft with its attached link is one driver. The internal gear z, instead of being fixed, is also rotated. In Fig. 22, if $z = 24$, $B = 60$ and $S = 3\frac{1}{2}$, with both drivers rotating in the same direction, then $F = 0$, thus indicating, in this case, the point where a larger value of S will reverse follower rotation.

Planetary Bevel Gears. — Two forms of planetary gears of the bevel type are shown in Figs. 23 and 24. The planet gear in Fig. 23 rotates about a fixed bevel gear at the center of which is the driven shaft. Fig. 24 illustrates the Humpage reduction gear. This is sometimes referred to as cone-pulley back-gearing because of its use within the cone pulleys of certain types of machine tools.

Ratios of Planetary or Epicyclic Gearing

D = rotation of *driver* per revolution of follower or driven member.

F = rotation of *follower* or driven member per revolution of driver. (In Figs. 1 to 4, inclusive, F = rotation of planet type follower about its axis.)

A = size of driving gear (use either number of teeth or pitch diameter). Note: When follower derives its motion both from A and from a secondary driving member, A = size of *initial* driving gear, and formula gives speed relationship between A and follower.

B = size of *driven gear or follower* (use either pitch diameter or number of teeth).

C = size of *fixed gear* (use either pitch diameter or number of teeth).

x = size of *planet gear* as shown by diagram (use either pitch diameter or number of teeth).

y = size of *planet gear* as shown by diagram (use either pitch diameter or number of teeth).

z = size of secondary or *auxiliary driving gear*, when follower derives its motion from two driving members.

S = rotation of *secondary driver*, per revolution of *initial* driver (Formulas in which S is used, give speed relationship between follower and the initial driver).

Note: In all cases, if D is known, $F = 1 \div D$, or, if F is known, $D = 1 \div F$.

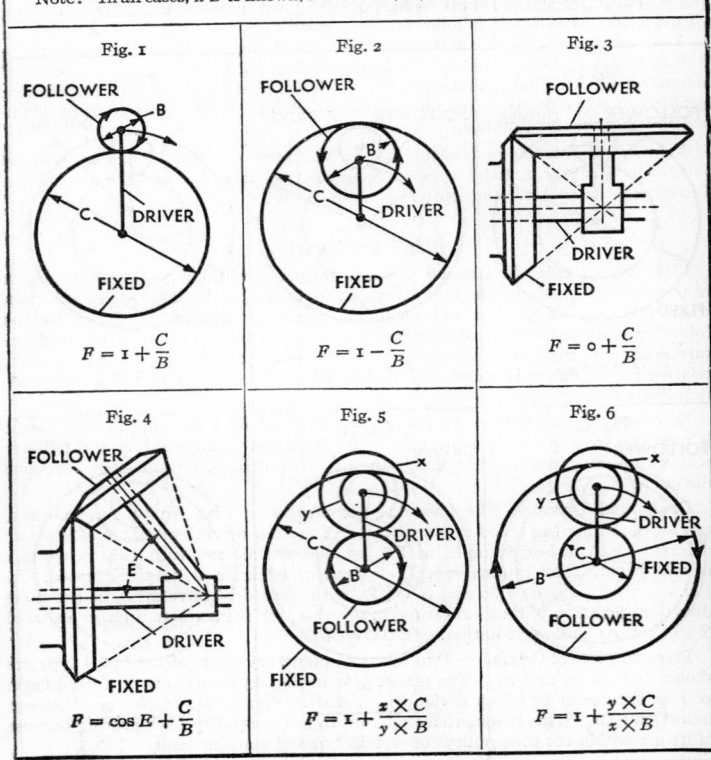

Fig. 1
$$F = 1 + \frac{C}{B}$$

Fig. 2
$$F = 1 - \frac{C}{B}$$

Fig. 3
$$F = 0 + \frac{C}{B}$$

Fig. 4
$$F = \cos E + \frac{C}{B}$$

Fig. 5
$$F = 1 + \frac{x \times C}{y \times B}$$

Fig. 6
$$F = 1 + \frac{y \times C}{x \times B}$$

Ratios of Planetary or Epicyclic Gearing

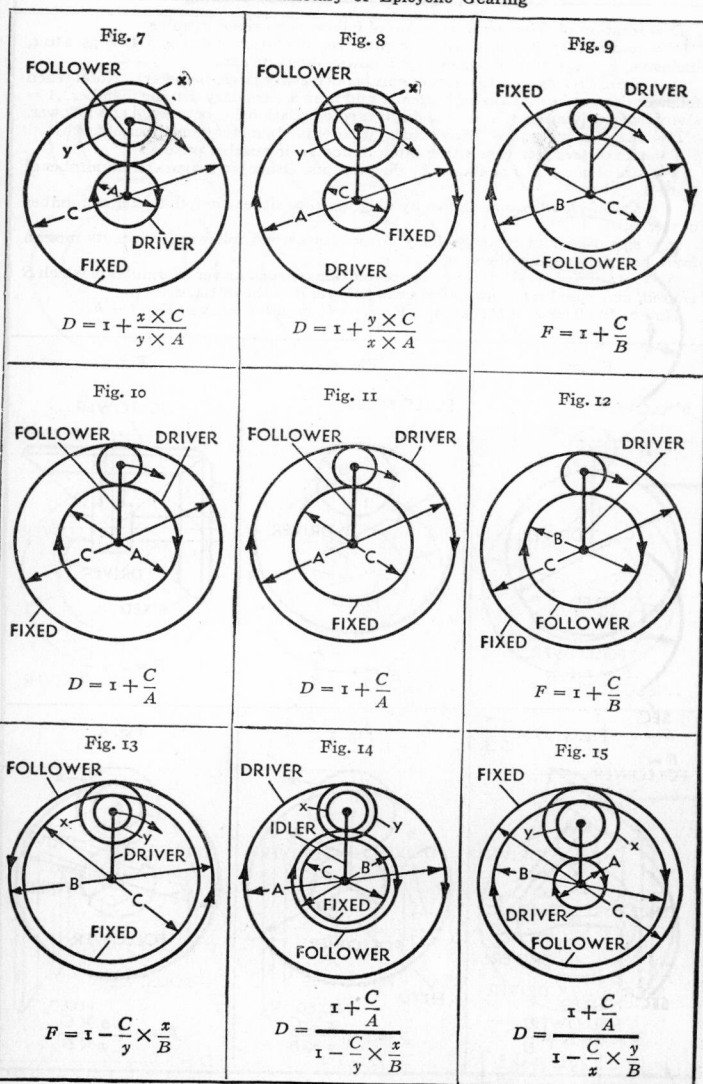

Fig. 7

$$D = 1 + \frac{x \times C}{y \times A}$$

Fig. 8

$$D = 1 + \frac{y \times C}{x \times A}$$

Fig. 9

$$F = 1 + \frac{C}{B}$$

Fig. 10

$$D = 1 + \frac{C}{A}$$

Fig. 11

$$D = 1 + \frac{C}{A}$$

Fig. 12

$$F = 1 + \frac{C}{B}$$

Fig. 13

$$F = 1 - \frac{C}{y} \times \frac{x}{B}$$

Fig. 14

$$D = \frac{1 + \dfrac{C}{A}}{1 - \dfrac{C}{y} \times \dfrac{x}{B}}$$

Fig. 15

$$D = \frac{1 + \dfrac{C}{A}}{1 - \dfrac{C}{x} \times \dfrac{y}{B}}$$

Ratios of Planetary or Epicyclic Gearing

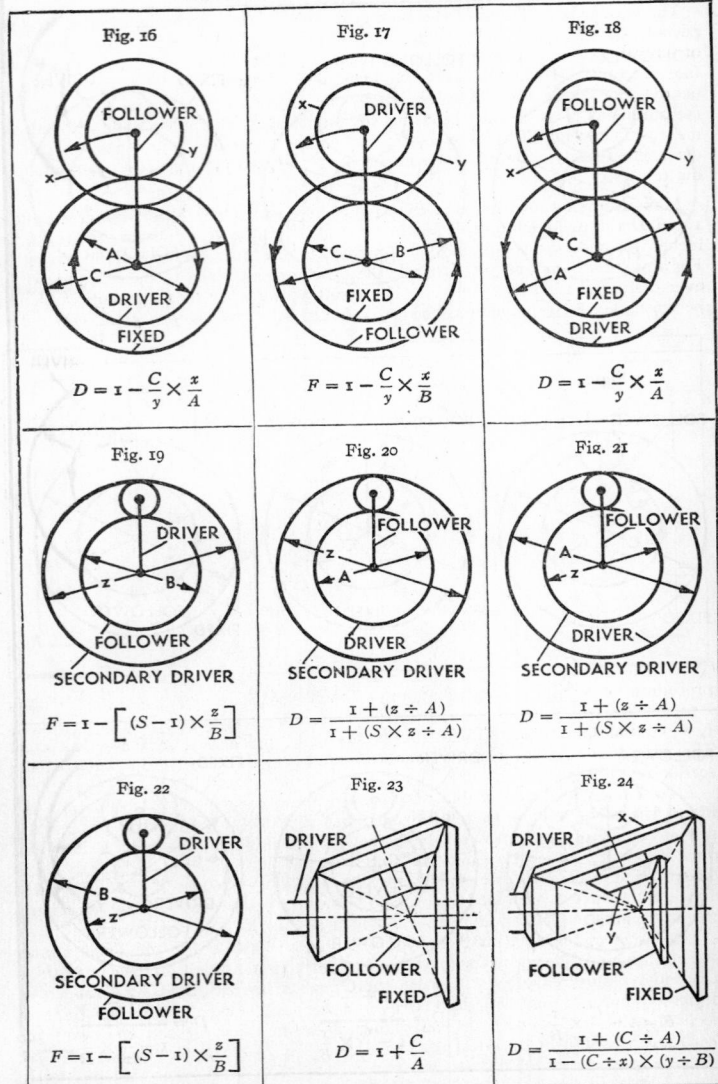

Fig. 16

$$D = 1 - \frac{C}{y} \times \frac{x}{A}$$

Fig. 17

$$F = 1 - \frac{C}{y} \times \frac{x}{B}$$

Fig. 18

$$D = 1 - \frac{C}{y} \times \frac{x}{A}$$

Fig. 19

$$F = 1 - \left[(S - 1) \times \frac{z}{B} \right]$$

Fig. 20

$$D = \frac{1 + (z \div A)}{1 + (S \times z \div A)}$$

Fig. 21

$$D = \frac{1 + (z \div A)}{1 + (S \times z \div A)}$$

Fig. 22

$$F = 1 - \left[(S - 1) \times \frac{z}{B} \right]$$

Fig. 23

$$D = 1 + \frac{C}{A}$$

Fig. 24

$$D = \frac{1 + (C \div A)}{1 - (C \div x) \times (y \div B)}$$

Checking Gear Size by Measurement Over Wires or Pins

The wire or pin method of checking gear sizes is accurate, easily applied, and especially useful in shops with limited inspection equipment. Two cylindrical wires or pins of predetermined diameter are placed in diametrically opposite tooth spaces (see diagram). If the gear has an odd number of teeth, the wires are located as nearly opposite as possible, as shown by the diagram at the right. The over-all measurement M is checked by using any sufficiently accurate method of measurement. The value of measurement M when the pitch diameter is correct can be determined easily and quickly by means of the calculated values in the accompanying tables.

Measurements for Checking External Spur Gears when Wire Diameter Equals 1.728 Divided by Diametral Pitch. Tables 1 and 2 give measurements M, in inches, for checking the pitch diameters of external spur gears of 1 diametral pitch. For any other diametral pitch, divide the measurement given in the table by whatever diametral pitch is required. The result shows what measurement M should be when the pitch diameter is correct *and there is no allowance for backlash.* The

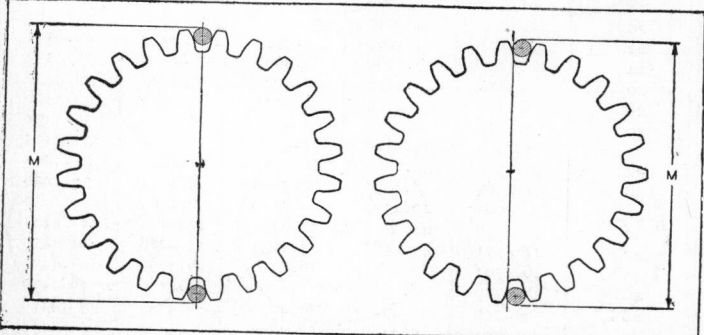

procedure for obtaining a given amount of backlash will be explained later. Tables 1 to 4 inclusive are based upon wire sizes conforming to the Van Keuren standard. For external spur gears the wire size equals 1.728 divided by the diametral pitch. The wire diameters for various diametral pitches will be found in the left-hand section of Table 5.

Even Number of Teeth: Table 1 is for even numbers of teeth. To illustrate the use of the table, assume that a spur gear has 32 teeth of 4 diametral pitch and a pressure angle of 20 degrees. Table 1 shows that the measurement for 1 diametral pitch is 34.4130; hence, for 4 diametral pitch, the measurement equals 34.4130 ÷ 4 = 8.6032 inches. This is the actual measurement over the wires when the pitch diameter is correct, provided there is no allowance for backlash. The wire diameter in this case equals 1.728 ÷ 4 = .432 inch (Table 5).

Measurement for even numbers of teeth above 170 and not in the Table 1, may be determined as shown by the following example: Assume that number of teeth = 240 and pressure angle 14½ degrees; then, for 1 diametral pitch, figure at left of decimal point = given No. of teeth + 2 = 240 + 2 = 242. Figure at right of decimal point lies between decimal values given in table for 200 teeth and 300 teeth and is obtained by interpolation. Thus, 240 − 200 = 40 (change to .40); .5395 − .5321 = .0074 = difference between decimal values for 300 and 200 teeth:

Table 1. Checking External Spur Gear Sizes by Measurement Over Wires

	EVEN NUMBERS OF TEETH				

Dimensions in table are for 1 diametral pitch and Van Keuren standard wire sizes. For any other diametral pitch, divide dimension in table by given pitch.

$$\text{Wire or pin diameter} = \frac{1.728}{\text{Diametral Pitch}}$$

No. of Teeth	Pressure Angle				
	14½°	17½°	20°	25°	30°
6	8.2846	8.2927	8.3032	8.3340	8.3759
8	10.3160	10.3196	10.3271	10.3533	10.3919
10	12.3399	12.3396	12.3445	12.3667	12.4028
12	14.3590	14.3552	14.3578	14.3768	14.4108
14	16.3746	16.3677	16.3683	16.3846	16.4169
16	18.3877	18.3780	18.3768	18.3908	18.4217
18	20.3989	20.3866	20.3840	20.3959	20.4256
20	22.4087	22.3940	22.3900	22.4002	22.4288
22	24.4172	24.4004	24.3952	24.4038	24.4315
24	26.4247	26.4060	26.3997	26.4069	26.4339
26	28.4314	28.4110	28.4036	28.4096	28.4358
28	30.4374	30.4154	30.4071	30.4120	30.4376
30	32.4429	32.4193	32.4102	32.4141	32.4391
32	34.4478	34.4228	34.4130	34.4159	34.4405
34	36.4523	36.4260	36.4155	36.4176	36.4417
36	38.4565	38.4290	38.4178	38.4191	38.4428
38	40.4603	40.4317	40.4198	40.4205	40.4438
40	42.4638	42.4341	42.4217	42.4217	42.4447
42	44.4671	44.4364	44.4234	44.4228	44.4455
44	46.4701	46.4385	46.4250	46.4239	46.4463
46	48.4729	48.4404	48.4265	48.4248	48.4470
48	50.4756	50.4422	50.4279	50.4257	50.4476
50	52.4781	52.4439	52.4292	52.4265	52.4482
52	54.4804	54.4454	54.4304	54.4273	54.4487
54	56.4826	56.4469	56.4315	56.4280	56.4492
56	58.4847	58.4483	58.4325	58.4287	58.4497
58	60.4866	60.4496	60.4335	60.4293	60.4501
60	62.4884	62.4509	62.4344	62.4299	62.4506
62	64.4902	64.4520	64.4352	64.4304	64.4510
64	66.4918	66.4531	66.4361	66.4309	66.4513
66	68.4933	68.4542	68.4369	68.4314	68.4517
68	70.4948	70.4552	70.4376	70.4319	70.4520
70	72.4963	72.4561	72.4383	72.4323	72.4523
72	74.4977	74.4570	74.4390	74.4327	74.4526
74	76.4990	76.4578	76.4396	76.4331	76.4529
76	78.5002	78.4586	78.4402	78.4335	78.4532
78	80.5014	80.4594	80.4408	80.4339	80.4534
80	82.5026	82.4601	82.4413	82.4342	82.4536
82	84.5037	84.4608	84.4418	84.4345	84.4538
84	86.5047	86.4615	86.4423	86.4348	86.4540
86	88.5057	88.4621	88.4428	88.4351	88.4542
88	90.5067	90.4627	90.4433	90.4354	90.4544

Table 1. Checking External Spur Gear Sizes by Measurement Over Wires

No. of Teeth	\multicolumn{5}{c}{EVEN NUMBERS OF TEETH}				
	14½°	17½°	20°	25°	30°
90	92.5076	92.4633	92.4437	92.4357	92.4546
92	94.5085	94.4639	94.4441	94.4359	94.4548
94	96.5094	96.4644	96.4445	96.4362	96.4550
96	98.5102	98.4649	98.4449	98.4364	98.4552
98	100.5110	100.4655	100.4453	100.4367	100.4554
100	102.5118	102.4660	102.4456	102.4369	102.4555
102	104.5125	104.4665	104.4460	104.4370	104.4557
104	106.5132	106.4669	106.4463	106.4372	106.4558
106	108.5139	108.4673	108.4466	108.4374	108.4560
108	110.5146	110.4678	110.4469	110.4376	110.4561
110	112.5152	112.4682	112.4472	112.4378	112.4562
112	114.5159	114.4686	114.4475	114.4380	114.4563
114	116.5165	116.4690	116.4478	116.4382	116.4564
116	118.5171	118.4693	118.4481	118.4384	118.4565
118	120.5177	120.4697	120.4484	120.4385	120.4566
120	122.5182	122.4701	122.4486	122.4387	122.4567
122	124.5188	124.4704	124.4489	124.4388	124.4568
124	126.5193	126.4708	126.4491	126.4390	126.4569
126	128.5198	128.4711	128.4493	128.4391	128.4570
128	130.5203	130.4714	130.4496	130.4393	130.4571
130	132.5208	132.4717	132.4498	132.4394	132.4572
132	134.5213	134.4720	134.4500	134.4395	134.4573
134	136.5217	136.4723	136.4502	136.4397	136.4574
136	138.5221	138.4725	138.4504	138.4398	138.4575
138	140.5226	140.4728	140.4506	140.4399	140.4576
140	142.5230	142.4730	142.4508	142.4400	142.4577
142	144.5234	144.4733	144.4510	144.4401	144.4578
144	146.5238	146.4736	146.4512	146.4402	146.4578
146	148.5242	148.4738	148.4513	148.4403	148.4579
148	150.5246	150.4740	150.4515	150.4404	150.4580
150	152.5250	152.4742	152.4516	152.4405	152.4580
152	154.5254	154.4745	154.4518	154.4406	154.4581
154	156.5257	156.4747	156.4520	156.4407	156.4581
156	158.5261	158.4749	158.4521	158.4408	158.4582
158	160.5264	160.4751	160.4523	160.4409	160.4582
160	162.5267	162.4753	162.4524	162.4410	162.4583
162	164.5270	164.4755	164.4526	164.4411	164.4584
164	166.5273	166.4757	166.4527	166.4411	166.4584
166	168.5276	168.4759	168.4528	168.4412	168.4585
168	170.5279	170.4760	170.4529	170.4413	170.4585
170	172.5282	172.4761	172.4531	172.4414	172.4586
180	182.5297	182.4771	182.4537	182.4418	182.4589
190	192.5310	192.4780	192.4542	192.4421	192.4591
200	202.5321	202.4786	202.4548	202.4424	202.4593
300	302.5395	302.4831	302.4579	302.4443	302.4606
400	402.5434	402.4854	402.4596	402.4453	402.4613
500	502.5458	502.4868	502.4606	502.4458	502.4619

Table 2. Checking External Spur Gear Sizes by Measurement Over Wires

ODD NUMBERS OF TEETH

Dimensions in table are for 1 diametral pitch and Van Keuren standard wire sizes. For any other diametral pitch, divide dimension in table by given pitch.

$$\text{Wire or pin diameter} = \frac{1.728}{\text{Diametral Pitch}}$$

No. of Teeth	Pressure Angle				
	14½°	17½°	20°	25°	30°
7	9.1116	9.1172	9.1260	9.1536	9.1928
9	11.1829	11.1844	11.1905	11.2142	11.2509
11	13.2317	13.2296	13.2332	13.2536	13.2882
13	15.2677	15.2617	15.2639	15.2814	15.3142
15	17.2957	17.2873	17.2871	17.3021	17.3329
17	19.3182	19.3072	19.3053	19.3181	19.3482
19	21.3368	21.3233	21.3200	21.3310	21.3600
21	23.3524	23.3368	23.3321	23.3415	23.3696
23	25.3658	25.3481	25.3423	25.3502	25.3775
25	27.3774	27.3579	27.3511	27.3576	27.3842
27	29.3876	29.3664	29.3586	29.3640	29.3899
29	31.3966	31.3738	31.3652	31.3695	31.3948
31	33.4047	33.3804	33.3710	33.3743	33.3991
33	35.4119	35.3863	35.3761	35.3786	35.4029
35	37.4185	37.3916	37.3807	37.3824	37.4063
37	39.4245	39.3964	39.3849	39.3858	39.4094
39	41.4299	41.4007	41.3886	41.3889	41.4120
41	43.4348	43.4047	43.3920	43.3917	43.4145
43	45.4394	45.4083	45.3951	45.3942	45.4168
45	47.4437	47.4116	47.3980	47.3965	47.4188
47	49.4477	49.4147	49.4007	49.3986	49.4206
49	51.4514	51.4175	51.4031	51.4006	51.4223
51	53.4547	53.4202	53.4053	53.4024	53.4239
53	55.4579	55.4227	55.4074	55.4041	55.4254
55	57.4609	57.4249	57.4093	57.4056	57.4267
57	59.4637	59.4271	59.4111	59.4071	59.4280
59	61.4664	61.4291	61.4128	61.4084	61.4292
61	63.4689	63.4310	63.4144	63.4097	63.4303
63	65.4712	65.4328	65.4159	65.4109	65.4313
65	67.4734	67.4344	67.4173	67.4120	67.4323
67	69.4755	69.4360	69.4186	69.4130	69.4332
69	71.4775	71.4375	71.4198	71.4140	71.4341
71	73.4795	73.4389	73.4210	73.4150	73.4349
73	75.4813	75.4403	75.4221	75.4159	75.4357
75	77.4830	77.4416	77.4232	77.4167	77.4364
77	79.4847	79.4428	79.4242	79.4175	79.4371
79	81.4863	81.4440	81.4252	81.4183	81.4378
81	83.4877	83.4451	83.4262	83.4190	83.4384
83	85.4892	85.4462	85.4271	85.4196	85.4390
85	87.4906	87.4472	87.4279	87.4203	87.4395
87	89.4919	89.4481	89.4287	89.4209	89.4400
89	91.4932	91.4490	91.4295	91.4215	91.4405

Table 2. Checking External Spur Gear Sizes by Measurement Over Wires

No. of Teeth	14½°	17½°	20°	25°	30°
	ODD NUMBERS OF TEETH				
91	93.4944	93.4499	93.4303	93.4221	93.4410
93	95.4956	95.4508	95.4310	95.4227	95.4415
95	97.4967	97.4516	97.4317	97.4232	97.4420
97	99.4978	99.4524	99.4323	99.4237	99.4424
99	101.4988	101.4532	101.4329	101.4242	101.4428
101	103.4998	103.4540	103.4335	103.4247	103.4432
103	105.5008	105.4546	105.4341	105.4252	105.4436
105	107.5017	107.4553	107.4346	107.4256	107.4440
107	109.5026	109.4559	109.4352	109.4260	109.4443
109	111.5035	111.4566	111.4357	111.4264	111.4447
111	113.5044	113.4572	113.4362	113.4268	113.4450
113	115.5052	115.4578	115.4367	115.4272	115.4453
115	117.5060	117.4584	117.4372	117.4275	117.4456
117	119.5068	119.4589	119.4376	119.4279	119.4459
119	121.5075	121.4594	121.4380	121.4282	121.4462
121	123.5082	123.4599	123.4384	123.4285	123.4465
123	125.5089	125.4604	125.4388	125.4288	125.4468
125	127.5096	127.4609	127.4392	127.4291	127.4471
127	129.5103	129.4614	129.4396	129.4294	129.4473
129	131.5109	131.4619	131.4400	131.4297	131.4476
131	133.5115	133.4623	133.4404	133.4300	133.4478
133	135.5121	135.4628	135.4408	135.4302	135.4480
135	137.5127	137.4632	137.4411	137.4305	137.4483
137	139.5133	139.4636	139.4414	139.4307	139.4485
139	141.5139	141.4640	141.4418	141.4310	141.4487
141	143.5144	143.4644	143.4421	143.4312	143.4489
143	145.5149	145.4648	145.4424	145.4315	145.4491
145	147.5154	147.4651	147.4427	147.4317	147.4493
147	149.5159	149.4655	149.4430	149.4319	149.4495
149	151.5164	151.4658	151.4433	151.4321	151.4497
151	153.5169	153.4661	153.4435	153.4323	153.4498
153	155.5174	155.4665	155.4438	155.4325	155.4500
155	157.5179	157.4668	157.4440	157.4327	157.4502
157	159.5183	159.4671	159.4443	159.4329	159.4504
159	161.5188	161.4674	161.4445	161.4331	161.4505
161	163.5192	163.4677	163.4448	163.4333	163.4507
163	165.5196	165.4680	165.4450	165.4335	165.4508
165	167.5200	167.4683	167.4453	167.4337	167.4510
167	169.5204	169.4686	169.4455	169.4338	169.4511
169	171.5208	171.4688	171.4457	171.4340	171.4513
171	173.5212	173.4691	173.4459	173.4342	173.4514
181	183.5230	183.4704	183.4469	183.4350	183.4520
191	193.5246	193.4715	193.4478	193.4357	193.4526
201	203.5260	203.4725	203.4487	203.4363	203.4532
301	303.5355	303.4790	303.4538	303.4402	303.4565
401	403.5404	403.4823	403.4565	403.4422	403.4582
501	503.5433	503.4843	503.4581	503.4434	503.4592

Table 3. Checking Internal Spur Gear Sizes by Measurement Between Wires

EVEN NUMBERS OF TEETH

Dimensions in table are for 1 diametral pitch and Van Keuren standard wire sizes. For any other diametral pitch, divide dimensions in table by given pitch.

$$\text{Wire or pin diameter} = \frac{1.44}{\text{Diametral Pitch}}$$

No. of Teeth	Pressure Angle				
	14½°	17½°	20°	25°	30°
10	8.8337	8.7383	8.6617	8.5209	8.3966
12	10.8394	10.7404	10.6623	10.5210	10.3973
14	12.8438	12.7419	12.6627	12.5210	12.3978
16	14.8474	14.7431	14.6630	14.5210	14.3982
18	16.8504	16.7441	16.6633	16.5210	16.3985
20	18.8529	18.7449	18.6635	18.5211	18.3987
22	20.8550	20.7456	20.6636	20.5211	20.3989
24	22.8569	22.7462	22.6638	22.5211	22.3991
26	24.8585	24.7467	24.6639	24.5211	24.3992
28	26.8599	26.7471	26.6640	26.5211	26.3993
30	28.8612	28.7475	28.6641	28.5211	28.3994
32	30.8623	30.7478	30.6642	30.5211	30.3995
34	32.8633	32.7481	32.6641	32.5211	32.3995
36	34.8642	34.7483	34.6643	34.5212	34.3996
38	36.8650	36.7486	36.6642	36.5212	36.3996
40	38.8658	38.7488	38.6644	38.5212	38.3997
42	40.8665	40.7490	40.6644	40.5212	40.3997
44	42.8672	42.7492	42.6645	42.5212	42.3998
46	44.8678	44.7493	44.6645	44.5212	44.3998
48	46.8683	46.7495	46.6646	46.5212	46.3999
50	48.8688	48.7496	48.6646	48.5212	48.3999
52	50.8692	50.7497	50.6646	50.5212	50.3999
54	52.8697	52.7499	52.6647	52.5212	52.4000
56	54.8701	54.7500	54.6647	54.5212	54.4000
58	56.8705	56.7501	56.6648	56.5212	56.4001
60	58.8709	58.7502	58.6648	58.5212	58.4001
62	60.8712	60.7503	60.6648	60.5212	60.4001
64	62.8715	62.7504	62.6648	62.5212	62.4001
66	64.8718	64.7505	64.6649	64.5212	64.4001
68	66.8721	66.7505	66.6649	66.5212	66.4001
70	68.8724	68.7506	68.6649	68.5212	68.4001
72	70.8727	70.7507	70.6649	70.5212	70.4002
74	72.8729	72.7507	72.6649	72.5212	72.4002
76	74.8731	74.7508	74.6649	74.5212	74.4002
78	76.8734	76.7509	76.6649	76.5212	76.4002
80	78.8736	78.7509	78.6649	78.5212	78.4002
82	80.8738	80.7510	80.6649	80.5212	80.4002
84	82.8740	82.7510	82.6649	82.5212	82.4002
86	84.8742	84.7511	84.6650	84.5212	84.4002
88	86.8743	86.7511	86.6650	86.5212	86.4003
90	88.8745	88.7512	88.6650	88.5212	88.4003

Table 3.   Checking Internal Spur Gear Sizes by Measurement Between Wires

No. of Teeth	14½°	17½°	20°	25°	30°
	EVEN NUMBERS OF TEETH				
92	90.8747	90.7512	90.6650	90.5212	90.4003
94	92.8749	92.7513	92.6650	92.5212	92.4003
96	94.8750	94.7513	94.6650	94.5212	94.4003
98	96.8752	96.7513	96.6650	96.5212	96.4003
100	98.8753	98.7514	98.6650	98.5212	98.4003
102	100.8754	100.7514	100.6650	100.5212	100.4003
104	102.8756	102.7514	102.6650	102.5212	102.4003
106	104.8757	104.7515	104.6650	104.5212	104.4003
108	106.8758	106.7515	106.6650	106.5212	106.4003
110	108.8759	108.7515	108.6651	108.5212	108.4004
112	110.8760	110.7516	110.6651	110.5212	110.4004
114	112.8761	112.7516	112.6651	112.5212	112.4004
116	114.8762	114.7516	114.6651	114.5212	114.4004
118	116.8763	116.7516	116.6651	116.5212	116.4004
120	118.8764	118.7517	118.6651	118.5212	118.4004
122	120.8765	120.7517	120.6651	120.5212	120.4004
124	122.8766	122.7517	122.6651	122.5212	122.4004
126	124.8767	124.7517	124.6651	124.5212	124.4004
128	126.8768	126.7518	126.6651	126.5212	126.4004
130	128.8769	128.7518	128.6652	128.5212	128.4004
132	130.8769	130.7518	130.6652	130.5212	130.4004
134	132.8770	132.7518	132.6652	132.5212	132.4004
136	134.8771	134.7519	134.6652	134.5212	134.4004
138	136.8772	136.7519	136.6652	136.5212	136.4004
140	138.8773	138.7519	138.6652	138.5212	138.4004
142	140.8773	140.7519	140.6652	140.5212	140.4004
144	142.8774	142.7519	142.6652	142.5212	142.4004
146	144.8774	144.7520	144.6652	144.5212	144.4004
148	146.8775	146.7520	146.6652	146.5212	146.4004
150	148.8775	148.7520	148.6652	148.5212	148.4005
152	150.8776	150.7520	150.6652	150.5212	150.4005
154	152.8776	152.7520	152.6652	152.5212	152.4005
156	154.8777	154.7520	154.6652	154.5212	154.4005
158	156.8778	156.7520	156.6652	156.5212	156.4005
160	158.8778	158.7520	158.6652	158.5212	158.4005
162	160.8779	160.7520	160.6652	160.5212	160.4005
164	162.8779	162.7521	162.6652	162.5212	162.4005
166	164.8780	164.7521	164.6652	164.5212	164.4005
168	166.8780	166.7521	166.6652	166.5212	166.4005
170	168.8781	168.7521	168.6652	168.5212	168.4005
180	178.8783	178.7522	178.6652	178.5212	178.4005
190	188.8785	188.7522	188.6652	188.5212	188.4005
200	198.8788	198.7523	198.6652	198.5212	198.4005
300	298.8795	298.7525	298.6654	298.5212	298.4005
400	398.8803	398.7527	398.6654	398.5212	398.4006
500	498.8810	498.7528	498.6654	498.5212	498.4006

Table 4. Checking Internal Spur Gear Sizes by Measurement Between Wires

	ODD NUMBERS OF TEETH				
Dimensions in table are for 1 diametral pitch and Van Keuren standard wire sizes. For any other diametral pitch, divide dimensions in table by given pitch. Wire or pin diameter $= \dfrac{1.44}{\text{Diametral Pitch}}$					

No. of Teeth	Pressure Angle				
	14½°	17½°	20°	25°	30°
7	5.6393	5.5537	5.4823	5.3462	5.2232
9	7.6894	7.5976	7.5230	7.3847	7.2618
11	9.7219	9.6256	9.5490	9.4094	9.2867
13	11.7449	11.6451	11.5669	11.4265	11.3040
15	13.7620	13.6594	13.5801	13.4391	13.3167
17	15.7752	15.6703	15.5902	15.4487	15.3265
19	17.7858	17.6790	17.5981	17.4563	17.3343
21	19.7945	19.6860	19.6045	19.4625	19.3405
23	21.8017	21.6918	21.6099	21.4676	21.3457
25	23.8078	23.6967	23.6143	23.4719	23.3501
27	25.8130	25.7009	25.6181	25.4755	25.3538
29	27.8176	27.7045	27.6214	27.4787	27.3571
31	29.8216	29.7076	29.6242	29.4814	29.3599
33	31.8251	31.7104	31.6267	31.4838	31.3623
35	33.8282	33.7128	33.6289	33.4860	33.3645
37	35.8311	35.7150	35.6310	35.4879	35.3665
39	37.8336	37.7169	37.6327	37.4896	37.3682
41	39.8359	39.7187	39.6343	39.4911	39.3698
43	41.8380	41.7203	41.6357	41.4925	41.3712
45	43.8399	43.7217	43.6371	43.4938	43.3725
47	45.8416	45.7231	45.6383	45.4950	45.3737
49	47.8432	47.7243	47.6394	47.4960	47.3748
51	49.8447	49.7254	49.6404	49.4970	49.3758
53	51.8461	51.7265	51.6414	51.4979	51.3768
55	53.8474	53.7274	53.6422	53.4988	53.3776
57	55.8486	55.7283	55.6431	55.4996	55.3784
59	57.8497	57.7292	57.6438	57.5003	57.3792
61	59.8508	59.7300	59.6445	59.5010	59.3799
63	61.8517	61.7307	61.6452	61.5016	61.3806
65	63.8526	63.7314	63.6458	63.5022	63.3812
67	65.8535	65.7320	65.6464	65.5028	65.3818
69	67.8543	67.7327	67.6469	67.5033	67.3823
71	69.8551	69.7332	69.6475	69.5038	69.3828
73	71.8558	71.7338	71.6480	71.5043	71.3833
75	73.8565	73.7343	73.6484	73.5048	73.3838
77	75.8572	75.7348	75.6489	75.5052	75.3842
79	77.8573	77.7352	77.6493	77.5056	77.3846
81	79.8584	79.7357	79.6497	79.5060	79.3850
83	81.8590	81.7361	81.6501	81.5064	81.3854
85	83.8595	83.7365	83.6505	83.5067	83.3858
87	85.8600	85.7369	85.6508	85.5071	85.3861
89	87.8605	87.7373	87.6511	87.5074	87.3864

Table 4. Checking Internal Spur Gear Sizes by Measurement Between Wires

	ODD NUMBERS OF TEETH				
No. of Teeth	14½°	17½°	20°	25°	30°
91	89.8610	89.7376	89.6514	89.5077	89.3867
93	91.8614	91.7379	91.6517	91.5080	91.3870
95	93.8619	93.7383	93.6520	93.5082	93.3873
97	95.8623	95.7386	95.6523	95.5085	95.3876
99	97.8627	97.7389	97.6526	97.5088	97.3879
101	99.8631	99.7391	99.6528	99.5090	99.3881
103	101.8635	101.7394	101.6531	101.5093	101.3883
105	103.8638	103.7397	103.6533	103.5095	103.3886
107	105.8642	105.7399	105.6535	105.5097	105.3888
109	107.8645	107.7402	107.6537	107.5099	107.3890
111	109.8648	109.7404	109.6539	109.5101	109.3893
113	111.8651	111.7406	111.6541	111.5103	111.3895
115	113.8654	113.7409	113.6543	113.5105	113.3897
117	115.8657	115.7411	115.6545	115.5107	115.3899
119	117.8660	117.7413	117.6547	117.5109	117.3900
121	119.8662	119.7415	119.6548	119.5110	119.3902
123	121.8663	121.7417	121.6550	121.5112	121.3904
125	123.8668	123.7418	123.6552	123.5114	123.3905
127	125.8670	125.7420	125.6554	125.5115	125.3907
129	127.8672	127.7422	127.6556	127.5117	127.3908
131	129.8675	129.7424	129.6557	129.5118	129.3910
133	131.8677	131.7425	131.6559	131.5120	131.3911
135	133.8679	133.7427	133.6560	133.5121	133.3913
137	135.8681	135.7428	135.6561	135.5123	135.3914
139	137.8683	137.7430	137.6563	137.5124	137.3916
141	139.8685	139.7431	139.6564	139.5125	139.3917
143	141.8687	141.7433	141.6565	141.5126	141.3918
145	143.8689	143.7434	143.6566	143.5127	143.3919
147	145.8691	145.7436	145.6568	145.5128	145.3920
149	147.8693	147.7437	147.6569	147.5130	147.3922
151	149.8694	149.7438	149.6570	149.5131	149.3923
153	151.8696	151.7439	151.6571	151.5132	151.3924
155	153.8698	153.7441	153.6572	153.5133	153.3925
157	155.8699	155.7442	155.6573	155.5134	155.3926
159	157.8701	157.7443	157.6574	157.5135	157.3927
161	159.8702	159.7444	159.6575	159.5136	159.3928
163	161.8704	161.7445	161.6576	161.5137	161.3929
165	163.8705	163.7446	163.6577	163.5138	163.3930
167	165.8707	165.7447	165.6578	165.5139	165.3931
169	167.8708	167.7448	167.6579	167.5139	167.3932
171	169.8710	169.7449	169.6580	169.5140	169.3933
181	179.8716	179.7453	179.6584	179.5144	179.3937
191	189.8721	189.7458	189.6588	189.5148	189.3940
201	199.8727	199.7461	199.6591	199.5151	199.3944
301	299.8759	299.7485	299.6612	299.5171	299.3965
401	399.8776	399.7496	399.6623	399.5182	399.3975
501	499.8786	499.7504	499.6629	499.5188	499.3981

hence, decimal required = .5321 + (.40 × .0074) = .53506. Total dimension = 242.53506 divided by the diametral pitch required.

Odd Number of Teeth: Table 2 is for odd numbers of teeth. Measurement for odd numbers above 171 and not in Table 2, may be determined as shown by the following example: Assume that number of teeth = 335 and pressure angle 20 degrees; then, for 1 diametral pitch, figure at left of decimal point = given No. of teeth + 2 = 335 + 2 = 337. Figure at right of decimal point lies between decimal values given in table for 301 and 401 teeth. Thus, 335 − 301 = 34 (change to .34); .4565 − .4538 = .0027; hence, decimal required = .4538 + (.34 × .0027) = .4547. Total dimension = 337.4547.

Table 5. Van Keuren Wire Diameters for Gears

External Gears Wire Diam. = 1.728 ÷ D.P.				Internal Gears Wire Diam. = 1.44 ÷ D.P.			
D.P.	Diam.	D.P.	Diam.	D.P.	Diam.	D.P.	Diam.
2	.86400	16	.10800	2	.72000	16	.09000
2½	.69120	18	.09660	2½	.57600	18	.08000
3	.57600	20	.08640	3	.48000	20	.07200
4	.43200	22	.07855	4	.36000	22	.06545
5	.34560	24	.07200	5	.28800	24	.06000
6	.28800	28	.06171	6	.24000	28	.05143
7	.24686	32	.05400	7	.20571	32	.04500
8	.21600	36	.04800	8	.18000	36	.04000
9	.19200	40	.04320	9	.16000	40	.03600
10	.17280	48	.03600	10	.14400	48	.03000
11	.15709	64	.02700	11	.13091	64	.02250
12	.14400	72	.02400	12	.12000	72	.02000
14	.12343	80	.02160	14	.10286	80	.01800

Measurements for Checking Internal Gears when Wire Diameter Equals 1.44 Divided by Diametral Pitch. Tables 3 and 4 give measurements between wires for checking internal gears of 1 diametral pitch. For any other diametral pitch, divide the measurement given in the table by the diametral pitch required. These measurements are based upon the Van Keuren standard wire size, which, for internal spur gears, equals 1.44 divided by the diametral pitch (see Table 5).

Even Number of Teeth: For an even number of teeth above 170 and not in Table 3, proceed as shown by the following example: Assume that the number of teeth = 380 and pressure angle is 14½ degrees; then, for 1 diametral pitch, figure at left of decimal point = given number of teeth − 2 = 380 − 2 = 378. Figure at right of decimal point lies between decimal values given in table for 300 and 400 teeth and is obtained by interpolation. Thus, 380 − 300 = 80 (change to .80); .8803 − .8795 = .0008; hence, decimal required = .8795 + (.80 × .0008) = .88014. Total dimension = 378.88014.

Odd Number of Teeth: Table 4 is for internal gears having odd numbers of teeth. For tooth numbers above 171 and not in the table, proceed as shown by the following example: Assume that number of teeth = 337 and pressure angle is 14½ degrees; then, for 1 diametral pitch, figure at left of decimal point = given No. of teeth − 2 = 337 − 2 = 335. Figure at right of decimal point lies between decimal values given in table for 301 and 401 teeth and is obtained by interpolation. Thus, 337 − 301 = 36 (change to .36); .8776 − .8759 = .0017; hence, decimal required = .8759 + (.36 × .0017) = .8765. Total dimension = 335.8765.

Measurements for Checking External Spur Gears when Wire Diameter Equals 1.68 Divided by Diametral Pitch. — Tables 7 and 8 give measurements M, in inches, for checking the pitch diameters of external spur gears of 1 diametral pitch. For any other diametral pitch, divide the measurement given in the table by whatever diametral pitch is required. The result shows what measurement M should be when the pitch diameter is correct and there is no allowance for backlash. The procedure for checking for a given amount of backlash when the diameter of the measuring wires equals 1.68 divided by the diametral pitch is explained under a subsequent heading. Tables 7 and 8 are based upon wire sizes equal to 1.68 divided by the diametral pitch. The corresponding wire diameters for various diametral pitches are given in Table 9.

To find measurement M of an external spur gear using wire sizes equal to 1.68 inches divided by the diametral pitch, the same method is followed in using Tables 7 and 8 as that outlined for Tables 1 and 2.

Allowance for Backlash. — Tables 1, 2, 7 and 8 give measurements over wires when the pitch diameters are correct and there is no allowance for backlash or play between meshing teeth. Backlash is obtained by cutting the teeth somewhat deeper than standard, thus reducing the thickness. Usually, the teeth of both mating gears are reduced in thickness an amount equal to one-half of the total backlash desired. However, if the pinion is small, it is common practice to reduce the gear teeth the full amount of backlash and pinion is made to standard size. The changes in measurements M over wires, for obtaining backlash in external spur gears, are listed in Table 6.

Table 6.   Backlash Allowances for External Spur Gears

For each 0.001 inch reduction in pitch-line tooth thickness, *reduce* measurement over wires given in Tables 1, 2, 7 or 8 by the amount shown below. Backlash on pitch line equals double tooth thickness reduction when teeth of *both* mating gears are reduced. If teeth of *one* gear only are reduced, backlash on pitch line equals amount of reduction.

No. of Teeth	14½°	17½°	20°	25°	30°
10	0.0024″	0.0022″	0.0020″	0.0017″	0.0015″
20	0.0028	0.0025	0.0023	0.0019	0.0016
30	0.0030	0.0026	0.0024	0.0020	0.0016
40	0.0031	0.0027	0.0025	0.0020	0.0017
50	0.0032	0.0028	0.0025	0.0020	0.0017
100	0.0035	0.0030	0.0026	0.0021	0.0017
200	0.0037	0.0031	0.0027	0.0021	0.0017

Measurements for Checking External Helical Gears when Wire Diameter Equals 1.68 Inches Divided by Normal Diametral Pitch. — This method makes use of Table 7 for even tooth external spur gears in checking both even-tooth and odd-tooth helical gears.

A convenient method of checking helical gears is to use three wires or pins held in place between the flat, parallel surfaces of plates. This measurement M between these plates and perpendicular to the gear axis, will be the same for both even and odd teeth numbers because the axial displacement of the wires with the odd numbers of teeth, does not affect the perpendicular measurement between the plates.

Table 7. Checking External Spur Gear Sizes by Measurement Over Wires

EVEN NUMBERS OF TEETH

Dimensions in table are for 1 diametral pitch and 1.68-inch series wire sizes (a Van Keuren standard). For any other diametral pitch, divide dimension in table by given pitch.

$$\text{Wire or pin diameter} = \frac{1.68}{\text{Diametral Pitch}}$$

No. of Teeth	Pressure Angle				
	$14\frac{1}{2}°$	$17\frac{1}{2}°$	20°	25°	30°
6	8.1298	8.1442	8.1600	8.2003	8.2504
8	10.1535	10.1647	10.1783	10.2155	10.2633
10	12.1712	12.1796	12.1914	12.2260	12.2722
12	14.1851	14.1910	14.2013	14.2338	14.2785
14	16.1964	16.2001	16.2091	16.2397	16.2833
16	18.2058	18.2076	18.2154	18.2445	18.2871
18	20.2137	20.2138	20.2205	20.2483	20.2902
20	22.2205	22.2190	22.2249	22.2515	22.2927
22	24.2265	24.2235	24.2286	24.2542	24.2949
24	26.2317	26.2275	26.2318	26.2566	26.2967
26	28.2363	28.2309	28.2346	28.2586	28.2982
28	30.2404	30.2339	30.2371	30.2603	30.2996
30	32.2441	32.2367	32.2392	32.2619	32.3008
32	34.2475	34.2391	34.2412	34.2632	34.3017
34	36.2505	36.2413	36.2430	36.2644	36.3026
36	38.2533	38.2433	38.2445	38.2655	38.3035
38	40.2558	40.2451	40.2460	40.2666	40.3044
40	42.2582	42.2468	42.2473	42.2675	42.3051
42	44.2604	44.2483	44.2485	44.2683	44.3057
44	46.2624	46.2497	46.2496	46.2690	46.3063
46	48.2642	48.2510	48.2506	48.2697	48.3068
48	50.2660	50.2522	50.2516	50.2704	50.3073
50	52.2676	52.2534	52.2525	52.2710	52.3078
52	54.2691	54.2545	54.2533	54.2716	54.3082
54	56.2705	56.2555	56.2541	56.2721	56.3086
56	58.2719	58.2564	58.2548	58.2726	58.3089
58	60.2731	60.2572	60.2555	60.2730	60.3093
60	62.2743	62.2580	62.2561	62.2735	62.3096
62	64.2755	64.2587	64.2567	64.2739	64.3099
64	66.2765	66.2594	66.2572	66.2742	66.3102
66	68.2775	68.2601	68.2577	68.2746	68.3104
68	70.2785	70.2608	70.2582	70.2749	70.3107
70	72.2794	72.2615	72.2587	72.2752	72.3109
72	74.2803	74.2620	74.2591	74.2755	74.3111
74	76.2811	76.2625	76.2596	76.2758	76.3113
76	78.2819	78.2631	78.2600	78.2761	78.3115
78	80.2827	80.2636	80.2604	80.2763	80.3117
80	82.2834	82.2641	82.2607	82.2766	82.3119
82	84.2841	84.2646	84.2611	84.2768	84.3121
84	86.2847	86.2650	86.2614	86.2771	86.3123
86	88.2854	88.2655	88.2617	88.2773	88.3124
88	90.2860	90.2659	90.2620	90.2775	90.3126

Table 7.   Checking External Spur Gear Sizes by Measurement Over Wires

No. of Teeth	14½°	17½°	20°	25°	30°
		EVEN NUMBERS OF TEETH			
90	92.2866	92.2662	92.2624	92.2777	92.3127
92	94.2872	94.2666	94.2627	94.2779	94.3129
94	96.2877	96.2670	96.2630	96.2780	96.3130
96	98.2882	98.2673	98.2632	98.2782	98.3131
98	100.2887	100.2677	100.2635	100.2784	100.3132
100	102.2892	102.2680	102.2638	102.2785	102.3134
102	104.2897	104.2683	104.2640	104.2787	104.3135
104	106.2901	106.2685	106.2642	106.2788	106.3136
106	108.2905	108.2688	108.2644	108.2789	108.3137
108	110.2910	110.2691	110.2645	110.2791	110.3138
110	112.2914	112.2694	112.2647	112.2792	112.3139
112	114.2918	114.2696	114.2649	114.2793	114.3140
114	116.2921	116.2699	116.2651	116.2794	116.3141
116	118.2925	118.2701	118.2653	118.2795	118.3142
118	120.2929	120.2703	120.2655	120.2797	120.3142
120	122.2932	122.2706	122.2656	122.2798	122.3143
122	124.2936	124.2708	124.2658	124.2799	124.3144
124	126.2939	126.2710	126.2660	126.2800	126.3145
126	128.2941	128.2712	128.2661	128.2801	128.3146
128	130.2945	130.2714	130.2663	130.2802	130.3146
130	132.2948	132.2716	132.2664	132.2803	132.3147
132	134.2951	134.2718	134.2666	134.2804	134.3147
134	136.2954	136.2720	136.2667	136.2805	136.3148
136	138.2957	138.2722	138.2669	138.2806	138.3149
138	140.2960	140.2724	140.2670	140.2807	140.3149
140	142.2962	142.2725	142.2671	142.2808	142.3150
142	144.2965	144.2727	144.2672	144.2808	144.3151
144	146.2967	146.2729	146.2674	146.2809	146.3151
146	148.2970	148.2730	148.2675	148.2810	148.3152
148	150.2972	150.2732	150.2676	150.2811	150.3152
150	152.2974	152.2733	152.2677	152.2812	152.3153
152	154.2977	154.2735	154.2678	154.2812	154.3153
154	156.2979	156.2736	156.2679	156.2813	156.3154
156	158.2981	158.2737	158.2680	158.2813	158.3155
158	160.2983	160.2739	160.2681	160.2814	160.3155
160	162.2985	162.2740	162.2682	162.2815	162.3155
162	164.2987	164.2741	164.2683	164.2815	164.3156
164	166.2989	166.2742	166.2684	166.2816	166.3156
166	168.2990	168.2744	168.2685	168.2816	168.3157
168	170.2992	170.2745	170.2686	170.2817	170.3157
170	172.2994	172.2746	172.2687	172.2818	172.3158
180	182.3003	182.2752	182.2691	182.2820	182.3160
190	192.3011	192.2757	192.2694	192.2823	192.3161
200	202.3018	202.2761	202.2698	202.2825	202.3163
300	302.3063	302.2790	302.2719	302.2839	302.3173
400	402.3087	402.2804	402.2730	402.2845	402.3178
500	502.3101	502.2813	502.2736	502.2850	502.3181

Table 8.   Checking External Spur Gear Sizes by Measurement Over Wires

ODD NUMBERS OF TEETH				

Dimensions in table are for 1 diametral pitch and 1.68-inch series wire sizes (a VanKeuren standard). For any other diametral pitch, divide dimension in table by given pitch.

$$\text{Wire or pin diameter} = \frac{1.68}{\text{Diametral Pitch}}$$

No. of Teeth	Pressure Angle				
	14½°	17½°	20°	25°	30°
5	6.8485	6.8639	6.8800	6.9202	6.9691
7	8.9555	8.9679	8.9822	9.0199	9.0675
9	11.0189	11.0285	11.0410	11.0762	11.1224
11	13.0615	13.0686	13.0795	13.1126	13.1575
13	15.0925	15.0973	15.1068	15.1381	15.1819
15	17.1163	17.1190	17.1273	17.1570	17.1998
17	19.1351	19.1360	19.1432	19.1716	19.2136
19	21.1505	21.1498	21.1561	21.1832	21.2245
21	23.1634	23.1611	23.1665	23.1926	23.2334
23	25.1743	25.1707	25.1754	25.2005	25.2408
25	27.1836	27.1788	27.1828	27.2071	27.2469
27	29.1918	29.1859	29.1892	29.2128	29.2522
29	31.1990	31.1920	31.1948	31.2177	31.2568
31	33.2053	33.1974	33.1997	33.2220	33.2607
33	35.2110	35.2021	35.2041	35.2258	35.2642
35	37.2161	37.2065	37.2079	37.2292	37.2674
37	39.2208	39.2104	39.2115	39.2323	39.2702
39	41.2249	41.2138	41.2147	41.2349	41.2726
41	43.2287	43.2170	43.2174	43.2374	43.2749
43	45.2323	45.2199	45.2200	45.2396	45.2769
45	47.2355	47.2226	47.2224	47.2417	47.2788
47	49.2385	49.2251	49.2246	49.2435	49.2805
49	51.2413	51.2273	51.2266	51.2452	51.2820
51	53.2439	53.2294	53.2284	53.2468	53.2835
53	55.2463	55.2313	55.2302	55.2483	55.2848
55	57.2485	57.2331	57.2318	57.2497	57.2861
57	59.2506	59.2348	59.2333	59.2509	59.2872
59	61.2526	61.2363	61.2347	61.2521	61.2883
61	63.2545	63.2378	63.2360	63.2532	63.2893
63	65.2562	65.2392	65.2372	65.2543	65.2902
65	67.2579	67.2406	67.2383	67.2553	67.2911
67	69.2594	69.2419	69.2394	69.2562	69.2920
69	71.2609	71.2431	71.2405	71.2571	71.2928
71	73.2623	73.2442	73.2414	73.2579	73.2935
73	75.2636	75.2452	75.2423	75.2586	75.2942
75	77.2649	77.2462	77.2432	77.2594	77.2949
77	79.2661	79.2472	79.2440	79.2601	79.2955
79	81.2673	81.2481	81.2448	81.2607	81.2961
81	83.2684	83.2490	83.2456	83.2614	83.2967
83	85.2694	85.2498	85.2463	85.2620	85.2972
85	87.2704	87.2506	87.2470	87.2625	87.2977
87	89.2714	89.2514	89.2476	89.2631	89.2982
89	91.2723	91.2521	91.2482	91.2636	91.2987

Table 8. Checking External Spur Gear Sizes by Measurement Over Wires

	ODD NUMBERS OF TEETH				
No. of Teeth	14½°	17½°	20°	25°	30°
91	93.2732	93.2528	93.2489	93.2641	93.2991
93	95.2741	95.2534	95.2495	95.2646	95.2996
95	97.2749	97.2541	97.2500	97.2650	97.3000
97	99.2757	99.2547	99.2506	99.2655	99.3004
99	101.2764	101.2553	101.2511	101.2659	101.3008
101	103.2771	103.2558	103.2516	103.2663	103.3011
103	105.2778	105.2563	105.2520	105.2667	105.3015
105	107.2785	107.2568	107.2525	107.2671	107.3018
107	109.2791	109.2573	109.2529	109.2674	109.3021
109	111.2798	111.2578	111.2533	111.2678	111.3024
111	113.2804	113.2583	113.2537	113.2681	113.3027
113	115.2809	115.2588	115.2541	115.2684	115.3030
115	117.2815	117.2592	117.2544	117.2687	117.3033
117	119.2821	119.2596	119.2548	119.2690	119.3036
119	121.2826	121.2601	121.2552	121.2693	121.3038
121	123.2831	123.2605	123.2555	123.2696	123.3041
123	125.2836	125.2608	125.2558	125.2699	125.3043
125	127.2841	127.2612	127.2562	127.2702	127.3046
127	129.2846	129.2615	129.2565	129.2704	129.3048
129	131.2851	131.2619	131.2568	131.2707	131.3050
131	133.2855	133.2622	133.2571	133.2709	133.3053
133	135.2859	135.2626	135.2574	135.2712	135.3055
135	137.2863	137.2629	137.2577	137.2714	137.3057
137	139.2867	139.2632	139.2579	139.2716	139.3059
139	141.2871	141.2635	141.2582	141.2718	141.3060
141	143.2875	143.2638	143.2584	143.2720	143.3062
143	145.2879	145.2641	145.2587	145.2722	145.3064
145	147.2883	147.2644	147.2589	147.2724	147.3066
147	149.2887	149.2647	149.2591	149.2726	149.3068
149	151.2890	151.2649	151.2594	151.2728	151.3069
151	153.2893	153.2652	153.2596	153.2730	153.3071
153	155.2897	155.2654	155.2598	155.2732	155.3073
155	157.2900	157.2657	157.2600	157.2733	157.3074
157	159.2903	159.2659	159.2602	159.2735	159.3076
159	161.2906	161.2661	161.2604	161.2736	161.3077
161	163.2909	163.2663	163.2606	163.2738	163.3078
163	165.2912	165.2665	165.2608	165.2740	165.3080
165	167.2915	167.2668	167.2610	167.2741	167.3081
167	169.2917	169.2670	169.2611	169.2743	169.3083
169	171.2920	171.2672	171.2613	171.2744	171.3084
171	173.2922	173.2674	173.2615	173.2746	173.3085
181	183.2936	183.2684	183.2623	183.2752	183.3091
191	193.2947	193.2692	193.2630	193.2758	193.3097
201	203.2957	203.2700	203.2636	203.2764	203.3101
301	303.3022	303.2749	303.2678	303.2798	303.3132
401	403.3056	403.2774	403.2699	403.2815	403.3147
501	503.3076	503.2789	503.2711	503.2825	503.3156

Table 9.   Wire Diameters for Spur and Helical Gears Based upon 1.68 Constant*

Diametral or Normal Diametral Pitch	Wire Diameter	Diametral or Normal Diametral Pitch	Wire Diameter	Diametral or Normal Diametral Pitch	Wire Diameter	Diametral or Normal Diametral Pitch	Wire Diameter
2	.840	8	.210	18	.09333	40	.042
2½	.672	9	.18666	20	.084	48	.035
3	.560	10	.168	22	.07636	64	.02625
4	.420	11	.15273	24	.070	72	.02333
5	.336	12	.140	28	.060	80	.021
6	.280	14	.120	32	.0525	..	......
7	.240	16	.105	36	.04667	..	......

* Pin diameter = 1.68 ÷ diametral pitch for spur gears and 1.68 ÷ normal diametral pitch for helical gears.

Measurement Over Balls: The measurement can be taken over two balls if they are kept in a plane of the gear's rotation. This can be done by holding them against a surface parallel to the face of the gear. In the case of odd-tooth helical gears, the two balls will not be diametrically opposite each other and hence a correction must be applied to the computed measurement M as described later under "Helical Gear with Odd Number of Teeth."

Helical Gear with Even Number of Teeth: First find a number N_e, by multiplying the number of teeth N in the helical gear by the secant of the helix angle. Next, multiply the number N of teeth in the helical gear by the cube of the secant of the helix angle, obtaining N_s. (N_s is the number of teeth which would be used in selecting a formed cutter in case the teeth are milled. The table on page 833 gives values of the secant cubed for various angles). Take that whole number which is nearest N_s and referring to Table 7 for spur gears with even tooth numbers, find the *decimal* value of the constant for this number of teeth, under the given *normal* pressure angle. Add to this decimal value the sum of $N_e + 2$ and divide the result by the normal diametral pitch to obtain the measurement M over the wires.

Example: Assume that a helical gear has 32 teeth of 6 normal diametral pitch, a helix angle of 23 degrees and normal pressure angle of 20 degrees. Determine the measurement M without allowance for backlash. The number N_e is equal to $32 \times \sec 23° = 32 \times 1.0864 = 34.7648$. The number of teeth N_s for which a formed cutter would be selected is equal to $32 \times \sec^3 23° = 32 \times 1.282 = 41.024$. The nearest whole number to N_s is 41 and the decimal part of the constant for 41 teeth must be found from Table 7 by interpolating halfway between the values given for 40 and 42 teeth. The decimal value given for 40 teeth is 0.2473 and for 42 teeth, 0.2485. The value for 41 teeth is halfway between, or 0.2479. Thus, M is computed as follows:

$$M = \frac{34.7648 + 2 + 0.2479}{6} = \frac{37.0127}{6} = 6.1688 \text{ inches}$$

Helical Gear with Odd Number of Teeth: The procedure is similar to that just outlined except that a correction is made in the final M value if the measurement is taken over two balls as previously described.

Example: Assume that a helical gear has 13 teeth of 8 normal diametral pitch, a helix angle of 45 degrees and a normal pressure angle of 14½ degrees. Wire diameter is 0.210 (see Table 9). To determine the measurement, M, without allowance for backlash, the number N_e is equal to $13 \times \sec 45° = 13 \times 1.4142 = 18.3846$. Multiply number of teeth N by cube of secant of helix angle, obtaining N_s Thus

$13 \times (\sec 45°) = 13 \times 2.828 = 36.764$. The nearest whole number to N_s is 37 and the decimal part of the constant for 37 teeth must be found from Table 7 by interpolating halfway between the values given for 36 and 38 teeth. The decimal value given for 36 teeth is 0.2533 and for 38 teeth, 0.2558. The value for 37 teeth is halfway between, or 0.2545. When the measurement is made over three wires and between parallel plates as previously described, M is computed as follows:

$$M = \frac{18.3846 + 2 + 0.2545}{8} = \frac{20.6391}{8} = 2.5799 \text{ inches}$$

When measurement is over two balls, the value of M is corrected for the balls not being diametrically opposite by one-half tooth interval, as follows:

$$M \text{ corrected} = (M - \text{Wire Diam.}) \times \cos \frac{90°}{N} + \text{Wire Diam.}$$

$$M \text{ corrected} = (2.5799 - 0.21) \cos \frac{90°}{13} + 0.21$$

$$= 2.3699 \times 0.99271 + 0.21 = 2.5626$$

Checking Spur Gear Size by Chordal Measurement Over Two or More Teeth. — Another method of checking gear sizes, that is generally available, is illustrated by the diagram accompanying Table 10. A vernier caliper is used to measure the distance M over two or more teeth. The diagram illustrates the measurement over two teeth (or with one intervening tooth space), but three or more teeth might be included, depending upon the pitch. The jaws of the caliper are merely held in contact with the sides or profiles of the teeth and perpendicular to the axis of the gear. Measurement M for involute teeth of the correct size, is determined as follows:

Table for Determining the Chordal Dimension: Table 10 gives the chordal dimensions for one diametral pitch when measuring over the number of teeth indicated in Table 11. To obtain any chordal dimension, it is simply necessary to divide chord M in the table (opposite the given number of teeth) by the diametral pitch of the gear to be measured and then subtract from the quotient one-half the total backlash between the mating pair of gears. In cases where a small pinion is used with a large gear and all of the backlash is to be obtained by reducing the gear teeth, the total amount of backlash is subtracted from the chordal dimension of the gear and nothing from the chordal dimension of the pinion. The application of the tables will be illustrated by an example.

Example — Determine the chordal dimension for checking the size of a gear having 30 teeth of 5 diametral pitch and a pressure angle of 20 degrees. A total backlash of 0.008 inch is to be obtained by reducing equally the teeth of both mating gears.

Table 10 shows that the chordal distance for 30 teeth of one diametral pitch and a pressure angle of 20 degrees is 10.7526 inches; one-half of the backlash equals 0.004 inch; hence,

$$\text{Chordal dimension} = \frac{10.7526}{5} - 0.004 = 2.1465 \text{ inches}$$

Table 11 shows that this is the chordal dimension when the vernier caliper spans four teeth, this being the number of teeth to gage over whenever gears of 20-degree pressure angle have any number of teeth from 28 to 36, inclusive.

If it is considered necessary to leave enough stock on the gear teeth for a shaving or finishing cut, this allowance is simply added to the chordal dimension of the finished teeth to obtain the required measurement over the teeth for the roughing

Table 10. Chordal Measurements over Spur Gear Teeth of 1 Diametral Pitch

Find value of *M* under pressure angle and opposite number of teeth; divide *M* by diametral pitch of gear to be measured and then subtract one-half total backlash to obtain a measurement *M* equivalent to given pitch and backlash. The number of teeth to gage or measure over is shown by Table 11.

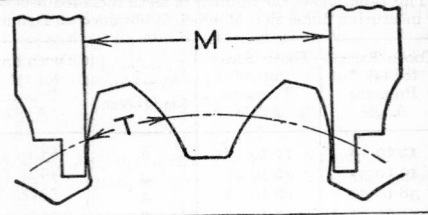

Number of Gear Teeth	M in Inches for 1 D. P.	Number of Gear Teeth	M in Inches for 1 D. P.	Number of Gear Teeth	M in Inches for 1 D. P.	Number of Gear Teeth	M in Inches for 1 D. P.
Pressure Angle, 14½ Degrees							
12	4.6267	37	7.8024	62	14.0197	87	20.2370
13	4.6321	38	10.8493	63	17.0666	88	23.2838
14	4.6374	39	10.8547	64	17.0720	89	23.2892
15	4.6428	40	10.8601	65	17.0773	90	23.2946
16	4.6482	41	10.8654	66	17.0827	91	23.2999
17	4.6536	42	10.8708	67	17.0881	92	23.3053
18	4.6589	43	10.8762	68	17.0934	93	23.3107
19	7.7058	44	10.8815	69	17.0988	94	23.3160
20	7.7112	45	10.8869	70	17.1042	95	23.3214
21	7.7166	46	10.8923	71	17.1095	96	23.3268
22	7.7219	47	10.8976	72	17.1149	97	23.3322
23	7.7273	48	10.9030	73	17.1203	98	23.3375
24	7.7326	49	10.9084	74	17.1256	99	23.3429
25	7.7380	50	10.9137	75	17.1310	100	23.3483
26	7.7434	51	13.9606	76	20.1779	101	26.3952
27	7.7488	52	13.9660	77	20.1833	102	26.4005
28	7.7541	53	13.9714	78	20.1886	103	26.4059
29	7.7595	54	13.9767	79	20.1940	104	26.4113
30	7.7649	55	13.9821	80	20.1994	105	26.4166
31	7.7702	56	13.9875	81	20.2047	106	26.4220
32	7.7756	57	13.9929	82	20.2101	107	26.4274
33	7.7810	58	13.9982	83	20.2155	108	26.4327
34	7.7863	59	14.0036	84	20.2208	109	26.4381
35	7.7917	60	14.0090	85	20.2262	110	26.4435
36	7.7971	61	14.0143	86	20.2316	...	....
Pressure Angle, 20 Degrees							
12	4.5963	30	10.7526	48	16.9090	66	23.0653
13	4.6103	31	10.7666	49	16.9230	67	23.0793
14	4.6243	32	10.7806	50	16.9370	68	23.0933
15	4.6383	33	10.7946	51	16.9510	69	23.1073
16	4.6523	34	10.8086	52	16.9650	70	23.1214
17	4.6663	35	10.8226	53	16.9790	71	23.1354
18	4.6803	36	10.8366	54	16.9930	72	23.1494
19	7.6464	37	13.8028	55	19.9591	73	26.1155
20	7.6604	38	13.8168	56	19.9731	74	26.1295
21	7.6744	39	13.8307	57	19.9872	75	26.1435
22	7.6884	40	13.8447	58	20.0012	76	26.1575
23	7.7024	41	13.8587	59	20.0152	77	26.1715
24	7.7165	42	13.8727	60	20.0292	78	26.1855
25	7.7305	43	13.8867	61	20.0432	79	26.1995
26	7.7445	44	13.9007	62	20.0572	80	26.2135
27	7.7585	45	13.9147	63	20.0712	81	26.2275
28	10.7246	46	16.8810	64	23.0373	...	....
29	10.7386	47	16.8950	65	23.0513	...	....

Table 11. Number of Teeth Included in Chordal Measurement

This table shows the number of teeth included between the jaws of the vernier caliper in measuring dimension M which is obtained as explained in connection with Table 10.

Tooth Range for 14½° Pressure Angle	Tooth Range for 20° Pressure Angle	Number of Teeth to Gage Over	Tooth Range for 14½° Pressure Angle	Tooth Range for 20° Pressure Angle	Number of Teeth to Gage Over
12 to 18	12 to 18	2	63 to 75	46 to 54	6
19 to 37	19 to 27	3	76 to 87	55 to 63	7
38 to 50	28 to 36	4	88 to 100	64 to 72	8
51 to 62	37 to 45	5	101 to 110	73 to 81	9

operation. It may be advisable to place this chordal dimension for roughing on the detail drawing.

Formula for Chordal Dimension M. — The required measurement M over spur gear teeth may be obtained by the following formula in which R = pitch radius of gear, A = pressure angle, T = tooth thickness along pitch circle, N = number of gear teeth, S = number of tooth *spaces* between caliper jaws, F = a factor depending upon the pressure angle = 0.01109 for 14½°; = 0.01973 for 17½°; = 0.0298 for 20°; = 0.04303 for 22½°; = 0.05995 for 25°. This factor F equals twice the involute function of the pressure angle.

$$M = R \times \cos A \times \left(\frac{T}{R} + \frac{6.2832 \times S}{N} + F \right)$$

Example — A spur gear has 30 teeth of 6 diametral pitch and a pressure angle of 14½ degrees. Determine measurement M over three teeth, there being two intervening tooth spaces.

The pitch radius = 2½ inches, the arc tooth thickness equivalent to 6 diametral pitch is 0.2618 inch (if no allowance is made for backlash) and factor F for 14½ degrees = 0.01109 inch.

$$M = 2.5 \times 0.96815 \times \left(\frac{0.2618}{2.5} + \frac{6.2832 \times 2}{30} + 0.01109 \right) = 1.2941 \text{ inches}$$

Checking Enlarged Pinions by Measuring Over Pins or Wires. — When the teeth of small spur gears or pinions would be undercut if generated by an unmodified straight-sided rack cutter or hob, it is common practice to make the outside diameter larger than standard. The amount of increase in outside diameter varies with the pressure angle and number of teeth, as shown by the table on page 670. In all cases, the teeth are cut to standard depth on a generating type of machine such as a gear hobber or gear shaper; and since the number of teeth and pitch are not changed, the pitch diameter also remains unchanged. The tooth thickness on the pitch circle, however, is increased and wire sizes suitable for standard gears are not large enough to extend above the tops of these enlarged gears or pinions; hence the Van Keuren wire size recommended for these enlarged pinions equals 1.92 ÷ diametral pitch. Table 12 gives measurements over wires of this size, for checking full-depth involute gears of 1 diametral pitch. For any other pitch, merely divide the measurement given in the table by the diametral pitch. Table 12 applies to pinions which have been enlarged by the same amounts as given in the table on page 670. These enlarged pinions will mesh with standard gears; but if the standard center distance is to be maintained, reduce the gear diameter below the standard size as much as the pinion diameter is increased.

Table 12. Checking Enlarged Spur Pinions by Measurement Over Wires

Measurements over wires are given in table for 1 diametral pitch. For any other diametral pitch, divide measurement in table by given pitch. Wire size equals 1.92 ÷ diametral pitch.

Number of Teeth	Outside or Major Diameter (Note 1)	Circular Tooth Thickness (Note 2)	Measurement Over Wires	Number of Teeth	Outside or Major Diameter (Note 1)	Circular Tooth Thickness (Note 2)	Measurement Over Wires
14½-degree full-depth involute teeth:				20-degree full-depth involute teeth:			
10	13.3731	1.9259	13.6186	10	12.8302	1.8730	13.4408
11	14.3104	1.9097	14.4966	11	13.7132	1.8304	14.2678
12	15.2477	1.8935	15.6290	12	14.5963	1.7878	15.3428
13	16.1850	1.8773	16.5211	13	15.4793	1.7452	16.1807
14	17.1223	1.8611	17.6244	14	16.3623	1.7027	17.2233
15	18.0597	1.8449	18.5260	15	17.2453	1.6601	18.0674
16	18.9970	1.8286	19.6075	16	18.1284	1.6175	19.0851
17	19.9343	1.8124	20.5156	17	19.0114	1.5749	19.9326
18	20.8716	1.7962	21.5806				
19	21.8089	1.7800	22.4934	Note 1: These enlargements, which are to improve the tooth form and avoid undercut, conform to those given in the table on page 670 where data will be found on the minimum number of teeth in the mating gear.			
20	22.7462	1.7638	23.5451				
21	23.6835	1.7476	24.4611				
22	24.6208	1.7314	25.5018				
23	25.5581	1.7151	26.4201				
24	26.4954	1.6989	27.4515	Note 2: The circular or arc thickness is at the standard pitch diameter. The corresponding chordal thickness may be found as follows: Multiply arc thickness by 90 and then divide product by 3.1416 × pitch radius; find sine of angle thus obtained and multiply it by pitch diameter.			
25	27.4328	1.6827	28.3718				
26	28.3701	1.6665	29.3952				
27	29.3074	1.6503	30.3168				
28	30.2447	1.6341	31.3333				
29	31.1820	1.6179	32.2558				
30	32.1193	1.6017	33.2661				
31	33.0566	1.5854	34.1889				

General Formula for Checking Spur Gears by Measurement Over Wires. —

The accompanying tables for checking spur gears by the wire or pin method are based upon the following formulas by Buckingham. These formulas may be required for pressure angles or wire sizes not covered by the tables. In these formulas, M = measurement over pins or wires for checking gear size; D = pitch diameter; T = arc tooth thickness on pitch circle; W = wire or pin diameter; N = number of gear teeth; A = pressure angle of gear; a = angle, the cosine of which is required in Formulas (2) and (3).

Formula (1) is used first to determine the involute function of angle a (inv a); then the corresponding angle a is found by referring to a table of involute functions (see "Manual of Gear Design," Section I, page 100). Note: If a = angle in degrees, then the involute function of that angle equals its tangent minus the angle expressed in radians or inv a = tan a − (π a ÷ 180).

Formulas (1), (2) and (3) apply to external gears

$$\text{inv } a = \frac{T}{D} + \text{inv } A + \frac{W}{D \cos A} - \frac{\pi}{N} \qquad (1)$$

For even number of teeth, $M = \dfrac{D \cos A}{\cos a} + W$ (2)

For odd number of teeth, $M = \left(\dfrac{D \cos A}{\cos a} \right) \cos \dfrac{90°}{N} + W$ (3)

Ratchet Gearing

Ratchet gearing may be used to transmit intermittent motion, or its only function may be to prevent the ratchet wheel from rotating backward. Ratchet gearing of this latter form is commonly used in connection with hoisting mechanisms of various kinds, to prevent the hoisting drum or shaft from rotating in a reverse direction under the action of the load.

Use of Multiple Pawls. — Some ratchet gearing is equipped with multiple pawls so that the relative motion between the pawl and ratchet wheel for engaging the pawl with successive teeth will be less than the pitch of the teeth. While the motion of the pawl lever that is necessary for engaging the pawl with successive teeth on the ratchet wheel may be reduced by making the pitch of the ratchet wheel teeth smaller, this weakens the teeth and is not always desirable. The effect of a smaller pitch may be obtained by using two or more pawls which are placed side by side and are pivoted on the same pin but are of different lengths. For example, if there are two pawls, one of these pawls is longer than the other by an amount equal to one-half the pitch of the ratchet wheel teeth, so that the practical effect is that of reducing the pitch one-half. By placing a number of pawls side by side and proportioning their lengths according to the pitch of the teeth, a very fine feed can be obtained with a ratchet wheel of comparatively coarse pitch.

Double-action Ratchet Mechanism. — Ratchet gearing is sometimes arranged so as to impart a rotary movement to the ratchet wheel for both the forward and backward motions of a lever to which two pawls are attached. The pawl lever is fulcrumed between the two pawls; consequently a movement of the pawl lever to the left causes one pawl to rotate the wheel while the other pawl is withdrawing for engaging the next successive tooth. As the pawl lever is moved in the opposite direction, this second pawl becomes the driving member.

Shape of Ratchet Wheel Teeth. — When designing ratchet gearing, it is important to so shape the teeth that the pawl will remain in engagement when a load is applied. The faces of the teeth which engage the end of the pawl should be in such relation with the center of the pawl pivot that a line perpendicular to the face of the engaging tooth will pass somewhere between the center of the ratchet wheel and the center of the pivot about which the pawl swings. If a line perpendicular to the face of the engaging tooth is beyond the pawl pivot, any load or pressure between the wheel and pawl would tend to disengage the latter, this tendency depending upon the inclination of the teeth and the amount of load which is applied. Ratchet teeth may be either cut by a milling cutter having the correct angle, or hobbed in a gear-hobbing machine by the use of a special hob.

Pitch of Ratchet Wheel Teeth. — The pitch of ratchet wheels used for holding suspended loads may be calculated by the following formula, in which $P =$ circular pitch, in inches, measured at the outside circumference; $M =$ turning moment acting upon the ratchet wheel shaft, in inch-pounds; $L =$ length of tooth face, in inches (thickness of ratchet gear); $S =$ safe stress (for steel, 2500 pounds per square inch when subjected to shock, and 4000 pounds per square inch when not subjected to shock); $N =$ number of teeth in ratchet wheel; $F =$ a factor the value of which is 50 for ratchet gears with 12 teeth or less, 35 for gears having from 12 to 20 teeth, and 20 for gears having over 20 teeth:

$$P = \sqrt{\frac{FM}{LSN}}$$

This formula has been used in the calculation of ratchet gears for crane design, and will give ample safety.

BELTS AND PULLEYS

Selection of Belting. — Oak-tanned leather is usually considered the best for belting, although many high-grade belts are no longer tanned by the use of oak bark. Assuming that a good grade of leather is used, uniformity in the material is of first importance; that is, the different sections of which the belt is made should all be of the same grade. The belts should also be thoroughly stretched so that they do not have to be "taken up" every few days. The leather for the best grades of belting is taken from the central part of the hide along the back of the animal. That part of the hide extending along the spine and for some distance down the sides is firm and close in texture and the strongest for a belt. If the leather is taken too far down the side, it will be flexible and lack strength and close-ness of texture. If the strips are cut too long, the ends will be taken from the neck of the animal, which is also inferior stock. A "short lap" belt is one made entirely from that part of the hide which comes from the back of the animal and the strips are not long enough to include any portion of the neck stock.

Application of Belts. — Whenever practicable, belts should be installed so that the slack side is above and the driving side below the pulleys. If this condition is reversed and the slack side is below, the arc of contact is materially lessened. Belts should also be placed on the pulleys with the hair or "grain" side next to the pulley rims.

Cemented Belt Joints. — The most satisfactory method of joining the ends of a belt is by making a cemented lap joint. The belt ends should be tapered to a smooth even surface, square with the edges, and the length of the lap should vary with the belt width approximately as given below:

Belt width in inches.........	1	2	3	4	5	6	7	8
Length of lap..............	5	5	6	6	7	8	8	9

For belting varying from 9 to 18 inches in width, the length of the lap is made equal to the belt width, and for widths above 18 inches, the lap need not be greater than 18 inches. Before cementing a joint, the belt should be placed over the pulleys and the proper tension obtained by means of clamps. These clamps are fastened across the belt on each side of the joint and are drawn together by threaded rods extending along the sides. Each clamp should be square with the belt and centrally located. After drawing the belt a little tighter than is desired, to allow for slack, bevel the ends to form the lap, and apply the cement to both surfaces while hot. If the belt is large, cement a few inches at a time, then rub with a "rub stone" and hammer down the cemented section thoroughly, proceeding this way until the entire lap has been cemented. The joint should then be carefully hammered, especially along the edges. The clamps should remain in position for about an hour, or longer if convenient.

The following preparation can be used for cementing leather belts: Place equal parts of glue and isinglass in a glue pot. Add enough water to cover the two in-gredients and let them soak ten hours. Then bring to boiling point and add pure tannin until the mixture appears like the white of an egg. Apply the cement while warm. For rubber belts use 16 parts gutta-percha, four parts India rubber, 2 parts caulker's pitch and one part linseed oil. These ingredients should be melted together and used while hot. This cement can also be applied to leather.

Inclination of Lap-joint. — The direction that the lap-joint of a belt should incline relative to the direction of the belt's motion is shown by the accompanying illustration. For a single-ply belt, the leading end or point of the lap is on the pulley side. The lap is inclined in this way to prevent the end from opening; when

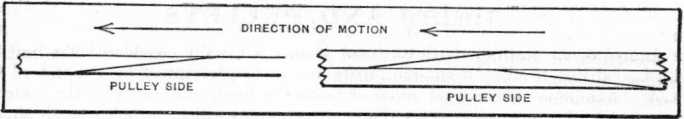

the leading end is on the outside, it tends to open up slightly, especially if the belt is operated at high speed, owing to the resistance of the air. As soon as there is a very slight opening, the atmospheric resistance tends to increase it, but when the leading end is next to the pulley, any tendency of the point to raise is overcome by frequent contact with the pulleys. To the right in the illustration is shown how the lap-joints of a double or two-ply belt should be inclined. In this case, the lap of the outer ply is in the same relation to the direction of motion as for a single belt, but the lap of the inner ply inclines in the opposite direction. With this arrangement, the leading ends of the laps in both plies will be inside and protected, and the outer ends are to the rear and not subjected to the atmospheric resistance. Opinions on this point, however, differ.

Laced Belt Joints. — When making a laced joint, cut the ends of the belt perfectly square and punch the holes exactly opposite one another in the two ends. In each end there should be two rows of staggered holes. The recommended number of holes for various widths is given in the table, "Belt Laces and Holes for Laced Joints." Begin to lace in the center of the belt and be careful to keep the belt ends exactly in line and to lace both sides with equal tension. The lacing should not be crossed on that side of the belt which runs next to the pulley.

Belt Laces and Holes for Laced Joints

Width of Belt, Inches	Width of Lace, Inches	No. of Holes	Distance of Holes from End		Width of Belt, Inches	Width of Lace, Inches	No. of Holes	Distance of Holes from End	
			First Row, Inches	Second Row, Inches				First Row, Inches	Second Row, Inches
1 –1¾	¼	2 or 3	⅜	...	6	⅜	9	¾	1¼
2 –2½	5⁄16	3	⅜	¾	8	½	11	¾	1⅜
2¾–3¼	5⁄16	5	½	1	10	½	13	1	1¾
3½–4½	⅜	5	⅝	1⅛	12	½	15	1	1¾
5	⅜	7	⅝	1⅛	14	½	17	1¼	2

Belt Dressings. — Belts should be cleaned and greased every five or six months to give the grain side a soft adherent surface. The following mixtures are recommended: Take two parts of beef tallow to one part of cod liver oil (by weight); melt the tallow and allow it to cool until the finger can be inserted without burning; then add the cod liver oil and stir until cooled. A light coat of this mixture should be applied to the driving side of the belt after it has been cleaned. Rosin or rosinous mixtures should never be used to prevent belts from slipping. They will cause temporary adhesion, but the belt soon becomes glazed and slips more than before the rosin was applied. Lubricating oils should not be permitted to drop onto belts. If a belt has become saturated with oil, scrape it and pack it in dry sawdust or some other absorbent material for three or four days. When belting becomes dry, all surface dirt should first be removed before applying the dressing; this usually can be done by rubbing the belt with a cloth dampened with kerosene. If necessary, use a wooden or metal scraper. A dressing recommended for rubber belts consists of equal parts of red lead, black lead, French yellow and litharge, mixed with boiled linseed oil and enough japan to make it dry quickly. Animal oil or grease should never be used on rubber belts.

Leather-covered Pulleys. — As the friction of leather on leather is much greater than of leather on iron or steel, leather-covered pulleys will transmit considerably more power than plain uncovered pulleys for the same belt tension. Before covering a pulley, clean the surface of all grease by washing it with naphtha or gasoline. Make the cover endless and about ⅛ inch to the foot shorter than the circumference of the pulley. Then place the endless cover on the pulley for a distance of about one inch. Next cover with glue the exposed inside surface of the cover and the exposed surface of the pulley. After applying the glue, drive the cover on by lifting the pulley and striking the cover edges against the floor or bench. This should be done quickly and by striking lightly to prevent bending the cover. When the cover is in place, rub the edges with a round stick or handle to secure a good contact. A properly covered pulley does not need rivets, although it is customary to insert a few copper rivets. Pulleys should be allowed to set two or three hours before using.

Direction of Belt Creep. — Belts connecting parallel shafts tend to run toward that part of the pulley which is largest in diameter; hence pulleys are crowned to keep the belt in the center of the rim. If the shafts are not parallel and the pulleys are cylindrical, the belt will run toward the "low" side of the pulley or the side where the centers of the shafts are closest.

Angular Belt Drives. — A general rule for aligning belt pulleys connecting shafts which are not parallel is as follows: The center of the face of the *driven* pulley must be aligned with the center of that face of the *driving* pulley from which the belt leaves, as at *A* in the illustrations. The manner in which the belt passes

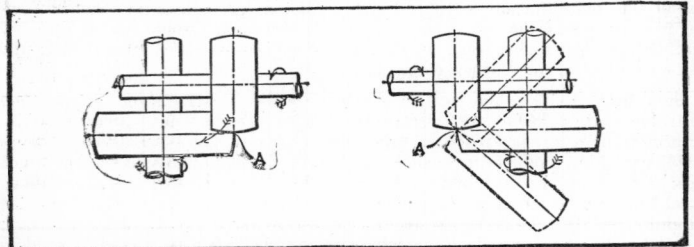

over the pulleys is indicated by the arrow heads showing the direction of rotation. The driven pulley can be set at any angle in relation to the driving pulley, provided it is turned about point *A*, as indicated by the dotted lines. The direction of rotation should not be reversed, unless the relative positions of the pulleys are changed in accordance with the foregoing rule.

Belt Width, Thickness and Speed. — The following conclusions are based upon tests. Narrow, thick belts are more desirable and work more satisfactorily than wide and thin belts. It is advisable to use double belts on pulleys 12 inches in diameter or larger and triple belts on pulleys 20 inches in diameter or larger. If thin belts are operated at high speed, they tend to run in waves on the slack side and travel laterally, especially if there are sudden load changes. This waving and snapping wears the belt rapidly and can be practically eliminated by having the thickness in proper proportion to the width. The speed at which belting runs has comparatively little effect upon its life until the velocity is higher than 2500 to 3000 feet per minute. The life is affected principally by the power transmitted, the method of fastening the ends, and the care of the belting. Tests made in France indicated that the greatest efficiency of transmission was obtained when oak-tanned belts ran at a speed of from 65 to 80 feet per second. What is termed "chromium-treated" leather belts ran most favorably at about 100 feet per second. The most satisfactory working tension was from 575 to 850 pounds per square inch of section. The tests indicated that the thickness of the belt should be from $\frac{1}{20}$ to $\frac{1}{30}$ of the radius of the pulley. When chromium-treated belts, which are more elastic, are used, a thickness of about $\frac{1}{15}$ of the radius is permissible.

Rubber Belting. — Rubber belts are used in places exposed to the weather or the action of steam, as they do not absorb moisture or stretch as readily as leather belts, under like conditions. The quality of rubber belting depends on the mixture (containing more or less rubber) that forms the coating, the cotton duck that gives strength to the belt and the method of manufacture. The best grades of rubber belting contain nothing but new rubber; the cheapest grades are composed largely of reclaimed rubber. The weight of the cotton duck is an important consideration. High-grade belts contain what is known as a 32-ounce cotton duck, and the cheaper grades have either a 30-ounce or 28-ounce duck. If the proper weight of duck is used, a 3- or 4-ply rubber belt is equal in strength to a single leather belt; a 5- or 6-ply rubber belt is equal to a double leather belt, and a 7- or 8-ply rubber belt is equal to a triple leather belt.

Canvas Belting. — Canvas stitched belting is made of several laps or plies of cotton duck stitched lengthwise and the belt is afterwards treated with a compound made principally of linseed oil. This oil saturates the cotton duck, which is thus protected from dampness, and the belt is not easily injured by heat, cold, steam, gas or acid fumes. Canvas stitched belting is often used where the material coming in contact with the belt or the surrounding atmosphere would ruin an ordinary leather, cotton or rubber belt. It is applicable to belt conveyors, when the material to be handled will not cut the cotton fiber.

Steel Belts. — Thin, flat steel belts have been used to some extent abroad, and tests are said to have demonstrated the following advantages: Steel belts can transmit much more power for the same width; they are not affected to any appreciable extent by temperature changes or changes in the humidity of the air, which adapts them for use in damp places; and there is little stretching or slipping. Steel belts can be run at speeds as high as 10,000 feet per minute. They must be carefully installed, however, to insure that the power is evenly distributed over the full width of the steel band, as otherwise one edge might be stressed beyond its breaking strength, with the result that the entire belt would fail. The pulleys for steel belts must be cylindrical and not crowned.

Horsepower Transmitted by Leather Belting. — The power-transmitting capacity of a belt should be less than the maximum possible capacity to insure a reasonable length of belt life and to avoid unnecessary expenses for repairs. The horsepower ratings for oak-tanned flat leather belting may be determined by means of the following Tables 1, 2 and 3, which were officially adopted in 1938 by the American Leather Belting Association. The nominal horsepower ratings per inch of belt width, as given in Table 1, are modified by certain important correction factors based upon practical experience. The application of these tables is illustrated by an example on a following page.

Table 1. Horsepower Ratings for Oak-tanned Flat Leather Belting

Officially adopted by the American Leather Belting Association

Belt Speed, Feet per Minute	SINGLE PLY		DOUBLE PLY			TRIPLE PLY	
	*1 1/64"	*1 3/64"	*1 8/64"	*2 0/64"	*2 3/64"	*3 0/64"	*3 4/64"
	Medium	Heavy	Light	Medium	Heavy	Medium	Heavy

Horsepower per Inch of Width — to be corrected by Factors from Tables 2 and 3

Belt Speed	Medium	Heavy	Light	Medium	Heavy	Medium	Heavy
600	1.1	1.2	1.5	1.8	2.2	2.5	2.8
800	1.4	1.7	2.0	2.4	2.9	3.3	3.6
1000	1.8	2.1	2.6	3.1	3.6	4.1	4.5
1200	2.1	2.5	3.1	3.7	4.3	4.9	5.4
1400	2.5	2.9	3.5	4.3	4.9	5.7	6.3
1600	2.8	3.3	4.0	4.9	5.6	6.5	7.1
1800	3.2	3.7	4.5	5.4	6.2	7.3	8.0
2000	3.5	4.1	4.9	6.0	6.9	8.1	8.9
2200	3.9	4.5	5.4	6.6	7.6	8.8	9.7
2400	4.2	4.9	5.9	7.1	8.2	9.5	10.5
2600	4.5	5.3	6.3	7.7	8.9	10.3	11.4
2800	4.9	5.6	6.8	8.2	9.5	11.0	12.1
3000	5.2	5.9	7.2	8.7	10.0	11.6	12.8
3200	5.4	6.3	7.6	9.2	10.6	12.3	13.5
3400	5.7	6.6	7.9	9.7	11.2	12.9	14.2
3600	5.9	6.9	8.3	10.1	11.7	13.4	14.8
3800	6.2	7.1	8.7	10.5	12.2	14.0	15.4
4000	6.4	7.4	9.0	10.9	12.6	14 5	16.0
4200	6.7	7.7	9.3	11.3	13.0	15.0	16.5
4400	6.9	7.9	9.6	11.7	13.4	15.4	16.9
4600	7.1	8.1	9.8	12.0	13.8	15.8	17.4
4800	7.2	8.3	10.1	12.3	14.1	16.2	17.8
5000	7.4	8.4	10.3	12.5	14.3	16.5	18.2
5200	7.5	8.6	10.5	12.8	14.6	16.8	18.5
5400	7.6	8.7	10.6	12.9	14.8	17.1	18.8
5600	7.7	8.8	10.8	13.1	15.0	17.3	19.0
5800	7.7	8.9	10.9	13.2	15.1	17.5	19.2
†6000	7.8	8.9	10.9	13.2	15.2	17.6	19.3

Minimum allowable pulley diameters for belt thicknesses listed above

	Medium	Heavy	Light	Medium	Heavy	Medium	Heavy
Belt Widths Under 8 in.	3"	5"	6"	8"	12"	20"	24"
Widths 8 in. and Over	5"	7"	8"	10"	14"	24"	30"

* The belt thicknesses are average thicknesses. See paragraph on Belt Thickness Specifications.

† For belt speeds over 6000 feet per minute, consult a leather belting manufacturer.

Table 2. Correction Factors for Small Pulley Diameter and Center Distance

Officially adopted by the American Leather Belting Association

Diam. Small Pulley Inches	CENTER DISTANCE IN FEET							
	Up to 10'		15'		20'		25' and Over	
	Tight Side		Tight Side		Tight Side		Tight Side	
	Above	Below	Above	Below	Above	Below	Above	Below
2"	.37	.37	.38	.41	.37	.43	.37	.44
2½"	.41	.41	.43	.46	.41	.48	.42	.49
3"	.45	.45	.48	.52	.48	.54	.48	.55
3½"	.49	.49	.53	.57	.53	.59	.53	.60
4"	.53	.53	.58	.63	.59	.65	.59	.66
4½"	.56	.56	.61	.66	.62	.68	.62	.70
5"	.59	.59	.65	.70	.66	.72	.66	.74
5½"	.60	.60	.66	.72	.67	.74	.68	.76
6"	.62	.62	.68	.74	.69	.76	.70	.78
7"	.64	.64	.70	.76	.71	.78	.72	.80
8"	.66	.66	.72	.78	.73	.80	.74	.82
9"	.67	.67	.73	.79	.74	.81	.75	.83
10"	.68	.68	.75	.81	.76	.83	.77	.85
11"	.69	.69	.76	.82	.77	.84	.78	.86
12"	.70	.70	.77	.83	.78	.86	.79	.88
13"	.71	.71	.78	.84	.79	.87	.80	.89
14"	.72	.72	.79	.85	.80	.88	.81	.90
15"	.73	.73	.80	.86	.81	.89	.82	.91
16"	.74	.74	.80	.87	.81	.89	.82	.91
17"	.74	.74	.81	.88	.82	.90	.83	.92
18"	.75	.75	.82	.89	.83	.91	.84	.93
20"	.75	.75	.83	.90	.84	.92	.85	.94
22"	.76	.76	.84	.91	.85	.93	.86	.95
24"	.77	.77	.85	.92	.86	.94	.87	.96
30"	.79	.79	.87	.94	.88	.96	.89	.98
36"	.80	.80	.88	.95	.89	.98	.90	1.00

Table 3. Service Correction Factors used in Determining Horsepower Rating

Select the one appropriate factor from each of the five divisions in this table
An example illustrating the application of Tables 1, 2 and 3 will be found on the next page

Condition of Atmosphere	Clean; scheduled maintenance on large drives 1.2 Normal................ 1.0 Oily, wet or dusty...... 0.7	Steady Loads	Steam engines, turbines, Diesel and multi-cylinder gas engines, fans, centrifugal pumps, steady line-shaft loads. 1.0
Angle of Center Line	Horizontal to 60°....... 1.0 60° to 75° from Hor..... 0.9 75° to 90° from Hor..... 0.8	Jerky Loads	Large induction motors compensator started, shunt wound D.C. motors, single cylinder gas engines, reciprocating machines such as compressors, punch presses, etc................... 0.8
Pulley Material	Fiber on motor and small pulleys..... 1.2 Cast iron or steel....... 1.0	Shock Loads	Shock and reversing belt loads, all motors 10 H.P and under. All cross the line start motors, wound rotor (slip ring) motors, synchronous motors.............. 0.6
Service	Temporary or infrequent 1.2 Normal................ 1.0 Important or continuous 0.8		

How to Apply Horsepower Rating Tables. — The application of the accompanying Tables 1, 2 and 3 (adopted by American Leather Belting Association) will be shown by an example. If H = horsepower to be transmitted; h = horsepower per inch of belt width (Table 1); W = total width of belt, inches; F = correction factor for center distance between pulleys and small pulley diameter (Table 2); A = factor for atmospheric condition (Table 3); B = factor for angle of center line between pulleys (Table 3); C = pulley material factor (Table 3); D = factor for class of service (Table 3); E = factor for character of load (Table 3),

$$W = \frac{H}{h\,F\,A\,B\,C\,D\,E}\,; \qquad H = W\,h\,F\,A\,B\,C\,D\,E$$

Example: A single-cylinder gas engine of 6 H.P. at 550 R.P.M. is to drive a compressor. Pulley diameters are 6 and 24 inches; fiber, on small pulley; center distance 6 feet; tight side of belt below; continuous service; normal atmospheric condition where belt is installed. Find width of belt.

Belt speed = $6 \times 550 \times 0.262$ = 864 feet per minute.

Selection of Factors: Table 1 shows that a light double belt is suitable for a 6-inch pulley. Horsepower rating h per inch of width (before applying correction factors) is 2.2 at 864 feet per minute (obtained by interpolating between values for 800 and 1000). Correction factor F from Table 2 is 0.62. Atmospheric condition factor $A = 1$ (Table 3); factor C for smallest pulley is 1.2; service factor D is 0.8; load condition factor E is 0.8.

$$\text{Width } W = \frac{6}{2.2 \times 0.62 \times 1 \times 1.2 \times 0.8 \times 0.8} = 5.7 \quad \text{(use 6-inch belt)}$$

Note: In checking the power-transmitting capacity of an available belt transmission, the calculated capacity may be less than the amount of power to be transmitted. In such cases, it may be possible to utilize the belt by making one or more of the following changes: (1) If small pulley is cast iron, change to fiber; (2) if drive is vertical, change to 60 degrees from horizontal or less; (3) improve atmospheric conditions if not normal. If these changes do not increase the horsepower capacity as much as required, an increase in belt width or thickness, or both, will be necessary. Note the relationship in Table 1 between the belt thickness and the small pulley diameter.

Belt Thickness Specifications. — The average belt thicknesses given in Table 1 have been adopted by the American Leather Belting Association. These average thicknesses are determined by measuring 20 coils and dividing this total measurement by the number of coils measured. If a belt roll contains less than 20 coils, measure all of the coils and divide by number. The allowable tolerance for all single- and double-ply belt thicknesses is plus or minus 1/64 inch. The thicknesses given in Table 1 for triple-ply belts are averages for general usage. The tolerances for single- and double-ply belts do not apply to triple-ply belts.

The Crowning of the Face of Pulleys. — The amount of "crowning" that should be given to a pulley differs with the conditions under which it works. The amount should be greater for leather belting than for cotton belting and also greater for low speeds than for high speeds. Different authorities recommend very different amounts of crown. One recommends a crown (or height at center) of 1/20 of the width of the pulley in the case of leather belting and 1/150 of the width for cotton belting. Another recommends 1/16 to 1/8 inch per foot width of crown for high speeds and 1/4 inch for low speeds, but these figures must be modified to meet individual conditions. The crowning of a pulley tends to keep the belt on only when the belt as a whole does not slip. A slipping belt will run off a crowned-face pulley quicker than from a straight-faced one.

Dimensions of Pulleys

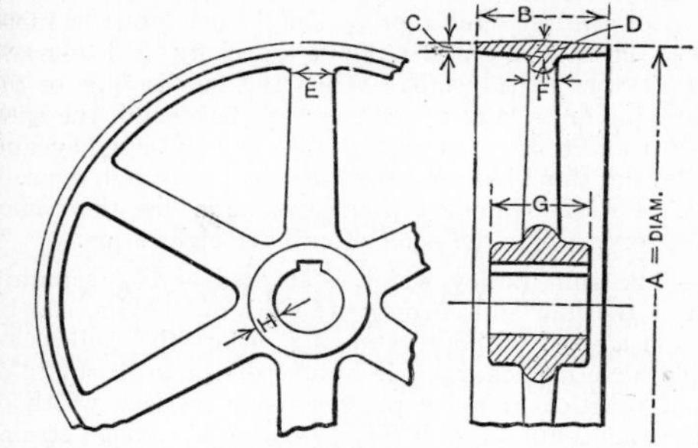

In all cases, the number of arms is 6. The arms increase in size towards the hub, the taper being ½ inch per foot. It is not safe to run cast-iron pulleys at a higher rim speed than 100 feet per second, and, in general, it is best to limit the speed to about 85 feet per second.

Diam. *A*	Face *B*	*C*	*D*	*E*	*F*	*G*	*H*
6	4	1/8	3/16	3/4	7/16	3	3/8
6	6	1/8	3/16	3/4	7/16	3 1/2	1/2
6	8	1/8	3/16	3/4	7/16	3 1/2	1/2
6	12	1/8	3/16	3/4	7/16	4	1/2
8	4	1/8	3/16	13/16	7/16	3	3/8
8	6	1/8	3/16	13/16	7/16	3 1/2	1/2
8	8	5/32	1/4	1 1/16	9/16	4 1/2	1/2
8	12	5/32	1/4	1 1/16	9/16	5 1/2	1/2
10	4	1/8	3/16	15/16	9/16	3	1/2
10	6	5/32	1/4	1 1/16	9/16	3 1/2	1/2
10	8	5/32	1/4	1 1/16	9/16	4 1/2	1/2
10	12	5/32	1/4	1 5/16	5/8	5 1/2	5/8
12	4	5/32	1/4	1	7/16	3 1/4	1/2
12	6	5/32	1/4	1 3/4	1/2	4	1/2
12	8	5/32	1/4	1 3/4	1/2	5	5/8
12	12	3/16	5/16	1 1/2	3/4	6 1/2	5/8
14	4	5/32	1/4	1 1/8	1/2	3 1/2	1/2
14	6	5/32	1/4	1 1/8	1/2	4 1/2	5/8
14	8	3/16	5/16	1 5/16	9/16	5	5/8
14	12	3/16	5/16	1 11/16	13/16	6 1/2	5/8
16	4	5/32	1/4	1 3/8	9/16	3 1/2	1/2
16	8	3/16	5/16	1 7/16	5/8	5	5/8
16	12	7/32	11/32	1 7/16	5/8	6 1/2	3/4
16	16	7/32	11/32	1 7/8	15/16	8 1/4	7/8
18	4	3/16	5/16	1 5/16	9/16	4	5/8
18	8	7/32	11/32	1 1/2	11/16	5 1/2	3/4
18	12	7/32	11/32	1 1/2	11/16	7 1/4	7/8
18	20	1/4	3/8	2 1/4	1 1/4	9	7/8
20	4	3/16	5/16	1 3/8	5/8	4	5/8
20	8	3/16	5/16	1 3/8	5/8	5	3/4
20	12	7/32	11/32	1 5/8	3/4	7	3/4
20	20	9/32	7/16	2 1/4	1 1/8	10	1
22	4	3/16	5/16	1 1/2	5/8	4	5/8
22	8	3/16	5/16	1 1/2	5/8	5	3/4
22	12	7/32	11/32	1 3/4	13/16	6 1/2	7/8
22	20	9/32	7/16	2 1/2	1 1/4	11	1 1/8
24	4	7/32	11/32	1 9/16	11/16	4	5/8
24	8	7/32	11/32	1 9/16	11/16	5 1/2	3/4

Cast-Iron Pulleys. — Cast-iron pulleys formed of one solid casting may or may not have a split or divided hub. The solid-hub pulley is held to its shaft either by a key, a key and one or two set-screws, or by simply using one or more set-screws without a key as in the case of small pulleys, especially on low-grade machinery where there is little power to transmit. When the hub is split or divided, it is provided with clamping bolts, and when these are tightened, the split hub grips the shaft tightly. In addition to clamping bolts, a key or a key and set-screws may be used. Pulleys of this kind are known as the clamp-hub type.

Most pulleys have six arms. For diameters less than 15 or 20 inches, there may be four arms, and pulleys 5 feet or larger in diameter often have eight arms.

Split Cast-iron Pulleys. — The split pulley which is formed of two separate sections bolted together both at the hub and on opposite sides of the rim, can be placed between other pulleys on a shaft without removing either the pulleys or the shaft. These pulleys often have interchangeable hub bushings to fit shafts of different diameter. It is good practice to make pulleys having a face width of 10 inches or over, either of the clamp-hub or split form, because shrinkage strains are either greatly reduced or practically eliminated, and the hub of the pulley can be firmly clamped to a shaft even though the bore is not an accurate fit. If the face width of a cast-iron pulley is greater than from 20 to 24 inches, there should be two sets of arms to provide better support for the rim.

Wood Pulleys. — Wood pulleys are not only much lighter than cast-iron pulleys but they are superior as transmitters of power; in fact it is claimed that they will transmit from 35 to 50 per cent more power for the same belt tension. Wood pulleys should not be used where they are exposed to excessive moisture. Ordinarily the rims are built up of segments, and the arrangement of the arms varies on different sizes and makes. Some wood pulleys intended for unusually severe duty have a rim which is joined to an iron center or hub by a solid web of wood. Other pulleys of the iron-center type have cast-iron hubs and arms and a wood rim. Internal shrinkage strains are thus eliminated and the pulleys are adapted to unusually high speeds. Well-seasoned maple is adapted to wood pulleys. Wood bushings are often inserted in the hubs to permit using the pulleys on shafts of different size.

Steel Pulleys. — Pulleys formed of sheet steel combine lightness with strength and they are free from the initial stresses which are such an uncertain factor in many cast-iron pulleys. The weight is ordinarily from 45 to 55 per cent less than the weight of a cast-iron pulley of equal power-transmitting capacity, which lessens the weight on the lineshaft and reduces the frictional losses. A series of tests showed that the percentage of slip was from 2.35 to 2.70 per cent less for steel pulleys than for cast-iron pulleys. Steel pulleys are ordinarily of the split type.

Safe Speeds for Pulleys. — The maximum safe rim speeds for solid cast-iron pulleys is as a general rule about 5000 feet per minute. If the pulley is split or formed of separate sections which are bolted together at the rim, the maximum speed should be limited to about 55 or 60 per cent of the maximum speed for solid pulleys. While the safe speeds of built-up steel pulleys are subject to some variation on account of differences in design or construction, in general such pulleys may be run at about 6000 feet per minute. The safe speeds recommended for wood pulleys vary considerably according to the type; thus, the maximum speeds recommended may be 5000 feet per minute for some pulleys and 10,000 feet per minute for others of different construction. A pulley having a cast-iron hub and arms, with a wood rim, has been operated under test at a rim speed of five and one-half miles per minute. For additional information on speeds see "Safe Speeds for Flywheels."

Short-center Flat-belt Drives. — There are two general methods of arranging short-center drives of the flat-belt type. One consists in applying an idler pulley or tension roller to the slack side of the belt near the smaller pulley. This idler is free to swing around the pulley to increase or decrease the arc of belt contact, and it usually is supported by a pivoted arm or frame which has an adjustable weight for varying the pressure on the slack side, if required.

Pivoted Motor Drive. — With drives of the pivoted-motor type, the motor base has a pivoted member to which the motor is attached. The pivot is so located that any swinging movement will either increase or decrease the belt tension. The motor may be adjusted toward or away from the pivot to change the initial belt tension. The tension also varies automatically with the load or amount of power being transmitted due to a counter-force or reaction torque which varies in proportion to the power output and tends to turn the pivoted motor frame, thus increasing or decreasing the tension.

V-Belt Drives. — Belts of the V-type provide a compact, resilient transmission and they have been applied extensively to automotive drives for fans, generators, and water pumps, and to many miscellaneous types of machines and industrial transmissions. Only the angular sides of a V-belt should be in contact with the sides of the pulley groove. The belt is approximately flush with the top of the pulley and the pulley groove should be deep enough to provide a clearance space at the bottom of about ⅛ to ³⁄₁₆ inch to insure a belt contact at the sides only. A multiple V-belt drive is commonly used instead of a single belt when required to increase the power-transmitting capacity. The driving and driven pulleys of these multiple drives are grooved for each belt, the grooves being spaced to provide a little clearance between the different belts.

S.A.E. Standard V-Belts. — The accompanying V-belt standard of the Society of Automotive Engineers, Inc., (see table) was formulated with the cooperation of a V-belt committee appointed by the Rubber Manufacturers' Association. The belts and pulleys specified are intended primarily for automotive applications, such as fan, generator, and pump drives. Where the load capacity of a single standard belt is inadequate, the required capacity usually can be obtained by using standard belts and pulleys in multiple. The S.A.E. standard ⅝- by ⅜-inch belt, was discontinued as a standard owing to extensive displacement by the 1¹⁄₁₆- by 1³⁄₃₂-inch size, but now is again included as a standard size.

Angle of Pulley and Belt. — Pulley diameters should never be smaller than shown in the table, and it is preferable to avoid using the minimum sizes listed whenever possible. The pulley diameters should be as large as possible without exceeding a belt speed of 7000 feet per minute. The included angle of the pulley groove varies from 28 to 38 degrees for different pulley diameters as shown by the table. The included angle of the belt itself, according to the S.A.E. specifications, is to be determined by the belt manufacturers to meet the specific requirements of each application.

Adjustable Pulley. — The adjustable pulley of the transmission should have an adjustment from the initial desired running position equal to the belt thickness to facilitate applying the belt. If such an adjustment is not provided, the belt may be injured by prying it over the pulley rim. The adjustable pulley should also have an adjustment in the other direction sufficient to take up at least 2½ per cent of the belt circumferential length.

Lengths of V-Belt and Designations of Size. — The belt lengths are measured on a standard fixture equipped with two grooved pulleys on which the belt is mounted and subjected to a tension of 40 pounds. These pulleys have an outside diameter of 4¾ inches. The grooves in them have an included angle of 34 degrees and a width at the top of 1⁵⁄₁₆ inch. After applying tension to the belt, the pulleys should be rotated at least one turn to seat the belt or they may be rotated continuously at slow speed. The belt length is checked by the center-to-center distance of the pulleys on the fixture with a tolerance of plus or minus ⅛ inch. The original center-to-center distance on the fixture is determined by using an original sample belt of correct length. Belts are specified and marked by the S.A.E. size number and the center-to-center distance in inches between the pulleys as established with this standard testing or checking fixture.

V-Belts for Industrial Applications. — The five common sizes of V-belts used for miscellaneous industrial applications include both smaller and larger sizes than those in the S.A.E. standard; moreover, the widths and thicknesses of industrial V-belts differ more or less from those conforming to the S.A.E. standard. The sizes of industrial V-belts are commonly designated by the letters A, B, C, D and E, or by the use of these letters in conjunction with the belt width at the top and its thickness. For example, size A, ½ by 1½₂ inch. The first dimension indicates the width at the top and the last one the belt thickness. The proportions of each of these

S.A.E. Standard V-Belts and Pulleys

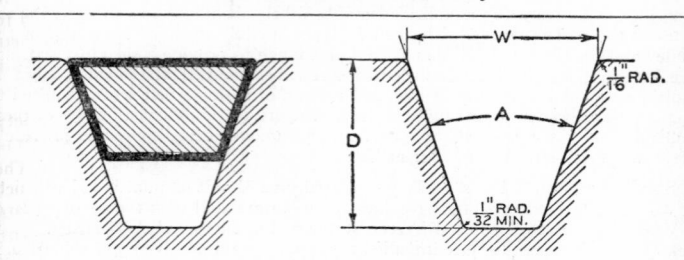

Sides of groove must be free of tool marks and rough spots.

S.A.E. Belt Size and Nominal Top Width, Inch	Nominal Belt Thickness, Inch	Outside Diameter of Pulley, ±0.010 Inch	Pulley Groove Dimensions		
			Top Width W, Inch ±0.010	Angle A ±½ Deg.	Depth D, Min. Inch
⅝	⅜	3 and larger	0.625	28	1 9⁄32
1 1⁄16	1 3⁄32	3 to 4 in., incl.* Over 4, to 6 in., incl. Over 6 in.	0.625	34 36 38	⅝
¾	7⁄16	3 to 4 in., incl.* Over 4, to 6 in., incl. Over 6 in.	0.688	34 36 38	1 1⁄16
⅞	½	3½ to 4½ in., incl.* Over 4½, to 6 in., incl. Over 6 in.	0.813	34 36 38	1 3⁄16
1	9⁄16	4 to 6 in., incl.* Over 6, to 8 in., incl. Over 8 in.	0.938	34 36 38	1 5⁄16

* In designing V-belt drives, these small-diameter pulleys should be used only in extreme cases because they reduce the power-transmitting capacity and belt life.

five letter sizes are given in the first column of the accompanying table, "Horse-power Ratings for V-Belt Drives."

Speed Ratios for V-Belt Drives. — Transmissions of the V-belt type commonly are applied to ratios varying from 1 to 1 up to 7½ to 1, and higher for some applications. As a general rule, the ratio should not be high enough to reduce the arc of belt contact with the smaller pulley below about 120 degrees. As the ratio increases, the power-transmitting capacity of a belt of given size decreases as shown by the table, "Horsepower Ratings for V-Belt Drives." The speed ratios are determined by using the *pitch* diameters of the belt sheaves or pulleys. These pitch diameters equal approximately the outside diameter of the sheave minus an amount equal

Horsepower Ratings for V-Belt Drives

These approximate ratings are intended as a general guide only in connection with preliminary estimates. More definite information about the power-transmitting capacity of a given type or make of belt may be obtained from the manufacturer.

Size of V-Belt (Top Width and Thickness)	Speed Ratio (Note 1)	Pitch Diameters of Sheaves		Horsepower per Belt			Range of Power, Using One or More Belts (Note 2)
		Driver	Driven	Motor 1720 R.P.M.	Motor 1140 R.P.M.	Motor 850 R.P.M.	
½″ × 11/32″ A	1	4	4	1.6	1.0	0.7	½ to 10 Horsepower
	1	6	6	2.2	1.5	1.1	
	3	4	12	1.3	0.8	0.6	
	3	5	15	1.6	1.1	0.8	
	6	3	18	0.9	0.6	0.4	
21/32″ × 7/16″ B	1	6	6	2.9	2	1.5	1 to 20 Horsepower
	1	7.4	7.4	3.5	2.4	1.8	
	3.07	6	18.4	2.6	1.8	1.3	
	6	5	30	2.1	1.3	1.0	
	7.6	5	38	2.1	1.3	1.0	
7/8″ × 5/8″ C	1	10	10	9.0	7.5	6.0	15 to 100 Horsepower
	3	10	30	8.4	7.0	5.6	
	5	10	50	7.9	6.6	5.3	
	7.11	9	64	7.4	6.2	5.0	
1¼″ × ¾″ D	1	15	15	17.7	15.7	13.3	50 to 250 Horsepower
	2.67	15	40	16.0	14.3	12.0	
	4.66	15	70	15.7	14.0	11.8	
	7.16	13.4	96	15.6	13	10.7	
1½″ × 1″ E	1	24	24	23.5	22.2	20.0	100 to 350 Horsepower
	2.09	22	46	22.0	19.7	17.6	
	3	22	66	21.4	19.0	17.0	
	4.36	22	96	20.9	18.7	16.6	

Note 1: The speed ratios given in Column 2 equal the *pitch* diameter of the driven sheave, divided by the pitch diameter of the driving sheave. The range of ratios selected for each belt size, show the effect of the ratio on the power-transmitting capacity due to the reduction in the arc of belt contact with the smaller pulley as the ratio increases.

Note 2: The last column gives a recommended range of power ratings for each belt size, two or more belts being used when the maximum power to be transmitted exceeds the power rating per belt. The number of belts for a given drive depends to some extent upon the application or possible overload requirements. The minimum number equals the horsepower rating of the motor divided by the power rating per belt for a given ratio and sheave combination. As the table shows, the rating per belt is affected by the speed ratio, sheave diameters, and speed.

approximately to the belt thickness plus from 1/16 to 1/8 inch, depending upon the belt size. For example, if the belt is size E or 1 1/2 by 1 inch, the pitch diameter would equal (approximately at least) the outside sheave diameter minus 1 1/8 inch. The pitch diameter represents the effective diameter and there may be some variation for belts of different make.

Sheaves for V-Belts. — Sheaves usually are made either of cast semi-steel, cast iron, or pressed steel. The sides of the grooves should be finished smoothly to avoid excessive belt wear, and the grooves of mating pulleys should be accurate as to width, angle, and alignment.

Minimum Sheave Diameters. — If the sheaves are too small in diameter, excessive bending of the belt will shorten its life and may result in considerable internal friction. The minimum pitch diameter of the sheave for one installation or kind of service might not be the minimum for different conditions; however, as a general rule, the minimum pitch diameters would be as follows: 3 inches for belt size A, 1/2 by 11/32 inch; 5.4 inches for belt size B, 21/32 by 7/16 inch; 9 inches for belt size C, 7/8 by 5/8 inch; 13 inches for belt size D, 1 1/4 by 3/4 inch; 21.6 inches for belt size E, 1 1/2 by 1 inch.

Center Distance between Sheaves. — Belt transmissions of the vee type are particularly adapted for short-center drives, and short-center distances are recommended especially for high speeds. One rule is to make the center distance slightly larger than the diameter of the larger pulley and smaller than the sum of the diameters of both pulleys; however, both longer and shorter distances are entirely practicable.

Adjustment of Center Distance. — There should always be provision for a center distance adjustment not merely to compensate for any slight stretching which might occur but to facilitate installing new belts without forcing them over the sheaves. Belts of the V-type do not require initial tension. In fact, it is only necessary to adjust the center distance so as to avoid excessive slack or undue sagging of the belt.

V-Belt Speeds. — The maximum speed depends upon the class of service and may be decidedly affected by the diameters of the sheaves. High speeds tend to shorten the life of the belt; on the other hand, if the speed is unnecessarily low, either a larger belt or more belts will be required for transmitting a given amount of power. In many installations, speeds should be limited to about 2500 to 3000 feet per minute, especially if the pitch diameters of the sheaves are near the minimum diameters previously given. On larger sheaves, under favorable conditions, the speeds may range from 4000 to 7000 feet per minute.

Arc of Belt Contact. — The arc of contact between the belt and the smaller sheave is found as follows: Multiply the difference in sheave diameters by 60; divide the product by the center distance in inches, and subtract the quotient from 180 degrees.

A reduction in the arc of contact from 180 to 160 degrees will reduce the power-transmitting capacity about 5 per cent; for a reduction to 145 degrees, 10 per cent; for 130 degrees, 15 per cent.

Example: Assume that a V-belt of size C (7/8 by 5/8) operates on 10- and 30-inch sheaves, the ratio being 3 to 1. Assume that the center distance is 34 inches. How much will the power capacity be reduced as compared with a 1-to-1 ratio?

By applying the arc of contact rule previously given, we find that this arc for the 3-to-1 drive is about 145 degrees; hence, if the power capacity is 7.5 for a 1-to-1 ratio, it will be reduced to approximately 7.5 × 0.90 = 6 3/4 horsepower.

Power-transmitting Capacity. — Belts of the V-type are now being used for many different types of drives with power capacities ranging from a fraction of a horsepower to several hundred horsepower. Information about the power-transmitting capacity of a given belt and for a given type of transmission should be obtained directly from the manufacturer of whatever belt is to be used. The accompanying table, " Horsepower Ratings for V-Belt Drives " is intended as a general guide only.

Belt Velocity or Circumferential Speed of Pulleys

Revolutions per Minute — Velocity in Feet per Minute

Pulley Diam. in Inches	70	80	90	100	110	120	130	140	150	160	170	180	190	200	210	220	230	250	260	280	300
6	110	126	141	157	173	188	204	220	235	251	267	282	298	314	330	346	361	392	408	440	471
7	128	146	165	183	201	220	238	256	275	293	312	330	348	367	385	403	421	458	477	513	550
8	146	167	188	210	230	251	272	293	314	335	356	377	398	419	440	461	481	523	545	586	628
9	165	188	212	236	259	282	306	330	353	377	400	424	447	471	495	518	542	588	613	660	707
10	183	209	235	262	288	314	340	366	392	419	445	471	497	524	549	576	602	654	681	733	785
12	220	252	282	314	346	377	408	440	471	503	534	565	597	628	659	691	722	785	817	880	942
14	256	293	330	366	403	440	476	513	550	586	623	659	696	733	769	806	843	916	953	1026	1100
16	293	335	377	419	460	502	544	586	628	670	712	754	796	838	879	921	963	1046	1089	1173	1257
18	330	377	424	471	518	565	612	659	707	754	801	848	895	942	989	1037	1084	1178	1225	1319	1414
20	366	419	471	524	576	628	681	733	785	838	890	942	995	1047	1099	1152	1204	1309	1361	1466	1571
22	403	460	518	576	634	691	749	806	864	921	979	1037	1094	1152	1209	1267	1325	1440	1497	1612	1728
24	440	502	565	628	691	754	817	880	942	1005	1068	1131	1194	1257	1319	1382	1445	1571	1633	1759	1885
26	476	545	612	681	749	817	885	953	1021	1089	1157	1225	1293	1361	1429	1497	1565	1701	1770	1906	2042
28	513	586	659	733	806	880	953	1026	1100	1173	1246	1319	1393	1466	1539	1613	1686	1832	1906	2052	2199
30	550	628	706	785	864	942	1022	1100	1178	1256	1335	1413	1492	1571	1649	1728	1806	1963	2042	2199	2356
32	586	670	754	838	921	1005	1089	1173	1257	1340	1424	1508	1592	1675	1759	1843	1927	2094	2178	2345	2513
34	623	712	801	890	979	1068	1157	1246	1335	1424	1513	1602	1691	1780	1869	1958	2047	2225	2314	2492	2670
36	659	754	848	942	1037	1131	1225	1319	1414	1508	1602	1696	1791	1885	1978	2073	2168	2356	2450	2639	2827
40	733	837	942	1047	1152	1256	1361	1466	1571	1675	1780	1885	1989	2094	2199	2304	2408	2618	2723	2932	3141
48	879	1005	1131	1257	1382	1508	1633	1759	1885	2010	2136	2262	2387	2513	2639	2765	2890	3142	3267	3518	3769
54	989	1131	1272	1414	1555	1696	1838	1979	2120	2262	2403	2545	2686	2827	2969	3110	3251	3534	3676	3959	4240
60	1099	1256	1414	1571	1728	1885	2042	2199	2356	2513	2670	2827	2984	3141	3298	3456	3613	3927	4084	4398	4712
66	1209	1382	1550	1728	1900	2073	2246	2419	2592	2764	2937	3110	3283	3455	3628	3801	3974	4319	4492	4838	5183
72	1319	1508	1696	1885	2073	2262	2450	2639	2827	3016	3204	3392	3581	3770	3958	4147	4335	4713	4900	5278	5654
78	1429	1633	1838	2042	2245	2450	2655	2859	3063	3267	3472	3676	3880	4084	4288	4492	4696	5105	5309	5717	6125
84	1539	1754	1978	2199	2419	2639	2859	3079	3298	3518	3738	3958	4178	4398	4618	4838	5058	5497	5717	6157	6597

Rules for Calculating Diameters and Speeds of Pulleys

Speed of Driven Pulley Required. — Diameter and speed of driving pulley, and diameter of driven pulley are known. *Rule:* Multiply the diameter of the driving pulley by its speed in revolutions per minute, and divide the product by the diameter of the driven pulley.

Example: — If the diameter of the driving pulley is 15 inches and its speed, 180 revolutions per minute, and the diameter of the driven pulley, 9 inches, then the speed of the driven pulley $= \dfrac{15 \times 180}{9} = 300$ revolutions per minute.

Diameter of Driven Pulley Required. — Diameter and speed of driving pulley, and revolutions per minute of driven pulley are known. *Rule:* Multiply the diameter of the driving pulley by its speed in revolutions per minute, and divide the product by the required speed of the driven pulley.

Example: — If the diameter of the driving pulley is 24 inches and its speed, 100 revolutions per minute, and the driven pulley is to rotate 600 revolutions per minute, then the diameter of the driven pulley $= \dfrac{24 \times 100}{600} = 4$ inches.

Diameter of Driving Pulley Required. — Diameter and speed of driven pulley, and speed of driving pulley are known. *Rule:* Multiply the diameter of the driven pulley by its speed in revolutions per minute, and divide the product by the speed of the driving pulley.

Example: — If the diameter of the driven pulley is 36 inches and its required speed, 150 revolutions per minute, and the speed of the driving pulley is 600 revolutions per minute, then the diameter of the driving pulley $= \dfrac{36 \times 150}{600} = 9$ inches.

Speed of Driving Pulley Required. — Diameters of driving and driven pulleys, and speed of driven pulley are known. *Rule:* Multiply the diameter of the driven pulley by its speed, and divide the product by the diameter of the driving pulley.

Example: — If the diameter of driven pulley is 4 inches, its required speed, 800 revolutions per minute, and the diameter of the driver, 26 inches, then the required speed of the driver $= \dfrac{4 \times 800}{26} = 123$ revolutions per minute, approximately.

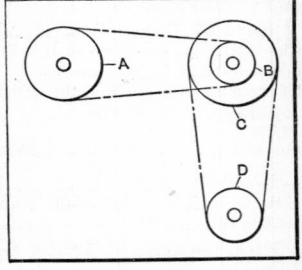

Speed of Driven Pulley in Compound Drive Required. — Diameters of pulleys A, B, C and D (see illustration), and speed of pulley A are known; find speed of pulley D. *Rule:* Divide product of diameters of driving pulleys by product of diameters of driven pulleys, and multiply quotient by speed of first driving pulley.

Example: — If the diameters of the driving pulleys A and C are 18 and 24 inches; the diameters of the driven pulleys B and D, 12 and 13 inches; and the speed of the driver A, 260 revolutions per minute; then the speed of the driven pulley $D = \dfrac{18 \times 24}{12 \times 13} \times 260 = 720$ revolutions per minute.

Pulley Diameters in Compound Drive Required. — Speeds of driving and driven pulleys are known; find diameters of the four pulleys A, B, C and D. *Rule:* Place the speed of the driving pulley as the numerator of a fraction, and the speed of driven pulley as the denominator, and reduce this fraction to its lowest terms; then resolve both the numerator and denominator into two factors, and multiply each "pair" of factors (a pair being one factor in the numerator and one in the denominator) by a trial number which will give pulleys of suitable diameters.

Example: — If the speed of pulley A is 260 revolutions per minute, and the required speed of pulley D is 720 revolutions per minute, find the diameters of the four pulleys. The fraction $\frac{260}{720}$ reduced to its lowest terms is $\frac{13}{36}$, which represents the required speed ratio. Resolve $\frac{13}{36}$ into two factors; $\frac{13}{36} = \frac{1 \times 13}{2 \times 18}$. Multiply by trial numbers 12 and 1:

$$\frac{(1 \times 12) \times (13 \times 1)}{(2 \times 12) \times (18 \times 1)} = \frac{12 \times 13}{24 \times 18}$$

The values 12 and 13 in the numerator represent the diameters of the *driven* pulleys B and D and values 24 and 18 in the denominator, the diameters of the *driving* pulleys.

Lengths of Open and Crossed Belts. — The following formulas for determining the lengths of belts on pulleys are accurate enough for practical purposes. No allowance is made for a lap joint. In these formulas, L = length of open belt; L_c = length of cross belt; D, C and R = diameter, circumference and radius, respectively, of large pulley; d, c and r = diameter, circumference and radius, respectively, of small pulley; x = center-to-center distance.

$$L = \frac{D+d}{2} \times 3\tfrac{1}{7} + 2x; \quad L_c = \frac{C}{2} + \frac{c}{2} + 2\sqrt{x^2 + (R+r)^2}$$

Rules for Calculating Speeds of Gearing

The relative speeds of shafts connected by spur or bevel gearing can be determined by the foregoing rules for pulley-and-belt drives, provided the *pitch diameter* or the number of teeth in the gear is substituted for the pulley diameter, in each case, as shown by the following examples:

Speed of Driven Gear Required. — Number of teeth in driving gear, its speed, and number of teeth in driven gear are known. *Rule:* Multiply the number of teeth in the driving gear by its speed in revolutions per minute, and divide by the number of teeth in the driven gear.

Example: — If the driving gear has 20 teeth and rotates 80 revolutions per minute, and the driven gear has 40 teeth, then the speed of the driven gear $= \frac{20 \times 80}{40}$ = 40 revolutions per minute.

If one or more intermediate gears are placed in a direct train between the driving and driven gears, the speed ratio will remain the same.

Pitch Diameter of Driven Gear Required. — The pitch diameter of the driving gear, its speed, and speed required for driven gear are known. *Rule:* Multiply the pitch diameter of the driving gear by its speed in revolutions per minute, and divide by the required speed of the driven gear.

Example: — If the pitch diameter of the driver is 8 inches, its speed, 75 revolutions per minute, and the speed required for the driven gear, 20 revolutions per minute, then the pitch diameter of the driven gear $= \frac{8 \times 75}{20}$ = 30 inches.

Machine Tool Drives

Machine Tool Drives with Speeds in Geometrical Ratio. — When designing a machine tool drive, the speeds obtainable on the machine should form a geometrical progression. Let n be the total number of required speeds; a, the slowest speed, in number of revolutions per minute; b, the fastest speed, in number of revolutions per minute; and r, the ratio of the geometrical progression, or the factor with which to multiply any speed to get the next higher speed. If the maximum and minimum speeds and the number of speed changes are known, the ratio of the progression may be found by the formula:

$$r = \sqrt[n-1]{\frac{b}{a}}$$

In most cases, this formula requires logarithms for its solution and can be written:

$$\text{Log } r = \frac{\log b - \log a}{n - 1}$$

As an example, assume that a drive is to be designed to give a range of 18 spindle speeds from 10 to 223 revolutions per minute. By means of the formula, ratio r is found to be 1.20, and by continued multiplication, the speeds are found to be:

10	12	14.4	17.25	20.7	24.85
29.8	35.8	43	51.6	62	74.4
89.4	107	129	155	186	223

Assume the use of a three-step cone, double back-gears, and two countershaft speeds. There are two methods of arranging the countershaft speeds; first, by shifting the machine belt over the entire range of the cone before changing the countershaft speed; and second, by changing the countershaft speed after each shifting of the machine belt. The design of the cone will be considerably different, according to which method is used. In the first case, there will be very small differences in the diameters of the steps, while in the second case these differences will be large, producing a cone with a steep incline. For the first arrangement, the following table may be made:

Cone	Open Belt		Small Ratio Back Gears in		Large Ratio Back Gears in	
	Fast Counter	Slow Counter	Fast Counter	Slow Counter	Fast Counter	Slow Counter
Step 1......	223	129.0	74.4	43.0	24.85	14.4
Step 2......	186	107.0	62.0	35.8	20.70	12.0
Step 3......	155	89.4	51.6	29.8	17.25	10.0
	1	2	3	4	5	6

From the above table, the ratio of the two sets of back-gears, the countershaft speeds, and the speeds off each step of the cone may be obtained. The ratio of the large ratio back-gears is found by dividing a term in column 2 by a corresponding term in column 6. The ratio of the small ratio gears is found by dividing a term in column 2 by a corresponding term in column 4. The ratio of countershaft speeds is obtained by dividing a term in column 5 by a corresponding term in column 6, and the ratio of speeds off each step of the cone, by dividing the term corresponding to step 1 in any column by a term corresponding to steps 2 or 3, as desired, in the same column. The results in the example given would be:

Ratio of large ratio gears is.................................... 8.94 to 1
Ratio of small ratio gears is.................................... 2.98 to 1
Ratio of countershaft speeds is.................................... 1.725 to 1
Ratio of speeds off step 1 to those off step 2.................... 1.2 to 1
Ratio of speeds off step 1 to those off step 3.................... 1.44 to 1

The diameter of the largest step of the cone is assumed to be 15 inches. The ratio of the speeds off step 1 and step 3 is 1.44 to 1; with equal pulleys on countershaft and on machine, this ratio also equals $(D \times D) \div (d \times d)$, where D is the diameter of the largest step and d is the diameter of the smallest step. Hence, $D^2 \div d^2 = 1.44$, and when D is 15 inches, $d = 12.5$ inches.

In the second case, where the countershaft speed is changed after each shifting of the machine belt, the speeds may be tabulated as follows:

Cone	Open Belt		Small Ratio Gears in		Large Ratio Gears in	
	Fast Counter Speed	Slow Counter Speed	Fast Counter Speed	Slow Counter Speed	Fast Counter Speed	Slow Counter Speed
Step 1......	223	186.0	74.4	62.0	24.85	20.7
Step 2......	155	129.0	51.6	43.0	17.25	14.4
Step 3......	107	89.4	35.8	29.8	12.00	10.0
	1	2	3	4	5	6

The various ratios are:

Large ratio gears.................................... 8.94 to 1
Small ratio gears.................................... 2.98 to 1
Countershaft speeds.................................... 1.2 to 1
Speeds off step 1 to those off step 2.................... 1.44 to 1
Speeds off step 1 to those off step 3.................... 2.07 to 1

In this case, if the large step is 15 inches in diameter, the smallest step will be 10.4 inches in diameter.

Ratio of Speed Changes for Machine Tools. — It is of little practical advantage to reduce the speed ratio below 1.2, and in the case of machine tools of ordinary type, a ratio of 1.3 is as small as is advisable. On the other hand, it is inadvisable to let the speed ratio be greater than 1.5, except in the case of cheap machinery, when ratios up to 1.7 may be permissible. In other words, if the lowest speed is 20 revolutions per minute, the next speed for ordinary machine tools should, as a rule, not be less than $20 \times 1.3 = 26$ revolutions per minute, and not more than $20 \times 1.5 = 30$ revolutions per minute. Succeeding speeds are found by multiplying each previous speed by the same factor.

The ratio between successive feeds should always be less than 1.3, and in the case of high-class machinery a value of 1.2 or less is preferable.

Table of Geometrical Progression. — The table of geometrical progression will be found useful in calculating speed ranges for machine tools. This table gives the values of consecutive terms in a geometrical progression when the increase of successive terms in per cent varies from 10 to 100, or when the ratio varies from 1.10 to 2. The columns 2, 3, 4, etc., give the values of the respective terms in the progression, when the first term is 1. For example, if the speed ratio is 1.15 and the first term in the progression is 1, then the eighth term in this geometrical progression would be 2.66. If the first term is any other value than 1, the value of the other terms may be found by multiplying the various tabulated values by the value of the first term. For example, if the speed ratio is 1.15 and the first speed is 20 revolutions per minute, then the eighth speed would be 20 × 2.66 = 53.2 revolutions per minute.

Table for Simplifying the Calculation of Cone Drive and Back-gear Designs. — The table "Geometrical Progressions for Spindle Speeds" gives the consecutive speeds in a properly arranged machine tool drive for ratios more finely subdivided than in the case of the previous table. The use of the table will be best shown by a practical example. Assume that the spindle of a lathe requires 18 speed changes, varying from 6 to 250 R.P.M., that the cone has three steps, the largest step being 15 inches in diameter, that the lathe is double back-geared, and that a two-speed countershaft is provided. The questions to be answered are then: What are the intermediate speeds between 6 and 250 R.P.M.? What are the diameters of the two remaining cone steps? What are the back-gear ratios and what should be the countershaft speeds?

In the table the maximum speed in every case is given as 1000, which, in the present case is four times greater than the maximum speed of the spindle. In order to reduce the figures given in the table to correspond with those of this example, divide the speeds given in the table by 4; (1000 ÷ 4 = 250); the slowest speed, given as 6 R.P.M., will then correspond to a speed given in the table equal to 24 R.P.M.; (24 ÷ 4 = 6). It will be seen that 24 and 1000 are in exactly the same ratio as 6 and 250. The number of spindle speeds being 18, follow the horizontal line from the figure 18 in the left-hand column of the table, until reaching the number nearest to 24, the number in this case being 22.5 in the 20 per cent column. The figures in this column, divided by 4, will give the range of the speeds desired, these speeds being as follows:

Range of Speeds

250	128	65.5	33.5	17.17	8.8
200	102.5	52.5	26.75	13.7	7.04
160	82	42	21.5	11	5.62

The speed ratio for the first back-gears is obtained by dividing 250, the fastest open belt speed, by 65.5, the fastest first back-gear speed; and the second back-gear ratio is found by dividing 250, the fastest open belt speed, by 17.17, the fastest second back-gear speed. These two ratios are then found to be 3.82 to 1, and 14.6 to 1, respectively. The countershaft speeds will be found to be 200 and 102.5 (the speeds of the middle cone steps), if consecutive spindle speeds are obtained by moving the belt from one step on the cone to another; but if consecutive speeds are obtained by shifting the countershaft, then this latter would be required to run at 160 and 128 R.P.M., which would then be the speeds of the middle cone steps. The diameter of the smallest cone step, if consecutive speeds are obtained by changing the countershaft speed, will equal $\frac{15 \times 160}{250} = 9.6$ inches. The diameter of the middle step would then be 12.3 inches approximately.

Table of Geometrical Progression

Ratio	Increase in Per cent	1	2	3	4	5	6	7	8	9	10	11	12
1.10	10	1	1.10	1.21	1.33	1.46	1.61	1.77	1.95	2.14	2.36	2.59	2.85
1.15	15	1	1.15	1.32	1.52	1.75	2.01	2.31	2.66	3.06	3.52	4.05	4.65
1.20	20	1	1.20	1.44	1.73	2.07	2.49	2.99	3.58	4.30	5.16	6.19	7.43
1.25	25	1	1.25	1.56	1.95	2.44	3.05	3.81	4.77	5.96	7.45	9.31	11.64
1.30	30	1	1.30	1.69	2.20	2.86	3.71	4.83	6.27	8.16	10.61	13.79	17.92
1.35	35	1	1.35	1.82	2.46	3.32	4.48	6.05	8.17	11.03	14.88	20.09	27.14
1.40	40	1	1.40	1.96	2.74	3.84	5.38	7.53	10.54	14.76	20.66	28.93	40.50
1.45	45	1	1.45	2.10	3.05	4.42	6.41	9.29	13.48	19.54	28.33	41.09	59.57
1.50	50	1	1.50	2.25	3.38	5.06	7.59	11.39	17.09	25.63	38.44	57.67	86.50
1.55	55	1	1.55	2.40	3.72	5.77	8.95	13.87	21.49	33.32	51.64	80.04	124.10
1.60	60	1	1.60	2.56	4.10	6.55	10.49	16.78	26.84	42.95	68.72	110.00	
1.65	65	1	1.65	2.72	4.49	7.41	12.23	20.18	33.30	54.94	90.65	149.60	
1.70	70	1	1.70	2.89	4.91	8.35	14.20	24.14	41.03	69.75	118.60		
1.75	75	1	1.75	3.06	5.36	9.38	16.41	28.72	50.27	87.96	153.90		
1.80	80	1	1.80	3.24	5.83	10.50	18.90	34.01	61.22	110.20			
1.85	85	1	1.85	3.42	6.33	11.71	21.67	40.09	74.17	137.20			
1.90	90	1	1.90	3.61	6.86	13.03	24.76	47.05	89.39	169.80			
1.95	95	1	1.95	3.80	7.41	14.46	28.20	54.98	107.20				
2.00	100	1	2.00	4.00	8.00	16.00	32.00	64.00	128.00				

Ratio	Per cent	13	14	15	16	17	18	19	20	21	22	23	24
1.10	10	3.14	3.45	3.80	4.18	4.60	5.05	5.56	6.11	6.73	7.40	8.14	8.95
1.15	15	5.35	6.15	7.08	8.14	9.36	10.76	12.38	14.23	16.37	18.82	21.65	24.89
1.20	20	8.92	10.70	12.84	15.41	18.49	22.19	26.62	31.95	38.34	46.01	55.21	66.25
1.25	25	14.55	18.19	22.74	28.42	35.53	44.41	55.51	69.39	86.74	108.40		
1.30	30	23.30	30.29	39.37	51.19	66.54	86.50	112.50					
1.35	35	36.64	49.47	66.78	90.37	121.70							
1.40	40	56.69	79.37	111.10									
1.45	45	86.38	125.30										
1.50	50	129.80											

Geometrical Progressions for Spindle Speeds. (See page 884.)

Percentage of Decrease of Consecutive Speeds

Number of Speed Changes Required	15	16	17	18	19	20	22	24	25	26	28	30	32	34	36	38	40	44	48	50
1	1000	1000	1000	1000	1000	1000	1000	1000	1000	1000	1000	1000	1000	1000	1000	1000	1000	1000	1000	1000
2	850	840	830	820	810	800	780	760	750	740	720	700	680	660	640	620	600	560	520	500
3	722	706	689	672	656	640	608	578	562	548	518	490	462	436	410	385	360	314	270	250
4	614	593	572	551	531	512	474	439	421	405	373	343	315	288	263	238	216	176	141	125
5	522	498	474	452	430	410	370	333	316	300	269	240	214	190	169	148	129	98	73.3	62.5
6	444	418	394	371	349	328	289	253	237	222	193	168	146	126	108	91.7	77.5	54.8	38.2	31.2
7	377	351	327	304	282	262	225	193	178	163	139	118	99	83	69.2	56.8	46.5	30.7	19.9	15.6
8	320	295	271	249	229	210	176	146	133	121	100	82.3	68.3	54.8	44.4	35.2	27.9	17.2	10.3	7.81
9	272	248	225	204	185	168	137	111	100	89.4	72.2	57.6	46.5	36.2	28.4	21.8	16.8	9.6	5.37	3.91
10	231	208	187	167	150	134	107	84.5	75	66.1	52.4	40.3	31.5	23.8	18.2	13.5	10.0	5.38	2.8	1.95
11	197	175	155	137	121	107	83.3	64.2	56.2	48.9	37.4	28.2	21.4	15.8	11.63	8.38	6.0	3.0	1.45	0.97
12	167	147	128	113	98.4	86	65	48.8	42.2	36.2	26.9	19.8	14.5	10.4	7.46	5.2	3.6	1.68	0.75	0.47
13	142	123	107	92.4	79.7	68.7	50.7	37.1	31.6	26.8	19.4	13.8	9.85	6.9	4.78	3.22	2.16	0.94		
14	121	103	88.5	75.7	64.5	55	39.5	28.2	23.7	19.8	13.9	9.7	6.7	4.55	3.06	2.0	1.29			
15	103	87	73.4	62.1	52.3	44	30.8	21.4	17.8	14.6	10	6.8	4.55	3.0	1.96	1.24	0.77			
16	87.3	73	60.9	50.9	42.3	35.2	24	16.3	13.3	10.8	7.23	4.7	3.09	1.99	1.25	0.77				
17	74.2	61.3	50.5	41.7	34.2	28.16	18.7	12.4	10	8.0	5.21	3.32	2.1	1.32	0.8					
18	63	51.5	41.5	34.2	27.7	22.5	14.6	9.4	7.5	5.9	3.75	2.32	1.43	0.87						
19	53.6	43.2	34.8	28	22.5	18	11.4	7.14	5.6	4.4	2.7	1.63	0.97							
20	45.5	36.3	28.9	23	18.1	14.9	8.9	5.42	4.2	3.25	1.94	1.14								
21	38.7	30.5	24	18.9	14.7	11.5	6.94	4.12	3.2	2.4	1.39									
22	32.9	25.6	19.9	15.5	11.9	9.2	5.4	3.13	2.4	1.78	1.00									
23	27.9	21.5	16.5	12.7	9.6	7.37	4.22	2.38	1.8	1.31										
24	23.7	18	13.7	10.4	7.8	5.9	3.29	1.81	1.3	0.97										

Cone Pulley Design. — When designing a pair of cone pulleys for belt power transmission, it is not possible to merely design the two pulleys with equal differences between the steps, because the length of belt required on the largest and smallest steps would be different from the length required on the two middle steps. If a crossed belt is used, all that is necessary is that the sum of the diameters of any pair of steps shall be equal to the sum of the diameters of any other pair of steps, but when an open belt is used, as is usually the case, the sum of the diameters of the steps at or near the middle of the cones must be somewhat greater than the sum of the diameters of the steps at or near the ends. The following method (Transactions of the American Society of Mechanical Engineers, Volume X, page 269) will be found a close approximation for determining the sizes of the steps of cone pulleys:

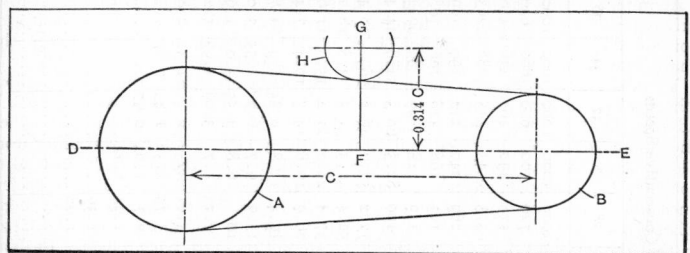

Let distance C be the distance between the centers of the shafts (see illustration) and draw circles A and B to represent a known pair of steps on the cones; at a point midway between the shaft centers erect a perpendicular FG. Then with a center on FG located at a distance from center-line DE equal to 0.314 × C, draw a circular arc H tangent to the belt line of the given pair of steps. The belt line of any other pair of steps should also be tangent to this arc.

Should the angle which the belt makes with the center-line DE exceed 18 degrees, a slight modification is made as follows: Draw a line tangent to the arc H at an angle of 18 degrees with DE, and with a center on FG, located at a distance from line DE equal to 0.298 × C, draw an arc tangent to this 18-degree line. All belt lines which make an angle with DE greater than 18 degrees should be made tangent to this new arc.

In all cases, 0.8 of the thickness of the belt should be subtracted from the diameters of the pulleys found by the graphical method, in order to obtain the actual diameter of the pulley. This is done because the length of the belt drawn tight around the pulleys is longer than the length of a tape line measured around them.

Length of Belt on Pulleys. — The following formula is given by Rankin for the length of belt required to pass over two pulleys:

$$\text{Length of belt} = 2\,C + \frac{11\,D + 11\,d}{7} + \frac{(D - d)^2}{4\,C}$$

in which

C = center distance between pulleys;
D = diameter of large pulley;
d = diameter of small pulley.

This formula, while not theoretically correct, is accurate enough for all practical purposes, and may be used as a check for cone pulley diameters; by means of this formula it can quickly be determined if the belt length is approximately correct for the various steps, as determined by a graphical method.

CHAIN TRANSMISSION

Chain drives are especially applicable when the distance between the driving and driven shafts is too short for belting and too long for gearing. The chain drive is positive, compact, and without the initial tension required for a belt drive. Chain drives frequently are substituted for belting when the driving and driven shafts are comparatively close, and, if correctly installed, the chain system of transmission is much more durable than belting. The initial cost is somewhat higher, but for many classes of service this extra cost amounts to little when compared with the effectiveness of the chain drive. A chain drive is more efficient than a belt drive, and a uniform turning movement is obtained. The chain may, in some cases, reduce impulses from the driving end. The slip which often occurs with non-positive drives seriously affects the uniformity of driving, in many cases. Frequently, a considerable saving in space may be effected, because the distance between the shafts may be much less with a chain than with a belt drive.

Various forms or types of chains have been developed for power transmission. The *block chain*, which consists of steel blocks connected by side links or plates, is adapted for light machine drives. The double width or twin type is used when the amount of power to be transmitted is relatively high. *Roller chains* differ from block chains in that bushings and rollers are inserted between the links instead of solid blocks. Roller chains are stronger than block chains and are used in preference when the speeds and amount of power to be transmitted are relatively high. The *bushing chain* resembles a roller chain somewhat, but differs from the latter in that the bushings between the side links are not provided with rollers. Bushing chains are used when considerable power is to be transmitted at relatively low speeds.

Number of Teeth in Sprockets. — The number of teeth in chain sprockets should be as large as is consistent with other conditions. A large number of teeth will reduce the noise, the wear of the chain on the sprockets, and the loss of energy from friction. The best results are obtained with sprockets having 16 teeth or more. Eight- or nine-tooth sprockets will almost invariably ruin a roller chain, and those having ten or eleven teeth are adapted for only medium and slow speeds, with other conditions favorable. The ratio between the driven and the driving sprocket should not be over 1 to 8 for block chains of the bicycle type, nor over 1 to 5 for roller chains of ¾-inch pitch and larger.

Chain Pitch and Sprocket Speed. — The maximum speed of the smaller sprocket should be considered when determining the pitch of the chain. A higher sprocket speed is allowable with a chain of short pitch than with a long pitch chain. Some chain manufacturers recommend maximum chain speeds of 1000 to 1200 feet per minute for roller chains and 700 to 800 feet per minute for block chains, but according to the Diamond Chain & Mfg. Co., if the conditions regarding sprocket speed and chain pull are favorable, chains may be run much faster than the maximum speeds which are based on chain speeds only. In fact, it is claimed that roller chains will operate under loads of from 1 to 150 horsepower at speeds up to 4000 feet per minute. A long series of observations and experiments demonstrated that the chain speed alone has very little to do with the destructive action between the chain and sprocket, but high sprocket speed combined with long pitch was found to be very destructive as well as noisy, because of the impact between the chain link and sprocket as the roller seats itself. The force of this impact increases in proportion to the weight of the chain and the square of the velocity with which the roller strikes the sprocket.

Table 1 gives the recommended maximum sprocket R.P.M. for various sprocket tooth numbers and chain pitches. These maximum R.P.M. apply also to idler sprockets.

Table 1. — Recommended Maximum R.P.M. of Sprockets
For American Standard Roller Chain

No. of Teeth	Chain No.						
	25	35	41	40	50	60	80
	Pitch						
	¼	⅜	½	½	⅝	¾	1
	Sprocket R.P.M.						
11	4310	2260	1020	1690	1220	920	525
12	4960	2590	1170	1940	1400	1050	670
13	5540	2900	1310	2180	1570	1180	750
14	6070	3170	1430	2380	1720	1290	820
15	6530	3420	1540	2560	1850	1390	880
16	6940	3630	1630	2720	1960	1480	935
17	7290	3810	1720	2860	2060	1550	985
18	7590	3970	1790	2980	2150	1610	1020
19	7840	4100	1850	3080	2220	1670	1060
20	8050	4210	1890	3160	2280	1720	1090
21	8230	4300	1940	3230	2330	1750	1110
22	8370	4380	1970	3290	2370	1780	1130
23	8480	4430	2000	3330	2400	1800	1150
24	8560	4480	2020	3360	2420	1820	1160
25	8610	4510	2030	3380	2440	1830	1160
30	8580	4490	2020	3370	2430	1830	1160
35	8200	4290	1930	3220	2320	1740	1110
40	7580	3970	1780	2970	2140	1610	1020
45	6820	3570	1600	2670	1930	1450	920
50	5950	3110	1400	2330	1680	1270	805
55	5010	2620	1180	1970	1420	1070	675
60	4020	2100	950	1580	1140	860	545

No. of Teeth	Chain No.						
	100	120	140	160	180	200	240
	Pitch						
	1¼	1½	1¾	2	2¼	2½	3
	Sprocket R.P.M.						
11	415	325	235	200	165	145	110
12	475	375	270	230	190	165	125
13	535	415	305	260	215	185	140
14	585	455	335	280	235	205	155
15	630	490	360	305	255	220	165
16	670	520	380	325	270	235	175
17	700	550	400	340	285	245	185
18	730	570	415	355	295	255	195
19	755	590	430	365	305	265	200
20	775	605	440	375	315	270	205
21	790	620	450	385	320	280	210
22	805	630	460	390	325	280	215
23	815	640	465	395	330	285	215
24	825	645	470	400	330	290	220
25	830	650	475	400	335	290	220
30	825	645	470	400	335	290	220
35	790	615	450	380	320	275	210
40	730	570	415	355	295	255	195
45	655	515	375	320	265	230	175
50	575	450	325	275	230	200	150
55	480	375	275	235	195	170	125
60	390	305	220	185	155	135	100

Horsepower Ratings for Roller Chain Drives. — The horsepower ratings shown in Table 2 are for American Standard single strand roller chain drives with two sprockets and have been established on a basis of approximately 15,000 hours life expectancy under optimum drive conditions and a service factor of 1.0.

Lubrication: A good grade of mineral oil, without additives, of medium or light consistency, free flowing at the prevailing temperature, should be used. The choice of type of lubrication is governed by the chain speed: up to 600 feet per minute use Type 1; from 600 to 1500 feet per minute use Type 2; 1500 feet per minute and above use Type 3 as described in Table 2. Heavy oils and greases are not recommended for roller chain lubrication except under unusual conditions of service.

Center distance between sprockets should be such as to provide approximately 135 degrees minimum arc of meshing of chain on the smaller sprocket. Means for adjustment of center distance is recommended, especially if there is load fluctuation or if sprockets are on vertical centers.

Alignment of shafting and sprocket tooth faces must be such as to provide distribution of the load across the entire chain width.

Table 2. — Horsepower Ratings for Roller Chain Drives

The ratings given are for a service factor of 1.0, which is for a uniform load and a 10-hour service day. For uniform load and a 24-hour service day, multiply the load by 1.2 to find what chain capacity is required; for moderate shock loads, multiply the load by 1.2 for a 10-hour service day and by 1.4 for a 24-hour service day; for heavy shock loads multiply the load by 1.4 for a 10-hour service day and by 1.7 for a 24-hour service day. These ratings are directly applicable only if the sprockets are on parallel, horizontal shafts.

For drives with multiple strand chain, multiply ratings shown by number of strands.

Lubrication. — The horsepower ratings listed in this table are divided into three sections for each pitch by heavy zigzag lines. For drives in the left-hand section use Type 1 lubrication; for drives in the center section use Type 2; for those in the right-hand section use Type 3.

Type 1: Drip (4 to 10 drops per minute), shallow bath, or manual with oil applied frequently with a brush or spout can to upper edges of all link plates in the lower span of chain.

Type 2: Rapid drip (20 drops per minute minimum) or continuous with shallow bath, disc or slinger.

Type 3: Continuous, with disc, slinger or circulating pump.

⅜-inch Pitch Standard Single Strand Roller Chain — No. 35

No. of Teeth Small Sprkt.	Revolutions per Minute — Small Sprocket										
	100	200	300	400	600	800	1000	1400	1800	2200	2800
	Horsepower Rating										
11	.165	.303	.426	.54	.74	.89	1.03	1.23	1.37	1.41	....
13	.198	.369	.523	.66	.92	1.13	1.31	1.61	1.83	1.96	2.07
15	.232	.432	.614	.78	1.08	1.35	1.59	1.96	2.25	2.46	2.65
17	.264	.494	.705	.90	1.25	1.56	1.83	2.29	2.65	2.92	3.20
19	.296	.556	.794	1.01	1.41	1.76	2.07	2.61	3.01	3.34	3.66
21	.328	.614	.879	1.12	1.56	1.95	2.30	2.89	3.35	3.71	4.08
23	.359	.673	.961	1.23	1.71	2.14	2.51	3.16	3.67	4.06	4.45
25	.389	.730	1.04	1.33	1.86	2.31	2.72	3.42	3.97	4.39	4.82
30	.465	.870	1.24	1.58	2.19	2.74	3.22	4.03	4.64	5.09	5.55
35	.540	1.01	1.43	1.82	2.52	3.13	3.67	4.55	5.21	5.69	6.10
40	.613	1.14	1.60	2.05	2.83	3.50	4.08	5.02	5.70	6.11	6.51
45	.684	1.27	1.79	2.27	3.12	3.84	4.46	5.45	6.12	6.56	6.78
50	.754	1.40	1.96	2.48	3.40	4.17	4.80	5.83	6.48	6.84	6.89

Table 2 (*Continued*). Horsepower Ratings for Roller Chain Drives

½-inch Pitch Standard Single Strand Roller Chain — No. 40

No. of Teeth Small Sprkt.	Revolutions per Minute — Small Sprocket										
	100	200	300	400	500	600	800	1000	1400	1800	2200
	Horsepower Rating										
11	.379	.687	.958	1.19	1.41	1.59	1.89	2.14	2.44	....	....
13	.458	.842	1.18	1.48	1.76	2.00	2.44	2.79	3.31	3.59	....
15	.535	.989	1.39	1.76	2.09	2.40	2.93	3.38	4.08	4.52	4.75
17	.611	1.13	1.59	2.02	2.41	2.77	3.41	3.95	4.80	5.38	5.72
19	.687	1.27	1.80	2.28	2.72	3.14	3.86	4.49	5.48	6.17	6.61
21	.758	1.41	1.99	2.52	3.01	3.47	4.27	4.97	6.07	6.86	7.35
23	.829	1.54	2.18	2.76	3.30	3.79	4.68	5.42	6.64	7.49	8.04
25	.902	1.67	2.36	3.00	3.58	4.11	5.07	5.90	7.19	8.10	8.67
30	1.08	1.99	2.81	3.56	4.24	4.86	5.95	6.93	8.40	9.38	9.95
35	1.25	2.30	3.24	4.09	4.86	5.56	6.86	7.86	9.42	10.4	10.9
40	1.41	2.60	3.65	4.59	5.44	6.22	7.57	8.67	10.3	11.2	11.6
45	1.58	2.89	4.04	5.07	5.99	6.80	8.27	9.43	11.0	11.9	12.0
50	1.74	3.17	4.42	5.53	6.52	7.40	8.92	10.1	11.7	12.3	12.3

⅝-inch Pitch Standard Single Strand Roller Chain — No. 50

No. of Teeth Small Sprkt.	Revolutions per Minute — Small Sprocket										
	50	100	200	300	400	500	600	800	1000	1200	1400
	Horsepower Rating										
11	.385	.72	1.29	1.78	2.19	2.56	2.85	3.33	3.68	3.88	....
13	.467	.87	1.59	2.20	2.74	3.23	3.65	4.36	4.91	5.30	5.57
15	.544	1.02	1.87	2.61	3.27	3.86	4.39	5.31	6.02	6.57	7.00
17	.620	1.16	2.14	2.99	3.77	4.46	5.09	6.17	7.05	7.75	8.31
19	.696	1.31	2.41	3.39	4.25	5.05	5.76	7.00	8.04	8.87	9.52
21	.769	1.45	2.66	3.75	4.70	5.59	6.38	7.77	8.90	9.84	10.6
23	.842	1.58	2.91	4.09	5.16	6.12	6.98	8.50	9.74	10.8	11.6
25	.914	1.72	3.17	4.45	5.59	6.62	7.58	9.20	10.6	11.6	12.5
30	1.09	2.06	3.77	5.28	6.63	7.84	8.93	10.8	12.4	13.6	14.5
35	1.27	2.38	4.35	6.07	7.59	8.96	10.2	12.3	13.9	15.2	16.1
40	1.44	2.70	4.91	6.82	8.51	10.0	11.3	13.6	15.3	16.6	17.5
45	1.61	3.01	5.44	7.54	9.37	11.0	12.4	14.7	16.5	17.7	18.5
50	1.78	3.31	5.86	8.22	10.2	11.9	13.4	15.8	17.5	18.6	19.0

¾-inch Pitch Standard Single Strand Roller Chain — No. 60

No. of Teeth Small Sprkt.	Revolutions per Minute — Small Sprocket										
	50	100	150	200	300	400	500	700	900	1100	1300
	Horsepower Rating										
11	.66	1.21	1.70	2.15	2.93	3.58	4.12	4.93	5.41	....	....
13	.79	1.48	2.09	2.65	3.65	4.52	5.27	6.46	7.32	7.88	....
15	.92	1.72	2.45	3.14	4.34	5.39	6.32	7.86	9.01	9.85	10.4
17	1.05	1.97	2.82	3.59	4.98	6.22	7.32	9.14	10.6	11.6	12.4
19	1.18	2.23	3.17	4.05	5.62	7.03	8.29	10.4	12.1	13.4	14.3
21	1.31	2.46	3.51	4.49	6.24	7.80	9.19	11.6	13.4	14.8	15.9
23	1.44	2.69	3.83	4.90	6.83	8.53	10.1	12.6	14.7	16.2	17.4
25	1.56	2.92	4.17	5.32	7.41	9.27	10.9	13.7	15.9	17.5	18.8
30	1.86	3.48	4.96	6.32	8.78	10.9	12.8	16.0	18.5	20.4	21.7
35	2.16	4.03	5.73	7.29	10.1	12.5	14.7	18.2	20.8	22.7	24.0
40	2.45	4.55	6.46	8.20	11.3	14.0	16.3	20.1	22.8	24.6	25.3
45	2.73	5.07	7.18	9.10	12.5	15.4	17.9	21.8	24.5	26.2	27.0
50	3.02	5.59	7.87	9.94	13.6	16.7	19.3	23.3	25.9	27.4	....

Table 2 (*Continued*). Horsepower Ratings for Roller Chain Drives

1-inch Pitch Standard Single Strand Roller Chain — No. 80

No. of Teeth Small Sprkt.	Revolutions per Minute — Small Sprocket										
	50	100	150	200	250	300	400	500	600	700	800
	Horsepower Rating										
11	1.52	2.76	3.83	4.78	5.62	6.36	7.60	8.56	....	....	....
13	1.83	3.36	4.72	5.93	7.03	8.03	9.75	11.2	12.3	13.2	....
15	2.14	3.95	5.57	7.03	8.37	9.59	11.8	13.6	15.1	16.3	17.3
17	2.44	4.52	6.39	8.09	9.65	11.1	13.6	15.8	17.6	19.2	20.5
19	2.74	5.09	7.20	9.13	10.9	12.5	15.4	17.9	20.1	21.9	23.4
21	3.03	5.62	7.96	10.1	12.1	13.9	17.1	19.9	22.3	24.3	26.0
23	3.32	6.16	8.72	11.0	13.2	15.2	18.7	21.8	24.4	26.6	28.4
25	3.61	6.69	9.45	12.0	14.3	16.4	20.3	23.6	26.4	28.8	30.8
30	4.30	7.96	11.2	14.2	17.0	19.5	23.9	27.7	30.9	33.6	35.8
35	4.99	9.20	13.0	16.4	19.4	22.3	27.2	31.4	34.9	37.7	40.0
40	5.65	10.4	14.6	18.4	21.8	24.9	30.3	34.7	38.4	41.2	43.5
45	6.31	11.6	16.2	20.3	24.0	27.3	33.1	37.7	41.4	44.2	46.2
50	6.95	12.7	17.7	22.1	26.1	29.6	35.6	40.4	44.0	46.7	48.3

1¼-inch Pitch Standard Single Strand Roller Chain — No. 100

No. of Teeth Small Sprkt.	Revolutions per Minute — Small Sprocket										
	25	50	75	100	125	150	200	300	400	500	600
	Horsepower Rating										
11	1.56	2.88	4.08	5.19	6.18	7.10	8.78	11.4	13.6	....	....
13	1.87	3.52	4.98	6.35	7.61	8.82	10.9	14.6	17.6	19.6	....
15	2.19	4.10	5.85	7.48	8.99	10.5	13.1	17.5	21.3	24.0	26.3
17	2.49	4.67	6.68	8.56	10.3	12.0	15.1	20.3	25.0	28.2	30.9
19	2.79	5.24	7.52	9.64	11.6	13.6	17.0	23.0	28.3	32.2	35.4
21	3.08	5.80	8.23	10.7	12.9	15.0	18.9	25.5	31.4	35.7	39.3
23	3.38	6.36	9.09	11.7	14.2	16.4	20.6	28.0	34.0	39.0	43.1
25	3.66	6.90	9.88	12.7	15.3	17.7	22.4	30.3	36.8	42.2	46.4
30	4.38	8.22	11.8	15.1	18.2	21.1	26.5	35.7	43.2	49.3	54.2
35	5.09	9.53	13.6	17.4	20.9	24.3	30.4	40.8	49.0	55.6	60.7
40	5.77	10.8	15.4	19.6	23.6	27.3	34.0	44.3	54.2	61.0	66.3
45	6.45	12.0	17.1	21.8	26.1	30.2	37.4	49.3	58.8	65.8	70.7
50	7.22	13.2	18.8	23.8	28.6	33.0	40.7	53.6	63.0	70.2	74.2

1½-inch Pitch Standard Single Strand Roller Chain — No. 120

No. of Teeth Small Sprkt.	Revolutions per Minute — Small Sprocket										
	25	50	75	100	125	150	175	200	250	300	400
	Horsepower Rating										
11	2.63	4.85	6.83	8.61	10.2	11.6	13.1	14.3	16.5	18.2	....
13	3.17	5.90	8.36	10.6	12.7	14.6	16.4	18.1	21.0	23.6	27.7
15	3.71	6.93	9.84	12.5	15.0	17.3	19.6	21.6	25.3	28.6	33.9
17	4.23	7.91	11.3	14.4	17.3	19.9	22.6	24.9	29.3	33.2	39.7
19	4.74	8.90	12.7	16.2	19.5	22.6	25.5	28.2	33.2	37.6	45.2
21	5.24	9.85	14.0	17.9	21.6	24.9	28.2	31.2	36.8	41.7	50.0
23	5.74	10.8	15.4	19.6	23.6	27.3	30.8	34.2	40.2	45.7	54.8
25	6.26	11.7	16.7	21.3	25.6	29.7	33.5	37.1	43.6	49.5	59.5
30	7.44	13.9	19.8	25.3	30.4	35.2	39.6	43.8	51.4	58.3	69.5
35	8.64	16.1	22.9	29.1	34.9	40.3	45.3	50.1	58.6	66.2	78.3
40	9.80	18.2	25.8	32.8	39.3	45.2	50.8	56.0	65.3	73.4	86.1
45	10.9	20.3	28.7	36.4	43.3	49.9	55.9	61.5	71.5	79.9	93.2
50	12.1	22.3	31.5	39.8	47.4	54.3	60.8	66.6	77.1	85.8	99.2

Table 2 (Continued). Horsepower Ratings for Roller Chain Drives

1¾-inch Pitch Standard Single Strand Roller Chain — No. 140

No. of Teeth Small Sprkt.	Revolutions per Minute — Small Sprocket										
	10	25	50	75	100	125	150	200	250	300	350
	Horsepower Rating										
11	1.79	4.12	7.55	10.6	13.3	15.7	17.8	21.5	....	....	....
13	2.13	5.07	9.19	13.0	16.3	19.5	22.3	27.3	31.6	35.2	....
15	2.48	5.94	10.8	15.2	19.3	23.1	26.6	32.8	38.2	42.8	46.7
17	2.83	6.77	12.3	17.5	22.2	26.6	30.6	38.0	44.3	49.9	54.7
19	3.17	7.60	13.9	19.7	25.1	30.0	34.7	43.0	50.3	56.7	62.3
21	3.49	8.40	15.3	21.7	27.7	33.2	38.4	47.6	55.7	62.8	69.0
23	3.83	9.18	16.8	23.9	30.3	36.4	42.0	52.1	61.0	68.7	75.5
25	4.17	10.4	18.2	25.9	32.9	39.4	45.5	56.5	66.1	74.5	81.7
30	4.98	11.9	21.7	30.8	39.1	46.8	53.9	66.7	77.8	87.3	95.7
35	5.78	13.8	25.0	35.5	44.9	53.7	61.8	76.1	88.4	98.9	108
40	6.58	15.7	28.3	40.0	50.6	60.3	69.1	84.9	98.2	109	118
45	7.36	17.5	31.6	44.4	56.0	66.5	76.2	92.9	107	112	127
50	8.14	19.2	34.7	48.7	61.1	72.4	82.7	100	115	125	....

2-inch Pitch Standard Single Strand Roller Chain — No. 160

No. of Teeth Small Sprkt.	Revolutions per Minute — Small Sprocket										
	10	20	40	60	80	100	120	140	180	220	260
	Horsepower Rating										
11	2.64	4.97	9.14	12.8	16.1	19.1	21.9	24.3	28.6	....	....
13	3.16	6.00	11.1	15.7	19.9	23.7	27.2	30.5	36.4	41.4	....
15	3.67	6.99	13.0	18.4	23.5	28.1	32.4	36.4	43.7	50.0	55.5
17	4.18	7.97	14.9	21.1	27.0	32.4	37.4	42.0	50.6	58.1	64.8
19	4.69	8.95	16.7	23.9	30.4	36.4	42.0	47.6	57.2	65.8	73.6
21	5.19	9.88	18.5	26.4	33.6	40.4	46.7	52.6	63.4	73.1	81.5
23	5.68	10.8	20.3	28.9	36.8	44.2	51.2	57.7	69.4	80.0	89.3
25	6.17	11.8	22.0	31.3	40.0	47.9	55.4	62.5	75.3	86.7	96.6
30	7.38	14.0	26.2	37.3	47.4	56.9	65.7	73.9	88.9	102	114
35	8.57	16.3	30.3	42.9	54.6	65.4	75.4	84.6	101	116	128
40	9.74	18.5	34.3	48.5	61.5	73.5	84.5	94.8	113	129	142
45	10.9	20.6	38.2	53.8	68.1	81.2	93.1	104	124	140	154
50	12.0	22.8	42.0	59.0	74.5	88.5	101	113	133	150	164

2½-inch Pitch Standard Single Strand Roller Chain — No. 200

No. of Teeth Small Sprkt.	Revolutions per Minute — Small Sprocket										
	10	20	30	40	50	60	80	100	120	160	200
	Horsepower Rating										
11	5.06	9.46	13.4	17.2	20.6	23.9	29.8	35.1	39.7	....	....
13	6.08	11.4	16.5	21.0	25.4	29.5	37.1	44.0	50.3	60.9	....
15	7.08	13.4	19.3	24.7	29.9	34.8	43.9	52.2	59.8	73.4	84.7
17	8.06	15.3	22.0	28.3	34.2	39.9	50.5	60.2	69.1	85.1	98.8
19	9.05	17.1	24.7	31.8	38.5	45.0	57.0	68.2	78.2	96.4	112
21	9.99	18.9	27.3	35.1	42.6	49.7	63.1	75.3	86.6	107	124
23	10.9	20.7	29.9	38.5	46.7	54.5	69.0	82.4	94.9	117	136
25	11.8	22.5	32.5	41.8	50.7	59.1	74.9	89.6	103	127	147
30	14.2	26.9	38.7	49.8	60.3	70.3	88.8	106	122	149	173
35	16.4	31.2	44.8	57.5	69.5	80.9	102	122	139	170	196
40	18.7	35.3	50.6	64.9	78.4	91.0	115	136	156	189	214
45	20.9	39.4	56.4	72.2	87.0	101	127	150	171	207	237
50	23.1	43.4	62.0	79.2	95.3	110	138	163	185	223	....

Revised Standard Roller Chains, Sprockets, and Cutters. — The roller chains and sprockets in this standard are those commonly used for the transmission of power in industrial machinery, machine tools, motor trucks, motorcycles and tractors and similar applications. This standard has been adopted by the Association of Roller and Silent Chain Manufacturers.

Standard Chain Nomenclature, Dimensions and Loads. — Standard nomenclature for roller chain parts are given in Table 3. Dimensions for Standard Series roller chain are given in Table 4.

Tolerances for Chain Length: New chains subjected to the standard measuring load are allowed an over-length of $\frac{1}{64}$ inch per foot, but must not be under-length.

The *Measuring Load* is the load under which a chain should be measured for length. It is equal to $125 \times (\text{Pitch})^2$, with a minimum of 18 pounds.

Minimum Ultimate Tensile Strength of Standard Series chain is equal to $12,500 \times (\text{Pitch})^2$.

Standard Chain Numbers. — The right-hand figure in the chain number is zero for roller chains of the usual proportions, 1 for a light-weight chain and 5 for a rollerless bushing chain. The numbers to the left of the right-hand figure denote the number of $\frac{1}{8}$ inches in the pitch. The letter H following the chain number denotes the heavy series; thus the number $80H$ denotes a 1-inch pitch heavy chain. The hyphenated number 2 suffixed to the chain number denotes a double strand, 3 a triple strand, 4 a quadruple strand chain and so on.

Heavy Series: These chains, made in $\frac{3}{4}$-inch and larger pitches, have thicker link plates than those of the regular standard. Their value is only in the acceptance of higher tensile or jerk loads at low speeds. The rollers, bushing diameters, pin diameters, and widths are the same as in the standard series.

Light-weight Machinery Chain: This chain is designated as No. 41. It is $\frac{1}{2}$ inch pitch; $\frac{1}{4}$ inch wide; has 0.306-inch diameter rollers; 0.141-inch pin diameter; and side plates 0.050 inch thick. The measuring load is 18 pounds.

Multiple-width Chains: The standard thickness of the center plates in these chains is equivalent to two thicknesses of the inside plates used on the roller links.

Types of Sprockets. — Four different designs or types of roller-chain sprockets are shown by the sectional views, Fig. 1. Type A is a plain plate; type B has a hub on one side only; type C, a hub on both sides; and type D, a detachable hub.

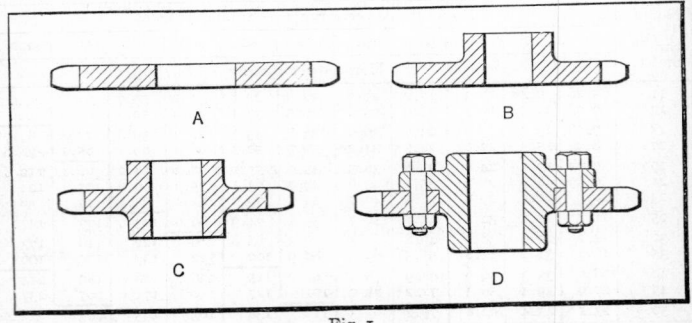

A

B

C

D

Fig. 1

Table 3. — American Standard Nomenclature for Roller Chain Parts

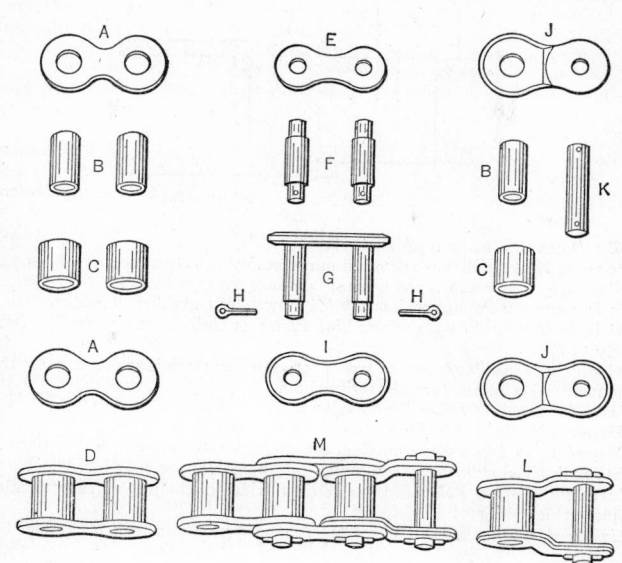

Roller Link D. — An inside link consisting of two inside plates, two bushings, and two rollers.

Pin Link G and E. — An outside link consisting of two pin-link plates assembled with two pins.

Inside Plate A. — One of the plates forming the tension members of a roller link.

Pin Link Plate E. — One of the plates forming the tension members of a pin link.

Pin F. — A stud articulating within a bushing of an inside link and secured at its ends by the pin-link plates.

Bushing B. — A cylindrical bearing in which the pin turns.

Roller C. — A ring or thimble which turns over a bushing.

Assembled Pins G. — Two pins assembled with one pin-link plate.

Connecting-Link G and I. — A pin link having one side plate detachable.

Connecting-Link Plate I. — The detachable pin-link plate belonging to a connecting link.

Offset Link L. — A link consisting of two offset plates assembled with a bushing and roller at one end and an offset link pin at the other.

Offset Plate J. — One of the plates forming the tension members of the offset link.

Offset Link Pin K. — A pin used in offset links.

Table 4. — Standard Roller Chain Dimensions

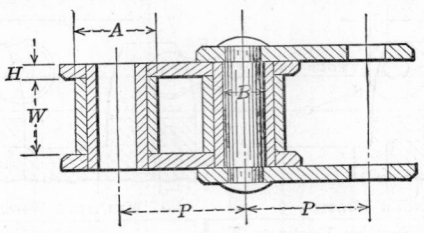

Roller Diameters A are approximately ⅝ *P*.

The *width W* is defined as the minimum distance between the link plates. In the wide series the width is the nearest common fraction to ⅝ *P*.

Pin Diameters B are approximately ⁵⁄₁₆ *P* or ½ of the roller diameter.

Thickness H of Inside and Outside Link Plates for the standard series is approximately ⅛ *P*.

Thickness of Link Plates for the heavy series of any pitch is approximately that of the next larger pitch standard series chain.

Maximum Width of Roller Link Plates = 0.95 Pitch.

Maximum Width of Pin Link Plates = 0.82 Pitch.

Maximum Pin Diameter = nominal pin diameter + 0.0005 inch.

Minimum Hole in Bushing = nominal pin diameter + 0.0015 inch.

Maximum Width of Roller Link = nominal width of chain + (2.12 × nominal link plate thickness.)

Minimum Distance between Pin Link Plates = maximum width of roller link + 0.002 inch.

| Pitch P | Max. Roller Diameter A | Standard Series | | | | | Heavy Series |
		Standard Chain No.	Width W	Pin Diameter B	Thickness of Link Plates H	Measuring Load, Lb.	Thickness of Link Plates H
¼	*0.130	25	⅛	0.0905	0.030	18	.....
⅜	*0.200	35	³⁄₁₆	0.141	0.050	18	.....
½	⁵⁄₁₆	40	⁵⁄₁₆	0.156	0.060	31	.....
⅝	0.400	50	⅜	0.200	0.080	49	.....
¾	15⁄32	60	½	0.234	0.094	70	0.125
1	⅝	80	⅝	0.312	0.125	125	0.156
1¼	¾	100	¾	0.375	0.156	195	0.187
1½	⅞	120	1	0.437	0.187	281	0.219
1¾	1	140	1	0.500	0.219	383	0.250
2	1⅛	160	1¼	0.562	0.250	500	0.281
2¼	1¹³⁄32	180	1¹³⁄32	0.687	0.281	633	0.375
2½	1⁹⁄₁₆	200	1½	0.781	0.312	781	0.375
3	1⅞	240	1⅞	0.937	0.375	1125	0.500

* This size chain has no rollers.

Table 5. — Standard Roller-Chain Sprocket Tooth Sections

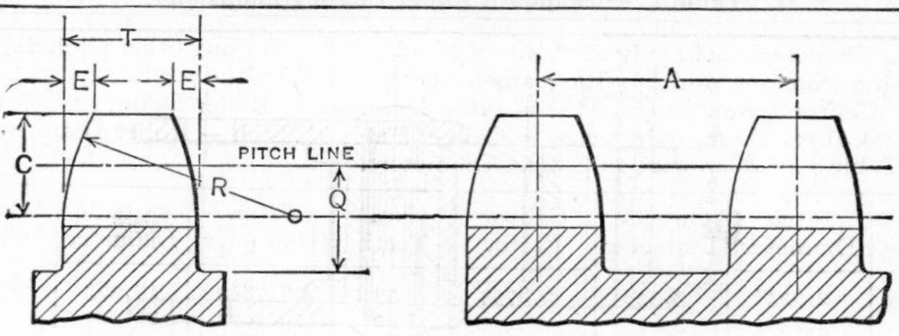

SINGLE WIDTH MULTIPLE WIDTH

Width of Chain W	Max. Sprocket Thickness (T) Single Strand	Double, Triple Strand	4 Strand and Over	Pitch P	Sprocket Chamfer Depth of Chamfer C	Width of Chamfer E	Minimum Radius R
1/8	0.110	0.107	0.096	1/4	1/8	1/32	0.265
3/16	0.168	0.162	0.149	3/8	3/16	3/64	0.398
1/4	0.227	.....	.....	1/2	1/4	1/16	0.531
5/16	0.284	0.275	0.256	5/8	5/16	5/64	0.664
3/8	0.343	0.332	0.311	3/4	3/8	3/32	0.796
1/2	0.459	0.444	0.418	1	1/2	1/8	1.062
5/8	0.575	0.557	0.526	1 1/4	5/8	5/32	1.327
3/4	0.692	0.669	0.633	1 1/2	3/4	3/16	1.593
1	0.924	0.894	0.848	1 3/4	7/8	7/32	1.858
1 1/4	1.156	1.119	1.063	2	1	1/4	2.124
1 13/32	1.301	1.259	1.197	2 1/4	1 1/8	9/32	2.392
1 1/2	1.389	1.344	1.278	2 1/2	1 1/4	5/16	2.654
1 7/8	1.738	1.682	1.601	3	1 1/2	3/8	3.187

P = pitch of chain; W = chain width; H = nominal thickness of link plates (Table 4)

$T = 0.93W - 0.006$ inch (maximum for single-width chains)

$T = 0.90W - 0.006$ inch (maximum for double- and triple-width chains)

$T = 0.86W - 0.012$ inch (maximum for quadruple-width chains and over)

$C = 0.5P$ = depth of chamfer; $E = \frac{1}{8}P$ approximately, but not to exceed $\frac{W}{3}$

R (minimum) $= 1.063P$ = chamfer radius; Maximum fillet radius $= 0.04P$.

$A = W + 4.22H$ = transverse pitch for multiple strand chains

Minus tolerance for overall measurement across one or more flange teeth = $0.01\,W + 0.006$ in. Maximum variation in thickness of any individual flange = 1/2 tolerance for overall measurement.

Sprocket Diameters. — The sprocket pitch diameters given in Table 6 are for 1-inch pitch and are based upon the following formula in which P = pitch, N = number of teeth:

$$\text{Pitch Diameter} = P \div \sin\left(\frac{180^\circ}{N}\right)$$

The maximum hub or groove diameter MHD is found by the formula:

$$MHD = P\left(\cot\frac{180^\circ}{N} - 1\right) - 0.030 \text{ inch}$$

Table 6. — Standard Roller Chain Sprocket Diameters

These diameters apply only to chains of 1-inch pitch. For any other pitch diameter or outside diameter, multiply the diameter given below by the pitch.

Caliper Diam. (even teeth) = Pitch Diameter — Roller Diam.

Caliper Diam. (odd teeth) = Caliper factor × Pitch — Roller Diam.

See Table 7 for tolerances on Caliper Diameters.

No. Teeth	Pitch Diameter	Outside Diameter	Caliper Factor	No. Teeth	Pitch Diameter	Outside Diameter	Caliper Factor
9	2.9238	3.348	2.8794	59	18.7892	19.363	18.7825
10	3.2361	3.678		60	19.1073	19.681	
11	3.5495	4.006	3.5133	61	19.4255	20.000	19.4190
12	3.8637	4.332		62	19.7437	20.318	
13	4.1786	4.657	4.1481	63	20.0618	20.637	20.0556
14	4.4940	4.981		64	20.3800	20.956	
15	4.8097	5.304	4.7834	65	20.6982	21.274	20.6921
16	5.1258	5.627		66	21.0164	21.593	
17	5.4422	5.949	5.4190	67	21.3346	21.911	21.3287
18	5.7588	6.271		68	21.6528	22.230	
19	6.0755	6.593	6.0548	69	21.9710	22.548	21.9653
20	6.3924	6.914		70	22.2892	22.867	
21	6.7095	7.235	6.6907	71	22.6074	23.185	22.6018
22	7.0267	7.555		72	22.9256	23.504	
23	7.3439	7.876	7.3268	73	23.2438	23.822	23.2384
24	7.6613	8.196		74	23.5620	24.141	
25	7.9787	8.516	7.9630	75	23.8802	24.459	23.8750
26	8.2962	8.836		76	24.1984	24.778	
27	8.6138	9.156	8.5992	77	24.5166	25.096	24.5116
28	8.9314	9.475		78	24.8349	25.415	
29	9.2491	9.795	9.2355	79	25.1531	25.733	25.1481
30	9.5668	10.114		80	25.4713	26.052	
31	9.8845	10.434	9.8718	81	25.7896	26.370	25.7847
32	10.2023	10.753		82	26.1078	26.689	
33	10.5201	11.073	10.5082	83	26.4260	27.007	26.4213
34	10.8379	11.392		84	26.7443	27.326	
35	11.1558	11.711	11.1446	85	27.0625	27.644	27.0579
36	11.4737	12.030		86	27.3807	27.962	
37	11.7916	12.349	11.7810	87	27.6990	28.281	27.6945
38	12.1095	12.668		88	28.0172	28.599	
39	12.4275	12.987	12.4174	89	28.3354	28.918	28.3310
40	12.7455	13.306		90	28.6537	29.236	
41	13.0635	13.625	13.0539	91	28.9719	29.555	28.9676
42	13.3815	13.944		92	29.2902	29.873	
43	13.6995	14.263	13.6904	93	29.6084	30.192	29.6042
44	14.0175	14.582		94	29.9267	30.510	
45	14.3355	14.901	14.3269	95	30.2449	30.828	30.2408
46	14.6536	15.219		96	30.5632	31.147	
47	14.9717	15.538	14.9634	97	30.8815	31.465	30.8774
48	15.2898	15.857		98	31.1997	31.784	
49	15.6079	16.176	15.5999	99	31.5180	32.102	31.5140
50	15.9260	16.495		100	31.8362	32.421	
51	16.2441	16.813	16.2364	101	32.1545	32.739	32.1506
52	16.5622	17.132		102	32.4727	33.057	
53	16.8803	17.451	16.8729	103	32.7910	33.376	32.7872
54	17.1984	17.769		104	33.1093	33.694	
55	17.5165	18.088	17.5094	105	33.4275	34.013	33.4238
56	17.8347	18.407		106	33.7458	34.331	
57	18.1528	18.725	18.1459	107	34.0641	34.649	34.0604
58	18.4710	19.044		108	34.3823	34.968	

Outside and Bottom Diameters of Roller-Chain Sprockets. — The outside diameter may be determined by the following formula in which O = approximate outside diameter; P = pitch of chain; N = number of sprocket teeth.

$$O = P \, [0.6 + \cot (180° \div N)]$$

The base or *bottom diameter* of a roller-chain sprocket equals the pitch diameter minus the diameter of the roller. The pitch and outside diameters are given in Table 6, and the roller diameters in Table 4.

The *bottom-diameter tolerance* is minus only and equals 0.003 inch + 0.001P $\sqrt{N}$. Tolerances for different pitches and numbers of teeth are given in Table 7.

Caliper Diameter. — If a sprocket has an odd number of teeth, the modified bottom diameter for calipering the sprocket may be determined by the following formula, in which D_r = the roller diameter:

$$\text{Caliper Diameter} = \text{Pitch Diameter} \times \cos (90° \div N) - D_r$$

Table 7. — Minus Tolerances on the Bottom Diameters of Cut Sprockets

Pitch	Number of Teeth				
	Up to 16	16–24	25–35	36–48	49–63
1/4	0.004	0.004	0.004	0.005	0.005
3/8	0.004	0.004	0.004	0.005	0.005
1/2	0.004	0.005	0.0055	0.006	0.0065
5/8	0.005	0.0055	0.006	0.007	0.008
3/4	0.005	0.006	0.007	0.008	0.009
1	0.006	0.007	0.008	0.009	0.010
1 1/4	0.007	0.008	0.009	0.010	0.012
1 1/2	0.007	0.009	0.0105	0.012	0.013
1 3/4	0.008	0.010	0.012	0.013	0.015
2	0.009	0.011	0.013	0.015	0.017
2 1/4	0.010	0.012	0.014	0.016	0.018
2 1/2	0.010	0.013	0.015	0.018	0.020
3	0.012	0.015	0.018	0.021	0.024

Pitch	Number of Teeth				
	64–80	81–99	100–120	121–143	144 up
1/4	0.005	0.005	0.006	0.006	0.006
3/8	0.006	0.006	0.006	0.007	0.007
1/2	0.007	0.0075	0.008	0.0085	0.009
5/8	0.009	0.009	0.009	0.010	0.011
3/4	0.010	0.010	0.011	0.012	0.013
1	0.011	0.012	0.013	0.014	0.015
1 1/4	0.013	0.014	0.016	0.017	0.018
1 1/2	0.015	0.016	0.018	0.019	0.021
1 3/4	0.017	0.019	0.020	0.022	0.024
2	0.019	0.021	0.023	0.025	0.027
2 1/4	0.021	0.023	0.025	0.028	0.030
2 1/2	0.023	0.025	0.028	0.030	0.033
3	0.027	0.030	0.033	0.036	0.039

Center Distance between Sprockets. — The center-to-center distance between sprockets, as a general rule, should not be less than $1\frac{1}{2}$ times the diameter of the larger sprocket and not less than thirty times the pitch nor more than about 60 times the pitch, although much depends upon the speed and other conditions. If roller-chain drives are designed correctly, the center-to-center distance for some transmissions may be so short that the sprocket teeth nearly touch each other, assuming that the load is not too great and the number of teeth is not too small. To avoid interference of the sprocket teeth, the center distance must, of course, be somewhat greater than one-half the sum of the outside diameters of the sprockets. The chain should extend around at least 120 degrees of the pinion circumference, and this minimum amount of contact is obtained for all center distances provided the ratio is less than $3\frac{1}{2}$ to 1. According to the Diamond Chain & Mfg. Co., the center distance should not be less than the difference between the sprocket diameters for ratios greater than $3\frac{1}{2}$ to 1. Other things being equal, a fairly long chain is recommended in preference to the shortest one allowed by the sprocket diameters, because the rate of chain elongation due to natural wear is inversely proportional to the length, and also because the greater elasticity of the longer strand tends to absorb irregularities of motion and to decrease the effect of shocks.

If possible, the center distance should be adjustable in order to take care of slack due to elongation from wear. An adjustment equal to the pitch of the chain is sufficient. A little slack is desirable as it allows the chain links to take the best position on the sprocket teeth and reduces the wear on the bearings. Too much sag or an excessive distance between the sprockets may cause the chain to whip up and down — a condition detrimental to smooth running and very destructive to the chain. The sprockets for machine-made chain should run in a vertical plane, the sprocket axes being approximately horizontal, unless an idler is used on the slack side to keep the chain in position. The most satisfactory results are obtained when the slack side of the chain is on the bottom.

Center Distance for a Given Chain Length. — When the distance between the driving and driven sprockets can be varied to suit the length of the chain, this center distance for a tight chain may be determined by the following formula, in which C = center-to-center distance in inches; L = chain length in pitches; P = pitch of chain; N = number of teeth in large sprocket; n = number of teeth in small sprocket.

$$C = \frac{P}{8}\left[2L - N - n + \sqrt{(2L - N - n)^2 - 0.824\,(N - n)^2}\right]$$

This formula is approximate, but the error is less than the variation in the length of the best chains. The length L in pitches should be an even number for a roller chain, so that the use of an offset connecting link will not be necessary.

Idler Sprockets. — When sprockets have a fixed center distance or are non-adjustable, it may be advisable to use an idler sprocket for taking up the slack. The idler should preferably be placed against the slack side between the two strands of the chain. When a sprocket is applied to the tight side of the chain to reduce vibration, it should be on the lower side and so located that the chain will run in a straight line between the two main sprockets. A sprocket will wear excessively if the number of teeth is too small and the speed too high, because there is impact between the teeth and rollers even though the idler carries practically no load.

Length of Driving Chain. — The total length of a block chain should be given in multiples of the pitch, whereas for a roller chain, the length should be in multiples of twice the pitch, because the ends must be connected with an outside and inside link. The length of a chain can be calculated accurately enough for ordinary practice by the use of the following formula, in which C = center distance in pitches; N = number of teeth in large sprocket; n = number of teeth in small sprocket:

$$\text{Chain length in pitches} = 2C + \frac{N}{2} + \frac{n}{2} + \left(\frac{N-n}{2\pi}\right)^2 \times \frac{1}{C}$$

To the length obtained by this formula, add enough to make a whole number (and for a roller chain, an even number) of pitches. If a roller chain has an odd number of pitches, it will be necessary to use an offset connecting link.

Another formula for obtaining chain length in which D = distance between centers of shafts; R = pitch radius of large sprocket; r = pitch radius of small sprocket; N = number of teeth in large sprocket; n = number of teeth in small sprocket; P = pitch of chain and sprockets; and L = required chain length in inches, is:

$$L = \frac{180° + 2\alpha}{360°} NP + \frac{180° - 2\alpha}{360°} nP + 2D \cos\alpha; \quad \text{where} \quad \sin\alpha = \frac{R-r}{D}$$

Cutting Standard Sprocket Tooth Form. — The proportions and seating curve data for the standard sprocket tooth form for roller chain are given in Table 8. Either formed or generating types of sprocket cutters may be employed.

Space Cutters: Five cutters of this type will be required to cut from 7 teeth up for any given roller diameter. The ranges are, respectively, 7–8, 9–11, 12–17, 18–34, and 35 teeth and over. If less than 7 teeth is necessary, special cutters conforming to the required number of teeth should be used.

The regular cutters are based upon an intermediate number of teeth N_a equal to $2N_1N_2 \div (N_1 + N_2)$ in which N_1 = minimum number of teeth and N_2 = maximum number of teeth for which cutter is intended; but the topping curve radius F (see diagram in Table 9) is designed to produce pointed teeth on a sprocket of N_2 teeth with $OD = P\left(0.7 + \cot\dfrac{180}{N_2}\right)$. The values of N_a for the several cutters are, respectively, 7.47, 9.9, 14.07, 23.54, and 56. Space cutters designed for a given roller diameter D_r will cut sprockets of any pitch. The formulas and construction data for space cutter layout are given in Table 9 and recommended cutter sizes are given in Table 10.

Straddle Cutters: Two of these cutters (designated as A and B) will be required to cut from 7 teeth up for any given pitch and roller diameter. Cutter B is recommended for 17 teeth and under (or for more than 17 teeth if a low pressure angle is desired). Cutter A is recommended for 18 teeth and over (or for less than 18 teeth if a large pressure angle is desired and the arc of contact between chain and sprocket is fairly large). Formulas and data for laying out straddle cutters are given in Table 11.

Hobs: Only one hob will be required to cut any number of teeth for a given pitch and roller diameter. All hobs should be marked with pitch and roller diameter to be cut. Formulas and data for standard hob design are given in Table 12.

Fellows Cutters: These are for use on the Fellows gear shaper. Only one will be required to cut any number of teeth for a given pitch and roller diameter. The manufacturer should be referred to for information concerning the cutter form.

Sprocket Materials. — Sprockets of 25 teeth and less should preferably be of steel, 180 Brinell minimum for speeds to about 600 feet per minute. For speeds greater than 600 feet per minute, either .20 carbon steel, carburized, hardened and drawn, or .40 or higher carbon steel, heat treated and drawn are generally recommended, the hardness being between 300 and 450 Brinell. Larger sprockets may be made from unhardened steel plates, bars, castings or forgings, or cast iron, depending upon the duty imposed.

Table 8. — Standard Sprocket Tooth Form for Roller Chain

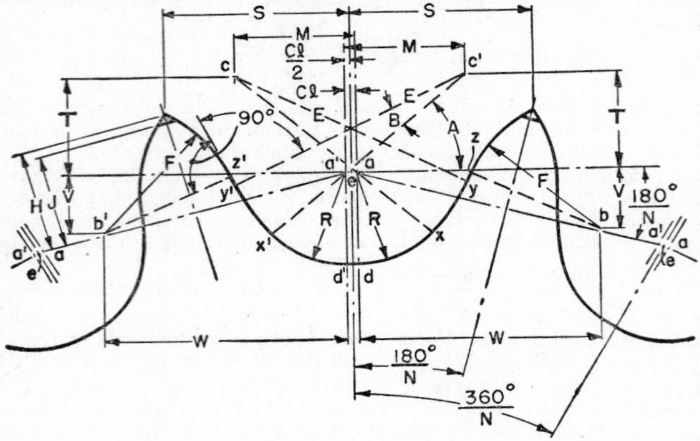

P = pitch (ee); N = number of teeth; D_r = nominal roller diameter
D_s = seating curve diameter = $1.005\ D_r + 0.003$; $R = \frac{1}{2} D_s$
Cl = pitch line clearance = $0.07\ (P - D_r) + 0.002$
D_s and Cl have only plus tolerance, which equals $0.003\ D_r + 0.005$
$A = 35° + (60° \div N)$; $B = 18° - (56° \div N)$; $ac = 0.8\ D_r$
$M = 0.8\ D_r \cos\ (35° + (60° \div N))$
$T = 0.8\ D_r \sin\ (35° + (60° \div N))$; $E = 1.3025\ D_r + 0.0015$
Chord $xy = (2.605\ D_r + 0.003) \sin\ (9° - (28° \div N))$
$yz = D_r\ [1.24 \sin\ (17° - (64° \div N)) - 0.8 \sin\ (18° - (56° \div N))]$
Length of a line between a and b = $1.24\ D_r$ (This line is parallel to ee)
Angle that line between a and b would make with horizontal = $180° \div N$
$W = 1.24\ D_r \cos\ (180° \div N)$; $V = 1.24\ D_r \sin\ (180° \div N)$
$F = D_r\ [0.8 \cos\ (18° - (56° \div N)) + 1.24 \cos\ (17° - (64° \div N)) - 1.3025] - 0.0015$
$H = \sqrt{F^2 - [1.24\ D_r - 0.5P + 0.5\ Cl \cos\ (180° \div N)]^2} + 0.5\ Cl \sin\ (180° \div N)$
$S = 0.5\ P \cos\ (180° \div N) + H \sin\ (180° \div N)$
Approximate O.D. of sprocket when J is $0.3\ P = P\ [0.6 + \cot\ (180° \div N)]$
O.D. of sprocket when tooth is pointed = $P \cot\ (180° \div N) + 2\ H$
Pressure angle for new chain = $xab = 35° - (120° \div N)$
Minimum pressure angle = $xab - B = 17° - (64° \div N)$; Average pressure angle $= 26° - (92° \div N)$

Seating Curve Data — Inches

P	D_r	Min. R	Min. Cl	D_s, Cl Tol.*	P	D_r	Min. R	Min. Cl	D_s, Cl Tol.*
¼	0.130	0.0670	0.010	0.0055	1¼	¾	0.3785	0.037	0.0070
⅜	0.200	0.1020	0.014	0.0055	1½	⅞	0.4410	0.046	0.0075
½	0.306	0.1585	0.015	0.0060	1¾	1	0.5040	0.055	0.0080
½	5/16	0.1585	0.015	0.0060	2	1⅛	0.5670	0.063	0.0085
⅝	0.400	0.2025	0.018	0.0060	2¼	1 13/32	0.7080	0.061	0.0090
¾	15/32	0.2370	0.022	0.0065	2½	1 9/16	0.7870	0.068	0.0095
1	⅝	0.3155	0.028	0.0070	3	1⅞	0.9435	0.081	0.0105

* Tolerance on D_s and Cl is plus only.

Table 9. — Standard Space Cutters for Roller-Chain Sprockets

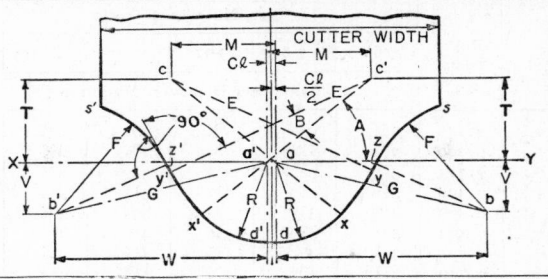

Construction: Draw XY. With a as a center and a radius equal to R draw circular arc xd; with a' as a center and with same radius draw circular arc $x'd'$. To complete seating curve xx', draw $d'd$ tangent to $d'x'$ and dx. Locate c and c' from dimensions M and T in table below. With c and c' as centers describe arcs xy and $x'y'$. Draw yz perpendicular to cy and $y'z'$ perpendicular to $c'y'$. Locate b and b' from dimensions W and V. Draw bz parallel to cy and $b'z'$ parallel to $c'y'$. With radii bs and $b'z'$ equal to F draw topping curves zs and $z's'$. The line yz is a common tangent to the two circular arcs xy and zs, similarly $y'z'$ is tangent to $x'y'$ and $z's'$.

Angle Yab is equal to $180° \div N$ when the cutter is made for a specific number of teeth, but has the values shown in the table below for cutters covering a given range of teeth. The following formulas are for cutters covering the standard ranges of teeth where N_a equals intermediate values given on page 901.

$$W = 1.24\ D_r \cos Yab; \qquad V = 1.24\ D_r \sin Yab$$

$$yz = D_r \left[1.24 \sin \left(17° + \frac{115°}{N_a} - Yab \right) - 0.8 \sin \left(18° - \frac{55°}{N_a} \right) \right]$$

$$F = D_r \left[0.8 \cos \left(18° - \frac{56°}{N_a} \right) + 1.24 \cos \left(17° + \frac{116°}{N_a} - Yab \right) - 1.3025 \right] - 0.0015 \text{ in.}$$

For other points, use the value of N_a for N in the standard formulas in Table 8.

Data for Laying Out Space Cutter

Range of Teeth	M	T	W	V
7–8	0.5848 D_r	0.5459 D_r	1.1328 D_r	0.5044 D_r
9–11	0.6032 D_r	0.5255 D_r	1.1782 D_r	0.3866 D_r
12–17	0.6194 D_r	0.5063 D_r	1.2129 D_r	0.2578 D_r
18–34	0.6343 D_r	0.4875 D_r	1.2353 D_r	0.1081 D_r
35 up	0.6466 D_r	0.4710 D_r	1.2400 D_r	0

Range of Teeth	F	Chord xy	yz	Angle Yab
7–8	0.7104 D_r — 0.0015	0.2384 D_r + 0.0003	0.0382 D_r	24°
9–11	0.6981 D_r — 0.0015	0.2800 D_r + 0.0003	0.0561 D_r	18°10′
12–17	0.6807 D_r — 0.0015	0.3181 D_r + 0.0004	0.0905 D_r	12°
18–34	0.6542 D_r — 0.0015	0.3540 D_r + 0.0004	0.1455 D_r	5°
35 up	0.6345 D_r — 0.0015	0.3850 D_r + 0.0004	0.1713 D_r	0°

E (same for all ranges) $= 1.3025\ D_r + 0.0015$; G (same for all ranges) $= 1.24\ D_r$

Table 10. — Recommended Space Cutter Sizes for Roller-Chain Sprockets

Pitch	Roller Diam.	Number of Teeth					
		6	7–8	9–11	12–17	18–34	35 up
		Cutter Diameter (Minimum)					
1/4	0.130	2 3/4	2 3/4	2 3/4	2 3/4	2 3/4	2 3/4
3/8	0.200	2 3/4	2 3/4	2 3/4	2 3/4	2 3/4	2 3/4
1/2 to 5/8	0.313	3	3	3 1/8	3 1/8	3 1/8	3 1/8
5/8	0.400	3 1/8	3 1/8	3 1/4	3 1/4	3 1/4	3 1/4
3/4	0.469	3 1/4	3 1/4	3 3/8	3 3/8	3 3/8	3 3/8
1	0.563	3 3/4	3 7/8	3 7/8	4	4	4
1 to 1 1/4	0.625	3 7/8	4	4 1/8	4 1/8	4 1/4	4 1/4
1 1/4 to 1 1/2	0.750	4 1/4	4 3/8	4 1/2	4 1/2	4 5/8	4 5/8
1 1/2	0.875	4 3/8	4 1/2	4 5/8	4 5/8	4 3/4	4 3/4
1 3/4	1.000	5	5 1/8	5 1/4	5 3/8	5 1/2	5 1/2
2	1.125	5 3/8	5 1/2	5 5/8	5 3/4	5 7/8	5 7/8
2 1/4	1.406	5 7/8	6	6 1/4	6 3/8	6 1/2	6 1/2
2 1/2	1.563	6 3/8	6 5/8	6 3/4	6 7/8	7	7 1/8
3	1.875	7 1/2	7 3/4	7 7/8	8	8	8 1/4

Pitch	Roller Diam.	Cutter Width (Minimum)					
1/4	0.130	5/16	5/16	5/16	5/16	9/32	9/32
3/8	0.200	15/32	15/32	15/32	7/16	7/16	13/32
1/2 to 5/8	0.313	3/4	3/4	3/4	3/4	23/32	11/16
5/8	0.400	3/4	3/4	3/4	3/4	23/32	11/16
3/4	0.469	29/32	29/32	29/32	7/8	27/32	13/16
1	0.563	1 1/4	1 1/4	1 3/16	1 5/32	1 1/8	1 3/32
1 to 1 1/4	0.625	1 1/2	1 1/2	1 15/32	1 15/32	1 13/32	1 11/32
1 1/4 to 1 1/2	0.750	1 13/16	1 13/16	1 25/32	1 3/4	1 11/16	1 5/8
1 1/2	0.875	1 13/16	1 13/16	1 25/32	1 3/4	1 11/16	1 5/8
1 3/4	1.000	2 3/32	2 3/32	2 1/16	2 1/32	1 31/32	1 7/8
2	1.125	2 13/32	2 13/32	2 3/8	2 5/16	2 1/4	2 5/32
2 1/4	1.406	2 11/16	2 11/16	2 21/32	2 19/32	2 15/32	2 13/32
2 1/2	1.563	3	3	2 15/16	2 29/32	2 3/4	2 11/16
3	1.875	3 19/32	3 19/32	3 17/32	3 15/32	3 11/32	3 7/32

Where the same roller diameter is commonly used with chains of two different pitches it is recommended that stock cutters be made wide enough to cut sprockets for both chains.

Marking of Cutters. — All cutters are to be marked, giving pitch, roller diameter and range of teeth to be cut.

Bores for Sprocket Cutters (recommended practice) are approximately as calculated from the formula:

$$\text{Bore} = 0.7\sqrt{(\text{Width of Cutter} + \text{Roller Diameter} + 0.7\ \text{Pitch})}$$

Minimum Outside Diameters of Space Cutters for 35 teeth and over (recommended practice) are approximately as calculated from the formula:

$$\text{Outside Diameter} = 1.2\ (\text{Bore} + \text{Roller Diameter} + 0.7\ \text{Pitch}) + 1\ \text{in.}$$

Table II. — American Standard Straddle Cutters for Roller-Chain Sprockets

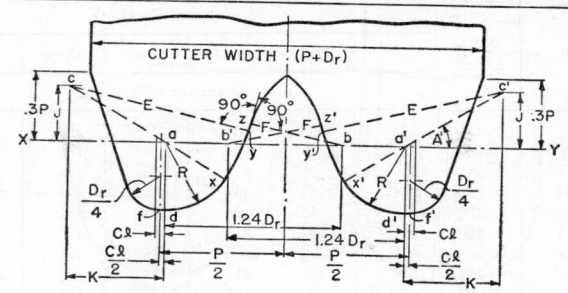

Construction. — P = Pitch, D_r = roller diameter, and N = number of teeth on which cutter is based. Draw XY and the two seating-curve circles xd and $x'd'$ as explained in Table 9. Locate c and c' from the dimensions K and J as given in this table. Locate b and b'. Draw cax and $c'a'x'$, and with centers c and c' draw the working curves xy and $x'y'$. Draw yz and $y'z'$ perpendicular to cy and $c'y'$ respectively. Draw bz and $b'z'$ parallel to cy and $c'y'$ respectively. With b and b' as centers and radius bz equal to F (see table), strike the arcs of the topping curves. Cutter width is $P + D_r$. Cutter diameters are as given in Table 10 for 35 and over teeth.

N = number of teeth on which cutter is based; $\qquad A' = 35° - \dfrac{120°}{N}$

$K = 0.8\ D_r \cos A'$; $\qquad J = 0.8\ D_r \sin A'$; $\qquad E = cx = 1.3025\ D_r + 0.0015$

$F = D_r \left[0.8 \cos\left(18° - \dfrac{56°}{N} \right) + 1.24 \cos\left(17° - \dfrac{64°}{N} \right) - 1.3025 \right] - 0.0015$

Maximum pressure angle (new chain) $xab = 35° - \dfrac{120°}{N} = 24.1°$ for " B " cutter and 32° for " A " cutter.

Minimum pressure angle $= xab - acy = 17° - \dfrac{64°}{N} = 11.2°$ for " B " cutter and 15.4° for " A " cutter.

Average pressure angle $= 26° - \dfrac{92°}{N} = 17.6°$ for " B " and 23.7° for " A " cutter.

There will be on the sprocket bottom diameter slight indentations for smaller, and slight projections for larger sprockets than the specific sprockets (11 and 40 teeth) for which cutters are designed.

Data for Laying Out Straddle Cutter				
Cutter*	No. of Teeth to be Cut	K	J	F
B	17 and under	$0.730\ D_r$	$0.327\ D_r$	$0.6937\ D_r - 0.0015$
A	18 and over	$0.678\ D_r$	$0.424\ D_r$	$0.6596\ D_r - 0.0015$

Cutter*	No. of Teeth to be Cut	Chord xy	yz	E
B	17 and under	$0.2928\ D_r + 0.0003$	$0.0617\ D_r$	$1.3025\ D_r + 0.0015$
A	18 and over	$0.3762\ D_r + 0.0004$	$0.1007\ D_r$	$1.3025\ D_r + 0.0015$

* Only two cutters of this type are required to cover the entire range of teeth. Cutter " A " is based on 40 teeth and is designed to be used for 18 teeth and over. Cutter " B " is based on 11 teeth and is designed to be used for 17 teeth and less.

Table 12. — Standard Hob Design for Roller-Chain Sprockets

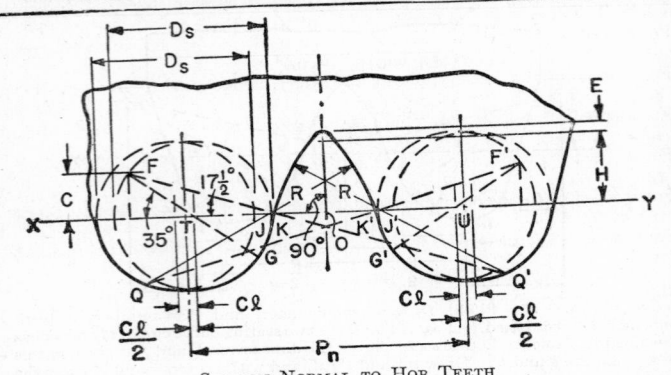

SECTION NORMAL TO HOB TEETH

Hobs designed for a given roller diameter (D_r) and chain pitch (P) will cut any number of teeth.

P = Pitch of Chain;　P_n = Normal Pitch of Hob = $1.011\ P$ inches

D_s = Minimum Diameter of Seating Curve = $1.005\ D_r + 0.003$

$Cl = 0.07\ (P - D_r) + 0.002$;　$C = 0.287\ D_s$

F = Radius Center for Arc GK;　$TO = GU = P_n \div 2$

$H = 0.27\ P$;　$E = 0.03\ P$ = Radius of Fillet Circle

Q' is located on line passing through F and J.　Point J is intersection of line XY with circle of diameter D_s.　R is found by trial and the arc of this radius is tangent to arc KG at K and to fillet radius.

OD = Outside Diameter = 1.7 (Bore + D_r + $0.7\ P$) approx.

D_h = Pitch Diameter = $OD - D_s$;　M = Helix Angle;　$\sin M = P_n \div \pi D_h$

L = Lead = $P_n \div \cos M$;　W = Width = Not less than $2 \times$ Bore, or $6\ D_r$, or $3.2\ P$

				Data for Laying Out Hob Outlines — Inches				
P	P_n	H	E	O.D.	W	Bore	Keyway	No. Gashes
¼	0.2527	0.0675	0.0075	2.640	2½	1.250	¼ × ⅛	13
⅜	0.379	0.101	0.012	3.125	2½	1.250	¼ × ⅛	13
½	0.506	0.135	0.015	3.375	2½	1.250	¼ × ⅛	12
⅝	0.632	0.170	0.018	3.625	2½	1.250	¼ × ⅛	12
¾	0.759	0.202	0.023	3.750	2⅞	1.250	¼ × ⅛	11
1	1.011	0.270	0.030	4.375	3¾	1.250	¼ × ⅛	11
1¼	1.264	0.337	0.038	4.750	4½	1.250	¼ × ⅛	10
1½	1.517	0.405	0.045	5.375	5¼	1.250	¼ × ⅛	10
1¾	1.770	0.472	0.053	6.375	6	1.500	⅜ × ³⁄₁₆	9
2	2.022	0.540	0.060	6.875	6¾	1.500	⅜ × ³⁄₁₆	9
2¼	2.275	0.607	0.068	8.000	8½	1.750	⅜ × ³⁄₁₆	8
2½	2.528	0.675	0.075	8.625	9⅜	1.750	⅜ × ³⁄₁₆	8
3	3.033	0.810	0.090	9.750	11¼	2.000	½ × ³⁄₁₆	8

Link-belt Driving Chains. — The working load recommended for detachable link-belting is determined as follows:

For a speed of 200 feet per minute and under, divide average ultimate strength by 6.

For a speed of 300 feet per minute and under, divide average ultimate strength by 8.

For a speed of 400 feet per minute and under, divide average ultimate strength by 10.

For a speed of 500 feet per minute and under, divide average ultimate strength by 12.

For a speed of 600 feet per minute and under, divide average ultimate strength by 16.

For a speed of 700 feet per minute and under, divide average ultimate strength by 20.

Average Ultimate Strength of Link-belts

Chain No.	Approx. Number of Links in 10 Feet	Average Ultimate Strength, Pounds	Chain No.	Approx. Number of Links in 10 Feet	Average Ultimate Strength, Pounds	Chain No.	Approx. Number of Links in 10 Feet	Average Ultimate Strength, Pounds
25	133	700	57	52	2800	93	30	7,500
32	104	1100	62	73	3100	95	30	8,700
33	86	1190	66	60	2600	103	39	9,600
34	86	1300	67	52	3300	108	25½	9,900
35	74	1200	75	46	4000	110	25½	12,700
42	88	1500	77	52	3600	114	37	11,000
45	74	1600	78	46	4900	122	20	15,000
51	104	1900	83	30	4950	124	30	12,700
52	80	2300	85	30	7600	146	20	14,000
55	74	2200	88	46	5750	....	......	......

Example: — The average ultimate strength of a No. 35 chain is 1200 pounds, as shown by the table "Average Ultimate Strength of Link-belts." Therefore, the working strength at a speed of 200 feet per minute equals 1200 ÷ 6 = 200 pounds.

In transmitting power, the engagement of each chain link with the sprocket wheel teeth is attended by a certain amount of shock and as this is intensified as the speed is increased, the working load of the chain should be reduced in a compensating ratio. If the load to be transmitted is irregular or subject to sudden variation, the working load should be reduced below what would be obtained by the foregoing figures.

To obtain the horsepower that can be transmitted by a link-belt, multiply the working strain (ascertained as in the foregoing) by the number of feet the chain travels per minute, and divide the result by 33,000.

Link-belt Size Numbers. — The sizes of detachable link-belting are designated by numbers. The numbers of Ewart link-belting and the average ultimate strength, in pounds, are given in the accompanying table. These chains are made in a number of different types or patterns suitable for different purposes. Some of these patterns are adapted for conveyor chains but are not suitable for power transmission, and *vice versa*. For ordinary transmission purposes, a chain of medium pitch is desirable. Typical chain numbers for power transmission are Nos. 35, 45, 67, 75, 77, 78, 88, 103, 114 and 124. Patterns such as Nos. 51, 52 and 62, which have a comparatively small tooth space are used for driving where back-lash or lost motion is objectionable. Sprocket wheels having a large number of teeth will not work well with these short-link chains, for a long period, because the small clearance between the teeth and chain links allows only a small amount of stretch before the chain tends to climb on top of the sprocket teeth.

Applying Link-belt Chains. — Whenever possible, a link-belt should run with the back of the coupling hook to the sprocket wheel. If it is necessary to run a

sprocket in contact with the face side of a link-belt or the side on which the coupling hook is open, use "face wheels." The accompanying illustrations A and C represent wheels which drive the belts, and B and D, wheels which are driven by the belts.

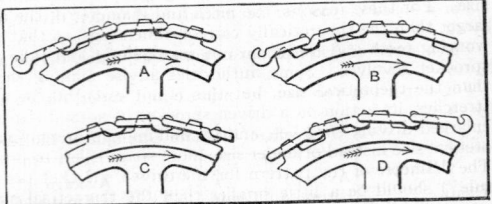

A long series of experiments based on conditions of wear on belts and sprockets at the points where they engage and disengage under strain, has demonstrated that for driving purposes or the transmission of power, the belt should run with the hook end of the link foremost, as at C and D; for ordinary elevator and conveyor work, the straight end-bar should run foremost, as at A and B, unless an elevator is handling fine gritty material which would have less tendency to work into the belt joints when running with the hook end foremost, as at C and D.

Sprockets for Detachable Chains. — In the design of sprockets for malleable and pressed steel chains of the detachable type, the ideal condition is to have the chordal pitch of the sprocket teeth exactly the same as the pitch of the chain, so that the load is equally distributed over all the teeth; but this is impracticable because the pitch of the chain lengthens as the result of the wear and stretching of the chain, which begins as soon as the chain is put into service. When the pitch of the chain has become greater than the chordal pitch of the sprocket, it is necessary for the chain to assume a larger pitch circle, and consequently it does not rest on the root circle, so that all the wear is on the faces of the teeth. In practice, this causes excessive wear on both the chain and the sprocket, and imparts a jerky, uneven motion to the drive. Therefore, it is considered good practice to anticipate this increase in the chain pitch and vary the sprocket sizes instead of making them to the dimensions which are theoretically correct.

Variations in Sizes of Sprockets. — To compensate for the elongation of the chain it is common practice to make the pitch of the driving sprocket larger than the theoretically correct pitch; the result is that the last tooth engaging the chain will carry the load and as it leaves the chain, the latter slips back until the next tooth takes the load. If the tooth curves are correct, this backward slipping or creeping movement of the chain will occur smoothly, the chain seating itself against the next tooth without shock. The entering tooth in this case has clearance and the chain comes quietly into contact with the root diameter of the sprocket. On the contrary, if the driving sprocket is smaller than the theoretical size, the entering tooth must "pick up" the load as the link slides into place on it. This means that the chain must be pushed ahead as the following tooth, in turn, picks up the load. As the tooth picks up the load while the chain is in the act of seating, this tends to prevent the link from seating to the full depth at once, which causes a jerking action of the chain and results in noisy operation.

The foregoing conditions are reversed when considering the driven sprocket. For example, if the driven sprocket is smaller than the theoretical diameter, the last tooth engaging the chain carries the load and, if properly shaped, it allows the chain to slip smoothly as it withdraws and as the succeeding link takes the load. The entering link also has plenty of clearance for seating to the full depth. If the driven sprocket, however, is made larger than the theoretical size, the entering tooth must pick up the load; hence there are the same objections previously mentioned in connection with the driving sprocket that is smaller than the theoretical size. For these reasons, the pitch and diameter of the driving sprocket should be larger than the theoretically correct dimensions, so that the *releasing* teeth are the working teeth and the chain can seat quietly and take the load gradually as the sprocket revolves. Some authorities advise making the driven sprocket smaller than the theoretical size, but this is not essential, because as soon as the chain stretches, its action on a driven sprocket of normal size will be the same as on an enlarged driving sprocket, and by making the driven sprocket the normal or theoretical size instead of under size, more space is left to provide for chain elongation. The diameter of the pattern for the driven sprocket (as measured with a "shrink rule") should be a little smaller than the theoretical size, however, to allow for

Average Pitches of Standard Link-belts

Chain No.	Average Pitch, Inches	Chain No.	Average Pitch, Inches	Chain No.	Average Pitch, Inches	Chain No.	Average Pitch, Inches	Chain No.	Average Pitch, Inches
25	0.902	45	1.630	66	2.013	85	4.000	110	4.720
32	1.154	51	1.155	67	2.308	88	2.609	114	3.250
33	1.394	52	1.506	75	2.609	93	4.033	122	6.050
34	1.398	55	1.631	77	2.293	95	3.967	124	4.063
35	1.630	57	2.308	78	2.609	103	3.075	146	6.150
42	1.375	62	1.654	83	4.000	108	4.720	....	.....

whatever increase there may be in the size of the casting as the result of the molding process, because over-size driven sprockets are as objectionable as under-size driving sprockets.

Pitch Diameter of Sprocket. — The pitch circle of a sprocket for malleable or detachable chains should intersect or pass through the pivot points or centers of the hook-shaped ends of the links. These chain links represent the sides of a polygon which is inscribed within the pitch circle. The following formulas, in which P = pitch diameter, p = pitch of chain, and N = number of teeth, give a theoretically correct pitch diameter:

$$P = \frac{p}{\sin\left(\frac{180}{N}\right)^\circ} = p \times \csc\left(\frac{180}{N}\right)^\circ$$

The theoretical pitch diameter obtained with one of these formulas may be increased in the case of a driver, or possibly decreased in the case of a driven sprocket, by adding or subtracting a fixed amount to compensate for chain elongation. The practice of the J. I. Case Threshing Machine Co., when making sprocket patterns, is first to obtain the correct or theoretical pitch diameter and then add a fixed amount to the driver and subtract a fixed amount from the driven sprocket so that the casting for the driver will be about 1/16 inch over size and the driven sprocket casting slightly under size. This practice is followed regardless of the size or number of the teeth in the sprockets. The exact amount to be allowed for variations in molding, shrinkage, etc., will depend somewhat upon the foundry doing the work. At the plant referred to, a driving sprocket pattern which is to be machine molded, is made $\frac{1}{32}$ inch larger than the calculated diameter, which results in a casting that is about $\frac{1}{16}$ inch over size. The driven sprocket pattern is made $\frac{1}{16}$ inch smaller than the calculated size because the castings tend to "grow" or increase in size in the foundry. In the case of driven sprockets, the closer the castings are to the theoretical size, the better, provided none of the castings are over size as a result of too small an allowance. Patterns for driving sprockets which are to be hand molded are made to the calculated or theoretical size and the driven sprockets $\frac{3}{32}$ inch under size. The patterns are, of course, measured with a shrink-rule.

Example: Find the pitch diameter of a machine molded pattern for a driving sprocket having 20 teeth and intended for a No. 52 malleable chain.

The pitch (see table "Average Pitches of Standard Link Belts") is 1.506 inch; hence,

$$P = \frac{1.506}{\sin\left(\frac{180}{20}\right)^\circ} = 9.627 \text{ inches.}$$

9.627 + 0.031 = 9.658 or $9\frac{21}{32}$ inches nearly, which is the pattern diameter as measured with a shrink-rule.

Root and Outside Diameters of Sprockets. — Root diameter D (see accompanying illustration) of a sprocket for detachable chain is found by subtracting

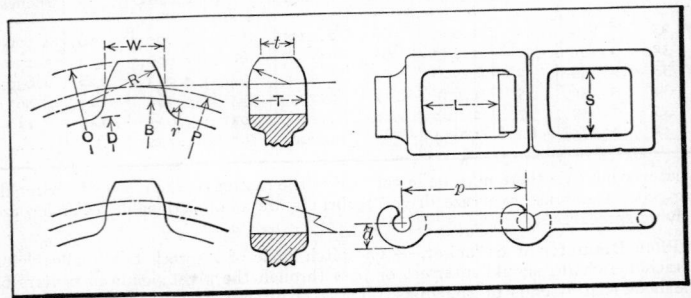

twice the dedendum d of the chain (or the distance from the center of the chain to the back of the hook-shaped end) from the pitch diameter. The outside diameter O is equal to the pitch diameter P plus twice the dedendum d of the chain, or the outside diameter may be reduced somewhat by adding to the pitch diameter from 1.6 to 1.8 times the dedendum instead of twice the dedendum. If the sprockets are originally designed as *driving* and *driven* sprockets, the shorter teeth or smaller outside diameter may be preferable, but a *combination sprocket* which is designed for use either as driver or driven should have the longer teeth, as otherwise the chain might become caught on top of a tooth. The cross-sectional shape of the shorter tooth should be modified by locating the center of the arc on the root line instead of the pitch line, as shown by the lower sectional view in the illustration.

Design of Sprocket Teeth. — The arcs forming the faces of the sprocket teeth have a radius R and their centers are located on a base circle B (see illustration). Radius R may be taken as $\frac{3}{4}$ of the chain pitch or it may be based upon the pitch diameter. According to one rule, R should equal 0.17 of the pitch diameter, but the minimum radius must not be less than the pitch p of the chain minus dedendum d. The radius of base circle B should be from 0.47 to 0.48 of the pitch circle diameter. The root radius r is usually from 0.6 to 0.7 of the dedendum d. The width W generally varies from 0.5 to 0.7 of the space L between the assembled links and may be as high as 0.8 L; but this will give, in most cases, a tooth that is wider than necessary, and in order to secure more clearance space to allow for chain elongation, the width W may be reduced. It is good practice to proportion width W with reference to the number of teeth in the sprocket, W being increased as the size of the sprocket or number of teeth decreases. If the width W is not increased in smaller sprockets, a tooth having the necessary clearance on the face may be either very narrow on top or entirely cut off below the circle representing the outside

Dimensions of Sprocket Teeth for Pressed Steel Chain *

All dimensions in inches

Number of Chain	Pitch of Chain	Face Radius	Pitch Circle to Base Circle	Backing b		Fillet Radius	Length of Opening	Thickness of Tooth	Height of Tooth	Width of Point	Width of Tooth	Width of Opening
	P	R	B	Mall.	Steel	r	O	T	H	S	W	U
25	0.902	1 1/16	1/8	0.203	0.177	3/32	9/16	5/16	3/8	3/16	11/32	7/16
32	1.154	7/8	1/8	0.245	0.227	1/8	11/16	7/16	7/16	1/4	1/2	19/32
34	1.398	1 1/16	1/8	0.262	0.257	5/32	27/32	1/2	1/2	5/16	9/16	21/32
35	1.630	1 1/4	3/16	0.262	0.300	3/16	1 1/8	5/8	9/16	3/8	11/16	25/32
42	1.375	1 1/16	1/8	0.282	0.262	5/32	27/32	9/16	9/16	11/32	5/8	3/4
45	1.630	1 1/4	3/16	0.293	0.300	3/16	1 1/16	5/8	9/16	3/8	11/16	25/32
52	1.506	1 1/8	3/16	0.346	0.300	3/16	7/8	5/8	5/8	13/32	3/4	13/16
55	1.631	1 1/4	3/16	0.353	0.317	3/16	1	5/8	9/16	3/8	11/16	25/32
62	1.654	1 1/4	3/16	0.410	0.332	3/16	1	5/8	5/8	1/2	7/8	1

* J. I. Case Threshing Machine Co.'s standard.

diameter. The tooth should have a flat on the top of at least 1/8 inch in width. The thickness T of the tooth should be from 0.85 to 0.90 of the space S between the sides of the links. The thickness t at the top usually varies from 0.55 to 0.60 of T.

Characteristics of Silent Chain Drives. — The silent or "inverted-tooth" driving chain has the following characteristics: The chain passes over the face of the wheel like a belt and the wheel teeth do not project through it; the chain engages the wheel by means of teeth extending across the full width of the under side, with the exception of those chains having a central guide link; the chain teeth and wheel teeth are of such a shape that as the chain pitch increases through wear at the joints, the chain shifts outward upon the teeth, thus engaging the wheel on

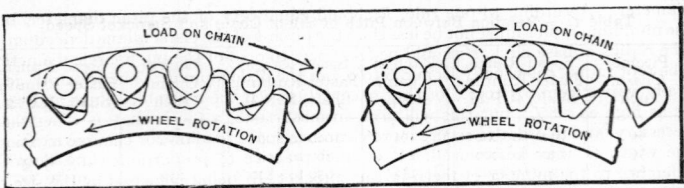

a pitch circle of increasing diameter; the result of this action is that the pitch of the wheel teeth increases at the same rate as the chain pitch. The accompanying illustration shows an unworn chain to the left, and a worn chain to the right, which has moved outward as the result of wear. Another distinguishing feature of the silent chain is that the power is transmitted by and to all the teeth in the arc of contact, irrespective of the increasing pitch due to elongation. The links have no sliding action either on or off the teeth, which results in a smooth and practically noiseless action, the chain being originally designed for the transmission of power at higher speeds than are suitable for roller chains. The efficiency of the silent chain itself may be as high as 99 per cent, and for the complete drive, from 96 to 97 per cent, under favorable conditions; from 94 to 96 per cent can be secured with well-designed drives under average conditions.

The life and upkeep of silent chains depend largely upon the design of the entire drive, including the provision for adjustment. If there is much slack, the whipping of the chain will greatly increase the wear, and means of adjustment may double the life of the chain. A slight amount of play is necessary for satisfactory operation. The minimum amount of sag should be about ⅛ inch. Although the silent chain shifts outward from the teeth and adjusts itself for an increase of pitch, it cannot take up the increased pitch in that portion of the chain between the wheels; therefore, the wheel must lag to the extent of the increased pitch in the straight portion of the chain.

Design of Silent Chain Drives. — The design of silent chain transmissions must be based not only upon the power to be transmitted and the ratio between driving and driven shafts, but also upon such factors as the speed of the faster running shaft, the available space, assuming that it affects the sprocket diameters, the character of the load and certain other factors. Determining the pitch of the chain and the number of teeth on the smallest sprocket are the important initial steps. Usually several combinations of pitches and sprocket sizes may be employed for a given installation. In attempting to select the best combination, it is advisable to consult with the manufacturer of the chain to be used. Some of the more important fundamental points governing the design of silent chain transmissions will be summarized.

Pitch of Silent Chain. — The pitch is selected with reference to the speed of the faster running shaft which ordinarily is the driver and holds the smaller sprocket. For example, if the speed of the smaller sprocket is somewhere between 1500 and 2000 R.P.M., a ½-inch pitch would be recommended by chain manufacturers, as a general rule. If the speed is between 800 and 1000 R.P.M., then a 1-inch pitch ordinarily would be selected. (Table 1 gives the recommendations of well-known manufacturers for trial selection.) As the normal operating speeds increase, the allowable pitch decreases. Recommendations relating to the relationship between pitch and operating speed are intended for normal or average conditions, and the speeds for a given pitch may be exceeded under favorable conditions and may have to be reduced when conditions are unfavorable. In general, smoother or quieter

Table 1. — Relation Between Pitch of Silent Chain and Sprocket Speed

Pitch of Chain, Inch	Speed Range, Faster Running Shaft, R.P.M.	Pitch of Chain, Inch	Speed Range, Faster Running Shaft, R.P.M.	Pitch of Chain, Inch	Speed Range, Faster Running Shaft, R.P.M.
⅜	2000 to 5000	¾	1000 to 1200	1½	500 to 650
½	1500 to 2000	1	800 to 1000	2	300 to 500
⅝	1200 to 1500	1¼	650 to 800	2½	up to 300

operation will result from using the smallest pitch suitable for a given speed and load. However, a larger pitch which might be applicable under the same conditions, will result in a narrower chain and a less expensive transmission. This usually is true when there is a small speed reduction and comparatively long center distance. If there is a large speed reduction and short center distance, drives having the smaller pitches may be less expensive.

Maximum Ratios for Silent Chain Drives. — The maximum permissible ratios between driving and driven sprockets vary somewhat for different conditions and usually range from 6- or 7-to-1 up to 10-to-1. Some drives have even higher ratios, especially when the operating conditions are exceptionally favorable. When a large speed reduction is necessary, it is preferable as a general rule to use a double reduction or compound type of transmission instead of obtaining the entire reduction with two sprockets. Drives should be so proportioned that the angle between the two strands of a tight chain does not exceed 45 degrees. When the angle is larger, the chain does not have sufficient contact with the driving sprocket.

Sprocket Size and Chain Speed: A driving sprocket with not less than 17 teeth is generally recommended. For the driven sprocket, one manufacturer recommends 127 teeth as a maximum limit and less than 100 as preferable. If practicable, the sprocket sizes should be small enough to limit the chain speed to from 1200 to 1400 feet per minute. If the chain speed exceeds these figures, this may indicate that the pitch is too large or that a smaller pitch, and, consequently, a reduction in sprocket diameters (and chain speed) will result in better operating conditions. Both sprockets should preferably have an odd number of teeth, because this causes a " hunting tooth " effect with a minimum and uniform distribution of wear.

If there is a small reduction in speed between the driving and driven shafts, both sprockets may be made as small as is consistent with satisfactory operation, either to obtain a compact drive or possibly to avoid excessive chain speed in cases where the rotative speed is high for a given horsepower. Under such conditions, one manufacturer recommends driving sprockets ranging from 17 to 30 teeth, and driven sprockets ranging from 19 to 33 teeth. If the number of revolutions per minute is low for a given horsepower and the center distance comparatively long, then the recommended range for driving sprockets is from 23 to 111 teeth, and driven sprockets from 27 to 129 teeth. The preferable range is from 17 to 75 teeth for the driving sprockets, and 19 to 102 teeth for the driven sprockets.

Sprocket Pitch Diameters. — The pitch diameters of silent chain sprockets are given in Table 2 which applies to a unit pitch of 1 inch. To obtain the pitch diameter for any other pitch, multiply the diameter given in the table by the pitch required. The general formula for pitch diameters is as follows:

$$\text{Pitch Diameter} = \frac{\text{Pitch}}{\sin (180° \div \text{No. of Teeth})}$$

Table 2. — Pitch Diameters of Silent Chain Sprockets*

Number of Teeth	Pitch Diam., Inches	Number of Teeth	Pitch Diam., Inches	Number of Teeth	Pitch Diam., Inches	Number of Teeth	Pitch Diam., Inches
15	4.810	59	18.789	103	32.791	147	46.795
16	5.126	60	19.107	104	33.109	148	47.113
17	5.442	61	19.425	105	33.428	149	47.432
18	5.759	62	19.744	106	33.746	150	47.750
19	6.076	63	20.062	107	34.064	151	48.068
20	6 393	64	20.380	108	34.382	152	48.387
21	6.710	65	20.698	109	34.701	153	48.705
22	7.027	66	21.016	110	35.019	154	49.023
23	7.344	67	21.335	111	35.337	155	49.341
24	7.661	68	21.653	112	35.655	156	49.660
25	7.979	69	21.971	113	35.974	157	49.978
26	8.296	70	22.289	114	36.292	158	50.296
27	8.614	71	22.607	115	36.610	159	50.615
28	8.932	72	22.926	116	36.928	160	50.933
29	9.249	73	23.244	117	37.247	161	51.251
30	9.567	74	23.562	118	37.565	162	51.569
31	9.885	75	23.880	119	37.883	163	51.888
32	10.202	76	24.198	120	38.202	164	52.206
33	10.520	77	24.517	121	38.520	165	52.524
34	10.838	78	24.835	122	38.838	166	52.843
35	11.156	79	25.153	123	39.156	167	53.161
36	11.474	80	25.471	124	39.475	168	53.479
37	11.792	81	25.790	125	39.793	169	53.797
38	12.110	82	26.108	126	40.111	170	54.116
39	12.429	83	26.426	127	40.429	171	54.434
40	12.746	84	26.744	128	40.748	172	54.752
41	13.064	85	27.063	129	41.066	173	55.071
42	13.382	86	27.381	130	41.384	174	55.389
43	13.700	87	27.699	131	41.703	175	55.707
44	14.018	88	28.017	132	42.021	176	56.026
45	14.336	89	28.335	133	42.339	177	56.344
46	14.654	90	28.654	134	42.657	178	56.662
47	14.972	91	28.972	135	42.976	179	56.980
48	15.290	92	29.290	136	43.294	180	57.299
49	15.608	93	29.608	137	43.612	181	57.617
50	15.926	94	29.927	138	43.931	182	57.935
51	16.244	95	30.245	139	44.249	183	58.253
52	16.562	96	30.563	140	44.567	184	58.572
53	16.880	97	30.881	141	44.885	185	58.890
54	17.198	98	31.200	142	45.204	186	59.208
55	17.517	99	31.518	143	45.522	187	59.527
56	17.835	100	31.836	144	45.840	188	59.845
57	18.153	101	32.154	145	46.158	189	60.163
58	18.471	102	32.473	146	46.477	190	60.482

These pitch diameters are for a unit pitch of 1 inch. The pitch diameter for any other pitch equals the pitch diameter given in the table multiplied by the given pitch.

Most silent chain manufacturers base their pitch diameters upon this formula. One prominent manufacturer uses somewhat larger pitch diameters for larger pitches and tooth numbers.

The outside diameters of Whitney silent chain sprockets are the same as the pitch diameters. According to Morse practice, the outside diameter is slightly less than the pitch diameter for tooth numbers below 33. This outside diameter reduction below the pitch diameter, ranges from about 0.020 to 0.030 inch for tooth numbers from 32 down to 17. The outside diameter for tooth numbers above 34 is somewhat larger than the pitch diameter, the increase ranging from about 0.020 to 0.085 inch for tooth numbers from 35 to 155.

Center Distance for Silent Chain Drives. — If the ratio of the drive is small, it is possible to locate the sprockets so close that the teeth just clear; however, as a general rule, the minimum center-to-center distance should equal the sum of the diameters of both sprockets. According to the Whitney Chain & Mfg. Co., if the speed ratio is not over 2½-to-1, the center distance may be equal to one-half the sum of the sprocket diameters plus tooth clearance, providing this distance is not less than the minimum given in Table 3.

Table 3. — Minimum Center Distances for Various Pitches

Pitch, Inches	⅜	½	⅝	¾	1	1¼	1½
Minimum Center Distance, Inches	6	9	12	15	21	27	33

If the speed ratio is greater than 2½-to-1, the center distance should not be less than the sum of the sprocket diameters.

When the chain length in pitches is known, the equivalent center distance for a tight chain may be determined by the formula for roller chain found on page 899.

Installation of Silent Chain Drives. — In installing chain transmissions of any kind, horizontal drives are those having driving and driven shafts in a horizontal plane, are always preferable to vertical drives, are those having a vertical center line intersecting the driving and driven shafts. If one sprocket must be higher than the other, avoid a vertical drive if possible by so locating the two sprockets that the common center line inclines from the vertical as far as is permitted by other conditions which might govern the installation. If practicable, an adjustment should be provided for the center distance between the driving and driven shafts. Driving motors are often mounted on adjustable base or slide rails to provide this adjustment for the center distance.

Slack Side of Chain: As a general rule, the slack strand of a chain should be on the lower side of a horizontal drive. If the drive is not horizontal but angular or at some angle less than 90 degrees from the vertical, the slack should preferably be on that side which causes the strand to curve outward or away from the center line of the driving and driven shafts. Whenever the slack strand is on the upper side of either a horizontal or inclined drive, adjustment for the center distance is especially important to compensate for possible chain elongation.

Lubrication: The life of a silent chain subjected to conditions such as are common to automobile drives, depends largely upon the wear of the joints. On account of the high speed and whipping action, it is important to have the chains well oiled. When splash lubrication is employed, the supply pipe should be placed so that the oil will be directed against the inside of the chain.

Table 1. Horsepower Ratings for Silent Chain Drives

The industrial standard horsepower ratings and service factors for silent chain drives are given in Tables 1 and 2. These ratings are recommended practice of the Association of Roller and Silent Chain Manufacturers.

The ratings in Table 1 may require modification by using the service factors given in Table 2. These factors, which apply to typical drives, are intended as a general guide only, and engineering judgment or experience may indicate different modifications to suit the nature of the load.

$$\text{Horsepower capacity of chain per inch of width} = \frac{\text{Rating in Table 1}}{\text{Service factor, Table 2}}$$

$$\text{Chain width for given total H.P. capacity} = \frac{\text{H.P.} \times \text{service factor}}{\text{Rating per inch, Table 1}}$$

Lubrication. — The horsepower ratings for each pitch listed in Table 1 are divided into three sections by heavy zigzag lines. For drives in the first or left-hand section, bath, splash, oil-cup or brush lubrication may be applied; for drives in the second or middle section, a disk or circulating pump is preferable; for drives in the third or right-hand section, consult the manufacturer's engineering department in regard to proper method of lubrication.

⅜″ Pitch — Horsepower per Inch of Chain Width — Max. Width, 4 Inches

No. of Teeth Small Sprkt.	Revolutions per Minute — Small Sprocket										
	100	500	1000	1500	2000	2500	3000	3500	4000	5000	6000
*17	.37	1.7	3.7	4.2	5.5	6.3	6.8	7.0	7.0	..	..
*19	.42	2.0	3.8	5.2	6.3	7.3	7.9	8.3	8.4	7.8	..
21	.46	2.2	4.1	5.8	7.2	8.3	9.1	9.6	9.9	9.5	8.2
23	.50	2.4	4.5	6.4	8.0	9.2	10	11	11	11	9.5
25	.55	2.6	4.9	7.0	8.8	10	11	12	12	12	11
27	.59	2.8	5.4	7.6	9.5	11	12	13	14	14	13
29	.64	3.0	5.8	8.2	10.3	12	13	14	15	15	14
31	.68	3.3	6.2	8.8	11	13	14	15	16	16	15
33	.72	3.5	6.6	9.4	12	14	15	17	17	17	16
35	.77	3.7	7.0	10	13	15	16	18	18	18	17
37	.82	3.9	7.3	11	13	16	17	19	19	19	..
40	.9	4.2	8.1	12	14	17	19	20	21	21	..
45	1.0	4.8	9.1	13	16	19	21	22	23	..	..
50	1.1	5.3	1C	14	18	21	23	24	..	..	..

½″ Pitch — Horsepower per Inch of Chain Width — Max. Width, 7 Inches

No. of Teeth Small Sprkt.	Revolutions per Minute — Small Sprocket										
	100	500	700	1000	1200	1800	2000	2500	3000	3500	4000
*17	.66	3	4	5	6	8	9	9	9	9	..
*19	.74	3	4	6	7	9	10	11	11	11	..
21	.81	4	5	7	8	11	11	12	13	13	..
23	.89	4	6	8	9	12	13	14	15	15	14
25	.97	4	6	8	10	13	14	16	17	17	16
27	1.0	5	7	9	10	14	15	17	19	19	18
29	1.1	5	7	10	11	15	17	19	20	20	20
31	1.2	6	8	10	12	17	18	20	22	22	22
33	1.3	6	8	11	13	18	19	22	23	24	23
35	1.4	6	9	12	14	19	20	23	25	25	24
37	1.5	7	9	13	15	20	21	24	26	26	..
40	1.6	7	10	14	16	22	23	26	28	28	..
45	2	8	11	15	18	24	24	29	31	..	..
50	2	9	12	17	20	27	29	32	..	..	..

* For best results, smaller sprocket should have at least 21 teeth.

Table 1 (*Continued*). Horsepower Ratings for Silent Chain Drives

⅝" Pitch — Horsepower per Inch of Chain Width — Max. Width, 8 Inches

No. of Teeth Small Sprkt.	Revolutions per Minute — Small Sprocket									
	100	500	700	1000	1200	1800	2000	2500	3000	3500
*19	1.1	5	7	10	11	13	14	14	..	..
21	1.3	6	8	10	12	15	16	16	16	..
23	1.4	6	9	12	13	17	18	19	18	..
25	1.5	7	9	13	15	19	20	21	21	19
27	1.6	8	10	14	16	21	22	23	23	21
29	1.7	8	11	15	17	22	24	25	25	23
31	1.9	9	12	16	18	24	25	27	27	25
33	2	9	13	17	20	26	27	29	29	27
35	2.1	10	13	18	21	27	29	31	31	28
37	2.2	10	14	19	22	29	31	34	33	..
40	2.4	11	15	21	24	31	33	35	..	..
45	2.7	13	17	23	27	35	37	..	..	..
50	3	14	19	26	30	38	40	..	..	..

¾" Pitch — Horsepower per Inch of Chain Width — Max. Width, 10 Inches

No. of Teeth Small Sprkt.	Revolutions per Minute — Small Sprocket								
	100	500	700	1000	1200	1500	1800	2000	2500
*19	1.6	7.4	10	12	14	16	17	17	..
21	1.8	8	11	14	16	18	19	20	19
23	2.0	9	12	16	18	20	22	22	22
25	2.2	10	13	17	20	23	25	25	24
27	2.3	11	14	19	22	25	27	28	28
29	2.5	12	16	21	24	27	29	30	30
31	2.7	12	17	22	25	29	32	33	33
33	2.9	13	18	24	27	31	34	35	35
35	3.0	14	19	25	29	33	36	37	37
37	3.2	15	20	27	31	35	38	39	39
40	3.5	16	22	29	33	38	41	42	42
45	3.9	18	24	32	37	42	45	46	..
50	4.3	20	27	36	42	46	49	..	..

1" Pitch — Horsepower per Inch of Chain Width — Max. Width, 14 Inches

No. of Teeth Small Sprkt.	Revolutions per Minute — Small Sprocket										
	100	200	300	400	500	700	1000	1200	1500	1800	2000
*19	3	6	8	10	12	16	20	21	22	..	..
21	3	6	9	12	14	18	23	25	26	26	..
23	3	7	10	13	15	20	25	28	30	30	..
25	4	7	11	14	17	22	28	31	33	33	33
27	4	8	12	15	19	24	31	34	37	37	36
29	4	9	13	16	20	26	33	37	40	41	40
31	5	9	13	18	22	28	36	40	43	44	43
33	5	10	14	19	23	30	39	43	47	47	46
35	5	10	15	20	24	32	41	45	49	50	49
37	5.4	11	16	21	26	34	43	48	52	53	..
40	6	12	18	23	28	36	47	52	56	..	..
45	7	13	20	25	31	41	52	57	61	..	..
50	8	15	22	28	34	45	57	62	..	..	..

* For best results, smaller sprocket should have at least 21 teeth.

Table 1 (*Continued*). **Horsepower Ratings for Silent Chain Drives**

1¼″ Pitch — Horsepower per Inch of Chain Width — Max. Width, 20 Inches											
No. of Teeth Small Sprkt.	Revolutions per Minute — Small Sprocket										
	100	200	300	400	500	600	700	800	1000	1200	1500
*19	4.5	8	12	16	19	21	23	25	27	28	..
21	5	9	14	18	21	24	26	29	32	33	..
23	5.5	10	15	19	23	27	29	32	36	37	37
25	6	11	16	21	25	29	32	35	40	42	42
27	6.4	12	18	23	28	32	35	39	43	46	46
29	6.9	13	19	25	30	34	38	42	47	50	51
31	7.4	14	21	27	32	37	41	45	51	54	55
33	7.9	15	22	28	34	39	44	48	55	58	59
35	8.4	16	23	30	36	42	47	51	58	62	62
37	9	17	24	32	38	44	50	54	61	65	..
40	9.6	19	27	35	42	48	54	59	66	70	..
45	10.7	21	30	39	47	54	60	65	73	..	..
50	12	23	34	43	52	59	66	72	80	..	..

1½″ Pitch — Horsepower per Inch of Chain Width — Max. Width, 24 Inches											
No. of Teeth Small Sprkt.	Revolutions per Minute — Small Sprocket										
	100	200	300	400	500	600	700	800	900	1000	1200
*19	6.4	12	17	22	25	28	31	32	33	34	..
21	7	13	19	24	29	32	35	37	39	39	..
23	8	15	21	27	32	36	39	42	44	45	44
25	8	16	23	30	35	40	44	47	49	52	51
27	9	18	25	32	38	43	48	51	54	56	56
29	10	19	27	35	41	47	52	56	59	60	61
31	11	20	29	37	44	51	56	60	63	65	66
33	11	22	31	40	47	54	60	64	68	70	71
35	12	23	33	42	50	57	63	68	72	74	75
37	13	24	35	47	53	61	67	72	77	79	..
40	14	26	38	53	58	66	72	78	84	..	..
45	15	30	43	54	65	74	81	86	90	..	..
50	17	33	47	60	71	81	89	94	..	..	..

2″ Pitch — Horsepower per Inch of Chain Width — Max. Width, 30 Inches									
No. of Teeth Small Sprkt.	Revolutions per Minute — Small Sprocket								
	100	200	300	400	500	600	700	800	900
*19	11	21	29	35	40	43	45	..	..
21	12.5	23	32	40	42	50	52	..	..
23	13.5	26	36	44	51	56	59	6c	..
25	14	28	39	49	56	62	66	68	68
27	16	30	43	53	62	68	73	75	75
29	17	33	46	58	67	74	79	82	82
31	18	35	50	62	72	80	85	88	88
33	20	37	53	66	77	85	91	94	94
35	21	40	57	70	82	91	97	100	100
37	22	42	60	74	88	99	102	105	..
40	24	46	65	81	94	103	110	113	..
45	27	51	72	90	105	115	121	..	..
50	30	57	80	100	115	125	..	..	..

* For best results, smaller sprocket should have at least 21 teeth.

Table 2.   Service Factors for Silent Chain Drives

Use factors in Col. 1 for service of 10 hours per day.
Use factors in Col. 2 for service of 24 hours per day or when extra-long chain life is desired.

Driven Machine	SOURCE OF POWER							
	Electric Motor or Turbine of Equal Rating		Oversize Motor or Turbine or Steam Engine*		Gasoline Engine 6 to 12 Cylinders		4 Cylinder Gas Engine or Diesel	
	Col. 1	Col. 2	Col. 1	Col. 2	Col. 1	Col. 2	Col. 1	Col. 2
Agitators								
Liquid	1.1	1.3	1.2	1.5	1.4	1.7	1.6	1.9
Semi-Liquid	1.1	1.3	1.2	1.5	1.4	1.7	1.6	1.9
Brick-Clay Mach.								
Auger Machines	1.3	1.6	1.4	1.7	1.5	1.8	1.7	2
Brick Machines	1.4	1.7	1.5	1.8	1.6	1.9	1.8	2.2
Cutting Table	1.3	1.6	1.4	1.7	1.5	1.8	1.7	2
Dry Press	1.4	1.7	1.5	1.8	1.6	1.9	1.8	2.2
Granulator	1.4	1.7	1.5	1.8	1.6	1.9	1.8	2.2
Mixer	1.4	1.7	1.5	1.8	1.6	1.9	1.8	2.2
Rolls	1.4	1.7	1.5	1.8	1.6	1.9	1.8	2.2
Cement Plants								
Kilns	1.4	1.7	1.5	1.8	1.6	1.9	1.8	2.2
Kominuters	1.5	1.8	1.6	1.9	1.7	2	2	2.5
Compressors Recip.								
Gas	1.4	1.7	1.5	1.8	1.6	1.9	...	...
Liquid	1.5	1.8	1.6	1.9	1.7	2	...	...
Cotton Oil Plants								
Linters	1.4	1.7	1.5	1.8	1.6	1.9	1.8	2.2
Cookers	1.4	1.7	1.5	1.8	1.6	1.9	1.8	2.2
Cranes	1	1.3	1.2	1.5	1.4	1.7	1.8	2.2
Crushing Machinery								
Ball Mills	1.5	1.8	1.6	1.9	1.7	2	2	2.5
Coal Breakers	1.4	1.7	1.5	1.8	1.6	1.9	1.8	2.2
Coal Pulverizers	1.4	1.7	1.5	1.8	1.6	1.9	1.8	2.2
Cone Crushers	1.5	1.8	1.6	1.9	1.7	2	2	2.5
Crushing Rolls	1.5	1.8	1.6	1.9	1.7	2	2	2.5
Gyratory Crushers	1.5	1.8	1.6	1.9	1.7	2	2	2.5
Hardinge Mills	1.5	1.8	1.6	1.9	1.7	2	2	2.5
Jaw Crushers	1.5	1.8	1.6	1.9	1.7	2	2	2.5
Linseed Crushers	1.4	1.7	1.5	1.8	1.6	1.9	1.8	2.2
Fans, Blowers								
Exhausters	1.2	1.5	1.4	1.7	1.6	1.9	1.8	2.2
Fans (Misc.)	1.1	1.4	1.3	1.6	1.6	1.9	1.8	2.2
Mine Fans	1.3	1.6	1.5	1.8	1.7	2	2	2.5
Positive Blowers	1.5	1.8	1.6	1.9	1.7	2	2	2.5
Propeller	1.1	1.4	1.3	1.6	1.6	1.9	1.8	2.2

* These same factors also apply to gas or Diesel engines with hydraulic drive.

Table 2 (*Continued*).   Service Factors for Silent Chain Drives

Use factors in Col. 1 for service of 10 hours per day.
Use factors in Col. 2 for service of 24 hours per day or when extra-long chain life is desired.

Driven Machine	Electric Motor or Turbine of Equal Rating		Oversize Motor or Turbine or Steam Engine*		Gasoline Engine 6 to 12 Cylinders		4 Cylinder Gas Engine or Diesel	
	Col. 1	Col. 2	Col. 1	Col. 2	Col. 1	Col. 2	Col. 1	Col. 2
Flour, Feed, Cereal Mach.								
Bolters, Sifters	1.1	1.4	1.2	1.5	1.3	1.6	1.5	1.8
Grinders	1.2	1.5	1.3	1.6	1.4	1.7	1.6	1.9
Purifiers, Reels	1.1	1.4	1.2	1.5	1.3	1.6	1.5	1.8
Roller Mills	1.3	1.6	1.4	1.7	1.5	1.8	1.7	2
Separator	1.1	1.4	...	...	...	...	...	...
Generators, Exciters	1.2	1.5	1.3	1.6	1.4	1.7	1.6	1.9
Hoists	1	1.3	1.2	1.5	1.3	1.6	1.5	1.8
Ice Machines	1.5	1.8	1.6	1.9	1.7	2	2	2.5
Laundry Machinery								
Dampeners	1.1	1.4	1.2	1.5	1.4	1.7	1.6	1.9
Extractors	1.1	1.4	1.2	1.5	1.4	1.7	1.6	1.9
Tumblers	1.2	1.5	1.3	1.6	1.4	1.7	1.6	1.9
Washers	1.1	1.4	1.2	1.5	1.4	1.7	1.6	1.9
Line Shafts								
Brick Plants	1.5	1.8	1.6	1.9	1.7	2	2	2.5
Coal Handling	1.2	1.5	1.3	1.6	1.4	1.7	1.5	1.8
Cotton Gins	1.1	1.4	1.2	1.5	1.3	1.6	1.5	1.8
Cotton Oil Plants	1.1	1.4	1.2	1.5	1.3	1.6	1.5	1.8
Grain Elevators	1	1.3	1.1	1.4	1.2	1.5	1.4	1.7
Paper Mills	1.3	1.6	1.4	1.7	1.5	1.8	1.7	2
Rubber Plants	1.4	1.7	1.5	1.8	1.6	1.9	1.8	2.2
Steel Mills	1.4	1.7	1.5	1.8	1.6	1.9	1.8	2.2
Machine Tools								
Boring Mills	1	1.3	1.2	1.5	1.4	1.7	...	...
Cam Cutters	1	1.3	1.2	1.5	1.4	1.7	...	...
Punch Presses	1.2	1.5	1.4	1.7	1.5	1.8	...	...
Drill Presses	1	1.3	1.1	1.4	1.3	1.6	...	...
Grinders	1.1	1.4	1.2	1.5	1.4	1.7	...	...
Lathes	1	1.3	1.2	1.5	1.4	1.7	...	...
Milling Machines	1.1	1.4	1.3	1.6	1.5	1.8	...	...
Mills								
Ball	1.6	1.9	1.7	2	1.8	2.2	...	...
Flaking	1.6	1.9	1.7	2	1.8	2.2	...	...
Pebble	1.6	1.9	1.7	2	1.8	2.2	...	...
Rod	1.6	1.9	1.7	2	1.8	2.2	...	...
Roller	1.6	1.9	1.7	2	1.8	2.2	...	...
Hardinge	1.6	1.9	1.7	2	1.8	2.2	...	...

* These same factors also apply to gas or Diesel engines with hydraulic drive.

Table 2 (*Continued*). Service Factors for Silent Chain Drives

Use factors in Col. 1 for service of 10 hours per day.
Use factors in Col. 2 for service of 24 hours per day or when extra-long chain life is desired.

Driven Machine	Electric Motor or Turbine of Equal Rating		Oversize Motor or Turbine or Steam Engine*		Gasoline Engine 6 to 12 Cylinders		4 Cylinder Gas Engine or Diesel	
	Col. 1	Col. 2	Col. 1	Col. 2	Col. 1	Col. 2	Col. 1	Col. 2
Oil Field Machinery								
Pipe Line Pumps	1.1	1.4	1.3	1.6	1.4	1.7	1.5	1.8
Pumping Units	1.4	1.7	1.5	1.8	1.6	1.9	1.7	2
Slush Pumps	1.3	1.6	1.4	1.7	1.5	1.8	1.6	1.9
Paper Machinery								
Agitators	1	1.3	1.2	1.5	1.3	1.6	1.5	1.8
Beaters	1.3	1.6	1.5	1.8	1.6	1.9	1.7	2
Calenders	1.2	1.5	1.4	1.7	1.5	1.8	1.6	1.9
Chippers	1.5	1.8	1.6	1.9	1.7	2	1.8	2.2
Dryers	1.2	1.5	1.4	1.7	1.5	1.8	1.6	1.9
Paper Machines	1.2	1.5	1.3	1.6	1.5	1.8	1.6	1.9
Washers	1.4	1.7	...	...	...	...	...	...
Winder Drums	1.5	1.8	1.6	1.9	1.7	2	...	...
Printing Machinery								
Embossing Press	1.2	1.5	1.3	1.6	1.5	1.8	1.6	1.9
Flat Bed Press	1.2	1.5	1.3	1.6	1.5	1.8	1.6	1.9
Folders	1.2	1.5	1.3	1.6	1.5	1.8	1.6	1.9
Linotype	1.1	1.4	1.2	1.5	1.3	1.6	1.5	1.8
Magazine Presses	1.2	1.5	1.4	1.7	1.5	1.8	1.6	1.9
Newspaper Presses	1	1.3	1.2	1.5	1.3	1.6	1.4	1.7
Paper Cutters	1.1	1.4	1.2	1.5	1.3	1.6	1.5	1.8
Rotary Press	1.1	1.4	1.2	1.5	1.3	1.6	1.5	1.8
Pumps								
Centrifugal	1.1	1.4	1.3	1.6	1.5	1.8	1.6	1.9
Dredge	1.5	1.8	1.6	1.9	1.7	2	2	2.5
Duplex	1.6	1.9	1.7	2	1.8	2.2	2	2.5
Gear	1.2	1.5	1.3	1.6	1.5	1.8	1.6	1.9
Rotary	1.1	1.4	1.3	1.6	1.5	1.8	1.6	1.9
Triplex	1.3	1.6	1.4	1.7	1.5	1.8	1.7	2
Steel Plants								
Rolling Mills	1.3	1.6	1.4	1.7	1.5	1.8	1.7	2
Wire Benches	1.2	1.5	1.3	1.6	1.5	1.8	1.6	1.9
Textile Machinery								
Looms	1.1	1.4	1.3	1.6	...	...	...	...
Reels	1	1.3	1.2	1.5	...	...	...	...
Spinning Frames	1	1.3	1.2	1.5	...	...	...	...
Twisters	1	1.3	1.2	1.5	...	...	...	...
Warpers	1	1.3	1.2	1.5	...	...	...	...

* These same factors also apply to gas or Diesel engines with hydraulic drive.

Sprocket Wheels for Ordinary Link Chain

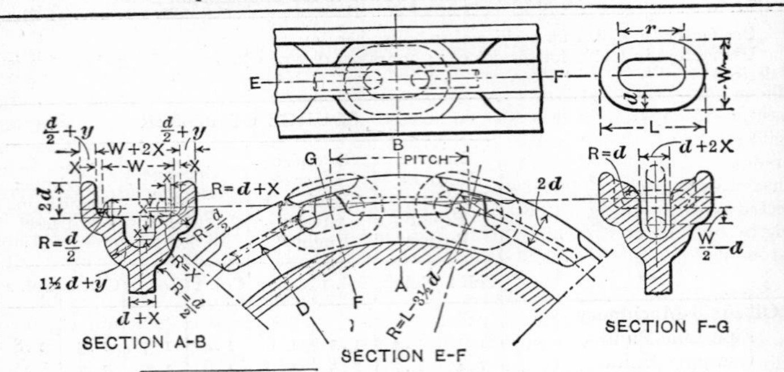

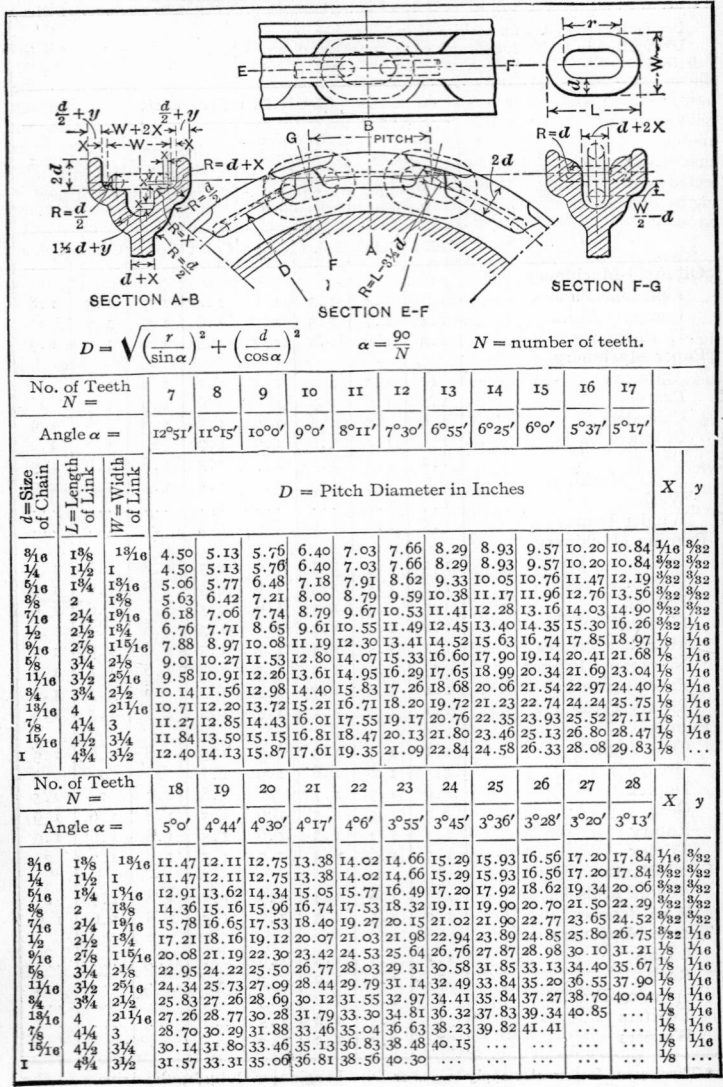

$$D = \sqrt{\left(\frac{r}{\sin\alpha}\right)^2 + \left(\frac{d}{\cos\alpha}\right)^2} \qquad \alpha = \frac{90}{N} \qquad N = \text{number of teeth.}$$

No. of Teeth $N =$			7	8	9	10	11	12	13	14	15	16	17		
Angle $\alpha =$			12°51′	11°15′	10°0′	9°0′	8°11′	7°30′	6°55′	6°25′	6°0′	5°37′	5°17′		
d = Size of Chain	L = Length of Link	W = Width of Link	D = Pitch Diameter in Inches											X	y
3/16	1 3/8	13/16	4.50	5.13	5.76	6.40	7.03	7.66	8.29	8.93	9.57	10.20	10.84	1/16	3/32
1/4	1 1/2	1	4.50	5.13	5.76	6.40	7.03	7.66	8.29	8.93	9.57	10.20	10.84	3/32	3/32
5/16	1 3/4	1 3/16	5.06	5.77	6.48	7.18	7.91	8.62	9.33	10.05	10.76	11.47	12.19	3/32	3/32
3/8	2	1 3/8	5.63	6.42	7.21	8.00	8.79	9.59	10.38	11.17	11.96	12.76	13.56	3/32	3/32
7/16	2 1/4	1 9/16	6.18	7.06	7.74	8.79	9.67	10.53	11.41	12.28	13.16	14.03	14.90	3/32	3/32
1/2	2 1/2	1 3/4	6.76	7.71	8.65	9.61	10.55	11.49	12.45	13.40	14.35	15.30	16.26	3/32	1/16
9/16	2 7/8	1 15/16	7.88	8.97	10.08	11.19	12.30	13.41	14.52	15.63	16.74	17.85	18.97	1/8	1/16
5/8	3 1/4	2 1/8	9.01	10.27	11.53	12.80	14.07	15.33	16.60	17.90	19.14	20.41	21.68	1/8	1/16
11/16	3 1/2	2 5/16	9.58	10.91	12.26	13.61	14.95	16.29	17.65	18.99	20.34	21.69	23.04	1/8	1/16
3/4	3 3/4	2 1/2	10.14	11.56	12.98	14.40	15.83	17.26	18.68	20.06	21.54	22.97	24.40	1/8	1/16
13/16	4	2 11/16	10.71	12.20	13.72	15.21	16.71	18.20	19.72	21.23	22.74	24.24	25.75	1/8	1/16
7/8	4 1/4	3	11.27	12.85	14.43	16.01	17.55	19.17	20.76	22.35	23.93	25.52	27.11	1/8	1/16
15/16	4 1/2	3 1/4	11.84	13.50	15.15	16.81	18.47	20.13	21.80	23.46	25.13	26.80	28.47	1/8	1/16
1	4 3/4	3 1/2	12.40	14.13	15.87	17.61	19.35	21.09	22.84	24.58	26.33	28.08	29.83	1/8	...

No. of Teeth $N =$			18	19	20	21	22	23	24	25	26	27	28	X	y
Angle $\alpha =$			5°0′	4°44′	4°30′	4°17′	4°6′	3°55′	3°45′	3°36′	3°28′	3°20′	3°13′		
3/16	1 3/8	13/16	11.47	12.11	12.75	13.38	14.02	14.66	15.29	15.93	16.56	17.20	17.84	1/16	3/32
1/4	1 1/2	1	11.47	12.11	12.75	13.38	14.02	14.66	15.29	15.93	16.56	17.20	17.84	3/32	3/32
5/16	1 3/4	1 3/16	12.91	13.62	14.34	15.05	15.77	16.49	17.20	17.92	18.62	19.34	20.06	3/32	3/32
3/8	2	1 3/8	14.36	15.16	15.96	16.74	17.53	18.32	19.11	19.90	20.70	21.50	22.29	3/32	3/32
7/16	2 1/4	1 9/16	15.78	16.65	17.53	18.40	19.27	20.15	21.02	21.90	22.77	23.65	24.52	3/32	3/32
1/2	2 1/2	1 3/4	17.21	18.16	19.12	20.07	21.03	21.98	22.94	23.89	24.85	25.80	26.75	3/32	1/16
9/16	2 7/8	1 15/16	20.08	21.19	22.30	23.42	24.53	25.64	26.76	27.87	28.98	30.10	31.21	1/8	1/16
5/8	3 1/4	2 1/8	22.95	24.22	25.50	26.77	28.03	29.31	30.58	31.85	33.13	34.40	35.67	1/8	1/16
11/16	3 1/2	2 5/16	24.34	25.73	27.09	28.44	29.79	31.14	32.49	33.84	35.20	36.55	37.90	1/8	1/16
3/4	3 3/4	2 1/2	25.83	27.26	28.69	30.12	31.55	32.97	34.41	35.84	37.27	38.70	40.04	1/8	1/16
13/16	4	2 11/16	27.26	28.77	30.28	31.79	33.30	34.81	36.32	37.83	39.34	40.85	...	1/8	1/16
7/8	4 1/4	3	28.70	30.29	31.88	33.46	35.04	36.63	38.23	39.82	41.41	...	...	1/8	1/16
15/16	4 1/2	3 1/4	30.14	31.80	33.46	35.13	36.83	38.48	40.15	...	...	...	...	1/8	1/16
1	4 3/4	3 1/2	31.57	33.31	35.06	36.81	38.56	40.30	...	...	...	...	...	1/8	...

CRANE CHAIN AND HOOKS

Material for Crane Chains. — The best material for crane and hoisting chains is a good grade of wrought iron, in which the percentage of phosphorus, sulphur, silicon and other impurities is comparatively low. The tensile strength of the best grades of wrought iron does not exceed 46,000 pounds per square inch, whereas mild steel with about 0.15 per cent carbon has a tensile strength nearly double this amount. The ductility and toughness of wrought iron, however, is greater than that of ordinary commercial steel, and for this reason it is preferable for chains subjected to heavy intermittent strains, because wrought iron will always give warning by bending or stretching, before breaking. Another important reason for using wrought iron in preference to steel is that a perfect weld can be effected more easily.

Strength of Chains. — When calculating the strength of chains, it should be observed that the strength of a link subjected to tensile stresses is not equal to twice the strength of an iron bar of the same diameter as the link stock, but is a certain amount less, owing to the bending action caused by the manner in which the load is applied to the link. The strength is also reduced somewhat by the weld. The following empirical formula is commonly used for calculating the breaking load, in pounds, of wrought-iron crane chains:

$$W = 54,000 D^2$$

in which W = breaking load in pounds, and D = diameter of bar (in inches) from which links are made. The working load for chains should not exceed one-third the value of W, and, in many cases, it is one-fourth or one-fifth of the breaking load. When a chain is wound around a casting and severe bending stresses are introduced, a greater factor of safety should be used.

Safe Loads in Tons for Ropes, Chains and Cables

Manila Rope*				Chains				Wire Cable			
Rope Diam.	Single Rope	Two Part	Four Part	Diam. Link Stock	Single Chain	Two Part	Four Part	Cable Diam.	Single Cable	Two Part	Four Part
½	⅛	¼	½	¼	½	⅞	1½	½	1	2	3½
⅝	¼	½	¾	⅜	1	1¾	3	⅝	1¾	3¼	6½
¾	⅜	¾	1¼	½	2	3½	6	¾	2½	4½	9
⅞	½	1	2	⅝	3	5	9	⅞	3¼	6	12
1	¾	1½	2½	¾	5	9	15	1	4	8	16
1¼	1	2	3	⅞	6	10½	18	1¼	6	12	24
1½	1¼	2½	4	1	8	14	24	1½	10	19	36
1¾	2	4	6	1⅛	11	19	33	1¾	13	25	48
2	2½	5	8	1¼	13	23	39	2	16	32	60
2¼	3½	6½	11	1½	18	32	54	...	...	...	...
2½	4½	8	13	....	...	...	...	...	...	...	...

* These figures apply only to a rope in fairly good condition.

Care of Hoisting and Crane Chains. — All chains used for hoisting heavy loads are subject to deterioration, both apparent and invisible. The links wear, and there is also an alteration in the nature or fiber of the material, owing to the strains, shocks, etc., producing crystallization. Chain wear can be reduced considerably by occasional lubrication. The life of a chain can also be prolonged by frequent annealing, as this restores the fibrous quality of the material to some extent, although there may be a slight decrease in the tensile strength. To anneal a chain, heat it to cherry-red and allow it to cool slowly. This should be done every six months, and oftener if the chain is subjected to unusually severe service. Chains should be examined periodically for twists, as a twisted chain will wear rapidly. Any links which have worn excessively should be replaced with new ones, so that every link will do its full share of work during the life of the chain, without exceeding the limit of safety. Chains for hoisting purposes should be made with short links, so that they will wrap closely around the sheaves or drums without bending. The diameter of the winding drums should be not less than 25 or 30 times the diameter of the iron used for the links.

Studded Chains. — Tests have demonstrated that the ultimate breaking strength of a chain with studded links is less than that of an unstudded chain. This is probably due to the fact that the open links of an unstudded chain collapse until the sides are approximately parallel, so that the stresses are lower than in the studded links, the sides of which are prevented from collapsing by the studs. The principal function of the stud is to prevent the chain from kinking and catching, so that it will run free from chain lockers, etc. The stud also prevents the chain from becoming rigid under heavy strains.

Studded Cable Chain

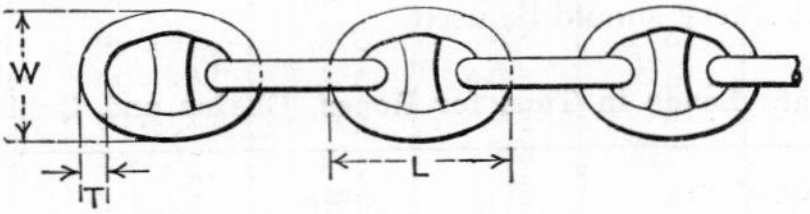

Size of Chain in Inches	Length of Link in Inches	Width of Link in Inches	Weight per Foot of Chain	Proof Test	Size of Chain in Inches	Length of Link in Inches	Width of Link in Inches	Weight per Foot of Chain	Proof Test
T	*L*	*W*	Pounds	Tons	*T*	*L*	*W*	Pounds	Tons
¾	4⅜	2¾	5.5	10.1	1½	8½	5⅜	21.2	40.5
13/16	4¾	3	6.3	12.0	1 9/16	8⅞	5⅝	23.8	44.0
⅞	5	3¼	8.2	13.7	1⅝	9¼	5⅞	25.0	47.5
15/16	5⅜	3½	9.2	15.7	1 11/16	9⅝	6	26.2	51.2
1	5⅞	3¾	10.2	18.0	1¾	10	6¼	28.8	55.2
1 1/16	6¼	3⅞	11.5	20.3	1⅞	10½	6¾	33.8	63.3
1⅛	6½	4⅛	12.3	22.8	1 15/16	10¾	7	35.8	67.5
1 3/16	6¾	4¼	13.5	25.5	2	11⅛	7¼	38.8	72.0
1¼	7⅛	4½	15.0	28.1	2 1/16	11½	7½	42.3	76.5
1 5/16	7⅜	4⅝	16.2	31.0	2⅛	12	7¾	46.0	81.2
1⅜	7¾	4⅞	18.3	34.0	2 3/16	12½	8	48.3	86.1
1 7/16	8⅛	5⅛	18.8	37.2	2¼	13	8¼	50.0	91.0

Note: Safe working loads are one-half of proof test loads.

Close-link Hoisting, Sling and Crane Chain

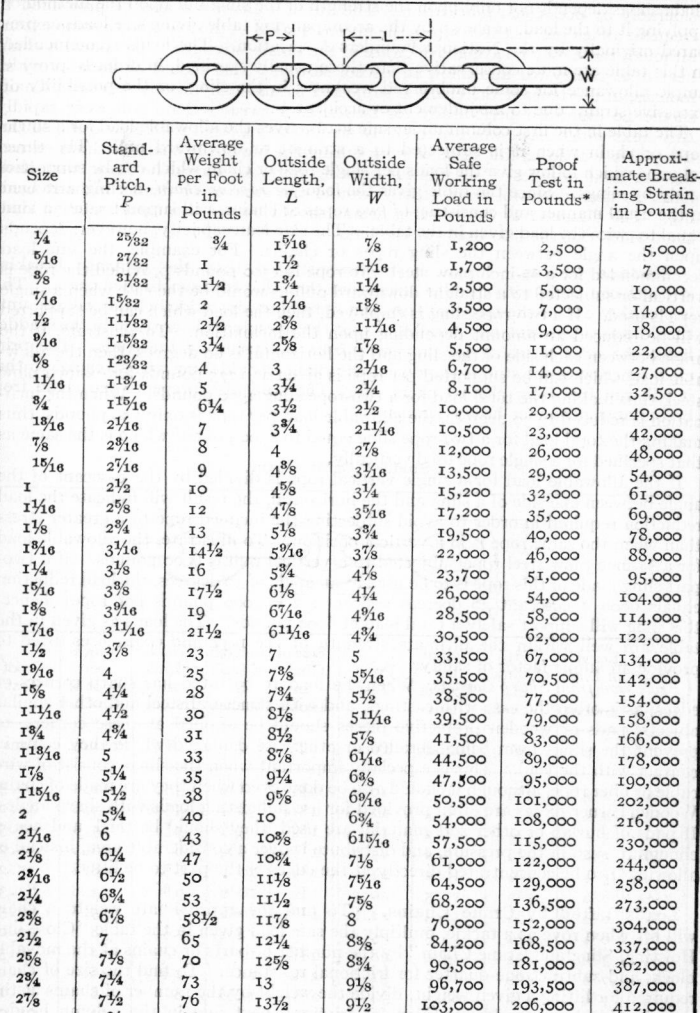

Size	Standard Pitch, P	Average Weight per Foot in Pounds	Outside Length, L	Outside Width, W	Average Safe Working Load in Pounds	Proof Test in Pounds*	Approximate Breaking Strain in Pounds
¼	25/32	¾	1 5/16	⅞	1,200	2,500	5,000
5/16	27/32	1	1½	1 1/16	1,700	3,500	7,000
⅜	31/32	1½	1¾	1¼	2,500	5,000	10,000
7/16	1 5/32	2	2 1/16	1⅜	3,500	7,000	14,000
½	1 11/32	2½	2⅜	1 11/16	4,500	9,000	18,000
9/16	1 15/32	3¼	2⅝	1⅞	5,500	11,000	22,000
⅝	1 23/32	4	3	2 1/16	6,700	14,000	27,000
11/16	1 13/16	5	3¼	2¼	8,100	17,000	32,500
¾	1 15/16	6¼	3½	2½	10,000	20,000	40,000
13/16	2 1/16	7	3¾	2 11/16	10,500	23,000	42,000
⅞	2 3/16	8	4	2⅞	12,000	26,000	48,000
15/16	2 7/16	9	4⅜	3 1/16	13,500	29,000	54,000
1	2½	10	4⅝	3¼	15,200	32,000	61,000
1 1/16	2⅝	12	4⅞	3 5/16	17,200	35,000	69,000
1⅛	2¾	13	5⅛	3¾	19,500	40,000	78,000
1 3/16	3 1/16	14½	5 9/16	3⅞	22,000	46,000	88,000
1¼	3⅛	16	5¾	4⅛	23,700	51,000	95,000
1 5/16	3⅜	17½	6⅛	4¼	26,000	54,000	104,000
1⅜	3 9/16	19	6 7/16	4 9/16	28,500	58,000	114,000
1 7/16	3 11/16	21½	6 11/16	4¾	30,500	62,000	122,000
1½	3⅞	23	7	5	33,500	67,000	134,000
1 9/16	4	25	7⅜	5 5/16	35,500	70,500	142,000
1⅝	4¼	28	7¾	5½	38,500	77,000	154,000
1 11/16	4½	30	8⅛	5 11/16	39,500	79,000	158,000
1¾	4¾	31	8½	5⅞	41,500	83,000	166,000
1 13/16	5	33	8⅞	6 1/16	44,500	89,000	178,000
1⅞	5¼	35	9¼	6⅜	47,500	95,000	190,000
1 15/16	5½	38	9⅝	6 9/16	50,500	101,000	202,000
2	5¾	40	10	6¾	54,000	108,000	216,000
2 1/16	6	43	10⅜	6 15/16	57,500	115,000	230,000
2⅛	6¼	47	10¾	7⅛	61,000	122,000	244,000
2 3/16	6½	50	11⅛	7 5/16	64,500	129,000	258,000
2¼	6¾	53	11½	7⅝	68,200	136,500	273,000
2⅜	6⅞	58½	11⅞	8	76,000	152,000	304,000
2½	7	65	12¼	8⅜	84,200	168,500	337,000
2⅝	7⅛	70	12⅝	8¾	90,500	181,000	362,000
2¾	7¼	73	13	9⅛	96,700	193,500	387,000
2⅞	7½	76	13½	9½	103,000	206,000	412,000
3	7¾	86	14	9⅞	109,000	218,000	436,000

* Chains tested to U. S. Government and American Bureau of Shipping requirements.

Safe Loads for Ropes and Chains. — Safe loads recommended for wire rope or chain slings depends not only upon the strength of the sling but upon the method of applying it to the load, as shown by the accompanying table giving safe loads as prepared originally by the National Founders Association. The loads recommended in this table are more conservative than those usually specified, in order to provide ample allowance for some unobserved weakness in the sling, or the possibility of excessive strains due to misjudgment or accident.

The table in the first column under safe loads, gives the allowable load for a single rope or chain when it is subjected to a straight or downward pull. The three columns which follow give the loads per single rope or chain which can be supported safely by slings. Since the table gives the load *per rope or chain*, a sling arranged in the usual manner and consisting of two ropes or chains, will support safely a load equal to twice the load given in the table. The safe load capacity, however, depends upon the angle between the sling ropes or chains. For example, the safe load recommended for a ⅜-inch plow steel wire rope is 1500 pounds provided the rope is vertical or subjected to a straight downward pull as would be the case when a single rope is used. If a two-rope sling is employed, then the load which can be supported will be reduced an amount depending upon the inclination. To illustrate, if the angle between each side of the sling and the horizontal is 60 degrees, then the allowable load which can be supported per rope is given as 1275 pounds for ⅜-inch plow steel, thus making the total load for a two-rope sling 2550 pounds. When the inclination is reduced to 30 degrees, the allowable load per rope is only 750 pounds, thus making the total load for a two-rope sling equal to 1500 pounds which is the same as that specified for a single rope used vertically.

If the allowable load for a single vertical rope is divided by the cosecant of the angle between one side of a sling and the horizontal, the result will indicate the load reduction required in order to avoid subjecting the inclined rope to a greater stress than when the same rope is in a vertical position. To illustrate, the allowable load for a ¾-inch plow steel rope subjected to a vertical pull is 6000 pounds. If a two-part sling made of this rope is to be used at an angle of 30 degrees, the load reduction equals 6000 ÷ cosecant 30 degrees = 6000 ÷ 2 = 3000 pounds per rope; hence, this sling will support safely a total load of 6000 pounds. The loads as given in the table are well within the ultimate strength of the rope and chain sizes listed to provide an ample factor of safety.

Protection from Sharp Corners: When the load to be lifted has sharp corners or edges, as is often the case with castings, and with structural steel and other similar objects, pads or wooden protective pieces should be applied at these corners, to prevent the slings from being abraded or otherwise damaged where they come in contact with the load. This is especially important when the slings consist of wire cable or fiber rope, although it should also be done even when they are made of chain. Wooden corner-pieces are often provided for use in hoisting loads with sharp angles. If pads of burlap or other soft material are used, they should be thick and heavy enough to sustain the pressure, and distribute it over a considerable area, instead of allowing it to be concentrated directly at the edges of the part to be lifted.

Loads Lifted by Crane Chains. — To find the approximate weight a chain will lift when rove as a tackle, multiply the safe load given in the table "Close-link Hoisting, Sling and Crane Chain" by the number of parts or chains at the movable block, and subtract one-quarter for frictional resistance. To find the size of chain required for lifting a given weight, divide the weight by the number of chains at the movable block, and add one-third for friction; next find in the column headed "Average Safe Working Load" the corresponding load, and then the corresponding size of chain in the column headed "Size." In case of heavy chain or where chain is unusually long, the weight of the chain itself should also be considered.

Safe Loads in Pounds for Ropes and Chains

Prepared by National Founders' Association. When handling molten metal, wire ropes and chains should be 25 per cent stronger than indicated in the table.

Kind of Rope or Chain	Diameter of Rope, or of Rod or Bar for Chain Links, Inch	The safe loads in table are for each *single* rope or chain. When used double or in other multiples, the loads may be increased proportionately.*			
		Rope or chain Vertical	Sling at 60°	Sling at 45°	Sling at 30°
			60°	45°	30°
PLOW STEEL WIRE ROPE (6 strands of 19 or 37 wires.) If crucible steel rope is used, reduce loads one-fifth.	3/8	1,500	1,275	1,050	750
	1/2	2,400	2,050	1,700	1,200
	5/8	4,000	3,400	2,800	2,000
	3/4	6,000	5,100	4,200	3,000
	7/8	8,000	6,800	5,600	4,000
	1	10,000	8,500	7,000	5,000
	1 1/8	13,000	11,000	9,000	6,500
	1 1/4	16,000	13,500	11,000	8,000
	1 3/8	19,000	16,000	13,000	9,500
	1 1/2	22,000	19,000	16,000	11,000
CRANE CHAIN (Best Grade of Wrought Iron, Hand-made, Tested, Short-linked chain.)	1/4	600	500	425	300
	3/8	1,200	1,025	850	600
	1/2	2,400	2,050	1,700	1,200
	5/8	4,000	3,400	2,800	2,000
	3/4	5,500	4,700	3,900	2,750
	7/8	7,500	6,400	5,200	3,700
	1	9,500	8,000	6,600	4,700
	1 1/8	12,000	10,200	8,400	6,000
	1 1/4	15,000	12,750	10,500	7,500
	1 3/8	22,000	19,000	16,000	11,000
MANILA ROPE (Best long Fiber Grade.)	3/8	120	100	85	60
	1/2	250	210	175	125
	5/8	360	300	250	180
	3/4	520	440	360	260
	7/8	620	520	420	300
	1	750	625	525	375
	1 1/8	1,000	850	700	500
	1 1/4	1,200	1,025	850	600
	1 1/2	1,600	1,350	1,100	800
	1 3/4	2,100	1,800	1,500	1,050
	2	2,800	2,400	2,000	1,400
	2 1/2	4,000	3,400	2,800	2,000
	3	6,000	5,100	4,200	3,000

* Note that when the angle between one side of sling and the horizontal, is reduced, the allowable load which may safely be supported per rope or chain, is also reduced. See "Safe Loads for Ropes and Chains."

Dimensions of Crane Hooks

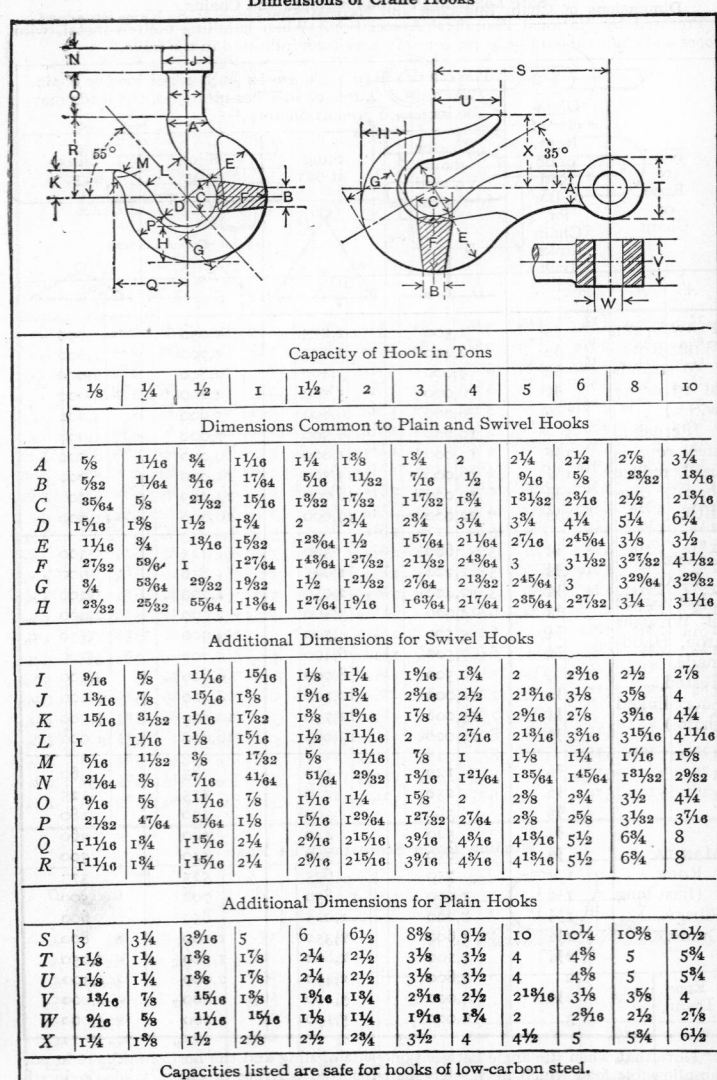

	Capacity of Hook in Tons											
	1/8	1/4	1/2	1	1½	2	3	4	5	6	8	10
Dimensions Common to Plain and Swivel Hooks												
A	5/8	11/16	3/4	1 1/16	1 1/4	1 3/8	1 3/4	2	2 1/4	2 1/2	2 7/8	3 1/4
B	5/32	11/64	9/16	17/64	5/16	11/32	7/16	1/2	9/16	5/8	23/32	13/16
C	35/64	5/8	21/32	15/16	1 3/32	1 7/32	1 17/32	1 3/4	1 31/32	2 3/16	2 1/2	2 13/16
D	1 5/16	1 3/8	1 1/2	1 3/4	2	2 1/4	2 3/4	3 1/4	3 3/4	4 1/4	5 1/4	6 1/4
E	1 1/16	3/4	1 3/16	1 5/32	1 23/64	1 1/2	1 57/64	2 11/64	2 7/16	2 45/64	3 1/8	3 1/2
F	27/32	59/64	1	1 4/64	1 43/64	1 27/32	2 11/32	2 43/64	3	3 29/64	4 11/32	
G	3/4	53/64	29/32	1 3/32	1 1/2	1 21/32	2 7/64	2 13/32	2 45/64	3	3 29/64	3 29/32
H	23/32	25/32	55/64	1 13/64	1 27/64	1 9/16	1 63/64	2 17/64	2 35/64	2 27/32	3 1/4	3 11/16
Additional Dimensions for Swivel Hooks												
I	9/16	5/8	11/16	15/16	1 1/8	1 1/4	1 9/16	1 3/4	2	2 3/16	2 1/2	2 7/8
J	13/16	7/8	15/16	1 3/8	1 9/16	1 3/4	2 3/16	2 1/2	2 13/16	3 1/8	3 5/8	4
K	15/16	1 1/32	1 1/16	1 7/32	1 3/8	1 9/16	1 7/8	2 1/4	2 9/16	2 7/8	3 3/16	4 1/4
L	1	1 1/16	1 1/8	1 5/16	1 1/2	1 11/16	2	2 7/16	2 13/16	3 3/16	3 15/16	4 11/16
M	5/16	11/32	3/8	17/32	5/8	11/16	7/8	1	1 1/8	1 1/4	1 7/16	1 5/8
N	21/64	3/8	7/16	41/64	51/64	29/32	1 3/16	1 21/64	1 35/64	1 45/64	1 31/32	2 9/32
O	9/16	5/8	11/16	7/8	1 1/16	1 1/4	1 5/8	2	2 3/8	2 3/4	3 1/2	4 1/4
P	21/32	47/64	51/64	1 1/8	1 5/16	1 29/64	1 27/32	2 7/64	2 3/8	2 5/8	3 7/32	3 7/16
Q	1 11/16	1 3/4	1 15/16	2 1/4	2 9/16	2 15/16	3 9/16	4 3/16	4 13/16	5 1/2	6 3/4	8
R	1 11/16	1 3/4	1 15/16	2 1/4	2 9/16	2 15/16	3 9/16	4 3/16	4 13/16	5 1/2	6 3/4	8
Additional Dimensions for Plain Hooks												
S	3	3 1/4	3 9/16	5	6	6 1/2	8 3/8	9 1/2	10	10 1/4	10 3/8	10 1/2
T	1 1/8	1 1/4	1 3/8	1 7/8	2 1/4	2 1/2	3 1/8	3 1/2	4	4 3/8	5	5 3/4
U	1 1/8	1 1/4	1 3/8	1 7/8	2 1/4	2 1/2	3 1/8	3 1/2	4	4 3/8	5	5 3/4
V	1 3/16	7/8	15/16	1 3/8	1 9/16	1 3/4	2 3/16	2 1/2	2 13/16	3 1/8	3 5/8	4
W	9/16	5/8	11/16	15/16	1 1/8	1 1/4	1 9/16	1 3/4	2	2 3/16	2 1/2	2 7/8
X	1 1/4	1 3/8	1 1/2	2 1/8	2 1/2	2 3/4	3 1/2	4	4 1/2	5	5 3/4	6 1/2

Capacities listed are safe for hooks of low-carbon steel.

Dimensions of Chain End-Link and Narrow Shackle — U. S. Navy Standard

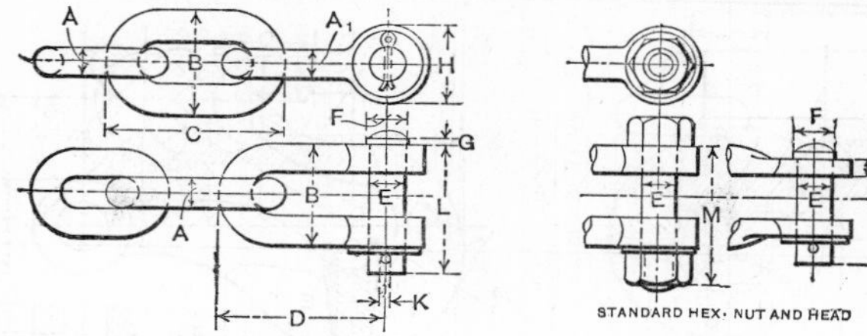

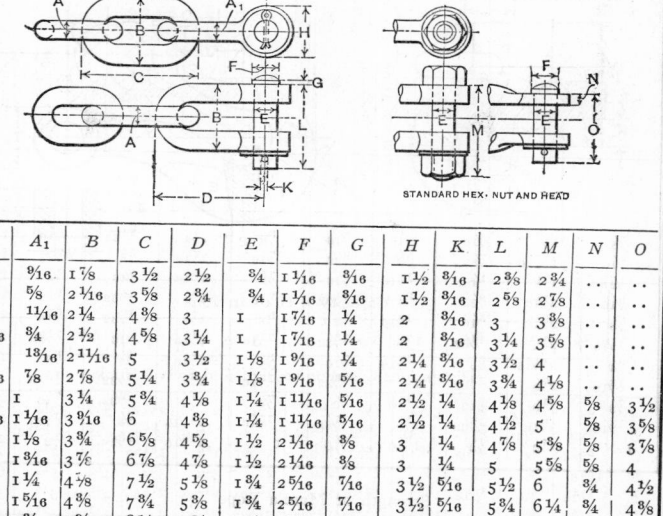

A	A1	B	C	D	E	F	G	H	K	L	M	N	O
1/2	9/16	1 7/8	3 1/2	2 1/2	3/4	1 1/16	3/16	1 1/2	3/16	2 3/8	2 3/4	..	..
9/16	5/8	2 1/16	3 5/8	2 3/4	3/4	1 1/16	3/16	1 1/2	3/16	2 5/8	2 7/8	..	..
5/8	11/16	2 1/4	4 3/8	3	1	1 7/16	1/4	2	3/16	3	3 3/8	..	..
11/16	3/4	2 1/2	4 5/8	3 1/4	1	1 7/16	1/4	2	3/16	3 1/4	3 5/8	..	..
3/4	13/16	2 11/16	5	3 1/2	1 1/8	1 9/16	1/4	2 1/4	3/16	3 1/2	4	..	..
13/16	7/8	2 7/8	5 1/4	3 3/4	1 1/8	1 9/16	5/16	2 1/4	3/16	3 3/4	4 1/8	..	..
7/8	1	3 1/4	5 3/4	4 1/8	1 1/4	1 11/16	5/16	2 1/2	1/4	4 1/8	4 5/8	5/8	3 1/2
15/16	1 1/16	3 9/16	6	4 3/8	1 1/4	1 11/16	5/16	2 1/2	1/4	4 1/2	5	5/8	3 5/8
1	1 1/8	3 3/4	6 5/8	4 5/8	1 1/2	2 1/16	3/8	3	1/4	4 7/8	5 3/8	5/8	3 7/8
1 1/16	1 3/16	3 7/8	6 7/8	4 7/8	1 1/2	2 1/16	3/8	3	1/4	5	5 5/8	5/8	4
1 1/8	1 1/4	4 1/8	7 1/2	5 1/8	1 3/4	2 5/16	7/16	3 1/2	5/16	5 1/2	6	3/4	4 1/2
1 3/16	1 5/16	4 3/8	7 3/4	5 3/8	1 3/4	2 5/16	7/16	3 1/2	5/16	5 3/4	6 1/4	3/4	4 3/8
1 1/4	1 3/8	4 9/16	8 1/8	5 3/4	1 7/8	2 7/16	7/16	3 3/4	5/16	6	6 5/8	3/4	4 3/4
1 5/16	1 7/16	4 3/4	8 3/8	5 7/8	1 7/8	2 7/16	1/2	3 3/4	5/16	6 1/4	6 3/4	3/4	4 7/8
1 3/8	1 1/2	5	8 3/4	6 1/4	2	2 11/16	1/2	4	5/16	6 1/2	7 1/8	7/8	5 1/4
1 7/16	1 9/16	5 3/16	9	6 1/2	2	2 11/16	1/2	4	5/16	6 3/4	7 3/8	7/8	5 3/8
1 1/2	1 5/8	5 3/8	9 5/8	6 7/8	2 1/4	3 1/16	9/16	4 1/2	3/8	7	7 3/4	7/8	5 1/2
1 9/16	1 11/16	5 5/8	9 7/8	7 1/8	2 1/4	3 1/16	9/16	4 1/2	3/8	7 1/4	8	7/8	5 5/8
1 5/8	1 3/4	5 13/16	10 1/2	7 3/8	2 1/2	3 7/16	5/8	5	3/8	7 1/2	8 1/2	1	6 1/8
1 11/16	1 13/16	6	10 3/4	7 3/4	2 1/2	3 7/16	5/8	5	3/8	7 3/4	8 3/4	1	6 1/4
1 3/4	1 7/8	6 1/4	11 3/8	8	2 3/4	3 11/16	11/16	5 1/2	7/16	8	9 1/8	1	6 3/8
1 13/16	1 15/16	6 7/16	11 5/8	8 1/4	2 3/4	3 11/16	11/16	5 1/2	7/16	8 1/4	9 3/8	1	6 1/2
1 7/8	2	6 11/16	11 3/4	8 1/2	2 3/4	3 11/16	11/16	5 1/2	7/16	8 1/2	9 5/8	1 1/8	6 3/4
1 15/16	2 1/16	6 7/8	12	8 3/4	2 3/4	3 11/16	11/16	5 1/2	7/16	8 3/4	9 7/8	1 1/8	6 7/8

Winding Drum Score for Wire Rope

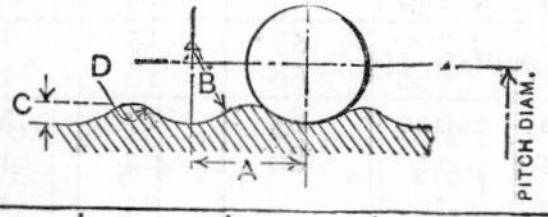

Rope Diam.	A	B	C	D
3/8	7/16	7/32	3/32	3/32
7/16	1/2	1/4	7/64	3/32
1/2	9/16	9/32	1/8	3/32
9/16	5/8	5/16	9/64	1/8
5/8	11/16	11/32	5/32	1/8
11/16	3/4	3/8	11/64	1/8
3/4	13/16	13/32	3/16	5/32
13/16	7/8	7/16	13/64	5/32
7/8	15/16	15/32	7/32	5/32
15/16	1	1/2	15/64	3/16
1	1 1/16	17/32	1/4	3/16

Winding Drum Scores for Chain

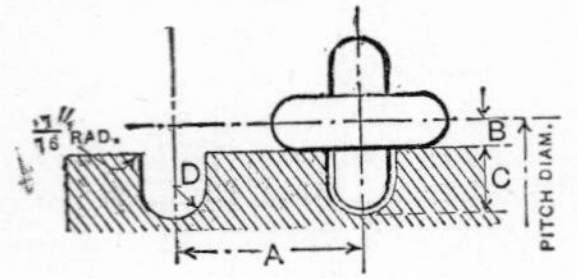

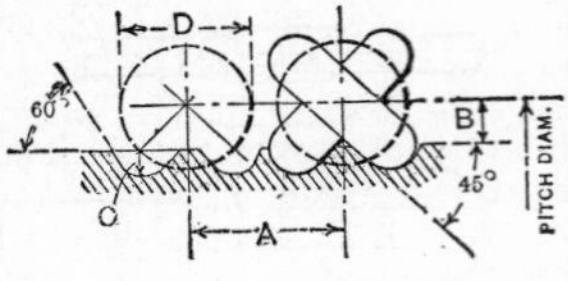

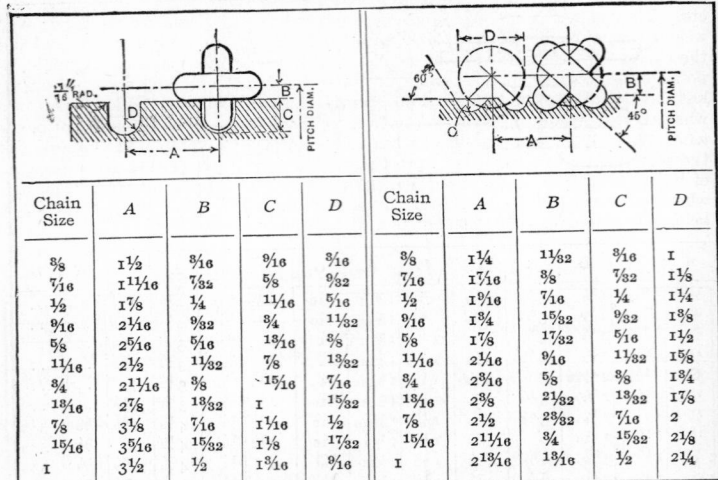

Chain Size	A	B	C	D	Chain Size	A	B	C	D
3/8	1 1/2	3/16	9/16	3/16	3/8	1 1/4	11/32	3/16	1
7/16	1 11/16	7/32	5/8	9/32	7/16	1 7/16	3/8	7/32	1 1/8
1/2	1 7/8	1/4	11/16	5/16	1/2	1 9/16	7/16	1/4	1 1/4
9/16	2 1/16	9/32	3/4	11/32	9/16	1 3/4	15/32	9/32	1 3/8
5/8	2 5/16	5/16	13/16	3/8	5/8	1 7/8	17/32	5/16	1 1/2
11/16	2 1/2	11/32	7/8	13/32	11/16	2 1/16	9/16	11/32	1 5/8
3/4	2 11/16	3/8	15/16	7/16	3/4	2 3/16	5/8	3/8	1 3/4
13/16	2 7/8	13/32	1	15/32	13/16	2 3/8	21/32	13/32	1 7/8
7/8	3 1/8	7/16	1 1/16	1/2	7/8	2 1/2	23/32	7/16	2
15/16	3 5/16	15/32	1 1/8	17/32	15/16	2 11/16	3/4	15/32	2 1/8
1	3 1/2	1/2	1 3/16	9/16	1	2 13/16	13/16	1/2	2 1/4

Strength of Manila Rope

Approximate Diameter, Inches	Circumference, Inches	Weight of 100 Feet of Rope, Pounds	Ultimate Tensile Strength of Rope, Pounds	Working Load, Total Area of Rope, in Lbs.			Minimum Diameter of Sheaves, in Inches		
				Rapid*	Medium†	Slow†	Rapid*	Medium†	Slow‡
3/16	9/16	2	230	10	20	40	8	3	1 1/2
5/16	1	4	630	20	40	100	13	5	2 1/2
3/8	1 1/8	5	900	30	60	140	15	6	3
1/2	1 1/2	7 2/3	1,620	50	100	250	20	8	4
5/8	2	13 1/3	2,880	90	180	450	25	10	5
13/16	2 1/2	20	4,500	150	300	650	35	11	7
1	3	28 1/3	6,480	200	400	1,000	40	12	8
1 1/8	3 1/2	38	8,820	250	500	1,250	45	13	9
1 5/16	4	52	11,500	350	700	1,700	55	15	11
1 1/2	4 1/2	65	14,600	450	900	2,200	60	16	12
1 5/8	5	80	18,000	550	1100	2,600	65	17	13
2	6	113	25,900	750	1500	3,700	80	22	16
2 1/4	7	153	35,300	....	2100	5,100	.....	24	18
2 5/8	8	211	46,100	....	2700	6,600	.....	28	21
3	9	262	58,300	....	3400	8,400	.....	32	24
3 1/4	10	325	72,000	....	4200	10,300	.....	35	26

* Speed from 400 to 800 feet per minute. † Hoisting speed from 150 to 300 feet per minute. ‡ Hoisting speed from 50 to 100 feet per minute.

Lifting Magnets. — Lifting magnets are especially adapted for handling pig-iron, metal plates, billets, scrap, iron and steel castings, rails, "skull crackers," etc. The magnet is energized by a direct current of any common voltage. The weight that a magnet of given size can lift depends upon the form of material and the evenness of the surfaces which must be gripped by the magnet. It might be possible to lift 20,000 pounds under favorable conditions and only 1000 pounds, or less, under adverse conditions. For example, a much greater weight can be lifted when there is a solid mass of steel or iron, than when there are a number of pieces which not only cling to the magnet but to each other. The table below represents the performance of magnets manufactured by Cutler-Hammer, Inc. The weights of billets, etc., that can be lifted, depend to some extent upon the dimensions and whether the material is in an irregular pile or stacked evenly. Brass and copper, being non-magnetic, cannot be handled with lifting magnets.

Average Lifting Capacities of Circular Magnets *

Class of Material to be Lifted	Magnet Diameter, Inches						
	18	24	29	39	45	55	65
	Average Lifting Capacity, Pounds						
Skull cracker balls, standard magnet	2100	4000	8000	12000	16000	20000	30000
Skull cracker balls, special pole shoe	3000	6000	10500	18000	24000	30000	40000
Slabs — up to	3300	6500	13000	20000	38000	50000	65000
Machine cast pig from stock pile	150	275	550	900	1580	2500	3500
Sand cast pig from stock pile	130	250	430	800	1420	2300	3000
Machine cast pig from railroad cars	130	250	430	800	1420	2300	3000
Sand cast pig from railroad cars	120	225	390	700	1300	2200	2850
Heavy melting scrap	150	275	550	900	1580	2500	3500
Plate scrap	130	250	500	700	1100	1500	2300
Broken scrap	110	200	350	600	1000	1400	1800
Cast iron borings	110	200	350	600	1100	1550	2400
Steel turnings	50	100	175	300	450	750	1200

*The lifting capacities shown are based on the average lifts when the magnet has attained maximum temperature on an all-day cycle of half-time excitation. When magnets are not operated continuously, lifting capacities are considerably higher.

Applications of Lifting Magnets. — The 18-inch magnet is used for general light work in handling finished parts or boxed material and for cleaning up scrap. It takes 2.2 amperes at 230 volts D.C. at working temperature. The 24-inch size is used for handling light finished parts, light iron and steel castings, and pipe, and draws 6.9 amperes at 230 volts D.C. at working temperature. The 29-inch size is especially adapted to crawler type cranes for general utility work, handling pipe, bar, scrap material, and miscellaneous steel pieces. It takes 8.5 amperes at 230 volts D.C. at working temperature. The 39-inch size is used for general service in handling pig iron, scrap, etc., where large capacity is not required. It draws 17.5 amperes at 230 volts D.C. at working temperature. The 45-inch size is primarily used with locomotive cranes and handles a high average load. It draws 33 amperes at 230 volts D.C. at working temperature. The 55-inch size is employed for general work and is used extensively in open hearth steel plants for handling stock. It draws 40 amperes at 230 volts D.C. at working temperature. The 65-inch size is used where large tonnage is to be handled and draws 58 amperes at 230 volts D.C. at working temperature.

Latches for Machine Doors

	A	B	C	D
	2	7/16	3/4	3/8
	2	7/16	3/4	3/8
	2	1/2	7/8	7/16

	E	F	G	α
	1	7/16	1/4	8°
	1	1/2	1/4	8°
	1 1/8	1/2	5/16	8°

Proportions of Large Handwheels

Diam.	A	B	C	D	E	F	G
8	3/4	3/4	5/8	1 1/2	3/8	5/16	1 1/8
9	13/16	13/16	11/16	1 5/8	13/32	11/32	1 1/4
10	7/8	7/8	3/4	1 3/4	7/16	3/8	1 5/16
11	15/16	15/16	3/4	1 7/8	15/32	3/8	1 3/8
12	1	1	13/16	2	1/2	13/32	1 1/2
13	1 1/16	1 1/16	13/16	2 1/8	17/32	13/32	1 5/8
14	1 1/8	1 1/8	7/8	2 1/4	9/16	7/16	1 11/16
15	1 3/16	1 3/16	15/16	2 3/8	19/32	15/32	1 3/4
16	1 1/4	1 1/4	1	2 1/2	5/8	1/2	1 7/8
17	1 5/16	1 5/16	1	2 5/8	21/32	1/2	1 15/16
18	1 3/8	1 3/8	1 1/16	2 3/4	11/16	17/32	2 1/16
19	1 7/16	1 7/16	1 1/8	2 7/8	23/32	9/16	2 1/8
20	1 1/2	1 1/2	1 3/16	3	3/4	19/32	2 1/4
21	1 9/16	1 9/16	1 1/4	3 1/8	25/32	5/8	2 5/16
22	1 5/8	1 5/8	1 1/4	3 1/4	13/16	5/8	2 7/16
23	1 11/16	1 11/16	1 5/16	3 3/8	27/32	21/32	2 1/2
24	1 3/4	1 3/4	1 3/8	3 1/2	7/8	11/16	2 5/8
27	1 15/16	1 15/16	1 1/2	3 7/8	31/32	3/4	2 7/8
30	2 1/8	2 1/8	1 5/8	4 1/4	1 1/16	13/16	3 3/16
33	2 5/16	2 5/16	1 3/4	4 5/8	1 5/32	7/8	3 7/16
36	2 1/2	2 1/2	2	5	1 1/4	1	3 3/4

Machine Handwheels. — The accompanying table gives complete dimensions for "dished-arm" machine handwheels. The following remarks relating to hubs, keyways, arms and rims apply to handwheels of the design illustrated. *Hubs.* In Column D, the minimum dimension that should be used is given. The hub may be increased in length on side a, if necessary. Length D is sufficient for Woodruff keys. *Keyway.* This is designed so that either a straight key or a Woodruff key may be used, without changing the dimensions. *Arms.* These incline to form a "dished" wheel. There are two reasons for this: First, it often happens that it is convenient, or necessary, to fasten the handwheel with a nut on the end of the shaft, and if the wheel is dished, there is a recess for this nut, so that the operator does not strike his arm when turning the handwheel with a handle. Second, when casting handwheels with straight arms, the arms often break due to strains, but if dished, the strains are taken up by the arms and hub. The arms are oval in section, as indicated; the taper from F to G is 1 inch to the foot for all sizes. In Column U for a 14-inch handwheel, it will be noted that the radius is less than for a 12-inch size. This is because the 14-inch wheel has six arms, whereas the 12-inch size has four arms. *Rims.* The inner half of the rim is reduced to permit finishing the outside half and to provide an even stopping place for the machined surface. This eliminates the filing that is otherwise required. Note that when a handle is to be used, a boss is cast on the outside of the rim at the end of one of the arms, and a smaller boss on the inside for the handle shank. The counterbore P receives the straight section Q on the handle, so that the latter will not project. Length R on the handle allows $\frac{1}{16}$ inch for riveting.

Machine Handwheels

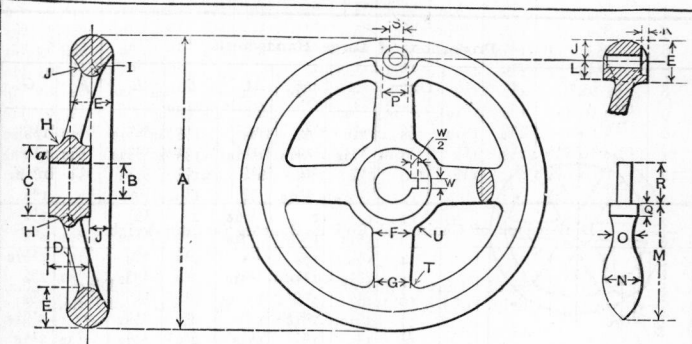

No. of Arms: 4 for sizes up to and including 12 inches; 6 for larger sizes.

A	B	C	D	E	F	G	H	I	J	K	L
6	$\frac{3}{4}$	$1\frac{3}{4}$	$\frac{7}{8}$	$\frac{7}{8}$	$\frac{7}{8}$	$\frac{25}{32}$	$\frac{7}{32}$	$\frac{3}{16}$	$\frac{7}{16}$	$\frac{3}{32}$	$\frac{5}{16}$
8	$\frac{7}{8}$	$1\frac{7}{8}$	1	$1\frac{1}{8}$	1	$\frac{27}{32}$	$\frac{1}{4}$	$\frac{13}{64}$	$\frac{1}{2}$	$\frac{3}{32}$	$\frac{3}{8}$
10	1	$2\frac{1}{8}$	$1\frac{1}{8}$	$1\frac{1}{4}$	$1\frac{1}{4}$	$1\frac{1}{16}$	$\frac{9}{32}$	$\frac{7}{32}$	$\frac{9}{16}$	$\frac{5}{32}$	$\frac{1}{2}$
12	$1\frac{1}{8}$	$2\frac{1}{4}$	$1\frac{1}{4}$	$1\frac{5}{16}$	$1\frac{3}{8}$	$1\frac{3}{32}$	$\frac{5}{16}$	$\frac{1}{4}$	$\frac{5}{8}$	$\frac{1}{4}$	$\frac{9}{16}$
14	$1\frac{1}{4}$	$2\frac{1}{2}$	$1\frac{3}{8}$	$1\frac{3}{8}$	$1\frac{3}{8}$	$1\frac{1}{16}$	$\frac{11}{32}$	$\frac{9}{32}$	$\frac{11}{16}$	$\frac{1}{4}$	$\frac{9}{16}$
16	$1\frac{3}{8}$	$2\frac{3}{4}$	$1\frac{1}{2}$	$1\frac{1}{2}$	$1\frac{1}{2}$	$1\frac{1}{8}$	$\frac{3}{8}$	$\frac{5}{16}$	$\frac{3}{4}$	...	....
18	$1\frac{1}{2}$	3	$1\frac{5}{8}$	$1\frac{5}{8}$	$1\frac{5}{8}$	$1\frac{3}{16}$	$\frac{13}{32}$	$\frac{3}{8}$	$1\frac{3}{16}$	...	....

A	M	N	O	P	Q	R	S	T	U	W	Size of Woodruff Key
6	$2\frac{1}{2}$	1	$\frac{7}{16}$	$\frac{1}{2}$	$\frac{3}{8}$	$\frac{7}{8}$	$\frac{1}{4}$	$\frac{1}{4}$	$\frac{1}{2}$	$\frac{5}{32}$	6
8	$2\frac{3}{4}$	$1\frac{1}{8}$	$\frac{1}{2}$	$\frac{5}{8}$	$\frac{3}{8}$	$1\frac{1}{16}$	$\frac{5}{16}$	$\frac{9}{32}$	$\frac{9}{16}$	$\frac{3}{16}$	11
10	$3\frac{1}{8}$	$1\frac{1}{4}$	$\frac{5}{8}$	$\frac{3}{4}$	$\frac{3}{8}$	$1\frac{3}{16}$	$\frac{3}{8}$	$\frac{5}{16}$	$\frac{5}{8}$	$\frac{1}{4}$	15
12	$3\frac{3}{8}$	$1\frac{3}{8}$	$\frac{3}{4}$	1	$\frac{1}{2}$	$1\frac{1}{8}$	$\frac{1}{2}$	$\frac{11}{32}$	$1\frac{1}{16}$	$\frac{1}{4}$	18
14	$3\frac{5}{8}$	$1\frac{3}{8}$	$\frac{3}{4}$	1	$\frac{1}{2}$	$1\frac{3}{16}$	$\frac{1}{2}$	$\frac{3}{8}$	$\frac{1}{4}$	$\frac{5}{16}$	D
16	...	...	...	...	...	...	...	$\frac{7}{16}$	$\frac{5}{16}$	$\frac{5}{16}$	23
18	...	...	...	...	...	...	...	$\frac{1}{2}$	$\frac{3}{8}$	$\frac{3}{8}$	F

Handwheels with Straight Arms

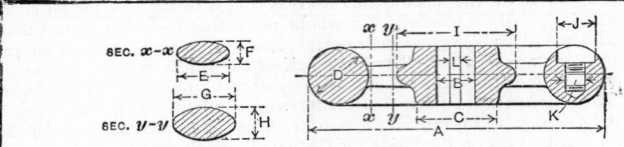

No. of Arms: 4 up to the 10-inch size; 5 in the 11-inch size; 6 in the 12-inch size.

A	B	C	D	E	F	G	H	I	J	K	L
4	3/8	7/8	11/16	1/2	1/4	5/8	5/16	1 3/8	15/32	5/16	1/16 by 1/32
5	7/16	1	13/16	9/16	9/32	11/16	11/32	1 5/8	15/32	3/8	3/32 by 3/64
6	9/16	1 3/16	15/16	5/8	5/16	3/4	3/8	1 7/8	1/2	3/8	3/32 by 3/64
7	11/16	1 3/8	1	11/16	11/32	7/8	7/16	2 1/8	19/32	3/8	1/8 by 1/16
8	3/4 to 7/8	1 1/2	1 1/8	3/4	3/8	15/16	15/32	2 3/8	19/32	3/8	1/8 by 1/16
9	13/16 to 1	1 5/8	1 3/16	13/16	13/32	1	1/2	2 5/8	19/32	3/8	1/8 by 1/16
10	7/8 to 1	1 3/4	1 5/16	7/8	7/16	1 1/8	9/16	2 7/8	21/32	7/16	3/16 by 3/32
11	15/16 to 1 1/8	1 7/8	1 3/8	15/16	15/32	1 3/16	9/16	3 1/8	21/32	7/16	3/16 by 3/32
12	1 to 1 1/4	2	1 1/2	1	1/2	1 1/4	5/8	3 3/8	3/4	1/2	1/4 by 1/8

Dimensions of Chain and Rod to Support Counter-weights

	Size of Chain, A	Diam. of Rod, B	Size of Bolt, C	Diam. of Cotter, E	F	G	Diam. of Hole, H	Max. Safe Load
	3/16	3/8	5/16	3/32	3/16	1	3/8	350
	1/4	1/2	3/8	1/8	1/4	1 1/4	7/16	650
	5/16	5/8	1/2	1/8	1/4	1 1/2	9/16	1300
	3/8	3/4	5/8	3/16	5/16	1 3/4	11/16	1900
	1/2	7/8	3/4	3/16	5/16	2 1/4	13/16	3300
	1/2	1	7/8	3/16	3/8	2 1/2	15/16	3400

Material for Aircraft Bolts and Nuts. — According to the S.A.E. standard, hexagon nuts are to be manufactured from bar steel having the following physical properties: Tensile strength, 70,000 pounds per square inch; yield point, 50,000 pounds per square inch; elongation in 2 inches, 10 per cent minimum; reduction of area, 40 per cent minimum. Test specimens for the flattening test shall be selected at random from the lot submitted for inspection. The nuts shall withstand being decreased in over-all diameter or distance between flats by an amount equal to 10 per cent of the nominal bolt diameter without visible cracks on the inside or outside of the nut. The flattening shall be done by steadily pressing the nuts edgewise in a vise or testing machine until the specified reduction has been made.

Machine Handles

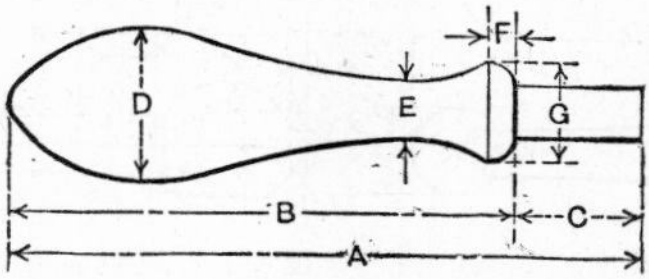

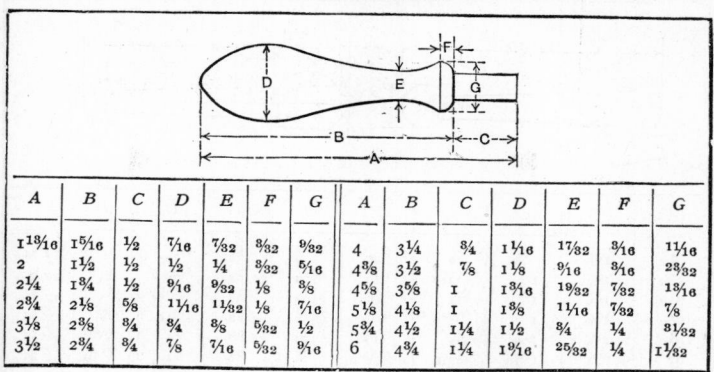

A	B	C	D	E	F	G	A	B	C	D	E	F	G
1 13/16	1 5/16	1/2	7/16	7/32	3/32	9/32	4	3 1/4	3/4	1 1/16	17/32	3/16	11/16
2	1 1/2	1/2	1/2	1/4	3/32	5/16	4 3/8	3 1/2	7/8	1 1/8	9/16	3/16	23/32
2 1/4	1 3/4	1/2	9/16	9/32	1/8	3/8	4 5/8	3 5/8	1	1 3/16	19/32	7/32	13/16
2 3/4	2 1/8	5/8	11/16	11/32	1/8	7/16	5 1/8	4 1/8	1	1 3/8	11/16	7/32	7/8
3 1/8	2 3/8	3/4	3/4	3/8	5/32	1/2	5 3/4	4 1/2	1 1/4	1 1/2	3/4	1/4	31/32
3 1/2	2 3/4	3/4	7/8	7/16	5/32	9/16	6	4 3/4	1 1/4	1 9/16	25/32	1/4	1 1/32

Ball-crank Machine Handles

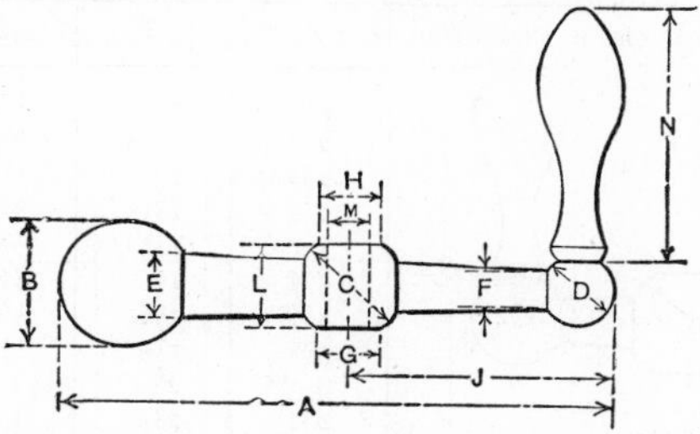

A	B	C	D	E	F	G	H	J	L	M	N
3	7/8	11/16	9/16	3/8	5/16	1/2	7/16	1 1/2	1/2	1/4	1 1/2
3 1/4	15/16	25/32	5/8	7/16	5/16	9/16	1/2	1 5/8	9/16	5/16	1 5/8
3 1/2	1 1/16	29/32	3/4	15/32	11/32	5/8	9/16	1 3/4	11/16	3/8	1 3/4
4	1 1/4	1	3/4	17/32	13/32	3/4	11/16	2	3/4	7/16	1 7/8
4 1/2	1 5/16	1 3/32	27/32	19/32	7/16	3/4	11/16	2 1/4	13/16	1/2	2
5	1 1/2	1 5/16	1	3/4	1/2	7/8	13/16	2 1/2	1	1/2	2 3/16
5 1/2	1 1/2	1 5/16	1	3/4	1/2	7/8	13/16	2 3/4	1	1/2	2 3/8
6	1 5/8	1 3/8	1	3/4	1/2	1	15/16	3	1	5/8	2 9/16
6 1/2	1 5/8	1 3/8	1	3/4	1/2	1	15/16	3 1/4	1	5/8	2 3/4
7	1 3/4	1 7/16	1	3/4	9/16	1	15/16	3 1/2	1 1/16	5/8	2 15/16
7 1/2	1 3/4	1 1/2	1	3/4	9/16	1	15/16	3 3/4	1 3/32	5/8	3 1/8
8	1 3/4	1 1/2	1 1/16	3/4	9/16	1	15/16	4	1 1/8	5/8	3 5/16
8 1/2	1 3/4	1 9/16	1 1/8	3/4	5/8	1 1/8	1 1/16	4 1/4	1 3/16	3/4	3 1/2
9	1 3/4	1 5/8	1 3/16	3/4	5/8	1 1/8	1 1/16	4 1/2	1 1/4	3/4	3 3/4

Two-ball Clamping Levers

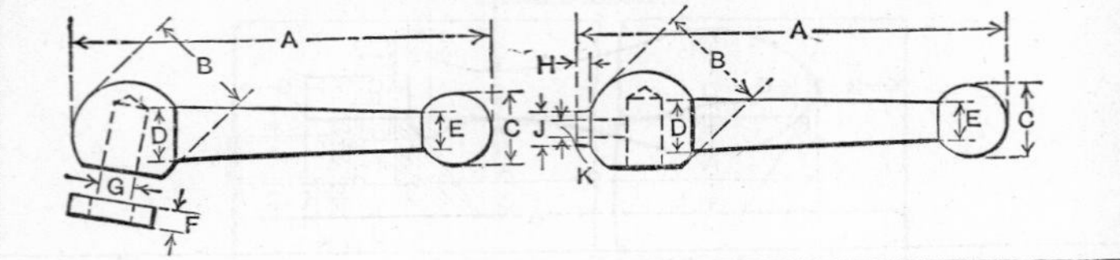

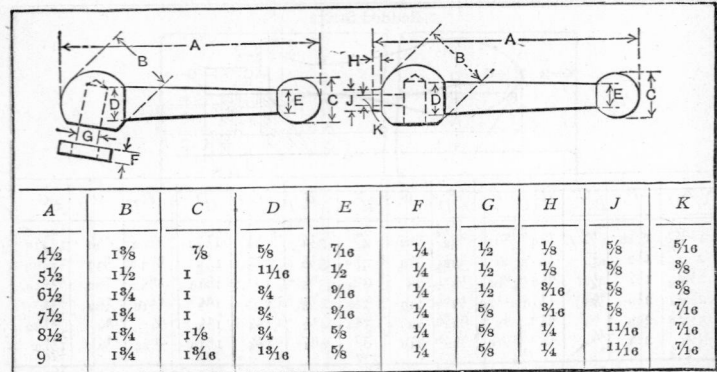

A	B	C	D	E	F	G	H	J	K
4½	1⅜	⅞	⅝	7/16	¼	½	⅛	⅝	5/16
5½	1½	1	11/16	½	¼	½	⅛	⅝	⅜
6½	1¾	1	¾	9/16	¼	½	3/16	⅝	⅜
7½	1¾	1	¾	9/16	¼	⅝	3/16	⅝	7/16
8½	1¾	1⅛	¾	⅝	¼	⅝	¼	11/16	7/16
9	1¾	1 3/16	13/16	⅝	¼	⅝	¼	11/16	7/16

Compound-rest Handles

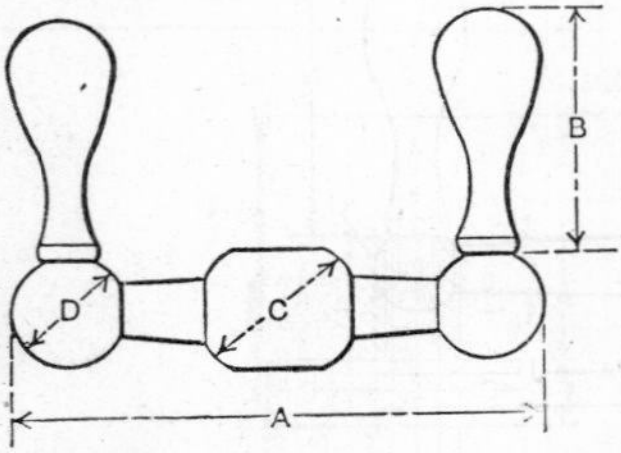

A	B	C	D
2½	1¼	13/16	21/32
2⅝	1 5/16	13/16	21/32
2¾	1⅜	13/16	11/16
2⅞	1 7/16	⅞	11/16
3	1½	⅞	23/32
3¼	1⅝	⅞	23/32
3½	1¾	15/16	¾
3¾	1⅞	15/16	¾
4	2	1	13/16
4¼	2⅛	1	13/16
4½	2¼	1 1/16	⅞

Knobs for Machine Doors

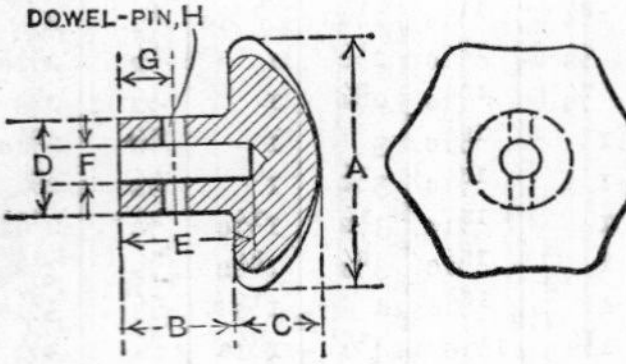

A	B	C	D
2¼	1 1/16	11/16	⅞
2¾	1 1/16	¾	1
3¼	1 1/16	15/16	1

E	F	G	H
1¼	7/16	½	3/16 by 15/16
1¼	½	½	3/16 by 1 1/16
1¼	½	½	3/16 by 1 1/16

Dimensions of Machine Slides

Bedded Strips

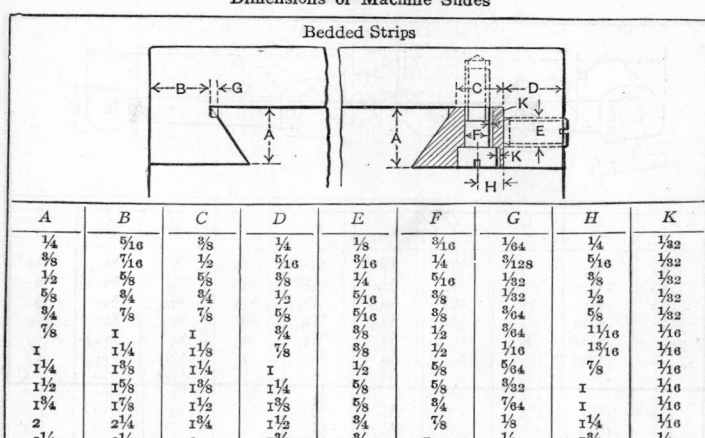

A	B	C	D	E	F	G	H	K
1/4	5/16	3/8	1/4	1/8	3/16	1/64	1/4	1/32
3/8	7/16	1/2	5/16	3/16	1/4	3/128	5/16	1/32
1/2	5/8	5/8	3/8	1/4	5/16	1/32	3/8	1/32
5/8	3/4	3/4	1/2	5/16	3/8	1/32	1/2	1/32
3/4	7/8	7/8	5/8	5/16	3/8	3/64	5/8	1/32
7/8	1	1	3/4	3/8	1/2	3/64	1 1/16	1/16
1	1 1/4	1 1/8	7/8	3/8	1/2	1/16	1 3/16	1/16
1 1/4	1 3/8	1 1/4	1	1/2	5/8	5/64	7/8	1/16
1 1/2	1 5/8	1 3/8	1 1/4	5/8	5/8	3/32	1	1/16
1 3/4	1 7/8	1 1/2	1 3/8	5/8	3/4	7/64	1	1/16
2	2 1/4	1 3/4	1 1/2	3/4	7/8	1/8	1 1/4	1/16
2 1/4	2 1/2	2	1 3/4	3/4	1	1/8	1 3/8	1/8
2 1/2	2 3/4	2 1/4	2	7/8	1	5/32	1 1/2	1/8
2 3/4	3	2 1/2	2 1/4	7/8	1 1/8	5/32	1 3/4	1/8
3	3 1/4	2 3/4	2 1/2	1	1 1/8	3/16	2	1/8

Square Strips

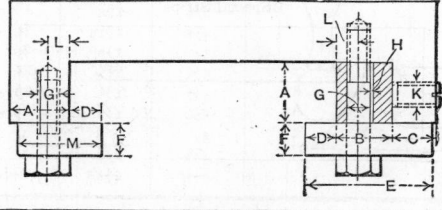

A	B	C	D	E	F	G	H	K	L	M
1/2	5/8	3/8	3/8	1 9/16	5/16	1/4	1/32	1/4	3/16	1 3/16
5/8	3/4	1/2	1/2	1 11/16	3/8	5/16	1/32	5/16	7/32	1 1/16
3/4	7/8	5/8	5/8	2 1/16	1/2	3/8	1/32	5/16	5/16	1 5/16
7/8	1	3/4	3/4	2 7/16	5/8	1/2	1/16	3/8	3/8	1 9/16
1	1 1/8	7/8	7/8	2 3/4	3/4	1/2	1/16	3/8	7/16	1 3/4
1 1/4	1 1/4	1	1	3 1/8	7/8	5/8	1/16	1/2	7/16	2 1/8
1 1/2	1 3/8	1 1/8	1 1/8	3 1/2	1	5/8	1/16	1/2	1/2	2 1/2
1 3/4	1 1/2	1 1/4	1 1/4	3 7/8	1 1/8	3/4	1/16	5/8	9/16	2 7/8
2	1 3/4	1 1/2	1 1/2	4 5/8	1 1/4	7/8	1/16	3/4	5/8	3 3/8
2 1/4	2	1 5/8	1 5/8	5	1 3/8	7/8	1/8	3/4	11/16	3 5/8
2 1/2	2 1/4	1 3/4	1 3/4	5 1/2	1 1/2	1	1/8	7/8	3/4	4
2 3/4	2 1/2	1 7/8	1 7/8	6	1 5/8	1	1/8	7/8	13/16	4 3/8
3	2 3/4	2	2	6 1/2	1 3/4	1 1/8	1/8	1	7/8	4 3/4
3 1/2	3 1/8	2 1/4	2 1/4	7 1/4	1 7/8	1 1/4	1/8	1 1/8	1	5 3/8
4	3 1/2	2 1/2	2 1/2	8	2	1 1/2	1/8	1 1/4	1 1/8	6

Dimensions of Machine Slides

Overhung Strips

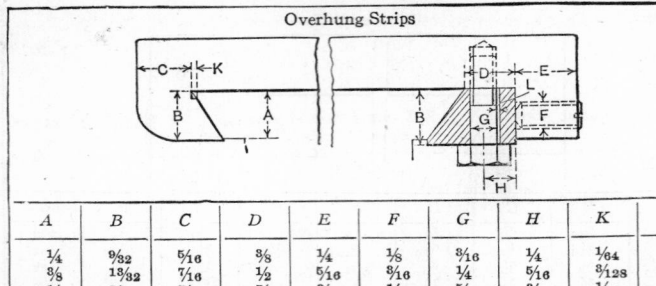

A	B	C	D	E	F	G	H	K	L
1/4	9/32	5/16	3/8	1/4	1/8	3/16	1/4	1/64	1/32
3/8	13/32	7/16	1/2	5/16	3/16	1/4	5/16	3/128	1/32
1/2	9/16	5/8	5/8	3/8	1/4	5/16	3/8	1/32	1/32
5/8	11/16	3/4	3/4	1/2	5/16	3/8	1/2	1/32	1/32
3/4	13/16	3/4	15/16	5/8	5/16	1/2	5/8	3/64	1/32
7/8	15/16	1	1	3/4	3/8	1/2	11/16	3/64	1/16
1	1 1/8	1 1/4	1	7/8	3/8	1/2	11/16	1/16	1/16
1 1/4	1 3/8	1 1/2	1 1/8	1	1/2	5/8	3/4	5/64	1/16
1 1/2	1 5/8	1 3/4	1 1/4	1 1/8	1/2	5/8	7/8	3/32	1/16
1 3/4	1 7/8	2	1 1/2	1 1/4	5/8	3/4	1	3/32	1/16
2	2 3/16	2 1/4	1 3/4	1 1/2	3/4	7/8	1 1/4	1/8	1/16
2 1/4	2 1/2	2 1/2	2	1 5/8	3/4	7/8	1 1/2	1/8	1/8
2 1/2	2 3/4	2 3/4	2 1/4	1 3/4	7/8	1	1 7/8	5/32	1/8
2 3/4	3	3	2 1/2	1 7/8	7/8	1	1 7/8	5/32	1/8
3	3 1/4	3 1/4	2 3/4	2	1	1 1/8	2	3/16	1/8

Special Strips

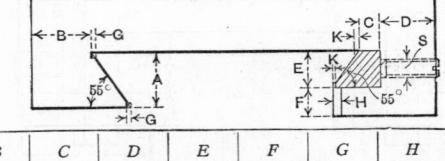

A	B	C	D	E	F	G	H	K	S
1	1 1/16	1/2	5/8	3/4	1/2	1/16	3/16	3/64	3/8
1 1/8	1 3/16	9/16	11/16	7/8	9/16	1/16	3/16	3/64	3/8
1 1/4	1 5/16	5/8	13/16	15/16	5/8	1/16	3/16	3/64	3/8
1 3/8	1 7/16	11/16	7/8	1 1/16	11/16	3/32	1/4	3/64	1/2
1 1/2	1 9/16	3/4	15/16	1 1/8	3/4	3/32	1/4	3/64	1/2
1 5/8	1 11/16	13/16	1	1 1/4	13/16	3/32	1/4	3/64	1/2
1 3/4	1 13/16	7/8	1 1/8	1 5/16	7/8	1/8	3/8	3/32	5/8
1 7/8	1 15/16	15/16	1 3/16	1 7/16	15/16	1/8	3/8	3/32	5/8
2	2 1/8	1	1 1/4	1 1/2	1	1/8	5/8	5/32	3/4
2 1/4	2 3/8	1 1/8	1 3/8	1 11/16	1 1/8	1/8	1/2	3/32	3/4
2 1/2	2 5/8	1 1/4	1 9/16	1 7/8	1 1/4	3/16	1/2	1/8	7/8
2 3/4	2 7/8	1 3/8	1 3/4	2 1/16	1 3/8	3/16	9/16	1/8	7/8
3	3 3/16	1 1/2	1 7/8	2 1/4	1 1/2	3/16	9/16	1/8	1
3 1/4	3 7/16	1 5/8	2	2 7/16	1 5/8	3/16	5/8	1/8	1 1/8
3 1/2	3 11/16	1 3/4	2 3/16	2 5/8	1 3/4	1/4	5/8	3/16	1 1/4
3 3/4	3 15/16	1 7/8	2 3/8	2 13/16	1 7/8	1/4	3/4	3/16	1 1/4
4	4 1/4	2	2 1/2	3	2	1/4	3/4	3/16	1 1/2

BOLTS, NUTS AND MACHINE DETAILS

In the following is given general information relating to the dimensions of bolts, nuts and screws used in machine construction. For detailed data relating to the proportions of various forms of screw threads, see the section on "Screw Thread Systems."

British Standard Whitworth (B.S.W.) and British Standard Fine (B.S.F.) Hexagon Bolts, Set Screws, Nuts and Washers

Diam. of Bolt	B.S.W. Threads per Inch	B.S.F. Threads per Inch	Bolt-heads, Set-screw-heads and Nuts			Bolts and Set-screws		Bolts		Nuts	
			Width across Flats		Approx. Width across Corner	Thickness		Minus Toler. on Bolt Diam.	Min. Length of Thread	Thickness	
			Max.	Min.		Max.	Min.			Max.	Min.
1/4	20	26	0.445	0.438	0.51	0.19	0.18	0.0035	1/2	0.200	0.190
5/16	18	22	0.525	0.518	0.61	0.22	0.21	0.0035	5/8	0.250	0.240
3/8	16	20	0.600	0.592	0.69	0.27	0.26	0.0035	3/4	0.312	0.302
7/16	14	18	0.710	0.702	0.82	0.33	0.32	0.004	7/8	0.375	0.365
1/2	12	16	0.820	0.812	0.95	0.38	0.37	0.004	1	0.437	0.427
9/16	12	16	0.920	0.912	1.06	0.44	0.43	0.004	1 1/8	0.500	0.490
5/8	11	14	1.010	1.000	1.17	0.49	0.48	0.006	1 1/4	0.562	0.552
3/4	10	12	1.200	1.190	1.39	0.60	0.59	0.006	1 1/2	0.687	0.677
7/8	9	11	1.300	1.288	1.50	0.66	0.65	0.006	1 3/4	0.750	0.740
1	8	10	1.480	1.468	1.71	0.77	0.76	0.008	2	0.875	0.865
1 1/8	7		1.670	1.658	1.93	0.88	0.87	0.008	2 1/4	1.000	0.990
1 1/4	7	9	1.860	1.845	2.15	0.98	0.96	0.008	2 1/2	1.125	1.105
*1 3/8	—	8	2.050	2.035	2.37	1.09	1.07	0.010	2 3/4	1.250	1.230
1 1/2	6	8	2.220	2.200	2.56	1.20	1.18	0.010	3	1.375	1.355
1 3/4	5	7	2.580	2.555	2.98	1.42	1.40	0.010	3 1/2	1.625	1.605
2	4.5	7	2.760	2.735	3.19	1.53	1.51	0.010	4	1.750	1.730

Diam. of Bolt	B.S.W. Threads per Inch	B.S.F. Threads per Inch	Lock Nuts		Washers				
			Thickness		Diameter of Hole		Outside Diam. Max.	Thickness	
			Max.	Min.	Max.	Min.		Max.	Min.
1/4	20	26	0.133	0.123	0.270	0.265	9/16	0.056	0.054
5/16	18	22	0.166	0.156	0.333	0.328	5/8	0.072	0.070
3/8	16	20	0.208	0.198	0.395	0.390	3/4	0.072	0.070
7/16	14	18	0.250	0.240	0.458	0.453	7/8	0.092	0.090
1/2	12	16	0.291	0.281	0.520	0.515	1	0.092	0.090
9/16	12	16	0.333	0.323	0.593	0.588	1 1/8	0.104	0.100
5/8	11	14	0.375	0.365	0.656	0.651	1 1/4	0.116	0.112
3/4	10	12	0.458	0.448	0.781	0.776	1 1/2	0.144	0.140
7/8	9	11	0.500	0.490	0.906	0.901	1 5/8	0.144	0.140
1	8	10	0.583	0.573	1.031	1.026	1 7/8	0.160	0.156
1 1/8	7	9	0.666	0.656	1.156	1.151	2 1/8	0.176	0.172
1 1/4	7	9	0.750	0.730	1.281	1.276	2 3/8	0.176	0.172
*1 3/8	—	8	0.833	0.813	1.406	1.401	2 5/8	0.192	0.188
1 1/2	6	8	0.916	0.896	1.531	1.526	2 7/8	0.192	0.188
1 3/4	5	7	1.083	1.063	1.781	1.776	3 3/8	0.212	0.208
2	4.5	7	1.166	1.146	2.031	2.026	3 5/8	0.212	0.208

All dimensions are in inches.
*Not a standard size for B.S.W. bolts and nuts.

Table 1. American Standard Bolt Heads

Diameter of Bolt	Width Across Flats		Width Across Corners, Min.		Height		
	Max. (Basic)	Min.	Sq.	Hex.	Nominal	Max.	Min.
REGULAR BOLT HEADS — Unfinished Square and Hexagon							
1/4	3/8	0.363	0.498	0.414	11/64	0.188	0.156
5/16	1/2	0.484	0.665	0.552	13/64	0.220	0.186
3/8	9/16	0.544	0.747	0.620	1/4	0.268	0.232
7/16	5/8	0.603	0.828	0.687	19/64	0.316	0.278
1/2	3/4	0.725	0.995	0.827	21/64	0.348	0.308
9/16	7/8	0.847	1.163	0.966	3/8	0.396	0.354
5/8	15/16	0.906	1.244	1.033	27/64	0.444	0.400
3/4	1 1/8	1.088	1.494	1.240	1/2	0.524	0.476
7/8	1 5/16	1.269	1.742	1.447	19/32	0.620	0.568
1	1 1/2	1.450	1.991	1.653	21/32	0.684	0.628
1 1/8	1 11/16	1.631	2.239	1.859	3/4	0.780	0.720
1 1/4	1 7/8	1.813	2.489	2.067	27/32	0.876	0.812
1 3/8	2 1/16	1.994	2.738	2.273	29/32	0.940	0.872
1 1/2	2 1/4	2.175	2.986	2.480	1	1.036	0.964
1 5/8	2 7/16	2.356	3.235	2.686	1 3/32	1.132	1.056
1 3/4	2 5/8	2.538	3.485	2.893	1 5/32	1.196	1.116
1 7/8	2 13/16	2.719	3.733	3.100	1 1/4	1.292	1.208
2	3	2.900	3.982	3.306	1 11/32	1.388	1.300
2 1/4	3 3/8	3.263	4.480	3.720	1 1/2	1.548	1.452
2 1/2	3 3/4	3.625	4.977	4.133	1 21/32	1.708	1.604
2 3/4	4 1/8	3.988	5.476	4.546	1 53/64	1.884	1.774
3	4 1/2	4.350	5.973	4.959	2	2.060	1.940
REGULAR BOLT HEADS — Semi-finished Hexagon							
1/4	3/8	0.363	.....	0.414	5/32	0.172	0.140
5/16	1/2	0.484	.....	0.552	3/16	0.205	0.171
3/8	9/16	0.544	.....	0.620	15/64	0.252	0.216
7/16	5/8	0.603	.....	0.687	9/32	0.300	0.262
1/2	3/4	0.725	.....	0.827	19/64	0.317	0.277
9/16	7/8	0.847	.....	0.966	11/32	0.365	0.323
5/8	15/16	0.906	.....	1.033	25/64	0.413	0.369
3/4	1 1/8	1.088	.....	1.240	15/32	0.493	0.445
7/8	1 5/16	1.269	.....	1.447	9/16	0.589	0.537
1	1 1/2	1.450	.....	1.653	19/32	0.622	0.566
1 1/8	1 11/16	1.631	.....	1.859	11/16	0.718	0.658
1 1/4	1 7/8	1.813	.....	2.067	25/32	0.813	0.749
1 3/8	2 1/16	1.994	.....	2.273	27/32	0.878	0.810
1 1/2	2 1/4	2.175	.....	2.480	15/16	0.974	0.902
1 5/8	2 7/16	2.356	.....	2.686	1 1/32	1.069	0.993
1 3/4	2 5/8	2.538	.....	2.893	1 3/32	1.134	1.054
1 7/8	2 13/16	2.719	.....	3.100	1 3/16	1.230	1.146
2	3	2.900	.....	3.306	1 7/32	1.263	1.175
2 1/4	3 3/8	3.263	.....	3.720	1 3/8	1.423	1.327
2 1/2	3 3/4	3.625	.....	4.133	1 17/32	1.583	1.479
2 3/4	4 1/8	3.988	.....	4.546	1 11/16	1.744	1.632
3	4 1/2	4.350	.....	4.959	1 7/8	1.935	1.815

All dimensions given in inches. *Regular bolt heads* are for general use. Unfinished bolt heads are not machined on any surface. Semi-finished bolt heads are machined under head only. Finished bolt heads made to same dimensions as semi-finished.

Table 2. American Standard Bolt Heads

Diameter of Bolt	Width Across Flats		Width Across Corners, Min.		Height		
	Max. (Basic)	Min.	Sq.	Hex.	Nominal	Max.	Min.
HEAVY BOLT HEADS — Unfinished Square and Hexagon							
1/2	7/8	0.850	1.167	0.969	7/16	0.458	0.418
9/16	15/16	0.906	1.244	1.033	15/32	0.490	0.448
5/8	1 1/16	1.031	1.416	1.175	17/32	0.553	0.509
3/4	1 1/4	1.213	1.665	1.383	5/8	0.649	0.601
7/8	1 7/16	1.394	1.914	1.589	23/32	0.745	0.693
1	1 5/8	1.575	2.162	1.796	13/16	0.841	0.785
1 1/8	1 13/16	1.756	2.411	2.002	29/32	0.936	0.876
1 1/4	2	1.938	2.661	2.209	1	1.032	0.968
1 3/8	2 3/16	2.119	2.909	2.416	1 3/32	1.128	1.060
1 1/2	2 3/8	2.300	3.158	2.622	1 3/16	1.224	1.152
1 5/8	2 9/16	2.481	3.406	2.828	1 9/32	1.319	1.243
1 3/4	2 3/4	2.663	3.656	3.036	1 3/8	1.415	1.335
1 7/8	2 15/16	2.844	3.905	3.242	1 15/32	1.511	1.427
2	3 1/8	3.025	4.153	3.449	1 9/16	1.607	1.519
2 1/4	3 1/2	3.388	4.652	3.862	1 3/4	1.798	1.702
2 1/2	3 7/8	3.750	5.149	4.275	1 15/16	1.990	1.886
2 3/4	4 1/4	4.113	5.647	4.689	2 1/8	2.181	2.069
3	4 5/8	4.475	6.144	5.102	2 5/16	2.373	2.253
HEAVY BOLT HEADS — Semi-finished Hexagon							
1/2	7/8	0.850	.....	0.969	13/32	0.426	0.386
9/16	15/16	0.906	.....	1.033	7/16	0.459	0.417
5/8	1 1/16	1.031	.....	1.175	1/2	0.522	0.478
3/4	1 1/4	1.213	.....	1.383	19/32	0.618	0.570
7/8	1 7/16	1.394	.....	1.589	11/16	0.714	0.662
1	1 5/8	1.575	.....	1.796	3/4	0.778	0.722
1 1/8	1 13/16	1.756	.....	2.002	27/32	0.874	0.814
1 1/4	2	1.938	.....	2.209	15/16	0.970	0.906
1 3/8	2 3/16	2.119	.....	2.416	1 1/32	1.065	0.997
1 1/2	2 3/8	2.300	.....	2.622	1 1/8	1.161	1.089
1 5/8	2 9/16	2.481	.....	2.828	1 7/32	1.257	1.181
1 3/4	2 3/4	2.663	.....	3.036	1 5/16	1.353	1.273
1 7/8	2 15/16	2.844	.....	3.242	1 13/32	1.448	1.364
2	3 1/8	3.025	.....	3.449	1 7/16	1.482	1.394
2 1/4	3 1/2	3.388	.....	3.862	1 5/8	1.673	1.577
2 1/2	3 7/8	3.750	.....	4.275	1 13/16	1.865	1.761
2 3/4	4 1/4	4.113	.....	4.689	2	2.056	1.944
3	4 5/8	4.475	.....	5.102	2 3/16	2.248	2.128

All dimensions given in inches. *Heavy bolt heads* are for use where greater bearing surface is desired. Finished bolt heads are made to same dimensions as semi-finished. Degree and character of finish to be specified.

Table 3. American Standard Nuts

Diameter of Bolt	Width Across Flats		Width Across Corners, Min.		Thickness, Nut		Thickness, Jam Nut	
	Max. (Basic)	Min.	Sq.	Hex.	Max.	Min.	Max.	Min.
REGULAR NUTS — Unfinished Square and Hexagon (Jam Nuts Hex. only)								
1/4	7/16	0.425	0.584	0.485	0.235	0.203	0.172	0.140
5/16	9/16	0.547	0.751	0.624	0.283	0.249	0.205	0.171
3/8	5/8	0.606	0.832	0.691	0.346	0.310	0.237	0.201
7/16	3/4	0.728	1.000	0.830	0.394	0.356	0.269	0.231
1/2	13/16	0.788	1.082	0.898	0.458	0.418	0.333	0.293
9/16	7/8	0.847	1.163	0.966	0.521	0.479	0.365	0.323
5/8	1	0.969	1.330	1.104	0.569	0.525	0.397	0.353
3/4	1 1/8	1.088	1.494	1.240	0.680	0.632	0.462	0.414
7/8	1 5/16	1.269	1.742	1.447	0.792	0.740	0.526	0.474
1	1 1/2	1.450	1.991	1.653	0.903	0.847	0.591	0.535
1 1/8	1 11/16	1.631	2.239	1.859	1.030	0.970	0.655	0.595
1 1/4	1 7/8	1.813	2.489	2.067	1.126	1.062	0.782	0.718
1 3/8	2 1/16	1.994	2.738	2.273	1.237	1.169	0.847	0.779
1 1/2	2 1/4	2.175	2.986	2.480	1.349	1.277	0.911	0.839
1 5/8	2 7/16	2.356	3.235	2.686	1.460	1.384	0.976	0.900
1 3/4	2 5/8	2.538	3.485	2.893	1.571	1.491	1.040	0.960
1 7/8	2 13/16	2.719	3.733	3.100	1.683	1.599	1.105	1.021
2	3	2.900	3.982	3.306	1.794	1.706	1.169	1.081
2 1/4	3 3/8	3.263	4.480	3.720	2.017	1.921	1.298	1.202
2 1/2	3 3/4	3.625	4.977	4.133	2.240	2.136	1.552	1.448
2 3/4	4 1/8	3.988	5.476	4.546	2.462	2.350	1.681	1.569
3	4 1/2	4.350	5.973	4.959	2.685	2.565	1.810	1.690
REGULAR NUTS — Semi-finished Hexagon								
1/4	7/16	0.425	.....	0.485	0.219	0.187	0.157	0.125
5/16	9/16	0.547	.....	0.624	0.267	0.233	0.189	0.155
3/8	5/8	0.606	.....	0.691	0.331	0.295	0.221	0.185
7/16	3/4	0.728	.....	0.830	0.378	0.340	0.253	0.215
1/2	13/16	0.788	.....	0.898	0.442	0.402	0.317	0.277
9/16	7/8	0.847	.....	0.966	0.505	0.463	0.349	0.307
5/8	1	0.969	.....	1.104	0.553	0.509	0.381	0.337
3/4	1 1/8	1.088	.....	1.240	0.665	0.617	0.446	0.398
7/8	1 5/16	1.269	.....	1.447	0.776	0.724	0.510	0.458
1	1 1/2	1.450	.....	1.653	0.887	0.831	0.575	0.519
1 1/8	1 11/16	1.631	.....	1.859	0.999	0.939	0.639	0.579
1 1/4	1 7/8	1.813	.....	2.067	1.094	1.030	0.751	0.687
1 3/8	2 1/16	1.994	.....	2.273	1.206	1.138	0.815	0.747
1 1/2	2 1/4	2.175	.....	2.480	1.317	1.245	0.880	0.808
1 5/8	2 7/16	2.356	.....	2.686	1.429	1.353	0.944	0.868
1 3/4	2 5/8	2.538	.....	2.893	1.540	1.460	1.009	0.929
1 7/8	2 13/16	2.719	.....	3.100	1.651	1.567	1.073	0.989
2	3	2.900	.....	3.306	1.763	1.675	1.138	1.050
2 1/4	3 3/8	3.263	.....	3.720	1.970	1.874	1.251	1.155
2 1/2	3 3/4	3.625	.....	4.133	2.193	2.089	1.505	1.401
2 3/4	4 1/8	3.988	.....	4.546	2.415	2.303	1.634	1.522
3	4 1/2	4.350	.....	4.959	2.638	2.518	1.763	1.643

Regular nuts are for general use. Unfinished nuts are threaded but not machined on any other surface. Semi-finished nuts are threaded, and machined on bearing surface. Finished nuts are made to same dimensions as semi-finished.

Table 4. American Standard Nuts

Diameter of Bolt	Across Flats		Across Corners		Nut Thickness		Jam Nut Thick.	
	Max.	Min.	Sq.	Hex.	Max.	Min.	Max.	Min.

HEAVY NUTS — Unfinished, Square and Hexagon (Jam Nuts, Hex. Only)

Diameter of Bolt	Across Flats Max.	Across Flats Min.	Across Corners Sq.	Across Corners Hex.	Nut Thickness Max.	Nut Thickness Min.	Jam Nut Thick. Max.	Jam Nut Thick. Min.
1/4	1/2	0.488	0.670	0.556	0.266	0.234	0.204	0.172
5/16	19/32	0.578	0.794	0.659	0.330	0.296	0.236	0.202
3/8	11/16	0.669	0.919	0.763	0.393	0.357	0.268	0.232
7/16	25/32	0.759	1.042	0.865	0.456	0.418	0.300	0.262
1/2	7/8	0.850	1.167	0.969	0.520	0.480	0.332	0.292
9/16	15/16	0.909	1.249	1.037	0.584	0.542	0.365	0.323
5/8	11/16	1.031	1.416	1.175	0.647	0.603	0.397	0.353
3/4	1 1/4	1.212	1.665	1.382	0.774	0.726	0.462	0.414
7/8	1 7/16	1.394	1.914	1.589	0.901	0.849	0.526	0.474
I	1 5/8	1.575	2.162	1.796	1.028	0.972	0.590	0.534
1 1/8	1 13/16	1.756	2.411	2.002	1.155	1.095	0.655	0.595
1 1/4	2	1.938	2.661	2.209	1.282	1.218	0.782	0.718
1 3/8	2 3/16	2.119	2.909	2.416	1.409	1.341	0.846	0.778
1 1/2	2 3/8	2.300	3.158	2.622	1.536	1.464	0.911	0.839
1 5/8	2 9/16	2.481	3.406	2.828	1.663	1.587	0.976	0.900
1 3/4	2 3/4	2.662	3.656	3.035	1.790	1.710	1.040	0.960
1 7/8	2 15/16	2.844	3.905	3.242	1.917	1.833	1.104	1.020
2	3 1/8	3.025	4.153	3.449	2.044	1.956	1.169	1.081
2 1/4	3 1/2	3.388	4.652	3.862	2.298	2.202	1.298	1.202
2 1/2	3 7/8	3.750	5.149	4.275	2.552	2.448	1.552	1.448
2 3/4	4 1/4	4.112	5 646	4.688	2.806	2.694	1.681	1.569
3	4 5/8	4.475	6.144	5.102	3.060	2.940	1.810	1.690
3 1/4	5	4.838	6.643	5.515	3.314	3.186	1.939	1.811
3 1/2	5 3/8	5.200	7.140	5.928	3.568	3.432	2.068	1.932
3 3/4	5 3/4	5.562	7.637	6.341	3.822	3.678	2.197	2.053
4	6 1/8	5.925	8.135	6.755	4.076	3.924	2.326	2.174

HEAVY NUTS — Semi-finished Hexagon

Diameter of Bolt	Across Flats Max.	Across Flats Min.	Across Corners Sq.	Across Corners Hex.	Nut Thickness Max.	Nut Thickness Min.	Jam Nut Thick. Max.	Jam Nut Thick. Min.
1/4	1/2	0.488	.....	0.556	0.250	0.218	0.188	0.156
5/16	19/32	0.578	.....	0.659	0.314	0.280	0.220	0.186
3/8	11/16	0.669	.....	0.763	0.377	0.341	0.252	0.216
7/16	25/32	0.759	.....	0.865	0.441	0.403	0.285	0.247
1/2	7/8	0.850	.....	0.969	0.504	0.464	0.317	0.277
9/16	15/16	0.909	.....	1.037	0.568	0.526	0.349	0.307
5/8	1 1/16	1.031	.....	1.175	0.631	0.587	0.381	0.337
3/4	1 1/4	1.212	.....	1.382	0.758	0.710	0.446	0.398
7/8	1 7/16	1.394	.....	1.589	0.885	0.833	0.510	0.458
I	1 5/8	1.575	.....	1.796	1.012	0.956	0.575	0.519
1 1/8	1 13/16	1.756	.....	2.002	1.139	1.079	0.639	0.579
1 1/4	2	1.938	.....	2.209	1.251	1.187	0.751	0.687
1 3/8	2 3/16	2.119	.....	2.416	1.378	1.310	0.815	0.747
1 1/2	2 3/8	2.300	.....	2.622	1.505	1.433	0.880	0.808
1 5/8	2 9/16	2.481	.....	2.828	1.632	1.556	0.944	0.868
1 3/4	2 3/4	2.662	.....	3.035	1.759	1.679	1.009	0.929
1 7/8	2 15/16	2.844	.....	3.242	1.886	1.802	1.073	0.989
2	3 1/8	3.025	.....	3.449	2.013	1.925	1.138	1.050
2 1/4	3 1/2	3.388	.....	3.862	2.251	2.155	1.251	1.155
2 1/2	3 7/8	3.750	.....	4.275	2.505	2.401	1.505	1.401
2 3/4	4 1/4	4.112	.....	4.688	2.759	2.647	1.634	1.522
3	4 5/8	4.475	.....	5.102	3.013	2.893	1.763	1.643
3 1/4	5	4.838	.....	5.515	3.252	3.124	1.876	1.748
3 1/2	5 3/8	5.200	.....	5.928	3.506	3.370	2.006	1.870
3 3/4	5 3/4	5.562	.....	6.341	3.760	3.616	2.134	1.990
4	6 1/8	5.925	.....	6.755	4.014	3.862	2.264	2.112

Finished nuts are made to same dimensions as semi-finished.

Table 5. American Standard Nuts

Diameter of Bolt	Width Across Flats		Width Across Corners	Thickness Light Nuts		Thickness Light Jam Nuts	
	Max. (Basic)	Min.	Min.	Max.	Min.	Max.	Min.
LIGHT NUTS — Semi-finished Hexagon							
1/4	7/16	0.428	0.488	0.226	0.212	0.163	0.150
5/16	1/2	0.489	0.557	0.273	0.258	0.195	0.180
3/8	9/16	0.551	0.628	0.337	0.320	0.227	0.210
7/16	5/8	0.612	0.698	0.385	0.365	0.260	0.240
1/2	3/4	0.736	0.840	0.448	0.427	0.323	0.302
9/16	7/8	0.861	0.982	0.496	0.473	0.324	0.301
5/8	15/16	0.922	1.051	0.559	0.534	0.387	0.363
3/4	1 1/16	1.045	1.191	0.670	0.642	0.389	0.361
7/8	1 1/4	1.231	1.403	0.782	0.750	0.454	0.421
1	1 7/16	1.417	1.615	0.893	0.857	0.518	0.482
1 1/8	1 5/8	1.602	1.826	1.004	0.964	0.582	0.543
1 1/4	1 13/16	1.788	2.038	1.116	1.072	0.647	0.603
1 3/8	2	1.973	2.249	1.227	1.180	0.774	0.726
1 1/2	2 3/16	2.159	2.461	1.338	1.287	0.838	0.787

All dimensions given in inches.
Semi-finished nuts are finished on bearing surface and threaded.

Table 6. American Standard Nuts

Diameter of Bolt	Width Across Flats		Width Across Corners	Thickness		
	Max. (Basic)	Min.	Min.	Nominal	Max.	Min.
LIGHT THICK NUTS — Semi-finished Hexagon						
1/4	7/16	0.428	0.488	9/32	0.288	0.274
5/16	1/2	0.489	0.557	21/64	0.336	0.320
3/8	9/16	0.551	0.628	13/32	0.415	0.398
7/16	5/8	0.612	0.698	29/64	0.463	0.444
1/2	3/4	0.736	0.840	9/16	0.573	0.552
9/16	7/8	0.861	0.982	39/64	0.621	0.598
5/8	15/16	0.922	1.051	23/32	0.731	0.706
3/4	1 1/16	1.045	1.191	13/16	0.827	0.798
7/8	1 1/4	1.231	1.403	29/32	0.922	0.890
1	1 7/16	1.417	1.615	1	1.018	0.982
1 1/8	1 5/8	1.602	1.826	1 5/32	1.176	1.136
1 1/4	1 13/16	1.788	2.038	1 1/4	1.272	1.228
1 3/8	2	1.973	2.249	1 3/8	1.399	1.351
1 1/2	2 3/16	2.159	2.461	1 1/2	1.526	1.474

All dimensions given in inches.
Semi-finished nuts are finished on bearing surface and threaded.

Table 7. American Standard Slotted Nuts

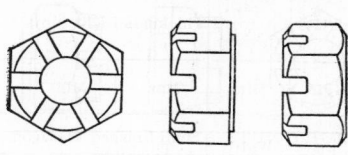

Diam. of Bolt	REGULAR Slotted Nuts (Note 1)		HEAVY Slotted Nuts (Note 2)		LIGHT Slotted Nuts (Note 3)		LIGHT THICK Slotted Nuts (Note 4)	
	Slot Width	Slot Depth	Slot Width	Slot Depth	Slot Width	Slot Depth	Slot Width	Slot Depth
1/4	5/64	3/32	5/64	3/32	5/64	3/32	5/64	3/32
5/16	3/32	3/32	3/32	3/32	3/32	3/32	3/32	3/32
3/8	1/8	1/8	1/8	1/8	1/8	1/8	1/8	1/8
7/16	1/8	5/32	1/8	5/32	1/8	5/32	1/8	5/32
1/2	5/32	5/32	5/32	5/32	5/32	5/32	5/32	5/32
9/16	5/32	3/16	5/32	3/16	5/32	3/16	5/32	3/16
5/8	3/16	7/32	3/16	7/32	3/16	7/32	3/16	7/32
3/4	3/16	1/4	3/16	1/4	3/16	1/4	3/16	1/4
7/8	3/16	1/4	3/16	1/4	3/16	1/4	3/16	1/4
1	1/4	9/32	1/4	9/32	1/4	9/32	1/4	9/32
1 1/8	1/4	11/32	1/4	11/32	1/4	11/32	1/4	11/32
1 1/4	5/16	3/8	5/16	3/8	5/16	3/8	5/16	3/8
1 3/8	5/16	3/8	5/16	3/8	5/16	3/8	5/16	3/8
1 1/2	3/8	7/16	3/8	7/16	3/8	7/16	3/8	7/16
1 5/8	3/8	7/16	3/8	7/16	...	...	...	.....
1 3/4	7/16	1/2	7/16	1/2	...	...	...	.....
1 7/8	7/16	9/16	7/16	9/16	...	...	...	.....
2	7/16	9/16	7/16	9/16	...	...	...	.....
2 1/4	7/16	9/16	7/16	9/16	...	...	...	.....
2 1/2	9/16	11/16	9/16	11/16	...	...	...	.....
2 3/4	9/16	11/16	9/16	11/16	...	...	...	.....
3	5/8	3/4	5/8	3/4	...	...	...	.....
3 1/4	..	...	5/8	3/4	...	...	...	.....
3 1/2	...	...	5/8	3/4	...	...	...	.....
3 3/4	...	...	5/8	3/4	...	...	...	.....
4	...	...	5/8	3/4	...	...	...	.....

Note 1: See lower half of Table 3 for other dimensions (nut thicknesses in columns 6 and 7).

Note 2: See lower half of Table 4 for other dimensions (nut thicknesses in columns 6 and 7).

Note 3: See Table 5 for other dimensions (nut thicknesses in columns 5 and 6).

Note 4: See Table 6 for other dimensions.

Slots may have either square or round bottoms, at the option of the manufacturer.

Table 8. American Standard Light Castle Nuts—Semi-finished Hexagon

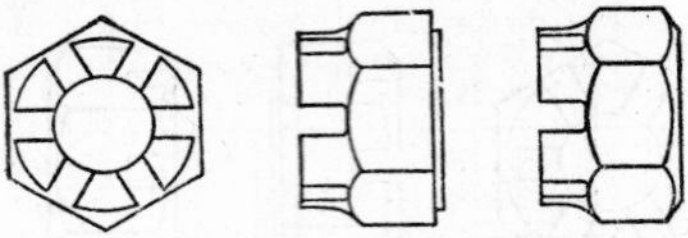

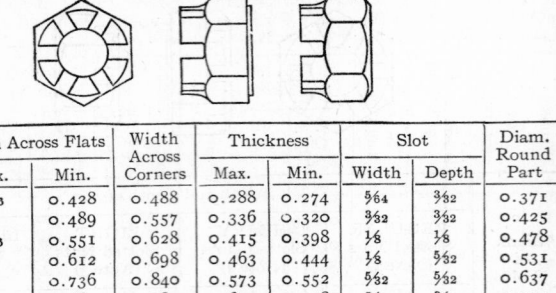

Diameter of Bolt	Width Across Flats		Width Across Corners	Thickness		Slot		Diam. Round Part
	Max.	Min.		Max.	Min.	Width	Depth	
¼	7/16	0.428	0.488	0.288	0.274	5/64	3/32	0.371
5/16	½	0.489	0.557	0.336	0.320	3/32	3/32	0.425
⅜	9/16	0.551	0.628	0.415	0.398	⅛	⅛	0.478
7/16	⅝	0.612	0.698	0.463	0.444	⅛	5/32	0.531
½	¾	0.736	0.840	0.573	0.552	5/32	5/32	0.637
9/16	⅞	0.861	0.982	0.621	0.598	5/32	3/16	0.744
⅝	15/16	0.922	1.051	0.731	0.706	3/16	7/32	0.797
¾	1 1/16	1.045	1.191	0.827	0.798	3/16	¼	0.903
⅞	1¼	1.231	1.403	0.922	0.890	3/16	¼	1.063
1	1 7/16	1.417	1.615	1.018	0.982	¼	9/32	1.222
1⅛	1⅝	1.602	1.826	1.176	1.136	¼	11/32	1.382
1¼	1 13/16	1.788	2.038	1.272	1.228	5/16	⅜	1.541
1⅜	2	1.973	2.249	1.399	1.351	5/16	⅜	1.700
1½	2 3/16	2.159	2.461	1.526	1.474	⅜	7/16	1.859

Extra Stock Required for Upsetting Screw Ends

Figures in body of table give extra length of rod (in inches) required for **upsetting** screw ends.

Diameters before and after Upsetting		Required Length of Upset End					Diameters before and after Upsetting		Required Length of Upset End				
From	To	1 In.	2 In.	3 In.	4 In.	5 In.	From	To	1 In.	2 In.	3 In.	4 In.	5 In.
¾	⅞	0.36	0.72	1.08	1.44	1.81	1¼	1½	0.44	0.88	1.32	1.76	2.20
¾	1	0.78	1.56	2.33	3.11	3.89	1¼	1⅝	0.69	1.38	2.07	2.76	3.45
¾	1⅛	1.25	2.50	3.75	5.00	6.25	1⅜	1½	0.19	0.38	0.57	0.76	0.95
⅞	1	0.31	0.61	0.92	1.22	1.53	1⅜	1⅝	0.40	0.79	1.19	1.59	1.98
⅞	1⅛	0.65	1.31	1.96	2.61	3.27	1⅜	1¾	0.62	1.24	1.86	2.48	3.10
⅞	1¼	1.04	2.08	3.12	4.16	5.20	1½	1⅝	0.17	0.35	0.52	0.69	0.87
1	1⅛	0.27	0.53	0.80	1.06	1.33	1½	1¾	0.36	0.72	1.08	1.44	1.81
1	1¼	0.56	1.13	1.69	2.25	2.81	1½	1⅞	0.56	1.13	1.69	2.25	2.81
1	1⅜	0.89	1.78	2.67	3.56	4.45	1⅝	1¾	0.16	0.32	0.48	0.64	0.80
1⅛	1¼	0.23	0.47	0.70	0.94	1.17	1⅝	1⅞	0.33	0.66	0.99	1.33	1.66
1⅛	1⅜	0.49	0.99	1.48	1.98	2.47	1⅝	2	0.51	1.03	1.54	2.06	2.57
1⅛	1½	0.78	1.56	2.33	3.11	3.89	1¾	1⅞	0.15	0.30	0.44	0.59	0.74
1¼	1⅜	0.21	0.42	0.63	0.84	1.05	1¾	2	0.31	0.61	0.92	1.22	1.53

U. S. Standard Threads, Bolts and Nuts

The United States Standard has largely been superseded by the American Standard but the former is sometimes used, especially for screw thread sizes above the present range of the American Standard. For American Standard bolts and nuts, see pages 940 to 946; also page 950; for screw threads, see pages 986 to 990.

Diameter	No. of Threads per Inch	Diameter at Root of Thread	Diameter of Tap Drill	Area in Sq. Inches Of Bolt	Area in Sq. Inches At Root of Thread	Tensile Strength at Stress of 6000 Pounds per Sq. Inch	Dimensions of Nuts and Bolt Heads				
1/4	20	0.185	13/64	0.049	0.026	160	1/2	0.578	0.707	1/4	1/4
5/16	18	0.240	1/4	0.076	0.045	270	19/32	0.686	0.840	5/16	19/64
3/8	16	0.294	5/16	0.110	0.068	410	11/16	0.794	0.972	3/8	11/32
7/16	14	0.345	23/64	0.150	0.093	560	25/32	0.902	1 105	7/16	25/64
1/2	13	0.400	27/64	0.196	0.126	760	7/8	1.011	1.237	1/2	7/16
9/16	12	0.454	15/32	0.248	0.162	1,000	31/32	1.119	1.370	9/16	31/64
5/8	11	0.507	17/32	0.307	0.202	1,210	1 1/16	1.227	1.502	5/8	17/32
3/4	10	0.620	41/64	0.442	0.302	1,810	1 1/4	1.444	1.768	3/4	5/8
7/8	9	0.731	3/4	0.601	0.419	2,520	1 7/16	1.660	2.033	7/8	23/32
1	8	0.838	55/64	0.785	0.551	3,300	1 5/8	1.877	2.298	1	13/16
1 1/8	7	0.939	31/32	0.994	0.694	4,160	1 13/16	2.093	2.563	1 1/8	29/32
1 1/4	7	1.064	1 3/32	1.227	0.893	5,350	2	2.310	2.828	1 1/4	1
1 3/8	6	1.158	1 7/32	1.485	1.057	6,340	2 3/16	2.527	3.093	1 3/8	1 3/32
1 1/2	6	1.283	1 11/32	1.767	1.295	7,770	2 3/8	2.743	3.358	1 1/2	1 3/16
1 5/8	5 1/2	1.389	1 27/64	2.074	1.515	9,090	2 9/16	2.960	3.623	1 5/8	1 9/32
1 3/4	5	1.490	1 17/32	2.405	1.746	10,470	2 3/4	3.176	3.889	1 3/4	1 3/8
1 7/8	5	1.615	1 21/32	2.761	2.051	12,300	2 15/16	3.393	4.154	1 7/8	1 15/32
2	4 1/2	1.711	1 49/64	3.142	2.302	13,800	3 1/8	3.609	4.419	2	1 9/16
2 1/4	4 1/2	1.961	2 1/64	3.976	3.023	18,100	3 1/2	4.043	4.949	2 1/4	1 3/4
2 1/2	4	2.175	2 15/64	4.909	3.719	22,300	3 7/8	4.476	5.479	2 1/2	1 15/16
2 3/4	4	2.425	2 31/64	5.940	4.620	27,700	4 1/4	4.909	6.010	2 3/4	2 1/8
3	3 1/2	2.629	2 11/16	7.069	5.428	32,500	4 5/8	5.342	6.540	3	2 5/16
3 1/4	3 1/2	2.879	2 15/16	8.296	6.510	39,000	5	5.775	7.070	3 1/4	2 1/2
3 1/2	3 1/4	3.100	3 11/64	9.621	7.548	45,300	5 3/8	6.208	7.500	3 1/2	2 11/16
3 3/4	3	3.317	3 3/8	11.045	8.641	51,800	5 3/4	6.641	8.131	3 3/4	2 7/8
4	3	3.567	3 5/8	12.566	9.963	59,700	6 1/8	7.074	8.661	4	3 1/16
4 1/4	2 7/8	3.798	3 27/32	14.186	11.340	68,000	6 1/2	7.508	9.191	4 1/4	3 1/4
4 1/2	2 3/4	4.028	4 3/32	15.904	12.750	76,500	6 7/8	7.941	9.721	4 1/2	3 7/16
4 3/4	2 5/8	4.255	4 5/16	17.721	14.215	85,500	7 1/4	8.374	10.252	4 3/4	3 5/8
5	2 1/2	4.480	4 9/16	19.635	15.760	94,000	7 5/8	8.807	10.782	5	3 13/16
5 1/4	2 1/2	4.730	4 13/16	21.648	17.570	105,500	8	9.240	11.312	5 1/4	4
5 1/2	2 3/8	4.953	5 1/32	23.758	19.260	116,000	8 3/8	9.673	11.842	5 1/2	4 3/16
5 3/4	2 3/8	5.203	5 9/32	25.967	21.250	127,000	8 3/4	10.106	12.373	5 3/4	4 3/8
6	2 1/4	5.423	5 1/2	28.274	23.090	138,000	9 1/8	10.539	12.903	6	4 9/16

Lengths of Machine Bolts — Approved by U. S. Department of Commerce; Bureau of Standards; American Institute of Bolt, Nut, and Rivet Manufacturers

Lengths, Inches	Diameters, Inch									
	1/4	5/16	3/8	7/16	1/2	5/8	3/4	7/8	1	1 1/8
Square-head Machine Bolts — Stock Sizes (See footnote)										
1/2	**	**	....	....	....	....	....	....	....	....
5/8	....	**	....	....	....	....	....	....	....	....
3/4	*	*	*	....	....	....	....	....	....	....
1	*	*	*	*	*	*	**	....	....	....
1 1/4	*	*	*	*	*	*	*	....	....	....
1 1/2	*	*	*	*	*	*	*	**	....	....
1 3/4	*	*	*	*	*	*	*	*	....	....
2	*	*	*	*	*	*	*	*	**	....
2 1/4	*	*	*	**	*	*	*	*	*	....
2 1/2	*	*	*	*	*	*	*	*	*	....
2 3/4	*	*	....	*	*	*	*	*	*	....
3	*	*	....	*	*	*	*	*	*	....
3 1/4	**	**	*	....	*	*	*	*	*	....
3 1/2	*	*	....	*	*	*	*	*	*	....
3 3/4	....	....	....	*	*	*	*	**	**	....
4	*	*	....	*	*	*	*	*	*	**
4 1/4	....	....	....	....	**	*	*	**	*	**
4 1/2	*	*	....	*	*	*	*	*	*	**
4 3/4	....	....	....	**	**	**	....	*	*	**
5	*	*	....	*	*	*	*	*	*	**
5 1/2	*	*	....	*	*	*	*	*	*	**
6	*	*	....	*	*	*	*	*	*	....
6 1/2	**	**	....	**	*	*	*	*	*	....
7	**	**	....	**	*	*	*	*	*	**
7 1/2	....	....	....	....	*	*	*	*	*	....
8	**	**	....	**	*	*	*	*	....	**
8 1/2	....	....	....	....	*	*	*	**	....	....
9	*	*	....	**	*	*	*	*	*	**
9 1/2	....	....	....	**	*	*	*	*	*	**
10	....	....	*	....	*	*	*	*	*	**
10 1/2	....	....	....	....	*	*	*	*	*	....
11	....	....	*	....	*	*	*	*	*	**
11 1/2	....	....	....	....	**	**	**	....	*	....
12	....	....	*	....	*	*	*	*	*	**
13	....	....	....	....	*	*	*	**	*	**
14	....	....	....	....	*	*	*	*	*	**
15	....	....	....	....	*	*	*	*	*	**
16	....	....	....	....	*	*	*	*	*	**
17	....	....	....	....	*	*	*	**	**	**
18	....	....	....	....	*	*	*	*	*	**
19	....	....	....	....	**	*	**	*	**	**
20	....	....	....	....	*	*	*	*	*	....
22	....	....	....	....	**	*	*	**	**	....
24	....	....	....	....	*	*	*	**	**	....
Hexagon-head Machine Bolts — Stock Sizes (See footnote)										
1/2	....	**	....	....	....	....	....	....	....	....
3/4	....	*	*	*	....	**	....	....	....	....
1	....	*	*	*	....	*	....	....	....	....
1 1/4	....	*	*	*	....	*	**	**	....	....
1 1/2	....	*	*	*	....	*	*	*	....	....
1 3/4	....	**	**	*	....	*	*	*	....	....
2	....	*	**	*	....	*	*	*	....	....
2 1/4	....	*	*	....	....	**	**	**	....	....
2 1/2	....	**	**	*	....	*	**	*	**	....
2 3/4	....	....	....	....	....	**	*	*	....	....
3	....	....	**	**	....	**	*	**	....	....
3 1/2	....	....	....	**	....	**	*	**	....	....
4	....	....	....	**	....	**	**	*	....	....
4 1/2	....	....	....	....	....	**	**	**	**	....
5	....	....	....	....	....	**	*	*	....	....
5 1/2	....	....	....	....	....	**	**	**	....	....
6	....	....	....	....	....	**	*	**	....	....

One asterisk (*) represents stock sizes of maximum demand, and two asterisks (**) stock sizes least frequently used. All other sizes are considered specials.

Weights in Pounds of Steel Bolts and Nuts, and Steel Bars*

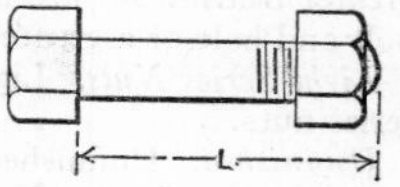

Length L, Inches	Diameter of Bolt												
	1/4	3/8	1/2	5/8	3/4	7/8	1	1⅛	1¼	1⅜	1½	1⅝	1¾
3/4	0.033	0.085	0.175	....	....	...	...	...					
7/8	0.034	0.089	0.182	....	....	...	...	...					
1	0.036	0.093	0.189	0.335	....	...	...	...					
1⅛	0.038	0.097	0.196	0.346	0.553	...	...	...					
1¼	0.040	0.101	0.203	0.357	0.568	0.849	...	...					
1⅜	0.041	0.105	0.210	0.367	0.584	0.870	1.23	...					
1½	0.041	0.116	0.230	0.391	0.612	0.899	1.26	1.61					
1¾	0.044	0.125	0.244	0.414	0.643	0.941	1.32	1.68	2.33	...	..	...	...
2	0.048	0.132	0.258	0.435	0.675	0.984	1.37	1.75	2.43	3.10	...	...	...
2¼	0.052	0.140	0.272	0.457	0.706	1.02	1.43	1.82	2.52	3.20	4.02	...	
2½	0.055	0.147	0.286	0.478	0.737	1.06	1.48	1.89	2.60	3.31	4.12	4.77	...
2¾	0.058	0.156	0.300	0.501	0.768	1.11	1.54	1.96	2.68	3.41	4.25	4.91	5.87
3	0.062	0.163	0.314	0.522	0.800	1.15	1.59	2.03	2.78	3.52	4.40	5.06	6.04
3½	0.069	0.178	0.342	0.565	0.862	1.23	1.71	2.17	2.95	3.73	4.65	5.35	6.38
4	0.076	0.194	0.370	0.609	0.925	1.32	1.83	2.31	3.13	3.94	4.90	5.65	6.72
4½	0.083	0.209	0.398	0.652	0.987	1.40	1.93	2.45	3.30	4.15	5.12	5.94	7.06
5	0.090	0.225	0.426	0.696	1.05	1.49	2.04	2.60	3.47	4.36	5.40	6.24	7.40
5½	0.097	0.240	0.454	0.739	1.11	1.57	2.15	2.74	3.65	4.57	5.62	6.53	7.74
6	0.104	0.256	0.482	0.783	1.17	1.66	2.26	2.88	3.82	4.78	5.90	6.82	8.08
6½	0.111	0.271	0.510	0.826	1.23	1.74	2.37	3.02	4.00	4.99	6.15	7.12	8.42
7	0.118	0.287	0.538	0.870	1.30	1.83	2.48	3.16	4.17	5.20	6.40	7.41	8.76
7½	0.125	0.302	0.566	0.913	1.36	1.91	2.59	3.30	4.34	5.41	6.62	7.71	9.10
8	0.132	0.318	0.594	0.957	1.42	2.00	2.70	3.44	4.52	5.62	6.90	8.00	9.44
8½	0.139	0.333	0.622	1.000	1.48	2.08	2.82	3.58	4.69	5.83	7.15	8.29	9.78
9	0.146	0.349	0.650	1.04	1.55	2.17	2.93	3.72	4.87	6.04	7.40	8.59	10.12
9½	0.157	0.364	0.678	1.08	1.61	2.25	3.04	3.86	5.04	6.25	7.62	8.88	10.46
10	0.160	0.380	0.706	1.13	1.67	2.34	3.15	4.00	5.21	6.46	7.90	9.18	10.81
11	0.174	0.411	0.762	1.21	1.80	2.51	3.37	4.28	5.56	6.88	8.40	9.76	11.49
12	0.188	0.442	0.818	1.30	1.92	2.68	3.61	4.56	5.91	7.30	8.90	10.35	12.17

Weight of Steel Bars

Length of Bar, Feet	Diameter of Bar												
	1/4	3/8	1/2	5/8	3/4	7/8	1	1⅛	1¼	1⅜	1½	1⅝	1¾
1	0.167	0.376	0.668	1.04	1.50	2.04	2.67	3.38	4.17	5.04	6.00	7.05	8.17
2	0.334	0.752	1.336	2.08	3.00	4.08	5.34	6.76	8.34	10.08	12.00	14.10	16.34
3	0.501	1.128	2.004	3.12	4.50	6.12	8.01	10.14	12.51	15.12	18.00	21.15	24.51
4	0.668	1.504	2.672	4.16	6.00	8.16	10.68	13.52	16.68	20.16	24.00	28.20	32.68
5	0.835	1.880	3.340	5.20	7.50	10.20	13.35	16.90	20.85	25.20	30.00	35.25	40.85
6	1.002	2.256	4.008	6.24	9.00	12.24	16.02	20.28	25.02	30.24	36.00	42.30	49.02
7	1.169	2.632	4.676	7.28	10.50	14.28	18.69	23.66	29.19	35.28	42.00	49.35	57.19
8	1.336	3.008	5.344	8.32	12.00	16.32	21.36	27.04	33.36	40.32	48.00	56.40	65.36
9	1.503	3.384	6.012	9.36	13.50	18.36	24.03	30.42	37.53	45.36	54.00	63.45	73.53
10	1.670	3.760	6.680	10.40	15.00	20.40	26.70	33.80	41.70	50.40	60.00	70.50	81.70

* When the length L of bolt is over 12 inches, compute by using table of weight of steel bars. Example: Weight of 1 inch bolt, 18 inches long = weight of 6 inches long bolt + weight of 1 foot long bar.

American Standard Bolts and Nuts. — These standards are intended for general use by all industries and to replace all other series of dimensions.

Regular Series Bolt Heads and Nuts: Regular bolt heads and nuts are for general use. The dimensions and the resulting strengths of these bolt heads and nuts are based on theoretical analysis of stresses and on results of numerous tests.

Heavy Series Bolt Heads and Nuts: Heavy bolt heads and nuts are for use where greater bearing surface is necessary; that is, where a larger clearance between the bolt and hole or a greater wrench bearing surface is considered essential.

Light Series Nuts: Light nuts have smaller dimensions across flats than regular series nuts.

Unfinished: Unfinished bolt heads or nuts are not machined or treated on any surface except in the threads.

Semi-finished: Semi-finished bolt heads or nuts are machined or otherwise formed or treated on the bearing surface so as to provide for nuts either a washer face or a circular bearing surface formed by chamfering the edges, and for bolt heads a washer face.

Finished: Finished bolt heads and nuts are the same as semi-finished except that the surfaces other than the bearing surface have been so treated as to provide a special appearance. (For dimensions, see table for semi-finished, in all cases.) The finish desired on all non-bearing surfaces of finished bolt heads and nuts should be specified by the purchaser.

Washer Face: The washer face is a circular boss turned or otherwise produced on the bearing surface of a bolt head or nut to relieve the corners. A circular bearing surface can also be produced by chamfering the corners of the nut.

American Standard T-Nuts

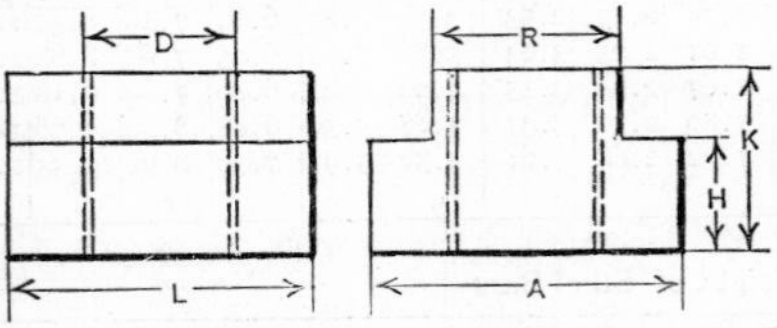

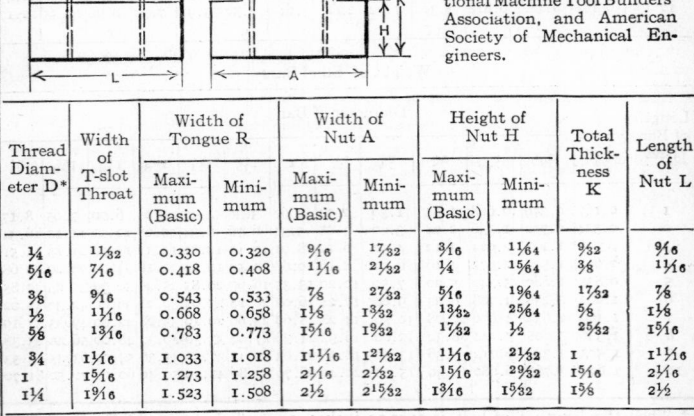

Approved by American Standards Association, National Machine Tool Builders' Association, and American Society of Mechanical Engineers.

Thread Diameter D*	Width of T-slot Throat	Width of Tongue R		Width of Nut A		Height of Nut H		Total Thickness K	Length of Nut L
		Maximum (Basic)	Minimum	Maximum (Basic)	Minimum	Maximum (Basic)	Minimum		
1/4	11/32	0.330	0.320	9/16	17/32	3/16	11/64	9/32	9/16
5/16	7/16	0.418	0.408	11/16	21/32	1/4	15/64	3/8	11/16
3/8	9/16	0.543	0.533	7/8	27/32	5/16	19/64	17/32	7/8
1/2	11/16	0.668	0.658	1 1/8	1 3/32	13/32	25/64	5/8	1 1/8
5/8	13/16	0.783	0.773	1 5/16	1 9/32	17/32	1/2	25/32	1 5/16
3/4	1 1/16	1.033	1.018	1 11/16	1 21/32	11/16	21/32	1	1 11/16
1	1 5/16	1.273	1.258	2 1/16	2 1/32	15/16	29/32	1 5/16	2 1/16
1 1/4	1 9/16	1.523	1.508	2 1/2	2 15/32	1 3/16	1 5/32	1 5/8	2 1/2

* Thread diameter in T-nut is made smaller than corresponding T-bolt, to insure full strength of T-nut.

American Standard T-Slots and T-Bolts

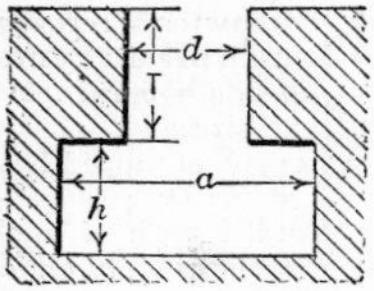

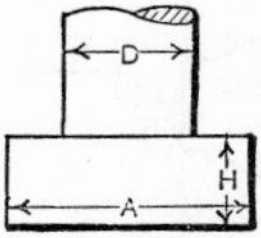

Approved by American Standards Association, National Machine Tool Builders' Association, and American Society of Mechanical Engineers.

Diameter of T-bolt*	Width of Throat d*†	Depth of Throat T		Head Space Dimensions and Tolerances					
				Width a			Depth h		
		Maximum	Minimum	Maximum (Basic)	Tolerance (Minus)	Minimum	Maximum (Basic)	Tolerance (Minus)	Minimum
1/4	9/32	3/8	1/8	9/16	0.063	1/2	15/64	0.031	13/64
5/16	11/32	7/16	5/32	21/32	0.063	19/32	17/64	0.031	15/64
3/8	7/16	9/16	7/32	25/32	0.063	23/32	21/64	0.031	19/64
1/2	9/16	11/16	5/16	31/32	0.063	29/32	25/64	0.031	23/64
5/8	11/16	7/8	7/16	1 1/4	0.063	1 3/16	31/64	0.031	29/64
3/4	13/16	1 1/16	9/16	1 15/32	0.094	1 3/8	5/8	0.031	19/32
1	1 1/16	1 1/4	3/4	1 27/32	0.094	1 3/4	53/64	0.047	25/32
1 1/4	1 5/16	1 9/16	1	2 7/32	0.094	2 1/8	1 3/32	0.063	1 1/32
1 1/2	1 9/16	1 15/16	1 1/4	2 21/32	0.094	2 9/16	1 11/32	0.063	1 9/32

All dimensions in inches.

* In addition to the width of throat given, a secondary standard is recognized, having the width of throat the same as the nominal diameter of the T-bolt. This is to provide for the use, during the transition period, of this standard on machine tools where it is already established.

† A tolerance of plus 0.001 is allowed for width of throat when tongues or other parts must fit.

Diameter of T-bolt D	Threads per Inch	Bolt Head Dimensions and Tolerances						
		Width across Flats A			Width across Corners	Height H		
		Maximum (Basic)	Tolerance (Minus)	Minimum		Maximum (Basic)	Tolerance (Minus)	Minimum
1/4	20	15/32	0.031	7/16	0.663	5/32	0.016	9/64
5/16	18	9/16	0.031	17/32	0.796	3/16	0.016	11/64
3/8	16	11/16	0.031	21/32	0.972	1/4	0.016	15/64
1/2	13	7/8	0.031	27/32	1.238	5/16	0.016	19/64
5/8	11	1 1/8	0.031	1 3/32	1.591	13/32	0.016	25/64
3/4	10	1 5/16	0.031	1 9/32	1.856	17/32	0.031	1/2
1	8	1 11/16	0.031	1 21/32	2.387	11/16	0.031	21/32
1 1/4	7	2 1/16	0.031	2 1/32	2.917	15/16	0.031	29/32
1 1/2	6	2 1/2	0.031	2 15/32	3.536	1 3/16	0.031	1 5/32

Dimensions of Turnbuckles

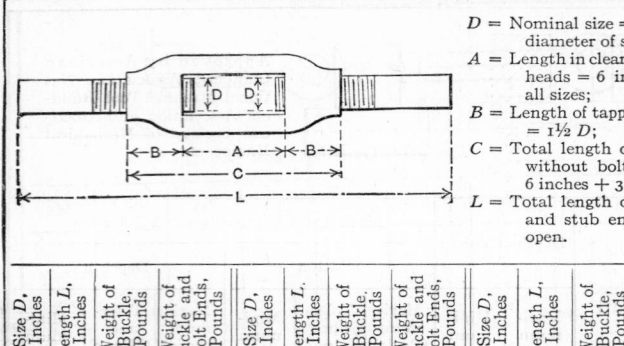

D = Nominal size = outside diameter of screws;
A = Length in clear between heads = 6 inches for all sizes;
B = Length of tapped heads = $1\frac{1}{2} D$;
C = Total length of buckle without bolt ends = 6 inches $+ 3 D$;
L = Total length of buckle and stub ends when open.

Size D, Inches	Length L, Inches	Weight of Buckle, Pounds	Weight of Buckle and Bolt Ends, Pounds	Size D, Inches	Length L, Inches	Weight of Buckle, Pounds	Weight of Buckle and Bolt Ends, Pounds	Size D, Inches	Length L, Inches	Weight of Buckle, Pounds	Weight of Buckle and Bolt Ends, Pounds
3/8	22	1	1 1/2	1 3/8	27	7	16	2 5/8	32	30	70
7/16	22	1	1 3/4	1 1/2	27	8	19	2 3/4	33	33	78
1/2	22	1	2	1 5/8	28	10	23	2 7/8	33	36	86
9/16	22	1 1/4	2 1/2	1 3/4	28	11	26	3	34	40	96
5/8	22	1 1/2	3	1 7/8	29	12	30	3 1/8	36	45	108
3/4	23	2	4	2	29	14	35	3 1/4	36	50	120
7/8	24	3	6	2 1/8	29	17	41	3 3/8	37	57	134
1	25	4	8	2 1/4	30	20	47	3 1/2	37	65	150
1 1/8	25	5	11	2 3/8	31	22	53	3 3/4	39	74	168
1 1/4	26	6	13	2 1/2	32	25	61	4	41	84	188

American Standard Cotter Pins

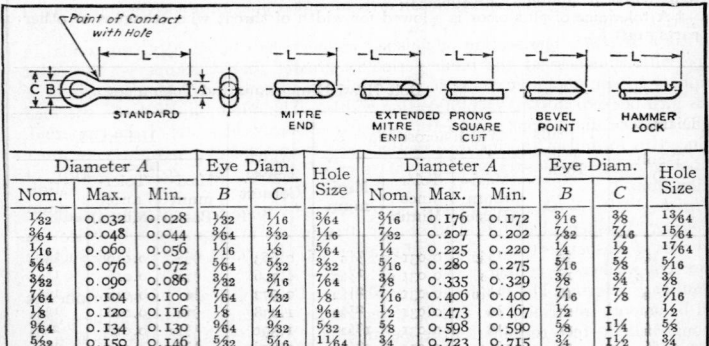

STANDARD · MITRE END · EXTENDED MITRE END · PRONG SQUARE CUT · BEVEL POINT · HAMMER LOCK

Diameter A			Eye Diam.		Hole Size	Diameter A			Eye Diam.		Hole Size
Nom.	Max.	Min.	B	C		Nom.	Max.	Min.	B	C	
1/32	0.032	0.028	1/32	1/16	3/64	3/16	0.176	0.172	3/16	3/8	13/64
3/64	0.048	0.044	3/64	3/32	1/16	7/32	0.207	0.202	7/32	7/16	15/64
1/16	0.060	0.056	1/16	1/8	5/64	1/4	0.225	0.220	1/4	1/2	17/64
5/64	0.076	0.072	5/64	5/32	3/32	5/16	0.280	0.275	5/16	5/8	5/16
3/32	0.090	0.086	3/32	3/16	7/64	3/8	0.335	0.329	3/8	3/4	3/8
7/64	0.104	0.100	7/64	7/32	1/8	7/16	0.406	0.400	7/16	7/8	7/16
1/8	0.120	0.116	1/8	1/4	9/64	1/2	0.473	0.467	1/2	1	1/2
9/64	0.134	0.130	9/64	9/32	5/32	5/8	0.598	0.590	5/8	1 1/4	5/8
5/32	0.150	0.146	5/32	5/16	11/64	3/4	0.723	0.715	3/4	1 1/2	3/4

Lengths L are measured as shown but are not included in standard. Prongs are to be parallel with ends closed as shown. Points may be blunt, mitre, extended-prong, bevel, or hammer-lock, as specified.

Cotter Pins — S.A.E. Standard

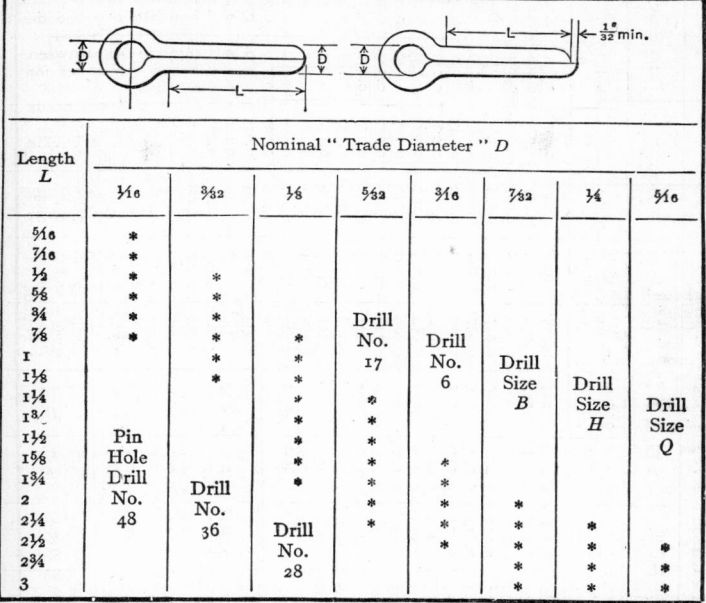

Length L	Nominal " Trade Diameter " D							
	1/16	3/32	1/8	5/32	3/16	7/32	1/4	5/16
5/16	*							
7/16	*							
1/2	*	*						
5/8	*	*						
3/4	*	*						
7/8	*	*	*	Drill No. 17				
1		*	*		Drill No. 6			
1 1/8		*	*	*		Drill Size B		
1 1/4			*	*			Drill Size H	
1 3/8			*	*				Drill Size Q
1 1/2	Pin Hole Drill No. 48		*	*				
1 5/8			*	*	*			
1 3/4		Drill No. 36	*	*	*			
2				*	*	*		
2 1/4			Drill No. 28	*	*	*	*	
2 1/2				*	*	*	*	*
2 3/4						*	*	*
3						*	*	*

American Standard Spring Lock Washers. — The carbon steel spring lock-washers covered by this specification are intended for automotive and general industrial application.

Washer Section: The section of finished washers shall be slightly trapezoidal in shape with thickness at the inner periphery greater than thickness at the outer periphery by an amount varying from a minimum of 0.0005 inch to a maximum of 0.001 inch per 0.0156 (1/64) inch of section width. The minimum thickness specified in the table of dimensions represents the *nominal* mean thickness of the trapezoid. Reduced to formulas, the increase in thickness from the outer periphery to inner periphery $= T - t = 0.032 \times$ width of section (min.) and $0.064 \times$ width of section (max.)

Finish: Plated washers shall be baked to relieve hydrogen or acid embrittlement.

Coiling: Washers shall be coiled so that free height is approximately twice the thickness of washer section. Gap and relationship of severed ends shall be such as to prevent washers tangling.

Quality of Finish: The flat faces of washers and the inner and outer peripheries shall be smooth and free from knurling, serrations, die marks, deep scratches, etc., although slight feed-roll marks are permissible. Washers shall also be free of burrs, rust, pit marks and loose scale, with internal and external circumferential edges rounded sufficiently to avoid heat checks.

Material and Hardness: Washers shall be made from carbon steel fabricated and heat-treated to a Rockwell hardness of 47–53 C scale. They shall be ground down

American Standard for Carbon Steel Spring Lock-Washers

Nom. Size	Outside Diam. Max.				Inside Diam. Min.	Clearance Bolt Size		Light		Med.		Heavy		Extra Heavy	
	Light	Med.	Heavy	Extra Heavy		Min.	Max.	Width	Thickness	Width	Thickness	Width	Thickness	Width	Thickness
0.086	0.165	0.175	0.185	0.211	0.088	0.002	0.011	0.030	0.015	0.035	0.020	0.040	0.025	0.053	0.027
0.099	0.188	0.198	0.212	0.242	0.102	0.002	0.011	0.035	0.020	0.040	0.025	0.047	0.031	0.062	0.034
0.112	0.202	0.212	0.226	0.256	0.115	0.003	0.012	0.035	0.020	0.040	0.025	0.047	0.031	0.062	0.034
0.125	0.225	0.239	0.255	0.303	0.128	0.003	0.012	0.040	0.025	0.047	0.031	0.055	0.040	0.079	0.045
0.138	0.237	0.251	0.267	0.315	0.141	0.003	0.013	0.040	0.025	0.047	0.031	0.055	0.040	0.079	0.045
0.164	0.280	0.296	0.310	0.378	0.168	0.004	0.014	0.047	0.031	0.055	0.040	0.062	0.047	0.096	0.057
0.190	0.323	0.337	0.353	0.437	0.194	0.004	0.015	0.055	0.040	0.062	0.047	0.070	0.056	0.112	0.068
0.216	0.364	0.380	0.394	0.500	0.221	0.005	0.016	0.062	0.047	0.070	0.056	0.077	0.063	0.130	0.080
1/4	0.489	0.493	0.495	0.539	0.255	0.005	0.017	0.107	0.047	0.109	0.062	0.110	0.077	0.132	0.084
5/16	0.575	0.591	0.601	0.627	0.319	0.006	0.020	0.117	0.056	0.125	0.078	0.130	0.097	0.143	0.108
3/8	0.678	0.688	0.696	0.746	0.382	0.007	0.023	0.136	0.070	0.141	0.094	0.145	0.115	0.170	0.123
7/16	0.780	0.784	0.792	0.844	0.446	0.008	0.026	0.154	0.085	0.156	0.109	0.160	0.133	0.186	0.143
1/2	0.877	0.879	0.889	0.945	0.509	0.009	0.029	0.170	0.099	0.171	0.125	0.176	0.151	0.204	0.162
9/16	0.975	0.979	0.989	1.049	0.573	0.010	0.032	0.186	0.113	0.188	0.141	0.193	0.170	0.223	0.182
5/8	1.082	1.086	1.100	1.164	0.636	0.011	0.035	0.201	0.126	0.203	0.156	0.210	0.189	0.242	0.202
11/16	1.178	1.184	1.200	1.266	0.700	0.012	0.038	0.216	0.138	0.219	0.172	0.227	0.207	0.260	0.221
3/4	1.277	1.279	1.299	1.369	0.763	0.013	0.041	0.233	0.153	0.234	0.188	0.244	0.226	0.279	0.241
13/16	1.375	1.377	1.401	1.473	0.827	0.014	0.044	0.249	0.168	0.250	0.203	0.262	0.246	0.298	0.261
7/8	1.470	1.474	1.504	1.586	0.890	0.015	0.047	0.264	0.179	0.266	0.219	0.281	0.266	0.322	0.285
15/16	1.562	1.570	1.604	1.698	0.954	0.016	0.050	0.277	0.191	0.281	0.234	0.298	0.284	0.345	0.308
1	1.656	1.672	1.716	1.810	1.017	0.017	0.053	0.289	0.202	0.297	0.250	0.319	0.306	0.366	0.330
1 1/16	1.746	1.768	1.820	1.922	1.081	0.018	0.056	0.301	0.213	0.312	0.266	0.338	0.326	0.389	0.352
1 1/8	1.837	1.865	1.921	2.031	1.144	0.019	0.059	0.314	0.224	0.328	0.281	0.356	0.345	0.411	0.375
1 3/16	1.923	1.963	2.021	2.137	1.208	0.020	0.062	0.324	0.234	0.344	0.297	0.373	0.364	0.431	0.396
1 1/4	2.012	2.058	2.126	2.244	1.271	0.021	0.065	0.336	0.244	0.359	0.312	0.393	0.384	0.452	0.417
1 5/16	2.098	2.156	2.226	2.350	1.335	0.022	0.068	0.346	0.254	0.375	0.328	0.410	0.403	0.472	0.438
1 3/8	2.183	2.253	2.325	2.453	1.398	0.023	0.071	0.356	0.264	0.391	0.344	0.427	0.422	0.491	0.458
1 7/16	2.269	2.349	2.421	2.555	1.462	0.024	0.074	0.366	0.273	0.406	0.359	0.442	0.440	0.509	0.478
1 1/2	2.352	2.446	2.518	2.654	1.525	0.025	0.077	0.375	0.282	0.422	0.375	0.458	0.458	0.526	0.496

to remove decarburization before testing hardness. They shall also meet the test requirements of this specification.

Size Designation: Washers shall be specified or designated by the nominal size and the series, i.e., ¼ inch light, ¼ inch medium, ¼ inch heavy, or ¼ inch extra heavy.

Temper Test: After a first compression to flat, the free height of a washer shall be at least five-sixths of the original free height. Subsequent compression under the same load shall not further reduce this free height.

High Nuts — S.A.E. Standard

Nut Size A	Width Across Flats B	Nut Height C	Counterbore Depth D*	Diam. at Top E	Slot Width F	Slot Depth G
¼	7/16	3/8	1/16	25/64	5/64	3/32
5/16	1/2	29/64	5/64	29/64	5/64	7/64
3/8	9/16	17/32	3/32	33/64	1/8	1/8
7/16	5/8	39/64	7/64	37/64	1/8	9/64
1/2	3/4	11/16	1/8	11/16	1/8	11/64
9/16	7/8	49/64	9/64	51/64	5/32	11/64
5/8	1	27/32	5/32	55/64	5/32	13/64
3/4	1 1/8	1	3/16	63/64	5/32	7/32
7/8	1 5/16	1 5/32	7/32	1 5/32	5/32	1/4
1	1 1/2	1 5/16	1/4	1 21/64	5/32	9/32

* The counterbore indicated at the bottom of the nut is optional. All screw threads are to be in accordance with the Free Fit or Class 2 of the American Standard. (See pages 1092 to 1095 for the Fine-thread Series and the Coarse-thread Series.) The angle of chamfer shall not exceed 40 degrees with the top face of the nut.

Plain Washers — S.A.E. Standard

Screw and Bolt Sizes	Inside Diam.	Outside Diam.	Thickness ±0.010	Screw and Bolt Sizes	Inside Diam.	Outside Diam.	Thickness ±0.010
2	3/32	1/4	1/32	9/16	19/32	1 3/16	3/32
4	1/8	5/16	1/32	5/8	21/32	1 5/16	3/32
6	5/32	3/8	3/64	11/16	23/32	1 3/8	3/32
8	3/16	7/16	3/64	3/4	13/16	1 1/2	1/8
10	7/32	1/2	1/16	7/8	15/16	1 3/4	1/8
12	1/4	9/16	1/16	1	1 1/16	2	1/8
1/4	9/32	5/8	1/16	1 1/8	1 3/16	2 1/4	1/8
5/16	11/32	11/16	1/16	1 1/4	1 5/16	2 1/2	5/32
3/8	13/32	13/16	1/16	1 3/8	1 7/16	2 3/4	5/32
7/16	15/32	15/16	1/16	1 1/2	1 9/16	3	5/32
1/2	17/32	1 1/16	3/32	....	....	....	....

Manufacturers' Regular Standard Plain Washers

Standard List Adopted February 4, 1935

Nominal Bolt Size, Inches	Outside Diam. Inches	Inside Diam. Inches	Thickness, Birmingham Wire Gage	Thickness, Inch	Approximate Number in 100 Pounds	Nominal Bolt Size, Inches	Outside Diam. Inches	Inside Diam. Inches	Thickness, Birmingham Wire Gage	Thickness, Inch	Approximate Number in 100 Pounds
$\frac{1}{4}$	$\frac{3}{4}$	$\frac{5}{16}$	16	0.065	14,900	$1\frac{1}{4}$	3	$1\frac{3}{8}$	8	0.165	384
$\frac{5}{16}$	$\frac{7}{8}$	$\frac{3}{8}$	16	0.065	11,100	$1\frac{3}{8}$	$3\frac{1}{4}$	$1\frac{1}{2}$	7	0.180	300
$\frac{3}{8}$	1	$\frac{7}{16}$	14	0.083	6,700	$1\frac{1}{2}$	$3\frac{1}{2}$	$1\frac{5}{8}$	7	0.180	260
$\frac{7}{16}$	$1\frac{1}{4}$	$\frac{1}{2}$	14	0.083	4,100	$1\frac{5}{8}$	$3\frac{3}{4}$	$1\frac{3}{4}$	7	0.180	227
$\frac{1}{2}$	$1\frac{3}{8}$	$\frac{9}{16}$	12	0.109	2,600	$1\frac{3}{4}$	4	$1\frac{7}{8}$	7	0.180	200
$\frac{9}{16}$	$1\frac{1}{2}$	$\frac{5}{8}$	12	0.109	2,200	$1\frac{7}{8}$	$4\frac{1}{4}$	2	7	0.180	176
$\frac{5}{8}$	$1\frac{3}{4}$	$1\frac{1}{16}$	10	0.134	1,300	2	$4\frac{1}{2}$	$2\frac{1}{8}$	7	0.180	159
$\frac{3}{4}$	2	$1\frac{3}{16}$	9	0.148	910	$2\frac{1}{4}$	$4\frac{3}{4}$	$2\frac{3}{8}$	5	0.220	121
$\frac{7}{8}$	$2\frac{1}{4}$	$1\frac{5}{16}$	8	0.165	652	$2\frac{1}{2}$	5	$2\frac{5}{8}$	4	0.238	104
1	$2\frac{1}{2}$	$1\frac{1}{16}$	8	0.165	532	$2\frac{3}{4}$	$5\frac{1}{4}$	$2\frac{7}{8}$	3	0.259	91
$1\frac{1}{8}$	$2\frac{3}{4}$	$1\frac{1}{4}$	8	0.165	454	3	$5\frac{1}{2}$	$3\frac{1}{8}$	2	0.284	77

Regular washers are for use with American Standard regular bolt heads, heavy bolt heads, regular nuts, heavy nuts, carriage bolts, stove bolts and cap screws.

Tolerances: Thickness — one gage plus or minus. Outside diameter — plus 0.010, minus 0.000, for $\frac{1}{4}$- to $1\frac{1}{4}$-inch bolt sizes; plus 0.015, minus 0.000 for $1\frac{3}{8}$- to 3-inch bolt sizes.

Spacing of Bolts for Wrench Clearance. — The spacing required for bolts, so as to obtain sufficient room between adjacent nuts for wrench clearance, may be determined by the following formulas, in which D = distance from center of bolt to nearest side of corner (see accompanying illustration); D_1 = distance between centers of adjacent bolts; d = diameter of bolt; C = distance across corners of nut; W = maximum width of head of wrench.

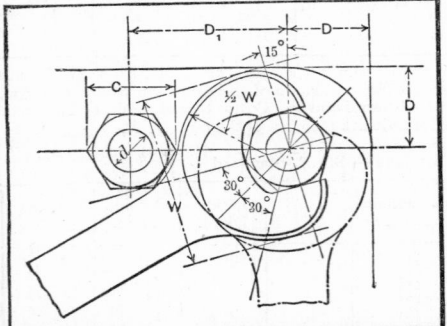

$$D = 0.48\ W$$

The value of W may be taken as $3\frac{1}{2}\ d + \frac{1}{8}$ inch which will be found ample for the wrenches on the market. The slight clearance at the sides, obtained with the formula for D, may need to be increased in some cases.

The following expression gives the distance D_1 between centers of adjacent bolts:

$$D_1 = \frac{1}{2}\ W + \frac{1}{2}\ C + \frac{1}{2}\ d$$

The distances C across the corners of the nuts may be found in the tables (pages 943 to 945) of the American Standard which is now in common use. For American Standard bolt heads, see pages 940 to 942.

Cap or Acorn Nuts — S.A.E. Recommended Practice

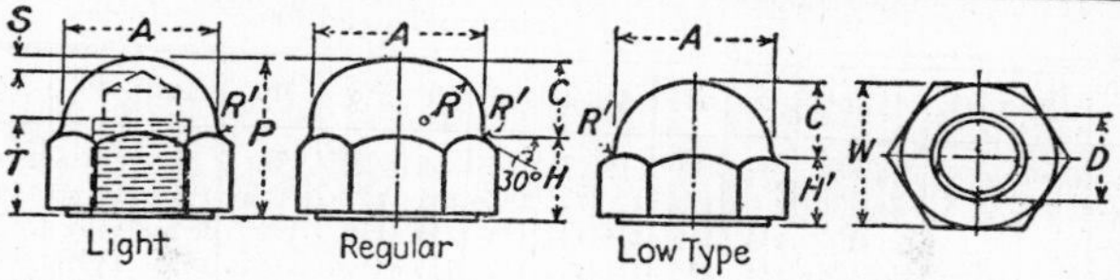

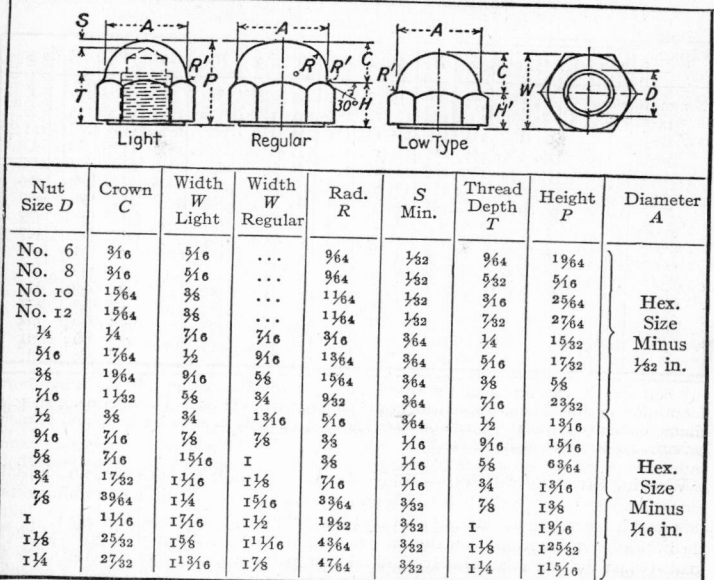

Nut Size D	Crown C	Width W Light	Width W Regular	Rad. R	S Min.	Thread Depth T	Height P	Diameter A
No. 6	3/16	5/16	...	9/64	1/32	9/64	19/64	Hex. Size Minus 1/32 in.
No. 8	3/16	5/16	...	9/64	1/32	5/32	5/16	
No. 10	15/64	3/8	...	11/64	1/32	3/16	25/64	
No. 12	15/64	3/8	...	11/64	1/32	7/32	27/64	
1/4	1/4	7/16	7/16	3/16	3/64	1/4	15/32	
5/16	17/64	1/2	9/16	13/64	3/64	5/16	17/32	
3/8	19/64	9/16	5/8	15/64	3/64	3/8	5/8	
7/16	11/32	5/8	3/4	9/32	3/64	7/16	23/32	
1/2	3/8	3/4	13/16	5/16	3/64	1/2	13/16	
9/16	7/16	7/8	7/8	3/8	1/16	9/16	15/16	Hex. Size Minus 1/16 in.
5/8	7/16	15/16	1	3/8	1/16	5/8	63/64	
3/4	17/32	1 1/16	1 1/8	7/16	1/16	3/4	1 3/16	
7/8	39/64	1 1/4	1 5/16	33/64	3/32	7/8	1 3/8	
1	11/16	1 7/16	1 1/2	19/32	3/32	1	1 9/16	
1 1/8	25/32	1 5/8	1 11/16	43/64	3/32	1 1/8	1 25/32	
1 1/4	27/32	1 13/16	1 7/8	47/64	3/32	1 1/4	1 15/16	

Height $H = D$ for No. 6 to No. 10 sizes, inc., and 7/8 D for larger sizes. Height H' for low nuts of the light series = 3/4 D.

For low nuts, reduce usable thread depth T an amount equal to H minus H'.

Radius R' = 1/64 inch for sizes Nos. 6 to 7/16, inc., and 1/32 inch for larger sizes.

Collar Screws

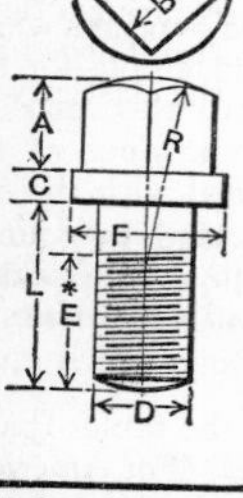

Outside Diameter of Screw, D	Number of Threads per Inch	Length of Head, A	Size of Square, B	Thickness of Collar, C	Diameter of Collar, F	Radius of Head, R
1/8	40	1/8	1/8	1/16	1/4	1/4
3/16	24	3/16	3/16	5/64	11/32	3/8
1/4	20	1/4	1/4	5/64	7/16	1/2
5/16	18	5/16	5/16	7/64	1/2	5/8
3/8	16	3/8	3/8	1/8	5/8	3/4
7/16	14	7/16	7/16	1/8	11/16	7/8
1/2	12 or 13	1/2	1/2	3/16	13/16	1
9/16	12	9/16	9/16	7/32	15/16	1 1/8
5/8	11	5/8	5/8	15/64	1	1 1/4
3/4	10	3/4	3/4	9/32	1 1/4	1 1/2

* On all screws four inches long and under, threads are cut 3/4 of the length L; longer than four inches, threads are cut half of the length L.

Thread Lengths for Bolts — Usual Practice of Bolt Manufacturers*

Bolt Diam.	Bolt Lengths and Minimum Thread Lengths, Inches																
	¾	1	1¼	1½	1¾	2	2½	3	4	5	6	8	10	12	16	20	30
No. 10–¼	½	¾	¾	¾	¾	¾	¾	⅞	⅞	⅞	⅞	⅞	⅞	⅞	1	1	...
5/16–⅜	½	¾	¾	⅞	⅞	1	1	1	1	1 3/16	1 3/16	1 3/16	1 3/16	1 3/16	1 3/16	1⅜	...
7/16–½	..	¾	1	1	1	1¼	1¼	1¼	1¼	1¼	1½	1½	1½	1½	1½	1½	1¾
9/16–⅝	..	¾	1	1⅛	1 3/16	1¼	1½	1½	1½	1½	1½	1 13/16	1 13/16	1 13/16	1 13/16	1 13/16	1 13/16
¾	..	..	1	1⅛	1⅜	1⅜	1½	1¾	1¾	1¾	1¾	2	2⅛	2⅛	2⅛	2⅛	2⅛
⅞	..	..	...	1⅛	1⅜	1 9/16	1 9/16	1¾	2	2	2	2	2 7/16	2 7/16	2 7/16	2 7/16	2 7/16
1	..	..	...	...	1⅜	1⅝	1¾	1¾	2¼	2¼	2¼	2¼	2½	2¾	2¾	2¾	2¾
1⅛–1¼	..	..	...	...	..	1⅝	2	2⅛	2¼	2¾	2¾	2¾	2¾	2¾	3¼	3⅜	3⅜
1⅜–1½	..	..	...	...	..	..	2	2½	2½	2¾	3¼	3¼	3¼	3¼	3¼	4	4
1⅝–1¾	..	..	...	...	..	..	..	2½	2⅞	2⅞	3¼	3¾	3¾	3¾	3¾	4⅝	4⅝
1⅞–2	..	..	...	...	..	..	..	...	3¼	3¼	3¼	4	4¼	4¼	4¼	4¾	5¼
2¼	..	..	...	...	..	..	..	...	3¼	3⅝	3⅝	4	4¾	4¾	4¾	4¾	5⅞
2½	..	..	...	...	..	..	..	...	3¼	4	4	4	4¾	5¼	5¼	5¼	6½
2¾	..	..	...	...	..	..	..	...	...	4⅛	4⅛	4⅛	4¾	5¾	5¾	5¾	6½
3	..	..	...	...	..	..	..	...	...	4¼	4¾	4¾	4¾	6¼	6¼	6¼	6½

* Bolt lengths recommended by American Standards Association. If bolt is too short for minimum thread length specified, cut thread to within ¼ inch of head or neck on bolt diameters up to ½ inch; ⅜ inch on sizes 9/16 to 1; ½ inch on sizes 1⅛ to 2; and ¾ inch on sizes 2⅛ to 3 inches, inclusive.

Working Strength of Bolts. — When the nut on a bolt is tightened, an initial tensile load is placed on the bolt which must be taken into account in determining its safe working strength or external load-carrying capacity. The total load on the bolt theoretically varies from a maximum equal to the sum of the initial and external loads (when the bolt is absolutely rigid and the parts held together are elastic) to a minimum equal to either the initial or external loads, whichever is the greater (where the bolt is elastic and the parts held together are absolutely rigid). Since no material is absolutely rigid, in practice the total load values fall somewhere between these maximum and minimum limits, depending upon the relative elasticity of the bolt and joint members.

Some experiments made at Cornell University to determine the initial stress due to tightening nuts on bolts sufficiently to make a packed joint steam tight, showed that experienced machinists tighten nuts with a pull roughly proportional to the bolt diameter. It was also found that the stress due to nut tightening was often sufficient to break a ½-inch bolt, but not larger sizes, assuming that the nut is tightened by an experienced mechanic. It may be concluded, therefore, that bolts smaller than ⅝ inch should not be used for holding cylinder heads or other parts requiring a tight joint. As a result of these tests, the following empirical formula was established for the working strength of bolts used for packed joints or joints where the elasticity of a gasket is greater than the elasticity of the studs or bolts.

$$W = S_t(0.55\,d^2 - 0.25\,d)$$

In this formula, W = working strength of bolt or permissible load, in pounds after allowance is made for initial load due to tightening; S_t = allowable working stress in tension, pounds per square inch; and d = nominal outside diameter of stud or bolt, inches. A somewhat more convenient formula, and one which gives approximately the same results, is:

$$W = S_t(A - 0.25\,d)$$

In this formula, W, S_t and d are as previously given, and A = area at the root of the thread, square inches.

Working Strength of Bolts — American Standard Coarse-Thread Series*

Bolt Size (Inches)	Allowable Stress (Pounds per Square Inch)			Bolt Size (Inches)	Allowable Stress (Pounds per Square Inch)		
	6,000 (Note 1)	10,000 (Note 2)	15,000 (Note 3)		6,000 (Note 1)	10,000 (Note 2)	15,000 (Note 3)
	Allowable Load on Bolt (Pounds)				Allowable Load on Bolt (Pounds)		
5/8	275	450	675	2	10800	18000	27000
3/4	700	1150	1700	2 1/4	14700	24600	36900
7/8	1200	2000	3000	2 1/2	18500	30900	46400
1	1800	3000	4500	2 3/4	23600	39300	59000
1 1/8	2500	4100	6200	3	29200	48700	73100
1 1/4	3500	5800	8700	3 1/4	35400	59100	88600
1 3/8	4300	7100	10700	3 1/2	42300	70400	105600
1 1/2	5500	9200	13800	3 3/4	49700	82800	124200
1 3/4	7800	13100	19600	4	57600	96100	144100

* Allowable working loads for bolts when ultimate strength of bolt material is 60,000 pounds per square inch and allowance is made for initial load produced in bolt by tightening. See accompanying text. Note 1: 6,000 pounds per square inch for shock loads requiring a factor of safety equal to 10. Note 2: 10,000 pounds per square inch for fluid-tight joints, live-loads, and variable loads requiring a factor of safety of 6. Note 3: 15,000 pounds per square inch for ordinary work, and dead loads requiring a factor of safety of 4.

Example. — What is the working strength of a 1-inch bolt which is screwed up tightly in a packed joint when the allowable working stress is 10,000 pounds per square inch?

$$W = 10,000(0.551 - 0.25 \times 1) = 3000 \text{ pounds approx.}$$

The accompanying table gives the working strengths of bolts of various sizes based on an ultimate stress of 60,000 pounds per square inch. For materials with higher ultimate stresses than 60,000 pounds per square inch, the working strength values given in this table may be increased proportionally, as shown by the following example.

Example. — What is the allowable working strength of a 1 1/4-inch S.A.E. 3130 steel stud used for a water-tight joint equipped with a gasket? The ultimate strength of S.A.E. 3130 steel is 150,000 pounds; the allowable load for a 1 1/4-inch bolt at 10,000 pounds per square inch unit stress, is 5800 pounds, as given in the table; hence the working strength of the bolt in this case is $5800 \times \dfrac{150,000}{60,000} = 14,500$ pounds.

The values given in this table are for applications in which the bolt or stud is less elastic than the elements which it holds together, as in a packed joint. If these values are applied to cases where the elasticity of the bolt equals or exceeds that of the elements held together, as in a cast-iron metal-to-metal joint fastened with steel bolts, the working strength values in the table will be somewhat lower than the actual values; consequently, bolt sizes obtained from the table will be somewhat larger than required and on the safe side.

Standard Machine Screws. — The American Standard for machine screws is very generally used in the United States, although there is still considerable demand for certain sizes or pitches conforming to the older A.S.M.E. standard. This continued use of the A.S.M.E. standard applies particularly to the No. 4 size with 36 threads per inch.

Machine Screw Sizes and Pitches
Comparison Between American Standard and the Superseded A.S.M.E. Standard

| Screw Number or Size | Outside Diameter of Screw Thread, Inch | Threads per Inch | | | | Other Pitches Previously Used by Some Manufacturers |
| | | American Standard | | A.S.M.E. Standard | | |
		Coarse Thread Series	Fine Thread Series	Standard	Special	
0	0.060	..	80	80	.....	.....
1	0.073	64	72	72	64	.....
2	0.086	56	64	64	56	48
3	0.099	48	56	56	48	.....
4	0.112	40	48	48	40–36	32
5	0.125	40	44	44	40–36	32
6	0.138	32	40	40	36–32	30
7	0.151	..	..	36	32–30	.....
8	0.164	32	36	36	32–30	.....
9	0.177	..	..	32	30–24	.....
10	0.190	24	32	30	32–24	.....
12	0.216	24	28	28	24	20
14	0.242	..	..	24	20	18
¼	0.250	20	28	..	.....	.....
16	0.268	..	..	22	20	18–16
18	0.294	..	..	20	18	16
5⁄16	0.3125	18	24	..	.....	.....
20	0.320	..	..	20	18	16
22	0.346	..	..	18	16	.....
24	0.372	..	..	16	18	14
3⁄8	0.375	16	24	..	.....	.....
26	0.398	..	..	16	14	.....
28	0.424	..	..	14	16	.....
7⁄16	0.4375	14	20	..	.....	.....
30	0.450	..	..	14	16	.....
½	0.500	13	20	..	.....	.....

American Standard Machine Screws and Cap-Screws. — The accompanying tables give the dimensions of American standard machine screws and cap-screws as revised in 1947. The screw threads of machine screws and cap screws may conform either to the American Standard Coarse-thread Series or the Fine-thread Series. For machine screws a Class 2 fit is specified and for cap-screws a Class 3 fit. Machine screws with the cross-recess type of head have the same general dimensions as the slotted type shown.

Thread Length on Machine Screws. — If the screw length is 2 inches or less, complete threads should extend to within two threads of the bearing surface of the head or closer if practicable. For longer screws, the minimum complete thread length is 1¾ inches.

Thread Length on Cap-Screws. — The minimum thread length = 2 × diam. + ¼ inch, with a plus tolerance of 2½ × pitch. If cap-screws are not long enough for this minimum length, complete threads should extend to within 2½ threads of the head.

Flat Head Machine Screws — American Standard

Nom. Size	Max. D	Max. A	Min. A	Max. S*	Max. H	Min. H	Max. J	Min. J	Max. T
0	0.060	0.119	0.105	0.002	0.035	0.026	0.023	0.016	0.015
1	0.073	0.146	0.130	0.003	0.043	0.033	0.026	0.019	0.019
2	0.086	0.172	0.156	0.003	0.051	0.040	0.031	0.023	0.023
3	0.099	0.199	0.181	0.004	0.059	0.048	0.035	0.027	0.027
4	0.112	0.225	0.207	0.004	0.067	0.055	0.039	0.031	0.030
5	0.125	0.252	0.232	0.005	0.075	0.062	0.043	0.035	0.034
6	0.138	0.279	0.257	0.005	0.083	0.069	0.048	0.039	0.038
8	0.164	0.332	0.308	0.006	0.100	0.084	0.054	0.045	0.045
10	0.190	0.385	0.359	0.007	0.116	0.098	0.060	0.050	0.053
12	0.216	0.438	0.410	0.008	0.132	0.112	0.067	0.056	0.060
1/4	0.250	0.507	0.477	0.009	0.153	0.131	0.075	0.064	0.070
5/16	0.3125	0.635	0.600	0.011	0.191	0.165	0.084	0.072	0.088
3/8	0.375	0.762	0.722	0.013	0.230	0.200	0.094	0.081	0.106
7/16	0.4375	0.812	0.771	0.016	0.223	0.190	0.094	0.081	0.103
1/2	0.500	0.875	0.831	0.018	0.223	0.186	0.106	0.091	0.103
9/16	0.5625	1.000	0.950	0.020	0.260	0.220	0.118	0.102	0.120
5/8	0.625	1.125	1.069	0.023	0.298	0.253	0.133	0.116	0.137
3/4	0.750	1.375	1.306	0.027	0.372	0.319	0.149	0.131	0.171

* Edge of head may be rounded (equivalent maximum flat S is given in table). Radius of fillet at base of head shall not exceed twice the pitch of thread.

Thread Series. — Threads on machine screws may be either American National Coarse- or Fine-thread Series, Class 2 fit. (See also pages 1108–1109.)

Thread Length. — If the screw length is 2 inches or less, complete threads should extend to within two threads of the bearing surface of the head or closer if practicable. For longer screws, the minimum complete thread length is 1¾ inches.

Unthreaded Diameter. — The diameter of the unthreaded portion of machine screws should not be less than the minimum pitch diameter nor more than the maximum major diameter of the screw thread.

Length Tolerance. — For lengths up to 1 inch, inclusive, minus 1/32 inch; for lengths from 1 inch to 2 inches, inclusive, minus 1/16 inch; for lengths over 2 inches, minus 3/32 inch.

Under-Cut Heads. — Short flat head screws having lengths equal to or less than those listed below, have under-cut heads with a conical bearing surface equal approximately to two-thirds of the standard height. Slot depths are also reduced proportionally. Head diameters are standard.

Size	Length	Size	Length	Size	Length
0	1/8 inch or less	6	3/16 inch or less	3/8	9/16 inch or less
1	1/8 " " "	8	1/4 " " "	7/16	5/8 " " "
2	1/8 " " "	10	5/16 " " "	1/2	3/4 " " "
3	1/8 " " "	12	3/8 " " "	9/16	13/16 " " "
4	3/16 " " "	1/4	7/16 " " "	5/8	15/16 " " "
5	3/16 " " "	5/16	1/2 " " "	3/4	1⅛ " " "

100-Degree Flat Head Machine Screws — American Standard

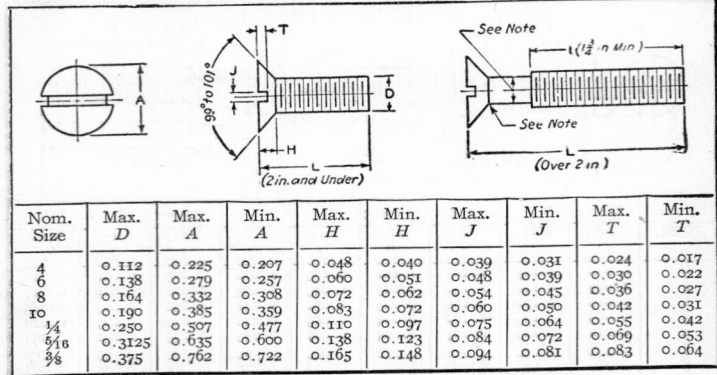

Nom. Size	Max. D	Max. A	Min. A	Max. H	Min. H	Max. J	Min. J	Max. T	Min. T
4	0.112	0.225	0.207	0.048	0.040	0.039	0.031	0.024	0.017
6	0.138	0.279	0.257	0.060	0.051	0.048	0.039	0.030	0.022
8	0.164	0.332	0.308	0.072	0.062	0.054	0.045	0.036	0.027
10	0.190	0.385	0.359	0.083	0.072	0.060	0.050	0.042	0.031
1/4	0.250	0.507	0.477	0.110	0.097	0.075	0.064	0.055	0.042
5/16	0.3125	0.635	0.600	0.138	0.123	0.084	0.072	0.069	0.053
3/8	0.375	0.762	0.722	0.165	0.148	0.094	0.081	0.083	0.064

Oval Head Machine Screws — American Standard

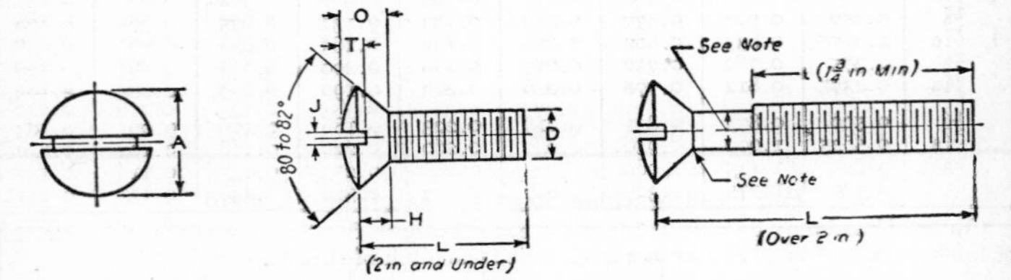

Nom. Size	Max. D	Max. A	Min. A	Max. H	Min. H	Max. O	Max. J	Min. J	Max. T
0	0.060	0.119	0.105	0.035	0.026	0.056	0.023	0.016	0.030
1	0.073	0.146	0.130	0.043	0.033	0.068	0.026	0.019	0.038
2	0.086	0.172	0.156	0.051	0.040	0.080	0.031	0.023	0.045
3	0.099	0.199	0.181	0.059	0.048	0.092	0.035	0.027	0.052
4	0.112	0.225	0.207	0.067	0.055	0.104	0.039	0.031	0.059
5	0.125	0.252	0.232	0.075	0.062	0.116	0.043	0.035	0.067
6	0.138	0.279	0.257	0.083	0.069	0.128	0.048	0.039	0.074
8	0.164	0.332	0.308	0.100	0.084	0.152	0.054	0.045	0.088
10	0.190	0.385	0.359	0.116	0.098	0.176	0.060	0.050	0.103
12	0.216	0.438	0.410	0.132	0.112	0.200	0.067	0.056	0.117
1/4	0.250	0.507	0.477	0.153	0.131	0.232	0.075	0.064	0.136
5/16	0.3125	0.635	0.600	0.191	0.165	0.290	0.084	0.072	0.171
3/8	0.375	0.762	0.722	0.230	0.200	0.347	0.094	0.081	0.206
7/16	0.4375	0.812	0.771	0.223	0.190	0.345	0.094	0.081	0.210
1/2	0.500	0.875	0.831	0.223	0.186	0.354	0.106	0.091	0.216
9/16	0.5625	1.000	0.950	0.260	0.220	0.410	0.118	0.102	0.250
5/8	0.625	1.125	1.069	0.298	0.253	0.467	0.133	0.116	0.285
3/4	0.750	1.375	1.306	0.372	0.319	0.578	0.149	0.131	0.353

Fillet radius at base of head should not exceed twice the pitch of thread. Diameter of unthreaded part should not be less than minimum pitch diameter nor more than the maximum major diameter of thread. For lengths of short oval head screw lengths having under-cut heads, see bottom of page 961.

Fillister Head Machine Screws — American Standard

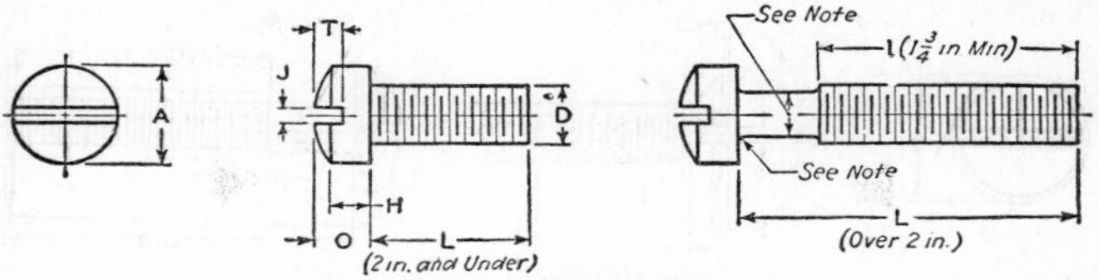

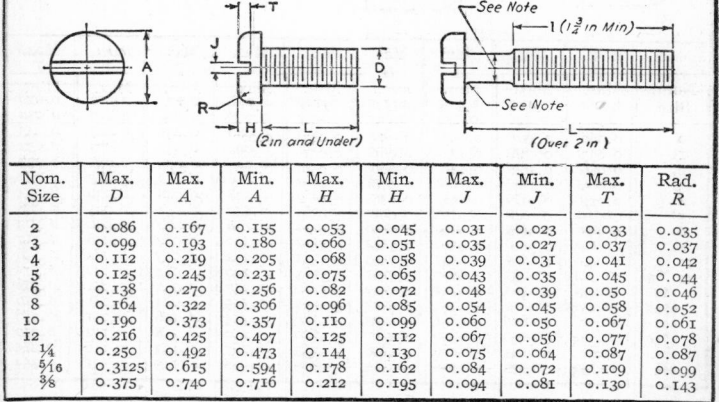

(2 in. and Under)   (Over 2 in.)

Nom. Size	Max. D	Max. A	Min. A	Max. H	Min. H	Max. O	Max. J	Min. J	Max. T
0	0.060	0.096	0.083	0.045	0.037	0.059	0.023	0.016	0.025
1	0.073	0.118	0.104	0.053	0.045	0.071	0.026	0.190	0.031
2	0.086	0.140	0.124	0.062	0.053	0.083	0.031	0.023	0.037
3	0.099	0.161	0.145	0.070	0.061	0.095	0.035	0.027	0.043
4	0.112	0.183	0.166	0.079	0.069	0.107	0.039	0.031	0.048
5	0.125	0.205	0.187	0.088	0.078	0.120	0.043	0.035	0.054
6	0.138	0.226	0.208	0.096	0.086	0.132	0.048	0.039	0.060
8	0.164	0.270	0.250	0.113	0.102	0.156	0.054	0.045	0.071
10	0.190	0.313	0.292	0.130	0.118	0.180	0.060	0.050	0.083
12	0.216	0.357	0.334	0.148	0.134	0.205	0.067	0.056	0.094
¼	0.250	0.414	0.389	0.170	0.155	0.237	0.075	0.064	0.109
5⁄16	0.3125	0.518	0.490	0.211	0.194	0.295	0.084	0.072	0.137
3⁄8	0.375	0.622	0.590	0.253	0.233	0.355	0.094	0.081	0.164
7⁄16	0.4375	0.625	0.589	0.265	0.242	0.368	0.094	0.081	0.170
½	0.500	0.750	0.710	0.297	0.273	0.412	0.106	0.091	0.190
9⁄16	0.5625	0.812	0.768	0.336	0.308	0.466	0.118	0.102	0.214
5⁄8	0.625	0.875	0.827	0.375	0.345	0.521	0.133	0.116	0.240
¾	0.750	1.000	0.945	0.441	0.406	0.612	0.149	0.131	0.281

Pan Head Machine Screws — American Standard

(2 in. and Under)   (Over 2 in.)

Nom. Size	Max. D	Max. A	Min. A	Max. H	Min. H	Max. J	Min. J	Max. T	Rad. R
2	0.086	0.167	0.155	0.053	0.045	0.031	0.023	0.033	0.035
3	0.099	0.193	0.180	0.060	0.051	0.035	0.027	0.037	0.037
4	0.112	0.219	0.205	0.068	0.058	0.039	0.031	0.041	0.042
5	0.125	0.245	0.231	0.075	0.065	0.043	0.035	0.045	0.044
6	0.138	0.270	0.256	0.082	0.072	0.048	0.039	0.050	0.046
8	0.164	0.322	0.306	0.096	0.085	0.054	0.045	0.058	0.052
10	0.190	0.373	0.357	0.110	0.099	0.060	0.050	0.067	0.061
12	0.216	0.425	0.407	0.125	0.112	0.067	0.056	0.077	0.078
¼	0.250	0.492	0.473	0.144	0.130	0.075	0.064	0.087	0.087
5⁄16	0.3125	0.615	0.594	0.178	0.162	0.084	0.072	0.109	0.099
3⁄8	0.375	0.740	0.716	0.212	0.195	0.094	0.081	0.130	0.143

Fillet radius at base of head should not exceed one-half pitch of thread. Diameter of unthreaded part should not be less than minimum pitch diameter nor more than maximum major diameter of thread.

Binding Head Machine Screws — American Standard

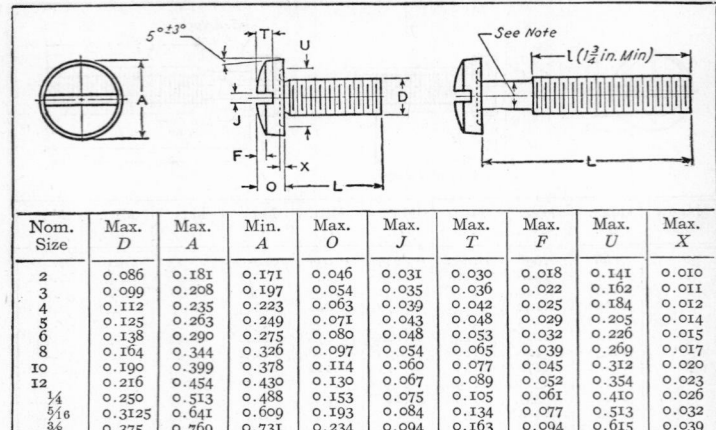

Nom. Size	Max. D	Max. A	Min. A	Max. O	Max. J	Max. T	Max. F	Max. U	Max. X
2	0.086	0.181	0.171	0.046	0.031	0.030	0.018	0.141	0.010
3	0.099	0.208	0.197	0.054	0.035	0.036	0.022	0.162	0.011
4	0.112	0.235	0.223	0.063	0.039	0.042	0.025	0.184	0.012
5	0.125	0.263	0.249	0.071	0.043	0.048	0.029	0.205	0.014
6	0.138	0.290	0.275	0.080	0.048	0.053	0.032	0.226	0.015
8	0.164	0.344	0.326	0.097	0.054	0.065	0.039	0.269	0.017
10	0.190	0.399	0.378	0.114	0.060	0.077	0.045	0.312	0.020
12	0.216	0.454	0.430	0.130	0.067	0.089	0.052	0.354	0.023
¼	0.250	0.513	0.488	0.153	0.075	0.105	0.061	0.410	0.026
5⁄16	0.3125	0.641	0.609	0.193	0.084	0.134	0.077	0.513	0.032
⅜	0.375	0.769	0.731	0.234	0.094	0.163	0.094	0.615	0.039

Round Head Machine Screws — American Standard

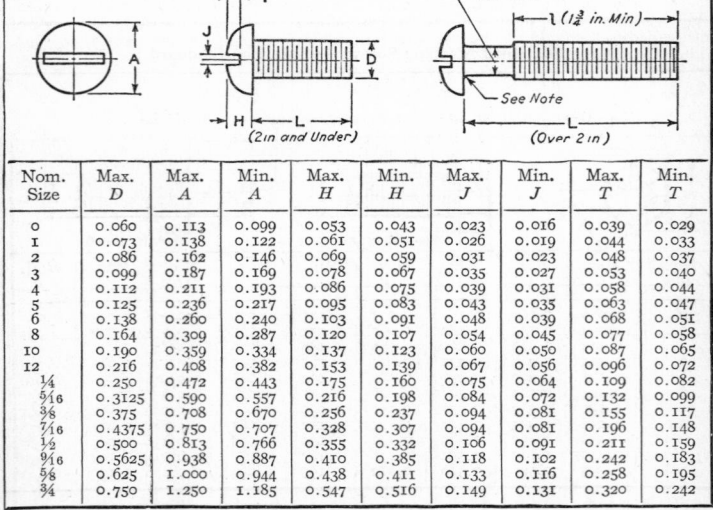

Nom. Size	Max. D	Max. A	Min. A	Max. H	Min. H	Max. J	Min. J	Max. T	Min. T
0	0.060	0.113	0.099	0.053	0.043	0.023	0.016	0.039	0.029
1	0.073	0.138	0.122	0.061	0.051	0.026	0.019	0.044	0.033
2	0.086	0.162	0.146	0.069	0.059	0.031	0.023	0.048	0.037
3	0.099	0.187	0.169	0.078	0.067	0.035	0.027	0.053	0.040
4	0.112	0.211	0.193	0.086	0.075	0.039	0.031	0.058	0.044
5	0.125	0.236	0.217	0.095	0.083	0.043	0.035	0.063	0.047
6	0.138	0.260	0.240	0.103	0.091	0.048	0.039	0.068	0.051
8	0.164	0.309	0.287	0.120	0.107	0.054	0.045	0.077	0.058
10	0.190	0.359	0.334	0.137	0.123	0.060	0.050	0.087	0.065
12	0.216	0.408	0.382	0.153	0.139	0.067	0.056	0.096	0.072
¼	0.250	0.472	0.443	0.175	0.160	0.075	0.064	0.109	0.082
5⁄16	0.3125	0.590	0.557	0.216	0.198	0.084	0.072	0.132	0.099
⅜	0.375	0.708	0.670	0.256	0.237	0.094	0.081	0.155	0.117
7⁄16	0.4375	0.750	0.707	0.328	0.307	0.094	0.081	0.196	0.148
½	0.500	0.813	0.766	0.355	0.332	0.106	0.091	0.211	0.159
9⁄16	0.5625	0.938	0.887	0.410	0.385	0.118	0.102	0.242	0.183
⅝	0.625	1.000	0.944	0.438	0.411	0.133	0.116	0.258	0.195
¾	0.750	1.250	1.185	0.547	0.516	0.149	0.131	0.320	0.242

Diameter of unthreaded part should not be less than minimum pitch diameter nor more than maximum major diameter of thread.

Truss Head Machine Screws — American Standard

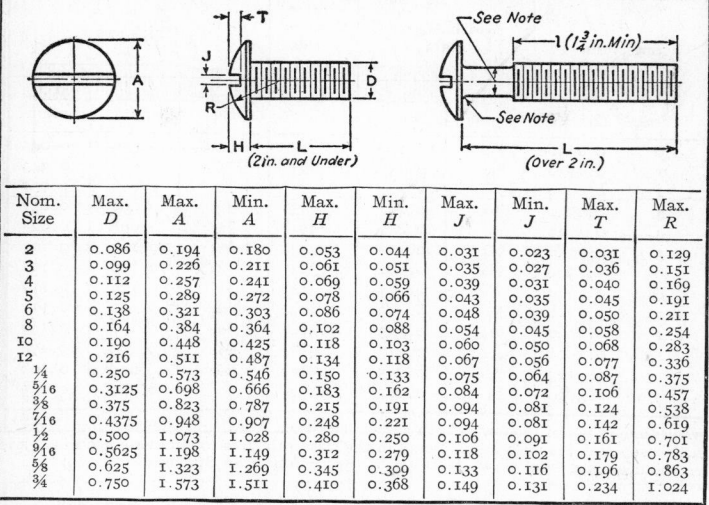

(2in. and Under)   (Over 2 in.)

Nom. Size	Max. D	Max. A	Min. A	Max. H	Min. H	Max. J	Min. J	Max. T	Max. R
2	0.086	0.194	0.180	0.053	0.044	0.031	0.023	0.031	0.129
3	0.099	0.226	0.211	0.061	0.051	0.035	0.027	0.036	0.151
4	0.112	0.257	0.241	0.069	0.059	0.039	0.031	0.040	0.169
5	0.125	0.289	0.272	0.078	0.066	0.043	0.035	0.045	0.191
6	0.138	0.321	0.303	0.086	0.074	0.048	0.039	0.050	0.211
8	0.164	0.384	0.364	0.102	0.088	0.054	0.045	0.058	0.254
10	0.190	0.448	0.425	0.118	0.103	0.060	0.050	0.068	0.283
12	0.216	0.511	0.487	0.134	0.118	0.067	0.056	0.077	0.336
$\frac{1}{4}$	0.250	0.573	0.546	0.150	0.133	0.075	0.064	0.087	0.375
$\frac{5}{16}$	0.3125	0.698	0.666	0.183	0.162	0.084	0.072	0.106	0.457
$\frac{3}{8}$	0.375	0.823	0.787	0.215	0.191	0.094	0.081	0.124	0.538
$\frac{7}{16}$	0.4375	0.948	0.907	0.248	0.221	0.094	0.081	0.142	0.619
$\frac{1}{2}$	0.500	1.073	1.028	0.280	0.250	0.106	0.091	0.161	0.701
$\frac{9}{16}$	0.5625	1.198	1.149	0.312	0.279	0.118	0.102	0.179	0.783
$\frac{5}{8}$	0.625	1.323	1.269	0.345	0.309	0.133	0.116	0.196	0.863
$\frac{3}{4}$	0.750	1.573	1.511	0.410	0.368	0.149	0.131	0.234	1.024

Fillet radius at base of head should not exceed one-half pitch of thread. Diameter of unthreaded part should not be less than minimum pitch diameter nor more than maximum major diameter of thread.

Hexagon Head Machine Screws — American Standard

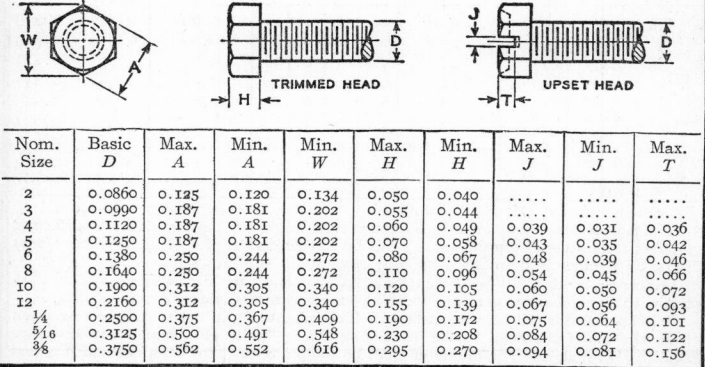

TRIMMED HEAD   UPSET HEAD

Nom. Size	Basic D	Max. A	Min. A	Min. W	Max. H	Min. H	Max. J	Min. J	Max. T
2	0.0860	0.125	0.120	0.134	0.050	0.040	.....	.....	.....
3	0.0990	0.187	0.181	0.202	0.055	0.044	.....	.....	.....
4	0.1120	0.187	0.181	0.202	0.060	0.049	0.039	0.031	0.036
5	0.1250	0.187	0.181	0.202	0.070	0.058	0.043	0.035	0.042
6	0.1380	0.250	0.244	0.272	0.080	0.067	0.048	0.039	0.046
8	0.1640	0.250	0.244	0.272	0.110	0.096	0.054	0.045	0.066
10	0.1900	0.312	0.305	0.340	0.120	0.105	0.060	0.050	0.072
12	0.2160	0.312	0.305	0.340	0.155	0.139	0.067	0.056	0.093
$\frac{1}{4}$	0.2500	0.375	0.367	0.409	0.190	0.172	0.075	0.064	0.101
$\frac{5}{16}$	0.3125	0.500	0.491	0.548	0.230	0.208	0.084	0.072	0.122
$\frac{3}{8}$	0.3750	0.562	0.552	0.616	0.295	0.270	0.094	0.081	0.156

Hexagon head screws usually are not slotted, the slot being optional.

Hexagonal and Square Machine Screw Nuts and Stove Bolt Nuts — American Standard

Screw Number and Outside Diam.		Width Across Flats		Across Corners of Hexagon	Thickness		
		Maximum	Minimum	Minimum	Nominal	Maximum	Minimum
0	0.0600	5/32	0.150	0.171	3/64	0.050	0.043
1	0.0730	5/32	0.150	0.171	3/64	0.050	0.043
2	0.0860	3/16	0.180	0.205	1/16	0.066	0.057
3	0.0990	3/16	0.180	0.205	1/16	0.066	0.057
4	0.1120	1/4	0.241	0.275	3/32	0.098	0.087
5	0.1250	5/16	0.302	0.344	7/64	0.114	0.102
6	0.1380	5/16	0.302	0.344	7/64	0.114	0.102
8	0.1640	11/32	0.332	0.378	1/8	0.130	0.117
10	0.1900	3/8	0.362	0.413	1/8	0.130	0.117
12	0.2160	7/16	0.423	0.482	5/32	0.161	0.148
1/4	0.2500	7/16	0.423	0.482	3/16	0.193	0.178
5/16	0.3125	9/16	0.545	0.621	7/32	0.225	0.208
3/8	0.3750	5/8	0.607	0.692	1/4	0.257	0.239

All dimensions in inches. Width across flats for screw diameters (D) from 1/4 to 1/2 inch = 1 1/2 D + 1/16 with adjustments in the sixteenth sizes to eliminate 32nd inch size wrench openings.

Finished Hexagonal Cap Screws — (American and S.A.E. Standards)

Diameter of Screw	Threads per Inch*		Width Across Flats		Minimum Width Across Corners	Height	
	Coarse	Fine	Maximum	Minimum		Maximum	Minimum
1/4	20	28	0.4375	0.428	0.488	0.194	0.181
5/16	18	24	0.5000	0.489	0.557	0.242	0.227
3/8	16	24	0.5625	0.551	0.628	0.289	0.273
7/16	14	20	0.6250	0.612	0.698	0.337	0.319
1/2	13	20	0.7500	0.737	0.840	0.385	0.365
9/16	12	18	0.8125	0.798	0.910	0.433	0.411
5/8	11	18	0.8750	0.860	0.980	0.481	0.457
3/4	10	16	1.0000	0.983	1.121	0.576	0.549
7/8	9	14	1.1250	1.106	1.261	0.672	0.641
1	8	14	1.3125	1.291	1.473	0.768	0.733
1 1/8	7	12	1.5000	1.477	1.684	0.863	0.824
1 1/4	7	12	1.6875	1.663	1.896	0.959	0.916

*Not included in American Standard.

The finished top shall be flat and chamfered, angle of chamfer with top surface 30 degrees; diameter of top flat circle shall be 100 per cent of the nominal width across flats. Tolerance in diameter of top flat circle shall be minus 15 per cent.

Cap-screw heads shall be at right angles to the body within 2 degrees and concentric with the body within a tolerance of 3 per cent of the distance across the flats.

All cap-screws shall be washer-faced. The height of the head shall be measured from the top of the head to the bearing surface. The thickness of the washer face shall be 1/64 inch and the diameter shall be 100 per cent of the nominal width across flats with tolerances of plus and minus 5 per cent.

Flat Head Cap-screws — American Standard

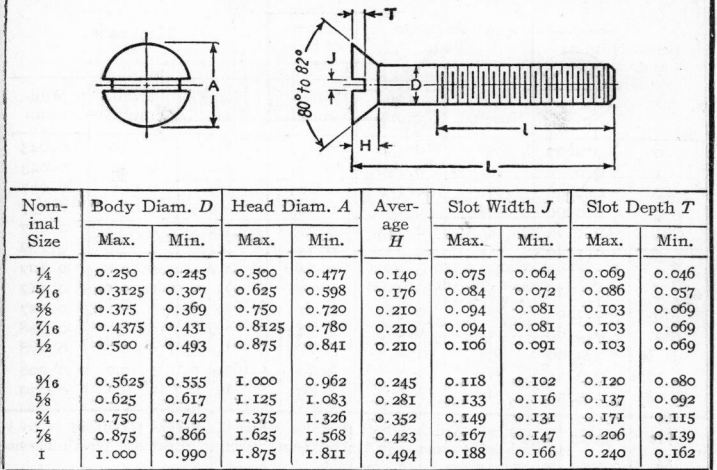

Nom-inal Size	Body Diam. D		Head Diam. A		Aver-age H	Slot Width J		Slot Depth T	
	Max.	Min.	Max.	Min.		Max.	Min.	Max.	Min.
¼	0.250	0.245	0.500	0.477	0.140	0.075	0.064	0.069	0.046
5⁄16	0.3125	0.307	0.625	0.598	0.176	0.084	0.072	0.086	0.057
3⁄8	0.375	0.369	0.750	0.720	0.210	0.094	0.081	0.103	0.069
7⁄16	0.4375	0.431	0.8125	0.780	0.210	0.094	0.081	0.103	0.069
½	0.500	0.493	0.875	0.841	0.210	0.106	0.091	0.103	0.069
9⁄16	0.5625	0.555	1.000	0.962	0.245	0.118	0.102	0.120	0.080
5⁄8	0.625	0.617	1.125	1.083	0.281	0.133	0.116	0.137	0.092
¾	0.750	0.742	1.375	1.326	0.352	0.149	0.131	0.171	0.115
7⁄8	0.875	0.866	1.625	1.568	0.423	0.167	0.147	0.206	0.139
1	1.000	0.990	1.875	1.811	0.494	0.188	0.166	0.240	0.162

Fillister Head Cap-screws — American Standard

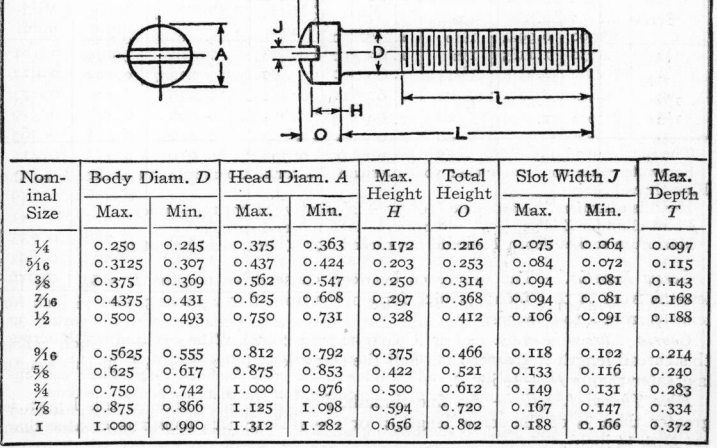

Nom-inal Size	Body Diam. D		Head Diam. A		Max. Height H	Total Height O	Slot Width J		Max. Depth T
	Max.	Min.	Max.	Min.			Max.	Min.	
¼	0.250	0.245	0.375	0.363	0.172	0.216	0.075	0.064	0.097
5⁄16	0.3125	0.307	0.437	0.424	0.203	0.253	0.084	0.072	0.115
3⁄8	0.375	0.369	0.562	0.547	0.250	0.314	0.094	0.081	0.143
7⁄16	0.4375	0.431	0.625	0.608	0.297	0.368	0.094	0.081	0.168
½	0.500	0.493	0.750	0.731	0.328	0.412	0.106	0.091	0.188
9⁄16	0.5625	0.555	0.812	0.792	0.375	0.466	0.118	0.102	0.214
5⁄8	0.625	0.617	0.875	0.853	0.422	0.521	0.133	0.116	0.240
¾	0.750	0.742	1.000	0.976	0.500	0.612	0.149	0.131	0.283
7⁄8	0.875	0.866	1.125	1.098	0.594	0.720	0.167	0.147	0.334
1	1.000	0.990	1.312	1.282	0.656	0.802	0.188	0.166	0.372

Threads may conform either to American National Coarse-thread Series or to the Fine-thread Series. Minimum thread length $l = 2D + ¼$ inch.

Table 1.   Hexagonal Socket Head Cap-screws — American Standard

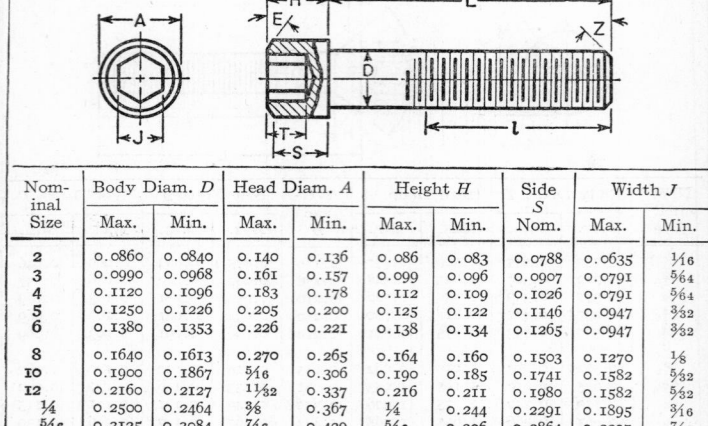

Nom- inal Size	Body Diam. D		Head Diam. A		Height H		Side S Nom.	Width J	
	Max.	Min.	Max.	Min.	Max.	Min.		Max.	Min.
2	0.0860	0.0840	0.140	0.136	0.086	0.083	0.0788	0.0635	1/16
3	0.0990	0.0968	0.161	0.157	0.099	0.096	0.0907	0.0791	5/64
4	0.1120	0.1096	0.183	0.178	0.112	0.109	0.1026	0.0791	5/64
5	0.1250	0.1226	0.205	0.200	0.125	0.122	0.1146	0.0947	3/32
6	0.1380	0.1353	0.226	0.221	0.138	0.134	0.1265	0.0947	3/32
8	0.1640	0.1613	0.270	0.265	0.164	0.160	0.1503	0.1270	1/8
10	0.1900	0.1867	5/16	0.306	0.190	0.185	0.1741	0.1582	5/32
12	0.2160	0.2127	11/32	0.337	0.216	0.211	0.1980	0.1582	5/32
1/4	0.2500	0.2464	3/8	0.367	1/4	0.244	0.2291	0.1895	3/16
5/16	0.3125	0.3084	7/16	0.429	5/16	0.306	0.2864	0.2207	7/32
3/8	0.3750	0.3705	9/16	0.553	3/8	0.368	0.3437	0.3155	5/16
7/16	0.4375	0.4326	5/8	0.615	7/16	0.430	0.4010	0.3155	5/16
1/2	0.5000	0.4948	3/4	0.739	1/2	0.492	0.4583	0.3780	3/8
9/16	0.5625	0.5569	13/16	0.801	9/16	0.554	0.5156	0.3780	3/8
5/8	0.6250	0.6191	7/8	0.863	5/8	0.616	0.5729	0.5030	1/2
3/4	0.7500	0.7436	1	0.987	3/4	0.741	0.6875	0.5655	9/16
7/8	0.8750	0.8680	1 1/8	1.111	7/8	0.865	0.8020	0.5655	9/16
1	1.0000	0.9924	1 5/16	1.297	1	0.989	0.9166	0.6290	5/8
1 1/8	1.1250	1.1165	1 1/2	1.483	1 1/8	1.113	1.0312	0.7540	3/4
1 1/4	1.2500	1.2415	1 3/4	1.733	1 1/4	1.238	1.1457	0.7540	3/4
1 3/8	1.3750	1.3649	1 7/8	1.855	1 3/8	1.361	1.2604	0.7540	3/4
1 1/2	1.5000	1.4899	2	1.979	1 1/2	1.485	1.3750	1.0040	1

The maximum body diam. D (unthreaded portion) is the basic screw size.
Screw threads conform either to American National Coarse-thread Series or to the Fine-thread Series.
Head is chamfered to an angle E of 30° ± 2° relative of flat top surface.
Point chamfer Z is 35° + 5° − 0 from plane of flat end surface.
Maximum socket depth T should not exceed 0.75 × min. head height H.

Screw Lengths. — The difference between consecutive lengths $L = \frac{1}{8}$ inch for lengths from 1/4 to 1 inch; 1/4 inch for lengths from 1 to 4 inches; and 1/2 inch for lengths from 4 to 6 inches.

Coarse Thread Length. — For Coarse-thread Series, $l = 2 D + \frac{1}{2}$ inch when this thread length is greater than half the screw length; or $l = \frac{1}{2} L$ (if this length is greater than $2 D + \frac{1}{2}$ inch).

Fine Thread Length. — For fine threads, $l = 1\frac{1}{2} D + \frac{1}{2}$ inch (if this length is greater than 3/8 of the screw length); or $l = \frac{3}{8} L$ (if this length is greater than $1\frac{1}{2} D + \frac{1}{2}$ inch).

Screws too short to allow application of these formulas should be threaded as close to the head as practicable.

Table 2.   Fluted Socket Head Cap-screws — American Standard

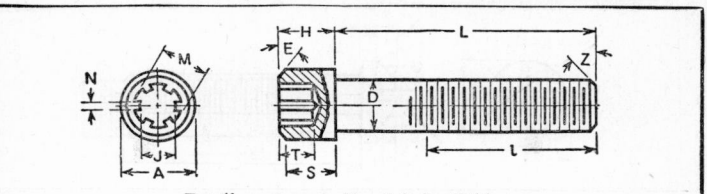

For dimensions *A*, *H* and *S*, See Table 1

Nominal Size	Body Diam. D		No. of Flutes	Diam. J		Diam. M		Width N	
	Max.	Min.		Max.	Min.	Max.	Min.	Max.	Min.
2	0.0860	0.0840	6	0.064	0.063	0.074	0.073	0.016	0.015
3	0.0990	0.0968	6	0.082	0.080	0.098	0.097	0.022	0.021
4	0.1120	0.1096	6	0.082	0.080	0.098	0.097	0.022	0.021
5	0.1250	0.1226	6	0.098	0.096	0.115	0.113	0.025	0.023
6	0.1380	0.1353	6	0.098	0.096	0.115	0.113	0.025	0.023
8	0.1640	0.1613	6	0.128	0.126	0.149	0.147	0.032	0.030
10	0.1900	0.1867	6	0.163	0.161	0.188	0.186	0.039	0.037
12	0.2160	0.2127	6	0.163	0.161	0.188	0.186	0.039	0.037
¼	0.2500	0.2464	6	0.190	0.188	0.221	0.219	0.050	0.048
5⁄16	0.3125	0.3084	6	0.221	0.219	0.256	0.254	0.060	0.058
3⁄8	0.3750	0.3705	6	0.319	0.316	0.380	0.377	0.092	0.089
7⁄16	0.4375	0.4326	6	0.319	0.316	0.380	0.377	0.092	0.089
½	0.5000	0.4948	6	0.386	0.383	0.463	0.460	0.112	0.109
9⁄16	0.5625	0.5569	6	0.386	0.383	0.463	0.460	0.112	0.109
5⁄8	0.6250	0.6191	6	0.509	0.506	0.604	0.601	0.138	0.134
¾	0.7500	0.7436	6	0.535	0.531	0.631	0.627	0.149	0.145
7⁄8	0.8750	0.8680	6	0.604	0.600	0.709	0.705	0.168	0.164
1	1.0000	0.9924	6	0.685	0.681	0.801	0.797	0.189	0.185
1⅛	1.1250	1.1165	6	0.828	0.824	0.970	0.966	0.231	0.227
1¼	1.2500	1.2415	6	0.828	0.824	0.970	0.966	0.231	0.227
1⅜	1.3750	1.3649	6	0.828	0.824	0.970	0.966	0.231	0.227
1½	1.5000	1.4899	6	1.007	1.003	1.275	1.271	0.298	0.294

Maximum body diam. *D* (unthreaded portion) is the basic screw size.

Screw threads conform either to the American National Coarse-thread Series or to the Fine-thread Series.

Head is chamfered to an angle *E* of 30° ± 2° relative to the flat top surface.

Point chamfer *Z* is 35° + 5° − o from plane of flat end surface.

The maximum socket depth *T* should not exceed 0.75 × min. head height *H*.

Screw Lengths. — The difference between consecutive lengths *L* = ⅛ inch for lengths from ¼ inch to 1 inch; ¼ inch for lengths from 1 to 4 inches; and ½ inch for lengths from 4 to 6 inches.

Coarse Thread Length. — For Coarse-thread Series, *l* = 2 *D* + ½ inch if this thread length is greater than half the screw length; or *l* = ½ *L* (if this length is greater than 2 *D* + ½ inch).

Fine Thread Length. — For fine threads, *l* = 1½ *D* + ½ inch (if this length is greater than ⅜ of the screw length); or *l* = ⅜ *L* (if this length is greater than 1½ *D* + ½ inch).

Screws too short to allow application of these formulas should be threaded as close to the head as practicable.

Round Head Cap-screws — American Standard

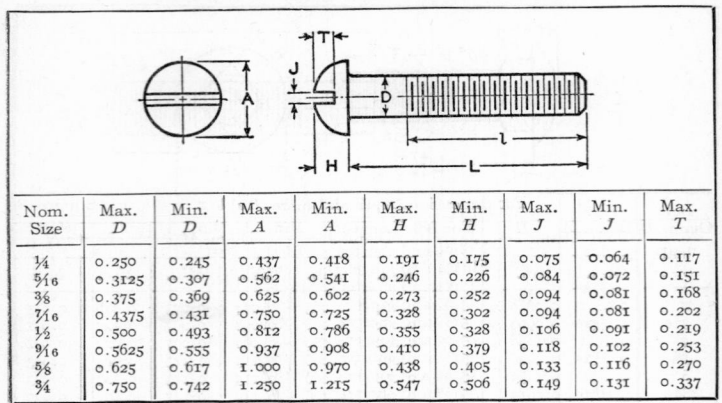

Nom. Size	Max. D	Min. D	Max. A	Min. A	Max. H	Min. H	Max. J	Min. J	Max. T
¼	0.250	0.245	0.437	0.418	0.191	0.175	0.075	0.064	0.117
⁵⁄₁₆	0.3125	0.307	0.562	0.541	0.246	0.226	0.084	0.072	0.151
⅜	0.375	0.369	0.625	0.602	0.273	0.252	0.094	0.081	0.168
⁷⁄₁₆	0.4375	0.431	0.750	0.725	0.328	0.302	0.094	0.081	0.202
½	0.500	0.493	0.812	0.786	0.355	0.328	0.106	0.091	0.219
⁹⁄₁₆	0.5625	0.555	0.937	0.908	0.410	0.379	0.118	0.102	0.253
⅝	0.625	0.617	1.000	0.970	0.438	0.405	0.133	0.116	0.270
¾	0.750	0.742	1.250	1.215	0.547	0.506	0.149	0.131	0.337

Button Head Machine Bolts — American Standard

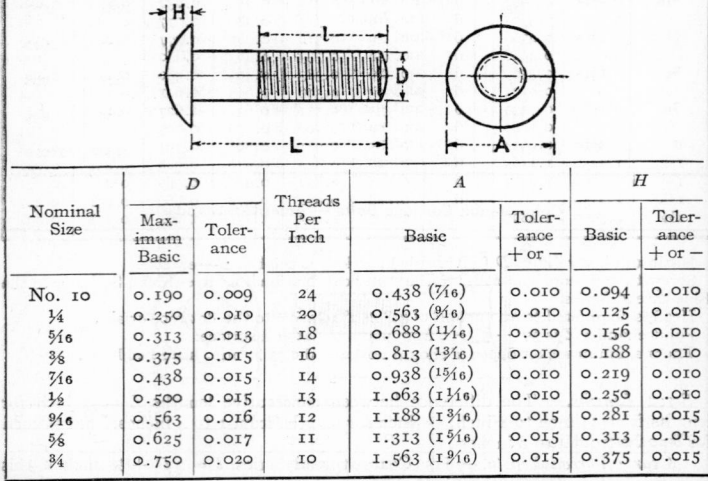

Nominal Size	D		Threads Per Inch	A			H	
	Max-imum Basic	Toler-ance		Basic	Toler-ance + or −		Basic	Toler-ance + or −
No. 10	0.190	0.009	24	0.438 (⁷⁄₁₆)	0.010		0.094	0.010
¼	0.250	0.010	20	0.563 (⁹⁄₁₆)	0.010		0.125	0.010
⁵⁄₁₆	0.313	0.013	18	0.688 (¹¹⁄₁₆)	0.010		0.156	0.010
⅜	0.375	0.015	16	0.813 (¹³⁄₁₆)	0.010		0.188	0.010
⁷⁄₁₆	0.438	0.015	14	0.938 (¹⁵⁄₁₆)	0.010		0.219	0.010
½	0.500	0.015	13	1.063 (1¹⁄₁₆)	0.010		0.250	0.010
⁹⁄₁₆	0.563	0.016	12	1.188 (1³⁄₁₆)	0.015		0.281	0.015
⅝	0.625	0.017	11	1.313 (1⁵⁄₁₆)	0.015		0.313	0.015
¾	0.750	0.020	10	1.563 (1⁹⁄₁₆)	0.015		0.375	0.015

The radius of fillet between body and head is ¹⁄₃₂ inch on the sizes No. 10 to ½ inch, inclusive; and ¹⁄₁₆ inch on the larger sizes. All screw threads are American Standard Coarse-thread Series Free Fit (Class 2). For tolerances see pages 1092 to 1095 under "Major Diameter, Min.," the tolerances being for unfinished hot-rolled material. (See also pages 1108–1109.) If the screw threads are produced by rolling, the body diameters are, of course, less than the diameters given in the table. The lengths (L) vary from ½ to 4 inches by ¼ inch steps and from 4 to 10 inches by ½ inch steps.

Square-neck Carriage Bolts — American Standard

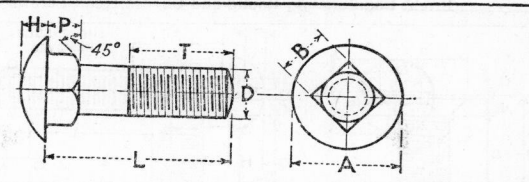

Bolt Diam., D	Head Diam., A	Height, H	Depth of Square, P			Width of Square, B	
			For Bolt Lengths	Min.	Max.	Min.	Max.
0.190	7⁄16	3⁄32	1⅛ and shorter	0.094	0.125	0.185	0.199
			1¼ and longer	.188	.219		
¼	9⁄16	⅛	1¼ and shorter	.125	.156	.245	.260
			1⅜ and longer	.219	.250		
5⁄16	11⁄16	5⁄32	1¼ and shorter	.156	.187	.307	.324
			1⅜ and longer	.250	.281		
⅜	13⁄16	3⁄16	1½ and shorter	.188	.219	.368	.388
			1⅝ and longer	.281	.312		
7⁄16	15⁄16	7⁄32	1½ and shorter	.219	.250	.431	.452
			1⅝ and longer	.313	.344		
½	1 1⁄16	¼	1⅞ and shorter	.250	.281	.492	.515
			2 and longer	.344	.375		
9⁄16	1 3⁄16	9⁄32	1⅞ and shorter	.281	.312	.554	.579
			2 and longer	.375	.406		
⅝	1 5⁄16	5⁄16	1⅞ and shorter	.313	.344	.616	.642
			2 and longer	.406	.437		
¾	1 9⁄16	⅜	1⅞ and shorter	.375	.406	.741	.768
			2 and longer	.469	.500		
⅞	1 13⁄16	7⁄16	1⅞ and shorter	.438	.469	.865	.895
			2 and longer	.531	.562		
1	2 1⁄16	½	1⅞ and shorter	.500	.531	.990	1.022
			2 and longer	.594	.625		

Countersunk Carriage Bolts — American Standard

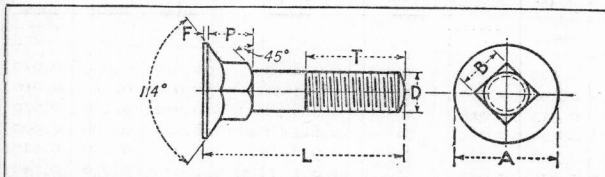

Bolt Diam., D	Head Diam., A		Width, F	Depth, P		Width of Square, B	
	Min.	Max.		Min.	Max.	Min.	Max.
0.190	0.500	0.520	0.016	0.219	0.250	0.185	0.199
¼	.625	.645	.016	.281	.312	.245	.260
5⁄16	.750	.770	.031	.344	.375	.307	.324
⅜	.875	.895	.031	.406	.437	.368	.388
7⁄16	1.000	1.020	.031	.469	.500	.431	.452
½	1.125	1.145	.031	.531	.562	.492	.515
9⁄16	1.250	1.275	.031	.594	.625	.554	.579
⅝	1.375	1.400	.031	.656	.687	.616	.642
¾	1.625	1.650	.047	.781	.812	.741	.768

British Standard Whitworth (B.S.W.) and British Standard Fine (B.S.F.) Bright Countersunk, Round and Cheese Head-Screws

Countersunk Head Screw   Round Head Screw   Cheese Head Screw

| Nominal Size, Inches | Number of Threads per Inch | | Countersunk Head Screw | | | | |
	B.S.W.	B.S.F.	Diam. of Head A	Depth of Countersunk Portion B	Depth of Parallel Portion C	Width of Slot D	Depth of Slot E
1/8	40	....	0.219	0.047	0.010	0.032	0.033
5/32	32	....	0.273	0.058	0.010	0.040	0.039
3/16	24	32	0.328	0.070	0.010	0.040	0.045
1/4	20	26	0.437	0.094	0.010	0.062	0.057
5/16	18	22	0.547	0.117	0.015	0.062	0.073
3/8	16	20	0.656	0.141	0.015	0.084	0.085
7/16	14	18	0.766	0.164	0.015	0.084	0.097
1/2	12	16	0.875	0.187	0.015	0.093	0.108
5/8	11	14	1.094	0.234	0.020	0.093	0.137
3/4	10	12	1.312	0.281	0.020	0.144	0.160
7/8	9	11	1.531	0.328	0.020	0.160	0.184
1	8	10	1.750	0.375	0.020	0.176	0.207

| Nominal Size, Inches | Number of Threads per Inch | | Round Head Screw* | | | Cheese Head Screw† | |
	B.S.W.	B.S.F.	Depth of Head G	Radius of Head H	Depth of Slot K	Diam. of Head L	Depth of Slot O
1/8	40	....	0.100	0.110	0.050	0.187	0.040
5/32	32	....	0.125	0.137	0.062	0.234	0.050
3/16	24	32	0.150	0.165	0.075	0.281	0.060
1/4	20	26	0.200	0.220	0.100	0.375	0.080
5/16	18	22	0.250	0.274	0.125	0.469	0.100
3/8	16	20	0.300	0.329	0.150	0.562	0.120
7/16	14	18	0.350	0.384	0.175	0.656	0.123
1/2	12	16	0.400	0.439	0.200	0.750	0.140
5/8	11	14	0.500	0.549	0.250	0.937	0.175
3/4	10	12	0.600	0.659	0.300	1.125	0.210
7/8	9	11	0.700	0.769	0.350	1.312	0.245
1	8	10	0.800	0.875	0.400	1.500	0.280

* Diameter of Head F and Width of Slot J same as for Countersunk Heads.
† Width of Slot N same as for Countersunk Heads. Depth M of head same as depth G for Round Heads.

British Standard Whitworth and British Standard Fine Studs. — Length of thread at long end equals over-all stud length minus twice the diameter. Radius of point at outer end equals stud diameter. Length of plain part between threaded ends equals stud diameter. Length of thread at short end equals stud diameter measured from flat end of stud to point where thread disappears.

American Standard Square Set-screw Heads (ASA B18.2)

Nominal Size or Basic Major Diameter of Thread		Width Across Flats		Width Across Corners	Height			Diameter of Neck	
		Max.	Min.	Min.	Nominal	Max.	Min.	Max.	Min.
1/4	0.2500	0.2500	0.241	0.331	3/16	0.196	0.178	0.185	0.170
5/16	0.3125	0.3125	0.302	0.415	15/64	0.245	0.224	0.240	0.225
3/8	0.3750	0.3750	0.362	0.497	9/32	0.293	0.270	0.294	0.279
7/16	0.4375	0.4375	0.423	0.581	21/64	0.341	0.315	0.345	0.330
1/2	0.5000	0.5000	0.484	0.665	3/8	0.389	0.361	0.400	0.385
9/16	0.5625	0.5625	0.545	0.748	27/64	0.437	0.407	0.454	0.439
5/8	0.6250	0.6250	0.606	0.833	15/32	0.485	0.452	0.507	0.492
3/4	0.7500	0.7500	0.729	1.001	9/16	0.582	0.544	0.620	0.605
7/8	0.8750	0.8750	0.852	1.170	21/32	0.678	0.635	0.731	0.716
1	1.0000	1.0000	0.974	1.337	3/4	0.774	0.726	0.838	0.823
1 1/8	1.1250	1.1250	1.096	1.505	27/32	0.870	0.817	0.939	0.914
1 1/4	1.2500	1.2500	1.219	1.674	15/16	0.966	0.908	1.064	1.039
1 3/8	1.3750	1.3750	1.342	1.843	1 1/32	1.063	1.000	1.159	1.134
1 1/2	1.5000	1.5000	1.464	2.010	1 1/8	1.159	1.091	1.284	1.259

All dimensions given in inches.
Width of neck under head shall be not over two times the pitch of the thread.
The under surface of the head shall be beveled not more than 40 deg.
Top or crown of head shall be rounded to a radius of two and a half times the major diameter of the thread.

American Standard Open End Wrench Openings (ASA B18.2)

Max.* Width Across Flats of Nut	Wrench Opening		Max.* Width Across Flats of Nut	Wrench Opening		Max.* Width Across Flats of Nut	Wrench Opening	
	Min.	Max.		Min.	Max.		Min.	Max.
9/32	0.158	0.163	1 1/16	1.068	1.077	2 5/8	2.639	2.656
3/16	0.190	0.195	1 1/8	1.132	1.142	2 3/4	2.766	2.783
1/4	0.252	0.257	1 1/4	1.257	1.267	2 13/16	2.827	2.845
5/16	0.316	0.322	1 5/16	1.320	1.331	2 15/16	2.954	2.973
11/32	0.347	0.353	1 3/8	1.383	1.394	3	3.016	3.035
3/8	0.378	0.384	1 7/16	1.446	1.457	3 1/8	3.142	3.162
7/16	0.440	0.446	1 1/2	1.508	1.520	3 3/8	3.393	3.414
1/2	0.504	0.510	1 5/8	1.634	1.646	3 1/2	3.518	3.540
9/16	0.566	0.573	1 11/16	1.696	1.708	3 3/4	3.770	3.793
19/32	0.598	0.605	1 13/16	1.822	1.835	3 7/8	3.895	3.918
5/8	0.629	0.636	1 7/8	1.885	1.898	4 1/8	4.147	4.172
11/16	0.692	0.699	2	2.011	2.025	4 1/4	4.272	4.297
3/4	0.755	0.763	2 1/16	2.074	2.088	4 1/2	4.524	4.550
25/32	0.786	0.794	2 3/16	2.200	2.215	4 5/8	4.649	4.676
13/16	0.818	0.826	2 1/4	2.262	2.277	5	5.026	5.055
7/8	0.880	0.888	2 3/8	2.388	2.404	5 3/8	5.403	5.434
15/16	0.944	0.953	2 7/16	2.450	2.466	5 3/4	5.780	5.813
1	1.006	1.015	2 9/16	2.576	2.593	6 1/8	6.157	6.192

All dimensions given in inches.
* Wrenches shall be marked with the "Nominal Size of Wrench" which is equal to the basic or maximum width across flats of the corresponding bolt head or nut.
Allowance (minimum clearance) between maximum width across flats of nut or bolt head and jaws of wrench equals (0.005 W + 0.001). Tolerance on wrench opening equals plus (0.005 W + 0.004) from minimum (W equals nominal size of wrench).

British Standard Whitworth (B.S.W.) and British Standard Fine (B.S.F.) Bright Square Head Set-Screws (With Flat Chamfered Ends)

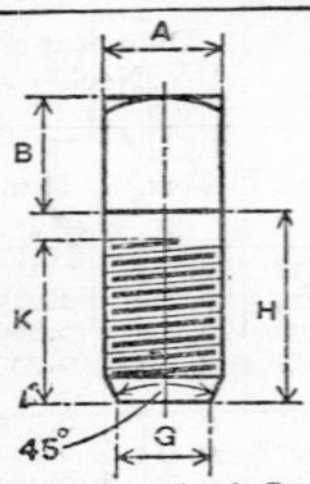

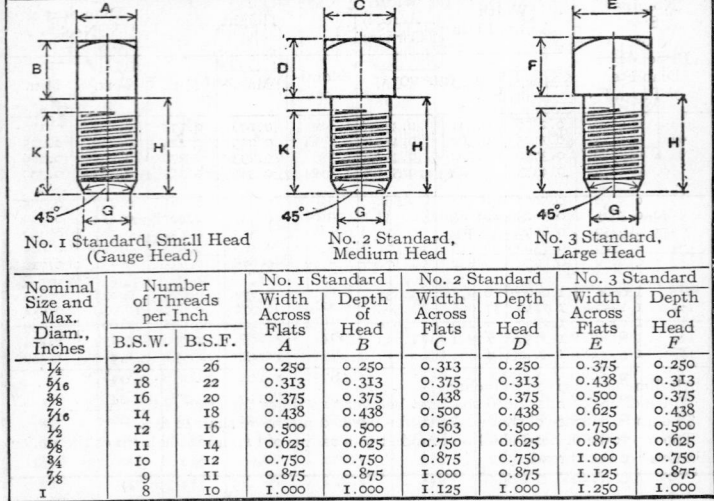

No. 1 Standard, Small Head (Gauge Head)

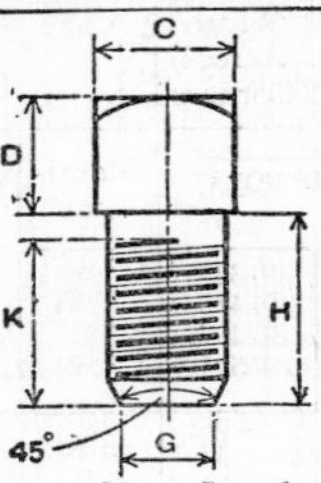

No. 2 Standard, Medium Head

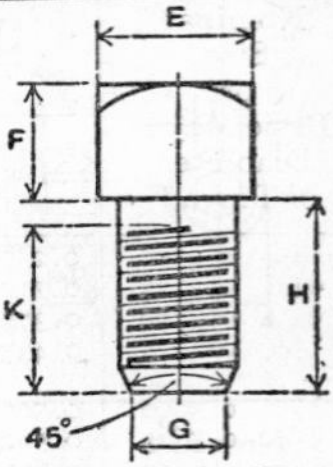

No. 3 Standard, Large Head

Nominal Size and Max. Diam., Inches	Number of Threads per Inch		No. 1 Standard		No. 2 Standard		No. 3 Standard	
	B.S.W.	B.S.F.	Width Across Flats *A*	Depth of Head *B*	Width Across Flats *C*	Depth of Head *D*	Width Across Flats *E*	Depth of Head *F*
1/4	20	26	0.250	0.250	0.313	0.250	0.375	0.250
5/16	18	22	0.313	0.313	0.375	0.313	0.438	0.313
3/8	16	20	0.375	0.375	0.438	0.375	0.500	0.375
7/16	14	18	0.438	0.438	0.500	0.438	0.625	0.438
1/2	12	16	0.500	0.500	0.563	0.500	0.750	0.500
5/8	11	14	0.625	0.625	0.750	0.625	0.875	0.625
3/4	10	12	0.750	0.750	0.875	0.750	1.000	0.750
7/8	9	11	0.875	0.875	1.000	0.875	1.125	0.875
1	8	10	1.000	1.000	1.125	1.000	1.250	1.000

* Depth of Head *B*, *D* and *F* same as for Width Across Flats, No. 1 Standard.
Reproduced from Report No. 451–1932 of the British Standards Institution.

Dimensions of Studs or Stud-Bolts

Engineering Standard of General Motors Corporation

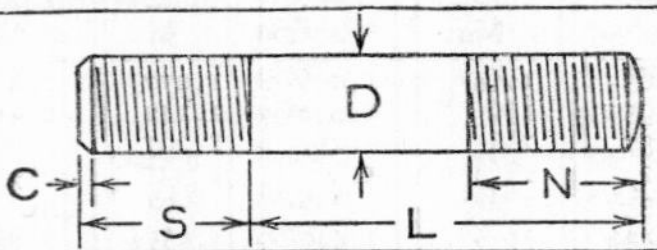

Stud Diam. *D*	Stud End *S*				Nut End *N*			
	Threads per Inch	Thread Length *S*	Pitch Diameter Max.	Pitch Diameter Min.	Threads per Inch	Thread Length *N*	Pitch Diameter Max.	Pitch Diameter Min.
Studs for Use in Cast Iron, Steel and Bronze								
5/16	18	1/2	.2815	.2795	24	9/16	.2854	.2834
3/8	16	9/16	.3394	.3374	24	5/8	.3479	.3459
7/16	14	1 1/16	.3961	.3941	20	3/4	.4050	.4030
1/2	13	3/4	.4550	.4530	20	13/16	.4675	.4655
3/4	10	1 1/8	.6910	.6880	16	1 1/16	.7094	.7064
Studs for Use in Aluminum								
1/4	20	3/8	.2245	.2225	28	7/16	.2268	.2248
7/16	14	1 1/16	.3981	.3961	20	3/4	.4050	.4030

The length *L* of these studs varies from 5/8 inch to 4 3/4 inches, depending upon the application. Studs of a given diameter may have more than one length *L*. The stud ends or tapped-hole ends have American Standard coarse threads, and the outer or nut ends, the American Standard fine threads. The 45-degree chamfer *C* extends from 1/32 to 3/32 inch.

Table 1. Set-screws of the Hexagon-socket Type — American Standard

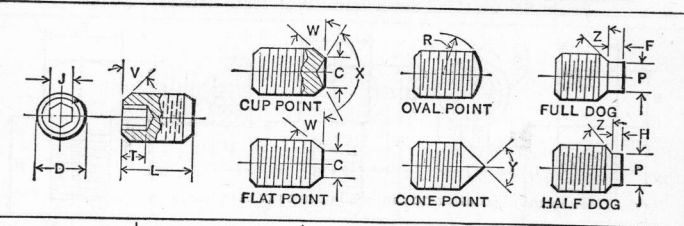

Nominal Diameter		Socket Width Across Flats J		Cup and Flat Point Diameter, Max. C	Dog Point Diameter, Max. P	Dog Point Length		Radius of Oval Point R
Size D	Decimal Equivalent	Max.	Min.			Full F	Half H	
5	0.1250	0.0635	1/16	0.067	0.083	0.06	0.03	3/32
6	0.1380	0.0635	1/16	0.074	0.092	0.07	0.03	7/64
8	0.1640	0.0791	5/64	0.087	0.109	0.08	0.04	1/8
10	0.1900	0.0947	3/32	0.102	0.127	0.09	0.04	9/64
12	0.2160	0.0947	3/32	0.115	0.144	0.11	0.06	5/32
1/4	0.2500	0.1270	1/8	0.132	5/32	1/8	1/16	3/16
5/16	0.3125	0.1582	5/32	0.172	13/64	5/32	5/64	15/64
3/8	0.3750	0.1895	3/16	0.212	1/4	3/16	3/32	9/32
7/16	0.4375	0.2207	7/32	0.252	19/64	7/32	7/64	21/64
1/2	0.5000	0.2520	1/4	0.291	11/32	1/4	1/8	3/8
9/16	0.5625	0.2520	1/4	0.332	25/64	9/32	9/64	27/64
5/8	0.6250	0.3155	5/16	0.371	15/32	5/16	5/32	15/32
3/4	0.7500	0.3780	3/8	0.450	9/16	3/8	3/16	9/16
7/8	0.8750	0.5030	1/2	0.530	21/32	7/16	7/32	21/32
1	1.0000	0.5655	9/16	0.609	3/4	1/2	1/4	3/4
1 1/8	1.1250	0.5655	9/16	0.689	27/32	9/16	9/32	27/32
1 1/4	1.2500	0.6290	5/8	0.767	15/16	5/8	5/16	15/16
1 3/8	1.3750	0.6290	5/8	0.848	1 1/32	11/16	11/32	1 1/32
1 1/2	1.5000	0.7540	3/4	0.926	1 1/8	3/4	3/8	1 1/8
1 3/4	1.7500	1.0040	1	1.086	1 5/16	7/8	7/16	1 5/16
2	2.0000	1.0040	1	1.244	1 1/2	1	1/2	1 1/2

All dimensions in inches.

The thread conforms to the American Standard.

The socket depth T is not included in the Standard.

Chamfer V and Z equals 35 degrees and W equals 45 degrees. Included angle X of the cup equals 118 degrees. Cone point angle Y equals 90 degrees if the set-screw length exceeds its diameter. If the lengths equal or are less than the diameter, Y equals 118 degrees.

The nominal length L of all socket type set-screws is the total or overall length. The difference between consecutive lengths equals 1/16 inch for screw lengths 1/4 to 5/8 inch; 1/8 inch for lengths 5/8 to 1 inch; 1/4 inch for lengths 1 to 4 inches; 1/2 inch for lengths 4 to 6 inches. The range of lengths is not standardized.

This standard for hollow- or socket-type set-screws is applied to most of the socket-type set-screws now produced in the United States.

Table 2. Set-screws of Fluted-socket Type — American Standard

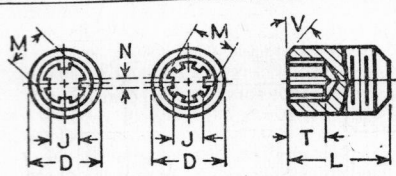

For different forms of points, and dimensions not given in the table below, see Table 1

Body Diam. D Nominal	Number of Flutes	Socket Diam. J		Socket Diam. M		Socket Land N	
		Max.	Min.	Max.	Min.	Max.	Min.
5	4	0.053	0.052	0.071	0.070	0.022	0.021
6	4	0.056	0.055	0.079	0.078	0.025	0.024
8	6	0.079	0.078	0.098	0.097	0.022	0.021
10	6	0.097	0.095	0.113	0.111	0.027	0.025
12	6	0.097	0.095	0.113	0.111	0.027	0.025
¼	6	0.127	0.125	0.147	0.145	0.032	0.030
5⁄16	6	0.160	0.158	0.185	0.183	0.041	0.040
3⁄8	6	0.190	0.188	0.219	0.217	0.052	0.050
7⁄16	6	0.221	0.219	0.256	0.254	0.062	0.060
½	6	0.254	0.252	0.297	0.295	0.072	0.070
9⁄16	6	0.254	0.252	0.297	0.295	0.072	0.070
5⁄8	6	0.315	0.312	0.380	0.377	0.092	0.089
¾	6	0.386	0.383	0.463	0.460	0.112	0.109
7⁄8	6	0.506	0.503	0.600	0.597	0.142	0.139
1	6	0.568	0.564	0.654	0.650	0.157	0.153
1⅛	6	0.568	0.564	0.654	0.650	0.157	0.153
1¼	6	0.631	0.627	0.790	0.786	0.184	0.180
1⅜	6	0.631	0.627	0.790	0.786	0.184	0.180
1½	6	0.756	0.752	0.958	0.954	0.221	0.217
1¾	6	1.007	1.003	1.275	1.271	0.298	0.294
2	6	1.007	1.003	1.275	1.271	0.298	0.294

All dimensions in inches.

The thread conforms to the American Standard.

The socket depth T is not included in the Standard.

Angles of chamfers and points for different forms of set-screws are the same as given in Table 1.

The nominal length L of all socket-type set-screws is the total or overall length. The difference between consecutive lengths equals ⅟16 inch for screw lengths ¼ to ⅝ inch; ⅛ inch for lengths ⅝ to 1 inch; ¼ inch for lengths 1 to 4 inches; ½ inch for lengths 4 to 6 inches. The range of lengths is not standardized. The allowable tolerance on length L for all set-screws of the socket type is 3 per cent for lengths of 2 inches or less, with a minimum of plus 0.010 or minus 0.010 inch. For lengths from 2 to 6 inches, the tolerance is plus or minus ⅟32 inch, and for lengths over 6 inches, plus or minus ⅟16 inch.

The half-dog point (see Table 1) is used for both hexagonal-socket and fluted-socket set-screws whenever the usable length of thread is less than the nominal diameter.

Holding Power of Set-screws. -- While the amount of power a set-screw of given size will transmit without slipping (when used for holding a pulley, gear, or other part from turning relative to a shaft) varies somewhat according to the physical properties of both set-screw and shaft and other variable factors, experiments have shown that the safe torsional holding power t in pound-inches for different diameters of cup-point set-screws should be approximately as follows: For $\frac{1}{4}$-inch diam., $t = 50$ pound-inches; $\frac{5}{16}$-inch diam., $t = 120$ pound-inches; $\frac{3}{8}$-inch diam., $t = 240$ pound-inches; $\frac{7}{16}$-inch diam., $t = 410$ pound-inches; $\frac{1}{2}$-inch diam., $t = 670$ pound-inches; $\frac{9}{16}$-inch diam., $t = 1000$ pound-inches; $\frac{5}{8}$-inch diam., $t = 1500$ pound-inches; $\frac{3}{4}$-inch diam., $t = 3000$ pound-inches; $\frac{7}{8}$-inch diam., $t = 5000$ pound-inches; and 1-inch diam., $t = 8100$ pound-inches. These values are computed by the empirical formula: $t = 8100 \times D^{3.6}$, where $t =$ holding power, in pound-inches and $D =$ diameter of set-screw, in inches. For round point set-screws, this formula becomes: $t = 7900 \times D^{3.6}$.

The holding-power T in pound-inches required for a given horsepower $H.P.$ and revolutions per minute n of the shaft is given by the formula: $T = 63,000\ H.P. \div n$. After determining the value of T by this formula, select a set-screw size having an equal or somewhat higher holding power t.

Example: What diameter of cup-point set-screw should be used to transmit 20 horsepower safely at a shaft speed of 550 revolutions per minute? In this case, T will be found to be 2290 pound-inches, so that a $\frac{3}{4}$-inch cup-point set-screw would be required since t for this size equals 3000 pound-inches.

Dowel-Pins. -- Dowel-pins are close-fitting pins which are inserted into adjacent parts of dies, jigs or other mechanical devices to supplement ordinary holding screws or bolts by preventing any lateral shifting of parts such as might result from thrust loads. Inasmuch as cap-screws and machine screws usually have some body clearance, a lateral thrust against whatever part is being held might result in a slight change in position and alignment. Dowel-pins are used primarily to prevent such lateral shifting, thus preserving the initial alignment between the parts. These pins are also useful in some cases for obtaining re-alignment as, for example, when parts which have been separated are re-assembled. The dowel-pins fit tightly or at least closely into their respective holes and about one-half of the pin body engages each part to be held in alignment; consequently, under normal conditions a properly fitted dowel-pin is subjected to shearing strain only and this strain occurs at the junction of the surfaces of the two parts.

Taper and Straight Dowel-Pins: Dowel-pins may either be tapering or cylindrical. The taper pin, which has a taper of $\frac{1}{4}$ inch per foot, is applied in machine work as a general rule. Taper pins are also preferable for parts which must be separated frequently, especially in cases where the removal of straight pins would tend to wear the holes. A taper pin is somewhat easier to fit than the cylindrical form. The latter, however, is extensively used, especially in connection with die, tool, or gage work.

Steel for Dowel-Pins: For some applications, a high-carbon steel is used such as S.A.E. 1095. This steel should be heat-treated to obtain a Rockwell hardness of 60-65 on the "C" scale. For applications where tool steel pins are too expensive it is common practice to use machine steel which is case-hardened. Soft dowel-pins made from drill or Bessemer rod are often used, but hardened and ground pins will not tear and stick as easily as soft pins; hence, hardening is preferable and pins usually are finished by centerless grinding.

Dowel-Pin Diameter: The nominal diameters of straight dowel-pins range from $\frac{1}{16}$ to $\frac{1}{2}$ inch according to the S.A.E. Aeronautical Standard (see accompanying table). The maximum and minimum diameters in this S.A.E. Standard are from 0.001 to 0.0015 inch under the nominal size. In the case of straight or cylindrical pins, however, it is common practice to grind pins to diameters varying from 0.0002 to 0.001 inch over the nominal size to provide a press or driving fit. The 0.001-inch over-size pins are generally used for repair work or in holes which have been machined over size. The following practice has also been recommended: If the doweled parts are hardened, grind or lap the hole 0.0002 to 0.0003 inch under size. For locating nests, gage-plates, etc., pins from ⅛ to 3⁄16 inch in diameter are usually satisfactory. For locating dies, the diameter usually should not be less than ¼ inch. The general rule is to use dowel-pins of the same size as the cap-screws or machine screws for fastening the parts together. Dowel-pins generally are obtained from diemakers' accessory supply houses.

Lengths of Dowel-Pins: The length, according to the S.A.E. Aeronautical Standard, for straight pins varies from ¼ to 2 inches. The length to use in any case should equal three to four times the pin diameter; hence the length of the bearing surface of a dowel-pin should equal about one and one-half to two times its diameter in each plate or part to be doweled. The general practice in using the smaller diameter pins is to make the length somewhat greater than three times the diameter to facilitate driving and insure adequate contact with both parts.

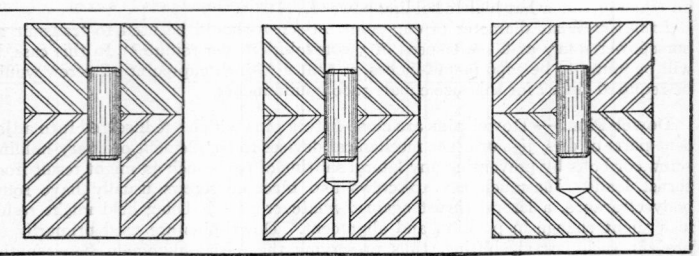

Dowel-Pins of "Through Type," "Semi-Blind" and "Blind" Types.

Holes for Dowel-Pins: When the dowel-pin hole is drilled and reamed through both parts (see illustration at left), the pin is known as a "through" type. The central diagram shows a "semi-blind" type. The smaller hole serves as an air vent; its diameter should not be less than one-half the diameter of the dowel-pin hole. A rod may be inserted in this smaller hole for driving out the pin. As a general rule, however, the diameter of a steel driving punch, such as is used to remove or "set" dowel-pins, should be about the same as the pin to prevent peening the end. If the smaller hole (shown by central diagram) is objectionable, the air vent hole is sometimes located at an angle of 90 degrees. In the latter case, the pin can be removed by placing the vent hole in a vertical position, filling it partially with oil, inserting a close-fitting rod, and tapping it with a hammer to create hydraulic pressure against the dowel-pin. The diagram at the right illustrates a "blind" type of hole. With this arrangement, a dowel-pin should always be a slip fit in the blind hole and a press fit in the mating part. A blind type of dowel-pin should never be used when it is feasible to employ either the through or semi-blind type.

Number of Dowel-Pins: Two dowel-pins usually are sufficient for retaining alignment between two parts, although the total lateral or thrust load should be considered. The load on each pin must not, of course, exceed the shearing strength of the material. Two dowel-pins are generally used to locate dies made of one piece of steel; the same is true regarding the punch. If the die is made of more than one piece, as in the case of follow-dies, each piece should have its own set of two pins.

American Standard Dimensions of Hardened and Ground Dowel-pins

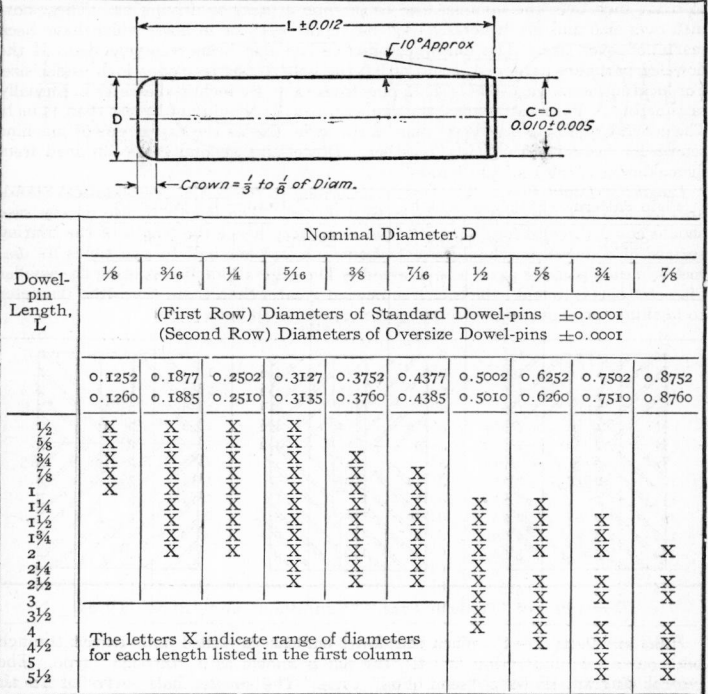

L ±0.012 — 10° Approx — D — C = D − 0.010±0.005 — Crown = ⅛ to ⅓ of Diam.

Dowel-pin Length, L	Nominal Diameter D									
	1/8	3/16	1/4	5/16	3/8	7/16	1/2	5/8	3/4	7/8
	(First Row) Diameters of Standard Dowel-pins ±0.0001									
	(Second Row) Diameters of Oversize Dowel-pins ±0.0001									
	0.1252	0.1877	0.2502	0.3127	0.3752	0.4377	0.5002	0.6252	0.7502	0.8752
	0.1260	0.1885	0.2510	0.3135	0.3760	0.4385	0.5010	0.6260	0.7510	0.8760
1/2	X	X	X	X						
5/8	X	X	X	X						
3/4	X	X	X	X	X					
7/8	X	X	X	X	X	X				
1	X	X	X	X	X	X				
1 1/4		X	X	X	X	X	X	X		
1 1/2		X	X	X	X	X	X	X		
1 3/4		X	X	X	X	X	X	X	X	
2		X	X	X	X	X	X	X	X	X
2 1/4			X		X	X	X	X		
2 1/2			X	X	X	X	X	X	X	X
3							X	X	X	X
3 1/2							X	X		
4							X	X		X
4 1/2								X	X	X
5									X	X
5 1/2									X	X

The letters X indicate range of diameters for each length listed in the first column

These dowel-pins are extensively used in the tool and machine industry and a machine reamer of nominal size may be used to produce the holes into which these pins tap or press fit.

American Standard Dimensions of Unhardened Ground Dowel-pins

Nom. Diam.	Max. Diam.	Min. Diam.	Chamfer Width	Nom. Diam.	Max. Diam.	Min. Diam.	Chamfer Width
1/16	0.0600	0.0595	0.010	5/16	0.3094	0.3089	1/32
3/32	0.0912	0.0907	0.010	3/8	0.3717	0.3712	1/32
7/64	0.1068	0.1063	0.010	7/16	0.4341	0.4336	1/32
1/8	0.1223	0.1218	0.010	1/2	0.4964	0.4959	1/32
5/32	0.1535	0.1530	1/64	5/8	0.6211	0.6206	3/64
3/16	0.1847	0.1842	1/64	3/4	0.7458	0.7453	3/64
7/32	0.2159	0.2154	1/64	7/8	0.8705	0.8700	1/16
1/4	0.2470	0.2465	1/64	1	0.9952	0.9947	1/16

Maximum diameters are graduated from 0.0005 on 1/16 inch pins to 0.0028 on 1-inch pins, under the minimum commercial bar stock sizes.

Drop-forged Weldless Eye-bolts of Carbon Steel*

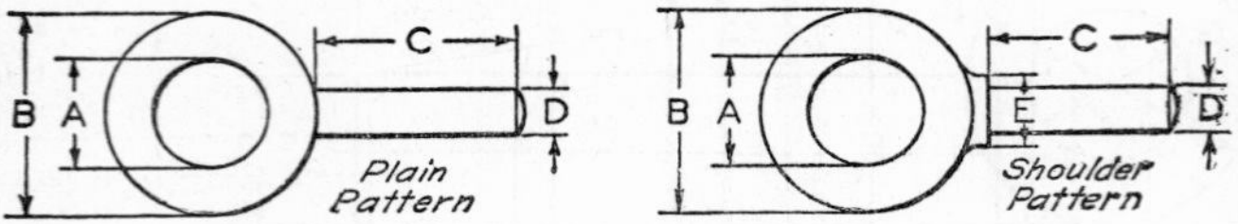

Plain Pattern — Standard Length				Plain Pattern — Extra Length				Safe Load, Tons*
Shank		Eye Diam.		Shank		Eye Diam.		
D	*C*	*A*	*B*	*D*	*C*	*A*	*B*	
¼	1⅜	½	⅞	....	....	....	....	0.2
5/16	1⅞	9/16	1 1/16	....	....	....	....	0.4
⅜	1⅛	1¼	2	....	....	....	....	0.7
7/16	1¼	1⅜	2⅛	⅜	4½	1	1 21/32	1.
½	1 7/16	1½	2⅜	7/16	4½	1 3/32	1 27/32	1.3
9/16	1⅝	1⅜	2⅜	½	4½	1 3/16	2 1/16	1.5
⅝	1 13/16	1 11/16	2 15/16	9/16	4½	1 9/32	2 9/32	2.
¾	2	1 13/16	3 5/16	⅝	4½	1⅜	2½	3.
⅞	2 3/16	1 15/16	3 9/16	¾	5	1½	2 13/16	3.5
1	2⅜	2 1/16	3 15/16	⅞	5	1 11/16	3¼	4.
1⅛	2½	2 3/16	4 5/16	1	5	1 13/16	3 9/16	5.
1¼	2¾	2 5/16	4 11/16	1⅛	5	2	4	7.5
1½	3⅛	2 9/16	5 5/16	1¼	6	2 3/16	4 7/16	9.
1¾	3½	3 1/16	6 1/16	1½	6	2½	5 3/16	11.
2	4	3 1/16	6 5/16	1¾	6	2⅞	6 1/16	13.
2½	5	4½	8½	2	6	3¼	6⅞	16.
2¾	4	5	9¾	2½	6	4	8 9/16	20.

Shoulder Pattern — Standard Length					Shoulder Pattern — Extra Length				Safe Load, Tons*
Shank		Eye Diam.		Diam.	Shank		Eye Diam.		
D	*C*	*A*	*B*	*E*	*D*	*C*	*A*	*B*	
¼	1	9/16	1	½	¼	3	¾	1 3/16	0.2
5/16	1⅛	⅞	1 7/16	9/16	5/16	4	⅞	1 7/16	0.4
⅜	1¼	1⅛	1 11/16	⅝	⅜	4½	1	1 21/32	0.7
7/16	1⅜	1 3/32	1 27/32	13/16	7/16	4½	1 3/32	1 27/32	1.
½	1 7/16	1¼	2⅜	⅞	½	4½	1 3/16	2 1/16	1.3
9/16	1⅝	1 9/32	2 9/32	1	9/16	4½	1 9/32	2 9/32	1.5
⅝	1¾	1⅜	2⅝	1	⅝	4½	1⅜	2½	2.
¾	2⅛	1½	3	1⅛	¾	5	1½	2 13/16	3.
⅞	2½	1⅝	3¼	1¼	⅞	5	1 11/16	3¼	3.5
1	3¼	1⅞	3⅝	1½	1	5	1 13/16	3 9/16	4.
1⅛	2¾	2	4	1 11/16	1⅛	5	2	4	5.
1¼	3	2 3/16	4 7/16	1 13/16	1¼	6	2 3/16	4 7/16	7.5
1½	3½	2½	5 3/16	2 3/16	1½	6	2½	5 3/16	9.
1¾	3¾	2⅞	6 1/16	2 7/16	1¾	6	2⅞	6 1/16	11.
2	4	3¼	6⅞	2⅞	2	6	3¼	6⅞	13.

* The Billings and Spencer Co. standard. The ultimate or breaking load is approximately 4 to 5 times the working load.

Eye-Bolts for Motor and Generator Frames, Transformer Covers, etc.

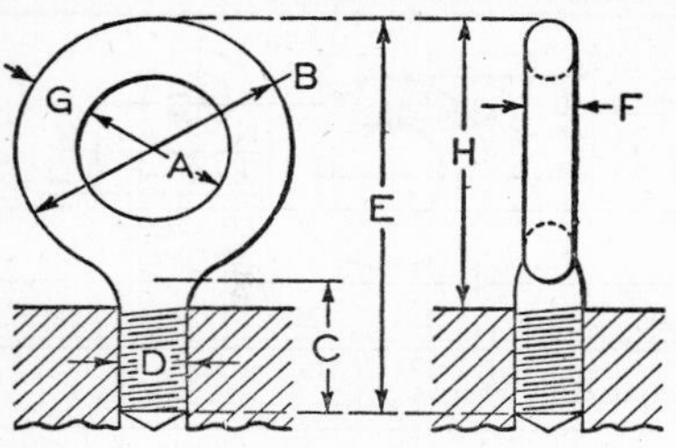

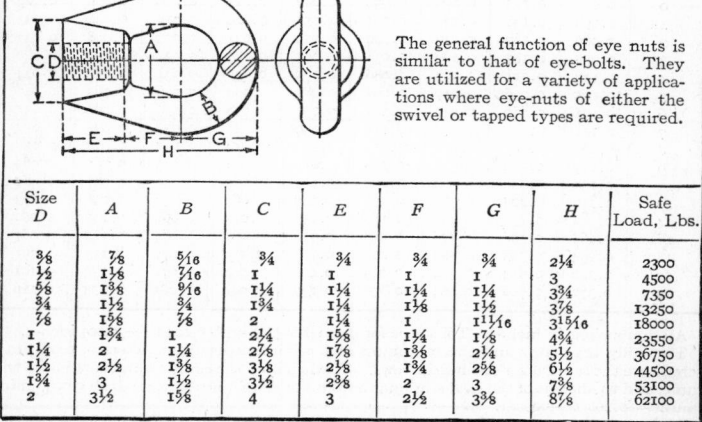

Thread Diam.	Pitch Diameter "Not Go" Gage	Pitch Diameter "Go" Gage
½–13	0.4500	0.4540
¾–10	0.6850	0.6900
1–8	0.9188	0.9238
1¼–7	1.1572	1.1632
1½–6	1.3917	1.3977
1¾–5	1.6201	1.6261
2–4½	1.8557	......
2½–4	2.3376	......

Shank		Eye Diam.		Length	Thick.	Width	Height	Safe
D	*C*	*A*	*B*	*E*	*F*	*G*	*H*	Load, Lbs.
½	1⅛	1½	2⅜	3½	13/32	7/16	2⅝	630
¾	1 9/16	1 13/16	3 5/16	4⅞	⅝	¾	3⅝	1500
1	1 15/16	2 1/16	3 15/16	5⅞	13/16	15/16	4¼	2760
1¼	2¾	2 5/16	4 11/16	7 7/16	1	1 3/16	5 1/16	4450
1½	3	3	5¾	8¾	1¼	1⅜	6⅛	6475
1¾	3⅝	4	7¼	10⅞	1½	1⅝	7⅝	8700
2	3⅝	4	7¼	10⅞	1½	1⅝	7⅝	11500
2½	4½	4½	8½	13	1 13/16	2	9¼	18580

Westinghouse Electric & Mfg. Co. standard. Maximum safe loads for direct tension at 5000 pounds per square inch.

Drop Forged Carbon Steel Eye-Nuts — Billings and Spencer Co. Standard

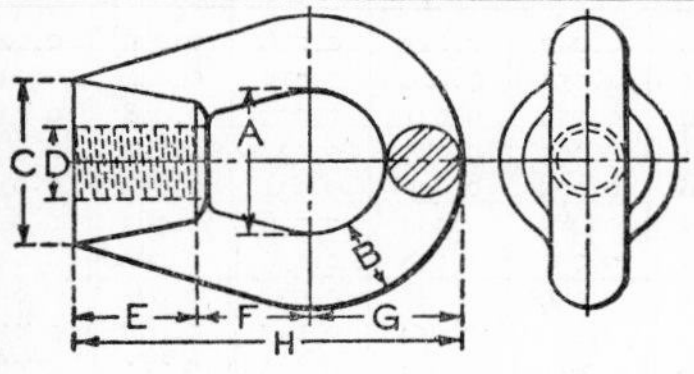

The general function of eye nuts is similar to that of eye-bolts. They are utilized for a variety of applications where eye-nuts of either the swivel or tapped types are required.

Size *D*	*A*	*B*	*C*	*E*	*F*	*G*	*H*	Safe Load, Lbs.
⅜	⅞	5/16	¾	¾	¾	¾	2¼	2300
½	1⅛	7/16	1	1	1	1	3	4500
⅝	1⅜	9/16	1¼	1¼	1¼	1¼	3¾	7350
¾	1½	¾	1¾	1¼	1⅛	1½	3⅞	13250
⅞	1⅝	⅞	2	1¼	1	1 11/16	3 15/16	18000
1	1¾	1	2¼	1⅝	1¼	1⅞	4¾	23550
1¼	2	1¼	2⅞	1⅞	1⅜	2¼	5½	36750
1½	2½	1⅜	3⅛	2⅛	1¾	2⅝	6½	44500
1¾	3	1½	3½	2⅜	2	3	7⅜	53100
2	3½	1⅝	4	3	2½	3⅜	8⅞	62100

Safe load applies to nut only and not to connecting bolt.

Flat Head and Round Head Wood Screws — American Standard

Screw Number	D	A Max.	A Min.	H Max.	H Min.	J Max.	J Min.	T Max.	T Min.
				Flat Head Screws					
0	0.060	0.119	0.105	0.035	0.026	0.023	0.016	0.015	0.010
1	0.073	0.146	0.130	0.043	0.033	0.026	0.019	0.019	0.012
2	0.086	0.172	0.156	0.051	0.040	0.031	0.023	0.023	0.015
3	0.099	0.199	0.181	0.059	0.048	0.035	0.027	0.027	0.017
4	0.112	0.225	0.207	0.067	0.055	0.039	0.031	0.030	0.020
5	0.125	0.252	0.232	0.075	0.062	0.043	0.035	0.034	0.022
6	0.138	0.279	0.257	0.083	0.069	0.048	0.039	0.038	0.024
7	0.151	0.305	0.283	0.091	0.076	0.048	0.039	0.041	0.027
8	0.164	0.332	0.308	0.100	0.084	0.054	0.045	0.045	0.029
9	0.177	0.358	0.334	0.108	0.091	0.054	0.045	0.049	0.032
10	0.190	0.385	0.359	0.116	0.098	0.060	0.050	0.053	0.034
12	0.216	0.438	0.410	0.132	0.112	0.067	0.056	0.060	0.039
14	0.242	0.491	0.461	0.148	0.127	0.075	0.064	0.068	0.044
16	0.268	0.544	0.512	0.164	0.141	0.075	0.064	0.075	0.049
18	0.294	0.597	0.563	0.180	0.155	0.084	0.072	0.083	0.054
20	0.320	0.650	0.614	0.196	0.170	0.084	0.072	0.090	0.059
24	0.372	0.756	0.716	0.228	0.198	0.094	0.081	0.105	0.069
No.				Round Head Screws					
0	0.060	0.113	0.099	0.053	0.042	0.023	0.016	0.039	0.029
1	0.073	0.138	0.122	0.061	0.051	0.026	0.019	0.044	0.033
2	0.086	0.162	0.146	0.070	0.059	0.031	0.023	0.048	0.037
3	0.099	0.187	0.169	0.078	0.067	0.035	0.027	0.053	0.040
4	0.112	0.211	0.193	0.086	0.075	0.039	0.031	0.058	0.044
5	0.125	0.236	0.217	0.095	0.083	0.043	0.036	0.063	0.047
6	0.138	0.260	0.240	0.103	0.091	0.048	0.039	0.068	0.051
7	0.151	0.285	0.264	0.111	0.099	0.048	0.039	0.072	0.055
8	0.164	0.309	0.287	0.119	0.107	0.054	0.045	0.077	0.058
9	0.177	0.334	0.311	0.128	0.115	0.054	0.045	0.082	0.062
10	0.190	0.359	0.334	0.136	0.124	0.060	0.050	0.087	0.065
12	0.216	0.408	0.382	0.152	0.140	0.067	0.056	0.096	0.073
14	0.242	0.457	0.429	0.169	0.156	0.075	0.064	0.106	0.080
16	0.268	0.506	0.476	0.185	0.172	0.075	0.064	0.115	0.087
18	0.294	0.555	0.523	0.202	0.188	0.084	0.072	0.125	0.094
20	0.320	0.604	0.570	0.219	0.205	0.084	0.072	0.134	0.101
24	0.372	0.702	0.664	0.252	0.237	0.094	0.081	0.154	0.116

All dimensions in inches. Tolerance for diameter $(D) = +$ 0.004 to $-$ 0.007 inches. The body diameters and the maximum and minimum head diameters of oval head screws are the same as for flat head screws. The height of the countersunk part is also the same, and the height of the oval section is as follows: Maximum $= 0.304 D + 0.003$; minimum $= 0.268 D - 0.001$.

Thread length l equals ⅔ L approximately. Revision approved by the American Standards Association, 1947.

American Standard Screw Lengths and Heads for Steel Wood Screws

Nominal Length, Inches	Screw Number								
	0	1	2	3	4	5	6	7	8
The letters below indicate the style of head for a given screw number and length. F = Flat Head, R = Round Head, O = Oval Head.									
1/4	FR	FR	FR	FR	FR				
3/8	FR	FR	FR	FRO	FRO	FR	FR	FR	FR
1/2		FR	FR	FR	FRO	FRO	FRO	FRO	FRO
5/8			FR	FR	FRO	FRO	FRO	FRO	FRO
3/4			FR	FR	FRO	FRO	FRO	FRO	FRO
7/8				FR	FR	FR	FR	FRO	FRO
1				FR	FR	FRO	FRO	FRO	FRO
1 1/4					FR	FR	FRO	FRO	FRO
1 1/2					FR	FR	FRO	FRO	FRO
1 3/4							FRO	FRO	FRO
2							FR	FR	FR
2 1/4							FR	FR	FR
2 1/2							FR	FR	FR
2 3/4									FR

Nominal Length, Inches	Screw Number								
	9	10	11	12	14	16	18	20	24
The letters below indicate the style of head for a given screw number and length. F = Flat Head, R = Round Head, O = Oval Head.									
1/2	FR	FR							
5/8	FR	FR	FR	FR					
3/4	FRO	FRO	FR	FR					
7/8	FRO	FRO	FR	FRO	FR				
1	FRO	FRO	FRO	FRO	FRO	FR			
1 1/4	FRO	FRO	FRO	FRO	FRO	FR	FR		
1 1/2	FRO	FRO	FRO	FRO	FRO	FRO	FRO	FRO	
1 3/4	FRO	FRO	FRO	FRO	FRO	FRO	FRO	FRO	
2	FR	FRO	FRO	FRO	FRO	FRO	FRO	FRO	
2 1/4	FR	FR	FR	FRO	FRO	FR	F	F	
2 1/2	FR	FR	FR	FRO	FRO	FR	FR	FR	
2 3/4	FR	FR	F	FR	FR	F	F	F	
3	FR	FR	F	FR	FR	FR	FR	F	F
3 1/2		FR	F	FR	FR	FR	F	F	F
4				FR	FR	FR	F	F	F
4 1/2					F	F	F	F	F
5					F	F	F	F	F

To illustrate the use of the table: Heads FR (flat and round heads) only are listed for a No. 4 screw of 1/4 inch length, but in lengths of from 3/8 to 3/4 inch, inclusive, heads FRO (flat, round, and oval) are included.

Standard Wire Nails and Spikes
(Size, Length and Approximate Number to Pound)

Size of Nail	Length, Inches	Gage	No. to Lb.	Gage	No. to Lb.	Gage	No. to Lb.	Gage	No. to Lb.	Gage	No. to Lb.
		Common Wire Nails and Brads		Flooring Brads		Fence Nails		Casing, Smooth and Barbed Box		Finishing Nails	
2 d	1	15	876	.....	....	.....	....	15½	1010	16½	1351
3 d	1¼	14	568	.....	....	.....	....	14½	635	15½	807
4 d	1½	12½	316	.....	....	.....	....	14	473	15	584
5 d	1¾	12½	271	.....	....	10	142	14	406	15	500
6 d	2	11½	181	11	157	10	124	12½	236	13½	309
7 d	2¼	11½	161	11	139	9	92	12½	210	13	238
8 d	2½	10¼	106	10	99	9	82	11½	145	12½	189
9 d	2¾	10¼	96	10	90	8	62	11½	132	12½	172
10 d	3	9	69	9	69	7	50	10½	94	11½	121
12 d	3¼	9	64	8	54	6	40	10½	87	11½	113
16 d	3½	8	49	7	43	5	30	10	71	11	90
20 d	4	6	31	6	31	4	23	9	52	10	62
30 d	4½	5	24	.....	....	.....	....	9	46	.....	....
40 d	5	4	18	.....	....	.....	....	8	35	.....	....
50 d	5½	3	16	.....	....	.....	....	.....	....	.....	....
60 d	6	2	11	.....	....	.....	....	.....	....	.....	....

Size and Length		Hinge Nails, Heavy		Hinge Nails, Light		Clinch Nails		Barbed Car Nails, Heavy		Barbed Car Nails, Light	
2 d	1	.....	....	.....	....	14	710	.....	....	.....	....
3 d	1¼	.....	....	.....	....	13	429	.....	....	.....	....
4 d	1½	3	50	6	82	12	274	10	165	12	274
5 d	1¾	3	38	6	62	12	235	9	118	10	142
6 d	2	3	30	6	50	11	157	9	103	10	124
7 d	2¼	00	12	3	25	11	139	8	76	9	92
8 d	2½	00	11	3	23	10	99	8	69	9	82
9 d	2¾	00	10	3	22	10	90	7	54	8	62
10 d	3	00	9	3	19	9	69	7	50	8	57
12 d	3¼	.....	....	.....	....	9	62	6	42	7	50
16 d	3½	.....	....	.....	....	8	49	6	35	7	43
20 d	4	.....	....	.....	....	7	37	5	26	6	31
30 d	4½	.....	....	.....	....	.....	....	5	24	6	28
40 d	5	.....	....	.....	....	.....	....	4	18	5	21
50 d	5½	.....	....	.....	....	.....	....	3	15	4	17
60 d	6	.....	....	.....	....	.....	....	3	13	4	15

Size and Length		Boat Nails, Heavy		Boat Nails, Light		Slating Nails	
2 d	1	.....	....	.....	....	12	411
3 d	1¼	.....	....	.....	....	10½	225
4 d	1½	¼	44	3/16	82	10½	187
5 d	1¾	.....	....	.....	....	10	142
6 d	2	¼	32	3/16	62	9	103
7 d	2¼	.....	....	.....	....	.....	....
8 d	2½	¼	26	3/16	50	.....	....
9 d	2¾	.....	....	.....	....	.....	....
10 d	3	3/8	14	¼	22	.....	....
12 d	3¼	3/8	13	¼	20	.....	....
16 d	3½	3/8	12	¼	18	.....	....
20 d	4	3/8	10	¼	16	.....	....
30 d	4½	.....	....	.....	....	.....	....
40 d	5	.....	....	.....	....	.....	....
50 d	5½	.....	....	.....	....	.....	....
60 d	6	.....	....	.....	....	.....	....

Spikes

Size and Length		Gage	No. to Lb.
10 d	3	6	41
12 d	3¼	6	38
16 d	3½	5	30
20 d	4	4	23
30 d	4½	3	17
40 d	5	2	13
50 d	5½	1	10
60 d	6	1	8
.....	7	0	7
.....	8	00	6
.....	9	00	5
.....	10	3/8	4
.....	12	3/8	3

SCREW THREAD SYSTEMS

American Standard Thread Form. — This thread form (formerly known as the United States Standard) is used for most of the screws, bolts, and miscellaneous

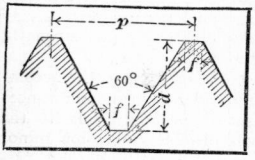

threaded products produced in the United States. The Unified and revised American Standard (referred to on page 986) includes certain modifications of the former American Standard. These revisions apply chiefly to new classes of tolerances (see section on Tolerances and Allowances for Standard Screw Threads). The basic thread angle in the axial plane of 60 degrees has been retained. The basic depth of an external thread now equals 0.61343 × pitch instead of 0.64952 × pitch as in the former standard. The previous thread form had a flat at the crest and root equal to 0.125 × pitch (although in practice some rounding gradually occurred at the root due to tool wear). The Unified and American thread form may have a rounded or a flat root. In American practice, a flat form (such as would be obtained from a new tool with a flat end) is permissible; hence the American standard does not specify a root radius. If the root form is flat, the width of flat at the minimum minor diameter of the external thread and at the minimum major diameter of the internal thread equals 0.125 × pitch. While the crest may be rounded, a flat crest with a minimum width of 0.125 × pitch is preferred American practice. See additional formulas and tabulated data on following pages.

Whitworth Standard Thread Form. — This screw thread, which is also known as the British Standard Whitworth (B.S.W.), is used principally in Great Britain. It was proposed by Sir Joseph Whitworth and a table of sizes published in 1841. The form of the thread is shown by the diagram.

If p = pitch of thread, d = depth of thread, and r = radius at top and bottom of thread, then:

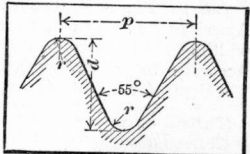

$$d = \frac{2}{3} \times \frac{p}{2} \times \cot 27 \deg. 30 \min. = 0.640\,327\,p$$

$$= \frac{0.640\,327}{\text{no. of threads per inch}}$$

$$r = 0.137\,329\,p = \frac{0.137\,329}{\text{number of threads per inch}}$$

Tables for the Whitworth or British standard thread will be found on the following pages.

Sharp V-thread. — The sides of the thread form an angle of 60 degrees with each other. The top and bottom of the thread are, theoretically, sharp, but

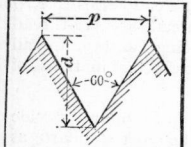

in practice it is necessary to make the thread with a slight flat. There is no standard adopted for this flat, but it is usually made about one-twenty-fifth of the pitch. If p = pitch of thread, and d = depth of thread, then:

$$d = p \times \cos 30 \deg. = 0.866\,p = \frac{0.866}{\text{no. of threads per inch}}$$

Some modified V-threads, for locomotive boiler taps particularly, have a depth of 0.8 × pitch.

Unified and American Screw Thread Standards. — The revised American Standard (ASA B1.1–1949), which is interchangeable with the previous one, includes a Unified Thread Series which was established by representatives of the United Kingdom, Canada and the United States to obtain screw thread interchangeability among these three nations. The American Standard contains, in addition to the Unified Series, certain other diameters and pitches which are used extensively in the United States. This revised standard provides greater fatigue strength, root clearance, easier assembly and longer life for cutting tools.

The Unified Series may readily be identified by the bold face type in the accompanying tables of basic dimensions and also in the tables of tolerances and allowances beginning on page 1084. The figures not in bold face type apply only to the American Standard. The Unified Series agreed upon provides for some minor variations in American and British practice but these differences do not prevent complete interchangeability within this series. The revised American Standard retains Class 2 and Class 3 limits of the former standard. It also includes three new classifications in the Unified Series which are designated as 1A, 1B (A for external, B for internal threads); 2A and 2B; 3A and 3B. The American Standard included thread angle of 60 degrees has been retained. (See also page 1108.)

External Thread. — The American Standard external thread may have either a rounded or flat root contour. The exact form is not specified since in practice the amount of rounding and the contour varies with tool wear. Any variation from a flat form, (which is permissible) to the rounding obtained with a worn tool, will not interfere with interchangeability. According to British specifications, the root is rounded to a radius of 0.14434 × pitch. The crest may either be flat (preferred American practice) or rounded (preferred British practice). The minimum width of a flat crest = 0.125 × pitch, and the radius of a rounded crest = 0.108 × pitch. The thread depth (or height) = 0.61343 × pitch.

Internal Thread. — The internal thread may have a flat crest and root (preferred American form) or a flat crest and rounded root (preferred British form). The width of the flat crest = 0.25 × pitch. The width of a flat root = 0.125 × pitch. According to British specifications, the radius of a rounded root = 0.10825 × pitch. The depth (or height) = 0.54127 × pitch.

Thread Series. — The revised standard includes the following series of threads.
Coarse-thread Series (NC). — The pitches for screw threads in this series are the same as for similar sizes in the Coarse-thread Series of the former American Standard (B1.1–1935). In the Unified Series of the American Standard, the ½-inch size has 12 threads per inch, but the American Standard also retains 13 threads per inch (in common use in the U. S.) as a possible alternate to 12 threads per inch.

Fine-thread Series (NF). — In this series the pitches coincide with those in the Fine-thread Series of the former American Standard (B1.1–1935), excepting the 1-inch size which now has 12 threads per inch as the Unified Standard, but the American Standard also retains 14 threads per inch as a possible alternate (1950 Revision).

Other Series. — The remaining series include an Extra-fine Thread Series (NEF) and three constant pitch series. The latter are designated 8-thread (8N), 12-thread (12N) and 16-thread (16N) Series, the pitch in each case being constant for all diameters. "Special threads" cover non-standard or special combinations of diameter, pitch and length of engagement.

Classes of Tolerances. — The Unified and revised American Standard provide for three new classes of limits and retain Classes 2 and 3 of the older standard, as previously mentioned. The limiting dimensions for different thread series and classes of tolerances will be found on pages 1081 to 1112.

Unified and American Standard Internal and External Screw Thread Forms

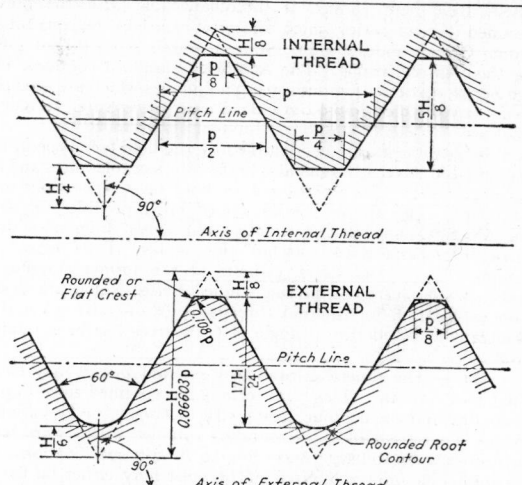

General Formulas for Finding Basic Dimensions of Unified and
American Standard Threads
(H = height of sharp V-thread = 0.86603 × pitch)

Pitch = $\dfrac{1}{\text{No. of threads per inch}}$		Crest truncation, external thread	= 0.10825 × pitch = $H \div 8$
Depth, external thread	= 0.61343 × pitch	Crest truncation, internal thread	= 0.21651 × pitch = $H \div 4$
Depth, internal thread	= 0.54127 × pitch	Root truncation, external thread	= 0.14434 × pitch = $H \div 6$
Flat at crest, external thread	= 0.125 × pitch	Root truncation, internal thread	= 0.10825 × pitch = $H \div 8$
Flat at crest, internal thread	= 0.25 × pitch	Addendum, external thread	= 0.32476 × pitch
Flat at root, internal thread	= 0.125 × pitch	Pitch diameter, Exter. and Inter.	= Major Diam. −2 × add. (Add. external thread)

Stress Area. — The stress areas given in the accompanying tables, which are used in computing the tensile strength of the threaded section, are based upon a diameter that is the mean of the pitch and root diameters. This mean diameter is to allow for the strengthening effect of the threads. Assume that A_s = stress area, sq. in.; E_m = mean pitch diam., Class 3 tolerance; K_m = mean minor diam., Class 3 tolerance. Then

$$A_s = 3.1416 \left(\frac{E_m + K_m}{4} \right)^2$$

Table 1. Thread Data, Unified and American Thread Form

Threads per Inch	Pitch	Depth of Sharp V-Thread	Depth of External Thread	Depth of Internal Thread	Depth of Thread Engagement	Flat at External Thread Crest	Truncation of External Thread Crest	Truncation of External Thread Root	Flat at Internal Thread Crest	Truncation of Internal Thread Crest	Flat at Internal Thread Root	Truncation of Internal Thread Root	Addendum of External Thread
n	p	0.86603p	0.61343p	0.54127p	0.54127p	0.125p	0.10825p	0.14434p	0.25p	0.21651p	0.125p	0.10825p	0.32476p
80	0.01250	0.01083	0.00767	0.00677	0.00677	0.00156	0.00135	0.00180	0.00312	0.00271	0.00156	0.00135	0.00406
72	0.01389	0.01203	0.00852	0.00752	0.00752	0.00174	0.00150	0.00200	0.00347	0.00301	0.00174	0.00150	0.00451
64	0.01563	0.01353	0.00958	0.00846	0.00846	0.00195	0.00169	0.00226	0.00391	0.00338	0.00195	0.00169	0.00507
56	0.01786	0.01546	0.01095	0.00967	0.00967	0.00223	0.00193	0.00258	0.00446	0.00387	0.00223	0.00193	0.00580
48	0.02083	0.01804	0.01278	0.01128	0.01128	0.00260	0.00226	0.00301	0.00521	0.00451	0.00260	0.00226	0.00677
44	0.02273	0.01968	0.01394	0.01230	0.01230	0.00284	0.00246	0.00328	0.00568	0.00492	0.00284	0.00246	0.00738
40	0.02500	0.02165	0.01534	0.01353	0.01353	0.00312	0.00271	0.00361	0.00625	0.00541	0.00312	0.00271	0.00812
36	0.02778	0.02406	0.01704	0.01504	0.01504	0.00347	0.00301	0.00401	0.00694	0.00601	0.00347	0.00301	0.00902
32	0.03125	0.02706	0.01917	0.01691	0.01691	0.00391	0.00338	0.00451	0.00781	0.00677	0.00391	0.00338	0.01015
28	0.03571	0.03093	0.02191	0.01933	0.01933	0.00446	0.00387	0.00515	0.00893	0.00773	0.00446	0.00387	0.01160
24	0.04167	0.03608	0.02556	0.02255	0.02255	0.00521	0.00451	0.00601	0.01042	0.00902	0.00521	0.00451	0.01353
20	0.05000	0.04330	0.03067	0.02706	0.02706	0.00625	0.00541	0.00722	0.01250	0.01083	0.00625	0.00541	0.01624
18	0.05556	0.04811	0.03408	0.03007	0.03007	0.00694	0.00601	0.00802	0.01389	0.01203	0.00694	0.00601	0.01804
16	0.06250	0.05413	0.03834	0.03383	0.03383	0.00781	0.00677	0.00902	0.01562	0.01353	0.00781	0.00677	0.02030
14	0.07143	0.06186	0.04382	0.03866	0.03866	0.00893	0.00773	0.01031	0.01786	0.01546	0.00893	0.00773	0.02320
13	0.07692	0.06662	0.04719	0.04164	0.04164	0.00962	0.00833	0.01110	0.01923	0.01665	0.00962	0.00833	0.02498
12	0.08333	0.07217	0.05112	0.04511	0.04511	0.01042	0.00902	0.01203	0.02083	0.01804	0.01042	0.00902	0.02706
11½	0.08696	0.07531	0.05334	0.04707	0.04707	0.01087	0.00941	0.01255	0.02174	0.01883	0.01087	0.00941	0.02824
11	0.09091	0.07873	0.05577	0.04921	0.04921	0.01136	0.00984	0.01312	0.02273	0.01968	0.01136	0.00984	0.02952
10	0.10000	0.08660	0.06134	0.05413	0.05413	0.01250	0.01083	0.01443	0.02500	0.02165	0.01250	0.01083	0.03248
9	0.11111	0.09623	0.06816	0.06014	0.06014	0.01389	0.01203	0.01604	0.02778	0.02406	0.01389	0.01203	0.03608
8	0.12500	0.10825	0.07668	0.06766	0.06766	0.01562	0.01353	0.01804	0.03125	0.02706	0.01562	0.01353	0.04059
7	0.14286	0.12372	0.08763	0.07732	0.07732	0.01786	0.01546	0.02062	0.03571	0.03093	0.01786	0.01546	0.04639
6	0.16667	0.14434	0.10224	0.09021	0.09021	0.02083	0.01804	0.02406	0.04167	0.03608	0.02083	0.01804	0.05413
5	0.20000	0.17321	0.12269	0.10825	0.10825	0.02500	0.02165	0.02887	0.05000	0.04330	0.02500	0.02165	0.06495
4½	0.22222	0.19245	0.13632	0.12028	0.12028	0.02778	0.02406	0.03208	0.05556	0.04811	0.02778	0.02406	0.07217
4	0.25000	0.21651	0.15336	0.13532	0.13532	0.03125	0.02706	0.03608	0.06250	0.05413	0.03125	0.02706	0.08119

Twice the external thread addendum (last column) is equivalent to the "basic height" of the original American National form.

Table 2.   Unified and American Standard Coarse-thread Series — Basic Dimensions

Size	Basic Major Diam. Inches	Thds. per Inch	Basic Pitch Diam. Inches	Minor Diam. Ext. Thds. Inches	Minor Diam. Int. Thds. Inches	Lead Angle, Basic Pitch Diam. Deg. Min.		Area, Minor Diam. Sq. In.	Stress Area, Sq. In. (See Note)
1 (.073)	0.0730	64	0.0629	0.0538	0.0561	4°	31'	0.0022	0.0026
2 (.086)	0.0860	56	0.0744	0.0641	0.0667	4°	22'	0.0031	0.0036
3 (.099)	0.0990	48	0.0855	0.0734	0.0764	4°	26'	0.0041	0.0048
4 (.112)	0.1120	40	0.0958	0.0813	0.0849	4°	45'	0.0050	0.0060
5 (.125)	0.1250	40	0.1088	0.0943	0.0979	4°	11'	0.0067	0.0079
6 (.138)	0.1380	32	0.1177	0.0997	0.1042	4°	50'	0.0075	0.0090
8 (.164)	0.1640	32	0.1437	0.1257	0.1302	3°	58'	0.0120	0.0139
10 (.190)	0.1900	24	0.1629	0.1389	0.1449	4°	39'	0.0145	0.0174
12 (.216)	0.2160	24	0.1889	0.1649	0.1709	4°	1'	0.0206	0.0240
1/4	0.2500	20	0.2175	0.1887	0.1959	4°	11'	0.0269	0.0317
5/16	0.3125	18	0.2764	0.2443	0.2524	3°	40'	0.0454	0.0522
3/8	0.3750	16	0.3344	0.2983	0.3073	3°	24'	0.0678	0.0773
7/16	0.4375	14	0.3911	0.3499	0.3602	3°	20'	0.0933	0.1060
*1/2	0.5000	13	0.4500	0.4056	0.4167	3°	7'	0.1257	0.1416
*1/2	0.5000	12	0.4459	0.3978	0.4098	3°	24'	0.1205	0.1374
9/16	0.5625	12	0.5084	0.4603	0.4723	2°	59'	0.1620	0.1816
5/8	0.6250	11	0.5660	0.5135	0.5266	2°	56'	0.2018	0.2256
3/4	0.7500	10	0.6850	0.6273	0.6417	2°	40'	0.3020	0.3340
7/8	0.8750	9	0.8028	0.7387	0.7547	2°	31'	0.4193	0.4612
1	1.0000	8	0.9188	0.8466	0.8647	2°	29'	0.5510	0.6051
1 1/8	1.1250	7	1.0322	0.9497	0.9704	2°	31'	0.6931	0.7627
1 1/4	1.2500	7	1.1572	1.0747	1.0954	2°	15'	0.8898	0.9684
1 3/8	1.3750	6	1.2667	1.1705	1.1946	2°	24'	1.0541	1.1538
1 1/2	1.5000	6	1.3917	1.2955	1.3196	2°	11'	1.2938	1.4041
1 3/4	1.7500	5	1.6201	1.5046	1.5335	2°	15'	1.7441	1.8983
2	2.0000	4 1/2	1.8557	1.7274	1.7594	2°	11'	2.3001	2.4971
2 1/4	2.2500	4 1/2	2.1057	1.9774	2.0094	1°	55'	3.0212	3.2464
2 1/2	2.5000	4	2.3376	2.1933	2.2294	1°	57'	3.7161	3.9976
2 3/4	2.7500	4	2.5876	2.4433	2.4794	1°	46'	4.6194	4.9326
3	3.0000	4	2.8376	2.6933	2.7294	1°	36'	5.6209	5.9659
3 1/4	3.2500	4	3.0876	2.9433	2.9794	1°	29'	6.7205	7.0992
3 1/2	3.5000	4	3.3376	3.1933	3.2294	1°	22'	7.9183	8.3268
3 3/4	3.7500	4	3.5876	3.4433	3.4794	1°	16'	9.2143	9.6546
4	4.0000	4	3.8376	3.6933	3.7294	1°	11'	10.6084	11.0805

Figures in bold type indicate Unified threads.

*In the Unified Series the ½ inch size has 12 threads per inch but the American Standard also retains 13 threads per inch (number in common use in the United States) as a possible alternate to 12 threads per inch.

In British practice, the term "Effective Diameter" is used instead of "Pitch Diameter."

The area designated as "Stress Area" (see last column) is determined by the formula on page 987 and is to allow for the strengthening effect of threads.

The Coarse-thread Series is recommended for general use in engineering work where conditions do not require a fine thread. The limiting dimensions for obtaining different classes of fits between external and internal threads will be found in the section on Tolerances and Allowances for Standard Screw Threads, beginning page 1081.

Table 3. Unified and American Standard Fine and
Extra-Fine Thread Series — Basic Dimensions

Size	Basic Major Diam. Inches	Thds. per Inch	Basic Pitch Diam. Inches	Minor Diam. Ext. Thds. Inches	Minor Diam. Int. Thds. Inches	Lead Angle, Pitch Diam. Deg. Min.	Area, Minor Diam. Sq. In.	Stress Area, Sq. In.
FINE THREAD SERIES								
0 (.060)	0.0600	80	0.0519	0.0447	0.0465	4° 23'	0.0015	0.0018
1 (.073)	0.0730	72	0.0640	0.0560	0.0580	3° 57'	0.0024	0.0027
2 (.086)	0.0860	64	0.0759	0.0668	0.0691	3° 45'	0.0034	0.0039
3 (.099)	0.0990	56	0.0874	0.0771	0.0797	3° 43'	0.0045	0.0052
4 (.112)	0.1120	48	0.0985	0.0864	0.0894	3° 51'	0.0057	0.0065
5 (.125)	0.1250	44	0.1102	0.0971	0.1004	3° 45'	0.0072	0.0082
6 (.138)	0.1380	40	0.1218	0.1073	0.1109	3° 44'	0.0087	0.0101
8 (.164)	0.1640	36	0.1460	0.1299	0.1339	3° 28'	0.0128	0.0146
10 (.190)	0.1900	32	0.1697	0.1517	0.1562	3° 21'	0.0175	0.0199
12 (.216)	0.2160	28	0.1928	0.1722	0.1773	3° 22'	0.0226	0.0257
1/4	0.2500	28	0.2268	0.2062	0.2113	2° 52'	0.0326	0.0362
5/16	0.3125	24	0.2854	0.2614	0.2674	2° 40'	0.0524	0.0579
3/8	0.3750	24	0.3479	0.3239	0.3299	2° 11'	0.0809	0.0876
7/16	0.4375	20	0.4050	0.3762	0.3834	2° 15'	0.1090	0.1185
1/2	0.5000	20	0.4675	0.4387	0.4459	1° 57'	0.1486	0.1597
9/16	0.5625	18	0.5264	0.4943	0.5024	1° 55'	0.1888	0.2026
5/8	0.6250	18	0.5889	0.5568	0.5649	1° 43'	0.2400	0.2555
3/4	0.7500	16	0.7094	0.6733	0.6823	1° 36'	0.3513	0.3724
7/8	0.8750	14	0.8286	0.7874	0.7977	1° 34'	0.4805	0.5088
1	1.0000	14	0.9536	0.9124	0.9227	1° 22'	0.6464	0.6791
1	1.0000	12	0.9459	0.8978	0.9098	1° 36'	0.6245	0.6624
1 1/8	1.1250	12	1.0709	1.0228	1.0348	1° 25'	0.8118	0.8549
1 1/4	1.2500	12	1.1959	1.1478	1.1598	1° 16'	1.0237	1.0721
1 3/8	1.3750	12	1.3209	1.2728	1.2848	1° 9'	1.2602	1.3137
1 1/2	1.5000	12	1.4459	1.3978	1.4098	1° 3'	1.5212	1.5799
EXTRA-FINE THREAD SERIES								
12 (.216)	0.2160	32	0.1957	0.1777	0.1822	2° 55'	0.0242	0.0269
1/4	0.2500	32	0.2297	0.2117	0.2162	2° 29'	0.0344	0.0377
5/16	0.3125	32	0.2922	0.2742	0.2787	1° 57'	0.0581	0.0622
3/8	0.3750	32	0.3547	0.3367	0.3412	1° 36'	0.0878	0.0929
7/16	0.4375	28	0.4143	0.3937	0.3988	1° 34'	0.1201	0.1270
1/2	0.5000	28	0.4768	0.4562	0.4613	1° 22'	0.1616	0.1695
9/16	0.5625	24	0.5354	0.5114	0.5174	1° 25'	0.2030	0.2134
5/8	0.6250	24	0.5979	0.5739	0.5799	1° 16'	0.2560	0.2676
11/16	0.6875	24	0.6604	0.6364	0.6424	1° 9'	0.3151	0.3280
3/4	0.7500	20	0.7175	0.6887	0.6959	1° 16'	0.3685	0.3855
13/16	0.8125	20	0.7800	0.7512	0.7584	1° 10'	0.4388	0.4573
7/8	0.8750	20	0.8425	0.8137	0.8209	1° 5'	0.5153	0.5352
15/16	0.9375	20	0.9050	0.8762	0.8834	1° 0	0.5979	0.6194
1	1.0000	20	0.9675	0.9387	0.9459	0° 57'	0.6866	0.7095
1 1/16	1.0625	18	1.0264	0.9943	1.0024	0° 59'	0.7702	0.7973
1 1/8	1.1250	18	1.0889	1.0568	1.0649	0° 56'	0.8705	0.8993
1 3/16	1.1875	18	1.1514	1.1193	1.1274	0° 53'	0.9770	1.0074
1 1/4	1.2500	18	1.2139	1.1818	1.1899	0° 50'	1.0895	1.1216
1 5/16	1.3125	18	1.2764	1.2443	1.2524	0° 48'	1.2082	1.2420
1 3/8	1.3750	18	1.3389	1.3068	1.3149	0° 45'	1.3330	1.3684
1 7/16	1.4375	18	1.4014	1.3693	1.3774	0° 43'	1.4640	1.5010
1 1/2	1.5000	18	1.4639	1.4318	1.4399	0° 42'	1.6011	1.6397
1 9/16	1.5625	18	1.5264	1.4943	1.5024	0° 40'	1.7444	1.7846
1 5/8	1.6250	18	1.5889	1.5568	1.5649	0° 38'	1.8937	1.9357
1 11/16	1.6875	18	1.6514	1.6193	1.6274	0° 37'	2.0493	2.0929
1 3/4	1.7500	16	1.7094	1.6733	1.6823	0° 40'	2.1873	2.2382
2	2.0000	16	1.9594	1.9233	1.9323	0° 35'	2.8917	2.9501

Bold face type indicates Unified threads.

Definitions of Screw Thread Terms. — The definitions which follow include only the more important terms.

Major Diameter: The largest diameter of a straight screw thread. The term major diameter applies to both internal and external threads and replaces the term "outside diameter" as applied to the thread of a screw and also the term "full diameter" as applied to the thread of a nut.

Minor Diameter: The smallest diameter of a straight screw thread. The term minor diameter applies to both internal and external threads and replaces the terms "core diameter" and "root diameter" as applied to the thread of a screw and also the term "inside diameter" as applied to the thread of a nut.

Pitch Diameter (Simple Effective Diameter): On a straight thread, the pitch diameter is the diameter of an imaginary co-axial cylinder, the surface of which would pass through the thread profiles at such points as to make the width of the groove equal to one-half of the basic pitch. On a perfect thread this occurs at the point where the widths of the thread and groove are equal.

On a taper thread, the pitch diameter at a given position on the thread axis, is the diameter of the pitch cone at that position.

Effective Size (or Virtual Effective Diameter): The effective size of an external or internal thread is the diameter derived by adding to the pitch diameter, in the case of an external thread, or subtracting from the pitch diameter, in the case of an internal thread, the cumulative effects of pitch and angle errors.

Pitch: The distance from a point on a screw thread to a corresponding point on the next thread measured parallel to the axis.

Lead: The distance a screw thread advances axially in one turn. On a single-thread screw, the lead and pitch are identical; on a double-thread screw, the lead is twice the pitch; on a triple-thread screw, the lead is three times the pitch, etc.

Angle of Thread: The angle included between the sides of the thread measured in an axial plane.

Lead Angle: The lead angle of a straight thread is the angle made by the helix of the thread at the pitch diameter with a plane perpendicular to the axis.

Crest: The top surface joining the two sides or flanks of a thread.

Root: The bottom surface joining adjacent sides or flanks of a thread.

Truncation: The truncation of the root or crest of a thread is the distance, measured perpendicular to the axis, between a sharp V-shaped root or crest (apex) and the cylinder or cone which bounds the root or crest.

Depth of Engagement: The depth of thread contact or overlap of two mating thread forms, measured radially.

Basic Size: The basic size is the theoretical size from which the size limits are derived by the application of the allowance and tolerance.

Tolerance: Tolerance is the difference between the maximum and minimum limits of size, or the total permissible variation.

Allowance: An allowance is an intentional difference in correlated dimensions of mating parts. According to American Standard terminology, it is the minimum clearance (positive allowance) or maximum interference (negative allowance) between such parts.

Fit: The fit between two mating parts is the relationship existing between them with respect to the amount of clearance or interference which is present when they are assembled.

Flank: The flank (or side) of a thread is either surface connecting the crest with the root, the intersection of which, with an axial plane, is a straight line.

Incomplete Thread: This is also known as the vanish or washout thread. On straight threads, the incomplete thread is that portion at the end having roots not fully formed because of the lead or chamfer on threading tools.

Effective Thread: The effective (or useful) thread includes the complete thread and that portion of the incomplete thread having fully formed roots but having crests not fully formed.

Blunt Start: "Blunt start" designates the removal of the partial thread at the entering end of thread. This is a feature of threaded parts which are repeatedly assembled by hand, such as hose couplings and thread plug gages, to prevent cutting of hands and crossing of threads, and which was formerly known as a "Higbee cut."

Nominal Size: The nominal size is the designation which is used for the purpose of general identification. For example, the nominal size of a ½-inch — 12 thread is ½-inch, but its actual size (major diameter) for Class 2A limits of size may range from 0.4985 to 0.4871 inch.

Table 4. American Standard 8-Pitch, 12-Pitch and 16-Pitch Thread Series

Diam. Inches	Threads per Inch			Diam. Inches	Threads per Inch		
	8-Pitch Series	12-Pitch Series	16-Pitch Series		8-Pitch Series	12-Pitch Series	16-Pitch Series
½	...	12	...	2 3/16	...	...	16
9/16	...	12	...	2 ¼	8	12	16
5/8	...	12	...	2 5/16	...	...	16
11/16	...	12	...	2 3/8	...	12	16
¾	...	12	16	2 7/16	...	...	16
13/16	...	12	16	2 ½	8	12	16
7/8	...	12	16	2 5/8	...	12	16
15/16	...	12	16	2 ¾	8	12	16
1	8	12	16	2 7/8	...	12	16
1 1/16	...	12	16	3	8	12	16
1 1/8	8	12	16	3 1/8	...	12	16
1 3/16	...	12	16	3 ¼	8	12	16
1 ¼	8	12	16	3 3/8	...	12	16
1 5/16	...	12	16	3 ½	8	12	16
1 3/8	8	12	16	3 5/8	...	12	16
1 7/16	...	12	16	3 ¾	8	12	16
1 ½	8	12	16	3 7/8	...	12	16
1 9/16	...	...	16	4	8	12	16
1 5/8	8	12	16	4 ¼	8	12	...
1 11/16	...	...	16	4 ½	8	12	...
1 ¾	8	12	16	4 ¾	8	12	...
1 13/16	...	...	16	5	8	12	...
1 7/8	8	12	16	5 ¼	8	12	...
1 15/16	...	...	16	5 ½	8	12	...
2	8	12	16	5 ¾	8	12	...
2 1/16	...	...	16	6	8	12	...
2 1/8	8	12	16				

The 8-pitch series is intended for such parts as cylinder-head studs, bolts for high-pressure pipe flanges, or similar fastenings requiring an initial tension and a pitch that remains the same for all diameters.

The 12-pitch series, from ½ to 1¾ inches inclusive, are used in boiler practice. The 12-pitch threads are also used widely in machine construction for thin nuts on shafts and sleeves.

The 16-pitch series is intended primarily for threaded adjusting collars and bearing retaining nuts or for any applications requiring a fine thread.

Table 5. S.A.E. Standard Series of Screw Threads

Size	Basic Major Diam.	Threads Per Inch					
		Coarse (NC) Note 1	Fine (NF)	Extra Fine (NEF) Note 2	8 Thread Series Note 2	12 Thread Series Note 3	16 Thread Series Note 4
0	0.0600	......	80	....	....	....	....
1	0.0730	64	72	....	....	....	....
2	0.0860	56	64	....	....	....	....
3	0.0990	48	56	....	....	....	....
4	0.1120	40	48	....	....	....	....
5	0.1250	40	44	....	....	....	....
6	0.1380	32	40	....	....	....	....
8	0.1640	32	36	....	....	....	....
10	0.1900	24	32	....	....	....	....
12	0.2160	24	28	....	....	....	....
¼	0.2500	20	28	32	....	....	....
5⁄16	0.3125	18	24	32	....	....	....
3⁄8	0.3750	16	24	32	....	....	....
7⁄16	0.4375	14	20	28	....	....	....
½	0.5000	13	20	28	....	....	....
9⁄16	0.5625	12	18	24	....	12	....
5⁄8	0.6250	11	18	24	....	12	....
11⁄16	0.6875	....	....	24	....	12	....
¾	0.7500	10	16	20	....	12	......
13⁄16	0.8125	....	....	20	....	12	16
7⁄8	0.8750	9	14	20	....	12	16
15⁄16	0.9375	....	....	20	....	12	16
1	1.0000	8	14	20	....	12	16
1 1⁄16	1.0625	....	....	18	8	12	16
1 1⁄8	1.1250	7	12	18	....	12	16
1 3⁄16	1.1875	....	....	18	8	12	16
1 ¼	1.2500	7	12	18	....	12	16
1 5⁄16	1.3125	....	....	18	8	12	16
1 3⁄8	1.3750	6	12	18	....	12	16
1 7⁄16	1.4375	....	....	18	8	12	16
1 ½	1.5000	6	12	18	....	12	16
1 9⁄16	1.5625	....	....	18	8	12	16
1 5⁄8	1.6250	....	....	18	....	....	16
1 11⁄16	1.6875	....	....	18	8	12	16
1 ¾	1.7500	5	For diameters over 1½ in., use 12 Thread Series	16	....	....	16
1 13⁄16	1.8125	....		....	8	12	16
1 7⁄8	1.8750	....		....	....	....	16
1 15⁄16	1.9375	....		....	8	....	16
2	2.0000	4½		16	8	12	16
2 1⁄16	2.0625	....		For diameters over 2 in., use 16 Thread Series	....	....	16
2 1⁄8	2.1250	....			8	12	16
2 3⁄16	2.1875	....			....	....	16
2 ¼	2.2500	4½			8	12	16
2 5⁄16	2.3125	....			....	....	16
2 3⁄8	2.3750	....			8	12	16
2 7⁄16	2.4375	....			....	12	16
2 ½	2.5000	4			8	12	16
2 5⁄8	2.625	....			....	12	16
2 ¾	2.750	4			8	12	16
2 7⁄8	2.875	....			....	12	16
3	3.000	4			8	12	16

Note 1. The Coarse (NC) series continues by ¼-inch steps or increments up to 4 inches diameter.

Note 2. The 8-pitch series continues by ¼-inch increments up to 6 inches diameter.

Note 3. The 12-pitch series continues by ⅛-inch increments up to 4 inches diameter and by ¼-inch increments from 4¼ to 6 inches diameter.

Note 4. The 16-pitch series continues by ⅛-inch increments up to 4 inches diameter and by ¼-inch increments from 4¼ to 6 inches diameter.

British Standard Whitworth Screw Thread

Diam., Inches	Threads per Inch	Pitch, Inch	Depth of Thread, Inch	Full or Major Diam., Max.	Effective Diam., Max.	Minor Diam.	Tap Drill Diam.,† Inch
1/8	40	0.02500	0.0160	0.1250	0.1090	0.0930	0.0980
3/16	24	0.04167	0.0267	0.1875	0.1608	0.1341	0.1405
1/4	20	0.05000	0.03200	0.2500	0.2180	0.1860	0.196
5/16	18	0.05556	0.03555	0.3125	0.2769	0.2414	1/4
3/8	16	0.06250	0.04000	0.3750	0.3350	0.2950	5/16
7/16	14	0.07143	0.04575	0.4375	0.3918	0.3460	23/64
1/2	12	0.08333	0.05335	0.5000	0.4466	0.3933	13/32
9/16	12	0.08333	0.05335	0.5625	0.5091	0.4558	15/32
5/8	11	0.09091	0.05820	0.6250	0.5668	0.5086	17/32
11/16*	11	0.09091	0.05820	0.6875	0.6293	0.5711	37/64
3/4	10	0.10000	0.06405	0.7500	0.6860	0.6219	41/64
13/16*	10	0.10000	0.06405	0.8125	0.7485	0.6844	45/64
7/8	9	0.11111	0.07115	0.8750	0.8039	0.7327	3/4
15/16*	9	0.11111	0.07115	0.9375	0.8664	0.7952	13/16
1	8	0.12500	0.08005	1.0000	0.9200	0.8399	55/64
1 1/8	7	0.14286	0.09150	1.1250	1.0335	0.9420	31/32
1 1/4	7	0.14286	0.09150	1.2500	1.1585	1.0670	1 3/32
1 3/8*	6	0.16667	0.10670	1.3750	1.2683	1.1616	1 3/16
1 1/2	6	0.16667	0.10670	1.5000	1.3933	1.2866	1 5/16
1 5/8*	5	0.20000	0.12806	1.6250	1.4969	1.3689	1 13/32
1 3/4	5	0.20000	0.12806	1.7500	1.6219	1.4939	1 33/64
1 7/8*	4 1/2	0.22222	0.14228	1.8750	1.7327	1.5904	1 5/8
2	4 1/2	0.22222	0.14228	2.0000	1.8577	1.7154	1 3/4
2 1/8*	4 1/2	0.22222	0.14228	2.1250	1.9827	1.8404	1 7/8
2 1/4	4	0.25000	0.16008	2.2500	2.0899	1.9298	1 31/32
2 3/8*	4	0.25000	0.16008	2.3750	2.2149	2.0548	2 3/32
2 1/2	4	0.25000	0.16008	2.5000	2.3399	2.1798	2 7/32
2 5/8*	4	0.25000	0.16008	2.6250	2.4649	2.3048	2 23/64
2 3/4	3 1/2	0.28571	0.18295	2.7500	2.5670	2.3841	2 7/16
2 7/8*	3 1/2	0.28571	0.18295	2.8750	2.6920	2.5091	2 9/16
3	3 1/2	0.28571	0.18295	3.0000	2.8170	2.6341	2 11/16
3 1/8*	3 1/2	0.28571	0.18295	3.1250	2.9420	2.7591	2 13/16
3 1/4	3 1/4	0.30769	0.19700	3.2500	3.0530	2.8560	
3 3/8*	3 1/4	0.30769	0.19700	3.3750	3.1780	2.9810	
3 1/2	3 1/4	0.30769	0.19700	3.5000	3.3030	3.1060	
3 5/8*	3 1/4	0.30769	0.19700	3.6250	3.4280	3.2310	
3 3/4	3	0.33333	0.21345	3.7500	3.5366	3.3231	
3 7/8*	3	0.33333	0.21345	3.8750	3.6616	3.4481	† Tap drill diam. = major diam. − 1.1328] × pitch (to yield about 88% full thread form).
4	3	0.33333	0.21345	4.0000	3.7866	3.5731	
4 1/8*	3	0.33333	0.21345	4.1250	3.9116	3.6981	
4 1/4*	2 7/8	0.34783	0.22270	4.2500	4.0273	3.8046	
4 3/8*	2 7/8	0.34783	0.22270	4.3750	4.1523	3.9296	
4 1/2	2 7/8	0.34783	0.22270	4.5000	4.2773	4.0546	
4 5/8*	2 7/8	0.34783	0.22270	4.6250	4.4023	4.1796	
4 3/4*	2 3/4	0.36364	0.23285	4.7500	4.5172	4.2843	
4 7/8*	2 3/4	0.36364	0.23285	4.8750	4.6422	4.4093	
5	2 3/4	0.36364	0.23285	5.0000	4.7672	4.5343	
5 1/4*	2 5/8	0.38095	0.24395	5.2500	5.0061	4.7621	
5 1/2	2 5/8	0.38095	0.24395	5.5000	5.2561	5.0121	
6	2 1/2	0.40000	0.25615	6.0000	5.7439	5.4877	

* Sizes marked (*) not recommended for general use by British Standards Institution.

Whitworth Thread Form — General Dimensions

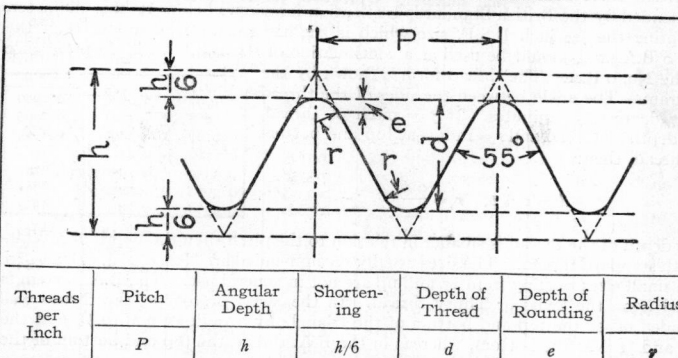

Threads per Inch	Pitch	Angular Depth	Shortening	Depth of Thread	Depth of Rounding	Radius
	P	h	h/6	d	e	r
60	0.016667	0.016008	0.002668	0.010672	0.001232	0.002289
48	0.020833	0.020010	0.003335	0.013340	0.001540	0.002861
40	0.025000	0.024012	0.004002	0.016008	0.001848	0.003433
36	0.027778	0.026680	0.004447	0.017787	0.002053	0.003815
32	0.031250	0.030015	0.005003	0.020010	0.002310	0.004292
28	0.035714	0.034303	0.005717	0.022869	0.002640	0.004905
24	0.041667	0.040021	0.006670	0.026680	0.003080	0.005722
20	0.050000	0.048025	0.008004	0.032016	0.003696	0.006866
19	0.052632	0.050552	0.008425	0.033702	0.003890	0.007228
18	0.055556	0.053361	0.008893	0.035574	0.004107	0.007629
16	0.062500	0.060031	0.010005	0.040021	0.004620	0.008583
14	0.071428	0.068607	0.011434	0.045737	0.005280	0.009809
12	0.083333	0.080041	0.013340	0.053361	0.006160	0.011444
11	0.090909	0.087318	0.014553	0.058212	0.006719	0.012485
10	0.100000	0.096049	0.016008	0.064033	0.007392	0.013733
9	0.111111	0.106722	0.017787	0.071148	0.008213	0.015259
8	0.125000	0.120062	0.020010	0.080041	0.009240	0.017166
7	0.142857	0.137213	0.022869	0.091475	0.010560	0.019618
6	0.166667	0.160082	0.026680	0.106721	0.012320	0.022888
5	0.200000	0.192098	0.032016	0.128065	0.014784	0.027466
4.5	0.222222	0.213443	0.035574	0.142295	0.016426	0.030518
4	0.250000	0.240123	0.040020	0.160082	0.018479	0.034332
3½	0.285714	0.274427	0.045737	0.182950	0.021119	0.039237

British Standard Brass Thread*

Diameter, In........	⅛	¼	⅜	½	⅝	¾
Core Diameter, In...	0.0758	0.2008	0.3258	0.4508	0.5758	0.7008
Diameter, In........	⅞	1	1⅛	1¼	1½	....
Core Diameter, In...	0.8258	0.9508	1.0758	1.2008	1.4508	....

* Used for brass tubing, gas-burner fittings, and general brass work. The thread is the Whitworth form. Threads per inch, 26, and thread depth, 0.0246 inch for all diameters. The sizes range from ¼ inch up to 1½ inches although some makers and dealers list a size as small as ⅛ inch.

British Association Standard Thread (B.A.) — This standard thread is recommended by the British Standards Institution for screws below ¼ inch diameter, excepting the 7⁄32 inch B.S.F. size which is slightly smaller in diameter than the No. 0 B.A. and should be used as a continuation of the B.S.F. series in preference to the No. 0 B.A. The thread form is shown by the diagram. The angle between the sides of the thread is 47 degrees, 30 minutes. If p = pitch of thread, d = depth of thread and r = radius at top and bottom of thread, then:

$$d = 0.6\ p, \quad r = \frac{2\ p}{11}$$

The depth of the thread is smaller in relation to the pitch than the depth of a Whitworth standard thread. The sizes usually recommended are Nos. 0, 2, 4, 6, 8 and 10. The small sizes ranging from 17 and up are not in general use. The B.A. system is based upon the Swiss or Thury thread. In the Swiss prototype, the thread was rounded off at the top and bottom of the triangle by a radius equal to ⅙ p at the top and ⅛ p at the bottom, whereas in the B.A. thread the top and bottom of the threads are both rounded to the same radius.

British Association Standard Thread

British Association Number	Diameter		Pitch		Depth of Thread	Radius	Threads per Inch Approx.
	Millimeters	Inches	Millimeters	Inches	Inches	Inches	
0	6.0	0.2362	1.0	0.0394	0.0236	0.0072	25.4
1	5.3	0.2087	0.90	0.0354	0.0212	0.0064	28.2
2	4.7	0.1850	0.81	0.0319	0.0191	0.0058	31.4
3	4.1	0.1614	0.73	0.0287	0.0172	0.0052	34.8
4	3.6	0.1417	0.66	0.0260	0.0156	0.0047	38.5
5	3.2	0.1260	0.59	0.0232	0.0139	0.0042	43.0
6	2.8	0.1102	0.53	0.0209	0.0125	0.0038	47.9
7	2.5	0.0984	0.48	0.0189	0.0113	0.0034	52.9
8	2.2	0.0866	0.43	0.0169	0.0101	0.0031	59.1
9	1.9	0.0748	0.39	0.0154	0.0092	0.0028	65.1
10	1.7	0.0669	0.35	0.0138	0.0083	0.0025	72.6
11	1.5	0.0591	0.31	0.0122	0.0073	0.0022	81.9
12	1.3	0.0511	0.28	0.0110	0.0066	0.0020	90.9
13	1.2	0.0472	0.25	0.0098	0.0059	0.0018	102.0
14	1.0	0.0394	0.23	0.0091	0.0055	0.0016	109.9
15	0.90	0.0354	0.21	0.0083	0.0050	0.0015	120.5
16	0.79	0.0311	0.19	0.0075	0.0045	0.0014	133.3
17	0.70	0.0276	0.17	0.0067	0.0040	0.0012	149.0
18	0.62	0.0244	0.15	0.0059	0.0035	0.0011	169.0
19	0.54	0.0213	0.14	0.0055	0.0033	0.0010	181.0
20	0.48	0.0189	0.12	0.0047	0.0028	0.0009	212.0
21	0.42	0.0165	0.11	0.0043	0.0026	0.0008	231.0
22	0.37	0.0146	0.098	0.0039	0.0023	0.0007	259.0
23	0.33	0.0130	0.090	0.0035	0.0021	0.0006	282.0

British Standard Fine Thread (B.S.F.) — This system supplements the Whitworth Standard where finer pitches are required. The thread form is the same as the Whitworth Standard. The dimensions given in the table below for the major, effective, and minor diameters are, respectively, the maximum limits of these diameters for bolts and the minimum limits for nuts.

In view of the tendency for closely fitting bolts and nuts of stainless steel to seize when tightened together, it is recommended that the maximum permissible size for all stainless steel bolts should be 0.001 inch below their basic size. The same manufacturing tolerances should be allowed as for bolts of other materials.

Three Grades of Fit: Under this specification, three grades of fit are provided. The close fit grade applies to screw threads requiring a fine, snug fit and is recommended only for special work where refined accuracy of pitch and thread form are particularly required. The medium fit applies to the better class of ordinary interchangeable screw threads. The free fit applies to the great bulk of screw threads of ordinary commercial quality. The three grades of fit are not intended to be applied to screw threads which have to mate with an interference fit.

British Standard Fine Thread (B.S.I. Report No. 84 — 1940)

Diameter, Inch	Threads per Inch*	Pitch, Inch	Depth of Thread, Inch	Major Diam.	Effective or Pitch Diam.	Minor Diam.	Tap Drill Size, Inch
³⁄₁₆	32	0.03125	0.02000	0.1875	0.1675	0.1475	No. 25
⁷⁄₃₂	28	0.03571	0.02290	0.2188	0.1959	0.1730	No. 16
¼	26	0.03846	0.0246	0.2500	0.2254	0.2008	No. 5
⁹⁄₃₂	26	0.03846	0.0246	0.2812	0.2566	0.2320	B
⁵⁄₁₆	22	0.04545	0.0291	0.3125	0.2834	0.2543	G
⅜	20	0.05000	0.0320	0.3750	0.3430	0.3110	O
⁷⁄₁₆	18	0.05556	0.0356	0.4375	0.4019	0.3663	³⁄₈
½	16	0.06250	0.0400	0.5000	0.4600	0.4200	27⁄64
⁹⁄₁₆	16	0.06250	0.0400	0.5625	0.5225	0.4825	½
⅝	14	0.07143	0.0457	0.6250	0.5793	0.5336	35⁄64
¹¹⁄₁₆	14	0.07143	0.0457	0.6875	0.6418	0.5961	39⁄64
¾	12	0.08333	0.0534	0.7500	0.6966	0.6432	21⁄32
¹³⁄₁₆	12	0.08333	0.0534	0.8125	0.7591	0.7057	23⁄32
⅞	11	0.09091	0.0582	0.8750	0.8168	0.7586	25⁄32
1	10	0.10000	0.0640	1.0000	0.9360	0.8720	57⁄64
1⅛	9	0.11111	0.0711	1.1250	1.0539	0.9828	1
1¼	9	0.11111	0.0711	1.2500	1.1789	1.1078	1⅛
1⅜	8	0.12500	0.0800	1.3750	1.2950	1.2150	1¹⁵⁄₆₄
1½	8	0.12500	0.0800	1.5000	1.4200	1.3400	1²³⁄₆₄
1⅝	8	0.12500	0.0800	1.6250	1.5450	1.4650	1³¹⁄₆₄
1¾	7	0.14286	0.0915	1.7500	1.6585	1.5670	1¹⁹⁄₃₂
2	7	0.14286	0.0915	2.0000	1.9085	1.8170	1²⁷⁄₃₂
2¼	6	0.16667	0.1067	2.2500	2.1433	2.0366	2¹⁄₁₆
2½	6	0.16667	0.1067	2.5000	2.3933	2.2866	2⁵⁄₁₆
2¾	6	0.16667	0.1067	2.7500	2.6433	2.5366	2⁹⁄₁₆
3	5	0.20000	0.1281	3.0000	2.8719	2.7438	2¾
3¼	5	0.20000	0.1281	3.2500	3.1219	2.9938	....
3½	4½	0.22222	0.1423	3.5000	3.3577	3.2154	....
3¾	4½	0.22222	0.1423	3.7500	3.6077	3.4654	....
4	4½	0.22222	0.1423	4.0000	3.8577	3.7154	....
4¼	4	0.25000	0.1601	4.2500	4.0899	3.9298	....

* For larger diameters, use 4 threads per inch.

British Standard Screw Thread Tolerance Formula. — The British Standards Institution has issued a revised three-term tolerance formula (BSI Report No. 84-1940), which includes, as factors, the diameter, length of engagement, and pitch. In this formula, T = tolerance on effective diameter in inches; D = major diameter; L = length of engagement; p = pitch of thread.

$$T = 0.002 \times \sqrt[3]{D} + 0.003 \times \sqrt{L} + 0.005 \times \sqrt{p} \qquad (1)$$

This formula is for British Standard Whitworth and British Standard Fine Screw Threads. Tolerances established by it are comparable to "medium fit" tolerances previously issued (see page **1107**). Tolerance for "close fit" = ⅔ of the tolerance and tolerance for "free fit" = 1½ × tolerance obtained by basic formula (1). For the British Association (BA) screw thread (dimensions in millimeters)

$$T = 0.0173 \times \sqrt[3]{D} + 0.0179 \times \sqrt{L} + 0.0218 \times \sqrt{p} \qquad (2)$$

Square Thread. — The sides of the square thread are parallel. The depth of the thread is equal to the width of space between the teeth; this space is, theoretically, equal to one-half of the pitch. It is necessary, in practice, however, to make the space in the nut a trifle wider than the thread, so as to permit of a sliding fit. The threads in the screws are made exactly according to the theoretical standard. The width of the point of the tool for cutting screws is, therefore, exactly one-half of the pitch, but the width of the point of the tool for cutting taps which are to be used for tapping nuts is slightly less than one-half the pitch, and the width of an inside thread tool for threading nuts is slightly more than one-half the pitch. The table below gives the width of tools for cutting taps, screws and nuts.

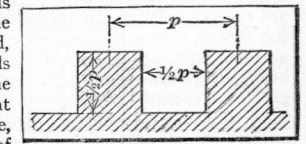

Tools for Square Thread

No. of Threads per Inch	Width of Point of Tool			No. of Threads per Inch	Width of Point of Tool		
	For Taps	For Screws	For Inside Thread Tools for Nuts		For Taps	For Screws	For Inside Thread Tools for Nuts
1	0.4965	0.5000	0.5035	8	0.0615	0.0625	0.0635
1⅓	0.3715	0.3750	0.3785	9	0.0546	0.0556	0.0566
1½	0.3303	0.3333	0.3363	10	0.0490	0.0500	0.0510
1¾	0.2827	0.2857	0.2887	11	0.0445	0.0455	0.0465
2	0.2475	0.2500	0.2525	12	0.0407	0.0417	0.0427
2½	0.1975	0.2000	0.2025	13	0.0375	0.0385	0.0395
3	0.1642	0.1667	0.1692	14	0.0352	0.0357	0.0362
3½	0.1409	0.1429	0.1449	15	0.0328	0.0333	0.0338
4	0.1235	0.1250	0.1265	16	0.0307	0.0312	0.0317
4½	0.1096	0.1111	0.1126	18	0.0273	0.0278	0.0283
5	0.0985	0.1000	0.1015	20	0.0245	0.0250	0.0255
5½	0.0894	0.0909	0.0924	22	0.0222	0.0227	0.0232
6	0.0818	0.0833	0.0848	24	0.0203	0.0208	0.0213
7	0.0699	0.0714	0.0729	......	......	......	......

Elements of the Square Thread

Threads per Inch	Depth of Thread	Double Depth of Thread	Threads per Inch	Depth of Thread	Double Depth of Thread	Threads per Inch	Depth of Thread	Double Depth of Thread
1	0.5000	1.0000	4½	0.1111	0.2222	12	0.0417	0.0833
1⅛	0.3750	0.7500	5	0.1000	0.2000	13	0.0385	0.0769
1½	0.3333	0.6667	5½	0.0909	0.1818	14	0.0357	0.0714
1¾	0.2857	0.5714	6	0.0833	0.1667	15	0.0333	0.0667
2	0.2500	0.5000	7	0.0714	0.1429	16	0.0312	0.0625
2½	0.2000	0.4000	8	0.0625	0.1250	18	0.0278	0.0556
3	0.1667	0.3333	9	0.0556	0.1111	20	0.0250	0.0500
3½	0.1429	0.2857	10	0.0500	0.1000	22	0.0227	0.0455
4	0.1250	0.2500	11	0.0455	0.0909	24	0.0208	0.0417

Difficulties in Cutting Square Threads with Taps and Dies. — The square form of thread is usually made about twice as coarse in pitch as the American standard threads. Partly for this reason and also because of the perpendicular walls of the thread, it is a troublesome thread to cut with taps and dies. Difficulties are also met with when more than one cut is made for producing the finished thread, owing to the succeeding taps or dies not having a lead exactly like the one of the partly cut thread, and hence the thread already formed is cut away. On account of these difficulties, the square thread, which was formerly used to a great extent on adjusting and power conveying screws, has been replaced in many cases, by screws provided with Acme threads because the Acme form is much easier to produce.

American Standard 10-Degree Modified Square Thread. — The included angle between the sides of the thread is 10 degrees (see accompanying diagram). The angle of 10 degrees results in a thread which is the practical equivalent of a "square thread," and yet is capable of economical production. Multiple thread milling cutters and ground thread taps should not be specified for modified square threads of the larger lead angles without consulting the cutting tool manufacturer.

Formulas: In the following formulas, D = basic major diameter; E = basic pitch diameter; K = basic minor diameter; p = pitch; h = basic depth of thread on screw (depth when there is no clearance between root of screw and crest of thread on nut); t = basic thickness of thread at pitch line; F = basic width of flat at crest of screw thread; G = basic width of flat at root of screw thread; C = clearance between root of screw and crest of thread on nut.

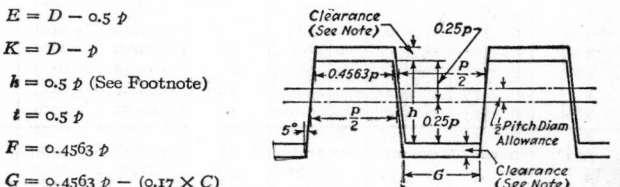

$$E = D - 0.5\,p$$

$$K = D - p$$

$$h = 0.5\,p \text{ (See Footnote)}$$

$$t = 0.5\,p$$

$$F = 0.4563\,p$$

$$G = 0.4563\,p - (0.17 \times C)$$

Note: A clearance should be added to depth h to avoid interference with threads of mating parts at minor or major diameters. The amount of clearance depends upon the application of the thread assembly.

American Standard General Purpose Acme Thread

Size	Threads per Inch *	Major Diameter		Pitch Diameter		Minor Diameter		Lead Angle, Deg. Min.
		Max.	Min.††	Max.	Min.	Max.†	Min.††	
		SCREW DIMENSIONS						
¼	16	0.2500	0.2469	0.2187	0.2087	0.1775	0.1744	5°12′
5⁄16	14	0.3125	0.3089	0.2768	0.2668	0.2311	0.2275	4°42′
3⁄8	12	0.3750	0.3708	0.3333	0.3233	0.2816	0.2774	4°33′
7⁄16	12	0.4375	0.4333	0.3958	0.3858	0.3441	0.3399	3°50′
½	10	0.5000	0.4950	0.4500	0.4400	0.3800	0.3750	4° 3′
5⁄8	8	0.6250	0.6187	0.5625	0.5495	0.4800	0.4737	4° 3′
¾	6	0.7500	0.7417	0.6667	0.6537	0.5633	0.5550	4°33′
7⁄8	6	0.8750	0.8667	0.7917	0.7757	0.6883	0.6800	3°50′
I	5	1.0000	0.9900	0.9000	0.8840	0.7800	0.7700	4° 3′
1⅛	5	1.1250	1.1150	1.0250	1.0060	0.9050	0.8950	3°33′
1¼	5	1.2500	1.2400	1.1500	1.1310	1.0300	1.0200	3°10′
1⅜	4	1.3750	1.3625	1.2500	1.2280	1.1050	1.0925	3°39′
1½	4	1.5000	1.4875	1.3750	1.3530	1.2300	1.2175	3°19′
1¾	4	1.7500	1.7375	1.6250	1.6000	1.4800	1.4675	2°48′
2	4	2.0000	1.9875	1.8750	1.8470	1.7300	1.7175	2°26′
2¼	3	2.2500	2.2333	2.0833	2.0523	1.8967	1.8800	2°55′
2½	3	2.5000	2.4833	2.3333	2.2993	2.1467	2.1300	2°43′
2¾	3	2.7500	2.7333	2.5833	2.5463	2.3967	2.3800	2°21′
3	2	3.0000	2.9750	2.7500	2.7100	2.4800	2.4550	3°19′
4	2	4.0000	3.9750	3.7500	3.7070	3.4800	3.4550	2°26′
5	2	5.0000	4.9750	4.7500	4.7070	4.4800	4.4550	1°55′
		NUT DIMENSIONS						
¼	16	......	0.2600	0.2337	0.2237	0.1906	0.1875	5°12′
5⁄16	14	......	0.3225	0.2918	0.2818	0.2447	0.2411	4°42′
3⁄8	12	......	0.3850	0.3483	0.3383	0.2959	0.2917	4°33′
7⁄16	12	......	0.4475	0.4108	0.4008	0.3584	0.3542	3°50′
½	10	......	0.5200	0.4650	0.4550	0.4050	0.4000	4° 3′
5⁄8	8	......	0.6450	0.5805	0.5675	0.5063	0.5000	4° 3′
¾	6	......	0.7700	0.6847	0.6717	0.5917	0.5833	4°33′
7⁄8	6	......	0.8950	0.8127	0.7967	0.7167	0.7083	3°50′
I	5	......	1.0200	0.9210	0.9050	0.8100	0.8000	4° 3′
1⅛	5	......	1.1450	1.0490	1.0300	0.9350	0.9250	3°33′
1¼	5	......	1.2700	1.1740	1.1550	1.0600	1.0500	3°10′
1⅜	4	......	1.3950	1.2770	1.2550	1.1375	1.1250	3°39′
1½	4	......	1.5200	1.4020	1.3800	1.2625	1.2500	3°19′
1¾	4	......	1.7700	1.6550	1.6300	1.5125	1.5000	2°48′
2	4	......	2.0200	1.9080	1.8800	1.7625	1.7500	2°26′
2¼	3	......	2.2700	2.1213	2.0903	1.9334	1.9167	2°55′
2½	3	......	2.5200	2.3743	2.3403	2.1834	2.1667	2°43′
2¾	3	......	2.7700	2.6273	2.5903	2.4334	2.4167	2°21′
3	2	......	3.0200	2.8000	2.7600	2.5250	2.5000	3°19′
4	2	......	4.0200	3.8030	3.7600	3.5250	3.5000	2°26′
5	2	......	5.0200	4.8030	4.7600	4.5250	4.5000	1°55′

Basic Dimensions: Maximum major and pitch diameters of screw; minimum minor diameter of nut.

* The number of threads per inch is recommended practice and is intended eventually to result in an established standard.

† Maximum minor diameter of a screw of given pitch is such as to result in a flat at the root equal in inches to 0.3707 p − (0.52 × clearance) when the pitch diameter of the screw is at its maximum value.

†† These dimensions result in tolerances on major and minor diameters equal to 0.05 × pitch.

American Standard Acme and Other Translating Threads. — This standard covers the design and dimensions of Acme and similar screw threads intended primarily for "translating screws," or those which traverse some slide, carriage or other driven part (motion of translation). Four series of translating screw threads are included in this standard: the General Purpose Acme Thread, the 29-Degree

American Standard General Purpose Acme Thread

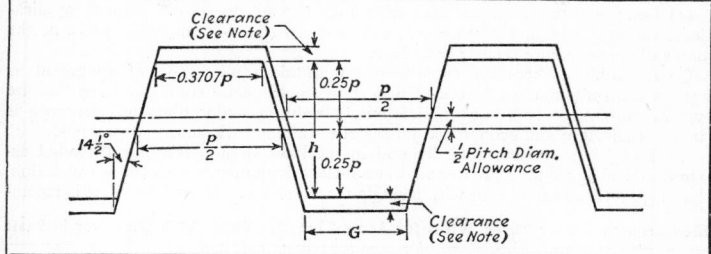

Thread Dimensions for Standard and Special Pitches

Threads per Inch	Pitch, Inch p	Depth of Thread (Basic) h	Total Depth of Thread *	Thickness (Basic)	Width of Flat at Crest of Screw (Basic)	Width of Flat at Root of Screw G
16	0.06250	0.0313	0.0363	0.0313	0.0232	0.0206
14	0.07143	0.0357	0.0407	0.0357	0.0265	0.0239
12	0.08333	0.0417	0.0467	0.0417	0.0309	0.0283
10	0.10000	0.0500	0.0600	0.0500	0.0371	0.0319
9	0.11111	0.0556	0.0656	0.0556	0.0412	0.0360
8	0.12500	0.0625	0.0725	0.0625	0.0463	0.0411
7	0.14286	0.0714	0.0814	0.0714	0.0530	0.0478
6	0.16667	0.0833	0.0933	0.0833	0.0618	0.0566
5	0.20000	0.1000	0.1100	0.1000	0.0741	0.0689
4	0.25000	0.1250	0.1350	0.1250	0.0927	0.0875
3½	0.28571	0.1429	0.1529	0.1429	0.1059	0.1007
3	0.33333	0.1667	0.1767	0.1667	0.1236	0.1184
2½	0.40000	0.2000	0.2100	0.2000	0.1483	0.1431
2	0.50000	0.2500	0.2600	0.2500	0.1853	0.1801
1½	0.66667	0.3333	0.3433	0.3333	0.2471	0.2419
1⅓	0.75000	0.3750	0.3850	0.3750	0.2780	0.2728
1	1.00000	0.5000	0.5100	0.5000	0.3707	0.3655

* A clearance of at least 0.010 inch is added to depth h on threads of 10 per inch and coarser, and 0.005 inch on finer pitches, to produce extra depth, thus avoiding interference with threads of mating parts at minor or major diameters. (Widths G of flat at root, as given in last column, apply to these minimum clearances.) It is recognized that there are conditions where a greater or less clearance may be desirable.

Basic depth $h = 0.5 \times$ pitch p; thread thickness at pitch line $= 0.5 \times$ pitch p; basic width of flat at crest of screw $= 0.3707 \times$ pitch p; width G of flat at root $= 0.3707 \times p -$ (0.52 $\times$ clearance); basic pitch diameter $=$ basic major diameter $- 0.5 \times$ pitch p.

Stub Thread, the 60-Degree Stub Thread, and a Modified Square Thread. The subject of Acme and kindred threads embraces a wide field and it is not possible to combine in a single standard all of the variables of all the uses. The following applications are recognized as common usages, but each may have special features which prevent inclusion in a general purpose standard.

(1) Feed- or lead-screws where backlash or end shake are objectionable. In such applications the nut is tapped first and then the screw is threaded to fit. The screw and nut so made are kept as a pair.

(2) Long lead-screws where sagging causes threads to seize. In such applications, the major diameter clearance is reduced so that bearing takes place at the major diameter before seizing can occur.

(3) Assemblies where the thread must maintain some degree of alignment as well as transmit motion. Desk chairs, shop stools, piano stools, and the like are typical examples. In these applications, a reduced major diameter clearance is the most effective and economical means of obtaining satisfactory assemblies.

(4) There is a considerable demand in mechanical industries for threaded assemblies which provide a greater advance of the driven member per screw revolution, than is practicable to obtain with a single-thread screw. In such cases, it is recom-

Measurements Over Three Wires for Acme Threads When Pitch Diameter is Basic

Size	Threads per Inch	Pitch Diameter (Basic)	Diameter Wires	Measurement Over Wires	Pitch Constant = 1.933355 p
¼	16	0.218,750	0.03500	0.27324	0.120,835
5⁄16	14	0.276,786	0.04000	0.33895	0.138,097
3⁄8	12	0.333,333	0.04500	0.39748	0.161,113
7⁄16	12	0.395,833	0.04500	0.45983	0.161,113
½	10	0.450,000	0.06000	0.55686	0.193,336
5⁄8	8	0.562,500	0.07000	0.67106	0.241,670
¾	6	0.666,667	0.09000	0.79496	0.322,226
7⁄8	6	0.791,667	0.09000	0.91965	0.322,226
1	5	0.900,000	0.11000	1.06369	0.386,671
1⅛	5	1.025,000	0.11000	1.18846	0.386,671
1¼	5	1.150,000	0.11000	1.31329	0.386,671
1⅜	4	1.250,000	0.13000	1.41686	0.483,339
1½	4	1.375,000	0.13000	1.54169	0.483,339
1¾	4	1.625,000	0.13000	1.79146	0.483,339
2	4	1.875,000	0.13000	2.04131	0.483,339
2¼	3	2.083,333	0.18000	2.33866	0.644,452
2½	3	2.333,333	0.18000	2.58849	0.644,452
2¾	3	2.583,333	0.18000	2.83836	0.644,452
3	2	2.750,000	0.25000	3.03337	0.966,678
4	2	3.750,000	0.25000	4.03265	0.966,678
5	2	4.750,000	0.25000	5.03233	0.966,678

Note: These measurements apply to single threads. For multiple threads or other diameter and pitch combinations, with resulting changes in lead angles, use the following formula in which S = tan lead angle.

$$\text{Measurement over wires} = (1.871778 \times S^2 + 4.993929) \times \text{wire diameter} + \text{pitch diameter} - \text{pitch constant}$$

To use larger or smaller wires than in above table: First calculate measurement, using wire size given in table; then either add to, or subtract from, the calculated wire measurement, an amount equal to the difference in wire diameters multiplied by 4.9939.

mended that no coarser thread for a given diameter than those listed (see table, page 1000) be used but instead that a multiple thread giving the desired lead be employed. Many applications in the valve industry are typical.

American Standard Acme General Purpose Thread. — The included angle between the sides of the thread is 29 degrees. This thread series should be used for all Acme thread applications except in special cases where design or operating considerations are such that the 29-Degree Stub, the 60-Degree Stub, or some other modified thread can be employed to better advantage. Dimensions of the Acme General Purpose Thread are given in an accompanying table.

American Standard 29-Degree Stub Thread. — The included angle between the sides of the thread is 29 degrees as in the case of the general purpose Acme series and the threads are truncated top and bottom, but the basic depth of thread is reduced to 0.30 of the pitch. The basic thread thickness is one-half the pitch as

American Standard 29-Degree Stub Thread

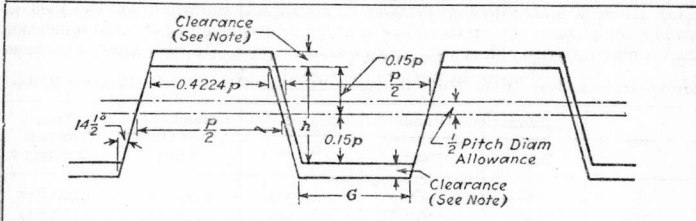

Threads per Inch	Pitch, Inch p	Depth of Thread (Basic) h	Total Depth of Thread *	Thickness (Basic)	Width of Flat at Crest of Screw (Basic)	Width of Flat at Root of Screw G
16	0.06250	0.0188	0.0238	0.0313	0.0264	0.0238
14	0.07143	0.0214	0.0264	0.0357	0.0302	0.0276
12	0.08333	0.0250	0.0300	0.0417	0.0352	0.0326
10	0.10000	0.0300	0.0400	0.0500	0.0422	0.0370
9	0.11111	0.0333	0.0433	0.0556	0.0469	0.0417
8	0.12500	0.0375	0.0475	0.0625	0.0528	0.0476
7	0.14286	0.0429	0.0529	0.0714	0.0603	0.0551
6	0.16667	0.0500	0.0600	0.0833	0.0704	0.0652
5	0.20000	0.0600	0.0700	0.1000	0.0845	0.0793
4	0.25000	0.0750	0.0850	0.1250	0.1056	0.1004
3½	0.28571	0.0857	0.0957	0.1429	0.1207	0.1155
3	0.33333	0.1000	0.1100	0.1667	0.1408	0.1356
2½	0.40000	0.1200	0.1300	0.2000	0.1690	0.1638
2	0.50000	0.1500	0.1600	0.2500	0.2112	0.2060

* A clearance of at least 0.010 inch is added to depth h on threads of 10 per inch and coarser, and 0.005 inch on finer pitches, to produce extra depth thus avoiding interference with threads of mating part at minor or major diameters. It is recognized that there are conditions where a greater or less clearance may be desirable.

Basic depth = 0.3 × pitch p; basic thickness at pitch line = 0.5 × pitch p; basic width of flat at crest of screw = 0.4224 × pitch p; width G of flat at root of screw = 0.4224 × pitch p − (0.52 × clearance); basic minor diameter = basic major diameter − (0.6 × pitch p).

before, and the threads are symmetrical about a line perpendicular to the axis of the screw. This produces a very strong thread section and, in addition, a thread admirably suited to applications where space limitations or other economic considerations make a shallow thread desirable. For dimensions see table.

American Standard 60-Degree Stub Thread. — The included angle between the sides of the thread is 60 degrees. The threads are truncated top and bottom, have a basic depth of 0.433 of the pitch, a basic thickness of one-half the pitch, and are symmetrical about a line perpendicular to the axis of the screw. See table.

Tolerances for American Standard Translating Threads. — The tolerances on diameters of the nuts or threaded holes are plus, and are applied from the minimum nut sizes to above the minimum nut sizes. The tolerances on diameters of the screws are minus, and are applied from the maximum screw sizes to below the maximum screw sizes. The tolerances on the thicknesses of threads are minus, and are applied from the maximum thread thickness to below the maximum thread thickness. The thread thickness tolerances for a screw and nut of the same diameter and pitch are equal. The thread thickness tolerances include lead and angle errors. The tolerances on the major diameters of the screws and minor diameters of the nuts are based upon the pitch of the thread.

American Standard 60-Degree Stub Thread

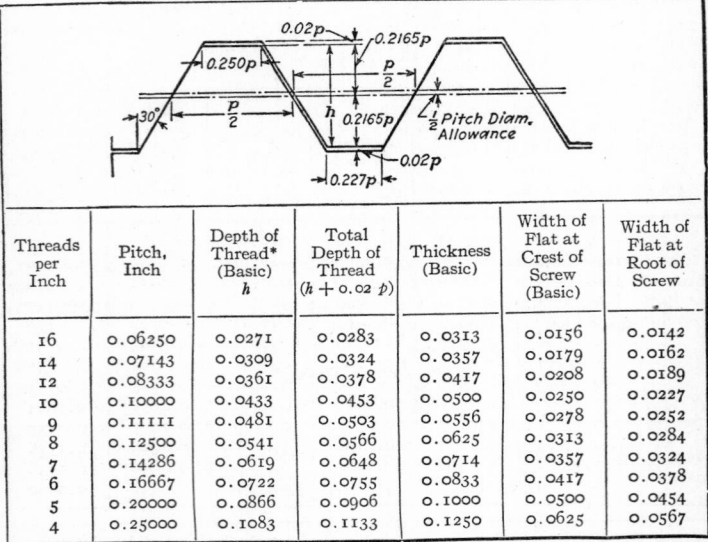

Threads per Inch	Pitch, Inch	Depth of Thread* (Basic) h	Total Depth of Thread ($h + 0.02\ p$)	Thickness (Basic)	Width of Flat at Crest of Screw (Basic)	Width of Flat at Root of Screw
16	0.06250	0.0271	0.0283	0.0313	0.0156	0.0142
14	0.07143	0.0309	0.0324	0.0357	0.0179	0.0162
12	0.08333	0.0361	0.0378	0.0417	0.0208	0.0189
10	0.10000	0.0433	0.0453	0.0500	0.0250	0.0227
9	0.11111	0.0481	0.0503	0.0556	0.0278	0.0252
8	0.12500	0.0541	0.0566	0.0625	0.0313	0.0284
7	0.14286	0.0619	0.0648	0.0714	0.0357	0.0324
6	0.16667	0.0722	0.0755	0.0833	0.0417	0.0378
5	0.20000	0.0866	0.0906	0.1000	0.0500	0.0454
4	0.25000	0.1083	0.1133	0.1250	0.0625	0.0567

* A clearance of at least 0.02 × pitch is added to depth h to produce extra depth, thus avoiding interference with threads of mating part at minor or major diameters.

Basic thread thickness at pitch line = 0.5 × pitch p; basic depth h = 0.433 × pitch; basic width of flat at crest = 0.25 × pitch; width of flat at root of screw thread = 0.227 × pitch; basic pitch diameter = basic major diameter − 0.433 × pitch; basic minor diameter = basic major diameter − 0.866 × pitch.

29-degree Worm Thread. — This worm thread resembles the Acme thread, in that the angle between the sides of the thread equals 29 degrees. The depth of thread, and width of the flat at top and bottom, differ. Multiple threaded worms may have thread angles up to 60 degrees. See Worm Gearing.

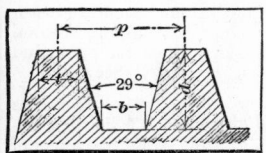

$$p = \text{pitch} = \frac{1}{\text{No. of threads per inch}}$$

$$d = \text{depth of thread} = 0.6866 \, p$$

$$= \frac{0.6866}{\text{No. of threads per inch}}$$

$$t = \text{width at top of thread} = 0.335 \, p;$$

$$b = \text{width at bottom of thread} = 0.310 \, p.$$

Elements of the 29-degree Worm Thread

Threads per Inch	Depth of Thread	Width of Flat at Top of Thread	Width of Flat at Bottom of Thread	Double Depth of Thread	Threads per Inch	Depth of Thread	Width of Flat at Top of Thread	Width of Flat at Bottom of Thread	Double Depth of Thread
1	0.6866	0.3350	0.3100	1.3732	5	0.1373	0.0670	0.0620	0.2746
1¼	0.5492	0.2680	0.2480	1.0984	6	0.1144	0.0558	0.0517	0.2289
1½	0.4577	0.2233	0.2066	0.9144	7	0.0981	0.0479	0.0443	0.1962
2	0.3433	0.1675	0.1550	0.6866	8	0.0858	0.0419	0.0388	0.1716
2½	0.2746	0.1340	0.1240	0.5492	9	0.0763	0.0372	0.0344	0.1526
3	0.2289	0.1117	0.1033	0.4577	10	0.0687	0.0335	0.0310	0.1373
3½	0.1962	0.0957	0.0886	0.3924	12	0.0572	0.0279	0.0258	0.1144
4	0.1716	0.0838	0.0775	0.3433	16	0.0429	0.0209	0.0194	0.0858
4½	0.1526	0.0744	0.0689	0.3052	20	0.0343	0.0167	0.0155	0.0687

Gas Fixture Threads. — Thin brass tubing is threaded with 27 threads per inch, irrespective of diameter. The so-called "ornament brass sizes" have 32 threads per inch. The standard sizes of the thread are 0.196 inch (large ornament brass size) and 0.148 inch (small ornament brass size).

Gas Fixture Threads

(Brass Pipe Sizes)

Nominal Size	Actual Diam. of Thread	Threads per Inch	Nominal Size	Actual Diam. of Thread	Threads per Inch	Nominal Size	Actual Diam. of Thread	Threads per Inch
0.148	0.148	32	⅜	0.390	27	¾	0.770	27
0.196	0.196	32	⁷⁄₁₆	0.459	27	⅞	0.885	27
No. 4	0.246	27	½	0.515	27	1	1.006	27
¼	0.260	27	⁹⁄₁₆	0.578	27	.....	.....	.....
⁵⁄₁₆	0.342	27	⅝	0.637	27	.....	.....	.....

Trapezoidal Metric Thread — DIN. Standard No. 103, Normal Series

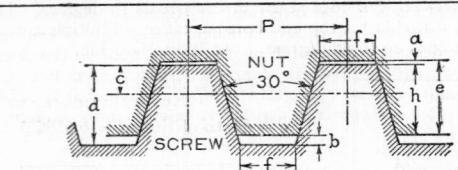

$$d = 0.5P + a; \quad f = 0.634P - 0.536d; \quad e = 0.5P + 2a - b; \quad c = 0.25P$$

Pitch, mm. P	Depth of Thread, mm. d	Contact Depth, mm. h	Clearance, mm.		Rounding, mm. (Optional)	Depth of Nut Thread, mm. e
			a	b		
3	1.75	1.25	0.25	0.5	0.25	1.50
4	2.25	1.75	0.25	0.5	0.25	2.00
5	2.75	2	0.25	0.75	0.25	2.25
6	3.25	2.5	0.25	0.75	0.25	2.75
7	3.75	3	0.25	0.75	0.25	3.25
8	4.25	3.5	0.25	0.75	0.25	3.75
9	4.75	4	0.25	0.75	0.25	4.25
10	5.25	4.5	0.25	0.75	0.25	4.75
12	6.25	5.5	0.25	0.75	0.25	5.75
14	7.5	6	0.5	1.5	0.5	6.5
16	8.5	7	0.5	1.5	0.5	7.5
18	9.5	8	0.5	1.5	0.5	8.5
20	10.5	9	0.5	1.5	0.5	9.5
22	11.5	10	0.5	1.5	0.5	10.5
24	12.5	11	0.5	1.5	0.5	11.5
26	13.5	12	0.5	1.5	0.5	12.5

Progress System Thread

Size Number	Diameter, mm.	Pitch, mm.	Size Number	Diameter, mm.	Pitch, mm.	
4	0.40	0.100	9½	0.95	0.225	....
4½	0.45	0.100	10	1.0	0.250	....
5	0.50	0.125	11	1.1	0.275	....
5½	0.55	0.125	12	1.2	0.300	....
6	0.60	0.150	13	1.3	0.325	....
6½	0.65	0.150	14	1.4	0.350	....
7	0.70	0.175	15	1.5	0.375	....
7½	0.75	0.175	16	1.6	0.32	0.457
8	0.80	0.200	17	1.7	0.34	0.486
8½	0.85	0.200	18	1.8	0.36	0.514
9	0.90	0.225	19	1.9	0.38	0.543
			20	2.0	0.40	0.571

Originated in Switzerland and used for watch screws. Included thread angle, 50 degrees. Depth of thread = 0.8 × pitch. Clearance or depth of rounding = 0.093 × pitch. Radius = 0.0732 × pitch.

Threads of Buttress Form. — Screw threads of the buttress type are designed to resist heavy axial loads in one direction. Diagram *A* shows a common form. The front or load-resisting face is perpendicular to the axis of the screw and the thread angle is 45 degrees. The pitch of the thread may be the same as for the American standard or the Whitworth standard. According to one rule, the pitch $P = 2 \times$ screw diameter $\div$ 15. The thread depth d may equal $\frac{3}{4} \times$ pitch, making the flat $f = \frac{1}{8} \times$ pitch. Sometimes depth d is reduced to $\frac{2}{3} \times$ pitch, making flat $f = \frac{1}{6} \times$ pitch.

Buttress Threads with Load-resisting Side Inclined. — The load-resisting side or flank may be inclined an amount (diagram *B*) ranging usually from 1 to 5 degrees to avoid cutter interference in milling the thread. With an angle of 5 degrees and an included thread angle of 50 degrees, if the width of the flat f at both crest and

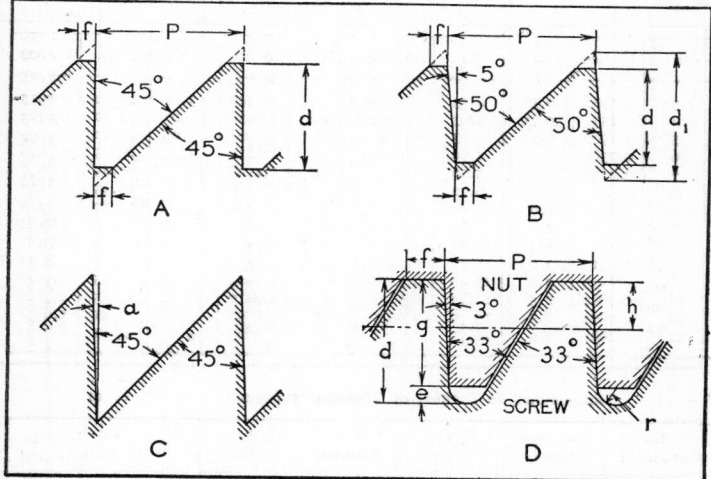

root equals $\frac{1}{8} \times$ pitch, then the thread depth equals 0.86777 $\times$ pitch or $\frac{3}{4}$ d_1. Diagram *C* shows a buttress thread of the sharp vee form with a front face angle a of 1 degree; some flat or rounding, however, at the crest and root of any screw thread is preferable.

Saw-Tooth Thread. — The saw-tooth form of thread illustrated by diagram *D* is known in Germany as the "Sägengewinde" and in Italy as the "Fillettatura a dente di Sega." Pitches are standardized from 2 millimeters up to 48 millimeters in the German and Italian specifications. The front face inclines 3 degrees from the perpendicular and the included angle is 33 degrees.

The thread depth d for the screw = 0.86777 $\times$ pitch P. The thread depth g for the nut = 0.75 $\times$ pitch. Dimension h = 0.341 $\times P$. The width f of flat at the crest of the thread on the screw = 0.26384 $\times$ pitch. Radius r at the root = 0.12427 $\times$ pitch. The clearance space e between the root of the screw thread and the crest of the nut = 0.11777 $\times$ pitch.

German Metric Thread. — This thread form is similar to the International Standard, excepting that the depth = 0.6945 × pitch and the clearance between crest and root = 0.045 × pitch; hence the core diameters are somewhat larger than those of the International Standard which has a depth of 0.703 646 × pitch and a maximum clearance equal to 0.054 × pitch. Radius of fillet at the root of the German metric thread = 0.0633 × pitch. The standard (DIN. 14) includes diameters from 6 to 149 millimeters. Pitches and effective diameters for sizes from 6 to 12 millimeters are given in the table International Metric Thread System.

French Thread (S.F.) — The French thread has the same form and proportions as the American standard (formerly U. S. standard). This French thread is being displaced gradually by the International Metric Thread System.

French Standard Thread

Diameter		Pitch, Mm.	Root Diameter		Diameter		Pitch, Mm.	Root Diameter	
Mm.	Inches		Mm.	Inches	Mm.	Inches		Mm.	Inches
3	0.1181	0.5	2.35	0.0925	24	0.9449	3.0	20.10	0.7915
4	0.1575	0.75	3.03	0.1191	26	1.0236	3.0	22.10	0.8702
5	0.1969	0.75	4.03	0.1585	28	1.1024	3.0	24.10	0.9490
6	0.2362	1.0	4.70	0.1851	30	1.1811	3.5	25.45	1.0020
7	0.2756	1.0	5.70	0.2245	32	1.2598	3.5	27.45	1.0807
8	0.3150	1.0	6.70	0.2639	34	1.3386	3.5	29.45	1.1595
9	0.3543	1.0	7.70	0.3032	36	1.4173	4.0	30.80	1.2126
10	0.3937	1.5	8.05	0.3170	38	1.4961	4.0	32.80	1.2914
12	0.4724	1.5	10.05	0.3957	40	1.5748	4.0	34.80	1.3701
14	0.5512	2.0	11.40	0.4489	42	1.6535	4.5	36.15	1.4232
16	0.6299	2.0	13.40	0.5276	44	1.7323	4.5	38.15	1.5020
18	0.7087	2.5	14.75	0.5808	46	1.8110	4.5	40.15	1.5807
20	0.7874	2.5	16.75	0.6595	48	1.8898	5.0	41.51	1.6343
22	0.8661	2.5	18.75	0.7382	50	1.9685	5.0	43.51	1.7130

Dimensions, in Inches, of Threads of French Standard Form

Pitch, Mm.	Depth of Thread, Inches	Width of Flat, Inches	Double Depth of Thread, Inches	Pitch, Mm.	Depth of Thread, Inches	Width of Flat, Inches	Double Depth of Thread, Inches
6.5	0.1662	0.0320	0.3324	2.5	0.0639	0.0123	0.1279
6	0.1534	0.0295	0.3068	2.25	0.0575	0.0111	0.1151
5.75	0.1470	0.0283	0.2940	2	0.0511	0.0098	0.1023
5.5	0.1406	0.0271	0.2812	1.75	0.0448	0.0086	0.0895
5.25	0.1343	0.0259	0.2685	1.5	0.0384	0.0074	0.0767
5	0.1279	0.0246	0.2557	1.25	0.0320	0.0062	0.0639
4.75	0.1215	0.0234	0.2429	1	0.0256	0.0049	0.0511
4.5	0.1151	0.0221	0.2301	0.9	0.0230	0.0044	0.0460
4.25	0.1087	0.0209	0.2174	0.85	0.0217	0.0042	0.0435
4	0.1023	0.0197	0.2046	0.8	0.0205	0.0039	0.0409
3.75	0.0959	0.0185	0.1918	0.75	0.0192	0.0037	0.0384
3.5	0.0895	0.0172	0.1790	0.7	0.0179	0.0034	0.0358
3.25	0.0831	0.0160	0.1662	0.6	0.0153	0.0030	0.0307
3	0.0767	0.0148	0.1534	0.55	0.0141	0.0027	0.0281
2.75	0.0703	0.0135	0.1406	0.5	0.0128	0.0025	0.0256

French Standard for Metric Threads

This series conforms to the specification of the Comité de Normalisation de la Mécanique. The thread form is the same as the International system. The accompanying table does not include sizes between 6 and 90 millimeters because these are the same as the International system. For sizes under 3 millimeters, the thread angle may be either 50 or 60 degrees. The thread depth = 0.704 × pitch and the clearance between the root of the thread and the mating crest = 0.054 × pitch. Sizes above 100 mm. increase by 5 mm.

Major Diam., mm.	Pitch, mm.	Effective or Pitch Diam.	Minor or Core Diam.	Major Diam., mm.	Pitch, mm.	Effective or Pitch, Diam.	Minor or Core Diam.
0.3	0.075	0.251	0.194	1.6	0.300	1.405	1.180
0.35	0.075	0.301	0.244	1.8	0.400	1.540	1.240
0.4	0.100	0.335	0.259	2	0.400	1.740	1.440
0.45	0.100	0.385	0.309	2.2	0.450	1.907	1.570
0.5	0.125	0.419	0.324	2.5	0.450	2.207	1.870
0.55	0.125	0.469	0.374	3	0.6	2.610	2.16
0.6	0.150	0.502	0.389	4	0.75	3.513	2.94
0.7	0.150	0.602	0.489	5	0.9	4.415	3.73
0.8	0.200	0.670	0.518	6	1	5.350	4.59
0.9	0.200	0.770	0.618				
1	0.250	0.837	0.650	90	6	86.103	81.56
1.2	0.250	1.037	0.850	95	6	91.103	86.56
1.4	0.300	1.205	0.980	100	6	96.103	91.56

Watch Screw Threads

Waltham Watch Co.			Elgin National Watch Co.					
Diam. of Thread, Inch	Diam. of Thread, Millimeters	Threads per Inch	Diam., Inch	Diam., Millimeters	Threads per Inch	Diam., Inch	Diam., Millimeters	Threads per Inch
0.0591	1.50	110	0.0132	0.33	360	0.0428	1.07	120
0.0473	1.20	110	0.0148	0.37	320	0.0448	1.12	110
0.0433	1.10	120	0.0168	0.42	260	0.0468	1.17	110
0.0394	1.00	140	0.0208	0.52	220	0.0488	1.22	140
0.0366	0.93	160	0.0228	0.57	260	0.0488	1.22	200
0.0528	1.34	170	0.0248	0.62	220	0.0508	1.27	110*
0.0394	1.00	180	0.0268	0.67	180	0.0548	1.37	180
0.0327	0.83	180	0.0288	0.72	220	0.0608	1.52	110
0.0256	0.65	200	0.0308	0.77	180	0.0608	1.52	110*
0.0217	0.55	220	0.0308	0.77	220	0.0708	1.77	180*
0.0177	0.45	240	0.0368	0.92	140	0.0768	1.92	110*
0.0138	0.35	254	0.0368	0.92	220	0.0772	1.93	80*
.....	......	.....	0.0408	1.02	120*	0.0892	2.23	80*
.....	......	.....	0.0408	1.02	200	....	.....	.....

Note: Asterisk (*) indicates left-hand threads.

American National Standard Gas Cylinder Valve Outlet

Type of Cyl. Valve Note(a)	Designation of Thread See Note (b)	Major Diam. Max.	Major Diam. Min.	Pitch Diam. Max.	Pitch Diam. Min.	Minor Diam. Max.	Thread Length, Min.
1	0.903″ — 14 NS-3	0.9030	0.8932	0.8566	0.8530	0.8154	5⁄8
2	0.830″ — 14 NS-2 LH	0.8300	0.8200	0.7836	0.7786	0.7424	5⁄8
3	½″ — 14 NPS form	0.8350	0.8290	0.7780	0.7740	......	..
4	½″ — 14 NPS form	0.8350	0.8290	0.7780	0.7740	......	..
5	⅜″ — 18 NPT (internal)	......	......	......	......	......	..
6	¾″ — 14 NPS form	1.031	1.025	0.9717	0.9677	......	..

Note a. The figures in the first column represent the following types of cylinder valves: (1) Oxygen, carbon-dioxide, or air; (2) Hydrogen, nitrogen, or helium; (3) Acetylene; (4) Ethyl-chloride; (5) Anhydrous ammonia; (6) Dichlorodifluoromethane.

Note b. Symbol NS represents American National Thread Form but special pitch; LH, left hand; NPS, American National Standard Straight Pipe Thread; NPT, American Standard Taper Pipe Thread. All threads are external except for anhydrous ammonia and all are right-hand except on valves for hydrogen, nitrogen or helium.

American National Standard Hose Connections for Welding and Cutting Torches

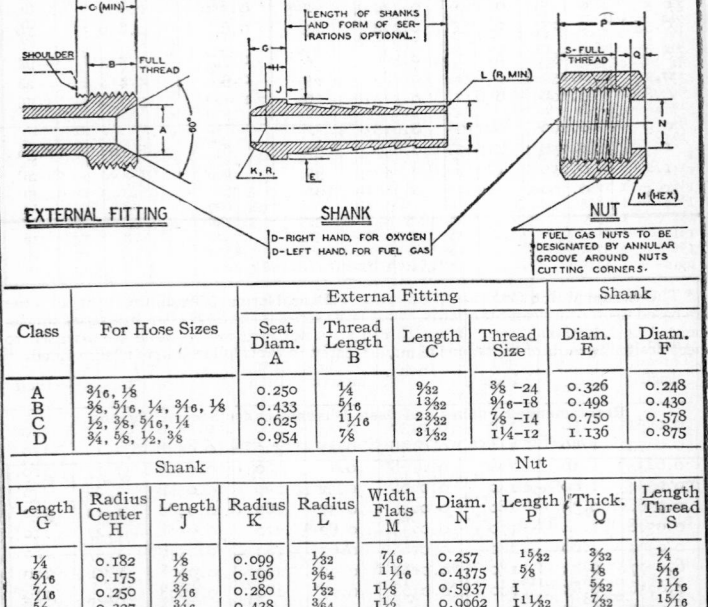

EXTERNAL FITTING   SHANK   NUT

D—RIGHT HAND, FOR OXYGEN
D—LEFT HAND, FOR FUEL GAS

FUEL GAS NUTS TO BE DESIGNATED BY ANNULAR GROOVE AROUND NUTS CUTTING CORNERS.

		External Fitting				Shank	
Class	For Hose Sizes	Seat Diam. A	Thread Length B	Length C	Thread Size	Diam. E	Diam. F
A	3⁄16, ⅛	0.250	¼	9⁄32	⅜ –24	0.326	0.248
B	⅜, 5⁄16, ¼, 3⁄16, ⅛	0.433	5⁄16	13⁄32	9⁄16–18	0.498	0.430
C	½, ⅜, 5⁄16, ¼	0.625	11⁄16	23⁄32	⅞ –14	0.750	0.578
D	¾, ⅝, ½, ⅜	0.954	⅞	31⁄32	1¼–12	1.136	0.875

Shank					Nut				
Length G	Radius Center H	Length J	Radius K	Radius L	Width Flats M	Diam. N	Length P	Thick. Q	Length Thread S
¼	0.182	⅛	0.099	1⁄32	7⁄16	0.257	15⁄32	3⁄32	¼
5⁄16	0.175	⅛	0.196	3⁄64	11⁄16	0.4375	⅝	⅛	5⁄16
7⁄16	0.250	3⁄16	0.280	1⁄32	1⅛	0.5937	1	5⁄32	11⁄16
⅝	0.327	3⁄16	0.438	3⁄64	1½	0.9062	1 1⁄32	7⁄32	15⁄16

Screw threads are American National form, fine-thread series and Class 3 fit. *Right-hand threads are specified for oxygen and left-hand threads for fuel gas.*

Tolerances: Dimension A ±.005 for Classes A to C inclusive, and ±.008 for Class D; dimension E ±.002 for Classes A and B and ±.004 for Classes C and D; dimension F −.005 for Classes A and B and −.010 for Classes C and D; radius H ±.005 for Classes A to C inclusive and ±0.008 for class D; diameter N +.003 −000 for Classes A and B; +.006 −.003 for Class C and +.006 −.002 for Class D.

Aeronautical Screw-thread Series*

Recommended selections from standard thread series for use in aircraft and aeronautical equipment — Data from "Screw Thread Standards for Federal Services" issued 1942 by U. S. Department of Commerce.

Size and Basic Major Diam.	Thread Series					Size and Basic Major Diam.	Thread Series			
	NC	NF	EF*	8N	12N		EF*	8N	12N	16N
	Threads per Inch						Threads per Inch			
0 — 0.0600		80	..	..	..	1½ — 1.5000	18	8	12	..
1 — 0.0730	64	72	..	..	..	1 9/16 — 1.5625	18	..	..	..
2 — 0.0860	56	64	..	..	..	1 5/8 — 1.6250	18	8	12	..
3 — 0.0990	48	56	..	..	..	1 11/16 — 1.6875	18	..	..	..
4 — 0.1120	40	48	..	..	..	1 ¾ — 1.7500	16	8	12	16
5 — 0.1250	40	44	..	..	..	1 13/16 — 1.8125	..	..	..	16
6 — 0.1380	32	40	..	..	..	1 7/8 — 1.8750	..	8	12	16
8 — 0.1640	32	36	..	..	..	1 15/16 — 1.9375	..	..	..	16
10 — 0.1900	24	32	..	..	..	2 — 2.0000	16	8	12	16
¼ — 0.2500	20	28	32	..	..	2 1/16 — 2.0625	..	..	..	16
5/16 — 0.3125	18	24	32	..	..	2 1/8 — 2.1250	..	8	12	16
3/8 — 0.3750	16	24	32	..	..	2 3/16 — 2.1875	..	..	..	16
7/16 — 0.4375	14	20	28	..	..	2 ¼ — 2.2500	..	8	12	16
½ — 0.5000	13	20	28	..	..	2 5/16 — 2.3125	..	..	..	16
9/16 — 0.5625	12	18	24	..	..	2 3/8 — 2.3750	..	..	12	16
5/8 — 0.6250	11	18	24	..	..	2 7/16 — 2.4375	..	..	..	16
11/16 — 0.6875	..	..	24	..	..	2 ½ — 2.5000	..	8	12	16
¾ — 0.7500	10	16	20	..	..	2 5/8 — 2.6250	..	..	12	16
13/16 — 0.8125	..	..	20	..	..	2 ¾ — 2.7500	..	8	12	16
7/8 — 0.8750	9	14	20	..	..	2 7/8 — 2.8750	..	..	12	16
15/16 — 0.9375	..	..	20	..	..	3 — 3.0000	..	8	12	16
1 — 1.0000	8	14	20	..	..	3 1/8 — 3.1250	..	..	12	16
1 1/16 — 1.0625	..	..	18	..	12	3 ¼ — 3.2500	..	8	12	16
1 1/8 — 1.1250	..	..	18	8	12	3 3/8 — 3.3750	..	..	12	16
1 3/16 — 1.1875	..	..	18	..	12	3 ½ — 3.5000	..	8	12	16
1 ¼ — 1.2500	..	..	18	8	12	3 5/8 — 3.6250	..	..	12	16
1 5/16 — 1.3125	..	..	18	..	12	3 ¾ — 3.7500	..	8	12	16
1 3/8 — 1.3750	..	..	18	8	12	3 7/8 — 3.8750	..	..	12	16
1 7/16 — 1.4375	..	..	18	..	12	4 — 4.0000	..	8	12	16

* The thread profile conforms to American National form. The different thread series are based upon American Standards. The (EF) series is the SAE extra-fine series supplemented by additional sizes. When thread sizes not included in table are essential to meet designing requirements, one of pitches listed in table following is recommended.

Recommended Pitches and Basic Dimensions for Special Threads

Data from "Screw Thread Standards for Federal Services"

Th'ds per Inch	Pitch	Depth of Th'd	Width of Flat		Th'ds per Inch	Pitch	Depth of Th'd	Width of Flat	
			Basic Width	Min. Nut*				Basic Width	Min. Nut*
64	.01562	.01015	.00195	.00065	18	.05556	.03608	.00694	.00231
56	.01786	.01160	.00223	.00074	16	.06250	.04059	.00781	.00260
48	.02083	.01353	.00260	.00087	14	.07143	.04639	.00893	.00298
40	.02500	.01624	.00312	.00104	12	.08333	.05413	.01042	.00347
36	.02778	.01804	.00347	.00116	10	.10000	.06495	.01250	.00417
32	.03125	.02030	.00391	.00130	8	.12500	.08119	.01562	.00521
28	.03571	.02320	.00446	.00149	6	.16667	.10825	.02083	.00694
24	.04167	.02706	.00521	.00174	4	.25000	.16238	.03125	.01042
20	.05000	.03248	.00625	.00208					

* The minimum width of flat for the nut applies to the major diameter and = pitch ÷ 24.

American Standard Taper Pipe Threads (ASA B2.1)

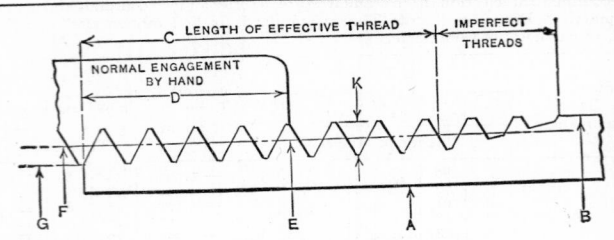

For all dimensions see corresponding reference letters in table.

Angle between sides of thread is 60 degrees.   Taper of thread, on diameter, is ¾ inch per foot.

The basic maximum thread depth, K, of the truncated thread is 0.8 × pitch of thread.   The crest and root are truncated a minimum of 0.033 × pitch for all pitches. Maximum truncation for crest and root is: 0.096 × pitch for 27 threads per inch, 0.088 × pitch for 18 threads per inch, 0.078 × pitch for 14 threads per inch, 0.073 × pitch for 11½ threads per inch, 0.062 × pitch for 8 threads per inch.

| Pipe Size | | Number of Threads per Inch | Pitch Diameter | | Length of Effective Thread | Length of Hand-tight Engagement | Imperfect Threads | Depth of Thread (Max.) |
| Nominal Pipe Size | Outside Diameter | | At End of External Thread | At End of Internal Thread | | | | |
	B		F	E	C	D		K
1/16	0.3125	27	0.27118	0.28118	0.2611	0.160	0.1285	0.02963
1/8	0.405	27	0.36351	0.37476	0.2639	0.180	0.1285	0.02963
1/4	0.540	18	0.47739	0.48989	0.4018	0.200	0.1928	0.04444
3/8	0.675	18	0.61201	0.62701	0.4078	0.240	0.1928	0.04444
1/2	0.840	14	0.75843	0.77843	0.5337	0.320	0.2478	0.05714
3/4	1.050	14	0.96768	0.98887	0.5457	0.339	0.2478	0.05714
1	1.315	11½	1.21363	1.23863	0.6828	0.400	0.3017	0.06957
1¼	1.660	11½	1.55713	1.58338	0.7068	0.420	0.3017	0.06957
1½	1.900	11½	1.79609	1.82234	0.7235	0.420	0.3017	0.06957
2	2.375	11½	2.26902	2.29627	0.7565	0.436	0.3017	0.06957
2½	2.875	8	2.71953	2.76216	1.1375	0.682	0.4337	0.10000
3	3.500	8	3.34062	3.38850	1.2000	0.766	0.4337	0.10000
3½	4.000	8	3.83750	3.88881	1.2500	0.821	0.4337	0.10000
4	4.500	8	4.33438	4.38712	1.3000	0.844	0.4337	0.10000
5	5.563	8	5.39073	5.44929	1.4063	0.937	0.4337	0.10000
6	6.625	8	6.44609	6.50597	1.5125	0.958	0.4337	0.10000
8	8.625	8	8.43359	8.50003	1.7125	1.063	0.4337	0.10000
10	10.750	8	10.54531	10.62094	1.9250	1.210	0.4337	0.10000
12	12.750	8	12.53281	12.61781	2.1500	1.360	0.4337	0.10000
14 OD	14.000	8	13.77500	13.87262	2.2500	1.562	0.4337	0.10000
16 OD	16.000	8	15.76250	15.87575	2.4500	1.812	0.4337	0.10000
18 OD	18.000	8	17.75000	17.87500	2.6500	2.000	0.4337	0.10000
20 OD	20.000	8	19.73750	19.87031	2.8500	2.125	0.4337	0.10000
24 OD	24.000	8	23.71250	23.86094	3.2500	2.375	0.4337	0.10000

American Standard Taper Pipe Threads (ASA B2.1)

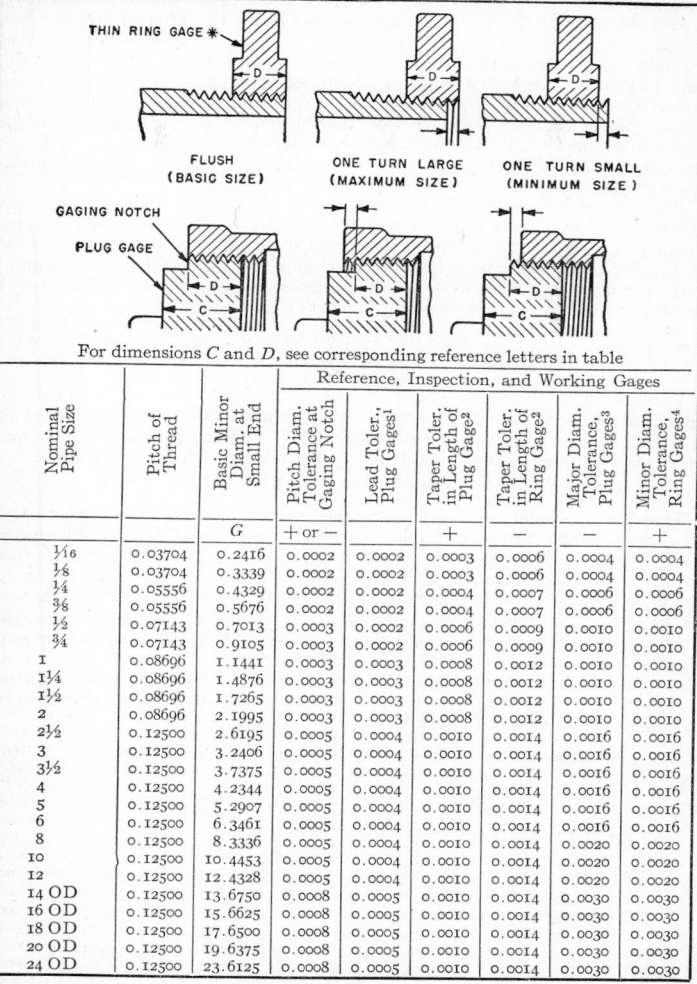

THIN RING GAGE *

FLUSH (BASIC SIZE) — ONE TURN LARGE (MAXIMUM SIZE) — ONE TURN SMALL (MINIMUM SIZE)

GAGING NOTCH

PLUG GAGE

For dimensions C and D, see corresponding reference letters in table

Nominal Pipe Size	Pitch of Thread	Basic Minor Diam. at Small End	Reference, Inspection, and Working Gages						
			Pitch Diam. Tolerance at Gaging Notch	Lead Toler., Plug Gages[1]	Taper Toler. in Length of Plug Gage[2]	Taper Toler. in Length of Ring Gage[2]	Major Diam. Tolerance, Plug Gages[3]	Minor Diam. Tolerance, Ring Gages[4]
		G	+ or −		+	−	−	+
1/16	0.03704	0.2416	0.0002	0.0002	0.0003	0.0006	0.0004	0.0004
1/8	0.03704	0.3339	0.0002	0.0002	0.0003	0.0006	0.0004	0.0004
1/4	0.05556	0.4329	0.0002	0.0002	0.0004	0.0007	0.0006	0.0006
3/8	0.05556	0.5676	0.0002	0.0002	0.0004	0.0007	0.0006	0.0006
1/2	0.07143	0.7013	0.0003	0.0002	0.0006	0.0009	0.0010	0.0010
3/4	0.07143	0.9105	0.0003	0.0002	0.0006	0.0009	0.0010	0.0010
1	0.08696	1.1441	0.0003	0.0003	0.0008	0.0012	0.0010	0.0010
1¼	0.08696	1.4876	0.0003	0.0003	0.0008	0.0012	0.0010	0.0010
1½	0.08696	1.7265	0.0003	0.0003	0.0008	0.0012	0.0010	0.0010
2	0.08696	2.1995	0.0003	0.0003	0.0008	0.0012	0.0010	0.0010
2½	0.12500	2.6195	0.0005	0.0004	0.0010	0.0014	0.0016	0.0016
3	0.12500	3.2406	0.0005	0.0004	0.0010	0.0014	0.0016	0.0016
3½	0.12500	3.7375	0.0005	0.0004	0.0010	0.0014	0.0016	0.0016
4	0.12500	4.2344	0.0005	0.0004	0.0010	0.0014	0.0016	0.0016
5	0.12500	5.2907	0.0005	0.0004	0.0010	0.0014	0.0016	0.0016
6	0.12500	6.3461	0.0005	0.0004	0.0010	0.0014	0.0016	0.0016
8	0.12500	8.3336	0.0005	0.0004	0.0010	0.0014	0.0020	0.0020
10	0.12500	10.4453	0.0005	0.0004	0.0010	0.0014	0.0020	0.0020
12	0.12500	12.4328	0.0005	0.0004	0.0010	0.0014	0.0020	0.0020
14 OD	0.12500	13.6750	0.0008	0.0005	0.0010	0.0014	0.0030	0.0030
16 OD	0.12500	15.6625	0.0008	0.0005	0.0010	0.0014	0.0030	0.0030
18 OD	0.12500	17.6500	0.0008	0.0005	0.0010	0.0014	0.0030	0.0030
20 OD	0.12500	19.6375	0.0008	0.0005	0.0010	0.0014	0.0030	0.0030
24 OD	0.12500	23.6125	0.0008	0.0005	0.0010	0.0014	0.0030	0.0030

* See page 1014 for uses of *full* ring gages.
[1] Lead tolerance for ring gages is 0.0001 inch more than for plug gages.
[2] Measured along the pitch line in length D with imperfect end threads omitted.
[3] The major diameter equals the pitch diameter (F or E) plus 0.666025 × pitch.
[4] The minor diameter equals the pitch diameter (F or E) minus 0.666025 × pitch.

American Standard Taper Pipe Threads. — The basic dimensions of the American standard taper pipe thread are given in the table, pages 1012 and 1013.

Form of Thread: The angle between the sides of the thread is 60 degrees when measured in an axial plane, and the line bisecting this angle is perpendicular to the axis. The depth of the truncated thread is based on factors entering into the manufacture of cutting tools and the making of tight joints and is given by the formulas on page 1012. While the standard shows flat surfaces at the crest and root of the thread, some rounding may occur in commercial practice, and it is the intention to include rounded crests which are not lower than the maximum flat at the center of the crest, and also rounded roots, provided all of the curvature is below the maximum flat.

Pitch Diameter Formulas: In the following formulas, which apply to the American Standard taper pipe thread, F = pitch diameter at the small end of the pipe thread; E = pitch diameter at the large end of the internal thread and also at the gaging notch; B = outside diameter of pipe; D = length of hand-tight or normal engagement between external and internal threads; C = length of effective thread; P = pitch = 1 ÷ number of threads per inch.

$$F = B - (0.050B + 1.1)P$$
$$E = F + (0.0625D)$$

Thread Length: The formula for C determines the length of the effective thread and includes approximately two usable threads which are slightly imperfect at the crest. The normal length of engagement D between external and internal taper threads, when assembled by hand, is controlled by the use of the gages.

$$C = (0.80B + 6.8)P$$

Pipe Thread Gages. — The master gages, reference gages and working gages all consist of taper threaded plug and thin ring gages, and are made of hardened steel. The thin ring gage has a length D and the plug gage a length C. (See sectional drawings of gages and dimensions D and C in table.) Diameters E in the table are also pitch diameters at the gaging notch. The roots of the threads on these gages should not be less than a sharp V. Preferably, they may be undercut beyond the sharp V to facilitate grinding, and the crests are truncated an amount equal to 0.10 × pitch.

Full Ring Gages: Army-Navy-Aeronautical Specification AN-GGG-P-363 requires the use of special full ring gages having a thickness equal to C in addition to the use of special thin ring gages.

Marking Gages. — Each gage should be marked so as to clearly indicate the nominal size of pipe, number of threads per inch, and the proper symbol to identify the thread form. Example: 3″–8 NPT. Symbols for use on gages are as follows:

NPT — American Standard Taper Pipe Threads

NPSC — American Standard Straight Pipe Thread in pipe couplings

NPTF — American Standard Taper Pipe Thread for pressure tight joints for use without lubricant or sealer

NPSF — American Standard Straight Pipe Thread for pressure tight joints for use without lubricant or sealer (Dryseal)

NPSI — American Standard Internal Straight Pipe Thread (Dryseal)

NPSM — American Standard Straight Pipe Thread for mechanical joints

NPSL — American Standard Straight Pipe Thread for lock-nuts and lock-nut pipe threads

NPSH — American Standard Straight Pipe Thread for hose couplings and nipples

NPTR — American Standard Taper Pipe Thread for railing fittings

Tolerances. — The set of master gages should be made to the basic dimensions as accurately as possible. The reference and working gage tolerances for individual elements are specified in the right-hand section of the taper pipe thread table.

Tolerance on Product: The maximum allowable variation for the commercial product, is one turn large or one turn small from the gaging notch on plug and gaging face of ring when using working gages. (See diagrams on page 1013.)

American Standard Straight Pipe Threads. — Straight pipe threads may be used to advantage for certain types of joints. The pitch, angle, and depth of a straight pipe thread are the same as for a taper thread on pipe of equal size.

Free-Fitting Mechanical Joints: Standard wrought iron, wrought steel and brass pipe are often used for special applications where there are no internal pressures but where straight pipe thread joints are required in connection with mechanical assemblies, adjustments, etc. The dimensions of these threads are given in the upper section of Table 1.

Table 1.   American Standard Straight Pipe Threads for Mechanical Joints

Nominal Pipe Size	Number of Threads per Inch	External Threads			Internal Threads		
		Maximum Major Diameter	Pitch Diameter		Pitch Diameter		Minimum Minor Diameter
			Max.	Min.	Max.	Min.	
Free-fitting Mechanical Joints for Fixtures							
⅛	27	0.404	0.3748	0.3713	0.3783	0.3748	0.345
¼	18	0.534	0.4899	0.4847	0.4951	0.4899	0.446
⅜	18	0.671	0.6270	0.6218	0.6322	0.6270	0.583
½	14	0.836	0.7784	0.7717	0.7851	0.7784	0.721
¾	14	1.046	0.9889	0.9822	0.9956	0.9889	0.932
1	11½	1.308	1.2386	1.2305	1.2467	1.2386	1.169
1¼	11½	1.653	1.5834	1.5753	1.5915	1.5834	1.514
1½	11½	1.892	1.8223	1.8142	1.8304	1.8223	1.753
2	11½	2.366	2.2963	2.2882	2.3044	2.2963	2.227
2½	8	2.861	2.7622	2.7505	2.7739	2.7622	2.664
3	8	3.487	3.3885	3.3768	3.4002	3.3885	3.290
3½	8	3.987	3.8888	3.8771	3.9005	3.8888	3.790
4	8	4.486	4.3871	4.3754	4.3988	4.3871	4.289
5	8	5.548	5.4493	5.4376	5.4610	5.4493	5.351
6	8	6.605	6.5060	6.4943	6.5177	6.5060	6.408
Mechanical Joints for Lock-nut Connections							
⅛	27	0.414	0.3840	0.3805	0.3898	0.3863	0.357
¼	18	0.548	0.5038	0.4986	0.5125	0.5073	0.463
⅜	18	0.685	0.6409	0.6357	0.6496	0.6444	0.600
½	14	0.853	0.7963	0.7896	0.8075	0.8008	0.744
¾	14	1.064	1.0067	1.0000	1.0179	1.0112	0.954
1	11½	1.330	1.2604	1.2523	1.2739	1.2658	1.196
1¼	11½	1.675	1.6051	1.5970	1.6187	1.6106	1.541
1½	11½	1.914	1.8441	1.8360	1.8576	1.8495	1.780
2	11½	2.388	2.3180	2.3099	2.3315	2.3234	2.254
2½	8	2.892	2.7934	2.7817	2.8129	2.8012	2.703
3	8	3.519	3.4198	3.4081	3.4393	3.4276	3.329
3½	8	4.019	3.9201	3.9084	3.9396	3.9279	3.829
4	8	4.517	4.4184	4.4067	4.4379	4.4262	4.328
5	8	5.579	5.4805	5.4688	5.5001	5.4884	5.390
6	8	6.636	6.5372	6.5255	6.5567	6.5450	6.447
8	8	8.630	8.5313	8.5196	8.5508	8.5391	8.441
10	8	10.751	10.6522	10.6405	10.6717	10.6600	10.562
12	8	12.748	12.6491	12.6374	12.6686	12.6569	12.558

Table 2. American Standard Straight Pipe Threads for Pressure-tight Joints

Nominal Pipe Size	Number of Threads per Inch	Internal Threads in Pipe Couplings			Internal Threads for Oil, Grease Cup or Other Lubrication Fittings		
		Pitch Diam., Max.	Pitch Diam., Min.	Minor Diam., Min.	Pitch Diam., Max.	Pitch Diam., Min.	Minor Diam., Min.
⅛	27	0.3783	0.3713	0.342	0.3713	0.3678	0.338
¼	18	0.4951	0.4847	0.440	0.4847	0.4795	0.435
⅜	18	0.6322	0.6218	0.577	0.6218	0.6166	0.572
½	14	0.7851	0.7717	0.715	0.7717	0.7650	0.708
¾	14	0.9956	0.9822	0.925	0.9822	0.9755	0.918
1	11½	1.2467	1.2305	1.161	1.2305	1.2224	1.153
1¼	11½	1.5915	1.5753	1.506	......	......	.....
1½	11½	1.8304	1.8142	1.745	......	......	.....
2	11½	2.3044	2.2882	2.219	......	......	.....
2½	8	2.7739	2.7505	2.652	......	......	.....
3	8	3.4002	3.3768	3.278	......	......	.....
3½	8	3.9005	3.8771	3.779	......	......	.....
4	8	4.3988	4.3754	4.277	......	......	.....

External Lock-nut Threads: Occasionally, a straight thread of the largest diameter that can be cut on standard pipe is required. (See lower section of Table 1.) Ordinarily, straight internal threads are used with these straight external threads, thus providing a comparatively loose fit which makes it necessary to use packing to seal the joint. The tank nipple thread joint shown by the accompanying illustration is an example.

Pressure-tight Joints: These joints are sometimes made with *straight* internal threads and standard *taper* external threads. (See Table 2.) One or both members are assumed to be sufficiently ductile to obtain the necessary adjustment and contact, but such joints are recommended for low pressures only.

Oil- or Grease-Cup Fittings: Such fittings may be attached to machine parts (1) by a regular taper pipe thread joint, external and internal; (2) by a *taper* external pipe thread in a *straight* internal thread; or (3) by external and internal machine screw threads. Dimensions for the second class of joint referred to are given in the right-hand section of Table 2.

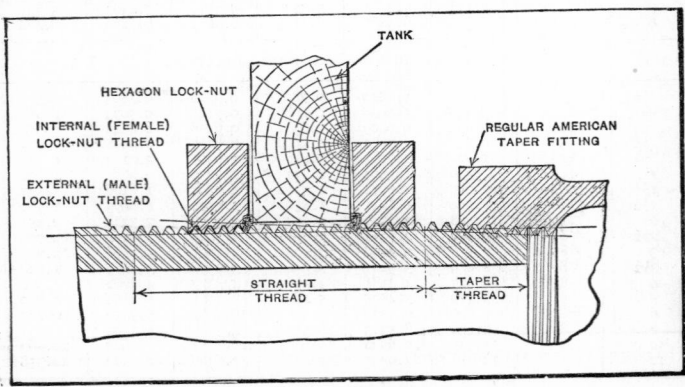

Gages for Straight Pipe Thread: Gages to properly control the production of these straight threads should be either straight "Go" and "Not Go" gages or the regular American Standard taper pipe thread gages. Straight "Go" and "Not Go" gages should be used for all types of threaded joints where both the external and internal threads are straight. Taper gages may be used for the internal threads of all types of mechanical thread joints where the external thread is tapered and the internal thread is straight. Taper thread gages should be used for all types of pressure-tight joints where the external thread is tapered and the internal thread is straight. The gaging notch on American Standard taper pipe thread plug gages should come flush with end of American Standard straight pipe threaded couplings or with the bottom of the chamfer, if chamfered, allowing a tolerance of one and one-half gage turns large or small. All "Not Go" gages should be truncated according to the practice for American Standard screw thread gages.

British Standard for Copper Tube Screw Threads

The standard screw threads for copper tubes previously adopted by the National Association of Master Heating and Domestic Engineers, has been standardized by the British Standards Institution with slight variation in the diameters of the ¼, ⅜ and ½-inch sizes, and the addition of ⅝ and ⅞-inch sizes. The table below applies to low (up to 50 lbs. per sq. inch) and medium (up to 125 lbs. per sq. inch) pressures. The dimensions for high pressure copper tubes are identical with those of the British Standard Pipe Thread.

Form of Thread: Whitworth.

Taper on Thread: ¹⁄₁₆-inch per inch of length.

Nominal Inside Diameter, Inch	Outside Diameter of Tube, Inch	Gage Diameter*	Threads per Inch	Depth of Thread, Inch	Core or Minor Diameter, Inch	Length of Thread, Inch
⅛	0.253	0.248	28	0.0229	0.202	⁵⁄₁₆
¼	0.394	0.389	20	0.0320	0.325	⅜
⅜	0.519	0.514	20	0.0320	0.450	½
½	0.644	0.639	20	0.0320	0.575	½
⅝	0.769	0.764	20	0.0320	0.700	⅝
¾	0.894	0.889	20	0.0320	0.825	⅝
⅞	1.019	1.014	20	0.0320	0.950	¾
1	1.160	1.155	20	0.0320	1.091	¾
1¼	1.410	1.405	20	0.0320	1.341	⅞
1½	1.660	1.655	20	0.0320	1.591	⅞
1¾	1.934	1.929	16	0.0400	1.849	1
2	2.184	2.179	16	0.0400	2.099	1
2¼	2.434	2.429	16	0.0400	2.349	1
2½	2.684	2.679	16	0.0400	2.599	1
2¾	2.934	2.929	16	0.0400	2.849	1
3	3.208	3.203	16	0.0400	3.123	1⅛
3¼	3.458	3.453	16	0.0400	3.373	1⅛
3½	3.732	3.727	16	0.0400	3.647	1⅛
3¾	3.982	3.977	16	0.0400	3.897	1⅛
4	4.256	4.251	16	0.0400	4.171	1¼

* The position of the gage diameter in a screwed connection is at the outer end of the connection.

British Standard Pipe Threads

The form of thread is that of the Whitworth system; the sides of the thread form an angle of 55 degrees with each other, and the top and bottom of the threads are rounded to a radius equal to 0.137278 × the pitch of the thread. Thread depth = 0.640327 × pitch. For taper pipe threads the taper is ¾ inch per foot, or 1/16 inch per inch, measured on the diameter. This system has been approved by the British Standards Institution as the standard pipe thread system in Great Britain. This standard is applied to iron and steel pipes and tubes for water, steam and gas. B.S.I. 21—1938.

Nominal Inside Diam.	Outside Diam. of Black Tube		No. of Threads per Inch	Depth of Thread	Length of Useful Thread	Major Diam. at Gage Plane (Basic)	Gage Plane to End of Pipe (Basic)
	Max.	Min.					
⅛	0.412	0.387	28	0.0229	0.25	0.383	0.1563
¼	0.550	0.525	19	0.0337	0.38	0.518	0.2367
⅜	0.688	0.663	19	0.0337	0.39	0.656	0.2500
½	0.859	0.834	14	0.0457	0.52	0.825	0.3214
¾	1.075	1.050	14	0.0457	0.57	1.041	0.3750
1	1.351	1.320	11	0.0582	0.66	1.309	0.4091
1¼	1.692	1.661	11	0.0582	0.75	1.650	0.5000
1½	1.924	1.893	11	0.0582	0.75	1.882	0.5000
2	2.403	2.358	11	0.0582	0.92	2.347	0.6250
2½	3.021	2.971	11	0.0582	1.05	2.960	0.6875
3	3.526	3.471	11	0.0582	1.18	3.460	0.8125
3½	4.021	3.961	11	0.0582	1.24	3.950	0.8750
4	4.526	4.461	11	0.0582	1.41	4.450	1.0000
5	5.536	5.461	11	0.0582	1.58	5.450	1.1250
6	6.541	6.461	11	0.0582	1.58	6.450	1.1250
7	7.575	7.463	10	0.0640	1.93	7.450	1.3750
8	8.585	8.463	10	0.0640	2.05	8.450	1.5000
9	9.595	9.463	10	0.0640	2.05	9.450	1.5000
10	10.605	10.463	10	0.0640	2.18	10.450	1.6250
11	11.615	11.465	8	0.0800	2.31	11.450	1.6250
12	12.625	12.465	8	0.0800	2.31	12.450	1.6250

This table contains revisions incorporated in Specification No. 21 issued by the British Standards Institution in 1938.

For tubes 7 inches and larger, the ends are to be specially sized prior to thread cutting in order to insure ample thickness below the root of the thread. This condition is to be complied with for the threading of cut tubes at the site.

British Standard Parallel Pipe Thread Series — Spec. No. 84-1940

Nominal Inside Diam.	Major Diam.	Threads per inch	Depth of Thread	Nominal Inside Diam.	Major Diam.	Threads per Inch	Depth of Thread
⅛	0.383	28	0.0229	1¼	1.650	11	0.0582
¼	0.518	19	0.0337	1½	1.882	11	0.0582
⅜	0.656	19	0.0337	1¾	2.116	11	0.0582
½	0.825	14	0.0457	2	2.347	11	0.0582
⅝	0.902	14	0.0457	2¼	2.587	11	0.0582
¾	1.041	14	0.0457	2½	2.960	11	0.0582
⅞	1.189	14	0.0457	2¾	3.210	11	0.0582
1	1.309	11	0.0582	3	3.460	11	0.0582

American Petroleum Institute (A.P.I.) Standard Casing Threads*

Size: Outside Diameter	Wall Thickness	Length: End of Pipe To Hand-tight Plane	Pitch Diameter At Handtight Plane	Total Thread Length	Size: Outside Diameter	Wall Thickness	Length: End of Pipe To Hand-tight Plane	Pitch Diameter At Handtight Plane	Total Thread Length
4½	.205	1.055	4.41174	2.000	8⅝	.264	1.988	8.53255	3.000
4½	.250	1.055	4.41174	2.000	8⅝	.304	2.363	8.53255	3.375
4½	.290	1.055	4.41174	2.000	8⅝	.352	2.363	8.53255	3.375
5	.220	1.555	4.91174	2.500	8⅝	.400	2.363	8.53255	3.375
5	.253	1.805	4.91174	2.750	8⅝	.450	2.363	8.53255	3.375
5	.296	1.805	4.91174	2.750	8⅝	.500	2.363	8.53255	3.375
5	.362	1.805	4.91174	2.750	8⅝	.557	2.363	8.53255	3.375
5½	.228	1.680	5.41174	2.625	9⅝	.281	2.238	9.53255	3.250
5½	.244	1.930	5.41174	2.875	9⅝	.312	2.363	9.53255	3.375
5½	.275	1.930	5.41174	2.875	9⅝	.352	2.363	9.53255	3.375
5½	.304	1.930	5.41174	2.875	9⅝	.395	2.363	9.53255	3.375
5½	.361	1.930	5.41174	2.875	9⅝	.435	2.363	9.53255	3.375
5½	.415	1.930	5.41174	2.875	9⅝	.472	2.363	9.53255	3.375
6	.238	2.055	5.91174	3.000	9⅝	.545	2.363	9.53255	3.375
6	.288	2.055	5.91174	3.000	10¾	.279	1.738	10.65755	2.750
6	.324	2.055	5.91174	3.000	10¾	.350	2.488	10.65755	3.500
6	.380	2.055	5.91174	3.000	10¾	.400	2.488	10.65755	3.500
6⅝	.245	2.180	6.53674	3.125	10¾	.450	2.488	10.65755	3.500
6⅝	.288	2.180	6.53674	3.125	10¾	.495	2.488	10.65755	3.500
6⅝	.352	2.180	6.53674	3.125	11¾	.300	2.238	11.65755	3.250
6⅝	.417	2.180	6.53674	3.125	11¾	.333	2.488	11.65755	3.500
6⅝	.475	2.180	6.53674	3.125	11¾	.375	2.488	11.65755	3.500
7	.231	1.430	6.91174	2.375	11¾	.435	2.488	11.65755	3.500
7	.272	2.180	6.91174	3.125	11¾	.489	2.488	11.65755	3.500
7	.317	2.180	6.91174	3.125	13⅜	.330	2.488	13.28255	3.500
7	.362	2.180	6.91174	3.125	13⅜	.380	2.488	13.28255	3.500
7	.408	2.180	6.91174	3.125	13⅜	.430	2.488	13.28255	3.500
7	.453	2.180	6.91174	3.125	13⅜	.480	2.488	13.28255	3.500
7	.498	2.180	6.91174	3.125	13⅜	.514	2.488	13.28255	3.500
7	.540	2.180	6.91174	3.125	16	.3125	2.862	15.87575	3.875
7⅝	.250	1.863	7.53255	2.875	16	.3750	2.862	15.87575	3.875
7⅝	.300	2.238	7.53255	3.250	16	.4375	2.862	15.87575	3.875
7⅝	.328	2.238	7.53255	3.250	16	.4950	2.862	15.87575	3.875
7⅝	.375	2.238	7.53255	3.250	20	.4170	2.862	19.87575	3.875
7⅝	.430	2.238	7.53255	3.250					
7⅝	.500	2.238	7.53255	3.250					

* Thread lengths for "short" threads and couplings. "Long" threads and couplings are available on order only. This table is based upon 1942 revision.

Pitch and Taper: All casing sizes have 8 threads per inch. The included taper of the thread is 0:0625 inch per inch, or ¾ inch per foot.

Rounded Thread Form: The included thread angle is 60 degrees. Threads for casing sizes up to 13⅜ inches, inclusive, have rounded crests and roots, and the depth, measured perpendicular to the axis of the pipe, equals 0.626 × pitch — 0.007 = 0.07125 inch.

Truncated Form: Threads for the 16- and 20-inch casing sizes have flat crests and roots. The depth equals 0.760 × pitch — 0.0950 inch. This truncated form is designated in the A.P.I. Standard as a "sharp thread."

Wall Thickness: The maximum total thread length is limited to that which will give a basic wall thickness at the end of the pipe and root of the thread, as determined by the following formula: Wall thickness at end = 0.009 × outside diameter + 0.040 inch. This wall thickness, however, must not in any case be less than 0.090 inch.

American Standard Hose Coupling Screw Threads
Basic Thread Form is American National Standard

COUPLING								
Nominal Size	Threads per Inch	Pitch	Depth of Thread	Major Diam. Min. (1)	Pitch Diameter		Minor Diameter	
					Max.	Min.	Max. (2)	Min.
Garden and Similar Hose								
½, ⅝, ¾	11½	0.08696	0.05648	1.0725	1.0245	1.0160	0.9765	0.9595
Chemical Engine and Booster Hose								
¾, 1	8	0.12500	0.08119	1.3870	1.3169	1.3058	1.2468	1.2246
Fire Protection Hose								
1½	9	0.11111	0.07217	2.0020	1.9409	1.9298	1.8799	1.8577
Steam, Water, Air, Oil, and All Other Hose Connections (3)								
½	14	0.07143	0.04639	0.8323	0.7929	0.7859	0.7535	0.7395
¾	14	0.07143	0.04639	1.0428	1.0034	0.9964	0.9640	0.9500
1	11½	0.08696	0.05648	1.3051	1.2571	1.2486	1.2091	1.1921
1¼	11½	0.08696	0.05648	1.6499	1.6019	1.5934	1.5539	1.5369
1½	11½	0.08696	0.05648	1.8888	1.8408	1.8323	1.7928	1.7758
2	11½	0.08696	0 05648	2.3628	2.3148	2.3063	2.2668	2.2498

NIPPLE								
Nominal Size	Threads per Inch	Pitch	Depth of Thread	Major Diameter		Pitch Diameter		Minor Diam.
				Max.	Min.	Max.	Min.	Max.
Garden and Similar Hose								
½, ⅝, ¾	11½	0.08696	0.05648	1.0625	1.0455	1.0060	0.9975	0.9495
Chemical Engine and Booster Hose								
¾, 1	8	0.12500	0.08119	1.3750	1.3528	1.2938	1.2827	1.2126
Fire Protection Hose								
1½	9	0.11111	0.07217	1.9900	1.9678	1.9178	1.9067	1.8457
Steam, Water, Air, Oil, and All Other Hose Connections (3)								
½	14	0.07143	0.04639	0.8248	0.8108	0.7784	0.7714	0.7320
¾	14	0.07143	0.04639	1.0353	1.0213	0.9889	0.9819	0.9425
1	11½	0.08696	0.05648	1.2951	1.2781	1.2386	1.2301	1.1821
1¼	11½	0.08696	0.05648	1.6399	1.6229	1.5834	1.5749	1.5269
1½	11½	0.08696	0.05648	1.8788	1.8618	1.8223	1.8138	1.7658
2	11½	0.08696	0.05648	2.3528	2.3358	2.2963	2.2878	2.2398

(1) Dimensions for the minimum major diam. of the coupling correspond to the basic flat (⅛ × pitch), and the profile at the major diam. produced by a worn tool must not fall below the basic outline. The maximum major diam. of the coupling shall be that corresponding to a flat at the major diam. of the coupling equal to 1⁄24 × pitch and may be determined by adding 0.7939 × pitch to the maximum pitch diam. of the coupling.

(2) Dimensions given for the maximum minor diameter of the nipple are figured to the intersection of the worn tool arc with a center line through crest and root. The minimum minor diameter of the nipple shall be that corresponding to a flat at the minor diameter of the nipple equal to 1⁄24 × pitch, and may be determined by subtracting 0.7939 × pitch from the minimum pitch diameter of the nipple.

(3) These dimensions permit hose connections to American Standard Straight Pipe Threads.

(All dimensions given in inches.)

American Standard Hose Coupling Screw Threads (*Continued*)

Dimensions of couplings and nipples (see dimension letters on illustration in table below)

Nominal Size	Threads per Inch	Length of Nipple *L*	Depth to Gasket Seat *H*	Thread Length in Coupling *T*	Length of Pilot A	Inside Diameter of Nipple *C*	Approx. Number of Threads in Length *T*
Garden and Similar Hose							
1/2, 5/8, 3/4	11 1/2	9/16	17/32	3/8	1/8	25/32	4 1/4
Chemical Engine and Booster Hose							
3/4, 1	8	5/8	19/32	15/32	5/32	1 1/32	3 3/4
Fire Protection Hose							
1 1/2	9	5/8	19/32	15/32	5/32	1 17/32	4 1/4
Steam, Water, Air, Oil and All Other Hose Connections							
1/2	14	1/2	15/32	5/16	1/8	17/32	4 1/4
3/4	14	9/16	17/32	3/8	1/8	25/32	5 1/4
1	11 1/2	9/16	17/32	3/8	5/32	1 1/32	4 1/4
1 1/4	11 1/2	5/8	19/32	15/32	5/32	1 9/32	5 1/2
1 1/2	11 1/2	5/8	19/32	15/32	5/32	1 17/32	5 1/2
2	11 1/2	3/4	23/32	19/32	3/16	2 1/32	6 3/4

All dimensions given in inches.

Thread at end of nipple and coupling thread is chamfered to angle of 35 degrees.

This American Standard applies to the threaded parts of hose couplings, valves, nozzles, and all other fittings used in direct connection with hose intended for fire protection or for domestic, industrial, and general service in nominal sizes of 1/2, 5/8, 3/4, 1, 1 1/4, 1 1/2, and 2 inches.

Table 1. National Standard Fire-hose Coupling Screw Thread

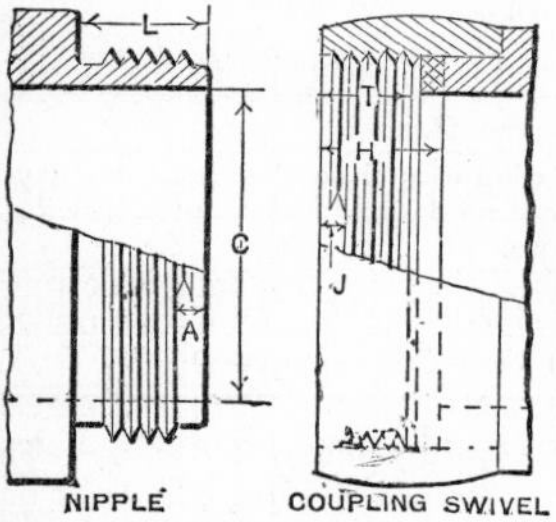

This standard has been approved and adopted by the American Water Works Association, Brass Hose Fittings Manufacturer's Association, Bureau of Standards — U. S. Department of Commerce, International Association of Fire Engineers, National Board of Fire Underwriters, National Fire Protection Association, National Screw Thread Commission, Railway Fire Protection Association, The American Society of Mechanical Engineers, The National Firemen's Association of the U. S., and other organizations.

Nominal Inside Diameter *C*	Number of Threads per Inch	Length *L**	Face to Start of Second Turn *A*	Depth to Washer Seat *H*	Face to Start of Second Turn *J*	Depth of Thread *T*
2 1/2	7 1/2	1	1/4	15/16	3/16	1 1/16
3	6	1 1/8	5/16	1 1/16	1/4	1 3/16
3 1/2	6	1 1/8	5/16	1 1/16	1/4	1 3/16
4 1/2	4	1 1/4	7/16	1 3/16	3/8	1 5/16

* Total length of threaded part of coupling and hydrant nipple.

Table 2. Limiting Dimensions for Internal Threads of Coupling Swivels and Hydrant Caps

Nominal Size	Threads per Inch	Min. Major Diameter*	Pitch Diameter		Minor Diameter	
			Maximum	Minimum	Maximum	Minimum
2.500	7.5	3.0836	3.0130	2.9970	2.9424	2.9104
3.000	6.0	3.6389	3.5486	3.5306	3.4583	3.4223
3.500	6.0	4.2639	4.1736	4.1556	4.0833	4.0473
4.500	4.0	5.7859	5.6485	5.6235	5.5111	5.4611

All dimensions given in inches.
* These dimensions correspond to the basic flat (⅛ pitch). The profile at the major diameter of the coupling, produced by a worn tool, must not fall below the basic outline, but a new tool may be made with a flat at the point as small as ¹⁄₂₄ pitch.

Table 3. Limiting Dimensions of External Threads of Coupling and Hydrant Nipples

Nominal Size	Threads per Inch	Major Diameter		Pitch Diameter		Max. Minor Diam.*
		Maximum	Minimum	Maximum	Minimum	
2.500	7.5	3.0686	3.0366	2.9820	2.9660	2.8954
3.000	6.0	3.6239	3.5879	3.5156	3.4976	3.4073
3.500	6.0	4.2439	4.2079	4.1356	4.1176	4.0273
4.500	4.0	5.7609	5.7109	5.5985	5.5735	5.4361

All dimensions given in inches.
The largest nipple is purposely made smaller in diameter than the smallest coupling in order to ensure a fit loose enough so that these threads can be assembled quickly regardless of the presence of dirt, burrs, bruises, etc.
*These dimensions are figured to the intersection of the worn tool arc with a center line through crest and root. New tools may be made to give a minimum minor diameter of the nipple as small as that corresponding to a flat of ¹⁄₂₄ pitch.

National (American) Standard Fire-Hose Coupling Screw Thread. — This standard is intended to cover the threaded part of fire-hose couplings, hydrant outlets, stand-pipe connections, Siamese connections, and all other special fittings on fire lines where fittings of 2½, 3, 3½, and 4½ inches nominal diameter are used. Table 1 gives the general dimensions, and shows a typical form of standard coupling. The limiting dimensions of the finished product are given in Tables 2 and 3. These dimensions are in perfect harmony with the nominal dimensions originally specified for couplings and nipples but are here expressed in a way to ensure the absolute interchangeability of the product. It should be noted also that they determine the size of the finished product and not of the threading tools. The basic form of the National (American) Standard Fire-Hose Coupling Screw Thread is the American (National) Standard form, formerly known as the "U. S. Standard Form." The outer ends of external and internal threads should be terminated by the "Higbee Cut" on the *full thread* to avoid crossing and mutilation of the thread (See illustration in Table 1).

International Metric Fine Thread. — The form of thread is the same as the International system but the pitch for a given diameter is smaller. The metric fine thread is used on the European continent, although there is not as yet complete uniformity. The dimensions given in the accompanying table are prescribed by the International Standards Association.

International Metric Fine Thread
All dimensions in millimeters

Major Diam.	Pitch	Effective or Pitch Diam.	Screw		Nut	
			Minor or Core Diam.	Core Area Sq. mm.	Major Diam.	Minor Diam.
1	0.2	0.870	0.72	0.41	1.02	0.74
1.2	0.2	1.070	0.92	0.66	1.22	0.94
1.4	0.2	1.270	1.12	0.98	1.42	1.14
1.7	0.2	1.570	1.42	1.58	1.72	1.44
2	0.25	1.838	1.65	2.13	2.03	1.68
2.3	0.25	2.138	1.95	2.98	2.33	1.98
2.6	0.35	2.373	2.11	3.49	2.64	2.15
3	0.35	2.773	2.51	4.94	3.04	2.55
3.5	0.35	3.273	3.01	7.10	3.54	3.05
4	0.5	3.675	3.30	8.53	4.05	3.35
4.5	0.5	4.175	3.80	11.32	4.55	3.85
5	0.5	4.675	4.30	14.50	5.05	4.35
6	0.75	5.513	4.94	19.20	6.08	5.03
7	0.75	6.513	5.94	27.75	7.08	6.03
8	1	7.350	6.59	34.14	8.11	6.70
9	1	8.350	7.59	45.28	9.11	7.70
10	1	9.350	8.59	57.99	10.11	8.70
12	1.5	11.026	9.89	76.81	12.16	10.05
14	1.5	13.026	11.89	111	14.16	12.05
16	1.5	15.026	13.89	152	16.16	14.05
18	1.5	17.026	15.89	198	18.16	16.05
20	1.5	19.026	17.89	251	20.16	18.05
22	1.5	21.026	19.89	311	22.16	20.05
24	2	22.701	21.19	353	24.22	21.40
27	2	25.701	24.19	459	27.22	24.40
30	2	28.701	27.19	580	30.22	27.40
33	2	31.701	30.19	716	33.22	30.40
36	3	34.051	31.78	793	36.32	32.10
39	3	37.051	34.78	950	39.32	35.10
42	3	40.051	37.78	1121	42.32	38.10
45	3	43.051	40.78	1306	45.32	41.10
48	3	46.051	43.78	1505	48.32	44.10
52	3	50.051	47.78	1793	52.32	48.10
56	4	53.402	50.37	1993	56.43	50.80
60	4	57.402	54.37	2322	60.43	54.80
64	4	61.402	58.37	2676	64.43	58.80
72	4	69.402	66.37	3460	72.43	66.80
80	4	77.402	74.37	4344	80.43	74.80

International Metric Thread System
(The Système Internationale Thread)

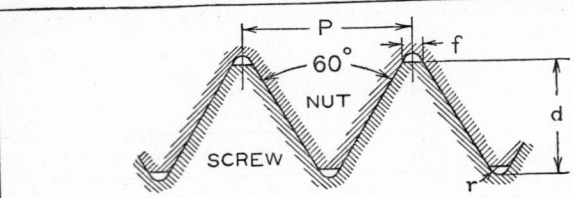

Depth $d = 0.7035\ P$ max.; $0.6855\ P$ min.   Radius $r = 0.0633\ P$ max.; $0.054\ P$ min.
Flat $f = 0.125\ P$ Tap drill diam. = major diam. — pitch

All dimensions are in millimeters

Major Diam., mm	Pitch P mm	Effective or Pitch Diam., mm	Screen Minor or Core Diam.	Thread Depth, Max.	Nut Major Diam.	Minor or Core Diam.
6	1	5.350	4.59	0.703	6.11	4.70
7	1	6.350	5.59	0.703	7.11	5.70
8	1.25	7.188	6.24	0.879	8.14	6.38
9	1.25	8.188	7.24	0.879	9.14	7.38
10	1.5	9.026	7.89	1.055	10.16	8.05
12	1.75	10.863	9.54	1.231	12.19	9.73
14	2	12.701	11.19	1.410	14.22	11.40
16	2	14.701	13.19	1.410	16.22	13.40
18	2.5	16.376	14.48	1.759	18.27	14.75
20	2.5	18.376	16.48	1.759	20.27	16.75
22	2.5	20.376	18.48	1.759	22.27	18.75
24	3	22.051	19.78	2.110	24.32	20.10
27	3	25.051	22.78	2.110	27.32	23.10
30	3.5	27.727	25.07	2.462	30.38	25.45
33	3.5	30.727	28.07	2.462	33.38	28.45
36	4	33.402	30.37	2.814	36.43	30.80
39	4	36.402	33.37	2.814	39.43	33.80
42	4.5	39.077	35.67	3.165	42.49	36.15
45	4.5	42.077	38.67	3.165	45.49	39.15
48	5	44.752	40.96	3.518	48.54	41.50
52	5	48.752	44.96	3.518	52.54	45.50
56	5.5	52.428	48.26	3.869	56.60	48.86
60	5.5	56.428	52.26	3.869	60.60	52.86
64	6	60.103	55.56	4.221	64.65	56.21
68	6	64.103	59.56	4.221	68.65	60.21
72	6	68.103	63.56	4.221	72.65	64.21
76	6	72.103	67.56	4.221	76.65	68.21
80*	6	76.103	71.56	4.221	80.65	72.21

* Above 80 mm. the diameters are 84, then 89 and so on, increasing by 5 mm. up to 149 mm. with a constant pitch of 6 mm.

The thread form is practically the same as the American standard excepting for the depth. A maximum clearance between the root and mating crest is equal to ⅟16 the height of the fundamental triangle or 0.054 × pitch. A root of rounded form is recommended but the shape is left to the manufacturer.

International Metric Thread System. — The Système Internationale Thread was adopted at the Internationale Congress for the standardization of screw threads held in Zurich in 1898. The thread form is similar to the American standard (formerly U. S. Standard), excepting the depth which is greater. There is a clearance between the root and mating crest fixed at a maximum of $\frac{1}{16}$ the height of the fundamental triangle or 0.054 × pitch. A rounded root profile is recommended. The angle in the plane of the axis is 60 degrees and the crest has a flat like the American standard equal to 0.125 × pitch. This system has been adopted as standard by the International Standards Association, by most European countries using the metric system, by Japan, and by the U.S.S.R., either wholly or in part. The original specification has been modified by the general adoption of a uniform pitch of 6 millimeters for the 72-, 76- and 80-millimeter sizes. The range of nominal diameters has also been extended beyond the original 80-millimeter maximum to 84 and then by increases of 5 millimeters with a constant pitch of 6 millimeters.

Thread depth $d = 0.7035\ P$ max. and $0.6855\ P$ min.; Width of flat f at crest $= 0.125\ P$; Radius r at root $= 0.0633\ P$ max. and $0.054\ P$ min.

Löwenherz Thread. — The Löwenherz thread has flats at the top and bottom the same as the U. S. standard form, but the angle is 53 degrees 8 minutes. The depth equals 0.75 × the pitch, and the width of the flats at the top and bottom is equal to 0.125 × the pitch. This screw thread is based on the metric system (see table) and is used extensively for the fine threads of measuring instruments, optical apparatus, etc., especially in Germany:

Löwenherz Thread

Diameter		Pitch, Millimeters	Approximate No. of Threads per Inch	Diameter		Pitch, Millimeters	Approximate No. of Threads per Inch
Millimeters	Inches			Millimeters	Inches		
1.0	0.0394	0.25	101.6	9.0	0.3543	1.30	19.5
1.2	0.0472	0.25	101.6	10.0	0.3937	1.40	18.1
1.4	0.0551	0.30	84.7	12.0	0.4724	1.60	15.9
1.7	0.0669	0.35	72.6	14.0	0.5512	1.80	14.1
2.0	0.0787	0.40	63.5	16.0	0.6299	2.00	12.7
2.3	0.0905	0.40	63.5	18.0	0.7087	2.20	11.5
2.6	0.1024	0.45	56.4	20.0	0.7874	2.40	10.6
3.0	0.1181	0.50	50.8	22.0	0.8661	2.80	9.1
3.5	0.1378	0.60	42.3	24.0	0.9450	2.80	9.1
4.0	0.1575	0.70	36.3	26.0	1.0236	3.20	7.9
4.5	0.1772	0.75	33.9	28.0	1.1024	3.20	7.9
5.0	0.1968	0.80	31.7	30.0	1.1811	3.60	7.1
5.5	0.2165	0.90	28.2	32.0	1.2599	3.60	7.1
6.0	0.2362	1.00	25.4	36.0	1.4173	4.00	6.4
7.0	0.2756	1.10	23.1	40.0	1.5748	4.40	5.7
8.0	0.3150	1.20	21.1	......	......	......	....

Threads for Shells of Electric Sockets and Lamp Bases. — This standard (see table on next page) applies to rolled threads of Edison-type screw shells used for lamp bases, plugs, and lamp and fuse holders. It has been sponsored by the National Electrical Manufacturers' Association and by the American Society of Mechanical Engineers.

Rolled Threads for Screw Shells of Electric Sockets and Lamp Bases — American Standard

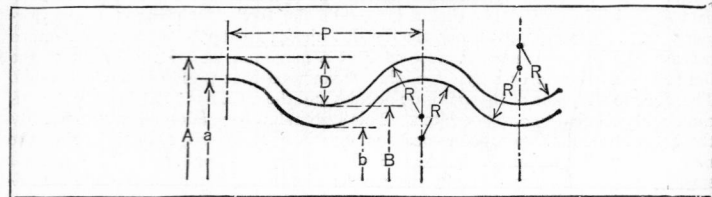

Male or Base Screw Shells Before Assembly

Size	Threads per Inch	Pitch P	Depth of Thread D	Radius Crest Root R	Major Diam. Max. A	Major Diam. Min. a	Minor Diam. Max. B	Minor Diam. Min. b
Miniature	14	0.07143	0.020	0.0210	0.375	0.370	0.335	0.330
Candelabra	10	0.10000	0.025	0.0312	0.465	0.460	0.415	0.410
Intermediate	9	0.11111	0.027	0.0353	0.651	0.645	0.597	0.591
Medium	7	0.14286	0.033	0.0470	1.037	1.031	0.971	0.965
Mogul	4	0.25000	0.050	0.0906	1.555	1.545	1.455	1.445

Socket Screw Shells Before Assembly

Size	Threads per Inch	Pitch P	Depth of Thread D	Radius Crest Root R	Major Diam. Max. A	Major Diam. Min. a	Minor Diam. Max. B	Minor Diam. Min. b
Miniature	14	0.07143	0.020	0.0210	0.3835	0.3775	0.3435	0.3375
Candelabra	10	0.10000	0.025	0.0312	0.476	0.470	0.426	0.420
Intermediate	9	0.11111	0.027	0.0353	0.664	0.657	0.610	0.603
Medium	7	0.14286	0.033	0.0470	1.053	1.045	0.987	0.979
Mogul	4	0.25000	0.050	0.0906	1.577	1.565	1.477	1.465

All dimensions given in inches.

Base Screw Shell Gage Tolerances: Threaded ring gages — "Go," Max. thread size to minus 0.0003 inch; "Not Go," Min. thread size to plus 0.0003 inch. Plain ring gages — "Go," Max. thread O.D. to minus 0.0002 inch; "Not Go," Min. thread O.D. to plus 0.0002. inch.

Socket Screw Shell Gages: Threaded plug gages — "Go," Min. thread size to plus 0.0003 inch; "Not Go," Max. thread size to minus 0.0003 inch. Plain plug gages — "Go," Min. minor diam. to plus 0.0002 inch; "Not Go," Max. minor diam. to minus 0.0002 inch.

Check Gages for Base Screw Shell Gages: Threaded plugs for checking threaded ring gages — "Go," Max. thread size to minus 0.0003 inch; "Not Go," Min. thread size to plus 0.0003 inch.

Instrument Makers' System. — The standard screw system of the Royal Microscopical Society of London, England, also known as the "Society Thread," is employed for microscope objectives and the nose pieces of the microscope into which these objectives screw. The form of the thread is the standard Whitworth form. The number of threads per inch is 36. The dimensions are as follows:

Male thread, outside diam.,	max. 0.7982 inch,	min. 0.7952 inch;
root diam.,	max. 0.7626 inch,	min. 0.7596 inch;
Female thread, root of thread,	max. 0.7674 inch,	min. 0.7644 inch;
top of thread,	max. 0.8030 inch,	min. 0.8000 inch.

Dardelet Self-locking Screw Thread — Standard Series

Nom. Size and Major Dia.	Thds. per Inch	Minor Dia. D, Bolt and Nut	External Thread			Internal Thread		
			Thread Depth E	Projected Width B	Width Crest C	Projected Width B_1	Width A	Tap Drill Stock Size
¼	16	0.2125	0.0188	0.0361	0.0176	0.0181	0.0351	No. 5
5⁄16	14	0.2697	0.0214	0.0413	0.0201	0.0207	0.0402	G
3⁄8	12	0.3250	0.0250	0.0482	0.0235	0.0242	0.0468	O
7⁄16	11	0.3830	0.0273	0.0526	0.0256	0.0264	0.0511	3⁄8
½	10	0.4400	0.0300	0.0578	0.0282	0.0290	0.0562	27⁄64
9⁄16	9	0.4959	0.0333	0.0642	0.0313	0.0322	0.0624	31⁄64
5⁄8	8	0.5500	0.0375	0.0723	0.0353	0.0363	0.0703	17⁄32
¾	8	0.6750	0.0375	0.0723	0.0353	0.0363	0.0703	21⁄32
7⁄8	7	0.7893	0.0429	0.0826	0.0403	0.0414	0.0804	25⁄32
1	6	0.9000	0.0500	0.0964	0.0470	0.0483	0.0937	57⁄64
1⅛	5	1.0050	0.0600	0.1156	0.0564	0.0580	0.1125	63⁄64
1¼	5	1.1300	0.0600	0.1156	0.0564	0.0580	0.1125	1 7⁄64
1½	4	1.3500	0.0750	0.1445	0.0705	0.0725	0.1406	1 21⁄64
1¾	4	1.6000	0.0750	0.1445	0.0705	0.0725	0.1406	1 37⁄64
2	4	1.8500	0.0750	0.1445	0.0705	0.0725	0.1406	1 53⁄64
2¼	4	2.1000	0.0750	0.1445	0.0705	0.0725	0.1406	2 3⁄32
2½	4	2.3500	0.0750	0.1445	0.0705	0.0725	0.1406	2 11⁄32
2¾	4	2.6000	0.0750	0.1445	0.0705	0.0725	0.1406	2 19⁄32
3	4	2.8500	0.0750	0.1445	0.0705	0.0725	0.1406	2 27⁄32

Dardelet Thread. — The Dardelet patented self-locking thread is designed to resist vibrations and remain tight without auxiliary locking devices. The locking surfaces are the tapered root of the bolt thread and the tapered crest of the nut thread. The nut is free to turn until seated tightly against a resisting surface, thus causing it to shift from the free position (indicated by dotted lines) to the locking position. The locking is due to a wedging action between the tapered crest of the nut thread and the tapered root or binding surface of the bolt thread. This self-locking thread is also applied to set-screws and cap-screws. The holes must, of course, be threaded with Dardelet taps. The abutment sides of the Dardelet thread carry the major part of the tensile load. The nut is unlocked simply by turning it backward with a wrench. The Dardelet thread can either be cut or rolled, using standard equipment provided with tools, taps, dies, or rolls made to suit the Dardelet thread profile. The included thread angle is 29 degrees; depth $E = 0.3\ P$; maximum axial movement $= 0.28\ P$. The major internal thread diameter (standard series) equals major external thread diameter plus 0.003 inch except for ¼-inch size which is plus 0.002 inch. The width of both external and internal threads at pitch line equals 0.36 P.

S.A.E. Standard Threads for Spark Plugs

Thread Size	Threads per Inch, Pitch	Major Diameter		Pitch Diameter		Minor Diameter	
		Max.	Min.	Max.	Min.	Max.	Min.
Spark Plug Threads							
⅞ in.	18	0.8750 in.	0.8668 in.	0.8384 in.	0.8343 in.	0.8068 in.	.....
18 mm.	1.5 mm.	0.7077 in.	0.7028 in.	0.6693 in.	0.6644 in.	0.6246 in.	.....
14 mm.	1.25 mm.	0.5505 in.	0.5455 in.	0.5185 in.	0.5142 in.	0.4904 in.	.....
10 mm.	1 mm.	0.3931 in.	0.3886 in.	0.3675 in.	0.3637 in.	0.3450 in.	.....
⅜ in.	24	0.3739 in.	0.3667 in.	0.3648 in.	0.3430 in.	0.3228 in.	.....
¼ in.	32	0.2490 in.	0.2431 in.	0.2287 in.	0.2255 in.	0.2107 in.	.....
Tapped Hole Threads							
⅞ in.	18	.....	0.8750 in.	0.8430 in.	0.8389 in.	0.8209 in.	0.8149 in.
18 mm.	1.5 mm.	.....	0.7160 in.	0.6762 in.	0.6713 in.	0.6378 in.	0.6329 in.
14 mm.	1.25 mm.	.....	0.5525 in.	0.5235 in.	0.5192 in.	0.4997 in.	0.4944 in.
10 mm.	1 mm.	.....	0.3948 in.	0.3719 in.	0.3681 in.	0.3525 in.	0.3482 in.
⅜ in.	24	.....	0.3750 in.	0.3512 in.	0.3479 in.	0.3364 in.	0.3299 in.
¼ in.	32	.....	0.2500 in.	0.2328 in.	0.2297 in.	0.2208 in.	0.2162 in.

Diameter of countersink or counterbore of the tapped hole in the cylinder head shall not exceed the minimum major thread diameter by more than 0.005 in. In order to keep the wear on the threading tools within permissible limits, the threads in the spark plug GO (ring) gage shall be truncated to the maximum minor diameter of the spark plug, and in the tapped hole, the GO (plug) gage to the minimum major diameter of the tapped hole. The plain plug gage for checking the minor diameter of the tapped hole shall be the minimum specified. The thread is the American National Form except that the root of the thread approximates the International Metric Form.

British Standards for Spark Plugs*

The International standard thread form is used

Recommended by Institution of Automobile Engineers (Where two diameters are given these are minimum and maximum)							
Thread Size, Nominal	Pitch	Major Diameter		Effective Diameter		Core Diameter	
		Plug	Hole	Plug	Hole	Plug	Hole
14	1.25	13.977	14.125	13.035	13.188	12.250	12.390
				13.165	13.278		
18	1.5	17.750	18.162	16.776	17.026	15.639	16.051
		17.950	18.337	16.976	17.201	15.839	16.226
Recommended by British Standards Institution							
Part	Pitch	Major Diameter		Effective Diameter		Core Diameter	
		Max.	Min.	Max.	Min.	Max.	Min.
Spark plugs for automobiles							
Plug	1.5	17.950	17.750	16.976	16.776	15.839	15.639
Hole		18.337	18.162	17.201	17.026	16.226	16.051
Spark plugs for aircraft							
Plug	1.5	17.975	17.850	17.001	16.876	15.864	15.739
Hole		18.312	18.187	17.176	17.051	16.201	16.076

* All dimensions in millimeters.

Aero-Thread Formulas and Basic Dimensions

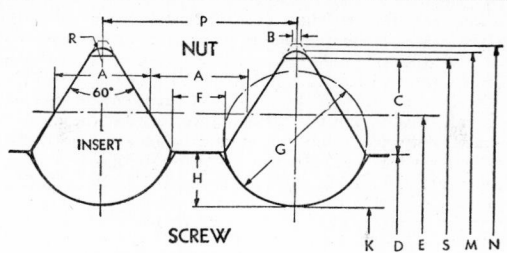

D = major screw diameter and minor diameter of tapped hole (see table); pitch $P = 1 \div$ number of threads per inch (see table); root diameter $K = D - 0.6P = E - P$; tapped hole pitch diameter $E = D + 0.4P$; insert diameter $S = D + 1.05P$; minimum major tap diameter $M = D + 1.122P$; maximum major tap diameter $N = D + 1.194P$; insert engagement $C = 0.525P$; depth $H = 0.3P$; flat $B = P \div 24$; radius $R = 0.072P$; thread form circle diameter $G = 0.75P$; $A = 0.5P$.

Major Diam. D	Threads per Inch	Pitch Diam. E	Root Diam. K	Major Diam. S Insert	Diam. G Form Circle	Major Tap Diameter Max. N	Major Tap Diameter Min. M
0.1875	24	0.2042	0.1625	0.2313	0.0313	0.2373	0.2343
0.2500	20	0.2700	0.2200	0.3024	0.0375	0.3098	0.3062
0.3125	18	0.3347	0.2792	0.3709	0.0417	0.3789	0.3749
0.3750	16	0.4000	0.3375	0.4406	0.0469	0.4496	0.4452
0.4375	14	0.4661	0.3946	0.5125	0.0536	0.5228	0.5177
0.5000	12	0.5333	0.4500	0.5876	0.0625	0.5996	0.5936
0.5625	12	0.5958	0.5125	0.6500	0.0625	0.6621	0.6561
0.6250	10	0.6650	0.5650	0.7300	0.0750	0.7444	0.7372
0.6875	10	0.7275	0.6275	0.7925	0.0750	0.8069	0.7997
0.7500	9	0.7944	0.6833	0.8666	0.0833	0.8826	0.8746
0.8750	8	0.9250	0.8000	1.0062	0.0938	1.0242	1.0152

The "Aero-Thread" is a patented form especially applicable where the internally threaded part is made from soft light materials, such as aluminum or magnesium alloys — as in aircraft construction — and the screw is made from high-strength steel. The spring-shaped insert, usually of phosphor bronze, prevents wear of the light alloy thread especially where frequent bolt removal is necessary. The insert also adjusts itself to bear evenly on all of the thread surfaces.

Lag Screw Thread Systems in Common Use

Diameter	Alternate Systems Threads per Inch	Alternate Systems Threads per Inch	Diameter	Alternate Systems Threads per Inch	Alternate Systems Threads per Inch	Diameter	Alternate Systems Threads per Inch	Alternate Systems Threads per Inch
¼	10	10	½	6	6	¾	4½	5
⁵⁄₁₆	9½	9	⁹⁄₁₆	5	6	⅞	4½	4
⅜	7	8	⅝	5	5	1	3	4
⁷⁄₁₆	7	7	1¹⁄₁₆	4½	5	....	......	......

Measuring Screw Threads

Pitch and Lead of Screw Threads. — The *pitch* of a screw thread is the distance from the center of one thread to the center of the next thread. This applies no matter whether the screw has a single, double, triple or quadruple thread. The *lead* of a screw thread is the distance the nut will move forward on the screw if it is turned around one full revolution. In a single-threaded screw, the pitch and lead are equal, because the nut would move forward the distance from one thread to the next, if turned around once. In a double-threaded screw, the nut will move forward two threads, or twice the pitch, so that in this case the lead equals twice the pitch. In a triple-threaded screw, the lead equals three times the pitch, and so on.

The word "pitch" is often, although improperly, used to denote the *number of threads per inch.* Screws are spoken of as having a 12-pitch thread, when twelve threads per inch is what is really meant. The number of threads per inch equals 1 divided by the pitch, or expressed as a formula:

$$\text{Number of threads per inch} = \frac{1}{\text{pitch}}$$

The pitch of a screw equals 1 divided by the number of threads per inch, or:

$$\text{Pitch} = \frac{1}{\text{number of threads per inch}}$$

If the number of threads per inch equals 16, the pitch = 1/16. If the pitch equals 0.05, the number of threads equals $1 \div 0.05 = 20$. If the pitch is 2/5 inch, the number of threads per inch equals $1 \div \frac{2}{5} = 2\frac{1}{2}$.

Confusion is often caused by the indefinite designation of multiple-thread screws (double, triple, quadruple, etc.). The expression, "four threads per inch, triple," for example, is not to be recommended. It means that the screw is cut with four triple threads or with twelve threads per inch, if the threads are counted by placing a scale alongside the screw. To cut this screw, the lathe would be geared to cut four threads per inch, but they would be cut only to the depth required for twelve threads per inch. The best expression, when a multiple-thread is to be cut, is to say, in this case, "¼ inch lead, 1/12 inch pitch, triple thread." For single-threaded screws, only the number of threads per inch and the form of the thread are specified. The word "single" is not required.

Measuring Screw Thread Pitch Diameters by Thread Micrometers. — As the pitch or angle diameter of a tap or screw is the most important dimension, it is

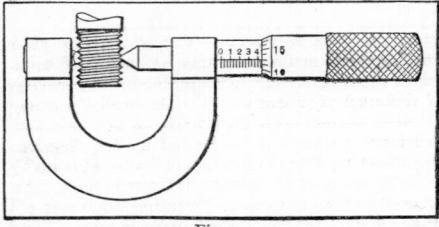

Fig. 1

necessary that the pitch diameter of screw threads be measured, in addition to the outside diameter. One method of measuring in the angle of a thread is by means of a special screw thread micrometer, as shown in the accompanying engraving, Fig. 1. The fixed anvil is V-shaped so as to fit over the thread, while the movable point is cone-shaped so as to enable it to enter the space between two threads, and at the same time be at liberty to revolve. The contact points are on the sides of the thread, as they necessarily must be in order that the pitch diameter may be determined. The cone-shaped point of the measuring screw is slightly rounded so that it will not bear in the bottom of the thread. There is also sufficient clearance at the bottom of the V-shaped anvil to prevent it from bearing on the top of the thread. The movable point is adapted to measuring all pitches, but the fixed anvil is limited in its capacity. To cover the whole range of pitches, from the finest to the coarsest, a number of fixed anvils are, therefore, required.

To find the theoretical pitch diameter, which is measured by the micrometer, subtract the single depth of the thread from the standard outside diameter. The depth of the thread for the American and other standard threads is given in the section on screw thread systems.

Ball-point Micrometers. — If standard plug gages are available, it is not necessary to actually measure the pitch diameter, but merely to compare it with the standard gage. In this case, a ball-point micrometer, as shown in Fig. 2, may be employed. Two types of ball-point micrometers are ordinarily used. One is simply a regular plain micrometer with ball points made to slip over both measuring points. (*See B*, Fig. 2.) This makes a kind of combination plain and ball-point micrometer, the ball points being easily removed. These ball points, however, do not fit solidly on their seats, even if they are split, as shown, and are apt to cause errors in the measurements. The best, and, in the long run, the cheapest, method is to use a regular micrometer arranged as shown at *A*. Drill and ream out both the end of the measuring screw or spindle and the anvil, and fit ball points into them as shown. Care should be taken to have the ball point in the spindle run true. The

holes in the micrometer spindle and anvil and the shanks on the points are tapered to insure a good fit. The hole *H* in spindle *G* is provided so that the ball point can be easily driven out when a change for a larger or smaller size of ball point is required.

A ball-point micrometer may be used for comparing the *angle* of a screw thread, with that of

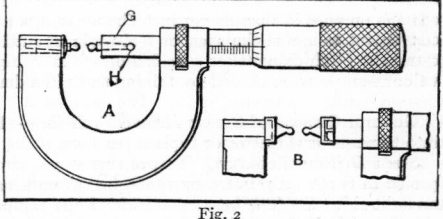

Fig. 2

a gage. This can be done by using different sizes of ball points, comparing the size first near the root of the thread, then (using a larger ball point) at about the point of the pitch diameter, and finally near the top of the thread (using in the latter case, of course, a much larger ball point). If the gage and thread measurements are the same at each of the three points referred to, this indicates that the thread angle is correct.

Measuring Screw Threads by Three-wire Method. — The *effective* or *pitch diameter* of a screw thread may be measured very accurately by means of some form of micrometer and three wires of equal diameter. This method is extensively used in checking the accuracy of threaded plug gages and other precision screw threads. Two of the wires are placed in contact with the thread on one side and the third wire in a position diametrically opposite as illustrated by the diagram, (see Table " Rules and Formulas for Checking Pitch Diameters of Screw Threads ") and the dimension over the wires is determined by means of a micrometer. An ordinary micrometer is commonly used but some form of " floating micrometer " is preferable, especially for measuring thread gages and other precision work. The floating micrometer is mounted upon a compound slide so that it can move freely in directions parallel or at right angles to the axis of the screw, which is held in a horizontal position between adjustable centers. With this arrangement the micrometer is held constantly at right angles to the axis of the screw so that only one wire on each side may be used instead of having two on one side and one on the other, as is necessary when using an ordinary micrometer. The accuracy of the pitch diameter may be determined provided the correct micrometer reading for wires of a given size is known.

Classes of Formulas for Three-wire Measurement. — Various formulas have been established for checking the pitch diameters of screw threads by measurement over wires of known size. These formulas differ in regard to their simplicity or complexity and resulting accuracy. They also differ in that some show what measurement M over the wires should be to obtain a given pitch diameter E, whereas others show the value of the pitch diameter E for a given measurement M.

Formulas for Finding Measurement M: In using a formula for finding the value of measurement M, the required pitch diameter E is inserted in the formula. Then, in cutting or grinding a screw thread, the *actual* measurement M is made to conform to the *calculated* value of M. Formulas for finding measurement M may be modified so that the basic major or outside diameter is inserted in the formula instead of the pitch diameter; however, the pitch diameter type of formula is preferable because this is a more important dimension than the major diameter.

Formulas for Finding Pitch Diameters E: Some formulas are arranged to show the value of the pitch diameter E when measurement M is known. Thus the value of M is first determined by actual measurement and then it is inserted in the formula for finding the corresponding pitch diameter E. This type of formula is useful for determining the pitch diameter of an existing thread gage or other screw thread in connection with inspection work. The formula for finding measurement M is more convenient to use in the shop or tool-room in cutting or grinding new threads, because the pitch diameter is specified on the drawing and the problem is to find the value of measurement M for obtaining this pitch diameter.

General Classes of Screw Thread Profiles. — Thread profiles may be divided into three general classes or types as follows:

Screw Helicoid: This type is represented by a screw thread having a straight-line profile in the axial plane. Such a screw thread may be cut in a lathe by using a straight-sided single-point tool, provided the top surface lies in the axial plane.

Involute Helicoid: This type is represented either by a screw thread or a helical gear tooth having an involute profile in a plane perpendicular to the axis. A rolled screw thread, theoretically at least, is an exact involute helicoid.

Intermediate Profiles: An intermediate profile which lies somewhere between the screw helicoid and the involute helicoid will be formed on a screw thread either by milling or grinding with a straight-sided wheel set in alignment with the thread groove. The resulting form will approach closely the involute helicoid form. In milling or grinding a thread, the included cutter or wheel angle may either equal the standard thread angle (which is always measured in the axial plane) or the cutter or wheel angle may be reduced to approximate, at least, the thread angle in the normal plane. These variations in practice all affect the three-wire measurement.

Accuracy of Formulas for Checking Pitch Diameters by Three-wire Method. — The exact measurement M for a given pitch diameter depends upon the lead angle, the thread angle, and the profile or cross-sectional shape of the thread. As pointed out in the preceding paragraph, the profile depends upon the method of cutting or forming the thread. In the case of a milled or ground thread, the profile is affected not only by the cutter or wheel angle but also by the diameter of the cutter or wheel; hence, because of these variations, an absolutely exact and reasonably simple general formula for measurement M cannot be established; however, if the lead angle is low, as in the case of a standard single-thread screw, and especially if the thread angle is high like a 60-degree thread, simple formulas which are not arranged to compensate for the lead angle are used ordinarily and meet most practical requirements, particularly in measuring 60-degree threads. If lead angles are large enough to decidedly affect the result, as in the case of most multiple threads (especially Acme or 29-degree worm threads), a formula should be used which compensates for the lead angle sufficiently to obtain the necessary accuracy.

The formulas which follow include (1) a very simple type in which the effect of the lead angle on measurement M is entirely ignored. This simple formula usually is applicable to the measurement of 60-degree single-thread screws, except possibly when gage-making accuracy is required; (2) formulas which do include the effect of the lead angle but, nevertheless, are approximations and not always suitable for the higher lead angles when extreme accuracy is required; (3) formulas for the higher lead angles and the most precise classes of work.

Where approximate formulas are applied consistently in the measurement of both thread plug gages and the threaded "setting plugs" for ring gages, interchangeability might be secured assuming that such approximate formulas were universally employed.

Wire Sizes for Checking Pitch Diameters of Screw Threads. — In checking screw threads by the 3-wire method, the general practice is to use measuring wires of the so-called "best size." The "best size" wire is one which contacts at the

Diameters of Wires for Measuring American Standard and British Standard Whitworth Screw Threads

Threads per Inch	Pitch, Inch	Wire Diameters for American Standard Threads			Wire Diameters for Whitworth Standard Threads		
		Max.	Min.	Pitch-line Contact	Max.	Min.	Pitch-line Contact
4	0.2500	0.2250	0.1400	0.1443	0.1900	0.1350	0.1409
4½	0.2222	0.2000	0.1244	0.1283	0.1689	0.1200	0.1253
5	0.2000	0.1800	0.1120	0.1155	0.1520	0.1080	0.1127
5½	0.1818	0.1636	0.1018	0.1050	0.1382	0.0982	0.1025
6	0.1667	0.1500	0.0933	0.0962	0.1267	0.0900	0.0939
7	0.1428	0.1286	0.0800	0.0825	0.1086	0.0771	0.0805
8	0.1250	0.1125	0.0700	0.0722	0.0950	0.0675	0.0705
9	0.1111	0.1000	0.0622	0.0641	0.0844	0.0600	0.0626
10	0.1000	0.0900	0.0560	0.0577	0.0760	0.0540	0.0564
11	0.0909	0.0818	0.0509	0.0525	0.0691	0.0491	0.0512
12	0.0833	0.0750	0.0467	0.0481	0.0633	0.0450	0.0470
13	0.0769	0.0692	0.0431	0.0444	0.0585	0.0415	0.0434
14	0.0714	0.0643	0.0400	0.0412	0.0543	0.0386	0.0403
16	0.0625	0.0562	0.0350	0.0361	0.0475	0.0337	0.0352
18	0.0555	0.0500	0.0311	0.0321	0.0422	0.0300	0.0313
20	0.0500	0.0450	0.0280	0.0289	0.0380	0.0270	0.0282
22	0.0454	0.0409	0.0254	0.0262	0.0345	0.0245	0.0256
24	0.0417	0.0375	0.0233	0.0240	0.0317	0.0225	0.0235
28	0.0357	0.0321	0.0200	0.0206	0.0271	0.0193	0.0201
32	0.0312	0.0281	0.0175	0.0180	0.0237	0.0169	0.0176
36	0.0278	0.0250	0.0156	0.0160	0.0211	0.0150	0.0156
40	0.0250	0.0225	0.0140	0.0144	0.0190	0.0135	0.0141

pitch line or mid-slope of the thread because then the measurement of the pitch diameter is least affected by an error in the thread angle. In the following formula for determining approximately the "best size" wire or the diameter for pitch-line contact, A = one-half included angle of thread in axial plane.

$$\text{Best size wire} = \frac{0.5 \text{ pitch}}{\cos A} = 0.5 \text{ pitch} \times \sec A$$

For 60-degree threads this formula reduces to

$$\text{Best size wire} = 0.57735 \times \text{pitch}$$

These formulas are based upon a thread groove of zero lead angle because ordinary variations in the lead angle have little effect on the wire diameter and it is desirable to use one wire size for a given pitch regardless of the lead angle. A theoretically correct solution for finding the *exact* size for pitch-line contact, involves the use of cumbersome indeterminate equations with solution by successive trials. The accompanying table gives the wire sizes for both American Standard (formerly U. S. Standard) and the Whitworth Standard Threads. The following formulas for determining wire diameters do not give the extreme theoretical limits but the smallest and largest sizes which are practicable. The diameters in the table are based upon these approximate formulas.

American Standard $\begin{cases} \text{Smallest wire diameter} = 0.56 \times \text{pitch} \\ \text{Largest wire diameter} = 0.90 \times \text{pitch} \\ \text{Diameter for pitch-line contact} = 0.57735 \times \text{pitch} \end{cases}$

Whitworth $\begin{cases} \text{Smallest wire diameter} = 0.54 \times \text{pitch} \\ \text{Largest wire diameter} = 0.76 \times \text{pitch} \\ \text{Diameter for pitch-line contact} = 0.56368 \times \text{pitch} \end{cases}$

Measuring Wire Accuracy. — A set of three measuring wires should have the same diameter within 0.00002 inch. In order to measure the pitch diameter of a screw-thread gage to an accuracy of 0.0001 inch by means of wires, it is necessary to know the wire diameters to 0.00002 inch. If the diameters of the wires are known only to an accuracy of 0.0001 inch, an accuracy better than 0.0003 inch in the measurement of pitch diameter cannot be expected. The wires should be accurately finished hardened steel cylinders of the maximum possible hardness without being brittle. The hardness should not be less than that corresponding to a Knoop indentation number of 630. A wire of this hardness can be cut with a file only with difficulty. The surface should not be rougher than the equivalent of one measuring 3 microinches root-mean-square deviation from a true cylindrical surface.

Measuring or Contact Pressure. — In measuring screw threads or screw thread gages by the 3-wire method, variations in contact pressure will result in different readings. The effect of a variation in contact pressure in measuring threads of fine pitches is indicated by the difference in readings obtained with pressures of 2 pounds and 5 pounds in checking a thread plug gage having 24 threads per inch. The reading over the wires with 5 pounds pressure was 0.00013 inch less than with 2 pounds pressure. For pitches finer than 20 threads per inch a pressure of 16 ounces is recommended by the National Bureau of Standards. For pitches of 20 threads per inch and coarser, a pressure of 2½ pounds is recommended.

In the case of Acme threads, the wire presses against the sides of the thread with a pressure of approximately twice that of the measuring instrument. To limit the tendency of the wires to wedge in between the sides of an Acme thread, it is recommended that pitch diameter measurements on 8 threads per inch and finer be made at 1 pound, and at 2½ pounds for pitches coarser than 8 threads per inch.

Notation Used in Formulas for Measuring Pitch Diameters by Three-wire Method

M = dimension over wires corresponding to pitch diameter E

D = basic major or outside diameter

E = pitch diameter or effective diameter = D − basic depth of thread

T = width of thread in axial plane at diameter E = 0.5 pitch P

T_a = arc thickness on pitch cylinder in plane perpendicular to axis

P = pitch = 1 ÷ number of threads per inch

W = wire or pin diameter

A = one-half included thread angle in the axial plane

A_n = one-half included thread angle in the normal plane or in plane perpendicular to sides of thread = one-half included angle of cutter when thread is milled (tan A_n = tan A × cos B). (Note: Included angle of milling cutter or grinding wheel may equal the nominal included angle of thread, or cutter angle may be reduced to whatever normal angle is required to make the thread angle standard in the axial plane. In either case, A_n = one-half cutter angle.)

S = number of "starts" or threads on a multiple-threaded worm or screw (2 for double thread, 3 for triple thread, etc.)

B = lead angle at pitch diameter. Tan $B = L ÷ 3.1416E$ = helix angle of thread as measured from a plane perpendicular to the axis

L = lead of thread = pitch P × number of threads S

H = helix angle at pitch diam. and measured from axis = $90° − B$ or tan H = cot B

H_b = helix angle at R_b measured from axis

R_b = radius required in Formulas (4e) and (4)

F = angle required in Formulas (4b), (4d) and (4e)

G = angle required in Formula (4)

Approximate Three-wire Formulas which do not Compensate for Lead Angle. — A general formula in which the effect of lead angle is ignored is as follows (see accompanying notation used in formulas):

$$M = E - T \cot A + W (1 + \operatorname{cosec} A) \qquad (1)$$

This formula can be simplified for any given thread angle and pitch. To illustrate, since $T = 0.5 P$, $M = E − 0.5 P \cot A + W (1 + 2)$, for a 60-degree thread, such as the American Standard,

$$M = E − 0.86603 \, P + 3 \, W$$

The accompanying table contains these simplified formulas for different standard threads. Two formulas are given in each case. The upper one includes the standard or basic major diameter and the lower one the pitch diameter or effective diameter. These formulas are sufficiently accurate for practically all checking of standard 60-degree single-thread screws because of the low lead angles which vary from 1° 11′ to 4° 31′ in the American Standard Coarse-thread Series.

Bureau of Standards General Formula. — The Formula (2) which follows compensates quite largely for the effect of the lead angle. It is from the National Bureau of Standards Handbook H 28 (1944). The formula, however, as here given has been arranged for finding the value of M (instead of E).

$$M = E − T \cot A + W (1 + \operatorname{cosec} A + 0.5 \tan^2 B \cos A \cot A) \qquad (2)$$

The Bureau of Standards uses Formula (2) in preference to Formula (1) when the value of $0.5 W \tan^2 B \cos A \cot A$ exceeds 0.00015, as in the case of the larger lead angles. If this test is applied to American Standard 60-degree threads it will show that Formula (1) is generally applicable; but in case of 29-degree Acme or worm threads, Formula (2) (or some other which includes effect of lead angle) should be employed.

Formulas for Checking Pitch Diameters of Screw Threads

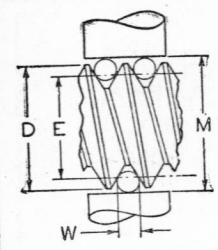

The formulas below do not compensate for the effect of the lead angle upon measurement M, but they are sufficiently accurate for checking standard single-thread screws unless exceptional accuracy is required. See accompanying information on effect of lead angle; also matter relating to measuring wire sizes, accuracy required for such wires, and contact or measuring pressure. The approximate best wire size for pitch-line contact may be obtained by the formula

$$W = 0.5 \times \text{pitch} \times \sec \tfrac{1}{2} \text{ included thread angle}$$

For 60-degree threads, $W = 0.57735 \times \text{pitch}$.

Form of Thread	Formulas for determining measurement M corresponding to correct pitch diameter. Diagram shows dimensions represented by letters in formulas.
American (National) Standard	When standard major diameter D is used in formula. $$M = D - (1.5155 \times P) + (3 \times W)$$ When pitch diameter E is used in formula. $$M = E - (0.86603 \times P) + (3 \times W)$$ The American Standard formerly was known as U. S. Standard.
British Standard Whitworth	When standard major diameter D is used in formula. $$M = D - (1.6008 \times P) + (3.1657 \times W)$$ When pitch diameter E is used in formula. $$M = E - (0.9605 \times P) + (3.1657 \times W)$$
British Association Standard	When standard major diameter D is used in formula. $$M = D - (1.7363 \times P) + (3.4829 \times W)$$ When pitch diameter E is used in formula. $$M = E - (1.1363 \times P) + (3.4829 \times W)$$
Lowenherz Thread	When standard major diameter D is used in formula. $$M = D - (1.75 \times P) + (3.2359 \times W)$$ When pitch diameter E is used in formula. $$M = E - P + (3.2359 \times W)$$
Sharp V-Thread	When standard major diameter D is used in formula. $$M = D - (1.732 \times P) + (3 \times W)$$ When pitch diameter E is used in formula. $$M = E - (0.86603 \times P) + (3 \times W)$$
International Standard	Use the formula given above for the American (National) Standard.
Pipe Thread	See accompanying paragraph on Measuring Taper Screw Threads by Three-wire Method.
Acme and Worm Threads	See Buckingham Formulas; also Three-wire Method for Checking Thickness of Acme Threads.
Buttress Form of Thread	Different forms of buttress threads are used. See paragraph on wire method applied to buttress threads.

The wires must be lapped to a uniform diameter and it is very important to insert in the rule or formula the wire diameter as determined by precise means of measurement. Any error will be multiplied. See paragraph on Wire Sizes for Checking Pitch Diameters.

Values of Constants Used in Formulas for Measuring Pitch Diameters of Screws by the Three-wire System

No. of Threads per Inch	V-Thread, 1.732 P	American Standard, 1.5155 P	Whitworth Thread, 1.6008 P	No. of Threads per Inch	V-Thread, 1.732 P	American Standard, 1.5155 P	Whitworth Thread, 1.6008 P
2¼	0.7698	0.6736	0.7115	18	0.0962	0.0842	0.0889
2⅜	0.7293	0.6381	0.6740	20	0.0866	0.0758	0.0800
2½	0.6928	0.6062	0.6403	22	0.0787	0.0689	0.0728
2⅝	0.6598	0.5773	0.6098	24	0.0722	0.0631	0.0667
2¾	0.6298	0.5511	0.5821	26	0.0666	0.0583	0.0616
2⅞	0.6025	0.5271	0.5568	28	0.0619	0.0541	0.0572
3	0.5774	0.5052	0.5336	30	0.0577	0.0505	0.0534
3¼	0.5329	0.4663	0.4926	32	0.0541	0.0474	0.0500
3½	0.4949	0.4330	0.4574	34	0.0509	0.0446	0.0471
4	0.4330	0.3789	0.4002	36	0.0481	0.0421	0.0445
4½	0.3849	0.3368	0.3557	38	0.0456	0.0399	0.0421
5	0.3464	0.3031	0.3202	40	0.0433	0.0379	0.0400
5½	0.3149	0.2755	0.2911	42	0.0412	0.0361	0.0381
6	0.2887	0.2526	0.2668	44	0.0394	0.0344	0.0364
7	0.2474	0.2165	0.2287	46	0.0377	0.0329	0.0348
8	0.2165	0.1894	0.2001	48	0.0361	0.0316	0.0334
9	0.1925	0.1684	0.1779	50	0.0346	0.0303	0.0320
10	0.1732	0.1515	0.1601	52	0.0333	0.0291	0.0308
11	0.1575	0.1378	0.1455	56	0.0309	0.0271	0.0286
12	0.1443	0.1263	0.1334	60	0.0289	0.0253	0.0267
13	0.1332	0.1166	0.1231	64	0.0271	0.0237	0.0250
14	0.1237	0.1082	0.1143	68	0.0255	0.0223	0.0235
15	0.1155	0.1010	0.1067	72	0.0241	0.0210	0.0222
16	0.1083	0.0947	0.1001	80	0.0217	0.0189	0.0200

Constants Used for Measuring Pitch Diameters of Metric Screws by the Three-wire System

Pitch in Mm.	Pitch in Inches	Metric Thread, 1.5155 P	Pitch in Mm.	Pitch in Inches	Metric Thread, 1.5155 P	Pitch in Mm.	Pitch in Inches	Metric Thread, 1.5155 P
0.5	0.0197	0.0298	2.5	0.0984	0.1492	6.0	0.2362	0.3580
0.75	0.0295	0.0447	3.0	0.1181	0.1790	6.5	0.2559	0.3878
1.0	0.0394	0.0597	3.5	0.1378	0.2088	7.0	0.2756	0.4177
1.25	0.0492	0.0746	4.0	0.1575	0.2387	7.5	0.2953	0.4475
1.5	0.0590	0.0895	4.5	0.1772	0.2685	8.0	0.3150	0.4773
1.75	0.0689	0.1044	5.0	0.1969	0.2983	9.0	0.3543	0.5370
2.0	0.0787	0.1193	5.5	0.2165	0.3282	10.0	0.3937	0.5966

This table may be used when a 60-degree metric thread (such as the International Standard or the French Thread) is to be checked, by first converting the metric dimensions into inches. The third column of the table gives the value of 1.5155 × pitch in inches equivalent to the pitch in millimeters given in the first column. The formula for the American Standard thread form is used.

Why Small Thread Angle Affects Accuracy of Three-wire Measurement. —

In measuring or checking Acme threads, or any others having a comparatively small thread angle A, it is particularly important to use a formula which compensates largely, if not entirely, for the effect of the lead angle, especially in all gage and precision work. The effect of the lead angle on the position of the wires and upon the resulting measurement M is much greater in the case of a 29-degree thread than in the case of a higher thread angle such, for example, as a 60-degree thread. This is because the cotangent of the thread angle increases as this angle becomes smaller; consequently, the reduction in the width of the thread groove in the normal plane due to the lead angle causes a wire of given size to rest higher in the groove of a thread having a small thread angle A (like a 29-degree thread) than in the groove with a larger angle (like a 60-degree American Standard).

Acme Threads: Three-wire measuring data for Acme threads will be found on page 1002. The measurements given in this table check with those obtained by Formula (2).

Dimensions Over Wires of Given Diameter for Checking Screw Threads of American National form (U. S. Standard) and the V-form

Diam. of Screw	No. of Threads per Inch	Diam. of Wire used	Dimension over Wires, V-Thread	Dimension over Wires, U. S. Thread	Diam. of Screw	No. of Threads per Inch	Diam. of Wire used	Dimension over Wires, V-Thread	Dimension over Wires, U. S. Thread
¼	18	0.035	0.2588	0.2708	⅞	8	0.090	0.9285	0.9556
¼	20	0.035	0.2684	0.2792	⅞	9	0.090	0.9525	0.9766
¼	22	0.035	0.2763	0.2861	⅞	10	0.090	0.9718	0.9935
¼	24	0.035	0.2828	0.2919	15⁄16	8	0.090	0.9910	1.0181
5⁄16	18	0.035	0.3213	0.3333	15⁄16	9	0.090	1.0150	1.0391
5⁄16	20	0.035	0.3309	0.3417	1	8	0.090	1.0535	1.0806
5⁄16	22	0.035	0.3388	0.3486	1	9	0.090	1.0775	1.1016
5⁄16	24	0.035	0.3453	0.3544	1⅛	7	0.090	1.1476	1.1785
⅜	16	0.040	0.3867	0.4003	1¼	7	0.090	1.2726	1.3035
⅜	18	0.040	0.3988	0.4108	1⅜	6	0.150	1.5363	1.5724
⅜	20	0.040	0.4084	0.4192	1½	6	0.150	1.6613	1.6974
7⁄16	14	0.050	0.4638	0.4793	1⅝	5½	0.150	1.7601	1.7995
7⁄16	16	0.050	0.4792	0.4928	1¾	5	0.150	1.8536	1.8969
½	12	0.050	0.5057	0.5237	1⅞	5	0.150	1.9786	2.0219
½	13	0.050	0.5168	0.5334	2	4½	0.150	2.0651	2.1132
½	14	0.050	0.5263	0.5418	2¼	4½	0.150	2.3151	2.3632
9⁄16	12	0.050	0.5682	0.5862	2½	4	0.150	2.5170	2.5711
9⁄16	14	0.050	0.5888	0.6043	2¾	4	0.150	2.7670	2.8211
⅝	10	0.070	0.6618	0.6835	3	3½	0.200	3.1051	3.1670
⅝	11	0.070	0.6775	0.6972	3¼	3½	0.200	3.3551	3.4170
⅝	12	0.070	0.6907	0.7087	3½	3¼	0.250	3.7171	3.7837
11⁄16	10	0.070	0.7243	0.7460	3¾	3	0.250	3.9226	3.9948
11⁄16	11	0.070	0.7400	0.7597	4	3	0.250	4.1726	4.2448
¾	10	0.070	0.7868	0.8085	4¼	2⅞	0.250	4.3975	4.4729
¾	11	0.070	0.8025	0.8222	4½	2¾	0.250	4.6202	4.6989
¾	12	0.070	0.8157	0.8337	4¾	2⅝	0.250	4.8402	4.9227
13⁄16	9	0.070	0.8300	0.8541	5	2½	0.250	5.0572	5.1438
13⁄16	10	0.070	0.8493	0.8710	....	....	.....	......	.....

Table for Measuring Whitworth Standard Threads by the Three-wire Method

Diam. of Thread	No. of Threads per Inch	Diam. of Wire used	Diam. Measured over Wires	Diam. of Thread	No. of Threads per Inch	Diam. of Wire used	Diam. Measured over Wires
1/8	40	0.018	0.1420	2 1/4	4	0.150	2.3247
3/16	24	0.030	0.2158	2 3/8	4	0.150	2.4497
1/4	20	0.035	0.2808	2 1/2	4	0.150	2.5747
5/16	18	0.040	0.3502	2 5/8	4	0.150	2.6997
3/8	16	0.040	0.4015	2 3/4	3 1/2	0.200	2.9257
7/16	14	0.050	0.4815	2 7/8	3 1/2	0.200	3.0507
1/2	12	0.050	0.5249	3	3 1/2	0.200	3.1757
9/16	12	0.050	0.5874	3 1/8	3 1/2	0.200	3.3007
5/8	11	0.070	0.7011	3 1/4	3 1/4	0.200	3.3905
11/16	11	0.070	0.7636	3 3/8	3 1/4	0.200	3.5155
3/4	10	0.070	0.8115	3 1/2	3 1/4	0.200	3.6405
13/16	10	0.070	0.8740	3 5/8	3 1/4	0.200	3.7655
7/8	9	0.070	0.9187	3 3/4	3	0.200	3.8495
15/16	9	0.070	0.9812	3 7/8	3	0.200	3.9745
1	8	0.090	1.0848	4	3	0.200	4.0995
1 1/16	8	0.090	1.1473	4 1/8	3	0.200	4.2245
1 1/8	7	0.090	1.1812	4 1/4	2 7/8	0.250	4.4846
1 3/16	7	0.090	1.2437	4 3/8	2 7/8	0.250	4.6096
1 1/4	7	0.090	1.3062	4 1/2	2 7/8	0.250	4.7346
1 5/16	7	0.090	1.3687	4 5/8	2 7/8	0.250	4.8596
1 3/8	6	0.120	1.4881	4 3/4	2 3/4	0.250	4.9593
1 7/16	6	0.120	1.5506	4 7/8	2 3/4	0.250	5.0843
1 1/2	6	0.120	1.6131	5	2 3/4	0.250	5.2093
1 9/16	6	0.120	1.6756	5 1/8	2 3/4	0.250	5.3343
1 5/8	5	0.120	1.6847	5 1/4	2 5/8	0.250	5.4316
1 11/16	5	0.120	1.7472	5 3/8	2 5/8	0.250	5.5566
1 3/4	5	0.120	1.8097	5 1/2	2 5/8	0.250	5.6816
1 13/16	5	0.120	1.8722	5 5/8	2 5/8	0.250	5.8066
1 7/8	4 1/2	0.150	1.9942	5 3/4	2 1/2	0.250	5.9011
1 15/16	4 1/2	0.150	2.0567	5 7/8	2 1/2	0.250	6.0261
2	4 1/2	0.150	2.1192	6	2 1/2	0.250	6.1511
2 1/8	4 1/2	0.150	2.2442	......	......	....	....

Buckingham Simplified Formula which Includes Effect of Lead Angle. — The Formula 3 which follows gives very accurate results for the lower lead angles in determining measurement M. However, if extreme accuracy is essential, it may be advisable to use the involute helicoid formulas as explained later.

$$M = E + W \left(1 + \sin A_n\right) \text{ where } W = \frac{T \times \cos B}{\cos A_n} \qquad \text{(3 and 3a)}$$

Theoretically correct equations for determining measurement M are complex and cumbersome to apply. Formula 3 combines simplicity with a degree of accuracy which meets all but the most exacting requirements, particularly for lead angles below 8 or 10 degrees and the higher thread angles. However, the wire diameter used in Formula (3) must conform to that obtained by Formula (3a) to permit a direct solution or one not involving indeterminate equations and successive trials.

Application of Buckingham Formula: In the application of Formula (3) to screw threads or to worms, there are two general cases to be considered.

Case 1: The screw thread or worm is to be milled with a cutter having an included angle equal to the nominal or standard thread angle which is assumed to be the angle in the axial plane. For example, a 60-degree cutter is to be used for milling a thread. In this case, the thread angle in the plane of the axis will exceed 60 degrees by an amount increasing with the lead angle. This variation from the standard angle may be of little or no practical importance if the lead angle is small or if the mating nut (or teeth in the case of worm gearing) is formed to suit the thread as milled.

Case 2: The screw thread or worm is to be milled with a cutter reduced to whatever normal angle is equivalent to the standard thread angle in the axial plane. For example, a 29-degree Acme thread is to be milled with a cutter having some angle smaller than 29 degrees (the reduction increasing with the lead angle) to make the thread angle standard in the plane of the axis. Theoretically, the milling cutter angle should always be corrected to suit the normal angle; but if the lead angle is small, such correction may be unnecessary.

If the thread is cut in a lathe to the standard angle as measured in the axial plane, Case 2 applies in determining the pin size W and the over-all measurement M.

In solving all problems under Case 1, the angle A_n used in Formulas (3) and (3a) equals one-half the included angle of the milling cutter.

When Case 2 applies, the angle A_n for milled threads also equals one-half the included angle of the cutter, but the cutter angle is reduced and is determined as follows:
$$\tan A_n = \tan A \times \cos B$$
The included angle of the cutter or the normal included angle of the thread groove $= 2 A_n$. Examples 1 and 2 which follow illustrate Cases 1 and 2.

Example 1 (Case 1): The example which follows illustrates the case of an Acme screw thread which is milled with a cutter having an included angle of 29 degrees; consequently, the angle of the thread is over 29 degrees in the axial section.

The outside or major diameter is 3 inches; the pitch, ½ inch; the lead, 1 inch; the number of threads or "starts," 2. Find pin size W and measurement M.

Pitch diameter $E = 2.75$; $T = 0.25$; $L = 1.0$; $A_n = 14.50°$; $\tan A_n = 0.258618$; $\sin A_n = 0.25038$; $\cos A_n = 0.968148$.

$$\tan B = \frac{1.0}{3.1416 \times 2.75} = 0.115749; \quad B = 6.6025°$$

$$W = \frac{0.25 \times 0.993368}{0.968148} = 0.25651 \text{ inch}$$

$$M = 2.75 + 0.25651 \times (1 + 0.25038) = 3.0707 \text{ inches.}$$

Note: This value of M is only 0.0001 inch larger than that obtained by using the very accurate involute helicoid formula (4) referred to on the following page.

Example 2 (Case 2): A triple-threaded worm has a pitch diameter of 2.481 inches; pitch of 1.5 inches; lead of 4.5 inches; lead angle of 30 degrees and nominal thread angle of 60 degrees in axial plane. Milling cutter angle is to be reduced. $T = 0.75$ inch; $\cos B = 0.866025$; $\tan A = 0.57735$. Again use Formula (3) to see if it is applicable in this case.

Tan $A_n = \tan A \times \cos B = 0.57735 \times 0.866025 = 0.5000$; hence $A_n = 26.565°$ making the included cutter angle 53.13°. $\cos A_n = 0.89443$; $\sin A_n = 0.44721$.

$$W = \frac{0.75 \times 0.866025}{0.89443} = 0.72618 \text{ inch.}$$

$$M = 2.481 + 0.72618 \times (1 + 0.44721) = 3.532 \text{ inches.}$$

Note: If the value of measurement M is determined by using the following

Formula (4) it will be found that $M = 3.515+$ inches; hence the error equals $3.532 - 3.515 = 0.017$ inch approximately, which indicates that Formula (3) is not accurate enough in this case. The application of this simpler Formula (3) will depend upon the lead angle and thread angle (as previously explained) and also upon the class of work.

Buckingham Exact Involute Helicoid Formula Applied to Screw Threads. — When extreme accuracy is required in finding measurement M for obtaining a given pitch diameter, the equations which follow, although somewhat cumbersome to apply, have the merit of providing a direct and very accurate solution; consequently, they are preferable to the indeterminate equations and successive trial solutions heretofore employed when extreme precision is required. These equations are exact for involute helical gears and, consequently, give theoretically correct results when applied to a screw thread of the involute helicoidal form; they also give very close approximations for threads having intermediate profiles.

Helical Gear Equation Applied to Screw Thread Measurement: In applying the helical gear equations to a screw thread, use either the axial or normal thread angle and the lead angle of the helix. In order to keep the solution on a practical basis, either thread angle A or A_n, as the case may be, is assumed to equal the cutter angle of a milled thread. Actually, the profile of a milled thread will have some curvature in both axial and normal sections; hence angles A and A_n represent the angular approximations of these slightly curved profiles. The equations which follow give the values needed to solve the screw thread problem as a helical gear problem.

$$M = \frac{2 R_b}{\cos G} + W \tag{4}$$

$$\tan F = \frac{\tan A}{\tan B} = \frac{\tan A_n}{\sin B} ; \quad R_b = \frac{E}{2} \cos F \tag{4a and 4b}$$

$$T_a = \frac{T}{\tan B} ; \quad \tan H_b = \cos F \tan H \tag{4c and 4d}$$

$$\operatorname{inv} G = \frac{T_a}{E} + \operatorname{inv} F + \frac{W}{2 R_b \cos H_b} - \frac{\pi}{S} \tag{4e}$$

A table of involute functions is required (see Manual of Gear Design, Section 1, pages 100 to 129).

Example 3: To illustrate the application of Formula (4) and the supplementary formulas, assume that the number of starts $S = 6$; pitch diameter $E = 0.6250$; normal thread angle $A_n = 20°$; lead of thread $L = 0.864$ inch; $T = 0.072$; $W = 0.07013$ inch.

$$\tan B = \frac{L}{\pi E} = \frac{0.864}{1.9635} = 0.44003 ; \quad B = 23.751°$$

Helix angle $H = 90° - 23.751° = 66.249°$

$$\tan F = \frac{\tan A_n}{\sin B} = \frac{0.36397}{0.40276} = 0.90369 ; \quad F = 42.104°$$

$$R_b = \frac{E}{2} \cos F = \frac{0.6250}{2} \times 0.74193 = 0.23185$$

$$T_a = \frac{T}{\tan B} = \frac{0.072}{0.44003} = 0.16362$$

$$\tan H_b = \cos F \tan H = 0.74193 \times 2.27257 = 1.68609 ; \quad H_b = 59.328°$$

The involute function of G is found next by Formula (4e).

$$\text{inv } G = \frac{0.16362}{0.625} + 0.16884 + \frac{0.07013}{2 \times 0.23185 \times 0.51012} - \frac{3.1416}{6} = 0.20351$$

A table of involute functions shows that 44.350° is the angular equivalent of 0.20351; hence $G = 44.350°$.

$$M = \frac{2 R_b}{\cos G} + W = \frac{2 \times 0.23185}{0.71508} + 0.07013 = 0.71859 \text{ inch}$$

Accuracy of Formulas (3) and (4) Compared. — With the involute helicoid Formula (4) any wire size which makes contact with the flanks of the thread may be used; however, in the preceding example, the wire diameter W was obtained by Formula (3a) in order to compare Formula (4) with (3). If Example (3) is solved by Formula (3), $M = 0.71912$; hence the difference between the values of M obtained with Formulas (3) and (4) equals $0.71912 - 0.71859 = 0.00053$ inch. The included thread angle in this case is 40 degrees. If Formulas (3) and (4) are applied to a 29-degree thread, the difference in measurements M or the error resulting from the use of Formula (3) will be larger. For example, in case of an Acme thread having a lead angle of about 34 degrees, the difference in values of M obtained by the two formulas equals 0.0008 inch.

Checking Thickness of Acme Screw Threads. — If the included angle of a screw thread is as small as 29 degrees, it may be preferable to check the thread thickness instead of the pitch diameter, especially if there is a thickness tolerance. There are three general methods of checking thread thickness.

A simple direct method applicable to the larger pitches is to use a vernier gear-tooth caliper for measuring the thickness normal or square to the sides of the thread. This measurement should be made at a distance from the top or crest of an Acme thread equal to one-fourth of the pitch. The thickness at this pitch-line depth and in the plane of the axis equals one-half the pitch (minus any slight allowance for clearance between screw and nut). The thickness normal or square to the sides of the thread will be less than in the plane of the axis, the amount depending upon the lead angle. Normal width = width in plane of axis × cos lead angle.

To find the lead angle, divide the pitch circumference by the pitch (or by the lead, if a multiple thread), thus obtaining the cotangent of the angle.

One-Wire Method Applied to Acme Threads. — The accompanying diagram shows how a single wire or pin may be used in checking the size of an Acme or other 29-degree thread of small lead angle. When the wire is flush with the top of a thread, the thickness is correct provided the wire diameter is correct for a given pitch and the outside or major diameter of the screw is also correct. If the lead angle is ignored,

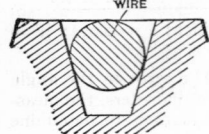

WIRE

Wire diameter for Acme thread = 0.48725 × pitch

Wire diam. for 29-deg. worm thread = 0.5149 × pitch

These formulas apply to threads which have straight sides in the plane of the axis and a basic thread thickness at the pitch line equal to one-half the pitch. The wire diameter may, of course, be increased slightly to provide clearance between screw and nut, but any such allowance should be reduced as the pitch decreases. The preceding formulas are accurate only when the lead angle is small. The points of contact and position of the wires will vary, especially with comparatively large lead angles. The formula which follows takes into account the lead angle.

Three-Wire Method for Checking Thickness of Acme Threads. — The application of the 3-wire method of checking the thickness of an Acme screw thread

Wire Sizes for American National Acme Threads

Threads per Inch	Best Size	Max.	Min.	Threads per Inch	Best Size	Max.	Min.
1	0.51645	0.65001	0.48726	5	0.10329	0.13000	0.09745
1¼	0.38734	0.48751	0.36545	6	0.08608	0.10834	0.08121
1½	0.34430	0.43334	0.32484	8	0.06456	0.08125	0.06091
2	0.25822	0.32501	0.24363	10	0.05164	0.06500	0.04873
2½	0.20658	0.26001	0.19491	12	0.04304	0.05417	0.04061
3	0.17215	0.21667	0.16242	14	0.03689	0.04643	0.03480
4	0.12911	0.16250	0.12182	16	0.03228	0.04063	0.03045

Based upon zero helix angle. Best size = 0.51645 × pitch; maximum size = 0.650013 × pitch; minimum size = 0.487263 × pitch.

is included in Report of the National Screw Thread Commission. In applying the 3-wire method for checking thread thickness, the procedure is the same as in checking pitch diameter although a different formula is required. Assume that D = basic major diameter of screw; M = measurement over wires; W = diameter of wires; a = half angle of thread; S = tangent of helix angle at pitch line; P = pitch; T = thread thickness at depth equal to $0.25P$.

$$T = 1.12931 \times P + 0.25862 \times (M - D) - W \times (1.29152 + 0.48407 \, S^2)$$

This formula transposed to show the correct measurement M equivalent to a given required thread thickness is as follows:

$$M = D + \frac{W \times (1.29152 + 0.48407 \times S^2) + T - 1.12931 \times P}{0.25862}$$

Example: An Acme screw thread has a basic major diameter of 5 inches and a quadruple thread of 0.5 inch pitch, making the lead of each thread equal 2 inches. Assume that the wire size is 0.258 inch (see table of wire sizes for Acme threads). Determine measurement M equivalent to a thread thickness T at the pitch line of 0.25 inch.

$$M = 5 + \frac{0.258 \times (1.29152 + 0.48407 \times 0.13402^2) + 0.25 - 1.12931 \times 0.5}{0.25862}$$

$$= 5.0804 \text{ inches}$$

Testing Angle of Thread by Three-wire Method. — The error in the angle of a thread may be determined by using sets of wires of two diameters, the measurement over the two sets of wires being followed by calculations to determine the amount of error, assuming that the angle cannot be tested by comparison with a standard plug gage which is known to be correct. The diameter of the small wires for the American standard thread is usually about 0.6 times the pitch and the diameter of the large wires, about 0.9 times the pitch. The total difference between the measurements over the large and small sets of wires is first determined. If the thread is an American standard or any other form having an included angle of 60 degrees, the difference between the two measurements should equal three times the difference between the diameters of the wires used. Thus, if the wires are 0.116 and 0.076 inch in diameter, respectively, the difference equals 0.116 − 0.076 = 0.040 inch. Therefore the difference between the micrometer readings for a standard angle of 60 degrees equals 3 × 0.040 = 0.120 inch in this case. If the angle is incorrect, the amount of error may be determined by the following formula, which applies to any thread regardless of angle:

$$\operatorname{Sin} a = \frac{A}{B - A}$$

In this formula,

A = difference in diameters of the large and small wires used;

B = total difference between the measurements over the large and small wires;

a = one-half the included thread angle.

Example: The diameter of the large wires used for testing the angle of a thread is 0.116 inch and of the small wires 0.076 inch. The measurement over the two sets of wires shows a total difference of 0.122 inch instead of the correct difference, 0.120 inch, for a standard angle of 60 degrees when using the sizes of wires mentioned. Therefore the amount of error is determined as follows:

$$\operatorname{Sin} a = \frac{0.040}{0.122 - 0.040} = \frac{0.040}{0.082} = 0.4878$$

By referring to a table of sines it will be seen that this value (0.4878) is the sine of 29 degrees 12 minutes, approximately. Therefore the angle of the thread is 58 degrees, 24 minutes or 1 degree 36 minutes less than the standard angle.

Measuring Taper Screw Threads by 3-Wire Method. — When the 3-wire method is used in measuring a taper screw thread the measurement is along a line that is not perpendicular to the axis of the screw thread, the inclination from the perpendicular equalling one-half the included angle of the taper. The formula which follows compensates for this inclination resulting from contact of the measuring instrument surfaces, with two wires on one side and one on the other. The taper thread is measured over the wires in the usual manner excepting that the single wire must be located in the thread at a point where the effective diameter is to be checked (as described more fully later). The formula shows the dimension equivalent to the correct pitch diameter at this given point. The general formula for taper screw threads follows:

M = measurement over the 3 wires; E = pitch diameter; a = one-half the angle of the thread; N = number of threads per inch; W = diameter of wires; b = one-half the angle of taper

$$M = \frac{E - \dfrac{\cot a}{2\,N} + W\,(1 + \operatorname{cosec} a)}{\sec b}$$

This formula is not theoretically correct but it is, however, accurate for screw threads having tapers of ¾ inch per foot or less. This general formula can be simplified for a given thread angle and taper. The simplified formula following (in which P = pitch) is for an American Standard Pipe Thread:

$$M = \frac{E - (0.86603 \times P) + 3 \times W}{1.00049}$$

Standard pitch diameters for pipe threads will be found in the table "American Standard Pipe Thread." The location of this pitch diameter or distance from the end of the pipe is also shown by the table. In using the formula for finding dimension M over the wires, the single wire is placed in whatever part of the thread groove locates it at the point where the pitch diameter is to be checked. The wire must be accurately located at this point. The other wires are then placed on each side of that thread which is diametrically opposite the single wire. If the pipe thread is straight or without taper,

$$M = E - (0.86603 \times P) + 3 \times W$$

Application of Formula to Pipe Thread: To illustrate the use of the formula for taper threads, assume that dimension M is required for an American Standard 3-inch pipe thread gage. The table " American Standard Pipe Thread " shows that the 3-inch size has 8 threads per inch or a pitch of 0.125 inch and a pitch diameter at the gaging notch of 3.3885 inches. Assume that the wire diameter is 0.07217 inch: Then when the pitch diameter is correct

$$M = \frac{3.3885 - (0.86603 \times 0.125) + 3 \times 0.07217}{1.00049} = 3.495 \text{ inch}$$

Pitch Diameter Equivalent to a Given Measurement Over the Wires: The formula following may be used to check the pitch diameter at any point along a tapering thread when measurement M over wires of a given diameter is known. In this formula E = the effective or pitch diameter at the position occupied by the single wire. The formula is not theoretically correct but gives very accurate results when applied to tapers of ¾ inch per foot or less.

$$E = 1.00049 \times M + (0.86603 \times P) - 3 \times W$$

Example: Measurement M = 3.495 inches at the gaging notch of a 3-inch pipe thread and the wire diameter = 0.07217 inch. Then:

$$E = 1.00049 \times 3.495 + (0.86603 \times 0.125) - 3 \times 0.07217 = 3.3885 \text{ inches}$$

Pitch Diameter at Any Point Along Taper Screw Thread: When the pitch diameter in any position along a tapering thread is known, the pitch diameter at any other position may be determined as follows:

Multiply the distance (measured along the axis) between the location of the known pitch diameter and the location of the required pitch diameter, by the taper per inch or by 0.0625 for American Standard Pipe Threads. Add this product to the known diameter, if the required diameter is at a larger part of the taper, or subtract if the required diameter is smaller.

Example: The pitch diameter of a 3-inch American Standard Pipe Thread is 3.3885 at the gaging notch. Determine the pitch diameter at the small end. The American Standard Pipe Thread Table shows that the distance between the gaging notch and the small end of a 3-inch pipe is 0.77 inch. Hence the pitch diameter at the small end = 3.3885 − (0.77 × 0.0625) = 3.3404 inches.

Three-Wire Method Applied to Buttress Threads. — The angles of buttress threads vary somewhat, especially on the front or load-resisting side. Formula (1) which follows may be applied to any angles required. In this formula M = measurement over wires when *pitch diameter E* is correct; A = included angle of thread and thread groove; a = angle of front face or load-resisting side, measured from a line perpendicular to screw thread axis; P = pitch of thread.

$$M = E - \left(\frac{P \times \sin(90 - a) \times \sin 90 - (A - a)}{\sin A} \right) + W \left(1 + \frac{\cos\left(\frac{A}{2} - a\right)}{\sin\frac{A}{2}} \right) \quad (1)$$

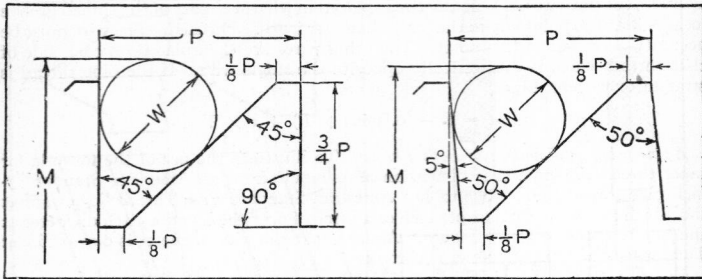

For given angles A and a, this general formula may be simplified as shown by the following examples. These simplified formulas contain constants with values depending upon angles A and a.

Best Wire Diameter: The wire diameter for obtaining pitch-line contact at the back of a buttress thread, may be determined by the following general formula (2).

$$W = \frac{P \times \sin(90 - a) \times \tan A \div 2}{\sin A} \qquad (2)$$

45-Degree Buttress Thread: The buttress thread shown by the diagram at the left, has a front or load-resisting side that is perpendicular to the axis of the screw. Measurement M equivalent to a correct pitch diameter E may be determined by formula (3):

$$M = E - P + (W \times 3.4142) \qquad (3)$$

Wire diameter W for pitch-line contact at back of thread = 0.5857 × pitch.

50-Degree Buttress Thread with Front-face Inclination of 5 Degrees: This buttress thread form is illustrated by the diagram at the right. Measurement M equivalent to the correct pitch diameter E may be determined by formula (4):

$$M = E - (P \times 0.91955) + (W \times 3.2235) \qquad (4)$$

Wire diameter W for pitch-line contact at back of thread = 0.60 × pitch. If the width of flat at crest and root = ⅛ × pitch, depth = 0.69 × pitch.

Checking International Standard Screw Threads by 3-Wire Method. — In applying the 3-wire method to the International standard thread (or to the French thread and German metric form), the measurement over the wires equivalent to a correct pitch diameter is determined by using the same formula as given in the accompanying table for the American standard. In using this formula, the dimensions for these 60-degree metric threads may all be in millimeters or they may be converted to inches.

Measurement of Pitch Diameter of Thread Ring Gages. — The application of direct methods of measurement to determine the pitch diameter of thread ring gages presents serious difficulties, particularly in securing proper contact pressure when a high degree of precision is required. The usual practice is to fit the ring gage to a master setting plug. When the thread ring gage is of correct lead, angle, and thread form, within close limits, this method is quite satisfactory and represents standard American practice. It is the only method available for small sizes of threads. For the larger sizes, various more or less satisfactory methods have been devised, but none of these have found wide application.

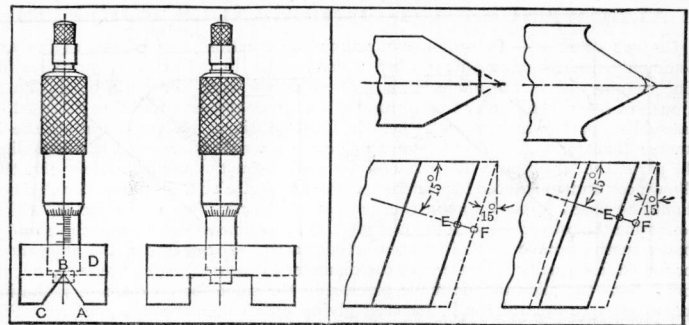

Measuring Flat or Radius at Point of Thread Tools. — To measure the width of the flat of an American standard thread tool or the radius of a Whitworth thread tool, a micrometer arranged as shown at the left may be used. The angle *ABC* of block *D* must be made to fit the angle of the tool, and a different block must be used for American standard and the Whitworth thread tools, on account of the different angles. By this micrometer, the distance *EF* can be measured from which the exact width of flat or the correct radius can be determined. Tables are given herewith showing what the distance *EF* should be for American standard (U. S. standard), and the Whitworth standard.

Table for Determining Flat or Radius at Point of Thread Tools
(American or U. S. Standard and Whitworth Threads — 15-degree Clearance Angle)

No. of Threads per Inch	U. S. Thread, *EF* on Thread Tool	Whitworth Thread, *EF* on Thread Tool	No. of Threads per Inch	U. S. U. S. Thread, *EF* on Thread Tool	Whitworth Thread, *EF* on Thread Tool	No. of Threads per Inch	U. S. Thread, *EF* on Thread Tool	Whitworth Thread, *EF* on Thread Tool
2¼	0.0465	0.0687	9	0.0116	0.0172	34	0.0031	0.0045
2⅜	0.0440	0.0651	10	0.0105	0.0155	36	0.0029	0.0043
2½	0.0418	0.0619	11	0.0095	0.0141	38	0.0027	0.0041
2⅝	0.0398	0.0589	12	0.0087	0.0129	40	0.0026	0.0039
2¾	0.0380	0.0562	13	0.0080	0.0119	42	0.0025	0.0037
2⅞	0.0364	0.0538	14	0.0075	0.0110	44	0.0024	0.0035
3	0.0349	0.0515	15	0.0070	0.0103	46	0.0023	0.0034
3¼	0.0322	0.0476	16	0.0065	0.0097	48	0.0022	0.0032
3½	0.0299	0.0442	18	0.0058	0.0086	50	0.0021	0.0031
4	0.0261	0.0387	20	0.0052	0.0077	52	0.0020	0.0030
4½	0.0232	0.0344	22	0.0048	0.0070	56	0.0019	0.0028
5	0.0209	0.0309	24	0.0044	0.0064	60	0.0017	0.0026
5½	0.0190	0.0281	26	0.0040	0.0059	64	0.0016	0.0024
6	0.0174	0.0258	28	0.0037	0.0055	68	0.0015	0.0023
7	0.0149	0.0221	30	0.0035	0.0052	72	0.0015	0.0021
8	0.0131	0.0193	32	0.0033	0.0048	80	0.0013	0.0019

ALLOWANCES AND TOLERANCES FOR FITS

Classes of Fits. — In ordinary machine construction, five classes of fits are commonly used: running fit; push fit; driving fit; forced fit; and shrinkage fit. The running fit, as the name implies, is employed when the parts must rotate; a push fit is not sufficiently free to rotate; the other classes referred to are used in assembling parts which must be held in fixed positions. When the allowance is smaller than for a running fit, and a moderate pressure is required in assembling the parts, the term "push fit" is sometimes used. The tables which follow give the allowances and tolerances for different classes of fits. The allowance or tolerance should be based primarily upon the function of the part but as the factors which determine the proper values differ considerably, the dimensions given in these tables may sometimes have to be increased or decreased. For example, the allowances for forced fits usually increase with the diameter to secure greater pressure, but in some shops the allowance is made practically the same for all diameters, the increased surface area of the larger sizes giving sufficient increase in pressure. For running fits, the allowances are also increased with the diameter, but may be varied according to the length of the bearing surface. The British standard limits and fits (see tables) include four standard grades of holes and a series of maximum and minimum shaft diameters providing fourteen different fits.

Basic Dimensions. — The basic size of a screw thread or machine part is the theoretical or nominal standard size from which variations are made. For example, a shaft may have a *basic* diameter of 2 inches, but a maximum variation of minus 0.010 inch may be permitted. The minimum hole should be of basic size in all cases where the use of standard tools represents the greatest economy. The maximum shaft should be of basic size in all cases where the use of standard purchased material, without further machining, represents the greatest economy, even though special tools are required to machine the mating part.

Tolerances. — Tolerance is the amount of variation permitted on dimensions or surfaces of machine parts. The tolerance is equal to the difference between the maximum and minimum limits of any specified dimension. For example, if the maximum limit for the diameter of a shaft is 2.000 inches and its minimum limit 1.990 inches, the tolerance for this diameter is 0.010 inch. By determining the maximum and minimum clearances required on operating surfaces, the extent of these tolerances is established. As applied to the fitting of machine parts, the word tolerance means the amount that duplicate parts are allowed to vary in size in connection with manufacturing operations, owing to unavoidable imperfections of workmanship. Tolerance may also be defined as the amount that duplicate parts are permitted to vary in size in order to secure sufficient accuracy without unnecessary refinement. The terms "tolerance" and "allowance" are often used interchangeably, but, according to common usage, *allowance* is a difference in dimensions prescribed in order to secure various classes of fits between different parts.

Unilateral and Bilateral Tolerances. — The term "unilateral tolerance" means that the total tolerance, as related to a basic dimension, is in *one* direction only. For example, if the basic dimension were 1 inch and the tolerance were expressed as 1.00 − 0.002, or as 1.00 + 0.002, these would be unilateral tolerances, since the total tolerance in each case is in one direction. On the contrary, if the tolerance were divided, so as to be partly plus and partly minus, it would be classed as "bilateral." Thus, $1.00 {+0.001 \atop -0.001}$ is an example of bilateral tolerance, because the total tolerance of 0.002 is given in two directions — plus and minus.

When unilateral tolerances are used, one of the three following methods should be used to express them:

(1) Specify limiting dimensions only as

      Diameter of hole: 2.250, 2.252
      Diameter of shaft: 2.249, 2.247

(2) One limiting size may be specified with its tolerances as

      Diameter of hole: 2.250 + 0.002, − 0.000
      Diameter of shaft: 2.249 + 0.000, − 0.002

(3) The nominal size may be specified for both parts, with a notation showing both allowance and tolerance, as

      Diameter of hole: 2¼ + 0.002, − 0.000
      Diameter of shaft: 2¼ − 0.001, − 0.003

Bilateral tolerances should be specified as such, usually with plus and minus tolerances of equal amount. Example of the expression of bilateral tolerances follow:

$$2 \pm 0.001 \quad \text{or} \quad 2 \begin{array}{c} + 0.001 \\ - 0.001 \end{array}$$

How to Apply Tolerances. — According to practice approved by the Society of Automotive Engineers, tolerances should show the permissible amount of variation in the direction that is less dangerous. When a variation in either direction is equally dangerous, a bilateral tolerance should be given. When a variation in one direction is more dangerous than a variation in another, a unilateral tolerance should be given in the less dangerous direction.

For non-mating surfaces, or atmospheric fits, the tolerances may be bilateral, or unilateral, depending entirely upon the nature of the variations that develop in manufacture. On mating surfaces, with but few exceptions, the tolerances should be unilateral.

Where tolerances are required on the distances between holes, usually they should be bilateral, as variation in either direction is usually equally dangerous. The variation in the distance between shafts carrying gears, however, should always be unilateral and plus; otherwise the gears might run too tight. A slight increase in the backlash between gears is seldom of much importance.

One exception to the use of unilateral tolerances on mating surfaces occurs when tapers are involved. In such cases either bilateral or unilateral tolerances may prove advisable, depending upon conditions. These should be determined in the same manner as the tolerances on the distances between holes. When a variation either in or out of the position of the mating taper surfaces is equally dangerous, the tolerances should be bilateral. When a variation in one direction is of less danger than a variation in the opposite direction, the tolerance should be unilateral and in the less dangerous direction.

Locating Tolerance Dimensions — Only one dimension in the same straight line can be controlled within fixed limits. That is the distance between the cutting surface of the tool and the locating or registering surface of the part being machined. Therefore, it is incorrect to locate any point or surface with tolerances from more than one point in the same straight line.

Every part of a mechanism must be located in each plane. Every operating part must be located with proper operating allowances. After such requirements of location are met, all other surfaces should have liberal clearances. Dimensions should be given between those points or surfaces that it is essential to hold in a specific relation to each other. This applies particularly to those surfaces in each plane which control the location of other component parts. Many dimensions are relatively unimportant in this respect. It is good practice in such cases to establish a common locating-point in each plane and give, so far as possible all such dimensions from these common locating-points. The locating points on the drawing, the locating or registering points used for machining the surfaces and the locating points for measuring should all be identical.

The initial dimensions placed on component drawings should be the exact dimensions that would be used if it were possible to work without tolerances. Tolerances should be given in that direction in which variations will cause the least harm or danger. When a variation in either direction is equally dangerous, the tolerances should be of equal amount in both directions, or bilateral. The initial clearance, or allowance, between operating parts should be as small as the operation of the mechanism will permit. The maximum clearance should be as great as the proper functioning of the mechanism will permit.

Direction of Tolerances on Gages. — The following fundamental principles have been adopted in connection with the American Standard Tolerances, Allowances and Gages for Metal Fits. The extreme sizes for all plain limit gages shall not exceed the extreme limits of the part to be gaged. All variations in the gages, whatever their cause or purpose, shall bring these gages within these extreme limits. Thus a gage which represents a minimum limit may be larger, but never smaller, than the minimum size specified for the part to be gaged, likewise the gage which represents a maximum limit may be smaller, but never larger, than the maximum size specified for the part to be gaged.

The final result sought by gaging is interchangeable manufacture in some degree. This means that the parts of a mechanism can be assembled without *fitting* one part to another and when assembled the parts will function properly.

Applied to manufactured material, the result sought is sufficient uniformity in size and contour to adapt the material without further fitting to the requirements of the industries. The fundamental principle involved in interchangeable manufacture requires that "a system of standardization and classification of fits shall establish a clearly defined line at which interference between mating parts begins." Hence, the standard or basic size, as physically represented by a correct standard master gage, represents the line at which this interference begins between mating parts. It is the minimum size of the external members of all mating parts of standardized practice, regardless of the kind of fit. It is the maximum size of internal members of all mating parts where interference begins or that fit metal to metal.

The limits of the component as physically represented by the limit master gages shall not be exceeded as a result either of tolerance of wear of the gages. "Go" gages, or the equivalent verification of all the factors involved in the fit, are necessary to prevent interference of mating parts. In the case of force fits, "go" gages are necessary to determine the maximum amount of interference between mating parts.

"Not go" gages, or the equivalent verification of the determining factor are necessary to prevent the maximum looseness of mating parts exceeding the limits specified. In the case of force fits, "not go" gages are necessary to determine the minimum amount of interference between mating parts.

Gage Tolerance Based upon Work Tolerance. — According to the plan to be described (which represents the practice of a prominent manufacturer of gages), a tolerance equal to 10 per cent of the tolerance on the work is generally allowed on ordinary working and inspection gages. Thus, if the work tolerance is 0.005 inch, the gage tolerance equals 0.0005 inch for both the working and inspection gages. There is a difference, however, between the maximum and minimum dimensions of the working and inspection gages. The minimum size of the working gage is made 10 per cent of the tolerance *larger* than the minimum size of the inspection gage, and the maximum size of the working gage is made 10 per cent of the tolerance *smaller* than the maximum size of the inspection gage.

Assume that the minimum and maximum diameters of a shaft are 1 and 1.005 inches respectively, the tolerance being 0.005 inch. The "not go" working gage will then measure 1.0005 inches, 10 per cent of the 0.005-inch tolerance being added to the minimum dimension of the shaft (1.000 + 10 per cent of 0.005 = 1.0005). The "go" working gage will measure 1.0045 inch, since 10 per cent of the tolerance, or 0.0005, is subtracted from the maximum size of the shaft (1.005 − 0.0005 = 1.0045).

When working gages are within the minimum and maximum limits allowed on the work and on the inspection gages, it is evident that all parts which pass the working gages will also pass the inspection gages. When the working gages are made the same size as the inspection gages, disputes are liable to arise and, moreover, working gages may wear faster and become larger than the inspection gages, provided they were both made the same size originally.

The tolerance of the gage itself should be properly applied to avoid any overlapping of dimensions between the working and inspection gages. This gage tolerance should be *minus* on "go" female gages and "not go" male gages, with the exception of the outside and root diameters of "not go" thread gages. The tolerance should be *plus* on "go" male gages and "not go" female gages, again excepting the outside and root diameters of "not go" thread gages. The dimensions on thread gages should be the same as corresponding diameters of "go" gages.

Allowance for Forced Fits. — The allowance per inch of diameter usually ranges from 0.001 inch to 0.0025 inch, 0.0015 being a fair average. Ordinarily the allowance per inch decreases as the diameter increases; thus the total allowance for a diameter of 2 inches might be 0.004 inch, whereas for a diameter of 8 inches the total allowance might not be over 0.009 or 0.010 inch. The parts to be assembled by forced fits are usually made cylindrical, although sometimes they are slightly tapered. The advantages of the taper form are that the possibility of abrasion of the fitted surfaces is reduced; that less pressure is required in assembling; and that the parts are more readily separated when renewal is required. On the other hand, the taper fit is less reliable, because if it loosens, the entire fit is free with but little axial movement. Some lubricant, such as white lead and lard oil mixed to the consistency of paint, should be applied to the pin and bore before assembling, to reduce the tendency of abrasion.

Pressure for Forced Fits. — The pressure required for assembling cylindrical parts depends not only upon the allowance for the fit, but also upon the area of the fitted surfaces, the pressure increasing in proportion to the distance that the inner member is forced in. The approximate ultimate pressure in tons can be determined by the use of the following formula in conjunction with the accompanying

Pressure Factors

Diameter, Inches	Pressure Factor	Diameter, Inches	Pressure Factor	Diameter, Inches	Pressure Factor	Diameter, Inches	Pressure Factor	Diameter, Inches	Pressure Factor
1	500	3½	132	6	75	9	48.7	14	30.5
1¼	395	3¾	123	6¼	72	9½	46.0	14½	29.4
1½	325	4	115	6½	69	10	43.5	15	28.3
1¾	276	4¼	108	6¾	66	10½	41.3	15½	27.4
2	240	4½	101	7	64	11	39.3	16	26.5
2¼	212	4¾	96	7¼	61	11½	37.5	16½	25.6
2½	189	5	91	7½	59	12	35.9	17	24.8
2¾	171	5¼	86	7¾	57	12½	34.4	17½	24.1
3	156	5½	82	8	55	13	33.0	18	23.4
3¼	143	5¾	78	8½	52	13½	31.7	....	....

Forced Fit Allowances — From Practice

For mild steel pins and shafts, pressed into cast-iron crank disks, except size marked * which had a cast steel crank disk.

Mean Diam. of Pin, Inches	Length of Fit, Inches	Mean Diam. of Hole, Inches	Total Allowance	Allowance per Inch of Diam.	Area of Fitted Surface, Square Inches	Volume within Fitted Surface, Cubic Inches	Pressure at Mid-position, Tons	Maximum Pressure, Tons
1.8798	6.125	1.8767	0.0031	0.0017	36.0	16.7	10	20
1.8819	6.125	1.8770	0.0042	0.0022	36.0	16.7	15	23
1.8774	4.375	1.8764	0.0010	0.0005	24.4	13.7	1	1
2.7455	4.500	2.7387	0.0068	0.0024	38.7	26.5	12	25
2.7465	4.500	2.7437	0.0028	0.0010	38.7	26.5	12	23
3.2610	5.000	3.2542	0.0068	0.0021	51.0	41.5	20	45
3.2625	5.000	3.2555	0.0070	0.0020	51.0	41.5	15	30
3.2670	5.000	3.2610	0.0060	0.0018	51.0	41.5	15	20
4.2505	6.000	4.2402	0.0103	0.0024	79.8	85.1	22	44
4.2388	6.625	4.2478	0.0091	0.0021	78.1	93.4	30	60
*4.2303	6.500	4.2224	0.0079	0.0019	95.8	91.0	60	125
5.9343	4.062	5.9216	0.0127	0.0022	75.7	112.2	16	25
5.9381	4.000	5.9252	0.0129	0.0022	74.4	110.4	18	35
5.9294	4.125	5.9194	0.0100	0.0017	76.7	113.8	15	25
6.8829	5.125	6.8697	0.0132	0.0020	110.7	190.1	20	42
6.8890	5.000	6.8785	0.0105	0.0015	108.0	185.9	22	45
6.8692	4.875	6.8550	0.0142	0.0021	104.8	180.4	35	65
7.8884	5.500	7.8730	0.0154	0.0020	135.9	267.3	32	64
7.8715	6.500	7.8575	0.0140	0.0018	160.5	315.9	25	50
7.8620	5.625	7.8460	0.0160	0.0020	138.2	272.8	40	80
8.9240	6.125	8.9050	0.0190	0.0021	170.8	378.9	45	68
8.9000	6.750	8.8848	0.0152	0.0017	188.4	419.9	47	96
8.8780	6.500	8.8669	0.0112	0.0013	180.7	401.0	45	92

Forced Fit Allowances — From Practice

For engine cranks of open-hearth steel castings, bored smooth and keyseated

Diameter of Hub	Diameter of Bore	Length of Hub	Allowance for Fit	Allowance per Inch Diameter	Pressure in Tons	Diameter of Hub	Diameter of Bore	Length of Hub	Allowance for Fit	Allowance per Inch Diameter	Pressure in Tons
4¼	2	2⅜	0.006	0.0030	3	8½	4½	5	0.012	0.0033	40
4½	2⅜	2⅜	0.007	0.0029	6	9½	4¾	5¼	0.015	0.0034	45
4½	2⅜	2½	0.008	0.0033	8	11	5½	5 9/16	0.015	0.0024	45
5½	2¾	2¾	0.008	0.0029	12	12	5¾	5¾	0.015	0.0026	55
6¼	3	3⅛	0.010	0.0033	18	14	6	6	0.015	0.0025	70
7¾	3½	3⅜	0.010	0.0028	25	14½	6¾	6¾	0.015	0.0022	75
8	3¾	3⅝	0.012	0.0034	35	15	7	7	0.015	0.0020	85
8½	4¼	4½	0.012	0.0028	35	...	...	...	....	....	...

table of "Pressure Factors." Assuming that A = area of surface in contact in "fit"; a = total allowance in inches; P = ultimate pressure required, in tons; F = pressure factor based upon assumption that the diameter of the hub is twice the diameter of the bore, that the shaft is of machine steel, and that the hub is of cast iron:

$$P = \frac{A \times a \times F}{2}$$

Allowance for Given Pressure. — By transposing the preceding formula, the approximate allowance for a required ultimate tonnage can be determined. Thus, $a = \frac{2\,P}{AF}$. The average ultimate pressure in tons commonly used ranges from 7 to 10 times the diameter in inches.

Expansion Fits. — In assembling certain classes of work requiring a very tight fit, the inner member is contracted by sub-zero cooling to permit insertion into the outer member and a tight fit is obtained as the temperature rises and the inner part expands. In order to obtain the sub-zero temperature, solid carbon dioxide or "dry ice" has been used but its temperature of about 109 degrees F. below zero will not contract some parts sufficiently to permit insertion in holes or recesses. Greater contraction may be obtained by using high purity liquid nitrogen which has a temperature of about 320 degrees F. below zero. During a temperature reduction from 75 degrees F. to —321 degrees F., the shrinkage per inch of diameter varies from about 0.002 to 0.003 inch for steel; 0.0042 inch for aluminum alloys; 0.0046 inch for magnesium alloys; 0.0033 inch for copper alloys; 0.0023 inch for monel metal; and 0.0017 inch for cast iron (not alloyed). The cooling equipment may vary from an insulated bucket to a special automatic unit, depending upon the kind and quantity of work. One type of unit is so arranged that parts are precooled by vapors from the liquid nitrogen before immersion. With another type, cooling is entirely by the vapor method.

Shrinkage Fits. — General practice seems to favor a smaller allowance for shrinkage fits than for forced fits, although in many shops the allowances are practically the same in each case, and for some classes of work, shrinkage allowances exceed those for forced fits. In any case, the shrinkage allowance varies to a great extent with the form and construction of the part which has to be shrunk into place. The thickness or amount of metal around the hole is the most important factor. The way in which the metal is distributed also has an influence on the results. Shrinkage allowances for locomotive driving wheel tires adopted by the American Railway Master Mechanics Association are as follows:

Center diameter, inches	38	44	50	56	62	66
Allowance, inches	0.040	0.047	0.053	0.060	0.066	0.070

Whether parts are to be assembled by forced or shrinkage fits depends upon conditions. For example, to press a tire over its wheel center, without heating, would ordinarily be a rather awkward and difficult job. On the other hand, pins, etc., are easily and quickly forced into place with a hydraulic press and there is the additional advantage of knowing the exact pressure required in assembling, whereas there is more or less uncertainty connected with a shrinkage fit, unless the stresses are calculated. Tests to determine the difference in the quality of shrinkage and forced fits showed that the resistance of a shrinkage fit to slippage was, for an axial pull, 3.66 times greater than that of a forced fit, and in rotation or torsion, 3.2 times greater. In each comparative test, the dimensions and allowances were the same.

Wheel and Axle Press Fits

	Axle					Wheel							Assembling Pressure, Tons
Size of Journal, Inches	Diameter Wheel Fit, Outside End	Diameter Wheel Fit, Inside End	Cutting Speed, Ft. per Minute	Depth of Cut	Feed, Inches	Diam., Inches	Material	Diameter of Bore, Outside End	Diameter of Bore, Inside End	Cutting Speed, Ft. per Minute	Feed, Inches	Cuts per Wheel	
4¼ × 8	5.708 5.704	5.706 5.704	40	1/32	1/8	33	C. I.	5.700 5.702	5.700 5.702	25	3/16	2	50
3¾ × 7	5.341 5.341	5.345 5.345	40	1/32	1/8	33	C. I.	5.332 5.332	5.336 5.331	25	5/16	2	65
3¾ × 7	5.339 5.339	5.338 5.338	40	1/32	1/8	33	C. I.	5.333 5.333	5.333 5.333	25	5/16	2	40
5½ × 10	5.480 5.480	5.480 5.480	25	1/32	1/8	30	S. T.	5.469 5.467	5.465 5.470	25	3/16	2	75*
4¼ × 8	5.763 5.763	5.761 5.763	50	1/32	1/16	33	C. I.	5.7445 5.7445	5.743 5.743	18	1/8	2	61
4¼ × 8	5.769 5.775	5.770 5.769	50	1/32	1/16	33	C. I.	5.756 5.756	5.7545 5.7545	18	1/8	2	62
5½ × 10	6.873 6.8715	6.872 6.869	50	1/32	1/16	33	C. I.	6.851 6.851	6.851 6.851	18	1/8	2	75
5½ × 10	6.969 6.969	6.972 6.971	50	1/32	1/16	33	C. I.	6.956 6.956	6.9545 6.9545	18	1/8	2	75
4¼ × 8	5.748 5.743	5.749 5.749	25	1/32	3/32	36	C. I.	5.740 5.740	5.740 5.740	16	9/16	2	57
5 × 9	6.371 6.371	6.380 6.382	25	1/32	3/32	33	C. I.	6.362 6.362	6.362 6.362	18	9/16	2	65
3¾ × 7	5.355 5.355	5.356 5.359	25	1/32	3/32	33	C. I.	5.352 5.352	5.348 5.348	18	3/32	1	60
3¾ × 7	5.388 5.390	5.395 5.398	25	1/32	3/32	33	C. I.	5.383 5.383	5.383 5.383	18	9/16	2	60
4¼ × 8	5.787 5.783	5.797 5.792	35	1/32	5/32	36	S.	5.785 5.785	5.785 5.785	18	1/16	2	119*
4¼ × 8	5.774 5.774	5.777 5.776	35	1/32	5/32	36	S.	5.767 5.771	5.775 5.776	18	1/16	2	51
5 × 9	6.436 6.438	6.432 6.433	35	1/32	5/32	33	C. I.	6.401 6.404	6.412 6.410	24	1/8	2	85
3¾ × 7	5.336 5.345	5.341 5.345	35	1/32	5/32	33	C. I.	5.333 5.333	5.337 5.337	24	1/8	2	64

* Wheel removed–pressure excessive. C. I. = cast iron; S. T. = steel tired; S. = steel. (The table represents practice in four railroad shops. Two dimensions are given for each axle or bore diameter, these dimensions being measured at right angles to each other.)

Allowances for Shrinkage Fits. — The most important point to consider when calculating shrinkage fits is the stress in the hub at the bore, which depends chiefly upon the shrinkage allowance. If the allowance is excessive, the elastic limit of the material will be exceeded and permanent set will occur, or, in extreme cases, the ultimate strength of the metal will be exceeded and the hub will burst. The intensity of the grip of the fit and the resistance to slippage depends mainly upon the thickness of the hub; the greater the thickness, the stronger the grip, and *vice versa*. Assuming the modulus of elasticity for steel to be 30,000,000, and for cast iron, 15,000,000, the shrinkage allowance per inch of nominal diameter can be determined by the following formula, in which A = allowance per inch of diameter; T = true tangential tensile stress at inner surface of outer member; C = factor taken from one of the accompanying tables, "Factors for Calculating Shrinkage Fit Allowances." For a cast-iron hub and steel shaft:

$$A = \frac{T(2+C)}{30,000,000} \tag{1}$$

When both hub and shaft are of steel:

$$A = \frac{T(1+C)}{30,000,000} \tag{2}$$

If the shaft is solid, the factor C is taken from Table 1; if it is hollow and the hub is of steel, factor C is taken from Table 2; if it is hollow and the hub is of cast iron, the factor is taken from Table 3.

Table 1.   Factors for Calculating Shrinkage Fit Allowances

Values of Ratio C for solid steel shafts of nominal diameter D_1, and hubs of steel or cast iron of nominal external and internal diameters D_2 and D_1, respectively.

Ratio of Diameters $\frac{D_2}{D_1}$	Steel Hub	Cast-iron Hub	Ratio of Diameters $\frac{D_2}{D_1}$	Steel Hub	Cast-iron Hub
1.5	0.227	0.234	2.8	0.410	0.432
1.6	0.255	0.263	3.0	0.421	0.444
1.8	0.299	0.311	3.2	0.430	0.455
2.0	0.333	0.348	3.4	0.438	0.463
2.2	0.359	0.377	3.6	0.444	0.471
2.4	0.380	0.399	3.8	0.450	0.477
2.6	0.397	0.417	4.0	0.455	0.482

Example 1: A steel crank web 15 inches outside diameter is to be shrunk on a 10-inch solid steel shaft. Required the allowance per inch of shaft diameter to produce a maximum tensile stress in the crank of 25,000 pounds per square inch, assuming the stresses in the crank to be equivalent to those in a ring of the diameter given.

The ratio of the external to the internal diameters equals $15 \div 10 = 1.5$; $T =$ 25,000 pounds; from Table 1, $C = 0.227$. Substituting in Formula (2):

$$A = \frac{25,000 \times (1 + 0.227)}{30,000,000} = 0.001 \text{ inch.}$$

Example 2: Find the allowance per inch of diameter for a 10-inch shaft having a 5-inch axial hole through it, other conditions being the same as in Example 1.

The ratio of external to internal diameters of the hub equals $15 \div 10 = 1.5$, as before, and the ratio of external to internal diameters of the shaft equals $10 \div 5 = 2$. From Table 2, we find that factor $C = 0.455$; $T = 25,000$ pounds. Substituting these values in Formula (2):

$$A = \frac{25,000 \times (1 + 0.455)}{30,000,000} = 0.0012 \text{ inch.}$$

The increase in allowance, as compared with Example 1, is due to the fact that the hollow shaft is more compressible.

Table 2. Factors for Calculating Shrinkage Fit Allowances

Values of Ratio C for hollow steel shafts of external and internal diameters D_1 and D_0, respectively, and steel hubs of nominal external diameter D_2.

$\frac{D_2}{D_1}$	$\frac{D_1}{D_0}$	C	$\frac{D_2}{D_1}$	$\frac{D_1}{D_0}$	C	$\frac{D_2}{D_1}$	$\frac{D_1}{D_0}$	C
1.5	2.0	0.455	2.4	2.0	0.760	3.4	2.0	0.876
	2.5	0.357		2.5	0.597		2.5	0.689
	3.0	0.313		3.0	0.523		3.0	0.602
	3.5	0.288		3.5	0.481		3.5	0.555
1.6	2.0	0.509	2.6	2.0	0.793	3.6	2.0	0.888
	2.5	0.400		2.5	0.624		2.5	0.698
	3.0	0.350		3.0	0.546		3.0	0.611
	3.5	0.322		3.5	0.502		3.5	0.562
1.8	2.0	0.599	2.8	2.0	0.820	3.8	2.0	0.900
	2.5	0.471		2.5	0.645		2.5	0.707
	3.0	0.412		3.0	0.564		3.0	0.619
	3.5	0.379		3.5	0.519		3.5	0.570
2.0	2.0	0.667	3.0	2.0	0.842	4.0	2.0	0.909
	2.5	0.524		2.5	0.662		2.5	0.715
	3.0	0.459		3.0	0.580		3.0	0.625
	3.5	0.422		3.5	0.533		3.5	0.576
2.2	2.0	0.718	3.2	2.0	0.860		.....	......
	2.5	0.565		2.5	0.676		.....	......
	3.0	0.494		3.0	0.591		.....	......
	3.5	0.455		3.5	0.544		.....	......

Example 3: If the crank web in Example 1 is of cast iron and 4000 pounds per square inch is the maximum tensile stress in the hub, what is the allowance per inch of diameter?

$$\frac{D_2}{D_1} = 1.5; \quad T = 4000.$$

In Table 1, we find that $C = 0.234$. Substituting in Formula (1), for cast-iron hubs, $A = 0.0003$ inch, which, owing to the lower tensile strength of cast iron, is about one-third the shrinkage allowance in Example 1, although the stress is two-thirds of the elastic limit.

Temperatures for Shrinkage Fits. — The temperature to which the outer member in a shrinkage fit should be heated for clearance in assembling the parts depends on the total expansion required and on the coefficient α of linear expansion of the metal (that is, the increase in length of any section of the metal in any direction for an increase in temperature of 1 degree F.). The total expansion in diameter which is required consists of the total allowance for shrinkage and an added amount for clearance. The value of the coefficient α is, for nickel-steel, 0.000007; for steel

Table 3. Factors for Calculating Shrinkage Fit Allowances

$\frac{D_2}{D_1}$	$\frac{D_1}{D_0}$	C	$\frac{D_2}{D_1}$	$\frac{D_1}{D_0}$	C	$\frac{D_2}{D_1}$	$\frac{D_1}{D_0}$	C
			Values of Ratio C for hollow steel shafts and cast-iron hubs. Notation as in Table 2.					
1.5	2.0	0.468	2.4	2.0	0.798	3.4	2.0	0.926
	2.5	0.368		2.5	0.628		2.5	0.728
	3.0	0.322		3.0	0.549		3.0	0.637
	3.5	0.296		3.5	0.506		3.5	0.587
1.6	2.0	0.527	2.6	2.0	0.834	3.6	2.0	0.941
	2.5	0.414		2.5	0.656		2.5	0.740
	3.0	0.362		3.0	0.574		3.0	0.647
	3.5	0.333		3.5	0.528		3.5	0.596
1.8	2.0	0.621	2.8	2.0	0.864	3.8	2.0	0.953
	2.5	0.488		2.5	0.679		2.5	0.749
	3.0	0.427		3.0	0.594		3.0	0.656
	3.5	0.393		3.5	0.547		3.5	0.603
2.0	2.0	0.696	3.0	2.0	0.888	4.0	2.0	0.964
	2.5	0.547		2.5	0.698		2.5	0.758
	3.0	0.479		3.0	0.611		3.0	0.663
	3.5	0.441		3.5	0.562		3.5	0.610
2.2	2.0	0.753	3.2	2.0	0.909	.....	.....	.....
	2.5	0.592		2.5	0.715		.....	.....
	3.0	0.518		3.0	0.625		.....	.....
	3.5	0.477		3.5	0.576		.....	.....

in general, 0.0000065; for cast iron, 0.0000062. As an example, take an outer member of steel to be expanded 0.005 inch per inch of internal diameter, 0.001 being the shrinkage allowance and the remainder for clearance. Then:

$$\alpha \times t^\circ = 0.005$$

$$t = \frac{0.005}{0.0000065} = 769 \text{ degrees F.}$$

The value t is the number of degrees F. which the temperature of the member must be raised above that of the room temperature.

Table 1. Free-fit Tolerances and Allowances — American Standard

For running fits with speeds of 600 R.P.M. or over, and journal pressures of 600 lb. per sq. in. or over.

Diameters	Tolerances				Min. Allowance	Max. Allowance
	Hole +	Hole −	Shaft −	Shaft −		
¼	0.0008	0.0000	0.0006	0.0014	0.0006	0.0022
½	0.0010	0.0000	0.0009	0.0019	0.0009	0.0029
¾	0.0012	0.0000	0.0012	0.0024	0.0012	0.0036
1	0.0013	0.0000	0.0014	0.0027	0.0014	0.0040
1¼	0.0014	0.0000	0.0016	0.0030	0.0016	0.0044
1½	0.0015	0.0000	0.0018	0.0033	0.0018	0.0048
2	0.0016	0.0000	0.0022	0.0038	0.0022	0.0054
2½	0.0018	0.0000	0.0026	0.0044	0.0026	0.0062
3	0.0019	0.0000	0.0029	0.0048	0.0029	0.0067
4	0.0021	0.0000	0.0035	0.0056	0.0035	0.0077
5	0.0022	0.0000	0.0041	0.0063	0.0041	0.0085
6	0.0024	0.0000	0.0046	0.0070	0.0046	0.0094
7	0.0025	0.0000	0.0051	0.0076	0.0051	0.0101
8	0.0026	0.0000	0.0056	0.0082	0.0056	0.0108

Table 2. Medium-fit Tolerances and Allowances — American Standard

For running fits under 600 R.P.M. and with journal pressures less than 600 lb. per sq. in.; also for sliding fits, and the more accurate machine-tool and automotive parts.

Diameters	Tolerances				Min. Allowance	Max. Allowance
	Hole +	Hole −	Shaft −	Shaft −		
¼	0.0005	0.0000	0.0004	0.0009	0.0004	0.0014
½	0.0006	0.0000	0.0006	0.0012	0.0006	0.0018
¾	0.0007	0.0000	0.0007	0.0014	0.0007	0.0021
1	0.0008	0.0000	0.0009	0.0017	0.0009	0.0025
1¼	0.0009	0.0000	0.0010	0.0019	0.0010	0.0028
1½	0.0009	0.0000	0.0012	0.0021	0.0012	0.0030
2	0.0010	0.0000	0.0014	0.0024	0.0014	0.0034
2½	0.0011	0.0000	0.0017	0.0028	0.0017	0.0039
3	0.0012	0.0000	0.0019	0.0031	0.0019	0.0043
4	0.0013	0.0000	0.0023	0.0036	0.0023	0.0049
5	0.0014	0.0000	0.0026	0.0040	0.0026	0.0054
6	0.0015	0.0000	0.0030	0.0045	0.0030	0.0060
7	0.0015	0.0000	0.0033	0.0048	0.0033	0.0063
8	0.0016	0.0000	0.0036	0.0052	0.0036	0.0068

Table 3. Snug-fit Tolerances and Allowances — American Standard

Closest fit which can be assembled by hand. It should be used where moving parts are not intended to move freely under load.

Diameters	Tolerances				Min. Allowance	Max. Allowance
	Hole +	Hole −	Shaft +	Shaft −		
¼	0.0004	0.0000	0.0000	0.0003	0.0000	0.0007
½	0.0005	0.0000	0.0000	0.0003	0.0000	0.0008
¾	0.0005	0.0000	0.0000	0.0004	0.0000	0.0009
1	0.0006	0.0000	0.0000	0.0004	0.0000	0.0010
1¼	0.0006	0.0000	0.0000	0.0004	0.0000	0.0010
1½	0.0007	0.0000	0.0000	0.0005	0.0000	0.0012
2	0.0008	0.0000	0.0000	0.0005	0.0000	0.0013
2½	0.0008	0.0000	0.0000	0.0005	0.0000	0.0013
3	0.0009	0.0000	0.0000	0.0006	0.0000	0.0015
4	0.0010	0.0000	0.0000	0.0006	0.0000	0.0016
5	0.0010	0.0000	0.0000	0.0007	0.0000	0.0017
6	0.0011	0.0000	0.0000	0.0007	0.0000	0.0018
7	0.0011	0.0000	0.0000	0.0008	0.0000	0.0019
8	0.0012	0.0000	0.0000	0.0008	0.0000	0.0020

Table 4. Tight-fit Tolerances and Allowances (Selective Assembly) American Standard

For drive fits in thin sections or extremely long fits in other sections; also for shrink fits in very light sections. Used in automotive, ordnance, and general machine manufacturing.

Diameters	Tolerances				Max. Allowance	Loosest Fit*	Selected Fit
	Hole +	Hole −	Shaft +	Shaft +			
¼	0.0004	0.0000	0.0005	0.0001	0.0005	+0.0003	0.0001
½	0.0005	0.0000	0.0006	0.0001	0.0006	+0.0004	0.0001
¾	0.0005	0.0000	0.0007	0.0002	0.0007	+0.0003	0.0002
1	0.0006	0.0000	0.0009	0.0003	0.0009	+0.0003	0.0003
1¼	0.0006	0.0000	0.0009	0.0003	0.0009	+0.0003	0.0003
1½	0.0007	0.0000	0.0011	0.0004	0.0011	+0.0003	0.0004
2	0.0008	0.0000	0.0013	0.0005	0.0013	+0.0003	0.0005
2½	0.0008	0.0000	0.0014	0.0006	0.0014	+0.0002	0.0006
3	0.0009	0.0000	0.0017	0.0008	0.0017	+0.0001	0.0008
4	0.0010	0.0000	0.0020	0.0010	0.0020	−0.0000	0.0010
5	0.0010	0.0000	0.0023	0.0013	0.0023	−0.0003	0.0013
6	0.0011	0.0000	0.0026	0.0015	0.0026	−0.0004	0.0015
7	0.0011	0.0000	0.0029	0.0018	0.0029	−0.0007	0.0018
8	0.0012	0.0000	0.0032	0.0020	0.0032	−0.0008	0.0020

* *Note:* — (−) denotes interference of metal; (+) denotes clearance or amount of looseness.

Table 5. Medium Force-fit Tolerances and Allowances (Selective Assembly) American Standard

For parts considered permanently assembled. These fits are used in fastening locomotive wheels, car wheels, armatures of dynamos and motors, and crank disks to their axles or shafts. They are also used for shrink fits on medium sections or long fits. These fits are the tightest which are recommended for cast-iron holes or external members as they stress cast iron to its elastic limit.

Diameters	Tolerances				Max. Allowance	Loosest Fit*	Selected Fit†
	Hole +	Hole −	Shaft +	Shaft +			
¼	0.0004	0.0000	0.0005	0.0001	0.0005	+0.0003	0.0001
½	0.0005	0.0000	0.0008	0.0003	0.0008	+0.0002	0.0003
¾	0.0005	0.0000	0.0009	0.0004	0.0009	+0.0001	0.0004
⅞	0.0006	0.0000	0.0010	0.0004	0.0010	+0.0002	0.0004
1	0.0006	0.0000	0.0011	0.0005	0.0011	+0.0001	0.0005
1⅛	0.0006	0.0000	0.0012	0.0006	0.0012	0.0000	0.0006
1¼	0.0006	0.0000	0.0012	0.0006	0.0012	0.0000	0.0006
1½	0.0007	0.0000	0.0015	0.0008	0.0015	−0.0001	0.0008
1¾	0.0007	0.0000	0.0016	0.0009	0.0016	−0.0002	0.0009
2	0.0008	0.0000	0.0018	0.0010	0.0018	−0.0002	0.0010
2¼	0.0008	0.0000	0.0019	0.0011	0.0019	−0.0003	0.0011
2½	0.0008	0.0000	0.0021	0.0013	0.0021	−0.0005	0.0013
3	0.0009	0.0000	0.0024	0.0015	0.0024	−0.0006	0.0015
3½	0.0009	0.0000	0.0027	0.0018	0.0027	−0.0009	0.0018
4	0.0010	0.0000	0.0030	0.0020	0.0030	−0.0010	0.0020
4½	0.0010	0.0000	0.0033	0.0023	0.0033	−0.0013	0.0023
5	0.0010	0.0000	0.0035	0.0025	0.0035	−0.0015	0.0025
6	0.0011	0.0000	0.0041	0.0030	0.0041	−0.0019	0.0030
7	0.0011	0.0000	0.0046	0.0035	0.0046	−0.0024	0.0035
8	0.0012	0.0000	0.0052	0.0040	0.0052	−0.0028	0.0040
9	0.0012	0.0000	0.0057	0.0045	0.0057	−0.0033	0.0045
10	0.0013	0.0000	0.0063	0.0050	0.0063	−0.0037	0.0050
12	0.0014	0.0000	0.0074	0.0060	0.0074	−0.0046	0.0060
14	0.0014	0.0000	0.0084	0.0070	0.0084	−0.0056	0.0070
16	0.0015	0.0000	0.0095	0.0080	0.0095	−0.0065	0.0080
18	0.0016	0.0000	0.0106	0.0090	0.0106	−0.0074	0.0090
20	0.0016	0.0000	0.0116	0.0100	0.0116	−0.0084	0.0100
24	0.0017	0.0000	0.0137	0.0120	0.0137	−0.0103	0.0120
28	0.0018	0.0000	0.0158	0.0140	0.0158	−0.0122	0.0140
32	0.0019	0.0000	0.0179	0.0160	0.0179	−0.0141	0.0160
36	0.0020	0.0000	0.0200	0.0180	0.0200	−0.0160	0.0180
40	0.0021	0.0000	0.0221	0.0200	0.0221	−0.0179	0.0200
48	0.0022	0.0000	0.0262	0.0240	0.0262	−0.0218	0.0240
56	0.0023	0.0000	0.0303	0.0280	0.0303	−0.0257	0.0280
64	0.0024	0.0000	0.0344	0.0320	0.0344	−0.0296	0.0320
72	0.0025	0.0000	0.0385	0.0360	0.0385	−0.0335	0.0360
80	0.0026	0.0000	0.0426	0.0400	0.0426	−0.0374	0.0400

* Note: — (−) denotes interference of metal; (+) denotes clearance or amount of looseness.

† The average interference of metal given under " Selected Fit " is the desired condition and must be obtained by selective assembly; that is, by mating large shafts in large holes and small shafts in small holes.

Table 6. Heavy Force- and Shrink-fit Tolerances and Allowances (Selective Assembly) American Standard

These fits are used for holes in steel. These fits cause excessive stress for cast-iron holes. Shrink fits are used where heavy force fits are impractical, as on locomotive wheel tires, heavy crank disks of large engines, etc.

Diameters	Tolerances				Max. Allowance	Loosest Fit*	Selected Fit†
	Hole +	Hole −	Shaft +	Shaft +			
¼	0.0004	0.0000	0.0007	0.0003	0.0007	+0.0001	0.0003
½	0.0005	0.0000	0.0010	0.0005	0.0010	0.0000	0.0005
¾	0.0005	0.0000	0.0013	0.0008	0.0013	−0.0003	0.0008
⅞	0.0006	0.0000	0.0015	0.0009	0.0015	−0.0003	0.0009
1	0.0006	0.0000	0.0016	0.0010	0.0016	−0.0004	0.0010
1⅛	0.0006	0.0000	0.0017	0.0011	0.0017	−0.0005	0.0011
1¼	0.0006	0.0000	0.0019	0.0013	0.0019	−0.0007	0.0013
1½	0.0007	0.0000	0.0022	0.0015	0.0022	−0.0008	0.0015
1¾	0.0007	0.0000	0.0025	0.0018	0.0025	−0.0011	0.0018
2	0.0008	0.0000	0.0028	0.0020	0.0028	−0.0012	0.0020
2¼	0.0008	0.0000	0.0031	0.0023	0.0031	−0.0015	0.0023
2½	0.0008	0.0000	0.0033	0.0025	0.0033	−0.0017	0.0025
3	0.0009	0.0000	0.0039	0.0030	0.0039	−0.0021	0.0030
3½	0.0009	0.0000	0.0044	0.0035	0.0044	−0.0026	0.0035
4	0.0010	0.0000	0.0050	0.0040	0.0050	−0.0030	0.0040
4½	0.0010	0.0000	0.0055	0.0045	0.0055	−0.0035	0.0045
5	0.0010	0.0000	0.0060	0.0050	0.0060	−0.0040	0.0050
6	0.0011	0.0000	0.0071	0.0060	0.0071	−0.0049	0.0060
7	0.0011	0.0000	0.0081	0.0070	0.0081	−0.0059	0.0070
8	0.0012	0.0000	0.0092	0.0080	0.0092	−0.0068	0.0080
9	0.0012	0.0000	0.0102	0.0090	0.0102	−0.0078	0.0090
10	0.0013	0.0000	0.0113	0.0100	0.0113	−0.0087	0.0100
12	0.0014	0.0000	0.0134	0.0120	0.0134	−0.0106	0.0120
14	0.0014	0.0000	0.0154	0.0140	0.0154	−0.0126	0.0140
16	0.0015	0.0000	0.0175	0.0160	0.0175	−0.0145	0.0160
18	0.0016	0.0000	0.0196	0.0180	0.0196	−0.0164	0.0180
20	0.0016	0.0000	0.0216	0.0200	0.0216	−0.0184	0.0200
24	0.0017	0.0000	0.0257	0.0240	0.0257	−0.0223	0.0240
28	0.0018	0.0000	0.0298	0.0280	0.0298	−0.0262	0.0280
32	0.0019	0.0000	0.0339	0.0320	0.0339	−0.0301	0.0320
36	0.0020	0.0000	0.0380	0.0360	0.0380	−0.0340	0.0360
40	0.0021	0.0000	0.0421	0.0400	0.0421	−0.0379	0.0400
48	0.0022	0.0000	0.0502	0.0480	0.0502	−0.0458	0.0480
56	0.0023	0.0000	0.0583	0.0560	0.0583	−0.0537	0.0560
64	0.0024	0.0000	0.0664	0.0640	0.0664	−0.0616	0.0640
72	0.0025	0.0000	0.0745	0.0720	0.0745	−0.0695	0.0720
80	0.0026	0.0000	0.0826	0.0800	0.0826	−0.0774	0.0800
96	0.0027	0.0000	0.0987	0.0960	0.0987	−0.0933	0.0960

* *Note:* — (−) denotes interference of metal; (+) denotes clearance or amount of looseness.

† The average interference of metal given under "Selected Fit" is the desired condition and must be obtained by selective assembly; that is, by mating large shafts in large holes and small shafts in small holes.

Table I. British Standard Limits and Fits for Holes

All dimensions except nominal sizes are expressed in thousandths of an inch

This table includes four standard grades of workmanship for holes designated as B, U, V and W for holes with unilateral tolerances and as K, X, Y and Z for holes with bilateral tolerances. Grade U (unilateral) and Grade X (bilateral) holes represent the grades most commonly employed. H = high limit of tolerance; L = low limit of tolerance. The + sign means clearance, and the − sign interference between mating parts. The use of the unilateral system of tolerances as applied to cylindrical mating surfaces is recommended in cases where it does not conflict with predominating present practice.

Nominal Sizes, Inches	Unilateral Holes — Low Limit of Hole is Nominal Size							
	B		U		V		W	
	H	L	H	L	H	L	H	L
0 to 0.29	+0.3	0	+0.6	0	+1.2	0	+ 2.4	0
0.3 " 0.59	+0.4	0	+0.8	0	+1.6	0	+ 3.2	0
0.6 " 0.99	+0.5	0	+1.0	0	+2.0	0	+ 4.0	0
1.0 " 1.49	+0.6	0	+1.2	0	+2.4	0	+ 4.8	0
1.5 " 2.09	+0.7	0	+1.4	0	+2.8	0	+ 5.6	0
2.1 " 2.79	+0.8	0	+1.6	0	+3.2	0	+ 6.4	0
2.8 " 3.59	+0.9	0	+1.8	0	+3.6	0	+ 7.2	0
3.6 " 4.49	+1.0	0	+2.0	0	+4.0	0	+ 8.0	0
4.5 " 5.49	+1.1	0	+2.2	0	+4.4	0	+ 8.8	0
5.5 " 6.59	+1.2	0	+2.4	0	+4.8	0	+ 9.6	0
6.6 " 7.79	+1.3	0	+2.6	0	+5.2	0	+10.4	0
7.8 " 9.09	+1.4	0	+2.8	0	+5.6	0	+11.2	0
9.1 " 10.49	+1.5	0	+3.0	0	+6.0	0	+12.0	0
10.5 " 11.99	+1.6	0	+3.2	0	+6.4	0	+12.8	0
12.0 " 13.59	+1.7	0	+3.4	0	+6.8	0	+13.6	0
13.6 " 15.29	+1.8	0	+3.6	0	+7.2	0	+14.4	0
15.3 " 17.09	+1.9	0	+3.8	0	+7.6	0	+15.2	0
17.1 " 18.99	+2.0	0	+4.0	0	+8.0	0	+16.0	0
19.0 " 20.99	+2.1	0	+4.2	0	+8.4	0	+16.8	0
21.0 " 23.09	+2.2	0	+4.4	0	+8.8	0	+17.6	0
23.1 " 25.29	+2.3	0	+4.6	0	+9.2	0	+18.4	0

Nominal Sizes, Inches	Bilateral Holes — Nominal Size of Hole lies between High and Low Limits							
	K		X		Y		Z	
	H	L	H	L	H	L	H	L
0 to 0.29	+0.1	−0.2	+0.3	−0.3	+0.6	−0.6	+1.2	−1.2
0.3 " 0.59	+0.2	−0.2	+0.4	−0.4	+0.8	−0.8	+1.6	−1.6
0.6 " 0.99	+0.2	−0.3	+0.5	−0.5	+1.0	−1.0	+2.0	−2.0
1.0 " 1.49	+0.3	−0.3	+0.6	−0.6	+1.2	−1.2	+2.4	−2.4
1.5 " 2.09	+0.3	−0.4	+0.7	−0.7	+1.4	−1.4	+2.8	−2.8
2.1 " 2.79	+0.4	−0.4	+0.8	−0.8	+1.6	−1.6	+3.2	−3.2
2.8 " 3.59	+0.4	−0.5	+0.9	−0.9	+1.8	−1.8	+3.6	−3.6
3.6 " 4.49	+0.5	−0.5	+1.0	−1.0	+2.0	−2.0	+4.0	−4.0
4.5 " 5.49	+0.5	−0.6	+1.1	−1.1	+2.2	−2.2	+4.4	−4.4
5.5 " 6.59	+0.6	−0.6	+1.2	−1.2	+2.4	−2.4	+4.8	−4.8
6.6 " 7.79	+0.6	−0.7	+1.3	−1.3	+2.6	−2.6	+5.2	−5.2
7.8 " 9.09	+0.7	−0.7	+1.4	−1.4	+2.8	−2.8	+5.6	−5.6
9.1 " 10.49	+0.7	−0.8	+1.5	−1.5	+3.0	−3.0	+6.0	−6.0
10.5 " 11.99	+0.8	−0.8	+1.6	−1.6	+3.2	−3.2	+6.4	−6.4
12.0 " 13.59	+0.8	−0.9	+1.7	−1.7	+3.4	−3.4	+6.8	−6.8
13.6 " 15.29	+0.9	−0.9	+1.8	−1.8	+3.6	−3.6	+7.2	−7.2
15.3 " 17.09	+0.9	−1.0	+1.9	−1.9	+3.8	−3.8	+7.6	−7.6
17.1 " 18.99	+1.0	−1.0	+2.0	−2.0	+4.0	−4.0	+8.0	−8.0
19.0 " 20.99	+1.0	−1.1	+2.1	−2.1	+4.2	−4.2	+8.4	−8.4
21.0 " 23.09	+1.1	−1.1	+2.2	−2.2	+4.4	−4.4	+8.8	−8.8
23.1 " 25.29	+1.1	−1.2	+2.3	−2.3	+4.6	−4.6	+9.2	−9.2

Table 1 (Continued).   British Standard Limits and Fits for Holes

All dimensions except nominal sizes are expressed in thousandths of an inch.

Nominal Sizes, Inches	Oversize Holes Low Limit of the Hole is larger than the Nominal Size					
	A		G		H	
	H	L	H	L	H	L
0 to 0.29	+1.2	+0.6	+ 1.8	+1.2	+ 2.4	+ 1.8
0.3 " 0.59	+1.6	+0.8	+ 2.4	+1.6	+ 3.2	+ 2.4
0.6 " 0.99	+2.0	+1.0	+ 3.0	+2.0	+ 4.0	+ 3.0
1.0 " 1.49	+2.4	+1.2	+ 3.6	+2.4	+ 4.8	+ 3.6
1.5 " 2.09	+2.8	+1.4	+ 4.2	+2.8	+ 5.6	+ 4.2
2.1 " 2.79	+3.2	+1.6	+ 4.8	+3.2	+ 6.4	+ 4.8
2.8 " 3.59	+3.6	+1.8	+ 5.4	+3.6	+ 7.2	+ 5.4
3.6 " 4.49	+4.0	+2.0	+ 6.0	+4.0	+ 8.0	+ 6.0
4.5 " 5.49	+4.4	+2.2	+ 6.6	+4.4	+ 8.8	+ 6.6
5.5 " 6.59	+4.8	+2.4	+ 7.2	+4.8	+ 9.6	+ 7.2
6.6 " 7.79	+5.2	+2.6	+ 7.8	+5.2	+10.4	+ 7.8
7.8 " 9.09	+5.6	+2.8	+ 8.4	+5.6	+11.2	+ 8.4
9.1 " 10.49	+6.0	+3.0	+ 9.0	+6.0	+12.0	+ 9.0
10.5 " 11.99	+6.4	+3.2	+ 9.6	+6.4	+12.8	+ 9.6
12.0 " 13.59	+6.8	+3.4	+10.2	+6.8	+13.6	+10.2
13.6 " 15.29	+7.2	+3.6	+10.8	+7.2	+14.4	+10.8
15.3 " 17.09	+7.6	+3.8	+11.4	+7.6	+15.2	+11.4
17.1 " 18.99	+8.0	+4.0	+12.0	+8.0	+16.0	+12.0
19.0 " 20.99	+8.4	+4.2	+12.6	+8.4	+16.8	+12.6
21.0 " 23.09	+8.8	+4.4	+13.2	+8.8	+17.6	+13.2
23.1 " 25.29	+9.2	+4.6	+13.8	+9.2	+18.4	+13.8

These " oversize holes " are common to both the unilateral and bilateral systems and are included to meet exceptional conditions.

British Standard Limits and Fits for Cylindrical Parts. — The British standard system of limits and fits for engineering (Report No. 164 of British Standards Institution) is based upon the adoption of the hole as basic or as the " constant member." The limiting dimensions of any hole of a particular quality and size remain unchanged, and varieties of fit are obtained by changing the actual dimensions of the shaft.

Unilateral Tolerances Recommended: The use of a unilateral system of tolerances as applied to cylindrical mating surfaces is recommended in cases where it does not conflict with predominating present practice. The British standard limits and fits, however, include bilateral as well as unilateral tolerances, and a series of standard graduated shafts suitable for use in holes having either system of tolerances. With the unilateral system, the tolerance is in one direction only from the nominal or basic size and usually is positive with every hole of nominal size or larger. A bilateral tolerance extends in both directions (but not always in equal amounts) from the nominal size and the holes may be smaller or larger than the nominal size. The effect of transferring any standard shaft from a bilateral hole to a unilateral hole tends either to increase the clearance or decrease the interference; in short, it makes the fit easier.

In deciding on the system of gaging and the amount of the tolerances to be employed, it is important to distinguish between mating surfaces, in which the interrelation between the surfaces in contact is the guiding feature, and non-mating surfaces in which only one surface has to be considered. The accompanying tables of British Standard Limits and Fits refer primarily to mating surfaces; but it is anticipated that they may be of service in other cases. The recommendation in favour of the unilateral system is confined definitely to mating surfaces because for non-mating surfaces either unilateral or bilateral tolerances may be used indiffer-

Table 2. British Standard Limits and Fits for Standard Shafts

All dimensions except nominal sizes are expressed in thousandths of an inch. For example, $+1.2 = +0.0012$ inch. The use of the unilateral system of tolerances as applied to cylindrical mating surfaces is recommended in cases where it does not conflict with predominating present practice.

The fourteen letters F, E, D, C, etc., (table is continued on next page), represent a standard series of graduated shafts suitable for use in holes having either unilateral or bilateral tolerances. This series of maximum and minimum shaft diameters provides fourteen different fits in any hole. To illustrate, if a shaft with the tolerance applied as at K is inserted in a hole of Grade U (Table 1), the resulting fit is designated as UK (see Table 3).

H = high limit of tolerance; L = low limit of tolerance. The + sign means clearance, and the − sign interference between mating parts.

Nominal Sizes, Inches	F		E		D		C		B	
	H	L	H	L	H	L	H	L	H	L
0 to 0.29	+1.2	+0.9	+0.9	+0.6	+0.6	+0.3	+0.4	+0.1	+0.3	0
0.3 " 0.59	+1.6	+1.2	+1.2	+0.8	+0.8	+0.4	+0.6	+0.2	+0.4	0
0.6 " 0.99	+2.0	+1.5	+1.5	+1.0	+1.0	+0.5	+0.7	+0.2	+0.5	0
1.0 " 1.49	+2.4	+1.8	+1.8	+1.2	+1.2	+0.6	+0.9	+0.3	+0.6	0
1.5 " 2.09	+2.8	+2.1	+2.1	+1.4	+1.4	+0.7	+1.0	+0.3	+0.7	0
2.1 " 2.79	+3.2	+2.4	+2.4	+1.6	+1.6	+0.8	+1.2	+0.4	+0.8	0
2.8 " 3.59	+3.6	+2.7	+2.7	+1.8	+1.8	+0.9	+1.3	+0.4	+0.9	0
3.6 " 4.49	+4.0	+3.0	+3.0	+2.0	+2.0	+1.0	+1.5	+0.5	+1.0	0
4.5 " 5.49	+4.4	+3.3	+3.3	+2.2	+2.2	+1.1	+1.6	+0.5	+1.1	0
5.5 " 6.59	+4.8	+3.6	+3.6	+2.4	+2.4	+1.2	+1.8	+0.6	+1.2	0
6.6 " 7.79	+5.2	+3.9	+3.9	+2.6	+2.6	+1.3	+1.9	+0.6	+1.3	0
7.8 " 9.09	+5.6	+4.2	+4.2	+2.8	+2.8	+1.4	+2.1	+0.7	+1.4	0
9.1 " 10.49	+6.0	+4.5	+4.5	+3.0	+3.0	+1.5	+2.2	+0.7	+1.5	0
10.5 " 11.99	+6.4	+4.8	+4.8	+3.2	+3.2	+1.6	+2.4	+0.8	+1.6	0
12.0 " 13.59	+6.8	+5.1	+5.1	+3.4	+3.4	+1.7	+2.5	+0.8	+1.7	0
13.6 " 15.29	+7.2	+5.4	+5.4	+3.6	+3.6	+1.8	+2.7	+0.9	+1.8	0
15.3 " 17.09	+7.6	+5.7	+5.7	+3.8	+3.8	+1.9	+2.8	+0.9	+1.9	0
17.1 " 18.99	+8.0	+6.0	+6.0	+4.0	+4.0	+2.0	+3.0	+1.0	+2.0	0
19.0 " 20.99	+8.4	+6.3	+6.3	+4.2	+4.2	+2.1	+3.1	+1.0	+2.1	0
21.0 " 23.09	+8.8	+6.6	+6.6	+4.4	+4.4	+2.2	+3.3	+1.1	+2.2	0
23.1 " 25.29	+9.2	+6.9	+6.9	+4.6	+4.6	+2.3	+3.4	+1.1	+2.3	0

Nominal Sizes, Inches	K		L		P		M		Q	
	H	L	H	L	H	L	H	L	H	L
0 to 0.29	+0.1	−0.2	0	−0.3	−0.2	−0.5	−0.3	−0.6	−0.5	−0.9
0.3 " 0.59	+0.2	−0.2	0	−0.4	−0.2	−0.6	−0.4	−0.8	−0.6	−1.2
0.6 " 0.99	+0.2	−0.3	0	−0.5	−0.3	−0.8	−0.5	−1.0	−0.8	−1.5
1.0 " 1.49	+0.3	−0.3	0	−0.6	−0.3	−0.9	−0.6	−1.2	−0.9	−1.8
1.5 " 2.09	+0.3	−0.4	0	−0.7	−0.4	−1.1	−0.7	−1.4	−1.1	−2.1
2.1 " 2.79	+0.4	−0.4	0	−0.8	−0.4	−1.2	−0.8	−1.6	−1.2	−2.4
2.8 " 3.59	+0.4	−0.5	0	−0.9	−0.5	−1.4	−0.9	−1.8	−1.4	−2.7
3.6 " 4.49	+0.5	−0.5	0	−1.0	−0.5	−1.5	−1.0	−2.0	−1.5	−3.0
4.5 " 5.49	+0.5	−0.6	0	−1.1	−0.6	−1.7	−1.1	−2.2	−1.7	−3.3
5.5 " 6.59	+0.6	−0.6	0	−1.2	−0.6	−1.8	−1.2	−2.4	−1.8	−3.6
6.6 " 7.79	+0.6	−0.7	0	−1.3	−0.7	−2.0	−1.3	−2.6	−2.0	−3.9
7.8 " 9.09	+0.7	−0.7	0	−1.4	−0.7	−2.1	−1.4	−2.8	−2.1	−4.2
9.1 " 10.49	+0.7	−0.8	0	−1.5	−0.8	−2.3	−1.5	−3.0	−2.3	−4.5
10.5 " 11.99	+0.8	−0.8	0	−1.6	−0.8	−2.4	−1.6	−3.2	−2.4	−4.8
12.0 " 13.59	+0.8	−0.9	0	−1.7	−0.9	−2.6	−1.7	−3.4	−2.6	−5.1
13.6 " 15.29	+0.9	−0.9	0	−1.8	−0.9	−2.7	−1.8	−3.6	−2.7	−5.4
15.3 " 17.09	+0.9	−1.0	0	−1.9	−1.0	−2.9	−1.9	−3.8	−2.9	−5.7
17.1 " 18.99	+1.0	−1.0	0	−2.0	−1.0	−3.0	−2.0	−4.0	−3.0	−6.0
19.0 " 20.99	+1.0	−1.1	0	−2.1	−1.1	−3.2	−2.1	−4.2	−3.2	−6.3
21.0 " 23.09	+1.1	−1.1	0	−2.2	−1.1	−3.3	−2.2	−4.4	−3.3	−6.6
23.1 " 25.29	+1.1	−1.2	0	−2.3	−1.2	−3.5	−2 3	−4.6	−3.5	−6.9

Table 2 (Continued). British Standard Limits and Fits for Standard Shafts

All dimensions except nominal sizes are expressed in thousandths of an inch.

Nominal Sizes, Inches	R		S		T		TT	
	H	L	H	L	H	L	H	L
0 to 0.29	−0.9	− 1.5	− 1.5	− 2.4	− 2.4	− 3.6	− 3.6	− 6.0
0.3 ″ 0.59	−1.2	− 2.0	− 2.0	− 3.2	− 3.2	− 4.8	− 4.8	− 8.0
0.6 ″ 0.99	−1.5	− 2.5	− 2.5	− 4.0	− 4.0	− 6.0	− 6.0	−10.0
1.0 ″ 1.49	−1.8	− 3.0	− 3.0	− 4.8	− 4.8	− 7.2	− 7.2	−12.0
1.5 ″ 2.09	−2.1	− 3.5	− 3.5	− 5.6	− 5.6	− 8.4	− 8.4	−14.0
2.1 ″ 2.79	−2.4	− 4.0	− 4.0	− 6.4	− 6.4	− 9.6	− 9.6	−16.0
2.8 ″ 3.59	−2.7	− 4 5	− 4.5	− 7.2	− 7.2	−10.8	−10.8	−18.0
3.6 ″ 4.49	−3.0	− 5.0	− 5.0	− 8.0	− 8.0	−12.0	−12.0	−20.0
4.5 ″ 5.49	−3.3	− 5.5	− 5.5	− 8.8	− 8.8	−13.2	−13.2	−22.0
5.5 ″ 6.59	−3.6	− 6.0	− 6.0	− 9.6	− 9.6	−14.4	−14.4	−24.0
6.6 ″ 7.79	−3.9	− 6.5	− 6.5	−10.4	−10.4	−15.6	−15.6	−26.0
7.8 ″ 9.09	−4.2	− 7.0	− 7.0	−11.2	−11.2	−16.8	−16.8	−28.0
9.1 ″ 10.49	−4.5	− 7.5	− 7.5	−12.0	−12.0	−18.0	−18.0	−30.0
10.5 ″ 11.99	−4.8	− 8.0	− 8.0	−12.8	−12.8	−19.2	−19.2	−32.0
12.0 ″ 13.59	−5.1	− 8.5	− 8.5	−13.6	−13.6	−20.4	−20.4	−34.0
13.6 ″ 15.29	−5.4	− 9.0	− 9.0	−14.4	−14.4	−21.6	−21.6	−36.0
15.3 ″ 17.09	−5.7	− 9.5	− 9.5	−15.2	−15.2	−22.8	−22.8	−38.0
17.1 ″ 18.99	−6.0	−10.0	−10.0	−16.0	−16.0	−24.0	−24.0	−40.0
19.0 ″ 20.99	−6.3	−10.5	−10.5	−16.8	−16.8	−25.2	−25.2	−42.0
21.0 ″ 23.09	−6.6	−11.0	−11.0	−17.6	−17.6	−26.4	−26.4	−44.0
23.1 ″ 25.29	−6.9	−11.5	−11.5	−18.4	−18.4	−27.6	−27.6	−46.0

ently, the choice depending mainly on the convenience of manufacture. Thus, if the tendency in the process of manufacture is for the article to become either bigger or smaller, due — for example — to wear of dies, the tolerance might be unilateral, while if the dimensions are also dependent upon adjustment of the producing apparatus, such as rolls, then a bilateral tolerance might be preferable.

British Standard Fits and Limits for Holes. — The accompanying Table 1 includes both unilateral and bilateral tolerances as applied to a range of nominal sizes up to 25 inches approximately. In the unilateral system, the nominal size is the low limit of the hole; in the bilateral system, the nominal size lies between the high and low limits of the hole. Table 1 provides four standard grades of workmanship for holes in which holes B (unilateral) and holes K (bilateral) represent the most accurate grade, while holes U (unilateral) and holes X (bilateral) are the grades most commonly employed. With each change in nominal size range, the tolerance increase of holes U and X is 0.0002 inch. Unilateral holes V and W and bilateral holes Y and Z have larger tolerances.

Table 1 (see continuation) also provides for the use of three holes A, G, H, each with two positive limits of tolerance. These are called " oversize holes." They are common to both the unilateral and bilateral systems, and are included in the table to meet exceptional conditions.

British Standard Fits and Limits for Shafts. — Table 2 (in two sections) shows the recommended limits for a standard series of shafts suitable for holes with either unilateral or bilateral tolerances. The letters F, E, D, C, B, K, etc., represent a series of fourteen different shaft fits for any particular hole. These fits are obtained by progressively changing the relation of the tolerance to the nominal or basic size. The tolerance itself remains unchanged for all shaft fits from F to M inclusive. These shafts are of the same grade of workmanship as a B hole. Shafts Q, R, S, T and TT are given increasing tolerances because they are all considerably under size and, therefore, result in increasing amounts of clearance when assembled in any hole.

Table 3. Clearance or Interference Between British Standard Shafts and Holes

All dimensions except nominal sizes are expressed in thousandths of an inch.

This table (continued on next page) shows the amount of clearance or interference between a series of fourteen standard shafts and holes with *unilateral* tolerances and of the U grade. Example: If shafts K of one inch nominal size are inserted in holes U of one inch nominal size, the resulting fits (designated as UK) may range from a maximum interference of −0.3 (−0.0003) to a maximum clearance of +1.5 (+0.0015) inch.

Nominal Sizes, Inches	Standard Shafts in Unilateral " U " Holes						
	UF	UE	UD	UC	UB	UK	UL
0 to 0.29	−1.2 −0.3	−0.9 0	−0.6 +0.3	−0.4 +0.5	−0.3 +0.6	−0.1 +0.8	0 +0.9
0.3 " 0.59	−1.6 −0.4	−1.2 0	−0.8 +0.4	−0.6 +0.6	−0.4 +0.8	−0.2 +1.0	0 +1.2
0.6 " 0.99	−2.0 −0.5	−1.5 0	−1.0 +0.5	−0.7 +0.8	−0.5 +1.0	−0.2 +1.3	0 +1.5
1.0 " 1.49	−2.4 −0.6	−1.8 0	−1.2 +0.6	−0.9 +0.9	−0.6 +1.2	−0.3 +1.5	0 +1.8
1.5 " 2.09	−2.8 −0.7	−2.1 0	−1.4 +0.7	−1.0 +1.1	−0.7 +1.4	−0.3 +1.8	0 +2.1
2.1 " 2.79	−3.2 −0.8	−2.4 0	−1.6 +0.8	−1.2 +1.2	−0.8 +1.6	−0.4 +2.0	0 +2.4
2.8 " 3.59	−3.6 −0.9	−2.7 0	−1.8 +0.9	−1.3 +1.4	−0.9 +1.8	−0.4 +2.3	0 +2.7
3.6 " 4.49	−4.0 −1.0	−3.0 0	−2.0 +1.0	−1.5 +1.5	−1.0 +2.0	−0.5 +2.5	0 +3.0
4.5 " 5.49	−4.4 −1.1	−3.3 0	−2.2 +1.1	−1.6 +1.7	−1.1 +2.2	−0.5 +2.8	0 +3.3
5.5 " 6.59	−4.8 −1.2	−3.6 0	−2.4 +1.2	−1.8 +1.8	−1.2 +2.4	−0.6 +3.0	0 +3.6
6.6 " 7.79	−5.2 −1.3	−3.9 0	−2.6 +1.3	−1.9 +2.0	−1.3 +2.6	−0.6 +3.3	0 +3.9
7.8 " 9.09	−5.6 −1.4	−4.2 0	−2.8 +1.4	−2.1 +2.1	−1.4 +2.8	−0.7 +3.5	0 +4.2
9.1 " 10.49	−6.0 −1.5	−4.5 0	−3.0 +1.5	−2.2 +2.3	−1.5 +3.0	−0.7 +3.8	0 +4.5
10.5 " 11.99	−6.4 −1.6	−4.8 0	−3.2 +1.6	−2.4 +2.4	−1.6 +3.2	−0.8 +4.0	0 +4.8
12.0 " 13.59	−6.8 −1.7	−5.1 0	−3.4 +1.7	−2.5 +2.6	−1.7 +3.4	−0.8 +4.3	0 +5.1
13.6 " 15.29	−7.2 −1.8	−5.4 0	−3.6 +1.8	−2.7 +2.7	−1.8 +3.6	−0.9 +4.5	0 +5.4
15.3 " 17.09	−7.6 −1.9	−5.7 0	−3.8 +1.9	−2.8 +2.9	−1.9 +3.8	−0.9 +4.8	0 +5.7
17.1 " 18.99	−8.0 −2.0	−6.0 0	−4.0 +2.0	−3.0 +3.0	−2.0 +4.0	−1.0 +5.0	0 +6.0
19.0 " 20.99	−8.4 −2.1	−6.3 0	−4.2 +2.1	−3.1 +3.2	−2.1 +4.2	−1.0 +5.3	0 +6.3
21.0 " 23.09	−8.8 −2.2	−6.6 0	−4.4 +2.2	−3.3 +3.3	−2.2 +4.4	−1.1 +5.5	0 +6.6
23.1 " 25.29	−9.2 −2.3	−6.9 0	−4.6 +2.3	−3.4 +3.5	−2.3 +4.6	−1.1 +5.8	0 +6.9

Table 3 (Continued). Clearance or Interference Between Standard Shafts and Holes

All dimensions except nominal sizes are expressed in thousandths of an inch

This table (continued from preceding page) shows the amount of clearance or interference between a series of fourteen standard shafts and holes with *unilateral* tolerances and of the *U* grade (Table 1). Example: If shafts *R* of 1½-inch nominal size are inserted in holes *U* of 1½-inch nominal size, the resulting fits (designated as *UR*) may range from a maximum clearance of +4.9 (0.0049) to a minimum clearance of +2.1 (+0.0021) inch.

Nominal Sizes, Inches	Standard Shafts in Unilateral " U " Holes						
	UP	UM	UQ	UR	US	UT	UTT
0 to 0.29	+0.2 / +1.1	+0.3 / +1.2	+ 0.5 / + 1.5	+ 0.9 / + 2.1	+ 1.5 / + 3.0	+ 2.4 / + 4.2	+ 3.6 / + 6.6
0.3 " 0.59	+0.2 / +1.4	+0.4 / +1.6	+ 0.6 / + 2.0	+ 1.2 / + 2.8	+ 2.0 / + 4.0	+ 3.2 / + 5.6	+ 4.8 / + 8.8
0.6 " 0.99	+0.3 / +1.8	+0.5 / +2.0	+ 0.8 / + 2.5	+ 1.5 / + 3.5	+ 2.5 / + 5.0	+ 4.0 / + 7.0	+ 6.0 / +11.0
1.0 " 1.49	+0.3 / +2.1	+0.6 / +2.4	+ 0.9 / + 3.0	+ 1.8 / + 4.2	+ 3.0 / + 6.0	+ 4.8 / + 8.4	+ 7.2 / +13.2
1.5 " 2.09	+0.4 / +2.5	+0.7 / +2.8	+ 1.1 / + 3.5	+ 2.1 / + 4.9	+ 3.5 / + 7.0	+ 5.6 / + 9.8	+ 8.4 / +15.4
2.1 " 2.79	+0.4 / +2.8	+0.8 / +3.2	+ 1.2 / + 4.0	+ 2.4 / + 5.6	+ 4.0 / + 8.0	+ 6.4 / +11.2	+ 9.6 / +17.6
2.8 " 3.59	+0.5 / +3.2	+0.9 / +3.6	+ 1.4 / + 4.5	+ 2.7 / + 6.3	+ 4.5 / + 9.0	+ 7.2 / +12.6	+10.8 / +19.8
3.6 " 4.49	+0.5 / +3.5	+1.0 / +4.0	+ 1.5 / + 5.0	+ 3.0 / + 7.0	+ 5.0 / +10.0	+ 8.0 / +14.0	+12.0 / +22.0
4.5 " 5.49	+0.6 / +3.9	+1.1 / +4.4	+ 1.7 / + 5 5	+ 3.3 / + 7.7	+ 5.5 / +11.0	+ 8.8 / +15.4	+13.2 / +24.2
5.5 " 6.59	+0.6 / +4.2	+1.2 / +4.8	+ 1.8 / + 6.0	+ 3.6 / + 8.4	+ 6.0 / +12.0	+ 9.6 / +16.8	+14.4 / +26.4
6.6 " 7.79	+0.7 / +4.6	+1.3 / +5.2	+ 2.0 / + 6.5	+ 3.9 / + 9.1	+ 6.5 / +13.0	+10.4 / +18.2	+15.6 / +28.6
7.8 " 9.09	+0.7 / +4.9	+1.4 / +5.6	+ 2.1 / + 7.0	+ 4.2 / + 9.8	+ 7.0 / +14.0	+11.2 / +19.6	+16.8 / +30.8
9.1 " 10.49	+0.8 / +5.3	+1.5 / +6.0	+ 2.3 / + 7.5	+ 4.5 / +10.5	+ 7.5 / +15.0	+12.0 / +21.0	+18.0 / +33.0
10.5 " 11.99	+0.8 / +5.6	+1.6 / +6.4	+ 2.4 / + 8.0	+ 4.8 / +11.2	+ 8.0 / +16.0	+12.8 / +22.4	+19.2 / +35.2
12.0 " 13.59	+0.9 / +6.0	+1.7 / +6.8	+ 2.6 / + 8.5	+ 5.1 / +11.9	+ 8.5 / +17.0	+13.6 / +23.8	+20.4 / +37.4
13.6 " 15.29	+0.9 / +6.3	+1.8 / +7.2	+ 2.7 / + 9.0	+ 5.4 / +12.6	+ 9.0 / +18.0	+14.4 / +25.2	+21.6 / +39.6
15.3 " 17.09	+1.0 / +6.7	+1.9 / +7.6	+ 2.9 / + 9.5	+ 5.7 / +13.3	+ 9.5 / +19.0	+15.2 / +26.6	+22.8 / +41.8
17.1 " 18.99	+1.0 / +7.0	+2.0 / +8.0	+ 3.0 / +10.0	+ 6.0 / +14.0	+10.0 / +20.0	+16.0 / +28.0	+24.0 / +44.0
19.0 " 20.99	+1.1 / +7.4	+2.1 / +8.4	+ 3.2 / +10.5	+ 6.3 / +14.7	+10.5 / +21.0	+16.8 / +29.4	+25.2 / +46.2
21.0 " 23.09	+1.1 / +7.7	+2.2 / +8.8	+ 3.3 / +11.0	+ 6.6 / +15.4	+11.0 / +22.0	+17.6 / +30.8	+26.4 / +48.4
23.1 " 25.29	+1.2 / +8.1	+2.3 / +9.2	+ 3.5 / +11.5	+ 6.9 / +16.1	+11.5 / +23.0	+18.4 / +32.2	+27.6 / +50.6

Table 4. Clearance or Interference Between Standard Shafts and Holes

All dimensions except nominal sizes are expressed in thousandths of an inch.

This table (continued on next page) shows the amount of clearance or interference between a series of fourteen standard shafts and holes with *bilateral* tolerances and of the X grade (Table I). Example: If shafts B of 4½-inch nominal size are inserted in holes X of 4½-inch nominal size, the resulting fits (designated as XB) may range from a maximum interference of −2.2 (−0.0022) to a maximum clearance of +1.1 (+0.0011) inch.

Nominal Sizes, Inches	Standard Shafts in Bilateral " X " Holes						
	XF	XE	XD	XC	XB	XK	XL
0 to 0.29	− 1.5 − 0.6	−1.2 −0.3	−0.9 0	−0.7 +0.2	−0.6 +0.3	−0.4 +0.5	−0.3 +0.6
0.3 " 0.59	− 2.0 − 0.8	−1.6 −0.4	−1.2 0	−1.0 +0.2	−0.8 +0.4	−0.6 +0.6	−0.4 +0.8
0.6 " 0.99	− 2.5 − 1.0	−2.0 −0.5	−1.5 0	−1.2 +0.3	−1.0 +0.5	−0.7 +0.8	−0.5 +1.0
1.0 " 1.49	− 3.0 − 1.2	−2.4 −0.6	−1.8 0	−1.5 +0.3	−1.2 +0.6	−0.9 +0.9	−0.6 +1.2
1.5 " 2.09	− 3.5 − 1.4	−2.8 −0.7	−2.1 0	−1.7 +0.4	−1.4 +0.7	−1.0 +1.1	−0.7 +1.4
2.1 " 2.79	− 4.0 − 1.6	−3.2 −0.8	−2.4 0	−2.0 +0.4	−1.6 +0.8	−1.2 +1.2	−0.8 +1.6
2.8 " 3.59	− 4.5 − 1.8	−3.6 −0.9	−2.7 0	−2.2 +0.5	−1.8 +0.9	−1.3 +1.4	−0.9 +1.8
3.6 " 4.49	− 5.0 − 2.0	−4.0 −1.0	−3.0 0	−2.5 +0.5	−2.0 +1.0	−1.5 +1.5	−1.0 +2.0
4.5 " 5.49	− 5.5 − 2.2	−4.4 −1.1	−3.3 0	−2.7 +0.6	−2.2 +1.1	−1.6 +1.7	−1.1 +2.2
5.5 " 6.59	− 6.0 − 2.4	−4.8 −1.2	−3.6 0	−3.0 +0.6	−2.4 +1.2	−1.8 +1.8	−1.2 +2.4
6.6 " 7.79	− 6.5 − 2.6	−5.2 −1.3	−3.9 0	−3.2 +0.7	−2.6 +1.3	−1.9 +2.0	−1.3 +2.6
7.8 " 9.09	− 7.0 − 2.8	−5.6 −1.4	−4.2 0	−3.5 +0.7	−2.8 +1.4	−2.1 +2.1	−1.4 +2.8
9.1 " 10.49	− 7.5 − 3.0	−6.0 −1.5	−4.5 0	−3.7 +0.8	−3.0 +1.5	−2.2 +2.3	−1.5 +3.0
10.5 " 11.99	− 8.0 − 3.2	−6.4 −1.6	−4.8 0	−4.0 +0.8	−3.2 +1.6	−2.4 +2.4	−1.6 +3.2
12.0 " 13.59	− 8.5 − 3.4	−6.8 −1.7	−5.1 0	−4.2 +0.9	−3.4 +1.7	−2.5 +2.6	−1.7 +3.4
13.6 " 15.29	− 9.0 − 3.6	−7.2 −1.8	−5.4 0	−4.5 +0.9	−3.6 +1.8	−2.7 +2.7	−1.8 +3.6
15.3 " 17.09	− 9.5 − 3.8	−7.6 −1.9	−5.7 0	−4.7 +1.0	−3.8 +1.9	−2.8 +2.9	−1.9 +3.8
17.1 " 18.99	−10.0 − 4.0	−8.0 −2.0	−6.0 0	−5.0 +1.0	−4.0 +2.0	−3.0 +3.0	−2.0 +4.0
19.0 " 20.99	−10.5 − 4.2	−8.4 −2.1	−6.3 0	−5.2 +1.1	−4.2 +2.1	−3.1 +3.2	−2.1 +4.2
21.0 " 23.09	−11.0 − 4.4	−8.8 −2.2	−6.6 0	−5.5 +1.1	−4.4 +2.2	−3.3 +3.3	−2.2 +4.4
23.1 " 25.29	−11.5 − 4.6	−9.2 −2.3	−6.9 0	−5.7 +1.2	−4.6 +2.3	−3.4 +3.5	−2.3 +4.6

Table 4 (Continued). Clearance or Interference Between Standard Shafts and Holes

All dimensions except nominal sizes are expressed in thousandths of an inch

This table (continued from preceding page) shows the amount of clearance or interference between a series of fourteen standard shafts and holes with *bilateral* tolerances and of the *X* grade (Table 1). Example: If shafts *R* of 4½-inch nominal size are inserted in holes *X* of 4½-inch nominal size, the resulting fits (designated as *XR*) may range from a maximum clearance of +6.6 (+0.0066) to a minimum clearance of +2.2 (+0.0022) inch.

Nominal Sizes, Inches	Standard Shafts in Bilateral " *X* " Holes						
	XP	*XM*	*XQ*	*XR*	*XS*	*XT*	*XTT*
0 to 0.29	−0.1 +0.8	0 +0.9	+0.2 +1.2	+ 0.6 + 1.8	+ 1.2 + 2.7	+ 2.1 + 3.9	+ 3.3 + 6.3
0.3 " 0.59	−0.2 +1.0	0 +1.2	+0.2 +1.6	+ 0.8 + 2.4	+ 1.6 + 3.6	+ 2.8 + 5.2	+ 4.4 + 8.4
0.6 " 0.99	−0.2 +1.3	0 +1.5	+0.3 +2.0	+ 1.5 + 3.0	+ 2.0 + 4.5	+ 3.5 + 6.5	+ 5.5 +10.5
1.0 " 1.49	−0.3 +1.5	0 +1.8	+0.3 +2.4	+ 1.2 + 3.6	+ 2.4 + 5.4	+ 4.2 + 7.8	+ 6.6 +12.6
1.5 " 2.09	−0.3 +1.8	0 +2.1	+0.4 +2.8	+ 1.4 + 4.2	+ 2.8 + 6.3	+ 4.9 + 9.1	+ 7.7 +14.7
2.1 " 2.79	−0.4 +2.0	0 +2.4	+0.4 +3.2	+ 1.6 + 4.8	+ 3.2 + 7.2	+ 5.6 +10.4	+ 8.8 +16.8
2.8 " 3.59	−0.4 +2.3	0 +2.7	+0.5 +3.6	+ 1.8 + 5.4	+ 3.6 + 8.1	+ 6.3 +11.7	+ 9.9 +18.9
3.6 " 4.49	−0.5 +2.5	0 +3.0	+0.5 +4.0	+ 2.0 + 6.0	+ 4.0 + 9.0	+ 7.0 +13.0	+11.0 +21.0
4.5 " 5.49	−0.5 +2.8	0 +3.3	+0.6 +4.4	+ 2.2 + 6.6	+ 4.4 + 9.9	+ 7.7 +14.3	+12.1 +23.1
5.5 " 6.59	−0.6 +3.0	0 +3.6	+0.6 +4.8	+ 2.4 + 7.2	+ 4.8 +10.8	+ 8.4 +15.6	+13.2 +25.2
6.6 " 7.79	−0.6 +3.3	0 +3.9	+0.7 +5.2	+ 2.6 + 7.8	+ 5.2 +11.7	+ 9.1 +16.9	+14.3 +27.3
7.8 " 9.09	−0.7 +3.5	0 +4.2	+0.7 +5.6	+ 2.8 + 8.4	+ 5.6 +12.6	+ 9.8 +18.2	+15.4 +29.4
9.1 " 10.49	−0.7 +3.8	0 +4.5	+0.8 +6.0	+ 3.0 + 9.0	+ 6.0 +13.5	+10.5 +19.5	+16.5 +31.5
10.5 " 11.99	−0.8 +4.0	0 +4.8	+0.8 +6.4	+ 3.2 + 9.6	+ 6.4 +14.4	+11.2 +20.8	+17.6 +33.6
12.0 " 13.59	−0.8 +4.3	0 +5.1	+0.9 +6.8	+ 3.4 +10.2	+ 6.8 +15.3	+11.9 +22.1	+18.7 +35.7
13.6 " 15.29	−0.9 +4.5	0 +5.4	+0.9 +7.2	+ 3.6 +10.8	+ 7.2 +16.2	+12.6 +23.4	+19.8 +37.8
15.3 " 17.09	−0.9 +4.8	0 +5.7	+1.0 +7.6	+ 3.8 +11.4	+ 7.6 +17.1	+13.3 +24.7	+20.9 +39.9
17.1 " 18.99	−1.0 +5.0	0 +6.0	+1.0 +8.0	+ 4.0 +12.0	+ 8.0 +18.0	+14.0 +26.0	+22.0 +42.0
19.0 " 20.99	−1.0 +5.3	0 +6.3	+1.1 +8.4	+ 4.2 +12.6	+ 8.4 +18.9	+14.7 +27.3	+23.1 +44.1
21.0 " 23.09	−1.1 +5.5	0 +6.6	+1.1 +8.8	+ 4.4 +13.2	+ 8.8 +19.8	+15.4 +28.6	+24.2 +46.2
23.1 " 25.29	−1.1 +5.8	0 +6.9	+1.2 +9.2	+ 4.6 +13.8	+ 9.2 +20.7	+16.1 +29.9	+25.3 +48.3

Range of Fits Between British Standard Shafts and Holes. — Tables 3 and 4 of the British Standard Fits and Limits show whether any fit or combination of shaft and hole will result in clearance or interference, and whether either clearance or interference is possible. To illustrate, a one-inch F shaft (Table 2) in a Grade U hole (Table 1) or a UF fit has interference ranging from a maximum (see Table 3) of −2.4 (−0.0024) to a minimum of −0.6 (−0.0006) inch. A one-inch D shaft in a Grade U hole (UD fit, Table 3) has a maximum interference of −1.2 (−0.0012) and a maximum clearance of +0.6 (+0.0006) inch. Table 3 is for unilateral tolerances and Table 4 for bilateral tolerances.

Terms Applied to General Classes of Fits. — The range of fits provided by the entire series of British Standard shaft limits is divided into three main classes which are defined as interference fits, transition fits, and clearance fits. These terms are recommended for use when specifying a general class of fit. The definitions of these three general classes of fits are as follows:

Interference Fit: Term applied when there is a negative allowance (or interference) between the largest hole and the smallest shaft, the shaft being larger than the hole.

Clearance Fit: Term indicating a positive allowance or clearance between the largest possible shaft and the smallest possible hole.

Transition Fit: Term applied when the limits admit of either clearance or interference fits being obtained.

Specific Designation of British Standard Fits. — Terms such as " push fit," "close-running fit," etc., although in common use, are not recommended because they have no numerically exact meaning. When the exact nature or class of fit has to be indicated, this can be done by using the symbols of the hole and shaft in combination, as, for example, UR. If UR is marked on the assembly drawing, the drawing of the hole would be marked U and of the shaft R in combination with the nominal size. For example, 2 inches U, 2 inches R, or the limits of tolerance can be specified in figures, if preferred.

Relation Between British Standard Fit Symbols and Terms in Common Use. — In order that these British standards may be more readily applied to existing practice, the approximate relation between general terms in common use and the symbols UF, UE, UD etc. representing various classes of fits (Tables 3 and 4) will be indicated.

Standard Shafts in Holes of Grade U — Unilateral Tolerances:	Standard Shafts in Holes of Grade X — Bilateral Tolerances:
Heavy drive fit — UF	Force fit — XF
Light drive fit — UE	Heavy drive fit — XE
Heavy keying fit — UD	Light drive fit — XD
Medium keying fit — UC	Extra light drive fit — XC
Light keying fit — UB	Heavy keying fit — XB
Push fit — UK	Medium keying fit — XK
Slide or easy push fit — UL	Light keying fit — XL
Easy slide or close-running fit — UP	Push fit — XP
Close-running fit (1) — UM	Slide or easy push fit — XM
Close-running fit (2) — UQ	Easy slide or close-running fit — XQ
Normal running fit — UR	Normal running fit — XR
Slack running fit — US	Slack running fit — XS
Extra slack running fit — UT	Extra slack running fit — XT
Coarse clearance fit — UTT	Coarse clearance fit — XTT

To illustrate, a push fit is similar to fit UK (Table 3) between a standard shaft and a hole U (unilateral tolerance). If the tolerance is bilateral, a push fit is equivalent to XP (Table 4) between a standard shaft and a hole X.

Tolerances and Allowances for Different Classes of Fits — 1

(Newall Engineering Co., Ltd.)

Diameter, Inches, to and Including	Hole Tolerances—Class A*			Hole Tolerances—Class B*		
	High Limit	Low Limit	Tolerance	High Limit	Low Limit	Tolerance
0 to ½	+.00025	−.00025	.0005	+.0005	−.0005	.001
½ to 1	+.0005	−.00025	.00075	+.00075	−.0005	.00125
1 to 2	+.00075	−.00025	.001	+.001	−.0005	.0015
2 to 3	+.001	−.0005	.0015	+.00125	−.00075	.002
3 to 4	+.001	−.0005	.0015	+.0015	−.00075	.00225
4 to 5	+.001	−.0005	.0015	+.00175	−.00075	.0025
5 to 6	+.0015	−.0005	.002	+.002	−.001	.003
6 to 7	+.0015	−.00075	.00225	+.00225	−.001	.00325
7 to 8	+.00175	−.00075	.0025	+.00225	−.00125	.0035
8 to 9	+.00175	−.001	.00275	+.0025	−.00125	.00375
9 to 10	+.00175	−.001	.00275	+.0025	−.00125	.00375
10 to 11	+.002	−.001	.003	+.00275	−.00125	.004
11 to 12	+.002	−.001	.003	+.00275	−.0015	.00425
12 to 13	+.002	−.001	.003	+.003	−.0015	.0045
13 to 14	+.00225	−.001	.00325	+.003	−.0015	.0045
14 to 15	+.00225	−.00125	.0035	+.003	−.00175	.00475
15 to 16	+.0025	−.00125	.00375	+.00325	−.00175	.005
16 to 17	+.0025	−.00125	.00375	+.00325	−.00175	.005
17 to 18	+.0025	−.00125	.00375	+.00325	−.00175	.005
18 to 19	+.0025	−.00125	.00375	+.0035	−.002	.0055
19 to 20	+.00275	−.00125	.004	+.0035	−.002	.0055
20 to 21	+.00275	−.00125	.004	+.00375	−.002	.00575
21 to 22	+.00275	−.0015	.00425	+.00375	−.002	.00575

Diameter, Inches	Forced Fit Allowances			Driving Fit Allowances		
	Max.	Min.	Tolerance	Max.	Min.	Tolerance
0 to ½	+.001	+.0005	.0005	+.0005	+.00025	.00025
½ to 1	+.002	+.0015	.0005	+.001	+.00075	.00025
1 to 2	+.004	+.003	.001	+.0015	+.001	.0005
2 to 3	+.006	+.0045	.0015	+.0025	+.0015	.001
3 to 4	+.008	+.006	.002	+.003	+.002	.001
4 to 5	+.010	+.008	.002	+.0035	+.0025	.001
5 to 6	+.012	+.010	.002	+.004	+.003	.001
6 to 7	+.014	+.012	.002	+.0045	+.003	.0015
7 to 8	+.016	+.014	.002	+.005	+.0035	.0015
8 to 9	+.018	+.016	.002	+.0055	+.004	.0015
9 to 10	+.020	+.018	.002	+.006	+.0045	.0015
10 to 11	+.022	+.020	.002	+.0065	+.0045	.002
11 to 12	+.024	+.022	.002	+.007	+.005	.002

*Tolerance is provided for holes, which ordinary standard reamers can produce, in two grades, Classes A and B, the selection of which is a question for the user's decision and dependent upon the quality of the work required; some prefer to use Class A as working limits and Class B as inspection limits.

Tolerances and Allowances for Different Classes of Fits — 2

Diameter, Inches	Push Fit Allowances			Running Fit Allowances—Class X		
	Min.	Max.	Tolerance	Min.	Max.	Tolerance
0 to ½	−.00025	−.00075	.0005	−.001	−.002	.001
½ to 1	−.00025	−.00075	.0005	−.00125	−.00275	.0015
1 to 2	−.00025	−.00075	.0005	−.00175	−.0035	.00175
2 to 3	−.0005	−.001	.0005	−.002	−.00425	.00225
3 to 4	−.0005	−.001	.0005	−.0025	−.005	.0025
4 to 5	−.0005	−.001	.0005	−.003	−.00575	.00275
5 to 6	−.0005	−.001	.0005	−.0035	−.0065	.003
6 to 7	−.0005	−.00125	.00075	−.0035	−.00675	.00325
7 to 8	−.0005	−.0015	.001	−.0035	−.007	.0035
8 to 9	−.0005	−.0015	.001	−.00375	−.0075	.00375
9 to 10	−.00075	−.002	.00125	−.004	−.008	.004
10 to 11	−.00075	−.002	.00125	−.004	−.00825	.00425
11 to 12	−.00075	−.002	.00125	−.00425	−.0085	.00425
12 to 13	−.00075	−.00225	.0015	−.00475	−.009	.00425
13 to 14	−.00075	−.00225	.0015	−.00475	−.00925	.0045
14 to 15	−.00075	−.00225	.0015	−.005	−.0095	.0045
15 to 16	−.001	−.0025	.0015	−.00525	−.00975	.0045
16 to 17	−.001	−.0025	.0015	−.00525	−.010	.00475
17 to 18	−.001	−.0025	.0015	−.0055	−.0105	.005
18 to 19	−.001	−.0025	.0015	−.0055	−.01075	.00525
19 to 20	−.001	−.00275	.00175	−.00575	−.01125	.0055

Diameter, Inches	Running Fit Allowances—Class Y			Running Fit Allowances—Class Z		
	Min.	Max.	Tolerance	Min.	Max.	Tolerance
0 to ½	−.00075	−.00125	.0005	−.0005	−.00075	.00025
½ to 1	−.001	−.002	.001	−.00075	−.00125	.0005
1 to 2	−.00125	−.0025	.00125	−.00075	−.0015	.00075
2 to 3	−.0015	−.003	.0015	−.001	−.002	.001
3 to 4	−.002	−.0035	.0015	−.001	−.00225	.00125
4 to 5	−.00225	−.004	.00175	−.00125	−.0025	.00125
5 to 6	−.0025	−.0045	.002	−.00125	−.00275	.0015
6 to 7	−.00275	−.00475	.002	−.00125	−.00275	.0015
7 to 8	−.00275	−.005	.00225	−.0015	−.003	.0015
8 to 9	−.003	−.0055	.0025	−.0015	−.003	.0015
9 to 10	−.00325	−.00575	.0025	−.0015	−.00325	.00175
10 to 11	−.00325	−.006	.00275	−.00175	−.0035	.00175
11 to 12	−.0035	−.00625	.00275	−.00175	−.0035	.00175
12 to 13	−.00375	−.0065	.00275	−.002	−.00375	.00175
13 to 14	−.00375	−.00675	.003	−.002	−.00375	.00175
14 to 15	−.004	−.007	.003	−.002	−.004	.002
15 to 16	−.0045	−.00775	.00325	−.0025	−.0045	.002
16 to 17	−.0045	−.00775	.00325	−.0025	−.0045	.002
17 to 18	−.0045	−.008	.0035	−.0025	−.0045	.002
18 to 19	−.0045	−.008	.0035	−.0025	−.0045	.002
19 to 20	−.005	−.0085	.0035	−.00275	−.005	.00225

Running fits, which are the most commonly required, are divided into three grades: Class X for engine and other work where easy fits are wanted; Class Y for high speeds and good average machine work; Class Z for fine tool work.

Preferred Series of Basic Sizes, Tolerances, and Allowances. — The American Standard Limits and Fits for Engineering and Manufacturing (Part I), approved in 1947, includes the following series of preferred basic sizes. In specifying fits, it is recommended that the sizes of mating parts (within the range listed) be selected from this series. The object is to reduce the number of different diameters commonly used in a given size range, thus reducing the number of sizes of bar stock, bushings, drills, reamers, and gages. The recommendations in this Standard apply particularly to fits between cylindrical parts. However, the data may also be applied to fits between mating parts other than cylindrical, in which case "size" refers to a length, width, or a dimension other than diameter.

Preferred Series of Basic Sizes

	0.0100	1/8	0.1250	7/8	0.8750	2 3/8	2.3750
	0.0125	5/32	0.15625	1	1.0000	2 1/2	2.5000
1/64	0.01562	3/16	0.1875	1 1/8	1.1250	2 5/8	2.6250
	0.0200	1/4	0.2500	1 1/4	1.2500	2 3/4	2.7500
	0.0250	5/16	0.3125	1 3/8	1.3750	2 7/8	2.8750
1/32	0.03125	3/8	0.3750	1 1/2	1.5000	3	3.0000
	0.0400	7/16	0.4375	1 5/8	1.6250	3 1/4	3.2500
	0.0500	1/2	0.5000	1 3/4	1.7500	3 1/2	3.5000
1/16	0.0625	9/16	0.5625	1 7/8	1.8750	3 3/4	3.7500
	0.0800	5/8	0.6250	2	2.0000	4	4.0000
3/32	0.09375	11/16	0.6875	2 1/8	2.1250	..	....
	0.1000	3/4	0.7500	2 1/4	2.2500		

Preferred Tolerances and Allowances. — In specifying tolerances and allowances it is recommended that suitable values be selected from the series listed below. These preferred tolerances and allowances are a logical complement to preferred sizes and also tend toward economies in stock parts, tools, and gages. The values in heavy type are recommended in preference to the others whenever they can be employed.

Preferred Series of Tolerances and Allowances

0.0001	0.0003	0.0008	**0.0020**	**0.0050**	0.0120	**0.0300**
0.00015	0.0004	**0.0010**	0.0025	0.0060	0.0150	....
0.0002	**0.0005**	0.0012	0.0030	0.0080	**0.0200**	....
0.00025	0.0006	0.0015	0.0040	**0.0100**	0.0250	....

Unilateral Tolerances. — The unilateral system was adopted as the one best suited to various types of fits and conducive to the greatest flexibility in manufacturing. A unilateral tolerance is in one direction only — plus for the hole and minus for the shaft.

Basic Hole and Basic Shaft Systems. — Both basic hole and basic shaft systems are included in this Standard.

With the *basic hole system* of fits, the minimum limit of each hole size is basic. The fit desired is obtained by varying the allowance of the shaft and the tolerances of the mating parts.

With the *basic shaft system* of fits the maximum limit of each shaft size is basic. The fit desired is obtained by varying the allowance of the hole and the tolerances of the mating parts.

Reference Temperature. — In determining the acceptance of parts, or whether they are within the specified limits, measurements for actual size should be made at the International Standard Reference Temperature of 68 F. (20 C.).

Johansson System of Tolerances with Diameter of Hole as Basic Size

Diameter of Hole, Inches	Tolerances for Plug Gage used in Hole *				Shaft Tolerances	
	Class A, Inch		Class B, Inch		Light Running Fit, Inch	
	Minimum	Maximum	Minimum	Maximum	Minimum	Maximum
1/32 – 1/8	−0.00016	+0.00016	−0.00008	+0.00008	−0.00083	−0.00043
1/8 – 1/4	−0.00024	+0.00024	−0.00012	+0.00012	−0.00122	−0.00063
1/4 – 13/32	−0.00031	+0.00031	−0.00016	+0.00016	−0.00165	−0.00087
13/32 – 23/32	−0.00043	+0.00043	−0.00024	+0.00020	−0.00217	−0.00118
23/32 – 1 1/8	−0.00055	+0.00055	−0.00028	+0.00028	−0.00276	−0.00157
1 1/8 – 1 7/8	−0.00067	+0.00067	−0.00035	+0.00031	−0.00335	−0.00197
1 7/8 – 2 15/16	−0.00083	+0.00083	−0.00043	+0.00039	−0.00402	−0.00236
2 15/16 – 4 17/32	−0.00098	+0.00098	−0.00051	+0.00047	−0.00473	−0.00276
4 17/32 – 6 7/8	−0.00118	+0.00118	−0.00059	+0.00059	−0.00551	−0.00315
6 7/8 – 10 7/16	−0.00138	+0.00138	−0.00071	+0.00067	−0.00630	−0.00354
10 7/16 – 15 3/4	−0.00157	+0.00157	−0.00079	+0.00079	−0.00709	−0.00394

Diameter of Hole, Inches	Shaft Tolerances					
	Running Fit, Inch		Sliding Fit, Inch		Push Fit, Inch	
	Minimum	Maximum	Minimum	Maximum	Minimum	Maximum
1/32 – 1/8	−0.00043	−0.00020	−0.00020	−0.00008	−0.00008	+0.00012
1/8 – 1/4	−0.00063	−0.00031	−0.00031	−0.00012	−0.00012	+0.00020
1/4 – 13/32	−0.00087	−0.00043	−0.00043	−0.00016	−0.00016	+0.00028
13/32 – 23/32	−0.00118	−0.00059	−0.00059	−0.00020	−0.00020	+0.00031
23/32 – 1 1/8	−0.00157	−0.00079	−0.00079	−0.00024	−0.00024	+0.00031
1 1/8 – 1 7/8	−0.00197	−0.00098	−0.00098	−0.00031	−0.00031	+0.00031
1 7/8 – 2 15/16	−0.00236	−0.00118	−0.00118	−0.00039	−0.00039	+0.00028
2 15/16 – 4 17/32	−0.00276	−0.00138	−0.00138	−0.00047	−0.00047	+0.00024
4 17/32 – 6 7/8	−0.00315	−0.00157	−0.00157	−0.00055	−0.00055	+0.00020
6 7/8 – 10 7/16	−0.00354	−0.00177	−0.00177	−0.00067	−0.00067	+0.00020
10 7/16 – 15 3/4	−0.00394	−0.00197	−0.00097	−0.00075	−0.00075	+0.00020

Diameter of Hole, Inches	Easy Driving Fit, Inch		Close Driving Fit, Inch		Forced Fit, Inch	
	Minimum	Maximum	Minimum	Maximum	Minimum	Maximum
1/32 – 1/8	+0.00012	+0.00024	+0.00024	+0.00039	+0.00039	+0.00059
1/8 – 1/4	+0.00020	+0.00035	+0.00035	+0.00059	+0.00059	+0.00098
1/4 – 13/32	+0.00028	+0.00047	+0.00047	+0.00083	+0.00083	+0.00146
13/32 – 23/32	+0.00031	+0.00059	+0.00059	+0.00110	+0.00110	+0.00197
23/32 – 1 1/8	+0.00031	+0.00071	+0.00071	+0.00142	+0.00142	+0.00252
1 1/8 – 1 7/8	+0.00031	+0.00087	+0.00087	+0.00177	+0.00177	+0.00319
1 7/8 – 2 15/16	+0.00028	+0.00102	+0.00102	+0.00213	+0.00213	+0.00394
2 15/16 – 4 17/32	+0.00024	+0.00118	+0.00118	+0.00256	+0.00256	+0.00481
4 17/32 – 6 7/8	+0.00020	+0.00138	+0.00138	+0.00303	+0.00303	+0.00579
6 7/8 – 10 7/16	+0.00020	+0.00157	+0.00157	+0.00354	+0.00354	+0.00689
10 7/16 – 15 3/4	+0.00020	+0.00177	+0.00177	+0.00414	+0.00414	+0.00808

* Use column A for ordinary work, where greater tolerances are allowable. Use column B for more accurate work, where smaller tolerances are required. The values, in inches, in the table above have been given to five decimals to give the exact value of the dimensions in millimeters in the original tables.

Limits for Holes in Gears. — The plus and minus limits given in the table "Limits for Holes in Gears" are recommended by the American Gear Manufacturers' Association. Holes in gears are divided into three groups or classes: Class 1

Limits for Holes in Gears

Diameter, Inches	Class 1 Precision Machines		Class 2 Automobiles, Machine Tools		Class 3 Standard Jobbing Gears	
	+ Limit "Not Go"	− Limit "Go"	+ Limit "Not Go"	− Limit "Go"	+ Limit "Not Go"	− Limit "Go"
0–½	0.000	0.00025	0.00025	0.00025	0.0005	0.0005
½–1	0.000	0.0005	0.0005	0.0005	0.00075	0.00075
1–2	0.000	0.00075	0.00075	0.00075	0.001	0.001
2–3	0.00025	0.00075	0.001	0.001	0.00125	0.00125
3–4	0.0005	0.00075	0.00125	0.001	0.0015	0.0015
4–5	0.0005	0.001	0.0013	0.0012	0.00175	0.00175
5–6	0.0005	0.001	0.00175	0.00125	0.002	0.002
8–9	0.00075	0.001	0.002	0.002	0.003	0.003
11–12	0.001	0.001	0.0025	0.0025	0.004	0.004

applies to precision gears, such as used in aircraft, printing machinery, etc.; Class 2 applies to gears for automobiles, machine tools, etc.; and Class 3 applies to pumps, hoisting machinery, and general jobbing gears. The recommendations cover hole diameters ranging from ½ to 12 inches. It is believed that these limits, if adopted as representative of standard practice in gear-making and used by all makers of gears, will produce a standard quality. It will be noted that the tolerance of Class 2 is about twice that of Class 1 and that of Class 3 about twice that of Class 2.

Tolerances for Cold-drawn Shafting. — The tolerances for cold-drawn shafting are usually on the minus side only and vary from 0.002 to 0.004 or 0.005 inch, depending upon the diameter of the shafting. According to the practice of several manufacturers of cold-drawn shafting, the tolerances are as follows: For shafting diameters smaller than 2 or 2½ inches, the tolerance is plus 0 and minus from 0.002 to 0.0025 inch. For diameters larger than 2 or 2½ inches, the tolerance is plus 0 and minus from 0.001 to 0.0015 inch per inch of diameter. For example, the minus tolerance for a 3-inch shaft would be 0.003 inch or possibly 0.0045 inch.

Tolerances for Cold-drawn Tool Steel. — The tolerances for cold-drawn tool steel or *drill* rod usually vary from 0.0005 to 0.001 inch, the tolerance increasing for the larger sizes. Some drill manufacturers want the tolerance divided equally plus and minus and others prefer the tolerance either on the plus or minus side. The tolerances for round stock, flats and other shapes are given in the accompanying table which covers both carbon and high-speed steel rods and bars.

S.A.E. Standard Tolerances for Bronze and Brass Sheets and Strips. — The thickness tolerances for cold-rolled sheets and strips of either brass or bronze are given in the accompanying table, which covers thicknesses from No. 0000 to No. 38, American or B. & S. gage and widths from 5 to 14 inches. The thickness of hot-rolled bronze sheets up to and including 48 inches wide, may vary 5 per cent under or over the gage. For widths over 48 inches up to and including 60 inches, the variation may be 7 per cent under or over the gage.

Permissible Variations in Sizes of Cold-finished and Hot-rolled Bars *

Tolerances for Cold-finished Bars and Shafting							
Nominal Size of Bar, Inches	ROUND BARS		Nominal Size of Bar, Inches	HEXAGON BARS		SQUARE BARS	
	Carbon Up to .30% +0.000	Carbon .31 to .50% +0.000		Carbon Up to .30% +0.000	Carbon .31 to .50% +0.000	Carbon Up to .30% +0.000	Carbon .31 to .50% +0.000
Up to 1 inc.	−0.002	−0.003	Up to .3 inc.	−0.002	−0.003	−0.003	−0.004
1 to 2 "	−0.003	−0.004	0.3 to 1 "	−0.003	−0.004	−0.004	−0.005
2 to 4 "	−0.004	−0.005	1 to 2½ "	−0.004	−0.005	−0.005	−0.006
4 to 6 "	−0.005	−0.006	2½ to 4 "	−0.006	−0.006	−0.006	−0.008
6 to 8 "	−0.006	−0.008	....	....	....	....	....

Tolerances for Cold-finished "Flats" or Rectangular Sections						
	Variations in Width and Thickness					
Nominal Thickness of Bar, Inches	Widths less than 1½ in.		Widths 1½ to 4 in., inc.		Widths 4 to 6 in., inc.	
	Carbon Up to .30% +0.000	Carbon .31 to .50% +0.000	Carbon Up to .30% +0.000	Carbon .31 to .50% +0.000	Carbon Up to .30% +0.000	Carbon .31 to .50% +0.000
Up to 0.3 inc.	−0.003	−0.004	−0.005	−0.006	−0.008	−0.010
0.3 to 1 "	−0.004	−0.005	−0.005	−0.006	−0.009	−0.012
1 to 2½ "	−0.005	−0.006	−0.006	−0.008	−0.010	−0.012

Tolerances for Hot-rolled Bars

ROUND OR SQUARE			HEXAGON			
Nominal Size, Inches	Tolerance		Nominal Size, Inches	Tolerance		
	Minus	Plus		Minus	Plus	Difference Across Flats
0–5⁄16	0.007	0.007	0–½	0.007	0.007	0.011
5⁄16–7⁄16	0.007	0.007	½–1	0.010	0.010	0.015
7⁄16–5⁄8	0.008	0.008	1–1½	0.013	0.021	0.025
5⁄8–7⁄8	0.009	0.009	1½–2	1⁄64	1⁄32	1⁄32
7⁄8–1	0.010	0.010	2–2½	1⁄64	3⁄64	3⁄64
1–1⁄8	0.012	0.012	2½–3½	1⁄64	1⁄16	1⁄16
1⅛–1¼	0.014	0.014				
1¼–1⅜	0.016	0.016	FLATS, SQUARE-EDGE AND ROUND-EDGE			
1⅜–1½	0.018	0.018				
1½–2	0.022	0.022				

Range of Widths	Width Tolerance	Thickness Range and Tolerance		
		¼" to ½"	½" to 1"	1" to 2"
To 1" inc.	−1⁄64+1⁄64	0.008	0.010	.....
1 to 2 "	−1⁄32+1⁄32	0.012	0.015	1⁄32
2 to 4 "	−1⁄32+1⁄16	0.015	0.020	1⁄32
4 to 6 "	−1⁄16+3⁄32	0.015	0.020	1⁄32

Remaining ROUND OR SQUARE rows:

Nominal Size, Inches	Minus	Plus
2–2½	0	1⁄16
2½–3½	0	5⁄64
3½–4½	0	3⁄32
4½–5½	0	7⁄64
5½–8	0	1⁄8

* Standard specifications of American Society for Testing Materials.

Tolerances for Cold-drawn Tool Steel Rods and Bars *

Grade of Steel	Kind of Rods or Bars	Finish	Size of Stock	Tolerance, Inch	Hardness Test Brinell Maximum	Sclero-scope
Carbon	Drill rod	Polished	Under ¼″	−0.00025	200	33
Carbon	Drill rod	Polished	¼″ to ½″	−0.0005	200	33
Carbon	Drill rod	Polished	½″ and over	±0.0005	220	36
Carbon	Drill rod	Lime Drawn	½″ and under	±0.0005	200	33
Carbon	Drill rod	Lime Drawn	Over ½″	±0.001	220	36
Carbon	Round	Rough Drawn	½″ and under	±0.001	210	35
Carbon	Round	Rough Drawn	Over ½″	±0.0015	228	38
Carbon	Round	Rough Drawn Annealed	½″ and under	±0.001	190	32
Carbon	Round	Rough Drawn Annealed	Over ½″	±0.0015	210	35
Carbon	Flats or Shapes	Lime Drawn	All dimensions	±0.001	220	36
Carbon	Flats or Shapes	Rough Drawn	All dimensions	±0.0015	228	38
High Speed	Drill Rod	Polished	All dimensions	±0.0005	250	42
High Speed	Drill Rod	Lime Drawn	All dimensions	±0.0005	250	42
High Speed	Rounds	Rough Drawn	All dimensions	±0.001	250	42
High Speed	Flats or Shapes	Lime Drawn	All dimensions	±0.001	250	42
High Speed	Flats or Shapes	Rough Drawn	All dimensions	±0.0015	250	42

* Atlas Crucible Steel Co.

Thickness Tolerances for Brass and Bronze Sheets and Strips
(S. A. E. Standard)

Thickness of Stock, American or Brown & Sharpe Gage	Tolerances for Different Widths Up to 5 in., inc.	5 to 8 in., inc.	8 to 11 in., inc.	11 to 14 in., inc.
No. 0000 to No. 0 inc. (0.4600–0.3249)	±0.0044″	±0.0048″	±0.0051″	±0.0055″
Below No. 0 to No. 4 inc. (0.3249–0.2043)	±0.0039	±0.0043	±0.0046	±0.0050
Below No. 4 to No. 8 inc. (0.2043–0.1285)	±0.0034	±0.0038	±0.0041	±0.0045
Below No. 8 to No. 14 inc. (0.1285–0.0641)	±0.0029	±0.0033	±0.0036	±0.0040
Below No. 14 to No. 18 inc. (0.0641–0.0403)	±0.0025	±0.0029	±0.0033	±0.0037
Below No. 18 to No. 24 inc. (0.0403–0.0201)	±0.0020	±0.0024	±0.0028	±0.0032
Below No. 24 to No. 28 inc. (0.0201–0.0126)	±0.0016	±0.0020	±0.0024	±0.0028
Below No. 28 to No. 32 inc. (0.0126–0.0080)	±0.0013	±0.0017	±0.0020	±0.0024
Below No. 32 to No. 35 inc. (0.0080–0.0056)	±0.0010	±0.0014	±0.0017	±0.0022
Below No. 35 to No. 38 inc. (0.0056–0.0040)	±0.0008	±0.0012	±0.0015	±0.0019

Screw-stock Tolerances
(Adopted by American Society for Testing Materials)

Diameter of Screw Stock	Over Size	Under Size	Eccentricity
Up to and including 0.3 inch	0	1% of diam.	0.5% of diam.
Over 0.3 inch to and including 1 inch	0	0.003 inch	0.0015 inch
Over 1 inch to and including 2½ inches	0	0.004 inch	0.0020 inch
Over 2½ inches	0	0.005 inch	0.0025 inch

Tolerances for Brass and Copper Tubing. — The S. A. E. standard tolerances for non-ferrous tubing, such as copper, brass and bronze, are given in the accompanying table which covers the tolerances for outside and inside diameters and the wall thickness tolerance. No combination of variations on the same tube is allowed

Tolerances for Brass and Bronze Tubing
(S. A. E. Standard)

Diameters, Outside and Inside	Tolerance, Inch	Thickness of Wall	Tolerance, Inch
Up to ½ inch, inc.......	±0.002	Up to ¹⁄₆₄ inch, inc.......	±0.001
Over ½ to ¾ in., inc....	±0.0025	Over ¹⁄₆₄ to ¹⁄₃₂ in., inc...	±0.002
Over ¾ to 1 in., inc......	±0.003	Over ¹⁄₃₂ to ¹⁄₁₆ in., inc...	±0.003
Over 1 to 1¼ in., inc....	±0.0035	Over ¹⁄₁₆ to ⅛ in., inc....	±0.005
Over 1¼ to 1½ in., inc...	±0.004	Over ⅛ to ¼ in., inc.....	±0.008
Over 1½ to 1¾ in., inc...	±0.0045	Over ¼ to ⁵⁄₁₆ in., inc....	±0.0125
Over 1¾ to 2 in., inc.....	±0.005	Over ⁵⁄₁₆ to ⅜ in., inc....	±0.015
Over 2 in................	±¼ of 1 per cent		

to make the thickness of the wall vary from the nominal size by more than the amounts given in that part of the table headed "Thickness of Wall." When the tolerances given in this table are not permissible, the tolerances should be specified in the order.

Standard Tolerances for Forgings. — The tolerances adopted by the Drop Forging Association in 1937 (see accompanying Tables 1 to 5) apply to forgings under 100 pounds each. Forging tolerances may either be "special" or "regular." *Special tolerances* are those which are particularly noted in the specifications and may state any or all tolerances in any way as required. Special tolerances apply only to the particular dimensions noted. In all cases where special tolerances are not specified, regular tolerances apply.

Regular tolerances are divided into two divisions — "Commercial Standard" and "Close Standard." "Commercial Standard" tolerances are for general forging practice, but when extra close work is desired involving additional expense and care in the production of forgings, "Close Standard" may be specified. When no standard is specified, "Commercial Standard" shall apply.

Regular tolerances are applicable to (1) thickness; (2) width, including shrinkage and die wear, mismatching, and trimmed size; (3) draft angle; (4) quantity in shipment; (5) fillets and corners.

Thickness Tolerances: Thickness tolerances shall apply to the overall thickness of a forging. (See Table 1.)

Width and Length Tolerances: Width and length tolerances shall be alike and shall apply to the width or length of a forging. When applied to drop hammer forgings, they shall apply to the width or length in a direction parallel to the main or fundamental parting plane of the die, but only to such dimensions as are enclosed by and actually formed by the die. When applied to upset forgings, they shall apply to the width or length in a direction perpendicular to the direction of travel of the ramp.

Width and length tolerances consist of the three subdivisions following: (*a*) Shrinkage and die wear tolerance: (*b*) mismatching tolerance; (*c*) trimmed size tolerance. The latter must not be greater nor less than the limiting sizes at the parting plane, imposed by the sum of the draft angle tolerances and the shrinkage and die wear tolerances.

Shrinkage and Die Wear: Shrinkage and die wear tolerances shall apply to that part of the forging formed by a single die block only. They shall not apply to any

Table 1.   Standard Tolerances for Forgings
Adopted, 1937, by Drop Forging Association for forgings under 100 pounds each

Thickness Tolerances, Inch*									
Net Weights, Pounds, up to —	Commercial		Close		Net Weights, Pounds, up to —	Commercial		Close	
	−	+	−	+		−	+	−	+
.2	.008	.024	.004	.012	20	.026	.078	.013	.039
.4	.009	.027	.005	.015	30	.030	.090	.015	.045
.6	.010	.030	.005	.015	40	.034	.102	.017	.051
.8	.011	.033	.006	.018	50	.038	.114	.019	.057
1	.012	.036	.006	.018	60	.042	.126	.021	.063
2	.015	.045	.008	.024	70	.046	.138	.023	.069
3	.017	.051	.009	.027	80	.050	.150	.025	.075
4	.018	.054	.009	.027	90	.054	.162	.027	.081
5	.019	.057	.010	.030	100	.058	.174	.029	.087
10	.022	.066	.011	.033					

* Thickness tolerances apply to the over-all thickness.   For drop-hammer forgings, they apply to the thickness in a direction perpendicular to the main or fundamental parting plane of the die.   For upset forgings, they apply to the thickness in the direction parallel to the travel of the ram, but only to such dimensions as are enclosed by and actually formed by the die.

Table 2.   Standard Tolerances for Forgings
Adopted, 1937, by Drop Forging Association for forgings under 100 pounds each

Shrinkage		Plus	Die Wear		Mismatching		
Lengths or widths up to — in.	Commercial + or −	Close + or −	Net wt. up to — lbs.	Commercial + or −	Close + or −	Net Weights, Pounds, up to —	Commercial	Close
1	.003	.002	1	.032	.016	1	.015	.010
2	.006	.003	3	.035	.018	7	.018	.012
3	.009	.005	5	.038	.019	13	.021	.014
4	.012	.006	7	.041	.021	19	.024	.016
5	.015	.008	9	.044	.022	25	.027	.018
6	.018	.009	11	.047	.024	31	.030	.020

For each additional inch under shrinkage, add 0.003 to the commercial tolerance and 0.0015 to the close tolerance.   For example, if length or width is 12 inches, the commercial tolerance is plus or minus 0.036 and the close tolerance plus or minus 0.018.

For each additional 2 pounds under die wear, add 0.003 to the commercial tolerance and 0.0015 to the close tolerance.   Thus, if the net weight is 21 pounds, the die wear commercial tolerance is 0.062 plus or minus, and the close tolerance 0.031 plus or minus.

For each additional 6 pounds under mismatching, add 0.003 to the commercial tolerance and 0.002 to the close tolerance.   Thus, if the net weight is 37 pounds, the mismatching commercial tolerance is 0.033 and the close tolerance 0.022.

Table 3. Standard Tolerances for Forgings
Adopted, 1937, by Drop Forging Association for forgings under 100 pounds each

Draft angle tolerances — the permissible variations from the standard or nominal draft angle							
Drop-Hammer Forgings				Upset Forgings			
Location of Surface	Nominal Angle Degrees	Commercial Limits	Close Limits	Location of Surface	Nominal Angle Degrees	Commercial Limits	Close Limits
Outside	7	0-10	0-8	Outside	3	0-5	0-4
Holes and Depressions	10	0-13	...	Holes and Depressions	5	0-8	0-7
	7	...	0-8				

Table 4. Standard Tolerances for Forgings
Adopted, 1937, by Drop Forging Association for forgings under 100 pounds each

Quantity Tolerances					
Number of Pieces on Order	Permissible Variation		Number of Pieces on Order	Permissible Variation	
	Over-run, Pieces	Under-run, Pieces		Over-run, Per cent	Under-run, Per cent
1- 2	1	0	100- 199	10	5.0
3- 5	2	1	200- 299	9	4.5
6-19	3	1	300- 599	8	4.0
20-29	4	2	600- 1,249	7	3.5
30-39	5	2	1,250- 2,999	6	3.0
40-49	6	3	3,000- 9,999	5	2.5
50-59	7	3	10,000- 39,999	4	2.0
60-69	8	4	40,000-299,999	3	1.5
70-79	9	4	300,000 up	2	1.0
80-99	10	5			

These quantity tolerances represent the permissible over-run or under-run allowed for each release or part shipment of an order. Any shipping quantity within the limits of over-run or under-run shall be considered as completing the order.

Table 5. Standard Tolerances for Forgings
Adopted, 1937, by Drop Forging Association for forgings under 100 pounds each

Maximum Radii of Fillets and Corners, Inch					
Net Weights, Pounds, up to —	Commercial	Close	Net Weights, Pounds, up to —	Commercial	Close
.3	3/32	3/64	10	3/16	3/32
1	1/8	1/16	30	7/32	7/64
3	5/32	5/64	100	1/4	1/8

dimension crossing the parting plane. They shall be the sum of the shrinkage tolerances and the die wear tolerances as given in Table 2 (left-hand section). The shrinkage tolerances and die wear tolerances shall not be applied separately, but shall only be used as the sum of the two. They shall not be so applied as to include draft.

Mismatching Tolerance: Mismatching is the displacement of a point in that part of a forging formed by one die block of a pair, from its desired position when located from the part of the forging formed in the other die block of the pair. Mismatching does not include any displacement caused by variation in thickness of the forging, but is only the displacement in a plane parallel to the main or fundamental parting plane of the dies. Mismatching tolerances are independent of, and in addition to, any other tolerances. See Table 2 (right-hand section).

Fillet and Corner Tolerances: Fillet and corner tolerances apply to all meeting surfaces even though drawings or models indicate sharp corners, unless such drawings or models have or indicate (even though actual dimensions are not specified) fillet or corner dimensions of larger radii than the standards in Table 5, in which case such actual or indicated larger dimensions shall be considered specified and the tolerances shall be "special tolerances."

Tolerances and Allowances for Standard Screw Threads

The standard tolerances and allowances given in the following tables have been established to provide the different fits required in various branches of machine building practice. With the exception of Classes 2 and 3, these tolerances and allowances differ somewhat from those in the former American Standard. The latest American Standard (ASA B1.1-1949) includes a Unified Thread Series. This Unified Series was established by representatives of the United Kingdom, Canada and the United States to obtain screw thread interchangeability among these three nations. The American Standard, as now revised, contains in addition to the Unified Series, certain screw thread diameters and pitches which are not in the Unified Series but are used extensively in the United States. In the tables, bold face type is used to indicate threads which are in both the Unified Series and the American Standard. The figures not in bold face apply only to the American Standard. This revision of the American Standard also incorporates certain changes resulting from practical experience in the manufacture, assembly and use of screw threads. The advantages include greater fatigue strength, root clearance, easier assembly, and longer life of thread cutting tools.

Thread Form. — The Unified and American Standard thread form is practically the same as the form which has long been used in the United States. The preferred American practice is to retain the truncated *flat* crest, and the preferred British practice is to round the crest. The root of the thread, according to American practice, may either be flat (as when cut by a new or unworn tool) or have whatever rounding may result from tool wear. The standard British root contour is round. These minor variations in American and British practice will not interfere with interchangeability of threads in the Unified Series.

Thread Series. — Threads are classified by pitch into several general series such as Coarse Thread, Fine Thread, Extra-Fine Thread, and three series with a uniform or constant pitch. The symbols used to designate different thread series will be found in an accompanying list.

Coarse-thread Series. — In this series the pitch for a given diameter is the same as in the former American Standard (B1.1-1935). In the Unified Series of the American Standard the ½ inch size has 12 threads per inch, but the American Standard also retains 13 threads per inch (in common use in the U.S.) as a possible alternate to 12 threads per inch. The Coarse Series is recommended for general use in engineering work where conditions do not require a fine thread. The limiting dimensions for the Unified and American National Coarse-thread Series are based upon a length of engagement equal to the nominal diameter (see Tables 1 to 10).

Fine-thread Series. — The pitches in this series are the same as in the former American Standard excepting that a 1-inch size with 12 threads has been added as a Unified Standard. The American Standard also retains the 1-inch 14-thread size as a possible alternate. This series is recommended for general use in automotive and aircraft work and where special conditions require a fine thread. The limiting dimensions are based upon a length of engagement equal to the nominal diameter.

Extra-Fine-thread Series. — This series is the same as the former SAE fine series and the present SAE extra-fine series. It is used particularly for aircraft and aeronautical equipment where (1) thin walled material is to be threaded, (2) thread depth of nuts must be held to a minimum to clear ferrules, coupling flanges, etc., and (3) a maximum practicable number of threads is required within a given thread length. Allowable limits are based on the length of engagement of 9 pitches.

8-thread Series. — This uniform pitch series with ⅛ inch pitch for all sizes in the series (1 inch to 6 inches inclusive) is used for high pressure pipe flanges, cylinder head studs, or whenever an initial pressure-resisting tension is required in a fastening. For such applications the 8-thread constant-pitch series has come into general use for many classes of engineering work in preference to the coarse-thread series. The limiting dimensions for Classes 2A and 2B, and for sizes up to 3 inches, inclusive, in Classes 2 and 3 are based upon a length of engagement equal to the nominal diameter; for larger sizes in Classes 2 and 3, upon a length equal to 3 inches.

12-thread Series. — This uniform pitch series is widely used for thin nuts on shafts and sleeves and in boiler practice. It provides a continuation of the fine-thread series for diameters larger than 1½ inches. For ½-, ⁹⁄₁₆-, 1-, 1⅛-, 1¼-, 1⅜-, and 1½-inch sizes, in Classes 2A and 2B, the tolerances are based on a length of engagement equal to the nominal diameter. All other sizes in Classes 2A and 2B, and those larger than 1½ inches in Classes 2 and 3, have pitch diameter tolerances based on a length of engagement of 9 pitches; for sizes ½ to 1½ inches, inclusive, in Classes 2 and 3, pitch diameter tolerances are as in the coarse- and fine-thread series.

16-thread Series. — This uniform pitch series is for adjusting collars, bearing retaining nuts or other applications requiring a fine thread. It provides a continuation of the extra-fine series for diameters larger than 2 inches. The limiting dimensions for the ¾-inch size in Classes 2A and 2B are based on a length of engagement equal to the nominal diameter; for larger sizes in Classes 2A and 2B and for sizes in Classes 2 and 3, except the ¾-inch size, on a length of engagement of 9 threads. The ¾-inch size has the same limits as in the fine-thread series.

If a thread is in the 8-, 12- or 16-thread series and also in the coarse, fine or extra-fine series, the symbols and tolerances of the latter apply.

Classes of Limits and Tolerances. — The tolerances and allowances in the latest American Standard (ASA B1.1–1949) have been revised with the exception of Classes 2 and 3 which remain unchanged. Three new series of tolerances are designated by Symbols 1A, 2A and 3A for external threads and 1B, 2B and 3B for internal threads (see following list of symbols). In selecting tolerances suitable for a given application, Class 2A, for example, may not invariably be combined with Class 2B, assuming that some other class for the internal thread, such as 1B, 3B, 2 or 3, is preferable for a specific application. Such interchangeable usage provides flexibility in the selection of tolerances and increases the range of usefulness. Selected combinations of special diameters and pitches should only be employed when a standard series will not meet requirements.

Classes 1A and 1B. — Class 1A for external and 1B for internal threads replace Class 1 of the former American Standard. They are, in general, based upon values equal to 1.5 times the tolerance for Classes 2A and 2B with the same allowance for 1A as for 2A. The maximum dimensions of Class 1A are less than basic, by the amount of the same allowance as applied to Class 2A and for the same purpose.

Classes 2A and 2B. — Tolerances represented by Classes 2A and 2B for external and internal threads, although smaller than Classes 1A and 1B, also provide a clearance under all conditions. Classes 2A and 2B are the recognized standard for normal production of screws, bolts and nuts. They are also suitable for many other applications. In Class 2A the maximum dimensions are less than basic, by the amount of allowance. This allowance provides a minimum clearance which minimizes galling and seizure. Plating applied to external threads may project into or fill this space.

Classes 3A and 3B. — The new classes of tolerances, 3A for external threads and 3B for internal threads, are, in general, for pitch diameters, 75 per cent of those allowed in Classes 2A and 2B, and for major diameters, the same as those allowed in Classes 2A and 2B.

Classes 2 and 3. — These two classes have the same limiting dimensions as Classes 2 and 3 of the former American Standard. They are not included in the Unified Series. Maximum external and minimum internal thread dimensions are basic. Tolerances for Class 3 are approximately 70 per cent of Class 2 tolerances.

Note: Class 4, formerly included in the American Standard, has been discontinued because it was seldom used and almost invariably to meet special requirements.

Symbols for Unified and American Standard Threads. — Standard symbols indicate the Thread Series and limit or tolerance classification. In the Unified Series, the number is followed by letter *A* for external and *B* for internal threads.

THREAD SERIES SYMBOLS:

UNC — Coarse-Thread Series in Unified part of American Standard

NC — Coarse-Thread Series not in Unified part of American Standard

UNF — Fine-Thread Series in Unified part of American Standard

NF — Fine-Thread Series not in Unified part of American Standard

N — Thread in American Standard 8-, 12-, or 16-Thread Constant-pitch Series; not in Unified part of American Standard

NS — Special thread not in Unified part of American Standard

UN or UNS — Special thread in Unified part of American Standard

UNEF — Extra-Fine Series in Unified part of American Standard

NEF — Extra-Fine Series not in Unified part of American Standard

LIMIT OR TOLERANCE CLASS SYMBOLS:

1A — Class 1A tolerance (external threads) in Unified part of American Standard

1B — Class 1B tolerance (internal threads) in Unified part of American Standard

2A — Class 2A tolerance (external threads) in Unified part of American Standard

2B — Class 2B tolerance (internal threads) in Unified part of American Standard

3A — Class 3A tolerance (external threads) in Unified part of American Standard

3B — Class 3B tolerance (internal threads) in Unified part of American Standard

2 — Class 2 tolerance (external and internal threads) not in Unified part of American Standard

3 — Class 3 tolerance (external and internal threads) not in Unified part of American Standard

The example below shows how screw thread size and symbols may be combined.

$$\frac{1}{4}''\text{--}20 \text{ UNC--}2A$$

This complete symbol indicates a nominal size of ¼ inch, 20 threads per inch (Coarse-thread Series) and Class 2A tolerance (external thread). The letters LH placed at end of symbol indicates a left-hand thread.

Table 1. Unified and American Standard Thread Series
Class 1A — External Thread Limits

Size	Thds. per Inch	Thread Symbol	Allowance	Major Diam. Limits		Pitch Diam. Limits		Minor Diam. Max
				Max.	Min.	Max.	Min.	
1/4	**20**	**UNC-1A**	**0.0011**	**0.2489**	**0.2367**	**0.2164**	**0.2108**	**0.1876**
1/4	**28**	**UNF-1A**	**0.0010**	**0.2490**	**0.2392**	**0.2258**	**0.2208**	**0.2052**
5/16	**18**	**UNC-1A**	**0.0012**	**0.3113**	**0.2982**	**0.2752**	**0.2691**	**0.2431**
5/16	**24**	**UNF-1A**	**0.0011**	**0.3114**	**0.3006**	**0.2843**	**0.2788**	**0.2603**
3/8	**16**	**UNC-1A**	**0.0013**	**0.3737**	**0.3595**	**0.3313**	**0.3266**	**0.2970**
3/8	**24**	**UNF-1A**	**0.0011**	**0.3739**	**0.3631**	**0.3468**	**0.3411**	**0.3228**
7/16	**14**	**UNC-1A**	**0.0014**	**0.4361**	**0.4206**	**0.3897**	**0.3826**	**0.3485**
7/16	**20**	**UNF-1A**	**0.0013**	**0.4362**	**0.4240**	**0.4037**	**0.3975**	**0.3749**
1/2	13	NC -1A	0.0015	0.4985	0.4822	0.4485	0.4411	0.4041
1/2	**12**	**UNC-1A**	**0.0015**	**0.4985**	**0.4813**	**0.4444**	**0.4367**	**0.3963**
1/2	**20**	**UNF-1A**	**0.0013**	**0.4987**	**0.4865**	**0.4662**	**0.4598**	**0.4374**
9/16	**12**	**UNC-1A**	**0.0016**	**0.5609**	**0.5437**	**0.5068**	**0.4990**	**0.4587**
9/16	**18**	**UNF-1A**	**0.0014**	**0.5611**	**0.5480**	**0.5250**	**0.5182**	**0.4929**
5/8	**11**	**UNC-1A**	**0.0016**	**0.6234**	**0.6052**	**0.5644**	**0.5561**	**0.5119**
5/8	**18**	**UNF-1A**	**0.0014**	**0.6236**	**0.6105**	**0.5875**	**0.5805**	**0.5554**
3/4	**10**	**UNC-1A**	**0.0018**	**0.7482**	**0.7288**	**0.6832**	**0.6744**	**0.6255**
3/4	**16**	**UNF-1A**	**0.0015**	**0.7485**	**0.7343**	**0.7079**	**0.7004**	**0.6718**
7/8	**9**	**UNC-1A**	**0.0019**	**0.8731**	**0.8523**	**0.8009**	**0.7914**	**0.7368**
7/8	**14**	**UNF-1A**	**0.0016**	**0.8734**	**0.8579**	**0.8270**	**0.8189**	**0.7858**
1	**8**	**UNC-1A**	**0.0020**	**0.9980**	**0.9755**	**0.9168**	**0.9067**	**0.8446**
1	**12**	**UNF-1A**	**0.0018**	**0.9982**	**0.9810**	**0.9441**	**0.9353**	**0.8960**
1	14	NF-1A	0.0017	0.9983	0.9828	0.9519	0.9435	0.9107
1 1/8	**7**	**UNC-1A**	**0.0022**	**1.1228**	**1.0982**	**1.0300**	**1.0191**	**0.9475**
1 1/8	**12**	**UNF-1A**	**0.0018**	**1.1232**	**1.1060**	**1.0691**	**1.0601**	**1.0210**
1 1/4	**7**	**UNC-1A**	**0.0022**	**1.2478**	**1.2232**	**1.1550**	**1.1439**	**1.0725**
1 1/4	**12**	**UNF-1A**	**0.0018**	**1.2482**	**1.2310**	**1.1941**	**1.1849**	**1.1460**
1 3/8	**6**	**UNC-1A**	**0.0024**	**1.3726**	**1.3453**	**1.2643**	**1.2523**	**1.1681**
1 3/8	**12**	**UNF-1A**	**0.0019**	**1.3731**	**1.3559**	**1.3190**	**1.3096**	**1.2709**
1 1/2	**6**	**UNC-1A**	**0.0024**	**1.4976**	**1.4703**	**1.3893**	**1.3772**	**1.2931**
1 1/2	**12**	**UNF-1A**	**0.0019**	**1.4981**	**1.4809**	**1.4440**	**1.4344**	**1.3959**
1 3/4	**5**	**UNC-1A**	**0.0027**	**1.7473**	**1.7165**	**1.6174**	**1.6040**	**1.5019**
2	**4½**	**UNC-1A**	**0.0029**	**1.9971**	**1.9641**	**1.8528**	**1.8385**	**1.7245**
2 1/4	**4½**	**UNC-1A**	**0.0029**	**2.2471**	**2.2141**	**2.1028**	**2.0882**	**1.9745**
2 1/2	**4**	**UNC-1A**	**0.0031**	**2.4969**	**2.4612**	**2.3345**	**2.3190**	**2.1902**
2 3/4	**4**	**UNC-1A**	**0.0032**	**2.7468**	**2.7111**	**2.5844**	**2.5686**	**2.4401**
3	**4**	**UNC-1A**	**0.0032**	**2.9968**	**2.9611**	**2.8344**	**2.8183**	**2.6901**
3 1/4	**4**	**UNC-1A**	**0.0033**	**3.2467**	**3.2110**	**3.0843**	**3.0680**	**2.9400**
3 1/2	**4**	**UNC-1A**	**0.0033**	**3.4967**	**3.4610**	**3.3343**	**3.3177**	**3.1900**
3 3/4	**4**	**UNC-1A**	**0.0034**	**3.7466**	**3.7109**	**3.5842**	**3.5674**	**3.4399**
4	**4**	**UNC-1A**	**0.0034**	**3.9966**	**3.9609**	**3.8342**	**3.8172**	**3.6899**

Bold face type indicates Unified threads.

A Class 1A thread need not be combined invariably with a Class 1B thread but may be used with a Class 2B, 3B, 2, or 3 thread where preferable for a specific application. Class 1A maximum dimensions are less than basic by the amount of an allowance which provides a minimum clearance for reducing galling and seizure during assembly and use. It also accommodates plated finishes or coatings.

Table 2. Unified and American Standard Thread Series
Class 1B — Internal Thread Limits

Size	Thds. per Inch	Thread Symbol	Minor Diam. Limits		Pitch Diam. Limits		Major Diam. Min.
			Min.	Max.	Min.	Max.	
1/4	**20**	**UNC-1B**	**0.1959**	**0.2067**	**0.2175**	**0.2248**	**0.2500**
1/4	**28**	**UNF-1B**	**0.2113**	**9.2190**	**0.2268**	**0.2333**	**0.2500**
5/16	**18**	**UNC-1B**	**0.2524**	**0.2630**	**0.2764**	**0.2843**	**0.3125**
5/16	**24**	**UNF-1B**	**0.2674**	**0.2754**	**0.2854**	**0.2925**	**0.3125**
3/8	**16**	**UNC-1B**	**0.3073**	**0.3182**	**0.3344**	**0.3429**	**0.3750**
3/8	**24**	**UNF-1B**	**0.3299**	**0.3372**	**0.3479**	**0.3553**	**0.3750**
7/16	**14**	**UNC-1B**	**0.3602**	**0.3717**	**0.3911**	**0.4003**	**0.4375**
7/16	**20**	**UNF-1B**	**0.3834**	**0.3916**	**0.4050**	**0.4131**	**0.4375**
1/2	13	NC-1B	0.4167	0.4284	0.4500	0.4597	0.5000
1/2	**12**	**UNC-1B**	**0.4098**	**0.4223**	**0.4459**	**0.4559**	**0.5000**
1/2	**20**	**UNF-1B**	**0.4459**	**0.4537**	**0.4675**	**0.4759**	**0.5000**
9/16	**12**	**UNC-1B**	**0.4723**	**0.4843**	**0.5084**	**0.5186**	**0.5625**
9/16	**18**	**UNF-1B**	**0.5024**	**0.5106**	**0.5264**	**0.5353**	**0.5625**
5/8	**11**	**UNC-1B**	**0.5266**	**0.5391**	**0.5660**	**0.5767**	**0.6250**
5/8	**18**	**UNF-1B**	**0.5649**	**0.5730**	**0.5889**	**0.5980**	**0.6250**
3/4	**10**	**UNC-1B**	**0.6417**	**0.6545**	**0.6850**	**0.6965**	**0.7500**
3/4	**16**	**UNF-1B**	**0.6823**	**0.6908**	**0.7094**	**0.7192**	**0.7500**
7/8	**9**	**UNC-1B**	**0.7547**	**0.7681**	**0.8028**	**0.8151**	**0.8750**
7/8	**14**	**UNF-1B**	**0.7977**	**0.8068**	**0.8286**	**0.8392**	**0.8750**
1	**8**	**UNC-1B**	**0.8647**	**0.8797**	**0.9188**	**0.9320**	**1.0000**
1	**12**	**UNF-1B**	**0.9098**	**0.9198**	**0.9459**	**0.9573**	**1.0000**
1	14	NF-1B	0.9227	0.9315	0.9536	0.9645	1.0000
1 1/8	**7**	**UNC-1B**	**0.9704**	**0.9875**	**1.0322**	**1.0463**	**1.1250**
1 1/8	**12**	**UNF-1B**	**1.0348**	**1.0448**	**1.0709**	**1.0826**	**1.1250**
1 1/4	**7**	**UNC-1B**	**1.0954**	**1.1125**	**1.1572**	**1.1716**	**1.2500**
1 1/4	**12**	**UNF-1B**	**1.1598**	**1.1698**	**1.1959**	**1.2079**	**1.2500**
1 3/8	**6**	**UNC-1B**	**1.1946**	**1.2146**	**1.2667**	**1.2822**	**1.3750**
1 3/8	**12**	**UNF-1B**	**1.2848**	**1.2948**	**1.3209**	**1.3332**	**1.3750**
1 1/2	**6**	**UNC-1B**	**1.3196**	**1.3396**	**1.3917**	**1.4075**	**1.5000**
1 1/2	**12**	**UNF-1B**	**1.4098**	**1.4198**	**1.4459**	**1.4584**	**1.5000**
1 3/4	**5**	**UNC-1B**	**1.5335**	**1.5575**	**1.6201**	**1.6375**	**1.7500**
2	**4 1/2**	**UNC-1B**	**1.7594**	**1.7861**	**1.8557**	**1.8743**	**2.0000**
2 1/4	**4 1/2**	**UNC-1B**	**2.0094**	**2.0361**	**2.1057**	**2.1247**	**2.2500**
2 1/2	**4**	**UNC-1B**	**2.2294**	**2.2594**	**2.3376**	**2.3578**	**2.5000**
2 3/4	**4**	**UNC-1B**	**2.4794**	**2.5094**	**2.5876**	**2.6082**	**2.7500**
3	**4**	**UNC-1B**	**2.7294**	**2.7594**	**2.8376**	**2.8585**	**3.0000**
3 1/4	**4**	**UNC-1B**	**2.9794**	**3.0094**	**3.0876**	**3.1088**	**3.2500**
3 1/2	**4**	**UNC-1B**	**3.2294**	**3.2594**	**3.3376**	**3.3591**	**3.5000**
3 3/4	**4**	**UNC-1B**	**3.4794**	**3.5094**	**3.5876**	**3.6094**	**3.7500**
4	**4**	**UNC-1B**	**3.7294**	**3.7594**	**3.8376**	**3.8597**	**4.0000**

Bold face type indicates Unified threads.

A Class 1B thread need not be combined invariably with a Class 1A thread, but may be used with a Class 2A, 3A, 2, or 3 thread where preferable for a specific application. The tolerances for pitch diameter in Class 1A and 1B are cumulative, that is, include the variations of lead and angle. Therefore, the full tolerance is not available for pitch diameter unless the lead and angle of the thread are perfect.

Table 3. Unified and American Standard Thread Series
Class 2A — External Thread Limits

No. or Size	Thds. per Inch	Thread Symbol	Allowance*	Major Diam. Limits			Pitch Diam. Limits		Minor Diam. Max.*
				Max.*	Min.[1]	Min.[2]	Max.*	Min.	
0	80	NF-2A	0.0005	0.0595	0.0563	....	0.0514	0.0496	0.0442
1	64	NC-2A	0.0006	0.0724	0.0686	....	0.0623	0.0603	0.0532
1	72	NF-2A	0.0006	0.0724	0.0689	....	0.0634	0.0615	0.0554
2	56	NC-2A	0.0006	0.0854	0.0813	....	0.0738	0.0717	0.0635
2	64	NF-2A	0.0006	0.0854	0.0816	....	0.0753	0.0733	0.0662
3	48	NC-2A	0.0007	0.0983	0.0938	....	0.0848	0.0825	0.0727
3	56	NF-2A	0.0007	0.0983	0.0942	....	0.0867	0.0845	0.0764
4	40	NC-2A	0.0008	0.1112	0.1061	....	0.0950	0.0925	0.0805
4	48	NF-2A	0.0007	0.1113	0.1068	....	0.0978	0.0954	0.0857
5	40	NC-2A	0.0008	0.1242	0.1191	....	0.1080	0.1054	0.0935
5	44	NF-2A	0.0007	0.1243	0.1195	....	0.1095	0.1070	0.0964
6	32	NC-2A	0.0008	0.1372	0.1312	....	0.1169	0.1141	0.0989
6	40	NF-2A	0.0008	0.1372	0.1321	....	0.1210	0.1184	0.1065
8	32	NC-2A	0.0009	0.1631	0.1571	....	0.1428	0.1399	0.1248
8	36	NF-2A	0.0008	0.1632	0.1577	....	0.1452	0.1424	0.1291
10	24	NC-2A	0.0010	0.1890	0.1818	....	0.1619	0.1586	0.1379
10	32	NF-2A	0.0009	0.1891	0.1831	....	0.1688	0.1658	0.1508
12	24	NC-2A	0.0010	0.2150	0.2078	....	0.1879	0.1845	0.1639
12	28	NF-2A	0.0010	0.2150	0.2085	....	0.1918	0.1886	0.1712
1/4	20	UNC-2A	0.0011	0.2489	0.2408	0.2367	0.2164	0.2127	0.1876
1/4	28	UNF-2A	0.0010	0.2490	0.2425	....	0.2258	0.2225	0.2052
5/16	18	UNC-2A	0.0012	0.3113	0.3026	0.2982	0.2752	0.2712	0.2431
5/16	24	UNF-2A	0.0011	0.3114	0.3042	....	0.2843	0.2806	0.2603
3/8	16	UNC-2A	0.0013	0.3737	0.3643	0.3595	0.3331	0.3287	0.2970
3/8	24	UNF-2A	0.0011	0.3739	0.3667	....	0.3468	0.3430	0.3228
7/16	14	UNC-2A	0.0014	0.4361	0.4258	0.4206	0.3897	0.3850	0.3485
7/16	20	UNF-2A	0.0013	0.4362	0.4281	....	0.4037	0.3995	0.3749
1/2	13	NC-2A	0.0015	0.4985	0.4876	0.4822	0.4485	0.4435	0.4041
1/2	12	UNC-2A	0.0015	0.4985	0.4871	0.4813	0.4444	0.4393	0.3963
1/2	20	UNF-2A	0.0013	0.4987	4.4906	....	0.4662	0.4619	0.4374
9/16	12	UNC-2A	0.0016	0.5609	0.5495	0.5437	0.5068	0.5016	0.4587
9/16	18	UNF-2A	0.0014	0.5611	0.5524	....	0.5250	0.5205	0.4929
5/8	11	UNC-2A	0.0016	0.6234	0.6113	0.6052	0.5644	0.5589	0.5119
5/8	18	UNF-2A	0.0014	0.6236	0.6149	....	0.5875	0.5828	0.5554
3/4	10	UNC-2A	0.0018	0.7482	0.7353	0.7288	0.6832	0.6773	0.6255
3/4	16	UNF-2A	0.0015	0.7485	0.7391	....	0.7079	0.7029	0.6718
7/8	9	UNC-2A	0.0019	0.8731	0.8592	0.8523	0.8009	0.7946	0.7368
7/8	14	UNF-2A	0.0016	0.8734	0.8631	....	0.8270	0.8216	0.7858
1	8	UNC-2A	0.0020	0.9980	0.9830	0.9755	0.9168	0.9100	0.8446
1	12	UNF-2A	0.0018	0.9982	0.9868	....	0.9441	0.9382	0.8960
1	14	NF-2A	0.0017	0.9983	0.9880	....	0.9519	0.9463	0.9107
1 1/8	7	UNC-2A	0.0022	1.1228	1.1064	1.0982	1.0300	1.0228	0.9475
1 1/8	8	N-2A	0.0021	1.1229	1.1079	1.1004	1.0417	1.0348	0.9695
1 1/8	12	UNF-2A	0.0018	1.1232	1.1118	....	1.0691	1.0631	1.0210

See footnotes at end of this table.

Table 3 (*Continued*). Unified and American Standard Thread Series
Class 2A — External Thread Limits

Size	Thds. per Inch	Thread Symbol	Allow-ance*	Major Diam. Limits			Pitch Diam. Limits		Minor Diam. Max.*
				Max.*	Min.[1]	Min.[2]	Max.*	Min.	
1 1/4	**7**	**UNC-2A**	**0.0022**	**1.2478**	**1.2314**	1.2232	**1.1550**	**1.1476**	1.0725
1 1/4	8	N-2A	0.0021	1.2479	1.2329	1.2254	1.1667	1.1597	1.0945
1 1/4	**12**	**UNF-2A**	**0.0018**	**1.2482**	**1.2368**	....	**1.1941**	**1.1879**	1.1460
1 3/8	**6**	**UNC-2A**	**0.0024**	**1.3726**	**1.3544**	1.3453	**1.2643**	**1.2563**	1.1681
1 3/8	8	N-2A	0.0022	1.3728	1.3578	1.3503	1.2916	1.2844	1.2194
1 3/8	**12**	**UNF-2A**	**0.0019**	**1.3731**	**1.3617**	....	**1.3190**	**1.3127**	1.2709
1 1/2	**6**	**UNC-2A**	**0.0024**	**1.4976**	**1.4794**	1.4703	**1.3893**	**1.3812**	1.2931
1 1/2	8	N-2A	0.0022	1.4978	1.4828	1.4753	1.4166	1.4093	1.3444
1 1/2	**12**	**UNF-2A**	**0.0019**	**1.4981**	**1.4867**	....	**1.4440**	**1.4376**	1.3959
1 5/8	8	N-2A	0.0022	1.6228	1.6078	1.6003	1.5416	1.5342	1.4694
1 3/4	**5**	**UNC-2A**	**0.0027**	**1.7473**	**1.7268**	1.7165	**1.6174**	**1.6085**	1.5019
1 3/4	8	N-2A	0.0023	1.7477	1.7327	1.7252	1.6665	1.6590	1.5943
1 7/8	8	N-2A	0.0023	1.8727	1.8577	1.8502	1.7915	1.7838	1.7193
2	**4 1/2**	**UNC-2A**	**0.0029**	**1.9971**	**1.9751**	1.9641	**1.8528**	**1.8433**	1.7245
2	8	N-2A	0.0023	1.9977	1.9827	1.9752	1.9165	1.9037	1.8443
2 1/8	8	N-2A	0.0024	2.1226	2.1076	2.1001	2.0414	2.0335	1.9692
2 1/4	**4 1/2**	**UNC-2A**	**0.0029**	**2.2471**	**2.2251**	2.2141	**2.1028**	**2.0931**	1.9745
2 1/4	8	N-2A	0.0024	2.2476	2.2326	2.2251	2.1664	2.1584	2.0942
2 1/2	**4**	**UNC-2A**	**0.0031**	**2.4969**	**2.4731**	2.4612	**2.3345**	**2.3241**	2.1902
2 1/2	8	N-2A	0.0024	2.4976	2.4826	2.4751	2.4164	2.4082	2.3442
2 3/4	**4**	**UNC-2A**	**0.0032**	**2.7468**	**2.7230**	2.7111	**2.5844**	**2.5739**	2.4401
2 3/4	8	N-2A	0.0025	2.7475	2.7325	2.7250	2.6663	2.6580	2.5941
3	**4**	**UNC-2A**	**0.0032**	**2.9968**	**2.9730**	2.9611	**2.8344**	**2.8237**	2.6901
3	8	N-2A	0.0026	2.9974	2.9824	2.9749	2.9162	2.9077	2.8440
3 1/4	**4**	**UNC-2A**	**0.0033**	**3.2467**	**3.2229**	3.2110	**3.0843**	**3.0734**	2.9400
3 1/4	8	N-2A	0.0026	3.2474	3.2324	3.2249	3.1662	3.1575	3.0940
3 1/2	**4**	**UNC-2A**	**0.0033**	**3.4967**	**3.4729**	3.4610	**3.3343**	**3.3233**	3.1900
3 1/2	8	N-2A	0.0026	3.4974	3.4824	3.4749	3.4162	3.4074	3.3440
3 3/4	**4**	**UNC-2A**	**0.0034**	**3.7466**	**3.7228**	3.7109	**3.5842**	**3.5730**	3.4399
3 3/4	8	N-2A	0.0027	3.7473	3.7323	3.7248	3.6661	3.6571	3.5939
4	**4**	**UNC-2A**	**0.0034**	**3.9966**	**3.9728**	3.9609	**3.8342**	**3.8229**	3.6899
4	8	N-2A	0.0027	3.9973	3.9823	3.9748	3.9161	3.9070	3.8439
4 1/4	8	N-2A	0.0028	4.2472	4.2322	4.2247	4.1660	4.1567	4.0938
4 1/2	8	N-2A	0.0028	4.4972	4.4822	4.4747	4.4160	4.4066	4.3438
4 3/4	8	N-2A	0.0029	4.7471	4.7321	4.7246	4.6659	4.6564	4.5937
5	8	N-2A	0.0029	4.9971	4.9821	4.9746	4.9159	4.9062	4.8437
5 1/4	8	N-2A	0.0029	5.2471	5.2321	5.2246	5.0659	5.0561	5.0937
5 1/2	8	N-2A	0.0030	5.4970	5.4820	5.4745	5.4158	5.4059	5.3436
5 3/4	8	N-2A	0.0030	5.7470	5.7320	5.7245	5.6658	5.6558	5.5936
6	8	N-2A	0.0030	5.9970	5.9820	5.9745	5.9158	5.9056	5.8436

Bold face type indicates Unified threads.

* Class 2A maximum dimensions are less than basic by the amount of an allowance which provides a minimum clearance for reducing galling and seizure during assembly and use. The maximum dimensions of threads which are electroplated or have coatings of similar thickness will be increased by the amount of the allowance.

[1] For semi-finished and finished screws and bolts, threaded portion only.

[2] For unfinished hot rolled material, threaded portion only.

Table 4. Unified and American Standard Thread Series
Class 2B — Internal Thread Limits

Size	Thds. per Inch	Thread Symbol	Minor Diam. Limits		Pitch Diam. Limits		Major Diam. Min.
			Min.	Max.	Min.	Max.	
0 (.060)	80	NF-2B	0.0465	0.0514	0.0519	0.0542	0.0600
1 (.073)	64	NC-2B	0.0561	0.0623	0.0629	0.0655	0.0730
1 (.073)	72	NF-2B	0.0580	0.0635	0.0640	0.0665	0.0730
2 (.086)	56	NC-2B	0.0667	0.0737	0.0744	0.0772	0.0860
2 (.086)	64	NF-2B	0.0691	0.0753	0.0759	0.0786	0.0860
3 (.099)	48	NC-2B	0.0764	0.0845	0.0855	0.0885	0.0990
3 (.099)	56	NF-2B	0.0797	0.0865	0.0874	0.0902	0.0990
4 (.112)	40	NC-2B	0.0849	0.0939	0.0958	0.0991	0.1120
4 (.112)	48	NF-2B	0.0894	0.0968	0.0985	0.1016	0.1120
5 (.125)	40	NC-2B	0.0979	0.1062	0.1088	0.1121	0.1250
5 (.125)	44	NF-2B	0.1004	0.1079	0.1102	0.1134	0.1250
6 (.138)	32	NC-2B	0.1042	0.1140	0.1177	0.1214	0.1380
6 (.138)	40	NF-2B	0.1109	0.1186	0.1218	0.1252	0.1380
8 (.164)	32	NC-2B	0.1302	0.1389	0.1437	0.1475	0.1640
8 (.164)	36	NF-2B	0.1339	0.1416	0.1460	0.1496	0.1640
10 (.190)	24	NC-2B	0.1449	0.1555	0.1629	0.1672	0.1900
10 (.190)	32	NF-2B	0.1562	0.1641	0.1697	0.1736	0.1900
12 (.216)	24	NC-2B	0.1709	0.1807	0.1889	0.1933	0.2160
12 (.216)	28	NF-2B	0.1773	0.1857	0.1928	0.1970	0.2160
1/4	20	UNC-2B	0.1959	0.2067	0.2175	0.2223	0.2500
1/4	28	UNF-2B	0.2113	0.2190	0.2268	0.2311	0.2500
5/16	18	UNC-2B	0.2524	0.2630	0.2764	0.2817	0.3125
5/16	24	UNF-2B	0.2674	0.2754	0.2854	0.2902	0.3125
3/8	16	UNC-2B	0.3073	0.3182	0.3344	0.3401	0.3750
3/8	24	UNF-2B	0.3299	0.3372	0.3479	0.3528	0.3750
7/16	14	UNC-2B	0.3602	0.3717	0.3911	0.3972	0.4375
7/16	20	UNF-2B	0.3834	0.3916	0.4050	0.4104	0.4375
1/2	13	NC-2B	0.4167	0.4284	0.4500	0.4565	0.5000
1/2	12	UNC-2B	0.4098	0.4223	0.4459	0.4525	0.5000
1/2	20	UNF-2B	0.4459	0.4537	0.4675	0.4731	0.5000
9/16	12	UNC-2B	0.4723	0.4843	0.5084	0.5152	0.5625
9/16	18	UNF-2B	0.5024	0.5106	0.5264	0.5323	0.5625
5/8	11	UNC-2B	0.5266	0.5391	0.5660	0.5732	0.6250
5/8	18	UNF-2B	0.5649	0.5730	0.5889	0.5949	0.6250
3/4	10	UNC-2B	0.6417	0.6545	0.6850	0.6927	0.7500
3/4	16	UNF-2B	0.6823	0.6908	0.7094	0.7159	0.7500
7/8	9	UNC-2B	0.7547	0.7681	0.8028	0.8110	0.8750
7/8	14	UNF-2B	0.7977	0.8068	0.8286	0.8356	0.8750
1	8	UNC-2B	0.8647	0.8797	0.9188	0.9276	1.0000
1	12	UNF-2B	0.9098	0.9198	0.9459	0.9535	1.0000
1	14	NF-2B	0.9227	0.9315	0.9536	0.9609	1.0000
1 1/8	7	UNC-2B	0.9704	0.9875	1.0322	1.0416	1.1250
1 1/8	8	N-2B	0.9897	1.0047	1.0438	1.0528	1.1250
1 1/8	12	UNF-2B	1.0348	1.0448	1.0709	1.0787	1.1250

See footnotes at end of this table.

Table 4 (*Continued*). **Unified and American Standard Thread Series**
Class 2B — Internal Thread Limits

Size	Threads per Inch	Thread Symbol	Minor Diam. Limits		Pitch Diam. Limits		Major Diam. Min.
			Min.	Max.	Min.	Max.	
1 1/4	**7**	**UNC-2B**	**1.0954**	**1.1125**	**1.1572**	**1.1668**	**1.2500**
1 1/4	8	N-2B	1.1147	1.1297	1.1688	1.1780	1.2500
1 1/4	**12**	**UNF-2B**	**1.1598**	**1.1698**	**1.1959**	**1.2039**	**1.2500**
1 3/8	**6**	**UNC-2B**	**1.1946**	**1.2146**	**1.2667**	**1.2771**	**1.3750**
1 3/8	8	N-2B	1.2397	1.2547	1.2938	1.3031	1.3750
1 3/8	**12**	**UNF-2B**	**1.2848**	**1.2948**	**1.3209**	**1.3291**	**1.3750**
1 1/2	**6**	**UNC-2B**	**1.3196**	**1.3396**	**1.3917**	**1.4022**	**1.5000**
1 1/2	8	N-2B	1.3647	1.3797	1.4188	1.4283	1.5000
1 1/2	**12**	**UNF-2B**	**1.4098**	**1.4198**	**1.4459**	**1.4542**	**1.5000**
1 5/8	8	N-2B	1.4897	1.5047	1.5438	1.5535	1.6250
1 3/4	**5**	**UNC-2B**	**1.5335**	**1.5575**	**1.6201**	**1.6317**	**1.7500**
1 3/4	8	N-2B	1.6147	1.6297	1.6688	1.6786	1.7500
1 7/8	8	N-2B	1.7397	1.7547	1.7938	1.8038	1.8750
2	**4½**	**UNC-2B**	**1.7594**	**1.7861**	**1.8557**	**1.8681**	**2.0000**
2	8	N-2B	1.8647	1.8797	1.9188	1.9289	2.0000
2 1/8	8	N-2B	1.9897	2.0047	2.0438	2.0540	2.1250
2 1/4	**4½**	**UNC-2B**	**2.0094**	**2.0361**	**2.1057**	**2.1183**	**2.2500**
2 1/4	8	N-2B	2.1147	2.1297	2.1688	2.1792	2.2500
2 1/2	**4**	**UNC-2B**	**2.2294**	**2.2594**	**2.3376**	**2.3511**	**2.5000**
2 1/2	8	N-2B	2.3647	2.3797	2.4188	2.4294	2.5000
2 3/4	**4**	**UNC-2B**	**2.4794**	**2.5094**	**2.5876**	**2.6013**	**2.7500**
2 3/4	8	N-2B	2.6147	2.6297	2.6688	2.6796	2.7500
3	**4**	**UNC-2B**	**2.7294**	**2.7594**	**2.8376**	**2.8515**	**3.0000**
3	8	N-2B	2.8647	2.8797	2.9188	2.9299	3.0000
3 1/4	**4**	**UNC-2B**	**2.9794**	**3.0094**	**3.0876**	**3.1017**	**3.2500**
3 1/4	8	N-2B	3.1147	3.1297	3.1688	3.1801	3.2500
3 1/2	**4**	**UNC-2B**	**3.2294**	**3.2594**	**3.3376**	**3.3519**	**3.5000**
3 1/2	8	N-2B	3.3647	3.3797	3.4188	3.4303	3.5000
3 3/4	**4**	**UNC-2B**	**3.4794**	**3.5094**	**3.5876**	**3.6021**	**3.7500**
3 3/4	8	N-2B	3.6147	3.6297	3.6688	3.6805	3.7500
4	**4**	**UNC-2B**	**3.7294**	**3.7594**	**3.8376**	**3.8523**	**4.0000**
4	8	N-2B	3.8647	3.8797	3.9188	3.9307	4.0000
4 1/4	8	N-2B	4.1147	4.1297	4.1688	4.1809	4.2500
4 1/2	8	N-2B	4.3647	4.3797	4.4188	4.4310	4.5000
4 3/4	8	N-2B	4.6147	4.6297	4.6688	4.6812	4.7500
5	8	N-2B	4.8647	4.8797	4.9188	4.9314	5.0000
5 1/4	8	N-2B	5.1147	5.1297	5.1688	5.1815	5.2500
5 1/2	8	N-2B	5.3647	5.3797	5.4188	5.4317	5.5000
5 3/4	8	N-2B	5.6147	5.6297	5.6688	5.6818	5.7500
6	8	N-2B	5.8647	5.8797	5.9188	5.9320	6.0000

Bold face type indicates Unified threads.

A Class 2B thread need not be combined invariably with a Class 2A thread but may be used with a Class 1A, 3A, 2, or 3 thread where preferable for a specific application. The tolerances for pitch diameter in Class 2A and 2B, are cumulative, that is, include the variations of lead and angle. Therefore, the full tolerance is not available for pitch diameter unless the lead and angle of the thread are perfect.

Table 5. Unified and American Standard Thread Series
Class 3A — External Thread Limits

Size	Thds. per Inch	Thread Symbol	Allow- ance	Major Diam. Limits		Pitch Diam. Limits		Minor Diam. Max.
				Max.	Min.	Max.	Min.	
1/4	20	UNC-3A	0.0000	0.2500	0.2419	0.2175	0.2147	0.1887
1/4	28	UNF-3A	0.0000	0.2500	0.2435	0.2268	0.2243	0.2062
5/16	18	UNC-3A	0.0000	0.3125	0.3038	0.2764	0.2734	0.2443
5/16	24	UNF-3A	0.0000	0.3125	0.3053	0.2854	0.2827	0.2614
3/8	16	UNC-3A	0.0000	0.3750	0.3656	0.3344	0.3311	0.2983
3/8	24	UNF-3A	0.0000	0.3750	0.3678	0.3479	0.3450	0.3239
7/16	14	UNC-3A	0.0000	0.4375	0.4272	0.3911	0.3876	0.3499
7/16	20	UNF-3A	0.0000	0.4375	0.4294	0.4050	0.4019	0.3762
1/2	13	NC-3A	0.0000	0.5000	0.4891	0.4500	0.4463	0.4056
1/2	12	UNC-3A	0.0000	0.5000	0.4886	0.4459	0.4421	0.3978
1/2	20	UNF-3A	0.0000	0.5000	0.4919	0.4675	0.4643	0.4387
9/16	12	UNC-3A	0.0000	0.5625	0.5511	0.5084	0.5045	0.4603
9/16	18	UNF-3A	0.0000	0.5625	0.5538	0.5264	0.5230	0.4943
5/8	11	UNC-3A	0.0000	0.6250	0.6129	0.5660	0.5619	0.5135
5/8	18	UNF-3A	0.0000	0.6250	0.6163	0.5889	0.5854	0.5568
3/4	10	UNC-3A	0.0000	0.7500	0.7371	0.6850	0.6806	0.6273
3/4	16	UNF-3A	0.0000	0.7500	0.7406	0.7094	0.7056	0.6733
7/8	9	UNC-3A	0.0000	0.8750	0.8611	0.8028	0.7981	0.7387
7/8	14	UNF-3A	0.0000	0.8750	0.8647	0.8286	0.8245	0.7874
1	8	UNC-3A	0.0000	1.0000	0.9850	0.9188	0.9137	0.8466
1	12	UNF-3A	0.0000	1.0000	0.9886	0.9459	0.9415	0.8978
1	14	NF-3A	0.0000	1.0000	0.9897	0.9536	0.9494	0.9124
1 1/8	7	UNC-3A	0.0000	1.1250	1.1086	1.0322	1.0268	0.9497
1 1/8	12	UNF-3A	0.0000	1.1250	1.1136	1.0709	1.0664	1.0228
1 1/4	7	UNC-3A	0.0000	1.2500	1.2336	1.1572	1.1517	1.0747
1 1/4	12	UNF-3A	0.0000	1.2500	1.2386	1.1959	1.1913	1.1478
1 3/8	6	UNC-3A	0.0000	1.3750	1.3568	1.2667	1.2607	1.1705
1 3/8	12	UNF-3A	0.0000	1.3750	1.3636	1.3209	1.3162	1.2728
1 1/2	6	UNC-3A	0.0000	1.5000	1.4818	1.3917	1.3856	1.2955
1 1/2	12	UNF-3A	0.0000	1.5000	1.4886	1.4459	1.4411	1.3978
1 3/4	5	UNC-3A	0.0000	1.7500	1.7295	1.6201	1.6134	1.5046
2	4 1/2	UNC-3A	0.0000	2.0000	1.9780	1.8557	1.8486	1.7274
2 1/4	4 1/2	UNC-3A	0.0000	2.2500	2.2280	2.1057	2.0984	1.9774
2 1/2	4	UNC-3A	0.0000	2.5000	2.4762	2.3376	2.3298	2.1933
2 3/4	4	UNC-3A	0.0000	2.7500	2.7262	2.5876	2.5797	2.4433
3	4	UNC-3A	0.0000	3.0000	2.9762	2.8376	2.8296	2.6933
3 1/4	4	UNC-3A	0.0000	3.2500	3.2262	3.0876	3.0794	2.9433
3 1/2	4	UNC-3A	0.0000	3.5000	3.4762	3.3376	3.3293	3.1933
3 3/4	4	UNC-3A	0.0000	3.7500	3.7262	3.5876	3.5792	3.4433
4	4	UNC-3A	0.0000	4.0000	3.9762	3.8376	3.8291	3.6933

Bold face type indicates Unified threads.

A Class 3A thread need not be combined invariably with a Class 3B thread but may be used with a Class 1B, 2B, 2, or 3 thread where preferable for a specific application. The tolerances for pitch diameter in Class 3A, are cumulative, that is, include the variations of lead and angle. Therefore, the full tolerance is not available for pitch diameter unless the lead and angle of the thread are perfect.

Table 6. Unified and American Standard Thread Series
Class 3B — Internal Thread Limits

Size	Thds. per Inch	Thread Symbol	Minor Diam. Limits		Pitch Diam. Limits		Major Diam. Min.
			Min.	Max.	Min.	Max.	
1/4	20	UNC-3B	0.1959	0.2067	0.2175	0.2211	0.2500
1/4	28	UNF-3B	0.2113	0.2190	0.2268	0.2300	0.2500
5/16	18	UNC-3B	0.2524	0.2630	0.2764	0.2803	0.3125
5/16	24	UNF-3B	0.2674	0.2754	0.2854	0.2890	0.3125
3/8	16	UNC-3B	0.3073	0.3182	0.3344	0.3387	0.3750
3/8	24	UNF-3B	0.3299	0.3372	0.3479	0.3516	0.3750
7/16	14	UNC-3B	0.3602	0.3717	0.3911	0.3957	0.4375
7/16	20	UNF-3B	0.3834	0.3916	0.4050	0.4091	0.4375
1/2	13	NC-3B	0.4167	0.4284	0.4500	0.4548	0.5000
1/2	12	UNC-3B	0.4098	0.4223	0.4459	0.4509	0.5000
1/2	20	UNF-3B	0.4459	0.4537	0.4675	0.4717	0.5000
9/16	12	UNC-3B	0.4723	0.4843	0.5084	0.5135	0.5625
9/16	18	UNF-3B	0.5024	0.5106	0.5264	0.5308	0.5625
5/8	11	UNC-3B	0.5266	0.5391	0.5660	0.5714	0.6250
5/8	18	UNF-3B	0.5649	0.5730	0.5889	0.5934	0.6250
3/4	10	UNC-3B	0.6417	0.6545	0.6850	0.6907	0.7500
3/4	16	UNF-3B	0.6823	0.6908	0.7094	0.7143	0.7500
7/8	9	UNC-3B	0.7547	0.7681	0.8028	0.8089	0.8750
7/8	14	UNF-3B	0.7977	0.8068	0.8286	0.8339	0.8750
1	8	UNC-3B	0.8647	0.8797	0.9188	0.9254	1.0000
1	12	UNF-3B	0.9098	0.9198	0.9459	0.9516	1.0000
1	14	NF-3B	0.9227	0.9315	0.9536	0.9590	1.0000
1 1/8	7	UNC-3B	0.9704	0.9875	1.0322	1.0393	1.1250
1 1/8	12	UNF-3B	1.0348	1.0448	1.0709	1.6768	1.1250
1 1/4	7	UNC-3B	1.0954	1.1125	1.1572	1.1644	1.2500
1 1/4	12	UNF-3B	1.1598	1.1698	1.1959	1.2019	1.2500
1 3/8	6	UNC-3B	1.1946	1.2146	1.2667	1.2745	1.3750
1 3/8	12	UNF-3B	1.2848	1.2948	1.3209	1.3270	1.3750
1 1/2	6	UNC-3B	1.3196	1.3396	1.3917	1.3996	1.5000
1 1/2	12	UNF-3B	1.4098	1.4198	1.4459	1.4522	1.5000
1 3/4	5	UNC-3B	1.5335	1.5575	1.6201	1.6288	1.7500
2	4 1/2	UNC-3B	1.7594	1.7861	1.8557	1.8650	2.0000
2 1/4	4 1/2	UNC-3B	2.0094	2.0361	2.1057	2.1152	2.2500
2 1/2	4	UNC-3B	2.2294	2.2594	2.3376	2.3477	2.5000
2 3/4	4	UNC-3B	2.4794	2.5094	2.5876	2.5979	2.7500
3	4	UNC-3B	2.7294	2.7594	2.8376	2.8480	3.0000
3 1/4	4	UNC-3B	2.9794	3.0094	3.0876	3.0982	3.2500
3 1/2	4	UNC-3B	3.2294	3.2594	3.3376	3.3484	3.5000
3 3/4	4	UNC-3B	3.4794	3.5094	3.5876	3.5985	3.7500
4	4	UNC-3B	3.7294	3.7594	3.8376	3.8487	4.0000

Bold face type indicates Unified threads.

A Class 3B thread need not be combined invariably with a Class 3A thread but may be used with a Class 1A, 2A, 2, or 3 thread where preferable for a specific application. The tolerances for pitch diameter in Class 3B are cumulative, that is, include the variations of lead and angle. Therefore, the full tolerance is not available for pitch diameter unless the lead and angle of the thread are perfect.

Table 7. American Standard Thread Series
Class 2 — External Thread Limits

No. or Size	Thds. per Inch	Thread Symbol	Major Diameter			Pitch Diam.		Minor Diam. Max.
			Max.	Min.[1]	Min.[2]	Max.	Min.	
0	80	NF-2	0.0600	0.0566	....	0.0519	0.0502	0.0447
1	64	NC-2	0.0730	0.0692	0.0678	0.0629	0.0610	0.0538
1	72	NF-2	0.0730	0.0694	....	0.0640	0.0622	0.0560
2	56	NC-2	0.0860	0.0820	0.0804	0.0744	0.0724	0.0641
2	64	NF-2	0.0860	0.0822	....	0.0759	0.0740	0.0668
3	48	NC-2	0.0990	0.0946	0.0928	0.0855	0.0833	0.0734
3	56	NF-2	0.0990	0.0950	....	0.0874	0.0854	0.0771
4	40	NC-2	0.1120	0.1072	0.1052	0.0958	0.0934	0.0813
4	48	NF-2	0.1120	0.1076	....	0.0985	0.0963	0.0864
5	40	NC-2	0.1250	0.1202	0.1182	0.1088	0.1064	0.0943
5	44	NF-2	0.1250	0.1204	....	0.1102	0.1079	0.0971
6	32	NC-2	0.1380	0.1326	0.1304	0.1177	0.1150	0.0997
6	40	NF-2	0.1380	0.1332	....	0.1218	0.1194	0.1073
8	32	NC-2	0.1640	0.1586	0.1564	0.1437	0.1410	0.1257
8	36	NF-2	0.1640	0.1590	....	0.1460	0.1435	0.1299
10	24	NC-2	0.1900	0.1834	0.1808	0.1629	0.1596	0.1389
10	32	NF-2	0.1900	0.1846	....	0.1697	0.1670	0.1517
12	24	NC-2	0.2160	0.2094	0.2068	0.1889	0.1856	0.1649
12	28	NF-2	0.2160	0.2098	....	0.1928	0.1897	0.1722
1/4	20	NC-2	0.2500	0.2428	0.2398	0.2175	0.2139	0.1887
1/4	28	NF-2	0.2500	0.2438	....	0.2268	0.2237	0.2062
5/16	18	NC-2	0.3125	0.3043	0.3011	0.2764	0.2723	0.2443
5/16	24	NF-2	0.3125	0.3059	....	0.2854	0.2821	0.2614
3/8	16	NC-2	0.3750	0.3660	0.3624	0.3344	0.3299	0.2983
3/8	24	NF-2	0.3750	0.3684	....	0.3479	0.3446	0.3239
7/16	14	NC-2	0.4375	0.4277	0.4235	0.3911	0.3862	0.3499
7/16	20	NF-2	0.4375	0.4303	....	0.4050	0.4014	0.3762
1/2	13	NC-2	0.5000	0.4896	0.4852	0.4500	0.4448	0.4056
1/2	20	NF-2	0.5000	0.4928	....	0.4675	0.4639	0.4387
9/16	12	NC-2	0.5625	0.5513	0.5467	0.5084	0.5028	0.4603
9/16	18	NF-2	0.5625	0.5543	....	0.5264	0.5223	0.4943
5/8	11	NC-2	0.6250	0.6132	0.6080	0.5660	0.5601	0.5135
5/8	18	NF-2	0.6250	0.6168	....	0.5889	0.5848	0.5568
3/4	10	NC-2	0.7500	0.7372	0.7316	0.6850	0.6786	0.6273
3/4	16	NF-2	0.7500	0.7410	....	0.7094	0.7049	0.6733
7/8	9	NC-2	0.8750	0.8610	0.8550	0.8028	0.7958	0.7387
7/8	14	NF-2	0.8750	0.8652	....	0.8286	0.8237	0.7874
1	8	NC-2	1.0000	0.9848	0.9778	0.9188	0.9112	0.8466
1	14	NF-2	1.0000	0.9902	....	0.9536	0.9487	0.9124

[1] For semi-finished and finished screws and bolts, threaded portion only.

[2] For unfinished hot rolled material, threaded portion only.

A Class 2 external thread need not be combined invariably with a Class 2 internal thread, but may be used with a Class 1B, 2B, 3B, or 3 thread where preferable for a specific application.

Table 7 (Continued). American Standard Thread Series
Class 2 — External Thread Limits

Size	Thds. per Inch	Thread Symbol	Major Diameter			Pitch Diam.		Minor Diam. Max.
			Max.	Min.[1]	Min.[2]	Max.	Min.	
1 1/8	7	NC-2	1.1250	1.1080	1.1002	1.0322	1.0237	0.9497
1 1/8	8	N-2	1.1250	1.1098	1.1028	1.0438	1.0359	0.9716
1 1/8	12	NF-2	1.1250	1.1138	....	1.0709	1.0653	1.0228
1 1/4	7	NC-2	1.2500	1.2330	1.2252	1.1572	1.1487	1.0747
1 1/4	8	N-2	1.2500	1.2348	1.2278	1.1688	1.1605	1.0966
1 1/4	12	NF-2	1.2500	1.2388	....	1.1959	1.1903	1.1478
1 3/8	6	NC-2	1.3750	1.3548	1.3460	1.2667	1.2566	1.1705
1 3/8	8	N-2	1.3750	1.3598	1.3528	1.2938	1.2852	1.2216
1 3/8	12	NF-2	1.3750	1.3638	....	1.3209	1.3153	1.2728
1 1/2	6	NC-2	1.5000	1.4798	1.4710	1.3917	1.3816	1.2955
1 1/2	8	N-2	1.5000	1.4848	1.4778	1.4188	1.4098	1.3466
1 1/2	12	NF-2	1.5000	1.4888	....	1.4459	1.4403	1.3978
1 5/8	8	N-2	1.6250	1.6098	1.6028	1.5438	1.5345	1.4716
1 3/4	5	NC-2	1.7500	1.7268	1.7162	1.6201	1.6085	1.5046
1 3/4	8	N-2	1.7500	1.7348	1.7278	1.6688	1.6591	1.5966
1 7/8	8	N-2	1.8750	1.8598	1.8528	1.7938	1.7838	1.7216
2	4½	NC-2	2.0000	1.9746	1.9632	1.8557	1.8430	1.7274
2	8	N-2	2.0000	1.9848	1.9778	1.9188	1.9084	1.8466
2 1/8	8	N-2	2.1250	2.1098	2.1028	2.0438	2.0331	1.9716
2 1/4	4½	NC-2	2.2500	2.2246	2.2132	2.1057	2.0930	1.9774
2 1/4	8	N-2	2.2500	2.2348	2.2278	2.1688	2.1578	2.0966
2 1/2	4	NC-2	2.5000	2.4720	2.4592	2.3376	2.3236	2.1933
2 1/2	8	N-2	2.5000	2.4848	2.4778	2.4188	2.4071	2.3466
2 3/4	4	NC-2	2.7500	2.7220	2.7092	2.5876	2.5736	2.4433
2 3/4	8	N-2	2.7500	2.7348	2.7278	2.6688	2.6564	2.5966
3	4	NC-2	3.0000	2.9720	2.9592	2.8376	2.8236	2.6933
3	8	N-2	3.0000	2.9848	2.9778	2.9188	2.9058	2.8466
3 1/4	4	NC-2	3.2500	3.2220	3.2092	3.0876	3.0736	2.9433
3 1/4	8	N-2	3.2500	3.2348	3.2278	3.1688	3.1556	3.0966
3 1/2	4	NC-2	3.5000	3.4720	3.4592	3.3376	3.3236	3.1933
3 1/2	8	N-2	3.5000	3.4848	3.4778	3.4188	3.4055	3.3466
3 3/4	4	NC-2	3.7500	3.7220	3.7092	3.5876	3.5736	3.4433
3 3/4	8	N-2	3.7500	3.7348	3.7278	3.6688	3.6554	3.5966
4	4	NC-2	4.0000	3.9720	3.9592	3.8376	3.8236	3.6933
4	8	N-2	4.0000	3.9848	3.9778	3.9188	3.9053	3.8466
4 1/4	8	N-2	4.2500	4.2348	4.2278	4.1688	4.1551	4.0966
4 1/2	8	N-2	4.5000	4.4848	4.4778	4.4188	4.4050	4.3466
4 3/4	8	N-2	4.7500	4.7348	4.7278	4.6688	4.6549	4.5966
5	8	N-2	5.0000	4.9848	4.9778	4.9188	4.9048	4.8466
5 1/4	8	N-2	5.2500	5.2348	5.2278	5.1688	5.1547	5.0966
5 1/2	8	N-2	5.5000	5.4848	5.4778	5.4188	5.4046	5.3466
5 3/4	8	N-2	5.7500	5.7348	5.7278	5.6688	5.6545	5.5966
6	8	N-2	6.0000	5.9848	5.9778	5.9188	5.9044	5.8466

[1] For semi-finished and finished screws and bolts, threaded portion only.
[2] For unfinished hot rolled material, threaded portion only.

A Class 2 external thread need not be combined invariably with a Class 2 internal thread but may be used with a Class 1B, 2B, 3B, or 3 thread where preferable for a specific application.

Table 8. American Standard Thread Series
Class 2 — Internal Thread Limits

No. or Size	Thds. per Inch	Thd. Symbol	Minor Diam.		Pitch Diam.		Major Diam. Min.
			Min.	Max.	Min.	Max.	
0	80	NF-2	0.0465	0.0514	0.0519	0.0536	0.0600
1	64	NC-2	0.0561	0.0623	0.0629	0.0648	0.0730
1	72	NF-2	0.0580	0.0634	0.0640	0.0658	0.0730
2	56	NC-2	0.0667	0.0737	0.0744	0.0764	0.0860
2	64	NF-2	0.0691	0.0746	0.0759	0.0778	0.0860
3	48	NC-2	0.0764	0.0841	0.0855	0.0877	0.0990
3	56	NF-2	0.0797	0.0856	0.0874	0.0894	0.0990
4	40	NC-2	0.0849	0.0938	0.0958	0.0982	0.1120
4	48	NF-2	0.0894	0.0960	0.0985	0.1007	0.1120
5	40	NC-2	0.0979	0.1062	0.1088	0.1112	0.1250
5	44	NF-2	0.1004	0.1068	0.1102	0.1125	0.1250
6	32	NC-2	0.1042	0.1145	0.1177	0.1204	0.1380
6	40	NF-2	0.1109	0.1179	0.1218	0.1242	0.1380
8	32	NC-2	0.1302	0.1384	0.1437	0.1464	0.1640
8	36	NF-2	0.1339	0.1402	0.1460	0.1485	0.1640
10	24	NC-2	0.1449	0.1559	0.1629	0.1662	0.1900
10	32	NF-2	0.1562	0.1624	0.1697	0.1724	0.1900
12	24	NC-2	0.1709	0.1801	0.1889	0.1922	0.2160
12	28	NF-2	0.1773	0.1835	0.1928	0.1959	0.2160
1/4	20	NC-2	0.1959	0.2060	0.2175	0.2211	0.2500
1/4	28	NF-2	0.2113	0.2173	0.2268	0.2299	0.2500
5/16	18	NC-2	0.2524	0.2630	0.2764	0.2805	0.3125
5/16	24	NF-2	0.2674	0.2739	0.2854	0.2887	0.3125
3/8	16	NC-2	0.3073	0.3184	0.3344	0.3389	0.3750
3/8	24	NF-2	0.3299	0.3364	0.3479	0.3512	0.3750
7/16	14	NC-2	0.3602	0.3721	0.3911	0.3960	0.4375
7/16	20	NF-2	0.3834	0.3906	0.4050	0.4086	0.4375
1/2	13	NC-2	0.4167	0.4290	0.4500	0.4552	0.5000
1/2	20	NF-2	0.4459	0.4531	0.4675	0.4711	0.5000
9/16	12	NC-2	0.4723	0.4850	0.5084	0.5140	0.5625
9/16	18	NF-2	0.5024	0.5100	0.5264	0.5305	0.5625
5/8	11	NC-2	0.5266	0.5397	0.5660	0.5719	0.6250
5/8	18	NF-2	0.5649	0.5725	0.5889	0.5930	0.6250
3/4	10	NC-2	0.6417	0.6553	0.6850	0.6914	0.7500
3/4	16	NF-2	0.6823	0.6903	0.7094	0.7139	0.7500
7/8	9	NC-2	0.7547	0.7689	0.8028	0.8098	0.8750
7/8	14	NF-2	0.7977	0.8062	0.8286	0.8335	0.8750
1	8	NC-2	0.8647	0.8795	0.9188	0.9264	1.0000
1	14	NF-2	0.9227	0.9312	0.9536	0.9585	1.0000

A Class 2 internal thread need not be combined invariably with a Class 2 external thread but may be used with a Class 1A, 2A, 3A, or 3 thread where preferable for a specific application.

Class 2 threads have no allowance since the maximum external and minimum internal thread dimensions are equal.

Table 8 (*Continued*). American Standard Thread Series
Class 2 — Internal Thread Limits

Size	Thds. per Inch	Thd. Symbol	Minor Diam.		Pitch Diam.		Major Diam. Min.
			Min.	Max.	Min.	Max.	
1 1/8	7	NC-2	0.9704	0.9858	1.0322	1.0407	1.1250
1 1/8	8	N-2	0.9897	1.0045	1.0438	1.0517	1.1250
1 1/8	12	NF-2	1.0348	1.0438	1.0709	1.0765	1.1250
1 1/4	7	NC-2	1.0954	1.1108	1.1572	1.1657	1.2500
1 1/4	8	N-2	1.1147	1.1295	1.1688	1.1771	1.2500
1 1/4	12	NF-2	1.1598	1.1688	1.1959	1.2015	1.2500
1 3/8	6	NC-2	1.1946	1.2126	1.2667	1.2768	1.3750
1 3/8	8	N-2	1.2397	1.2545	1.2938	1.3024	1.3750
1 3/8	12	NF-2	1.2848	1.2938	1.3209	1.3265	1.3750
1 1/2	6	NC-2	1.3196	1.3376	1.3917	1.4018	1.5000
1 1/2	8	N-2	1.3647	1.3795	1.4188	1.4278	1.5000
1 1/2	12	NF-2	1.4098	1.4188	1.4459	1.4515	1.5000
1 5/8	8	N-2	1.4897	1.5045	1.5438	1.5531	1.6250
1 3/4	5	NC-2	1.5335	1.5551	1.6201	1.6317	1.7500
1 3/4	8	N-2	1.6147	1.6295	1.6688	1.6785	1.7500
1 7/8	8	N-2	1.7397	1.7545	1.7938	1.8038	1.8750
2	4 1/2	NC-2	1.7594	1.7835	1.8557	1.8684	2.0000
2	8	N-2	1.8647	1.8795	1.9188	1.9292	2.0000
2 1/8	8	N-2	1.9897	2.0045	2.0438	2.0545	2.1250
2 1/4	4 1/2	NC-2	2.0094	2.0335	2.1057	2.1184	2.2500
2 1/4	8	N-2	2.1147	2.1295	2.1688	2.1798	2.2500
2 1/2	4	NC-2	2.2294	2.2564	2.3376	2.3516	2.5000
2 1/2	8	N-2	2.3647	2.3795	2.4188	2.4305	2.5000
2 3/4	4	NC-2	2.4794	2.5064	2.5876	2.6016	2.7500
2 3/4	8	N-2	2.6147	2.6295	2.6688	2.6812	2.7500
3	4	NC-2	2.7294	2.7564	2.8376	2.8516	3.0000
3	8	N-2	2.8647	2.8795	2.9188	2.9318	3.0000
3 1/4	4	NC-2	2.9794	3.0064	3.0876	3.1016	3.2500
3 1/4	8	N-2	3.1147	3.1295	3.1688	3.1820	3.2500
3 1/2	4	NC-2	3.2294	3.2564	3.3376	3.3516	3.5000
3 1/2	8	N-2	3.3647	3.3795	3.4188	3.4321	3.5000
3 3/4	4	NC-2	3.4794	3.5064	3.5876	3.6016	3.7500
3 3/4	8	N-2	3.6147	3.6295	3.6688	3.6822	3.7500
4	4	NC-2	3.7294	3.7564	3.8376	3.8516	4.0000
4	8	N-2	3.8647	3.8795	3.9188	3.9323	4.0000
4 1/4	8	N-2	4.1147	4.1295	4.1688	4.1825	4.2500
4 1/2	8	N-2	4.3647	4.3795	4.4188	4.4326	4.5000
4 3/4	8	N-2	4.6147	4.6295	4.6688	4.6827	4.7500
5	8	N-2	4.8647	4.8795	4.9188	4.9328	5.0000
5 1/4	8	N-2	5.1147	5.1295	5.1688	5.1829	5.2500
5 1/2	8	N-2	5.3647	5.3795	5.4188	5.4330	5.5000
5 3/4	8	N-2	5.6147	5.6295	5.6688	5.6831	5.7500
6	8	N-2	5.8647	5.8795	5.9188	5.9332	6.0000

A Class 2 internal thread need not be combined invariably with a Class 2 external thread but may be used with a Class 1A, 2A, 3A, or 3 thread where preferable for a specific application.

Table 9.   American Standard Thread Series
Class 3 — External Thread Limits

No. or Size	Thds. per Inch	Thd. Symbol	Major Diam.		Pitch Diam.		Minor Diam. Max.
			Max.	Min.	Max.	Min.	
0	80	NF-3	0.0600	0.0566	0.0519	0.0506	0.0447
1	64	NC-3	0.0730	0.0692	0.0629	0.0615	0.0538
1	72	NF-3	0.0730	0.0694	0.0640	0.0627	0.0560
2	56	NC-3	0.0860	0.0820	0.0744	0.0729	0.0641
2	64	NF-3	0.0860	0.0822	0.0759	0.0745	0.0668
3	48	NC-3	0.0990	0.0946	0.0855	0.0839	0.0734
3	56	NF-3	0.0990	0.0950	0.0874	0.0859	0.0771
4	40	NC-3	0.1120	0.1072	0.0958	0.0941	0.0813
4	48	NF-3	0.1120	0.1076	0.0985	0.0969	0.0864
5	40	NC-3	0.1250	0.1202	0.1088	0.1071	0.0943
5	44	NF-3	0.1250	0.1204	0.1102	0.1086	0.0971
6	32	NC-3	0.1380	0.1326	0.1177	0.1158	0.0997
6	40	NF-3	0.1380	0.1332	0.1218	0.1201	0.1073
8	32	NC-3	0.1640	0.1586	0.1437	0.1418	0.1257
8	36	NF-3	0.1640	0.1590	0.1460	0.1442	0.1299
10	24	NC-3	0.1900	0.1834	0.1629	0.1605	0.1389
10	32	NF-3	0.1900	0.1846	0.1697	0.1678	0.1517
12	24	NC-3	0.2160	0.2094	0.1889	0.1865	0.1649
12	28	NF-3	0.2160	0.2098	0.1928	0.1906	0.1722
1/4	20	NC-3	0.2500	0.2428	0.2175	0.2149	0.1887
1/4	28	NF-3	0.2500	0.2438	0.2268	0.2246	0.2062
5/16	18	NC-3	0.3125	0.3043	0.2764	0.2734	0.2443
5/16	24	NF-3	0.3125	0.3059	0.2854	0.2830	0.2614
3/8	16	NC-3	0.3750	0.3660	0.3344	0.3312	0.2983
3/8	24	NF-3	0.3750	0.3684	0.3479	0.3455	0.3239
7/16	14	NC-3	0.4375	0.4277	0.3911	0.3875	0.3499
7/16	20	NF-3	0.4375	0.4303	0.4050	0.4024	0.3762
1/2	13	NC-3	0.5000	0.4896	0.4500	0.4463	0.4056
1/2	20	NF-3	0.5000	0.4928	0.4675	0.4649	0.4387
9/16	12	NC-3	0.5625	0.5513	0.5084	0.5044	0.4603
9/16	18	NF-3	0.5625	0.5543	0.5264	0.5234	0.4943
5/8	11	NC-3	0.6250	0.6132	0.5660	0.5618	0.5135
5/8	18	NF-3	0.6250	0.6168	0.5889	0.5859	0.5568
3/4	10	NC-3	0.7500	0.7372	0.6850	0.6805	0.6273
3/4	16	NF-3	0.7500	0.7410	0.7094	0.7062	0.6733
7/8	9	NC-3	0.8750	0.8610	0.8028	0.7979	0.7387
7/8	14	NF-3	0.8750	0.8652	0.8286	0.8250	0.7874
1	8	NC-3	1.0000	0.9848	0.9188	0.9134	0.8466
1	14	NF-3	1.0000	0.9902	0.9536	0.9500	0.9124

A Class 3 external thread need not be combined invariably with a Class 3 internal thread but may be used with a Class 1B, 2B, 3B, or 2 thread where preferable for a specific application.

Class 3 threads have no allowance; the maximum external and minimum internal thread dimensions are basic.

Table 9 (*Continued*).   American Standard Thread Series
Class 3 — External Thread Limits

Size	Thds. per Inch	Thd. Symbol	Major Diam.		Pitch Diam.		Minor Diam. Max.
			Max.	Min.	Max.	Min.	
1 1/8	7	NC-3	1.1250	1.1080	1.0322	1.0263	0.9497
1 1/8	8	N-3	1.1250	1.1098	1.0438	1.0383	0.9716
1 1/8	12	NF-3	1.1250	1.1138	1.0709	1.0669	1.0228
1 1/4	7	NC-3	1.2500	1.2330	1.1572	1.1513	1.0747
1 1/4	8	N-3	1.2500	1.2348	1.1688	1.1630	1.0966
1 1/4	12	NF-3	1.2500	1.2388	1.1959	1.1919	1.1478
1 3/8	6	NC-3	1.3750	1.3548	1.2667	1.2596	1.1705
1 3/8	8	N-3	1.3750	1.3598	1.2938	1.2877	1.2216
1 3/8	12	NF-3	1.3750	1.3638	1.3209	1.3169	1.2728
1 1/2	6	NC-3	1.5000	1.4798	1.3917	1.3846	1.2955
1 1/2	8	N-3	1.5000	1.4848	1.4188	1.4125	1.3466
1 1/2	12	NF-3	1.5000	1.4888	1.4459	1.4419	1.3978
1 5/8	8	N-3	1.6250	1.6098	1.5438	1.5373	1.4716
1 3/4	5	NC-3	1.7500	1.7268	1.6201	1.6119	1.5046
1 3/4	8	N-3	1.7500	1.7348	1.6688	1.6620	1.5966
1 7/8	8	N-3	1.8750	1.8598	1.7938	1.7868	1.7216
2	4½	NC-3	2.0000	1.9746	1.8557	1.8468	1.7274
2	8	N-3	2.0000	1.9848	1.9188	1.9115	1.8466
2 1/8	8	N-3	2.1250	2.1098	2.0438	2.0363	1.9716
2 1/4	4½	NC-3	2.2500	2.2246	2.1057	2.0968	1.9774
2 1/4	8	N-3	2.2500	2.2348	2.1688	2.1611	2.0966
2 1/2	4	NC-3	2.5000	2.4720	2.3376	2.3279	2.1933
2 1/2	8	N-3	2.5000	2.4848	2.4188	2.4106	2.3466
2 3/4	4	NC-3	2.7500	2.7220	2.5876	2.5779	2.4433
2 3/4	8	N-3	2.7500	2.7348	2.6688	2.6601	2.5966
3	4	NC-3	3.0000	2.9720	2.8376	2.8279	2.6933
3	8	N-3	3.0000	2.9848	2.9188	2.9096	2.8466
3 1/4	4	NC-3	3.2500	3.2220	3.0876	3.0779	2.9433
3 1/4	8	N-3	3.2500	3.2348	3.1688	3.1595	3.0966
3 1/2	4	NC-3	3.5000	3.4720	3.3376	3.3279	3.1933
3 1/2	8	N-3	3.5000	3.4848	3.4188	3.4095	3.3466
3 3/4	4	NC-3	3.7500	3.7220	3.5876	3.5779	3.4433
3 3/4	8	N-3	3.7500	3.7348	3.6688	3.6594	3.5966
4	4	NC-3	4.0000	3.9720	3.8376	3.8279	3.6933
4	8	N-3	4.0000	3.9848	3.9188	3.9093	3.8466
4 1/4	8	N-3	4.2500	4.2348	4.1688	4.1592	4.0966
4 1/2	8	N-3	4.5000	4.4848	4.4188	4.4091	4.3466
4 3/4	8	N-3	4.7500	4.7348	4.6688	4.6590	4.5966
5	8	N-3	5.0000	4.9848	4.9188	4.9089	4.8466
5 1/4	8	N-3	5.2500	5.2348	5.1688	5.1589	5.0966
5 1/2	8	N-3	5.5000	5.4848	5.4188	5.4088	5.3466
5 3/4	8	N-3	5.7500	5.7348	5.6688	5.6587	5.5966
6	8	N-3	6.0000	5.9848	5.9188	5.9086	5.8466

A Class 3 external thread need not be combined invariably with a Class 3 internal thread but may be used with a Class 1B, 2B, 3B, or 2 thread where preferable for a specific application.

Table 10. American Standard Thread Series
Class 3 — Internal Thread Limits

No. or Size	Thds. per Inch	Thd. Symbol	Minor Diam.		Pitch Diam.		Major Diam. Min.
			Min.	Max.	Min.	Max.	
0	80	NF-3	0.0465	0.0514	0.0519	0.0532	0.0600
1	64	NC-3	0.0561	0.0623	0.0629	0.0643	0.0730
1	72	NF-3	0.0580	0.0634	0.0640	0.0653	0.0730
2	56	NC-3	0.0667	0.0737	0.0744	0.0759	0.0860
2	64	NF-3	0.0691	0.0746	0.0759	0.0773	0.0860
3	48	NC-3	0.0764	0.0841	0.0855	0.0871	0.0990
3	56	NF-3	0.0797	0.0856	0.0874	0.0889	0.0990
4	40	NC-3	0.0849	0.0938	0.0958	0.0975	0.1120
4	48	NF-3	0.0894	0.0960	0.0985	0.1001	0.1120
5	40	NC-3	0.0979	0.1062	0.1088	0.1105	0.1250
5	44	NF-3	0.1004	0.1068	0.1102	0.1118	0.1250
6	32	NC-3	0.1042	0.1145	0.1177	0.1196	0.1380
6	40	NF-3	0.1109	0.1179	0.1218	0.1235	0.1380
8	32	NC-3	0.1302	0.1384	0.1437	0.1456	0.1640
8	36	NF-3	0.1339	0.1402	0.1460	0.1478	0.1640
10	24	NC-3	0.1449	0.1559	0.1629	0.1653	0.1900
10	32	NF-3	0.1562	0.1624	0.1697	0.1716	0.1900
12	24	NC-3	0.1709	0.1801	0.1889	0.1913	0.2160
12	28	NF-3	0.1773	0.1835	0.1928	0.1950	0.2160
1/4	20	NC-3	0.1959	0.2060	0.2175	0.2201	0.2500
1/4	28	NF-3	0.2113	0.2173	0.2268	0.2290	0.2500
5/16	18	NC-3	0.2524	0.2630	0.2764	0.2794	0.3125
5/16	24	NF-3	0.2674	0.2739	0.2854	0.2878	0.3125
3/8	16	NC-3	0.3073	0.3184	0.3344	0.3376	0.3750
3/8	24	NF-3	0.3299	0.3364	0.3479	0.3503	0.3750
7/16	14	NC-3	0.3602	0.3721	0.3911	0.3947	0.4375
7/16	20	NF-3	0.3834	0.3906	0.4050	0.4076	0.4375
1/2	13	NC-3	0.4167	0.4290	0.4500	0.4537	0.5000
1/2	20	NF-3	0.4459	0.4531	0.4675	0.4701	0.5000
9/16	12	NC-3	0.4723	0.4850	0.5084	0.5124	0.5625
9/16	18	NF-3	0.5024	0.5100	0.5264	0.5294	0.5625
5/8	11	NC-3	0.5266	0.5397	0.5660	0.5702	0.6250
5/8	18	NF-3	0.5649	0.5725	0.5889	0.5919	0.6250
3/4	10	NC-3	0.6417	0.6553	0.6850	0.6895	0.7500
3/4	16	NF-3	0.6823	0.6903	0.7094	0.7126	0.7500
7/8	9	NC-3	0.7547	0.7689	0.8028	0.8077	0.8750
7/8	14	NF-3	0.7977	0.8062	0.8286	0.8322	0.8750
1	8	NC-3	0.8647	0.8795	0.9188	0.9242	1.0000
1	14	NF-3	0.9227	0.9312	0.9536	0.9572	1.0000

A Class 3 internal thread need not be combined invariably with a Class 3 external thread but may be used with a Class 1A, 2A, 3A, or 2 thread where preferable for a specific application.

Class 3 threads have no allowance since the maximum external and minimum internal thread dimensions are equal.

Table 10 *(Continued)*. American Standard Thread Series
Class 3 — Internal Thread Limits

Size	Thds. per Inch	Thd. Symbol	Minor Diam.		Pitch Diam.		Major Diam. Min.
			Min.	Max.	Min.	Max.	
1 1/8	7	NC-3	0.9704	0.9858	1.0322	1.0381	1.1250
1 1/8	8	N-3	0.9897	1.0045	1.0438	1.0493	1.1250
1 1/8	12	NF-3	1.0348	1.0438	1.0709	1.0749	1.1250
1 1/4	7	NC-3	1.0954	1.1108	1.1572	1.1631	1.2500
1 1/4	8	N-3	1.1147	1.1295	1.1688	1.1746	1.2500
1 1/4	12	NF-3	1.1598	1.1688	1.1959	1.1999	1.2500
1 3/8	6	NC-3	1.1946	1.2126	1.2667	1.2738	1.3750
1 3/8	8	N-3	1.2397	1.2545	1.2938	1.2999	1.3750
1 3/8	12	NF-3	1.2848	1.2938	1.3209	1.3249	1.3750
1 1/2	6	NC-3	1.3196	1.3376	1.3917	1.3988	1.5000
1 1/2	8	N-3	1.3647	1.3795	1.4188	1.4251	1.5000
1 1/2	12	NF-3	1.4098	1.4188	1.4459	1.4499	1.5000
1 5/8	8	N-3	1.4897	1.5045	1.5438	1.5503	1.6250
1 3/4	5	NC-3	1.5335	1.5551	1.6201	1.6283	1.7500
1 3/4	8	N-3	1.6147	1.6295	1.6688	1.6756	1.7500
1 7/8	8	N-3	1.7397	1.7545	1.7938	1.8008	1.8750
2	4 1/2	NC-3	1.7594	1.7835	1.8557	1.8646	2.0000
2	8	N-3	1.8647	1.8795	1.9188	1.9261	2.0000
2 1/8	8	N-3	1.9897	2.0045	2.0438	2.0513	2.1250
2 1/4	4 1/2	NC-3	2.0094	2.0335	2.1057	2.1146	2.2500
2 1/4	8	N-3	2.1147	2.1295	2.1688	2.1765	2.2500
2 1/2	4	NC-3	2.2294	2.2564	2.3376	2.3473	2.5000
2 1/2	8	N-3	2.3647	2.3795	2.4188	2.4270	2.5000
2 3/4	4	NC-3	2.4794	2.5064	2.5876	2.5973	2.7500
2 3/4	8	N-3	2.6147	2.6295	2.6688	2.6775	2.7500
3	4	NC-3	2.7294	2.7564	2.8376	2.8473	3.0000
3	8	N-3	2.8647	2.8795	2.9188	2.9280	3.0000
3 1/4	4	NC-3	2.9794	3.0064	3.0876	3.0973	3.2500
3 1/4	8	N-3	3.1147	3.1295	3.1688	3.1781	3.2500
3 1/2	4	NC-3	3.2294	3.2564	3.3376	3.3473	3.5000
3 1/2	8	N-3	3.3647	3.3795	3.4188	3.4281	3.5000
3 3/4	4	NC-3	3.4794	3.5064	3.5876	3.5973	3.7500
3 3/4	8	N-3	3.6147	3.6295	3.6688	3.6782	3.7500
4	4	NC-3	3.7294	3.7564	3.8376	3.8473	4.0000
4	8	N-3	3.8647	3.8795	3.9188	3.9283	4.0000
4 1/4	8	N-3	4.1147	4.1295	4.1688	4.1784	4.2500
4 1/2	8	N-3	4.3647	4.3795	4.4188	4.4285	4.5000
4 3/4	8	N-3	4.6147	4.6295	4.6688	4.6786	4.7500
5	8	N-3	4.8647	4.8795	4.9188	4.9287	5.0000
5 1/4	8	N-3	5.1147	5.1295	5.1688	5.1787	5.2500
5 1/2	8	N-3	5.3647	5.3795	5.4188	5.4288	5.5000
5 3/4	8	N-3	5.6147	5.6295	5.6688	5.6789	5.7500
6	8	N-3	5.8647	5.8795	5.9188	5.9290	6.0000

A Class 3 internal thread need not invariably be combined with a Class 3 external thread but may be used with a Class 1A, 2A, 3A, or 2 thread where preferable for a specific application.

Table II. Unified and American Special Threads*
Class 2A — External Thread Limits†

Size	Thds. per Inch	Thread Symbol	9 × Pitch	Allow-ance	Major Diam. Limits		Pitch Diam. Limits		Minor Diam. Max.
					Max.	Min.	Max.	Min.	
1/4	24	NS-2A	0.3750	0.0011	0.2489	0.2417	0.2218	0.2181	0.1978
1/4	32	NEF-2A	0.2812	0.0010	0.2490	0.2430	0.2287	0.2255	0.2107
1/4	**36**	**UN-2A**	**0.2500**	**0.0009**	**0.2491**	**0.2436**	**0.2311**	**0.2280**	**0.2150**
1/4	40	NS-2A	0.2250	0.0009	0.2491	0.2440	0.2329	0.2300	0.2184
1/4	48	NS-2A	0.1875	0.0008	0.2492	0.2447	0.2357	0.2330	0.2236
1/4	56	NS-2A	0.1607	0.0008	0.2492	0.2451	0.2376	0.2350	0.2273
5/16	20	NS-2A	0.4500	0.0012	0.3113	0.3032	0.2788	0.2748	0.2500
5/16	28	NS-2A	0.3214	0.0010	0.3115	0.3050	0.2883	0.2849	0.2677
5/16	32	NEF-2A	0.2812	0.0010	0.3115	0.3055	0.2912	0.2880	0.2732
5/16	**36**	**UN-2A**	**0.2500**	**0.0009**	**0.3116**	**0.3061**	**0.2936**	**0.2905**	**0.2775**
5/16	40	NS-2A	0.2250	0.0009	0.3116	0.3065	0.2954	0.2925	0.2809
5/16	48	NS-2A	0.1875	0.0008	0.3117	0.3072	0.2982	0.2955	0.2861
3/8	18	NS-2A	0.5000	0.0013	0.3737	0.3650	0.3376	0.3333	0.3055
3/8	20	NS-2A	0.4500	0.0012	0.3738	0.3657	0.3413	0.3372	0.3125
3/8	28	NS-2A	0.3214	0.0011	0.3739	0.3674	0.3507	0.3471	0.3301
3/8	32	NEF-2A	0.2812	0.0010	0.3740	0.3680	0.3537	0.3503	0.3357
3/8	**36**	**UN-2A**	**0.2500**	**0.0010**	**0.3740**	**0.3685**	**0.3560**	**0.3528**	**0.3399**
3/8	40	NS-2A	0.2250	0.0009	0.3741	0.3690	0.3579	0.3548	0.3434
7/16	16	NS-2A	0.5625	0.0014	0.4361	0.4267	0.3955	0.3909	0.3594
7/16	18	NS-2A	0.5000	0.0013	0.4362	0.4275	0.4001	0.3958	0.3680
7/16	24	NS-2A	0.3750	0.0011	0.4364	0.4292	0.4093	0.4055	0.3853
7/16	**28**	**UNEF-2A**	**0.3214**	**0.0011**	**0.4364**	**0.4299**	**0.4132**	**0.4096**	**0.3926**
7/16	32	NS-2A	0.2812	0.0010	0.4365	0.4305	0.4162	0.4128	0.3982
1/2	14	NS-2A	0.6429	0.0015	0.4985	0.4882	0.4521	0.4471	0.4109
1/2	16	NS-2A	0.5625	0.0014	0.4986	0.4892	0.4580	0.4533	0.4219
1/2	18	NS-2A	0.5000	0.0013	0.4987	0.4900	0.4626	0.4582	0.4305
1/2	24	NS-2A	0.3750	0.0012	0.4988	0.4916	0.4717	0.4678	0.4477
1/2	**28**	**UNEF-2A**	**0.3214**	**0.0011**	**0.4989**	**0.4924**	**0.4757**	**0.4720**	**0.4551**
1/2	32	NS-2A	0.2812	0.0010	0.4990	0.4930	0.4787	0.4752	0.4607
9/16	14	NS-2A	0.6429	0.0015	0.5610	0.5507	0.5146	0.5096	0.4734
9/16	16	NS-2A	0.5625	0.0014	0.5611	0.5517	0.5205	0.5158	0.4844
9/16	20	NS-2A	0.4500	0.0013	0.5612	0.5531	0.5287	0.5245	0.4999
9/16	24	NEF-2A	0.3750	0.0012	0.5613	0.5541	0.5342	0.5303	0.5102
9/16	**28**	**UN-2A**	**0.3214**	**0.0011**	**0.5614**	**0.5549**	**0.5382**	**0.5345**	**0.5176**
9/16	32	NS-2A	0.2812	0.0010	0.5615	0.5555	0.5412	0.5377	0.5232
5/8	12	N-2A	0.7500	0.0016	0.6234	0.6120	0.5693	0.5639	0.5212
5/8	14	NS-2A	0.6429	0.0015	0.6235	0.6132	0.5771	0.5720	0.5359
5/8	16	NS-2A	0.5625	0.0014	0.6236	0.6142	0.5830	0.5782	0.5469
5/8	20	NS-2A	0.4500	0.0013	0.6237	0.6156	0.5912	0.5869	0.5624
5/8	24	NEF-2A	0.3750	0.0012	0.6238	0.6166	0.5967	0.5927	0.5727
5/8	**28**	**UN-2A**	**0.3214**	**0.0011**	**0.6239**	**0.6174**	**0.6007**	**0.5969**	**0.5801**
5/8	32	NS-2A	0.2812	0.0011	0.6239	0.6179	0.6036	0.6000	0.5856
11/16	12	N-2A	0.7500	0.0016	0.6859	0.6745	0.6318	0.6264	0.5837
11/16	24	NEF-2A	0.3750	0.0012	0.6863	0.6791	0.6592	0.6552	0.6352
3/4	12	N-2A	0.7500	0.0017	0.7483	0.7369	0.6942	0.6887	0.6461
3/4	14	NS-2A	0.6429	0.0015	0.7485	0.7382	0.7021	0.6970	0.6609
3/4	18	NS-2A	0.5000	0.0014	0.7486	0.7399	0.7125	0.7079	0.6804
3/4	**20**	**UNEF-2A**	**0.4500**	**0.0013**	**0.7487**	**0.7406**	**0.7162**	**0.7118**	**0.6874**
3/4	24	NS-2A	0.3750	0.0012	0.7488	0.7416	0.7217	0.7176	0.6977
3/4	**28**	**UN-2A**	**0.3214**	**0.0012**	**0.7488**	**0.7423**	**0.7256**	**0.7218**	**0.7050**
3/4	32	NS-2A	0.2812	0.0011	0.7489	0.7429	0.7286	0.7250	0.7106

Bold face type indicates Unified threads.

* Selected combinations of special diameter and pitch.

† Based on lengths of engagement of 9 times the pitch, but applicable to lengths of engagement of from 5 to 15 times the pitch, inclusive. The maximum dimensions of threads which are electroplated or have coatings of similar thickness will be increased by the amount of the allowance.

Table 11 (*Continued*). Unified and American Special Threads*
Class 2A — External Thread Limits†

Size	Thds. per Inch	Thread Symbol	9 × Pitch	Allow-ance	Major Diam. Limits		Pitch Diam. Limits		Minor Diam. Max.
					Max.	Min.	Max.	Min.	
13/16	12	N-2A	0.7500	0.0017	0.8108	0.7994	0.7567	0.7512	0.7086
13/16	**16**	**UN-2A**	**0.5625**	**0.0015**	**0.8110**	**0.8016**	**0.7704**	**0.7655**	**0.7343**
13/16	**20**	**UNEF-2A**	**0.4500**	**0.0013**	**0.8112**	**0.8031**	**0.7787**	**0.7743**	**0.7498**
7/8	10	NS-2A	0.9000	0.0018	0.8732	0.8603	0.8082	0.8022	0.7505
7/8	12	N-2A	0.7500	0.0017	0.8733	0.8619	0.8192	0.8137	0.7711
7/8	**16**	**UN-2A**	**0.5625**	**0.0015**	**0.8735**	**0.8641**	**0.8329**	**0.8280**	**0.7968**
7/8	18	NS-2A	0.5000	0.0014	0.8736	0.8649	0.8375	0.8329	0.8054
7/8	**20**	**UNEF-2A**	**0.4500**	**0.0013**	**0.8737**	**0.8656**	**0.8412**	**0.8368**	**0.8124**
7/8	24	NS-2A	0.3750	0.0012	0.8738	0.8666	0.8467	0.8426	0.8227
7/8	**28**	**UN-2A**	**0.3214**	**0.0012**	**0.8738**	**0.8673**	**0.8596**	**0.8468**	**0.8300**
7/8	32	NS-2A	0.2812	0.0011	0.8739	0.8679	0.8536	0.8500	0.8356
15/16	**12**	**UN-2A**	**0.7500**	**0.0017**	**0.9358**	**0.9244**	**0.8817**	**0.8760**	**0.8336**
15/16	**16**	**UN-2A**	**0.5625**	**0.0015**	**0.9360**	**0.9266**	**0.8954**	**0.8904**	**0.8593**
15/16	**20**	**UNEF-2A**	**0.4500**	**0.0014**	**0.9361**	**0.9280**	**0.9036**	**0.8991**	**0.8748**
1	10	NS-2A	0.9000	0.0018	0.9982	0.9853	0.9332	0.9270	0.8755
1	**16**	**UN-2A**	**0.5625**	**0.0015**	**0.9985**	**0.9891**	**0.9579**	**0.9529**	**0.9218**
1	18	NS-2A	0.5000	0.0014	0.9986	0.9899	0.9625	0.9578	0.9304
1	**20**	**UNEF-2A**	**0.4500**	**0.0014**	**0.9986**	**0.9905**	**0.9661**	**0.9616**	**0.9373**
1	24	NS-2A	0.3750	0.0013	0.9987	0.9915	0.9716	0.9674	0.9476
1	**28**	**UN-2A**	**0.3214**	**0.0012**	**0.9988**	**0.9923**	**0.9756**	**0.9716**	**0.9550**
1	32	NS-2A	0.2812	0.0011	0.9989	0.9929	0.9786	0.9748	0.9606
1 1/16	**12**	**UN-2A**	**0.7500**	**0.0017**	**1.0608**	**1.0494**	**1.0067**	**1.0010**	**0.9586**
1 1/16	**16**	**UN-2A**	**0.5625**	**0.0015**	**1.0610**	**1.0516**	**1.0204**	**1.0154**	**0.9843**
1 1/16	18	NEF-2A	0.5000	0.0014	1.0611	1.0524	1.0250	1.0203	0.9929
1 1/8	10	NS-2A	0.9000	0.0018	1.1232	1.1103	1.0582	1.0520	1.0005
1 1/8	14	NS-2A	0.6429	0.0016	1.1234	1.1131	1.0770	1.0717	1.0358
1 1/8	**16**	**UN-2A**	**0.5625**	**0.0015**	**1.1235**	**1.1141**	**1.0829**	**1.0779**	**1.0468**
1 1/8	18	NEF-2A	0.5000	0.0014	1.1236	1.1149	1.0875	1.0828	1.0554
1 1/8	**20**	**UN-2A**	**0.4500**	**0.0014**	**1.1236**	**1.1155**	**1.0911**	**1.0866**	**1.0623**
1 1/8	24	NS-2A	0.3750	0.0013	1.1237	1.1165	1.0966	1.0924	1.0726
1 1/8	**28**	**UN-2A**	**0.3214**	**0.0012**	**1.1238**	**1.1173**	**1.1006**	**1.0966**	**1.0800**
1 3/16	**12**	**UN-2A**	**0.7500**	**0.0017**	**1.1858**	**1.1744**	**1.1317**	**1.1259**	**1.0836**
1 3/16	**16**	**UN-2A**	**0.5625**	**0.0015**	**1.1860**	**1.1766**	**1.1454**	**1.1403**	**1.1093**
1 3/16	18	NEF-2A	0.5000	0.0015	1.1860	1.1773	1.1499	1.1450	1.1178
1 1/4	10	NS-2A	0.9000	0.0019	1.2481	1.2352	1.1831	1.1768	1.1254
1 1/4	14	NS-2A	0.6429	0.0016	1.2484	1.2381	1.2020	1.1966	1.1608
1 1/4	**16**	**UN-2A**	**0.5625**	**0.0015**	**1.2485**	**1.2391**	**1.2079**	**1.2028**	**1.1718**
1 1/4	18	NEF-2A	0.5000	0.0015	1.2485	1.2398	1.2124	1.2075	1.1803
1 1/4	**20**	**UN-2A**	**0.4500**	**0.0014**	**1.2486**	**1.2405**	**1.2161**	**1.2114**	**1.1873**
1 1/4	24	NS-2A	0.3750	0.0013	1.2487	1.2415	1.2216	1.2173	1.1976
1 5/16	**12**	**UN-2A**	**0.7500**	**0.0017**	**1.3108**	**1.2994**	**1.2567**	**1.2509**	**1.2086**
1 5/16	**16**	**UN-2A**	**0.5625**	**0.0015**	**1.3110**	**1.3016**	**1.2704**	**1.2653**	**1.2343**
1 5/16	18	NEF-2A	0.5000	0.0015	1.3110	1.3023	1.2749	1.2700	1.2428
1 3/8	10	NS-2A	0.9000	0.0019	1.3731	1.3602	1.3081	1.3018	1.2504
1 3/8	14	NS-2A	0.6429	0.0016	1.3734	1.3631	1.3270	1.3216	1.2858
1 3/8	**16**	**UN-2A**	**0.5625**	**0.0015**	**1.3735**	**1.3641**	**1.3329**	**1.3278**	**1.2968**
1 3/8	18	NEF-2A	0.5000	0.0015	1.3735	1.3648	1.3374	1.3325	1.3053

Bold face type indicates Unified threads.

* Selected combinations of special diameter and pitch.

† Based on lengths of engagement of 9 times the pitch, but applicable to lengths of engagement of from 5 to 15 times the pitch, inclusive. The maximum dimensions of threads which are electroplated or have coatings of similar thickness will be increased by the amount of the allowance.

Table II (Continued). Unified and American Special Threads*
Class 2A — External Thread Limits†

Size	Thds. per Inch	Thread Symbol	9 × Pitch	Allow-ance	Major Diam. Limits		Pitch Diam. Limits		Minor Diam. Max.
					Max.	Min.	Max.	Min.	
1 7/16	12	UN-2A	0.7500	0.0018	1.4357	1.4243	1.3816	1.3757	1.3335
1 7/16	16	UN-2A	0.5625	0.0016	1.4359	1.4265	1.3953	1.3901	1.3592
1 7/16	18	NEF-2A	0.5000	0.0015	1.4360	1.4273	1.3999	1.3949	1.3678
1 1/2	10	NS-2A	0.9000	0.0019	1.4981	1.4852	1.4331	1.4267	1.3754
1 1/2	14	NS-2A	0.6429	0.0017	1.4983	1.4880	1.4519	1.4464	1.4107
1 1/2	16	UN-2A	0.5625	0.0016	1.4984	1.4890	1.4578	1.4526	1.4217
1 1/2	18	NEF-2A	0.5000	0.0015	1.4985	1.4898	1.4624	1.4574	1.4303
1 1/2	20	UN-2A	0.4500	0.0014	1.4986	1.4905	1.4661	1.4613	1.4373
1 1/2	24	NS-2A	0.3750	0.0013	1.4987	1.4915	1.4716	1.4672	1.4476
1 9/16	16	N-2A	0.5625	0.0016	1.5609	1.5515	1.5203	1.5151	1.4842
1 9/16	18	NEF-2A	0.5000	0.0015	1.5610	1.5523	1.5249	1.5199	1.4928
1 5/8	6	NS-2A	1.5000	0.0024	1.6226	1.6044	1.5143	1.5062	1.4181
1 5/8	7	NS-2A	1.2857	0.0023	1.6227	1.6063	1.5299	1.5224	1.4474
1 5/8	10	NS-2A	0.9000	0.0019	1.6231	1.6102	1.5581	1.5517	1.5004
1 5/8	12	N-2A	0.7500	0.0018	1.6232	1.6118	1.5691	1.5632	1.5210
1 5/8	14	NS-2A	0.6429	0.0017	1.6233	1.6130	1.5769	1.5714	1.5357
1 5/8	16	N-2A	0.5625	0.0016	1.6234	1.6140	1.5828	1.5776	1.5467
1 5/8	18	NEF-2A	0.5000	0.0015	1.6235	1.6148	1.5874	1.5824	1.5553
1 5/8	20	NS-2A	0.4500	0.0014	1.6236	1.6155	1.5911	1.5863	1.5623
1 5/8	24	NS-2A	0.3750	0.0013	1.6237	1.6165	1.5966	1.5922	1.5726
1 11/16	16	N-2A	0.5625	0.0016	1.6859	1.6765	1.6453	1.6400	1.6092
1 11/16	18	NEF-2A	0.5000	0.0015	1.6860	1.6773	1.6499	1.6448	1.6178
1 3/4	6	NS-2A	1.5000	0.0025	1.7475	1.7293	1.6392	1.6310	1.5430
1 3/4	7	NS-2A	1.2857	0.0023	1.7477	1.7313	1.6549	1.6473	1.5724
1 3/4	8	UN-2A	1.1250	0.0021	1.7479	1.7329	1.6667	1.6596	1.5945
1 3/4	10	NS-2A	0.9000	0.0019	1.7481	1.7352	1.6831	1.6766	1.6254
1 3/4	12	UN-2A	0.7500	0.0018	1.7482	1.7368	1.6941	1.6881	1.6460
1 3/4	14	NS-2A	0.6429	0.0017	1.7483	1.7380	1.7019	1.6963	1.6607
1 3/4	16	UNEF-2A	0.5625	0.0016	1.7484	1.7399	1.7078	1.7025	1.6717
1 3/4	18	NS-2A	0.5000	0.0015	1.7485	1.7398	1.7124	1.7073	1.6803
1 3/4	20	UN-2A	0.4500	0.0015	1.7485	1.7404	1.7160	1.7112	1.6872
1 13/16	16	N-2A	0.5625	0.0016	1.8109	1.8015	1.7703	1.7650	1.7342
1 7/8	6	NS-2A	1.5000	0.0025	1.8725	1.8543	1.7642	1.7560	1.6680
1 7/8	7	NS-2A	1.2857	0.0023	1.8727	1.8563	1.7799	1.7723	1.6974
1 7/8**	8	NS-2A	1.1250	0.0021	1.8729	1.8579	1.7917	1.7846	1.7195
1 7/8	10	NS-2A	0.9000	0.0019	1.8731	1.8602	1.8081	1.8016	1.7504
1 7/8	12	N-2A	0.7500	0.0018	1.8732	1.8618	1.8191	1.8131	1.7710
1 7/8	14	NS-2A	0.6429	0.0017	1.8733	1.8630	1.8269	1.8213	1.7857
1 7/8	16	N-2A	0.5625	0.0016	1.8734	1.8640	1.8328	1.8275	1.7967
1 7/8	18	NS-2A	0.5000	0.0015	1.8735	1.8648	1.8374	1.8323	1.8053
1 7/8	20	NS-2A	0.4500	0.0015	1.8735	1.8654	1.8410	1.8362	1.8122
1 15/16	16	N-2A	0.5625	0.0016	1.9359	1.9265	1.8953	1.8899	1.8592
2	6	NS-2A	1.5000	0.0025	1.9975	1.9793	1.8892	1.8809	1.7930
2	7	NS-2A	1.2857	0.0023	1.9977	1.9813	1.9049	1.8972	1.8224
2	8	UN-2A	1.1250	0.0022	1.9978	1.9828	1.9166	1.9094	1.8444
2	10	NS-2A	0.9000	0.0020	1.9980	1.9851	1.9330	1.9265	1.8753
2	12	UN-2A	0.7500	0.0018	1.9982	1.9868	1.9441	1.9380	1.8960
2	14	NS-2A	0.6429	0.0017	1.9983	1.9880	1.9519	1.9462	1.9107

Bold face type indicates Unified threads.

* Selected combinations of special diameter and pitch.

** Standard size of the 8-thread series. These limits are for special applications only.

† Based on lengths of engagement of 9 times the pitch, but applicable to lengths of engagement of from 5 to 15 times the pitch, inclusive. The maximum dimensions of threads which are electroplated or have coatings of similar thickness will be increased by the amount of the allowance.

Table 11 (Continued). Unified and American Special Threads*
Class 2A — External Thread Limits†

Size	Thds. per Inch	Thread Symbol	9 × Pitch	Allowance	Major Diam. Limits		Pitch Diam. Limits		Minor Diam. Max.
					Max.	Min.	Max.	Min.	
2	16	UNEF-2A	0.5625	0.0016	1.9984	1.9890	1.9578	1.9524	1.9217
2	18	NS-2A	0.5000	0.0015	1.9985	1.9898	1.9624	1.9573	1.9303
2	20	UN-2A	0.4500	0.0015	1.9985	1.9904	1.9660	1.9611	1.9372
2 1/16	16	N-2A	0.5625	0.0016	2.0609	2.0515	2.0203	2.0149	1.9842
2 1/8	12	N-2A	0.7500	0.0018	2.1232	2.1118	2.0691	2.0630	2.0210
2 1/8	16	N-2A	0.5625	0.0016	2.1234	2.1140	2.0828	2.0774	2.0467
2 3/16	16	N-2A	0.5625	0.0016	2.1859	2.1765	2.1453	2.1399	2.1092
2 1/4	6	NS-2A	1.5000	0.0025	2.2475	2.2293	2.1392	2.1309	2.0430
2 1/4	7	NS-2A	1.2857	0.0024	2.2476	2.2312	2.1548	2.1471	2.0723
2 1/4	8	UN-2A	1.1250	0.0022	2.2478	2.2328	2.1666	2.1594	2.0944
2 1/4	10	NS-2A	0.9000	0.0020	2.2480	2.2351	2.1830	2.1765	2.1253
2 1/4	12	UN-2A	0.7500	0.0018	2.2482	2.2368	2.1941	2.1880	2.1460
2 1/4	14	NS-2A	0.6429	0.0017	2.2483	2.2380	2.2019	2.1962	2.1607
2 1/4	16	UN-2A	0.5625	0.0016	2.2484	2.2390	2.2078	2.2024	2.1717
2 1/4	18	NS-2A	0.5000	0.0015	2.2485	2.2398	2.2124	2.2073	2.1803
2 1/4	20	UN-2A	0.4500	0.0015	2.2485	2.2404	2.2160	2.2111	2.1872
2 5/16	16	N-2A	0.5625	0.0017	2.3108	2.3014	2.2702	2.2647	2.2341
2 3/8	12	N-2A	0.7500	0.0019	2.3731	2.3617	2.3190	2.3128	2.2709
2 3/8	16	N-2A	0.5625	0.0017	2.3733	2.3639	2.3327	2.3272	2.2966
2 7/16	16	N-2A	0.5625	0.0017	2.4358	2.4264	2.3952	2.3897	2.3591
2 1/2	6	NS-2A	1.5000	0.0025	2.4975	2.4793	2.3892	2.3808	2.2930
2 1/2	7	NS-2A	1.2857	0.0024	2.4976	2.4812	2.4048	2.3970	2.3223
2 1/2	8	UN-2A	1.1250	0.0022	2.4978	2.4828	2.4166	2.4092	2.3444
2 1/2	10	NS-2A	0.9000	0.0020	2.4980	2.4851	2.4330	2.4263	2.3753
2 1/2	12	UN-2A	0.7500	0.0019	2.4981	2.4867	2.4440	2.4378	2.3959
2 1/2	14	NS-2A	0.6429	0.0017	2.4983	2.4880	2.4519	2.4461	2.4107
2 1/2	16	UN-2A	0.5625	0.0017	2.4983	2.4889	2.4577	2.4522	2.4216
2 1/2	18	NS-2A	0.5000	0.0016	2.4984	2.4897	2.4623	2.4570	2.4302
2 1/2	20	UN-2A	0.4500	0.0015	2.4985	2.4904	2.4660	2.4609	2.4372
2 5/8	12	N-2A	0.7500	0.0019	2.6231	2.6117	2.5690	2.5628	2.5209
2 5/8	16	N-2A	0.5625	0.0017	2.6233	2.6139	2.5827	2.5772	2.5466
2 3/4	6	NS-2A	1.5000	0.0025	2.7475	2.7293	2.6392	2.6308	2.5430
2 3/4	7	NS-2A	1.2857	0.0024	2.7476	2.7312	2.6548	2.6470	2.5723
2 3/4	8	UN-2A	1.1250	0.0022	2.7478	2.7328	2.6666	2.6592	2.5944
2 3/4	10	NS-2A	0.9000	0.0020	2.7480	2.7351	2.6830	2.6763	2.6253
2 3/4	12	UN-2A	0.7500	0.0019	2.7481	2.7367	2.6940	2.6878	2.6459
2 3/4	14	NS-2A	0.6429	0.0017	2.7483	2.7380	2.7019	2.6961	2.6607
2 3/4	16	UN-2A	0.5625	0.0017	2.7483	2.7389	2.7077	2.7022	2.6716
2 3/4	18	NS-2A	0.5000	0.0016	2.7484	2.7397	2.7123	2.7070	2.6802
2 7/8	12	N-2A	0.7500	0.0019	2.8731	2.8617	2.8190	2.8127	2.7709
2 7/8	16	N-2A	0.5625	0.0017	2.8733	2.8639	2.8327	2.8271	2.7966
3	6	NS-2A	1.5000	0.0026	2.9974	2.9792	2.8891	2.8806	2.7929
3	7	NS-2A	1.2857	0.0024	2.9976	2.9812	2.9048	2.8968	2.8223
3	8	UN-2A	1.1250	0.0023	2.9977	2.9827	2.9165	2.9090	2.8443
3	10	NS-2A	0.9000	0.0020	2.9980	2.9851	2.9330	2.9262	2.8753
3	12	UN-2A	0.7500	0.0019	2.9981	2.9867	2.9440	2.9377	2.8959
3	14	NS-2A	0.6429	0.0018	2.9982	2.9879	2.9518	2.9459	2.9106
3	16	UN-2A	0.5625	0.0017	2.9983	2.9889	2.9577	2.9521	2.9216
3	18	NS-2A	0.5000	0.0016	2.9984	2.9897	2.9623	2.9569	2.9302

Bold face type indicates Unified threads.

* Selected combinations of special diameter and pitch.

† Based on lengths of engagement of 9 times the pitch, but applicable to lengths of engagement of from 5 to 15 times the pitch, inclusive. The maximum dimensions of threads which are electroplated or have coatings of similar thickness will be increased by the amount of the allowance.

Table 12.　Unified and American Special Threads*
Class 2B — Internal Thread Limits†

Size	Thds. per Inch	Thread Symbol	9 × Pitch	Minor Diam. Limits		Pitch Diam. Limits		Major Diam. Min.
				Min.	Max.	Min.	Max.	
1/4	24	NS-2B	0.3750	0.2049	0.2139	0.2229	0.2277	0.2500
1/4	32	NEF-2B	0.2812	0.2162	0.2229	0.2297	0.2339	0.2500
1/4	**36**	**UN-2B**	**0.2500**	**0.2199**	**0.2258**	**0.2320**	**0.2360**	**0.2500**
1/4	40	NS-2B	0.2250	0.2229	0.2282	0.2338	0.2376	0.2500
1/4	48	NS-2B	0.1875	0.2274	0.2317	0.2365	0.2401	0.2500
1/4	56	NS-2B	0.1607	0.2307	0.2343	0.2384	0.2417	0.2500
5/16	20	NS-2B	0.4500	0.2584	0.2680	0.2800	0.2852	0.3125
5/16	28	NS-2B	0.3214	0.2738	0.2807	0.2893	0.2937	0.3125
5/16	32	NEF-2B	0.2812	0.2787	0.2847	0.2922	0.2964	0.3125
5/16	**36**	**UN-2B**	**0.2500**	**0.2824**	**0.2877**	**0.2945**	**0.2985**	**0.3125**
5/16	40	NS-2B	0.2250	0.2854	0.2902	0.2963	0.3001	0.3125
5/16	48	NS-2B	0.1875	0.2899	0.2940	0.2990	0.3026	0.3125
3/8	18	NS-2B	0.5000	0.3149	0.3246	0.3389	0.3445	0.3750
3/8	20	NS-2B	0.4500	0.3209	0.3297	0.3425	0.3479	0.3750
3/8	28	NS-2B	0.3214	0.3363	0.3426	0.3518	0.3564	0.3750
3/8	32	NEF-2B	0.2812	0.3412	0.3469	0.3547	0.3591	0.3750
3/8	**36**	**UN-2B**	**0.2500**	**0.3449**	**0.3501**	**0.3570**	**0.3612**	**0.3750**
3/8	40	NS-2B	0.2250	0.3479	0.3527	0.3588	0.3628	0.3750
7/16	16	NS-2B	0.5625	0.3698	0.3800	0.3969	0.4028	0.4375
7/16	18	NS-2B	0.5000	0.3774	0.3865	0.4014	0.4070	0.4375
7/16	24	NS-2B	0.3750	0.3924	0.3994	0.4104	0.4153	0.4375
7/16	**28**	**UNEF-2B**	**0.3214**	**0.3988**	**0.4051**	**0.4143**	**0.4189**	**0.4375**
7/16	32	NS-2B	0.2812	0.4037	0.4094	0.4172	0.4216	0.4375
1/2	14	NS-2B	0.6429	0.4227	0.4336	0.4536	0.4601	0.5000
1/2	16	NS-2B	0.5625	0.4323	0.4419	0.4594	0.4655	0.5000
1/2	18	NS-2B	0.5000	0.4399	0.4485	0.4639	0.4697	0.5000
1/2	24	NS-2B	0.3750	0.4549	0.4619	0.4729	0.4780	0.5000
1/2	**28**	**UNEF-2B**	**0.3214**	**0.4613**	**0.4676**	**0.4768**	**0.4816**	**0.5000**
1/2	32	NS-2B	0.2812	0.4662	0.4719	0.4797	0.4842	0.5000
9/16	14	NS-2B	0.6429	0.4852	0.4956	0.5161	0.5226	0.5625
9/16	16	NS-2B	0.5625	0.4948	0.5040	0.5219	0.5280	0.5625
9/16	20	NS-2B	0.4500	0.5084	0.5162	0.5300	0.5355	0.5625
9/16	24	NEF-2B	0.3750	0.5174	0.5244	0.5354	0.5405	0.5625
9/16	**28**	**UN-2B**	**0.3214**	**0.5238**	**0.5301**	**0.5393**	**0.5441**	**0.5625**
9/16	32	NS-2B	0.2812	0.5287	0.5344	0.5422	0.5467	0.5625
5/8	12	N-2B	0.7500	0.5348	0.5463	0.5709	0.5780	0.6250
5/8	14	NS-2B	0.6429	0.5477	0.5577	0.5786	0.5852	0.6250
5/8	16	NS-2B	0.5625	0.5573	0.5662	0.5844	0.5906	0.6250
5/8	20	NS-2B	0.4500	0.5709	0.5787	0.5925	0.5981	0.6250
5/8	24	NEF-2B	0.3750	0.5799	0.5869	0.5979	0.6031	0.6250
5/8	**28**	**UN-2B**	**0.3214**	**0.5863**	**0.5926**	**0.6018**	**0.6067**	**0.6250**
5/8	32	NS-2B	0.2812	0.5912	0.5969	0.6047	0.6093	0.6250
11/16	12	N-2B	0.7500	0.5973	0.6085	0.6334	0.6405	0.6875
11/16	24	NEF-2B	0.3750	0.6424	0.6494	0.6604	0.6656	0.6875
3/4	12	N-2B	0.7500	0.6598	0.6707	0.6959	0.7031	0.7500
3/4	14	NS-2B	0.6429	0.6727	0.6822	0.7036	0.7103	0.7500
3/4	18	NS-2B	0.5000	0.6899	0.6980	0.7139	0.7199	0.7500
3/4	**20**	**UNEF-2B**	**0.4500**	**0.6959**	**0.7037**	**0.7175**	**0.7232**	**0.7500**
3/4	24	NS-2B	0.3750	0.7049	0.7119	0.7229	0.7282	0.7500
3/4	**28**	**UN-2B**	**0.3214**	**0.7113**	**0.7176**	**0.7268**	**0.7318**	**0.7500**
3/4	32	NS-2B	0.2812	0.7162	0.7219	0.7297	0.7344	0.7500

Bold face type indicates Unified threads.

* Selected combinations of special diameter and pitch.
† Based on lengths of engagement of 9 times pitch, but applicable to lengths of engagement of from 5 to 15 times the pitch, inclusive.

Table 12 (*Continued*). Unified and American Special Threads*
Class 2B — Internal Thread Limits†

Size	Thds. per Inch	Thread Symbol	9 × Pitch	Minor Diam. Limits		Pitch Diam. Limits		Major Diam. Min.
				Min.	Max.	Min.	Max.	
13/16	12	N-2B	0.7500	0.7223	0.7329	0.7584	0.7656	0.8125
13/16	**16**	**UN-2B**	**0.5625**	**0.7448**	**0.7533**	**0.7719**	**0.7782**	**0.8125**
13/16	**20**	**UNEF-2B**	**0.4500**	**0.7584**	**0.7662**	**0.7800**	**0.7857**	**0.8125**
7/8	10	NS-2B	0.9000	0.7667	0.7789	0.8100	0.8178	0.8750
7/8	12	N-2B	0.7500	0.7848	0.7952	0.8209	0.8281	0.8750
7/8	**16**	**UN-2B**	**0.5625**	**0.8073**	**0.8158**	**0.8344**	**0.8407**	**0.8750**
7/8	18	NS-2B	0.5000	0.8149	0.8230	0.8389	0.8449	0.8750
7/8	**20**	**UNEF-2B**	**0.4500**	**0.8209**	**0.8287**	**0.8425**	**0.8482**	**0.8750**
7/8	24	NS-2B	0.3750	0.8299	0.8369	0.8479	0.8532	0.8750
7/8	**28**	**UN-2B**	**0.3214**	**0.8363**	**0.8426**	**0.8518**	**0.8568**	**0.8750**
7/8	32	NS-2B	0.2812	0.8412	0.8469	0.8547	0.8594	0.8750
15/16	**12**	**UN-2B**	**0.7500**	**0.8473**	**0.8575**	**0.8834**	**0.8908**	**0.9375**
15/16	**16**	**UN-2B**	**0.5625**	**0.8698**	**0.8783**	**0.8969**	**0.9034**	**0.9375**
15/16	**20**	**UNEF-2B**	**0.4500**	**0.8834**	**0.8912**	**0.9050**	**0.9109**	**0.9375**
1	10	NS-2B	0.9000	0.8917	0.9037	0.9350	0.9430	1.0000
1	**16**	**UN-2B**	**0.5625**	**0.9323**	**0.9408**	**0.9594**	**0.9659**	**1.0000**
1	18	NS-2B	0.5000	0.9399	0.9480	0.9639	0.9701	1.0000
1	**20**	**UNEF-2B**	**0.4500**	**0.9459**	**0.9537**	**0.9675**	**0.9734**	**1.0000**
1	24	NS-2B	0.3750	0.9549	0.9619	0.9729	0.9784	1.0000
1	**28**	**UN-2B**	**0.3214**	**0.9613**	**0.9676**	**0.9768**	**0.9820**	**1.0000**
1	32	NS-2B	0.2812	0.9662	0.9719	0.9797	0.9846	1.0000
1 1/16	**12**	**UN-2B**	**0.7500**	**0.9723**	**0.9823**	**1.0084**	**1.0158**	**1.0625**
1 1/16	**16**	**UN-2B**	**0.5625**	**0.9948**	**1.0033**	**1.0219**	**1.0284**	**1.0625**
1 1/16	**18**	**NEF-2B**	**0.5000**	**1.0024**	**1.0105**	**1.0264**	**1.0326**	**1.0625**
1 1/8	10	NS-2B	0.9000	1.0167	1.0287	1.0600	1.0680	1.1250
1 1/8	14	NS-2B	0.6429	1.0477	1.0565	1.0786	1.0855	1.1250
1 1/8	**16**	**UN-2B**	**0.5625**	**1.0573**	**1.0658**	**1.0844**	**1.0910**	**1.1250**
1 1/8	**18**	**NEF-2B**	**0.5000**	**1.0649**	**1.0730**	**1.0889**	**1.0951**	**1.1250**
1 1/8	**20**	**UN-2B**	**0.4500**	**1.0709**	**1.0787**	**1.0925**	**1.0984**	**1.1250**
1 1/8	24	NS-2B	0.3750	1.0799	1.0869	1.0979	1.1034	1.1250
1 1/8	**28**	**UN-2B**	**0.3214**	**1.0863**	**1.0926**	**1.1018**	**1.1070**	**1.1250**
1 3/16	**12**	**UN-2B**	**0.7500**	**1.0973**	**1.1073**	**1.1334**	**1.1409**	**1.1875**
1 3/16	**16**	**UN-2B**	**0.5625**	**1.1198**	**1.1283**	**1.1469**	**1.1535**	**1.1875**
1 3/16	**18**	**NEF-2B**	**0.5000**	**1.1274**	**1.1355**	**1.1514**	**1.1577**	**1.1875**
1 1/4	10	NS-2B	0.9000	1.1417	1.1537	1.1850	1.1932	1.2500
1 1/4	14	NS-2B	0.6429	1.1727	1.1815	1.2036	1.2106	1.2500
1 1/4	**16**	**UN-2B**	**0.5625**	**1.1823**	**1.1908**	**1.2094**	**1.2160**	**1.2500**
1 1/4	18	NEF-2B	0.5000	1.1899	1.1980	1.2139	1.2202	1.2500
1 1/4	**20**	**UN-2B**	**0.4500**	**1.1959**	**1.2037**	**1.2175**	**1.2236**	**1.2500**
1 1/4	24	NS-2B	0.3750	1.2049	1.2119	1.2229	1.2285	1.2500
1 5/16	**12**	**UN-2B**	**0.7500**	**1.2223**	**1.2323**	**1.2584**	**1.2659**	**1.3125**
1 5/16	**16**	**UN-2B**	**0.5625**	**1.2448**	**1.2533**	**1.2719**	**1.2785**	**1.3125**
1 5/16	**18**	**NEF-2B**	**0.5000**	**1.2524**	**1.2605**	**1.2764**	**1.2827**	**1.3125**
1 3/8	10	NS-2B	0.9000	1.2667	1.2787	1.3100	1.3182	1.3750
1 3/8	14	NS-2B	0.6429	1.2977	1.3065	1.3286	1.3356	1.3750
1 3/8	**16**	**UN-2B**	**0.5625**	**1.3073**	**1.3158**	**1.3344**	**1.3410**	**1.3750**
1 3/8	**18**	**NEF-2B**	**0.5000**	**1.3149**	**1.3230**	**1.3389**	**1.3452**	**1.3750**

Bold face type indicates Unified threads.

* Selected combinations of diameter and pitch.
† Based on lengths of engagement of 9 times pitch, but applicable to lengths of engagement of from 5 to 15 times the pitch, inclusive.

Table 12 (*Continued*).   Unified and American Special Threads*
Class 2B — Internal Thread Limits†

Size	Thds. per Inch	Thread Symbol	9 × Pitch	Minor Diam. Limits		Pitch Diam. Limits		Major Diam. Min.
				Min.	Max.	Min.	Max.	
1 7/16	**12**	**UN-2B**	**0.7500**	**1.3473**	**1.3573**	**1.3834**	**1.3910**	**1.4375**
1 7/16	**16**	**UN-2B**	**0.5625**	**1.3698**	**1.3783**	**1.3969**	**1.4037**	**1.4375**
1 7/16	18	NEF-2B	0.5000	1.3774	1.3855	1.4014	1.4079	1.4375
1 1/2	10	NS-2B	0.9000	1.3917	1.4037	1.4350	1.4433	1.5000
1 1/2	14	NS-2B	0.6429	1.4227	1.4315	1.4536	1.4608	1.5000
1 1/2	**16**	**UN-2B**	**0.5625**	**1.4323**	**1.4408**	**1.4594**	**1.4662**	**1.5000**
1 1/2	18	NEF-2B	0.5000	1.4399	1.4480	1.4639	1.4704	1.5000
1 1/2	**20**	**UN-2B**	**0.4500**	**1.4459**	**1.4537**	**1.4675**	**1.4737**	**1.5000**
1 1/2	24	NS-2B	0.3750	1.4549	1.4619	1.4729	1.4787	1.5000
1 9/16	16	N-2B	0.5625	1.4948	1.5033	1.5219	1.5287	1.5625
1 9/16	18	NEF-2B	0.5000	1.5024	1.5105	1.5264	1.5329	1.5625
1 5/8	6	NS-2B	1.5000	1.4446	1.4646	1.5167	1.5272	1.6250
1 5/8	7	NS-2B	1.2857	1.4704	1.4875	1.5322	1.5420	1.6250
1 5/8	10	NS-2B	0.9000	1.5167	1.5287	1.5600	1.5683	1.6250
1 5/8	12	N-2B	0.7500	1.5348	1.5448	1.5709	1.5785	1.6250
1 5/8	14	NS-2B	0.6429	1.5477	1.5565	1.5786	1.5858	1.6250
1 5/8	16	N-2B	0.5625	1.5573	1.5658	1.5844	1.5912	1.6250
1 5/8	18	NEF-2B	0.5000	1.5649	1.5730	1.5889	1.5954	1.6250
1 5/8	20	NS-2B	0.4500	1.5709	1.5787	1.5925	1.5987	1.6250
1 5/8	24	NS-2B	0.3750	1.5799	1.5869	1.5979	1.6037	1.6250
1 11/16	16	N-2B	0.5625	1.6198	1.6283	1.6469	1.6538	1.6875
1 11/16	18	NEF-2B	0.5000	1.6274	1.6355	1.6514	1.6580	1.6875
1 3/4	6	NS-2B	1.5000	1.5696	1.5896	1.6417	1.6523	1.7500
1 3/4	7	NS-2B	1.2857	1.5954	1.6125	1.6572	1.6671	1.7500
1 3/4	**8**	**UN-2B**	**1.1250**	**1.6147**	**1.6297**	**1.6688**	**1.6781**	**1.7500**
1 3/4	10	NS-2B	0.9000	1.6417	1.6537	1.6850	1.6934	1.7500
1 3/4	**12**	**UN-2B**	**0.7500**	**1.6598**	**1.6698**	**1.6959**	**1.7037**	**1.7500**
1 3/4	14	NS-2B	0.6429	1.6727	1.6815	1.7036	1.7109	1.7500
1 3/4	**16**	**UNEF-2B**	**0.5625**	**1.6823**	**1.6908**	**1.7094**	**1.7163**	**1.7500**
1 3/4	18	NEF-2B	0.5000	1.6899	1.6980	1.7139	1.7205	1.7500
1 3/4	**20**	**UN-2B**	**0.4500**	**1.6959**	**1.7037**	**1.7175**	**1.7238**	**1.7500**
1 13/16	16	N-2B	0.5625	1.7448	1.7533	1.7719	1.7788	1.8125
1 7/8	6	NS-2B	1.5000	1.6946	1.7146	1.7667	1.7773	1.8750
1 7/8	7	NS-2B	1.2857	1.7204	1.7375	1.7822	1.7921	1.8750
1 7/8**	8	NS-2B	1.1250	1.7397	1.7547	1.7938	1.8031	1.8750
1 7/8	10	NS-2B	0.9000	1.7667	1.7787	1.8100	1.8184	1.8750
1 7/8	12	N-2B	0.7500	1.7848	1.7948	1.8209	1.8287	1.8750
1 7/8	14	NS-2B	0.6429	1.7977	1.8065	1.8286	1.8359	1.8750
1 7/8	16	N-2B	0.5625	1.8073	1.8158	1.8344	1.8413	1.8750
1 7/8	18	NS-2B	0.5000	1.8149	1.8230	1.8389	1.8455	1.8750
1 7/8	20	NS-2B	0.4500	1.8209	1.8287	1.8425	1.8488	1.8750
1 15/16	16	N-2B	0.5625	1.8698	1.8783	1.8969	1.9039	1.9375
2	6	NS-2B	1.5000	1.8196	1.8396	1.8917	1.9025	2.0000
2	7	NS-2B	1.2857	1.8454	1.8625	1.9072	1.9172	2.0000
2	**8**	**UN-2B**	**1.1250**	**1.8647**	**1.8797**	**1.9188**	**1.9282**	**2.0000**
2	10	NS-2B	0.9000	1.8917	1.9037	1.9350	1.9435	2.0000
2	**12**	**UN-2B**	**0.7500**	**1.9098**	**1.9198**	**1.9459**	**1.9538**	**2.0000**
2	14	NS-2B	0.6429	1.9227	1.9315	1.9536	1.9610	2.0000

Bold face type indicates Unified threads.

* Selected combinations of special diameter and pitch.

** Standard size of the 8-thread series.   These limits are for special applications only.

† Based on lengths of engagement of 9 times pitch, but applicable to lengths of engagement of from 5 to 15 times the pitch, inclusive.

Table 12 (*Continued*). Unified and American Special Threads*
Class 2B — Internal Thread Limits†

Size	Thds. per Inch	Thread Symbol	9 × Pitch	Minor Diam. Limits		Pitch Diam. Limits		Major Diam. Min.
				Min.	Max.	Min.	Max.	
2	16	UNEF-2B	0.5625	1.9323	1.9408	1.9594	1.9664	2.0000
2	18	NS-2B	0.5000	1.9399	1.9480	1.9639	1.9706	2.0000
2	20	UN-2B	0.4500	1.9459	1.9537	1.9675	1.9739	2.0000
2 1/16	16	N-2B	0.5625	1.9948	2.0033	2.0219	2.0289	2.0625
2 1/8	12	N-2B	0.7500	2.0348	2.0448	2.0709	2.0788	2.1250
2 1/8	16	N-2B	0.5625	2.0573	2.0658	2.0844	2.0914	2.1250
2 3/16	16	N-2B	0.5625	2.1198	2.1283	2.1469	2.1539	2.1875
2 1/4	6	NS-2B	1.5000	2.0696	2.0896	2.1417	2.1525	2.2500
2 1/4	7	NS-2B	1.2857	2.0954	2.1125	2.1572	2.1672	2.2500
2 1/4	8	UN-2B	1.1250	2.1147	2.1297	2.1688	2.1782	2.2500
2 1/4	10	NS-2B	0.9000	2.1417	2.1537	2.1850	2.1935	2.2500
2 1/4	12	UN-2B	0.7500	2.1598	2.1698	2.1959	2.2038	2.2500
2 1/4	14	NS-2B	0.6429	2.1727	2.1815	2.2036	2.2110	2.2500
2 1/4	16	UN-2B	0.5625	2.1823	2.1908	2.2094	2.2164	2.2500
2 1/4	18	NS-2B	0.5000	2.1899	2.1980	2.2139	2.2206	2.2500
2 1/4	20	UN-2B	0.4500	2.1959	2.2037	2.2175	2.2239	2.2500
2 5/16	16	N-2B	0.5625	2.2448	2.2533	2.2719	2.2791	2.3125
2 3/8	12	N-2B	0.7500	2.2848	2.2948	2.3209	2.3290	2.3750
2 3/8	16	N-2B	0.5625	2.3073	2.3158	2.3344	2.3416	2.3750
2 7/16	16	N-2B	0.5625	2.3698	2.3783	2.3969	2.4041	2.4375
2 1/2	6	NS-2B	1.5000	2.3196	2.3396	2.3917	2.4026	2.5000
2 1/2	7	NS-2B	1.2857	2.3454	2.3625	2.4072	2.4174	2.5000
2 1/2	8	UN-2B	1.1250	2.3647	2.3797	2.4188	2.4284	2.5000
2 1/2	10	NS-2B	0.9000	2.3917	2.4037	2.4350	2.4437	2.5000
2 1/2	12	UN-2B	0.7500	2.4098	2.4198	2.4459	2.4540	2.5000
2 1/2	14	NS-2B	0.6429	2.4227	2.4315	2.4536	2.4612	2.5000
2 1/2	16	UN-2B	0.5625	2.4323	2.4408	2.4594	2.4666	2.5000
2 1/2	18	NS-2B	0.5000	2.4399	2.4480	2.4639	2.4708	2.5000
2 1/2	20	UN-2B	0.4500	2.4459	2.4537	2.4675	2.4741	2.5000
2 5/8	12	N-2B	0.7500	2.5348	2.5448	2.5709	2.5790	2.6250
2 5/8	16	N-2B	0.5625	2.5573	2.5658	2.5844	2.5916	2.6250
2 3/4	6	NS-2B	1.5000	2.5696	2.5896	2.6417	2.6526	2.7500
2 3/4	7	NS-2B	1.2857	2.5954	2.6125	2.6572	2.6674	2.7500
2 3/4	8	UN-2B	1.1250	2.6147	2.6297	2.6688	2.6784	2.7500
2 3/4	10	NS-2B	0.9000	2.6417	2.6537	2.6850	2.6937	2.7500
2 3/4	12	UN-2B	0.7500	2.6598	2.6698	2.6959	2.7040	2.7500
2 3/4	14	NS-2B	0.6429	2.6727	2.6815	2.7036	2.7112	2.7500
2 3/4	16	UN-2B	0.5625	2.6823	2.6908	2.7094	2.7166	2.7500
2 3/4	18	NS-2B	0.5000	2.6899	2.6980	2.7139	2.7208	2.7500
2 7/8	12	N-2B	0.7500	2.7848	2.7948	2.8209	2.8291	2.8750
2 7/8	16	N-2B	0.5625	2.8073	2.8158	2.8344	2.8417	2.8750
3	6	NS-2B	1.5000	2.8196	2.8396	2.8917	2.9028	3.0000
3	7	NS-2B	1.2857	2.8454	2.8625	2.9072	2.9176	3.0000
3	8	UN-2B	1.1250	2.8647	2.8797	2.9188	2.9286	3.0000
3	10	NS-2B	0.9000	2.8917	2.9037	2.9350	2.9439	3.0000
3	12	UN-2B	0.7500	2.9098	2.9198	2.9459	2.9541	3.0000
3	14	NS-2B	0.6429	2.9227	2.9315	2.9536	2.9613	3.0000
3	16	UN-2B	0.5625	2.9323	2.9408	2.9594	2.9667	3.0000
3	18	NS-2B	0.5000	2.9399	2.9480	2.9639	2.9709	3.0000

Bold face type indicates Unified threads.

* Selected combinations of diameter and pitch.
† Based on lengths of engagement of 9 times pitch, but applicable to lengths of engagement of from 5 to 15 times the pitch, inclusive.

Relation between Revised and Former American Standards. — The revised and former American Standards are interchangeable. The Unified Series of Screw Threads (which constitutes an important part of the revised American Standard) also provides an interchangeable system for the Dominion of Canada, United Kingdom, and United States. Just how the new thread standard affects the manufacturers and users of threaded products has been summarized by Herman H. Lind, President, American Institute of Bolt, Nut, and Rivet Manufacturers. The achievement of screw thread unification by the adoption of international specifications is given as the principal reason for the new standard. Additional reasons and facts of importance will be found in the following paragraphs.

Minimum Clearance between Mating Parts. — Modern practice in producing both external and internal screw threads makes it possible to obtain very precise dimensions. One of the difficulties arising from these small tolerances has been that the mating threaded parts may approach or have the same basic dimensions; hence a nut thread made to the minimum allowed limit, and a bolt thread made to the maximum limit, may not assemble readily. The new American standard corrects such faults by introducing limits of Classes 1A, 1B and 2A, 2B which provide a *minimum clearance* between mating parts. Thus, tight fits during wrenching and seizure at high temperatures are prevented, and room is allowed for plating.

Increase in Working Tolerance. — The revised standard is designed to correct certain production difficulties resulting from the former standard. Often, under the old system, the tolerances of the product were practically absorbed by the combined tool and gage tolerances, leaving little for a working tolerance in manufacture. Somewhat greater tolerances are now provided for nut threads. As contrasted with the old " classes of fit " 1, 2, and 3, for each of which the pitch diameter tolerance on the external and internal threads were equal, the Classes 1B, 2B, and 3B (internal) threads in the new standard have, respectively, a 30 per cent larger pitch diameter tolerance than the 1A, 2A, and 3A (external) threads. Relatively more tolerance is provided for fine threads than for coarse threads of the same pitch. In cases where previous tolerances were more liberal than is required in manufacture, they were reduced.

Relative Strengths of New and Old Standard. — The strength or holding power of a bolt and nut has not been changed by the new standard. In fact, bolts made according to the old or new British standard and those conforming to the old or new American standard are all about equally strong as fasteners.

Transition from Old to New Standards. — The interchangeability between the new and former American standards is fortunate because procurement of gages and tools, and utilizing existing stocks, will require considerable time. The producers of threaded parts doubtless will introduce tools for the new threads as fast as the old tools wear out. Most users can accept the new threads in lieu of the old without any trouble.

Specifying the Revised Standard. — Specifications for the revised standard should be made with the following reservations:

Where the screw is to be assembled into a precision tapped hole and where a wrench-tight stud fit is desired, a definite statement to that effect should be made by the purchaser. If the assembly is with a nut or in a tapped hole where a free fit is desired, there are few, if any, cases where either the new or the old standard thread would not be usable and fully satisfactory. It is not practical or possible to go instantly from the old standard to the new. Specifying the new standard and accepting either the old or the new will speed the transition period and make it less costly for all concerned, because the new tools and gages can be introduced into the production line as the old ones are worn out.

When Class 2 or Class 3 tolerances of the old American standard tolerances are now specified, the user's specifications should permit the supplier the option of furnishing Class 2A for bolts and Class 2B for nuts when, as, and if available. These Classes 2A and 2B are the recognized standards for the normal production of bolts, screws, and nuts.

Avoiding Difficulties during Transition Period. — During the transition period it is absolutely essential that an inspection of the product both by the producer and user should be related to its usability rather than to extreme precision which may not appreciably affect application. Thus, a reasonable inspection policy resulting in a practical approach and based primarily upon *function* or *application* will prevent much trouble between producer and user.

Are Present Stocks Obsolete? — The answer is "No." This again is because the limits of the old and the new are such that assemblies can be made without interference.

Class 5 Fit for Threaded Studs.

— The Class 5 fit (see table on next page) applies to steel studs set into hard materials such as cast iron, semi-steel and bronze. These specifications are not intended for studs set into aluminum, since a larger interference of metal is permissible. Class 5 fit is based partly upon experimental data obtained in an investigation conducted by the National Bureau of Standards, and partly upon the existing practice of manufacturers.

Thread Form: The American National form of thread profile is used but the thread form in the tapped hole is modified by truncating the crest of the thread an amount greater than standard. This truncation may be such that the minimum depth of thread engagement is one-half of the basic thread depth, to provide clearance space into which the metal can flow. The maximum depth of engagement is governed by the tolerances specified for the major diameter of the stud and the minor diameter of the tapped hole.

Minimum Interferences: The minimum interferences are such that a wrench-tight fit will result in all cases. If the thread surfaces are smooth and thread form is maintained, these interferences will permit disassembly and reassembly of the same stud and hole as many as four times and still produce a wrench-tight fit. In the coarse-threaded stud series, the *minimum* pitch diameter interference ranges from 0.0003 inch for a ¼-inch stud, up to 0.0013 inch for a 1½-inch stud. In the fine-threaded series, the minimum pitch diameter interference ranges from 0.0005 inch for a ¼-inch stud, up to 0.0012 inch for a 1½-inch stud.

Maximum Interferences: The maximum interferences are such that all conditions necessary for a good wrench fit are fulfilled. If threads are well lubricated with a suitable lute, no galling or seizing of the threads will result; also, mild steel studs, even of the smaller sizes, will not break if the rate of assembly is not excessive. The wrench fit class is intended to cover the manufacture of threaded studs and holes which are to be assembled permanently by the application of power.

In the coarse-threaded series, the *maximum* pitch diameter interference ranges from 0.0018 inch for a ¼-inch stud, up to 0.0070 inch for a 1½-inch stud. In the fine-threaded series, the maximum pitch diameter interference ranges from 0.0034 inch for a ¼-inch stud, up to 0.0050 inch for a 1½-inch stud.

When a mixture of white lead and oil is used as a lute, it is important that it be of a thick fluid consistency in order to prevent galling or seizing (particularly for fine threads in hard materials), and that it be applied liberally. If a lute consisting of 40 per cent zinc dust, which has passed through a 200-mesh sieve, and 60 per cent petrolatum is used, the tendency for the threads to gall or seize with maximum interference is materially reduced.

Minor and Major Diameters: Dimensions given in the table for the maximum minor diameter of the screw, are figured to the intersection of the worn tool arc with a center line through crest and root. The minimum minor diameter of the screw shall be that corresponding to a flat at the minor diameter of the screw equal

Class 5 Fit for Threaded Steel Studs — American Standard Coarse- and Fine-thread Series

Sizes in coarse and fine series	Threads per inch	Stud sizes					Tapped-hole sizes					Tap-drill diam. See Footnote	Approx. torque at full engagement of 1½D. Inch-pounds	
		Major diameter		Pitch diameter		Minor diam., Max.	Minor diameter		Pitch diameter		Major diam., Min.			
		Max.	Min.	Max.	Min.		Min.	Max.	Min.	Max.			Max.	Min.
¼*	20	0.2500	0.2428	0.2193	0.2186	0.1904	0.2049	0.2103	0.2175	0.2183	0.2500	0.2090	105	35
5⁄16	18	0.3125	0.3043	0.2804	0.2784	0.2483	0.2622	0.2682	0.2764	0.2779	0.3125	0.2656	265	80
3⁄8	16	0.3750	0.3660	0.3389	0.3305	0.3028	0.3186	0.3254	0.3344	0.3360	0.3750	0.3230	420	120
7⁄16	14	0.4375	0.4277	0.3961	0.3935	0.3549	0.3736	0.3813	0.3911	0.3929	0.4375	0.3750	610	180
½	13	0.5000	0.4896	0.4555	0.4526	0.4111	0.4313	0.4396	0.4500	0.4519	0.5000	0.4375	850	265
9⁄16	12	0.5625	0.5513	0.5144	0.5112	0.4663	0.4882	0.4972	0.5084	0.5104	0.5625	0.4921	1,170	360
5⁄8	11	0.6250	0.6132	0.5720	0.5689	0.5195	0.5444	0.5542	0.5660	0.5681	0.6250	0.5469	1,450	450
¾	10	0.7500	0.7372	0.6915	0.6882	0.6338	0.6614	0.6722	0.6850	0.6873	0.7500	0.6719	2,300	730
⅞	9	0.8750	0.8610	0.8093	0.8062	0.7452	0.7708	0.7888	0.8028	0.8052	0.8750	0.7812	3,200	1,080
1	8	1.0000	0.9848	0.9253	0.9226	0.8531	0.8901	0.9036	0.9188	0.9215	1.0000	0.8906	4,250	1,500
1⅛	7	1.1250	1.1080	1.0387	1.0363	0.9552	0.9998	1.0152	1.0322	1.0352	1.1250	1.0000	5,300	1,875
1¼	7	1.2500	1.2330	1.1637	1.1614	1.0812	1.1248	1.1402	1.1572	1.1602	1.2500	1.1250	6,950	2,535
1⅜	6	1.3750	1.3548	1.2732	1.2715	1.1770	1.2286	1.2466	1.2667	1.2703	1.3750	1.2344	8,159	2,970
1½	6	1.5000	1.4798	1.3987	1.3966	1.3025	1.3536	1.3716	1.3917	1.3953	1.5000	1.3594	10,400	3,900
¼	28	0.2500	0.2438	0.2302	0.2284	0.2096	0.2167	0.2206	0.2268	0.2279	0.2500	0.2187	140	45
5⁄16	24	0.3125	0.3059	0.2891	0.2871	0.2650	0.2743	0.2788	0.2854	0.2866	0.3125	0.2770	230	70
3⁄8	24	0.3750	0.3684	0.3523	0.3497	0.3282	0.3368	0.3413	0.3479	0.3491	0.3750	0.3390	410	125
7⁄16	20	0.4375	0.4303	0.4094	0.4069	0.3805	0.3924	0.3978	0.4050	0.4063	0.4375	0.3970	540	170
½	20	0.5000	0.4928	0.4725	0.4695	0.4436	0.4549	0.4603	0.4675	0.4688	0.5000	0.4576	810	260
9⁄16	18	0.5625	0.5543	0.5314	0.5286	0.4993	0.5122	0.5182	0.5264	0.5279	0.5625	0.5156	1,040	330
5⁄8	18	0.6250	0.6168	0.5944	0.5912	0.5623	0.5747	0.5807	0.5889	0.5904	0.6250	0.5781	1,430	460
¾	16	0.7500	0.7410	0.7153	0.7118	0.6792	0.6936	0.7004	0.7094	0.7110	0.7500	0.6970	2,200	685
⅞	14	0.8750	0.8652	0.8347	0.8312	0.7935	0.8111	0.8188	0.8286	0.8304	0.8750	0.8125	3,070	945
1	14	1.0000	0.9902	0.9605	0.9563	0.9193	0.9361	0.9438	0.9536	0.9554	1.0000	0.9375	4,590	1,410
1⅛	12	1.1250	1.1138	1.0776	1.0738	1.0295	1.0507	1.0597	1.0709	1.0729	1.1250	1.0552	5,620	1,750
1¼	12	1.2500	1.2388	1.2019	1.1990	1.1538	1.1757	1.1847	1.1959	1.1979	1.2500	1.1811	6,900	2,530
1⅜	12	1.3750	1.3638	1.3264	1.3240	1.2782	1.3007	1.3097	1.3209	1.3229	1.3750	1.3052	8,440	3,225
1½	12	1.5000	1.4888	1.4509	1.4491	1.4028	1.4257	1.4347	1.4459	1.4479	1.5000	1.4302	10,070	4,215

* Selective assembly in the case of the ¼-inch size may be required on account of the small tolerances necessary on pitch diameter. To avoid breaking a mild steel stud, the maximum interference on pitch diameter of 0.0018 inch must not be exceeded. The use of ¼"-28, instead of ¼"-20, is recommended.

The recommended tap-drill size for 9⁄16—12 thread, is 12.5 mm. or 0.4921 inch; for 1¼—12 thread, 30 mm. or 1.1811 inch.

Pitch Diameters for Alternative System of Class 5 Stud Fits *

Nom. Stud Diam.	Coarse-thread Series				Fine-thread Series			
	Threads per Inch	Stud Pitch Diam. Max	Stud Pitch Diam. Min.	Hole Pitch D. Max.	Threads per Inch	Stud Pitch Diam. Max.	Stud Pitch Diam. Min.	Hole Pitch D. Max.
1/4	..	......	......	......	28	0.2307	0.2296	0.2290
5/16	18	0.2810	0.2795	0.2790	24	0.2896	0.2884	0.2878
3/8	16	0.3395	0.3379	0.3374	24	0.3523	0.3511	0.3503
7/16	14	0.3968	0.3950	0.3943	20	0.4097	0.4084	0.4076
1/2	13	0.4562	0.4543	0.4534	20	0.4725	0.4712	0.4701
9/16	12	0.5150	0.5130	0.5119	18	0.5320	0.5305	0.5294
5/8	11	0.5729	0.5708	0.5696	18	0.5945	0.5930	0.5919
3/4	10	0.6923	0.6900	0.6887	16	0.7153	0.7137	0.7126
7/8	9	0.8102	0.8078	0.8065	14	0.8351	0.8333	0.8322
1	8	0.9263	0.9238	0.9225	14	0.9605	0.9587	0.9572
1 1/8	7	1.0398	1.0373	1.0359	12	1.0784	1.0764	1.0749
1 1/4	7	1.1648	1.1623	1.1609	12	1.2031	1.2011	1.1996
1 3/8	6	1.2743	1.2718	1.2704	12	1.3276	1.3256	1.3241
1 1/2	6	1.3998	1.3973	1.3957	12	1.4521	1.4501	1.4486

* For all other dimensions, see table on preceding page.

to $1/8 \times p$, and may be determined by subtracting the basic thread depth (or $0.6495p$) from the minimum pitch diameter of the screw.

Dimensions for the minimum major diameter of the tapped hole correspond to the basic flat ($1/8 \times p$), and the profile at the major diameter produced by a worn tool must not fall below the basic outline. The maximum major diameter of the tapped hole shall be that corresponding to a flat at the major diameter of the tapped hole equal to $1/24 \times p$, and may be determined by adding $1\frac{2}{9} \times$ thread depth (or $0.7939p$) to the maximum pitch diameter of the nut.

Alternative System of Stud Fits. — An alternative Class 5 fit for threaded studs is the same as the one just referred to, excepting the pitch diameters listed in the table on this page. This alternative system is intended to avoid difficulty in maintaining tapped holes within the tolerances specified. Regarding the studs, the threads can readily be made within smaller tolerances than those specified. There has also been some indication that the minimum interference is too small, and that the theoretical maximum interference can be increased slightly. The interferences, as determined experimentally, were based on direct pitch diameter measurements of the stud and of the tap. If, in practice, the interferences are controlled by "go" and "not go" thread gages, the actual maximum and minimum interferences obtained may be less than those tabulated, on account of lead, angle, and pitch diameter tolerances of gages; hence it should be possible to increase the theoretical maximum interferences, and it is desirable to increase the minimum interferences.

Some commercial practice agrees with this alternative Class 5 fit. Gages for this alternative system should have "W" tolerances (see pages 1113 and 1114) for the ring and plug gages to control thread sizes of both studs and tapped holes. The maximum interferences have been increased, in general (with slight deviations for rounding of tables), by the diameter equivalent of pitch diameter, lead, and angle gage tolerances of W gages. This equivalent is taken for one W gage, and therefore represents an average condition. In order to maintain minimum interferences, it is important that the "not go" gages should not assemble with the product more than 1 1/2 turns.

Threaded Steel Studs for Parts Made of Aluminum and Magnesium Alloys

(Aeronautical Recommended Practice of the Society of Automotive Engineers)

Nominal Size of Stud, Inch	Number of Threads per Inch	Tapped Hole		Stud Diameters and Fit Allowances			
		Pitch Diam., Max. Min. (Note 1)	Tap Drill +0.005 −0.002 (Note 2)	Major Diam., Max. Min.	Pitch Diam., Max. Min.	Pitch Diam., Fit Allowances	Pitch Diam. of Leading Threads (Note 3)
.2500	20	0.2198 0.2175	No. 7 (.201)	0.2500 0.2440	0.2221 0.2208	0.0046 0.0010	0.2165 0.2145
.3125	18	0.2789 0.2764	F (.257)	0.3125 0.3065	0.2814 0.2799	0.0050 0.0010	0.2754 0.2734
.3750	16	0.3370 0.3344	0.3125	0.3750 0.3690	0.3396 0.3380	0.0052 0.0010	0.3334 0.3314
.4375	14	0.3939 0.3911	U (.368)	0.4375 0.4315	0.3967 0.3949	0.0056 0.0010	0.3901 0.3881
.5000	13	0.4529 0.4500	0.4219	0.5000 0.4940	0.4558 0.4539	0.0058 0.0010	0.4490 0.4470
.5625	12	0.5114 0.5084	0.4844	0.5625 0.5565	0.5144 0.5124	0.0060 0.0010	0.5074 0.5054
.6250	11	0.5691 0.5660	0.5312	0.6250 0.6190	0.5722 0.5701	0.0062 0.0010	0.5650 0.5630

Note 1: Dimensions for pitch diameters of studs are before plating. If studs are cadmium plated, the thickness specified in AMS 2400–1 shall be followed.

Note 2: Optional drill sizes to produce approximately 75 per cent full thread may be used. The depth of the tapped hole should provide the following length L of stud engagement for stud diameter D: For straight studs, L = 2 D in aluminum and 2.5 D in magnesium. For stepped studs with enlarged end in tapped hole, L = 1.5 D in aluminum and 2 D in magnesium.

Note 3: A lead of one thread minimum and three threads maximum may be provided on entering end of stud (optional). For pitch diameters see table.

To avoid overstressing a stud when assembling, it is necessary to control torque so that stress will be lower than yield point of material. Fits giving required torque may be obtained by selecting a stud and tapping the hole to suit, within the limits of the pitch diameters listed in table. Torque values should be determined by each manufacturer according to individual stud requirements.

It is preferred that the studded end of stud be straight, although a taper of 0.001 per inch maximum is permitted, the smaller end being the entering end.

The out-of-roundness of the pitch diameter of the studded end shall not exceed 0.00030. Lead errors and errors due to angularity shall be within Class 4 tolerance.

Surface roughness: Rolled or ground threads not to exceed 40 RMS micro-inches; die-cut threads not to exceed 130 RMS micro-inches.

A suitable lubricant should be used for driving studs.

Aluminum and magnesium may be divided into three classes for hardness designation: Brinell 45–65, 65–105, 105–160; the range of fit allowances shall be as follows: From 45–65, the fit should be from the mean value to the high limit; from 65–105, the fit should be approximately the mean value; from 105–160, the fit should be from the low limit to the mean value.

Material AMS 6317 or equivalent. Rockwell C26–32.

Thread Gage Tolerances. — Gage tolerances for the four classes of American Standard screw thread fits are designated as W, X and Y gage tolerances (see table, page 1114). These tolerances are applicable to the National Coarse (NC) and National Fine (NF) Series, and to comparable diameters and pitches. The recommended uses for W, X and Y gage tolerances are as follows:

Working Gages. For Classes 1 and 2 fits, use Y tolerances; for Class 3, use X tolerances; for Class 4, use W tolerances.

Inspection Gages. Recommended uses are same as given under Working Gages.

Setting Gages. These thread plug gages are used in adjusting thread ring gages, thread snap gages, or other thread comparators. For Classes 1 and 2 fits, use X tolerances; for Class 3 fit, use W or X tolerances; for Class 4, use W tolerances.

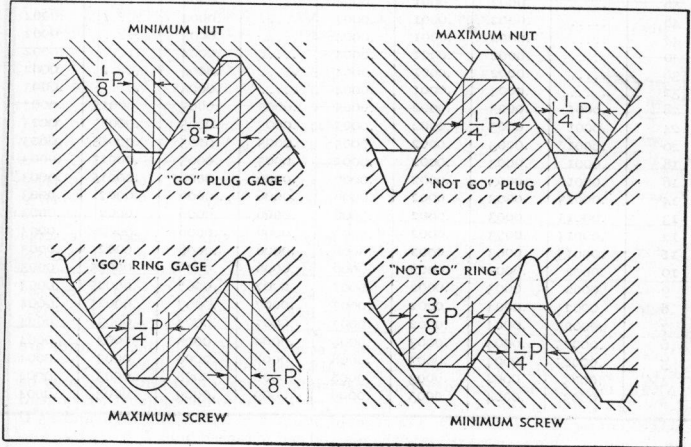

" Go " Gages for Screw Threads. — A " Go " gage should check simultaneously as many elements as possible, whereas a "Not Go" gage usually checks one element only. A "Go" gage checks the maximum limit of a threaded plug and the minimum limit of the threaded hole.

Pitch Diameter. The pitch diameter of W and X *"Go" plug gages* is the same as the minimum pitch diameter of the threaded hole or nut. (See tables beginning on page 1084, giving limiting dimensions for the required class of screw thread fit.) The tolerance is plus for plugs. The pitch diameter of the W and X " Go " *ring gages* is the same as the maximum pitch diameter of the screw. The tolerance is minus for rings.

Major and Minor Diameters. The major diameter of the " Go " *plug gage* is the same as the basic major diameter, with a plus tolerance. The minor diameter of the *Go ring gage* is the same as the minimum minor diameter of the nut or tapped hole, with a minus tolerance.

" Not Go " Gages for Screw Threads. — A " Not Go " thread gage which checks the pitch diameter only, usually meets practical requirements. The " Not Go " gage checks the minimum limit of a threaded plug and the maximum limit of a threaded hole.

ALLOWANCES AND TOLERANCES

American Standard Thread Gage Tolerances

For recommended applications, see Thread Gage Tolerances, page 1113.

Threads per Inch	Pitch Diameter Tolerances				Major or Minor Diam. Tolerances		Lead* Tolerances	
	W Gages	X Gages	Y Gages		W	X and Y	W	X and Y
			From	To				
80	.....	.0002	.0001	.0003	.....	.0003	.....	.0002
72	.....	.0002	.0001	.0003	.....	.0003	.....	.0002
64	.....	.0002	.0001	.0004	.....	.0004	.....	.0002
56	.....	.0002	.0001	.0004	.....	.0004	.....	.0002
48	.....	.0002	.0001	.0004	.....	.0004	.....	.0002
44	.....	.0002	.0001	.0004	.....	.0004	.....	.0002
40	.....	.0002	.0001	.0004	.....	.0004	.....	.0002
36	.....	.0002	.0001	.0004	.....	.0004	.....	.0002
32	.....	.0003	.0001	.0004	.....	.0004	.....	.0003
28	.0001	.0003	.0002	.0005	.0005	.0005	.00015	.0003
24	.0001	.0003	.0002	.0005	.0005	.0005	.00015	.0003
20	.0001	.0003	.0002	.0005	.0005	.0005	.00015	.0003
18	.0001	.0003	.0002	.0005	.0005	.0005	.00015	.0003
16	.0001	.0003	.0002	.0006	.0006	.0006	.00015	.0003
14	.00015	.0003	.0002	.0006	.0006	.0006	.0002	.0003
13	.00015	.0003	.0002	.0006	.0006	.0006	.0002	.0003
12	.00015	.0003	.0002	.0006	.0006	.0006	.0002	.0003
11	.00015	.0003	.0002	.0006	.0006	.0006	.0002	.0003
10	.0002	.0003	.0002	.0006	.0006	.0006	.00025	.0003
9	.0002	.0003	.0002	.0007	.0007	.0007	.00025	.0003
8	.0002	.0004	.0002	.0007	.0007	.0007	.00025	.0004
7	.00025	.0004	.0002	.0007	.0007	.0007	.0003	.0004
6	.00025	.0004	.0003	.0008	.0008	.0008	.0003	.0004
5	.00025	.0004	.0003	.0008	.0008	.0008	.0003	.0004
4½	.0003	.0004	.0003	.0008	.0008	.0008	.0003	.0004
4	.0003	.0004	.0003	.0009	.0009	.0009	.0003	.0004

Tolerances on Half Angle of Thread, Minutes

Threads per Inch	W Gage	X Gage	Y Gage	Threads per Inch	W Gage	X Gage	Y Gage
80	....	30'	45'	16	8'	10'	15'
72	....	30'	45'	14	6'	10'	15'
64	....	30'	45'	13	6'	10'	15'
56	....	30'	45'	12	6'	10'	10'
48	....	30'	45'	11	6'	10'	10'
44	....	20'	30'	10	5'	10'	10'
40	....	20'	30'	9	5'	10'	10'
36	....	20'	30'	8	5'	5'	5'
32	....	15'	20'	7	4'	5'	5'
28	8'	15'	20'	6	4'	5'	5'
24	8'	15'	20'	5	4'	5'	5'
20	8'	15'	20'	4½	4'	5'	5'
18	8'	10'	15'	4	4'	5'	5'

* Allowable variation in lead between any two threads not farther apart than the standard length of engagement, which is equal to the basic major diameter.

Pitch Diameter. The pitch diameter of a "*Not Go*" *plug gage* equals the maximum pitch diameter of the threaded hole or nut. (See tables beginning on page 1084.) The tolerance is minus but may be plus. All gages used for the *production* of screw threads, and "Go" gages for inspection, should be within the extreme limits of the product. However, to avoid needless controversy about parts close to "Not Go" limits because of possible small differences in gage sizes, the pitch diameter tolerances on all "Not Go" gages used for *final inspection* and for inspection of purchased products, may be outside of the product limits *is specially authorized*.

The pitch diameter of the "*Not Go*" *thread ring gage* is the same as the minimum pitch diameter of the screw. The tolerance is plus but may be minus for the reason given in the preceding paragraph.

Thread Form on Gages. — The illustration on page 1113, shows approved thread forms for both plug and ring gages. The crest of the thread on "Not Go" plug and ring gages is partly removed to insure proper contact. There is also a clearance groove at the root of "Not Go" plug and ring gages to insure pitch diameter contact. The "Go" plug and ring gages may have clearance grooves at the roots to facilitate grinding and lapping.

Truncated Setting Plugs. — The major diameter of the full portion of the "*Go*" *setting plug* is that of a full American National form, based on maximum pitch diameter of the screw. The tolerance is plus. The major diameter of the truncated portion of the "Go" setting plug is that of a full American National form minus one-third the basic thread depth, with a minus tolerance.

The major diameter of the full portion of the "*Not Go*" *setting plug* is the same as that of the "Go" plug of the same nominal size, except that the truncation from a theoretical vee should not be less than 0.058 times pitch. The latter condition might arise in the case of fine pitches and especially wide tolerances. The tolerance is minus. The major diameter of the truncated portion of the "Not Go" setting plug is that of a full American National form minus one-third the basic thread depth, with a minus tolerance.

American Standard Tolerances for Plain Gages

Diam. Range	X	Y	Z	Diam. Range	X	Y	Z
0.029–0.825	.00004	.00007	.00010	4.510–6.510	.00013	.00019	.00025
0.825–1.510	.00006	.00009	.00012	6.510–9.010	.00016	.00024	.00032
1.510–2.510	.00008	.00012	.00016	9.010–12.01	.00020	.00030	.00040
2.510–4.510	.00010	.00015	.00020	......	......	......	......

The X tolerances are for master gages. The Y and Z tolerances are for the working gages used in gaging major and minor diameters. The Y tolerances are also recommended for inspection gages.

Tolerances for Machining Operations

The following tolerances for different classes of machine work are based upon the experience and practice of the Pratt & Whitney Co. in making equipment for rifle manufacture. These figures are subject to variation, and are given as a guide. It is assumed that the machines in each case are in good condition. The figures are also intended to apply only to the manufacture of duplicate parts on an interchangeable basis, and are not given as representing the greatest degree of accuracy obtainable.

Lathe Work: — Rough turning: Minimum tolerance of 0.005 inch for diameters from ¼ to ½ inch; 0.007 inch for diameters from ½ to 1 inch; 0.010 inch for diameters from 1 inch to 2 inches; and 0.015 inch for larger diameters. **Finish turning:** Tolerance of 0.002 inch for diameters from ¼ to ½ inch; 0.003 inch for diameters from ½ to 1 inch; 0.005 inch for diameters from 1 inch to 2 inches; and 0.007 inch for larger diameters. The most accurate as well as most economical method of finishing many classes of cylindrical work is by grinding, so that accurate lathe work prior to grinding is not necessary.

Automatic Screw Machine Work: — Tolerance of 0.003 inch for turning with box tools; tolerance of 0.003 inch for forming tools less than ¾ inch wide; and 0.004 inch for widths between ¾ inch and 1½ inches. Tolerance of 0.006 inch for hollow milling from ³⁄₁₆ to ½ inch diameter; 0.008 inch from ½ to ¾ inch diameter; and 0.010 inch from ¾ to 1 inch diameter. For drilling, tolerances range from 0.002 inch for drills from No. 60 to No. 30, to about 0.007 inch for drills from ¾ to 1 inch in diameter. Reaming enables the tolerance to be reduced to 0.001 for sizes up to ½ inch diameter and to 0.0015 for sizes from ½ to 1 inch.

Milling Operations: — While a tolerance of 0.002 inch is feasible, it should, if possible, be increased to 0.004 or 0.005 inch to secure greater economy in manufacturing. If a single surface is to be milled, the tolerance may be from 0.002 to 0.003 inch; but when there are two or more surfaces to be milled, all but the most important one should be given tolerances of about 0.005 inch, if practicable. The tolerance for straddle-milling may be 0.003 inch; for form-milling, 0.005 inch; for end-milling, when the depth of the slot is little deeper than the mill diameter, 0.004 inch for widths from ¼ to ½ inch, 0.006 inch for widths from ½ to ¾ inch, and 0.008 inch for widths from ¾ to 1 inch. Somewhat greater tolerances should be allowed for hand-milling than for power-milling, because the feeding motion is not so even.

Drilling: — For drills from Nos. 60 to 30, 0.002 inch tolerance; for Nos. 30 to 1, 0.003 inch tolerance; for drill diameters from ¼ to ½ inch, 0.004 inch tolerance; for diameters from ½ to ¾ inch, 0.005 inch tolerance; for diameters from ¾ to 1 inch, 0.007 inch tolerance; and for diameters from 1 inch to 2 inches, 0.010 inch tolerance.

Grinding: — Cylindrical and surface grinding, 0.0005 inch tolerance. Vertical surface-grinding machine, 0.002 inch, which tolerance may be reduced to 0.001 inch under favorable conditions.

Planing Operations: — Tolerances varying from 0.005 to 0.010 inch may be maintained in planing comparatively large parts, such as machine tool slides, etc.

Thread-cutting: — When screw threads are cut in a lathe, tolerances on the pitch diameter of from 0.0015 to 0.002 inch may be maintained. When milling screw threads, it is possible, with a machine extremely well taken care of and when using a very accurate form of cutter, to maintain a tolerance of 0.001 inch for short pieces on the pitch diameter, and a tolerance of 0.002 inch on the outside and bottom diameter; but it is impracticable to give tolerances for interchangeable manufacture more accurate than 0.002 inch for the pitch diameter and 0.004 inch for the outside and bottom diameter. Tolerances on the outside diameter refer only to Whitworth or other threads with a formed top of thread. The larger tolerance given for the outside diameter does not affect the accuracy or working of the thread, because the apex of the thread is of little value and the important dimension is the pitch diameter.

Hand- and Machine-reaming: — For diameters up to 1 inch, a tolerance of 0.0004 inch may be maintained for hand-reaming; for diameters above 1 inch, the tolerance may be 0.0006 inch. These tolerances are increased somewhat for machine-reaming. For diameters up to ½ inch, the tolerance may be about 0.0005 inch; for diameters from ½ to 1 inch, from 0.00075 inch to 0.001 inch; and for **diameters** above 1 inch, 0.0015 inch.

MEASURING INSTRUMENTS AND GAGING METHODS

Reading a Vernier. — A general rule for taking readings with a vernier scale is as follows: Note the number of inches and sub-divisions of an inch that the zero mark of the vernier scale has moved along the true scale, and then 'add to this reading as many thousandths, or hundredths, or whatever fractional part of an inch the vernier reads to, as there are spaces between the vernier zero and that line on the vernier which coincides with one on the true scale. For example, if the zero line of a vernier which reads to thousandths is slightly beyond the 0.5 inch division on the main or true scale, as shown in Fig. 1, and graduation line 10 on the vernier coincides exactly with one on the true scale, the reading is 0.5 + 0.010 or 0.510 inch. In order to determine the reading or fractional part of an inch that can be obtained by a vernier, multiply the denominator of the finest sub-division given on the true scale by the total number of divisions on the vernier. For example, if one inch on the true scale is divided into 40 parts or fortieths (as in Fig. 1), and the vernier into twenty-five parts, the vernier will read to thousandths of an inch, as 25 × 40 = 1000. Similarly, if there are sixteen divisions to the inch on the true scale and a total of eight on the vernier, the latter will enable readings within one-hundred-twenty-eighths of an inch to be taken, as 8 × 16 = 128.

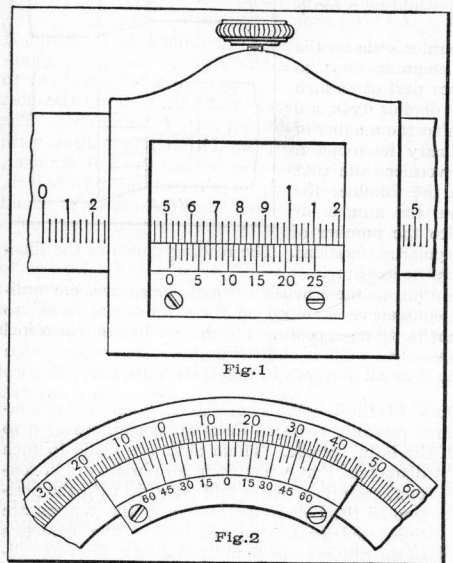

Fig. 1

Fig. 2

If the vernier is on a protractor, note the whole number of degrees passed by the vernier zero mark and then count the spaces between the vernier zero and that line which coincides with a graduation on the protractor scale. If the vernier indicates angles within five minutes or one-twelfth degree (as in Fig. 2), the number of spaces multiplied by 5 will, of course, give the number of minutes to be added to the whole number of degrees. The reading of the protractor set as illustrated would be 14 whole degrees (the number passed by the zero mark on the vernier) plus 30 minutes, as the graduation 30 on the vernier is the only one to the right of the vernier zero which exactly coincides with a line on the protractor scale. It will be noted that there are duplicate scales on the vernier, one being to the right and the other to the left of zero. The left-hand scale is used when the vernier zero is moved to the left of the zero of the protractor scale, whereas the right-hand graduations are used when the movement is to the right.

Reading a Micrometer. — To read a micrometer, count the number of whole divisions that are visible on the scale of the frame, multiply this number by 25 (the number of thousandths of an inch that each division represents) and add to the product the number of that division on the thimble which coincides with the axial zero line on the frame. The result will be the diameter expressed in thousandths of an inch. As the numbers 1, 2, 3, etc., opposite every fourth sub-division on the frame, indicate hundreds of thousandths, the reading can easily be taken mentally. Suppose the thimble were screwed out so that graduation 2, and three additional sub-divisions, were visible (as shown in Fig. 1), and that graduation 10 on the thimble coincided with the axial line on the frame. The reading then would be 0.200 + 0.075 + 0.010, or 0.285 inch.

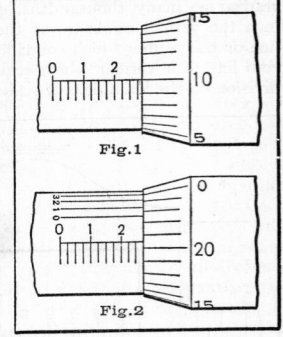

Fig. 1

Fig. 2

Some micrometers have a vernier scale on the frame in addition to the regular graduations, so that measurements within 0.0001 part of an inch can be taken. Micrometers of this type are read as follows: First determine the number of thousandths, as with an ordinary micrometer, and then find a line on the vernier scale that exactly coincides with one on the thimble; the number of this line represents the number of ten-thousandths to be added to the number of thousandths obtained by the regular graduations. The reading shown in the illustration, Fig. 2, is 0.270 + 0.0003 = 0.2703 inch.

Micrometers graduated according to the English system of measurement ordinarily have a table of decimal equivalents stamped on the sides of the frame, so that fractions such as sixty-fourths, thirty-seconds, etc., can readily be converted into decimals. The decimal equivalent table is omitted on micrometers graduated according to the metric system, since all divisions in this system are decimal.

Locating Holes by the Disk Method. — When machining holes in comparatively small precision work, three carefully centered disks are sometimes used to align the respective holes with the lathe spindle. These disks are made to such diameters that when their peripheries are in contact, each disk center will coincide with the position of the hole to be machined; the centers are then used for locating the work. The diameters of the disks can be found as follows: Subtract dimension y from x, thus obtaining the difference between the radii of disks C and A; add this difference to dimension z to obtain the diameter of disk A; subtract the radius of disk A from the center distance x to obtain the radius of B; subtract the radius of B from dimension y to obtain the radius of C.

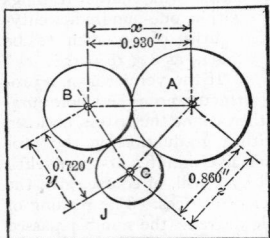

Example: 0.930 − 0.720 = 0.210, or the difference between the radii of disks C and A. The diameter of A equals 0.210 + 0.860 = 1.070 inch, and the radius equals 1.070 ÷ 2 = 0.535 inch. The radius of B = 0.930 − 0.535 = 0.395 inch. The radius of C = 0.720 − 0.395 = 0.325.

The center-to-center distance between two disks is determined accurately by first measuring the over-all distance with a micrometer or vernier caliper, and then deducting the radius of each disk from the over-all dimension.

Sine-bar. — The sine-bar is used either for very accurate angular measurements or for locating work at a given angle as, for example, in surface grinding templets, gages, etc. The sine-bar is especially useful in measuring or checking angles when the limit of accuracy is 5 minutes or less. Some bevel protractors are equipped with verniers which read to 5 minutes but the setting depends upon the alignment of graduations whereas a sine-bar usually is located by positive contact with precision gage-blocks selected for whatever dimension is required for obtaining a given angle.

Types of Sine-bars. — A sine-bar consists of a hardened, ground and lapped steel bar which has very accurate cylindrical plugs of equal diameter attached to or near each end. The form illustrated by Fig. 1 has notched ends for receiving the cylindrical plugs which are held firmly against both faces of the notch. The standard center-to-center distance C between the plugs is either 5 or 10 inches. The upper and lower sides of sine-bars are parallel to the center line of the plugs within very close limits. The body of the sine-bar ordinarily has several holes through it to reduce the weight. In the making of the sine-bar shown in Fig. 2, if too much material is removed from one locating notch, regrinding the shoulder at the opposite end would make it possible to obtain the correct center distance. That is the reason for this change in form. The type of sine-bar illustrated by Fig. 3 has the cylindrical disks or plugs attached to one side. These differences in form or arrangement do not, of course, affect the principle governing the use of the sine-bar. An accurate surface plate or master flat is always used in conjunction with a sine-bar in order to form the base from which the vertical measurements are made.

Setting 5-inch Sine-bar to Given Angle. — Since many sine-bars have a length of 5 inches, the accompanying table of constants is based upon that length. These constants represent the vertical distances H for setting a 5-inch sine-bar to the required angle. Assume that the angle is 31° 20′; the table shows that height H

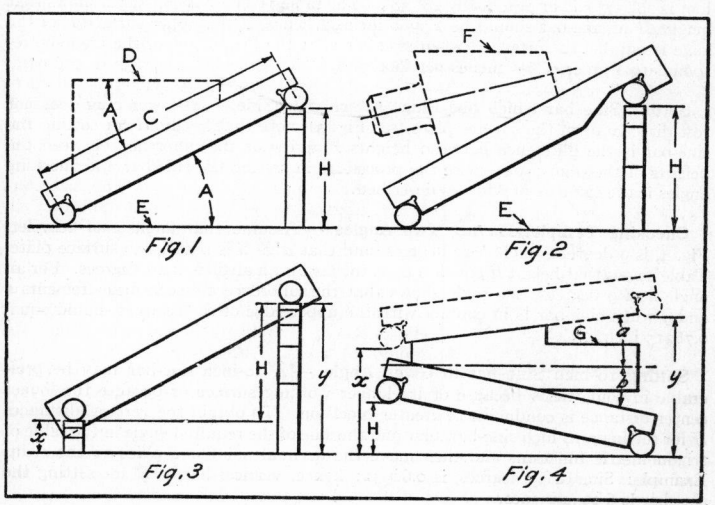

Fig. 1   Fig. 2   Fig. 3   Fig. 4

(Figs. 1, 2 and 3) should equal 2.6001 inches. Note: The constants in table equal five times sine of angle; thus the sine of 31° 20′ (see table of trigonometric functions) is 0.52002, and 0.52002 × 5 = 2.6001 inches.

Finding Angle when Height H of Sine-bar is Known. — In finding the angle equivalent to a given height H, the table of constants is used in reverse order. To illustrate, if the height H is 1.4061 inches, the angle to which the sine-bar is set is 16° 20′. (Note: In using the regular table of sines, divide height H by length of sine-bar, find sine equal to quotient and its angle; thus 1.4061 ÷ 5 = 0.2812. Table of sines shows that this is the sine of 16° 20′.)

Checking Angle of Templet or Gage by Using Sine-bar. — Place templet or gage on sine-bar as indicated by dotted lines, Fig. 1. Clamps may be used to hold work in place. Place upper end of sine-bar on gage-blocks having total height H corresponding to the required angle. If upper edge D of work is parallel with surface plate E, then angle A of work equals angle A to which sine-bar is set. Parallelism between edge D and surface plate may be tested by checking the height at each end with a dial gage or some indicating type of comparator.

Measuring Angle of Templet or Gage with Sine-bar. — Adjust height of gage-blocks and sine-bar until edge D, Fig. 1, of gage or templet is parallel with surface plate E; then find angle corresponding to height H of gage-blocks. For example, if height H is 2.5938 inches when D and E are parallel, the table of sine-bar constants shows that angle A of work is 31° 15′.

Checking Taper per Foot with Sine-bar. — As an example, assume that plug gage, Fig. 2, is supposed to have a taper of 6⅛ inches per foot and taper is to be checked by using a 5-inch sine-bar. The accompanying table, Tapers per Foot and Corresponding Angles, shows that the included angle for a taper of 6⅛ inches per foot is 28° 37′ 59″ or practically 28° 38′. The table of sine-bar constants shows that height H of sine-bar should be 2.3960 inches; hence, if the upper surface F of the gage is parallel to surface E when sine-bar is at the height given, the angle corresponds to a taper of 6⅛ inches per foot.

Setting Sine-bar which has Plugs Attached to Side. — If lower plug does not rest directly upon the surface plate (see Fig. 3), note that height H for setting the sine-bar is the difference between heights x and y or the difference between the heights of the plugs; otherwise the procedure in setting the sine-bar and checking angles is the same as previously described.

Checking Templet Having Two Angles. — Assume that angle a of templet, Fig. 4, is 9 degrees, angle b 12 degrees, and that edge G is parallel to surface plate. Table shows that height H equals 1.0395 inches for an angle b of 12 degrees. For an angle a of 9 degrees, the table shows that the difference between measurements x and y when sine-bar is in contact with the upper edge of the templet should equal 0.78215 inch.

Setting 10-inch Sine-bar to Given Angle. — A 10-inch sine-bar may be preferable in some cases because of its longer working surface or because the longer center distance is conducive to greater precision. To obtain the vertical distances H for setting a 10-inch sine-bar, first find the sine of the required angle in the table of trigonometric functions and then move the decimal point one place to the right. Example: Sine of 39 degrees, is 0.62932; hence, vertical height H for setting the sine-bar is 6.2932 inches.

Constants for Setting a 5-inch Sine-bar

Min.	0°	1°	2°	3°	4°	5°	6°	7°
0	0.00000	0.08725	0.17450	0.26170	0.34880	0.43580	0.52265	0.60935
1	.00145	.08870	.17595	.26315	.35025	.43720	.52410	.61080
2	.00290	.09015	.17740	.26460	.35170	.43865	.52555	.61225
3	.00435	.09160	.17885	.26605	.35315	.44010	.52700	.61370
4	.00580	.09310	.18030	.26750	.35460	.44155	.52845	.61510
5	0.00725	0.09455	.18175	0.26895	0.35605	.44300	0.52985	0.61655
6	.00875	.09600	.18320	.27040	.35750	.44445	.53130	.61800
7	.01020	.09745	.18465	.27185	.35895	.44590	.53275	.61945
8	.01165	.09890	.18615	.27330	.36040	.44735	.53420	.62090
9	.01310	.10035	.18760	.27475	.36185	.44880	.53565	.62235
10	0.01455	0.10180	0.18905	0.27620	0.36330	0.45025	0.53710	0.62380
11	.01600	.10325	.19050	.27765	.36475	.45170	.53855	.62520
12	.01745	.10470	.19195	.27910	.36620	.45315	.54000	.62665
13	.01890	.10615	.19340	.28055	.36765	.45460	.54145	.62810
14	.02035	.10760	.19485	.28200	.36910	.45605	.54290	.62955
15	0.02180	0.10905	.19630	0.28345	0.37055	.45750	0.54435	0.63100
16	.02325	.11055	.19775	.28490	.37200	.45895	.54580	.63245
17	.02475	.11200	.19920	.28635	.37345	.46040	.54725	.63390
18	.02620	.11345	.20065	.28780	.37490	.46185	.54865	.63530
19	.02765	.11490	.20210	.28925	.37635	.46330	.55010	.63675
20	0.02910	0.11635	0.20355	0.29070	0.37780	0.46475	0.55155	0.63820
21	.03055	.11780	.20500	.29220	.37925	.46620	.55300	.63965
22	.03200	.11925	.20645	.29365	.38070	.46765	.55445	.64110
23	.03345	.12070	.20795	.29510	.38215	.46910	.55590	.64255
24	.03490	.12215	.20940	.29655	.38360	.47055	.55735	.64400
25	0.03635	0.12360	.21085	0.29800	0.38505	.47200	0.55880	0.64540
26	.03780	.12505	.21230	.29945	.38650	.47345	.56025	.64685
27	.03925	.12650	.21375	.30090	.38795	.47490	.56170	.64830
28	.04070	.12800	.21520	.30235	.38940	.47635	.56315	.64975
29	.04220	.12945	.21665	.30380	.39085	.47780	.56455	.65120
30	0.04365	0.13090	0.21810	0.30525	0.39230	0.47925	0.56600	0.65265
31	.04510	.13235	.21955	.30670	.39375	.48070	.56745	.65405
32	.04655	.13380	.22100	.30815	.39520	.48210	.56890	.65550
33	.04800	.13525	.22245	.30960	.39665	.48355	.57035	.65695
34	.04945	.13670	.22390	.31105	.39810	.48500	.57180	.65840
35	0.05090	0.13815	.22535	0.31250	0.39955	.48645	0.57325	0.65985
36	.05235	.13960	.22680	.31395	.40100	.48790	.57470	66130
37	.05380	.14105	.22825	.31540	.40245	.48935	.57615	.66270
38	.05525	.14250	.22970	.31685	.40390	.49080	.57760	.66415
39	.05670	.14395	.23115	.31830	.40535	.49225	.57900	.66560
40	0.05820	0.14540	0.23265	0.31975	0.40680	0.49370	0.58045	0.66705
41	.05965	.14690	.23410	.32120	.40825	.49515	.58190	.66850
42	.06110	.14835	.23555	.32265	.40970	.49660	.58335	.66995
43	.06255	.14980	.23700	.32410	.41115	.49805	.58480	.67135
44	.06400	.15125	#23845	.32555	.41260	.49950	.58625	.67280
45	0.06545	0.15270	0.23990	0.32700	0.41405	0.50095	0.58770	0.67425
46	.06690	.15415	.24135	.32845	.41550	.50240	.58915	.67570
47	.06835	.15560	.24280	.32990	.41695	.50385	.59060	.67715
48	.06980	.15705	.24425	.33135	.41840	.50530	.59200	.67860
49	.07125	.15850	.24570	.33280	.41985	.50675	.59345	.68000
50	0.07270	0.15995	0.24715	0.33425	0.42130	0.50820	0.59490	0.68145
51	.07415	.16140	.24860	.33570	.42275	.50960	.59635	.68290
52	.07565	.16285	.25005	.33715	.42420	.51105	.59780	.68435
53	.07710	.16430	.25150	.33865	.42565	.51250	.59925	.68580
54	.07855	.16580	.25295	.34010	.42710	.51395	.60070	.68720
55	0.08000	0.16725	0.25440	0.34155	0.42855	.51540	0.60215	0.68865
56	.08145	.16870	.25585	.34300	.43000	.51685	.60355	.69010
57	.08290	.17015	.25730	.34445	.43145	.51830	.60500	.69155
58	.08435	.17160	.25875	.34590	.43290	.51975	.60645	.69300
59	.08580	.17305	.26028	.34735	.43435	.52120	.60790	.69445
60	0.08725	0.17450	0.26170	0.34880	0.43580	0.52265	0.60935	0.69585

Constants for Setting a 5-inch Sine-bar

Min.	8°	9°	10°	11°	12°	13°	14°	15°
0	0.69585	0.78215	0.86825	0.95405	1.0395	1.1247	1.2096	1.2941
1	.69730	.78360	.86965	.95545	.0410	.1261	.2110	.2955
2	.69875	.78505	.87110	.95690	.0424	.1276	.2124	.2969
3	.70020	.78650	.87255	.95835	.0438	.1290	.2138	.2983
4	.70165	.78790	.87395	.95975	.0452	.1304	.2152	.2997
5	0.70305	0.78935	0.87540	0.96120	1.0466	1.1318	1.2166	1.3011
6	.70450	.79080	.87685	.96260	0481	.1332	.2181	.3025
7	.70595	.79225	.87825	.96405	.0495	.1346	.2195	.3039
8	.70740	.79365	.87970	.96545	.0509	.1361	.2209	.3053
9	.70885	.79510	.88115	.96690	.0523	.1375	.2223	.3067
10	0.71025	0.79655	0.88255	0.96830	1.0538	1.1389	1.2237	1.3081
11	.71170	.79795	.88400	.96975	.0552	.1403	.2251	.3095
12	.71315	.79940	.88540	.97115	.0566	.1417	.2265	.3109
13	.71460	.80085	.88685	.97260	.0580	.1431	.2279	.3123
14	.71600	.80230	.88830	.97405	.0594	.1446	.2293	.3137
15	0.71745	0.80370	0.88970	0.97545	1.0609	1.1460	1.2307	1.3151
16	.71890	.80515	.89115	.97690	.0623	.1474	.2322	.3165
17	.72035	.80660	.89260	.97830	.0637	.1488	.2336	.3179
18	.72180	.80800	.89400	.97975	.0651	.1502	.2350	.3193
19	.72320	.80945	.89545	.98115	.0665	.1516	.2364	.3207
20	0.72465	0.81090	0.89685	0.98260	1.0680	1.1531	1.2378	1.3221
21	.72610	.81230	.89830	.98400	.0694	.1545	.2392	.3235
22	.72755	.81375	.89975	.98545	.0708	.1559	.2406	.3250
23	.72900	.81520	.90115	.98685	.0722	.1573	.2420	.3264
24	.73040	.81665	.90260	.98830	.0737	.1587	.2434	.3278
25	0.73185	0.81805	0.90405	0.98970	1.0751	1.1601	1.2448	1.3292
26	.73330	.81950	.90545	.99115	.0765	.1615	.2462	.3306
27	.73475	.82095	.90690	.99255	.0779	.1630	.2477	.3320
28	.73615	.82235	.90830	.99400	.0793	.1644	.2491	.3334
29	.73760	.82380	.90975	.99540	.0808	.1658	.2505	.3348
30	0.73905	0.82525	0.91120	0.99685	1.0822	1.1672	1.2519	1.3362
31	.74050	.82665	.91260	.99825	.0836	.1686	.2533	.3376
32	.74190	.82810	.91405	.99970	.0850	.1700	.2547	.3390
33	.74335	.82955	.91545	1.0011	.0864	.1714	.2561	.3404
34	.74480	.83100	.91690	.0026	.0879	.1729	.2575	.3418
35	0.74625	0.83240	0.91835	1.0039	1.0893	1.1743	1.2589	1.3432
36	.74770	.83385	.91975	.0054	.0907	.1757	.2603	.3446
37	.74910	.83530	.92120	.0068	.0921	.1771	.2617	.3460
38	.75055	.83670	.92260	.0082	.0935	.1785	.2631	.3474
39	.75200	.83815	.92405	.0096	.0949	.1799	.2645	.3488
40	0.75345	0.83960	0.92545	1.0110	1.0964	1.1813	1.2660	1.3502
41	.75485	.84100	.92690	.0125	.0978	.1828	.2674	.3516
42	.75630	.84245	.92835	.0139	.0992	.1842	.2688	.3530
43	.75775	.84390	.92975	.0153	.1006	.1856	.2702	.3544
44	.75920	.84530	.93120	.0168	.1020	.1870	.2716	.3558
45	0.76060	0.84675	0.93260	1.0182	1.1035	1.1884	1.2730	1.3572
46	.76205	.84820	.93405	.0196	.1049	.1898	.2744	.3586
47	.76350	.84960	.93550	.0210	.1063	.1912	.2758	.3600
48	.76495	.85105	.93690	.0225	.1077	.1926	.2772	.3614
49	.76635	.85250	.93835	.0239	.1091	.1941	.2786	.3628
50	0.76780	0.85390	0.93975	1.0253	1.1106	1.1955	1.2800	1.3642
51	.76925	.85535	.94120	.0267	.1120	.1969	.2814	.3656
52	.77070	.85680	.94260	.0281	.1134	.1983	.2828	.3670
53	.77210	.85820	.94405	.0296	.1148	.1997	.2842	.3684
54	.77355	.85965	.94550	.0310	.1162	.2011	.2856	.3698
55	0.77500	0.86110	0.94690	1.0324	1.1176	1.2025	1.2870	1.3712
56	.77645	.86250	.94835	.0338	.1191	.2039	.2884	.3726
57	.77785	.86395	.94975	.0353	.1205	.2054	.2899	.3740
58	.77930	.86540	.95120	.0367	.1219	.2068	.2913	.3754
59	.78075	.86680	.95260	.0381	.1233	.2082	.2927	.3768
60	0.78215	0.86825	0.95405	1.0395	1.1247	1.2096	1.2941	1.3782

Constants for Setting a 5-inch Sine-bar

Min.	16°	17°	18°	19°	20°	21°	22°	23°
0	1.3782	1.4618	1.5451	1.6278	1.7101	1.7918	1.8730	1.9536
1	.3796	.4632	.5464	.6292	.7114	.7932	.8744	.9550
2	.3810	.4646	.5478	.6306	.7128	.7945	.8757	.9563
3	.3824	.4660	.5492	.6319	.7142	.7959	.8771	.9576
4	.3838	.4674	.5506	.6333	.7155	.7972	.8784	.9590
5	1.3852	1.4688	.5520	1.6347	.7169	1.7986	1.8797	1.9603
6	.3865	.4702	.5534	.6361	.7183	.8000	.8811	.9617
7	.3879	.4716	.5547	.6374	.7196	.8013	.8824	.9630
8	.3893	.4730	.5561	.6388	.7210	.8027	.8838	.9643
9	.3907	.4743	.5575	.6402	.7224	.8040	.8851	.9657
10	1.3921	1.4757	1.5589	1.6416	1.7237	1.8054	1.8865	1.9670
11	.3935	.4771	.5603	.6429	.7251	.8067	.8878	.9683
12	.3949	.4785	.5616	.6443	.7265	.8081	.8892	.9697
13	.3963	.4799	.5630	.6457	.7278	.8094	.8905	.9710
14	.3977	.4813	.5644	.6471	.7292	.8108	.8919	.9724
15	1.3991	1.4827	.5658	1.6484	.7306	1.8122	1.8932	1.9737
16	.4005	.4841	.5672	.6498	.7319	.8135	.8946	.9750
17	.4019	.4855	.5686	.6512	.7333	.8149	.8959	.9764
18	.4033	.4868	.5699	.6525	.7347	.8162	.8973	.9777
19	.4047	.4882	.5713	.6539	.7360	.8176	.8986	.9790
20	1.4061	1.4896	1.5727	1.6553	1.7374	1.8189	1.8999	1.9804
21	.4075	.4910	.5741	.6567	.7387	.8203	.9013	.9817
22	.4089	.4924	.5755	.6580	.7401	.8217	.9026	.9830
23	.4103	.4938	.5768	.6594	.7415	.8230	.9040	.9844
24	.4117	.4952	.5782	.6608	.7428	.8244	.9053	.9857
25	1.4131	1.4966	1.5796	1.6622	1.7442	1.8257	1.9067	1.9870
26	.4145	.4980	.5810	.6635	.7456	.8271	.9080	.9884
27	.4159	.4993	.5824	.6649	.7469	.8284	.9094	.9897
28	.4173	.5007	.5837	.6663	.7483	.8298	.9107	.9911
29	.4187	.5021	.5851	.6676	.7496	.8311	.9120	.9924
30	1.4201	1.5035	1.5865	1.6690	1.7510	1.8325	1.9134	1.9937
31	.4214	.5049	.5879	.6704	.7524	.8338	.9147	.9951
32	.4228	.5063	.5893	.6718	.7537	.8352	.9161	.9964
33	.4242	.5077	.5906	.6731	.7551	.8365	.9174	.9977
34	.4256	.5091	.5920	.6745	.7565	.8379	.9188	.9991
35	1.4270	1.5104	1.5934	1.6759	1.7578	1.8392	1.9201	2.0004
36	.4284	.5118	.5948	.6772	.7592	.8406	.9215	.0017
37	.4298	.5132	.5961	.6786	.7605	.8419	.9228	.0031
38	.4312	.5146	.5975	.6800	.7619	.8433	.9241	.0044
39	.4326	.5160	.5989	.6813	.7633	.8447	.9255	.0057
40	1.4340	1.5174	1.6003	1.6827	1.7646	1.8460	1.9268	2.0070
41	.4354	.5188	.6017	.6841	.7660	.8474	.9282	.0084
42	.4368	.5201	.6030	.6855	.7673	.8487	.9295	.0097
43	.4382	.5215	.6044	.6868	.7687	.8501	.9308	.0110
44	.4396	.5229	.6058	.6882	.7701	.8514	.9322	.0124
45	1.4410	1.5243	1.6072	1.6896	1.7714	1.8528	1.9335	2.0137
46	.4423	.5257	.6085	.6909	.7728	.8541	.9349	.0150
47	.4437	.5271	.6099	.6923	.7742	.8555	.9362	.0164
48	.4451	.5285	.6113	.6937	.7755	.8568	.9376	.0177
49	.4465	.5298	.6127	.6950	.7769	.8582	.9389	.0190
50	1.4479	1.5312	1.6141	1.6964	1.7782	1.8595	1.9402	2.0204
51	.4493	.5326	.6154	.6978	.7796	.8609	.9416	.0217
52	.4507	.5340	.6168	.6991	.7809	.8622	.9429	.0230
53	.4521	.5354	.6182	.7005	.7823	.8636	.9443	.0244
54	.4535	.5368	.6196	.7019	.7837	.8649	.9456	.0257
55	1.4549	1.5381	1.6209	1.7032	1.7850	1.8663	1.9469	2.0270
56	.4563	.5395	.6223	.7046	.7864	.8676	.9483	.0283
57	.4577	.5409	.6237	.7060	.7877	.8690	.9496	.0297
58	.4591	.5423	.6251	.7073	.7891	.8703	.9510	.0310
59	.4604	.5437	.6264	.7087	.7905	.8717	.9523	.0323
60	1.4618	1.5451	1.6278	1.7101	1.7918	1.8730	1.9536	2.0337

Constants for Setting a 5-inch Sine-bar

Min.	24°	25°	26°	27°	28°	29°	30°	31°
0	2.0337	2.1131	2.1918	2.2699	2.3473	2.4240	2.5000	2.5752
1	.0350	.1144	.1931	.2712	.3486	.4253	.5012	.5764
2	.0363	.1157	.1944	.2725	.3499	.4266	.5025	.5777
3	.0376	.1170	.1958	.2738	.3512	.4278	.5038	.5789
4	.0390	.1183	.1971	.2751	.3525	.4291	.5050	.5802
5	2.0403	2.1197	.1984	2.2764	.3538	2.4304	2.5063	2.5814
6	.0416	.1210	.1997	.2777	.3550	.4317	.5075	.5826
7	.0430	.1223	.2010	.2790	.3563	.4329	.5088	.5839
8	.0443	.1236	.2023	.2803	.3576	.4342	.5100	.5851
9	.0456	.1249	.2036	.2816	.3589	.4355	.5113	.5864
10	2.0469	2.1262	2.2049	2.2829	2.3602	2.4367	2.5126	2.5876
11	.0483	.1276	.2062	.2842	.3614	.4380	.5138	.5889
12	.0496	.1289	.2075	.2855	.3627	.4393	.5151	.5901
13	.0509	.1302	.2088	.2868	.3640	.4405	.5163	.5914
14	.0522	.1315	.2101	.2881	.3653	.4418	.5176	.5926
15	2.0536	2.1328	2.2114	2.2893	2.3666	.4431	2.5188	2.5938
16	.0549	.1341	.2127	.2906	.3679	.4444	.5201	.5951
17	.0562	.1354	.2140	.2919	.3691	.4456	.5214	.5963
18	.0575	.1368	.2153	.2932	.3704	.4469	.5226	.5976
19	.0589	.1381	.2166	.2945	.3717	.4482	.5239	.5988
20	2.0602	2.1394	2.2179	2.2958	2.3730	2.4494	2.5251	2.6001
21	.0615	.1407	.2192	.2971	.3743	.4507	.5264	.6013
22	.0628	.1420	.2205	.2984	.3755	.4520	.5276	.6025
23	.0642	.1433	.2218	.2997	.3768	.4532	.5289	.6038
24	.0655	.1447	.2232	.3010	.3781	.4545	.5301	.6050
25	2.0668	2.1460	2.2245	2.3023	.3794	2.4558	2.5314	2.6063
26	.0681	.1473	.2258	.3036	.3807	.4570	.5327	.6075
27	.0695	.1486	.2271	.3048	.3819	.4583	.5339	.6087
28	.0708	.1499	.2284	.3061	.3832	.4596	.5352	.6100
29	.0721	.1512	.2297	.3074	.3845	.4608	.5364	.6112
30	2.0734	2.1525	2.2310	2.3087	2.3858	2.4621	2.5377	2.6125
31	.0748	.1538	.2323	.3100	.3870	.4634	.5389	.6137
32	.0761	.1552	.2336	.3113	.3883	.4646	.5402	.6149
33	.0774	.1565	.2349	.3126	.3896	.4659	.5414	.6162
34	.0787	.1578	.2362	.3139	.3909	.4672	.5427	.6174
35	.0801	2.1591	2.2375	2.3152	.3922	2.4684	2.5439	2.6187
36	.0814	.1604	.2388	.3165	.3934	.4697	.5452	.6199
37	.0827	.1617	.2401	.3177	.3947	.4709	.5464	.6211
38	.0840	.1630	.2414	.3190	.3960	.4722	.5477	.6224
39	.0853	.1643	.2427	.3203	.3973	.4735	.5489	.6236
40	2.0867	2.1656	2.2440	2.3216	2.3985	2.4747	2.5502	2.6249
41	.0880	.1670	.2453	.3229	.3998	.4760	.5514	.6261
42	.0893	.1683	.2466	.3242	.4011	.4773	.5527	.6273
43	.0906	.1696	.2479	.3255	.4024	.4785	.5539	.6286
44	.0920	.1709	.2492	.3268	.4036	.4798	.5552	.6298
45	.0933	2.1722	2.2505	2.3280	2.4049	2.4811	2.5564	2.6310
46	.0946	.1735	.2518	.3293	.4062	.4823	.5577	.6323
47	.0959	.1748	.2531	.3306	.4075	.4836	.5589	.6335
48	.0972	.1761	.2544	.3319	.4087	.4848	.5602	.6348
49	.0986	.1774	.2557	.3332	.4100	.4861	.5614	.6360
50	2.0999	2.1787	2.2570	2.3345	2.4113	2.4874	2.5627	2.6372
51	.1012	.1801	.2583	.3358	.4126	.4886	.5639	.6385
52	.1025	.1814	.2596	.3371	.4138	.4899	.5652	.6397
53	.1038	.1827	.2609	.3383	.4151	.4912	.5664	.6409
54	.1052	.1840	.2621	.3396	.4164	.4924	.5677	.6422
55	.1065	.1853	.2634	2.3409	.4177	2.4937	2.5689	2.6434
56	.1078	.1866	.2647	.3422	.4189	.4949	.5702	.6446
57	.1091	.1879	.2660	.3435	.4202	.4962	.5714	.6459
58	.1104	.1892	.2673	.3448	.4215	.4975	.5727	.6471
59	.1117	.1905	.2686	.3460	.4228	.4987	.5739	.6483
60	2.1131	2.1918	2.2699	2.3473	2.4240	2.5000	2.5752	2.6496

Constants for Setting a 5-inch Sine-bar

Min.	32°	33°	34°	35°	36°	37°	38°	39°
0	2.6496	2.7232	2.7959	2.8679	2.9389	3.0091	3.0783	3.1466
1	.6508	.7244	.7971	.8690	.9401	.0102	.0794	.1477
2	.6520	.7256	.7984	.8702	.9413	.0114	.0806	.1488
3	.6533	.7268	.7996	.8714	.9424	.0125	.0817	.1500
4	.6545	.7280	.8008	.8726	.9436	.0137	.0829	.1511
5	2.6557	2.7293	2.8020	2.8738	2.9448	3.0149	3.0840	3.1522
6	.6570	.7305	.8032	.8750	.9460	.0160	.0852	.1534
7	.6582	.7317	.8044	.8762	.9471	.0172	.0863	.1545
8	.6594	.7329	.8056	.8774	.9483	.0183	.0874	.1556
9	.6607	.7341	.8068	.8786	.9495	.0195	.0886	.1567
10	2.6619	2.7354	2.8080	2.8798	2.9507	3.0207	3.0897	3.1579
11	.6631	.7366	.8092	.8809	.9518	.0218	.0909	.1590
12	.6644	.7378	.8104	.8821	.9530	.0230	.0920	.1601
13	.6656	.7390	.8116	.8833	.9542	.0241	.0932	.1612
14	.6668	.7402	.8128	.8845	.9554	.0253	.0943	.1624
15	2.6680	2.7414	2.8140	2.8857	2.9565	3.0264	3.0954	3.1635
16	.6693	.7427	.8152	.8869	.9577	.0276	.0966	.1646
17	.6705	.7439	.8164	.8881	.9589	.0288	.0977	.1658
18	.6717	.7451	.8176	.8893	.9600	.0299	.0989	.1669
19	.6730	.7463	.8188	.8905	.9612	.0311	.1000	.1680
20	2.6742	2.7475	2.8200	2.8916	2.9624	3.0322	3.1012	3.1691
21	.6754	.7487	.8212	.8928	.9636	.0334	.1023	.1703
22	.6767	.7499	.8224	.8940	.9647	.0345	.1034	.1714
23	.6779	.7512	.8236	.8952	.9659	.0357	.1046	.1725
24	.6791	.7524	.8248	.8964	.9671	.0369	.1057	.1736
25	2.6803	2.7536	2.8260	2.8976	2.9682	3.0380	3.1069	3.1748
26	.6816	.7548	.8272	.8988	.9694	.0392	.1080	.1759
27	.6828	.7560	.8284	.8999	.9706	.0403	.1091	.1770
28	.6840	.7572	.8296	.9011	.9718	.0415	.1103	.1781
29	.6852	.7584	.8308	.9023	.9729	.0426	.1114	.1792
30	2.6865	2.7597	2.8320	2.9035	2.9741	3.0438	3.1125	3.1804
31	.6877	.7609	.8332	.9047	.9753	.0449	.1137	.1815
32	.6889	.7621	.8344	.9059	.9764	.0461	.1148	.1826
33	.6902	.7633	.8356	.9070	.9776	.0472	.1160	.1837
34	.6914	.7645	.8368	.9082	.9788	.0484	.1171	.1849
35	2.6926	2.7657	2.8380	2.9094	2.9799	3.0495	3.1182	3.1860
36	.6938	.7669	.8392	.9106	.9811	.0507	.1194	.1871
37	.6951	.7681	.8404	.9118	.9823	.0519	.1205	.1882
38	.6963	.7694	.8416	.9130	.9834	.0530	.1216	.1893
39	.6975	.7706	.8428	.9141	.9846	.0542	.1228	.1905
40	2.6987	2.7718	2.8440	2.9153	2.9858	3.0553	3.1239	3.1916
41	.7000	.7730	.8452	.9165	.9869	.0565	.1251	.1927
42	.7012	.7742	.8464	.9177	.9881	.0576	.1262	.1938
43	.7024	.7754	.8476	.9189	.9893	.0588	.1273	.1949
44	.7036	.7766	.8488	.9200	.9904	.0599	.1285	.1961
45	2.7048	2.7778	2.8500	2.9212	2.9916	3.0611	3.1296	3.1972
46	.7061	.7790	.8512	.9224	.9928	.0622	.1307	.1983
47	.7073	.7802	.8523	.9236	.9939	.0634	.1319	.1994
48	.7085	.7815	.8535	.9248	.9951	.0645	.1330	.2005
49	.7097	.7827	.8547	.9259	.9963	.0657	.1341	.2016
50	2.7110	2.7839	2.8559	2.9271	2.9974	3.0668	3.1353	3.2028
51	.7122	.7851	.8571	.9283	.9986	.0680	.1364	.2039
52	.7134	.7863	.8583	.9295	.9997	.0691	.1375	.2050
53	.7146	.7875	.8595	.9307	3.0009	.0703	.1387	.2061
54	.7158	.7887	.8607	.9318	.0021	.0714	.1398	.2072
55	2.7171	2.7899	2.8619	2.9330	3.0032	3.0725	3.1409	3.2083
56	.7183	.7911	.8631	.9342	.0044	.0737	.1421	.2095
57	.7195	.7923	.8643	.9354	.0056	.0748	.1432	.2106
58	.7207	.7935	.8655	.9365	.0067	.0760	.1443	.2117
59	.7220	.7947	.8667	.9377	.0079	.0771	.1454	.2128
60	2.7232	2.7959	2.8679	2.9389	3.0091	3.0783	3.1466	3.2139

Constants for Setting a 5-inch Sine-bar

Min.	40°	41°	42°	43°	44°	45°	46°	47°
0	3.2139	3.2803	3.3456	3.4100	3.4733	3.5355	3.5967	3.6567
1	.2150	.2814	.3467	.4110	.4743	.5365	.5977	.6577
2	.2161	.2825	.3478	.4121	.4754	.5376	.5987	.6587
3	.2173	.2836	.3489	.4132	.4764	.5386	.5997	.6597
4	.2184	.2847	.3499	.4142	.4774	.5396	.6007	.6607
5	3.2195	3 2858	3.3510	3.4153	.4785	3.5406	3.6017	3.6617
6	.2206	.2869	.3521	.4163	.4795	.5417	.6027	.6627
7	.2217	.2879	.3532	.4174	.4806	.5427	.6037	.6637
8	.2228	.2890	.3543	.4185	.4816	.5437	.6047	.6647
9	.2239	.2901	.3553	.4195	.4827	.5448	.6058	.6657
10	3.2250	3.2912	3.3564	3.4206	.4837	3.5458	3.6068	3.6666
11	.2262	.2923	.3575	.4217	.4848	.5468	.6078	.6676
12	.2273	.2934	.3586	.4227	.4858	.5478	.6088	.6686
13	.2284	.2945	.3597	.4238	.4868	.5489	.6098	.6696
14	.2295	.2956	.3607	.4248	.4879	.5499	.6108	.6706
15	3.2306	3.2967	3.3618	3.4259	.4889	3.5509	3.6118	3.6716
16	.2317	.2978	.3629	.4269	.4900	.5519	.6128	.6726
17	.2328	.2989	.3640	.4280	.4910	.5529	.6138	.6736
18	.2339	.3000	.3650	.4291	.4921	.5540	.6148	.6745
19	.2350	.3011	.3661	.4301	.4931	.5550	.6158	.6755
20	3.2361	3.3022	3.3672	3.4312	.4941	3.5560	3.6168	3.6765
21	.2373	.3033	.3683	.4322	.4952	.5570	.6178	.6775
22	.2384	.3044	.3693	.4333	.4962	.5581	.6188	.6785
23	.2395	.3054	.3704	.4344	.4973	.5591	.6198	.6795
24	.2406	.3065	.3715	.4354	.4983	.5601	.6208	.6805
25	3.2417	3.3076	3.3726	3.4365	.4993	3.5611	3.6218	3.6814
26	.2428	.3087	.3736	.4375	.5004	.5621	.6228	.6824
27	.2439	.3098	.3747	.4386	.5014	.5632	.6238	.6834
28	.2450	.3109	.3758	.4396	.5024	.5642	.6248	.6844
29	.2461	.3120	.3769	.4407	.5035	.5652	.6258	.6854
30	3.2472	3.3131	3.3779	3.4417	.5045	3.5662	3.6268	3.6864
31	.2483	.3142	.3790	.4428	.5056	.5672	.6278	.6873
32	.2494	.3153	.3801	.4439	.5066	.5683	.6288	.6883
33	.2505	.3163	.3811	.4449	.5076	.5693	.6298	.6893
34	.2516	.3174	.3822	.4460	.5087	.5703	.6308	.6903
35	3.2527	3.3185	3.3833	3.4470	.5097	3.5713	3.6318	3.6913
36	.2538	.3196	.3844	.4481	.5107	.5723	.6328	.6923
37	.2550	.3207	.3854	.4491	.5118	.5734	.6338	.6932
38	.2561	.3218	.3865	.4502	.5128	.5744	.6348	.6942
39	.2572	.3229	.3876	.4512	.5138	.5754	.6358	.6952
40	3.2583	3.3240	3.3886	3.4523	.5149	3.5764	3.6368	3.6962
41	.2594	.3250	.3897	.4533	.5159	.5774	.6378	.6972
42	.2605	.3261	.3908	.4544	.5169	.5784	.6388	.6981
43	.2616	.3272	.3918	.4554	.5180	.5795	.6398	.6991
44	.2627	.3283	.3929	.4565	.5190	.5805	.6408	.7001
45	3.2638	3.3294	3.3940	3.4575	.5200	3.5815	3.6418	3.7011
46	.2649	.3305	.3950	.4586	.5211	.5825	.6428	.7020
47	.2660	.3316	.3961	.4596	.5221	.5835	.6438	.7030
48	.2671	.3326	.3972	.4607	.5231	.5845	.6448	.7040
49	.2682	.3337	.3982	.4617	.5242	.5855	.6458	.7050
50	3.2693	3.3348	3.3993	3.4628	.5252	3.5866	3.6468	3.7060
51	.2704	.3359	.4004	.4638	.5262	.5876	.6478	.7069
52	.2715	.3370	.4014	.4649	.5273	.5886	.6488	.7079
53	.2726	.3381	.4025	.4659	.5283	.5896	.6498	.7089
54	.2737	.3391	.4036	.4670	.5293	.5906	.6508	.7099
55	3.2748	3.3402	3.4046	3.4680	.5304	3.5916	3.6518	3.7108
56	.2759	.3413	.4057	.4691	.5314	.5926	.6528	.7118
57	.2770	.3424	.4068	.4701	.5324	.5936	.6538	.7128
58	.2781	.3435	.4078	.4712	.5335	.5947	.6548	.7138
59	.2792	.3445	.4089	.4722	.5345	.5957	.6558	.7147
60	3.2803	3.3456	3.4100	3.4733	3.5355	3.5967	3.6567	3.7157

Constants for Setting a 5-inch Sine-bar

Min.	48°	49°	50°	51°	52°	53°	54°.	55°
0	3.7157	3.7735	3.8302	3.8857	3.9400	3.9932	4.0451	4.0957
1	.7167	.7745	.8311	.8866	.9409	.9940	.0459	.0966
2	.7176	.7754	.8321	.8875	.9418	.9949	.0468	.0974
3	.7186	.7764	.8330	.8884	.9427	.9958	.0476	.0982
4	.7196	.7773	.8339	.8894	.9436	.9967	.0485	.0991
5	3.7206	3.7783	3.8349	3.8903	3.9445	3.9975	4.0493	4.0999
6	.7215	.7792	.8358	.8912	.9454	.9984	.0502	.1007
7	.7225	.7802	.8367	.8921	.9463	.9993	.0510	.1016
8	.7235	.7811	.8377	.8930	.9472	4.0001	.0519	.1024
9	.7244	.7821	.8386	.8939	.9481	.0010	.0527	.1032
10	3.7254	3.7830	3.8395	3.8948	3.9490	4.0019	4.0536	4.1041
11	.7264	.7840	.8405	.8958	.9499	.0028	.0544	.1049
12	.7274	.7850	.8414	.8967	.9508	.0036	.0553	.1057
13	.7283	.7859	.8423	.8976	.9516	.0045	.0561	.1066
14	.7293	.7869	.8433	.8985	.9525	.0054	.0570	.1074
15	3.7303	3.7878	3.8442	3.8994	3.9534	4.0062	4.0578	4.1082
16	.7312	.7887	.8451	.9003	.9543	.0071	.0587	.1090
17	.7322	.7897	.8460	.9012	.9552	.0080	.0595	.1099
18	.7332	.7906	.8470	.9021	.9561	.0089	.0604	.1107
19	.7341	.7916	.8479	.9030	9570	.0097	.0612	.1115
20	3.7351	3.7925	3.8488	3.9039	3.9579	4.0106	4.0621	4.1124
21	.7361	.7935	.8498	.9049	.9588	.0115	.0629	.1132
22	.7370	.7944	.8507	.9058	.9596	.0123	.0638	.1140
23	.7380	.7954	.8516	.9067	.9605	.0132	.0646	.1148
24	.7390	.7963	.8525	.9076	.9614	.0141	.0655	.1157
25	3.7399	3.7973	3.8535	3.9085	3.9623	4.0149	4.0663	4.1165
26	.7409	.7982	.8544	.9094	.9632	.0158	.0672	.1173
27	.7419	.7992	.8553	.9103	.9641	.0167	.0680	.1181
28	.7428	.8001	.8562	.9112	.9650	.0175	.0689	.1190
29	.7438	.8011	.8572	.9121	.9659	.0184	.0697	.1198
30	3.7448	3.8020	3.8581	3.9130	3.9667	4.0193	4.0706	4.1206
31	.7457	.8029	.8590	.9139	.9676	.0201	.0714	.1214
32	.7467	.8039	.8599	.9148	.9685	.0210	.0722	.1223
33	.7476	.8048	.8609	.9157	.9694	.0219	.0731	.1231
34	.7486	.8058	.8618	.9166	.9703	.0227	.0739	.1239
35	3.7496	3.8067	3.8627	3.9175	3.9712	4.0236	4.0748	4.1247
36	.7505	.8077	.8636	.9184	.9720	.0244	.0756	.1255
37	.7515	.8086	.8646	.9193	.9729	.0253	.0765	.1264
38	.7525	.8096	.8655	.9202	.9738	.0262	.0773	.1272
39	.7534	.8105	.8664	.9212	.9747	.0270	.0781	.1280
40	3.7544	3.8114	3.8673	3.9221	3.9756	4.0279	4.0790	4.1288
41	.7553	.8124	.8683	.9230	.9765	.0288	.0798	.1296
42	.7563	.8133	.8692	.9239	.9773	.0296	.0807	.1305
43	.7573	.8143	.8701	.9248	.9782	.0305	.0815	.1313
44	.7582	.8152	.8710	.9257	.9791	.0313	.0823	.1321
45	3.7592	3.8161	3.8719	3.9266	3.9800	4.0322	4.0832	4.1329
46	.7601	.8171	.8729	.9275	.9809	.0331	.0840	.1337
47	.7611	.8180	.8738	.9284	.9817	.0339	.0849	.1346
48	.7620	.8190	.8747	.9293	.9826	.0348	.0857	.1354
49	.7630	.8199	.8756	.9302	.9835	.0356	.0865	.1362
50	3.7640	3.8208	3.8765	3.9311	3.9844	4.0365	4.0874	4.1370
51	.7649	.8218	.8775	.9320	.9853	.0374	.0882	.1378
52	.7659	.8227	.8784	.9329	.9861	.0382	.0891	.1386
53	.7668	.8236	.8793	.9338	.9870	.0391	.0899	.1395
54	.7678	.8246	.8802	.9347	.9879	.0399	.0907	.1403
55	3.7687	3.8255	3.8811	3.9355	3.9888	4.0408	4.0916	4.1411
56	.7697	.8265	.8820	.9364	.9896	.0416	.0924	.1419
57	.7707	.8274	.8830	.9373	.9905	.0425	.0932	.1427
58	.7716	.8283	.8839	.9382	.9914	.0433	.0941	.1435
59	.7726	.8293	.8848	.9391	.9923	.0442	.0949	.1443
60	3.7735	3.8302	3.8857	3.9400	3.9932	4.0451	4.0957	4.1452

To Lay Out Angles Accurately. — Angles can be laid out accurately without the use of a protractor, provided a table of natural tangents is available. *Example:* A line is to be drawn at an angle of 29 degrees 54 minutes with another line, as

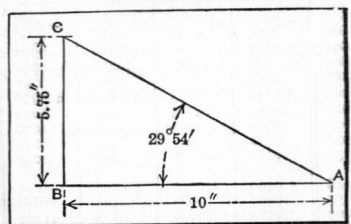

shown in the illustration. First draw a line AB of indefinite length, and then erect a perpendicular BC at a distance from A of, say 10 inches; then find in a table the tangent of 29 degrees 54 minutes, which equals 0.57503 for a radius of 1; hence, BC equals 0.57503 × 10 = 5.7503, or 5¾ inches. Measure 5¾ inches from B to C, at right angles to line AB, and draw a line from A to C, thus obtaining the required angle. Conversely, the angularity of two lines can be determined by measuring line BC and dividing by length AB; the quotient equals the tangent; then find the corresponding angle.

This method of laying out or measuring angles will give more accurate results than an ordinary protractor.

Measuring Dovetail Slides. — Dovetail slides which must be machined accurately to a given width are commonly gaged by using pieces of cylindrical rod or wire and measuring as indicated by the dimensions x and y of the accompanying

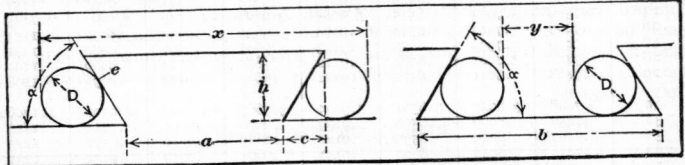

illustrations. To obtain dimension x for measuring male dovetails, add 1 to the cotangent of one-half the dovetail angle α, multiply by diameter D of the rods used, and add the product to dimension a. To obtain dimension y for measuring a female dovetail, add 1 to the cotangent of one-half the dovetail angle α, multiply by diameter D of the rod used, and subtract the result from dimension b. Expressing these rules as formulas:

$$x = D\ (1 + \cot \tfrac{1}{2}\, \alpha) + a.$$
$$y = b - D\ (1 + \cot \tfrac{1}{2}\, \alpha).$$

Dimension c equals $h \times \cot \alpha$.

The rod or wire used should be small enough so that the point of contact e is somewhat below the corner or edge of the dovetail.

Taper Turning with Combined Feeds. — When it is necessary to machine, on the boring mill, a conical surface which has such a large included angle that the tool-bar cannot be swiveled far enough to permit turning by the usual method, the combined vertical and horizontal feeds are sometimes used to obtain the required taper. Suppose a conical casting is to be turned to an angle α of 30 degrees (see illustration), and that the tool-head of the boring mill feeds horizontally ¼ inch per turn of the screw and has a vertical movement of ⁹⁄₁₆ inch per turn of the vertical feed shaft. If the two feeds are used simultaneously with the tool-bar at right angles to the table, the tool will move a distance h of eight inches, while it moves downward a distance of six inches, thus turning the surface to an angle β. This angle β is greater than the required angle α, but if the tool-bar is swiveled to an angle γ, the tool, as it moves downward, will be advanced horizontally in addition to the regular horizontal feeding movement. Hence, if the tool-bar is set over to the proper angle γ, the surface can be turned to an angle α. The problem, then,

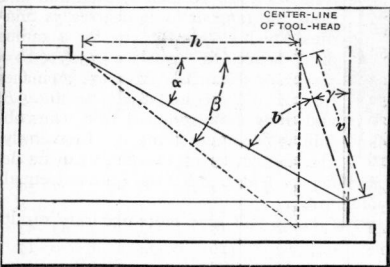

is to determine what the angle γ should be for turning to a given angle α.

Angle γ can be calculated as follows: $\sin b = \dfrac{\sin \alpha \times h}{v}$ in which h represents the rate of horizontal feed and v the rate of vertical feed. Having angles α and b, the desired angle γ is obtained by subtracting the sum of the former angles from 90 degrees. To illustrate (using the values given in the foregoing) the sine of 30 degrees is 0.5; then,

$$\sin b = \frac{0.5 \times \frac{1}{4}}{\frac{8}{16}} = 0.6666.$$ Hence, angle $b = 41$ degrees 48 minutes and $\gamma = 90°$ − $(30° + 41° \ 48') = 18$ degrees 12 minutes. If angle α were greater than angle β obtained from the combined feeds with the tool-bar in the vertical position, it would be necessary to swing the lower end of the bar to the left rather than to the right of the vertical plane; that is, the lower end of the bar would be inclined to the left of the vertical an amount equal to the sum of angles α and b subtracted from 90 degrees.

Rules for Figuring Tapers

Given	To Find	Rule
The taper per foot.	The taper per inch.	Divide the taper per foot by 12.
The taper per inch.	The taper per foot.	Multiply the taper per inch by 12.
End diameters and length of taper in inches.	The taper per foot.	Subtract small diameter from large; divide by length of taper, and multiply quotient by 12.
Large diameter and length of taper in inches, and taper per foot.	Diameter at small end in inches.	Divide taper per foot by 12; multiply by length of taper, and subtract result from large diameter.
Small diameter and length of taper in inches, and taper per foot.	Diameter at large end in inches.	Divide taper per foot by 12; multiply by length of taper, and add result to small diameter.
The taper per foot and two diameters in inches.	Distance between two given diameters in inches.	Subtract small diameter from large; divide remainder by taper per foot, and multiply quotient by 12.
The taper per foot.	Amount of taper in a certain length given in inches.	Divide taper per foot by 12; multiply by given length of tapered part.

Tapers per Foot and Corresponding Angles

Taper per Foot	Included Angle			Angle with Center Line			Taper per Foot	Included Angle			Angle with Center Line		
1/64	0°	4'	28"	0°	2'	14"	1 7/8	8°	56'	2"	4°	28'	1"
1/32	0	8	58	0	4	29	1 15/16	9	13	51	4	36	56
1/16	0	17	53	0	8	57	2	9	31	37	4	45	49
3/32	0	26	52	0	13	26	2 1/8	10	7	11	5	3	35
1/8	0	35	47	0	17	54	2 1/4	10	42	41	5	21	21
5/32	0	44	45	0	22	23	2 3/8	11	18	12	5	39	6
3/16	0	53	44	0	26	52	2 1/2	11	53	38	5	56	49
7/32	1	2	39	0	31	20	2 5/8	12	29	2	6	14	31
1/4	1	11	38	0	35	49	2 3/4	13	4	25	6	32	13
9/32	1	20	33	0	40	16	2 7/8	13	39	44	6	49	52
5/16	1	29	31	0	44	46	3	14	15	0	7	7	30
1 1/32	1	38	30	0	49	15	3 1/8	14	50	15	7	25	8
3/8	1	47	25	0	53	42	3 1/4	15	25	27	7	42	43
13/32	1	56	24	0	58	12	3 3/8	16	0	34	8	0	17
7/16	2	5	18	1	2	39	3 1/2	16	35	41	8	17	50
15/32	2	14	17	1	7	8	3 5/8	17	10	42	8	35	21
1/2	2	23	12	1	11	36	3 3/4	17	45	40	8	52	50
17/32	2	32	10	1	16	5	3 7/8	18	20	35	9	10	18
9/16	2	41	7	1	20	34	4	18	55	31	9	27	45
19/32	2	50	4	1	25	2	4 1/8	19	30	18	9	45	9
5/8	2	59	3	1	29	31	4 1/4	20	5	1	10	2	31
21/32	3	7	57	1	33	59	4 3/8	20	39	44	10	19	52
11/16	3	16	56	1	38	28	4 1/2	21	14	20	10	37	10
23/32	3	25	51	1	42	55	4 5/8	21	48	55	10	54	28
3/4	3	34	48	1	47	24	4 3/4	22	23	27	11	11	43
25/32	3	43	44	1	51	52	4 7/8	22	57	50	11	28	55
13/16	3	52	42	1	56	21	5	23	32	12	11	46	6
27/32	4	1	38	2	0	49	5 1/8	24	6	28	12	3	14
7/8	4	10	32	2	5	16	5 1/4	24	40	43	12	20	21
29/32	4	19	31	2	9	46	5 3/8	25	14	50	12	37	25
15/16	4	28	26	2	14	13	5 1/2	25	48	53	12	54	27
31/32	4	37	25	2	18	42	5 5/8	26	22	52	13	11	26
1	4	46	19	2	23	10	5 3/4	26	56	48	13	28	24
1 1/16	5	4	12	2	32	6	5 7/8	27	30	35	13	45	18
1 1/8	5	22	2	2	41	1	6	28	4	20	14	2	10
1 3/16	5	39	55	2	49	58	6 1/8	28	37	59	14	19	0
1 1/4	5	57	45	2	58	53	6 1/4	29	11	36	14	35	48
1 5/16	6	15	38	3	7	49	6 3/8	29	45	4	14	52	32
1 3/8	6	33	29	3	16	44	6 1/2	30	18	28	15	9	14
1 7/16	6	51	21	3	25	41	6 5/8	30	51	49	15	25	55
1 1/2	7	9	10	3	34	35	6 3/4	31	25	2	15	42	31
1 9/16	7	27	0	3	43	30	6 7/8	31	58	11	15	59	5
1 5/8	7	44	49	3	52	24	7	32	31	14	16	15	37
1 11/16	8	2	38	4	1	19	7 1/8	33	4	10	16	32	5
1 3/4	8	20	28	4	10	14	7 1/4	33	37	3	16	48	32
1 13/16	8	38	17	4	19	8	7 3/8	34	9	49	17	4	55

Accurate Measurement of Angles and Tapers. — When great accuracy is required in the measurement of angles, or when originating tapers, disks are commonly used. The principle of the disk method of taper measurement is that if two disks of unequal diameters are placed either in contact or a certain distance apart, lines tangent to their peripheries will represent an angle or taper, the degree of which depends upon the diameters of the two disks and the distance between them. The

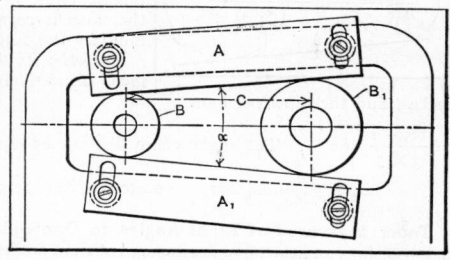

gage shown in the accompanying illustration, which is a form commonly used for originating tapers or measuring angles accurately, is set by means of disks. This gage consists of two adjustable straight-edges A and A_1, which are in contact with disks B and B_1. The angle α or the taper between the straight-edges depends, of course, upon the diameters of the disks and the center distance C, and as these three dimensions can be measured accurately, it is possible to set the gage to a given angle within very close limits. Moreover, if a record of the three dimensions is kept, the exact setting of the gage can be reproduced quickly at any time. The following rules may be used for adjusting a gage of this type, and cover all problems likely to arise in practice. Disks are also occasionally used for the setting of parts in angular positions for accurately machining them to a given angle; the rules will be found applicable to these conditions also.

To Find Angle for Given Taper per Foot. — When the taper in inches per foot is known, and the corresponding angle α is required. *Rule:* Divide the

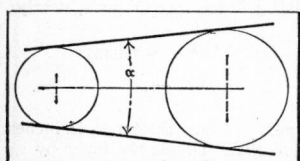

taper in inches per foot by 24; find the angle corresponding to the quotient, in a table of tangents, and double this angle.

Example: What angle α is equivalent to a taper of 1½ inch per foot?

$\dfrac{1.5}{24} = 0.0625$. The angle whose tangent is 0.0625 equals 3 degrees 35 minutes, nearly; then, 3 deg. 35 min. × 2 = 7 deg. 10 min.

To Find Angle for Given Disk Dimensions. — When the diameters D and d of the large and small disks and the center distance are given, to determine the angle α. *Rule:* Divide the difference between the disk diameters by twice the center distance; find the angle corresponding to the quotient, in a table of sines, and double the angle.

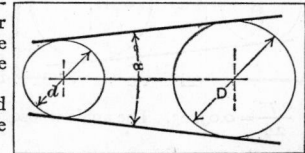

Example: If the disk diameters are 1 and 1.5 inch, respectively, and the center distance is 5 inches, find the included angle α.

$\dfrac{1.5 - 1}{2 \times 5} = 0.05$. The angle whose sine is 0.05 equals 2 degrees 52 minutes; then, 2 deg. 52 min. × 2 = 5 deg. 44 min. = angle α.

To Find the Taper per Foot. — When the diameters D and d of the large and small disks and the center distance C are given, to determine the taper per foot (measured at right angles to line through disk centers). *Rule:* Divide the difference between the disk diameters by twice the center distance; find the angle corresponding to the quotient, in a table of sines; then find the tangent corresponding to this angle, and multiply the tangent by 24.

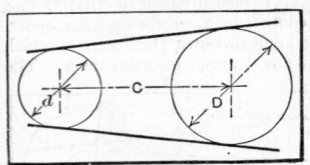

Example: If disk diameters are 1 and 1.5 inch, respectively, and center distance is 5 inches, find the taper per foot.

$$\frac{1.5 - 1}{2 \times 5} = 0.05.$$ The angle whose sine is 0.05 equals 2 degrees 52 minutes;

$$\tan 2° \ 52' = 0.05007; \qquad 0.05007 \times 24 = 1.2017 \text{ inch taper per foot.}$$

Taper Measured at Right Angles to One Side. — When one side is taken as a base line, and the taper is measured at right angles to that side, use the following rule for determining the taper per foot. *Rule:* Divide the difference between the disk diameters D and d by twice the center distance C; find the angle corresponding to the quotient, in a table of sines; double this angle and find the corresponding tangent; then multiply the tangent by 12.

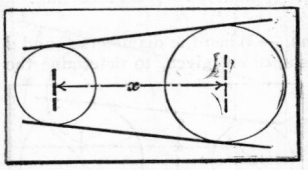

Example: If the disk diameters are 2 and 3 inches, respectively, and the center distance is 5 inches, what is the taper per foot measured at right angles to one side?

$$\frac{3 - 2}{2 \times 5} = 0.1.$$ The angle whose sine is 0.1 equals 5 degrees 45 minutes, **nearly;**

then, 2×5 deg. 45 min. $= 11$ deg. 30 min.; $\tan 11° \ 30' = 0.20345$;

$$0.20345 \times 12 = 2.4414 \text{ inches taper per foot.}$$

To Find Center Distance for a Given Taper. — When the taper, in inches per foot, is given, to determine center distance x. *Rule:* Divide the taper by 24 and find the angle corresponding to the quotient in a table of tangents; then find the sine corresponding to this angle and divide the difference between the disk diameters by twice the sine.

Example: Gage is to be set to ¾ inch per foot, and disk diameters are 1.25 and 1.5 inch, respectively. Find the required center distance for the disks.

$$\frac{0.75}{24} = 0.03125.$$ The angle whose tangent is 0.03125 equals 1 degree 47.4 minutes;

$$\sin 1° \ 47.4' = 0.03123; \qquad 1.50 - 1.25 = 0.25 \text{ inch;}$$

$$\frac{0.25}{2 \times 0.03123} = 4.002 \text{ inches} = \text{center distance } x.$$

To Find Center Distance for a Given Angle. — When straight-edges must be set to a given angle α, to determine center distance x between disks of known diameter. *Rule:* Find the sine of half the angle α in a table of sines; divide the difference between the disk diameters by double this sine.

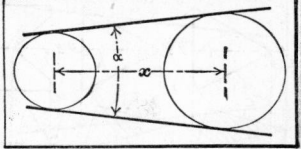

Example: If an angle α of 20 degrees is required, and the disks are 1 and 3 inches in diameter, respectively, find the required center distance x.

$$\frac{20}{2} = 10 \text{ degrees}; \quad \sin 10° = 0.17365;$$

$$\frac{3 - 1}{2 \times 0.17365} = 5.759 \text{ inches} = \text{center distance } x.$$

Center Distance when Taper is Measured from One Side. — When taper is measured at right angles to one side, use the following rule for determining the center distance x.

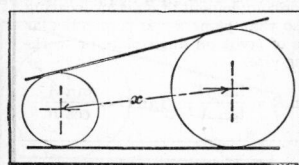

Rule: Divide the taper in inches per foot by 12; find the angle corresponding to the quotient, in a table of tangents; find the sine of one-half this angle, and then divide the difference between the disk diameters by double the sine.

Example: If taper measured at right angles to one side is 6.9 inches per foot, and the disks are 2 and 5 inches in diameter, respectively, what is center distance x?

$\dfrac{6.9}{12} = 0.575$. The angle whose tangent is 0.575 equals 29 degrees 54 minutes;

then, $\dfrac{29 \text{ deg. } 54 \text{ min.}}{2} = 14 \text{ deg. } 57 \text{ min}; \quad \sin 14° 57' = 0.25798;$

$$\frac{5 - 2}{2 \times 0.25798} = 5.814 \text{ inches, center distance.}$$

Angular Measurements with Disks in Contact. — When the two disks are to be in contact and the diameter of the small disk is known, the diameter D of the large disk for a given angle α can be obtained as follows. *Rule:* Multiply twice the diameter of the small disk by the sine of one-half the required angle; divide this product by 1 minus the sine of one-half the required angle; add the quotient to the diameter of the small disk to obtain the diameter of the large disk.

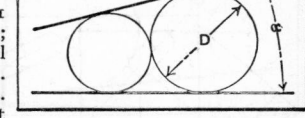

Example: The required angle α is 15 degrees. Find diameter of large disk, to be in contact with a standard 1-inch reference disk.

$$\sin 7° 30' = 0.13053. \quad 2 \times 1 \times 0.13053 = 0.26106;$$

$$\frac{0.26106}{1 - 0.13053} = 0.3002. \quad 1 + 0.3002 = 1.3002 = \text{diameter of large disk.}$$

Formulas for Compound Angles

C = compound angle in plane x-x and is the resultant of angles A and B

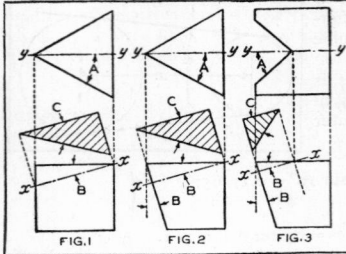

FIG. 1　　　FIG. 2　　　FIG. 3

For given angles A and B, find the resultant angle C in plane x-x. Angle B is measured in vertical plane y-y of midsection.

(Fig. 1) $\text{Tan } C = \tan A \times \cos B$

(Fig. 2) $\text{Tan } C = \dfrac{\tan A}{\cos B}$

(Fig. 3) (Same formula as for Fig. 2)

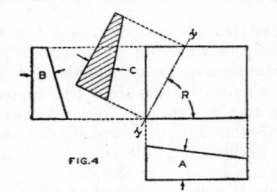

FIG. 4

Fig. 4. In machining plate to angles A and B, it is held at angle C in plane x-x. Angle of rotation R in plane parallel to base (or complement of R) is for locating plate so that plane x-x is perpendicular to axis of pivot on angle-plate or work-holding vise.

$$\text{Tan } R = \frac{\tan B}{\tan A} ; \quad \text{Tan } C = \frac{\tan A}{\cos R}$$

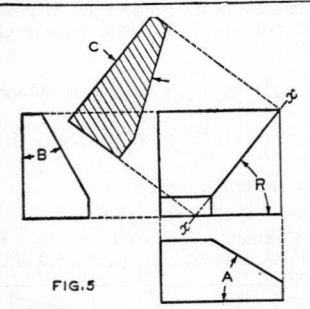

FIG. 5

Fig. 5. Angle R in plane parallel to base is angle from plane x-x to side having angle A.

$$\text{Tan } R = \frac{\cot B}{\cot A}$$

$$\text{Cot } C = \sqrt{\cot^2 A + \cot^2 B}$$

Compound angle C is angle in plane x-x from base to corner formed by intersection of planes inclined to angles A and B. This formula for C may be used to find cot of complement of C_1, Fig. 6.

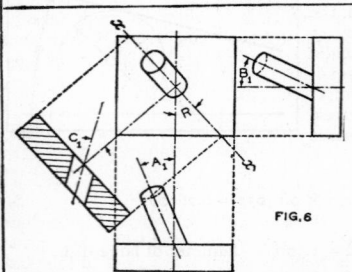

FIG. 6

Fig. 6. Angles A_1 and B_1 are measured in vertical planes of front and side elevations. Plane x-x is located by angle R from center-line or from plane of angle B_1.

$$\text{Tan } C_1 = \sqrt{\tan^2 A_1 + \tan^2 B_1}$$

$$\text{Tan } R = \frac{\tan A_1}{\tan B_1}$$

The resultant angle C_1 would be required in drilling hole for pin.

Compound Angles. — Three types of compound angles are illustrated by Figs. 1–6. The first type is shown in Figs. 1, 2 and 3; the second type in Fig. 4; and the third type in Figs. 5 and 6.

In Fig. 1 is shown what might be considered as a thread-cutting tool without front clearance. A is a known angle in plane y–y of the top surface. C is the corresponding angle in plane x–x which is at some given angle B with plane y–y. Thus, angles A and B are components of the compound angle C.

Problem Referring to Fig. 1: The angle $2A$ in plane y–y is known, as is also the angle B between planes x–x and y–y. It is required to find the compound angle $2C$ in plane x–x.

Solution: Let $2A = 60°$ and $B = 15°$
Then
$$\tan C = \tan A \cos B$$
$$\tan C = \tan 30° \cos 15°$$
$$\tan C = 0.57735 \times 0.96592$$
$$\tan C = 0.55767$$
$$C = 29° 8.8' \qquad 2C = 58° 17.6'$$

Fig. 2 shows a thread-cutting tool with front clearance angle B. Angle A equals one-half the angle between the cutting edges in plane y–y of the top surface and compound angle C is one-half the angle between the cutting edges in a plane x–x at right angles to the inclined front edge of the tool. The angle between planes y–y and x–x is, therefore, equal to clearance angle B.

Problem Referring to Fig. 2: Find the angle $2C$ between the front faces of a thread-cutting tool having a known clearance angle B, which will permit the grinding of these faces so that their top edges will form the desired angle $2A$ for cutting the thread.

Solution: Let $2A = 60°$ and $B = 15°$
Then
$$\tan C = \frac{\tan A}{\cos B} = \frac{\tan 30°}{\cos 15°} = \frac{0.57735}{0.96592}$$
$$\tan C = 0.59772$$
$$C = 30° 52' \qquad 2C = 61° 44'$$

In Fig. 3 is shown a form-cutting tool in which A is one-half the angle between the cutting edges in plane y–y of the top surface; B is the front clearance angle; and C is one-half the angle between the cutting edges in plane x–x at right angles to the front edges of the tool. The formula for finding angle C when angles A and B are known is the same as that for Fig. 2.

Problem Referring to Fig. 3: Find the angle $2C$ between the front faces of a form-cutting tool having a known clearance angle B which will permit the grinding of these faces so that their top edges will form the desired angle $2A$ for form cutting.

Solution: Let $2A = 46°$ and $B = 12°$
Then
$$\tan C = \frac{\tan A}{\cos B} = \frac{\tan 23°}{\cos 12°} = \frac{0.42447}{0.97815}$$
$$\tan C = 0.43395$$
$$C = 23° 27.5' \qquad 2C = 46° 55'$$

In Fig. 4 is shown a wedge-shaped block, the top surface of which is inclined at compound angle C with the base in a plane at right angles with the base and at angle R with the front edge. Angle A in the vertical plane of the front of the plate and angle B in the vertical plane of one side which is at right angles to the front are components of angle C.

Problem Referring to Fig. 4: Find the compound angle C of a wedge-shaped block having known component angles A and B in sides at right angles to each other.

Solution: Let $A = 47° 14'$ and $B = 38° 10'$

$$\tan R = \frac{\tan B}{\tan A} = \frac{\tan 38° 10'}{\tan 47° 14'}$$

$$\tan R = \frac{0.78598}{1.0812} = 0.72695$$

$$R = 36° 0.9'$$

$$\tan C = \frac{\tan A}{\cos R} = \frac{\tan 47° 14'}{\cos 36° 0.9'}$$

$$\tan C = \frac{1.0812}{0.80887} = 1.3367$$

$$C = 53° 12'$$

In Fig. 5 is shown a four-sided block, two sides of which are at right angles to each other and to the base of the block. The other two sides are inclined at an oblique angle with the base. Angle C is a compound angle formed by the intersection of these two inclined sides and the intersection of a vertical plane passing through x–x, and the base of the block. The components of angle C are angles A and B and angle R is the angle in the base plane of the block between the plane of angle C and the plane of angle A.

Problem Referring to Fig. 5: Find the angles C and R in the block shown in Fig. 5 when angles A and B are known.

Solution: Let angle $A = 27°$ and $B = 36°$

$$\tan R = \frac{\cot B}{\cot A} = \frac{\cot 36°}{\cot 27°} = \frac{1.3764}{1.9626}$$

$$\tan R = 0.70131 \qquad R = 35° 2.5'$$

$$\cot C = \sqrt{\cot^2 A + \cot^2 B} = \sqrt{(1.9626)^2 + (1.3764)^2}$$

$$\cot C = \sqrt{5.74627572} = 2.3971$$

$$C = 22° 38.6'$$

Problem Referring to Fig. 6: A rod or pipe is inserted into a rectangular block at an angle. Angle C_1 is the compound angle of inclination (measured from the vertical) in a plane passing through the center line of the rod or pipe and at right angles to the top surface of the block. Angles A_1 and B_1 are the angles of inclination of the rod or pipe when viewed respectively in the front and side planes of the block. Angle R is the angle between the plane of angle C_1 and the plane of angle B_1. Find angles C_1 and R when a rod or pipe is inclined at known angles A_1 and B_1.

Solution: Let $A_1 = 39°$ and $B_1 = 34°$

Then $$\tan C_1 = \sqrt{\tan^2 A_1 + \tan^2 B_1} = \sqrt{(0.80978)^2 + (0.67451)^2}$$

$$\tan C_1 = \sqrt{1.1107074} = 1.0539$$

$$C_1 = 46° 30.2'$$

$$\tan R = \frac{\tan A_1}{\tan B_1} = \frac{0.80978}{0.67451}$$

$$\tan R = 1.2005 \qquad R = 50° 12.4'$$

Woodruff Key-slot Gages — Former S.A.E. Production Standard

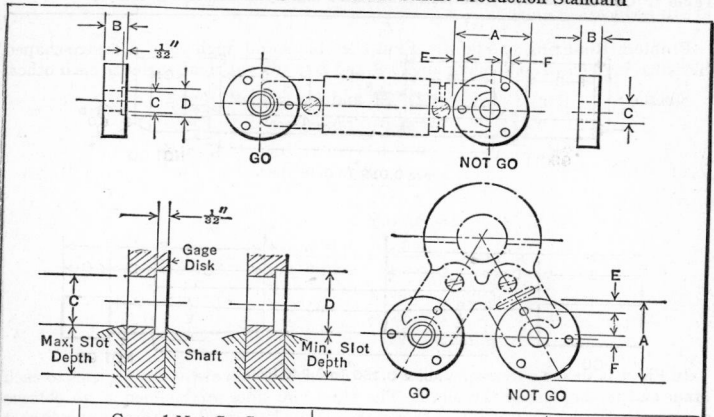

Key Size	Go and Not Go Gage			Go Gage			Not Go Gage	
	A	E	F	B	C	D	B	C
1/16 × 1/2	0.5000	0.0781	1/16	0.0615	0.1564	0.1664	0.0630	3/16
3/32 × 1/2	0.5000	0.0781	1/16	0.0928	0.1878	0.1978	0.0943	3/16
1/8 × 1/2	0.5000	0.0781	1/16	0.1240	0.2190	0.2290	0.1255	3/16
3/32 × 5/8	0.6250	0.0938	3/32	0.0928	0.2188	0.2288	0.0943	3/16
1/8 × 5/8	0.6250	0.0938	3/32	0.1240	0.2500	0.2600	0.1255	7/32
5/32 × 5/8	0.6250	0.0938	3/32	0.1553	0.2812	0.2912	0.1568	7/32
1/8 × 3/4	0.7500	0.0938	3/32	0.1240	0.2490	0.2590	0.1255	7/32
5/32 × 3/4	0.7500	0.0938	3/32	0.1553	0.2802	0.2902	0.1568	1/4
3/16 × 3/4	0.7500	0.0938	3/32	0.1863	0.3114	0.3214	0.1568	1/4
5/32 × 7/8	0.8750	0.1094	1/8	0.1553	0.2812	0.2912	0.1880	1/4
3/16 × 7/8	0.8750	0.1094	1/8	0.1863	0.3124	0.3224	0.1568	9/32
1/4 × 7/8	0.8750	0.1094	1/8	0.2487	0.3750	0.3850	0.1880	9/32
3/16 × 1	1.0000	0.1250	1/8	0.1863	0.3114	0.3214	0.2505	9/32
1/4 × 1	1.0000	0.1250	1/8	0.2487	0.3740	0.3840	0.1880	5/16
5/16 × 1	1.0000	0.1250	1/8	0.3111	0.4364	0.4464	0.2505	5/16
3/16 × 1 1/8	1.1250	0.1562	1/8	0.1863	0.3444	0.3544	0.3130	5/16
1/4 × 1 1/8	1.1250	0.1562	1/8	0.2487	0.4070	0.4170	0.1880	11/32
5/16 × 1 1/8	1.1250	0.1562	1/8	0.3111	0.4694	0.4794	0.2505	11/32
1/4 × 1 1/4	1.2500	0.1719	1/8	0.2487	0.4060	0.4160	0.3130	11/32
5/16 × 1 1/4	1.2500	0.1719	1/8	0.3111	0.4684	0.4784	0.2505	3/8
3/8 × 1 1/4	1.2500	0.1719	1/8	0.3735	0.5310	0.5410	0.3130	3/8
1/4 × 1 3/8	1.3750	0.1875	1/8	0.2487	0.4370	0.4470	0.3755	3/8
5/16 × 1 3/8	1.3750	0.1875	1/8	0.3111	0.4994	0.5094	0.2505	7/16
3/8 × 1 3/8	1.3750	0.1875	1/8	0.3735	0.5620	0.5720	0.3130	7/16
1/4 × 1 1/2	1.5000	0.2187	1/8	0.2487	0.4680	0.4780	0.3755	7/16
5/16 × 1 1/2	1.5000	0.2187	1/8	0.3111	0.5304	0.5404	0.3130	1/2
3/8 × 1 1/2	1.5000	0.2187	1/8	0.3735	0.5930	0.6030	0.3755	1/2

All dimensions in inches. Tolerances: All diameters A plus 0.0002 minus 0.000 for Go gage; plus or minus 0.001 for Not Go. All widths B plus 0.0002 minus 0.000 for both Go and Not-Go gages. All diameters C plus 0.0004 minus 0.000 for Go gage and plus or minus 0.005 for drilled holes in Not-Go gage. All diameters D plus 0.0004 minus 0.000.

The detail sectional views above table show use of hole C and counterbore D for checking the maximum and minimum slot depths.

The three equally spaced holes F provide for shifting the disk to three positions relative to the handle, thus increasing the disk life three times as compared with a single-position disk. Use oil-hardening steel, or its equivalent.

The straight handle is intended for gaging key sizes up to 5/16 by 1 1/8 and the V-shaped handle for larger sizes.

Table 1. Commercial and American Standard Plain Cylindrical Plug Gaging Members

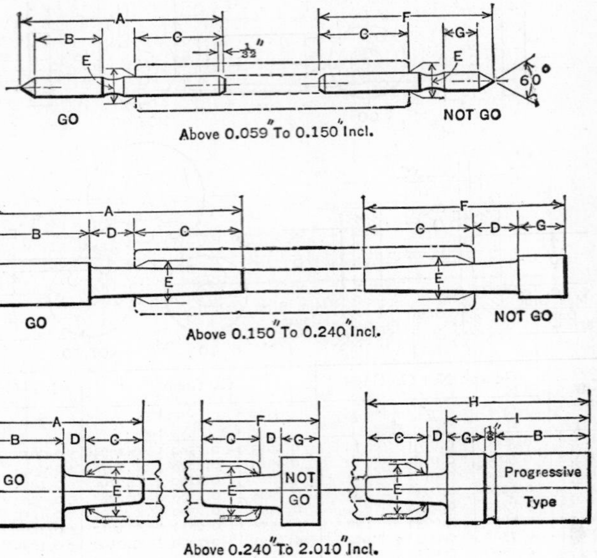

Above 0.059" To 0.150" Incl.

Above 0.150" To 0.240" Incl.

Above 0.240" To 2.010" Incl.

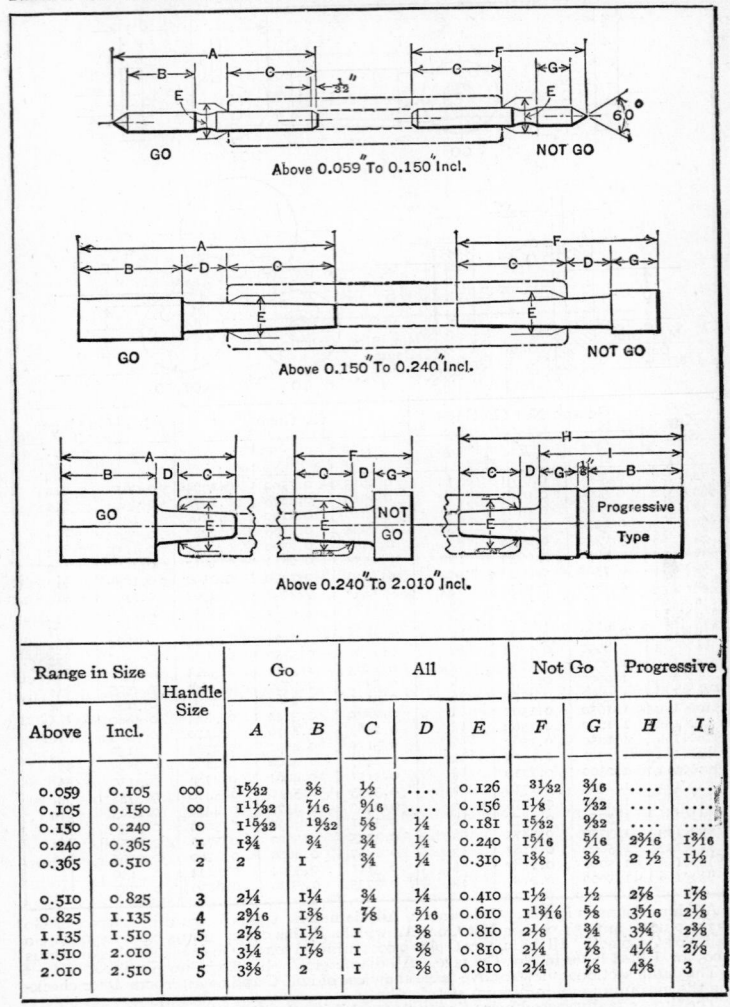

Range in Size		Handle Size	Go		All			Not Go		Progressive	
Above	Incl.		*A*	*B*	*C*	*D*	*E*	*F*	*G*	*H*	*I*
0.059	0.105	000	1 5/32	3/8	1/2	....	0.126	31/32	3/16	....	....
0.105	0.150	00	1 11/32	7/16	9/16	....	0.156	1 1/8	7/32	....	....
0.150	0.240	0	1 15/32	19/32	5/8	1/4	0.181	1 5/32	9/32	....	....
0.240	0.365	1	1 3/4	3/4	3/4	1/4	0.240	1 5/16	5/16	2 3/16	1 3/16
0.365	0.510	2	2	1	3/4	1/4	0.310	1 3/8	3/8	2 1/2	1 1/2
0.510	0.825	3	2 1/4	1 1/4	3/4	1/4	0.410	1 1/2	1/2	2 7/8	1 7/8
0.825	1.135	4	2 9/16	1 3/8	7/8	5/16	0.610	1 13/16	5/8	3 5/16	2 1/8
1.135	1.510	5	2 7/8	1 1/2	1	3/8	0.810	2 1/8	3/4	3 3/4	2 3/8
1.510	2.010	5	3 1/4	1 7/8	1	3/8	0.810	2 1/4	7/8	4 1/4	2 7/8
2.010	2.510	5	3 3/8	2	1	3/8	0.810	2 1/4	7/8	4 3/8	3

All dimensions in inches. Tapers of all plug-gage shanks 0.25 inch per foot.

Maximum diameters *E* are given (minimum diameters are 0.001 inch less up to 0.365-inch plug size inclusive, and 0.002 inch less for larger sizes).

Break all sharp corners on plug gages.

Table 2. Handles for Cylindrical and Thread Plug Gages — Taper Lock Design

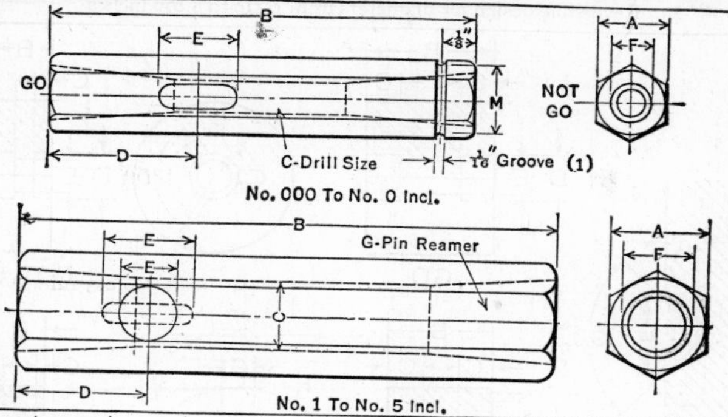

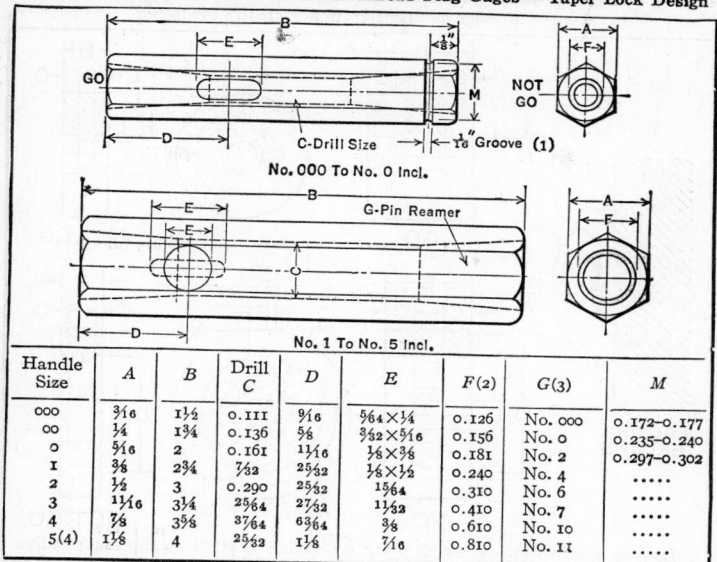

Handle Size	*A*	*B*	Drill *C*	*D*	*E*	*F*(2)	*G*(3)	*M*
000	3/16	1 1/2	0.111	9/16	5/64 × 1/4	0.126	No. 000	0.172–0.177
00	1/4	1 3/4	0.136	5/8	3/32 × 5/16	0.156	No. 0	0.235–0.240
0	5/16	2	0.161	11/16	1/8 × 3/8	0.181	No. 2	0.297–0.302
1	3/8	2 3/4	7/32	25/32	1/8 × 1/2	0.240	No. 4	.....
2	1/2	3	0.290	25/32	15/64	0.310	No. 6	.....
3	11/16	3 1/4	25/64	27/32	11/32	0.410	No. 7	.....
4	7/8	3 5/8	37/64	63/64	3/8	0.610	No. 10	.....
5(4)	1 1/8	4	25/32	1 1/8	7/16	0.810	No. 11	.....

(1) Groove to indicate the Not-Go end. (2) Maximum diameters given (Minimum 0.001 inch less). (3) Pin reamer numbers (see table p. 1320); taper of holes at ends 0.25 inch per foot. (4) Use No. 5 size handle for optional range of cylindrical plugs with diameters above 1.510 to 2.510 inclusive. All dimensions in inches.

Steel for Gages. — Machine steel, plain carbon steel and special alloy steels are used for making various classes of gages. Machine steel is used extensively for gage work. The carbon content of machine steel for gages usually ranges from 0.15 to 0.25 per cent, although it may be as high as 0.50 per cent, especially for ring or plug gages. A 0.20-per cent carbon steel, containing from 0.90 to 1.10 per cent manganese and about 0.05 per cent of phosphorus and sulphur is considered very satisfactory for gages. This steel should not contain silicon as this causes warping in hardening. The carbon in the so-called 0.20-per cent carbon steel may vary from 0.15 to 0.25 per cent and many gage-makers prefer the steel having the smaller amount. This general class of steel is extensively used for making drop-forged snap gages. Plug gages, ring gages or other forms which may be ground easily after hardening are often made of steel containing about 0.50 per cent carbon.

A high-carbon or tool steel is sometimes preferred to machine steel because it can be hardened in much less time than is required for carburizing and hardening machine steel gages. High-carbon steel for gages often contains about 0.90 per cent carbon, about 0.30 per cent manganese, a phosphorus and sulphur content not exceeding 0.025 per cent, and about 0.15 per cent silicon. Special alloy steels have been developed which are adapted to fine gage work partly because changes due to hardening are exceedingly small.

Table 3. Commercial and American Standard Plain Cylindrical Plug Gaging Members

Reversible design for diameters from 1.510 to 8.010 inches

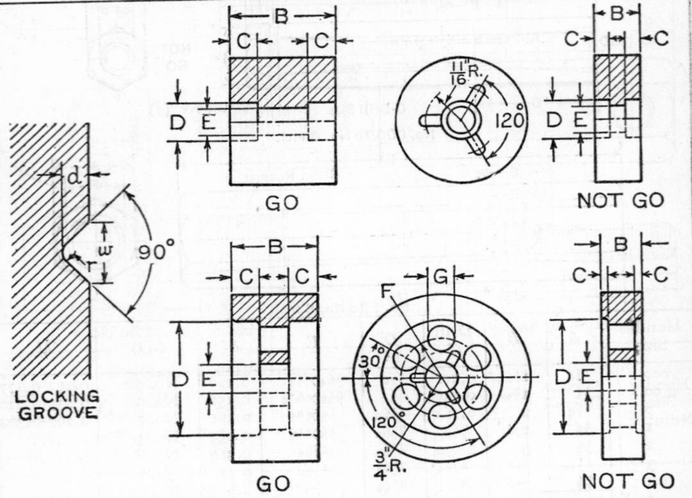

Locking groove width $w = 0.198$ max.; 0.188 min.; depth $d = 0.073$ min.; radius $r = 0.030$ to 0.050 inch.

Range of Diameters		Go Gages		Not Go		Go and Not Go			
Above	To and Including	*B*	*C*	*B*	*C*	*D*	*E*	*F*	*G*
1.510	2.010	1 7/8	1/2	7/8	9/32	25/32	17/32	....	....
2.010	2.510	2	1/2	7/8	9/32	25/32	17/32	....	....
2.510	3.010	2 1/8	11/16	1	1/8	1 7/8	29/32	....	....
3.010	3.510	2 1/4	3/4	1	1/8	2 1/4	29/32	....	....
3.510	4.010	2 1/4	3/4	1	1/8	2 5/8	29/32	....	....
4.010	4.510	2 1/4	3/4	1	1/8	3	29/32	1 1/16	3/4
4.510	5.010	2 1/4	3/4	1	1/8	3 7/16	29/32	1 3/16	13/16
5.010	5.510	2 1/4	3/4	1	1/8	3 7/8	29/32	1 1/4	7/8
5.510	6.010	2 1/4	3/4	1	1/8	4 5/16	29/32	1 3/8	1
6.010	6.510	2 1/4	3/4	1	1/8	4 3/4	29/32	1 1/2	1 1/8
6.510	7.010	2 1/4	3/4	1	1/8	5 1/4	29/32	1 5/8	1 1/4
7.010	7.510	2 1/4	3/4	1	1/8	5 3/4	29/32	1 3/4	1 3/8
7.510	8.010	2 1/4	3/4	1	1/8	6 1/4	29/32	1 7/8	1 1/2

Three equally spaced locking grooves (see enlarged section) are required on both ends of all gages. Use handle size No. 6 for diameters up to 2.510 and No. 7 for larger gages. See Table 4 for handle dimensions.

With the reversible design of gage, the gaging end or plug can be reversed when one end is worn, thus increasing the useful life of a gage.

The "taper lock" design (see Table 1) is optional for diameters above 1.510 up to and including 2.510 inches.

Table 4. Handles for Plain Cylindrical and Thread Plug Gages — Reversible Design

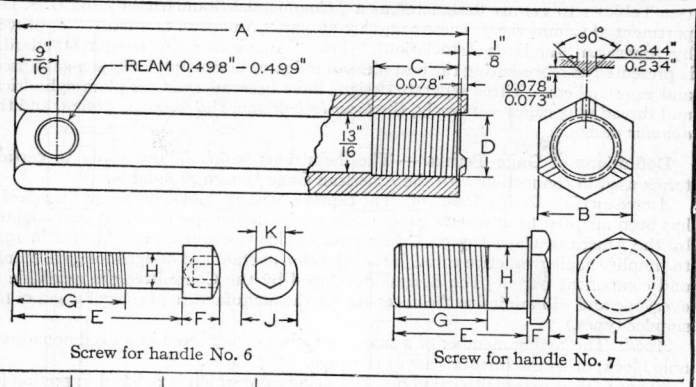

Screw for handle No. 6   Screw for handle No. 7

Handle Size Number	Length Overall A	Width Across Flats B	Tapped Hole in Handle*				
			Length C	Major Diam. D	Pitch Diam., Min.	Pitch Diam., Max.	Threads per Inch
6	5	1⅛	⅝	0.500	0.4675	0.4711	20
7	6	1¼	1¼	0.875	0.8286	0.8335	14

Handle Size Number	E	F	G	Body Diam. H, Go and Not Go	Screw Head Diam. J	Hexagon Socket K	Hexagon Head L
6	Not Go 1½ Go 2¼	Not Go ⅜ Go ½	Not Go 1¼ Go 1½	.5000 Max. .4928 Min.	¾	⅜	......
7†	1 25⁄32	9⁄32	1¼	.875 Max. .867 Min.	......	......	1⅛

* Class 2 fit is specified for screws and tapped holes.
† With No. 7 handle, " Not Go " and " Go " gages have the same screw dimensions *E*, *F* and *G*.

Two sizes of standard gage handles listed in this table are for both plain cylindrical plug gages (Table 3) and thread plug gages (Table 7) ranging in diameter from approximately 1½ to 8 inches. The gaging member is attached to the handle so that its position can be reversed readily when one end of the gage has become worn. Three wedge-shaped locking prongs on one end of the handle are forced into corresponding grooves in the gaging member by a single screw, thus providing a self-centering support and a positive lock. The result is a degree of rigidity equivalent to that of a solid gage. The carefully worked-out dimensional limits insure interchangeability between the gaging members and the handles regardless of where they may be manufactured.

The use of a cross-bar in the hole at the end of the handle is optional. The length of this cross-bar is 5½ inches and the maximum and minimum diameters are 0.5005 and 0.4995 inch. For maximum and minimum diameters of the reamed hole, see illustration above.

Commercial Standard for Gages. — The accompanying gage design standards (see Tables 1 to 11) are designated as a " Commercial Standard " by the U. S. Department of Commerce. These gages are also an " American Standard " (approved by American Standards Association). This " American Gage Design Standard " is presented as representing the best ideas of industry in general, including gage users and gage makers. Three separate designs have been adopted for plain cylindrical and thread plug gages — namely, the *taper lock* design, the *reversible* design, and the *annular* design.

Definitions of Gage Terms. — The definitions which follow apply to certain terms used in connection with the American Gage Design Standards.

American Gage Design Standard: The caption " American Gage Design Standard " has been adopted to designate gages made to the design specifications promulgated by the American Gage Design Committee. (This Committee was formed in 1926 to simplify gaging practice through the adoption of standard designs for gage blanks and component parts. The designs developed by the Committee are available to everyone and will minimize the necessity for the manufacture of special gages of the simpler types.)

Anvil: The gaging member of a snap gage when constructed as a fixed nonadjustable block, or as the integral jaw of the gage.

Flange: That external portion of a large ring gage which is reduced in section for the purpose of lightening the gage.

Gaging Button: is an adjustable gaging member of a snap gage consisting of a shank and a flanged portion, the latter constituting the gaging section.

Gaging Member· That integral unit of a gage which is accurately finished to size and is employed for size control of the work. In taper lock plug gages, the gaging member consists of a shank and a gaging section.

Gaging Pin: A straight, unflanged adjustable gaging member of an adjustable snap gage.

Adjustable Snap Gage: An external caliper gage employed for the size control of external dimensions, comprising an open frame, in both jaws of which gaging members are so held that one or more pairs can be set and locked to any predetermined size within the range of adjustment.

Solid Snap Gage: An external caliper gage employed for the size control of external dimensions, comprising an open frame and jaws, the latter carrying gaging members in the form of fixed, parallel, nonadjustable anvils.

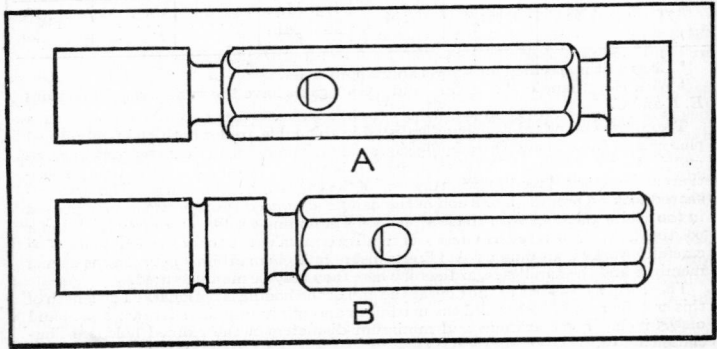

Fig. 1.

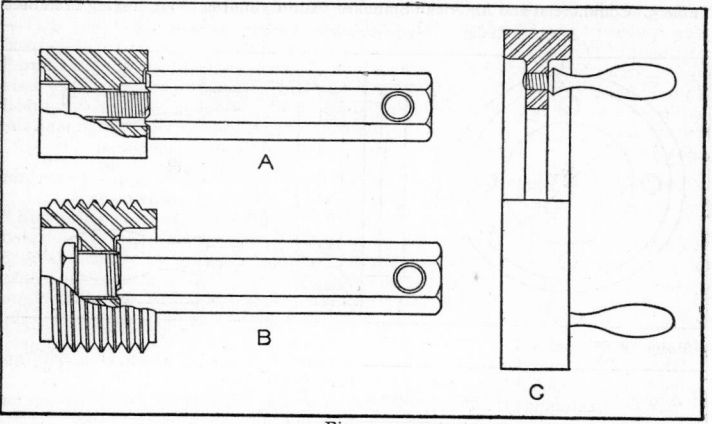

Fig. 2.

Taper Lock: Term designating that construction in which the gaging member has a taper shank, which is forced into a taper hole in the handle.

Lightening Holes: Unfinished drilled holes provided in the heavier sizes of gaging members for the sole purpose of reducing the weight of the gage.

Marking Disk: A plate which can be attached to a gage frame to provide, when suitably marked, a means of identification for the gage.

Annular Plug Gage: A shell type plug gage in which the gaging member is in the form of a ring, the external surface of which is the gaging section, the central portion of the web being machined away for the purpose of reducing weight, ball handles being provided for convenience in handling. This construction is employed for plain and thread plug gages in the ranges above 8.010 inches.

Plain Cylindrical Plug Gage: A complete unthreaded internal gage of single- or double-ended type for the size control of holes. It consists of handle and gaging member or members, with suitable locking means.

Progressive Cylindrical Plug Gage: A complete unthreaded internal gage consisting of handle and gaging member in which the " go " and " not go " gaging sections are combined in a single unit secured to one end of the handle.

Reversible Plug Gage: A plug gage in which three wedge-shaped *locking prongs* on the handle are forced into corresponding *locking grooves* in the gaging member by means of a single through screw, thus providing a self-centering support with a positive lock.

Thread Plug Gage: A complete internal thread gage of either single- or double-ended type, comprising handle and threaded gaging member or members, with suitable locking means.

Plain Ring Gage: An unthreaded external gage of circular form employed for the size control of external diameters. In the smaller sizes it consists of a gage body into which is pressed a *bushing*, that is accurately finished to size for gaging purposes.

Thread Ring Gage: An external thread gage employed for the size control of threaded work, means of adjustment being provided integral with the gage body.

Thread Ring Gage Locking Device: Means of expanding and contracting the thread ring gage during the manufacturing or resizing processes. It also provides an effectual lock

Table 5. Commercial and American Standard Plain Cylindrical Plug Gaging Members

Annular design for diameters from 8.010 to 12.010 inches

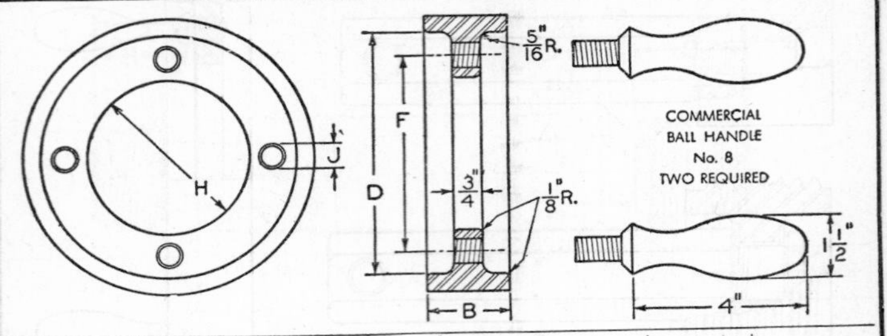

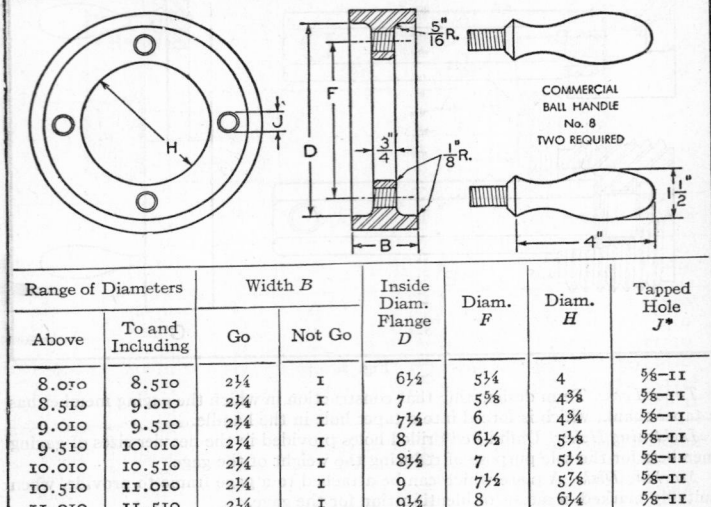

Range of Diameters		Width *B*		Inside Diam. Flange *D*	Diam. *F*	Diam. *H*	Tapped Hole *J**
Above	To and Including	Go	Not Go				
8.010	8.510	2¼	1	6½	5¼	4	⅝–11
8.510	9.010	2¼	1	7	5⅝	4⅜	⅝–11
9.010	9.510	2¼	1	7½	6	4¾	⅝–11
9.510	10.010	2¼	1	8	6½	5⅛	⅝–11
10.010	10.510	2¼	1	8½	7	5½	⅝–11
10.510	11.010	2¼	1	9	7½	5⅞	⅝–11
11.010	11.510	2¼	1	9½	8	6¼	⅝–11
11.510	12.010	2¼	1	10	8½	6⅝	⅝–11

* A Class 2 fit is specified for the tapped holes (⅝–11 NC–2). The web of the gage is provided with four tapped holes for convenience in bolting to faceplate during manufacture. Two of these holes are employed for attaching No. 8 ball handles to the gaging member. (For handle dimensions, see illustration above.)

Shank: That portion of the gaging member which is inserted in the handle or frame.

Taper Lock Design of Gage. — The term "taper lock" indicates that the gaging member has a taper shank which is forced into a taper hole in the gage handle (see Fig. 1 and Tables 1 and 2). This gage possesses the rigidity of a solid gage. The taper lock is used for plain plug gages in diameters ranging from above 0.059 to and including 1.510 inches. The use of this design for diameters above 1.510 to and including 2.510 is optional. The "go" and "not go" gages may be combined in one gaging member of the progressive type (B, Fig. 1) for diameters above 0.240 to 2.510 inches as shown by Table 1. Table 2 gives the dimensions of the handles for gaging members in Table 1. A drift slot or hole is provided near one end of the handle to permit removing a gaging member when replacement is necessary. One end of a double-end gage is removed by inserting a rod through the hollow handle. In the smaller sizes (above 0.059 inch to and including 0.240 inch) a groove is cut near the "not go" end to clearly distinguish it from the "go" end. This groove is considered unnecessary for sizes above 0.240 inch.

Reversible Design of Gage. — The reversible type of plug gage is so arranged that the plug can be reversed when one end is worn, thus increasing the life of the

Table 6. Commercial and American Standard Thread Plug Gaging Members

Taper lock design for diameters from ¼ to 1½ inches inclusive

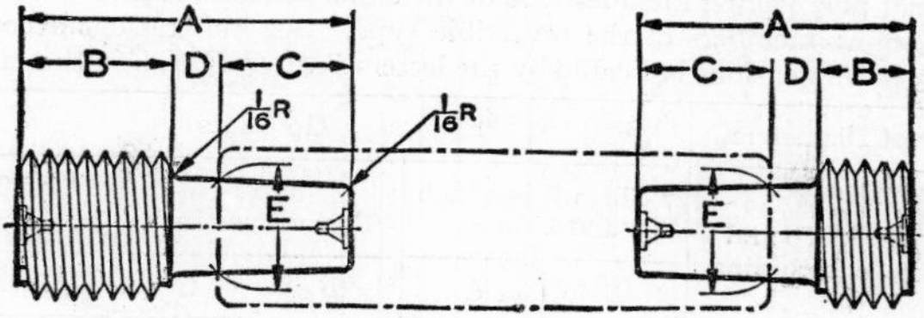

Range of Diameters		Go Gages				Go and Not Go	
Above	To and Including	A	B	C	D	Min. E	Max. E
0.240	0.365	1½	½	¾	¼	0.239	0.240
0.365	0.510	1¾	¾	¾	¼	0.309	0.310
0.510	0.825	1⅞	⅞	¾	¼	0.408	0.410
0.825	1.135	2³⁄₁₆	1	⅞	⁵⁄₁₆	0.608	0.610
*1.135	1.510	2⅝	1¼	1	⅜	0.808	0.810
†1.135	1.510	2⅜	1	1	⅜	0.808	0.810

Range of Diameters		Not Go Gages				Handle Size No.	Taper of Gage Shank
Above	To and Including	A	B	C	D		
0.240	0.365	1⁵⁄₁₆	⁵⁄₁₆	¾	¼	1	0.25 inch per foot for all gage shanks
0.365	0.510	1⅜	⅜	¾	¼	2	
0.510	0.825	1½	½	¾	¼	3	
0.825	1.135	1¹³⁄₁₆	⅝	⅞	⁵⁄₁₆	4	
*1.135	1.510	2⅛	¾	1	⅜	5	
†1.135	1.510	2⅛	¾	1	⅜	5	

* Less than 12 threads per inch. † 12 threads per inch and over.

For dimensions of handles see Table 2.

The "Not Go" plug must have not less than 3 full threads.

Taper lock gaging members are standard for all taper pipe thread plug gages up to and including 2 inch nominal pipe size.

gage (see A and B, Fig. 2). This reversible design has three wedge-shaped locking prongs on the handle which engage locking grooves in the gaging member, the two members being held together by a screw thus providing a self-centering support and a positive lock. This design is standard for all plain and thread plug gages in the range of diameters above 1.510 to and including 8.010 inches, with the exception of pipe thread plug gages for which the design is standard in the range above 2 inch nominal pipe size to and including 6 inch nominal pipe size. The design shown at B, Fig. 2, is used for plain and thread plug gages above 2.510 to and including 8.010 inches. For dimensions of the reversible design of gaging members and handles, see Tables 3 and 4. The handles for these standard gages may, of course, be used with new gaging members whenever necessary, so that with reasonable care the life of the handle is indefinite.

Table 7. Commercial and American Standard Thread Plug Gaging Members

Reversible design for diameters from 1.510 to 8.010 inches

Thread plug gaging members are of the same general form as the plain cylindrical gaging members of the reversible type. See illustrations accompanying Table 3 for dimensions indicated by the letters *B*, *C*, *D*, *E*, *F*, *G* in the table below.

Range of Diameters		Go Gages					
		7 Threads per Inch and Under		8 to 14 Threads per Inch		16 Threads per Inch and Over	
Above	To and Including	*B*	*C*	*B*	*C*	*B*	*C*
1.510	2.010	1 7/8	1/2	1 1/4	3/8	7/8	9/32
2.010	2.510	2	1/2	1 3/8	3/8	7/8	9/32
2.510	3.010	2 1/8	11/16	1 1/2	3/8	1	1/8
3.010	3.510	2 1/4	3/4	1 1/2	3/8	1	1/8
3.510	4.010	2 1/4	3/4	1 1/2	3/8	1	1/8
4.010	4.510	2 1/4	3/4	1 1/2	3/8	1	1/8
4.510	5.010	2 1/4	3/4	1 1/2	3/8	1	1/8
5.010	5.510	2 1/4	3/4	1 1/2	3/8	1	1/8
5.510	6.010	2 1/4	3/4	1 1/2	3/8	1	1/8
6.010	6.510	2 1/4	3/4	1 1/2	3/8	1	1/8
6.510	7.010	2 1/4	3/4	1 1/2	3/8	1	1/8
7.010	7.510	2 1/4	3/4	1 1/2	3/8	1	1/8
7.510	8.010	2 1/4	3/4	1 1/2	3/8	1	1/8

Range of Diameters		Not Go Gages All Pitches		Go and Not Go Gages All Pitches			
Above	To and Including	*B*	*C*	*D*	*E*	*F*	*G*
1.510	2.010	7/8	9/32	25/32	17/32	......	......
2.010	2.510	7/8	9/32	25/32	17/32	......	......
2.510	3.010	1	1/8	1 7/8	29/32	......	......
3.010	3.510	1	1/8	2 1/4	29/32	......	......
3.510	4.010	1	1/8	2 5/8	29/32	......	......
4.010	4.510	1	1/8	3	29/32	1 1/16	3 1/4
4.510	5.010	1	1/8	3 7/16	29/32	1 3/16	13/16
5.010	5.510	1	1/8	3 7/8	29/32	1 1/4	7/8
5.510	6.010	1	1/8	4 5/16	29/32	1 3/8	1
6.010	6.510	1	1/8	4 3/4	29/32	1 1/2	1 1/8
6.510	7.010	1	1/8	5 1/4	29/32	1 5/8	1 1/4
7.010	7.510	1	1/8	5 3/4	29/32	1 3/4	1 3/8
7.510	8.010	1	1/8	6 1/4	29/32	1 7/8	1 1/2

Three equally spaced locking grooves (see enlarged section, Table 3 are required on both ends of all gages. Use handle size No. 6 for diameters up to 2.510 inclusive, and No. 7 for larger gages. See Table 4 for handle dimensions.

With the reversible design of gage, the gaging end or plug can be reversed when one end is worn, thus increasing the useful life of a gage.

"Not Go" gages having 16 threads per inch or more are relieved on both ends 1/32 inch below the root of the thread and 1/8 inch in from each end, the thread being removed. Not less than 3 full threads must remain on any "Not Go" plug.

Table 8. Commercial and American Standard Thread Plug Gaging Members
Annular design for diameters from 8.010 to 12.010 inches

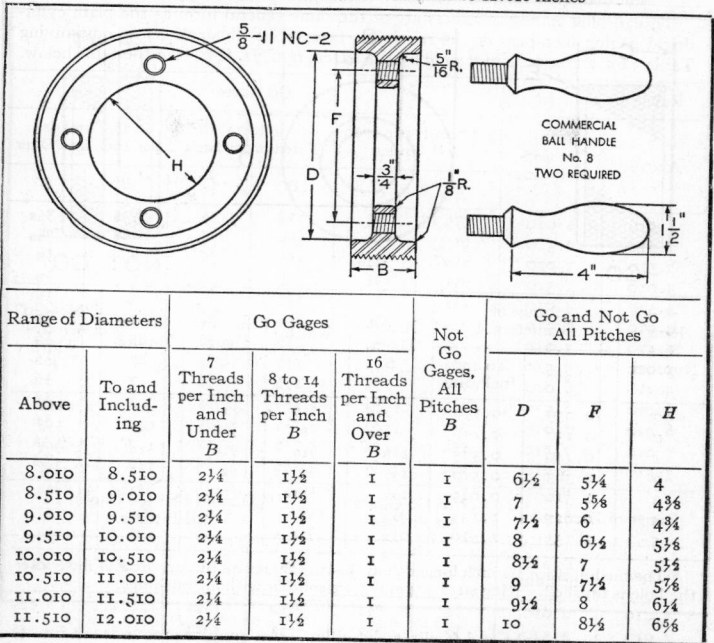

Range of Diameters		Go Gages			Not Go Gages, All Pitches *B*	Go and Not Go All Pitches		
Above	To and Including	7 Threads per Inch and Under *B*	8 to 14 Threads per Inch *B*	16 Threads per Inch and Over *B*		*D*	*F*	*H*
8.010	8.510	2¼	1½	1	1	6½	5¼	4
8.510	9.010	2¼	1½	1	1	7	5⅝	4⅜
9.010	9.510	2¼	1½	1	1	7½	6	4¾
9.510	10.010	2¼	1½	1	1	8	6½	5⅛
10.010	10.510	2¼	1½	1	1	8½	7	5½
10.510	11.010	2¼	1½	1	1	9	7½	5⅞
11.010	11.510	2¼	1½	1	1	9½	8	6¼
11.510	12.010	2¼	1½	1	1	10	8½	6⅝

Annular Design of Gage. — As large plug gages are heavy and difficult to handle, a design was adopted for sizes above 8.010 inches having a minimum of weight consistent with strength and permanence. This annular design (C, Fig. 2 and Table 5) has a rim and a web the center of which is bored out to reduce the weight. The web is provided with four tapped holes for convenience in holding during manufacturing. Two of these holes are further employed for attaching ball handles to the gaging member. These handles are a commercial design.

Thread Plug Gages. — The taper lock, reversible and annular designs have been adopted for thread plug gages, the designs being similar to those used for plain cylindrical plug gages, excepting that the length of the thread gaging members differs in some instances. (See Tables 6, 7 and 8.) The taper lock type of gage is used for pipe thread gages ranging from ⅛ to 2 inches nominal pipe sizes. The reversible design is used for 2½ to 6 inch nominal pipe sizes and the annular design for 8-inch nominal size.

Plain Ring Gages. — For external size control, the American Gage Design Standard includes plain ring gages above 0.059 to and including 12.260 (see Tables 9 and 10). Ring gages for diameters above 0.059 to and including 0.510 inch (Table 9) consist of a hardened bushing pressed into a soft gage body. The solid or one-piece gage is employed for sizes above 0.510 inch, but sizes above 1.510 inch are

Table 9. Commercial and American Standard Plain Ring Gages

For diameters ranging from above 0.059 to, and including, 1.510 inches

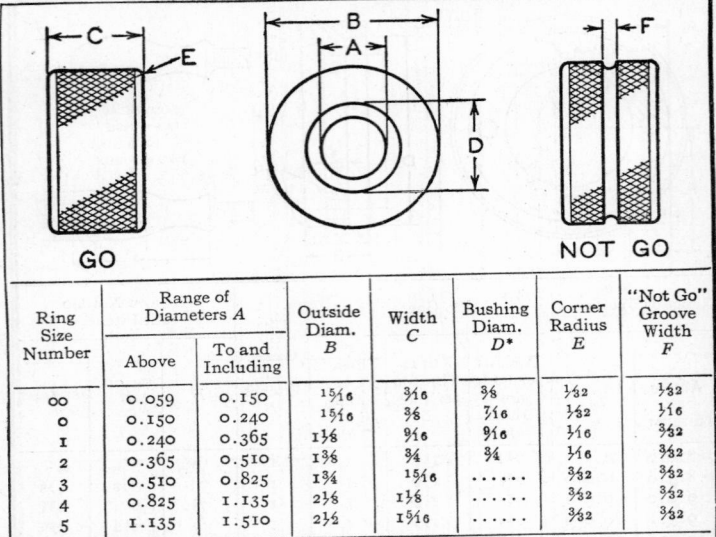

GO   NOT GO

Ring Size Number	Range of Diameters A		Outside Diam. B	Width C	Bushing Diam. D*	Corner Radius E	"Not Go" Groove Width F
	Above	To and Including					
00	0.059	0.150	$1\frac{5}{16}$	$\frac{3}{16}$	$\frac{3}{8}$	$\frac{1}{32}$	$\frac{1}{32}$
0	0.150	0.240	$1\frac{5}{16}$	$\frac{3}{8}$	$\frac{7}{16}$	$\frac{1}{32}$	$\frac{1}{16}$
1	0.240	0.365	$1\frac{1}{8}$	$\frac{9}{16}$	$\frac{9}{16}$	$\frac{1}{16}$	$\frac{3}{32}$
2	0.365	0.510	$1\frac{3}{8}$	$\frac{3}{4}$	$\frac{3}{4}$	$\frac{1}{16}$	$\frac{3}{32}$
3	0.510	0.825	$1\frac{3}{4}$	$1\frac{5}{16}$	. . . . . .	$\frac{3}{32}$	$\frac{3}{32}$
4	0.825	1.135	$2\frac{1}{8}$	$1\frac{1}{8}$	. . . . . .	$\frac{3}{32}$	$\frac{3}{32}$
5	1.135	1.510	$2\frac{1}{2}$	$1\frac{9}{16}$	. . . . . .	$\frac{3}{32}$	$\frac{3}{32}$

* The bushings are $\frac{1}{16}$ inch longer than the ring thickness but are ground flush after the hole is finished.   Ring sizes 3, 4 and 5 are solid or without bushings.

flanged to reduce weight and facilitate handling. An annular groove is cut into the periphery of "not go" gages to distinguish them from the "go" gages (see illustrations accompanying Tables 9 and 10). Ring gages in sizes above 5.510 inches are provided with ball handles. The general outside and over-all dimensions of large plain and thread ring gage blanks are the same so that one set of dies may be utilized to make forgings for both types of gages.

Thread Ring Gage Blanks. — All American Gage Design Standard thread ring gage blanks are equipped with an effective device for adjusting and locking the gage in the manufacturing or resizing processes. Of the many locking devices considered, the single-unit locking device was finally adopted as standard, as it permits a minimum diameter of blank for a given size range, and provides a simple adjustment and positive lock without introducing any mechanical stresses into the gage body which might tend to create distortion after setting.

The adjusting screw, (see Fig. 3), is threaded externally and internally and split longitudinally. Turning this screw to the right exerts pressure on the sleeve and against a shoulder on the other side of the gage, thus spreading the ring. Once the ring has been properly adjusted by means of the adjusting screw, the adjustment is locked by tightening the locking screw. The tightening of the locking screw exerts a pull between the shoulder immediately under its head and the internal threads of the adjusting screw, which causes the adjusting screw to expand into the threads in the wall of the gage, the thrust of this action being taken up longitudinally by the

Table 10. Commercial and American Standard Plain Ring Gages

For diameters ranging from above 1.510 to, and including, 12.260 inches

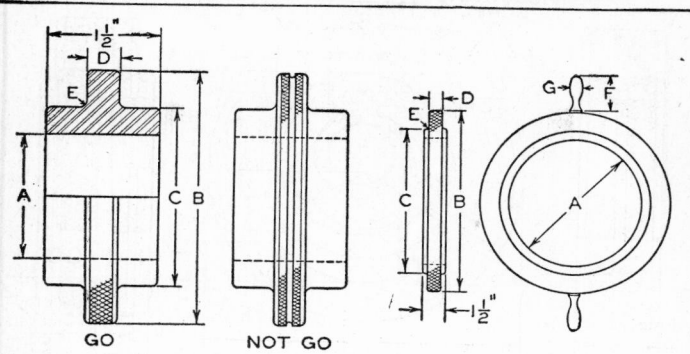

GO　　　　　NOT GO

Ring Size Number	Range of Diam. A		Outside Diam. B	Hub Diam. C	Flange Width D	Fillet Radius E	Handle Size No.*
	Above	To and Including					
6	1.510	2.010	4	A +⅞	½	⅛	......
7	2.010	2.510	4½	A +⅞	⁹⁄₁₆	⅛	......
8	2.510	3.010	5	A +1	⅝	⁵⁄₃₂	......
9	3.010	3.510	5½	A +1	¹¹⁄₁₆	⁵⁄₃₂	......
10	3.510	4.010	6⅜	A +1⅛	¾	⁵⁄₃₂	......
11	4.010	4.760	7¼	A +1⅛	⅞	⁵⁄₃₂	......
12	4.760	5.510	8¼	A +1⅛	1	³⁄₁₆	......
13	5.510	6.260	9¼	A +1⅛	1	³⁄₁₆	6
14	6.260	7.010	10¼	A +1⅛	1	³⁄₁₆	6
15	7.010	7.760	11¼	A +1⅛	1	³⁄₁₆	6
16	7.760	8.510	12¼	A +1⅛	1	³⁄₁₆	6
17	8.510	9.260	13¼	A +1⅛	1	³⁄₁₆	7
18	9.260	10.010	14¼	A +1⅛	1	³⁄₁₆	7
19	10.010	10.760	15¼	A +1⅛	1	³⁄₁₆	7
20	10.760	11.510	16¼	A +1⅛	1	³⁄₁₆	7
21	11.510	12.260	17¼	A +1⅛	1	³⁄₁₆	7

Overall width is 1½ inches for all sizes.

* Diameters above 5.510 inches are provided with commercial ball handles as shown by the illustration at the right. Diameters above 5.510 to, and including, 8.510 inches have two handles and larger sizes, four handles. Handle No. 6 has a length F of 3⅜ inches and a handle diameter G of 1¼ inches; handle No. 7 has a length F of 3¾ inches and a diameter G of 1⅜ inches. These handles fit into tapped holes in the ring gage flange. This thread for both handle sizes is American Standard, ½ inch diameter and 13 threads per inch. The fit is Class 2. (See Allowances and Tolerances for American Standard Screw Threads.)

The "Not Go Gage" has an annular groove, cut around the knurled flange as shown and the "Go Gage" flange is without a groove.

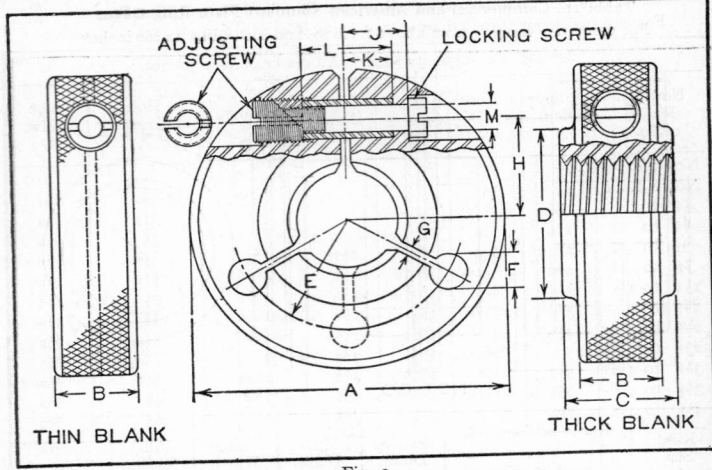

Fig. 3.

sleeve; therefore, the clamping is accomplished by expansion of the adjusting screw equally in all directions and not by the application of any eccentric forces that tend to distort the gage or change the adjustment. The locking pressure, it is seen, is taken up centrally in the locking screw itself as the reacting support is directly under the head of the locking screw in the form of a shoulder in the gage. The sleeve around the locking screw is accurately fitted and serves as a large dowel to maintain the alignment of the gage. Dimensions for thread ring gage blanks in the range from No. 0 to 4¾ inches are given in Table 11.

Plain Adjustable Snap Gages. — This type of gage which is used for controlling external dimensions consists of an open C-shaped frame with gaging members inserted in both jaws and so arranged that they can be set and locked to any predetermined size within the range of adjustment. The American Gage Design Standard includes four designs of adjustable snap gages designated as Models A, B, C, and MC. Model A, Fig. 4, has four gaging pins. Model B is the same as A, excepting that four gaging " buttons " are used instead of pins. These buttons are pins with flanged or enlarged gaging ends (as shown at C).

Model C (Fig. 4) has two gaging buttons and a single block anvil opposite. Model MC is a miniature snap gage with two gaging buttons and a single block anvil.

Models A, B and C are made in sixteen different sizes as indicated by frame Nos. 1 to 16. Model A is for all diameters up to 12 inches inclusive; Model B is for diameters ranging from ½ to 11¼ inches inclusive; Model C is for all diameters up to 11⅝ inches inclusive; and Model MC is for diameters up to 0.760 inch inclusive. Model MC is made in two sizes only.

In establishing this snap gage standard, the intention was to embody the most desirable features of gages previously manufactured and make it possible to produce snap gages conforming to a common standard.

The gaging pins or buttons may be adjusted by screws which bear against the ends. The locking device for the pins or buttons consists of a locking screw, a locking bushing, and a locking nut. The locking bushing and nut are beveled on one

Table 11. Commercial and American Standard Thread Ring Gages

For nominal screw thread diameters ranging from No. 0 to 4 3/4 inches inclusive.

See Fig. 3 on opposite page — All dimensions in inches.

Nominal Range of Sizes	Outside Diam. *A*	Blank Width *B*	Blank Width *C*	Hub Diam. *D*	Radius *E*	Hole Diameter *F*	Slot Width *G*
Nos. 0 to 6	1	1/4	.....	.....	5/16	5/32	0.010
Nos. 8 to 12	1	1/4	.....	.....	5/16	5/32	1/64
1/4 to 5/16	1 3/8	11/32	.....	.....	7/16	3/16	1/32
3/8 to 1/2	1 3/4	7/16	.....	.....	19/32	1/4	1/32
9/16 to 3/4	2 3/16	9/16	3/4	1 1/16	3/4	5/16	1/16
7/8 to 1 1/8	2 5/8	11/16	15/16	1 1/2	31/32	5/16	1/16
1 1/4 to 1 1/2	3 1/4	3/4	1 1/8	1 7/8	1 3/16	3/8	1/16
1 5/8 to 2	3 3/4	13/16	1 1/4	2 3/8	1 7/16	3/8	1/16
2 1/8 to 2 1/2	4 1/2	7/8	1 5/16	2 7/8	1 3/4	7/16	3/32
2 5/8 to 3	5	7/8	1 3/8	3 3/8	2	7/16	3/32
3 1/8 to 3 1/2	5 1/2	15/16	1 7/16	3 7/8	2 7/32	7/16	3/32
3 5/8 to 4	6 3/8	15/16	1 1/2	4 5/8	2 5/8	1/2	3/32
4 1/8 to 4 3/4	7 1/4	1	1 1/2	5 3/8	3 1/32	1/2	3/32

Nominal Range of Sizes	Locking and Adjusting Screw Dimensions *H*	*J*	*K*	Sleeve Length *L*	Adjusting Screw External Thread	Adjusting Screw Internal Thread	Max. Diam. *M**
Nos. 0 to 6	5/16	7/32	5/32	1/4	No. 8–36	No. 2–64	0.0860
Nos. 8 to 12	5/16	7/32	5/32	1/4	No. 8–36	No. 2–64	0.0860
1/4 to 5/16	3/8	11/32	1/4	7/16	No. 12–28	No. 4–48	0.1120
3/8 to 1/2	15/32	1/2	3/8	5/8	1/4–28	No. 6–40	0.1380
9/16 to 3/4	11/16	17/32	13/32	3/4	5/16–24	No. 10–32	0.1900
7/8 to 1 1/8	7/8	17/32	13/32	13/16	3/8–24	No. 12–28	0.2160
1 1/4 to 1 1/2	1 1/8	5/8	7/16	13/16	7/16–20	1/4–28	0.2500
1 5/8 to 2	1 3/8	5/8	7/16	13/16	7/16–20	1/4–28	0.2500
2 1/8 to 2 1/2	1 11/16	13/16	9/16	1 1/16	1/2–20	5/16–24	0.3125
2 5/8 to 3	1 15/16	13/16	9/16	1 1/16	1/2–20	5/16–24	0.3125
3 1/8 to 3 1/2	2 3/16	13/16	9/16	1 1/16	1/2–20	5/16–24	0.3125
3 5/8 to 4	2 9/16	1	3/4	1 1/2	5/8–18	3/8–24	0.3750
4 1/8 to 4 3/4	3	1	3/4	1 1/2	5/8–18	3/8–24	0.3750

* The locking screw body diameters have a minus tolerance of 0.002 inch on all sizes.

Use "thin" form of blank for 9/16- to 1 1/8-inch sizes inclusive, and 12 or more threads per inch (excepting 9/16–12 size). Also use thin blank for diameters above 1 1/8 inch if there are 10 or more threads per inch. The "thick" form is used for 9/16- to 1 1/8-inch sizes if threads per inch are less than 12 and for sizes above 1 1/8 inch if threads per inch are less than 10.

Gage blanks for screw sizes No. 0 to 6 are counterbored on each side to a depth of 1/32 inch and to a diameter of 1/2 inch. Gages for screw sizes from No. 0 to 5/16 inclusive have only one adjusting slot and terminal hole as indicated by the dotted lines on the illustration.

An annular groove is cut in the center of the knurled ring of the "Not Go" gage to distinguish it from the "Go" gage. These grooves range in width from 1/32 to 1/8 inch with depths equal to one-half the width.

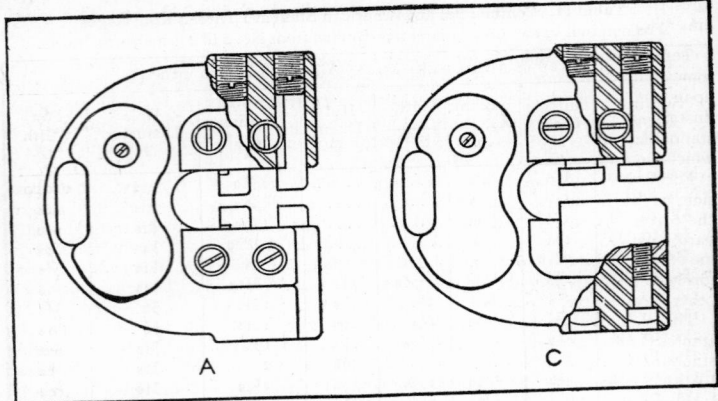

Fig. 4.

side to an angle of 30 degrees, and, as the screw is tightened, these beveled surfaces are drawn against corresponding flats on the shank of the gaging button or pin. This locking device was adopted because it has stood the test of time. The front edge or corner of the pins or buttons are beveled where they first engage the work. In the development of these gages exceptional care was taken to insure embodying all of the best features of snap-gage design including:

1. A design of frame which has proved to be exceptionally rigid under severe tests. 2. Reduction of weight to as low a point as strength of materials permits. 3. Distribution of metal to assure a nice balance and feel. 4. An effective and proved locking device. 5. Suitable construction of gaging pins, buttons, and anvils to give ample rigidity and maintain accuracy. 6. Ease and simplicity of adjustment. 7. Provision for sealing. 8. Careful selection of limits and tolerances to preserve accuracy and permit interchangeability.

Glass Gages. — Glass gages have proved satisfactory for gaging parts of steel and brass, but they are not recommended for aluminum. The cost of glass gages is relatively low compared with steel. They also resist corrosion and have low thermal conductivity. If a glass gage is dropped, breakage may occur, but this is preferable to distortion which, in the case of a steel gage, is not always apparent.

Norbide Gages. — Norbide (Boron Carbide B_4 C) is said to be the hardest artificial material made for commercial use. Tests made with plug gages on a production job showed a life of only four hours for hardened tool steel, eight hours for chromium-plated tool steel, two weeks for tungsten carbide, and after five months of wear of only 0.00001 inch for Norbide gages.

Sapphire Gages. — The sapphire is next to the diamond in the mineral hardness scale; hence, plug and ring gages of sapphire offer exceptional resistance to abrasion and wear; in fact they may be made without wear allowance. Sapphire gages resist ordinary shocks and are not subject to burring. Exceptional gaging records have been made with sapphire gages.

Carbide Gages. — Cemented carbide is another wear and corrosion-resistant material that has proven successful for gage blocks, plug gages and ring gages. Carbide gage blocks are practically non-magnetic and their adhesive factor facilitates the wringing together of the thinner blocks in building them up to a given dimension.

Temperature Standards for Gages. — Inasmuch as the length of a gage varies somewhat with temperature changes, it is evident that the length should be based upon some standard temperature. In the standardization of precision gages for industrial use, 68 degrees F. has been adopted generally in the United States as the standard temperature, because it is the common or average working temperature to which gages are ordinarily subjected in practice.

Formerly 62 degrees F. was the temperature used for precision gage standardization, as this is the temperature, approximately, at which the standard yard bar is at the correct length. While 62 degrees F. still applies to the fundamental standard yard bar in Washington, a temperature of 68 degrees F. is the generally used working standard for the calibration of industrial gages. This temperature not only conforms to average working temperatures, but it has been widely employed for many other physical tests, and moreover, it is the exact equivalent of 20 degrees C.

This same temperature of 20 degrees C., or 68 degrees F., has been adopted as the standard for gage work and other industrial measuring instruments, by engineering standardization bodies in Germany, Holland, Sweden, and Switzerland. In Great Britain 62 degrees F., applies to the fundamental standard yard bar, but 68 degrees F. is the temperature for industrial gage and instrument calibration.

Standard for Metric Instruments: Two temperatures — o degrees C. (32 degrees F.) and 20 degrees C. (68 degrees F.) — are employed for the industrial standardization of metric measuring instruments. The o degrees C. temperature is the standard at which the fundamental standard meter bar is of correct length, but as this temperature is far below ordinary working temperatures, materials having different coefficients of expansion would show measurable differences in length when the temperatures were increased from o degrees C. to ordinary working temperatures. For this reason the director of the International Bureau of Weights and Measures recommended the following practice, which, incidentally, has been very generally adopted in France.

Gages and other measuring instruments used in the manufacture of metal parts should be so made that when calibrated at a temperature of 20 degrees C., they will have an assumed coefficient of expansion of eleven millionths per unit of length per degree centigrade. In other words, at 20 degrees C. the actual length of such standards will be 220 millionths per unit of length longer than the corresponding subdivision of the fundamental standard of the meter at o degrees C. This assumed coefficient of eleven millionths is approximately correct for steel and cast iron, and the error due to the difference between this arbitrary coefficient and the actual coefficient of ordinary gage materials is so small that it may safely be ignored in industrial gage standardization.

Inspection of Tapped Holes. — One method of inspecting tapped holes is to inspect the tap first and then test the tapped holes periodically with " Go " and " Not Go " gages. The tap can be checked for wear by testing the tapped holes with a " Go " gage. A generally accepted plan consists of using a " Go " thread plug gage and " Not Go " thread plug gage for the minor diameter. Taps may be inspected by measuring the various elements, such as the pitch diameter, angle, and lead. Another method consists in tapping a hole with each tap before it is placed in use; the tapped hole is then checked with a " Go " and " Not Go " plug gage. " Go " and " Not Go " plain cylindrical plug gages are used for inspecting the minor diameter of the tapped hole. Plain ring or snap gages are used for inspecting the major diameter of the screw. When used, it is recommended that the " Go " inspection gage be a ring gage and the " Not Go " inspection gage be a snap gage. The working gages may be combined as a " Go " and " Not Go " snap gage.

Specifications for Thread Gages. — The following specifications of the National Screw Thread Commission will be helpful in the design and construction of gages used for producing threaded work. Specific information regarding the tolerances for working gages, inspection gages, and "setting" gages will be found on pages 1113 to 1115. The table on 1114 includes three grades of standard tolerances.

Gage Steel. — Gages may be made of a good grade of machine steel pack-hardened, or of straight carbon steel of not less than 1 per cent carbon; or preferably of an oil-hardening steel of approximately 1.10 per cent carbon and 1.40 per cent chromium. The handles should be made of a good grade of machine steel plainly marked to identify the gage.

Plug Gages. — All plug gages, whether plain or threaded, should be single-ended. Plug gages of 2 inches and less in diameter should be made with a plug inserted in the handle and fastened thereto by means of a pin. Plug gages of more than 2 inches in diameter should have the gaging blank so made as to be reversible. This can be accomplished by having a finished hole in the gage blank fitting a shouldered projection on the end of the handle, the gage blank being held on with a nut and keyed in the case of a threaded plug gage. The "go" plug gage should be noticeably longer than the "not go" gage, or some distinguishing feature in the design of the handle should be used to serve as a ready means of identification, such as a chamfer on the handle of the "go" gage.

Plain Ring Gages. — Both the "go" and "not go" gages should have their outside diameters knurled if made circular. The "go" gage should have a decided chamfer in order to provide a ready means of identification for distinguishing the "go" from the "not go" gage.

Snap Gages. — Snap gages may be either adjustable or nonadjustable. It is recommended that all snap gages up to and including ⅛ inch be of the built-up type. For larger snap gages, forged blanks, flat plate stock or other suitable construction may be used. Sufficient clearance beyond the mouth of the gage should be provided to permit the gaging of cylindrical work. Snap gages for measuring lengths and diameters may have one gaging dimension only, or may have a maximum and minimum gaging dimension, both on one end, or maximum and minimum gaging dimension on opposite ends of the gage. When the maximum and minimum gaging dimensions are placed on opposite ends of the gage, the maximum or "go" end of the snap gage should be distinguished from the minimum or " not go " end by having the corners of the gage on the " not go " end decidedly chamfered.

Plug Thread Gages. — End threads on plug thread gages should not be chamfered, but the first half turn of the end thread should be flattened to avoid a feather edge.

Dirt Grooves. — Inspection and working thread plug gages should be provided with dirt grooves which extend into the gage for a depth of from one to four threads.

Length of Thread. — The length of thread parallel to the axis of the gage should, for all standard "go" thread plug and ring gages, be at least as much as the quantity expressed in the following formula, in which L = length of thread and D = basic major diameter of thread: $L = 1.5 D$.

For threaded work of shorter length of engagement than $1.5 D$, the length of thread on the "go" gage may be correspondingly shorter.

"Not Go" Gage for Pitch Diameter only. — All "not go" thread plug gages should be made to check the pitch diameter only. This necessitates removal of the crest of the thread so that the dimension of the major diameter is never greater than that specified for the "go" gage, and also removing the portion of the thread at the root of the standard thread form.

Ring Thread Gages. — All ring thread gages should be made adjustable. The "go" gage should be distinguished from the "not go" gage by having a decided chamfer, and both gages should have their outside diameter knurled if made circular. The end threads on ring thread gages should not be chamfered but the first half turn of the end thread should be flattened to avoid a feather edge.

"Not go" ring thread gages should be made to check the pitch diameter only. This necessitates removal of the crest of the thread (so that the dimension of the minor diameter is never less than that specified for the maximum or "go" gage) and also removing the portion of the thread at the root of the standard form.

The Marking of Gages. — The maximum and minimum limits or sizes of gages may be marked in different ways. In the case of a plug gage, for example, the larger end may be marked either "max." (maximum), "high," " + " (plus), or "not go," while the small end would be marked "min." (minimum), "low," " — " (minus), or "go." In the case of a snap gage, the maximum dimension would be marked "max.," "high," " +," or "go," and the minimum, "min.," "low," " —," or "not go." The markings "max.," "min.," "high," and "low" refer to the dimension, while the markings "go" and "not go" refer to the use of the gage. When plug gages are marked "max." and "min.," it is evident that the "min." size is intended to pass into the hole while the "max." size is not supposed to enter. With a snap gage, however, the conditions are reversed: the "max." size should pass over the shaft, while the "min." size should not. Were the gages marked "go" and "not go," the meaning of these words would, in both cases, be the same, which is an advantage. That part of a gage marked "go" would pass over or into the work, while the part marked "not go" would not pass over or into the work.

Working and inspection double-ended plug gages should have the "go" end longer than the "not go" end. Working and inspection double-ended snap gages should have the "go" end rounded to a radius of about ⅛ inch, while the "not go" end should be beveled for a distance of about ⅛ inch. This makes it possible to see at a glance which is the "go" and which the "not go" end.

In marking the sizes on gages, the marking, when expressed in inches, should always be carried to at least three decimals, whether the last decimal is a o or not; for example, 0.370 and 0.200, etc. When the exact size requires more than three decimals, as, for example, 0.5798, the required number of decimals should, of course, be stamped on the gage. When the size is expressed in millimeters, the marking should be carried to at least two decimals. For example, 6.00 and 7.40; and if more than two decimals are required to express the exact size, the required number of decimals will, of course, be given.

Allowance for Lapping Thread Gages. — The allowance for lapping usually varies from 0.0002 to 0.0005 inch, although, in some cases, the allowance may be as high as 0.001 inch or more, the amount left for lapping increasing with the size of the gage.

As to the material for laps, some gage-makers prefer cast iron and others, soft steel. It is essential to use laps which are accurate as to lead and thread form, although some laps intended for correcting errors have thread angles which are slightly greater or less than the standard, the object being to change the angle of the gage thread more readily.

Abrasives for Lapping Gages. — Flour of emery is extensively used for lapping gages, and artificial abrasives are also used. The abrasive is mixed with some oil such as lard oil, sperm oil, or possibly kerosene oil. When a very slow cutting abrasive is required and the amount to be removed by lapping is small, rouge and lard oil may be used. Information regarding the different kinds of artificial abrasives adapted for lapping may be obtained from the manufacturers. After lapping a gage, it should be washed in gasoline before measuring it. If the gage has been heated appreciably as the result of lapping, it should be cooled in water down to the room temperature before measuring.

Dial Indicators — Commercial Standard CS8-41

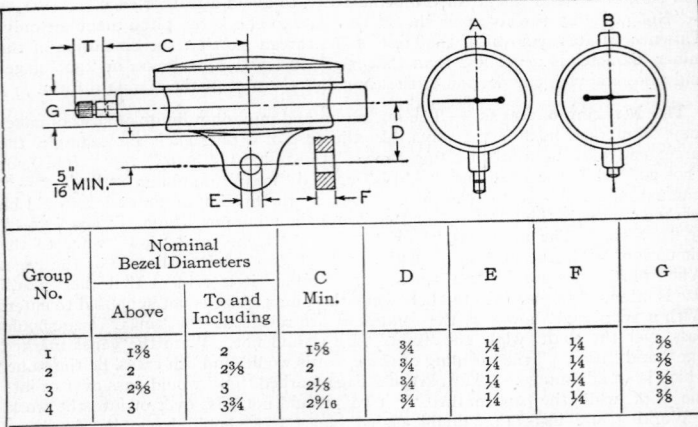

Group No.	Nominal Bezel Diameters		C Min.	D	E	F	G
	Above	To and Including					
1	1⅜	2	1⅝	¾	¼	¼	⅜
2	2	2⅜	2	¾	¼	¼	⅜
3	2⅜	3	2⅛	¾	¼	¼	⅜
4	3	3¾	2⁹⁄₁₆	¾	¼	¼	⅜

These standard basic dimensions are to permit mounting, interchangeably, dial gages of various makes and models. To secure uniformity between total spindle movement T and the magnification, total travel T should be equivalent to 2½ revolutions of indicator hand, except for special applications requiring greater movement. The indicator hand should swing to the 9 o'clock position or ¼ revolution to left of zero (as shown at A) when spindle is in its outer or extended position, to permit measuring on both the plus and minus sides of zero without making a full revolution of the indicating hand. Diagram B shows the position of the hand when the spindle has moved its full range inward.

Spirit Levels. — The accuracy of a spirit level depends upon the curvature of the glass tube. This tube is ground on the inside to a barrel shape, except in cheap levels which have a tube bent to the approximate curve. The bent tube type is only for work which does not require great accuracy. The tube is nearly filled with spirits of wine, ether, or some similar fluid and is hermetically sealed at each end. The larger radius of curvature the glass has, the more sensitive will be the level. The following table gives the curvature for various degrees of sensitiveness, the graduations being in tenths of an inch:

	Seconds					Min.	Deg.
Angular Value of Each Graduation	2	5	10	20	30	1	1
Corresponding Diameter of Curvature in Feet	1718	687	343	171	114	57	0.95

The air space in a ground glass is much longer than in a bent one, being ordinarily from ¼ to ⅓ the length of the tube. Modern levels are graduated to tenths and twentieths of an inch, except when they are divided according to the metric system. The leveling glass or "bubble" is generally fixed in a brass tube with plaster-of-paris. This method is satisfactory for all levels having an accuracy of about five seconds angular measurement to each one-tenth inch graduation. For finer levels, it is better to fix one end only with plaster-of-paris and the other end with cork.

TAPPING AND THREAD CUTTING

Diameter of Tap Drill. — Tapping troubles are often caused by using tap drills that are too small in diameter. For ordinary manufacturing, not more than 75 or 80 per cent of the standard thread depth is necessary, and for some classes of work, not more than 50 per cent is required. Tap drill sizes, especially for machine screws, should be varied according to the material to be tapped and the depth of the tapped hole. In general, if the screws enter more than one and one-half times the diameter, one-half of the full thread is sufficient. Soft tough material, such as copper, Norway iron, drawn aluminum, etc., should have a larger hole for the tap than hard crystalline materials, such as cast metals. When tapping soft materials, if the hole is too small, the threads will be torn off to some extent, thus actually decreasing the effective thread depth as compared to what it would be if the tap drill had been of larger diameter; but if the hole is drilled rather large, when tapping tenacious materials, the metal at the top of the thread is drawn somewhat, thereby increasing the depth of the threads. This is more likely to occur after the keen edge of the tap has been slightly dulled by use.

The diameters of tap drills can be found by the formula, $D = T - 0.75 \times 2\,d$, in which D = drill diameter, T = diameter of tap or thread and d = depth of thread. The depth of thread for various numbers of threads per inch and thread forms, are given in the tables in the section "Screw Thread Systems." The diameters obtained by this formula allow for a thread having 75 per cent of the standard depth which is sufficient for general work. The formula applies to the American (National) thread form. The diameter of the tap drill should not be smaller than is necessary to give the required strength of thread, as every decrease of even 0.001 inch in diameter of the tap drill materially increases the power required for tapping and the percentage of broken taps.

Simplified Rule for Tap Drill Diameter. — If a table of tap drill sizes is not at hand, the following rule may be used:

Rule: To find the tap drill diameter in inches, subtract from the outside diameter of the tap an amount equal to 1 divided by the number of threads per inch. In the practical application of this rule, the nearest commercial drill size is always used.

Tap Drills for Pipe Taps *

Size of Tap	Drills for Briggs Pipe Taps	Drills for Whitworth Pipe Taps	Size of Tap	Drills for Briggs Pipe Taps	Drills for Whitworth Pipe Taps	Size of Tap	Drills for Briggs Pipe Taps	Drills for Whitworth Pipe Taps
⅛	11/32	5/16	1¼	1½	1 15/32	3¼	....	3½
¼	7/16	27/64	1½	1 23/32	1 25/32	3½	3¾	3¾
⅜	19/32	9/16	1¾	....	1 15/16	3¾	....	4
½	23/32	11/16	2	2 3/16	2 5/32	4	4¼	4¼
⅝	....	25/32	2¼	....	2 13/32	4½	4¾	4¾
¾	15/16	29/32	2½	2⅝	2 25/32	5	5 5/16	5¼
⅞	....	1 1/16	2¾	....	3 1/32	5½	....	5¾
1	1 5/32	1⅛	3	3¼	3 9/32	6	6⅜	6¼

* To secure the best results, the hole should be reamed before tapping with a reamer having a taper of ¾ inch per foot.

Tap Drill Sizes for Threads of American Standard Form
(Adopted by Tap and Die Manufacturers)

Screw Thread		Commercial Tap Drills*		Screw Thread		Commercial Tap Drills*	
Outside Diam. Pitch	Root Diam.	Size or Number	Decimal Equiv.	Outside Diam. Pitch	Root Diam.	Size or Number	Decimal Equiv.
1/16-64	0.0422	3/64	0.0469	27	0.4519	15/32	0.4687
72	0.0445	3/64	0.0469	9/16-12	0.4542	31/64	0.4844
5/64-60	0.0563	1/16	0.0625	18	0.4903	33/64	0.5156
72	0.0601	52	0.0635	27	0.5144	17/32	0.5312
3/32-48	0.0667	49	0.0730	5/8-11	0.5069	17/32	0.5312
50	0.0678	49	0.0730	12	0.5168	35/64	0.5469
7/64-48	0.0823	43	0.0890	18	0.5528	37/64	0.5781
1/8-32	0.0844	3/32	0.0937	27	0.5769	19/32	0.5937
40	0.0925	38	0.1015	11/16-11	0.5694	19/32	0.5937
9/64-40	0.1081	32	0.1160	16	0.6063	5/8	0.6250
5/32-32	0.1157	1/8	0.1250	3/4-16	0.6201	21/32	0.6562
36	0.1202	30	0.1285	12	0.6418	43/64	0.6719
11/64-32	0.1313	9/64	0.1406	16	0.6688	11/16	0.6875
3/16-24	0.1334	26	0.1470	27	0.7019	23/32	0.7187
32	0.1469	22	0.1570	13/16-10	0.6826	23/32	0.7187
13/64-32	0.1490	20	0.1610	7/8-9	0.7307	49/64	0.7656
7/32-24	0.1646	16	0.1770	12	0.7668	51/64	0.7969
32	0.1782	12	0.1890	14	0.7822	13/16	0.8125
15/64-24	0.1806	10	0.1935	18	0.8028	53/64	0.8281
1/4-20	0.1850	7	0.2010	27	0.8269	27/32	0.8437
24	0.1959	4	0.2090	15/16-9	0.7932	53/64	0.8281
27	0.2019	3	0.2130	1 - 8	0.8376	7/8	0.8750
28	0.2036	3	0.2130	12	0.8918	59/64	0.9219
32	0.2094	7/32	0.2187	14	0.9072	15/16	0.9375
5/16-18	0.2403	F	0.2570	27	0.9519	31/32	0.9687
20	0.2476	17/64	0.2656	1 1/8- 7	0.9394	63/64	0.9844
24	0.2584	I	0.2720	12	1.0168	1 3/64	1.0469
27	0.2644	J	0.2770	1 1/4- 7	1.0644	1 7/64	1.1094
32	0.2719	9/32	0.2812	12	1.1418	1 11/64	1.1719
3/8-16	0.2938	5/16	0.3125	1 3/8- 6	1.1585	1 7/32	1.2187
20	0.3100	21/64	0.3281	12	1.2668	1 19/64	1.2969
24	0.3209	Q	0.3320	1 1/2- 6	1.2835	1 11/32	1.3437
27	0.3269	R	0.3390	12	1.3918	1 27/64	1.4219
7/16-14	0.3447	U	0.3680	1 5/8- 5 1/2	1.3888	1 29/64	1.4531
20	0.3726	25/64	0.3906	1 3/4- 5	1.4902	1 9/16	1.5625
24	0.3834	X	0.3970	1 7/8- 5	1.6152	1 11/16	1.6875
27	0.3894	Y	0.4040	2 - 4 1/2	1.7113	1 25/32	1.7812
1/2-12	0.3918	27/64	0.4219	2 1/8- 4 1/2	1.8363	1 29/32	1.9062
13	0.4001	27/64	0.4219	2 1/4- 4 1/2	1.9613	2 1/32	2.0312
20	0.4351	29/64	0.4531	2 3/8- 4	2.0502	2 1/8	2.1250
24	0.4459	29/64	0.4531	2 1/2- 4	2.1752	2 1/4	2.2500

* These tap drill diameters allow approximately 75 per cent of a full thread.

Tap Drills and Clearance Drills for Machine Screws

Size of Screw		No. of Threads per Inch	Tap Drills		Clearance Hole Drills			
					Close Fit		Free Fit	
No. or Diam.	Decimal Equiv.		Drill Size	Decimal Equiv.	Drill Size	Decimal Equiv.	Drill Size	Decimal Equiv.
0	.060	80	3/64	.0469	52	.0635	50	.0700
1	.073	64 72	53 53	.0595 .0595	48	.0760	46	.0810
2	.086	56 64	50 50	.0700 .0700	43	.0890	41	.0960
3	.099	48 56	47 45	.0785 .0820	37	.1040	35	.1100
4	.112	36* 40 48	44 43 42	.0860 .0890 .0935	32	.1160	30	.1285
5	.125	40 44	38 37	.1015 .1040	30	.1285	29	.1360
6	.138	32 40	36 33	.1065 .1130	27	.1440	25	.1495
8	.164	32 36	29 29	.1360 .1360	18	.1695	16	.1770
10	.190	24 32	25 21	.1495 .1590	9	.1960	7	.2010
12	.216	24 28	16 14	.1770 .1820	2	.2210	1	.2280
14	.242	20* 24*	10 7	.1935 .2010	D	.2460	F	.2570
1/4	.250	20 28	7 3	.2010 .2130	F	.2570	H	.2660
5/16	.3125	18 24	F I	.2570 .2720	P	.3230	Q	.3320
3/8	.375	16 24	5/16 Q	.3125 .3320	W	.3860	X	.3970
7/16	.4375	14 20	U 25/64	.3680 .3906	29/64	.4531	15/32	.4687
1/2	.500	13 20	27/64 29/64	.4219 .4531	33/64	.5156	17/32	.5312

* Screws marked with asterisk (*) are not in the American Standard but are from the former A.S.M.E. Standard and are still used — especially the No. 4 size with 36 threads per inch.

Removing a Broken Tap. — Whenever practicable, a broken tap should be removed by using a tap extractor. A design which has proved successful is equipped with projecting fingers which enter the flutes of the tap which is backed out of the hole by turning the extractor with a wrench. This extractor is adjustable so as to support the fingers close to the tap, even when the broken end is below the surface of the work. Another method of removing broken taps, which has proved effective in some cases, is to inject into the hole a little nitric acid, diluted in the proportion of about one part acid to five parts water. The action of the acid upon the steel loosens the tap so that it usually can be removed either with an extractor or an ordinary pair of pliers. The remaining acid should afterwards be washed out of the hole so that it will not continue to eat the threads. A third method consists in adding, by electric arc welding, metal onto the shank of the broken tap, up to or above the level of the work. Care must be exercised to prevent depositing metal onto the threads in the tapped hole. After the shank has been built up, the head of a bolt or a nut is tacked to it and then the tap may be backed out. Broken taps may also be removed by burning. The tap is aligned with a copper tube of an electrical burning equipment. The tube diameter is slightly smaller than the root diameter of the tap. Both electricity and compressed air are used and a hole is burned through the tap as the copper tube is automatically vibrated and moved inward.

Power Required for Tapping. — The power required for tapping depends upon the diameter of the tap drill hole; the kind of lubricant used; the shape of the tap flutes; amount that the end of the tap is ground back, that is, the "chamfer"; and the condition of the tap. The accompanying table, "Average Torque in Inch-pounds for Tapping Different Materials," contains figures which are the average of a large number of tests. The maximum and minimum torque in inch-pounds is given. The taps were ½ inch U. S. standard; depth of tapped hole, ½ inch; and diameter of tap drill, 0.420 inch. The table, "Effect of Lubricants and Tap Drill Diameters when Tapping," shows the variation in power, the number of breakages and the quality of thread resulting from the use of different lubricants and three different sizes of tap drills. These data represent a long series of tests. For comparative purposes, the breaking strength is taken as 100, and the power required for tapping is given as a percentage of this number. The test pieces were common hexagon, cold-punched nuts accurately reamed to the sizes specified, and regular ½ inch U. S. standard taps were used. The torque required to break a properly made ½ inch U. S. standard tap is approximately 1000 inch-pounds; hence, by multiplying the percentage given in the table, by 10, the average actual torque in inch-pounds can be obtained. (From paper by Mr. F. O. Wells, read before the American Society of Mechanical Engineers.)

Average Torque in Inch-pounds for Tapping Different Materials
(One-half inch U. S. tap; diameter of tap drill, 0.420 inch.)

Material Tapped	Torque in Inch-pounds	
	Maximum	Minimum
Hexagon Drawn Brass................	64	63
Crucible Tool Steel................	261	258
Cold Punched Hexagon Steel Nuts........	182	176
Hexagon Screw Stock................	205	189
Drawn Hexagon Phosphor Bronze.........	234	221

Effect of Lubricants and Tap Drill Diameters when Tapping

Lubricant	Diameter Tap Hole, 0.425 inch (75 per cent Thread)			Diameter Tap Hole, 0.410 inch (90 per cent Thread)			Diameter Tap Hole, 0.400 inch (Full Thread)		
	Power Required*	Per cent of Breakages	Quality of Thread	Power Required*	Per cent of Breakages	Quality of Thread	Power Required*	Per cent of Breakages	Quality of Thread
Animal Lard Oil	15.9	0	Smooth	.....	....	....	.....	....	....
Sperm Oil	16.5	0	Smooth	23	0	Smooth	35.5	0	Smooth, Taps Torn
Graphite, 10 per cent; Tallow, 90 per cent	16.9	0	Smooth	.....	....	....	.....	....	....
Cataract Soap Compound	18.9	0	Smooth	25.1	0	Smooth	41	0	Slightly Rough, Taps Torn
Mineral Lard Oil	19.9	0	Smooth	36.5	0	Smooth	57.5	0	Smooth, Taps Torn
Tapped Without Oil	29.9	14	Rough	60.2	50	Rough	71.8	66	Torn, Partly Stripped
Machine Oil	34.2	15	Torn	62.5	71.5	Badly Torn	100	100	Torn, Chips Wedged

* In per cent of breaking strength of tap.

Power for Pipe Taps. — The power required for driving pipe taps is given in the following table, which includes nominal pipe tap sizes from 2 to 8 inches.

Power Required for Pipe Taps

Nominal Tap Size	Rev. per Min.	Net H.P.	Thickness of Metal	Nominal Tap Size	Rev. per Min.	Net H.P.	Thickness of Metal
2	40	4.24	1⅛	3½	25.6	7.20	1¾
2½	40	5.15	1⅛	4	18	6.60	2
*2½	38.5	9.14	1⅛	5	18	7.70	2
3	40	5.75	1⅛	6	17.8	8.80	2
*3	38.5	9.70	1⅛	8	14	7.96	2½

* Tapping steel casting; other tests in cast iron.

The holes to be tapped were reamed with standard pipe tap reamers before tapping. The horsepower recorded was read off just before the tap was reversed.

The table gives the net horsepower, deductions being made for the power required to run the machine without a load. The material tapped was cast iron, except in two instances, where steel casting was tapped. It will be seen that nearly double the power is required for tapping steel casting. The power varies, of course, with the conditions. More power than that indicated in the table will be required if the cast iron is of a harder quality or if the taps are not properly relieved. The taps used in these experiments were of the inserted-blade type, the blades being made of high-speed steel.

Recommended Tapping Fluids or Lubricants

Material to be Tapped	Kind of Lubricant	Material to be Tapped	Kind of Lubricant
Cast Brass or Bronze.........	Light mineral or soluble oil	Nitriding Steels..	Sulphurized mineral oil
Forged Brass or Copper.........	Mineral with lard base	Magnesium Alloys	Dry or mixture of 10 per cent lard oil and 90 per cent light mineral oil diluted with 30–40 per cent kerosene
Cast Iron.........	Light mineral or soluble oil		
Aluminum, Aluminum Alloys, etc.	Add kerosene to light mineral oils, and sometimes also add good lard oil		
		High-Nickel Alloys............	Sulphurized mineral lard oil
Alloy Steel, Low-Carbon Steel Forgings.......	Good grade of sulphur-base oil	Beryllium Copper	Lard oil
		Nickel Silvers and Cupro-Nickels..	Sulphur-base oil
Stainless Steels...	Soluble oil with sulphur added. On tough jobs, use paste of white lead and a high sulphur-base lard oil	Aluminum Bronze	⅓ kerosene and ⅔ lard oil
		Copper-Silicon Alloys............	Kerosene and lard oil mixture
		Laminated Plastics............	Dry or water
SAE Nickel Alloy Steels..........	Sulphurized mineral oil	Hard Rubber....	Any good grade tapping oil
Carbon Sheet Steel..........	Sulphur-base oil		

Tapping Speeds for Different Materials

These speeds are intended as a general guide only. The most effective speed should be determined by actual test with a given tap, material, machine, and tapping fluid.

Material to be Tapped	Speed, Feet per minute, High-speed Steel Taps*	Material to be Tapped	Speed, Feet per minute, High-speed Steel Taps*
Cast Iron.................	70 to 90	Copper...................	85 to 110
Malleable Iron...........	35 to 70	Monel Metal.............	20 to 30
Machine Steel............	40 to 70	Aluminum Alloys........	90 to 110
Alloy Steels.............	20 to 40	Magnesium Alloys.......	25 to 50
Tool Steel...............	20 to 40	Duralumin..............	90 to 100
Stainless Steel...........	15 to 30	Bakelite................	60 to 80
Steel Castings...........	20 to 35	Hard Rubber............	80 to 100
Brass...................	90 to 120	Fiber..................	80 to 100
Bronze..................	40 to 70	Nickel Silver............	75 to 90
Manganese Bronze.......	30 to 50		....

* The speeds in this table should be reduced about one-half for carbon steel taps.

Planing Clearance on Threading Tools. — In the following are given formulas for finding the angle to which the planer or shaper head should be set when planing threading tools with both side and front clearance. The expression "leading" side indicates the side of the tool which first enters the work when a thread is cut; the "following" side is that which enters the work last. In the formulas, a = depth of thread; b = width of flat on offset tool; c = actual width of flat; d = outside diameter of screw; v = front clearance angle; w = one-half angle of thread; y = angle of thread helix; and x = angle to which to set the planer head when planing the tool on the side. Then, for tools with side clearance:

$$\tan y = \frac{\text{lead of thread}}{3.1416\,(d-a)}$$

and angle x is found from:

$$\tan x = \frac{\cos y \pm (\cot w \times \sin v \times \sin y)}{\cot w \times \cos v}$$

Use + for leading side and − for following side.

For Acme (29-degree) thread and 15 degrees clearance angle, the formula can, for all practical purposes, be written:

$$\tan x = \frac{\cos y \pm \sin y}{3.735}$$

The width of flat on the offset tool is figured from the formula:

$$b = c \times \cos y$$

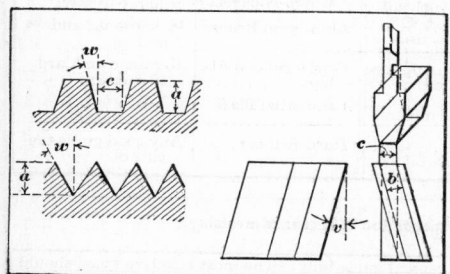

If the tool has no side clearance, the angle of helix can be considered equal to 0 degrees, and the formula reduces itself to $\tan x = \dfrac{\tan w}{\cos v}$

For a 60-degree screw thread, U. S. standard, the formula will then be:

$$\tan x = \frac{\tan 30°}{\cos 15°} = 0.5977;$$
$$x = 30 \text{ deg. } 52 \text{ min.}$$

Example: Find the angles to which to set the planer heads when planing the sides of an Acme thread tool for a screw 2 inches in diameter having 2 threads per inch.

$$\tan y = \frac{0.5}{3.1416\,(2-0.26)} = 0.0915; \quad y = 5° \ 14'.$$

$$\tan x = \frac{\cos 5° \ 14' \pm \sin 5° \ 14'}{3.735} = \frac{0.9958 \pm 0.0912}{3.735}$$

$\tan x$ (for "leading" side) = 0.291; $x = 16° \ 14'$.

$\tan x$ (for "following" side) = 0.242; $x = 13° \ 37'$

Helix Angles of Screw Threads — Based Upon Pitch Diameters — I

Helix Angles (Degrees and Minutes) Based Upon Pitch Diameters of Screw Threads of American Standard or U. S. Form.

Outside Diameter, Inches	Threads per Inch												
	11	11½	12	13	14	16	18	20	22	24	26	28	32
3/16	....	....	....	....	....	7°-43'	6°-40'	5°-52'	5°-14'	4°-44'	4°-19'	3°-57'	3°-24'
1/4	....	....	....	6°-59'	6°-22'	5°-26'	4°-44'	4°-11'	3°-45'	3°-24'	3°-7'	2°-52'	2°-29'
5/16	....	....	5°-52'	5°-20'	4°-53'	4°-11'	3°-40'	3°-15'	2°-56'	2°-40'	2°-26'	2°-15'	1°-57'
3/8	....	....	4°-44'	4°-19'	3°-57'	3°-24'	2°-59'	2°-40'	2°-24'	2°-11'	2°-0'	1°-51'	1°-36'
7/16	4°-22'	....	3°-57'	3°-37'	3°-20'	2°-52'	2°-31'	2°-15'	2°-2'	1°-51'	1°-42'	1°-34'	1°-22'
1/2	3°-45'	....	3°-24'	3°-7'	2°-52'	2°-31'	2°-11'	1°-57'	1°-46'	1°-36'	1°-29'	1°-22'	1°-11'
9/16	3°-17'	....	2°-59'	2°-44'	2°-31'	2°-11'	1°-55'	1°-43'	1°-33'	1°-25'	1°-18'	1°-12'	1°-3'
5/8	2°-56'	....	2°-40'	2°-26'	2°-15'	1°-57'	1°-43'	1°-32'	1°-23'	1°-16'	1°-10'	1°-5'	0°-57'
3/4	2°-24'	2°-17'	2°-11'	2°-6'	1°-51'	1°-36'	1°-25'	1°-16'	1°-9'	1°-3'	0°-58'	0°-54'	0°-47'
7/8	2°-2'	1°-56'	1°-51'	1°-42'	1°-34'	1°-22'	1°-12'	1°-5'	0°-59'	0°-54'	0°-50'	0°-46'	0°-40'
1	1°-46'	1°-41'	1°-36'	1°-29'	1°-22'	1°-11'	1°-3'	0°-57'	0°-51'	0°-47'	0°-43'	0°-40'	0°-35'
1⅛	1°-33'	1°-29'	1°-25'	1°-20'	1°-12'	1°-3'	0°-56'	0°-50'	0°-45'	0°-42'	0°-38'	0°-35'	0°-31'
1¼	1°-23'	1°-20'	1°-16'	1°-10'	1°-5'	0°-57'	0°-50'	0°-45'	0°-41'	0°-37'	0°-34'	0°-32'	0°-28'
1⅜	1°-16'	1°-12'	1°-9'	1°-4'	0°-59'	0°-51'	0°-45'	0°-41'	0°-37'	0°-34'	0°-31'	0°-29'	0°-25'
1½	1°-9'	1°-6'	1°-3'	0°-58'	0°-54'	0°-47'	0°-42'	0°-37'	0°-34'	0°-31'	0°-29'	0°-26'	0°-23'
1⅝	1°-3'	1°-1'	0°-58'	0°-53'	0°-49'	0°-43'	0°-38'	0°-34'	0°-31'	0°-29'	0°-26'	0°-24'	0°-21'
1¾	0°-59'	0°-56'	0°-54'	0°-49'	0°-46'	0°-40'	0°-35'	0°-32'	0°-29'	0°-26'	0°-24'	0°-23'	0°-20'
1⅞	0°-55'	0°-52'	0°-50'	0°-43'	0°-43'	0°-37'	0°-33'	0°-30'	0°-27'	0°-25'	0°-21'	0°-21'	0°-18'
2	0°-51'	0°-49'	0°-47'	0°-38'	0°-40'	0°-35'	0°-31'	0°-28'	0°-25'	0°-23'	0°-19'	0°-20'	0°-17'
2¼	0°-45'	0°-43'	0°-42'	0°-31'	0°-35'	0°-31'	0°-27'	0°-25'	0°-22'	0°-21'	0°-17'	0°-18'	0°-15'
2½	0°-41'	0°-39'	0°-37'	0°-29'	0°-32'	0°-28'	0°-25'	0°-22'	0°-20'	0°-18'	0°-15'	0°-16'	....
2¾	0°-37'	0°-35'	0°-34'	0°-26'	0°-29'	0°-25'	0°-22'	0°-20'	0°-18'	0°-17'	....	....	....
3	0°-34'	0°-32'	0°-31'	0°-24'	0°-26'	0°-23'	0°-21'	0°-18'	0°-17'	0°-15'	....	....	....
3¼	0°-31'	0°-30'	0°-29'	0°-23'	0°-23'	0°-21'	0°-19'	0°-17'	0°-15'	0°-14'	....	....	....
3½	0°-29'	0°-28'	0°-26'	0°-21'	0°-21'	0°-20'	0°-18'	0°-16'	0°-14'	0°-13'	....	....	....
3¾	0°-27'	0°-26'	0°-25'	....	0°-20'	0°-18'	0°-16'	0°-15'	0°-13'	0°-12'	....	....	....
4	0°-25'	0°-24'	0°-23'	....	....	0°-17'	0°-15'	0°-14'	0°-12'	0°-11'	....	....	....

Helix Angles of Screw Threads — Based Upon Pitch Diameters — 2

Helix Angles (Degrees and Minutes) Based Upon Pitch Diameters of Screw Threads of American Standard or U. S. Form.*

Outside Diameter, Inches	Threads per Inch												
	2	3	3¼	3½	4	4½	5	5½	6	7	8	9	10
7/16	....	....	....	....	....	....	....	....	....	....	....	....	4°-53'
1/2	....	....	....	....	....	....	....	....	....	....	5°-26'	4°-44'	4°-11'
9/16	....	....	....	....	....	....	....	....	....	....	4°-44'	4°-8'	3°-40'
5/8	....	....	....	....	....	....	....	....	....	4°-53'	4°-11'	3°-40'	3°-15'
3/4	....	....	....	....	....	....	....	....	4°-44'	3°-58'	3°-24'	2°-59'	2°-40'
7/8	....	....	....	....	....	....	....	4°-22'	3°-58'	3°-20'	2°-52'	2°-31'	2°-15'
1	....	....	....	....	5°-26'	4°-44'	4°-11'	3°-45'	3°-24'	2°-52'	2°-29'	2°-11'	1°-57'
1⅛	....	....	....	5°-32'	4°-44'	4°-7'	3°-40'	3°-17'	2°-59'	2°-31'	2°-11'	1°-55'	1°-43'
1¼	....	5°-52'	5°-20'	4°-53'	4°-11'	3°-40'	3°-15'	2°-56'	2°-40'	2°-15'	1°-57'	1°-43'	1°-32'
1⅜	....	5°-14'	4°-46'	4°-22'	3°-45'	3°-17'	2°-56'	2°-38'	2°-24'	2°-2'	1°-46'	1°-33'	1°-24'
1½	....	4°-44'	4°-19'	3°-57'	3°-24'	2°-59'	2°-40'	2°-24'	2°-11'	1°-51'	1°-36'	1°-25'	1°-16'
1⅝	6°-59'	4°-18'	3°-56'	3°-37'	3°-7'	2°-44'	2°-26'	2°-12'	2°-00'	1°-42'	1°-29'	1°-18'	1°-10'
1¾	6°-22'	3°-57'	3°-37'	3°-20'	2°-52'	2°-31'	2°-15'	2°-2'	1°-51'	1°-34'	1°-22'	1°-12'	1°-5'
1⅞	5°-52'	3°-40'	3°-21'	3°-5'	2°-40'	2°-20'	2°-5'	1°-53'	1°-43'	1°-28'	1°-16'	1°-7'	1°-00'
2	5°-26'	3°-24'	3°-7'	2°-52'	2°-29'	2°-11'	1°-57'	1°-46'	1°-36'	1°-22'	1°-11'	1°-3'	0°-57'
2¼	4°-44'	2°-59'	2°-44'	2°-31'	2°-11'	1°-55'	1°-43'	1°-33'	1°-25'	1°-12'	1°-3'	0°-56'	0°-50'
2½	4°-11'	2°-40'	2°-26'	2°-15'	1°-57'	1°-43'	1°-32'	1°-24'	1°-16'	1°-5'	0°-57'	0°-50'	0°-45'
2¾	3°-45'	2°-24'	2°-12'	2°-2'	1°-46'	1°-33'	1°-24'	1°-16'	1°-9'	0°-59'	0°-51'	0°-45'	0°-41'
3	3°-24'	2°-11'	2°-00'	1°-51'	1°-36'	1°-25'	1°-16'	1°-9'	1°-3'	0°-54'	0°-47'	0°-42'	0°-37'
3¼	3°-7'	2°-00'	1°-50'	1°-42'	1°-29'	1°-18'	1°-10'	1°-4'	0°-58'	0°-49'	0°-43'	0°-38'	0°-34'
3½	2°-52'	1°-51'	1°-42'	1°-34'	1°-22'	1°-12'	1°-5'	0°-59'	0°-54'	0°-46'	0°-40'	0°-35'	0°-32'
3¾	2°-40'	1°-43'	1°-35'	1°-28'	1°-16'	1°-7'	1°-00'	0°-55'	0°-50'	0°-43'	0°-37'	0°-33'	0°-30'
4	2°-29'	1°-36'	1°-29'	1°-22'	1°-11'	1°-3'	0°-57'	0°-51'	0°-47'	0°-40'	0°-35'	0°-31'	0°-28'

* To find the tangent of the helix angle equivalent to a given pitch diameter, divide the lead of the thread by 3.1416 × pitch diameter. Pitch diameter = outside diameter − depth of thread.

Lathe Change Gears

Change Gears for Thread Cutting. — To determine the change gears to use for cutting a thread of given pitch, first find what number of threads per inch will be cut when gears of the same size are placed on the lead-screw and spindle stud, either by actual trial or by referring to the index plate; then multiply this number, called the "lathe screw constant," by some trial number to obtain the number of teeth in the gear for the spindle stud, and multiply the threads per inch to be cut by the *same* trial number to obtain the number of teeth in the gear for the lead-screw. Expressing this rule as a formula:

$$\frac{\text{Trial number} \times \text{lathe screw constant}}{\text{Trial number} \times \text{threads per inch to be cut}} = \frac{\text{teeth in gear on spindle stud}}{\text{teeth in gear on lead-screw}}$$

For example, suppose the available change gears supplied with the lathe have 24, 28, 32, 36 teeth, etc., the number increasing by four up to one hundred, and that 10 threads per inch are to be cut in a lathe having a lathe screw constant of 6; then, if the screw constant is written as the numerator, and the number of threads per inch to be cut, as the denominator of a fraction, and both numerator and denominator are multiplied by some trial number, say 4, it is found that gears having 24 and 40 teeth can be used. Thus:

$$\frac{6}{10} = \frac{6 \times 4}{10 \times 4} = \frac{24}{40}$$

The 24-tooth gear goes on the spindle stud and the 40-tooth gear on the lead-screw.

The lathe screw constant is, of course, equal to the number of threads per inch on the lead-screw, provided the spindle stud and spindle are geared in the ratio of 1 to 1, which, however, is not always the case.

Compound Gearing. — To find the change gears used in compound gearing, place the screw constant as the numerator, and the number of threads per inch to be cut as the denominator of a fraction; resolve both numerator and denominator into two factors each, and multiply each "pair" of factors by the same number, until values are obtained representing suitable numbers of teeth for the change gears. (One factor in the numerator and one in the denominator make a "pair" of factors.)

Example: — $1\frac{3}{4}$ threads per inch are to be cut in a lathe having a screw constant of 8; the available gears have 24, 28, 32, 36, 40 teeth, etc., increasing by four up to one hundred. Following the rule:

$$\frac{8}{1\frac{3}{4}} = \frac{2 \times 4}{1 \times 1\frac{3}{4}} = \frac{(2 \times 36) \times (4 \times 16)}{(1 \times 36) \times (1\frac{3}{4} \times 16)} = \frac{72 \times 64}{36 \times 28}$$

The gears having 72 and 64 teeth are the *driving* gears and those with 36 and 28 teeth are the *driven* gears.

Fractional Threads. — Sometimes the lead of a thread is given as a fraction of an inch instead of stating the number of threads per inch. For example, a thread may be required to be cut, having $\frac{3}{8}$ inch lead. The expression "$\frac{3}{8}$ inch lead" should first be transformed to "number of threads per inch." The number of threads per inch (the thread being single) equals:

$$\frac{1}{\frac{3}{8}} = 1 \div \frac{3}{8} = \frac{8}{3} = 2\frac{2}{3}$$

To find the change gears to cut $2\frac{2}{3}$ threads per inch in a lathe having a screw constant 8 and change gears running from 24 to 100 teeth, increasing by 4, proceed as below·

$$\frac{8}{2\frac{2}{3}} = \frac{2 \times 4}{1 \times 2\frac{2}{3}} = \frac{(2 \times 36) \times (4 \times 24)}{(1 \times 36) \times (2\frac{2}{3} \times 24)} = \frac{72 \times 96}{36 \times 64}$$

Change Gears for Metric Pitches. — When screws are cut in accordance with the metric system, it is the usual practice to give the lead of the thread in millimeters, instead of the number of threads per unit of measurement. To find the change gears for cutting metric threads, when using a lathe having an English lead-screw, first determine the number of threads per inch corresponding to the given lead in millimeters. Suppose a thread of 3 millimeters lead is to be cut in a lathe having an English lead-screw and a screw constant of 6. As there are 25.4 millimeters per inch, the number of threads per inch will equal 25.4 ÷ 3. Place the screw constant as the numerator, and the number of threads per inch to be cut as the denominator:

$$\frac{6}{\frac{25.4}{3}} = 6 \div \frac{25.4}{3} = \frac{6 \times 3}{25.4}$$

The numerator and denominator of this fractional expression of the change gear ratio is next multiplied by some trial number to determine the size of the gears. The first whole number by which 25.4 can be multiplied so as to get a whole number as the result is 5. Thus, $25.4 \times 5 = 127$. Hence, one gear having 127 teeth is always used when cutting metric threads with an English lead-screw. The other gear required in this case has 90 teeth. Thus:

$$\frac{6 \times 3 \times 5}{25.4 \times 5} = \frac{90}{127}$$

Therefore, the following rule can be used to find the change gears for cutting metric pitches with an English lead-screw:

Rule: Place the lathe screw constant multiplied by the lead of the required thread in millimeters multiplied by 5, as the numerator of the fraction, and 127 as the denominator. The product of the numbers in the numerator equals the number of teeth for the spindle-stud gear, and 127 is the number of teeth for the lead-screw gear.

If the lathe has a metric pitch lead-screw, and a screw having a given number of threads per inch is to be cut, first find the "metric screw constant" of the lathe or the lead of thread in millimeters that would be cut with change gears of equal size on the lead-screw and spindle stud; then the method of determining the change gears is simply the reverse of the one already explained for cutting a metric thread with an English lead-screw.

Rule: To find the change gears for cutting English threads with a metric lead-screw, place 127 in the numerator and the threads per inch to be cut, multiplied by the metric screw constant multiplied by 5, in the denominator; 127 is the number of teeth on the spindle-stud gear and the product of the numbers in the denominator equals the number of teeth in the lead-screw gear.

Threads per Inch Obtained with a Given Combination of Gears. — To determine the number of threads per inch that will be obtained with a given combination of gearing, multiply the lathe screw constant by the number of teeth in the *driven* gear (or by the product of the numbers of teeth in both driven gears of compound gearing), and divide the product thus obtained by the number of teeth in the *driving* gear (or by the product of the two driving gears of a compound train). The quotient equals the number of threads per inch.

Change Gears for Fractional Ratios. — When gear ratios cannot be expressed exactly in whole numbers which are within the range of ordinary gearing, the combination of gearing required for the fractional ratio may be determined quite easily, in some cases, by the "cancellation method." To illustrate this method, assume that the speeds of two gears are to be in the ratio of 3.423 to 1. The number 3.423 is first changed to $\frac{3423}{1000}$ to clear it of decimals. Then, in order to secure a fraction that can be reduced, 3423 is changed to 3420;

$$\frac{3420}{1000} = \frac{342}{100} = \frac{3 \times 2 \times 57}{2 \times 50} = \frac{3 \times 57}{1 \times 50}$$

Then, multiplying $\frac{3}{1}$ by some trial number, say, 24, the following gear combination is obtained:

$$\frac{72}{24} \times \frac{57}{50} = \frac{4104}{1200} = \frac{3.42}{1}$$

As the desired ratio is 3.423 to 1, there is an error of 0.003. When the ratios are comparatively simple, the cancellation method is not difficult and is frequently used; but by the logarithmic method to be described, more accurate results are possible in most cases.

Logarithms of Change-gear Ratios. — Change-gear problems can be solved readily by the use of the accompanying tables which contain the six-place logarithms of the ratios of all gear combinations between 16 and 120 teeth, inclusive, excepting the 1 to 1 ratios. To illustrate how these logarithms of ratios are obtained, take as an example gears having 72 and 41 teeth, respectively; the ratio equals 72 divided by 41, and to divide by means of logarithms, the logarithm of one number is subtracted from the logarithm of the other, thus:

$$\log 72 = 1.857333$$
$$\log 41 = 1.612784$$
$$\text{ratio log} = 0.244549$$

The logarithms for ratios of gear combinations between 16 and 120 have been arranged in numerical order in the tables. In a number of cases, more than one combination gives the same logarithm, so that the different gears that equal the logarithm have been repeated. In some simple cases, only the ratio has been given in order to shorten the table; for instance, all the gear combinations that equal a 2 to 1 ratio have been omitted and only the ratio is given.

There are nearly 5000 different ratios represented in the gear tables between the extremes 1.0084+ to 1 (120 : 119) and 7½ to 1 (120 : 16). As the sum of any two two-gear logarithms equals a four-gear logarithm, the tables represent over 12,000,000 four-gear combinations; and by using three pairs of gears in a train, there are over 20,000,000,000 six-gear combinations available.

Solving Change-gear Problems by Use of Logarithms. — To show how the tables of logarithms for different gear ratios are used, suppose that gears having the ratio 3.423 : 1 are desired. Log 3.423 = 0.534407. From the table, log 89 : 26 = 0.534417; therefore, the gears having 89 and 26 teeth are the nearest to the ratio 3.423 to 1, and as 89 ÷ 26 = 3.423077, the ratio error is only 0.000077.

When solving gear problems the ratio should be reduced to terms of 1. For example, what two gears will drive two shafts at a speed ratio of 7.182 to 3.902? $\frac{7.182}{3.902} = \frac{1.84059}{1}$; the log of 1.84059 is 0.264957. From the table, 81 : 44 = log 0.265032. As 81 ÷ 44 = 1.84091, the error is only 0.00032.

A more rapid solution of the same problem, which may be used by those familiar with logarithms, is:

$$\log 7.182 = 0.856245$$
$$\log 3.902 = \underline{0.591287}$$
$$\text{ratio log} = 0.264958$$

From the table, log 81 : 44 = 0.265032. To find the error, proceed thus:

$$\log 0.265032$$
$$\log \underline{0.264958}$$
$$\text{log of ratio error } 0.000074$$

Finding Four-gear Ratios. — When four gears must be used, the gear logarithms make it possible to obtain more accurate results than any other method. For example, suppose it is desired to find four gears that will have a ratio of 2.105399 to 1. Log 2.105399 = 0.323334. To keep the reduction about equal in each pair of gears, it is necessary to select from the table that set of gears the logarithm of which is equal to about one-half the ratio logarithm, as log 57 : 37 = 0.187673. By subtracting this from log 0.323334, the other logarithm is found to be 0.135661. From the table, log 41 : 30 = 0.135663, so the error is log 0.000002. Thus this result is obtained:

$$\tfrac{57}{37} \times \tfrac{41}{30} = \tfrac{2337}{1110} = 2.105405$$

As the ratio of the gears is 2.105405 and the desired ratio is 2.105399, the error in the ratio is 0.000006. The two largest gears will be drivers or driven, whichever the case may be.

In case no combination can be found that nearly equals the logarithm of the ratio, a suitable four-gear combination may be found by reversing the second ratio selected from the table. For example, what gears will drive two shafts at a ratio of 595 to 594? Taking the logarithms from a six-place table,

$$\log 595 = 2.774517$$
$$\log 594 = \underline{2.773786}$$
$$\text{log ratio} = 0.000731$$

From the table of logarithms for gear ratios, select any ratio, say log 72 : 70 = 0.012235, and add the logarithm of the ratio 595 : 594, or 0.000731; the sum is 0.012966. Select the logarithm nearest the sum from the table; this is found to be log 68 : 66 = 0.012965. Now by reversing this pair the difference of the ratios, or 594 : 595, will be obtained. Reversing 68 : 66 gives 66 : 68; therefore, the gears required are $\tfrac{72}{70} \times \tfrac{66}{68}$. The proof of this is: $\tfrac{72}{70} \times \tfrac{66}{68} = \tfrac{4752}{4760} = \tfrac{594}{595}$.

Driving and Driven Gears. — Gears for the ratio 7.32 : 4.17 are selected in the same manner as gears for the ratio 4.17 : 7.32. The logarithm of the smaller number is subtracted from the logarithm of the larger, giving the logarithm of the ratio. The first figure or term of a gear ratio is usually considered to be the driver. For example, if two shafts are to run at a ratio of 3 to 1, it is implied that 3 is the driver and the gear with the largest number of teeth will be placed on the driving shaft. In so far as the use of the gear logarithm tables is concerned, it is immaterial which is the driver and which is the driven gear, and by comparing the gears selected with the ratio, no confusion should result.

Lathe Change-gears. — For calculating the change-gears to cut any pitch on a lathe, the "constant" of the machine must be known. For any lathe, $C : L$ = driver : driven gear, in which C = constant of machine and L = thds. per inch.

For example, what change-gears are required to cut 1.7345 threads per inch on a lathe having a constant of 4?

$$C : L = 4 : 1.7345$$
$$\log 4 = 0.602060$$
$$\log 1.7345 = \underline{0.239174}$$
$$\text{ratio } \log = 0.362886$$

From the table, $\log 113 : 49 = \underline{0.362882}$

$$\log \text{ of ratio error} = 0.000004$$

Therefore, the driver has 113 teeth, and the driven gear, 49 teeth.

Relieving Helical Fluted Hobs. — The problem of relieving hobs that have been fluted at right angles to the thread is an example of the special application of the gear logarithms to difficult problems. The usual method is to alter the angle of the helical flutes to agree with previously calculated change-gears. The ratio between the hob and relieving attachment cam is expressed by the following terms:

$$\frac{N}{\cos^2\alpha} : C = \text{drivers : driven gears}$$

$$\text{Tan } \alpha = \frac{P}{H_c}$$

in which

N = number of flutes in hob;
α = helix angle of thread from plane perpendicular to axis;
C = constant of relieving attachment;
P = axial lead of hob;
H_c = hob pitch circumference, or 3.1416 × pitch diameter.

The constant of a relieving attachment can be found on its index-plate, and is determined by the number of flutes that require equal gears on the change-gear studs. This will vary with different makes of lathes.

Example. — What four change-gears must be used to relieve a helical fluted worm-gear hob, 24 diametral pitch, sextuple thread, 13 degrees, 41 minutes helix angle of thread, with eleven helical flutes, assuming that a relieving attachment having a constant of 4 is to be used?

$$\text{Cos 13 degrees, 41 minutes} = 0.97162$$
$$0.97162^2 = 0.944045$$

$$\frac{N \div \cos^2\alpha}{C} = \frac{N}{C \times \cos^2\alpha}; \quad \frac{11}{4 \times 0.944045} = \frac{11}{3.776}$$

$$\log 11 = 1.04139$$
$$\log 3.776 = \underline{0.57703}$$
$$\log \text{ ratio} = 0.46436$$

From tables, $\log 67 : 39 = \underline{0.23501}$

Subtracting from log ratio = 0.22935

From table, $\log 78 : 46 = 0.22933$

Therefore, the gears are $\dfrac{67}{39} \times \dfrac{78}{46} = \dfrac{\text{drivers}}{\text{driven}}$

The ratio of these gears equals 2.913 which is the ratio represented by 11 ÷ 3.776. In relieving hobs for spur gears, the *normal* pitch (or lead of a single-threaded hob) should equal the circular pitch of the gear, and the *axial* pitch = normal pitch ÷ cos α. Sine α = normal pitch ÷ H_c.

Logarithms of Gear Ratios from 1.0084+ to 7.5

Numbers of Teeth	Logarithm of Ratio	Numbers of Teeth	Logarithm of Ratio	Numbers of Teeth	Logarithm of Ratio	Numbers of Teeth	Logarithm of Ratio
120 : 16	0.875061	99 : 16	0.791515	101 : 18	0.749049	115 : 22	0.718275
119 : 16	.871427	105 : 17	.790740	112 : 20	.748188	94 : 18	.717855
118 : 16	.867762	111 : 18	.790051	95 : 17	.747275	120 : 23	.717453
117 : 16	.864065	98 : 16	.787106	106 : 19	.746552	99 : 19	.716882
116 : 16	.860338	104 : 17	.786584	117 : 21	.745967	109 : 21	.715207
115 : 16	.856578	110 : 18	.786120	89 : 16	.745270	83 : 16	.714958
114 : 16	.852785	116 : 19	.785704	100 : 18	.744728	114 : 22	.714482
113 : 16	.848958	97 : 16	.782652	111 : 20	.744293	88 : 17	.714034
120 : 17	0.848732	103 : 17	0.782388	94 : 17	0.742680	119 : 23	0.713819
119 : 17	.845098	109 : 18	.782154	105 : 19	.742436	93 : 18	.713210
112 : 16	.845098	115 : 19	.781944	116 : 21	.742239	98 : 19	.712473
118 : 17	.841433	114 : 19	.778151	110 : 20	.740363	103 : 20	.711807
111 : 16	.841203	108 : 18	.778151	99 : 18	.740363	108 : 21	.711205
117 : 17	.837737	102 : 17	.778151	88 : 16	.740363	113 : 22	.710656
110 : 16	.837272	96 : 16	.778151	115 : 21	.738479	118 : 23	.710154
116 : 17	.834009	119 : 20	.774517	104 : 19	.738280	82 : 16	.709694
109 : 16	0.833307	113 : 19	0.774325	93 : 17	0.738034	87 : 17	0.709070
115 : 17	.830249	107 : 18	.774111	120 : 22	.736759	92 : 18	.708515
108 : 16	.829304	101 : 17	.773873	109 : 20	.736397	97 : 19	.708018
114 : 17	.826456	95 : 16	.773604	98 : 18	.735954	102 : 20	.707570
107 : 16	.825264	112 : 19	.770464	87 : 16	.735400	107 : 21	.707165
120 : 18	.823909	106 : 19	.770033	114 : 21	.734686	112 : 22	.706795
113 : 17	.822629	100 : 17	.769551	103 : 19	.734084	117 : 23	.706458
106 : 16	.821186	94 : 16	.769008	92 : 17	.733339	81 : 16	.704365
119 : 18	0.820275	117 : 20	0.767156	119 : 22	0.733124	86 : 17	0.704050
112 : 17	.818769	111 : 19	.766570	108 : 20	.732394	91 : 18	.703769
105 : 16	.817069	105 : 18	.765917	97 : 18	.731499	96 : 19	.703518
118 : 18	.816609	99 : 17	.765186	113 : 21	.730859	101 : 20	.703291
111 : 17	.814874	93 : 16	.764363	86 : 16	.730379	106 : 21	.703087
117 : 18	.812913	116 : 20	.763429	102 : 19	.729847	111 : 22	.702900
104 : 16	.812913	110 : 19	.762639	118 : 22	.729459	116 : 23	.702730
110 : 17	.810944	104 : 18	.761761	91 : 17	.728593	120 : 24	.698970
116 : 18	0.809186	98 : 17	0.760777	107 : 20	0.728354	115 : 23	0.698970
103 : 16	.808717	115 : 20	.759668	112 : 21	.726999	110 : 22	.698970
109 : 17	.806978	92 : 16	.759668	96 : 18	.726999	105 : 21	.698970
115 : 18	.805425	109 : 19	.758673	117 : 22	.725763	100 : 20	.698970
102 : 16	.804480	103 : 18	.757565	101 : 19	.725568	95 : 19	.698970
108 : 17	.802975	120 : 21	.756962	85 : 16	.725299	90 : 18	.698970
114 : 18	.801632	114 : 20	.755875	106 : 20	.724276	85 : 17	.698970
120 : 19	.800428	91 : 16	.754921	90 : 17	.723794	80 : 16	.698970
101 : 16	0.800201	108 : 19	0.754670	111 : 21	0.723104	119 : 24	0.695336
107 : 17	.798936	119 : 21	.753328	95 : 18	.722451	114 : 23	.695171
113 : 18	.797806	102 : 18	.753328	116 : 22	.722035	109 : 22	.695004
119 : 19	.796793	113 : 20	.752048	100 : 19	.721246	104 : 21	.694814
100 : 16	.795880	96 : 17	.751822	105 : 20	.720159	99 : 20	.694605
106 : 17	.794857	107 : 19	.750630	84 : 16	.720159	94 : 19	.694374
112 : 18	.793946	90 : 16	.750123	110 : 21	.719173	89 : 18	0.694118
118 : 19	.793128	118 : 21	.749663	89 : 17	.718941	84 : 17	.693830

Logarithms of Gear Ratios from 1.0084+ to 7.5

Numbers of Teeth	Logarithm of Ratio	Numbers of Teeth	Logarithm of Ratio	Numbers of Teeth	Logarithm of Ratio	Numbers of Teeth	Logarithm of Ratio
79 : 16	0.693507	103 : 22	0.670415	76 : 17	0.650365	90 : 21	0.632023
118 : 24	.691671	117 : 25	.670246	116 : 26	.649485	107 : 25	.631444
113 : 23	.691351	112 : 24	.669007	107 : 24	.649173	77 : 18	.631218
108 : 22	.691001	98 : 21	.669007	98 : 22	.648803	94 : 22	.630705
103 : 21	.690618	84 : 18	.669007	89 : 20	.648360	111 : 26	.630350
98 : 20	.690196	107 : 23	.667656	80 : 18	.647817	81 : 19	.629731
93 : 19	.689729	93 : 20	.667453	120 : 27	.647817	98 : 23	.629498
88 : 18	.689210	79 : 17	.667178	111 : 25	.647383	115 : 27	.629334
83 : 17	0.688629	116 : 25	0.666518	71 : 16	0.647138	119 : 28	0.628389
117 : 24	.687975	102 : 22	.666178	102 : 23	.646872	85 : 20	.628389
78 : 16	.687975	88 : 19	.665730	93 : 21	.646264	68 : 16	.628389
112 : 23	.687490	111 : 24	.665112	115 : 26	.645725	106 : 25	.627366
107 : 22	.686961	74 : 16	.665112	84 : 19	.645526	89 : 21	.627171
102 : 21	.686381	97 : 21	.664552	106 : 24	.645095	72 : 17	.626884
97 : 20	.685742	120 : 26	.664208	75 : 17	.644612	110 : 26	.626419
92 : 19	.685034	83 : 18	.663806	97 : 22	.644349	93 : 22	.626060
116 : 24	0.684247	106 : 23	0.663578	119 : 27	0.644183	114 : 27	0.625541
87 : 18	.684247	115 : 25	.662758	110 : 25	.643453	76 : 18	.625541
111 : 23	.683595	92 : 20	.662758	88 : 20	.643453	97 : 23	.625044
82 : 17	.683365	101 : 22	.661899	101 : 23	.642594	118 : 28	.624724
106 : 22	.682883	78 : 17	.661645	79 : 18	.642355	80 : 19	.624336
77 : 16	.682371	110 : 24	.661182	114 : 26	.641932	101 : 24	.624110
101 : 21	.682102	87 : 19	.660766	92 : 21	.641569	105 : 25	.623249
120 : 25	.681241	119 : 26	.660574	105 : 24	.640978	84 : 20	.623249
96 : 20	0.681241	96 : 21	0.660052	70 : 16	0.640978	109 : 26	0.622453
115 : 24	.680487	105 : 23	.659462	118 : 27	.640518	88 : 21	.622263
91 : 19	.680288	73 : 16	.659203	83 : 19	.640324	67 : 16	.621955
110 : 23	.679665	114 : 25	.658965	96 : 22	.639849	113 : 27	.621715
86 : 18	.679226	82 : 18	.658541	109 : 25	.639487	92 : 22	.621365
105 : 22	.678767	91 : 20	.658011	74 : 17	.638783	117 : 28	.621028
81 : 17	.678036	100 : 22	.657577	87 : 20	.638489	71 : 17	.620809
100 : 21	.677781	109 : 24	.657215	100 : 23	.638272	96 : 23	.620543
119 : 25	0.677607	118 : 26	0.656909	113 : 26	0.638105	100 : 24	0.619789
114 : 24	.676694	77 : 17	.656042	117 : 27	.636822	75 : 18	.619789
95 : 20	.676694	86 : 19	.655745	104 : 24	.636822	120 : 29	.619093
76 : 16	.676694	95 : 21	.655504	91 : 21	.636822	79 : 19	.618874
109 : 23	.675699	104 : 23	.655306	78 : 18	.636822	108 : 26	.618451
90 : 19	.675489	113 : 25	.655138	108 : 25	.635484	83 : 20	.618048
104 : 22	.674611	117 : 26	.653213	95 : 22	.635301	112 : 27	.617854
85 : 18	.674146	108 : 24	.653213	82 : 19	.635060	116 : 28	.617300
118 : 25	0.673942	99 : 22	0.653213	69 : 16	0.634729	87 : 21	0.617300
99 : 21	.673416	90 : 20	.653213	112 : 26	.634245	120 : 29	.616783
113 : 24	.672867	81 : 18	.653213	99 : 23	.633907	91 : 22	.616619
80 : 17	.672641	72 : 16	.653213	86 : 20	.633469	95 : 23	.615996
94 : 20	.672098	112 : 25	.651278	116 : 27	.633094	99 : 24	.615424
108 : 23	.671696	103 : 23	.651109	73 : 17	.632874	66 : 16	.615424
75 : 16	.670941	94 : 21	.650909	103 : 24	.632626	103 : 25	.614897
89 : 19	.670636	85 : 19	.650665	120 : 28	.632023	70 : 17	.614649

Logarithms of Gear Ratios from 1.0084+ to 7.5

Numbers of Teeth	Logarithm of Ratio	Numbers of Teeth	Logarithm of Ratio	Numbers of Teeth	Logarithm of Ratio	Numbers of Teeth	Logarithm of Ratio
107 : 26	0.614411	67 : 17	0.595626	99 : 26	0.580662	81 : 22	0.566062
111 : 27	.613959	63 : 16	.595221	118 : 31	.580520	92 : 25	.565848
74 : 18	.613959	118 : 30	.594761	114 : 30	.579784	103 : 28	.565679
115 : 28	.613540	114 : 29	.594507	95 : 25	.579784	114 : 31	.565543
78 : 19	.613341	110 : 28	.594235	76 : 20	.579784	88 : 24	.564271
119 : 29	.613149	106 : 27	.593942	110 : 29	.578995	110 : 30	.564271
82 : 20	.612784	102 : 26	.593627	91 : 24	.578830	99 : 27	.564271
86 : 21	.612279	98 : 25	.593286	72 : 19	.578579	77 : 21	.564271
90 : 22	0.611820	94 : 24	0.592917	106 : 28	0.578148	66 : 18	0.564271
94 : 23	.611400	90 : 23	.592515	87 : 23	.577792	117 : 32	.563036
98 : 24	.611015	86 : 22	.592076	102 : 27	.577236	106 : 29	.562908
102 : 25	.610660	82 : 21	.591595	68 : 18	.577236	95 : 26	.562750
106 : 26	.610333	117 : 30	.591065	117 : 31	.576824	84 : 23	.562552
110 : 27	.610029	78 : 20	.591065	83 : 22	.576655	73 : 20	.562293
114 : 28	.609747	113 : 29	.590680	98 : 26	.576253	62 : 17	.561943
118 : 29	.609484	74 : 19	.590478	113 : 30	.575957	113 : 31	.561717
65 : 16	0.608793	109 : 28	0.590269	64 : 17	0.575731	102 : 28	0.561442
69 : 17	.608400	105 : 27	.589826	79 : 21	.575408	91 : 25	.561101
73 : 18	.608050	70 : 18	.589826	94 : 25	.575188	120 : 33	.560667
77 : 19	.607737	101 : 26	.589348	109 : 29	.575029	80 : 22	.560667
81 : 20	.607455	66 : 17	.589105	120 : 32	.574031	109 : 30	.560305
85 : 21	.607200	97 : 25	.588832	105 : 28	.574031	69 : 19	.560096
89 : 22	.606967	62 : 16	.588272	90 : 24	.574031	98 : 27	.559862
93 : 23	.606755	93 : 24	.588272	75 : 20	.574031	116 : 32	.559308
97 : 24	0.606561	120 : 31	0.587820	60 : 16	0.574031	87 : 24	0.559308
101 : 25	.606381	89 : 23	.587662	116 : 31	.573096	105 : 29	.558791
105 : 26	.606216	116 : 30	.587337	86 : 23	.572770	76 : 21	.558594
109 : 27	.606063	85 : 22	.586996	71 : 19	.572505	94 : 26	.558155
113 : 28	.605920	112 : 29	.586820	112 : 30	.572097	112 : 31	.557856
117 : 29	.605788	108 : 28	.586266	97 : 26	.571798	65 : 18	.557641
64 : 16		81 : 21	.586266	82 : 22	.571391	83 : 23	.557350
or		104 : 27	.585670	108 : 29	.571026	101 : 28	.557163
any	0.602060	77 : 20	0.585461	67 : 18	0.570802	119 : 33	0.557033
4 to 1		100 : 26	.585027	93 : 25	.570543	108 : 30	.556303
ratio		73 : 19	.584569	119 : 32	.570397	90 : 25	.556303
119 : 30	.598426	96 : 25	.584331	104 : 28	.569875	72 : 20	.556303
115 : 29	.598300	119 : 31	.584185	78 : 21	.569875	115 : 32	.555548
111 : 28	.598165	115 : 30	.583577	115 : 31	.569336	97 : 27	.555408
107 : 27	.598020	92 : 24	.583577	89 : 24	.569179	79 : 22	.555204
103 : 26	.597864	69 : 18	.583577	63 : 17	.568892	61 : 17	.554881
99 : 25	0.597695	111 : 29	0.582925	100 : 27	0.568636	104 : 29	0.554635
95 : 24	.597512	88 : 23	.582755	111 : 30	.568202	86 : 24	.554287
91 : 23	.597314	65 : 17	.582465	74 : 20	.568202	111 : 31	.553961
87 : 22	.597097	107 : 28	.582226	85 : 23	.567691	68 : 19	.553755
83 : 21	.596859	84 : 22	.581857	96 : 26	.567298	93 : 26	.553510
79 : 20	.596597	103 : 27	.581473	107 : 29	.566986	118 : 33	.553368
75 : 19	.596308	61 : 16	.581210	118 : 32	.566732	100 : 28	.552842
71 : 18	.595986	80 : 21	.580871	70 : 19	.566344	75 : 21	.552842

Logarithms of Gear Ratios from 1.0084+ to 7.5

Numbers of Teeth	Logarithm of Ratio	Numbers of Teeth	Logarithm of Ratio	Numbers of Teeth	Logarithm of Ratio	Numbers of Teeth	Logarithm of Ratio
107 : 30	0.552263	76 : 22	0.538391	104 : 31	0.525672	101 : 31	0.512960
82 : 23	.552086	107 : 31	.538022	114 : 34	.525426	114 : 35	.512837
114 : 32	.551755	69 : 20	.537819	67 : 20	.525045	117 : 36	.511883
89 : 25	.551450	100 : 29	.537602	77 : 23	.524763	104 : 32	.511883
96 : 27	.550907	93 : 27	.537119	87 : 26	.524546	91 : 28	.511883
64 : 18	.550907	62 : 18	.537119	97 : 29	.524374	65 : 20	.511883
103 : 29	.550439	117 : 34	.536707	107 : 32	.524234	120 : 37	.510980
71 : 20	.550228	86 : 25	.536559	117 : 35	.524118	107 : 33	.510870
110 : 31	0.550031	110 : 32	0.536243	120 : 36	0.522879	94 : 29	0.510730
117 : 33	.549672	55 : 16	.536243	110 : 33	.522879	81 : 25	.510545
78 : 22	.549672	79 : 23	.535899	100 : 30	.522879	68 : 21	.510290
85 : 24	.549208	103 : 30	.535716	90 : 27	.522879	110 : 34	.509914
92 : 26	.548815	120 : 35	.535113	80 : 24	.522879	97 : 30	.509650
99 : 28	.548477	96 : 28	.535113	70 : 21	.522879	84 : 26	.509306
106 : 30	.548185	72 : 21	.535113	60 : 18	.522879	113 : 35	.509010
113 : 32	.547928	113 : 33	.534565	113 : 34	.521600	71 : 22	.508836
120 : 34	0.547702	89 : 26	0.534417	103 : 31	0.521476	100 : 31	0.508638
67 : 19	.547321	65 : 19	.534160	93 : 28	.521325	116 : 36	.508156
74 : 21	.547012	106 : 31	.533944	83 : 25	.521138	87 : 27	.508156
81 : 23	.546757	82 : 24	.533603	73 : 22	.520900	103 : 32	.507687
88 : 25	.546543	99 : 29	.533237	63 : 19	.520587	74 : 23	.507504
95 : 27	.546360	116 : 34	.532980	116 : 35	.520390	119 : 37	.507345
102 : 29	.546202	75 : 22	.532639	106 : 32	.520165	90 : 28	.507085
109 : 31	.546065	92 : 27	.532424	96 : 29	.519873	106 : 33	.506792
119 : 34	0.544068	109 : 32	0.532277	86 : 26	0.519525	61 : 19	0.506576
112 : 32	.544068	119 : 35	.531479	119 : 36	.519245	77 : 24	.506280
105 : 30	.544068	102 : 30	.531479	76 : 23	.519086	93 : 29	.506085
98 : 28	.544068	85 : 25	.531479	109 : 33	.518913	109 : 34	.505948
91 : 26	.544068	68 : 20	.531479	99 : 30	.518514	112 : 35	.505150
84 : 24	.544068	112 : 33	.530704	89 : 27	.518026	96 : 30	.505150
77 : 22	.544068	95 : 28	.530566	112 : 34	.517739	80 : 25	.505150
70 : 20	.544068	78 : 23	.530367	79 : 24	.517416	64 : 20	.505150
63 : 18	0.544068	61 : 18	0.530057	102 : 31	0.517239	115 : 36	0.504395
56 : 16	.544068	105 : 31	.529828	115 : 35	.516630	99 : 31	.504274
115 : 33	.542184	88 : 26	.529509	69 : 21	.516630	83 : 26	.504105
108 : 31	.542062	115 : 34	.529219	92 : 28	.516629	67 : 21	.503856
101 : 29	.541923	71 : 21	.529039	105 : 32	.516039	118 : 37	.503680
87 : 25	.541579	98 : 29	.528828	82 : 25	.515874	102 : 32	.503450
80 : 23	.541362	108 : 32	.528274	118 : 36	.515580	86 : 27	.503135
73 : 21	.541104	81 : 24	.528274	95 : 29	.515326	105 : 33	.502675
66 : 19	0.540790	118 : 35	0.527814	108 : 33	0.514910	70 : 22	0.502675
118 : 34	.540403	91 : 27	.527678	72 : 22	.514910	89 : 28	.502232
111 : 32	.540173	64 : 19	.527426	85 : 26	.514446	108 : 34	.501945
104 : 30	.539912	101 : 30	.527200	98 : 30	.514105	73 : 23	.501595
97 : 28	.539614	111 : 33	.526809	111 : 34	.513844	92 : 29	.501390
90 : 26	.539269	74 : 22	.526809	62 : 19	.513638	111 : 35	.501255
83 : 24	.538867	84 : 25	.526339	75 : 23	.513334	95 : 30	.500602
114 : 33	.538391	94 : 28	.525970	88 : 27	.513119	76 : 24	.500602

Logarithms of Gear Ratios from 1.0084+ to 7.5

Numbers of Teeth	Logarithm of Ratio	Numbers of Teeth	Logarithm of Ratio	Numbers of Teeth	Logarithm of Ratio	Numbers of Teeth	Logarithm of Ratio
117 : 37	0.499984	120 : 39	0.488117	92 : 31	0.472426	81 : 28	0.461327
98 : 31	.499864	80 : 26	.488117	89 : 30	.472269	107 : 37	.461182
79 : 25	.499687	83 : 27	.487714	86 : 29	.472101	104 : 36	.460731
120 : 38	.499398	86 : 28	.487341	83 : 28	.471920	78 : 27	.460731
101 : 32	.499171	89 : 29	.486992	80 : 27	.471726	101 : 35	.460258
82 : 26	.498841	92 : 30	.486667	77 : 26	.471517	75 : 26	.460088
104 : 33	.498519	95 : 31	.486362	74 : 25	.471291	98 : 34	.459747
63 : 20	.498311	98 : 32	.486076	71 : 24	.471047	72 : 25	.459393
85 : 27	0.498055	101 : 33	0.485808	68 : 23	0.470781	95 : 33	0.459210
107 : 34	.497905	104 : 34	.485554	65 : 22	.470491	118 : 41	.459098
110 : 35	.497325	107 : 35	.485316	62 : 21	.470172	115 : 40	.458638
88 : 28	.497325	110 : 36	.485090	118 : 40	.469822	92 : 32	.458638
113 : 36	.496776	113 : 37	.484877	115 : 39	.469633	69 : 24	.458638
91 : 29	.496643	116 : 38	.484674	112 : 38	.469434	112 : 39	.458153
69 : 22	.496426	119 : 39	.484482	109 : 37	.469225	89 : 31	.458028
116 : 37	.496256	61 : 20	.484300	106 : 36	.469003	66 : 23	.457816
94 : 30	0.496007	64 : 21	0.483961	103 : 35	0.468769	109 : 38	0.457643
119 : 38	.495763	67 : 22	.483652	100 : 34	.468521	86 : 30	.457377
72 : 23	.495605	70 : 23	.483370	97 : 33	.468258	106 : 37	.457104
97 : 31	.495410	73 : 24	.483112	94 : 32	.467978	63 : 22	.456918
100 : 32	.494850	76 : 25	.482874	91 : 31	.467680	83 : 29	.456680
75 : 24	.494850	79 : 26	.482654	88 : 30	.467361	103 : 36	.456535
103 : 33	.494323	82 : 27	.482450	85 : 29	.467021	120 : 42	.455932
78 : 25	.494155	85 : 28	.482261	82 : 28	.466656	100 : 35	.455932
106 : 34	0.493827	88 : 29	0.482085	120 : 41	0.466397	80 : 28	0.455932
81 : 26	.493511	91 : 30	.481920	79 : 27	.466263	60 : 21	.455932
109 : 35	.493359	94 : 31	.481766	117 : 40	.466126	117 : 41	.455402
112 : 36	.492916	97 : 32	.481622	114 : 39	.465840	97 : 34	.455293
84 : 27	.492916	100 : 33	.481486	76 : 26	.465840	77 : 27	.455127
115 : 37	.492496	103 : 34	.481358	111 : 38	.465539	114 : 40	.454845
87 : 28	.492361	106 : 35	.481237	73 : 25	.465383	94 : 33	.454614
118 : 38	.492098	109 : 36	.481124	108 : 37	.465222	111 : 39	.454258
90 : 29	0.491845	112 : 37	0.481016	70 : 24	0.464887	74 : 26	0.454258
93 : 30	.491362	115 : 38	.480914	102 : 35	.464532	91 : 32	.453891
62 : 20	.491362	118 : 39	.480817	67 : 23	.464347	71 : 25	.453318
96 : 31	.490910	48 : 16		99 : 34	.464156	88 : 31	.453121
65 : 21	.490694	or any	.477121	96 : 33	.463757	105 : 37	.452988
99 : 32	.490485	3 to 1		64 : 22	.463757	119 : 42	.452298
102 : 33	.490086	ratio		93 : 32	.463333	102 : 36	.452298
68 : 22	.490086	119 : 40	.473487	61 : 21	.463111	85 : 30	.452298
105 : 34	0.489710	116 : 39	0.473393	90 : 31	0.462881	68 : 24	0.452298
71 : 23	.489531	113 : 38	.473295	119 : 41	.462763	116 : 41	.451674
108 : 35	.489356	110 : 37	.473191	116 : 40	.462398	99 : 35	.451567
111 : 36	.489021	107 : 36	.473081	87 : 30	.462398	82 : 29	.451416
74 : 24	.489021	104 : 35	.472965	58 : 20	.462398	65 : 23	.451186
114 : 37	.488703	101 : 34	.472843	113 : 39	.462013	113 : 40	.451018
77 : 25	.488551	98 : 33	.472712	84 : 29	.461881	96 : 34	.450792
117 : 38	.488402	95 : 32	.472574	110 : 38	.461609	79 : 28	.450469

Logarithms of Gear Ratios from 1.0084+ to 7.5

Numbers of Teeth	Logarithm of Ratio	Numbers of Teeth	Logarithm of Ratio	Numbers of Teeth	Logarithm of Ratio	Numbers of Teeth	Logarithm of Ratio
110 : 39	0.450328	88 : 32	0.439333	94 : 35	0.429060	84 : 32	0.419129
93 : 33	.449969	77 : 28	.439333	102 : 38	.428817	118 : 45	.418670
62 : 22	.449969	118 : 43	.438414	110 : 41	.428609	97 : 37	.418570
107 : 38	.449600	107 : 39	.438319	59 : 22	.428429	76 : 29	.418416
76 : 27	.449450	96 : 35	.438203	67 : 25	.428135	55 : 21	.418143
90 : 32	.449092	85 : 31	.438057	75 : 28	.427903	89 : 34	.417911
104 : 37	.448832	74 : 27	.437868	83 : 31	.427716	102 : 39	.417536
118 : 42	.448633	63 : 23	.437613	91 : 34	.427563	68 : 26	.417536
73 : 26	0.448350	115 : 42	0.437449	99 : 37	0.427434	115 : 44	0.417245
87 : 31	.448158	104 : 38	.437250	107 : 40	.427324	81 : 31	.417123
101 : 36	.448019	93 : 34	.437004	115 : 43	.427229	94 : 36	.416825
115 : 41	.447914	82 : 30	.436693	120 : 45	.425969	107 : 41	.416600
98 : 35	.447158	112 : 41	.436434	112 : 42	.425969	60 : 23	.416424
84 : 30	.447158	71 : 26	.436285	104 : 39	.425969	73 : 28	.416165
112 : 40	.447158	101 : 37	.436120	96 : 36	.425969	86 : 33	.415985
70 : 25	.447158	90 : 33	.435729	88 : 33	.425969	99 : 38	.415852
109 : 39	0.446362	60 : 22	0.435729	80 : 30	0.425969	112 : 43	0.415750
95 : 34	.446245	109 : 40	.435367	72 : 27	.425969	117 : 45	.414973
81 : 29	.446087	79 : 29	.435229	64 : 24	.425969	91 : 35	.414973
67 : 24	.445864	98 : 36	.434924	56 : 21	.425969	78 : 30	.414973
120 : 43	.445713	117 : 43	.434717	117 : 44	.424733	52 : 20	.414973
106 : 38	.445522	68 : 25	.434569	109 : 41	.424643	109 : 42	.414177
92 : 33	.445274	87 : 32	.434369	101 : 38	.424538	96 : 37	.414070
117 : 42	.444937	106 : 39	.434241	93 : 35	.424415	83 : 34	.413928
78 : 28	0.444937	114 : 42	0.433656	85 : 32	0.424269	70 : 27	0.413734
103 : 37	.444636	95 : 35	.433656	77 : 29	.424093	57 : 22	.413452
64 : 23	.444452	76 : 28	.433656	69 : 26	.423876	101 : 39	.413257
89 : 32	.444240	57 : 21	.433656	61 : 23	.423602	88 : 34	.413004
114 : 41	.444121	103 : 38	.433054	114 : 43	.423436	119 : 46	.412789
100 : 36	.443698	84 : 31	.432918	106 : 40	.423246	75 : 29	.412663
75 : 27	.443698	65 : 24	.432702	98 : 37	.423024	106 : 41	.412522
111 : 40	.443263	111 : 41	.432539	90 : 34	.422764	62 : 24	.412180
86 : 31	0.443137	92 : 34	0.432309	82 : 31	0.422452	93 : 36	0.412180
61 : 22	.442907	119 : 44	.432094	119 : 45	.422335	111 : 43	.411855
97 : 35	.442704	73 : 27	.431959	111 : 42	.422074	80 : 31	.411728
72 : 26	.442359	100 : 37	.431798	74 : 28	.422074	98 : 38	.411443
108 : 39	.442359	108 : 40	.431364	103 : 39	.421773	116 : 45	.411246
119 : 43	.442079	81 : 30	.431364	95 : 36	.421421	67 : 26	.411102
83 : 30	.441957	54 : 20	.431364	87 : 33	.421005	85 : 33	.410905
94 : 34	.441649	116 : 43	.430990	58 : 22	.421005	103 : 40	.410777
105 : 38	0.441406	89 : 33	0.430876	108 : 41	0.420640	90 : 35	0.410175
58 : 21	.441209	62 : 23	.430664	79 : 30	.420506	72 : 28	.410175
69 : 25	.440909	97 : 36	.430469	100 : 38	.420216	54 : 21	.410175
80 : 29	.440692	105 : 39	.430125	71 : 27	.419895	113 : 44	.409626
91 : 33	.440528	70 : 26	.430125	92 : 35	.419720	95 : 37	.409522
102 : 37	.440399	113 : 42	.429829	113 : 43	.419610	77 : 30	.409369
113 : 41	.440295	78 : 29	.429697	105 : 40	.419130	59 : 23	.409124
99 : 36	.439333	86 : 32	.429349	63 : 24	.419130	100 : 39	.408935

Logarithms of Gear Ratios from 1.0084+ to 7.5

Numbers of Teeth	Logarithm of Ratio	Numbers of Teeth	Logarithm of Ratio	Numbers of Teeth	Logarithm of Ratio	Numbers of Teeth	Logarithm of Ratio
82 : 32	0.408664	40 : 16 or any 2½ to 1 ratio	0.397940	110 : 45	0.388180	48 : 20	0.380211
105 : 41	.408405			88 : 36	.388180	115 : 48	.379457
64 : 25	.408240			66 : 27	.388180	103 : 43	.379369
87 : 34	.408040	117 : 47	.396088	105 : 43	.387721	91 : 38	.379258
110 : 43	.407924	112 : 45	.396006	83 : 34	.387599	79 : 33	.379113
115 : 45	.407485	107 : 43	.395915	61 : 25	.387390	67 : 28	.378916
92 : 36	.407485	102 : 41	.395816	100 : 41	.387216	55 : 23	.378635
69 : 27	.407485	97 : 39	0.395707	117 : 48	.386945	98 : 41	.378442
120 : 47	0.407083	92 : 37	.395586	78 : 32	0.386945	86 : 36	0.378196
97 : 38	.406988	87 : 35	.395451	95 : 39	.386659	117 : 49	.377990
74 : 29	.406834	82 : 33	.395300	112 : 46	.386460	74 : 31	.377870
51 : 20	.406540	77 : 31	.395129	56 : 23	.386460	105 : 44	.377737
79 : 31	.406265	72 : 29	.394935	73 : 30	.386202	93 : 39	.377418
107 : 42	.406135	67 : 27	.394711	90 : 37	.386041	62 : 26	.377418
84 : 33	.405765	62 : 25	.394452	107 : 44	.385931	112 : 47	.377120
56 : 22	.405765	119 : 48	0.394306	102 : 42	.385351	81 : 34	.377006
117 : 46	0.405428	57 : 23	.394147	119 : 49	0.385351	100 : 42	0.376751
89 : 35	.405322	109 : 44	.393974	85 : 35	.385351	50 : 21	.376751
61 : 24	.405119	52 : 21	.393784	68 : 28	.385351	119 : 50	.376577
94 : 37	.404926	99 : 40	.393575	51 : 21	.385351	69 : 29	.376451
99 : 39	.404571	94 : 38	.393344	114 : 47	.384807	88 : 37	.376281
66 : 26	.404571	89 : 36	.393088	97 : 40	.384712	107 : 45	.376171
104 : 41	.404249	84 : 34	.392800	80 : 33	.384576	95 : 40	.375664
71 : 28	.404100	79 : 32	0.392477	63 : 26	.384367	76 : 32	.375664
109 : 43	0.403958	116 : 47	.392360	109 : 45	0.384214	57 : 24	0.375664
114 : 45	.403692	111 : 45	.392111	92 : 38	.384004	102 : 43	.375132
76 : 30	.403692	74 : 30	.392111	75 : 31	.383700	83 : 35	.375010
119 : 47	.403449	106 : 43	.391837	104 : 43	.383565	64 : 27	.374816
81 : 32	.403335	69 : 28	.391691	87 : 36	.383217	109 : 46	.374669
86 : 34	.403020	101 : 41	.391538	58 : 24	.383217	90 : 38	.374459
91 : 36	.402739	96 : 39	.391207	99 : 41	.382851	116 : 49	.374262
96 : 38	.402488	64 : 26	0.391207	70 : 29	.382700	71 : 30	.374137
101 : 40	0.402261	91 : 37	.390840	111 : 46	0.382565	97 : 41	0.373988
53 : 21	.402057	59 : 24	.390641	82 : 34	.382335	78 : 33	.373581
111 : 44	.401870	86 : 35	.390431	94 : 39	.382063	52 : 22	.373581
58 : 23	.401700	113 : 46	.390321	53 : 22	.381853	111 : 47	.373225
63 : 25	.401401	108 : 44	.389971	118 : 49	.381686	85 : 36	.373116
68 : 27	.401145	81 : 33	.389971	65 : 27	.381550	59 : 25	.372912
73 : 29	.400925	54 : 22	.389971	77 : 32	.381341	92 : 39	.372723
78 : 31	.400733	103 : 42	0.389588	89 : 37	.381188	66 : 28	.372386
83 : 33	0.400564	76 : 31	.389452	101 : 42	0.381072	99 : 42	0.372386
88 : 35	.400415	98 : 40	.389166	113 : 47	.380981	106 : 45	.372093
93 : 37	.400281	49 : 20	.389166	120 : 50	.380211	73 : 31	.371961
98 : 39	.400162	120 : 49	.388985	108 : 45	.380211	113 : 48	.371837
103 : 41	.400053	71 : 29	.388860	96 : 40	.380211	120 : 51	.371611
108 : 43	.399955	93 : 38	.388699	84 : 35	.380211	80 : 34	.371611
113 : 45	.399866	115 : 47	.388600	72 : 30	.380211	87 : 35	.371318
118 : 47	.399784			60 : 25	.380211	94 : 40	.371068

Logarithms of Gear Ratios from 1.0084+ to 7.5

Numbers of Teeth	Logarithm of Ratio	Numbers of Teeth	Logarithm of Ratio	Numbers of Teeth	Logarithm of Ratio	Numbers of Teeth	Logarithm of Ratio
47 : 20	0.371068	115 : 50	0.361728	70 : 31	0.353736	62 : 28	0.345234
101 : 43	.370853	92 : 40	.361728	79 : 35	.353559	104 : 47	.344935
54 : 23	.370666	69 : 30	.361728	88 : 39	.353418	73 : 33	.344809
115 : 49	.370502	46 : 20	.361728	97 : 43	.353303	115 : 52	.344695
61 : 26	.370357	108 : 47	.361326	106 : 47	.353208	84 : 38	.344496
68 : 29	.370111	85 : 37	.361217	115 : 51	.353128	95 : 43	.344255
75 : 32	.369911	62 : 27	.361028	117 : 52	.352183	53 : 24	.344065
82 : 35	.369746	101 : 44	.360869	108 : 48	.352183	117 : 53	.343910
89 : 38	0.369606	117 : 51	0.360616	99 : 44	0.352183	64 : 29	0.343782
96 : 41	.369487	78 : 34	.360616	90 : 40	.352183	75 : 34	.343582
103 : 44	.369385	94 : 41	.360344	81 : 36	.352183	86 : 39	.343434
110 : 47	.369295	55 : 24	.360152	72 : 32	.352183	97 : 44	.343319
117 : 50	.369216	71 : 31	.359897	63 : 28	.352183	108 : 49	.343228
119 : 51	.367977	87 : 38	.359736	45 : 20	.352183	119 : 54	.343153
105 : 45	.367977	103 : 45	.359625	119 : 53	.351271	99 : 45	.342423
98 : 42	.367977	119 : 52	.359544	110 : 49	.351197	88 : 40	.342423
91 : 39	0.367977	112 : 49	0.359022	101 : 45	0.351109	77 : 35	0.342423
84 : 36	.367977	96 : 42	.359022	92 : 41	.351004	66 : 30	.342423
77 : 33	.367977	80 : 35	.359022	83 : 37	.350876	55 : 25	.342423
70 : 30	.367977	64 : 28	.359022	74 : 33	.350718	112 : 51	.341648
63 : 27	.367977	48 : 21	.359022	65 : 29	.350515	101 : 46	.341564
56 : 24	.367977	105 : 46	.358432	56 : 25	.350248	90 : 41	.341459
49 : 21	.367977	89 : 39	.358325	103 : 46	.350079	79 : 36	.341325
114 : 49	.366709	73 : 32	.358173	94 : 42	.349879	57 : 26	.340902
107 : 46	0.366626	57 : 25	0.357935	85 : 38	0.349635	103 : 47	0.340739
100 : 43	.366552	98 : 43	.357758	114 : 51	.349335	92 : 42	.340539
93 : 40	.366423	82 : 36	.357511	76 : 34	.349335	46 : 21	.340539
86 : 37	.366297	107 : 47	.357286	105 : 47	.349091	81 : 37	.340283
79 : 34	.366148	66 : 29	.357146	67 : 30	.348954	116 : 53	.340182
72 : 31	.365971	91 : 40	.356981	96 : 43	.348803	105 : 48	.339948
65 : 28	.365755	116 : 51	.356888	87 : 39	.348455	70 : 32	.339948
58 : 25	.365488	75 : 33	.356547	58 : 26	.348455	94 : 43	.339659
109 : 47	0.365329	50 : 22	0.356547	107 : 48	0.348143	118 : 54	0.339488
102 : 44	.365148	100 : 44	.356547	78 : 35	.348027	59 : 27	.339488
95 : 41	.364940	109 : 48	.356185	98 : 44	.347773	83 : 38	.339295
88 : 38	.364700	84 : 37	.356078	49 : 22	.347773	107 : 49	.339188
81 : 35	.364417	59 : 26	.355879	118 : 53	.347606	120 : 55	.338819
118 : 51	.364312	93 : 41	.355699	69 : 31	.347487	96 : 44	.338819
111 : 48	.364082	102 : 45	.355388	89 : 40	.347330	72 : 33	.338819
74 : 32	.364082	68 : 30	.355388	109 : 49	.347230	48 : 22	.338819
104 : 45	0.363821	111 : 49	0.355127	100 : 45	0.346788	109 : 50	0.338457
67 : 29	.363677	77 : 34	.355012	80 : 36	.346788	85 : 39	.338354
90 : 39	.363178	120 : 53	.354905	60 : 27	.346788	61 : 28	.338172
60 : 26	.363178	86 : 38	.354715	111 : 50	.346353	98 : 45	.338014
113 : 49	.362882	95 : 42	.354444	91 : 41	.346258	111 : 51	.337753
53 : 23	.362548	52 : 23	.354276	51 : 23	.345842	74 : 34	.337753
76 : 33	.362300	113 : 50	.354108	113 : 51	.345508	87 : 40	.337459
99 : 43	.362167	61 : 27	.353966	93 : 42	.345234	100 : 46	.337242

Logarithms of Gear Ratios from 1.0084+ to 7.5

Numbers of Teeth	Logarithm of Ratio	Numbers of Teeth	Logarithm of Ratio	Numbers of Teeth	Logarithm of Ratio	Numbers of Teeth	Logarithm of Ratio
113 : 52	0.337075	111 : 52	0.329320	88 : 42	0.321233	107 : 52	0.313381
63 : 29	.336943	96 : 45	.329059	44 : 21	.321233	72 : 35	.313265
76 : 35	.336746	64 : 30	.329059	111 : 53	.321047	109 : 53	.313151
89 : 41	.336606	113 : 53	.328803	67 : 32	.320925	74 : 36	.312929
102 : 47	.336502	81 : 38	.328701	90 : 43	.320774	111 : 54	.312929
115 : 53	.336422	98 : 46	.328468	113 : 54	.320685	113 : 55	.312716
117 : 54	.335792	115 : 54	.328304	115 : 55	.320335	76 : 37	.312612
91 : 42	.335792	66 : 31	.328182	92 : 44	.320335	115 : 56	.312510
78 : 36	0.335792	83 : 39	0.328014	69 : 33	0.320335	117 : 57	0.312311
65 : 30	.335792	100 : 47	.327902	46 : 22	.320335	78 : 38	.312311
52 : 24	.335792	117 : 55	.327823	117 : 56	.319998	119 : 58	.312119
119 : 55	.335184	119 : 56	.327359	71 : 34	.319779	80 : 39	.312025
106 : 49	.335110	85 : 40	.327359	119 : 57	.319672	82 : 40	.311754
93 : 43	.335014	68 : 32	.327359	96 : 46	.319513	41 : 20	.311754
80 : 37	.334888	51 : 24	.327359	73 : 35	.319255	84 : 41	.311495
67 : 31	.334713	104 : 49	.326837	98 : 47	.319128	86 : 42	.311249
54 : 25	0.334454	87 : 41	0.326735	100 : 48	0.318759	43 : 21	0.311249
95 : 44	.334271	70 : 33	.326584	75 : 36	.318759	88 : 43	.311014
82 : 38	.334030	89 : 42	.326141	102 : 49	.318404	90 : 44	.310790
110 : 51	.333823	108 : 51	.325854	77 : 37	.318289	45 : 22	.310790
69 : 32	.333699	72 : 34	.325854	52 : 25	.318063	92 : 45	.310575
97 : 45	.333559	91 : 43	.325573	79 : 38	.317844	94 : 46	.310370
84 : 39	.333215	55 : 26	.325389	106 : 51	.317736	96 : 47	.310173
56 : 26	.333215	74 : 35	.325164	81 : 39	.317420	98 : 48	.309985
99 : 46	0.332877	93 : 44	.325030	110 : 53	0.317117	100 : 49	0.309804
71 : 33	.332744	112 : 53	.324942	83 : 40	.317018	102 : 50	.309630
114 : 53	.332629	95 : 45	.324511	112 : 54	.316824	51 : 25	.309630
86 : 40	.332439	76 : 36	.324511	85 : 41	.316635	104 : 51	.309463
43 : 20	.332439	57 : 27	.324511	114 : 55	.316542	53 : 26	.309303
101 : 47	.332224	116 : 55	.324095	87 : 42	.316270	108 : 53	.309148
58 : 27	.332064	97 : 46	.324014	58 : 28	.316270	55 : 27	.308999
73 : 34	.331844	78 : 37	.323893	118 : 57	.316007	112 : 55	.308855
88 : 41	0.331699	59 : 28	0.323694	89 : 43	0.315922	57 : 28	0.308717
103 : 48	.331596	99 : 47	.323537	120 : 58	.315753	116 : 57	.308583
118 : 55	.331519	120 : 57	.323306	60 : 29	.315753	59 : 29	.308454
105 : 49	.330993	80 : 38	.323306	91 : 44	.315589	118 : 58	.308454
90 : 42	.330993	101 : 48	.323080	93 : 45	.315270	120 : 59	.308329
75 : 35	.330993	61 : 29	.322932	62 : 30	.315270	61 : 30	.308209
60 : 28	.330993	82 : 39	.322749	95 : 46	.314966	63 : 31	.307979
45 : 21	.330993	103 : 49	.322641	64 : 31	.314818	65 : 32	.307763
107 : 50	0.330414	105 : 50	0.322219	97 : 47	0.314674	67 : 33	.307561
92 : 43	.330319	84 : 40	.322219	99 : 48	.314394	69 : 34	.307370
77 : 36	.330188	63 : 30	.322219	66 : 32	.314394	71 : 35	.307190
62 : 29	.329994	42 : 20	.322219	101 : 49	.314125	73 : 36	.307020
109 : 51	.329855	107 : 51	.321814	68 : 33	.313995	75 : 37	.306860
94 : 44	.329675	86 : 41	.321715	103 : 50	.313867	77 : 38	.306707
47 : 22	.329675	65 : 31	.321552	105 : 51	.313619	79 : 39	.306563
79 : 37	.329425	109 : 52	.321423	70 : 34	.313619	81 : 40	.306425

Logarithms of Gear Ratios from 1.0084+ to 7.5

Numbers of Teeth	Logarithm of Ratio	Numbers of Teeth	Logarithm of Ratio	Numbers of Teeth	Logarithm of Ratio	Numbers of Teeth	Logarithm of Ratio
83 : 41	0.306294	71 : 36	0.294956	93 : 48	0.287242	99 : 52	0.279632
85 : 42	.306170	69 : 35	.294781	62 : 32	.287242	59 : 31	.279490
87 : 43	.306051	67 : 34	.294596	91 : 47	.286944	78 : 41	.279311
89 : 44	.305937	65 : 33	.294400	120 : 62	.286790	97 : 51	.279202
91 : 45	.305829	63 : 32	.294191	89 : 46	.286632	116 : 61	.279128
93 : 46	.305725	61 : 31	.293968	118 : 61	.286552	95 : 50	.278754
95 : 47	.305626	120 : 61	.293851	116 : 60	.286307	76 : 40	.278754
97 : 48	.305531	59 : 30	.293731	58 : 30	.286307	57 : 30	.278754
99 : 49	0.305439	116 : 59	0.293606	114 : 59	0.286053	38 : 20	0.278754
101 : 50	.305351	57 : 29	.293477	85 : 44	.285966	112 : 59	.278366
103 : 51	.305267	112 : 57	.293343	56 : 29	.285790	93 : 49	.278287
105 : 52	.305186	55 : 28	.293205	83 : 43	.285610	74 : 39	.278167
107 : 53	.305108	108 : 55	.293061	110 : 57	.285518	55 : 29	.277965
109 : 54	.305033	53 : 27	.292912	81 : 42	.285236	91 : 48	.277800
111 : 55	.304960	104 : 53	.292757	54 : 28	.285235	108 : 57	.277549
113 : 56	.304890	51 : 26	.292597	106 : 55	.284943	72 : 38	.277549
115 : 57	0.304823	100 : 51	0.292430	79 : 41	0.284843	89 : 47	0.277292
117 : 58	.304758	98 : 50	.292256	52 : 27	.284640	53 : 28	.277118
119 : 59	.304695	96 : 49	.292075	77 : 40	.284431	87 : 46	.276762
32 : 16		94 : 48	.291887	102 : 53	.284324	104 : 55	.276671
or		92 : 47	.291690	100 : 52	.283997	119 : 63	.276207
any	.301030	90 : 46	.291485	75 : 39	.283997	85 : 45	.276207
2 to 1		88 : 45	.291270	98 : 51	.283656	68 : 36	.276206
ratio		86 : 44	.291046	73 : 38	.283540	117 : 62	.275794
119 : 60	0.297396	84 : 43	0.290811	96 : 50	0.283301	100 : 53	0.275724
117 : 59	.297334	82 : 42	.290565	119 : 62	.283155	83 : 44	.275625
115 : 58	.297270	41 : 21	.290565	71 : 37	.283057	66 : 35	.275476
113 : 57	.297204	80 : 41	.290306	94 : 49	.282932	115 : 61	.275368
111 : 56	.297135	119 : 61	.290217	117 : 61	.282856	98 : 52	.275223
109 : 55	.297064	78 : 40	.290035	92 : 48	.282547	81 : 43	.275017
107 : 54	.296990	39 : 20	.290035	69 : 36	.282547	113 : 60	.274927
105 : 53	.296913	115 : 59	.289846	113 : 59	.282226	96 : 51	.274701
103 : 52	0.296833	76 : 39	0.289749	90 : 47	0.282145	64 : 34	0.274701
101 : 51	.296751	113 : 58	.289650	67 : 35	.282007	111 : 59	.274471
99 : 50	.296665	111 : 57	.289448	111 : 58	.281895	79 : 42	.274378
97 : 49	.296576	74 : 38	.289448	88 : 46	.281725	94 : 50	.274158
95 : 48	.296482	109 : 56	.289239	109 : 57	.281552	109 : 58	.273999
93 : 47	.296385	72 : 37	.289131	65 : 34	.281435	62 : 33	.273878
91 : 46	.296284	107 : 55	.289021	86 : 45	.281286	77 : 41	.273707
89 : 45	.296178	70 : 36	.288796	107 : 56	.281196	92 : 49	.273592
87 : 44	0.296067	103 : 53	0.288561	84 : 44	0.280827	107 : 57	0.273509
85 : 43	.295950	68 : 35	.288441	63 : 33	.280827	120 : 64	.273001
83 : 42	.295829	101 : 52	.288318	103 : 54	.280443	105 : 56	.273001
81 : 41	.295701	66 : 34	.288065	82 : 43	.280345	90 : 48	.273001
79 : 40	.295567	99 : 51	.288065	61 : 32	.280180	75 : 40	.273001
77 : 39	.295426	97 : 50	.287802	101 : 53	.280046	60 : 32	.273001
75 : 38	.295278	64 : 33	.287666	80 : 42	.279841	118 : 63	.272542
73 : 37	.295121	95 : 49	.287528	40 : 21	.279841	103 : 55	.272475

Logarithms of Gear Ratios from 1.0084+ to 7.5

Numbers of Teeth	Logarithm of Ratio	Numbers of Teeth	Logarithm of Ratio	Numbers of Teeth	Logarithm of Ratio	Numbers of Teeth	Logarithm of Ratio
88 : 47	0.272385	94 : 51	0.265558	87 : 48	0.258278	116 : 65	0.251545
73 : 39	.272258	70 : 38	.265314	58 : 32	.258278	91 : 51	.251471
58 : 31	.272066	116 : 63	.265118	96 : 53	.257995	66 : 37	.251342
101 : 54	.271928	81 : 44	.265032	67 : 37	.257873	107 : 60	.251233
86 : 46	.271741	92 : 50	.264818	105 : 58	.257761	82 : 46	.251056
114 : 61	.271575	103 : 56	.264649	38 : 21	.257564	98 : 55	.250863
99 : 53	.271360	68 : 37	.264307	76 : 42	.257564	57 : 32	.250725
112 : 60	.271067	79 : 43	.264159	85 : 47	.257321	73 : 41	.250539
84 : 45	0.271067	90 : 49	0.264046	94 : 52	0.257125	89 : 50	0.250420
56 : 30	.271067	101 : 55	.263959	103 : 57	.256962	105 : 59	.250337
97 : 52	.270768	112 : 61	.263888	112 : 62	.256826	112 : 63	.249878
69 : 37	.270647	110 : 60	.263241	56 : 31	.256826	96 : 54	.249878
110 : 59	.270541	99 : 54	.263241	65 : 36	.256611	80 : 45	.249878
82 : 44	.270361	88 : 48	.263241	74 : 41	.256448	64 : 36	.249878
41 : 22	.270361	77 : 42	.263241	83 : 46	.256320	119 : 67	.249472
95 : 51	.270153	66 : 36	.263241	92 : 51	.256218	103 : 58	.249409
54 : 29	0.269996	55 : 30	0.263241	101 : 56	0.256133	87 : 49	0.249323
67 : 36	.269772	119 : 65	.262634	110 : 61	.256063	71 : 40	.249198
80 : 43	.269622	108 : 59	.262572	119 : 66	.256003	110 : 62	.249001
93 : 50	.269513	97 : 53	.262496	99 : 55	.255273	55 : 31	.249001
106 : 57	.269431	86 : 47	.262401	90 : 50	.255273	94 : 53	.248852
119 : 64	.269367	75 : 41	.262277	81 : 45	.255273	117 : 66	.248642
117 : 63	.268845	64 : 35	.262112	72 : 40	.255273	78 : 44	.248642
91 : 49	.268845	53 : 29	.261878	63 : 35	.255273	101 : 57	.248447
78 : 42	0.268845	95 : 52	0.261720	54 : 30	0.255273	62 : 35	0.248324
65 : 35	.268845	84 : 46	.261522	115 : 64	.254518	85 : 48	.248178
52 : 28	.268845	115 : 63	.261357	106 : 59	.254454	108 : 61	.248094
39 : 21	.268845	73 : 40	.261262	97 : 54	.254378	115 : 65	.247785
115 : 62	.268306	104 : 57	.261158	88 : 49	.254287	92 : 52	.247785
102 : 55	.268238	62 : 34	.260913	79 : 44	.254174	69 : 39	.247785
89 : 48	.268149	93 : 51	.260912	70 : 39	.254033	99 : 56	.247447
76 : 41	.268030	113 : 62	.260687	61 : 34	.253851	76 : 43	.247345
63 : 34	0.267862	82 : 45	0.260601	113 : 63	0.253738	106 : 60	0.247155
113 : 61	.267749	51 : 28	.260412	52 : 29	.253605	53 : 30	.247155
100 : 54	.267606	71 : 39	.260194	95 : 53	.253448	83 : 47	.246980
87 : 47	.267421	91 : 50	.260071	86 : 48	.253257	113 : 64	.246898
111 : 60	.267172	111 : 61	.259993	120 : 67	.253106	120 : 68	.246672
74 : 40	.267172	100 : 55	.259637	77 : 43	.253022	90 : 51	.246672
37 : 20	.267172	80 : 44	.259637	111 : 62	.252931	60 : 34	.246672
98 : 53	.266950	40 : 22	.259637	102 : 57	.252725	97 : 55	.246409
61 : 33	0.266816	109 : 60	0.259275	68 : 38	0.252725	67 : 38	0.246291
85 : 46	.266661	89 : 49	.259194	93 : 52	.252480	104 : 59	.246181
109 : 59	.266575	69 : 38	.259066	118 : 66	.252338	111 : 63	.245982
96 : 52	.266268	118 : 65	.258969	59 : 33	.252338	74 : 42	.245982
72 : 39	.266268	98 : 54	.258832	84 : 47	.252181	37 : 21	.245982
107 : 58	.265956	78 : 43	.258626	109 : 61	.252097	118 : 67	.245807
118 : 64	.265702	107 : 59	.258532	100 : 56	.251812	81 : 46	.245727
59 : 32	.265702	116 : 64	.258278	75 : 42	.251812	88 : 50	.245513

Logarithms of Gear Ratios from 1.0084+ to 7.5

Numbers of Teeth	Logarithm of Ratio	Numbers of Teeth	Logarithm of Ratio	Numbers of Teeth	Logarithm of Ratio	Numbers of Teeth	Logarithm of Ratio
95 : 54	0.245330	52 : 30	0.238882	111 : 65	0.232410	111 : 66	0.225779
51 : 29	.245172	97 : 56	.238584	70 : 41	.232314	74 : 44	.225779
109 : 62	.245035	71 : 41	.238474	87 : 51	.231949	116 : 69	.225609
58 : 33	.244914	116 : 67	.238383	58 : 34	.231949	79 : 47	.225529
65 : 37	.244712	90 : 52	.238239	104 : 61	.231704	84 : 50	.225309
72 : 41	.244549	109 : 63	.238086	75 : 44	.231608	89 : 53	.225114
79 : 45	.244415	64 : 37	.237978	92 : 54	.231394	94 : 56	.224940
86 : 49	.244302	83 : 48	.237837	109 : 64	.231247	99 : 59	.224783
93 : 53	0.244207	102 : 59	0.237748	63 : 37	0.231139	52 : 31	0.224642
100 : 57	.244125	95 : 55	.237361	80 : 47	.230992	109 : 65	.224513
107 : 61	.244054	76 : 44	.237361	97 : 57	.230897	114 : 68	.224396
114 : 65	.243992	57 : 33	.237361	114 : 67	.230830	57 : 34	.224396
119 : 68	.243038	38 : 22	.237361	85 : 50	.230449	119 : 71	.224289
112 : 64	.243038	107 : 62	.236992	68 : 40	.230449	62 : 37	.224190
98 : 56	.243038	88 : 51	.236913	51 : 30	.230449	67 : 40	.224015
91 : 52	.243038	69 : 40	.236789	107 : 63	.230043	72 : 43	.223864
84 : 48	0.243038	119 : 69	0.236698	90 : 53	0.229967	77 : 46	0.223733
77 : 44	.243038	100 : 58	.236572	73 : 43	.229854	82 : 49	.223618
70 : 40	.243038	50 : 29	.236572	112 : 66	.229674	87 : 52	.223516
63 : 36	.243038	81 : 47	.236387	56 : 33	.229674	92 : 55	.223425
35 : 20	.243038	112 : 65	.236305	95 : 56	.229536	97 : 58	.223344
117 : 67	.242111	62 : 36	.236089	117 : 69	.229337	102 : 61	.223270
110 : 63	.242052	93 : 54	.236089	78 : 46	.229337	107 : 64	.223204
103 : 59	.241985	105 : 61	.235860	100 : 59	.229148	112 : 67	.223143
96 : 55	0.241909	74 : 43	0.235763	61 : 36	0.229027	117 : 70	0.223088
89 : 51	.241820	117 : 68	.235677	83 : 49	.228882	100 : 60	.221849
82 : 47	.241716	86 : 50	.235529	105 : 62	.228798	95 : 57	.221849
75 : 43	.241593	98 : 57	.235351	110 : 65	.228479	90 : 54	.221849
68 : 39	.241444	110 : 64	.235213	88 : 52	.228479	85 : 51	.221849
61 : 35	.241262	55 : 32	.235213	66 : 39	.228479	80 : 48	.221849
115 : 66	.241154	67 : 39	.235010	115 : 68	.228187	75 : 45	.221849
108 : 62	.241032	79 : 46	.234869	93 : 55	.228120	70 : 42	.221849
54 : 31	0.241032	91 : 53	0.234766	71 : 42	0.228009	65 : 39	0.221849
101 : 58	.240893	103 : 60	.234686	120 : 71	.227923	60 : 36	.221849
94 : 54	.240734	115 : 67	.234623	98 : 58	.227798	55 : 33	.221849
87 : 50	.240549	96 : 56	.234083	76 : 45	.227601	50 : 30	.221849
120 : 69	.240332	84 : 49	.234083	103 : 61	.227507	118 : 71	.220624
80 : 46	.240332	72 : 42	.234083	81 : 48	.227244	113 : 68	.220570
113 : 65	.240165	60 : 35	.234083	54 : 32	.227244	108 : 65	.220510
73 : 42	.240074	113 : 66	.233535	113 : 67	.227004	103 : 62	.220446
106 : 61	0.239976	101 : 59	0.233469	86 : 51	0.226928	98 : 59	0.220374
99 : 57	.239760	89 : 52	.233388	59 : 35	.226784	93 : 56	.220295
66 : 38	.239760	77 : 45	.233278	91 : 54	.226648	88 : 53	.220207
92 : 53	.239512	65 : 38	.233130	64 : 38	.226396	83 : 50	.220109
59 : 34	.239373	118 : 69	.233033	96 : 57	.226396	78 : 47	.219997
85 : 49	.239223	53 : 31	.232914	101 : 60	.226170	73 : 44	.219870
111 : 64	.239143	94 : 55	.232765	69 : 41	.226065	68 : 41	.219725
78 : 45	.238882	82 : 48	.232573	106 : 63	.225965	63 : 38	.219557

Logarithms of Gear Ratios from 1.0084+ to 7.5

Numbers of Teeth	Logarithm of Ratio	Numbers of Teeth	Logarithm of Ratio	Numbers of Teeth	Logarithm of Ratio	Numbers of Teeth	Logarithm of Ratio
58 : 35	0.219360	116 : 71	0.213200	29 : 18	0.207126	81 : 51	0.200915
111 : 67	.219248	98 : 60	.213075	95 : 59	.206872	54 : 34	.200915
53 : 32	.219126	49 : 30	.213075	66 : 41	.206760	100 : 63	.200660
101 : 61	.218992	80 : 49	.212894	103 : 64	.206657	73 : 46	.200565
96 : 58	.218843	111 : 68	.212814	111 : 69	.206474	119 : 75	.200486
91 : 55	.218679	93 : 57	.212608	74 : 46	.206474	92 : 58	.200360
86 : 52	.218495	62 : 38	.212608	119 : 74	.206315	111 : 70	.200225
81 : 49	.218289	106 : 65	.212393	82 : 51	.206244	65 : 41	.200130
119 : 72	0.218215	75 : 46	0.212304	90 : 56	0.206055	84 : 53	0.200003
76 : 46	.218056	119 : 73	.212224	98 : 61	.205896	103 : 65	.199924
109 : 66	.217883	88 : 54	.212089	53 : 33	.205762	114 : 72	.199572
71 : 43	.217790	101 : 62	.211930	114 : 71	.205647	95 : 60	.199572
104 : 63	.217693	57 : 35	.211807	61 : 38	.205546	76 : 48	.199572
66 : 40	.217484	70 : 43	.211630	69 : 43	.205380	57 : 36	.199572
94 : 57	.217253	96 : 59	.211419	77 : 48	.205250	106 : 67	.199231
61 : 37	.217128	109 : 67	.211352	85 : 53	.205143	87 : 55	.199157
89 : 54	0.216996	117 : 72	0.210853	93 : 58	0.205055	68 : 43	0.199040
117 : 71	.216928	91 : 56	.210853	101 : 63	.204981	117 : 74	.198954
112 : 68	.216709	78 : 48	.210853	109 : 68	.204918	98 : 62	.198834
84 : 51	.216709	65 : 40	.210853	117 : 73	.204863	49 : 31	.198834
56 : 34	.216709	112 : 69	.210369	96 : 60	.204120	79 : 50	.198657
107 : 65	.216470	99 : 61	.210305	88 : 55	.204120	109 : 69	.198577
79 : 48	.216386	86 : 53	.210223	80 : 50	.204120	90 : 57	.198368
102 : 62	.216209	73 : 45	.210110	72 : 45	.204120	60 : 38	.198368
51 : 31	0.216209	120 : 74	0.209950	64 : 40	0.204120	101 : 64	0.198141
74 : 45	.216019	60 : 37	.209950	56 : 35	.204120	71 : 45	.198046
97 : 59	.215920	107 : 66	.209840	32 : 20	.204120	112 : 71	.197960
120 : 73	.215858	94 : 58	.209700	115 : 72	.203365	82 : 52	.197811
115 : 70	.215600	81 : 50	.209515	107 : 67	.203309	93 : 59	.197631
92 : 56	.215600	115 : 71	.209440	99 : 62	.203244	52 : 33	.197489
69 : 42	.215600	68 : 42	.209260	91 : 57	.203167	115 : 73	.197375
110 : 67	.215318	34 : 21	.209260	83 : 52	.203075	63 : 40	.197281
87 : 53	0.215243	89 : 55	0.209027	75 : 47	0.202963	74 : 47	0.197134
64 : 39	.215115	55 : 34	.208884	67 : 42	.202826	85 : 54	.197025
105 : 64	.215009	76 : 47	.208716	59 : 37	.202650	96 : 61	.196941
82 : 50	.214844	97 : 60	.208620	110 : 69	.202544	107 : 68	.196875
100 : 61	.214670	118 : 73	.208559	51 : 32	.202420	118 : 75	.196821
118 : 72	.214550	84 : 52	.208276	94 : 59	.202276	110 : 70	.196295
59 : 36	.214550	63 : 39	.208276	86 : 54	.202105	99 : 63	.196295
77 : 47	.214393	113 : 70	.207980	78 : 49	.201899	88 : 56	.196295
95 : 58	0.214296	92 : 57	0.207913	113 : 71	0.201820	77 : 49	0.196295
113 : 69	.214229	71 : 44	.207806	105 : 66	.201645	66 : 42	.196295
90 : 55	.213880	100 : 62	.207608	70 : 44	.201645	55 : 35	.196295
72 : 44	.213880	50 : 31	.207608	97 : 61	.201442	113 : 72	.195746
54 : 33	.213880	79 : 49	.207431	62 : 39	.201327	91 : 58	.195613
36 : 22	.213880	108 : 67	.207349	89 : 56	.201202	102 : 65	.195687
103 : 63	.213497	87 : 54	.207126	116 : 73	.201135	69 : 44	.195396
67 : 41	.213291	58 : 36	.207126	108 : 68	.200915	58 : 37	.195226

Logarithms of Gear Ratios from 1.0084+ to 7.5

Numbers of Teeth	Logarithm of Ratio	Numbers of Teeth	Logarithm of Ratio	Numbers of Teeth	Logarithm of Ratio	Numbers of Teeth	Logarithm of Ratio
105 : 67	0.195115	99 : 64	0.189455	110 : 72	0.184060	71 : 47	0.179160
94 : 60	.194977	116 : 75	.189397	55 : 36	.184060	74 : 49	.179036
47 : 30	.194977	119 : 77	.189056	84 : 55	.183917	77 : 51	.178921
83 : 53	.194802	102 : 66	.189056	113 : 74	.183847	80 : 53	.178814
119 : 76	.194733	85 : 55	.189056	116 : 76	.183644	83 : 55	.178715
108 : 69	.194575	68 : 44	.189056	87 : 57	.183644	86 : 57	.178624
97 : 62	.194380	51 : 33	.189056	58 : 38	.183644	89 : 59	.178538
61 : 39	.194265	34 : 22	.189056	119 : 78	.183452	92 : 61	.178458
86 : 55	0.194136	105 : 68	0.188680	90 : 59	0.183391	95 : 63	0.178383
111 : 71	.194065	88 : 57	.188608	61 : 40	.183270	98 : 65	.178312
100 : 64	.193820	71 : 46	.188501	93 : 61	.183153	101 : 67	.178247
75 : 48	.193820	54 : 35	.188326	96 : 63	.182931	104 : 69	.178184
50 : 32	.193820	91 : 59	.188190	64 : 42	.182931	107 : 71	.178126
114 : 73	.193582	111 : 72	.187991	32 : 21	.182931	110 : 73	.178070
89 : 57	.193515	74 : 48	.187991	99 : 65	.182724	113 : 75	.178017
64 : 41	.193396	94 : 61	.187798	67 : 44	.182622	116 : 77	.177967
103 : 66	0.193293	57 : 37	0.187673	102 : 67	0.182525	119 : 79	0.177920
117 : 75	.193125	77 : 50	.187521	105 : 69	.182340	24 : 16	
78 : 50	.193125	97 : 63	.187431	70 : 46	.182340	or	
92 : 59	.192936	117 : 76	.187372	108 : 71	.182166	any	.176091
53 : 34	.192797	100 : 65	.187087	73 : 48	.182082	3 to 2	
120 : 77	.192691	80 : 52	.187087	111 : 73	.182000	ratio	
67 : 43	.192606	60 : 39	.187087	114 : 75	.181844	118 : 79	.174255
81 : 52	.192482	103 : 67	.186762	76 : 50	.181844	115 : 77	.174207
95 : 61	0.192394	83 : 54	0.186684	117 : 77	0.181695	112 : 75	0.174157
109 : 70	.192329	63 : 41	.186557	79 : 52	.181624	109 : 73	.174104
112 : 72	.191886	106 : 69	.186457	120 : 79	.181554	106 : 71	.174048
98 : 63	.191886	86 : 56	.186311	82 : 54	.181420	103 : 69	.173988
84 : 54	.191886	109 : 71	.186168	85 : 56	.181231	100 : 67	.173925
70 : 45	.191886	66 : 43	.186075	88 : 58	.181055	97 : 65	.173858
56 : 36	.191886	89 : 58	.185962	91 : 60	.180890	94 : 63	.173787
115 : 74	.191466	112 : 73	.185895	94 : 62	.180736	91 : 61	.173712
101 : 65	0.191408	115 : 75	0.185637	47 : 31	0.180736	88 : 59	0.173631
87 : 56	.191331	92 : 60	.185637	97 : 64	.180592	85 : 57	.173544
73 : 47	.191225	69 : 45	.185637	100 : 66	.180456	82 : 55	.173451
59 : 38	.191068	46 : 30	.185637	50 : 33	.180456	79 : 53	.173351
104 : 67	.190959	118 : 77	.185391	103 : 68	.180328	76 : 51	.173243
90 : 58	.190815	95 : 62	.185332	106 : 70	.180208	73 : 49	.173127
76 : 49	.190618	72 : 47	.185235	53 : 35	.180208	70 : 47	.173000
107 : 69	.190535	98 : 64	.185046	109 : 72	.180094	67 : 45	.172862
93 : 60	0.190332	49 : 32	0.185046	112 : 74	0.179986	64 : 43	0.172712
62 : 40	.190332	75 : 49	.185046	56 : 37	.179986	61 : 41	.172546
110 : 71	.190134	101 : 66	.184778	115 : 76	.179884	119 : 80	.172457
79 : 51	.190057	104 : 68	.184524	118 : 78	.179787	58 : 39	.172363
96 : 62	.189880	78 : 51	.184524	59 : 39	.179787	113 : 76	.172265
113 : 73	.189756	52 : 34	.184524	62 : 41	.179608	55 : 37	.172161
65 : 42	.189664	107 : 70	.184286	65 : 43	.179445	107 : 72	.172051
82 : 53	.189538	81 : 53	.184209	68 : 45	.179296	104 : 70	.171935

Logarithms of Gear Ratios from 1.0084+ to 7.5

Numbers of Teeth	Logarithm of Ratio	Numbers of Teeth	Logarithm of Ratio	Numbers of Teeth	Logarithm of Ratio	Numbers of Teeth	Logarithm of Ratio
52 : 35	0.171935	47 : 32	0.166948	77 : 53	0.162215	102 : 71	0.157342
101 : 68	.171813	116 : 79	.166831	61 : 42	.162081	79 : 55	.157264
98 : 66	.171682	69 : 47	.166751	106 : 73	.161983	112 : 78	.157123
49 : 33	.171682	91 : 62	.166650	90 : 62	.161851	56 : 39	.157123
95 : 64	.171544	113 : 77	.166588	45 : 31	.161851	89 : 62	.156998
92 : 62	.171396	110 : 75	.166331	119 : 82	.161733	99 : 69	.156786
46 : 31	.171396	88 : 60	.166331	74 : 51	.161662	66 : 46	.156786
89 : 60	.171239	66 : 45	.166331	103 : 71	.161579	109 : 76	.156613
86 : 58	0.171071	44 : 30	0.166331	116 : 80	0.161368	76 : 53	0.156538
83 : 56	.170890	107 : 73	.166061	87 : 60	.161368	119 : 83	.156469
120 : 81	.170696	85 : 58	.165991	58 : 40	.161368	86 : 60	.156347
80 : 54	.170696	63 : 43	.165872	100 : 69	.161151	43 : 30	.156347
117 : 79	.170559	104 : 71	.165775	71 : 49	.161062	96 : 67	.156196
77 : 52	.170487	82 : 56	.165626	113 : 78	.160984	106 : 74	.156074
114 : 77	.170414	101 : 69	.165472	84 : 58	.160851	53 : 37	.156074
111 : 75	.170262	120 : 82	.165367	97 : 67	.160697	116 : 81	.155973
74 : 50	0.170262	60 : 41	0.165367	110 : 76	0.160579	63 : 44	0.155888
108 : 73	.170101	79 : 54	.165233	55 : 38	.160579	73 : 51	.155753
71 : 48	.170017	98 : 67	.165151	68 : 47	.160411	93 : 65	.155570
105 : 71	.169931	117 : 80	.165096	81 : 56	.160297	103 : 72	.155505
68 : 46	.169751	114 : 78	.164810	94 : 65	.160215	113 : 79	.155451
99 : 67	.169560	95 : 65	.164810	107 : 74	.160152	120 : 84	.154902
65 : 44	.169461	76 : 52	.164810	120 : 83	.160103	110 : 77	.154902
96 : 65	.169358	57 : 39	.164810	117 : 81	.159701	100 : 70	.154902
93 : 63	0.169142	111 : 76	0.164509	104 : 72	0.159701	90 : 63	0.154902
62 : 42	.169142	92 : 63	.164447	91 : 63	.159701	80 : 56	.154902
31 : 21	.169142	73 : 50	.164353	78 : 54	.159701	70 : 49	.154902
90 : 61	.168913	108 : 74	.164192	65 : 45	.159701	60 : 42	.154902
59 : 40	.168792	54 : 37	.164192	52 : 36	.159701	30 : 21	.154902
118 : 80	.168792	89 : 61	.164060	114 : 79	.159278	117 : 82	.154372
87 : 59	.168667	105 : 72	.163857	101 : 70	.159223	107 : 75	.154323
115 : 78	.168603	70 : 48	.163857	88 : 61	.159153	97 : 68	.154263
112 : 76	0.168404	86 : 59	0.163647	75 : 52	0.159058	87 : 61	0.154190
84 : 57	.168404	102 : 70	.163502	62 : 43	.158923	77 : 54	.154097
56 : 38	.168404	51 : 35	.163502	111 : 77	.158832	67 : 47	.153977
109 : 74	.168196	118 : 81	.163397	98 : 68	.158717	114 : 80	.153815
81 : 55	.168122	67 : 46	.163317	49 : 34	.158717	57 : 40	.153815
106 : 72	.167973	83 : 57	.163203	85 : 59	.158567	104 : 73	.153710
53 : 36	.167973	99 : 68	.163126	108 : 75	.158363	94 : 66	.153584
78 : 53	.167819	115 : 79	.163071	72 : 50	.158363	47 : 33	.153584
103 : 70	0.167739	112 : 77	0.162727	95 : 66	0.158180	84 : 59	0.153427
100 : 68	.167491	96 : 66	.162727	59 : 41	.158068	111 : 78	.153228
75 : 51	.167491	80 : 55	.162727	82 : 57	.157939	74 : 52	.153228
50 : 34	.167491	64 : 44	.162727	105 : 73	.157866	101 : 71	.153063
97 : 66	.167228	48 : 33	.162727	115 : 80	.157608	64 : 45	.152968
72 : 49	.167136	32 : 22	.162727	92 : 64	.157608	91 : 64	.152861
119 : 81	.167062	109 : 75	.162365	69 : 48	.157608	118 : 83	.152804
94 : 64	.166948	93 : 64	.162303	46 : 32	.157608	108 : 76	.152610

Logarithms of Gear Ratios from 1.0084+ to 7.5

Numbers of Teeth	Logarithm of Ratio	Numbers of Teeth	Logarithm of Ratio	Numbers of Teeth	Logarithm of Ratio	Numbers of Teeth	Logarithm of Ratio
81 : 57	0.152610	45 : 32	0.148063	114 : 82	0.143091	106 : 77	0.138815
54 : 38	.152610	97 : 69	.147923	57 : 41	.143091	117 : 85	.138767
98 : 69	.152377	104 : 74	.147802	82 : 59	.142962	110 : 80	.138303
71 : 50	.152288	52 : 37	.147802	107 : 77	.142893	99 : 72	.138303
115 : 81	.152213	111 : 79	.147696	100 : 72	.142668	88 : 64	.138303
88 : 62	.152091	118 : 84	.147603	75 : 54	.142668	77 : 56	.138303
44 : 31	.152091	66 : 47	.147446	50 : 36	.142668	66 : 48	.138303
105 : 74	.151958	73 : 52	.147320	118 : 85	.142463	55 : 40	.138303
61 : 43	0.151861	80 : 57	0.147215	93 : 67	0.142408	44 : 32	0.138303
78 : 55	.151732	87 : 62	.147128	68 : 49	.142313	114 : 83	.137827
95 : 67	.151649	94 : 67	.147053	111 : 80	.142233	103 : 75	.137776
112 : 79	.151591	101 : 72	.146989	86 : 62	.142107	92 : 67	.137713
119 : 84	.151268	108 : 77	.146933	43 : 31	.142107	81 : 59	.137633
102 : 72	.151268	115 : 82	.146884	104 : 75	.141972	70 : 51	.137528
85 : 60	.151268	98 : 70	.146128	61 : 44	.141877	118 : 86	.137384
68 : 48	.151268	91 : 65	.146128	79 : 57	.141752	59 : 43	.137384
51 : 36	0.151268	84 : 60	0.146128	97 : 70	0.141674	107 : 78	0.137289
109 : 77	.150936	77 : 55	.146128	115 : 83	.141620	96 : 70	.137173
92 : 65	.150874	70 : 50	.146128	108 : 78	.141329	48 : 35	.137173
75 : 53	.150785	63 : 45	.146128	90 : 65	.141329	85 : 62	.137027
116 : 82	.150644	56 : 40	.146128	72 : 52	.141329	111 : 81	.136838
58 : 41	.150644	49 : 35	.146128	54 : 39	.141329	74 : 54	.136838
99 : 70	.150537	42 : 30	.146128	119 : 86	.141049	100 : 73	.136677
82 : 58	.150386	35 : 25	.146128	101 : 73	.140999	63 : 46	.136583
106 : 75	0.150245	116 : 83	0.145380	83 : 60	0.140927	89 : 65	0.136477
65 : 46	.150156	109 : 78	.145332	65 : 47	.140816	115 : 84	.136419
89 : 63	.150050	102 : 73	.145277	112 : 81	.140733	104 : 76	.136220
113 : 80	.149988	88 : 63	.145142	94 : 68	.140619	78 : 57	.136220
120 : 85	.149762	81 : 58	.145057	47 : 34	.140619	52 : 38	.136220
96 : 68	.149762	74 : 53	.144956	76 : 55	.140451	119 : 87	.136028
72 : 51	.149762	67 : 48	.144834	105 : 76	.140376	93 : 68	.135974
48 : 34	.149762	120 : 86	.144683	116 : 84	.140179	67 : 49	.135879
103 : 73	0.149514	60 : 43	0.144683	87 : 63	0.140179	108 : 79	0.135797
79 : 56	.149439	113 : 81	.144593	58 : 42	.140179	82 : 60	.135663
110 : 78	.149298	106 : 76	.144492	29 : 21	.140179	41 : 30	.135663
55 : 39	.149298	53 : 38	.144492	98 : 71	.139968	97 : 71	.135513
86 : 61	.149169	99 : 71	.144377	69 : 50	.139879	112 : 82	.135404
117 : 83	.149108	92 : 66	.144244	109 : 79	.139799	56 : 41	.135404
93 : 66	.148939	46 : 33	.144244	120 : 87	.139662	71 : 52	.135255
62 : 44	.148939	85 : 61	.144089	80 : 58	.139662	86 : 63	.135158
31 : 22	0.148939	117 : 84	0.143907	91 : 66	0.139498	101 : 74	0.135090
100 : 71	.148742	78 : 56	.143907	102 : 74	.139369	116 : 85	.135039
69 : 49	.148653	110 : 79	.143766	51 : 37	.139369	105 : 77	.134699
107 : 76	.148570	71 : 51	.143688	113 : 82	.139265	90 : 66	.134699
114 : 81	.148420	103 : 74	.143606	62 : 45	.139179	75 : 55	.134699
76 : 54	.148420	96 : 69	.143422	73 : 53	.139047	60 : 44	.134699
83 : 59	.148226	64 : 46	.143422	84 : 61	.138950	45 : 33	.134699
90 : 64	.148063	89 : 64	.143210	95 : 69	.138875	30 : 22	.134699

Logarithms of Gear Ratios from 1.0084+ to 7.5

Numbers of Teeth	Logarithm of Ratio	Numbers of Teeth	Logarithm of Ratio	Numbers of Teeth	Logarithm of Ratio	Numbers of Teeth	Logarithm of Ratio
109 : 80	0.134337	58 : 43	0.129960	104 : 78	0.124939	95 : 72	0.120391
94 : 69	.134279	89 : 66	.129846	88 : 66	.124939	62 : 47	.120294
79 : 58	.134199	120 : 89	.129791	84 : 63	.124939	91 : 69	.120192
64 : 47	.134082	93 : 69	.129634	64 : 48	.124939	120 : 91	.120140
113 : 83	.134000	62 : 46	.129634	60 : 45	.124939	116 : 88	.119975
98 : 72	.133894	97 : 72	.129439	44 : 33	.124939	87 : 66	.119975
49 : 36	.133894	66 : 49	.129348	40 : 30	▼ .124939	58 : 44	.119975
83 : 61	.133748	101 : 75	.129260	28 : 21	.124939	29 : 22	.119975
117 : 86	0.133687	105 : 78	0.129095	117 : 88	0.123703	112 : 85	0.119799
102 : 75	.133539	70 : 52	.129095	113 : 85	.123660	83 : 63	.119738
68 : 50	.133539	109 : 81	.128942	109 : 82	.123613	108 : 82	.119610
87 : 64	.133339	74 : 55	.128869	105 : 79	.123562	54 : 41	.119610
106 : 78	.133211	113 : 84	.128799	101 : 76	.123508	79 : 60	.119476
72 : 53	.133057	117 : 87	.128667	97 : 73	.123449	104 : 79	.119406
91 : 67	.132967	78 : 58	.128667	93 : 70	.123385	100 : 76	.119186
110 : 81	.132908	82 : 61	.128484	89 : 67	.123315	75 : 57	.119186
114 : 84	0.132626	86 : 64	0.128319	85 : 64	0.123238	50 : 38	0.119186
95 : 70	.132626	43 : 32	.128319	81 : 61	.123155	96 : 73	.118948
76 : 56	.132626	90 : 67	.128168	77 : 58	.123063	71 : 54	.118865
57 : 42	.132626	94 : 70	.128030	73 : 55	.122960	117 : 89	.118796
118 : 87	.132363	47 : 35	.128030	69 : 52	.122846	92 : 70	.118690
99 : 73	.132312	98 : 73	.127903	65 : 49	.122717	46 : 35	.118690
80 : 59	.132238	102 : 76	.127787	61 : 46	.122552	113 : 86	.118580
61 : 45	.132117	51 : 38	.127787	118 : 89	.122492	67 : 51	.118505
103 : 76	0.132024	106 : 79	0.127679	114 : 86	0.122406	88 : 67	0.118408
84 : 62	.131888	110 : 82	.127579	57 : 43	.122406	109 : 83	.118348
42 : 31	.131888	55 : 41	.127579	110 : 83	.122315	84 : 64	.118099
107 : 79	.131757	114 : 85	.127486	53 : 40	.122216	63 : 48	.118099
65 : 48	.131672	118 : 88	.127399	106 : 80	.122216	42 : 32	.118099
88 : 65	.131570	59 : 44	.127399	102 : 77	.122110	105 : 80	.118090
111 : 82	.131509	63 : 47	.127243	98 : 74	.121994	101 : 77	.117831
115 : 85	.131279	67 : 50	.127105	49 : 37	.121994	80 : 61	.117760
92 : 68	0.131279	71 : 53	0.126982	94 : 71	0.121870	118 : 90	.117640
69 : 51	.131279	75 : 56	.126873	90 : 68	.121734	59 : 45	0.117640
46 : 34	.131279	79 : 59	.126775	45 : 34	.121734	97 : 74	.117540
119 : 88	.131064	83 : 62	.126686	86 : 65	.121585	114 : 87	.117386
96 : 71	.131013	87 : 65	.126606	82 : 62	.121422	76 : 58	.117386
73 : 54	.130929	91 : 68	.126533	41 : 31	.121422	93 : 71	.117225
100 : 74	.130768	95 : 71	.126465	119 : 90	.121305	110 : 84	.117113
50 : 37	.130768	99 : 74	.126404	78 : 59	.121243	55 : 42	.117113
77 : 57	0.130616	103 : 77	0.126347	115 : 87	0.121179	72 : 55	0.116970
104 : 77	.130543	107 : 80	.126294	111 : 84	.121044	89 : 68	.116881
81 : 60	.130334	111 : 83	.126245	74 : 56	.121044	106 : 81	.116821
54 : 40	.130334	115 : 86	.126199	107 : 81	.120899	119 : 91	.116506
27 : 20	.130334	119 : 89	.126157	70 : 53	.120822	102 : 78	.116506
112 : 83	.130140	120 : 90	.124939	103 : 78	.120743	85 : 65	.116506
85 : 63	.130078	112 : 84	.124939	99 : 75	.120574	68 : 52	.116506
116 : 86	.129960	108 : 81	.124939	66 : 50	.120574	51 : 39	.116506

Logarithms of Gear Ratios from 1.0084+ to 7.5

Numbers of Teeth	Logarithm of Ratio	Numbers of Teeth	Logarithm of Ratio	Numbers of Teeth	Logarithm of Ratio	Numbers of Teeth	Logarithm of Ratio
34 : 26	0.116506	101 : 78	0.112227	118 : 92	0.108094	75 : 59	0.104209
115 : 88	.116215	110 : 85	.111974	59 : 46	.108094	61 : 48	.104089
98 : 75	.116165	88 : 68	.111974	109 : 85	.108008	108 : 85	.104005
81 : 62	.116093	44 : 34	.111974	100 : 78	.107905	94 : 74	.103896
64 : 49	.115984	66 : 51	.111974	50 : 39	.107905	47 : 37	.103896
111 : 85	.115904	119 : 92	.111759	91 : 71	.107783	80 : 63	.103750
94 : 72	.115795	97 : 75	.111710	82 : 64	.107634	113 : 89	.103688
47 : 36	.115795	75 : 58	.111633	41 : 32	.107634	99 : 78	.103541
77 : 59	0.115639	106 : 82	0.111492	114 : 89	0.107515	66 : 52	0.103541
107 : 82	.115570	53 : 41	.111492	73 : 57	.107448	118 : 93	.103399
120 : 92	.115393	84 : 65	.111366	105 : 82	.107375	85 : 67	.103344
90 : 69	.115393	115 : 89	.111308	96 : 75	.107210	104 : 82	.103219
60 : 46	.115393	93 : 72	.111151	64 : 50	.107210	52 : 41	.103219
30 : 23	.115393	62 : 48	.111151	119 : 93	.107064	90 : 71	.102984
103 : 79	.115210	102 : 79	.110973	87 : 68	.107010	109 : 86	.102928
73 : 56	.115135	71 : 55	.110896	110 : 86	.106894	95 : 75	.102662
116 : 89	0.115068	111 : 86	0.110825	55 : 43	0.106894	76 : 60	0.102662
86 : 66	.114955	120 : 93	.110698	78 : 61	.106765	57 : 45	.102662
43 : 33	.114955	80 : 62	.110698	101 : 79	.106694	38 : 30	.102662
99 : 76	.114822	40 : 31	.110698	115 : 90	.106455	119 : 94	.102419
112 : 86	.114720	89 : 69	.110541	92 : 72	.106455	100 : 79	.102373
56 : 43	.114720	98 : 76	.110413	69 : 54	.106455	81 : 64	.102305
69 : 53	.114573	49 : 38	.110413	46 : 36	.106455	62 : 49	.102196
82 : 63	.114473	107 : 83	.110306	106 : 83	.106228	105 : 83	.102111
95 : 73	0.114401	116 : 90	0.110216	83 : 65	0.106165	86 : 68	0.101990
108 : 83	.114346	58 : 45	.110216	120 : 94	.106053	43 : 34	.101990
117 : 90	.113943	67 : 52	.110072	60 : 47	.106053	110 : 87	.101873
104 : 80	.113943	76 : 59	.109962	97 : 76	.105958	67 : 53	.101799
91 : 70	.113943	85 : 66	.109875	111 : 87	.105804	91 : 72	.101709
78 : 60	.113943	94 : 73	.109805	74 : 58	.105804	115 : 91	.101656
65 : 50	.113943	103 : 80	.109747	88 : 69	.105634	120 : 95	.101458
52 : 40	.113943	112 : 87	.109699	102 : 80	.105510	96 : 76	.101458
39 : 30	0.113943	117 : 91	0.109145	51 : 40	0.105510	72 : 57	0.101458
26 : 20	.113943	108 : 84	.109145	116 : 91	.105417	48 : 38	.101458
113 : 87	.113559	99 : 77	.109145	65 : 51	.105343	101 : 80	.101231
100 : 77	.113509	90 : 70	.109145	79 : 62	.105235	77 : 61	.101161
87 : 67	.113445	81 : 63	.109145	93 : 73	.105160	106 : 84	.101027
74 : 57	.113357	72 : 56	.109145	107 : 84	.105105	53 : 42	.101027
61 : 47	.113232	63 : 49	.109145	112 : 88	.104735	82 : 65	.100901
109 : 84	.113147	54 : 42	.109145	98 : 77	.104735	111 : 88	.100840
96 : 74	0.113040	45 : 35	0.109145	84 : 66	0.104735	116 : 92	0.100670
48 : 37	.113040	27 : 21	.109145	70 : 55	.104735	87 : 69	.100670
83 : 64	.112898	113 : 88	.108596	56 : 44	.104735	58 : 46	.100670
118 : 91	.112841	104 : 81	.108548	42 : 33	.104735	29 : 23	.100670
70 : 54	.112704	95 : 74	.108492	28 : 22	.104735	92 : 73	.100465
92 : 71	.112530	86 : 67	.108424	117 : 92	.104398	63 : 50	.100371
57 : 44	.112422	77 : 60	.108339	103 : 81	.104352	97 : 77	.100281
79 : 61	.112297	68 : 53	.108233	89 : 70	.104292	102 : 81	.100115

Logarithms of Gear Ratios from 1.0084+ to 7.5

Numbers of Teeth	Logarithm of Ratio	Numbers of Teeth	Logarithm of Ratio	Numbers of Teeth	Logarithm of Ratio	Numbers of Teeth	Logarithm of Ratio
68 : 54	0.100115	117 : 94	0.095058	74 : 60	0.091080	88 : 72	0.087150
34 : 27	.100115	56 : 45	.094976	37 : 30	.091080	77 : 63	.087150
107 : 85	.099964	107 : 86	.094885	90 : 73	.090920	66 : 54	.087150
73 : 58	.099894	102 : 82	.094786	106 : 86	.090807	55 : 45	.087150
112 : 89	.099828	51 : 41	.094786	53 : 43	.090807	44 : 36	.087150
78 : 62	.099703	97 : 78	.094677	69 : 56	.090661	116 : 95	.086734
39 : 31	.099703	92 : 74	.094556	85 : 69	.090570	105 : 86	.086691
83 : 66	.099534	46 : 37	.094556	101 : 82	.090508	94 : 77	.086637
88 : 70	0.099385	87 : 70	0.094421	117 : 95	0.090462	83 : 68	0.086569
44 : 35	.099385	82 : 66	.094270	112 : 91	.090177	72 : 59	.086481
93 : 74	.099251	41 : 33	.094270	96 : 78	.090177	61 : 50	.086360
98 : 78	.099132	118 : 95	.094158	80 : 65	.090177	111 : 91	.086282
49 : 39	.099132	77 : 62	.094099	64 : 52	.090177	100 : 82	.086186
103 : 82	.099023	113 : 91	.094037	48 : 39	.090177	50 : 41	.086186
108 : 86	.098925	108 : 87	.093905	107 : 87	.089865	89 : 73	.086067
54 : 43	.098925	72 : 58	.093905	91 : 74	.089811	117 : 96	.085915
113 : 90	0.098836	103 : 83	0.093759	75 . 61	0.089732	78 : 64	0.085915
118 : 94	.098754	67 : 54	.093681	118 : 96	.089611	39 : 32	.085915
59 : 47	.098754	98 : 79	.093599	59 : 48	.089611	106 : 87	.085787
64 : 51	.098610	93 : 75	.093422	102 : 83	.089522	67 : 55	.085712
69 : 55	.098486	62 : 50	.093422	86 : 70	.089401	95 : 78	.085629
74 : 59	.098380	119 : 96	.093276	43 : 35	.089401	112 : 92	.085430
79 : 63	.098287	88 : 71	.093224	113 : 92	.089291	84 : 69	.085430
84 : 67	.098205	114 : 92	.093117	70 : 57	.089223	56 : 46	.085430
89 : 71	0.098132	57 : 46	0.093117	97 : 79	0.089145	28 : 23	0.085430
94 : 75	.098067	83 : 67	.093003	108 : 88	.088941	101 : 83	.085243
99 : 79	.098008	109 : 88	.092944	81 : 66	.088941	118 : 97	.085110
104 : 83	.097955	104 : 84	.092754	54 : 44	.088941	90 : 74	.085011
109 : 87	.097907	78 : 63	.092754	27 : 22	.088941	45 : 37	.085011
114 : 91	.097864	52 : 42	.092754	119 : 97	.088775	107 : 88	.084901
119 : 95	.097823	26 : 21	.092754	65 : 53	.088663	62 : 51	.084822
20 : 16		99 : 80	.092545	103 : 84	.088558	79 : 65	.084714
or		73 : 59	0.092471	114 : 93	0.088422	96 : 79	0.084644
any	0.096910	120 : 97	.092410	76 : 62	.088422	113 : 93	.084596
5 to 4		94 : 76	.092314	38 : 31	.088422	119 : 98	.084321
ratio		47 : 38	.092314	87 : 71	.088261	102 : 84	.084321
116 : 93	.095975	68 : 55	.092146	98 : 80	.088136	85 : 70	.084321
111 : 89	.095933	115 : 93	.092215	49 : 40	.088136	68 : 56	.084321
106 : 85	.095887	89 : 72	.092058	109 : 89	.088037	51 : 42	.084321
101 : 81	.095836	110 : 89	.092003	120 : 98	.087955	108 : 89	.084034
96 : 77	0.095781	105 : 85	0.091770	60 : 49	0.087955	91 : 75	0.083980
91 : 73	.095719	84 : 68	.091770	71 : 58	.087830	74 : 61	.083902
86 : 69	.095649	63 : 51	.091770	82 : 67	.087739	114 : 94	.083777
81 : 65	.095572	42 : 34	.091770	93 : 76	.087669	57 : 47	.083777
76 : 61	.095484	116 : 94	.091330	104 : 85	.087614	97 : 80	.083682
71 : 57	.095383	58 : 47	.091330	115 : 94	.087570	120 : 99	.083546
66 : 53	.095268	95 : 77	0.091233	110 : 90	.087150	80 : 66	.083546
61 : 49	.095134	111 : 90	.091080	99 : 81	.087150	40 : 33	.083546

Logarithms of Gear Ratios from 1.0084+ to 7.5

Numbers of Teeth	Logarithm of Ratio	Numbers of Teeth	Logarithm of Ratio	Numbers of Teeth	Logarithm of Ratio	Numbers of Teeth	Logarithm of Ratio
103 : 85	0.083418	115 : 96	0.078427	114 : 96	0.074634	73 : 62	0.070931
63 : 52	.083337	109 : 91	.078385	95 : 80	.074634	93 : 79	.070856
86 : 71	.083240	103 : 86	.078339	76 : 64	.074634	113 : 96	.070808
109 : 90	.083184	97 : 81	.078287	57 : 48	.074634	100 : 85	.070581
115 : 95	.082974	91 : 76	.078228	38 : 32	.074634	80 : 68	.070581
92 : 76	.082974	85 : 71	.078161	108 : 91	.074382	60 : 51	.070581
69 : 57	.082974	79 : 66	.078083	89 : 75	.074329	40 : 34	.070581
46 : 38	.082974	73 : 61	.077993	70 : 59	.074246	107 : 91	.070342
98 : 81	0.082741	67 : 56	0.077887	102 : 86	0.074102	87 : 74	0.070288
75 : 62	.082670	61 : 51	.077760	51 : 43	.074102	67 : 57	.070200
52 : 43	.082535	116 : 97	.077686	83 : 70	.073980	114 : 97	.070133
81 : 67	.082410	55 : 46	.077605	115 : 97	.073927	94 : 80	.070038
110 : 91	.082351	104 : 87	.077514	96 : 81	.073786	47 : 40	.070038
116 : 96	.082187	98 : 82	.077412	64 : 54	.073786	74 : 63	.069891
87 : 72	.082187	49 : 41	.077412	109 : 92	.073639	101 : 86	.069823
58 : 48	.082187	92 : 77	.077297	77 : 65	.073577	81 : 69	.069636
29 : 24	0.082187	86 : 72	0.077166	90 : 76	0.073429	54 : 46	0.069636
93 : 77	.081992	43 : 36	.077166	45 : 38	.073429	115 : 98	.069472
64 : 53	.081904	80 : 67	.077015	103 : 87	.073318	88 : 75	.069421
99 : 82	.081821	117 : 98	.076960	116 : 98	.073232	61 : 52	.069327
105 : 87	.081670	111 : 93	.076840	58 : 49	.073232	95 : 81	.069239
70 : 58	.081670	74 : 62	.076840	71 : 60	.073107	68 : 58	.069081
76 : 63	.081473	37 : 31	.076840	84 : 71	.073021	109 : 93	.068944
117 : 97	.081414	105 : 88	.076707	97 : 82	.072958	75 : 64	.068881
82 : 68	0.081305	68 : 57	0.076634	110 : 93	0.072910	116 : 99	0.068823
41 : 34	.081305	99 : 83	.076557	117 : 99	.072551	82 : 70	.068716
88 : 73	.081160	93 : 78	.076388	104 : 88	.072551	41 : 35	.068716
94 : 78	.081033	62 : 52	.076388	91 : 77	.072551	89 : 76	.068576
47 : 39	.081033	118 : 99	.076247	78 : 66	.072551	96 : 82	.068457
100 : 83	.080922	87 : 73	.076196	65 : 55	.072551	48 : 41	.068457
106 : 88	.080823	112 : 94	.076090	39 : 33	.072551	103 : 88	.068355
53 : 44	.080823	56 : 47	.076090	52 : 44	.072551	55 : 47	.068265
118 : 98	0.080656	81 : 68	0.075976	111 : 94	0.072195	117 : 100	0.068186
59 : 49	.080656	106 : 89	.075916	98 : 83	.072148	62 : 53	.068116
65 : 54	.080520	100 : 84	.075721	85 : 72	.072086	69 : 59	.067997
71 : 59	.080406	75 : 63	.075721	72 : 61	.072003	76 : 65	.067900
77 : 64	.080311	50 : 42	.075721	118 : 100	.071882	83 : 71	.067820
83 : 69	.080229	25 : 21	.075721	59 : 50	.071882	90 : 77	.067752
89 : 74	.080158	119 : 100	0.075547	105 : 89	.071797	97 : 83	.067694
95 : 79	.080097	94 : 79	.075501	92 : 78	.071693	104 : 89	.067643
107 : 89	0.079994	69 : 58	0.075421	46 : 39	.071693	111 : 95	0.067599
113 : 94	.079951	113 : 95	.075355	79 : 67	0.071552	98 : 84	.066947
119 : 99	.079912	88 : 74	.075251	112 : 95	.071494	91 : 78	.066947
30 : 25		44 : 37	.075251	99 : 84	.071356	84 : 72	.066947
or		107 : 90	.075141	66 : 56	.071356	77 : 66	.066947
any	.079181	63 : 53	.075065	86 : 73	.071176	70 : 60	.066947
6 to 5		82 : 69	.074965	106 : 90	.071063	63 : 54	.066947
ratio		101 : 85	.074903	53 : 45	.071063	56 : 48	.066947

Logarithms of Gear Ratios from 1.0084+ to 7.5

Numbers of Teeth	Logarithm of Ratio	Numbers of Teeth	Logarithm of Ratio	Numbers of Teeth	Logarithm of Ratio	Numbers of Teeth	Logarithm of Ratio
49 : 42	0.066947	75 : 65	0.062148	113 : 99	0.057443	69 : 61	0.053519
42 : 36	.066947	60 : 52	.062148	105 : 92	.057402	95 : 84	.053444
35 : 30	.066947	45 : 39	.062148	97 : 85	.057353	78 : 69	.053246
113 : 97	.066307	113 : 98	.061852	89 : 78	.057295	52 : 46	.053246
106 : 91	.066265	98 : 85	.061807	81 : 71	.057227	113 : 100	.053078
99 : 85	.066216	83 : 72	.061746	73 : 64	.057143	87 : 77	.053029
92 : 79	.066161	68 : 59	.061657	65 : 57	.057039	61 : 54	.052936
85 : 73	.066096	53 : 46	.061518	57 : 50	.056905	96 : 85	.052852
78 : 67	0.066020	91 : 79	0.061414	106 : 93	0.056823	70 : 62	0.052706
71 : 61	.065929	76 : 66	.061270	98 : 86	.056728	35 : 31	.052706
64 : 55	.065817	38 : 33	.061270	49 : 43	.056728	79 : 70	.052529
57 : 49	.065679	99 : 86	.061137	90 : 79	.056615	88 : 78	.052388
107 : 92	.065596	61 : 53	.061054	82 : 72	.056481	44 : 39	.052388
100 : 86	.065502	84 : 73	.060956	41 : 36	.056481	97 : 86	.052273
50 : 43	.065502	107 : 93	.060901	74 : 65	.056318	53 : 47	.052178
93 : 80	.065393	92 : 80	.060698	107 : 94	.056256	62 : 55	.052029
86 : 74	0.065267	69 : 60	0.060698	99 : 87	0.056116	71 : 63	0.051918
43 : 37	.065267	46 : 40	.060698	66 : 58	.056116	80 : 71	.051832
79 : 68	.065118	100 : 87	.060481	91 : 80	.055951	89 : 79	.051763
115 : 99	.065063	77 : 67	.060416	58 : 51	.055858	98 : 87	.051707
72 : 62	.064941	54 : 47	.060296	83 : 73	.055755	107 : 95	.051660
36 : 31	.064941	85 : 74	.060187	108 : 95	.055700	99 : 88	.051153
101 : 87	.064802	93 : 81	.059998	100 : 88	.055517	90 : 80	.051153
65 : 56	.064725	62 : 54	.059998	75 : 66	.055517	81 : 72	.051153
94 : 81	0.064643	101 : 88	0.059839	50 : 44	0.055517	72 : 64	0.051153
87 : 75	.064558	70 : 61	.059768	92 : 81	.055303	63 : 56	.051153
109 : 94	.064299	109 : 95	.059703	67 : 59	.055223	54 : 48	.051153
80 : 69	.064241	78 : 68	.059586	109 : 96	.055155	45 : 40	.051153
102 : 88	.064118	39 : 34	.059586	84 : 74	.055048	36 : 32	.051153
51 : 44	.064118	86 : 75	.059437	42 : 37	.055048	109 : 97	.050655
73 : 63	.063982	47 : 41	.059314	101 : 89	.054931	100 : 89	.050610
95 : 82	.063910	94 : 82	.059314	59 : 52	.054849	91 : 81	.050556
88 : 76	0.063669	102 : 89	0.059210	76 : 67	0.054739	82 : 73	0.050491
66 : 57	.063669	55 : 48	.059122	93 : 82	.054669	73 : 65	.050410
44 : 38	.063669	63 : 55	.058978	110 : 97	.054621	64 : 57	.050305
103 : 89	.063447	71 : 62	.058867	102 : 90	.054358	55 : 49	.050167
81 : 70	.063387	79 : 69	.058778	85 : 75	.054358	101 : 90	.050079
59 : 51	.063282	87 : 76	.058706	68 : 60	.054358	92 : 82	.049974
96 : 83	.063193	95 : 83	.058646	51 : 45	.054358	46 : 41	.049974
74 : 64	.063052	103 : 90	.058595	34 : 30	.054358	83 : 74	.049846
37 : 32	0.063052	96 : 84	0.057992	111 : 98	0.054097	74 : 66	0.049688
89 : 77	.062899	88 : 77	.057992	94 : 83	.054050	37 : 33	.049688
52 : 45	.062791	80 : 70	.057992	77 : 68	.053982	102 : 91	.049558
67 : 58	.062647	72 : 63	.057992	60 : 53	.053875	65 : 58	.049485
82 : 71	.062556	64 : 56	.057992	103 : 91	.053796	93 : 83	.049405
97 : 84	.062493	56 : 49	.057992	86 : 76	.053685	56 : 50	.049218
112 : 97	.062446	48 : 42	.057992	43 : 38	.053685	84 : 75	.049218
90 : 78	.062148	40 : 35	.057992	112 : 99	.053583	103 : 92	.049049

Logarithms of Gear Ratios from 1.0084+ to 7.5

Numbers of Teeth	Logarithm of Ratio	Numbers of Teeth	Logarithm of Ratio	Numbers of Teeth	Logarithm of Ratio	Numbers of Teeth	Logarithm of Ratio
75 : 67	0.048987	41 : 37	0.044582	57 : 52	0.039872	38 : 35	0.035716
94 : 84	.048849	72 : 65	.044419	80 : 73	.039767	89 : 82	.035576
47 : 42	.048849	103 : 93	.044354	103 : 94	.039709	51 : 47	.035472
66 : 59	.048692	93 : 84	.044204	92 : 84	.039509	64 : 59	.035328
85 : 76	.048605	62 : 56	.044204	69 : 63	.039509	77 : 71	.035232
104 : 93	.048550	83 : 75	.044017	46 : 42	.039509	90 : 83	.035164
95 : 85	.048305	52 : 47	.043905	104 : 95	.039310	103 : 95	.035114
76 : 68	.048305	73 : 66	.043779	81 : 74	.039253	91 : 84	.034762
57 : 51	0.048305	94 : 85	0.043709	58 : 53	0.039152	78 : 72	0.034762
38 : 34	.048305	84 : 76	.043466	93 : 85	.039064	65 : 60	.034762
105 : 94	.048061	63 : 57	.043466	105 : 96	.038918	52 : 48	.034762
86 : 77	.048008	42 : 38	.043466	70 : 64	.038918	39 : 36	.034762
67 : 60	.047924	95 : 86	.043225	35 : 32	.038918	105 : 97	.034418
96 : 86	.047773	74 : 67	.043157	82 : 75	.038753	92 : 85	.034369
48 : 43	.047773	53 : 48	.043035	94 : 86	.038629	79 : 73	.034304
77 : 69	.047642	85 : 77	.042928	47 : 43	.038629	66 : 61	.034214
106 : 95	0.047582	96 : 87	0.042752	106 : 97	0.038534	53 : 49	0.034080
87 : 78	.047425	64 : 58	.042752	59 : 54	.038458	93 : 86	.033984
58 : 52	.047425	107 : 97	.042612	71 : 65	.038345	80 : 74	.033858
29 : 26	.047425	75 : 68	.042552	83 : 76	.038265	40 : 37	.033858
97 : 87	.047252	86 : 78	.042404	95 : 87	.038204	107 : 99	.033749
39 : 35	.046997	43 : 39	.042404	107 : 98	.038158	67 : 62	.033683
88 : 79	.046856	97 : 88	.042289	96 : 88	.037898	94 : 87	.033609
98 : 88	.046743	54 : 49	.042198	84 : 77	0.037789	81 : 75	.033424
49 : 44	0.046743	65 : 59	0.042061	72 : 66	.037789	54 : 50	0.033424
108 : 97	.046652	76 : 69	.041965	60 : 55	.037789	95 : 88	.033241
59 : 53	.046576	87 : 79	.041892	48 : 44	.037789	68 : 63	.033168
69 : 62	.046457	98 : 89	.041836	36 : 33	.037789	82 : 76	.033000
79 : 71	.046369	109 : 99	.041791	109 : 100	.037427	41 : 38	.033000
89 : 80	.046300	99 : 90	.041393	97 : 89	.037382	96 : 89	.032881
99 : 89	.046245	88 : 80	.041393	85 : 78	.037273	55 : 51	.032793
109 : 98	.046200	77 : 70	.041393	73 : 67	.037248	69 : 64	.032669
100 : 90	0.045758	66 : 60	0.041393	61 : 56	0.037142	83 : 77	0.032587
90 : 81	.045758	55 : 50	.041393	98 : 90	.036984	97 : 90	.032529
80 : 72	.045758	44 : 40	.041393	49 : 45	.036984	98 : 91	.032185
70 : 63	.045758	33 : 30	.041393	86 : 79	.036871	84 : 78	.032185
60 : 54	.045758	100 : 91	.040959	74 : 68	.036723	70 : 65	.032185
50 : 45	.045758	89 : 81	.040905	37 : 34	.036723	56 : 52	.032185
40 : 36	.045758	78 : 71	.040836	99 : 91	.036594	42 : 39	.032185
111 : 100	.045323	67 : 61	.040745	62 : 57	.036517	99 : 92	.031847
101 : 91	0.045280	56 : 51	0.040618	87 : 80	0.036429	85 : 79	0.031792
91 : 82	.045228	101 : 92	.040534	100 : 92	.036212	71 : 66	.031714
81 : 73	.045162	90 : 82	.040429	75 : 69	.036212	57 : 53	.031599
71 : 64	.045078	45 : 41	.040429	50 : 46	.036212	100 : 93	.031517
61 : 55	.044967	79 : 72	.040295	88 : 81	.035998	86 : 80	.031409
51 : 46	.044812	68 : 62	.040117	63 : 58	.035913	43 : 40	.031409
92 : 83	.044710	34 : 31	.040117	101 : 93	.035839	72 : 67	.031258
82 : 74	.044582	91 : 83	.039963	76 : 70	.035716	101 : 94	.031194

Logarithms of Gear Ratios from 1.0084+ to 7.5

Numbers of Teeth	Logarithm of Ratio	Numbers of Teeth	Logarithm of Ratio	Numbers of Teeth	Logarithm of Ratio	Numbers of Teeth	Logarithm of Ratio
87 : 81	0.031034	50 : 47	0.026872	80 : 76	0.022276	100 : 96	0.017729
58 : 54	.031034	67 : 63	.026734	60 : 57	.022276	75 : 72	.017729
102 : 95	.030877	84 : 79	.026652	40 : 38	.022276	50 : 48	.017729
73 : 68	.030814	101 : 95	.026598	20 : 19	.022276	101 : 97	.017550
88 : 82	.030669	85 : 80	.026329	101 : 96	.022050	76 : 73	.017491
44 : 41	.030669	68 : 64	.026329	81 : 77	.021994	51 : 49	.017374
103 : 96	.030566	51 : 48	.026329	61 : 58	.021902	77 : 74	.017259
59 : 55	.030489	34 : 32	.026329	103 : 98	.021611	103 : 99	.017202
74 : 69	0.030383	103 : 97	0.026066	62 : 59	0.021540	78 : 75	0.017033
89 : 83	.030312	86 : 81	.026014	83 : 79	.021451	52 : 50	.017033
104 : 97	.030262	69 : 65	.025936	104 : 99	.021398	79 : 76	.016814
105 : 98	.029963	52 : 49	.025807	84 : 80	.021189	53 : 51	.016706
90 : 84	.029963	87 : 82	.025705	63 : 60	.021189	80 : 77	.016599
75 : 70	.029963	70 : 66	.025554	42 : 40	.021189	81 : 78	.016391
60 : 56	.029963	35 : 33	.025554	85 : 81	.020934	54 : 52	.016391
45 : 42	.029963	88 : 83	.025405	64 : 61	.020850	82 : 79	.016187
106 : 99	0.029671	53 : 50	0.025306	86 : 82	0.020685	55 : 53	0.016087
91 : 85	.029623	71 : 67	.025184	43 : 41	.020685	83 : 80	.015988
76 : 71	.029555	89 : 84	.025111	65 : 62	.020522	84 : 81	.015794
61 : 57	.029455	90 : 85	.024824	87 : 83	.020441	56 : 54	.015794
107 : 100	.029384	72 : 68	.024824	88 : 84	.020203	85 : 82	.015605
92 : 84	.029289	54 : 51	.024824	66 : 63	.020203	57 : 55	.015512
46 : 43	.029289	36 : 34	.024824	44 : 42	.020203	86 : 83	.015420
77 : 72	.029158	91 : 86	.024543	89 : 85	.019971	87 : 84	.015240
93 : 87	0.028964	73 : 69	0.024474	67 : 64	0.019895	58 : 56	0.015240
62 : 58	.028964	55 : 52	.024359	90 : 86	.019744	88 : 85	.015064
78 : 73	.028772	92 : 87	.024269	45 : 43	.019744	59 : 57	.014977
47 : 44	.028645	74 : 70	.024134	68 : 65	.019596	89 : 86	.014892
94 : 88	.028645	37 : 35	.024134	91 : 87	.019522	90 : 87	.014723
63 : 59	.028489	93 : 88	.024000	92 : 88	.019305	60 : 58	.014723
79 : 74	.028395	56 : 53	.023912	69 : 66	.019305	91 : 88	.014559
95 : 89	.028334	75 : 71	.023803	46 : 44	.019305	61 : 59	.014478
96 : 90	0.028029	94 : 89	0.023738	93 : 89	0.019093	92 : 89	0.014398
80 : 75	.028029	95 : 90	.023481	70 : 67	.019023	93 : 90	.014240
64 : 60	.028029	76 : 72	.023481	94 : 90	.018885	62 : 60	.014240
48 : 45	.028029	57 : 54	.023481	47 : 45	.018885	31 : 30	.014240
32 : 30	.028029	38 : 36	.023481	71 : 68	.018749	94 : 91	.014087
97 : 91	.027730	96 : 91	.023230	95 : 91	.018682	63 : 61	.014011
81 : 76	.027671	77 : 73	.023168	96 : 92	.018483	95 : 92	.013936
65 : 61	.027584	58 : 55	.023065	72 : 69	.018483	96 : 93	.013788
98 : 92	0.027438	97 : 92	0.022984	48 : 46	0.018483	64 : 62	0.013788
49 : 46	.027438	78 : 74	.022863	24 : 23	.018483	32 : 31	.013788
82 : 77	.027323	39 : 37	.022863	97 : 93	.018289	97 : 94	.013644
99 : 93	.027152	98 : 93	.022743	73 : 70	.018225	65 : 63	.013573
66 : 62	.027152	59 : 56	.022664	98 : 94	.018098	98 : 95	.013503
33 : 31	.027152	79 : 75	.022566	49 : 47	.018098	99 : 96	.013364
83 : 78	.026984	99 : 94	.022507	74 : 71	.017973	66 : 64	.013364
100 : 94	.026872	100 : 95	.022276	99 : 95	.017912	33 : 32	.013364

Logarithms of Gear Ratios from 1.0084+ to 7.5

Numbers of Teeth	Logarithm of Ratio	Numbers of Teeth	Logarithm of Ratio	Numbers of Teeth	Logarithm of Ratio	Numbers of Teeth	Logarithm of Ratio
100 : 97	0.013228	87 : 85	0.010100	61 : 60	0.007179	93 : 92	0.004695
67 : 65	.013161	88 : 86	.009984	62 : 61	.007062	94 : 93	.004645
101 : 98	.013095	44 : 43	.009984	63 : 62	.006949	95 : 94	.004596
68 : 66	.012965	89 : 87	.009871	64 : 63	.006840	96 : 95	.004548
34 : 33	.012965	90 : 88	.009760	65 : 64	.006733	97 : 96	.004501
103 : 100	.012837	45 : 44	.009760	66 : 65	.006631	98 : 97	.004454
69 : 67	.012774	91 : 89	.009651	67 : 66	.006531	99 : 98	.004409
70 : 68	.012589	92 : 90	.009545	68 : 67	.006434	100 : 99	.004365
35 : 34	0.012589	46 : 45	0.009545	69 : 68	0.006340	101 : 100	0.004321
72 : 70	.012235	93 : 91	.009442	70 : 69	.006249	102 : 101	.004279
36 : 35	.012235	94 : 92	.009340	71 : 70	.006160	103 : 102	.004237
73 : 71	.012065	47 : 46	.009340	72 : 71	.006074	104 : 103	.004196
74 : 72	.011899	95 : 93	.009241	73 : 72	.005990	105 : 104	.004156
37 : 36	.011899	96 : 94	.009143	74 : 73	.005909	106 : 105	.004117
75 : 73	.011738	48 : 47	.009143	75 : 74	.005830	107 : 106	.004078
76 : 74	.011582	97 : 95	.009048	76 : 75	.005752	108 : 107	.004040
38 : 37	0.011582	98 : 96	0.008955	77 : 76	0.005677	109 : 108	0.004002
77 : 75	.011429	49 : 48	.008955	78 : 77	.005604	110 : 109	.003967
78 : 76	.011281	99 : 97	.008864	79 : 78	.005533	111 : 110	.003930
39 : 38	.011281	100 : 98	.008774	80 : 79	.005463	112 : 111	.003895
79 : 77	.011136	50 : 49	.008774	81 : 80	.005395	113 : 112	.003860
80 : 78	.010995	101 : 99	.008686	82 : 81	.005329	114 : 113	.003827
40 : 39	.010995	51 : 50	.008600	83 : 82	.005264	115 : 114	.003793
81 : 79	.010858	52 : 51	.008433	84 : 83	.005201	116 : 115	.003760
82 : 80	0.010724	53 : 52	0.008273	85 : 84	0.005140	117 : 116	0.003728
41 : 40	.010724	54 : 53	.008118	86 : 85	.005080	118 : 117	.003696
83 : 81	.010593	55 : 54	.007969	87 : 86	.005021	119 : 118	.003665
84 : 82	.010465	56 : 55	.007825	88 : 87	.004963	120 : 119	.003634
42 : 41	.010465	57 : 56	.007687	89 : 88	.004907	......	......
85 : 83	.010341	58 : 57	.007553	90 : 89	.004853	......	......
86 : 84	.010219	59 : 58	.007424	91 : 90	.004799	......	......
43 : 42	.010219	60 : 59	.007299	92 : 91	.004746	......	......

Example: A driven shaft is to rotate 6.9078 revolutions while the driving shaft rotates 1.3961 revolutions. Determine sizes of driving and driven gears.

$$\frac{\text{Driving gear size}}{\text{Driven gear size}} = \frac{\text{Driven gear speed}}{\text{Driving gear speed}} = \frac{6.9078}{1.3961}$$

Log 6.9078 = 0.8393398

Log 1.3961 = 0.1449165

0.6944233 = log $\dfrac{\text{Driving gear size}}{\text{Driven gear size}}$

The nearest logarithm in table is 0.694374 which is the log for ratio 94/19. The driving gear is to have 94 teeth and the driven gear 19 teeth.

Actual revolutions of driven shaft (while driving shaft makes 1.3961 turns) = 1.3961 × 94/19 = 6.9070 or a difference from the desired rotation of 0.0008 revolution. Should a more exact solution be required, some form of compound gearing might be used. (See also examples preceding table.)

THREAD MILLING

Single-cutter Method: Whenever a single cutter is used, the axis of the cutter is inclined an amount equal to the lead angle of the screw thread, in order to locate the cutter in line with the thread groove at the point where the cutting action takes place. Tangent of lead angle = lead of screw thread ÷ pitch circumference of screw.

The helical thread groove is generated in practically the same way as when a lathe is used. The single cutter process is especially applicable to the milling of large screw threads of coarse pitch, and either single or multiple threads.

The cutter should revolve as fast as possible without dulling the cutting edges excessively, in order to mill a smooth thread and prevent the unevenness that would result with a slow-moving cutter, on account of the tooth spaces. As the cutter rotates, the part on which a thread is to be milled is also revolved, but at a very slow rate (a few inches per minute), since this rotation of the work is practically a feeding movement. The cutter is ordinarily set to the full depth of the thread groove and finishes a single thread in one passage, although deep threads of coarse pitch may require two or even three cuts. For fine pitches and short threads, the multiple-cutter method (described in the next paragraph) usually is preferable, because it is more rapid. The milling of taper screw threads may be done on a single-cutter type of machine by traversing the cutter laterally as it feeds along in a lengthwise direction, the same as when using a taper attachment on a lathe.

Multiple-cutter Method: The multiple cutter for thread milling is practically a series of single cutters, although formed of one solid piece of steel, at least so far as the cutter proper is concerned. The rows of teeth do not lie in a helical path, like the teeth of a hob or tap, but they are annular or without lead. If the cutter had helical teeth the same as a gear hob, it would have to be geared to revolve in a certain fixed ratio with the screw being milled, but a cutter having annular teeth may rotate at any desired cutting speed, while the screw blank is rotated slowly to provide a suitable rate of feed. (The multiple cutters used for thread milling are frequently called "hobs," but the term hob should be applied only to cutters having a helical row of teeth like a gear-cutting hob.)

The object in using a multiple cutter instead of a single cutter is to finish a screw thread complete in approximately one revolution of the work, a slight amount of over-travel being allowed to insure milling the thread to the full depth where the end of cut joins the starting point. The cutter which is at least one or two threads or pitches wider than the thread to be milled, is fed in to the full thread depth and then either the cutter or screw blank is moved in a lengthwise direction a distance equal to the lead of the thread during one revolution of the work.

The multiple cutter is used for milling comparatively short threads and usually medium or fine pitches. The accompanying illustration shows typical examples of external and internal work for which the multiple-cutter type of thread milling has proved very efficient, although its usefulness is not confined to shoulder work and "blind" holes.

In using multiple cutters either for internal or external thread milling, the axis of the cutter is set parallel with the axis of the work, instead of inclining the cutter to suit the lead angle of the thread, as when using a single cutter. Theoretically, this is not the correct position for a cutter, since each cutting edge is revolving in a plane at right angles to the screw's axis while milling a thread groove of helical form. However, as a general rule, interference between the cutter and the thread, does not result a decided change in the standard thread form. Usually the defect is very slight and may be disregarded except when milling threads which incline considerably relative to the axis like a thread of multiple form and large lead angle. Multiple cutters are suitable for external threads having lead angles under $3\frac{1}{2}$ degrees and for internal threads having lead angles under $2\frac{1}{2}$ degrees. Threads

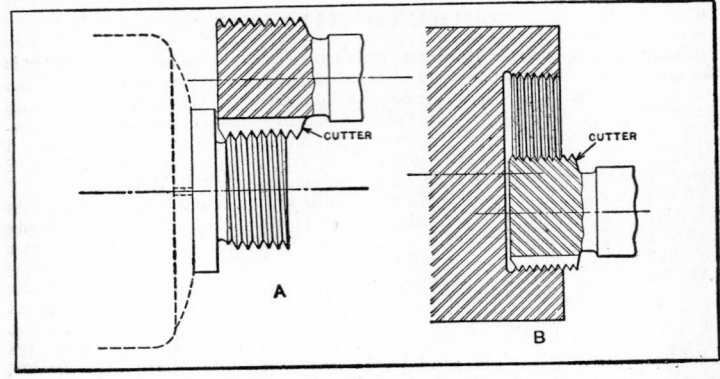

Examples of External and Internal Thread Milling with
a Multiple Type of Cutter

which have steeper sides or smaller included angles than the American Standard
or Whitworth forms should ordinarily be milled with a single cutter, assuming that
the milling process is preferable to other methods. For instance, in milling an Acme
thread which has an included angle between the sides of 29 degrees, there might be
considerable interference if a multiple cutter were used, unless the screw thread
diameter were large enough in proportion to the pitch to prevent such interference.
If an attempt were made to mill a square thread with a multiple cutter, the results
would be unsatisfactory owing to the interference.

Interference between the cutter and work is more pronounced when milling internal threads, because the cutter does not clear itself so well. Experiments have
shown that multiple cutters for internal work should preferably not exceed one-
third the diameter of the hole to be threaded. A cutter that is one-quarter the
diameter of the thread will do very satisfactory work. It is preferable to use as
small a cutter as practicable, either for internal or external work, not only to avoid
interference, but to reduce the strain on the driving mechanism. Some thread milling cutters, known as "topping cutters," are made for milling the outside diameter
of the thread as well as the angular sides and root.

Planetary Method: The planetary method of thread milling is similar in principle
to planetary milling. The part to be threaded is held stationary and the thread
milling cutter, which is held by it, is given a planetary movement
around the work in order to mill the thread in one planetary revolution. The machine spindle and the cutter which is held by it is moved longitudinally for thread
milling, an amount equal to the thread lead during one planetary revolution. This
operation is applicable to both internal and external threads. For the latter operation, the thread milling cutter surrounds the work. This thread milling is frequently accompanied by milling operations on other adjoining surfaces. For example, a planetary type of machine may be used for milling a screw thread and a
concentric cylindrical surface simultaneously. When the milling operation begins,
the eccentrically mounted cutter-spindle feeds the cutter into the right depth and
then the planetary movement begins, thus milling the thread and the cylindrical
surface. Thin sharp starting edges are eliminated on threads milled by the planetary method and the thread begins with a smooth gradual approach. One design of

machine will mill internal and external threads simultaneously. These threads may be of the same hand or one may be right hand and the other left hand. The threads may also be either of the same pitch or of a different pitch, and either straight or tapered.

Classes of Work for Thread Milling Machines. — Thread milling machines are used in preference to lathes or taps and dies for certain threading operations. There are four general reasons why a thread milling machine may be preferred: (1) Because the pitch of the thread is too coarse for cutting with a die; (2) because the milling process is more efficient than using a single-point tool in a lathe; (3) to secure a smoother and more accurate thread than would be obtained with a tap or die; (4) because the thread is so located relative to a shoulder or other surface that the milling method is superior, if not the only practicable way. A thread milling machine having a single cutter is especially adapted for coarse pitches, multiple-threaded screws, or any form or size of thread requiring the removal of a relatively large amount of metal, particularly if the pitch of the thread is large in proportion to the screw diameter, since the torsional strain due to the milling process is relatively small. While thread milling has little, if any, advantage over the lathe in regard to accuracy of lead, it gives a higher rate of production, and a thread is usually finished by means of a single passage of the cutter. The multiple-cutter type of thread milling machine frequently comes into competition with dies and taps, and especially self-opening dies and collapsing taps. The use of a multiple cutter is desirable when a thread must be cut close to a shoulder or to the bottom of a shallow recess, although the usefulness of the multiple cutter is not confined to shoulder work and "blind" holes.

Maximum Pitches of Die-cut Threads. — Dies of special design could be constructed for practically any pitch, if the screw blank were strong enough to resist the cutting strains and the size and cost of the die were immaterial; but, as a general rule, when the pitch is coarser than four or five threads per inch, the difficulty of cutting threads with dies increases rapidly, although in a few cases some dies are used successfully on screw threads having two or three threads per inch or less. Much depends upon the design of the die, the finish or smoothness required, and the relation between the pitch of the thread and the diameter of the screw. When the screw diameter is relatively small in proportion to the pitch, there may be considerable distortion due to the twisting strains set up when the thread is being cut. If the number of threads per inch is only one or two less than the standard number for a given diameter, a screw blank ordinarily will be strong enough to permit the use of a die.

Changing Pitch of Screw Thread Slightly. — A very slight change in the pitch of a screw thread may be necessary as, for example, when the pitch of a tap is increased a small amount to compensate for shrinkage in hardening. One method of obtaining slight variations in pitch is by means of a taper attachment. This attachment is set at an angle and the work is located at the same angle by adjusting the tailstock center. The result is that the tool follows an angular path relative to the movement of the carriage and, consequently, the pitch of the thread is increased slightly, the amount depending upon the angle to which the work and taper attachment are set. The cosine of this angle, for obtaining a given increase in pitch, equals the standard pitch (which would be obtained with the lathe used in the regular way) divided by the increased pitch necessary to compensate for shrinkage.

Example: — If the pitch of a ¾-inch American standard screw is to be increased from 0.100 to 0.1005, the cosine of the angle to which the taper attachment and work should be set is found as follows:

$$\text{Cosine of required angle} = \frac{0.100}{0.1005} = 0.9950$$

which is the cosine of 5 degrees 45 minutes, nearly.

THREAD GRINDING

Thread grinding is employed for precision tool and gage work and also in producing certain classes of threaded parts. Thread grinding may be utilized (1) because of the accuracy and finish obtained, (2) hardness of material to be threaded, (3) economy in grinding certain classes of screw threads when using modern machines, wheels, and thread-grinding oils. In some cases pre-cut threads are finished by grinding; but usually, threads are ground "from the solid," being formed entirely by the grinding process. Examples of work include thread gages and taps of steel and tungsten carbide, hobs, worms, lead-screws, adjusting or traversing screws, alloy steel studs, etc. Grinding is applied to external, internal, straight, and tapering threads, and to various thread forms.

Accuracy Obtainable by Thread Grinding. — With single-edge or single-ribbed wheels it is possible to grind threads on gages to a degree of accuracy that requires but very little lapping to produce a so-called "master" thread gage. As far as lead is concerned, some thread grinding machine manufacturers guarantee to hold the lead within 0.0001 inch per inch of thread; and while it is not guaranteed that a higher degree of accuracy for lead is obtainable, it is known that threads have been ground to closer tolerances than this on the lead. Pitch diameter accuracies for either Class 3 or Class 4 fits are obtainable according to the grinding method used; with single-edge wheels, the thread angle can be ground to an accuracy of within two or three minutes in half the angle.

Wheels for Thread Grinding. — The wheels used for steel have an aluminous abrasive and, ordinarily, either a resinoid bond or a vitrified bond. The general rule is to use resinoid wheels when extreme tolerances are not required, and it is desirable to form the thread with a minimum number of passes, as in grinding threaded machine parts, such as studs, adjusting screws which are not calibrated, and for some classes of taps. *Resinoid Wheels*, as a rule, will hold a fine edge longer than a vitrified wheel but they are more flexible and, consequently, less suitable for accurate work, especially when there is lateral grinding pressure that causes wheel deflection. *Vitrified wheels* are utilized for obtaining extreme accuracy in thread form and lead because they are very rigid and not easily deflected by side pressure in grinding. This rigidity is especially important in grinding pre-cut threads on such work as gages, taps and lead-screws. The progressive lead errors in long lead-screws, for example, might cause an increasing lateral pressure that would deflect a resinoid wheel. Vitrified wheels are also recommended for internal grinding.

Diamond Wheels: Diamond wheels set in a rubber or plastic bond are also used for thread grinding, especially for grinding threads in carbide materials and in other hardened alloys. Thread grinding is now being done successfully on a commercial basis on both taps and gages made from carbides. Gear hobs made from carbides have also been tested with successful results. Diamond wheels are dressed by means of silicon-carbide grinding wheels which travel past the diamond-wheel thread form at the angle required for the flanks of the thread to be ground. The action of the dressing wheels is, perhaps, best described as a "scrubbing" of the bond which holds the diamond grits. Obviously, the silicon-carbide wheels do not dress the diamonds, but they loosen the bond until the diamonds not wanted drop out.

Thread Grinding with Single-Edge Wheel. — With this type of wheel, the edge is trued to the cross-sectional shape of the thread groove. The wheel, when new, may have a diameter of 18 or 20 inches and, when grinding a thread, the wheel is inclined to align it with the thread groove. On some machines, lead variations are obtained by means of change-gears which transmit motion from the work-driving spindle to the lead-screw. Other machines are so designed that a lead-screw is selected to suit the lead of thread to be ground and transmits motion directly to the work-driving spindle.

Wheels with Edges for Roughing and Finishing. — The "three-ribbed" type of wheel has a roughing edge or rib which removes about two-thirds of the metal. This is followed by an intermediate rib which leaves about 0.005 inch for the third or finishing rib. The accuracy obtained with this triple-edge type compares with

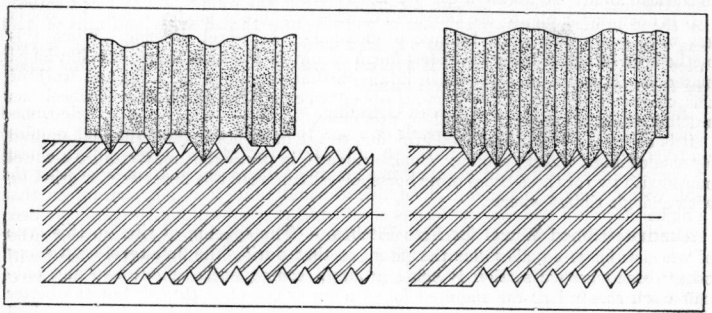

Fig. 1. Wheel with Edges for Roughing and Finishing

Fig. 2. Multi-ribbed Type of Thread-grinding Wheel

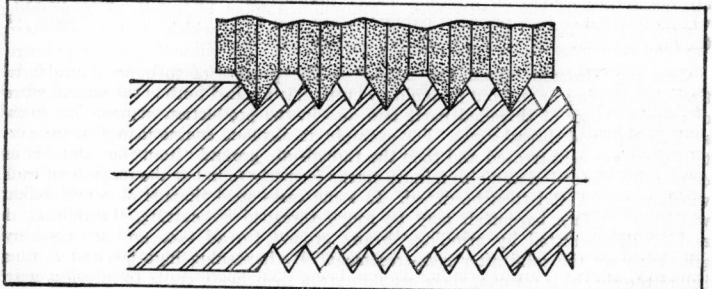

Fig. 3. Alternate-ribbed Wheel for Grinding the Finer Pitches

that of a single-edge wheel, which means that it may be used for the greatest accuracy obtainable in thread grinding. When the accuracy required makes it necessary, this wheel can be inclined to the helix angle of the thread, the same as is the single-edge wheel.

The three-ribbed wheel is recommended not only for precision work but for grinding threads which are too long for the multi-ribbed wheel referred to later. It is also well adapted to tap grinding, because it is possible to dress a portion of the wheel adjacent to the finish rib for the purpose of grinding the outside diameter of the thread, as indicated in Fig. 1. Furthermore, the wheel can be dressed for grinding or relieving both crests and flanks at the same time.

Multi-ribbed Wheels. — This type of wheel is employed when rapid production is more important than extreme accuracy, which means that it is intended primarily for the grinding of duplicate parts in manufacturing. A wheel 1¼ to 2 inches wide has formed upon its face a series of annular thread-shaped ridges (see Fig. 2); hence, if the length of the thread is not greater than the wheel width, a thread may be ground in one work revolution plus about one-half revolution for feeding in and withdrawing the wheel. The principle of operation is the same as that of thread milling with a multiple type cutter. This type of wheel is not inclined to the lead angle. To obtain a Class 3 fit, the lead angle should not exceed 4 degrees.

It is not practicable, to use this form of wheel on thread pitches where the root is less than 0.007 inch wide, because of difficulties in wheel dressing. When this method can be applied, it is the fastest means known of producing threads in hardened materials. It is not recommended, however, that thread gages, taps, and work of this character be ground with multi-ribbed wheels. The single-ribbed wheel has a definite field for accurate, small-lot production.

It is necessary, in multi-ribbed grinding, to use more horsepower than is required for single-ribbed wheel grinding. Coarse threads, in particular, may require a wheel motor with two or three times more horsepower than would be necessary for grinding with a single-ribbed wheel.

Alternate-ribbed Wheel for Fine Pitches. — The spacing of ribs on this type of wheel (Fig. 3) equals twice the pitch, so that during the first revolution every other thread groove section is being ground; consequently, about two and one-half work revolutions are required for grinding a complete thread, but the better distribution of cooling oil and resulting increase in work speeds makes this wheel very efficient. This alternate-type of wheel is adapted for grinding threads of fine pitch. Since these wheels cannot be tipped to the helix angle of the thread, they are not recommended for anything closer than Class 3 fits. The "three-ribbed" wheels referred to in a previous paragraph are also made in the alternate type for the finer pitches.

Grinding Threads "from the Solid." — The process of forming threads entirely by grinding, or without preliminary cutting, is applied both in the manufacture of certain classes of threaded parts and also in the production of precision tools, such as taps and thread gages. For example, in airplane engine manufacture, certain parts are heat-treated and then the threads are ground "from the solid," thus eliminating distortion and also minute cracks formerly found at the roots of threads which were cut and then hardened. In some cases steel threads of coarse pitch, which are surface hardened, may be rough threaded by cutting, then hardened and finally corrected by grinding. Many ground thread taps are produced by grinding from the solid after heat-treatment. By hardening high-speed steel taps before the thread is formed, there are no narrow or delicate crests to interfere with the application of the high temperature required for uniform hardness and the best steel structure.

Number of Wheel Passes. — The number of cuts or passes for grinding from the solid depends upon the type of wheel and accuracy required. In general, threads of 12 or 14 per inch and finer may be ground in one pass of a single-edge wheel unless the "unwrapped" thread length is much greater than normal. Unwrapped length = pitch circumference × total number of thread turns, approximately. For example, a thread gage 1¼ inches long with 24 threads per inch would have an unwrapped length equal to 30 × pitch circumference. (If more convenient, outside circumference may be used instead of pitch circumference.) Assume that there are 6 or 7 feet of unwrapped length on a screw thread having 12 threads per inch. In this case, one pass might be sufficient for a Class 3 fit, whereas two passes might be recommended for a Class 4 fit. When two passes are required, too deep a roughing cut may break down the narrow edge of the wheel. To prevent this, try a roughing cut depth equal to about two-thirds the total thread depth, thus leaving one-third for the finishing cut.

Wheel and Work Rotation. — When a screw thread, on the side being ground, is moving *upward* or *against* the grinding wheel rotation, less heat is generated and the grinding operation is more efficient than when wheel and work are moving in the same direction on the grinding side; however, to avoid running a machine idle during its return stroke, many screw threads are ground during both the forward and return traversing movements, by reversing the work rotation at the end of the forward stroke. For this reason, thread grinders generally are equipped so that both forward and return work speeds may be changed; they may also be designed to accelerate the return movement when grinding in one direction only.

Wheel Speeds. — Wheel speeds should always be limited to the maximum specified on the wheel by the manufacturer. According to the American Standard Safety Code, resinoid wheels are limited to 9,500 and vitrified wheels to 6,500 surface feet per minute; however, according to Norton Co., the most efficient speeds are from 9,000 to 10,500 for resinoid wheels and 7,500 to 9,500 for vitrified wheels. Only tested wheels recommended by the wheel manufacturer should be used. After a suitable surface speed has been established, it should be maintained by increasing the R.P.M. of the wheel, as the latter is reduced in diameter by wear. Since thread grinding wheels work close to the limit of their stock-removing capacity, some adjustment of the wheel or work speed may be required to get the best results. If the wheel speed is too slow for a given job and excessive heat is generated, try an increase in speed, assuming that such increase is within the safety limits. If the wheel is too soft and the edge wears excessively, again an increase in wheel speed will give the effect of a harder wheel and result in better form-retaining qualities.

Work Speeds. — The work speed usually ranges from 3 to 10 feet per minute. In grinding with a comparatively heavy feed, and a minimum number of passes, the speed may not exceed 2½ or 3 feet per minute. If very light feeds are employed as in grinding hardened high-speed steel, the work speed may be much higher than 3 feet per minute and should be determined by test. If excessive heat is generated by removing stock too rapidly, a work speed reduction is one remedy. If a wheel is working below its normal capacity, an increase in work speed would prevent dulling of the grains and reduce the tendency to heat or "burn" the work. An increase in work speed and reduction in feed may also be employed to prevent burning while grinding hardened steel.

Truing Grinding Wheels. — Thread grinding wheels are trued both to maintain the required thread form and also an efficient grinding surface. Thread grinders ordinarily are equipped with precision truing devices which function automatically. One type automatically dresses the wheel and also compensates for the slight amount removed in dressing, thus automatically maintaining size control of the work. While truing the wheel, a small amount of grinding oil should be used to reduce diamond wear. Light truing cuts are advisable, especially in truing resinoid wheels which may be deflected by excessive truing pressure. A master former for controlling the path followed by the truing diamond may require a modified profile to prevent distortion of the thread form, especially when the lead angles are comparatively large. Such modification usually is not required for 60-degree threads when the pitches for a given diameter are standard because then the resulting lead angles are less than 4½ degrees. In grinding Acme threads or 29-degree worm threads having lead angles greater than 4 or 5 degrees, modified formers may be required to prevent a bulge in the thread profile. The highest point of this bulge is approximately at the pitch line. A bulge of about 0.001 inch may be within allowable limits on some commercial worms but precision worms for gear hobbers, etc., require straight flanks in the axial plane.

Crushing Method: Thread grinding wheels are also dressed or formed by the crushing method, which is used in connection with some types of thread grinding machines. When this method is used, the annular ridge or ridges on the wheel are formed by a hardened steel cylindrical dresser or crusher. The crusher has a series of smooth annular ridges which are shaped and spaced like the thread that is to be ground. During the wheel dressing operation, the crusher is positively driven instead of the grinding wheel, and the ridges on the wheel face are formed by the rotating crusher being forced inward.

Wheel Hardness or Grade. — Wheel hardness or grade selection is based upon a compromise between efficient cutting and durability of the grinding edge. Grade selection depends on the bond and the character of the work. The following general recommendations are based upon Norton grading.

Vitrified wheels usually range from J to M, and resinoid wheels from R to U. For heat-treated screws or studs and the American Standard Thread, try the following. For 8 to 12 threads per inch, grade S resinoid wheel; for 14 to 20 threads per inch, grade T resinoid; for 24 threads per inch and finer, grades T or U resinoid. For high-speed steel taps 4 to 12 threads per inch, grade J vitrified or S resinoid; 14 to 20 threads per inch, grade K vitrified or T resinoid; 24 to 36 threads per inch, grade M vitrified or T resinoid.

Grain Size. — A thread grinding wheel usually operates close to its maximum stock-removing capacity, and the narrow edge which forms the root of the thread is the most vulnerable part. In grain selection, the general rule is to use the coarsest grained wheel that will hold its form while grinding a reasonable amount of work. Pitch of thread and quality of finish are two governing factors. Thus, to obtain an exceptionally fine finish, the grain size might be smaller than is needed to retain the edge profile. The usual grain sizes range from 120 to 150. For heat-treated screws and studs with American Standard Threads, 100 to 180 is the usual range. For precision screw threads of very fine pitch, the grain size may range from 220 to 320. For high-speed steel taps, the usual range is from 150 to 180 for American Standard Threads, and from 80 to 150 for pre-cut Acme threads.

Thread Grinding by Centerless Method. — Screw threads may be ground from the solid by the centerless method. A centerless thread grinder is similar in its operating principle to a centerless grinder designed for general work, in that it has a grinding wheel, a regulating or feed wheel (with speed adjustments), and a work-rest. Adjustments are provided to accommodate work of different sizes and for varying the rates of feed. The grinding wheel is a multi-ribbed type, being a series of annular ridges across the face. These ridges conform in pitch and profile with the thread to be ground. The grinding wheel is inclined to suit the helix or lead angle of the thread. In grinding threads on such work as socket type set-screws, the blanks are fed automatically and passed between the grinding and regulating wheels in a continuous stream. To illustrate production possibilities, hardened socket set-screws of ¼-20 size may be ground from the solid at the rate of 60 to 70 per minute and with the wheel operating continuously for 8 hours without redressing. The lead errors of centerless ground screw threads may be limited to 0.0005 inch per inch or even less by reducing the production rate. The pitch diameter tolerances are within 0.0002 to 0.0003 inch of the basic size. The grain size for the wheel is selected with reference to the pitch of the thread, the following sizes being recommended: For 11 to 13 threads per inch, 150; for 16 threads per inch, 180; for 18 to 20 threads per inch, 220; for 24 to 28 threads per inch, 320; for 40 threads per inch, 400.

THREAD ROLLING

Screw threads may be formed by rolling either by using some type of thread-rolling machine or by equipping an automatic screw machine or turret lathe with a suitable threading roll. If a thread-rolling machine is used, the unthreaded screw, bolt or other "blank," is placed (either automatically or by hand) between dies having thread-shaped ridges which sink into the blank, and by displacing the metal, form a thread of the required shape and pitch. The thread-rolling process is applied where bolts, screws, studs, threaded rods, etc., are required in large quantities. Screw threads that are within the range of the rolling process may be produced more rapidly by this method than in any other way. The rolled thread, due to the cold-working action of the dies, is 10 to 20 per cent stronger than a cut or ground thread, and the increase may be much higher when tested for fatigue resistance. Another advantage of the rolling process is that no stock is wasted in forming the thread, and the surface of a rolled thread is harder than that of a cut thread, thus increasing wear resistance.

Thread-Rolling Machine of Flat-die Type. — One type of machine which is used extensively is equipped with a pair of flat or straight dies   One die is stationary and the other has a reciprocating movement when the machine is in use. The ridges on these dies, which form the screw thread, incline at an angle equal to the helix angle of the thread. In making dies for precision thread rolling, the threads may be formed either by milling and grinding after heat-treatment, or by grinding "from the solid" after heat-treating. A vitrified wheel is used. The thread is formed in one passage of the work, which is inserted at one end of the dies, either by hand or automatically, and then rolls between the die faces until it is ejected at the opposite end. The relation between the position of the dies and a screw thread being rolled is such that the top of the thread-shaped ridge of one die, at the point of contact with the screw thread, is directly opposite the bottom of the thread groove in the other die at the point of contact. Some form of mechanism insures starting the blank at the right time and also square with the dies.

Thread-Rolling Machine of Cylindrical Die Type. — With machines of this type, the blank is threaded while being rolled between two or three cylindrical dies (depending upon type of machine) which are pressed into the blank at a rate of penetration adjusted to the hardness of the material, or wall thickness in the case of threading operations on tubing or hollow parts. The dies have ground or ground and lapped threads and a pitch diameter that is a multiple of the pitch diameter of the thread to be rolled. As the dies are much larger in diameter than the work, a multiple thread is required to obtain the same lead angle as that of the work. The thread may be formed in one die revolution or even less, or several revolutions may be required (as in rolling hard materials) to obtain a gradual rate of penetration equivalent to that obtained with flat or straight dies if extended to a length of possibly 15 or 20 feet. Provisions for accurately adjusting or matching the thread rolls to bring them into proper alignment with each other, are important features of these machines.

Two-Roll Type of Machine: With a two-roll type of machine, the work is rotated between two horizontal power-driven threading rolls and is supported by a hardened rest bar on the lower side. One roll is fed inward by hydraulic pressure to a depth that is governed automatically.

Three-Roll Type of Machine: With this machine the blank to be threaded is held in a "floating position" while being rolled between three cylindrical dies which, through toggle arms, are moved inward at a predetermined rate of penetration until the required pitch diameter is obtained. The die movement is governed by a cam driven through change gears selected to give the required cycle of squeeze, dwell and release.

Rate of Production. — Production rates in thread rolling depend upon the type of machine, the size of both machine and work, and whether the parts to be threaded are inserted by hand or automatically. A reciprocating flat die type of machine, applied to ordinary steels, may thread 30 or 40 parts per minute in diameters ranging from about ⅝ to 1⅛ inch, and 150 to 175 per minute in machine screw sizes from No. 10 (.190) to No. 6 (.138). In the case of heat-treated alloy steels in the usual hardness range of 26 to 32 Rockwell C, the production may be 30 or 40 per minute or less. With a cylindrical die type of machine, which is designed primarily for precision work and hard metals, 10 to 30 parts per minute are common production rates, the amount depending upon the hardness of material and allowable rate of die penetration per work revolution. These production rates are intended as a general guide only. The diameters of rolled threads usually range from the smallest machine screw sizes up to 1 or 1½ inches, depending upon the type and size of machine.

Precision Thread Rolling. — Both flat and cylindrical dies are used in aeronautical and other plants for precision work. With accurate dies and blank diameters held to close limits, it is practicable to produce rolled threads for American Standard Class 3 and Class 4 fits. The blank sizing may be by centerless grinding or by means of a die in conjunction with the heading operations. The blank should be round, and, as a general rule, the diameter tolerance should not exceed ½ to ⅔ the pitch diameter tolerance. The blank diameter should range from the correct size (which is close to the pitch diameter, but should be determined by actual trial), down to the allowable minimum, the tolerance being minus to insure a correct pitch diameter, even though the major diameter may vary slightly. Precision thread rolling has become an important method of threading alloy steel studs and other threaded parts, especially in aeronautical work where precision and high-fatigue resistance are required. Micrometer screws are also an outstanding example of precision thread rolling. This process has also been applied in tap making, although it is the general practice to finish rolled taps by grinding when the Class 3 and Class 4 fits are required.

Steels for Thread Rolling. — Steels vary from soft low-carbon types for ordinary screws and bolts, to nickel, nickel-chromium and molybdenum steels for aircraft studs, bolts, etc., or for any work requiring exceptional strength and fatigue resistance. Typical SAE alloy steels are No. 2330, 3135, 3140, 4027, 4042, 4640 and 6160. The hardness of these steels after heat-treatment usually ranges from 26 to 32 Rockwell C, with tensile strengths varying from 130,000 to 150,000 pounds per square inch. While harder materials might be rolled, grinding is more practicable when the hardness exceeds 40 Rockwell C. Thread rolling is applicable not only to a wide range of steels but for non-ferrous materials, especially if there is difficulty in cutting due to "tearing" the threads.

Diameter of Blank for Thread Rolling. — The diameter of the screw blank or cylindrical part upon which a thread is to be rolled should be less than the outside screw diameter by an amount that will just compensate for the metal that is displaced and raised above the original surface by the rolling process. The increase in diameter is approximately equal to the depth of one thread. While there are rules and formulas for determining blank diameters, it may be necessary to make slight changes in the calculated size in order to secure a well-formed thread. The blank diameter should be verified by trial, especially when rolling accurate screw threads. Some stock offers greater resistance to displacement than other stock, owing to the greater hardness or tenacity of the metal. The following figures may prove useful in establishing trial sizes. The blank diameters for screws varying from ¼ to ½ inch are from 0.002 to 0.0025 inch larger than the pitch diameter, and for screws varying from ½ to 1 inch or larger, the blank diameters are from 0.0025 to

0.003 inch larger than the pitch diameter. Blanks which are slightly less than the pitch diameter are intended for bolts, screws, etc., which are to have a comparatively free fit. Blanks for this class of work may vary from 0.002 to 0.003 inch less than the pitch diameter for screw thread sizes varying from ¼ to ½ inch, and from 0.003 to 0.005 inch less than the pitch diameter for sizes above ½ inch. If the screw threads are smaller than ¼ inch, the blanks are usually from 0.001 to 0.0015 inch less than the pitch diameter for ordinary grades of work.

Thread Rolling in Automatic Screw Machines. — Screw threads are sometimes rolled in automatic screw machines and turret lathes when the thread is behind a shoulder so that it cannot be cut with a die. In such cases, the advantage of rolling the thread is that a second operation is avoided. A circular roll is used for rolling threads in screw machines. The roll may be presented to the work either in a tangential direction or radially, either method producing a satisfactory thread. In the former case, the roll gradually comes into contact with the periphery of the work and completes the thread as it passes across the surface to be threaded. When the roll is held in a radial position, it is simply forced against one side until a complete thread is formed. The method of applying the roll may depend upon the relation between the threading operation and other machining operations. Thread rolling in automatic screw machines is generally applied only to brass and other relatively soft metals, owing to the difficulty of rolling threads in steel. Thread rolls made of chrome-nickel steel containing from 0.15 to 0.20 per cent of carbon have given fairly good results, however, when applied to steel. A 3 per cent nickel steel containing about 0.12 per cent carbon has also proved satisfactory for threading brass.

Factors Governing the Diameter of Thread Rolling. — The threading roll used in screw machines may be about the same diameter as the screw thread, but for sizes smaller than, say, ¾ inch, the roll diameter is some multiple of the thread diameter minus a slight amount to obtain a better rolling action. When the diameters of the thread and roll are practically the same, a single-threaded roll is used to form a single thread on the screw. If the diameter of the roll is made double that of the screw, in order to avoid using a small roll, then the roll must have a double thread. If the thread roll is three times the size of the screw thread, a triple thread is used, and so on. These multiple threads are necessary when the roll diameter is some multiple of the work, in order to obtain corresponding helix angles on the roll and work.

Diameter of Threading Roll. — The pitch diameter of a threading roll having a single thread, is slightly less than the pitch diameter of the screw thread to be rolled, and in the case of multiple-thread rolls, the pitch diameter is not an exact multiple of the screw thread pitch diameter but is also reduced somewhat. The amount of reduction recommended by different screw machine manufacturers varies as shown by Formulas 1 and 2 which follow. Evidently, the reduction may vary over a limited range without appreciably affecting the quality of the rolled thread. If D = pitch diameter of threading roll, d = pitch diameter of screw thread, N = number of single threads or "starts" on the roll (this number is selected with reference to diameter of roll desired), T = single depth of thread:

$$D = N\left(d - \frac{T}{2}\right) - T \text{ (Formula 1)}; \quad D = N\left(d - \frac{T}{4}\right) - T \text{ (Formula 2)}$$

Example: Find by using Formula 1, the pitch diameter of a double-thread roll for rolling a ½-inch American standard screw thread. Pitch diameter d = 0.4500 inch and thread depth T = 0.0499 inch.

$$D = 2\left(0.4500 - \frac{0.0499}{2}\right) - 0.0499 = 0.8001 \text{ inch}$$

Kind of Thread on Roll and Its Shape. — The thread (or threads) on the roll should be left hand for rolling a right-hand thread, and *vice versa*. The roll should be wide enough to overlap the part to be threaded, provided there are clearance spaces at the ends, which should be formed if possible. The thread on the roll should be sharp on top for rolling an American (National) standard form of thread, so that less pressure will be required to displace the metal when rolling the thread. The bottom of the thread groove on the roll may also be left sharp or it may have a flat. If the bottom is sharp, the roll is sunk only far enough into the blank to form a thread having a flat top, assuming that the thread is the American form. The number of threads on the roll (whether double, triple, quadruple, etc.) is selected, as a rule, so that the diameter of the thread roll will be somewhere between 1¼ and 2¼ inches. In making a thread roll, the ends are beveled at an angle of 45 degrees, to prevent the threads on the ends of the roll from chipping. Precautions should be taken in hardening, because if the sharp edges are burnt, the roll will be useless. Thread rolls, as a rule, are lapped after hardening. This is done by holding them on an arbor in the lathe and using emery and oil on a piece of hard wood. A thread roll, to give good results, should fit closely in the holder. If the roll is made to fit loosely, it will mar the threads.

Application of Thread Roll. — The shape of the work, and the character of the operations necessary to produce it, govern, to a large extent, the method employed in applying the thread roll. Some of the points to consider are as follows: 1. Diameter of the part to be threaded. 2. Location of the part to be threaded. 3. Length of the part to be threaded. 4. Relation that the thread rolling operation bears to the other operations. 5. Shape of the part to be threaded, whether straight, tapered or otherwise. 6. Method of applying the support. When the diameter to be rolled is much smaller than the diameter of the shoulder preceding it, a cross-slide knurl-holder should be used. If the part to be threaded is not behind a shoulder, a holder on the swing principle should be used. When the work is long (greater in length than two-and-one-half times its diameter) a swing roll-holder should be employed, carrying a support. When the work can be cut off after the thread is rolled, a cross-slide roll-holder should be used. The method of applying the support to the work also governs to some extent the method of applying the thread roll. When no other tool is working at the same time as the thread roll, and when there is freedom from chips, the roll can be held more rigidly by passing it under instead of over the work. When passing the roll over the work, it has a tendency to raise the cross-slide. Where the part to be threaded is tapered, the roll can best be presented to the work by holding it in a cross-slide roll-holder.

Speeds and Feeds for Thread Rolling. — When the thread roll is made from high-carbon steel and used on brass, a surface speed as high as 200 feet per minute can be used. Better results, however, are obtained by using a lower speed than this. When the roll is held in a holder attached to the cross-slide, and is presented either tangentially or radially to the work, a considerably higher speed can be used than if it is held in a swing tool. This is due to the lack of rigidity in a holder of the swing type. The feeds to be used when a cross-slide roll-holder is used are given in the upper half of the table "Feeds for Thread Rolling"; the lower half of the table gives the feeds for thread rolling with swing tools. These feeds are applicable for rolling threads without a support, when the root diameter of the blank is not less than five times the double depth of the thread. When the root diameter is less than this, a support should be used. A support should also be used when the width of the roll is more than two-and-one-half times the smallest diameter of the piece to be rolled, irrespective of the pitch of the thread. When the smallest diameter of the piece to be rolled is much less than the root diameter of the thread, the smallest diameter should be taken as the deciding factor for the feed to be used.

Feeds for Thread Rolling

Cross-slide Holders — Feed per Revolution in Inches

Root Diam. of Blank	| Number of Threads per Inch													
	14	18	20	22	24	28	32	36	40	44	48	56	64	72
1/8	....	....	....	....	....	0.0005	0.0010	0.0015	0.0020	0.0025	0.0030	0.0035	0.0040	0.0045
3/16	....	....	....	....	0.0005	0.0010	0.0015	0.0020	0.0025	0.0030	0.0035	0.0040	0.0045	0.0050
1/4	....	....	....	0.0005	0.0010	0.0015	0.0020	0.0025	0.0030	0.0035	0.0040	0.0045	0.0050	0.0055
5/16	....	0.0005	0.0005	0.0010	0.0015	0.0020	0.0025	0.0030	0.0035	0.0040	0.0045	0.0050	0.0055	0.0060
3/8	0.0005	0.0010	0.0010	0.0015	0.0020	0.0025	0.0030	0.0035	0.0040	0.0045	0.0050	0.0055	0.0060	0.0065
7/16	0.0010	0.0015	0.0015	0.0020	0.0025	0.0030	0.0035	0.0040	0.0045	0.0050	0.0055	0.0060	0.0065	0.0070
1/2	0.0015	0.0020	0.0020	0.0025	0.0030	0.0035	0.0040	0.0045	0.0050	0.0055	0.0060	0.0065	0.0070	0.0075
5/8	0.0020	0.0025	0.0025	0.0030	0.0035	0.0040	0.0045	0.0050	0.0055	0.0060	0.0065	0.0070	0.0075	0.0080
3/4	0.0025	0.0030	0.0030	0.0035	0.0040	0.0045	0.0050	0.0055	0.0060	0.0065	0.0070	0.0075	0.0080	0.0085
7/8	0.0030	0.0035	0.0035	0.0040	0.0045	0.0050	0.0055	0.0060	0.0065	0.0070	0.0075	0.0080	0.0085	0.0090
1	0.0035	0.0040	0.0040	0.0045	0.0050	0.0055	0.0060	0.0065	0.0070	0.0075	0.0080	0.0085	0.0090	0.0095

Swing Holders — Feed per Revolution in Inches

Root Diam.	14	18	20	22	24	28	32	36	40	44	48	56	64	72
1/8	....	....	....	....	....	....	....	....	....	0.0005	0.0010	0.0015	0.0020	0.0025
3/16	....	....	....	....	....	....	....	....	0.0005	0.0008	0.0015	0.0020	0.0025	0.0028
1/4	....	....	....	....	....	....	0.0005	0.0005	0.0010	0.0010	0.0020	0.0025	0.0030	0.0030
5/16	....	....	....	....	....	0.0005	0.0010	0.0010	0.0015	0.0015	0.0025	0.0030	0.0035	0.0035
3/8	....	....	....	0.0005	0.0005	0.0010	0.0015	0.0015	0.0020	0.0020	0.0030	0.0035	0.0040	0.0040
7/16	....	0.0005	0.0005	0.0010	0.0010	0.0015	0.0020	0.0020	0.0025	0.0025	0.0035	0.0040	0.0045	0.0045
1/2	0.0005	0.0010	0.0010	0.0015	0.0015	0.0020	0.0025	0.0025	0.0030	0.0030	0.0040	0.0045	0.0048	0.0048
5/8	0.0010	0.0015	0.0015	0.0020	0.0020	0.0025	0.0030	0.0030	0.0035	0.0035	0.0043	0.0048	0.0050	0.0050
3/4	0.0013	0.0018	0.0020	0.0025	0.0025	0.0028	0.0035	0.0035	0.0040	0.0040	0.0045	0.0050	0.0052	0.0055
7/8	0.0015	0.0022	0.0025	0.0028	0.0028	0.0030	0.0038	0.0040	0.0043	0.0045	0.0048	0.0052	0.0055	0.0058
1	0.0018	0.0025	0.0028	0.0030	0.0032	0.0035	0.0040	0.0043	0.0047	0.0048	0.0050	0.0054	0.0058	0.0060

CHANGE GEARS FOR HELICAL MILLING

Lead of a Milling Machine. — If gears with an equal number of teeth are placed on the table feed-screw and the worm-gear stud, then the *lead of the milling machine* is the distance the table will travel while the index spindle makes one complete revolution. This distance is a constant used in figuring the change gears.

The lead of a helix or "spiral" is the distance, measured along the axis of the work, in which the helix makes one full turn around the work. The lead of the milling machine may, therefore, also be expressed as the lead of the helix that will be cut when gears with an equal number of teeth are placed on the feed-screw and the worm-gear stud, and an idler of suitable size is interposed between the gears.

Rule: To find the lead of a milling machine, place equal gears on the worm-gear stud and on the feed-screw, and multiply the number of revolutions made by the feed-screw to produce one revolution of the index head spindle, by the lead of the thread on the feed-screw. Expressing the rule given as a formula:

$$\text{lead of milling machine} = \frac{\text{rev. of feed-screw for one}}{\text{revolution of index spindle}} \times \frac{\text{lead of}}{\text{feed-screw.}}$$
$$\text{with equal gears}$$

Assume that it is necessary to make 40 revolutions of the feed-screw to turn the index head spindle one complete revolution, when the gears are equal, and that the lead of the thread on the feed-screw of the milling machine is ¼ inch; then the lead of the machine equals 40 × ¼ inch = 10 inches.

Change Gears for Helical Milling. — To find the change gears to be used in the compound train of gears for helical milling, place the lead of the helix to be cut in the numerator and the lead of the milling machine in the denominator of a fraction; divide numerator and denominator into two factors each; and multiply each "pair" of factors by the *same* number until suitable numbers of teeth for the change gears are obtained. (One factor in the numerator and one in the denominator are considered as one "pair" in this calculation.)

Example: Assume that the lead of a machine is 10 inches, and that a helix having a 48-inch lead is to be cut. Following the method explained:

$$\frac{48}{10} = \frac{6 \times 8}{2 \times 5} = \frac{(6 \times 12) \times (8 \times 8)}{(2 \times 12) \times (5 \times 8)} = \frac{72 \times 64}{24 \times 40}$$

The gear having 72 teeth is placed on the worm-gear stud and meshes with the 24-tooth gear on the intermediate stud. On the same intermediate stud is then placed the gear having 64 teeth, which is driven by the gear having 40 teeth placed on the feed-screw. This makes the gears having 72 and 64 teeth the driven gears, and the gears having 24 and 40 teeth the driving gears. In general, for compound gearing, the following formula may be used:

$$\frac{\text{lead of helix to be cut}}{\text{lead of machine}} = \frac{\text{product of driven gears}}{\text{product of driving gears}}$$

Short-lead Milling. — If lead to be milled is exceptionally short, the drive may be direct from table feed-screw to dividing head spindle to avoid excessive load on feed-screw and change-gears. If table feed-screw has 4 threads per inch (usual standard), then

$$\text{Change-gear ratio} = \frac{\text{Lead to be milled}}{0.25} = \frac{\text{Driven gears}}{\text{Driving gears}}$$

For indexing, number of teeth on spindle change-gear should be some multiple number of divisions required, to permit indexing by disengaging and turning the gear.

Helix. — A helix is a curve generated by a point moving about a cylindrical surface (real or imaginary) at a constant rate in the direction of the cylinder's axis. The curvature of a screw thread is one common example of a helical curve.

Lead of Helix: The lead of a helix is the distance that it advances in an axial direction, in one complete turn about the cylindrical surface. To illustrate, the lead of a screw thread equals the distance that a thread advances in one turn; it also equals the distance that a nut would advance in one turn.

Development of Helix: If one turn of a helical curve were unrolled onto a plane surface (as shown by diagram), the helix would become a straight line forming the hypotenuse of a right angle triangle. The length of one side of this triangle would equal the circumference of the cylinder with which the helix coincides, and the length of the other side of the triangle would equal the lead of the helix.

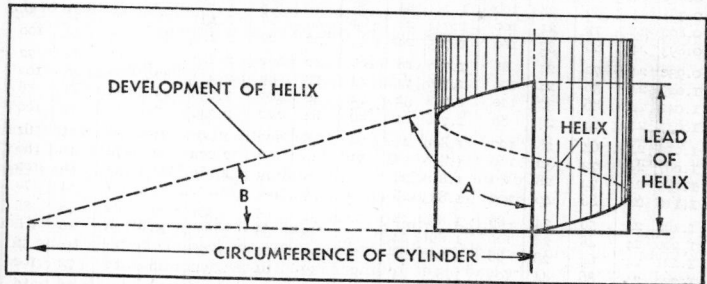

Helix Angles. — The triangular development of a helix has one angle *A* subtended by the circumference of the cylinder, and another angle *B* subtended by the lead of the helix. The term "helix angle" indicates angle *A* in some cases and angle *B* in others. For example, the helix angle of a helical gear, according to the general usage of the term, is always angle *A*, because this is the angle used in helical gear-designing formulas. Helix angle *A* would also be applied in milling the helical teeth of cutters, reamers, etc. Angle *A* of a gear or cutter tooth is a measure of its inclination relative to the axis of the gear or cutter.

Lead Angle: Angle *B* is applied to screw threads and worm threads. This angle *B* is a measure of the inclination of a screw thread from a plane that is perpendicular to the screw thread axis. Angle *B* is often called the "lead angle" because it is subtended by the lead of the thread, and to distinguish it from the term "helix angle" as applied to helical gears.

Finding Helix Angle of Helical Gear: A helical gear tooth has an infinite number of helix angles, but the angle at the pitch diameter or mid-working depth is the one required in gear designing and gear cutting. This angle *A*, relative to the axis of the gear, is found as follows:

$$\text{Cot helix angle} = \frac{\text{Lead of gear tooth}}{3.1416 \times \text{pitch diameter of gear}}$$

Finding Lead Angle of Screw Thread: The lead or helix angle at the pitch diameter of a screw thread usually is required when, for example, a thread milling cutter must be aligned with the thread. This angle measured from a plane perpendicular to the screw thread axis, is found as follows:

$$\text{Cot helix angle} = \frac{3.1416 \times \text{pitch diameter of screw thread}}{\text{Lead of screw thread}}$$

Change Gears for Different Leads — 0.670 Inch to 2.658 Inches

Lead in Inches	Driven Gear on Worm	Driver First Gear on Stud	Driven Second Gear on Stud	Driver Gear on Screw	Lead in Inches	Driven Gear on Worm	Driver First Gear on Stud	Driven Second Gear on Stud	Driver Gear on Screw	Lead in Inches	Driven Gear on Worm	Driver First Gear on Stud	Driven Second Gear on Stud	Driver Gear on Screw
0.670	24	86	24	100	1.711	28	72	44	100	2.182	24	44	40	100
0.781	24	86	28	100	1.714	24	56	40	100	2.188	24	48	28	64
0.800	24	72	24	100	1.744	24	64	40	86	2.193	24	56	44	86
0.893	24	86	32	100	1.745	24	44	32	100	2.200	24	48	44	100
0.930	24	72	24	86	1.750	28	64	40	100	2.222	24	48	32	72
1.029	24	56	24	100	1.776	24	44	28	86	2.233	40	86	48	100
1.042	28	86	32	100	1.778	32	72	40	100	2.238	28	64	44	86
1.047	24	64	24	86	1.786	24	86	64	100	2.240	28	40	32	100
1.050	24	64	28	100	1.800	24	64	48	100	2.250	24	40	24	64
1.067	24	72	32	100	1.809	28	72	40	86	2.274	32	72	44	86
1.085	24	72	28	86	1.818	24	44	24	72	2.286	32	56	40	100
1.116	24	86	40	100	1.823	28	86	56	100	2.292	24	64	44	72
1.196	24	56	24	86	1.860	28	56	32	86	2.326	32	64	40	86
1.200	24	48	24	100	1.861	24	72	48	86	2.333	28	48	40	100
1.221	24	64	28	86	1.867	28	48	32	100	2.338	24	44	24	56
1.228	24	86	44	100	1.875	24	48	24	64	2.344	28	86	72	100
1.240	24	72	32	86	1.886	24	56	44	100	2.368	28	44	32	86
1.250	24	64	24	72	1.905	24	56	32	72	2.381	32	86	64	100
1.302	28	86	40	100	1.919	24	64	44	86	2.386	24	44	28	64
1.309	24	44	24	100	1.920	24	40	32	100	2.392	24	56	48	86
1.333	24	72	40	100	1.925	28	64	44	100	2.400	28	56	48	100
1.340	24	86	48	100	1.944	24	48	28	72	2.424	24	44	32	72
1.371	24	56	32	100	1.954	24	40	28	86	2.431	28	64	40	72
1.395	24	48	24	86	1.956	32	72	44	100	2.442	24	32	28	86
1.400	24	48	28	100	1.990	28	72	44	86	2.445	40	72	44	100
1.429	24	56	24	72	1.993	24	56	40	86	2.450	28	64	56	100
1.440	24	40	24	100	2.000	24	40	24	72	2.456	44	86	48	100
1.458	24	64	28	72	2.009	24	86	72	100	2.481	32	72	48	86
1.467	24	72	44	100	2.030	24	44	32	86	2.489	32	72	56	100
1.488	32	86	40	100	2.035	28	64	40	86	2.500	24	48	28	56
1.500	24	64	40	100	2.036	28	44	32	100	2.514	32	56	44	100
1.522	24	44	24	86	2.045	24	44	24	64	2.532	28	72	56	86
1.550	24	72	40	86	2.047	40	86	44	100	2.537	24	44	40	86
1.563	24	86	56	100	2.057	24	28	24	100	2.546	28	44	40	100
1.595	24	56	32	86	2.067	32	72	40	86	2.558	32	64	44	86
1.600	24	48	32	100	2.083	24	64	40	72	2.567	28	48	44	100
1.607	24	56	24	64	2.084	28	86	64	100	2.571	24	40	24	56
1.628	24	48	28	86	2.093	24	64	48	86	2.593	28	48	32	72
1.637	32	86	44	100	2.100	24	64	56	100	2.605	28	40	32	86
1.650	24	64	44	100	2.121	24	44	28	72	2.618	24	44	48	100
1.667	24	56	28	72	2.133	24	72	64	100	2.619	24	56	44	72
1.674	24	40	24	86	2.143	24	56	32	64	2.625	24	40	28	64
1.680	24	40	28	100	2.171	24	72	56	86	2.640	24	40	44	100
1.706	24	72	44	86	2.178	28	72	56	100	2.658	32	56	40	86

Change Gears for Different Leads — 2.667 Inches to 4.040 Inches

Lead in Inches	Driven — Gear on Worm	Driver — First Gear on Stud	Driven — Second Gear on Stud	Driver — Gear on Screw	Lead in Inches	Driven — Gear on Worm	Driver — First Gear on Stud	Driven — Second Gear on Stud	Driver — Gear on Screw	Lead in Inches	Driven — Gear on Worm	Driver — First Gear on Stud	Driven — Second Gear on Stud	Driver — Gear on Screw
2.667	40	72	48	100	3.140	24	86	72	64	3.588	72	56	24	86
2.674	28	64	44	72	3.143	40	56	44	100	3.600	72	48	24	100
2.678	24	56	40	64	3.150	28	100	72	64	3.618	56	72	40	86
2.679	32	86	72	100	3.175	32	56	40	72	3.636	24	44	32	48
2.700	24	64	72	100	3.182	28	44	32	64	3.637	48	44	24	72
2.713	28	48	40	86	3.189	32	56	48	86	3.646	40	48	28	64
2.727	24	44	32	64	3.190	24	86	64	56	3.655	40	56	44	86
2.743	24	56	64	100	3.198	40	64	44	86	3.657	64	56	32	100
2.750	40	64	44	100	3.200	28	100	64	56	3.663	72	64	28	86
2.778	32	64	40	72	3.214	24	56	48	64	3.667	40	48	44	100
2.791	28	56	48	86	3.225	24	100	86	64	3.673	24	28	24	56
2.800	24	24	28	100	3.241	28	48	40	72	3.684	44	86	72	100
2.812	24	32	24	64	3.256	24	24	28	86	3.686	86	56	24	100
2.828	28	44	32	72	3.267	28	48	56	100	3.704	32	48	40	72
2.843	40	72	44	86	3.273	24	40	24	44	3.721	24	24	32	86
2.845	32	72	64	100	3.275	44	86	64	100	3.733	48	72	56	100
2.849	28	64	56	86	3.281	24	32	28	64	3.750	24	32	24	48
2.857	24	48	32	56	3.300	44	64	48	100	3.763	86	64	28	100
2.865	44	86	56	100	3.308	32	72	64	86	3.771	44	56	48	100
2.867	86	72	24	100	3.333	32	64	48	72	3.772	24	28	44	100
2.880	24	40	48	100	3.345	28	100	86	72	3.799	56	48	28	86
2.894	28	72	64	86	3.349	40	86	72	100	3.809	24	28	32	72
2.909	32	44	40	100	3.360	56	40	24	100	3.810	64	56	24	72
2.917	24	64	56	72	3.383	32	44	40	86	3.818	24	40	28	44
2.924	32	56	44	86	3.403	28	64	56	72	3.819	24	64	44	72
2.933	44	72	48	100	3.409	24	44	40	64	3.822	86	72	32	100
2.934	32	48	44	100	3.411	32	48	44	86	3.837	24	44	44	86
2.946	24	56	44	64	3.422	44	72	56	100	3.840	64	40	24	100
2.960	28	44	40	86	3.428	24	40	32	56	3.850	44	64	56	100
2.977	40	86	64	100	3.429	40	28	24	100	3.876	24	72	100	86
2.984	28	48	44	86	3.438	24	48	44	64	3.889	32	64	56	72
3.000	24	40	28	56	3.488	40	64	48	86	3.896	24	44	40	56
3.030	24	44	40	72	3.491	64	44	24	100	3.907	56	40	24	86
3.044	24	44	48	86	3.492	32	56	44	72	3.911	44	72	64	100
3.055	28	44	48	100	3.500	40	64	56	100	3.920	28	40	56	100
3.056	32	64	44	72	3.520	32	40	44	100	3.927	72	44	24	100
3.070	24	40	44	86	3.535	28	44	40	72	3.929	32	56	44	64
3.080	28	44	40	100	3.552	56	44	24	86	3.977	28	44	40	64
3.086	24	56	72	100	3.556	40	72	64	100	3.979	44	72	56	86
3.101	40	72	48	86	3.564	56	44	28	100	3.987	24	28	40	86
3.111	28	40	32	72	3.565	28	48	44	72	4.000	24	40	32	48
3.117	24	44	32	56	3.571	24	48	40	56	4.011	28	48	44	64
3.125	28	56	40	64	3.572	48	86	64	100	4.019	72	86	48	100
3.126	48	86	56	100	3.582	44	40	28	86	4.040	32	44	40	72

Change Gears for Different Leads — 4.059 Inches to 5.568 Inches

Lead in Inches	Driven — Gear on Worm	Driver — First Gear on Stud	Driven — Second Gear on Stud	Driver — Gear on Screw	Lead in Inches	Driven — Gear on Worm	Driver — First Gear on Stud	Driven — Second Gear on Stud	Driver — Gear on Screw	Lead in Inches	Driven — Gear on Worm	Driver — First Gear on Stud	Driven — Second Gear on Stud	Driver — Gear on Screw
4.059	32	44	48	86	4.567	72	44	24	86	5.105	28	48	56	64
4.060	64	44	24	86	4.572	40	56	64	100	5.116	44	24	24	86
4.070	28	32	40	86	4.582	72	44	28	100	5.119	86	56	24	72
4.073	64	44	28	100	4.583	44	64	48	72	5.120	64	40	32	100
4.074	32	48	44	72	4.584	32	48	44	64	5.133	56	48	44	100
4.091	24	44	48	64	4.651	40	24	24	86	5.134	44	24	28	100
4.093	32	40	44	86	4.655	64	44	32	100	5.142	72	56	40	100
4.114	48	28	24	100	4.667	28	40	32	48	5.143	24	28	24	40
4.125	24	40	44	64	4.675	24	28	24	44	5.156	44	32	24	64
4.135	40	72	64	86	4.687	40	32	24	64	5.160	86	40	24	100
4.144	56	44	28	86	4.688	56	86	72	100	5.168	100	72	32	86
4.167	28	48	40	56	4.691	86	44	24	100	5.185	28	24	32	72
4.186	72	64	32	86	4.714	44	40	24	56	5.186	64	48	28	72
4.200	48	64	56	100	4.736	64	44	28	86	5.195	32	44	40	56
4.242	28	44	32	48	4.762	40	28	24	72	5.209	100	64	24	72
4.253	64	56	32	86	4.773	24	32	28	44	5.210	64	40	28	86
4.264	40	48	44	86	4.778	86	72	40	100	5.226	86	64	28	72
4.267	64	48	32	100	4.784	72	56	32	86	5.233	72	64	40	86
4.278	28	40	44	72	4.785	48	28	24	86	5.236	72	44	32	100
4.286	24	28	24	48	4.800	48	24	24	100	5.238	44	28	24	72
4.300	86	56	28	100	4.813	44	40	28	64	5.250	24	32	28	40
4.320	72	40	24	100	4.821	72	56	24	64	5.256	86	72	44	100
4.341	48	72	56	86	4.849	32	44	48	72	5.280	48	40	44	100
4.342	64	48	28	86	4.861	40	32	28	72	5.303	28	44	40	48
4.361	100	64	24	86	4.884	48	64	56	86	5.316	40	28	32	86
4.363	24	40	32	44	4.889	32	40	44	72	5.328	72	44	28	86
4.364	40	44	48	100	4.898	24	28	32	56	5.333	40	24	32	100
4.365	40	56	44	72	4.900	56	32	28	100	5.347	44	64	56	72
4.375	24	24	28	64	4.911	40	56	44	64	5.348	44	32	28	72
4.386	24	28	44	86	4.914	86	56	32	100	5.357	40	28	24	64
4.400	24	24	44	100	4.950	56	44	28	72	5.358	64	86	72	100
4.444	64	56	28	72	4.961	64	48	32	86	5.375	86	64	40	100
4.465	64	40	24	86	4.978	56	72	64	100	5.400	72	32	24	100
4.466	48	40	32	86	4.984	100	56	24	86	5.413	64	44	32	86
4.477	44	32	28	86	5.000	24	40	28	56	5.426	40	24	28	86
4.479	86	64	24	72	5.017	86	48	28	100	5.427	40	48	56	86
4.480	56	40	32	100	5.023	72	40	24	86	5.444	56	40	28	72
4.500	72	64	40	100	5.029	44	28	32	100	5.455	48	44	28	56
4.522	100	72	28	86	5.040	72	40	28	100	5.469	40	32	28	64
4.537	56	48	28	72	5.074	40	44	48	86	5.473	86	44	28	100
4.545	24	44	40	48	5.080	64	56	32	72	5.486	64	28	24	100
4.546	28	44	40	56	5.088	100	64	28	86	5.500	44	40	24	48
4.548	44	72	64	86	5.091	56	44	40	100	5.556	40	24	24	72
4.558	56	40	28	86	5.093	40	48	44	72	5.568	56	44	28	64

Change Gears for Different Leads — 5.581 Inches to 7.500 Inches

Lead in Inches	Driven — Gear on Worm	Driver — First Gear on Stud	Driven — Second Gear on Stud	Driver — Gear on Screw	Lead in Inches	Driven — Gear on Worm	Driver — First Gear on Stud	Driven — Second Gear on Stud	Driver — Gear on Screw	Lead in Inches	Driven — Gear on Worm	Driver — First Gear on Stud	Driven — Second Gear on Stud	Driver — Gear on Screw
5.581	64	32	24	86	6.172	72	28	24	100	6.825	86	56	32	72
5.582	48	24	24	86	6.202	40	24	32	86	6.857	32	28	24	40
5.600	56	24	24	100	6.222	64	40	28	72	6.875	44	24	24	64
5.625	48	32	24	64	6.234	32	28	24	44	6.880	86	40	32	100
5.657	56	44	32	72	6.250	24	24	40	64	6.944	100	48	24	72
5.698	56	32	28	86	6.255	86	44	32	100	6.945	100	56	28	72
5.714	48	28	24	72	6.279	72	64	48	86	6.968	86	48	28	72
5.730	40	48	44	64	6.286	44	40	32	56	6.977	48	32	40	86
5.733	86	48	32	100	6.300	72	32	28	100	6.982	64	44	48	100
5.756	72	64	44	86	6.343	100	44	24	86	6.984	44	28	32	72
5.759	86	56	24	64	6.350	40	28	32	72	7.000	28	24	24	40
5.760	72	40	32	100	6.364	56	44	24	48	7.013	72	44	24	56
5.788	64	72	56	86	6.379	64	28	24	86	7.040	64	40	44	100
5.814	100	64	32	86	6.396	44	32	40	86	7.071	56	44	40	72
5.818	64	44	40	100	6.400	64	24	24	100	7.104	56	44	48	86
5.833	28	24	24	48	6.417	44	40	28	48	7.106	100	72	44	86
5.847	64	56	44	86	6.429	24	28	24	32	7.111	64	40	32	72
5.848	44	28	32	86	6.450	86	64	48	100	7.130	44	24	28	72
5.861	72	40	28	86	6.460	100	72	40	86	7.143	40	28	32	64
5.867	44	24	32	100	6.465	64	44	32	72	7.159	72	44	28	64
5.893	44	32	24	56	6.482	56	48	40	72	7.163	56	40	44	86
5.912	86	64	44	100	6.512	56	24	24	86	7.167	86	40	24	72
5.920	56	44	40	86	6.515	86	44	24	72	7.176	72	28	24	86
5.926	64	48	32	72	6.534	56	24	28	100	7.200	72	24	24	100
5.952	100	56	24	72	6.545	48	40	24	44	7.268	100	64	40	86
5.954	64	40	32	86	6.548	44	48	40	56	7.272	64	44	28	56
5.969	44	24	28	86	6.563	56	32	24	64	7.273	32	24	24	44
5.972	86	48	24	72	6.578	72	56	44	86	7.292	56	48	40	64
5.980	72	56	40	86	6.600	48	32	44	100	7.310	44	28	40	86
6.000	48	40	28	56	6.645	100	56	32	86	7.314	64	28	32	100
6.016	44	32	28	64	6.667	64	48	28	56	7.326	72	32	28	86
6.020	86	40	28	100	6.689	86	72	56	100	7.330	86	44	24	64
6.061	40	44	32	48	6.697	100	56	24	64	7.333	44	24	40	100
6.077	100	64	28	72	6.698	72	40	32	86	7.334	44	40	32	48
6.089	72	44	32	86	6.719	86	48	24	64	7.347	48	28	24	56
6.109	56	44	48	100	6.720	56	40	48	100	7.371	86	56	48	100
6.112	24	24	44	72	6.735	44	28	24	56	7.372	86	28	24	100
6.122	40	28	24	56	6.750	72	40	24	64	7.400	100	44	28	86
6.125	56	40	28	64	6.757	86	56	44	100	7.408	40	24	32	72
6.137	72	44	24	64	6.766	64	44	40	86	7.424	56	44	28	48
6.140	48	40	44	86	6.784	100	48	28	86	7.442	64	24	24	86
6.143	86	56	40	100	6.806	56	32	28	72	7.465	86	64	40	72
6.160	56	40	44	100	6.818	40	32	24	44	7.467	64	24	28	100
6.171	72	56	48	100	6.822	44	24	32	86	7.500	48	24	24	64

Change Gears for Different Leads — 7.525 Inches to 9.598 Inches

Lead in Inches	Driven (Gear on Worm)	Driver (First Gear on Stud)	Driven (Second Gear on Stud)	Driver (Gear on Screw)	Lead in Inches	Driven (Gear on Worm)	Driver (First Gear on Stud)	Driven (Second Gear on Stud)	Driver (Gear on Screw)	Lead in Inches	Driven (Gear on Worm)	Driver (First Gear on Stud)	Driven (Second Gear on Stud)	Driver (Gear on Screw)
7.525	86	32	28	100	8.140	56	32	40	86	8.800	48	24	44	100
7.543	48	28	44	100	8.145	64	44	56	100	8.838	100	44	28	72
7.576	100	44	24	72	8.148	64	48	44	72	8.839	72	56	44	64
7.597	56	24	28	86	8.149	44	24	32	72	8.909	56	40	28	44
7.601	86	44	28	72	8.163	40	28	32	56	8.929	100	48	24	56
7.611	72	44	40	86	8.167	56	40	28	48	8.930	64	40	48	86
7.619	64	48	32	56	8.182	48	32	24	44	8.953	56	32	44	86
7.620	64	28	24	72	8.186	64	40	44	86	8.959	86	48	28	56
7.636	56	40	24	44	8.212	86	64	44	72	8.960	64	40	56	100
7.639	44	32	40	72	8.229	72	28	32	100	8.980	44	28	32	56
7.644	86	72	64	100	8.250	44	32	24	40	9.000	48	32	24	40
7.657	56	32	28	64	8.306	100	56	40	86	9.044	100	72	56	86
7.674	72	48	44	86	8.312	64	44	32	56	9.074	56	24	28	72
7.675	48	32	44	86	8.333	40	24	24	48	9.091	40	24	24	44
7.679	86	48	24	56	8.334	40	24	28	56	9.115	100	48	28	64
7.680	64	40	48	100	8.361	86	40	28	72	9.134	72	44	48	86
7.700	56	32	44	100	8.372	72	24	24	86	9.137	100	56	44	86
7.714	72	40	24	56	8.377	86	44	24	56	9.143	64	40	32	56
7.752	100	48	32	86	8.400	72	24	28	100	9.164	72	44	56	100
7.778	32	24	28	48	8.437	72	32	24	64	9.167	44	24	24	48
7.792	40	28	24	44	8.457	100	44	32	86	9.210	72	40	44	86
7.813	100	48	24	64	8.484	32	24	28	44	9.214	86	40	24	56
7.815	56	40	48	86	8.485	64	44	28	48	9.260	100	48	32	72
7.818	86	44	40	100	8.485	56	44	32	48	9.302	48	24	40	86
7.838	86	48	28	64	8.506	64	28	32	86	9.303	56	28	40	86
7.855	72	44	48	100	8.523	100	44	24	64	9.333	64	40	28	48
7.857	44	24	24	56	8.527	44	24	40	86	9.334	32	24	28	40
7.872	44	28	32	64	8.532	86	56	40	72	9.351	48	28	24	44
7.875	72	40	28	64	8.534	64	24	32	100	9.375	48	32	40	64
7.883	86	48	44	100	8.552	86	44	28	64	9.382	86	44	48	100
7.920	72	40	44	100	8.556	56	40	44	72	9.385	86	56	44	72
7.936	100	56	32	72	8.572	64	32	24	56	9.406	86	40	28	64
7.954	40	32	28	44	8.572	48	24	24	56	9.428	44	28	24	40
7.955	56	44	40	64	8.594	44	32	40	64	9.429	48	40	44	56
7.963	86	48	32	72	8.600	86	24	24	100	9.460	86	40	44	100
7.974	48	28	40	86	8.640	72	40	48	100	9.472	64	44	56	86
7.994	100	64	44	86	8.681	100	64	40	72	9.524	40	28	32	48
8.000	64	32	40	100	8.682	64	24	28	86	9.545	72	44	28	48
8.021	44	32	28	48	8.687	86	44	32	72	9.546	56	32	24	44
8.035	72	56	40	64	8.721	100	32	24	86	9.547	56	44	48	64
8.063	86	40	24	64	8.727	48	40	32	44	9.549	100	64	44	72
8.081	64	44	40	72	8.730	44	28	40	72	9.556	86	40	32	72
8.102	100	48	28	72	8.750	28	24	24	32	9.569	72	28	32	86
8.119	64	44	48	86	8.772	48	28	44	86	9.598	86	56	40	64

Change Gears for Different Leads — 9.600 Inches to 12.375 Inches

Lead in Inches	Driven (Gear on Worm)	Driver (First Gear on Stud)	Driven (Second Gear on Stud)	Driver (Gear on Screw)	Lead in Inches	Driven (Gear on Worm)	Driver (First Gear on Stud)	Driven (Second Gear on Stud)	Driver (Gear on Screw)	Lead in Inches	Driven (Gear on Worm)	Driver (First Gear on Stud)	Driven (Second Gear on Stud)	Driver (Gear on Screw)
9.600	72	24	32	100	10.370	64	24	28	72	11.314	72	28	44	100
9.625	44	32	28	40	10.371	64	48	56	72	11.363	100	44	24	48
9.643	72	32	24	56	10.390	40	28	32	44	11.401	86	44	28	48
9.675	86	64	72	100	10.417	100	32	24	72	11.429	32	24	24	28
9.690	100	48	40	86	10.419	64	40	56	86	11.454	72	40	28	44
9.697	64	48	32	44	10.451	86	32	28	72	11.459	44	24	40	64
9.723	40	24	28	48	10.467	72	32	40	86	11.467	86	24	32	100
9.741	100	44	24	56	10.473	72	44	64	100	11.512	72	32	44	86
9.768	72	48	56	86	10.476	44	24	32	56	11.518	86	28	24	64
9.773	86	44	24	48	10.477	48	28	44	72	11.520	72	40	64	100
9.778	64	40	44	72	10.500	56	32	24	40	11.574	100	48	40	72
9.796	64	28	24	56	10.558	86	56	44	64	11.629	100	24	24	86
9.818	72	40	24	44	10.571	100	44	40	86	11.638	64	40	32	44
9.822	44	32	40	56	10.606	56	44	40	48	11.667	56	24	24	48
9.828	86	28	32	100	10.631	64	28	40	86	11.688	72	44	40	56
9.844	72	32	28	64	10.655	72	44	56	86	11.695	64	28	44	86
9.900	72	32	44	100	10.659	100	48	44	86	11.719	100	32	24	64
9.921	100	56	40	72	10.667	64	40	48	72	11.721	72	40	56	86
9.923	64	24	32	86	10.694	44	24	28	48	11.728	86	40	24	44
9.943	100	44	28	64	10.713	40	28	24	32	11.733	64	24	44	100
9.954	86	48	40	72	10.714	48	32	40	56	11.757	86	32	28	64
9.967	100	56	48	86	10.750	86	40	24	48	11.785	72	48	44	56
9.968	100	28	24	86	10.800	72	32	48	100	11.786	44	28	24	32
10.000	56	28	24	48	10.853	56	24	40	86	11.825	86	32	44	100
10.033	86	24	28	100	10.859	86	44	40	72	11.905	100	28	24	72
10.046	72	40	48	86	10.909	72	44	32	48	11.938	56	24	44	86
10.057	64	28	44	100	10.913	100	56	44	72	11.944	86	24	44	72
10.078	86	32	24	64	10.937	56	32	40	64	11.960	72	28	40	86
10.080	72	40	56	100	10.945	86	44	56	100	12.000	48	24	24	40
10.101	100	44	32	72	10.949	86	48	44	72	12.031	56	32	44	64
10.159	64	28	32	72	10.972	64	28	48	100	12.040	86	40	56	100
10.175	100	32	28	86	11.000	44	24	24	40	12.121	40	24	32	44
10.182	64	40	28	44	11.021	72	28	24	56	12.153	100	32	28	72
10.186	44	24	40	72	11.057	86	56	72	100	12.178	72	44	64	86
10.209	56	24	28	64	11.111	40	24	32	48	12.216	86	44	40	64
10.228	72	44	40	64	11.137	56	32	28	44	12.222	44	24	24	48
10.233	48	24	44	86	11.160	100	56	40	64	12.245	48	28	40	56
10.238	86	28	24	72	11.163	72	24	32	86	12.250	56	32	28	40
10.267	56	24	44	100	11.169	86	44	32	56	12.272	72	32	24	44
10.286	48	28	24	40	11.198	86	48	40	64	12.277	100	56	44	64
10.312	48	32	44	64	11.200	56	24	48	100	12.286	86	28	40	100
10.313	72	48	44	64	11.225	44	28	40	56	12.318	86	48	44	64
10.320	86	40	48	100	11.250	72	24	24	64	12.343	72	28	48	100
10.336	100	72	64	86	11.313	64	44	56	72	12.375	72	40	44	64

Change Gears for Different Leads — 12.403 Inches to 16.000 Inches

Lead in Inches	Driven / Gear on Worm	Driver / First Gear on Stud	Driven / Second Gear on Stud	Driver / Gear on Screw	Lead in Inches	Driven / Gear on Worm	Driver / First Gear on Stud	Driven / Second Gear on Stud	Driver / Gear on Screw	Lead in Inches	Driven / Gear on Worm	Driver / First Gear on Stud	Driven / Second Gear on Stud	Driver / Gear on Screw
12.403	64	24	40	86	13.438	86	24	24	64	14.668	44	24	32	40
12.444	64	40	56	72	13.469	48	28	44	56	14.694	72	28	32	56
12.468	64	28	24	44	13.500	72	32	24	40	14.743	86	28	48	100
12.500	40	24	24	32	13.514	86	28	44	100	14.780	86	40	44	64
12.542	86	40	28	48	13.566	100	24	28	86	14.800	100	44	56	86
12.508	86	44	64	100	13.611	56	24	48	100	14.815	64	24	40	72
12.558	72	32	48	86	13.636	48	28	40	44	14.849	56	24	28	44
12.571	64	40	44	56	13.643	64	24	44	86	14.880	100	48	40	56
12.572	44	28	32	40	13.650	86	28	32	72	14.884	64	28	56	86
12.600	72	32	56	100	13.672	100	32	28	64	14.931	86	32	40	72
12.627	100	44	40	72	13.682	86	40	28	44	14.933	64	24	56	100
12.686	100	44	48	86	13.713	64	40	48	56	14.950	100	56	72	86
12.698	64	28	40	72	13.715	64	28	24	40	15.000	48	24	24	32
12.727	64	32	28	44	13.750	44	24	24	32	15.050	86	32	56	100
12.728	56	24	24	44	13.760	86	40	64	100	15.150	100	44	32	48
12.732	100	48	44	72	13.889	100	24	24	72	15.151	100	44	48	72
12.758	64	28	48	86	13.933	86	48	56	72	15.202	86	44	56	72
12.791	100	40	44	86	13.935	86	24	28	72	15.238	64	28	48	72
12.798	86	48	40	56	13.953	72	24	40	86	15.239	64	28	32	48
12.800	64	28	56	100	13.960	86	44	40	56	15.272	56	40	48	44
12.834	56	40	44	48	13.968	64	28	44	72	15.278	44	24	40	48
12.857	72	28	32	64	14.000	56	24	24	40	15.279	100	40	44	72
12.858	48	28	24	32	14.025	72	44	48	56	15.306	100	28	24	56
12.900	86	32	48	100	14.026	72	28	24	44	15.349	72	24	44	86
12.963	56	24	40	72	14.063	72	32	40	64	15.357	86	28	24	48
12.987	100	44	32	56	14.071	86	44	72	100	15.429	72	40	48	56
13.020	100	48	40	64	14.078	86	48	44	56	15.469	72	32	44	64
13.024	56	24	48	86	14.142	72	40	44	56	15.480	86	40	72	100
13.030	86	44	32	48	14.204	100	44	40	64	15.504	100	48	64	86
13.062	64	28	32	56	14.260	56	24	44	72	15.556	64	32	56	72
13.082	100	64	72	86	14.286	40	24	24	28	15.584	48	28	40	44
13.090	72	40	32	44	14.318	72	32	28	44	15.625	100	24	24	64
13.096	44	28	40	48	14.319	72	44	56	64	15.636	86	40	32	44
13.125	72	32	28	48	14.322	100	48	44	64	15.677	86	32	28	48
13.139	86	40	44	72	14.333	86	40	32	48	15.714	64	24	24	28
13.157	72	28	44	86	14.352	72	28	48	86	15.750	72	32	28	40
13.163	86	28	24	56	14.400	72	24	48	100	15.767	86	24	44	100
13.200	72	24	44	100	14.536	100	32	40	86	15.873	100	56	64	72
13.258	100	44	28	48	14.545	64	24	24	44	15.874	100	28	32	72
13.289	100	28	32	86	14.583	56	32	40	48	15.909	100	40	28	44
13.333	64	24	24	48	14.584	40	24	28	32	15.925	86	48	64	72
13.393	100	56	48	64	14.651	72	32	56	86	15.926	86	24	32	72
13.396	72	40	64	86	14.659	86	44	48	64	15.989	100	32	44	86
13.437	86	32	28	56	14.667	64	40	44	48	16.000	64	24	24	40

Change Gears for Different Leads — 16.042 Inches to 21.39 Inches

Lead in Inches	Driven (Gear on Worm)	Driver (First Gear on Stud)	Driven (Second Gear on Stud)	Driver (Gear on Screw)	Lead in Inches	Driven (Gear on Worm)	Driver (First Gear on Stud)	Driven (Second Gear on Stud)	Driver (Gear on Screw)	Lead in Inches	Driven (Gear on Worm)	Driver (First Gear on Stud)	Driven (Second Gear on Stud)	Driver (Gear on Screw)
16.042	56	24	44	64	17.442	100	32	48	86	19.350	86	32	72	100
16.043	44	24	28	32	17.454	64	40	48	44	19.380	100	24	40	86
16.071	72	32	40	56	17.500	56	24	24	32	19.394	64	24	32	44
16.125	86	32	24	40	17.550	86	28	32	56	19.444	40	24	28	24
16.204	100	24	28	72	17.677	100	44	56	72	19.480	100	28	24	44
16.233	100	44	40	56	17.679	72	32	44	56	19.531	100	32	40	64
16.280	100	40	56	86	17.778	64	24	32	48	19.535	72	24	56	86
16.288	86	44	40	48	17.858	100	24	24	56	19.545	86	24	24	44
16.296	64	24	44	72	17.917	86	24	32	64	19.590	64	28	48	56
16.327	64	28	40	56	17.918	86	24	24	48	19.635	72	40	48	44
16.333	56	24	28	40	17.959	64	28	44	56	19.642	100	40	44	56
16.364	72	24	24	44	18.000	72	24	24	40	19.643	44	28	40	32
16.370	100	48	44	56	18.181	56	28	40	44	19.656	86	28	64	100
16.423	86	32	44	72	18.182	48	24	40	44	19.687	72	32	56	64
16.456	72	28	64	100	18.229	100	32	28	48	19.710	86	40	44	48
16.500	72	40	44	48	18.273	100	28	44	86	19.840	100	28	40	72
16.612	100	28	40	86	18.285	64	28	32	40	19.886	100	44	56	64
16.623	64	28	32	44	18.333	56	28	44	48	19.887	100	32	28	44
16.667	56	28	40	48	18.367	72	28	40	56	19.908	86	24	40	72
16.722	86	40	56	72	18.428	86	28	24	40	19.934	100	28	48	86
16.744	72	24	48	86	18.476	86	32	44	64	20.00	72	24	32	48
16.752	86	44	48	56	18.519	100	24	32	72	20.07	86	24	56	100
16.753	86	28	24	44	18.605	100	40	64	86	20.09	100	56	72	64
16.797	86	32	40	64	18.663	100	64	86	72	20.16	86	48	72	64
16.800	72	24	56	100	18.667	64	24	28	40	20.20	100	44	64	72
16.875	72	32	48	64	18.700	72	44	64	56	20.35	100	32	56	86
16.892	86	40	44	56	18.750	100	32	24	40	20.36	64	40	56	44
16.914	100	44	64	86	18.750	72	32	40	48	20.41	100	28	32	56
16.969	64	44	56	48	18.770	86	28	44	72	20.42	56	24	28	32
16.970	64	24	28	44	18.812	86	32	28	40	20.45	72	32	40	44
17.045	100	32	24	44	18.858	48	28	44	40	20.48	86	48	64	56
17.046	100	44	48	64	18.939	100	44	40	48	20.57	72	40	64	56
17.062	86	28	40	72	19.029	100	44	72	86	20.63	72	32	44	48
17.101	86	44	56	64	19.048	40	24	32	28	20.74	64	24	56	72
17.102	86	32	28	44	19.090	56	32	48	44	20.78	64	28	40	44
17.141	64	32	48	56	19.091	72	24	28	44	20.83	100	32	48	72
17.143	64	28	24	32	19.096	100	32	44	72	20.90	86	32	56	72
17.144	48	24	24	28	19.111	86	40	64	72	20.93	100	40	72	86
17.188	100	40	44	64	19.136	72	28	64	86	20.95	64	28	44	48
17.200	86	32	64	100	19.197	86	32	40	56	21.00	56	32	48	40
17.275	86	56	72	64	19.200	72	24	64	100	21.12	86	32	44	56
17.361	100	32	40	72	19.250	56	32	44	40	21.32	100	24	44	86
17.364	64	24	56	86	19.285	72	32	48	56	21.33	100	56	86	72
17.373	86	44	64	72	19.286	72	28	24	32	21.39	44	24	28	24

Change Gears for Different Leads — 21.43 Inches to 32.09 Inches

Lead in Inches	Driven — Gear on Worm	Driver — First Gear on Stud	Driven — Second Gear on Stud	Driver — Gear on Screw	Lead in Inches	Driven — Gear on Worm	Driver — First Gear on Stud	Driven — Second Gear on Stud	Driver — Gear on Screw	Lead in Inches	Driven — Gear on Worm	Driver — First Gear on Stud	Driven — Second Gear on Stud	Driver — Gear on Screw
21.43	100	40	48	56	24.88	100	72	86	48	28.05	72	28	48	44
21.48	100	32	44	64	24.93	64	28	48	44	28.06	100	28	44	56
21.50	86	24	24	40	25.00	72	24	40	48	28.13	100	40	72	64
21.82	72	44	64	48	25.08	86	24	28	40	28.15	86	28	44	48
21.88	100	40	56	64	25.09	86	40	56	48	28.29	72	28	44	40
21.90	86	24	44	72	25.13	86	44	72	56	28.41	100	32	40	44
21.94	86	28	40	56	25.14	64	28	44	40	28.57	100	56	64	40
21.99	86	44	72	64	25.45	64	44	56	32	28.64	72	44	56	32
22.00	64	32	44	40	25.46	100	24	44	72	28.65	100	32	44	48
22.04	72	28	48	56	25.51	100	28	40	56	28.67	86	40	64	48
22.11	86	28	72	100	25.57	100	64	72	44	29.09	64	24	48	44
22.22	100	40	64	72	25.60	86	28	40	48	29.17	100	40	56	48
22.34	86	44	64	56	25.67	56	24	44	40	29.22	100	56	72	44
22.40	86	32	40	48	25.71	72	24	48	56	29.32	86	48	72	44
22.50	72	24	48	64	25.72	72	24	24	28	29.34	64	24	44	40
22.73	100	24	24	44	25.80	86	24	72	100	29.39	72	28	64	56
22.80	86	48	56	44	25.97	100	44	64	56	29.56	86	32	44	40
22.86	64	24	24	28	26.04	100	32	40	48	29.76	100	28	40	48
22.91	72	44	56	40	26.06	86	44	64	48	29.86	100	40	86	72
22.92	100	40	44	48	26.16	100	32	72	86	29.90	100	28	72	86
22.93	86	24	64	100	26.18	72	40	64	44	30.00	56	28	48	32
23.04	86	56	72	48	26.19	44	24	40	28	30.23	86	32	72	64
23.14	100	24	40	72	26.25	72	32	56	48	30.30	100	48	64	44
23.26	100	32	64	86	26.33	86	28	48	56	30.48	64	24	32	28
23.33	64	32	56	48	26.52	100	44	56	48	30.54	100	44	86	64
23.38	72	28	40	44	26.58	100	28	64	86	30.56	44	24	40	24
23.44	100	48	72	64	26.67	64	28	56	48	30.61	100	28	48	56
23.45	86	40	48	44	26.79	100	48	72	56	30.71	86	24	48	56
23.52	86	32	56	64	26.88	86	28	56	64	30.72	86	24	24	28
23.57	72	28	44	48	27.00	72	32	48	40	30.86	72	28	48	40
23.81	100	48	64	56	27.13	100	24	56	86	31.01	100	24	64	86
23.89	86	32	64	72	27.15	100	44	86	72	31.11	64	24	56	48
24.00	64	40	72	48	27.22	56	24	28	24	31.25	100	28	56	64
24.13	86	28	44	56	27.27	100	40	48	44	31.27	86	40	64	44
24.19	86	40	72	64	27.30	86	28	64	72	31.35	86	32	56	48
24.24	64	24	40	44	27.34	100	32	56	64	31.36	86	24	28	32
24.31	100	32	56	72	27.36	86	40	56	44	31.43	64	28	44	32
24.43	86	32	40	44	27.43	64	28	48	40	31.50	72	32	56	40
24.44	44	24	32	24	27.50	56	32	44	28	31.75	100	72	64	28
24.54	72	32	48	44	27.64	86	40	72	56	31.82	100	44	56	40
24.55	100	32	44	56	27.78	100	32	64	72	31.85	86	24	64	72
24.57	86	40	64	56	27.87	86	24	56	72	31.99	100	56	86	48
24.64	86	24	44	64	27.92	86	28	40	44	32.00	64	28	56	40
24.75	72	32	44	40	28.00	100	64	86	48	32.09	56	24	44	32

Change Gears for Different Leads — 32.14 Inches to 60.00 Inches

Lead in Inches	Driven (Gear on Worm)	Driver (First Gear on Stud)	Driven (Second Gear on Stud)	Driver (Gear on Screw)	Lead in Inches	Driven (Gear on Worm)	Driver (First Gear on Stud)	Driven (Second Gear on Stud)	Driver (Gear on Screw)	Lead in Inches	Driven (Gear on Worm)	Driver (First Gear on Stud)	Driven (Second Gear on Stud)	Driver (Gear on Screw)
32.14	100	56	72	40	38.20	100	24	44	48	46.07	86	28	72	48
32.25	86	48	72	40	38.39	100	40	86	56	46.67	64	24	56	32
32.41	100	24	56	72	38.57	72	28	48	32	46.88	100	32	72	48
32.47	100	28	40	44	38.89	56	24	40	24	47.15	72	24	44	28
32.58	86	24	40	44	38.96	100	28	48	44	47.62	100	28	64	48
32.73	72	32	64	44	39.09	86	32	64	44	47.78	86	24	64	48
32.74	100	28	44	48	39.29	100	28	44	40	47.99	100	32	86	56
32.85	86	24	44	48	39.42	86	24	44	40	48.00	72	24	64	40
33.00	72	24	44	40	39.49	86	28	72	56	48.38	86	32	72	40
33.33	100	24	32	40	39.77	100	32	56	44	48.61	100	24	56	48
33.51	86	28	48	44	40.00	72	24	64	48	48.86	100	40	86	44
33.59	100	64	86	40	40.18	100	32	72	56	48.89	64	24	44	24
33.79	86	28	44	44	40.31	86	32	72	48	49.11	100	28	44	32
33.94	64	24	56	44	40.72	100	44	86	48	49.14	86	28	64	40
34.09	100	48	72	44	40.82	100	28	64	56	49.27	86	24	44	32
34.20	86	44	56	32	40.91	100	40	72	44	49.77	100	24	86	72
34.29	72	48	64	28	40.95	86	28	64	48	50.00	100	28	56	40
34.38	100	32	44	40	40.96	86	24	32	28	50.17	86	24	56	40
34.55	86	32	72	56	41.14	72	28	64	40	50.26	86	28	72	44
34.72	100	24	40	48	41.25	72	24	44	32	51.14	100	32	72	44
34.88	100	24	72	86	41.67	100	32	64	48	51.19	86	24	40	28
34.90	100	56	86	44	41.81	86	24	56	48	51.43	72	28	64	32
35.00	72	24	56	48	41.91	64	24	44	28	51.95	100	28	64	44
35.10	86	28	64	56	41.99	100	32	86	64	52.12	86	24	64	44
35.16	100	32	72	64	42.00	72	24	56	40	52.50	72	24	56	32
35.18	86	44	72	40	42.23	86	28	44	32	53.03	100	24	56	44
35.36	72	32	44	28	42.66	100	28	86	72	53.33	64	24	56	28
35.56	64	24	32	24	42.78	56	24	44	24	53.57	100	28	72	48
35.71	100	32	64	56	42.86	100	28	48	40	53.75	86	24	48	32
35.72	100	24	28	40	43.00	86	32	64	40	54.85	100	28	86	56
35.83	86	32	64	48	43.64	72	24	64	44	55.00	72	24	44	24
36.00	72	32	64	40	43.75	100	32	56	40	55.28	86	28	72	40
36.36	100	44	64	40	43.98	86	32	72	44	55.56	100	24	32	24
36.46	100	48	56	32	44.44	64	24	40	24	55.99	100	24	86	64
36.67	48	24	44	24	44.64	100	28	40	32	56.25	100	32	72	40
36.86	86	28	48	40	44.68	86	28	64	44	56.31	86	24	44	28
37.04	100	24	64	72	44.79	100	40	86	48	57.14	100	24	64	40
37.33	100	32	86	72	45.00	72	28	56	32	57.30	100	24	44	32
37.40	72	28	64	44	45.45	100	32	64	40	57.33	86	24	64	40
37.50	100	48	72	40	45.46	100	28	56	44	58.33	100	24	56	40
37.63	86	32	56	40	45.61	86	24	56	44	58.44	100	28	72	44
37.88	64	24	40	44	45.72	64	24	48	28	58.64	86	24	72	44
38.10	64	24	40	28	45.84	100	24	44	40	59.53	100	24	40	28
38.18	72	24	56	44	45.92	100	28	72	56	60.00	72	24	64	32

Lead of Helix for Given Helix Angle Relative to Axis, When Diameter = 1

Deg.	0'	6'	12'	18'	24'	30'	36'	42'	48'	54'	60'
0	Infin.	1800.001	899.997	599.994	449.993	359.992	299.990	257.130	224.986	199.983	179.982
1	179.982	163.616	149.978	138.438	128.545	119.973	112.471	105.851	99.967	94.702	89.964
2	89.964	85.676	81.778	78.219	74.956	71.954	69.183	66.617	64.235	62.016	59.945
3	59.945	58.008	56.191	54.485	52.879	51.365	49.934	48.581	47.299	46.082	44.927
4	44.927	43.827	42.780	41.782	40.829	39.918	39.046	38.212	37.412	36.645	35.909
5	35.909	35.201	34.520	33.866	33.235	32.627	32.040	31.475	30.928	30.400	29.890
6	29.890	29.397	28.919	28.456	28.008	27.573	27.152	26.743	26.346	25.961	25.586
7	25.586	25.222	24.868	24.524	24.189	23.863	23.545	23.236	22.934	22.640	22.354
8	22.354	22.074	21.801	21.535	21.275	21.021	20.773	20.530	20.293	20.062	19.835
9	19.835	19.614	19.397	19.185	18.977	18.773	18.574	18.379	18.188	18.000	17.817
10	17.817	17.637	17.460	17.287	17.117	16.950	16.787	16.626	16.469	16.314	16.162
11	16.162	16.013	15.866	15.722	15.581	15.441	15.305	15.170	15.038	14.908	14.780
12	14.780	14.654	14.530	14.409	14.289	14.171	14.055	13.940	13.828	13.717	13.608
13	13.608	13.500	13.394	13.290	13.187	13.086	12.986	12.887	12.790	12.695	12.600
14	12.600	12.507	12.415	12.325	12.237	12.148	12.061	11.975	11.890	11.807	11.725
15	11.725	11.643	11.563	11.484	11.405	11.328	11.252	11.177	11.102	11.029	10.956
16	10.956	10.884	10.813	10.743	10.674	10.606	10.538	10.471	10.405	10.340	10.276
17	10.276	10.212	10.149	10.086	10.025	9.964	9.904	9.844	9.785	9.727	9.669
18	9.669	9.612	9.555	9.499	9.444	9.389	9.335	9.281	9.228	9.176	9.124
19	9.124	9.072	9.021	8.971	8.921	8.872	8.823	8.774	8.726	8.679	8.631
20	8.631	8.585	8.539	8.493	8.447	8.403	8.358	8.314	8.270	8.227	8.184
21	8.184	8.142	8.099	8.058	8.016	7.975	7.935	7.894	7.855	7.815	7.776
22	7.776	7.737	7.698	7.660	7.622	7.584	7.547	7.510	7.474	7.437	7.401
23	7.401	7.365	7.330	7.295	7.260	7.225	7.191	7.157	7.123	7.089	7.056
24	7.056	7.023	6.990	6.958	6.926	6.894	6.862	6.830	6.799	6.768	6.737
25	6.737	6.707	6.676	6.646	6.617	6.586	6.557	6.528	6.499	6.470	6.441
26	6.441	6.413	6.385	6.357	6.329	6.300	6.274	6.246	6.219	6.192	6.166
27	6.166	6.139	6.113	6.087	6.061	6.035	6.009	5.984	5.959	5.933	5.908
28	5.908	5.884	5.859	5.835	5.810	5.786	5.762	5.738	5.715	5.691	5.668
29	5.668	5.644	5.621	5.598	5.575	5.553	5.530	5.508	5.486	5.463	5.441

Lead of Helix for Given Helix Angle Relative to Axis, When Diameter = 1

Deg.	0'	6'	12'	18'	24'	30'	36'	42'	48'	54'	60'
30	5.441	5.420	5.398	5.376	5.355	5.333	5.312	5.291	5.270	5.249	5.228
31	5.228	5.208	5.187	5.167	5.147	5.127	5.107	5.087	5.067	5.047	5.028
32	5.028	5.008	4.989	4.969	4.950	4.931	4.912	4.894	4.875	4.856	4.838
33	4.838	4.819	4.801	4.783	4.764	4.746	4.728	4.711	4.693	4.675	4.658
34	4.658	4.640	4.623	4.605	4.588	4.571	4.554	4.537	4.520	4.503	4.487
35	4.487	4.470	4.453	4.437	4.421	4.404	4.388	4.372	4.356	4.340	4.324
36	4.324	4.308	4.292	4.277	4.261	4.246	4.230	4.215	4.199	4.184	4.169
37	4.169	4.154	4.139	4.124	4.109	4.094	4.079	4.065	4.050	4.036	4.021
38	4.021	4.007	3.992	3.978	3.964	3.950	3.935	3.921	3.907	3.893	3.880
39	3.880	3.866	3.852	3.838	3.825	3.811	3.798	3.784	3.771	3.757	3.744
40	3.744	3.731	3.718	3.704	3.691	3.678	3.665	3.652	3.640	3.627	3.614
41	3.614	3.601	3.589	3.576	3.563	3.551	3.538	3.526	3.514	3.501	3.489
42	3.489	3.477	3.465	3.453	3.440	3.428	3.416	3.405	3.393	3.381	3.369
43	3.369	3.358	3.346	3.334	3.322	3.311	3.299	3.287	3.276	3.265	3.253
44	3.253	3.242	3.231	3.219	3.208	3.197	3.186	3.175	3.164	3.153	3.142
45	3.142	3.131	3.120	3.109	3.098	3.087	3.076	3.066	3.055	3.044	3.034
46	3.034	3.023	3.013	3.002	2.992	2.981	2.971	2.960	2.950	2.940	2.930
47	2.930	2.919	2.909	2.899	2.889	2.879	2.869	2.859	2.849	2.839	2.829
48	2.829	2.819	2.809	2.799	2.789	2.779	2.770	2.760	2.750	2.741	2.731
49	2.731	2.721	2.712	2.702	2.693	2.683	2.674	2.664	2.655	2.645	2.636
50	2.636	2.627	2.617	2.608	2.599	2.590	2.581	2.571	2.562	2.553	2.544
51	2.544	2.535	2.526	2.517	2.508	2.499	2.490	2.481	2.472	2.463	2.454
52	2.454	2.446	2.437	2.428	2.419	2.411	2.402	2.393	2.385	2.376	2.367
53	2.367	2.359	2.350	2.342	2.333	2.325	2.316	2.308	2.299	2.291	2.282
54	2.282	2.274	2.266	2.257	2.249	2.241	2.233	2.224	2.216	2.208	2.200
55	2.200	2.192	2.183	2.175	2.167	2.159	2.151	2.143	2.135	2.127	2.119
56	2.119	2.111	2.103	2.095	2.087	2.079	2.072	2.064	2.056	2.048	2.040
57	2.040	2.032	2.025	2.017	2.009	2.001	1.994	1.986	1.978	1.971	1.963
58	1.963	1.955	1.948	1.940	1.933	1.925	1.918	1.910	1.903	1.895	1.888
59	1.888	1.880	1.873	1.865	1.858	1.851	1.843	1.836	1.828	1.821	1.814

Lead of Helix for Given Helix Angle Relative to Axis, When Diameter = 1

Deg.	0'	6'	12'	18'	24'	30'	36'	42'	48'	54'	60'
60	1.814	1.806	1.799	1.792	1.785	1.777	1.770	1.763	1.756	1.749	1.741
61	1.741	1.734	1.727	1.720	1.713	1.706	1.699	1.692	1.685	1.677	1.670
62	1.670	1.663	1.656	1.649	1.642	1.635	1.628	1.621	1.615	1.608	1.601
63	1.601	1.594	1.587	1.580	1.573	1.566	1.559	1.553	1.546	1.539	1.532
64	1.532	1.525	1.519	1.512	1.505	1.498	1.492	1.485	1.478	1.472	1.465
65	1.465	1.458	1.452	1.445	1.438	1.432	1.425	1.418	1.412	1.405	1.399
66	1.399	1.392	1.386	1.379	1.372	1.366	1.359	1.353	1.346	1.340	1.334
67	1.334	1.327	1.321	1.314	1.308	1.301	1.295	1.288	1.282	1.276	1.269
68	1.269	1.263	1.257	1.250	1.244	1.237	1.231	1.225	1.219	1.212	1.206
69	1.206	1.200	1.193	1.187	1.181	1.175	1.168	1.162	1.156	1.150	1.143
70	1.143	1.137	1.131	1.125	1.119	1.112	1.106	1.100	1.094	1.088	1.082
71	1.082	1.076	1.069	1.063	1.057	1.051	1.045	1.039	1.033	1.027	1.021
72	1.021	1.015	1.009	1.003	0.997	0.991	0.985	0.978	0.972	0.966	0.960
73	0.960	0.954	0.948	0.943	0.937	0.931	0.925	0.919	0.913	0.907	0.901
74	0.901	0.895	0.889	0.883	0.877	0.871	0.865	0.859	0.854	0.848	0.842
75	0.842	0.836	0.830	0.824	0.818	0.812	0.807	0.801	0.795	0.789	0.783
76	0.783	0.777	0.772	0.766	0.760	0.754	0.748	0.743	0.737	0.731	0.725
77	0.725	0.720	0.714	0.708	0.702	0.696	0.691	0.685	0.679	0.673	0.668
78	0.668	0.662	0.656	0.651	0.645	0.639	0.633	0.628	0.622	0.616	0.611
79	0.611	0.605	0.599	0.594	0.588	0.582	0.577	0.571	0.565	0.560	0.554
80	0.554	0.548	0.543	0.537	0.531	0.526	0.520	0.514	0.509	0.503	0.498
81	0.498	0.492	0.486	0.481	0.475	0.469	0.464	0.458	0.453	0.447	0.441
82	0.441	0.436	0.430	0.425	0.419	0.414	0.408	0.402	0.397	0.391	0.386
83	0.386	0.380	0.375	0.369	0.363	0.358	0.352	0.347	0.341	0.336	0.330
84	0.330	0.325	0.319	0.314	0.308	0.302	0.297	0.291	0.286	0.280	0.275
85	0.275	0.269	0.264	0.258	0.253	0.247	0.242	0.236	0.231	0.225	0.220
86	0.220	0.214	0.209	0.203	0.198	0.192	0.187	0.181	0.176	0.170	0.165
87	0.165	0.159	0.154	0.148	0.143	0.137	0.132	0.126	0.121	0.115	0.110
88	0.110	0.104	0.099	0.093	0.088	0.082	0.077	0.071	0.066	0.060	0.055
89	0.055	0.049	0.044	0.038	0.033	0.027	0.022	0.016	0.011	0.005	0.000

Leads, Change Gears and Angles for Helical Milling

Lead of Helix, Inches	Gear on Worm	1st Intermediate Gear	2d Intermediate Gear	Gear on Screw	Diameter of Work, Inches									
					1/8	1/4	3/8	1/2	5/8	3/4	7/8	1	1 1/4	1 1/2
0.67	24	86	24	100	30 1/4	...	...	...	Approximate Angles for Milling Machine Table					
0.78	24	86	28	100	26	44 1/2	...	...						
0.89	24	86	32	100	23 1/2	41	...	...						
1.12	24	86	40	100	19	34 1/2	...	...						
1.34	24	86	48	100	16	30 1/4	41 1/2	...	...	...	...	...	...	...
1.46	24	64	28	72	14 3/4	28	38 1/2	...	...	...	...	...	...	...
1.56	24	86	56	100	13 3/4	26 1/2	37	...	...	...	...	...	...	...
1.67	24	64	32	72	12 3/4	25	34 3/4	43 1/4	...	...	...	...	...	...
1.94	32	64	28	72	11 1/4	21 3/4	31	39	45	...	...	...	...	...
2.08	24	64	40	72	10 1/4	20 1/2	29 1/2	37	43 1/4	...	...	...	...	...
2.22	32	56	28	72	9 3/4	19 1/4	27 1/2	35	41 1/4	...	...	...	...	...
2.50	24	64	48	72	8 3/4	17	25	32	38	43 1/4	...	...	...	...
2.78	40	56	28	72	8	15 1/2	23	29 1/2	35 1/4	40 1/2	44 3/4	...	...	...
2.92	24	64	56	72	7 1/2	15	21 3/4	28 1/4	34	39	43 1/4	...	...	...
3.24	40	48	28	72	6 3/4	13 1/4	19 3/4	25 3/4	31 1/4	36	40 1/2	44 1/4	...	...
3.70	40	48	32	72	6	11 3/4	17 1/2	23	28	32 1/2	36 1/2	40 1/2	...	...
3.89	56	48	24	72	5 1/2	11 1/4	16 3/4	22	26 3/4	31 1/4	35 1/4	39	...	...
4.17	40	72	48	64	5 1/4	10 1/2	15 3/4	20 1/2	25 1/4	29 1/2	33 1/2	37	43 1/4	...
4.46	48	40	32	86	4 3/4	9 3/4	14 3/4	19 1/4	23 3/4	27 3/4	31 1/2	35	41 1/2	...
4.86	40	64	56	72	4 1/2	9	13 1/2	17 3/4	22	25 3/4	29 1/2	33	39	44 1/4
5.33	48	40	32	72	4	8 1/4	12 1/4	16 1/2	20 1/4	23 3/4	27 1/4	30 1/2	36 1/2	41 1/2
5.44	56	40	28	72	4	8	12	16	20	23 1/2	26 3/4	30	36	41
6.12	56	40	28	64	3 1/2	7 1/4	11	14 1/2	17 3/4	21	24 1/4	27	33	37 3/4
6.22	56	40	32	72	3 1/2	7	10 3/4	14 1/4	17 1/2	20 3/4	23 3/4	26 3/4	32 1/2	37 1/4
6.48	56	48	40	72	3 1/4	6 3/4	10 1/4	13 1/2	16 3/4	20	23	25 3/4	31 1/2	36 1/4
6.67	64	48	28	56	3 1/4	6 1/2	10	13 1/4	16 1/2	19 1/2	22 1/2	25 1/4	30 3/4	35 1/4
7.29	56	48	40	64	3	6 1/4	9 1/4	12 1/4	15	18	20 1/2	23 1/2	28 1/2	33
7.41	64	48	40	72	3	6	9	12	14 3/4	17 3/4	20 1/4	22 3/4	28 1/4	32 1/2
7.62	64	48	32	56	2 3/4	5 3/4	8 3/4	11 1/2	14 1/2	17 1/4	19 3/4	22 1/4	27 1/2	32
8.33	48	32	40	72	2 1/2	5 1/4	8	10 1/2	13 1/4	15 3/4	18 1/4	20 1/2	25 1/2	29 1/2
8.95	86	48	28	56	2 1/2	5	7 1/2	10	12 1/2	14 3/4	17	19 1/4	24	28
9.33	56	40	48	72	2 1/4	4 3/4	7 1/4	9 1/2	11 3/4	14	16 1/4	18 1/2	23	27
9.52	64	48	40	56	2 1/4	4 1/2	7	9 1/4	11 1/2	13 3/4	16	18 1/4	22 1/2	26 1/2
10.29	72	40	32	56	2	4 1/4	6 1/2	8 3/4	10 3/4	12 3/4	15	17 1/4	21	24 3/4
10.37	64	48	56	72	2	4 1/4	6 1/2	8 1/2	10 1/2	12 3/4	14 3/4	17	20 3/4	24 1/2
10.50	48	40	56	64	2	4 1/4	6 1/4	8 1/2	10 1/2	12 1/2	14 1/2	16 3/4	20 1/2	24 1/4
10.67	64	40	48	72	2	4	6 1/4	8 1/4	10 1/4	12 1/4	14 1/4	16 1/2	20 1/4	24
10.94	56	32	40	64	2	4	6	8 1/4	10 1/4	12	14	16 1/4	20	23 1/2
11.11	64	32	40	72	2	4	6	8	10	11 3/4	13 3/4	16	19 3/4	23
11.66	56	32	48	72	1 3/4	3 3/4	5 3/4	7 1/2	9 1/2	11 1/4	13 1/4	15 1/4	18 3/4	22
12.00	72	40	32	48	1 3/4	3 3/4	5 1/2	7 1/4	9 1/4	11	12 3/4	15	18 1/4	21 1/2
13.12	56	32	48	64	1 1/2	3 1/2	5 1/4	6 3/4	8 1/2	10 1/4	11 3/4	13 1/2	16 3/4	20
13.33	56	28	48	72	1 1/2	3 1/4	5	6 1/2	8 1/4	10	11 1/2	13 1/4	16 1/2	19 1/2
13.71	64	40	48	56	1 1/2	3 1/4	4 3/4	6 1/2	8	9 3/4	11 1/4	13	16	19
15.24	64	28	48	72	1 1/2	3	4 1/2	5 3/4	7 1/4	8 3/4	10 1/4	11 3/4	14 1/2	17 1/4
15.56	64	32	56	72	1 1/4	2 3/4	4 1/4	5 3/4	7 1/4	8 3/4	10	11 1/2	14 1/4	17
15.75	56	64	72	40	1 1/4	2 3/4	4 1/4	5 1/2	7	8 1/2	9 3/4	11 1/4	14	16 3/4
16.87	72	32	48	64	1 1/4	2 1/2	4	5 1/4	6 3/4	7 3/4	9 1/4	10 1/2	13 1/4	15 3/4
17.14	64	32	48	56	1 1/4	2 1/2	4	5 1/4	6 1/2	7 3/4	9	10 1/4	13	15 1/2
18.75	72	32	40	48	1	2 1/4	3 1/2	4 3/4	6	7 1/4	8 1/4	9 1/2	12	14 1/4
19.29	72	32	48	56	1	2 1/4	3 1/2	4 1/2	5 3/4	7	8	9 1/4	11 1/2	13 3/4
19.59	64	28	48	56	1	2 1/4	3 1/4	4 1/2	5 3/4	6 3/4	8	9 1/4	11 1/2	13 1/2
19.69	72	32	56	64	1	2 1/4	3 1/4	4 1/2	5 3/4	6 3/4	8	9	11 1/2	13 1/2
21.43	72	24	40	56	1	2	3 1/4	4 1/4	5 1/4	6 1/4	7 1/2	8 1/2	10 1/2	12 1/2
22.50	72	28	56	64	1	2	3	4	5	6	7	8	10	12
23.33	64	32	56	48	1	2	3	4	5	5 3/4	6 3/4	7 3/4	9 3/4	11 1/2
26.25	72	24	56	64	1	1 3/4	2 3/4	3 1/2	4 1/4	5	6	7	8 1/2	10 1/4
26.67	64	28	56	48	3/4	1 3/4	2 3/4	3 1/2	4 1/4	5	6	6 3/4	8 1/2	10
28.00	64	32	56	40	3/4	1 3/4	2 1/2	3 1/4	4	4 3/4	5 3/4	6 1/2	8	9 1/2
30.86	72	28	48	40	3/4	1 1/2	2 1/4	3	3 3/4	4 1/2	5	5 3/4	7 1/4	8 3/4

Leads, Change Gears and Angles for Helical Milling

Lead of Helix, Inches	Gear on Worm	1st Intermediate Gear	2d Intermediate Gear	Gear on Screw	Diameter of Work, Inches									
					1¾	2	2¼	2½	2¾	3	3¼	3½	3¾	4
6.12	56	40	28	64	42	...	...	...	Approximate Angles for					
6.22	56	40	32	72	41½	...	...	...	Milling Machine Table					
6.48	56	48	40	72	40¼	44¼	...	...						
6.67	64	48	28	56	39½	43½	...	...	...	...	...	...	...	...
7.29	56	48	40	64	37	41	44¼	...	...	...	...	...	...	...
7.41	64	48	40	72	36½	40¼	43¾	...	...	...	...	...	...	...
7.62	64	48	32	56	36	39½	43	...	...	...	...	...	...	...
8.33	48	32	40	72	33½	37	40½	43½	...	...	...	...	...	...
8.95	86	48	28	56	31¾	35¼	38½	41¼	44	...	...	...	...	...
9.33	56	40	48	72	30½	34	37¼	40¼	43	...	...	...	...	...
9.52	64	48	40	56	30	33½	36½	39½	42¼	45	...	...	...	...
10.29	72	40	32	56	28¼	31½	34½	37½	40	42½	45	...	...	...
10.37	64	48	56	72	28	31¼	34¼	37¼	39¾	42¼	44¾	...	...	...
10.50	48	40	56	64	27¾	31	34	36¾	39½	42	44¼	...	...	...
10.67	64	40	48	72	27¼	30½	33½	36½	39	41½	43¾	...	...	...
10.94	56	32	40	64	26¾	30	33	35¾	38¼	40¾	43	...	...	...
11.11	64	32	40	72	26½	29½	32½	35¼	38	40¼	42½	44¾	...	...
11.66	56	32	48	72	25¼	28½	31¼	34	36½	39	41¼	43½	...	...
12.00	72	40	32	48	24¾	27¾	30½	33¼	35¾	38	40¼	42½	44¾	...
13.12	56	32	48	64	22¾	25¾	28¼	31	33¼	35¾	37¾	40	42	43¾
13.33	56	28	48	72	22½	25½	28	30½	33	35¼	37½	39½	41½	43¼
13.71	64	40	48	56	22	24¾	27¼	30	32¼	34½	36½	38¾	40¾	42½
15.24	64	28	48	72	20	22½	25	27¼	29½	31¾	34	35¾	37¾	39½
15.56	64	32	56	72	19½	22	24½	27	29	31¼	33¼	35¼	37	39
15.75	56	64	72	40	19¼	21¾	24¼	26½	28¾	31	33	35	36¾	38½
16.87	72	32	48	64	18¼	20½	22¾	25	27	29¼	31¼	33¼	35	36½
17.14	64	32	48	56	17¾	20¼	22¼	24¾	26¾	29	30¾	32¾	34½	36
18.75	72	32	40	48	16¼	18½	20¾	22¾	25	26¾	28½	30¼	32	33¾
19.29	72	32	48	56	16	18¼	20¼	22¼	24	26	28	29¾	31½	33
19.59	64	28	48	56	15¾	18	20	22	23¾	25¾	27½	29¼	31	32¾
19.69	72	32	56	64	15¾	17¾	20	21¾	23¾	25½	27½	29¼	31	32½
21.43	72	24	40	56	14½	16½	18½	20¼	22	23¾	25½	27¼	29	30¼
22.50	72	28	56	64	13¾	15¾	17½	19¼	21	22¾	24½	26	27¾	29¼
23.33	64	32	56	48	13¼	15¼	17	18¾	20¼	22	23½	25¼	27	28¼
26.25	72	24	56	64	12	13½	15	16¾	18¼	19¾	21¼	22¾	24¼	25½
26.67	64	28	56	48	11¾	13¼	14¾	16½	18	19½	21	22¼	23¾	25¼
28.00	64	32	56	40	11¼	12¾	14¼	15¾	17¼	18¾	20	21½	22¾	24
30.86	72	28	48	40	10	11½	13	14¼	15½	17	18½	19½	21	22
31.50	72	32	56	40	10	11¼	12¾	14	15¼	16½	18	19¼	20½	21¾
36.00	72	32	64	40	8¾	10	11	12¼	13½	14¾	16	17	18¼	19¼
41.14	72	28	64	40	7¾	8¾	9¾	10¾	11¾	13	14	15	16	17
45.00	72	28	56	32	7	8	9	10	11	11¾	12¾	13¾	14¾	15½
48.00	72	24	64	40	6½	7½	8½	9¼	10¼	11¼	12	13	13¾	14½
51.43	72	28	64	32	6	7	7¾	8¾	9½	10½	11¼	12	12¾	13¾
60.00	72	24	64	32	5¼	6	6¾	7½	8¼	9	9½	10¼	11	11¾
68.57	72	24	64	28	4¼	5¼	5¾	6½	7¼	8	8½	9	9¾	10¼

Helix Angle for Given Lead and Diameter. — The table on this and the preceding page gives helix angles (relative to axis) equivalent to a range of leads and diameters. The expression " Diameter of Work " at the top of the table might mean pitch diameter or outside diameter, depending upon the class of work. Assume, for example, that a plain milling cutter 4 inches in diameter is to have helical teeth and a helix angle of about 25 degrees is desired. The table shows that this angle will be obtained approximately by using change-gears which will give a lead of 26.67 inches. As the outside diameter of the cutter is 4 inches, the helix angle of 25¼ degrees is at the tops of the teeth. The angles listed for different diameters are used in setting the table of a milling machine. In milling a right-hand helix (or cutter teeth which turn to the right as seen from the end of the cutter), swivel the right-hand end of the machine table toward the rear, and, inversely, for a left-hand helix, swivel the left-hand end of the table toward the rear. The angles in the table are based upon the following formula:

$$\text{Cot helix angle relative to axis} = \frac{\text{Lead of helix}}{3.1416 \times \text{diameter}}$$

Lead of Helix for Given Angle. — The lead of a helix or "spiral" for given angles measured with the axis of the work is given in the table, pages 1220–1222, for a diameter of 1. For other diameters, lead equals the value found in the table multiplied by the given diameter. Suppose the angle is 55 degrees, and the diameter 5 inches, what would be the lead? By referring to the table (Part 2), it is found that the lead for a diameter of 1 and an angle of 55 degrees 0 minutes equals 2.200. Multiply this value by 5; 5 × 2.200 = 11 inches, which is the required lead. If the lead and diameter are given, and the angle is wanted, divide the given lead by the given diameter, thus obtaining the lead for a diameter equal to 1; then find the angle corresponding to this lead in the table. If the lead and angle are given, and the diameter is wanted, divide the lead by the value in the table for the angle.

SIMPLE, COMPOUND, DIFFERENTIAL AND BLOCK INDEXING

Simple Indexing. — A general rule for determining the number of turns the crank of a dividing head must make, to obtain a given number of divisions, is as follows: Divide the number of turns required for one revolution of the dividing-head spindle by the number of divisions into which the periphery of the work is to be divided.

Example: — If 40 turns of the index crank are required for one revolution of the spindle, and 12 divisions are required, the number of turns of the index crank for each indexing would equal 40 ÷ 12 = 3⅓ turns.

Compound Indexing. — This method is sometimes used to obtain divisions which are beyond the range of those secured by the simple method. The crank is first turned a definite amount in the regular way, and then the index plate is also turned either in the same or opposite direction, in order to locate the index crank in the proper position. Thus, there are two separate movements which are, in reality, two simple indexing operations. The following rule is for determining what circles of holes can be used for indexing by the compound method.

Rule: Resolve into its factors the number of divisions required; then choose at random two circles of holes, subtract one from the other, and factor the difference; place the two sets of factors thus obtained above a horizontal line. Next factor the number of turns of the crank required for one revolution of the spindle, and also the number of holes in each of the chosen circles; place the three sets of factors thus obtained below the horizontal line. If all the factors *above* the line can be canceled by those below, the two circles chosen will give the required number of divisions; if not, other circles must be chosen and another trial made.

Example: — Assume that 69 divisions are required, and that circles having 33 and 23 holes are chosen for the first trial. Then, by applying the foregoing rule, it is found that all the factors above the line cancel:

$$\frac{3 \times 23 \times 2 \times 5}{2 \times 2 \times 2 \times 5 \times 3 \times 11 \times 23} = \frac{1}{2 \times 2 \times 11}$$

Compound Indexing *

No. of Divisions	Indexing Movements	No. of Times Around	No. of Divisions	Indexing Movements	No. of Times Around	No. of Divisions	Indexing Movements	No. of Times Around
51	$8\frac{4}{47}-1\frac{2}{49}$	11	133	$3\frac{23}{29}-16\frac{6}{53}$	11	198*	$\frac{3}{27}+\frac{3}{23}$	...
53	$6\frac{4}{47}-\frac{9}{49}$	9	134	$3\frac{27}{47}+1\frac{5}{49}$	13	199	$2\frac{13}{41}-\frac{5}{49}$	11
57	$4\frac{4}{47}+\frac{3}{49}$	7	137	$3\frac{17}{43}-\frac{9}{49}$	11	201	$2\frac{18}{47}+1\frac{9}{49}$	13
59	$7\frac{19}{47}+1\frac{2}{49}$	11	138*	$1\frac{1}{3}-\frac{1}{23}$	...	202	$3\frac{10}{41}+\frac{6}{49}$	17
61	$3\frac{4}{47}+\frac{2}{49}$	6	139	$2\frac{25}{37}+2\frac{4}{49}$	11	203	$1\frac{23}{59}+\frac{9}{49}$	9
63	$4\frac{19}{49}+1\frac{15}{53}$	8	141	$1\frac{32}{59}+2\frac{2}{49}$	8	204	$2\frac{29}{41}+\frac{3}{49}$	13
67	$2\frac{27}{41}+1\frac{9}{49}$	5	142	$4\frac{1}{47}+1\frac{9}{49}$	15	206	$2\frac{35}{59}+\frac{3}{49}$	15
69*	$2\frac{1}{23}-1\frac{1}{53}$	...	143	$1\frac{36}{47}-1\frac{8}{49}$	5	207	$3\frac{9}{41}-2\frac{5}{49}$	14
71	$3\frac{34}{41}-2\frac{7}{49}$	6	146	$2\frac{3}{37}-\frac{8}{49}$	7	208	$1\frac{19}{47}+1\frac{9}{49}$	9
73	$6\frac{28}{47}-\frac{1}{49}$	12	147*	$\frac{13}{29}-\frac{3}{49}$	...	209	$\frac{8}{49}+\frac{9}{41}$	2
77*	$\frac{9}{21}+\frac{3}{23}$	...	149	$3\frac{5}{43}-\frac{8}{49}$	11	211	$1\frac{25}{59}+1\frac{8}{49}$	11
79	$2\frac{42}{43}+\frac{3}{49}$	6	151	$1\frac{42}{43}-\frac{6}{49}$	7	212	$3\frac{5}{47}+\frac{9}{49}$	17
81	$5\frac{5}{41}-\frac{9}{49}$	10	153	$2\frac{45}{47}-\frac{5}{49}$	11	213	$1\frac{15}{59}+\frac{2}{49}$	8
83	$3\frac{45}{47}-\frac{5}{49}$	8	154*	$\frac{9}{21}-\frac{4}{23}$	...	214	$3\frac{9}{47}-1\frac{9}{49}$	15
87*	$\frac{23}{29}-1\frac{1}{53}$	...	157	$2\frac{23}{51}+\frac{2}{53}$	11	217	$2\frac{3}{43}+1\frac{9}{49}$	13
89	$3\frac{28}{29}-\frac{9}{49}$	8	158	$5\frac{5}{43}-1\frac{5}{49}$	19	218	$1\frac{2}{47}-\frac{9}{49}$	7
91*	$\frac{9}{49}+1\frac{5}{49}$	...	159	$2\frac{7}{37}+1\frac{9}{49}$	10	219	$3\frac{29}{43}-1\frac{9}{49}$	19
93*	$\frac{3}{21}+1\frac{1}{53}$	...	161	$2\frac{19}{29}-\frac{1}{49}$	9	221	$1\frac{5}{47}-\frac{1}{49}$	6
96*	$3\frac{1}{8}+\frac{5}{20}$	...	162	$1\frac{39}{59}-\frac{2}{49}$	7	222	$2\frac{9}{43}-1\frac{9}{49}$	11
97	$4\frac{27}{41}-\frac{9}{49}$	11	163	$3\frac{7}{37}-2\frac{4}{49}$	11	223	$2\frac{25}{43}+1\frac{3}{49}$	16
99*	$1\frac{5}{27}-\frac{5}{23}$	...	166	$1\frac{19}{43}+1\frac{2}{49}$	7	224	$2\frac{9}{23}+\frac{2}{53}$	13
101	$4\frac{32}{43}-1\frac{9}{49}$	11	167	$2\frac{1}{29}+\frac{5}{53}$	9	225*	$\frac{5}{18}-\frac{3}{20}$	...
102	$4\frac{17}{43}-\frac{5}{49}$	11	169	$1\frac{32}{37}+1\frac{3}{49}$	9	226	$1\frac{35}{59}+1\frac{9}{49}$	13
103	$1\frac{8}{43}+1\frac{8}{49}$	4	171	$1\frac{29}{47}+\frac{1}{49}$	7	227	$3\frac{3}{43}+\frac{5}{49}$	18
106	$2\frac{38}{41}+2\frac{3}{49}$	9	173	$1\frac{7}{43}+1\frac{1}{49}$	6	228	$2\frac{3}{41}-1\frac{3}{49}$	11
107	$2\frac{2}{51}-\frac{7}{23}$	7	174*	$1\frac{1}{33}-\frac{3}{29}$	...	229	$2\frac{19}{41}-1\frac{8}{49}$	12
109	$2\frac{19}{29}+\frac{5}{49}$	7	175	$1\frac{31}{41}+\frac{8}{53}$	6	231*	$\frac{3}{21}+\frac{1}{53}$	...
111	$3\frac{29}{47}+1\frac{7}{49}$	11	176	$1\frac{14}{43}+1\frac{3}{49}$	7	233	$1\frac{39}{47}+\frac{9}{49}$	11
112	$4\frac{19}{51}-1\frac{3}{53}$	11	177	$2\frac{19}{47}+\frac{4}{49}$	11	234	$2\frac{21}{29}+\frac{6}{53}$	17
113	$3\frac{26}{47}-1\frac{8}{49}$	9	178	$3\frac{28}{47}+1\frac{1}{49}$	17	236	$2\frac{39}{43}+\frac{9}{49}$	17
114	$1\frac{35}{37}+2\frac{5}{49}$	7	179	$2\frac{33}{47}-1\frac{3}{49}$	11	237	$2\frac{12}{47}-\frac{3}{49}$	13
117	$7\frac{1}{47}-\frac{9}{49}$	20	181	$2\frac{3}{43}+1\frac{2}{49}$	11	238	$2\frac{3}{51}+1\frac{1}{53}$	15
118	$1\frac{9}{29}+2\frac{4}{49}$	5	182*	$\frac{3}{29}+\frac{7}{49}$	...	239	$1\frac{23}{43}+1\frac{5}{49}$	11
119	$3\frac{1}{23}-1\frac{6}{53}$	8	183	$1\frac{24}{41}+\frac{8}{49}$	8	241	$1\frac{1}{41}+2\frac{3}{49}$	9
121	$1\frac{14}{47}-1\frac{5}{49}$	3	186*	$\frac{17}{51}-1\frac{1}{53}$	...	242	$2\frac{23}{41}-\frac{5}{49}$	15
122	$3\frac{41}{43}-1\frac{7}{49}$	11	187	$1\frac{29}{47}+1\frac{5}{49}$	8	243	$1\frac{29}{41}-\frac{3}{49}$	10
123	$1\frac{12}{43}+1\frac{7}{49}$	5	189	$2\frac{26}{41}-1\frac{5}{49}$	11	244	$2\frac{15}{51}+1\frac{19}{53}$	17
125	$2\frac{33}{41}-1\frac{2}{49}$	8	191	$1\frac{38}{47}+1\frac{4}{49}$	10	246	$1\frac{9}{43}-1\frac{6}{49}$	5
126	$3\frac{19}{19}-\frac{7}{20}$	11	192	$2\frac{22}{41}-1\frac{3}{49}$	11	247	$2\frac{15}{43}-\frac{5}{49}$	14
127	$2\frac{23}{29}+1\frac{2}{49}$	9	193	$1\frac{5}{37}-1\frac{5}{49}$	4	249	$3\frac{5}{43}-\frac{2}{49}$	19
129	$5\frac{24}{41}+1\frac{5}{49}$	19	194	$2\frac{22}{37}-1\frac{9}{49}$	11	250	$2\frac{9}{37}-\frac{8}{49}$	13
131	$2\frac{40}{43}+2\frac{1}{49}$	11	197	$1\frac{39}{43}+1\frac{9}{49}$	11	...	....	...

* The indexing movements are exact for the divisions marked with an asterisk (*); the errors of the other divisions are so slight as to be negligible for all ordinary classes of work, such as gear-cutting, etc.

This shows that these circles can be used. The factors 2, 2 and 11 remain uncanceled below the line. The amount the crank and index plate must be moved in their respective circles is next determined by multiplying together all these uncanceled factors. Thus $2 \times 2 \times 11 = 44$. This means that we can index $\frac{1}{19}$ revolution by turning the crank forward 44 holes in the 23-hole circle, and the index plate backward 44 holes in the 33-hole circle. The movement could also be forward 44 holes in the 33-hole circle and backward 44 holes in the 23-hole circle, without affecting the result. The movements obtained by the foregoing rule are expressed in compound indexing tables in the form of fractions, as, for example: $+ \frac{44}{23} - \frac{44}{33}$. The numerators represent the number of holes indexed and the denominators the circles used; the + and − signs show that the movements of the crank and index plate are opposite in direction. These fractions can often be reduced and simplified, so that it will not be necessary to move so many holes, by adding some number to them algebraically. The number is chosen by trial, and its sign should be opposite that of the fraction to which it is added. Suppose, for example, a fraction is added representing one complete turn, to each of the fractions referred to; then there will be a movement of 21 holes in the 23-hole circle, and a movement of 11 holes in the opposite direction, in the 33-hole circle.

Differential Indexing. — This method is the same, in principle, as compound indexing, but differs from the latter in that the index plate is rotated by suitable gearing which connects it to the spiral-head spindle. This rotation or differential motion of the index plate takes place when the crank is turned, the plate moving either in the same direction as the crank or opposite to it, as may be required. The result is that the *actual* movement of the crank, at every indexing, is either greater or less than its movement with relation to the index plate. The differential method makes it possible to obtain almost any division, by using only one circle of holes for that division and turning the index crank in one direction, the same as for plain indexing. The gears to use for moving the index plate the required amount (when gears are required) are shown by the tables, "Simple and Differential Indexing." This table shows what divisions can be obtained by plain indexing, and also when it is necessary to use gears and the differential system. For example, if 50 divisions are required, the 20-hole index circle is used and the crank is moved 16 holes, but no gears are required. For 51 divisions, a 24-tooth gear is placed on the worm-shaft and a 48-tooth gear is mounted on the spindle. These two gears are connected by two idler gears having 24 and 44 teeth, respectively. To illustrate the principle of differential indexing, suppose a dividing head is to be geared for 271 divisions. The table calls for a gear on the worm-shaft having 56 teeth; a spindle gear with 72 teeth; and a 24-toothed idler which serves to rotate the index plate in the same direction as the crank. The sector should be set for giving the crank a movement of 3 holes in the 21-hole circle. If the spindle and index plate were not connected through gearing, 280 divisions would be obtained by successively moving the crank 3 holes in the 21-hole circle, but the gears cause the index plate to turn in the same direction as the crank at such a rate that, when 271 indexings have been made, the work is turned one complete revolution; therefore, we have 271 divisions instead of 280, the number being reduced because the total movement of the crank, for each indexing, is equal to its movement relative to the index plate, *plus* the movement of the plate itself when (as in this case) the crank and plate rotate in the same direction. If they were rotated in opposite directions, the crank would have a total movement equal to that which it turned relative to the plate, *minus* the plate's movement. Sometimes it is necessary to use compound gearing, in order to move the index plate the required amount for each turn of the crank. The differential method cannot be used in connection with helical or spiral milling, because the spiral head is then geared to the lead-screw of the machine.

To Find Ratio of Gearing for Differential Indexing. — To find the gearing ratio for differential indexing, first select some approximate number A of divisions either greater or less than the required number N. To illustrate, if the required number N is 67, the approximate number A might be 70; then if 40 turns of the index crank are required for 1 revolution of the spindle,

$$\text{Gearing ratio } R = (A - N) \times \frac{40}{A}$$

If the approximate number A is less than N, the formula is the same as above except that $A - N$ is replaced by $N - A$.

Example: Find the gearing ratio and indexing movement for 67 divisions. If $A = 70$,

$$\text{Gearing ratio} = (70 - 67) \times \frac{40}{70} = \frac{12}{7} = \frac{\text{Gear on spindle (driver)}}{\text{Gear on worm (driven)}}$$

The fraction $\frac{12}{7}$ is raised to obtain a numerator and denominator equivalent to available gears. For example, $\frac{12}{7} = \frac{48}{28}$.

Various combinations of gearing and index circles are possible for a given number of divisions. The index movements and gear combinations in the accompanying table apply to a given series of index circles and gear-tooth numbers. The approximate number A upon which any combination is based may be determined by dividing 40 by the fraction representing the indexing movement. For example, the approximate number used for 109 divisions equals $40 \div \frac{6}{16}$ or $40 \times \frac{16}{6} = 106\frac{2}{3}$. If this approximate number is inserted in the preceding formula, it will be found that the gear ratio is $\frac{7}{8}$ as shown in the table.

Second Method of Determining Gear Ratio. — In illustrating a somewhat different method of determining the gear ratio, 67 divisions will again be used. If 70 is selected as the approximate number, then $\frac{40}{70} = \frac{4}{7}$ or $1\frac{2}{7}$ turn of the index crank will be required. If the crank is indexed four-sevenths of a turn sixty-seven times, it will make $\frac{4}{7} \times 67 = 38\frac{2}{7}$ revolutions. This is $1\frac{5}{7}$ turns less than the forty required for one revolution of the work (indicating that the gearing should be arranged to rotate the index plate in the same direction as the index crank to increase the indexing movement); hence the gear ratio $= 1\frac{5}{7} = \frac{12}{7}$.

To Find the Indexing Movement. — The indexing movement is represented by the fraction $\frac{40}{A}$. For example, if 70 is the approximate number A used in calculating the gear ratio for 67 divisions, then, to find the required movement of the index crank, reduce $\frac{40}{70}$ to any fraction of equal value and having as denominator any number equal to the number of holes available in an index circle. To illustrate,

$$\frac{40}{70} = \frac{4}{7} = \frac{12}{21} = \frac{\text{number of holes indexed}}{\text{number of holes in index circle}}$$

Use of Idler Gears. — In differential indexing, idler gears are used (1) to rotate the index plate in the same direction as the index crank, thus *increasing* the actual indexing movement, or (2) to rotate the index plate in the opposite direction, thus *reducing* the actual indexing movement.

Case 1: If the approximate number A is *greater* than the actual number of divisions N, simple gearing will require one idler, and compound gearing no idler. Index plate and crank rotate in the same direction.

Case 2: If the approximate number A is *less* than the actual number of divisions N, simple gearing requires two idlers, and compound gearing one idler. Index plate and crank rotate in opposite directions.

When Compound Gearing Is Required. — In some cases, as will be noted by referring to the table, it is necessary to use a train of four gears in order to obtain the required ratio with gear-tooth numbers in the available series.

Example: Find the gear combination and indexing movement for 99 divisions, assuming that an approximate number A of 100 is used.

$$\text{Ratio} = (100 - 99) \times \frac{40}{100} = \frac{4}{10} = \frac{4 \times 1}{5 \times 2} = \frac{32}{40} \times \frac{28}{56}$$

These final numbers conform to available gear sizes. The gears having 32 and 28 teeth are the drivers (gear on spindle and first gear on stud), and gears having 40 and 56 teeth are driven (second gear on stud and gear on worm). The indexing movement is represented by the fraction $\frac{40}{100}$ which is reduced to $\frac{8}{20}$, the 20-hole index circle being used in this case.

Example: Determine the gear combination to use for indexing 53 divisions. If 56 is used as an approximate number (possibly after one or more trial solutions to find an approximate number and resulting gear ratio coinciding with available gears).

$$\text{Gearing ratio} = (56 - 53) \times \frac{40}{56} = \frac{15}{7} = \frac{3 \times 5}{1 \times 7} = \frac{72 \times 40}{24 \times 56}$$

The tooth numbers above the line represent *gear on spindle* and *first gear on stud.* The numbers below the line represent *second gear on stud* and *gear on worm.*

$$\text{Indexing movement} = \frac{40}{56} = \frac{5}{7} = \frac{5 \times 7}{7 \times 7} = \frac{35 \text{ holes}}{49\text{-hole circle}}$$

In setting sector arms, do not count the hole containing the index crank pin.

To Check the Number of Divisions Obtained with a Given Gear Ratio and Index Movement. — Invert the fraction representing the indexing movement and let C equal this inverted fraction. R = gearing ratio.

Case 1: If simple gearing is used with one idler or compound gearing with no idler,

$$\text{Number of divisions } N = 40\,C - RC$$

Case 2: If simple gearing is used with two idlers or compound gearing with one idler,

$$\text{Number of divisions } N = 40\,C + RC$$

Example: The gear ratio is $\frac{12}{7}$; there is simple gearing and one idler (Case 1), and the indexing movement is $\frac{12}{21}$, making the inverted fraction $C = \frac{21}{12}$; find the number of divisions N

$$N = (40 \times \tfrac{21}{12}) - (\tfrac{12}{7} \times \tfrac{21}{12}) = 70 - \tfrac{21}{7} = 67$$

Example: The gear ratio is $\frac{7}{8}$; two idlers are used with simple gearing (Case 2) and the indexing movement is 6 holes in the 16-hole circle. Then

$$N = (40 \times \tfrac{16}{6}) + (\tfrac{7}{8} \times \tfrac{16}{6}) = 109$$

Simple and Differential Indexing — Brown & Sharpe Milling Machines

GEAR ON SPINDLE 64 T.
IDLER 24 T.
NO. 1 HOLE
NO. 2 HOLE
GEAR ON WORM 40 T.
GEARED FOR 107 DIVISIONS
2D GEAR ON STUD 32 T.
1ST GEAR ON STUD 56 T.
A
B

Note: Graduations in table indicate setting for sector arms when index crank moves through arc *A*, except figures marked *, when crank moves through arc *B*.

Note: Certain divisions such as 51, 53, 57, etc. are obtained by differential indexing. Change-gears are used to transmit motion from main spindle of dividing head to index plate which turns (either in the same direction as the index crank, or in the opposite direction) whatever amount is required to obtain the correct indexing movement.

Number of Divisions	Index Circle	Number of Turns of Crank	Graduation on Sector	Number of Divisions	Index Circle	Number of Turns of Crank	Graduation on Sector	Gear on Worm	First Gear on Stud	Second Gear on Stud	Gear on Spindle	No. 1 Hole	No. 2 Hole†
									No. 1 Hole	No. 1 Hole		Idlers	Idlers
2	Any	20	....	33	33	1 7/33	41						
3	39	13 13/39	65	34	17	1 3/17	33						
4	Any	10	....	35	49	1 7/49	26						
5	Any	8	....	36	27	1 3/27	21						
6	39	6 26/39	132	37	37	1 3/37	15						
7	49	5 35/49	140	38	19	1 1/19	9						
8	Any	5	....	39	39	1 1/39	3						
9	27	4 15/27	88	40	Any	1	...						
10	Any	4	....	41	41	40/41	3*						
11	33	3 21/33	126	42	21	20/21	9*						
12	39	3 13/39	65	43	43	40/43	12*						
13	39	3 3/39	14	44	33	30/33	17*						
14	49	2 42/49	169	45	27	24/27	21*						
15	39	2 26/39	132	46	23	20/23	172						
16	20	2 10/20	98	47	47	40/47	168						
17	17	2 6/17	69	48	18	15/18	165						
18	27	2 6/27	43	49	49	40/49	161						
19	19	2 2/19	19	50	20	16/20	158						
20	Any	2	....	51	17	14/17	33*	24	...	...	48	24	44
21	21	1 19/21	18*	52	39	30/39	152	...	...	...	...	...	...
22	33	1 27/33	161	53	49	35/49	140	56	40	24	72	...	...
23	23	1 17/23	147	54	27	20/27	147	...	...	...	...	...	...
24	39	1 26/39	132	55	33	24/33	144	...	...	...	...	...	...
25	20	1 15/20	118	56	49	35/49	140	56	...	...	40	24	44
26	39	1 21/39	106	57	21	15/21	142	...	...	...	...	...	...
27	27	1 18/27	95	58	29	20/29	136	...	...	...	...	...	...
28	49	1 21/49	83	59	39	26/39	132	48	...	...	32	44	...
29	29	1 11/29	75	60	39	26/39	132	...	...	...	...	...	...
30	39	1 13/39	65	61	39	26/39	132	48	...	...	32	24	44
31	31	1 9/31	56	62	31	20/31	127	...	...	...	...	...	...
32	20	1 5/20	48	63	39	26/39	132	24	...	...	48	24	44

† On Nos. 1, 1½ and 2 machines, No. 2 hole is in machine table. On Nos. 3 and 4 machines, No. 2 hole is in head.

Simple and Differential Indexing

No. of Divisions	Index Circle	No. of Turns of Crank	Graduation on Sector	Gear on Worm	No. 1 Hole		Gear on Spindle	Idlers	
					First Gear on Stud	Second Gear on Stud		No. 1 Hole	No. 2 Hole
64	16	$\frac{10}{16}$	123	....	....	....	....	....	....
65	39	$\frac{24}{39}$	121	....	....	....	....	....	....
66	33	$\frac{20}{33}$	120	....	....	....	....	....	....
67	21	$\frac{12}{21}$	113	28	....	....	48	44	....
68	17	$\frac{10}{17}$	116	....	....	....	....	....	....
69	20	$\frac{12}{20}$	118	40	....	....	56	24	44
70	49	$\frac{28}{49}$	112	....	....	....	....	....	....
71	18	$\frac{10}{18}$	109	72	....	....	40	24	....
72	27	$\frac{15}{27}$	110	....	....	....	....	....	....
73	21	$\frac{12}{21}$	113	28	....	....	48	24	44
74	37	$\frac{20}{37}$	107	....	....	....	....	....	....
75	15	$\frac{8}{15}$	105	....	....	....	....	....	....
76	19	$\frac{10}{19}$	103	....	....	....	....	....	....
77	20	$\frac{10}{20}$	98	32	....	....	48	44	....
78	39	$\frac{20}{39}$	101	....	....	....	....	....	....
79	20	$\frac{10}{20}$	98	48	....	....	24	44	....
80	20	$\frac{10}{20}$	98	....	....	....	....	....	....
81	20	$\frac{10}{20}$	98	48	....	....	24	24	44
82	41	$\frac{20}{41}$	96	....	....	....	....	....	....
83	20	$\frac{10}{20}$	98	32	....	....	48	24	44
84	21	$\frac{10}{21}$	94	....	....	....	....	....	....
85	17	$\frac{8}{17}$	92	....	....	....	....	....	....
86	43	$\frac{20}{43}$	91	....	....	....	....	....	....
87	15	$\frac{7}{15}$	92	40	....	....	24	24	44
88	33	$\frac{15}{33}$	89	....	....	....	....	....	....
89	18	$\frac{8}{18}$	87	72	....	....	32	44	....
90	27	$\frac{12}{27}$	88	....	....	....	....	....	....
91	39	$\frac{18}{39}$	91	24	....	....	48	24	44
92	23	$\frac{10}{23}$	86	....	....	....	....	....	....
93	18	$\frac{8}{18}$	87	24	....	....	32	24	44
94	47	$\frac{20}{47}$	83	....	....	....	....	....	....
95	19	$\frac{8}{19}$	82	....	....	....	....	....	....
96	21	$\frac{9}{21}$	85	28	....	....	32	24	44
97	20	$\frac{8}{20}$	78	40	....	....	48	44	....
98	49	$\frac{20}{49}$	79	....	....	....	....	....	....
99	20	$\frac{8}{20}$	78	56	28	40	32	....	....
100	20	$\frac{8}{20}$	78	....	....	....	....	....	....
101	20	$\frac{8}{20}$	78	72	24	40	48	....	24
102	20	$\frac{8}{20}$	78	40	....	....	32	24	44
103	20	$\frac{8}{20}$	78	40	....	....	48	24	44
104	39	$\frac{15}{39}$	75	....	....	....	....	....	....
105	21	$\frac{8}{21}$	75	....	....	....	....	....	....
106	43	$\frac{16}{43}$	73	86	24	24	48	....	....

Simple and Differential Indexing

No. of Divisions	Index Circle	No. of Turns of Crank	Graduation on Sector	Gear on Worm	No. 1 Hole		Gear on Spindle	Idlers	
					First Gear on Stud	Second Gear on Stud		No. 1 Hole	No. 2 Hole
107	20	8/20	78	40	56	32	64	....	24
108	27	10/27	73	....	....	....	....	....	....
109	16	9/16	73	32	....	....	28	24	44
110	33	12/33	71	....	....	....	....	....	....
111	39	13/39	65	24	....	....	72	32	....
112	39	13/39	65	24	....	....	64	44	....
113	39	13/39	65	24	....	....	56	44	....
114	39	13/39	65	24	....	....	48	44	....
115	23	8/23	68	....	....	....	....	....	....
116	29	10/29	68	....	....	....	....	....	....
117	39	13/39	65	24	....	....	24	56	....
118	39	13/39	65	48	....	....	32	44	....
119	39	13/39	65	72	....	....	24	44	....
120	39	13/39	65	....	....	....	....	....	....
121	39	13/39	65	72	....	....	24	24	44
122	39	13/39	65	48	....	....	32	24	44
123	39	13/39	65	24	....	....	24	24	44
124	31	10/31	63	....	....	....	....	....	....
125	39	13/39	65	24	....	....	40	24	44
126	39	13/39	65	24	....	....	48	24	44
127	39	13/39	65	24	....	....	56	24	44
128	16	5/16	61	....	....	....	....	....	....
129	39	13/39	65	24	....	....	72	24	44
130	39	12/39	60	....	....	....	....	....	....
131	20	9/20	58	40	....	....	28	44	....
132	33	10/33	59	....	....	....	....	....	....
133	21	9/21	56	24	....	....	48	44	....
134	21	9/21	56	28	....	....	48	44	....
135	27	8/27	58	....	....	....	....	....	....
136	17	5/17	57	....	....	....	....	....	....
137	21	9/21	56	28	....	....	24	56	....
138	21	9/21	56	56	....	....	32	44	....
139	21	9/21	56	56	32	48	24	....	....
140	49	14/49	55	....	....	....	....	....	....
141	18	5/18	54	48	....	....	40	44	....
142	21	9/21	56	56	....	....	32	24	44
143	21	9/21	56	28	....	....	24	24	44
144	18	5/18	54	....	....	....	....	....	....
145	29	8/29	54	....	....	....	....	....	....
146	21	9/21	56	28	....	....	48	24	44
147	21	9/21	56	24	....	....	48	24	44
148	37	10/37	53	....	....	....	....	....	....
149	21	9/21	56	28	....	....	72	24	44

Simple and Differential Indexing

No. of Divisions	Index Circle	No. of Turns of Crank	Graduation on Sector	Gear on Worm	No. 1 Hole		Gear on Spindle	Idlers	
					First Gear on Stud	Second Gear on Stud		No. 1 Hole	No. 2 Hole
150	15	4/15	52	....	....	....		....	....
151	20	5/20	48	32	....	....	72	44	....
152	19	5/19	51	....	....	....		....	....
153	20	5/20	48	32	....	....	56	44	....
154	20	5/20	48	32	....	....	48	44	....
155	31	8/31	50	....	....	....	....	....	....
156	39	10/39	50	....	....	....	....	....	....
157	20	5/20	48	32	....	....	24	56	....
158	20	5/20	48	48	....	....	24	44	....
159	20	5/20	48	64	32	56	28	....	....
160	20	5/20	48	....	....	....		....	....
161	20	5/20	48	64	32	56	28	....	24
162	20	5/20	48	48	....	....	24	24	44
163	20	5/20	48	32	....	....	24	24	44
164	41	10/41	47	....	....	....	....	....	....
165	33	8/33	47	....	....	....	....	....	....
166	20	5/20	48	32	....	....	48	24	44
167	20	5/20	48	32	....	....	56	24	44
168	21	5/21	47	....	....	....	....	....	....
169	20	5/20	48	32	....	....	72	24	44
170	17	4/17	45	....	....	....		....	....
171	21	5/21	47	56	....	....	40	24	44
172	43	10/43	44	....	....	....	....	....	....
173	18	4/18	43	72	56	32	64	....	....
174	18	4/18	43	24	....	....	32	56	....
175	18	4/18	43	72	40	32	64	....	....
176	18	4/18	43	72	24	24	64	....	....
177	18	4/18	43	72	....	....	48	24	....
178	18	4/18	43	72	....	....	32	44	....
179	18	4/18	43	72	24	48	32	....	....
180	18	4/18	43	....	....	....	....	....	....
181	18	4/18	43	72	24	48	32	....	24
182	18	4/18	43	72	....	....	32	24	44
183	18	4/18	43	48	....	....	32	24	44
184	23	5/23	42	....	....	....	....	....	....
185	37	8/37	42	....	....	....	....	....	....
186	18	4/18	43	48	....	....	64	24	44
187	18	4/18	43	72	48	24	56	....	24
188	47	10/47	40	....	....	....	....	....	....
189	18	4/18	43	32	....	....	64	24	44
190	19	4/19	40	....	....	....		....	....
191	20	4/20	38	40	....	....	72	24	....
192	20	4/20	38	40	....	....	64	44	....

Simple and Differential Indexing

No. of Divisions	Index Circle	No. of Turns of Crank	Graduation on Sector	Gear on Worm	No. 1 Hole		Gear on Spindle	Idlers	
					First Gear on Stud	Second Gear on Stud		No. 1 Hole	No. 2 Hole
193	20	4/20	38	40	....	....	56	44	....
194	20	4/20	38	40	....	....	48	44	....
195	39	8/39	39	....	....	....	....	....	....
196	49	10/49	38	....	....	....	....	....	....
197	20	4/20	38	40	....	....	24	56	....
198	20	4/20	38	56	28	40	32	....	....
199	20	4/20	38	100	40	64	32	....	....
200	20	4/20	38	....	....	....	....	....	....
201	20	4/20	38	72	24	40	24	....	24
202	20	4/20	38	72	24	40	48	....	24
203	20	4/20	38	40	....	....	24	24	44
204	20	4/20	38	40	....	....	32	24	44
205	41	8/41	37	....	....	....	....	....	....
206	20	4/20	38	40	....	....	48	24	44
207	20	4/20	38	40	....	....	56	24	44
208	20	4/20	38	40	....	....	64	24	44
209	20	4/20	38	40	....	....	72	24	44
210	21	4/21	37	....	....	....	....	....	....
211	16	3/16	36	64	....	....	28	44	....
212	43	8/43	35	86	24	24	48	....	....
213	27	5/27	36	72	....	....	40	44	....
214	20	4/20	38	40	56	32	64	....	24
215	43	8/43	35	....	....	....	....	....	....
216	27	5/27	36	....	....	....	....	....	....
217	21	4/21	37	48	....	....	64	24	44
218	16	3/16	36	64	....	....	56	24	44
219	21	4/21	37	28	....	....	48	24	44
220	33	6/33	35	....	....	....	....	....	....
221	17	3/17	33	24	....	....	24	56	....
222	18	3/18	32	24	....	....	72	44	....
223	43	8/43	35	86	48	24	64	....	24
224	18	3/18	32	24	....	....	64	44	....
225	27	5/27	36	24	....	....	40	24	44
226	18	3/18	32	24	....	....	56	44	....
227	49	8/49	30	56	64	28	72	....	....
228	18	3/18	32	24	....	....	48	44	....
229	18	3/18	32	24	....	....	44	48	....
230	23	4/23	34	....	....	....	....	....	....
231	18	3/18	32	32	....	....	48	44	....
232	29	5/29	33	....	....	....	....	....	....
233	18	3/18	32	48	....	....	56	44	....
234	18	3/18	32	24	....	....	24	56	....
235	47	8/47	32	....	....	....	....	....	....

Simple and Differential Indexing

No. of Divisions	Index Circle	No. of Turns of Crank	Graduation on Sector	Gear on Worm	No. 1 Hole		Gear on Spindle	Idlers	
					First Gear on Stud	Second Gear on Stud		No. 1 Hole	No. 2 Hole
236	18	8/18	32	48	....	....	32	44	....
237	18	8/18	32	48	....	....	24	44	....
238	18	8/18	32	72	....	....	24	44	....
239	18	8/18	32	72	24	64	32	....	....
240	18	8/18	32	....	....	....	....	....	....
241	18	8/18	32	72	24	64	32	....	24
242	18	8/18	32	72	....	....	24	24	44
243	18	8/18	32	64	....	....	32	24	44
244	18	8/18	32	48	....	....	32	24	44
245	49	8/49	30	....	....	....	....	....	....
246	18	8/18	32	24	....	....	24	24	44
247	18	8/18	32	48	....	....	56	24	44
248	31	5/31	31	....	....	....	....	....	....
249	18	8/18	32	32	....	....	48	24	44
250	18	8/18	32	24	....	....	40	24	44
251	18	8/18	32	48	44	32	64	....	24
252	18	8/18	32	24	....	....	48	24	44
253	33	5/33	29	24	....	....	40	56	....
254	18	8/18	32	24	....	....	56	24	44
255	18	8/18	32	48	40	24	72	....	24
256	18	8/18	32	24	....	....	64	24	44
257	49	8/49	30	56	48	28	64	....	24
258	43	7/43	31	32	....	....	64	24	44
259	21	8/21	28	24	....	....	72	44	....
260	39	9/39	29	....	....	....	....	....	....
261	29	4/29	26	48	64	24	72	....	....
262	20	3/20	28	40	....	....	28	44	....
263	49	8/49	30	56	64	28	72	....	24
264	33	5/33	29	....	....	....	....	....	....
265	21	3/21	28	56	40	24	72	....	....
266	21	3/21	28	32	....	....	64	44	....
267	27	4/27	28	72	....	....	32	44	....
268	21	3/21	28	28	....	....	48	44	....
269	20	3/20	28	64	32	40	28	....	24
270	27	4/27	28	....	....	....	....	....	....
271	21	3/21	28	56	24	24	72	....	....
272	21	3/21	28	56	....	....	64	24	....
273	21	3/21	28	24	....	....	24	56	....
274	21	3/21	28	56	....	....	48	44	....
275	21	3/21	28	56	....	....	40	44	....
276	21	3/21	28	56	....	....	32	44	....
277	21	3/21	28	56	....	....	24	44	....
278	21	3/21	28	56	32	48	24	....	....

Simple and Differential Indexing

No. of Divisions	Index Circle	No. of Turns of Crank	Graduation on Sector	Gear on Worm	No. 1 Hole		Gear on Spindle	Idlers	
					First Gear on Stud	Second Gear on Stud		No. 1 Hole	No. 2 Hole
279	27	4/27	28	24	....	....	32	24	44
280	49	7/49	26	....	....	....	....	....	....
281	21	8/21	28	72	24	56	24	....	24
282	43	6/43	26	86	24	24	56	....	....
283	21	8/21	28	56	....	....	24	24	44
284	21	8/21	28	56	....	....	32	24	44
285	21	8/21	28	56	....	....	40	24	44
286	21	8/21	28	56	....	....	48	24	44
287	21	8/21	28	24	....	....	24	24	44
288	21	8/21	28	28	....	....	32	24	44
289	21	8/21	28	56	24	24	72	....	24
290	29	4/29	26	....	....	....	....	....	....
291	15	2/15	25	40	....	....	48	44	....
292	21	8/21	28	28	....	....	48	24	44
293	15	2/15	25	48	32	40	56	....	....
294	21	8/21	28	24	....	....	48	24	44
295	15	2/15	25	48	....	....	32	44	....
296	37	5/37	26	....	....	....	....	....	....
297	33	4/33	23	28	48	24	56	....	....
298	21	8/21	28	28	....	....	72	24	44
299	23	8/23	25	24	....	....	24	56	....
300	15	2/15	25	....	....	....	....	....	....
301	43	6/43	26	24	....	....	48	24	44
302	16	2/16	24	32	....	....	72	24	....
303	15	2/15	25	72	24	40	48	....	24
304	16	2/16	24	24	....	....	48	44	....
305	15	2/15	25	48	....	....	32	24	44
306	15	2/15	25	40	....	....	32	24	44
307	15	2/15	25	72	48	40	56	....	24
308	16	2/16	24	32	....	....	48	44	....
309	15	2/15	25	40	....	....	48	24	44
310	31	4/31	24	....	....	....	....	....	....
311	16	2/16	24	64	24	24	72	....	....
312	39	5/39	24	....	....	....	....	....	....
313	16	2/16	24	32	....	....	28	56	....
314	16	2/16	24	32	....	....	24	56	....
315	16	2/16	24	64	....	....	40	24	....
316	16	2/16	24	64	....	....	32	44	....
317	16	2/16	24	64	....	....	24	44	....
318	16	2/16	24	56	28	48	24	....	....
319	29	4/29	26	48	64	24	72	....	24
320	16	2/16	24	....	....	....	....	....	....
321	16	2/16	24	72	24	64	24	....	24

Simple and Differential Indexing

No. of Divisions	Index Circle	No. of Turns of Crank	Gradution on Sector	Gear on Worm	No. 1 Hole		Gear on Spindle	Idlers	
					First Gear on Stud	Second Gear on Stud		No. 1 Hole	No. 2 Hole
322	23	8/23	25	32	....	....	64	24	44
323	16	2/16	24	64	....	....	24	24	44
324	16	2/16	24	64	....	....	32	24	44
325	16	2/16	24	64	....	....	40	24	44
326	16	2/16	24	32	....	....	24	24	44
327	16	2/16	24	32	....	....	28	24	44
328	41	5/41	23	....	....	....	....	....	....
329	16	2/16	24	64	24	24	72	....	24
330	33	4/33	23	....	....	....	....	....	....
331	16	2/16	24	64	44	24	48	....	24
332	16	2/16	24	32	....	....	48	24	44
333	18	2/18	21	24	....	....	72	44	....
334	16	2/16	24	32	....	....	56	24	44
335	33	4/33	23	72	48	44	40	....	24
336	16	2/16	24	32	....	....	64	24	44
337	43	5/43	21	86	40	32	56	....	....
338	16	2/16	24	32	....	....	72	24	44
339	18	2/18	21	24	....	....	56	44	....
340	17	2/17	22	....	....	....	....	....	....
341	43	5/43	21	86	24	32	40	....	....
342	18	2/18	21	32	....	....	64	44	....
343	15	2/15	25	40	64	24	86	....	24
344	43	5/43	21	....	....	....	....	....	....
345	18	2/18	21	24	....	....	40	56	....
346	18	2/18	21	72	56	32	64	....	....
347	43	5/43	21	86	24	32	40	....	24
348	18	2/18	21	24	....	....	32	56	....
349	18	2/18	21	72	44	24	48	....	....
350	18	2/18	21	72	40	32	64	....	....
351	18	2/18	21	24	....	....	24	56	....
352	18	2/18	21	72	24	24	64	....	....
353	18	2/18	21	72	24	24	56	....	....
354	18	2/18	21	72	....	....	48	24	....
355	18	2/18	21	72	....	....	40	24	....
356	18	2/18	21	72	....	....	32	24	....
357	18	2/18	21	72	....	....	24	44	....
358	18	2/18	21	72	32	48	24	....	....
359	43	5/43	21	86	48	32	100	....	24
360	18	2/18	21	....	....	....	....	....	....
361	19	2/19	19	32	....	....	64	44	....
362	18	2/18	21	72	28	56	32	....	24
363	18	2/18	21	72	....	....	24	24	44
364	18	2/18	21	72	....	....	32	24	44

Indexing Movements for Standard Index Plate — Cincinnati Milling Machine

The standard index plate indexes all numbers up to and including 60; all even numbers and those divisible by 5 up to 120; and all divisions listed below up to 400. This plate is drilled on both sides, and has holes as follows:

First side: 24, 25, 28, 30, 34, 37, 38, 39, 41, 42, 43.

Second side: 46, 47, 49, 51, 53, 54, 57, 58, 59, 62, 66.

No. of Divisions	Circle	Turns	Holes	No. of Divisions	Circle	Holes	No. of Divisions	Circle	Holes	No. of Divisions	Circle	Holes
2	Any	20	...	44	66	60	104	39	15	205	41	8
3	24	13	8	45	54	48	105	42	16	210	42	8
4	Any	10	...	46	46	40	106	53	20	212	53	10
5	Any	8	...	47	47	40	108	54	20	215	43	8
6	24	6	16	48	24	20	110	66	24	216	54	10
7	28	5	20	49	49	40	112	28	10	220	66	12
8	Any	5	...	50	25	20	114	57	20	224	28	5
9	54	4	24	51	51	40	115	46	16	228	57	10
10	Any	4	...	52	39	30	116	58	20	230	46	8
11	66	3	42	53	53	40	118	59	20	232	58	10
12	24	3	8	54	54	40	120	66	22	235	47	8
13	39	3	3	55	66	48	124	62	20	236	59	10
14	49	2	42	56	28	20	125	25	8	240	66	11
15	24	2	16	57	57	40	130	39	12	245	49	8
16	24	2	12	58	58	40	132	66	20	248	62	10
17	34	2	12	59	59	40	135	54	16	250	25	4
18	54	2	12	60	42	28	136	34	10	255	51	8
19	38	2	4	62	62	40	140	28	8	260	39	6
20	Any	2	...	64	24	15	144	54	15	264	66	10
21	42	1	38	65	39	24	145	58	16	270	54	8
22	66	1	54	66	66	40	148	37	10	272	34	5
23	46	1	34	68	34	20	150	30	8	280	28	4
24	24	1	16	70	28	16	152	38	10	290	58	8
25	25	1	15	72	54	30	155	62	16	296	37	5
26	39	1	21	74	37	20	156	39	10	300	30	4
27	54	1	26	75	30	16	160	28	7	304	38	5
28	42	1	18	76	38	20	164	41	10	310	62	8
29	58	1	22	78	39	20	165	66	16	312	39	5
30	24	1	8	80	34	17	168	42	10	320	24	3
31	62	1	18	82	41	20	170	34	8	328	41	5
32	28	1	7	84	42	20	172	43	10	330	66	8
33	66	1	14	85	34	16	176	66	15	336	42	5
34	34	1	6	86	43	20	180	54	12	340	34	4
35	28	1	4	88	66	30	184	46	10	344	43	5
36	54	1	6	90	54	24	185	37	8	360	54	6
37	37	1	3	92	46	20	188	47	10	368	46	5
38	38	1	2	94	47	20	190	38	8	370	37	4
39	39	1	1	95	38	16	192	24	5	376	47	5
40	Any	1	...	96	24	10	195	39	8	380	38	4
41	41	...	40	98	49	20	196	49	10	390	39	4
42	42	...	40	100	25	10	200	30	6	392	49	5
43	43	...	40	102	51	20	204	51	10	400	30	3

Indexing Movements for High Numbers — Cincinnati Milling Machine

This set of 3 index plates indexes all numbers up to and including 200; all even numbers and those divisible by 5 up to and including 400. The plates are drilled on each side, making six sides A, B, C, D, E and F.

Example: — It is required to index 35 divisions. The preferred side is F, since this requires the least number of holes; but should one of plates D, A or E be in place, either can be used, thus avoiding the changing of plates.

No. of Divisions	Side	Circle	Turns	Holes	No. of Divisions	Side	Circle	Turns	Holes	No. of Divisions	Side	Circle	Turns	Holes
2	Any	Any	20	....	15	C	93	2	62	28	D	77	1	33
3	A	30	13	10	15	F	159	2	106	28	A	91	1	39
3	B	36	13	12	16	E	26	2	13	29	E	87	1	33
3	E	42	13	14	16	F	28	2	14	30	A	30	1	10
3	C	93	13	31	16	A	30	2	15	30	B	36	1	12
3	F	159	13	53	16	D	32	2	16	30	E	42	1	14
4	Any	Any	10	....	16	C	34	2	17	30	C	93	1	31
5	Any	Any	8	....	16	B	36	2	18	30	F	159	1	53
6	A	30	6	20	17	C	34	2	21	31	C	93	1	27
6	B	36	6	24	17	E	119	2	42	32	F	28	1	7
6	E	42	6	28	17	C	153	2	54	32	D	32	1	8
6	C	93	6	62	17	F	187	2	66	32	B	36	1	9
6	F	159	6	106	18	B	36	2	8	32	A	48	1	12
7	F	28	5	20	18	A	99	2	22	33	A	99	1	21
7	E	42	5	30	18	C	153	2	34	34	C	34	1	6
7	D	77	5	55	19	F	38	2	4	34	E	119	1	21
7	A	91	5	65	19	E	133	2	14	34	F	187	1	33
8	Any	Any	5	....	19	A	171	2	18	35	F	28	1	4
9	B	36	4	16	20	Any	Any	2	....	35	D	77	1	11
9	A	99	4	44	21	E	42	1	38	35	A	91	1	13
9	C	153	4	68	21	A	147	1	133	35	E	119	1	17
10	Any	Any	4	....	22	D	44	1	36	36	B	36	1	4
11	D	44	3	28	22	A	99	1	81	36	A	99	1	11
11	A	99	3	63	22	F	143	1	117	36	C	153	1	17
11	F	143	3	91	23	C	46	1	34	37	B	111	1	9
12	A	30	3	10	23	A	69	1	51	38	F	38	1	2
12	B	36	3	12	23	E	161	1	119	38	E	133	1	7
12	E	42	3	14	24	A	30	1	20	38	A	171	1	9
12	C	93	3	31	24	B	36	1	24	39	A	117	1	3
12	F	159	3	53	24	E	42	1	28	40	Any	Any	1	....
13	E	26	3	2	24	C	93	1	62	41	C	123	....	120
13	A	91	3	7	24	F	159	1	106	42	E	42	....	40
13	F	143	3	11	25	A	30	1	18	42	A	147	....	140
13	B	169	3	13	25	E	175	1	105	43	A	129	....	120
14	F	28	2	24	26	F	26	1	14	44	D	44	....	40
14	E	42	2	36	26	A	91	1	49	44	A	99	....	90
14	D	77	2	66	26	B	169	1	91	44	F	143	....	130
14	A	91	2	78	27	B	81	1	39	45	B	36	....	32
15	A	30	2	20	27	A	189	1	91	45	A	99	....	88
15	B	36	2	24	28	F	28	1	12	45	C	153	....	136
15	E	42	2	28	28	E	42	1	18	46	C	46	....	40

Indexing Movements for High Numbers — Cincinnati Milling Machine

No. of Divisions	Side	Circle	Holes	No. of Divisions	Side	Circle	Holes	No. of Divisions	Side	Circle	Holes
46	A	69	60	70	E	119	68	96	B	36	15
46	E	161	140	71	F	71	40	96	A	48	20
47	B	141	120	72	B	36	20	97	B	97	40
48	A	30	25	72	A	117	65	98	A	147	60
48	B	36	30	72	C	153	85	99	A	99	40
49	A	147	120	73	E	73	40	100	A	30	12
50	A	30	24	74	B	111	60	100	E	175	70
50	E	175	140	75	A	30	16	101	F	101	40
51	C	153	120	76	F	38	20	102	C	153	60
52	E	26	20	76	E	133	70	103	E	103	40
52	A	91	70	76	A	171	90	104	E	26	10
52	F	143	110	77	D	77	40	104	A	91	35
52	B	169	130	78	A	117	60	104	F	143	55
53	F	159	120	79	C	79	40	104	B	169	65
54	B	81	60	80	E	26	13	105	E	42	16
54	A	189	140	80	F	28	14	105	A	147	56
55	D	44	32	80	A	30	15	106	F	159	60
55	F	143	104	80	D	32	16	107	D	107	40
56	F	28	20	80	C	34	17	108	B	81	30
56	E	42	30	80	B	36	18	108	A	189	70
56	D	77	55	80	E	42	21	109	C	109	40
56	A	91	65	81	B	81	40	110	D	44	16
57	A	171	120	82	C	123	60	110	A	99	36
58	E	87	60	83	F	83	40	110	F	143	52
59	A	177	120	84	E	42	20	111	B	111	40
60	A	30	20	84	A	147	70	112	F	28	10
60	B	36	24	85	C	34	16	112	E	42	15
60	E	42	28	85	E	119	56	113	F	113	40
60	F	159	106	85	F	187	88	114	A	171	60
61	B	183	120	86	A	129	60	115	C	46	16
62	C	93	60	87	E	87	40	115	A	69	24
63	A	189	120	88	D	44	20	115	E	161	56
64	D	32	20	88	A	99	45	116	E	87	30
64	A	48	30	88	F	143	65	117	A	117	40
65	E	26	16	89	D	89	40	118	A	177	60
65	A	91	56	90	B	36	16	119	E	119	40
65	F	143	88	90	A	99	44	120	A	30	10
65	B	169	104	90	C	153	68	120	B	36	12
66	A	99	60	91	A	91	40	120	E	42	14
67	B	67	40	92	C	46	20	120	C	93	31
68	C	34	20	92	A	69	30	120	F	159	53
68	E	119	70	92	E	161	70	121	D	121	40
68	F	187	110	93	C	93	40	122	B	183	60
69	A	69	40	94	B	141	60	123	C	123	40
70	F	28	16	95	F	38	16	124	C	93	30
70	D	42	24	95	E	133	56	125	E	175	56
70	A	91	52	95	A	171	72	126	A	189	60

Indexing Movements for High Numbers—Cincinnati Milling Machine

No. of Divisions	Side	Circle	Holes	No. of Divisions	Side	Circle	Holes	No. of Divisions	Side	Circle	Holes
127	B	127	40	160	A	48	12	198	A	99	20
128	D	32	10	161	E	161	40	199	B	199	40
128	A	48	15	162	B	81	20	200	A	30	6
129	A	129	40	163	D	163	40	200	E	175	35
130	E	26	8	164	C	123	30	202	F	101	20
130	A	91	28	165	A	99	24	204	C	153	30
130	F	143	44	166	F	83	20	205	C	123	24
130	B	169	52	167	C	167	40	206	E	103	20
131	F	131	40	168	E	42	10	208	E	26	5
132	A	99	30	168	A	147	35	210	E	42	8
133	E	133	40	169	B	169	40	210	A	147	28
134	B	67	20	170	C	34	8	212	F	159	30
135	B	81	24	170	E	119	28	214	D	107	20
135	A	189	56	170	F	187	44	215	A	129	24
136	C	34	10	171	A	171	40	216	B	81	15
136	E	119	35	172	A	129	30	216	A	189	35
137	D	137	40	173	F	173	40	218	C	109	20
138	A	69	20	174	E	87	20	220	D	44	8
139	C	139	40	175	E	175	40	220	A	99	18
140	F	28	8	176	D	44	10	220	F	143	26
140	E	42	12	177	A	177	40	222	B	111	20
140	D	77	22	178	D	89	20	224	F	28	5
140	A	91	26	179	D	179	40	226	F	113	20
141	B	141	40	180	B	36	8	228	A	171	30
142	F	71	20	180	A	99	22	230	C	46	8
143	F	143	40	180	C	153	34	230	A	69	12
144	B	36	10	181	C	181	40	230	E	161	28
145	E	87	24	182	A	91	20	232	E	87	15
146	E	73	20	183	B	183	40	234	A	117	20
147	A	147	40	184	C	46	10	235	B	141	24
148	B	111	30	184	A	69	15	236	A	177	30
149	E	149	40	184	E	161	35	238	E	119	20
150	A	30	8	185	B	111	24	240	A	30	5
151	D	151	40	186	C	93	20	240	B	36	6
152	F	38	10	187	F	187	40	240	E	42	7
152	E	133	35	188	B	141	30	240	A	48	8
152	A	171	45	189	A	189	40	242	D	121	20
153	C	153	40	190	F	38	8	244	B	183	30
154	D	77	20	190	E	133	28	245	A	147	24
155	C	93	24	190	A	171	36	246	C	123	20
156	A	117	30	191	E	191	40	248	C	93	15
157	B	157	40	192	A	48	10	250	E	175	28
158	C	79	20	193	D	193	40	252	A	189	30
159	F	159	40	194	B	97	20	254	B	127	20
160	F	28	7	195	A	117	24	255	C	153	24
160	D	32	8	196	A	147	30	256	D	32	5
160	B	36	9	197	C	197	40	258	A	129	20

Indexing Movements for High Numbers — Cincinnati Milling Machine

No. of Divisions	Side	Circle	Holes	No. of Divisions	Side	Circle	Holes	No. of Divisions	Side	Circle	Holes
260	E	26	4	304	F	38	5	354	A	177	20
260	A	91	14	305	B	183	24	355	F	71	8
260	F	143	22	306	C	153	20	356	D	89	10
260	B	169	26	308	D	77	10	358	D	179	20
262	F	131	20	310	C	93	12	360	B	36	4
264	A	99	15	312	A	117	15	360	A	99	11
265	F	159	24	314	B	157	20	360	C	153	17
266	E	133	20	315	A	189	24	362	C	181	20
268	B	67	10	316	C	79	10	364	A	91	10
270	B	81	12	318	F	159	20	365	E	73	8
270	A	189	28	320	D	32	4	366	B	183	20
272	C	34	5	320	A	48	6	368	C	46	5
274	D	137	20	322	E	161	20	370	B	111	12
276	A	69	10	324	B	81	10	372	C	93	10
278	C	139	20	326	D	163	20	374	F	187	20
280	F	28	4	328	C	123	15	376	B	141	15
280	E	42	6	330	A	99	12	378	A	189	20
280	D	77	11	332	F	83	10	380	F	38	4
280	A	91	13	334	C	167	20	380	E	133	14
282	B	141	20	335	B	67	8	380	A	171	18
284	F	71	10	336	E	42	5	382	E	191	20
285	A	171	24	338	B	169	20	384	A	48	5
286	F	143	20	340	C	34	4	385	D	77	8
288	B	36	5	340	E	119	14	386	D	193	20
290	E	87	12	340	F	187	22	388	B	97	10
292	E	73	10	342	A	171	20	390	A	117	12
294	A	147	20	344	A	129	15	392	A	147	15
295	A	177	24	345	A	69	8	394	C	197	20
296	B	111	15	346	F	173	20	395	C	79	8
298	E	149	20	348	E	87	10	396	A	99	10
300	A	30	4	350	E	175	20	398	B	199	20
302	D	151	20	352	D	44	5	400	A	30	3

Angular Indexing. — With the ordinary indexing head, in which 40 turns of the index crank are required for one revolution of the work, one turn of the index crank equals 9 degrees. Hence, when one complete turn of the index crank equals 9 degrees, two holes in the 18-hole circle, or 3 holes in the 27-hole circle, must correspond to one degree. The first principle or rule for indexing for angles is therefore that two holes in the 18-hole circle or 3 holes in the 27-hole circle equals a movement of one degree of the index head spindle and the work.

Assume that an indexing movement of 35 degrees is required. One complete turn of the index crank equals 9 degrees; therefore, first divide the number of degrees for which to index, by 9, in order to find how many complete turns the index crank should make. The number of degrees left to turn after having completed the full turns are indexed by taking two holes in the 18-hole circle for each degree. In this case, $\frac{35}{9} = 3\frac{8}{9}$, which indicates that the index crank must be turned three full revolutions, and then 8 degrees more are indexed by moving 16 holes in the 18-hole circle.

To index for 11½ degrees, for example, first turn the index crank one revolution, this being a 9-degree movement. Then to index 2½ degrees, move the index crank 5 holes in the 18-hole circle (4 holes for the two whole degrees and one hole for the ½ degree equals the total movement of 5 holes).

Below is shown how this calculation may be carried out to plainly indicate the movement required for this angle:

11½ deg. = 9 deg. + 2 deg. + ½ deg.
1 turn + 4 holes + 1 hole in the 18-hole circle.

Should it be required to index only ⅓ degree, this may be done by using the 27-hole circle. In this circle a three-hole movement equals one degree, and a one-hole movement in that circle thus equals ⅓ degree, or 20 minutes. Assume that it is required to index the work through an angle of 48 degrees 40 minutes. Below is plainly shown how this calculation may be carried out:

48 deg. 40 min. = 45 deg. + 3 deg. + 40 min.
5 turns + 9 holes + 2 holes in the 27-hole circle.

Angular Values of One-Hole Moves — B. & S. Index Plates

15-hole circle = 36 minutes	29-hole circle = 18.620 minutes
16-hole circle = 33.750 minutes	31-hole circle = 17.419 minutes
17-hole circle = 31.764 minutes	33-hole circle = 16.363 minutes
18-hole circle = 30 minutes	37-hole circle = 14.594 minutes
19-hole circle = 28.421 minutes	39-hole circle = 13.846 minutes
20-hole circle = 27 minutes	41-hole circle = 13.170 minutes
21-hole circle = 25.714 minutes	47-hole circle = 11.489 minutes
23-hole circle = 23.478 minutes	49-hole circle = 11.020 minutes
27-hole circle = 20 minutes	....

Approximate Indexing for Angles. — The following general rule for *approximate* indexing of small angles is applicable to any index head requiring 40 revolutions of the index crank for one revolution of the work.

Rule: Divide 540 by the total number of minutes to be indexed. If the quotient is approximately equal to the number of holes in any index circle available, the angular movement is obtained by moving the crank one hole in this index circle; but if the quotient is not approximately equal, multiply it by any trial number which will give a product equal to the number of holes in an available index circle and move the index crank as many holes as are indicated by the trial number. (If the quotient of 540 divided by the total number of minutes is greater than the number of holes in any of the index circles, it is not possible to obtain the required movement for the angle by simple indexing.)

Example: — Assume that it is required to index to an angle of 2 degrees 46 minutes. Changing this to minutes gives a total of 166 minutes. Dividing 540 by 166 we have 540 ÷ 166 = 3.253. This quotient is next multiplied by some trial number to obtain a product which equals the number of holes in an available index circle. Multiplying by 12, we have 3.253 × 12 = 39.036. Therefore, for indexing 2 degrees 46 minutes, the 39-hole circle can be used and the index crank would be moved 12 holes.

Tables for Angular Indexing. — The table, "Angular Indexing," gives the number of turns of the index crank for indexing various angles. In the column headed, "Turns of Index Crank," the whole number (where given) indicates the number of full revolutions; the numerator of the fraction, the number of holes additional; and the denominator, the number of holes in the index circle to be used. The angular movement obtained for a movement of one hole, in various index plates is given in the table, "Angular Values of One-Hole Moves."

Angular Indexing

Angle in Degs.	Turns of Index Crank	Angle in Degs.	Turns of Index Crank	Angle in Degs.	Turns of Index Crank	Angle in Degs.	Turns of Index Crank	Angle in Degs.	Turns of Index Crank
1	2/18	10	1 7/18	19	2 9/18	28	3 7/18	37	4 7/18
1 1/3	4/27	10 1/3	1 4/27	19 1/3	2 4/27	28 1/3	3 4/27	37 1/3	4 4/27
1 1/2	3/18	10 1/2	1 8/18	19 1/2	2 8/18	28 1/2	3 8/18	37 1/2	4 8/18
1 2/3	5/27	10 2/3	1 5/27	19 2/3	2 5/27	28 2/3	3 5/27	37 2/3	4 5/27
2	4/18	11	1 4/18	20	2 4/18	29	3 4/18	38	4 4/18
2 1/3	7/27	11 1/3	1 7/27	20 1/3	2 7/27	29 1/3	3 7/27	38 1/3	4 7/27
2 1/2	5/18	11 1/2	1 5/18	20 1/2	2 5/18	29 1/2	3 5/18	38 1/2	4 5/18
2 2/3	8/27	11 2/3	1 8/27	20 2/3	2 8/27	29 2/3	3 8/27	38 2/3	4 8/27
3	6/18	12	1 6/18	21	2 6/18	30	3 6/18	39	4 6/18
3 1/3	10/27	12 1/3	1 10/27	21 1/3	2 10/27	30 1/3	3 10/27	39 1/3	4 10/27
3 1/2	7/18	12 1/2	1 7/18	21 1/2	2 7/18	30 1/2	3 7/18	39 1/2	4 7/18
3 2/3	11/27	12 2/3	1 11/27	21 2/3	2 11/27	30 2/3	3 11/27	39 2/3	4 11/27
4	8/18	13	1 8/18	22	2 8/18	31	3 8/18	40	4 8/18
4 1/3	13/27	13 1/3	1 13/27	22 1/3	2 13/27	31 1/3	3 13/27	40 1/3	4 13/27
4 1/2	9/18	13 1/2	1 9/18	22 1/2	2 9/18	31 1/2	3 9/18	40 1/2	4 9/18
4 2/3	14/27	13 2/3	1 14/27	22 2/3	2 14/27	31 2/3	3 14/27	40 2/3	4 14/27
5	10/18	14	1 10/18	23	2 10/18	32	3 10/18	41	4 10/18
5 1/3	16/27	14 1/3	1 16/27	23 1/3	2 16/27	32 1/3	3 16/27	41 1/3	4 16/27
5 1/2	11/18	14 1/2	1 11/18	23 1/2	2 11/18	32 1/2	3 11/18	41 1/2	4 11/18
5 2/3	17/27	14 2/3	1 17/27	23 2/3	2 17/27	32 2/3	3 17/27	41 2/3	4 17/27
6	12/18	15	1 12/18	24	2 12/18	33	3 12/18	42	4 12/18
6 1/3	19/27	15 1/3	1 19/27	24 1/3	2 19/27	33 1/3	3 19/27	42 1/3	4 19/27
6 1/2	13/18	15 1/2	1 13/18	24 1/2	2 13/18	33 1/2	3 13/18	42 1/2	4 13/18
6 2/3	20/27	15 2/3	1 20/27	24 2/3	2 20/27	33 2/3	3 20/27	42 2/3	4 20/27
7	14/18	16	1 14/18	25	2 14/18	34	3 14/18	43	4 14/18
7 1/3	22/27	16 1/3	1 22/27	25 1/3	2 22/27	34 1/3	3 22/27	43 1/3	4 22/27
7 1/2	15/18	16 1/2	1 15/18	25 1/2	2 15/18	34 1/2	3 15/18	43 1/2	4 15/18
7 2/3	23/27	16 2/3	1 23/27	25 2/3	2 23/27	34 2/3	3 23/27	43 2/3	4 23/27
8	16/18	17	1 16/18	26	2 16/18	35	3 16/18	44	4 16/18
8 1/3	25/27	17 1/3	1 25/27	26 1/3	2 25/27	35 1/3	3 25/27	44 1/3	4 25/27
8 1/2	17/18	17 1/2	1 17/18	26 1/2	2 17/18	35 1/2	3 17/18	44 1/2	4 17/18
8 2/3	26/27	17 2/3	1 26/27	26 2/3	2 26/27	35 2/3	3 26/27	44 2/3	4 26/27
9	1	18	2	27	3	36	4	45	5
9 1/3	1 1/27	18 1/3	2 1/27	27 1/3	3 1/27	36 1/3	4 1/27	45 1/3	5 1/27
9 1/2	1 1/18	18 1/2	2 1/18	27 1/2	3 1/18	36 1/2	4 1/18	45 1/2	5 1/18
9 2/3	1 2/27	18 2/3	2 2/27	27 2/3	3 2/27	36 2/3	4 2/27	45 2/3	5 2/27

Accurate Angular Indexing Movements — 1 *

Fractional Indexing Movement	B. & S., Becker, Hendey, K. & T. and Rockford	Cincinnati and LeBlond *
0.0152	.....	1/66
0.0161	.....	1/62
0.0169	.....	1/59
0.0172	.....	1/58
0.0175	.....	1/57
0.0185	.....	1/54
0.0189	.....	1/53
0.0196	.....	1/51
0.0204	1/49	1/49
0.0213	1/47	1/47
0.0217	.....	1/46
0.0233	1/43	1/43
0.0238	.....	1/42
0.0244	1/41	1/41
0.0256	1/39	1/39
0.0263	.....	1/38
0.0270	1/37	1/37
0.0294	.....	1/34
0.0303	1/33	2/66
0.0323	1/31	2/62
0.0333	.....	1/30
0.0338	.....	2/59
0.0345	1/29	2/58
0.0351	.....	2/57
0.0357	.....	1/28
0.0370	1/27	2/54
0.0377	.....	2/53
0.0392	.....	2/51
0.0400	.....	1/25
0.0408	2/49	2/49
0.0417	.....	1/24
0.0426	2/47	2/47
0.0435	1/23	2/46
0.0454	.....	3/66
0.0465	2/43	2/43
0.0476	1/21	2/42
0.0484	.....	3/62
0.0488	2/41	2/41
0.0500	1/20	.....
0.0508	.....	3/59
0.0513	2/39	2/39
0.0517	.....	3/58
0.0526	1/19	2/38
0.0526	.....	3/57
0.0541	2/37	2/37
0.0556	1/18	3/54
0.0566	.....	3/53
0.0588	1/17	3/51
0.0588	.....	3/51
0.0606	2/33	4/66
0.0612	3/49	3/49
0.0625	1/16	.....
0.0638	3/47	3/47
0.0645	2/31	4/62
0.0652	.....	3/46
0.0667	.....	2/30
0.0678	.....	4/59
0.0690	2/29	4/58
0.0698	3/43	3/43
0.0702	.....	4/57
0.0714	.....	2/28
0.0714	.....	3/42
0.0732	3/41	3/41
0.0741	2/27	4/54
0.0755	.....	4/53
0.0758	.....	5/66
0.0769	3/39	3/39
0.0784	.....	4/51
0.0789	.....	3/38
0.0800	.....	2/25
0.0806	.....	5/62
0.0811	3/37	3/37
0.0816	4/49	4/49
0.0833	.....	2/24
0.0847	.....	5/59
0.0851	4/47	4/47
0.0862	.....	5/58
0.0870	2/23	4/46
0.0877	.....	5/57
0.0882	.....	3/34
0.0909	3/33	6/66
0.0926	.....	5/54
0.0930	4/43	4/43
0.0943	.....	5/53
0.0952	2/21	4/42
0.0968	3/31	6/62
0.0976	4/41	4/41
0.0980	.....	5/51
0.1000	2/20	3/30
0.1017	.....	6/59
0.1020	5/49	5/49
0.1026	4/39	4/39
0.1034	3/29	6/58
0.1053	2/19	4/38
0.1053	.....	6/57
0.1061	.....	7/66
0.1064	5/47	5/47
0.1071	.....	3/28
0.1081	4/37	4/37
0.1087	.....	5/46
0.1111	2/18	.....
0.1111	3/27	6/54
0.1129	.....	7/62
0.1132	.....	6/53
0.1163	5/43	5/43
0.1176	2/17	4/34
0.1176	.....	6/51
0.1186	.....	7/59
0.1190	.....	5/42
0.1200	.....	3/25
0.1207	.....	7/58
0.1212	4/33	8/66
0.1220	5/41	5/41
0.1224	6/49	6/49
0.1228	.....	7/57
0.1250	2/16	3/24
0.1277	6/47	6/47
0.1282	5/39	5/39
0.1290	4/31	8/62
0.1296	.....	7/54
0.1304	3/23	6/46
0.1316	.....	5/38
0.1321	.....	7/53
0.1333	2/15	4/30
0.1351	5/37	5/37
0.1356	.....	8/59
0.1364	.....	9/66
0.1372	.....	7/51
0.1379	4/29	8/58
0.1395	6/43	6/43
0.1404	.....	8/57
0.1429	.....	4/28

* See explanatory note below Table 8.

Accurate Angular Indexing Movements — 2 *

Fractional Indexing Movement	B. & S., Becker, Hendey, K. & T. and Rockford	Cincinnati and LeBlond *	Fractional Indexing Movement	B. & S., Becker, Hendey, K. & T. and Rockford	Cincinnati and LeBlond *	Fractional Indexing Movement	B. & S., Becker, Hendey, K. & T. and Rockford	Cincinnati and LeBlond *
0.1429	3/21	9/42	0.1864	.....	11/59	0.2308	9/39	9/39
0.1429	7/49	7/49	0.1875	3/16	.....	0.2326	10/43	10/43
0.1452	.....	9/62	0.1887	.....	10/53	0.2333	.....	7/30
0.1463	9/41	9/41	0.1892	7/37	7/37	0.2340	11/47	11/47
0.1471	.....	5/34	0.1897	.....	11/58	0.2353	4/17	8/34
0.1481	9/27	9/64	0.1905	4/21	8/42	0.2353	.....	12/51
0.1489	7/47	7/47	0.1915	9/47	9/47	0.2368	.....	9/38
0.1500	3/20	.....	0.1930	.....	11/57	0.2373	.....	14/59
0.1509	.....	8/53	0.1935	9/31	.....	0.2381	5/21	10/42
0.1515	5/33	10/66	0.1951	8/41	.....	0.2391	.....	11/46
0.1522	.....	7/46	0.1957	.....	9/46	0.2400	.....	9/25
0.1525	.....	9/59	0.1961	.....	10/51	0.2407	.....	13/54
0.1538	9/49	9/59	0.1970	.....	13/66	0.2414	7/29	14/58
0.1552	.....	9/58	0.2000	3/15	5/25	0.2419	.....	15/62
0.1569	.....	8/51	0.2000	4/20	9/45	0.2424	8/33	16/66
0.1579	3/19	9/48	0.2034	.....	12/59	0.2432	9/37	9/37
0.1579	.....	9/57	0.2037	.....	11/54	0.2439	10/41	10/41
0.1600	.....	4/25	0.2041	10/49	10/49	0.2449	12/49	12/49
0.1613	5/31	10/62	0.2051	.....	8/39	0.2453	.....	13/53
0.1622	6/37	9/37	0.2059	.....	7/34	0.2456	.....	14/57
0.1628	7/43	7/43	0.2069	6/29	12/58	0.2500	4/16	9/24
0.1633	8/49	8/49	0.2075	.....	11/53	0.2500	5/20	7/28
0.1667	3/18	11/66	0.2083	.....	5/24	0.2542	.....	15/59
0.1667	.....	9/54	0.2093	9/43	9/43	0.2549	.....	13/51
0.1667	.....	7/42	0.2097	.....	13/62	0.2553	12/47	12/47
0.1667	.....	5/30	0.2105	4/19	8/38	0.2558	11/43	11/43
0.1667	.....	4/24	0.2105	.....	12/57	0.2564	10/39	10/39
0.1695	.....	10/59	0.2121	7/33	14/66	0.2576	.....	17/66
0.1698	.....	9/53	0.2128	10/47	10/47	0.2581	8/31	16/62
0.1702	8/47	8/47	0.2143	.....	9/42	0.2586	.....	15/58
0.1707	7/41	7/41	0.2143	.....	6/28	0.2593	7/27	14/54
0.1724	5/29	10/58	0.2157	.....	11/51	0.2609	6/23	12/46
0.1739	4/23	8/46	0.2162	8/37	8/37	0.2619	.....	11/42
0.1754	.....	10/57	0.2174	5/23	10/46	0.2632	5/19	10/38
0.1765	3/17	9/54	0.2195	9/41	9/41	0.2632	.....	15/57
0.1765	.....	9/51	0.2203	.....	13/59	0.2642	.....	14/53
0.1774	.....	11/62	0.2222	4/18	.....	0.2647	.....	9/34
0.1786	.....	5/28	0.2222	6/27	.....	0.2653	13/49	13/49
0.1795	7/39	7/39	0.2241	.....	13/58	0.2667	4/15	8/30
0.1818	6/33	12/66	0.2245	11/49	11/49	0.2683	11/41	11/41
0.1839	9/49	9/49	0.2258	7/31	14/62	0.2703	10/37	10/37
0.1842	.....	7/38	0.2264	.....	12/53	0.2712	.....	16/59
0.1852	5/27	10/64	0.2273	.....	15/66	0.2727	9/33	18/66
0.1860	8/43	8/43	0.2281	.....	13/57	0.2742	.....	17/62

* See explanatory note below Table 8.

Accurate Angular Indexing Movements — 3 *

Fractional Indexing Movement	B. & S., Becker Hendey, K. & T. and Rockford	Cincinnati and LeBlond *	Fractional Indexing Movement	B. & S., Becker, Hendey, K. & T. and Rockford	Cincinnati and LeBlond *	Fractional Indexing Movement	B. & S., Becker, Hendey, K. & T. and Rockford	Cincinnati and LeBlond *
0.2745	....	14/51	0.3191	15/47	15/47	0.3617	17/47	17/47
0.2759	8/29	19/58	0.3200	....	8/25	0.3621	....	21/58
0.2766	13/47	13/47	0.3208	....	17/53	0.3636	12/33	24/66
0.2778	5/18	15/54	0.3214	....	9/28	0.3659	15/41	15/41
0.2791	12/43	12/43	0.3220	....	19/59	0.3667	....	11/30
0.2800	....	7/25	0.3226	10/31	20/62	0.3673	18/49	18/49
0.2807	....	16/57	0.3235	....	11/34	0.3684	7/19	14/38
0.2821	11/39	11/39	0.3243	12/37	12/37	0.3684	....	21/57
0.2826	....	13/46	0.3256	14/43	14/43	0.3696	....	17/46
0.2830	....	15/53	0.3261	....	15/46	0.3704	10/27	20/54
0.2857	....	8/28	0.3265	16/49	16/49	0.3710	....	23/62
0.2857	14/49	14/49	0.3276	....	19/58	0.3721	16/43	16/43
0.2857	9/21	12/42	0.3333	6/18	8/24	0.3725	....	19/51
0.2879	....	19/66	0.3333	5/15	19/30	0.3729	....	22/59
0.2881	....	17/59	0.3333	13/39	13/39	0.3750	6/16	9/24
0.2895	....	11/38	0.3333	7/21	14/42	0.3774	....	20/53
0.2903	9/31	18/62	0.3333	....	17/51	0.3784	14/37	14/37
0.2917	....	7/24	0.3333	9/27	18/54	0.3788	....	25/66
0.2927	12/41	12/41	0.3333	....	19/57	0.3793	11/29	22/58
0.2931	....	17/58	0.3333	11/33	22/66	0.3810	8/21	16/42
0.2941	....	15/51	0.3387	....	21/62	0.3824	....	13/34
0.2941	5/17	10/34	0.3390	....	20/59	0.3830	18/47	18/47
0.2963	8/27	16/54	0.3396	....	18/53	0.3846	15/39	15/39
0.2973	11/37	11/37	0.3404	16/47	16/47	0.3860	....	22/57
0.2979	14/47	14/47	0.3415	14/41	14/41	0.3871	12/31	24/62
0.2982	....	17/57	0.3421	....	13/38	0.3878	19/49	19/49
0.3000	6/20	9/30	0.3448	10/29	20/58	0.3889	7/18	21/54
0.3019	....	16/53	0.3469	17/49	17/49	0.3898	....	23/59
0.3023	13/43	13/43	0.3478	8/23	16/46	0.3902	16/41	16/41
0.3030	10/33	20/66	0.3485	....	23/66	0.3913	9/23	18/46
0.3043	7/23	14/46	0.3488	15/43	15/43	0.3922	....	20/51
0.3051	....	18/59	0.3500	7/20	....	0.3929	....	11/28
0.3061	15/49	15/49	0.3509	....	20/57	0.3939	13/33	26/66
0.3065	....	19/62	0.3514	13/37	13/37	0.3947	....	15/38
0.3077	12/39	12/39	0.3519	....	19/54	0.3953	17/43	17/43
0.3095	....	13/42	0.3529	9/17	12/34	0.3962	....	21/53
0.3103	9/29	18/58	0.3529	....	18/51	0.3966	....	23/58
0.3125	5/16	....	0.3548	11/31	22/62	0.4000	6/15	10/25
0.3137	....	16/51	0.3559	....	21/59	0.4000	8/20	12/30
0.3148	....	17/54	0.3571	....	10/28	0.4032	....	25/62
0.3158	9/19	12/38	0.3571	....	15/42	0.4035	....	23/57
0.3158	....	18/57	0.3585	....	19/53	0.4043	19/47	19/47
0.3171	13/41	13/41	0.3590	14/39	14/39	0.4048	....	17/42
0.3182	....	21/66	0.3600	....	9/25	0.4054	15/37	15/37

* See explanatory note below Table 8.

Accurate Angular Indexing Movements — 4 *

Fractional Indexing Movement	B. & S., Becker, Hendey, K. & T. and Rockford	Cincinnati and LeBlond *	Fractional Indexing Movement	B. & S., Becker, Hendey, K. & T. and Rockford	Cincinnati and LeBlond *	Fractional Indexing Movement	B. & S., Becker, Hendey, K. & T. and Rockford	Cincinnati and LeBlond *
0.4068		24/59	0.4490	22/49	22/49	0.4912		28/57
0.4074	11/27	22/54	0.4500	9/20		0.4915		29/59
0.4082	20/49	20/49	0.4510		23/51	0.5000	8/16	12/24
0.4091		27/66	0.4516	14/31	28/62	0.5000	9/18	14/28
0.4103	16/39	16/39	0.4524		19/42	0.5000	10/20	15/30
0.4118	7/17	14/34	0.4528		24/53	0.5000		17/34
0.4118		21/51	0.4545	15/33	30/66	0.5000		19/38
0.4130		19/46	0.4561		26/57	0.5000		21/42
0.4138	12/29	24/58	0.4565		21/46	0.5000		23/46
0.4146	17/41	17/41	0.4576		27/59	0.5000		27/54
0.4151		22/53	0.4583		11/24	0.5000		29/58
0.4167		10/24	0.4595	17/37	17/37	0.5000		31/62
0.4186	18/43	18/43	0.4615	18/39	18/39	0.5000		33/66
0.4194	13/31	26/62	0.4630		25/54	0.5085		30/59
0.4211	8/19	16/38	0.4634	19/41	19/41	0.5088		29/57
0.4211		24/57	0.4643		13/28	0.5094		27/53
0.4237		25/59	0.4651	20/43	20/43	0.5098		26/51
0.4242	14/33	28/66	0.4655		27/58	0.5102	25/49	25/49
0.4255	20/47	20/47	0.4667	7/15	14/30	0.5106	24/47	24/47
0.4259		23/54	0.4677		29/62	0.5116	22/43	22/43
0.4286		12/28	0.4681	22/47	22/47	0.5122	21/41	21/41
0.4286	9/21	18/42	0.4694	23/49	23/49	0.5128	20/39	20/39
0.4286	21/49	21/49	0.4697		31/66	0.5135	19/37	19/37
0.4310		25/58	0.4706	8/17	16/34	0.5152	17/33	34/66
0.4314		22/51	0.4706		24/51	0.5161	16/31	32/62
0.4324	16/37	16/37	0.4717		25/53	0.5172	15/29	30/58
0.4333		13/30	0.4737	9/19	27/57	0.5185	14/27	28/54
0.4340		23/53	0.4746		28/59	0.5200		13/25
0.4348	10/23	20/46	0.4762	10/21	20/42	0.5217	12/23	24/46
0.4355		27/62	0.4783	11/23	22/46	0.5238	11/21	22/42
0.4359	17/39	17/39	0.4800		12/25	0.5254		31/59
0.4375	7/16		0.4814		26/54	0.5263	10/19	20/38
0.4386		25/57	0.4815	13/27		0.5263		30/57
0.4390	18/41	18/41	0.4828	14/29	28/58	0.5283		28/53
0.4394		29/66	0.4839	15/31	30/62	0.5294	9/17	18/34
0.4400		11/25	0.4848	16/33	32/66	0.5294		27/51
0.4407		26/59	0.4865	18/37	18/37	0.5303		35/66
0.4412		15/34	0.4872	19/39	19/39	0.5306	26/49	26/49
0.4419	19/43	19/43	0.4878	20/41	20/41	0.5319	25/47	25/47
0.4444	8/18		0.4884	21/43	21/43	0.5323		33/62
0.4444	12/27	24/54	0.4894	23/47	23/47	0.5333	8/15	16/30
0.4468	21/47	21/47	0.4898	24/49	24/49	0.5345		31/58
0.4474		17/38	0.4902		25/51	0.5349	23/43	23/43
0.4483	13/29	26/58	0.4906		26/53	0.5357		15/28

* See explanatory note below, Table 8.

Accurate Angular Indexing Movements — 5 *

Fractional Indexing Movement	B. & S., Becker, Hendey, K. & T. and Rockford	Cincinnati and LeBlond *	Fractional Indexing Movement	B. & S., Becker, Hendey, K. & T. and Rockford	Cincinnati and LeBlond *	Fractional Indexing Movement	B. & S., Becker, Hendey, K. & T. and Rockford	Cincinnati and LeBlond *
0.5366	22/41	22/41	0.5789	....	33/57	0.6250	10/16	15/24
0.5370	....	29/54	0.5806	18/31	36/62	0.6271	....	37/59
0.5385	21/39	21/39	0.5814	25/43	25/43	0.6275	....	32/51
0.5405	20/37	20/37	0.5833	....	14/24	0.6279	27/43	27/43
0.5417	....	13/24	0.5849	....	31/53	0.6290	....	39/62
0.5424	....	32/59	0.5854	24/41	24/41	0.6296	17/27	34/54
0.5435	....	25/46	0.5862	17/29	34/58	0.6304	....	29/46
0.5439	....	31/57	0.5870	....	27/46	0.6316	12/19	24/38
0.5455	18/33	39/66	0.5882	10/17	....	0.6316	....	36/57
0.5472	....	29/53	0.5882	....	20/34	0.6327	31/49	31/49
0.5476	....	23/42	0.5897	23/39	23/39	0.6333	....	19/30
0.5484	17/31	34/62	0.5909	....	39/66	0.6341	26/41	26/41
0.5490	....	28/51	0.5918	29/49	29/49	0.6364	21/33	42/66
0.5500	11/20	....	0.5926	16/27	....	0.6379	....	37/58
0.5510	27/49	27/49	0.5932	....	35/59	0.6383	30/47	30/47
0.5517	19/29	32/58	0.5946	22/37	22/37	0.6400	....	16/25
0.5526	....	21/38	0.5952	....	25/42	0.6410	25/39	25/39
0.5532	29/47	29/47	0.5957	28/47	28/47	0.6415	....	34/53
0.5556	10/18	....	0.5965	....	34/57	0.6429	....	18/28
0.5556	15/27	39/54	0.5968	....	37/62	0.6429	....	27/42
0.5581	24/43	24/43	0.6000	9/15	15/25	0.6441	....	38/59
0.5588	....	19/34	0.6000	12/20	18/30	0.6452	20/31	40/62
0.5593	....	33/59	0.6034	....	35/58	0.6471	11/17	22/34
0.5600	....	14/25	0.6038	....	32/53	0.6471	....	33/51
0.5606	....	37/66	0.6047	26/43	26/43	0.6481	....	35/54
0.5610	23/41	23/41	0.6053	....	23/38	0.6486	24/37	24/37
0.5614	....	32/57	0.6061	20/33	40/66	0.6491	....	37/57
0.5625	9/16	....	0.6071	....	17/28	0.6500	13/20	....
0.5641	22/39	22/39	0.6078	....	31/51	0.6512	28/43	28/43
0.5645	....	35/62	0.6087	14/23	28/46	0.6515	....	43/66
0.5652	13/23	26/46	0.6098	25/41	25/41	0.6522	15/23	30/46
0.5660	....	30/53	0.6102	....	36/59	0.6531	32/49	32/49
0.5667	....	17/30	0.6111	11/18	33/54	0.6552	19/29	38/58
0.5676	21/37	21/37	0.6122	30/49	30/49	0.6579	....	25/38
0.5686	....	29/51	0.6129	19/31	38/62	0.6585	27/41	27/41
0.5690	....	33/58	0.6140	....	35/57	0.6596	31/47	31/47
0.5714	....	16/28	0.6154	24/39	24/39	0.6604	....	35/53
0.5714	12/21	24/42	0.6170	29/47	29/47	0.6610	....	39/59
0.5714	28/49	28/49	0.6176	....	21/34	0.6613	....	41/62
0.5741	....	31/54	0.6190	13/21	26/42	0.6667	12/18	16/24
0.5745	27/47	27/47	0.6207	18/29	36/58	0.6667	10/15	20/30
0.5758	19/33	38/66	0.6212	....	41/66	0.6667	20/30	26/39
0.5763	....	34/59	0.6216	23/37	23/37	0.6667	14/21	28/42
0.5789	11/19	22/38	0.6226	....	33/53	0.6667	....	34/51

* See explanatory note below Table 8.

Accurate Angular Indexing Movements — 6 *

Fractional Indexing Movement	B. & S., Becker, Hendey, K. & T. and Rockford	Cincinnati and LeBlond *	Fractional Indexing Movement	B. & S., Becker, Hendey, K. & T. and Rockford	Cincinnati and LeBlond *	Fractional Indexing Movement	B. & S., Becker, Hendey, K. & T. and Rockford	Cincinnati and LeBlond *
0.6667	$\frac{18}{27}$	$\frac{36}{54}$	0.7119	.....	$\frac{42}{59}$	0.7576	$\frac{25}{33}$	$\frac{50}{66}$
0.6667	.....	$\frac{38}{57}$	0.7121	.....	$\frac{47}{66}$	0.7581	.....	$\frac{47}{62}$
0.6667	$\frac{22}{33}$	$\frac{44}{66}$	0.7143	.....	$\frac{20}{28}$	0.7586	$\frac{22}{29}$	$\frac{44}{58}$
0.6724	.....	$\frac{39}{58}$	0.7143	$\frac{15}{21}$	$\frac{30}{42}$	0.7593	.....	$\frac{41}{54}$
0.6735	$\frac{33}{49}$	$\frac{33}{49}$	0.7143	$\frac{35}{49}$	$\frac{35}{49}$	0.7600	.....	$\frac{19}{25}$
0.6739	.....	$\frac{31}{46}$	0.7170	.....	$\frac{38}{53}$	0.7609	.....	$\frac{35}{46}$
0.6744	$\frac{29}{43}$	$\frac{29}{43}$	0.7174	.....	$\frac{33}{46}$	0.7619	$\frac{16}{21}$	$\frac{32}{42}$
0.6757	$\frac{25}{37}$	$\frac{25}{37}$	0.7179	$\frac{28}{39}$	$\frac{28}{39}$	0.7627	.....	$\frac{45}{59}$
0.6765	.....	$\frac{23}{34}$	0.7193	.....	$\frac{41}{57}$	0.7632	.....	$\frac{29}{38}$
0.6774	$\frac{21}{31}$	$\frac{42}{62}$	0.7200	$\frac{18}{25}$	$\frac{18}{25}$	0.7647	$\frac{13}{17}$	$\frac{26}{34}$
0.6780	.....	$\frac{40}{59}$	0.7209	$\frac{31}{43}$	$\frac{31}{43}$	0.7647	.....	$\frac{39}{51}$
0.6786	.....	$\frac{19}{28}$	0.7222	$\frac{13}{18}$	$\frac{39}{54}$	0.7660	$\frac{36}{47}$	$\frac{36}{47}$
0.6792	.....	$\frac{36}{53}$	0.7234	$\frac{34}{47}$	$\frac{34}{47}$	0.7667	.....	$\frac{23}{30}$
0.6800	.....	$\frac{17}{25}$	0.7241	$\frac{21}{29}$	$\frac{42}{58}$	0.7674	$\frac{33}{43}$	$\frac{33}{43}$
0.6809	$\frac{32}{47}$	$\frac{32}{47}$	0.7255	.....	$\frac{37}{51}$	0.7692	$\frac{30}{39}$	$\frac{30}{39}$
0.6818	.....	$\frac{45}{66}$	0.7258	.....	$\frac{45}{62}$	0.7719	.....	$\frac{44}{57}$
0.6829	$\frac{28}{41}$	$\frac{28}{41}$	0.7273	$\frac{24}{33}$	$\frac{48}{66}$	0.7727	.....	$\frac{51}{66}$
0.6842	$\frac{13}{19}$	$\frac{26}{38}$	0.7288	.....	$\frac{43}{59}$	0.7736	.....	$\frac{41}{53}$
0.6842	.....	$\frac{39}{57}$	0.7297	$\frac{27}{37}$	$\frac{27}{37}$	0.7742	$\frac{24}{31}$	$\frac{48}{62}$
0.6852	.....	$\frac{37}{54}$	0.7317	$\frac{30}{41}$	$\frac{30}{41}$	0.7755	$\frac{38}{49}$	$\frac{38}{49}$
0.6863	.....	$\frac{35}{51}$	0.7333	$\frac{11}{15}$	$\frac{22}{30}$	0.7759	.....	$\frac{45}{58}$
0.6875	$\frac{11}{16}$	.....	0.7347	.....	$\frac{36}{49}$	0.7778	$\frac{14}{18}$	$\frac{42}{54}$
0.6897	$\frac{20}{29}$	$\frac{40}{58}$	0.7353	.....	$\frac{25}{34}$	0.7778	$\frac{21}{27}$	.....
0.6905	.....	$\frac{29}{42}$	0.7358	.....	$\frac{39}{53}$	0.7797	.....	$\frac{46}{59}$
0.6923	$\frac{27}{39}$	$\frac{27}{39}$	0.7368	$\frac{14}{19}$	$\frac{28}{38}$	0.7805	$\frac{32}{41}$	$\frac{32}{41}$
0.6935	.....	$\frac{43}{62}$	0.7368	.....	$\frac{42}{57}$	0.7826	$\frac{18}{23}$	$\frac{36}{46}$
0.6939	$\frac{34}{49}$	$\frac{34}{49}$	0.7381	.....	$\frac{31}{42}$	0.7838	$\frac{29}{37}$	$\frac{29}{37}$
0.6949	.....	$\frac{41}{59}$	0.7391	$\frac{17}{23}$	$\frac{34}{46}$	0.7843	.....	$\frac{40}{51}$
0.6957	$\frac{16}{23}$	$\frac{32}{46}$	0.7407	$\frac{20}{27}$	$\frac{40}{54}$	0.7857	.....	$\frac{22}{28}$
0.6970	$\frac{23}{33}$	$\frac{46}{66}$	0.7414	.....	$\frac{43}{58}$	0.7857	.....	$\frac{33}{42}$
0.6977	$\frac{30}{43}$	$\frac{30}{43}$	0.7419	$\frac{23}{31}$	$\frac{46}{62}$	0.7872	$\frac{37}{47}$	$\frac{37}{47}$
0.6981	.....	$\frac{37}{53}$	0.7424	.....	$\frac{49}{66}$	0.7879	$\frac{26}{33}$	$\frac{52}{66}$
0.7000	$\frac{14}{20}$	$\frac{21}{30}$	0.7436	.....	$\frac{29}{39}$	0.7895	$\frac{15}{19}$	$\frac{30}{38}$
0.7018	.....	$\frac{40}{57}$	0.7442	.....	$\frac{32}{43}$	0.7895	.....	$\frac{45}{57}$
0.7021	$\frac{33}{47}$	$\frac{33}{47}$	0.7447	$\frac{35}{47}$	$\frac{35}{47}$	0.7903	.....	$\frac{49}{62}$
0.7027	$\frac{26}{37}$	$\frac{26}{37}$	0.7451	.....	$\frac{38}{51}$	0.7907	$\frac{34}{43}$	$\frac{34}{43}$
0.7037	$\frac{19}{27}$	$\frac{38}{54}$	0.7458	.....	$\frac{44}{59}$	0.7917	.....	$\frac{19}{24}$
0.7059	$\frac{12}{17}$	$\frac{24}{34}$	0.7500	$\frac{12}{16}$	$\frac{18}{24}$	0.7925	.....	$\frac{42}{53}$
0.7059	.....	$\frac{36}{51}$	0.7500	$\frac{15}{20}$	$\frac{30}{40}$	0.7931	$\frac{23}{29}$	$\frac{46}{58}$
0.7069	.....	$\frac{41}{58}$	0.7544	.....	$\frac{43}{57}$	0.7941	.....	$\frac{27}{34}$
0.7073	$\frac{29}{41}$	$\frac{29}{41}$	0.7547	.....	$\frac{40}{53}$	0.7949	$\frac{31}{39}$	$\frac{31}{39}$
0.7083	.....	$\frac{17}{24}$	0.7551	$\frac{37}{49}$	$\frac{37}{49}$	0.7959	$\frac{39}{49}$	$\frac{39}{49}$
0.7097	$\frac{22}{31}$	$\frac{44}{62}$	0.7561	$\frac{31}{41}$	$\frac{31}{41}$	0.7963	.....	$\frac{43}{54}$
0.7105	.....	$\frac{27}{38}$	0.7568	$\frac{28}{37}$	$\frac{28}{37}$	0.7966	.....	$\frac{47}{59}$

* See explanatory note below Table 8.

Accurate Angular Indexing Movements — 7 *

Fractional Indexing Movement	B. & S., Becker, Hendey, K. & T. and Rockford	Cincinnati and LeBlond *
0.8000	$\frac{16}{20}$	$\frac{20}{25}$
0.8000	$\frac{12}{15}$	$\frac{24}{30}$
0.8030	.....	$\frac{53}{66}$
0.8039	.....	$\frac{41}{51}$
0.8043	.....	$\frac{37}{46}$
0.8049	$\frac{33}{41}$	$\frac{33}{41}$
0.8065	$\frac{25}{31}$	$\frac{50}{62}$
0.8070	.....	$\frac{46}{57}$
0.8085	$\frac{38}{47}$	$\frac{38}{47}$
0.8095	$\frac{17}{21}$	$\frac{34}{42}$
0.8103	.....	$\frac{47}{58}$
0.8108	$\frac{30}{37}$	$\frac{30}{37}$
0.8113	.....	$\frac{43}{53}$
0.8125	$\frac{13}{16}$	.....
0.8136	.....	$\frac{48}{59}$
0.8140	.....	$\frac{35}{43}$
0.8148	.....	$\frac{44}{54}$
0.8158	.....	$\frac{31}{38}$
0.8163	$\frac{40}{49}$	$\frac{40}{49}$
0.8182	$\frac{27}{33}$	$\frac{54}{66}$
0.8205	$\frac{32}{39}$	$\frac{32}{39}$
0.8214	.....	$\frac{23}{28}$
0.8226	.....	$\frac{51}{62}$
0.8235	$\frac{14}{17}$	$\frac{28}{34}$
0.8235	.....	$\frac{42}{51}$
0.8246	.....	$\frac{47}{57}$
0.8261	$\frac{19}{23}$	$\frac{38}{46}$
0.8276	$\frac{24}{29}$	$\frac{48}{58}$
0.8293	$\frac{34}{41}$	$\frac{34}{41}$
0.8298	$\frac{39}{47}$	$\frac{39}{47}$
0.8302	.....	$\frac{44}{53}$
0.8305	.....	$\frac{49}{59}$
0.8333	$\frac{15}{18}$	$\frac{20}{24}$
0.8333	.....	$\frac{25}{30}$
0.8333	.....	$\frac{35}{42}$
0.8333	.....	$\frac{45}{54}$
0.8333	.....	$\frac{55}{66}$
0.8367	$\frac{41}{49}$	$\frac{41}{49}$
0.8372	$\frac{36}{43}$	$\frac{36}{43}$
0.8378	$\frac{31}{37}$	$\frac{31}{37}$
0.8387	$\frac{26}{31}$	$\frac{52}{62}$
0.8400	.....	$\frac{21}{25}$
0.8421	.....	$\frac{32}{38}$
0.8421	$\frac{16}{19}$	$\frac{48}{57}$
0.8431	.....	$\frac{43}{51}$
0.8448	.....	$\frac{49}{58}$
0.8462	$\frac{33}{39}$	$\frac{33}{39}$
0.8475	.....	$\frac{50}{59}$
0.8478	.....	$\frac{39}{46}$
0.8485	$\frac{28}{33}$	$\frac{56}{66}$
0.8491	.....	$\frac{45}{53}$
0.8500	$\frac{17}{20}$	.....
0.8511	$\frac{40}{47}$	$\frac{40}{47}$
0.8519	$\frac{23}{27}$	$\frac{46}{54}$
0.8529	.....	$\frac{29}{34}$
0.8537	$\frac{35}{41}$	$\frac{35}{41}$
0.8548	.....	$\frac{53}{62}$
0.8571	.....	$\frac{24}{28}$
0.8571	$\frac{18}{21}$	$\frac{36}{42}$
0.8571	$\frac{42}{49}$	$\frac{42}{49}$
0.8596	.....	$\frac{49}{57}$
0.8605	$\frac{37}{43}$	$\frac{37}{43}$
0.8621	$\frac{25}{29}$	$\frac{50}{58}$
0.8627	.....	$\frac{44}{51}$
0.8636	.....	$\frac{57}{66}$
0.8644	.....	$\frac{51}{59}$
0.8649	$\frac{32}{37}$	$\frac{32}{37}$
0.8667	$\frac{13}{15}$	$\frac{26}{30}$
0.8679	.....	$\frac{46}{53}$
0.8684	.....	$\frac{33}{38}$
0.8696	$\frac{20}{23}$	$\frac{40}{46}$
0.8704	.....	$\frac{47}{54}$
0.8710	$\frac{27}{31}$	$\frac{54}{62}$
0.8718	$\frac{34}{39}$	$\frac{34}{39}$
0.8723	$\frac{41}{47}$	$\frac{41}{47}$
0.8750	$\frac{14}{16}$	$\frac{21}{24}$
0.8772	.....	$\frac{50}{57}$
0.8776	$\frac{43}{49}$	$\frac{43}{49}$
0.8780	$\frac{36}{41}$	$\frac{36}{41}$
0.8788	$\frac{29}{33}$	$\frac{58}{66}$
0.8793	.....	$\frac{51}{58}$
0.8800	.....	$\frac{22}{25}$
0.8810	.....	$\frac{37}{42}$
0.8814	.....	$\frac{52}{59}$
0.8824	$\frac{15}{17}$	$\frac{30}{34}$
0.8824	.....	$\frac{45}{51}$
0.8837	$\frac{38}{43}$	$\frac{38}{43}$
0.8868	.....	$\frac{47}{53}$
0.8871	.....	$\frac{55}{62}$
0.8889	$\frac{16}{18}$	.....
0.8889	$\frac{24}{27}$	$\frac{48}{54}$
0.8913	.....	$\frac{41}{46}$
0.8919	$\frac{33}{37}$	$\frac{33}{37}$
0.8929	.....	$\frac{25}{28}$
0.8936	$\frac{42}{47}$	$\frac{42}{47}$
0.8939	.....	$\frac{59}{66}$
0.8947	$\frac{17}{19}$	$\frac{34}{38}$
0.8947	.....	$\frac{51}{57}$
0.8966	$\frac{26}{29}$	$\frac{52}{58}$
0.8974	$\frac{35}{39}$	$\frac{35}{39}$
0.8980	$\frac{44}{49}$	$\frac{44}{49}$
0.8983	.....	$\frac{53}{59}$
0.9000	$\frac{18}{20}$	$\frac{27}{30}$
0.9020	.....	$\frac{46}{51}$
0.9024	$\frac{37}{41}$	$\frac{37}{41}$
0.9032	$\frac{28}{31}$	$\frac{56}{62}$
0.9048	$\frac{19}{21}$	$\frac{38}{42}$
0.9057	.....	$\frac{48}{53}$
0.9070	$\frac{39}{43}$	$\frac{39}{43}$
0.9074	.....	$\frac{49}{54}$
0.9090	$\frac{30}{33}$	$\frac{60}{66}$
0.9118	.....	$\frac{31}{34}$
0.9123	.....	$\frac{52}{57}$
0.9130	$\frac{21}{23}$	$\frac{42}{46}$
0.9138	.....	$\frac{53}{58}$
0.9149	$\frac{43}{47}$	$\frac{43}{47}$
0.9153	.....	$\frac{54}{59}$
0.9167	.....	$\frac{22}{24}$
0.9184	$\frac{45}{49}$	$\frac{45}{49}$
0.9189	$\frac{34}{37}$	$\frac{34}{37}$
0.9194	.....	$\frac{57}{62}$
0.9200	.....	$\frac{23}{25}$
0.9211	.....	$\frac{35}{38}$
0.9216	.....	$\frac{47}{51}$
0.9231	$\frac{36}{39}$	$\frac{36}{39}$
0.9242	.....	$\frac{61}{66}$
0.9245	.....	$\frac{49}{53}$
0.9259	$\frac{25}{27}$	$\frac{50}{54}$
0.9268	$\frac{38}{41}$	$\frac{38}{41}$
0.9286	.....	$\frac{26}{28}$
0.9286	.....	$\frac{39}{42}$
0.9298	.....	$\frac{53}{57}$

* See explanatory note below Table 8.

Accurate Angular Indexing Movements — 8 *

Fractional Indexing Movement	B. & S., Becker, Hendey, K. & T. and Rockford	Cincinnati and LeBlond *	Fractional Indexing Movement	B. & S., Becker, Hendey, K. & T. and Rockford	Cincinnati and LeBlond *	Fractional Indexing Movement	B. & S., Becker, Hendey, K. & T. and Rockford	Cincinnati and LeBlond *
0.9302	40/43	40/43	0.9500	19/20	....	0.9697	32/33	64/66
0.9310	27/29	54/58	0.9512	39/41	39/41	0.9706	....	33/34
0.9322	....	55/59	0.9516	....	59/62	0.9730	36/37	36/37
0.9333	14/15	28/30	0.9524	20/21	40/42	0.9737	....	37/38
0.9348	....	43/46	0.9535	41/43	41/43	0.9744	38/39	38/39
0.9355	29/31	58/62	0.9545	....	63/66	0.9756	40/41	40/41
0.9362	44/47	44/47	0.9565	22/23	44/46	0.9762	....	41/42
0.9375	15/16	....	0.9574	45/47	45/47	0.9767	42/43	42/43
0.9388	46/49	46/49	0.9583	....	23/24	0.9783	....	45/46
0.9394	31/33	62/66	0.9592	47/49	47/49	0.9787	46/47	46/47
0.9412	16/17	32/34	0.9600	....	24/25	0.9796	48/49	48/49
0.9412	....	48/51	0.9608	....	49/51	0.9804	....	50/51
0.9434	....	50/53	0.9623	....	51/53	0.9811	....	52/53
0.9444	17/18	51/54	0.9630	26/27	52/54	0.9815	....	53/54
0.9459	35/37	35/37	0.9643	....	27/28	0.9825	....	56/57
0.9474	18/19	36/38	0.9649	....	55/57	0.9828	....	57/58
0.9474	....	54/57	0.9655	28/29	56/58	0.9831	....	58/59
0.9483	....	55/58	0.9661	....	57/59	0.9839	....	61/62
0.9487	37/39	37/39	0.9667	....	29/30	0.9848	....	65/66
0.9492	....	56/59	0.9677	30/31	60/62		....	....

* The foregoing tables may be used when indexing for angles in degrees, minutes or seconds. The tables are used as follows: Reduce the angle to seconds and divide the value thus obtained by 32,400. The quotient gives the number of complete turns and decimal fraction of a turn required. Then find the decimal (or nearest decimal) to this decimal fraction in the tables. Opposite this decimal will be found the fractional number indicating the indexing movement.

Example: — Assume that an angle of 10 degrees, 32 minutes, 12 seconds is to be indexed. Then, $10° \ 32' \ 12'' = 37,932$ seconds and $37,932 \div 32,400 = 1.1707$; therefore this indexing can be made by one complete turn and 0.1707 part of a turn. The second table shows that 0.1707 part of a turn is obtained by moving 7 holes in the 41-hole circle.

Example: — Two slots are to be milled in the edge of a disk and the angle between their center-lines is 58 degrees 51 minutes and 53 seconds. Determine the indexing movement.

The angle $58° \ 51' \ 53''$ reduced to seconds $= 211,913$ seconds and $211,913 \div 32,400 = 6.5405$; therefore this indexing movement requires six complete turns and 0.5405 part of a turn. The fifth table shows that 0.5405 part of a turn is obtained by moving 20 holes in the 37-hole circle.

The number of holes in the index circles of the indexing-heads made by the Brown & Sharpe Mfg. Co., Becker Milling Machine Co., Hendey Machine Co., Kearney & Trecker Co., and the Rockford Milling Machine Co. are the same. The index circles of the Cincinnati Milling Machine Co. differ from these; hence, a separate column is given in the table for the "Cincinnati" index-head. The R. K. LeBlond Machine Tool Co.'s dividing head has the same index circles as that of the Cincinnati Milling Machine Co., except that the former does not have the 24-, 25-, 28-, and 30-hole circles, but has, instead, 36-, 48-, and 56-hole circles. The movements in the 24- and 28-hole circles of the Cincinnati index-head may be made on the LeBlond index-head by taking double the number of holes in the 48-hole and 56-hole circles, respectively. In this way, the table can be used for practically all movements with LeBlond milling machines.

Block or Multiple Indexing for Gear Cutting

Teeth to be Cut	Number Indexed at Once	First Driver	First Follower	Second Driver	Second Follower	Turns of Locking Disk	Teeth to be Cut	Number Indexed at Once	First Driver	First Follower	Second Driver	Second Follower	Turns of Locking Disk
25	4	100	50	72	30	4	77	4	100	70	96	44	2
26	3	100	50	90	52	4	78	5	100	30	90	78	2
27	2	100	50	60	54	4	80	3	100	50	90	80	2
28	3	100	50	90	56	4	81	7	100	30	84	52	2
29	3	100	50	90	58	4	82	5	100	30	90	82	2
30	1	100	50	60	60	2	84	5	100	30	90	84	2
31	3	100	50	90	62	4	85	4	100	50	96	68	2
32	3	100	50	90	64	4	86	5	100	30	90	86	2
33	4	100	50	80	44	4	87	7	100	30	84	58	2
34	3	100	50	90	68	4	88	5	100	30	90	88	2
35	4	100	50	96	56	4	90	7	100	30	70	50	2
36	5	100	48	80	40	4	91	3	100	70	72	52	2
37	5	100	30	90	74	4	92	5	100	30	90	92	2
38	5	100	30	90	76	4	93	7	100	30	84	62	2
39	5	100	30	90	78	4	94	5	100	30	90	94	2
40	3	100	50	90	80	4	95	4	100	50	96	76	2
41	5	100	30	90	82	4	96	5	100	30	90	96	2
42	5	100	30	90	84	4	98	5	100	30	90	98	2
43	5	100	30	90	86	4	99	10	100	30	80	44	2
44	5	100	30	90	88	4	100	7	100	50	84	40	2
45	7	100	50	70	30	4	102	5	100	30	60	68	2
46	5	100	30	90	92	4	104	5	100	60	90	52	2
47	5	100	30	90	94	4	105	4	100	70	96	60	2
48	5	100	30	90	96	4	108	7	100	30	70	60	2
49	5	100	30	90	98	4	110	7	100	50	84	44	2
50	7	100	50	84	40	4	111	5	100	74	80	40	2
51	4	100	30	96	68	2	112	5	100	60	90	56	2
52	5	100	30	90	52	2	114	7	100	30	84	76	2
54	5	100	30	90	54	2	115	8	100	50	96	46	2
55	4	100	50	96	44	2	116	5	100	60	90	58	2
56	5	100	30	90	56	2	117	8	100	30	96	78	2
57	4	100	30	96	76	2	119	3	100	70	72	68	2
58	5	100	30	90	58	2	120	7	100	50	70	40	2
60	7	100	30	84	40	2	121	4	60	66	96	44	2
62	5	100	30	90	62	2	123	7	100	30	84	82	2
63	5	100	30	80	56	2	124	5	100	60	90	62	2
64	5	100	30	90	64	2	125	7	100	50	84	50	2
65	4	100	50	96	52	2	126	5	100	50	50	42	2
66	5	100	44	80	40	2	128	5	100	60	90	64	2
67	5	100	30	90	67	2	129	7	100	30	84	86	2
68	5	100	30	90	68	2	130	7	100	50	84	52	2
69	5	100	46	80	40	2	132	5	100	88	80	40	2
70	3	100	50	90	70	2	133	4	100	70	96	76	2
72	5	100	30	90	72	2	134	5	100	60	90	67	2
74	5	100	30	90	74	2	135	7	100	50	84	54	2
75	7	100	30	84	50	2	136	5	100	60	90	68	2
76	5	100	30	90	76	2	138	5	100	92	80	40	2

Block or Multiple Indexing for Gear Cutting

Teeth to be Cut	Number Indexed at Once	First Driver	First Follower	Second Driver	Second Follower	Turns of Locking Disk	Teeth to be Cut	Number Indexed at Once	First Driver	First Follower	Second Driver	Second Follower	Turns of Locking Disk
140	3	50	50	90	70	2	170	7	100	50	84	68	2
141	5	100	94	80	40	2	171	5	70	42	80	76	2
143	6	90	66	96	52	2	172	5	100	60	90	86	2
144	5	100	60	90	72	2	174	7	100	60	84	58	2
145	6	100	50	72	58	2	175	8	100	50	96	70	2
147	5	100	98	80	40	2	176	5	100	60	90	88	2
148	5	100	60	90	74	2	180	7	100	60	70	50	2
150	7	100	60	84	50	2	182	9	90	56	96	52	2
152	5	100	60	90	76	2	184	5	100	60	90	92	2
153	5	100	68	80	60	2	185	6	100	50	72	74	2
154	5	100	56	72	66	2	186	7	100	60	84	62	2
155	6	100	50	72	62	2	187	5	100	44	48	68	2
156	5	100	60	90	78	2	188	5	100	60	90	94	2
160	7	100	50	84	64	2	189	5	100	60	80	84	2
161	5	100	70	60	46	2	190	7	100	50	84	76	2
162	7	100	60	84	52	2	192	5	100	60	90	96	2
164	5	100	60	90	82	2	195	7	100	50	84	78	2
165	7	100	50	84	66	2	196	5	100	60	90	98	2
168	5	100	60	90	84	2	198	7	100	50	70	66	2
169	6	96	52	90	78	2	200	7	60	60	84	40	2

Block or Multiple Indexing for Gear Cutting. — With the block system of indexing, a number of teeth are indexed at one time, instead of cutting the teeth consecutively, and the gear is revolved several times before the teeth are all finished. For example, when cutting a gear having 25 teeth, the indexing mechanism is geared to index four teeth at once (see table) and the first time around, six widely separated tooth spaces are cut. The second time around, the cutter is one tooth behind the spaces previously milled. On the third indexing, the cutter has dropped back another tooth, thus finishing the gear (in this case) by indexing it around four times. The various combinations of change gears to use for block or multiple indexing are given in the accompanying table. The advantage claimed for block indexing is that the heat generated by the cutter (especially when cutting cast-iron gears of coarse pitch) is distributed more evenly about the rim and dissipated to a greater extent, thus avoiding distortion due to local heating and permitting higher speeds and feeds. The table given is intended for use with Brown & Sharpe automatic gear-cutting machines, but the gears for any other machine equipped with a similar indexing mechanism can be calculated. Assume, for example, that a gear cutter requires the following change gears for indexing a certain number of teeth: Driving gears having 20 and 30 teeth, respectively, and driven gears having 50 and 60 teeth. Then if it is desired to cut, say, every fifth tooth, multiply the fractions $\frac{20}{60}$ and $\frac{30}{50}$ by 5. Then, $\frac{20}{60} \times \frac{30}{50} \times \frac{5}{1} = \frac{1}{1}$. In this particular instance, then, the blank could be divided so that every fifth space would be cut, by using gears of equal size. The number of teeth in the gear and the number of teeth indexed in each block, must not have a common factor.

Indexing Movements for 60-Tooth Worm-Wheel Dividing Head

Divisions	Index Circle	No. of Turns	No. of Holes	Divisions	Index Circle	No. of Turns	No. of Holes	Divisions	Index Circle	No. of Turns	No. of Holes	Divisions	Index Circle	No. of Holes
2	Any	30	..	50	60	1	12	98	49		30	146	73	30
3	Any	20	..	51	17	1	3	99	33		20	147	49	20
4	Any	15	..	52	26	1	4	100	60		36	148	37	15
5	Any	12	..	53	53	1	7	101	101		60	149	149	60
6	Any	10	..	54	27	1	3	102	17		10	150	60	24
7	21	8	12	55	33	1	3	103	103		60	151	151	60
8	26	7	13	56	28	1	2	104	26		15	152	76	30
9	21	6	14	57	19	1	1	105	21		12	153	51	20
10	Any	6	..	58	29	1	1	106	53		30	154	77	30
11	33	5	15	59	59	1	1	107	107		60	155	31	12
12	Any	5	..	60	Any	1	..	108	27		15	156	26	10
13	26	4	16	61	61	..	60	109	109		60	157	157	60
14	21	4	6	62	31	..	30	110	33		18	158	79	30
15	Any	4	..	63	21	..	20	111	37		20	159	53	20
16	28	3	21	64	32	..	30	112	28		15	160	32	12
17	17	3	9	65	26	..	24	113	113		60	161	161	60
18	21	3	7	66	33	..	30	114	19		10	162	27	10
19	19	3	3	67	67	..	60	115	23		12	163	163	60
20	Any	3	..	68	17	..	15	116	29		15	164	41	15
21	21	2	18	69	23	..	20	117	39		20	165	33	12
22	33	2	24	70	21	..	18	118	59		30	166	83	30
23	23	2	14	71	71	..	60	119	119		60	167	167	60
24	26	2	13	72	60	..	50	120	26		13	168	28	10
25	60	2	24	73	73	..	60	121	121		60	169	169	60
26	26	2	8	74	37	..	30	122	61		30	170	17	6
27	27	2	6	75	60	..	48	123	41		20	171	57	20
28	21	2	3	76	19	..	15	124	31		15	172	43	15
29	29	2	2	77	77	..	60	125	100		48	173	173	60
30	Any	2	..	78	26	..	20	126	21		10	174	29	10
31	31	1	29	79	79	..	60	127	127		60	175	35	12
32	32	1	28	80	28	..	21	128	32		15	176	44	15
33	33	1	27	81	27	..	20	129	43		20	177	59	20
34	17	1	13	82	41	..	30	130	26		12	178	89	30
35	21	1	15	83	83	..	60	131	131		60	179	179	60
36	21	1	14	84	21	..	15	132	33		15	180	21	7
37	37	1	23	85	17	..	12	133	133		60	181	181	60
38	19	1	11	86	43	..	30	134	67		30	182	91	30
39	26	1	14	87	29	..	20	135	27		12	183	61	20
40	26	1	13	88	44	..	30	136	68		30	184	46	15
41	41	1	19	89	89	..	60	137	137		60	185	37	12
42	21	1	9	90	21	..	14	138	23		10	186	31	10
43	43	1	17	91	91	..	60	139	139		60	187	187	60
44	33	1	12	92	23	..	15	140	21		9	188	47	15
45	21	1	7	93	31	..	20	141	47		20	189	63	20
46	23	1	7	94	47	..	30	142	71		30	190	19	6
47	47	1	13	95	19	..	12	143	143		60	191	191	60
48	28	1	7	96	32	..	20	144	60		25	192	32	10
49	49	1	11	97	97	..	60	145	29		12	193	193	60

Indexing for Rack Cutting. — When racks are cut on a milling machine, there are two general methods of indexing. One is by using the graduated dial on the feed-screw and the other is by using an indexing attachment. The accompanying table shows the indexing movements when the first method is employed. This table applies to milling machines having feed-screws with the usual lead of ¼ inch and 250 dial graduations each equivalent to 0.001 inch of table movement.

$$\text{Actual rotation of feed-screw} = \frac{\text{Linear pitch of rack}}{\text{Lead of feed-screw}}$$

Multiply *decimal* part of turn (obtained by above formula) by 250, to obtain dial reading for fractional part of indexing movement, assuming that dial has 250 graduations.

Indexing Movements for Cutting Rack Teeth on Milling Machine

These movements are for table feed-screws having the usual lead of ¼ inch

Pitch of Rack Tooth		Indexing, Movement		Pitch of Rack Teeth		Indexing, Movement	
Diametral Pitch	Linear or Circular	No. of Whole Turns	No. of .001 Inch Divisions	Diametral Pitch	Linear or Circular	No. of Whole Turns	No. of .001 Inch Divisions
2	1.5708	6	70.8	12	0.2618	1	11.8
2¼	1.3963	5	146.3	13	0.2417	0	241.7
2½	1.2566	5	6.6	14	0.2244	0	224.4
2¾	1.1424	4	142.4	15	0.2094	0	208.4
3	1.0472	4	47.2	16	0.1963	0	196.3
3½	0.8976	3	147.6	17	0.1848	0	184.8
4	0.7854	3	35.4	18	0.1745	0	174.8
5	0.6283	2	128.3	19	0.1653	0	165.3
6	0.5236	2	23.6	20	0.1571	0	157.1
7	0.4488	1	198.8	22	0.1428	0	142.8
8	0.3927	1	142.7	24	0.1309	0	130.9
9	0.3491	1	99.1	26	0.1208	0	120.8
10	0.3142	1	64.2	28	0.1122	0	112.2
11	0.2856	1	35.6	30	0.1047	0	104.7

Note: The linear pitch of the rack equals the circular pitch of gear or pinion which is to mesh with the rack. The table gives both standard diametral pitches and their equivalent linear or circular pitches.

Example: Find indexing movement for cutting rack to mesh with a pinion of 10 diametral pitch.

Indexing movement equals 1 whole turn of feed-screw plus 64.2 thousandths or divisions on feed-screw dial. The feed-screw may be turned this fractional amount by setting dial back to its zero position for each indexing (without backward movement of feed-screw), or, if preferred, 64.2 (in this example) may be added to each successive dial position as shown below.

Dial reading for second position = 64.2 × 2 = 128.4 (complete movement = 1 turn + 64.2 additional divisions by turning feed-screw until dial reading is 128.4).

Third dial position = 64.2 × 3 = 192.6 (complete movement = 1 turn + 64.2 additional divisions by turning until dial reading is 192.6).

Fourth position = 64.2 × 4 = 250 = 6.8 (1 turn + 64.2 additional divisions by turning feed-screw until dial reading is 6.8 divisions past the zero mark); or, to simplify operation, set dial back to zero for fourth indexing (without moving feed-screw) and then repeat settings for the three previous indexings or whatever number can be made before making a complete turn of the dial.

SMALL TOOLS

The expression "small tools" is applied in the machine-building and metal-working industries to such tools as drills, taps, dies or other threading tools, reamers, counterbores, countersinks, milling cutters, hobs, broaches, etc. In a broad sense, the term "small tools" might include all classes of hand-operated or auxiliary tools used in the production of metal products.

Standards have been established for certain small tools as will be seen by referring to some of the tables in this section. These standards apply to various classes of small tools such as taps, reamers, twist drills, and milling cutters. The standardization applies particularly to the more important dimensions so that small tools made by different manufacturers may be used interchangeably. In tap standardization, for example, the American standard dimensions include the over-all length, the length of the full thread, diameter of the shank, size and length of the square, and the number of flutes. Standards for reamers and milling cutters also apply to the important over-all dimensions. The standardization of small tools is especially important in connection with tool engineering.

Taps and Threading Dies

American Standard Taps. — This standard for cut- and ground-thread taps includes general dimensions, limiting dimensions, and markings or thread-identifying symbols. It was approved by the American Standard Association and sponsored by the Society of Automotive Engineers, Inc.; National Machine Tool Builders' Association; and the American Society of Mechanical Engineers. The thread form specified for taps covered by this standard is known as the American National Form. See Screw Thread Systems.

Hand Taps. — The Regular (Standard) Hand Taps are so called because they are primarily for use by hand, although at the present time these taps are used extensively in machines. A regular hand tap is comparatively short and has a thread and shank approximately the same length. The shank has a square end to accommodate a tap wrench, or other driving device. These taps are made in fractional sizes only. Regular (standard) hand taps are made in "taper," "plug," and "bottoming" types which differ in regard to the number of threads chamfered. The number is approximately as follows: Taper taps have 7 to 9 threads chamfered; plug taps, 2½ to 5 threads; and bottoming taps, 1 to 1½ threads. For general dimensions see Table 1.

Two- or Three-Fluted Hand Taps: These are similar to regular (standard) hand taps, excepting the number of flutes which is smaller. They are suitable for machines used in tapping tough stringy metal. See Table 2.

Spiral-Pointed Hand Taps: Regular (standard) hand taps having the cutting face of the first few threads ground at an angle to force the chips ahead, thus preventing clogging in the flutes. These taps only have two or three flutes and the lands are comparatively wide. See Table 2.

Serial Hand Taps: These are regular (standard) hand taps made in sets of three, with a progressive increase in size. Thus, the pitch diameter of No. 1 is smaller than No. 2, the No. 2 is smaller than No. 3, so that the work is distributed. These taps are used when a full thread cannot be cut into tough metal at one pass. They are identified by rings on the shank near the square. See Table 2.

Machine Screw Taps. — Regular (standard) machine screw taps are similar to the regular (standard) hand taps, excepting that they are made in the numbered or machine screw sizes. See Table 3.

Spiral-Pointed Type: This type is a regular machine screw tap having two flutes,

Table 1. American Standard Hand Taps — Regular Standard

Diameter of Tap	Threads per Inch		Number of Flutes	Length Overall	Length Full Thread	Length of Square	Diam. of Shank	Size of Square
	NC	NF						
1/16	*	*	3	1 5/8	5/16	3/16	0.141	0.110
3/32	*	*	3	1 3/4	7/16	3/16	0.141	0.110
1/8	*	*	3	1 15/16	5/8	3/16	0.141	0.110
5/32	*	*	4	2 1/16	3/4	1/4	0.160	0.125
3/16	*	*	4	2 3/8	7/8	1/4	0.192	0.149
7/32	*	*	4	2 3/8	15/16	1/4	0.223	0.167
1/4	20	28	4	2 1/2	1	9/32	0.255	0.191
5/16	18	24	4	2 23/32	1 1/8	5/16	0.318	0.238
3/8	16	24	4	2 15/16	1 1/4	3/8	0.381	0.286
7/16	14	20	4	3 5/32	1 7/16	13/32	0.323	0.242
1/2	13	20	4	3 3/8	1 21/32	7/16	0.367	0.275
9/16	12	18	4	3 19/32	1 21/32	1/2	0.429	0.322
5/8	11	18	4	3 13/16	1 13/16	9/16	0.480	0.360
11/16	...	..	4	4 1/32	1 13/16	5/8	0.542	0.406
3/4	10	16	4	4 1/4	2	11/16	0.590	0.442
7/8	9	14	4	4 11/16	2 7/32	3/4	0.697	0.523
1	8	14	4	5 1/8	2 1/2	13/16	0.800	0.600
1 1/8	7	12	**4	5 7/16	2 9/16	7/8	0.896	0.672
1 1/4	7	12	**4	5 3/4	2 9/16	1	1.021	0.766
1 3/8	6	12	**4	6 1/16	3	1 1/16	1.108	0.831
1 1/2	6	12	**4	6 3/8	3	1 1/8	1.233	0.925
1 5/8	...	..	6	6 11/16	3 3/16	1 1/8	1.305	0.979
1 3/4	5	..	6	7	3 3/16	1 1/4	1.430	1.072
1 7/8	...	..	6	7 5/16	3 9/16	1 1/4	1.519	1.139
2	4 1/2	..	6	7 5/8	3 9/16	1 3/8	1.644	1.233

Tolerances for General Dimensions

Element	Diameter Range	Tolerance		Element	Diameter Range	Tolerance	
		Cut Thread	Ground Thread			Cut Thread	Ground Thread
Overall Length	1/16 to 1	±1/32	±1/32	Shank Diameter	1/16 to 7/32	−0.004	−0.0015
	1 1/8 to 2	±1/16	±1/16		1/4 to 5/8	−0.005	−0.0015
					11/16 to 1	−0.005	−0.002
Thread Length	1/16 to 7/32	±3/64	±3/64		1 1/8 to 1 1/2	−0.007	−0.002
	1/4 to 1/2	±1/16	±1/16		1 5/8 to 2	−0.007	−0.003
	9/16 to 1 1/2	±3/32	±3/32	Size of Square	1/16 to 1/2	−0.004	−0.004
	1 5/8 to 2	±1/8	±1/8		9/16 to 1	−0.006	−0.006
Square Length	1/16 to 1	±1/32	±1/32		1 1/8 to 2	−0.008	−0.008
	1 1/8 to 2	±1/16	±1/16				

All dimensions are given in inches.

These taps are furnished with American National Form of thread in taper, plug, or bottoming style. Cut thread taps up to 9/16 inch, inclusive, have external center on thread end; sizes 3/8 inch and larger have internal center in thread end. All ground thread taps 1/4 inch and larger have internal center in thread end.

* Machine screw taps are recommended for sizes under 1/4 inch.

** These tap sizes have six flutes in the fine-thread series.

comparatively wide lands, and the cutting face of the first few threads ground at an angle to force the chips ahead and prevent clogging in the flutes. See Table 3.

Stub Type: The thread of this type is considerably shorter than on a regular (standard) machine screw tap. The stub type is not included in the revised American Standard, issued 1948.

Spiral-Pointed Stub Type: This is a two-fluted tap with cutting face of the first few threads ground at an angle to force the chips ahead and prevent clogging. (Not included in the revised American Standard, issued 1948).

Nut Taps. — Designed for use in machine shops which tap their own nuts — generally from blanks supplied by a nut manufacturer. The entering threads, according to general practice, have a slight taper in both pitch diameter and root diameter for approximately three-fourths of the thread length. This is done to insure tapping a nut with a full-formed thread. The overall length, thread length and shank length are longer than on a regular (standard) hand tap. See Table 4.

Tapper Taps: The straight-shank tapper taps are used by nut manufacturers in vertical-spindle nut-tapping machines. They are made 12 or 15 inches long, and the nuts are allowed to accumulate on the shank during the tapping operation. These taps are made both in fractional and machine screw sizes. See Tables 5 and 6.

Bent-Shank Tapper Taps: Bent-shank taps are designed for use in one type of automatic tapping machine. The tapped nuts pass over the bent shank and are ejected, thus obtaining continuous production without stopping or reversal. These taps are made in both fractional and machine screw sizes.

Pipe Taps. — The taper pipe tap is a hand tap used for tapping taper fittings either by machine or by hand. See Table 7.

Straight Pipe Taps: This form is similar to a taper pipe tap, excepting the threaded portion which is straight and conforms to the proper size for tapping American standard straight pipe threads. See Table 7.

Combined Pipe Tap and Drill: This is a taper pipe tap having an extended point suitable for drilling. It is often used for drilling and tapping in range boilers and for similar work. See Table 8. (Not in revised American Standard, 1948).

Boiler Taps. — Straight boiler taps are hand taps having 12 threads per inch. They are used by railroads and locomotive builders for tapping straight holes in boiler plate. See Table 9.

Taper Boiler Taps: These are hand taps having a taper of ¾ inch per foot and 12 threads per inch. They are used by locomotive builders and in railroad shops. See Table 9.

Mud or Washout Taps: These are hand taps having a taper of 1¼ inches per foot and 12 threads per inch. They are used in tapping or retapping the holes in mud drums of boilers.

Staybolt Taps: These taps have a long shank and also a reamer section. They are used by boilermakers in tapping the inner and outer sheets preparatory to inserting the staybolts. All sizes have 12 threads per inch. See Table 10.

Pulley Taps. — This form of tap was designed originally for tapping set-screw holes in pulley hubs, but it is also used where exceptionally long hand taps are required. The thread length equals approximately that of a regular (standard) hand tap. The shank, which is slightly larger than the major diameter of the tap thread, comes in various lengths. See Table 11.

Tap Marking. — The American Standard includes marks or symbols to identify the thread form or series. All taps, dies, and other threading tools should be marked to show the nominal size, number of threads per inch, and with a standard symbol to identify the thread form. See accompanying table Marks or Symbols for Identifying Threads on Taps.

Table 2. Other Classes of American Standard Hand Taps

Diameter of Tap	Threads per Inch		Number of Flutes	Length Overall	Length Full Thread	Length of Square	Diam. of Shank	Size of Square
	NC	NF						

Three-Fluted Hand Taps

Regular (standard) hand taps in every way except that they have only three flutes. Suitable for machine use in tapping tough stringy metal.

Diameter of Tap	NC	NF	Number of Flutes	Length Overall	Length Full Thread	Length of Square	Diam. of Shank	Size of Square
¼	20	28	3	2½	1	9/32	0.255	0.191
5/16	18	24	3	2 23/32	1⅛	5/16	0.318	0.238
⅜	16	24	3	2 15/16	1¼	⅜	0.381	0.286
7/16	14	20	3	3 5/32	1 7/16	13/32	0.323	0.242
½	13	20	3	3⅜	1 21/32	7/16	0.367	0.275

Spiral-Pointed Hand Taps

Regular (standard) hand taps having a fewer number of flutes and wider lands and having the cutting face of the first few threads ground at an angle to force the chips ahead thus preventing clogging in the flutes.

Diameter of Tap	NC	NF	Number of Flutes	Length Overall	Length Full Thread	Length of Square	Diam. of Shank	Size of Square
⅛	..	..	2	1 15/16	⅝	3/16	0.141	0.110
3/16	..	..	2	2⅜	⅞	¼	0.192	0.149
¼	20	28	2	2½	1	9/32	0.255	0.191
5/16	18	24	2	2 23/32	1⅛	5/16	0.318	0.238
⅜	16	24	3	2 15/16	1¼	⅜	0.381	0.286
7/16	14	20	3	3 5/32	1 7/16	13/32	0.323	0.242
½	13	20	3	3⅜	1 21/32	7/16	0.367	0.275

Serial Hand Taps

A set consists of one each No. 1, No. 2, and No. 3 taps. The No. 1 is first used to rough out the thread and is followed by the No. 2, which being larger in pitch and major diameter, cuts the thread a little fuller. Finally the No. 3 tap is used, which finishes the thread to full size, the work thus being distributed among three taps. These taps are used when a full thread cannot be cut into tough metal at one pass. Serial taps are identified by rings on the shank near the square.

Diameter of Tap	NC	NF	Number of Flutes	Length Overall	Length Full Thread	Length of Square	Diam. of Shank	Size of Square
¼	20	..	4	2½	1	9/32	0.255	0.191
5/16	18	..	4	2 23/32	1⅛	5/16	0.318	0.238
⅜	16	..	4	2 15/16	1¼	⅜	0.381	0.286
7/16	14	..	4	3 5/32	1 7/16	13/32	0.323	0.242
½	13	..	4	3⅜	1 21/32	7/16	0.367	0.275
9/16	12	..	4	3 19/32	1 21/32	½	0.429	0.322
⅝	11	..	4	3 13/16	1 13/16	9/16	0.480	0.360
¾	10	..	4	4¼	2	11/16	0.590	0.442
⅞	9	..	4	4 11/16	2 7/32	¾	0.697	0.523
1	8	..	4	5⅛	2½	13/16	0.800	0.600

Marks or Symbols for Identifying Threads on Taps

Mark or Symbol	Thread Represented
NC	American Standard Coarse-thread Series.
NF	American Standard Fine-thread Series.
N	American Standard 8-Pitch, 12-Pitch, or 16-Pitch Series.
NS	Special threads with the American National form.
NH	American National Hose Coupling Threads.
NPT	American Standard Taper Pipe Threads.
NPS	American Standard Straight Pipe Threads.
NPSG	A standardized undersize straight pipe thread tap for grease-cup fittings.
V	A 60-degree V-thread usually with both the crest and root flatted several thousandths from the theoretical to users' specifications.
Acme	American Standard 29-degree Acme type thread.

Identifying Marks on Ground Thread Taps: All *commercial* ground-thread taps made to the thread limits specified in Tables 13 and 14 (upper part of table in each case) should be marked with one ring on the shank near the thread in addition to the standard marking. All *precision* ground-thread taps made to the thread limits specified in Table 13, and all precision ground-thread machine screw taps, Table 14, should be marked with a limit number. Other precision-ground thread taps are also marked with these limit numbers.

Limit number 01 is for a pitch diameter between basic and minus 0.0005; 1 is for a pitch diameter between basic and plus 0.0005; 2 is for a pitch diameter between 0.0005 and 0.0010 inch over basic size.

Ground thread pipe taps conforming to the limits given in Tables 16 and 18 should be marked CG.

Other special ground thread taps should be marked CG if the pitch diameter grinding tolerance is equal to, or greater than, the following: 0.0020 inch for 4 to 5½ threads per inch, inclusive; 0.0018 inch for 6 threads per inch; 0.0015 inch for 7 threads per inch; 0.0014 inch for 8 threads per inch; 0.0012 inch for 9 threads per inch; 0.0011 inch for 10 and 11½ threads per inch; 0.0010 inch for 12 threads per inch and finer. If the tolerances are less than those just given, the mark PG is used.

Special taps (excepting ground thread taps marked with the limit numbers previously referred to) varying only slightly from standard dimensions are to be marked with the letter S enclosed in a circle. Taps varying in pitch diameter up to 0.015 inch, over or under the basic size, should be marked with the actual amount the low limit is over or under this basic size, in addition to the standard size.

Left-Hand Taps. — Left-hand taps should be marked either "Left Hand" or LH, in addition to the other marking.

Multiple Thread Taps and Dies. — Taps and dies with multiple threads should be marked to give (1) diameter, (2) number of threads per inch, (3) thread form, (4) lead designated in fractions, and (5) whether the thread is double, triple, quadruple, etc.

Example: Assume that a special 1-inch tap has a double thread of American National form and a pitch of 1⁄16 inch or a lead of 1⁄8 inch; then the marking would be as follows:

1″ — 16 NS
1⁄8 Lead Double

Table 2a. Special Fine-pitch Hand Taps

Diam. of Tap	Length Overall	Length of Full Thread	Diameter of Shank	Size of Square	Diam. of Tap	Length Overall	Length of Full Thread	Diameter of Shank	Size of Square
1⅛	4	1½	0.896	0.672	2⅝	5½	2	2.100	1.575
1¼	4	1½	1.021	0.766	2¾	5½	2	2.100	1.575
1⅜	4	1½	1.108	0.831	2⅞	5½	2	2.100	1.575
1½	4	1½	1.233	0.925	3	5½	2	2.100	1.575
1⅝	5	2	1.305	0.979	3⅛	5¾	2	2.100	1.575
1¾	5	2	1.430	1.072	3¼	5¾	2	2.100	1.575
1⅞	5	2	1.519	1.139	3⅜	5¾	2	2.100	1.575
2	5	2	1.644	1.233	3½	5¾	2	2.100	1.575
2⅛	5¼	2	1.769	1.327	3⅝	6	2	2.100	1.575
2¼	5¼	2	1.894	1.420	3¾	6	2	2.100	1.575
2⅜	5¼	2	2.019	1.514	3⅞	6	2	2.100	1.575
2½	5¼	2	2.100	1.575	4	6	2	2.100	1.575

Pitches are not specified. It is recommended that special hand taps 1⅛ to 1½ in. in diameter, inclusive, having 14 or more threads per inch, and sizes over 1½ in. in diameter with 10 or more threads per inch, be manufactured to the dimensions shown.

Table 3. American Standard Machine Screw Taps

Screw Size Number	Basic Major Diameter	Threads per Inch NC	NF	Number of Flutes	Length Overall	Length Full Thread	Length of Square	Diam. of Shank	Size of Square
Regular (Standard) Machine Screw Taps									
0	0.060	..	80	2	1⅝	5/16	3/16	0.141	0.110
1	0.073	64	72	2	1¹¹⁄₁₆	3/8	3/16	0.141	0.110
2	0.086	56	64	3	1¾	7/16	3/16	0.141	0.110
3	0.099	48	56	3	1¹³⁄₁₆	1/2	3/16	0.141	0.110
4	0.112	40	48	3	1⅞	9/16	3/16	0.141	0.110
5	0.125	40	44	3	1¹⁵⁄₁₆	5/8	3/16	0.141	0.110
6	0.138	32	40	3	2	11/16	3/16	0.141	0.110
8	0.164	32	36	4	2⅛	3/4	1/4	0.168	0.131
10	0.190	24	32	4	2⅜	7/8	1/4	0.194	0.152
12	0.216	24	28	4	2⅜	15/16	9/32	0.220	0.165
14	0.242	..	..	4	2½	1	9/32	0.247	0.185
Spiral-Pointed Machine Screw Taps									
Cutting face of first few threads ground at an angle to force chips ahead and prevent clogging in the flutes.									
3	0.099	48	56	2	1¹³⁄₁₆	1/2	3/16	0.141	0.110
4	0.112	40	48	2	1⅞	9/16	3/16	0.141	0.110
5	0.125	40	44	2	1¹⁵⁄₁₆	5/8	3/16	0.141	0.110
6	0.138	32	40	2	2	11/16	3/16	0.141	0.110
8	0.164	32	36	2	2⅛	3/4	1/4	0.168	0.131
10	0.190	24	32	2	2⅜	7/8	1/4	0.194	0.152
12	0.216	24	28	2	2⅜	15/16	9/32	0.220	0.165
14	0.242	..	..	2	2½	1	9/32	0.247	0.185

All machine screw taps have the American National Form of thread. The regular (standard) machine screw taps are similar to hand taps except that they are made in numbered sizes. No. 14 size has special pitches of either 20 or 24 threads per inch.

Table 4. American Standard Nut Taps

Tap Diam.	Threads per Inch		Number of Flutes	Length Overall	Length of Full Thread		Length of Square	Diam. of Shank	Size of Square
	NC	NF			NC	NF			
1/4	20	28	4	5	1 5/8	1 1/4	9/16	0.185	0.139
5/16	18	24	4	5 1/2	1 13/16	1 3/8	5/8	0.240	0.180
3/8	16	24	4	6	2	1 1/2	11/16	0.294	0.220
7/16	14	20	4	6 1/2	2 3/8	1 3/4	3/4	0.345	0.259
1/2	13	20	4	7	2 1/2	1 7/8	7/8	0.400	0.300
9/16	12	18	4	7 1/2	2 3/4	2	7/8	0.450	0.337
5/8	11	18	4	8	3	2 1/4	15/16	0.503	0.377
3/4	10	16	4	9	3 1/4	2 1/2	1	0.616	0.462
7/8	9	14	4	10	3 5/8	2 3/4	1 1/16	0.727	0.545
1	8	14	4	11	4	3	1 1/8	0.834	0.625

Table 5. American Standard Straight-shank Tapper Taps — Fractional Sizes

Tap Diam.	Threads per Inch		Number of Flutes	Length Overall	Length of Full Thread		Diam. of Shank
	NC	NF			NC	NF	
1/4	20	28	3	12	1 1/4	1	0.185
5/16	18	24	3	12	1 3/8	1 1/16	0.240
3/8	16	24	3	12	1 9/16	1 3/16	0.294
7/16	14	20	3	12	1 13/16	1 3/8	0.345
1/2	13	20	3	12, 15	1 7/8	1 3/8	0.400
9/16	12	18	4	12, 15	2 1/8	1 9/16	0.450
5/8	11	18	4	12, 15	2 9/16	1 11/16	0.503
3/4	10	16	4	12, 15	2 1/2	1 3/4	0.616
7/8	9	14	4	12, 15	2 3/4	1 7/8	0.727
1	8	14	4	12, 15	3 1/8	2 1/8	0.834
1 1/8	7	12	4	15	3 1/2	2 3/8	0.933
1 1/4	7	12	4	15	3 1/2	2 3/8	1.058
1 3/8	6	12	4	15	4	2 5/8	1.153
1 1/2	6	12	4	15	4	2 5/8	1.278

Number of threads chamfered is 11 to 12 for NC threads and 15 to 17 for NF threads.

Table 6. American Standard Straight-shank Tapper Taps — Machine Screw Sizes

Screw Size Number	Basic Major Diameter	Threads per Inch		Number of Flutes	Length Overall	Length Full Thread	Diam. of Shank
		NC	NF				
*4	0.112	*	*	3	6	9/16	0.076
4	0.112	40	..	3	6	1/2	0.080
4	0.112	..	48	3	6	13/32	0.085
5	0.125	40	..	3	8	1/2	0.093
5	0.125	..	44	3	8	7/16	0.096
6	0.138	32	..	3	8	5/8	0.097
6	0.138	..	40	3	8	1/2	0.106
8	0.164	32	..	3	9	5/8	0.123
8	0.164	..	36	3	9	9/16	0.128
10	0.190	24	..	3	11	13/16	0.136
10	0.190	..	32	3	11	5/8	0.149
12	0.216	24	..	3	11	13/16	0.162
12	0.216	..	28	3	11	23/32	0.170

* First No. 4 size listed has 36 threads per inch — the pitch in general use.

Table 7. American Standard Taper and Straight Pipe Taps

Nominal Size	Threads per Inch	Number of Flutes: Regular Thread	Number of Flutes: Interrupted Thread	Length Overall	Length of Full Thread	Length of Square	Diam. of Shank	Size of Square
Taper Pipe Taps								
1/8	27	4	5	2 1/8	3/4	3/8	0.3125	0.234
1/8	27	4	5	2 1/8	3/4	3/8	0.4375	0.328
1/4	18	4	5	2 7/16	1 1/16	7/16	0.5625	0.421
3/8	18	4	5	2 9/16	1 1/16	1/2	0.7000	0.531
1/2	14	4	5	3 1/8	1 3/8	5/8	0.6875	0.515
3/4	14	5	5	3 1/4	1 3/8	11/16	0.9063	0.679
1	11 1/2	5	5	3 3/4	1 3/4	13/16	1.1250	0.843
1 1/4	11 1/2	5	5	4	1 3/4	15/16	1.3125	0.984
1 1/2	11 1/2	6	7	4 1/4	1 3/4	1	1.5000	1.125
2	11 1/2	6	7	4 1/2	1 3/4	1 1/8	1.8750	1.406
2 1/2	8	8	.	5 1/2	2 9/16	1 1/4	2.2500	1.687
3	8	8	.	6	2 5/8	1 3/8	2.6250	1.968
3 1/2	8	9	.	6 1/2	2 11/16	1 1/2	2.8125	2.108
4	8	9	.	6 3/4	2 3/4	1 5/8	3.0000	2.250

These taps have American Standard pipe thread and taper of 3/4 inch per foot.

The following steels and threads are considered standard: For tap sizes from 1/8 to 4 inches, inclusive, carbon steel and either right-hand or left-hand regular threads; from 1/8 to 2 inches, high-speed steel and a regular cut thread, right hand; from 1/8 to 2 inches, high-speed steel with either an interrupted cut thread or a regular ground thread, right hand.

Nominal Size	Threads per Inch	Number of Flutes: Regular Thread	Number of Flutes: Interrupted Thread	Length Overall	Length of Full Thread	Length of Square	Diam. of Shank	Size of Square
Straight Pipe Taps								
1/8	27	4	..	2 1/8	3/4	3/8	0.3125	0.234
1/8	27	4	..	2 1/8	3/4	3/8	0.4375	0.328
1/4	18	4	..	2 7/16	1 1/16	7/16	0.5625	0.421
3/8	18	4	..	2 9/16	1 1/16	1/2	0.7000	0.531
1/2	14	4	..	3 1/8	1 3/8	5/8	0.6875	0.515
3/4	14	5	..	3 1/4	1 3/8	11/16	0.9063	0.679
1	11 1/2	5	..	3 3/4	1 3/4	13/16	1.1250	0.843
1 1/4	11 1/2	5	..	4	1 3/4	15/16	1.3125	0.984
1 1/2	11 1/2	6	..	4 1/4	1 3/4	1	1.5000	1.125
2	11 1/2	6	..	4 1/2	1 3/4	1 1/8	1.8750	1.406

Table 8. Combined Pipe Tap and Drill*

Nominal Size	Threads per Inch	Length Overall	Length of Full Thread	Length of Square	Size Square*: Small End	Size Square*: Large End	Gage† Measurement
1/8	27	Manufacturers Individual Practice	3/4	1 3/4	1/2	3/4	0.312
1/4	18		1 1/16	1 3/4	1/2	3/4	0.459
3/8	18		1 1/16	1 3/4	1/2	3/4	0.454
1/2	14		1 3/8	1 3/4	1/2	3/4	0.579
3/4	14		1 3/8	1 3/4	1/2	3/4	0.565
1	11 1/2		1 3/4	1 3/4	1/2	3/4	0.678
1 1/4	11 1/2		1 3/4	1 3/4	1/2	3/4	0.686
1 1/2	11 1/2		1 3/4	1 3/4	1/2	3/4	0.699
2	11 1/2		1 3/4	2	3/4	1	0.667

* Not included in the American Standard (B5.4-1948).

† Distance that the small end of tap projects through American Standard Pipe Thread Ring Gage.

Table 9. American Standard Taper and Straight Boiler Taps

Diameter of Tap	Threads per Inch	Number of Flutes	Length Overall	Length of Full Thread	Length of Square	Diam. of Shank	Size of Square
Taper Boiler Taps							
Hand taps having a taper of ¾ inch per foot. These taps are used by locomotive builders and railroad shops for tapping taper holes in boiler plate.							
½	12	4	4¼	2¼	½	0.5000	0.375
9⁄16	12	4	4⅝	2⅜	9⁄16	0.5625	0.421
⅝	12	4	5	2½	⅝	0.6250	0.468
11⁄16	12	4	5¼	2⅝	11⁄16	0.6875	0.515
¾	12	4	5½	2¾	¾	0.7500	0.562
13⁄16	12	4	5¾	2¾	13⁄16	0.8125	0.609
⅞	12	4	6	2¾	⅞	0.8750	0.656
15⁄16	12	4	6¼	2¾	15⁄16	0.9375	0.702
1	12	4	6½	2¾	1	1.0000	0.750
1 1⁄16	12	4	6¾	2¾	1 1⁄16	1.0625	0.796
1⅛	12	4	6⅞	2¾	1⅛	1.1250	0.843
1 3⁄16	12	4	7	2¾	1⅛	1.1875	0.890
1¼	12	5	7⅛	2 13⁄16	1¼	1.2500	0.937
1 5⁄16	12	5	7¼	2⅞	1¼	1.3125	0.984
1⅜	12	5	7⅜	2 15⁄16	1⅜	1.3750	1.031
1 7⁄16	12	5	7½	3	1⅜	1.4375	1.078
1½	12	5	7⅝	3	1⅜	1.5000	1.125
Straight Boiler Taps							
These are hand taps used by railroads and locomotive builders for tapping straight holes in boiler plate.							
½	12	4	4¼	2	½	0.5000	0.375
9⁄16	12	4	4⅝	2⅛	9⁄16	0.5625	0.421
⅝	12	4	5	2¼	⅝	0.6250	0.468
11⁄16	12	4	5¼	2⅜	11⁄16	0.6875	0.515
¾	12	4	5½	2½	¾	0.7500	0.562
13⁄16	12	4	5¾	2 11⁄16	13⁄16	0.8125	0.609
⅞	12	4	6	2⅞	⅞	0.8750	0.656
15⁄16	12	4	6¼	3	15⁄16	0.9375	0.702
1	12	4	6½	3 3⁄16	1	1.0000	0.750
1 1⁄16	12	4	6¾	3⅜	1 1⁄16	1.0625	0.796
1⅛	12	4	6⅞	3 7⁄16	1⅛	1.1250	0.843
1 3⁄16	12	4	7	3½	1⅛	1.1875	0.890
1¼	12	6	7⅛	3 9⁄16	1¼	1.2500	0.937
1 5⁄16	12	6	7¼	3⅝	1¼	1.3125	0.984
1⅜	12	6	7⅜	3¾	1⅜	1.3750	1.031
1 7⁄16	12	6	7½	3⅞	1⅜	1.4375	1.078
1½	12	6	7⅝	4	1⅜	1.5000	1.125

All dimensions are given in inches.
These taps are furnished with American National Form or "V" Form of thread.
The diameter of taper boiler taps is measured ⅝ in. from the large end of the thread.
All taps have internal center in thread end.   Sizes and dimensions not listed are special.
Left-hand taps are special.

Table 10. American Standard Staybolt Taps

This form of tap has a long shank and a reamer section, and it is used by boilermakers in tapping boiler sheets preparatory to inserting the staybolts.

Diameter of Tap	Threads per Inch	Length Overall	Length of Straight Thread	Length of Taper Thread	Length of Square	Diam. of Shank	Size of Square	Length of Reamer	Length of Shank
7/8	12	24	2	6	1	0.750	5/8	7	8
7/8	12	27	2	6½	1	0.750	5/8	7½	10
15/16	12	24	2	6	1	0.812	5/8	7	8
15/16	12	27	2	6½	1	0.812	5/8	7½	10
1	12	24	2	6	1	0.875	5/8	7	8
1	12	27	2	6½	1	0.875	5/8	7½	10
1 1/16	12	24	2	6	1	0.937	5/8	7	8
1 1/16	12	27	2	6½	1	0.937	5/8	7½	10
1 1/8	12	24	2	6	1	1.000	3/4	7	8
1 1/8	12	27	2	6½	1	1.000	3/4	7½	10
1 3/16	12	24	2	6	1	1.062	3/4	7	8
1 3/16	12	27	2	6½	1	1.062	3/4	7½	10
1 1/4	12	24	2	6	1	1.125	3/4	7	8
1 1/4	12	27	2	6½	1	1.125	3/4	7½	10
1 5/16	12	24	2	6	1	1.187	3/4	7	8
1 5/16	12	27	2	6½	1	1.187	3/4	7½	10
1 3/8	12	24	2	6	1	1.250	1	7	8
1 3/8	12	27	2	6½	1	1.250	1	7½	10
1 7/16	12	24	2	6	1	1.312	1	7	8
1 7/16	12	27	2	6½	1	1.312	1	7½	10
1 1/2	12	24	2	6	1	1.375	1	7	8
1 1/2	12	27	2	6½	1	1.375	1	7½	10

All dimensions are given in inches.

These taps are furnished with American National Form or "V" Form of thread. All sizes have 5 flutes.

All taps have internal center in reamer end.

Sizes and dimensions nor listed are special. Left-hand taps are special.

Table 11. American Standard Pulley Taps

This form of tap was designed originally for tapping set-screw holes in the hubs of pulleys, but it is also used where exceptionally long hand taps are required.

Diameter of Tap	Threads per Inch	Number of Flutes	Length Overall	Length of Full Thread	Length of Square	Diam. of Shank	Size of Square
1/4	20	4	6, 8	1	5/16	0.255	0.191
5/16	18	4	6, 8	1 1/8	3/8	0.318	0.238
3/8	16	4	6, 8, 10	1 1/4	7/16	0.381	0.286
7/16	14	4	6, 8, 10	1 7/16	1/2	0.444	0.333
1/2	13	4	6, 8, 10, 12	1 21/32	9/16	0.507	0.380
5/8	11	4	6, 8, 10, 12	1 13/16	11/16	0.633	0.475
3/4	10	4	10, 12	2	3/4	0.759	0.569

All dimensions are given in inches.

These taps are furnished with American National Form of thread in plug style.

Cut thread taps up to 5/16 inch inclusive have external center on thread end; sizes 3/8 inch and larger have internal center in thread end.

Ground thread taps have internal center in thread end.

Sizes and dimensions not listed are special. Taper and bottoming taps are special. Left-hand taps are special.

Table 12. American Standard Limits for Cut-thread Fractional-size Taps

Tap Size	Threads per Inch			Major Diameter			Pitch Diameter		
	NC	NF	NS	Basic	Min	Max	Basic	Min	Max
1/4	20	..	..	0.2500	0.2532	0.2557	0.2175	0.2180	0.2200
1/4	..	..	24	0.2500	0.2528	0.2553	0.2229	0.2234	0.2254
1/4	..	..	27	0.2500	0.2525	0.2550	0.2259	0.2264	0.2284
1/4	..	28	..	0.2500	0.2524	0.2549	0.2268	0.2273	0.2288
1/4	..	..	32	0.2500	0.2522	0.2547	0.2297	0.2302	0.2317
5/16	18	..	..	0.3125	0.3160	0.3185	0.2764	0.2769	0.2789
5/16	..	..	20	0.3125	0.3157	0.3182	0.2800	0.2805	0.2825
5/16	..	24	..	0.3125	0.3153	0.3178	0.2854	0.2859	0.2874
5/16	..	..	27	0.3125	0.3150	0.3175	0.2884	0.2889	0.2904
5/16	..	..	32	0.3125	0.3147	0.3172	0.2922	0.2927	0.2942
3/8	16	..	..	0.3750	0.3789	0.3814	0.3344	0.3349	0.3369
3/8	..	..	20	0.3750	0.3782	0.3807	0.3425	0.3430	0.3450
3/8	..	24	..	0.3750	0.3778	0.3803	0.3479	0.3484	0.3499
3/8	..	..	27	0.3750	0.3775	0.3800	0.3509	0.3514	0.3529
7/16	14	..	..	0.4375	0.4419	0.4449	0.3911	0.3916	0.3941
7/16	..	..	20	0.4375	0.4407	0.4437	0.4050	0.4055	0.4075
7/16	..	..	24	0.4375	0.4403	0.4433	0.4104	0.4109	0.4129
7/16	..	..	27	0.4375	0.4400	0.4430	0.4134	0.4139	0.4159
1/2	..	..	12	0.5000	0.5050	0.5080	0.4459	0.4464	0.4489
1/2	13	..	..	0.5000	0.5047	0.5077	0.4500	0.4505	0.4530
1/2	..	..	20	0.5000	0.5032	0.5062	0.4675	0.4680	0.4700
1/2	..	..	24	0.5000	0.5028	0.5058	0.4729	0.4734	0.4754
1/2	..	..	27	0.5000	0.5025	0.5055	0.4759	0.4764	0.4784
9/16	12	..	..	0.5625	0.5675	0.5705	0.5084	0.5089	0.5114
9/16	..	18	..	0.5625	0.5660	0.5690	0.5264	0.5269	0.5289
9/16	..	..	27	0.5625	0.5650	0.5680	0.5384	0.5389	0.5409
5/8	11	..	..	0.6250	0.6304	0.6334	0.5660	0.5665	0.5690
5/8	..	..	12	0.6250	0.6300	0.6330	0.5709	0.5714	0.5739
5/8	..	18	..	0.6250	0.6285	0.6315	0.5889	0.5894	0.5914
5/8	..	..	27	0.6250	0.6275	0.6305	0.6009	0.6014	0.6034
11/16	..	..	11	0.6875	0.6929	0.6969	0.6285	0.6290	0.6320
11/16	..	..	16	0.6875	0.6914	0.6954	0.6469	0.6474	0.6499
3/4	10	..	..	0.7500	0.7559	0.7599	0.6850	0.6855	0.6885
3/4	..	..	12	0.7500	0.7550	0.7590	0.6959	0.6964	0.6994
3/4	..	16	..	0.7500	0.7539	0.7579	0.7094	0.7099	0.7124
3/4	..	..	27	0.7500	0.7525	0.7565	0.7259	0.7264	0.7289
7/8	9	..	..	0.8750	0.8820	0.8860	0.8028	0.8038	0.8068
7/8	..	..	12	0.8750	0.8805	0.8845	0.8209	0.8219	0.8249
7/8	..	14	..	0.8750	0.8799	0.8839	0.8286	0.8296	0.8321
7/8	..	..	27	0.8750	0.8780	0.8820	0.8509	0.8519	0.8544
1	8	..	..	1.0000	1.0078	1.0118	0.9188	0.9198	0.9228
1	..	..	12	1.0000	1.0055	1.0095	0.9459	0.9469	0.9499
1	..	14	..	1.0000	1.0049	1.0089	0.9536	0.9546	0.9571
1	..	..	27	1.0000	1.0030	1.0070	0.9759	0.9769	0.9794
1 1/8	7	..	..	1.1250	1.1337	1.1382	1.0322	1.0332	1.0367
1 1/8	..	12	..	1.1250	1.1305	1.1350	1.0709	1.0719	1.0749
1 1/4	7	..	..	1.2500	1.2587	1.2632	1.1572	1.1582	1.1617
1 1/4	..	12	..	1.2500	1.2555	1.2600	1.1959	1.1969	1.1999
1 3/8	6	..	..	1.3750	1.3850	1.3895	1.2667	1.2677	1.2712
1 3/8	..	12	..	1.3750	1.3805	1.3850	1.3209	1.3219	1.3249
1 1/2	6	..	..	1.5000	1.5100	1.5145	1.3917	1.3927	1.3962
1 1/2	..	12	..	1.5000	1.5055	1.5100	1.4459	1.4469	1.4499
1 5/8	..	..	5 1/2	1.6250	1.6344	1.6399	1.5069	1.5084	1.5124
1 3/4	5	..	..	1.7500	1.7602	1.7657	1.6201	1.6216	1.6256
1 7/8	..	..	5	1.8750	1.8852	1.8907	1.7451	1.7466	1.7506
2	4 1/2	..	..	2.0000	2.0111	2.0166	1.8557	1.8572	1.8612

Lead Tolerance: Plus or minus 0.003 inch max. per inch of thread.

Angle Tolerance: Plus or minus 35 min. in half angle or 53 min. in full angle for 4½ to 5½ thds. per in.; 40 min. half angle and 60 min. full angle for 6 to 9 thds.; 45 min. half angle and 68 min. full angle for 10 to 28 thds.; 60 min. half angle and 90 min. full angle for 30 to 64 thds. per in.

Table 13. American Standard Limits for Ground-thread Fractional-size Taps

Tap Size	Threads per Inch		Commercial Ground Threads					
	NC	NF	Basic Major Diam.	Min Major Diam.	Max Major Diam.	Basic Pitch Diam.	Min Pitch Diam.	Max Pitch Diam.
1/4	20	..	0.2500	0.2540	0.2550	0.2175	0.2180	0.2190
1/4	..	28	0.2500	0.2525	0.2535	0.2268	0.2273	0.2283
5/16	18	..	0.3125	0.3170	0.3180	0.2764	0.2769	0.2779
5/16	..	24	0.3125	0.3155	0.3165	0.2854	0.2859	0.2869
3/8	16	..	0.3750	0.3800	0.3810	0.3344	0.3349	0.3359
3/8	..	24	0.3750	0.3780	0.3790	0.3479	0.3484	0.3494
7/16	14	..	0.4375	0.4435	0.4445	0.3911	0.3916	0.3926
7/16	..	20	0.4375	0.4415	0.4425	0.4050	0.4055	0.4065
1/2	13	..	0.5000	0.5065	0.5075	0.4500	0.4505	0.4515
1/2	..	20	0.5000	0.5040	0.5050	0.4675	0.4680	0.4690
9/16	12	..	0.5625	0.5690	0.5700	0.5084	0.5089	0.5099
9/16	..	18	0.5625	0.5670	0.5680	0.5264	0.5269	0.5279
5/8	11	..	0.6250	0.6320	0.6330	0.5660	0.5665	0.5676
5/8	..	18	0.6250	0.6295	0.6305	0.5889	0.5894	0.5904
3/4	10	..	0.7500	0.7575	0.7590	0.6850	0.6855	0.6866
3/4	..	16	0.7500	0.7550	0.7560	0.7094	0.7099	0.7109
7/8	9	..	0.8750	0.8835	0.8850	0.8028	0.8038	0.8050
7/8	..	14	0.8750	0.8810	0.8820	0.8286	0.8296	0.8306
1	8	..	1.0000	1.0095	1.0110	0.9188	0.9198	0.9212
1	..	14	1.0000	1.0060	1.0070	0.9536	0.9546	0.9556
1 1/8	7	..	1.1250	1.1350	1.1370	1.0322	1.0332	1.0347
1 1/8	..	12	1.1250	1.1315	1.1325	1.0709	1.0719	1.0729
1 1/4	7	..	1.2500	1.2600	1.2620	1.1572	1.1582	1.1597
1 1/4	..	12	1.2500	1.2565	1.2575	1.1959	1.1969	1.1979
1 3/8	6	..	1.3750	1.3870	1.3890	1.2667	1.2677	1.2695
1 3/8	..	12	1.3750	1.3815	1.3825	1.3209	1.3219	1.3229
1 1/2	6	..	1.5000	1.5120	1.5140	1.3917	1.3927	1.3945
1 1/2	..	12	1.5000	1.5065	1.5075	1.4459	1.4469	1.4479

Tap Size	Threads per Inch		Precision Ground Threads						
			Major Diameter		Basic Pitch Diam.	Pitch Diameter Limits*			
	NC	NF	Min	Max		Minor	Max or Min 1	Max 1 Min 2	Max 2
1/4	20	..	0.2540	0.2550	0.2175	0.2170	0.2175	0.2180	0.2185
1/4	..	28	0.2525	0.2535	0.2268	......	0.2268	0.2273	0.2278
5/16	18	..	0.3170	0.3180	0.2764	0.2759	0.2764	0.2769	0.2774
5/16	..	24	0.3155	0.3165	0.2854	......	0.2854	0.2859	0.2864
3/8	16	..	0.3800	0.3810	0.3344	0.3339	0.3344	0.3349	0.3354
3/8	..	24	0.3780	0.3790	0.3479	......	0.3479	0.3484	0.3489
7/16	14	..	0.4435	0.4445	0.3911	0.3906	0.3911	0.3916	0.3921
7/16	..	20	0.4415	0.4425	0.4050	......	0.4050	0.4055	0.4060
1/2	13	..	0.5065	0.5075	0.4500	0.4495	0.4500	0.4505	0.4510
1/2	..	20	0.5040	0.5050	0.4675	......	0.4675	0.4680	0.4685
9/16	12	..	0.5690	0.5700	0.5084	......	0.5084	0.5089	0.5094
9/16	..	18	0.5670	0.5680	0.5264	......	0.5264	0.5269	0.5274
5/8	11	..	0.6320	0.6330	0.5660	......	0.5660	0.5665	0.5670
5/8	..	18	0.6295	0.6305	0.5889	......	0.5889	0.5894	0.5899
3/4	10	..	0.7575	0.7590	0.6850	......	0.6850	0.6855	0.6860
3/4	..	16	0.7550	0.7560	0.7094	......	0.7094	0.7099	0.7104
7/8	9	..	0.8835	0.8850	0.8028	......	0.8028	0.8033	0.8038
7/8	..	14	0.8810	0.8820	0.8286	......	0.8286	0.8291	0.8296
1	8	..	1.0095	1.0110	0.9188	......	0.9188	0.9193	0.9198
1	..	14	1.0060	1.0070	0.9536	......	0.9536	0.9541	0.9546

Lead Tolerance (for both "Commercial" and "Precision Ground" Taps): Plus or minus 0.0005 inch per inch of thread. *Angle Tolerance:* Plus or minus 25 min. in half angle for 6 to 9 threads, commercial ground, and 8 to 9 threads per inch, precision ground; in both cases 30 min. for 10 to 28 threads per inch inc.

* See Identifying Marks on Ground Thread Taps, page 1261.

Table 14. American Standard Limits for Ground-thread Machine-screw Taps

Screw Size Number	Threads per Inch			Major Diameter			Pitch Diameter		
	NC	NF	NS	Basic	Min	Max	Basic	Min	Max
Commercial Ground Thread									
3	48	..	..	0.0990	0.1000	0.1010	0.0855	0.0857	0.0867
3	..	56	..	0.0990	0.0995	0.1005	0.0874	0.0876	0.0886
4	..	..	36	0.1120	0.1135	0.1145	0.0940	0.0942	0.0952
4	40	..	..	0.1120	0.1135	0.1145	0.0958	0.0960	0.0970
4	..	48	..	0.1120	0.1130	0.1140	0.0985	0.0987	0.0997
5	40	..	..	0.1250	0.1265	0.1275	0.1088	0.1090	0.1100
5	..	44	..	0.1250	0.1260	0.1270	0.1102	0.1104	0.1114
6	32	..	..	0.1380	0.1400	0.1410	0.1177	0.1182	0.1192
6	..	40	..	0.1380	0.1395	0.1405	0.1218	0.1220	0.1230
8	32	..	..	0.1640	0.1660	0.1670	0.1437	0.1442	0.1452
8	..	36	..	0.1640	0.1655	0.1665	0.1460	0.1462	0.1472
10	24	..	..	0.1900	0.1930	0.1940	0.1629	0.1634	0.1644
10	..	32	..	0.1900	0.1920	0.1930	0.1697	0.1702	0.1712
12	24	..	..	0.2160	0.2190	0.2200	0.1889	0.1894	0.1904
12	..	28	..	0.2160	0.2185	0.2195	0.1928	0.1933	0.1943
14	..	..	20	0.2420	0.2460	0.2470	0.2095	0.2100	0.2110
14	..	..	24	0.2420	0.2450	0.2460	0.2149	0.2154	0.2164
Precision Ground Thread									
0	..	80	..	0.0600	0.0605	0.0615	0.0519	0.0519	0.0524
1	..	..	56	0.0730	0.0735	0.0745	0.0614	0.0614	0.0619
1	64	..	..	0.0730	0.0735	0.0745	0.0629	0.0629	0.0634
1	..	72	..	0.0730	0.0735	0.0745	0.0640	0.0640	0.0645
2	56	..	..	0.0860	0.0865	0.0875	0.0744	0.0744	0.0749
2	..	64	..	0.0860	0.0865	0.0875	0.0759	0.0759	0.0764
3	48	..	..	0.0990	0.1000	0.1010	0.0855	0.0855	0.0860
3	..	56	..	0.0990	0.0995	0.1005	0.0874	0.0874	0.0879
4	..	..	36	0.1120	0.1135	0.1145	0.0940	0.0940	0.0945
4	40	..	..	0.1120	0.1135	0.1145	0.0958	0.0958	0.0963
4	..	48	..	0.1120	0.1130	0.1140	0.0985	0.0985	0.0990
5	40	..	..	0.1250	0.1265	0.1275	0.1088	0.1088	0.1093
5	..	44	..	0.1250	0.1260	0.1270	0.1102	0.1102	0.1107
6	32	..	..	0.1380	0.1400	0.1410	0.1177	0.1177	0.1182
6	..	40	..	0.1380	0.1395	0.1405	0.1218	0.1218	0.1223
8	32	..	..	0.1640	0.1660	0.1670	0.1437	0.1437	0.1442
8	..	36	..	0.1640	0.1655	0.1665	0.1460	0.1460	0.1465
10	24	..	..	0.1900	0.1930	0.1940	0.1629	0.1629	0.1634
10	..	32	..	0.1900	0.1920	0.1930	0.1697	0.1697	0.1702
12	24	..	..	0.2160	0.2190	0.2200	0.1889	0.1889	0.1894
12	..	28	..	0.2160	0.2185	0.2195	0.1928	0.1928	0.1933

All dimensions are given in inches.
Lead Tolerance: Plus or minus 0.0005 inch per inch of thread.
Angle Tolerance: Plus or minus 30 min. in half angle for 20 to 80 threads per inch inc.

Table 15. American Standard Limits for Cut-thread Machine Screw Taps

Screw Size Number	Threads per Inch			Major Diameter			Pitch Diameter		
	NC	NF	NS	Basic	Min	Max	Basic	Min	Max
0	..	80	..	0.0600	0.0609	0.0624	0.0519	0.0521	0.0531
1	64	..	..	0.0730	0.0740	0.0755	0.0629	0.0631	0.0641
1	..	72	..	0.0730	0.0740	0.0755	0.0640	0.0642	0.0652
2	56	..	..	0.0860	0.0872	0.0887	0.0744	0.0746	0.0756
2	..	64	..	0.0860	0.0870	0.0885	0.0759	0.0761	0.0771
3	48	..	..	0.0990	0.1003	0.1018	0.0855	0.0857	0.0867
3	..	56	..	0.0990	0.1002	0.1017	0.0874	0.0876	0.0886
4	..	..	36	0.1120	0.1137	0.1157	0.0940	0.0942	0.0957
4	40	..	..	0.1120	0.1136	0.1156	0.0958	0.0960	0.0975
4	..	48	..	0.1120	0.1133	0.1153	0.0985	0.0987	0.1002
5	40	..	..	0.1250	0.1266	0.1286	0.1088	0.1090	0.1105
5	..	44	..	0.1250	0.1264	0.1284	0.1102	0.1104	0.1119
6	32	..	..	0.1380	0.1402	0.1422	0.1177	0.1182	0.1197
6	..	40	..	0.1380	0.1396	0.1416	0.1218	0.1220	0.1235
8	32	..	..	0.1640	0.1662	0.1682	0.1437	0.1442	0.1457
8	..	36	..	0.1640	0.1657	0.1677	0.1460	0.1462	0.1477
10	24	..	..	0.1900	0.1928	0.1948	0.1629	0.1634	0.1649
10	..	32	..	0.1900	0.1922	0.1942	0.1697	0.1702	0.1717
12	24	..	..	0.2160	0.2188	0.2208	0.1889	0.1894	0.1909
12	..	28	..	0.2160	0.2184	0.2204	0.1928	0.1933	0.1948
14	..	..	20	0.2420	0.2452	0.2477	0.2095	0.2100	0.2120
14	..	..	24	0.2420	0.2448	0.2473	0.2149	0.2154	0.2174

Lead Tolerance: Plus or minus 0.003 inch per inch of thread.   *Angle Tolerance:* Plus or minus 45 min. in half angle and 68 min. in full angle for 20 to 28 threads per inch; plus or minus 60 min. in half angle and 90 min. in full angle for 30 or more threads per inch.

Table 16. American Standard Taper Pipe Taps — Cut and Ground Threads

Nominal Tap Size	Threads per Inch	Gage Measurement*			Lead Tolerance per Inch of Thread, Plus or Minus		Angle Tolerance		
		Projection, Inches	Tolerance, Plus or Minus				Half Angle, Plus or Minus		Full Angle
			Cut Thread	Ground Thread	Cut Thread	Ground Thread	Cut Thread	Ground Thread	Cut Thread
1/8	27	0.312	1/16	1/16	0.003	0.0005	45'	30'	68'
1/4	18	0.459	1/16	1/16	0.003	0.0005	45'	30'	68'
3/8	18	0.454	1/16	1/16	0.003	0.0005	45'	30'	68'
1/2	14	0.579	1/16	1/16	0.003	0.0005	45'	30'	68'
3/4	14	0.565	1/16	1/16	0.003	0.0005	45'	30'	68'
1	11½	0.678	3/32	3/32	0.003	0.0005	45'	30'	68'
1¼	11½	0.686	3/32	3/32	0.003	0.0005	45'	30'	68'
1½	11½	0.699	3/32	3/32	0.003	0.0005	45'	30'	68'
2	11½	0.667	3/32	3/32	0.003	0.0005	45'	30'	68'
2½	8	0.925	3/32	3/32	0.003	0.0005	40'	25'	60'
3	8	0.925	3/32	3/32	0.003	0.0005	40'	25'	60'
3½	8	0.938	1/8	1/8	0.003	0.0005	40'	25'	60'
4	8	0.950	1/8	1/8	0.003	0.0005	40'	25'	60'

* Distance that small end of tap projects through standard pipe thread ring gage.
Lead Error: For cut thread 0.003 inch per inch; for ground thread, 0.0005 inch per inch of thread.

Table 17. American Standard Straight Pipe Taps — Cut Thread

Nominal Size	Threads per Inch, NPS	Size at Gaging Notch	Pitch Diameter		Values to use in Formulas		
			Min	Max	*A*	*B*	*C*
⅛	27	0.3748	0.3733	0.3763	0.0267	0.0296	0.0257
¼	18	0.4899	0.4884	0.4914	0.0408	0.0444	0.0401
⅜	18	0.6270	0.6253	0.6288			
½	14	0.7784	0.7767	0.7802	0.0535	0.0571	0.0525
¾	14	0.9889	0.9869	0.9909			
1	11½	1.2386	1.2366	1.2406	0.0658	0.0696	0.0647
1¼	11½	1.5834	1.5811	1.5856			
1½	11½	1.8223	1.8201	1.8246			
2	11½	2.2963	2.2938	2.2988			

If M = actual or measured pitch diameter, inches

Major diam. min. = $M + A$ Minor diam. min. = $M - B$

Major diam. max. = $M + B$ Minor diam. max. = $M - C$

Max. lead tolerance ±0.003 inch per inch of thread. Angle tolerance, all pitches, ±45 min. in half angle and 68 min. in full angle. The thread is the American Standard pipe form.

Table 18. American Standard Straight Pipe Taps — Ground Thread

Nominal Size, Inches	Threads per Inch	Major Diameter			Pitch Diameter		
		Plug at Gaging Notch	Min *G*	Max *H*	Plug at Gaging Notch *E*	Min *K*	Max *L*
⅛	27	0.3994	0.4034	0.4044	0.3748	0.3753	0.3763
¼	18	0.5269	0.5323	0.5333	0.4899	0.4904	0.4914
⅜	18	0.6640	0.6694	0.6704	0.6270	0.6275	0.6285
½	14	0.8260	0.8335	0.8345	0.7784	0.7789	0.6799
¾	14	1.0364	1.0440	1.0450	0.9889	0.9894	0.7904
1	11½	1.2966	1.3057	1.3072	1.2386	1.2396	1.2407

Formulas For American Standard Pipe Form*

Nominal Size	Major Diameter		Minor Diameter		Pitch Diameter	
	Min *G*	Max *H*	Min	Max	Min *K*	Max *L*
⅛	$H - 0.0010$	$(K + A) - 0.0005$	$M - A$	$M - B$	$E + 0.0005$	$K + C$
¼ to ¾	$H - 0.0010$	$(K + A) - 0.0015$	$M - A$	$M - B$	$E + 0.0005$	$K + C$
1	$H - 0.0015$	$(K + A) - 0.0020$	$M - A$	$M - B$	$E + 0.0010$	$K + C$

Threads per Inch	*A*	*B*	*C*	Threads per Inch	*A*	*B*	*C*
27	0.0296	0.0257	0.0010	14	0.0571	0.0525	0.0010
18	0.0444	0.0401	0.0010	11½	0.0696	0.0647	0.0011

* In the formulas, M equals the actual or measured pitch diameter. Max. lead tolerance ±0.0005 inch per inch of thread. Angle tolerance, all pitches, ±30 min. in half angle. The thread is the American Standard pipe form.

Table 19.   American Standard Straight Boiler and Staybolt Taps — Cut Thread

Size	Threads per Inch, NF	Major Diameter			Pitch Diameter		
		Basic	Min	Max	Basic	Min	Max
½	12	0.5000	0.5010	0.5040	0.4459	0.4464	0.4489
9⁄16	12	0.5625	0.5635	0.5665	0.5084	0.5089	0.5114
5⁄8	12	0.6250	0.6260	0.6290	0.5709	0.5714	0.5739
11⁄16	12	0.6875	0.6885	0.6925	0.6334	0.6339	0.6369
¾	12	0.7500	0.7510	0.7550	0.6959	0.6964	0.6994
13⁄16	12	0.8125	0.8135	0.8175	0.7584	0.7589	0.7619
7⁄8	12	0.8750	0.8760	0.8800	0.8209	0.8214	0.8244
15⁄16	12	0.9375	0.9385	0.9425	0.8834	0.8839	0.8869
1	12	1.0000	1.0010	1.0050	0.9459	0.9464	0.9494
1 1⁄16	12	1.0625	1.0635	1.0675	1.0084	1.0089	1.0119
1⅛	12	1.1250	1.1265	1.1310	1.0709	1.0714	1.0749
1 3⁄16	12	1.1875	1.1890	1.1935	1.1334	1.1339	1.1374
1¼	12	1.2500	1.2515	1.2560	1.1959	1.1964	1.1999
1 5⁄16	12	1.3125	1.3140	1.3185	1.2584	1.2589	1.2624
1⅜	12	1.3750	1.3765	1.3810	1.3209	1.3214	1.3249
1 7⁄16	12	1.4375	1.4390	1.4435	1.3834	1.3839	1.3874
1½	12	1.5000	1.5015	1.5060	1.4459	1.4464	1.4499

Lead Tolerance: Plus or minus 0.003 inch per inch of thread.   *Angle Tolerance:* Plus or minus 45 min. in half angle and 68 min. in full angle.

Acme and Square-threaded Taps. — These taps are usually made in sets, three taps in a set undoubtedly being the most common.   For very fine pitches, two taps in a set will be found sufficient, while as many as five taps in a set are used for coarse pitches.   Tables are given herewith for proportioning both Acme and square-threaded taps when made in sets.   One leading tap maker in cutting the threads of square-threaded taps makes them according to the following rules: The width of the groove between two threads is made equal to one-half the pitch of the thread, less 0.004 inch.   This makes the width of the thread itself equal to one-half of the pitch, plus 0.004 inch.   The depth of the thread is made equal to 0.45 times the pitch, plus 0.0025 inch.   This latter rule produces a thread which for all the ordinarily used pitches for square-threaded taps has a depth less than the generally accepted standard depth, this latter depth being equal to one-half the pitch.   The object of this shallow thread is to insure that if the hole to be threaded by the tap is not bored out so as to provide clearance at the bottom of the thread, the tap will cut its own clearance.   The hole should, however, always be drilled out large enough so that the cutting of the clearance is not required of the tap.

Another maker follows under ordinary conditions the dimensions given in the accompanying tables, making the diameter at the end of the chamfer of the first tap equal to the root diameter of the thread, plus 0.010 inch.   The diameter at the end of the chamfer of the second and third taps is made equal to the diameter of the straight portion of the next previous tap, minus 0.005 inch.

For Acme thread taps, this manufacturer makes the actual root diameter on the first tap 0.010 inch, and on the second tap 0.005 inch less than the standard root diameter.   The finishing tap is made with standard root diameter, and a standard thread tool is used for all three taps in a set.

The table, "Dimensions of Acme Thread Taps in Sets of Three Taps" may be used for the length dimensions for Acme taps.   The dimensions in this table apply to single-threaded taps.   For multiple-threaded taps or taps with very coarse pitch, relative to the diameter, the length of the chamfered part of the thread may be increased.   Square-threaded taps are made to the same table as Acme taps, with the exception of the figures in column K, which for square-threaded taps should be equal to the nominal diameter of the tap, no oversize allowance being customary in these taps. The first tap in a set of Acme taps (not square-threaded taps) should be turned taper in bottom of the thread for a distance of about one-quarter of the length of the threaded part. The taper should be so selected that the root diameter is about 1/32 inch smaller at the point than the proper root diameter of the tap. The first tap should preferably be provided with a short pilot at the point. For very coarse pitches, the first tap may be provided with spiral flutes at right angles to the angle of the thread. Acme and square-threaded taps should be relieved or backed off on the top of the thread of the chamfered portion on all of the taps in the set. When the taps are used as machine taps, rather than as hand taps, they should be relieved in the angle of the thread, as well as on the top, for the whole length of the chamfered portion. Acme taps should also always be relieved on the front side of the thread to within 1/32 inch of the cutting edge.

Table for Making Acme Thread Taps in Sets of Three Taps

No. of Threads per Inch	Amount in Inches to be Added to Root Diameter of Tap to Obtain Diameter of Straight Part of Thread of		No. of Threads per Inch	Amount in Inches to be Added to Root Diameter of Tap to Obtain Diameter of Straight Part of Thread of	
	1st Tap	2d Tap		1st Tap	2d Tap
1	0.468	0.832	5	0.108	0.192
1½	0.318	0.566	5½	0.100	0.178
2	0.243	0.432	6	0.093	0.166
2½	0.198	0.352	7	0.082	0.146
3	0.168	0.298	8	0.074	0.132
3½	0.147	0.261	9	0.068	0.121
4	0.130	0.232	10	0.063	0.112
4½	0.118	0.210	12	0.055	0.098

Table for Making Square-threaded Taps in Sets of Three Taps

No. of Threads per Inch	Amount in Inches to be Added to Root Diameter of Tap to Obtain Diameter of Straight Part of Thread of		No. of Threads per Inch	Amount in Inches to be Added to Root Diameter of Tap to Obtain Diameter of Straight Part of Thread of	
	1st Tap	2d Tap		1st Tap	2d Tap
1	0.410	0.800	5	0.082	0.160
1½	0.273	0.533	5½	0.075	0.146
2	0.205	0.400	6	0.068	0.133
2½	0.164	0.320	7	0.059	0.114
3	0.137	0.267	8	0.051	0.100
3½	0.117	0.229	9	0.046	0.089
4	0.102	0.200	10	0.041	0.080
4½	0.091	0.178	12	0.034	0.067

Proportions of Acme and Square-threaded Taps Made in Sets

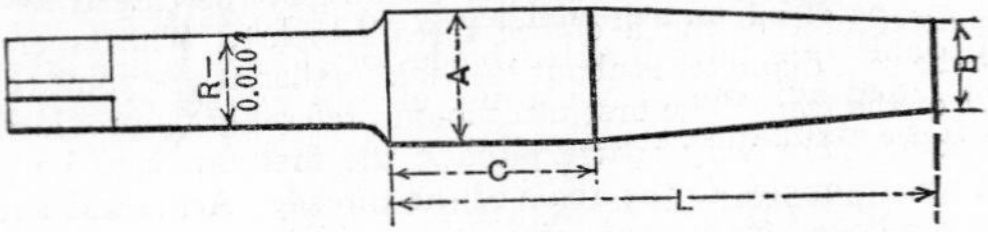

R = root diameter of thread.   D = full diameter of tap.
T = double depth of full thread.

Kind of Tap	No. of Taps in Set	Order of Tap in Set	A	B	C
Acme Thread Taps	2	1st 2d	$R + 0.65\,T$ D	$R + 0.010$ A on 1st tap — 0.005	⅛ L to ⅙ L ¼ L to ⅓ L
	3	1st 2d 3d	$R + 0.45\,T$ $R + 0.80\,T$ D	$R + 0.010$ A on 1st tap — 0.005 A on 2d tap — 0.005	⅛ L to ⅙ L ⅙ L to ¼ L ¼ L to ⅓ L
	4	1st 2d 3d 4th	$R + 0.40\,T$ $R + 0.70\,T$ $R + 0.90\,T$ D	$R + 0.010$ A on 1st tap — 0.005 A on 2d tap — 0.005 A on 3d tap — 0.005	⅛ L ⅙ L ⅕ L ¼ L to ⅓ L
	5	1st 2d 3d 4th 5th	$R + 0.37\,T$ $R + 0.63\,T$ $R + 0.82\,T$ $R + 0.94\,T$ D	$R + 0.010$ A on 1st tap — 0.005 A on 2d tap — 0.005 A on 3d tap — 0.005 A on 4th tap — 0.005	⅛ L ⅙ L ⅕ L ⅕ L to ¼ L ¼ L to ⅓ L
Square-threaded Taps	2	1st 2d	$R + 0.67\,T$ D	R A on 1st tap — 0.005	⅛ L to ⅙ L ¼ L to ⅓ L
	3	1st 2d 3d	$R + 0.41\,T$ $R + 0.80\,T$ D	R A on 1st tap — 0.005 A on 2d tap — 0.005	⅛ L to ⅙ L ⅙ L to ¼ L ¼ L to ⅓ L
	4	1st 2d 3d 4th	$R + 0.32\,T$ $R + 0.62\,T$ $R + 0.90\,T$ D	R A on 1st tap — 0.005 A on 2d tap — 0.005 A on 3d tap — 0.005	⅛ L ⅙ L ⅕ L ¼ L to ⅓ L
	5	1st 2d 3d 4th 5th	$R + 0.26\,T$ $R + 0.50\,T$ $R + 0.72\,T$ $R + 0.92\,T$ D	R A on 1st tap — 0.005 A on 2d tap — 0.005 A on 3d tap — 0.005 A on 4th tap — 0.005	⅛ L ⅙ L ⅕ L ⅕ L to ¼ L ¼ L to ⅓ L

Die Hobs. — Die hobs for taps are designed for sizing or tapping threads in dies. Short die hobs as made by Pratt & Whitney are used for sizing dies. They have 5 threads chamfered and are not relieved. Long die hobs are suitable for finishing dies from the solid in one operation. They are relieved and are provided with a pilot of the same diameter as the root or minor diameter of the thread to be cut. There are also taper pipe hobs designed for finishing pipe dies.

Adjustable Taps. — Many adjustable taps are now used, especially for accurate work. Some taps of this class are made of a solid piece of steel which is split and provided with means of expanding sufficiently to compensate for wear. Most of the larger adjustable taps have inserted blades or chasers which are rigidly held, but capable of radial adjustment. The use of taps of this general class enables standard sizes to be maintained readily.

Advantages of Collapsing Taps. — Collapsing taps are similar in principle to self-opening dies, except that the action is reversed, the tap chasers moving inward to permit the rapid removal of the tap from the hole. This collapsing action may be due to the engagement of a collar gage-plate or lever on the tap with the

Dimensions of Acme Thread Taps in Sets of Three Taps

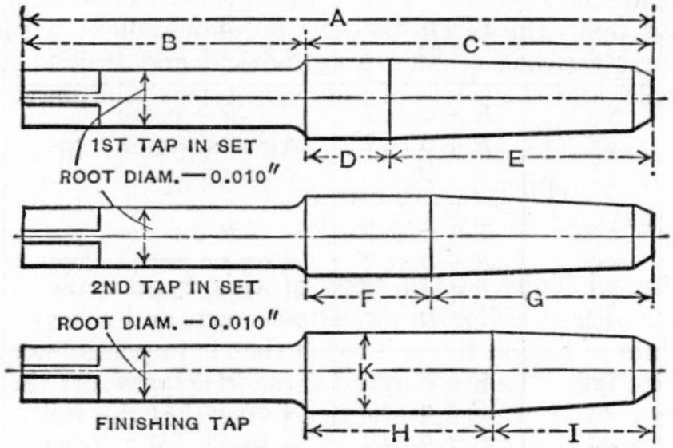

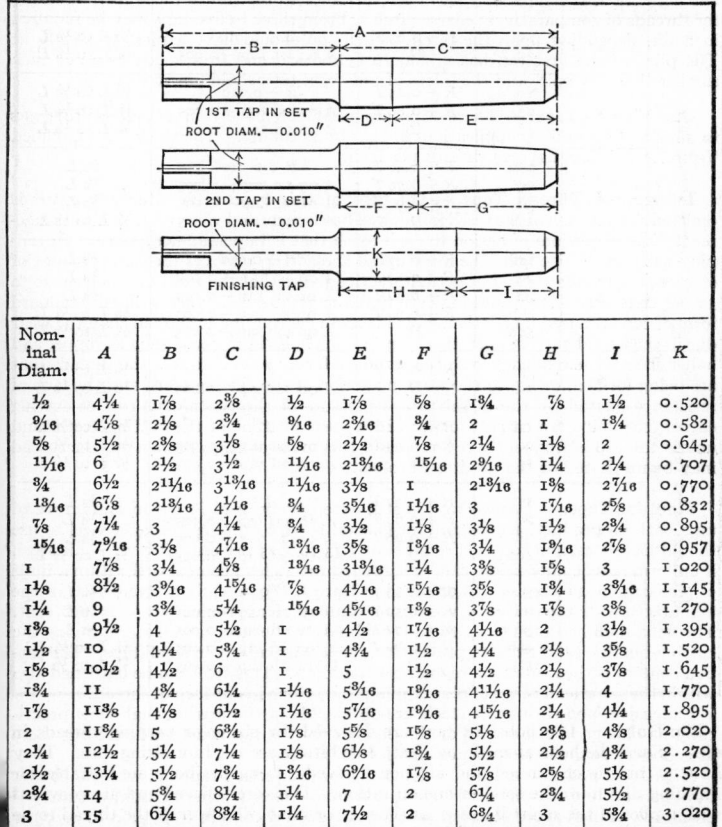

Nominal Diam.	A	B	C	D	E	F	G	H	I	K
1/2	4 1/4	1 7/8	2 3/8	1/2	1 7/8	5/8	1 3/4	7/8	1 1/2	0.520
9/16	4 7/8	2 1/8	2 3/4	9/16	2 3/16	3/4	2	1	1 3/4	0.582
5/8	5 1/2	2 3/8	3 1/8	5/8	2 1/2	7/8	2 1/4	1 1/8	2	0.645
11/16	6	2 1/2	3 1/2	11/16	2 13/16	15/16	2 9/16	1 1/4	2 1/4	0.707
3/4	6 1/2	2 11/16	3 13/16	11/16	3 1/8	1	2 13/16	1 3/8	2 7/16	0.770
13/16	6 7/8	2 13/16	4 1/16	3/4	3 5/16	1 1/16	3	1 7/16	2 5/8	0.832
7/8	7 1/4	3	4 1/4	3/4	3 1/2	1 1/8	3 1/8	1 1/2	2 3/4	0.895
15/16	7 9/16	3 1/8	4 7/16	13/16	3 5/8	1 3/16	3 1/4	1 9/16	2 7/8	0.957
1	7 7/8	3 1/4	4 5/8	13/16	3 13/16	1 1/4	3 3/8	1 5/8	3	1.020
1 1/8	8 1/2	3 9/16	4 15/16	7/8	4 1/16	1 5/16	3 5/8	1 3/4	3 3/16	1.145
1 1/4	9	3 3/4	5 1/4	15/16	4 5/16	1 3/8	3 7/8	1 7/8	3 3/8	1.270
1 3/8	9 1/2	4	5 1/2	1	4 1/2	1 7/16	4 1/16	2	3 1/2	1.395
1 1/2	10	4 1/4	5 3/4	1	4 3/4	1 1/2	4 1/4	2 1/8	3 5/8	1.520
1 5/8	10 1/2	4 1/2	6	1	5	1 1/2	4 1/2	2 1/8	3 7/8	1.645
1 3/4	11	4 3/4	6 1/4	1 1/16	5 3/16	1 9/16	4 11/16	2 1/4	4	1.770
1 7/8	11 3/8	4 7/8	6 1/2	1 1/16	5 7/16	1 9/16	4 15/16	2 1/4	4 1/4	1.895
2	11 3/4	5	6 3/4	1 1/8	5 5/8	1 5/8	5 1/8	2 3/8	4 3/8	2.020
2 1/4	12 1/2	5 1/4	7 1/4	1 1/8	6 1/8	1 3/4	5 1/2	2 1/2	4 3/4	2.270
2 1/2	13 1/4	5 1/2	7 3/4	1 3/16	6 9/16	1 7/8	5 7/8	2 5/8	5 1/8	2.520
2 3/4	14	5 3/4	8 1/4	1 1/4	7	2	6 1/4	2 3/4	5 1/2	2.770
3	15	6 1/4	8 3/4	1 1/4	7 1/2	2	6 3/4	3	5 3/4	3.020

surface of the work or with a fixed stop. With some designs, the collapsing action occurs only after the travel of the turret-slide is discontinued and is due to the relative motion between parts or sections of the tap itself. Collapsing taps not only reduce the time for the tapping period, but they avoid marring the thread.

Combination Taps and Dies. — Combination tools arranged for cutting an external thread and tapping a hole at the same time may be used to advantage in some cases. If the tap of a combination tool is used for cutting threads of different pitch, the difference in the rate at which they advance is compensated for by providing a floating movement for either the tap or the die.

Tapping Square Threads. — If it is necessary to tap square threads, this should be done by using a set of taps that will form the thread by a progressive cutting action, the taps varying in size in order to distribute the work, especially for threads of comparatively coarse pitch. From three to five taps may be required in a set, depending upon the pitch. Each tap should have a pilot to steady it. The pilot of the first tap has a smooth cylindrical end from 0.003 to 0.005 inch smaller than the hole, and the pilots of following taps should have teeth.

Gas Fixture Taps. — These taps are used extensively in manufacturing gas fixtures and for various applications of thin brass tubing. The thread is a modified V-form. All sizes have 27 threads per inch.

Interrupted Thread Taps. — On taps of this type each alternate tooth is omitted so that each of the teeth is followed by a space, and vice versa. This arrangement gives a freedom of action to each tooth that is impossible otherwise. In tapping out a given size hole, the interrupted thread tap removes the same amount of stock as the standard tap but actual practice shows that the resistance is from 30 to 50 per cent less. This would indicate that the greater resistance with the standard form of tap is caused by friction, which is more destructive to the tap than the wear due in the actual cutting operation. In tapping holes in material such as copper and boiler sheets, the tendency with the standard form of tap is to tear the threads that are being formed, owing to the wedging action of the cutting teeth and the lack of resistance offered by the metal to the pressure of the continuous row of cutting edges; the chips are carried forward in a mass in front of the cutting teeth, and unless the tap is frequently reversed and this mass of chips broken off, the thread may be mutilated or the tap itself broken.

Steel for Taps. — *Carbon steel* is still extensively used in the manufacture of taps both on production jobs and for general service tapping. A good steel to use should have a carbon content from about 1.15 to 1.25 per cent carbon. This steel, if uniform in its composition, can be hardened with a lead control well within a limit of plus or minus 0.003 inch in one inch of thread. Some carbon steels used in the manufacture of taps have a vanadium content of approximately 0.25 per cent. The vanadium has a tendency to add toughness to the steel as well as improving the cutting qualities and helps to prevent breakage particularly in small taps. The carbon content is the same as in regular carbon steels. This steel can be hardened also within the same lead range of plus or minus 0.003 inch in one inch of thread.

Expensive, non-shrinkable steels are obtainable in the market that show practically no change in either lead or the diameter of the tap when hardened but these are not used commercially on account of their high cost.

High-speed steel taps are used extensively for production tapping, with *cut threads* for a general line of commercial work, and *ground threads* where greater accuracy is essential. A high-speed steel suitable for taps should contain from 0.60 to 0.75 per cent carbon and from 17 to 19 per cent tungsten. This steel hardens at from 2200 to 2350 degrees F. The temper should be drawn at from 1000 to 1125 degrees F.

Due to the progress steel makers have made in the manufacture of high-speed steels and advances made by tap makers in the heat treatment, high-speed steel taps are especially good for production tapping and great savings have been accomplished by their use. The high-speed steel ground-thread tap is extensively used in production where accuracy is the controlling factor. The grinding of the blank and the threads corrects inaccuracies caused by distortion in heat treatment and insures accuracy for the pitch, outside, and shank diameters as well as in the lead of the thread. The introduction of the ground-thread tap is a modern achievement that has filled a long-felt need.

Classes of Fits Obtained with Ground-Thread Taps. — The majority of the taps used by the automotive industry are high-speed steel commercial and precision ground-thread taps. The precision ground tap usually is employed where a Class 3 fit is specified. (For information about Class 3 and other classes of fits, see Allowances and Tolerances for American Standard Screw Threads.) Commercial ground-thread taps produce a satisfactory Class 2 fit in the majority of cases. In some of the larger sizes, commercial ground taps produce a Class 3 fit. Many variables, however, affect the tapped hole size, such as type and condition of the tapping machine and equipment, analysis and physical properties of the material being tapped, cutting fluid employed, etc. Many nuts for the automotive industry are tapped to a Class 4 fit, using precision high-speed steel ground-thread hook taps. Naturally the life of these taps is not so great as that of taps producing Class 2 and Class 3 fits, due to the very close tolerance of the Class 4 product. A great deal depends also on the type of steel from which the nuts are fabricated. Medium-carbon steel nuts, low in manganese, phosphorus, and sulphur, are considerably harder to tap than the usual run of low-carbon steel nuts.

High-speed steel cut-thread taps are used in many shops where close tolerances are not specified. These taps are marketed at a lower price than the ground-thread product. Owing to improved manufacturing methods and the use of properly designed hardening equipment, the high-speed steel cut-thread tap comes well within the tolerances specified in the trade catalogues.

Right-hand spiral-fluted taps with highly polished flutes are adapted to aluminum alloy parts; interrupted thread taps, to very soft, stringy steel parts and thin-wall jobs; stub machine-screw taps to thin metal work; and spiral-pointed taps to many through-hole jobs.

Hardness of Taps. — Tests made over many years of tapping with high-speed steel ground-thread taps show that the ideal hardness of a tap should be about 63 Rockwell C. It should never be below 61 or above 65. If the hardness is below 61 Rockwell C., the corners of the teeth wear very rapidly; if the tap is harder than 65 Rockwell C., the teeth show a tendency of slightly chipping at the chamfer, especially when tapping hard or tough materials.

Tapping Fixtures. — The fixture should locate the hole to be tapped in alignment with the tap. This may be difficult due to variations in size of work. Clamping the parts in the fixture requires additional time, and in most cases, is not necessary, if proper consideration is given to the locating points in relation to the fixture, as it is usually possible to find some points that can be used for locating where no great variations are present.

In high-speed tapping, especially with taps 5/16 inch or less in diameter, the tapping time is usually much less than the time required for handling the work. In such cases, it is important that the fixture be designed to require the minimum of handling time. This involves consideration of such points as the height of the fixture, so that the hand is not crowded while placing the piece in it; the angle at which the part is placed in the fixture relative to the operator; whether the part should be inserted from the right-hand or from the left-hand side; whether it is easier and quicker to push it into position from the front of the machine.

Threading Dies

Steel for Die Chasers. — High-speed steels now are used extensively for die chasers. Such steels can now be hardened without injuring the finished surfaces; moreover, when the design of the chaser is such that grinding of the thread form after hardening is practicable, even keener cutting edges and smoother surfaces can be obtained. The National Acme Co. recommends high-speed steel for practically all threading chasers. In some cases, carbon steel has been recommended for threading copper and also for cutting Acme or worm threads.

Types of Die Chasers and Methods of Forming Teeth. — One common type of die chaser has the teeth formed on the end. The teeth of such chasers may be formed by three different methods. The first is by using a hob having helical teeth like the teeth of a tap. The second is by using a milling cutter which has annular rows of teeth that are perpendicular to the axis. This cutter is set to the helix angle of the screw thread when milling the chaser teeth, and it is fed across the end of the blank and forms a series of straight teeth. The third method is by using a milling cutter like the one just referred to. This cutter is set to the proper helix angle as in the previous case, and is then sunk into the end of the chaser blank, thus forming concave or circular teeth instead of straight teeth. Another form of milled chaser which has straight teeth is found in the Landis die-heads. In this case, the chasers are set tangentially to the work and the milled teeth, instead of being across the ends of the chasers, extend the full length of the chasers; the latter are sharpened by grinding on the ends.

The National Acme circular chasers are like circular forming tools. The circumferential thread grooves are annular and have no lead. This type of chaser is sharpened by grinding the cutting face back in a circumferential direction, the same as in grinding circular formed tools.

Angle of Chamfer for Die Chasers. — The leading side or "throat" of a die is chamfered to provide a more gradual cutting action, unless it is necessary to cut a full thread close to a shoulder. The throat angle should preferably be such that the work of cutting a thread to the full depth will be distributed over at least two or three teeth on the leading side of the die. The chamfer, according to common practice, extends from the root or base of the most advanced tooth in a set of chasers back to the top of the third tooth, which may be slightly beveled. Each chaser should be ground to the same angle so that each throat will be the same distance from the die axis. The angles recommended for Hartness dies vary according to the pitch of the thread, the angle being 15 degrees relative to the axis of the die for threads varying from 4 to 5½ per inch, 20 degrees for threads varying from 6 to 8 per inch, and 25 degrees for nine or more threads per inch.

Relief of Die Chasers. — The throat or chamfered edge of each chaser should have clearance back of the cutting edge or in a circumferential direction. This clearance should be just enough to insure free cutting. If there is not enough relief, the cutting action will be either prevented entirely or retarded, and the die will not advance as fast as it should. On the contrary, excessive relief tends to increase the rate of advance, assuming that the die is self-leading. It is of especial importance that die chasers for brass have as little clearance as possible, because the throats of the chasers steady the die when starting a thread. The sides of the chaser teeth are sometimes relieved instead of the leading sides or corners being chamfered, when a thread must be cut close to a shoulder in brass. This relieving is done by using a brass lap which has an angle of about 50 degrees for a 60-degree chaser tooth.

Amount of Rake for Threading Dies. — The front face of each die chaser should lie in a plane intersecting the axis of a die that is used for cutting threads on parts of cast brass, cast iron, or brittle materials of a granular structure. For the more tenacious or tougher materials which are not brittle, such as wrought iron, steel, copper and yellow brass, the chasers should have positive rake, the cutting faces lying in planes that are in advance of the die axis. Most aluminum castings, on account of the zinc in their composition, cut very much like cast brass, and should preferably be threaded with dies having little or no rake. Many of the dies used for cutting threads in machine steel have the front faces of the chasers located ahead of the die axis a distance equal to about one-fifth of the die radius. When grinding the front faces of die chasers, care should be taken to maintain the rake angles. According to experiments of the National Tube Co., the rake angles of dies for pipe threading should vary from 15 to 25 degrees, the latter angle being suitable for threading open-hearth steel pipe.

Number of Chasers for Pipe Dies. — To obtain the best results with pipe dies, the number of chasers should vary according to the size of the die, four chasers being used for diameters up to 1¼ inch; six chasers for diameters of from 1½ to 4 inches; eight chasers for diameters of from 4½ to 8 inches; twelve chasers for diameters of from 9 to 12 inches; fourteen chasers for diameters of from 13 to 16 inches; and sixteen chasers for diameters of from 17 to 20 inches. This information is based on experiments of the National Tube Co.

Dies for Cutting Taper Threads. — While short taper threads are commonly cut with solid dies, the type of die to use for accurate work, particularly when the length of thread exceeds ordinary die widths, is one having chasers which taper to correspond to the taper on the work and are arranged to move outward radially as the die moves along. Such dies are of the self-opening type. The radial outward movement of the chasers is controlled by a taper plate which allows the cam or scroll ring of the die-head to turn slowly as the die advances. When the thread is finished, the chasers spring out rapidly to clear the work. In dies of this class, the taper plate for controlling the movement of the chasers serves about the same purpose as the adjustable slide or bar of a lathe taper attachment.

Dies for Cutting Square Threads. — If dies are to be used for cutting square threads, the sides of the teeth should be relieved to prevent the teeth from binding and breaking. If the die is to be self-leading (the feeding movement not being controlled by a lead-screw), this side relief or clearance should be very slight because, if there is too much relief on the sides of the chaser teeth, the die will not be supported properly and is liable to cut a thread that is quite incorrect in lead. The use of a lead-screw is preferable when cutting square threads with a die. The Acme thread may be cut readily with dies.

Positive Control of Die-feeding Movement. — While most dies are self-leading, it is sometimes advisable to control positively the longitudinal motion of the die relative to the work. This control may be utilized merely to start the die, or the arrangement may be such that the longitudinal motion of the die is controlled positively throughout the entire screw-cutting operation. This positive action may be derived from a lead-screw or from a cam, depending upon the type of machine. A lead-screw is sometimes applied to a threading machine of the bolt-cutter type, especially when cutting square threads, or special forms. For screw-cutting operations of this kind, if the die follows its own lead, the accumulated error is often considerable. It is essential that the pitch of the die teeth correspond to the leading movement obtained from the lead-screw. The general method of cutting threads on the automatic screw machine is to use a cam that starts a die on the work and then allows the turret-slide to lag behind somewhat so that the die can lead itself on. The die-holder is designed to allow the die to follow its own lead or move independently of the turret-slide.

Non-opening Dies. — The non-opening dies are capable in some cases of hand adjustment, but the object of this adjustment is to vary the size of the die. There are four types of non-opening dies in common use, which may be designated as (1) solid dies, or those that are rigid and incapable of any adjustment for varying the diameter; (2) flexible dies, or those that are split in one or more places and may be adjusted to some extent by compressing or expanding; (3) sectional dies, or those formed of two adjustable sections; (4) rigid adjustable dies of the chaser type, having inserted chasers that may be adjusted radially within certain limits either for maintaining a standard size or for varying the size slightly. A non-opening die may be removed from the work in three different ways: (1) the work rotation may be reversed after the thread is cut; (2) the die itself may be reversed, thus unscrewing it from the threaded part; (3) the die may be revolved in the same direction as the work, but at a somewhat slower speed while cutting the thread and then at a faster rate so that the die backs off the threaded part.

Automatic or Self-opening Dies. — Dies which open automatically to permit their removal when the thread is finished, not only save time, but may prevent injury to the thread, which sometimes results when the chips wedge between the teeth of a non-opening die and the work. Self-opening dies differ both in regard to the mechanism for opening the die chasers automatically at the completion of a cut, and as to the method of resetting the chasers in the working or cutting position after the die has been removed. These dies, in general, are formed of two main sections, which have a certain relative motion for opening and closing the die. This motion may be parallel to the axis of the die, or it may be rotary. The radial movement of the chasers is derived from either cam surfaces or the conical surface of a slide in contact with the chasers. Dies of this class may be opened or tripped (1) by stopping the travel of the turret, (2) by the engagement of an outside tripping latch with a fixed stop, or (3) by the engagement of the end of the work with a tripping plate located in the center of the die back of the chasers. Most of the self-opening dies are of the non-revolving type, but some are designed for attachment to a revolving spindle.

Spring Screw Threading Dies. — These dies are usually tapped with a straight tap and hob, although this practice is somewhat objectionable on account of the fact that a slight inaccuracy is produced in the shape of the threads of the screw to be threaded when the prongs of the die are forced in by the adjustment of the clamp collar. It is, therefore, better to tap out this die from the back end with a tap that tapers an amount equal to the clearance required in the die when cutting. In that case, the die should be cut to the correct cutting size at the point, and not oversize, as is the case when it is cut with a straight tap. The amount of back taper may be made from about 0.005 to 0.010 inch per inch for iron and steel, and from 0.008 to 0.015 inch per inch for dies cutting brass, copper and metals of similar structure. Spring screw dies are generally made with four flutes, but for several reasons three flutes would be preferable. When four flutes are used, as a rule only two of the lands are cutting. If a die is made with three flutes, it should be fluted with a 60-degree angular cutter. If made with four flutes, the cutter should be a 48-, 45- or 40-degree angular cutter, according to the size of the die, the 48-degree cutter being used for the smallest dies and the 45-degree cutter for all ordinary sizes. Dies ½ inch in outside diameter or smaller are never made with more than three lands. If the die is not to cut close to a shoulder, about three threads should be chamfered off at the end. When dies are to cut close to a shoulder, not more than 1 or 1½ threads should be chamfered. The threads should be relieved on the chamfered part. It is common practice to make the length of the thread in a spring screw die about seven times the pitch. Tables are given herewith showing the general dimensions of spring screw threading dies as ordinarily manufactured, the length of the thread for various pitches, and the oversize required in taps for hobbing spring screw dies when these are cut with straight taps.

Clamp Collars for Spring Screw Threading Dies

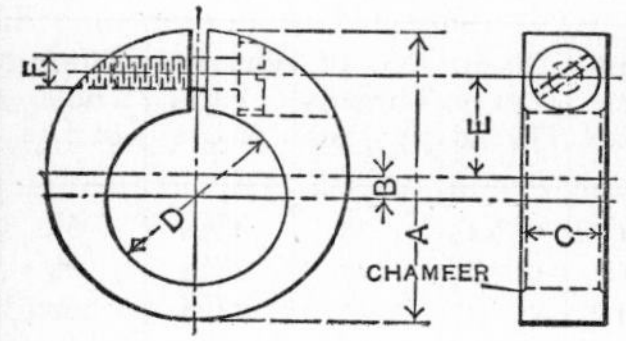

D	A	B	C	E	F
½	1	9/64	3/8	5/16	3/16
¾	1 5/16	9/64	7/16	13/32	7/32
1	1 11/16	11/64	½	9/16	¼
1 3/16	1 7/8	5/32	9/16	21/32	¼
1¼	1 7/8	1/8	9/16	23/32	¼
1 3/8	2 3/16	5/32	5/8	¾	5/16
1 5/8	2 5/8	7/32	11/16	7/8	3/8
2	3 1/8	9/32	13/16	1 1/16	3/8
2½	3 ¾	5/16	7/8	1 5/16	3/8
3¼	4½	5/16	15/16	1 11/16	3/8

Spring Screw Threading Dies

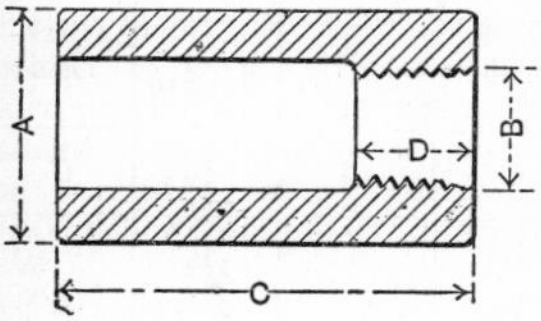

Out-side Diam.	Diam. of Thread	Length of Die	Out-side Diam.	Diam. of Thread	Length of Die
A	B	C	A	B	C
½	3/32–¼	1¼	1 3/8	½– ¾	2½
¾	¼–3/8	1¾	1 5/8	5/8–1	2½
1	5/16–½	2	2	¾–1¼	3
1 3/16	5/8–¾	2¼	2½	1 –1½	3½
1¼	3/8–¾	2½	3¼	1 5/8–2 1/8	4

Length of Thread for Different Pitches

No. of Threads per Inch	Length of Thread, D	No. of Threads per Inch	Length of Thread, D	No. of Threads per Inch	Length of Thread, D	No. of Threads per Inch	Length of Thread, D	No. of Threads per Inch	Length of Thread, D
40	3/16	24	5/16	14	½	10	¾	6	1 3/16
36	7/32	20	3/8	13	9/16	9	13/16	5½	1 5/16
32	¼	18	13/32	12	5/8	8	7/8	5	1 7/16
28	9/32	16	7/16	11	11/16	7	1	4½	1 9/16

Oversize of Taps for Hobbing Spring Screw Dies

No. of Threads per Inch	Over-size	No. of Threads per Inch	Over-size	No. of Threads per Inch	Over-size	No. of Threads per Inch	Over-size	No. of Threads per Inch	Over-size
4½	0.015	8	0.007	13	0.006	22	0.005	40	0.003
5	0.013	9	0.007	14	0.005	24	0.004	48	0.003
5½	0.012	10	0.006	16	0.005	28	0.004	56	0.003
6	0.010	11	0.006	18	0.005	32	0.004	64	0.002
7	0.008	12	0.006	20	0.005	36	0.004	72	0.002

Solid Round Gas Fixture Dies

(For fixtures and thin brass tubing—60-degree V-thread with slight flat top and bottom)

Nominal Size	Diam. of Thread	No. of Threads per Inch	Outside Diam. of Die	Thickness of Die	Nominal Size	Diam. of Thread	No. of Threads per Inch	Outside Diam. of Die	Thickness of Die
0.148	0.148	32	⅝	¼	½	0.515	27	1⁷⁄₁₆	⅜
0.196	0.196	32	⅝	¼	⁹⁄₁₆	0.578	27	1⁷⁄₁₆	⅜
No. 4	0.246	27	⅝	¼	⅝	0.637	27	1⁷⁄₁₆	⅜
¼	0.260	27	1	⁵⁄₁₆	¾	0.770	27	2	½
⁵⁄₁₆	0.342	27	1	⁵⁄₁₆	⅞	0.885	27	2	½
⅜	0.390	27	1⁷⁄₁₆	⅜	1	1.006	27	2	½
⁷⁄₁₆	0.459	27	1⁷⁄₁₆	⅜	....	....	.....	.....	.....

Solid Square Bolt Dies

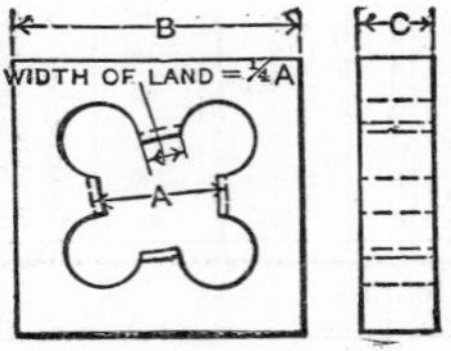

WIDTH OF LAND = ¾ A

Diam. of Thread	Size of Square	Thickness	Diam. of Thread	Size of Square	Thickness
A	B	C	A	B	C
¼	2½	½	¹⁵⁄₁₆	2½	¾
⁵⁄₁₆	2½	½	1	2½	1
⅜	2½	½	1⅛	2½	1
⁷⁄₁₆	2½	½	1¼	2½	1
½	2½	¾	1⅜	2½	1
⁹⁄₁₆	2½	¾	1½	3	1
⅝	2½	¾	1⅝	3	1
11⁄16	2½	¾	1¾	3	1¼
¾	2½	¾	1⅞	3½	1½
13⁄16	2½	¾	2	3¾	2
⅞	2½	¾	....	.....	.....

Hexagon Rethreading Dies. — These dies are of hexagon form and resemble a nut. They are intended for repair work in the reconditioning of battered or rusty threads and are rotated either by a wrench, or by inserting in a bit brace socket. The commercial sizes cover the common range of bolt diameters.

Solid Square Pipe Dies

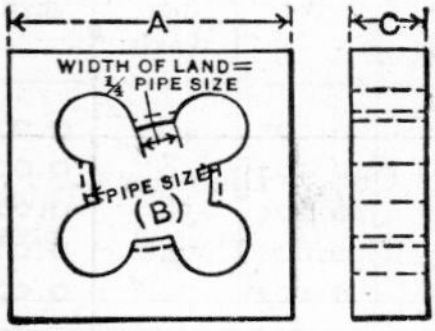

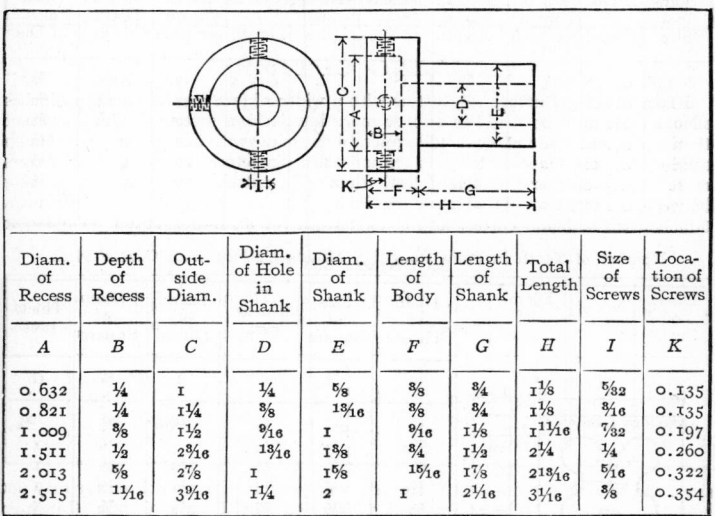

Size of Square A	Pipe Size (Nominal) B	Thickness C	Size of Square A	Pipe Size (Nominal) B	Thickness C
2	1/8–1/2	1/2	3 7/8	1 1/4–2	7/8
2 3/8	1/4–1	3/4	3 7/8	1 1/4–2	1
2 1/2	1/4–1	3/4	4	1 1/4–2	7/8
2 7/8	3/4–1 1/4	3/4	4	1 1/4–2	1
3	3/4–1 1/4	3/4	5	2 1/2–3	1 1/4

Lathe Die Holders

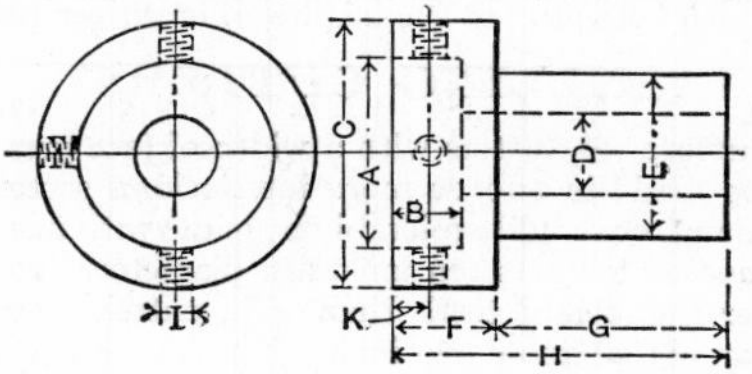

Diam. of Recess A	Depth of Recess B	Outside Diam. C	Diam. of Hole in Shank D	Diam. of Shank E	Length of Body F	Length of Shank G	Total Length H	Size of Screws I	Location of Screws K
0.632	1/4	1	1/4	5/8	3/8	3/4	1 1/8	5/32	0.135
0.821	1/4	1 1/4	3/8	13/16	3/8	3/4	1 1/8	3/16	0.135
1.009	3/8	1 1/2	9/16	1	9/16	1 1/8	1 11/16	7/32	0.197
1.511	1/2	2 3/16	13/16	1 3/8	3/4	1 1/2	2 1/4	1/4	0.260
2.013	5/8	2 7/8	1	1 5/8	15/16	1 7/8	2 13/16	5/16	0.322
2.515	11/16	3 9/16	1 1/4	2	1	2 1/16	3 1/16	3/8	0.354

Solid Dies. — A solid die, as a rule, is of square shape and is used principally for threading in bolt cutters and for pipe dies. In pipe dies the thread, of course, is tapered. A tapered die, in order to cut a thread smoothly and correctly, should be relieved in the angle of the thread, but as the difficulties of relieving an internal thread like that of a pipe die are very great, this is not ordinarily done and, therefore, pipe dies, as well as other taper dies, cannot be used for cutting the threads of taps, where the thread is required to be smooth and cut closely to the correct shape, but can be used only on pipes and similar soft metal where a perfect thread shape is not essential. Solid square dies are always provided with four lands, except when very large, when five lands are preferable. The width of the land should be about 1/4 of the diameter of the thread to be cut.

Round Split Adjustable Dies. — These dies have three lands for sizes up to and including 3/16 inch. For all larger sizes, four lands are used. When hardening these dies, draw to a blue back of the clearance holes in order to insure a good spring temper. About three threads should be chamfered and relieved on the top of the chamfer on the leading side of the die.

Round Split Adjustable Dies

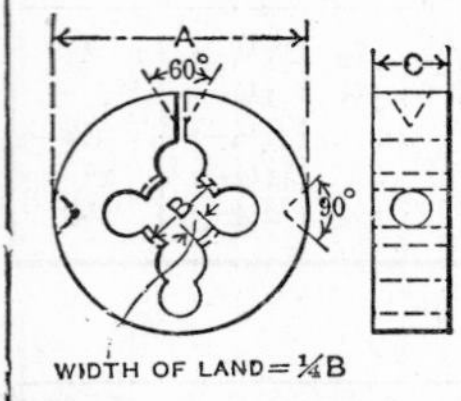

Outside Diam. A	Diameter of Thread B	Thickness C	Outside Diam. A	Diameter of Thread B	Thickness C
5/8	1/16–17/64	1/4	1 1/2	1/4–5/8	1/2
13/16	1/16–5/16	1/4	2	3/8–7/8	5/8
1	3/16–1/2	3/8	2 1/2	1/2–1 1/4	11/16

MILLING CUTTERS

Plain Milling Cutters. — Cutters with a width of face greater than four inches should preferably be made in two or more interlocking sections. Cutters larger than five inches in diameter should preferably be made with inserted teeth, although solid cutters are made as large as ten inches in diameter. Inserted blade cutters must have a smaller number of teeth than solid cutters. The pitch or spacing between the teeth should be about 1 1/2 inch. This gives about twelve teeth for a 6-inch inserted blade cutter, and sixteen teeth for an 8-inch cutter. On larger

Number of Teeth in Plain Roughing Milling Cutters With Coarse Pitch

Diam. of Cutter	No. of Teeth	Diam. of Cutter	No. of Teeth	Diam. of Cutter	No. of Teeth	Diam. of Cutter	No. of Teeth	Diam. of Cutter	No. of Teeth
2	8	3	8	5	10	7	14	9	18
2 1/4	8	3 1/2	9	5 1/2	11	7 1/2	14	9 1/2	18
2 1/2	8	4	9	6	12	8	16	10	20
2 3/4	8	4 1/2	10	6 1/2	12	8 1/2	16	....	...

sizes, the spacing should be still coarser. For example, a 10-inch cutter may not have over 18 teeth. The thickness of an inserted steel blade should be 7/16 inch on cutters up to six inches in diameter, 1/2 inch for cutters up to 10 inches, and 9/16 inch for larger cutters. Two tables are given herewith showing numbers of teeth in solid plain milling cutters. In one table the number of teeth for the finer pitches is given, and in the other, the number of teeth in roughing milling cutters with the coarse pitch now used extensively. In end mills with coarse pitch teeth use 4 teeth in mills up to 1 inch; use 5 in 1 1/4-inch; 6 in 1 1/2-inch; and 8 in 2-inch mills. When cutters are to be used exclusively on brass, the number of teeth may be made 25 per cent less than that given for the ordinary plain milling cutter. The teeth in plain milling cutters should be cut with a regular 60-degree angular cutter if the teeth are cut straight. If they are cut spiral, they should be cut either with 60-degree double-angle cutters (12 degrees on one side and 48 on the other) or with 65-degree, double-angle cutters (12 degrees on one side and 53 on the other). The angular cutter for the teeth should have a slightly rounded point so as not to produce a sharp corner in the bottom of the tooth being cut. The backing off of the teeth by grinding is made to an angle of about five degrees with the tangent to the cylindrical surface of the cutter. When the teeth are cut spiral, the lead should be so selected that the angle of spiral equals about fifteen degrees.

Plain and Side Milling Cutters

Diameter of Cutter	Plain Milling Cutter		Side Milling Cutter		Width of Land on Teeth	Diameter of Cutter	Plain Milling Cutter		Side Milling Cutter		Width of Land on Teeth
	Number of Teeth	Radius of Point of Fluting Cutter	Number of Teeth	Angle of Cutter for Side Teeth			Number of Teeth	Radius of Point of Fluting Cutter	Number of Teeth	Angle of Cutter for Side Teeth	
2	14	5/64	22	For wide cutters, use 70- or 75-degree angle cutter. For thin cutters, use 80-, and in extreme cases, 85-degree cutter.	1/32	5½	22	9/64	28	For wide cutters, use 70- or 75-degree angle cutter. For thin cutters, use 80-, and in extreme cases, 85-degree cutter.	3/64
2¼	14	5/64	22		1/32	6	24	5/32	30		1/16
2½	16	3/32	24		1/32	6½	24	5/32	30		1/16
2¾	16	3/32	24		1/32	7	26	3/16	30		1/16
3	18	7/64	24		1/32	7½	26	3/16	30		1/16
3½	18	7/64	24		3/64	8	28	3/16	30		5/64
4	20	1/8	26		3/64	8½	28	3/16	32		5/64
4½	20	1/8	26		3/64	9	30	3/16	32		5/64
5	22	9/64	28		3/64	10	30	3/16	32		9/64

Plain Milling Cutters — American Standard

Cutter Diameter			Range of Face Widths, Nom.	Hole Diameter		
Nom.	Max.	Min.		Nom.	Max.	Min.
Heavy-duty Cutters — Helical Teeth						
2½	2.515	2.485	2 to 4	1	1.001	1.000
3	3.015	2.985	2 to 6	1¼	1.251	1.250
4	4.015	3.985	2 to 6	1½	1.501	1.500
4½	4.515	4.485	6 and 12	2	2.001	2.000
Light-duty Cutters						
2¼	2.265	2.235	½ and 1	⅞	0.876	0.875
2½	2.515	2.485	3/16 to 3	1	1.001	1.000
3	3.015	2.985	3/16 to ⅜	1	1.001	1.000
3	3.015	2.985	⅜ to 6	1¼	1.251	1.250
4	4.015	3.985	¼, 5/16, ⅜	1	1.001	1.000
4	4.015	3.985	¼, 5/16; ⅜ to 4	1¼	1.251	1.250
4	4.015	3.985	6	1½	1.501	1.500

All dimensions in inches. "Plain cutters" have teeth on the circumferential surface only. Heavy-duty cutters have helical teeth. Light-duty cutters less than ¾ inch width have straight teeth; widths of ¾ inch and over have helical teeth.

Hand of spiral and construction optional with cutter manufacturer.

American Standard Woodruff Key-slot Cutters† — Shank-Type and Arbor-Type.
(ASA B5.3)

SHANK-TYPE CUTTERS

American Standard Number¹	M'f'rs' Number²	A	B	American Standard Number¹	M'f'rs' Number²	A	B	American Standard Number¹	M'f'rs' Number²	A	B
202	201	1/16	1/4	506	8	5/32	3/4	610	19	3/16	1 1/4
202½	206	1/16	5/16	806	91	1/4	3/4	710	20	7/32	1 1/4
302½	207	3/32	5/16	507	10	5/32	7/8	810	21	1/4	1 1/4
203	211	1/16	3/8	606	9	3/16	3/4	811	22	1/4	1 3/8
303	212	3/32	3/8	607	11	3/16	7/8	812	24	1/4	1 1/2
403	213	1/8	3/8	707	12	7/32	7/8	1008	B	5/16	1
204	1	1/16	1/2	608	13	3/16	1	1009	C	5/16	1 1/8
304	2	3/32	1/2	708	14	7/32	1	1010	D	5/16	1 1/4
305	4	3/32	5/8	1208	152	3/8	1	1011	23	5/16	1 3/8
404	3	1/8	1/2	609	16	3/16	1 1/8	1012	25	5/16	1 1/2
405	5	1/8	5/8	807	A	1/4	7/8	1210	E	3/8	1 1/4
406	7	1/8	3/4	808	15	1/4	1	1211	F	3/8	1 3/8
505	6	5/32	5/8	709	17	7/32	1 1/8	1212	G	3/8	1 1/2
605	61	3/16	5/8	809	18	1/4	1 1/8	....	...	...	...

ARBOR-TYPE CUTTERS

American Standard Number	M'f'rs' Number	A	B	American Standard Number	M'f'rs' Number	A	B	American Standard Number	M'f'rs' Number	A	B
617	26	3/16	2 1/8	1222	T	3/8	2 3/4	1828	33	9/16	3 1/2
817	27	1/4	2 1/8	1422	U	7/16	2 3/4	2028	34	5/8	3 1/2
1017	28	5/16	2 1/8	1622	V	1/2	2 3/4	2228	35	11/16	3 1/2
1217	29	3/8	2 1/8	1228	30	3/8	3 1/2	2428	36	3/4	3 1/2
822	R	1/4	2 3/4	1428	31	7/16	3 1/2	....	..	...	...
1022	S	5/16	2 3/4	1628	32	1/2	3 1/2	....	..	...	...

All dimensions are given in inches. All cutters are high-speed steel.

¹ American Standard Number indicates the nominal key dimension or size cutter, that is, the last two digits give diameter B in eighths of an inch; the digits preceding the last two give width A in thirty-seconds. Thus, 204 indicates a cutter size 2/32 × 4/8 or 1/16 inch wide × 1/2 inch diameter.

² Manufacturers' Numbers formerly used to designate key and cutter sizes.

† For Woodruff key and key-slot dimensions, see pages 587 and 588. For key number 126 use cutter number 617; for 127 use 817; for 128 use 1017; for 129 use 1217; for Rx use 822; for Sx use 1022; for Tx use 1222; for Ux use 1422; for Vx use 1622.

* Diameter of hole H: for cutter numbers 617, 817, 1017, and 1217, H = 3/4 inch; for other cutters, H = 1 inch.

Tolerances: Face width A of all sizes: +0.0000, −0.0005 inch. Hole size H: +0.00075, −0.0000 inch.

American Standard Keys and Keyways for Milling Cutters and Arbors* (ASA B5.3)

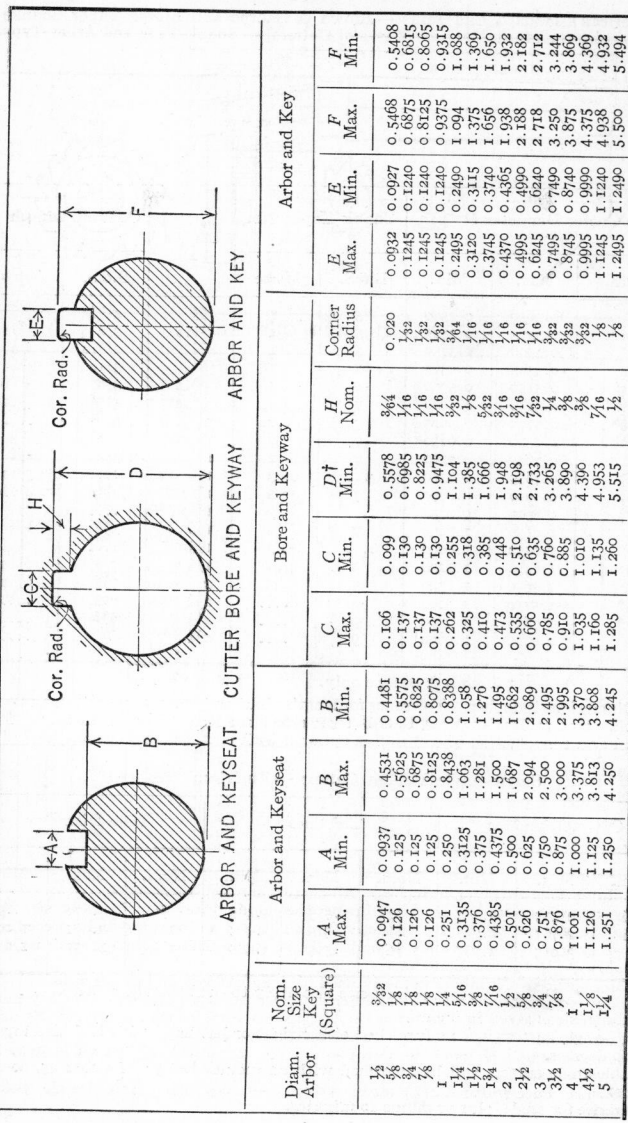

ARBOR AND KEYSEAT · CUTTER BORE AND KEYWAY · ARBOR AND KEY

Diam. Arbor	Nom. Size Key (Square)	Arbor and Keyseat				Cutter Bore and Keyway					Arbor and Key			
		A Max.	A Min.	B Max.	B Min.	C Max.	C Min.	D† Min.	H Nom.	Corner Radius	E Max.	E Min.	F Max.	F Min.
1/2	3/32	0.0947	0.0937	0.4531	0.4481	0.106	0.099	0.5578	3/64	0.020	0.0932	0.0927	0.5468	0.5408
5/8	1/8	0.126	0.125	0.5625	0.5575	0.137	0.130	0.6985	1/16	1/32	0.1245	0.1240	0.6875	0.6815
3/4	1/8	0.126	0.125	0.6875	0.6825	0.137	0.130	0.8225	1/16	1/32	0.1245	0.1240	0.8125	0.8065
7/8	1/8	0.126	0.125	0.8125	0.8075	0.137	0.130	0.9475	1/16	1/32	0.1245	0.1240	0.9375	0.9315
1	1/4	0.251	0.250	0.8438	0.8338	0.262	0.255	1.104	3/32	3/64	0.2495	0.2490	1.094	1.088
1 1/4	5/16	0.3135	0.3125	1.063	1.058	0.325	0.318	1.385	1/8	1/16	0.3120	0.3115	1.375	1.369
1 1/2	3/8	0.376	0.375	1.281	1.276	0.410	0.385	1.666	5/32	1/16	0.3745	0.3740	1.656	1.650
1 3/4	7/16	0.4385	0.4375	1.500	1.495	0.473	0.448	1.948	3/16	1/16	0.4370	0.4365	1.938	1.932
2	1/2	0.501	0.500	1.687	1.682	0.535	0.510	2.198	3/16	1/16	0.4995	0.4990	2.188	2.182
2 1/2	5/8	0.626	0.625	2.094	2.089	0.660	0.635	2.733	7/32	3/32	0.6245	0.6240	2.718	2.712
3	3/4	0.751	0.750	2.500	2.495	0.785	0.760	3.265	1/4	1/16	0.7495	0.7490	3.250	3.244
3 1/2	7/8	0.876	0.875	3.000	2.995	0.910	0.885	3.890	3/8	3/32	0.8745	0.8740	3.875	3.869
4	1	1.001	1.000	3.375	3.370	1.035	1.010	4.390	3/8	3/32	0.9995	0.9990	4.375	4.369
4 1/2	1 1/8	1.126	1.125	3.813	3.808	1.160	1.135	4.953	7/16	1/8	1.1245	1.1240	4.938	4.932
5	1 1/4	1.251	1.250	4.250	4.245	1.285	1.260	5.515	1/2	1/8	1.2495	1.2490	5.500	5.494

All dimensions given in inches. † D max. is 0.010 inches larger than D min. * Keys and keyways for hobs on the basis of hole size are not the same as for milling cutters in all cases.

American Standard End Mills — Brown & Sharpe and Morse Taper Shanks

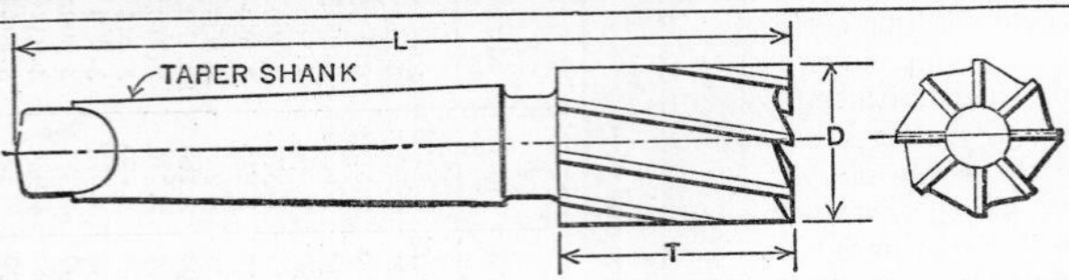

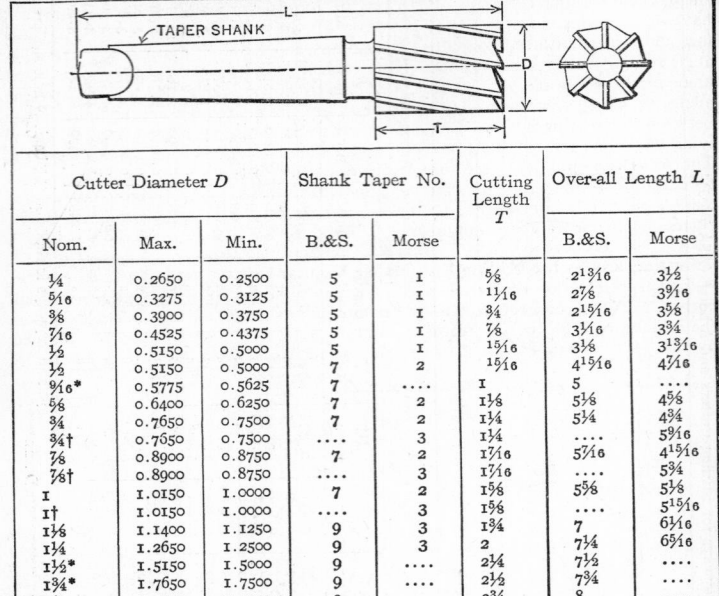

Cutter Diameter *D*			Shank Taper No.		Cutting Length *T*	Over-all Length *L*	
Nom.	Max.	Min.	B.&S.	Morse		B.&S.	Morse
1/4	0.2650	0.2500	5	1	5/8	2 13/16	3 1/2
5/16	0.3275	0.3125	5	1	11/16	2 7/8	3 9/16
3/8	0.3900	0.3750	5	1	3/4	2 15/16	3 5/8
7/16	0.4525	0.4375	5	1	7/8	3 1/16	3 3/4
1/2	0.5150	0.5000	5	1	15/16	3 1/8	3 13/16
1/2	0.5150	0.5000	7	2	15/16	4 15/16	4 7/16
9/16*	0.5775	0.5625	7	....	1	5	....
5/8	0.6400	0.6250	7	2	1 1/8	5 1/8	4 5/8
3/4	0.7650	0.7500	7	2	1 1/4	5 1/4	4 3/4
3/4†	0.7650	0.7500	....	3	1 1/4	....	5 9/16
7/8	0.8900	0.8750	7	2	1 7/16	5 7/16	4 15/16
7/8†	0.8900	0.8750	....	3	1 7/16	....	5 3/4
1	1.0150	1.0000	7	2	1 5/8	5 5/8	5 1/8
1†	1.0150	1.0000	....	3	1 5/8	....	5 15/16
1 1/8	1.1400	1.1250	9	3	1 3/4	7	6 1/16
1 1/4	1.2650	1.2500	9	3	2	7 1/4	6 5/16
1 1/2*	1.5150	1.5000	9	....	2 1/4	7 1/2	....
1 3/4*	1.7650	1.7500	9	....	2 1/2	7 3/4	....
2*	2.0150	2.0000	9	....	2 3/4	8	....

* Brown & Sharpe only. † Morse only.

All dimensions in inches. Tolerance for length of cut and length over-all, plus or minus 1/32 inch. End mills with No. 5 B. & S. taper shank are furnished without tang. Hand of spiral and construction of end mill is optional with cutter manufacturer.

Single-Angle Milling Cutters — American Standard*

Cutter Diameter			Thickness			Hole Diameter		
Nom.	Max.	Min.	Nom.	Max.	Min.	Nom.	Max.	Min.
2 1/2	2.515	2.485	1/2	.515	.485	7/8	.876	.875
2 3/4*	2.765	2.735	1/2	.515	.485	1	1.001	1.000
3	3.015	2.985	1/2	.515	.485	1 1/4	1.251	1.250

* Dimensions for 2 3/4-inch size also apply to double-angle cutters.

All dimensions given in inches.

Single-angle cutters will be furnished either right or left hand with included angle of 45 or 60 degrees.

Double-angle cutters will be furnished with an included angle of either 45, 60 or 90 degrees.

Tolerance for angle, plus or minus 10 minutes.

American Standard Single- and Double-angle Milling Cutters. — A single-angle milling cutter has teeth on the conical surface and may or may not have teeth on one or both of the flat sides. The included angle between the conical face and larger flat face designates the cutter as, for example, 45° or 60°. A double-angle milling cutter has two intersecting conical surfaces with teeth on both. The angle of the teeth may or may not be symmetrical with respect to a plane at right angles to axis. Symmetrical angle cutters are designated by the included angle between the cutting edges. Unsymmetrical angle cutters are designated by specifying angle of each side with the plane of intersection at right angles to the axis. The American Standard (see table) includes three diameters for single-angle cutters and one diameter for double-angle cutters. The single-angle cutters are made either right- or left-hand. The tolerance for the angle on both classes of cutters is plus or minus 10 minutes.

Setting-angles for Milling End Mills, Angular Cutters and Taper Reamers. — In the calculation of setting-angles for the dividing head for milling angular cutters, end mills and taper reamers, the number of angles involved usually makes the calculation difficult and uncertain, and, in general, the settings can be obtained by the "cut-and-try" method in less time than it takes to compute them. It is,

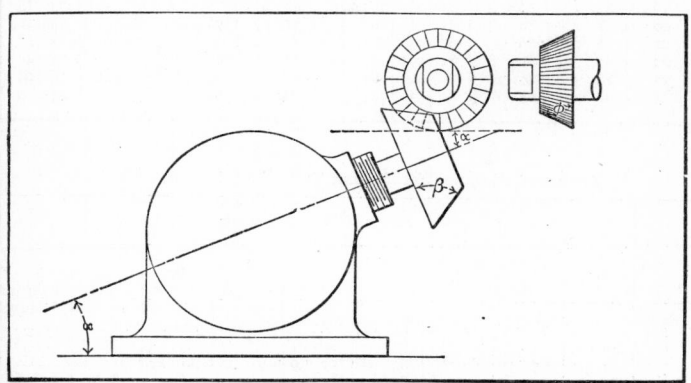

however, preferable to have the drawings contain all the information relating to the work. The accompanying tables, therefore, give the angles required for setting the dividing head for a great number of combinations. The angle to which the dividing head must be set depends upon two factors; the number of the teeth in the mill to be cut and the angle of the cutter with which the teeth are cut or fluted. When the number of teeth in the cutter to be made and the angle of the cutter used for milling the teeth are given, the setting-angle of the dividing head is found in the body of the tables. For example, assume that twelve teeth are to be cut in the end of an end mill with a 60-degree cutter. By following the horizontal line from twelve teeth, we read in the column under 60 degrees that the dividing head should be set to an angle of 70 degrees 32 minutes. This is the angle α in the accompanying engraving. The angle of the blank in which the teeth are to be milled is designated β, and tables are given for every 5-degree variation in this angle. The angle of the fluting cutter is designated ϕ in the illustration, and the tables give data for fluting cutters with nine different angles.

Angles of Elevation for Milling Teeth in End Mills

No. of Teeth	Angle of Fluting Cutter							
	85	80	75	70	65	60	55	50
5	74° 23'	57° 8'	34° 27'	....	....	....	....	....
6	81 17	72 13	62 21	50° 55'	36° 8'	....	....	....
7	83 42	77 13	70 22	62 50	54 12	43° 36'	....	....
8	84 59	79 51	74 27	68 39	62 12	54 44	45° 33'	32° 57'
9	85 47	81 29	77 0	72 13	66 58	61 1	54 1	45 15
10	86 21	82 38	78 46	74 40	70 12	65 12	59 25	52 26
11	86 47	83 29	80 5	76 28	72 34	68 13	63 15	57 22
12	87 6	84 9	81 6	77 52	74 23	70 32	66 9	61 2
13	87 22	84 41	81 54	78 59	75 48	72 21	68 26	63 52
14	87 35	85 8	82 35	79 54	77 1	73 51	70 17	66 10
15	87 46	85 30	83 9	80 40	78 1	75 6	71 50	68 4
16	87 55	85 49	83 38	81 20	78 52	76 10	73 8	69 40
17	88 3	86 5	84 3	81 53	79 36	77 4	74 15	71 1
18	88 11	86 19	84 24	82 23	80 14	77 52	75 14	72 13
19	88 17	86 32	84 43	82 49	80 47	78 34	76 6	73 15
20	88 22	86 43	85 0	83 13	81 17	79 11	76 51	74 11
21	88 27	86 53	85 15	83 33	81 44	79 44	77 31	74 59
22	88 32	87 2	85 29	83 52	82 8	80 14	78 8	75 44
23	88 36	87 10	85 42	84 9	82 30	80 42	78 41	76 24
24	88 39	87 18	85 53	84 24	82 49	81 6	79 11	77 0

Angles of Elevation for Milling Teeth in 5-degree Blank

No. of Teeth	Angle of Fluting Cutter								
	90	85	80	75	70	65	60	55	50
5	74° 12'	59° 11'	42° 43'	21° 41'	......	......	......	......	......
6	80 4	71 29	62 34	53 52	41° 41'	27° 22'	......	......	......
7	82 1	75 47	69 22	62 35	55 9	46 33	36° 12'	21° 36'	......
8	82 57	77 58	72 52	67 32	61 47	55 23	48 0	38 56	25° 40'
9	83 29	79 18	75 2	70 35	65 49	60 36	54 43	47 46	38 30
10	83 50	80 13	76 31	72 41	68 35	64 9	59 11	53 27	46 4
11	84 4	80 52	77 36	74 12	70 37	66 43	62 24	57 28	51 15
12	84 14	81 21	78 25	75 23	72 10	68 42	64 52	60 31	55 5
13	84 21	81 44	79 4	76 13	73 23	70 15	66 48	62 54	58 4
14	84 27	82 3	79 36	77 4	74 24	71 32	68 23	64 50	60 28
15	84 32	82 19	80 3	77 43	75 15	72 30	69 42	66 27	62 28
16	84 35	82 31	80 25	78 14	75 57	73 30	70 49	67 48	64 7
17	84 38	82 42	80 44	78 42	76 34	74 16	71 46	68 58	65 33
18	84 41	82 52	81 1	79 7	77 6	74 57	72 36	69 59	66 47
19	84 43	83 0	81 16	79 28	77 34	75 33	73 20	70 52	67 42
20	84 45	83 8	81 29	79 47	77 59	76 4	73 59	71 39	68 50
21	84 46	83 14	81 40	80 3	77 21	76 32	75 4	72 20	69 40
22	84 47	83 19	81 50	80 17	78 40	76 57	75 4	72 58	70 26
23	84 48	83 24	81 59	80 30	78 58	77 20	75 32	73 32	71 7
24	84 49	83 29	82 7	80 43	79 15	77 40	75 57	74 3	71 44

Angles of Elevation for Milling Teeth in 10-degree Blank

No. of Teeth	Angle of Fluting Cutter								
	90	85	80	75	70	65	60	55	50
5	60° 16′	46° 45′	32° 9′	14° 31′	......	......	......	. . . .	......
6	70 34	62 11	53 50	44 37	34° 5′	20° 57′	......	......	......
7	74 12	68 8	61 55	55 20	48 9	39 57	30° 2′	16° 32′	......
8	76 0	71 8	66 9	60 56	55 19	49 6	41 56	33 12	20° 39′
9	77 2	72 56	68 45	64 23	59 21	54 7	48 52	42 6	33 8
10	77 42	74 8	70 31	66 44	62 44	57 22	53 30	47 54	40 42
11	78 10	75 1	71 48	68 28	64 56	61 6	56 52	52 2	45 56
12	78 30	75 40	72 46	69 47	66 37	63 12	59 26	55 10	49 50
13	78 44	76 9	73 31	70 48	67 56	64 51	61 26	57 36	52 51
14	78 56	76 34	74 9	71 39	69 2	66 12	63 6	59 36	55 19
15	79 5	76 54	74 40	72 21	69 56	67 19	64 28	61 15	57 20
16	79 12	77 10	75 5	72 57	70 41	68 16	65 37	62 39	59 1
17	79 18	77 23	75 27	73 27	71 20	69 4	66 36	63 51	60 28
18	79 22	77 34	75 45	73 52	71 53	69 46	67 27	64 58	61 43
19	79 26	77 44	76 1	74 15	72 23	70 23	68 12	65 46	62 48
20	79 30	77 54	76 9	74 35	72 44	70 56	68 52	66 34	63 47
21	79 33	78 2	76 29	74 53	73 12	71 25	69 28	67 17	64 38
22	79 35	78 8	76 40	75 9	73 33	71 51	69 59	67 55	65 25
23	79 37	78 18	76 50	75 23	73 52	72 14	70 28	68 29	66 6
24	79 39	78 20	76 59	75 30	74 9	72 35	70 54	69 1	66 44

Angles of Elevation for Milling Teeth in 15-degree Blank

No. of Teeth	Angle of Fluting Cutter								
	90	85	80	75	70	65	60	55	50
5	49° 4′	37° 3′	24° 52′	10° 32′	......	......	......	......	......
6	61 49	54 9	46 12	37 40	28° 4′	16° 26′	......	......	......
7	66 44	60 57	55 1	48 45	41 57	34 14	25° 2′	12° 57′	......
8	69 15	64 33	59 46	54 44	49 21	43 24	36 34	28 21	17° 34′
9	70 43	66 45	62 41	58 28	53 58	49 3	43 30	37 2	29 4
10	71 40	68 12	64 41	61 1	57 8	52 55	48 12	42 47	36 18
11	72 20	69 16	66 8	62 54	59 27	55 44	51 37	46 56	41 24
12	72 48	70 2	67 13	64 18	61 13	57 54	54 14	50 5	45 13
13	73 10	70 39	68 5	65 26	62 38	59 37	56 18	52 34	48 14
14	73 26	71 7	68 46	66 20	63 46	61 0	57 59	54 35	50 38
15	73 39	71 30	69 20	67 5	64 42	62 10	59 22	56 15	52 39
16	73 50	71 50	69 49	67 43	65 30	63 9	60 33	57 40	54 20
17	73 58	72 6	70 12	68 14	66 11	63 58	61 33	58 51	55 46
18	74 5	72 20	70 33	68 42	66 46	64 41	62 26	59 54	57 0
19	74 11	72 32	70 51	69 6	67 17	65 19	63 11	60 49	58 6
20	74 16	72 42	71 6	69 28	67 44	65 53	63 52	61 37	59 3
21	74 20	72 51	71 20	69 46	68 7	66 22	64 27	62 20	59 54
22	74 24	72 59	71 32	70 3	68 29	66 49	65 0	62 59	60 40
23	74 27	73 6	71 43	70 18	68 49	67 13	65 29	63 33	61 22
24	74 30	73 12	71 53	70 32	69 6	67 35	65 56	64 5	61 59

Angles of Elevation for Milling Teeth in 20-degree Blank

No. of Teeth	Angle of Fluting Cutter								
	90	85	80	75	70	65	60	55	50
5	40° 20'	30° 4'	19° 46'	8° 4'	......	......	......	......	......
6	53 57	46 55	39 39	31 55	23° 18'	13° 11'	......	......	......
7	59 43	54 17	48 42	42 51	36 30	29 23	21° 1'	10° 23'	......
8	62 46	58 18	53 45	48 59	43 53	38 16	31 53	24 16	14° 31'
9	64 35	60 47	56 54	52 52	48 34	43 53	38 38	32 32	25 5
10	65 47	62 28	59 4	55 33	51 50	47 47	43 18	38 9	32 1
11	66 36	63 39	60 38	57 30	54 12	50 38	46 11	42 12	36 56
12	67 12	64 32	61 49	59 0	56 2	52 50	49 18	45 19	40 40
13	67 39	65 13	62 44	60 11	57 28	54 34	51 22	47 47	43 36
14	68 0	65 46	63 29	61 8	58 39	55 59	53 4	49 47	46 0
15	68 17	66 13	64 6	61 55	59 38	57 10	54 28	51 27	47 58
16	68 30	66 34	64 36	62 34	60 26	58 9	55 39	52 51	49 38
17	68 41	66 53	65 2	63 8	61 8	59 0	56 40	54 3	51 4
18	68 50	67 8	65 24	63 37	61 44	59 44	57 32	55 5	52 17
19	68 57	67 21	65 43	64 2	62 15	60 22	58 18	55 59	53 21
20	69 3	67 32	65 59	64 23	62 43	60 55	58 58	56 47	54 18
21	69 9	67 42	66 14	64 42	63 8	61 25	59 34	57 30	55 9
22	69 14	67 51	66 28	64 59	63 30	61 52	60 7	58 9	55 55
23	69 18	67 59	66 39	65 15	63 50	62 16	60 36	58 44	56 36
24	69 21	68 5	66 49	65 30	64 7	62 38	61 2	59 14	57 12

Angles of Elevation for Milling Teeth in 25-degree Blank

No. of Teeth	Angle of Fluting Cutter								
	90	85	80	75	70	65	60	55	50
5	33° 32'	25° 0'	16° 5'	6° 27'	......	......	......	......	......
6	47 0	40 38	34 6	27 10	19° 33'	10° 48'	......	......	......
7	53 12	48 10	43 0	37 35	31 43	25 17	17° 44'	8° 31'	......
8	56 36	52 25	48 8	43 40	38 55	33 41	27 47	20 50	11° 33'
9	58 40	55 4	51 24	47 36	43 33	39 8	34 13	28 33	21 15
10	60 2	56 53	53 40	50 21	46 47	42 58	38 43	32 53	27 47
11	61 0	58 11	55 18	52 20	49 12	45 48	42 4	37 49	32 32
12	61 42	59 9	56 33	53 52	51 2	47 59	44 38	40 51	36 10
13	62 14	59 54	57 32	55 5	52 30	49 44	46 41	43 15	39 2
14	62 38	60 29	58 19	56 3	53 41	51 8	48 20	45 12	41 22
15	62 57	61 0	58 57	56 52	54 39	52 18	49 43	46 50	43 18
16	63 13	61 22	59 29	57 32	55 29	53 17	50 53	48 13	44 57
17	63 26	61 42	59 54	58 6	56 11	54 8	51 54	49 23	46 21
18	63 37	61 59	60 19	58 36	56 48	54 52	52 46	50 25	47 34
19	63 46	62 13	60 38	59 1	57 20	55 30	53 31	51 19	48 38
20	63 53	62 25	60 56	59 23	57 47	56 4	54 11	52 6	49 33
21	63 59	62 36	61 11	59 43	58 11	56 34	54 47	52 48	50 23
22	64 5	62 46	61 25	60 1	58 34	57 1	55 19	53 26	51 9
23	64 10	62 55	61 37	60 17	58 54	57 25	55 48	54 0	51 50
24	64 14	63 3	61 47	60 31	59 12	57 46	56 13	54 30	52 26

Angles of Elevation for Milling Teeth in 30-degree Blank

No. of Teeth	Angle of Fluting Cutter								
	90	85	80	75	70	65	60	55	50
5	28° 9'	20° 51'	13° 17'	......	......	8° 59'	......	......	......
6	40 54	35 12	29 22	23° 13'	16° 32'	......	......	......	......
7	47 12	42 35	37 52	32 56	27 38	21 47	15° 6'	7° 5'	......
8	50 46	46 53	42 55	38 47	34 24	29 36	24 12	17 55	10° 14'
9	53 0	49 38	46 13	42 40	38 53	34 48	30 14	25 1	18 47
10	54 29	51 31	48 30	45 22	42 3	38 29	34 31	30 1	24 44
11	55 32	52 52	50 10	47 22	44 25	41 13	37 43	33 45	29 8
12	56 18	53 53	51 26	48 54	46 14	43 21	40 12	36 38	32 32
13	56 54	54 42	52 27	50 8	47 41	45 4	42 12	38 58	35 15
14	57 21	55 19	53 15	51 7	48 52	46 27	43 49	40 51	37 27
15	57 42	55 49	53 54	51 55	49 50	47 35	45 9	42 25	39 17
16	58 0	56 14	54 27	52 36	50 39	48 34	46 19	43 47	40 52
17	58 14	56 35	54 54	53 10	51 21	49 24	47 17	44 55	42 12
18	58 26	56 53	55 18	53 40	51 57	50 7	48 7	45 53	43 20
19	58 36	57 8	55 38	54 6	52 29	50 45	48 51	46 46	44 22
20	58 44	57 21	55 55	54 28	52 56	51 18	49 30	47 31	45 15
21	58 51	57 32	56 10	54 47	53 20	51 47	50 5	48 12	46 3
22	58 57	57 42	56 24	55 5	53 42	52 13	50 36	48 44	46 46
23	59 3	57 51	56 37	55 21	54 2	52 37	51 4	49 21	47 25
24	59 8	57 59	56 48	55 36	54 20	52 59	51 30	49 52	48 0

Angles of Elevation for Milling Teeth in 35-degree Blank

No. of Teeth	Angle of Fluting Cutter								
	90	85	80	75	70	65	60	55	50
5	23° 49'	17° 35'	11° 10'	4° 22'	......	......	......	......	......
6	35 32	30 29	25 19	19 53	14° 3'	7° 1'	......	......	......
7	41 41	37 20	33 14	28 46	24 1	18 48	12° 54'	5° 58'	......
8	45 17	41 43	38 5	34 19	30 18	25 56	21 4	15 27	8° 41'
9	47 34	44 28	41 18	38 1	34 32	30 47	26 37	21 52	16 16
10	49 7	46 22	43 33	40 39	37 35	34 17	30 38	26 30	21 40
11	50 14	47 46	45 14	42 38	39 53	36 55	33 40	30 0	25 44
12	51 3	48 48	46 30	44 8	41 39	38 58	36 2	32 44	28 55
13	51 40	49 36	47 30	45 20	43 3	40 36	37 55	34 55	31 28
14	52 9	50 15	48 19	46 18	44 12	41 57	39 28	36 42	33 33
15	52 32	50 46	48 58	47 6	45 9	43 4	40 46	38 12	35 17
16	52 50	51 11	49 20	47 46	45 56	43 59	41 51	39 28	36 45
17	53 5	51 32	49 57	48 20	46 37	44 47	42 47	40 33	38 1
18	53 18	51 50	50 21	48 49	47 12	45 29	43 36	41 31	39 8
19	53 29	52 6	50 42	49 14	47 43	46 5	44 19	42 21	40 6
20	53 38	52 19	50 59	49 36	48 10	46 37	44 57	43 5	40 57
21	53 46	52 31	51 15	49 56	48 34	47 6	45 31	43 44	41 43
22	53 53	52 42	51 29	50 14	48 56	47 32	46 1	44 19	42 24
23	53 59	52 51	51 42	50 30	49 15	47 55	46 28	44 51	43 1
24	54 4	52 59	51 53	50 44	49 32	48 16	46 52	45 20	43 35

Angles of Elevation for Milling Teeth in 40-degree Blank

No. of Teeth	Angle of Fluting Cutter								
	90	85	80	75	70	65	60	55	50
5	20° 13′	14° 53′	9° 24′	3° 39′	......	......	......	......	......
6	30 48	26 21	21 48	17 3	11° 58′	6° 22′	......	......	......
7	36 37	32 52	29 2	25 3	20 49	16 12	11° 1′	5° 2′	......
8	40 7	36 53	33 36	30 10	26 33	22 38	18 16	13 20	7° 23′
9	42 24	39 34	36 41	33 41	30 31	27 26	23 20	19 4	14 3
10	43 57	41 26	38 51	36 11	33 32	30 21	27 3	23 16	18 55
11	45 4	42 48	40 28	38 4	35 32	32 49	29 50	26 29	22 38
12	45 54	43 50	41 43	39 32	37 14	34 45	32 3	29 2	25 33
13	46 33	44 38	42 42	40 41	38 35	36 19	33 50	31 4	27 54
14	47 3	45 17	43 29	41 38	39 41	37 36	35 19	32 46	29 51
15	47 26	45 47	44 7	42 24	40 35	38 39	36 32	34 10	31 28
16	47 45	46 13	44 39	43 3	41 21	39 32	37 33	35 21	32 50
17	48 1	46 34	45 6	43 36	42 0	40 18	38 27	36 23	34 2
18	48 14	46 52	45 29	44 4	42 34	40 58	39 13	37 17	35 5
19	48 25	47 8	45 49	44 28	43 3	41 33	39 54	38 4	35 59
20	48 35	47 22	46 7	44 50	43 30	42 4	40 30	38 46	36 47
21	48 43	47 33	46 23	45 9	43 53	42 31	41 2	39 23	37 30
22	48 50	47 43	46 36	45 26	44 13	42 55	41 30	39 56	38 8
23	48 56	47 52	46 48	45 41	44 31	43 17	41 55	40 25	38 42
24	49 1	48 0	46 58	45 55	44 48	43 36	42 19	40 57	39 15

Angles of Elevation for Milling Teeth in 45-degree Blank

No. of Teeth	Angle of Fluting Cutter								
	90	85	80	75	70	65	60	55	50
5	17° 10′	12° 36′	7° 57′	3° 5′	......	......	......	......	......
6	26 34	22 41	18 43	14 35	10° 11′	5° 23′	......	......	......
7	31 56	28 36	25 13	21 42	17 56	13 55	9° 24′	4° 15′	......
8	35 16	32 22	29 25	26 22	23 8	19 39	15 48	11 25	5° 58′
9	37 27	34 54	32 17	29 36	26 45	23 41	20 19	16 31	11 49
10	38 58	36 41	34 21	31 57	29 24	26 40	23 40	20 18	16 10
11	40 4	38 0	35 53	33 42	31 24	28 57	26 15	23 14	19 32
12	40 54	39 0	37 5	35 5	33 0	30 45	28 18	25 33	22 13
13	41 32	39 47	38 1	36 11	34 15	32 12	29 57	27 36	24 23
14	42 1	40 24	38 46	37 4	35 17	33 22	31 18	28 58	26 9
15	42 25	40 55	39 23	37 48	36 9	34 22	32 26	30 17	27 40
16	42 44	41 20	39 54	38 25	36 52	35 12	33 24	31 23	28 57
17	43 0	41 41	40 20	38 57	37 29	35 55	34 14	32 20	30 4
18	43 13	41 58	40 42	39 24	38 1	36 33	34 56	33 10	31 1
19	43 24	42 13	41 1	39 47	38 28	37 5	35 34	33 54	31 51
20	43 34	42 26	41 18	40 6	38 53	37 34	36 8	34 33	32 37
21	43 42	42 37	41 33	40 26	39 15	38 0	36 38	35 7	33 17
22	43 49	42 47	41 46	40 42	39 34	38 23	37 5	35 38	33 53
23	43 55	42 56	41 57	40 56	39 52	38 43	37 29	36 6	34 26
24	44 0	43 4	42 7	41 9	40 7	39 1	37 50	36 31	35 55

Angles of Elevation for Milling Teeth in 50-degree Blank

No. of Teeth	Angle of Fluting Cutter								
	90	85	80	75	70	65	60	55	50
5	14° 32'	10° 39'	6° 42'	2° 33'	......	......	......	......	......
6	22 45	19 23	15 58	12 24	8° 38'	4° 32'	......	......	......
7	27 37	24 42	21 44	18 39	15 24	11 54	8° 1'	3° 36'	......
8	30 41	28 8	25 31	22 50	19 59	16 55	13 33	9 45	5° 20'
9	32 44	30 28	28 9	25 45	23 14	20 31	17 32	14 13	10 22
10	34 10	32 7	30 2	27 54	25 39	23 12	20 32	17 34	14 9
11	35 13	33 22	31 28	29 31	27 28	25 16	22 52	20 11	17 6
12	36 0	34 18	32 34	30 47	28 53	26 54	24 42	22 15	19 27
13	36 36	35 2	33 26	31 48	30 3	28 13	26 11	23 56	21 22
14	37 5	35 38	34 9	32 47	31 1	29 18	27 26	25 21	22 58
15	37 28	36 7	34 44	33 18	31 49	30 13	28 28	26 32	24 20
16	37 47	36 31	35 13	33 53	32 29	31 0	29 22	27 33	25 30
17	38 2	36 50	35 37	34 22	33 3	31 38	30 7	28 24	26 29
18	38 15	37 7	35 58	34 47	33 33	32 13	30 46	29 10	27 21
19	38 26	37 22	36 17	35 9	33 59	32 43	31 21	29 50	28 7
20	38 35	37 34	36 32	35 28	34 21	33 9	31 52	30 25	28 47
21	38 43	37 45	36 46	35 45	34 41	33 33	32 19	30 57	29 24
22	38 50	37 55	36 58	36 0	34 59	33 55	32 44	31 26	29 57
23	38 56	38 3	37 9	36 14	35 15	34 14	33 6	31 51	30 26
24	39 1	38 10	37 19	36 25	35 30	34 30	33 25	32 14	30 52

Angles of Elevation for Milling Teeth in 55-degree Blank

No. of Teeth	Angle of Fluting Cutter								
	90	85	80	75	70	65	60	55	50
5	12° 13'	8° 57'	5° 37'	2° 10'	......	......	......	......	......
6	19 17	16 25	13 30	10 28	7° 15'	3° 48'	......	......	......
7	23 35	21 4	18 31	15 51	13 4	10 3	6° 44'	3° 1'	......
8	26 21	24 8	21 52	19 31	17 3	14 25	11 30	8 17	4° 17'
9	28 13	26 14	24 12	22 7	19 55	17 34	14 59	12 6	8 34
10	29 32	27 45	25 55	24 2	22 3	19 55	17 36	15 1	11 52
11	30 30	28 52	27 12	25 29	23 41	21 45	19 39	17 18	14 27
12	31 14	29 44	28 12	26 38	24 59	23 13	21 17	19 8	16 32
13	31 48	30 25	29 0	27 33	26 2	24 24	22 37	20 38	18 15
14	32 15	30 58	29 39	28 18	26 53	25 25	23 43	21 53	19 40
15	32 36	31 24	30 11	28 55	27 35	26 11	24 38	22 56	20 52
16	32 54	31 47	30 38	29 27	28 12	26 53	25 26	23 51	21 54
17	33 9	32 6	31 1	29 54	28 44	27 29	26 7	24 38	22 49
18	33 21	32 21	31 20	30 17	29 10	28 0	26 43	25 18	23 35
19	33 31	32 34	31 36	30 36	29 33	28 27	27 14	25 54	24 17
20	33 40	32 46	31 51	30 54	29 54	28 51	27 42	26 25	24 53
21	33 47	32 56	32 3	31 9	30 12	29 12	28 6	26 53	25 25
22	33 54	33 5	32 15	31 23	30 29	29 31	28 28	27 19	25 55
23	34 0	33 13	32 25	31 36	30 44	29 48	28 48	27 42	26 22
24	34 5	33 20	32 34	31 47	30 57	30 4	29 7	28 3	26 46

Angles of Elevation for Milling Teeth in 60-degree Blank

No. of Teeth	Angle of Fluting Cutter								
	90	85	80	75	70	65	60	55	50
5	10° 7′	7° 25′	4° 39′	1° 47′	......	......	......	......	......
6	16 6	13 41	11 12	8 42	6° 2′	3° 9′	......	......	......
7	19 48	17 40	15 30	13 16	10 55	8 22	5° 36′	2° 30′	......
8	22 13	20 19	18 24	16 24	14 19	12 4	9 37	6 53	3° 44′
9	23 52	22 10	20 26	18 39	16 46	14 46	12 34	10 7	7 19
10	25 2	23 30	21 56	20 19	18 37	16 48	14 49	12 36	10 5
11	25 54	24 30	23 4	21 35	20 2	18 23	16 34	14 34	12 16
12	26 34	25 16	23 57	22 36	21 10	19 39	17 59	16 9	14 13
13	27 5	25 53	24 40	23 25	22 6	20 41	19 9	17 27	15 31
14	27 29	26 22	25 14	24 4	22 51	21 32	20 6	18 32	16 44
15	27 49	26 46	25 43	24 37	23 29	22 15	20 55	19 27	17 47
16	28 5	27 6	26 7	25 5	24 1	22 52	21 37	20 14	18 40
17	28 18	27 23	26 27	25 29	24 28	23 23	22 13	20 55	19 26
18	28 29	27 37	26 44	25 49	24 52	23 50	22 44	21 30	20 6
19	28 38	27 49	26 58	26 7	25 12	24 14	23 11	22 1	20 42
20	28 46	27 59	27 11	26 22	25 30	24 35	23 35	22 29	21 14
21	28 53	28 8	27 23	26 36	25 46	24 54	23 57	22 54	21 42
22	29 0	28 17	27 34	26 49	26 2	25 12	24 17	23 17	22 8
23	29 5	28 24	27 43	27 0	26 15	25 27	24 35	23 37	22 32
24	29 9	28 30	27 50	27 9	26 26	25 40	24 50	23 55	22 52

Angles of Elevation for Milling Teeth in 65-degree Blank

No. of Teeth	Angle of Fluting Cutter								
	90	85	80	75	70	65	60	55	50
5	8° 12′	6° 0′	3° 46′	1° 27′	......	......	......	......	......
6	13 7	11 10	9 8	7 4	4° 53′	2° 33′	......	......	......
7	16 13	14 28	12 41	10 50	8 54	6 49	4° 33′	2° 1′	......
8	18 15	16 40	15 6	13 26	11 42	9 51	7 50	5 30	3° 1′
9	19 39	18 14	16 48	15 19	13 45	12 5	10 16	8 14	5 57
10	20 40	19 23	18 4	16 44	15 19	13 48	12 9	10 19	8 15
11	21 25	20 14	19 3	17 49	16 31	15 9	13 38	11 58	10 4
12	21 59	20 54	19 48	18 40	17 28	16 12	14 49	13 17	11 32
13	22 26	21 26	20 35	19 22	18 15	17 5	15 48	14 23	12 46
14	22 48	21 52	20 55	19 56	18 54	17 48	16 37	15 17	13 48
15	23 5	22 13	21 19	20 24	19 26	18 24	17 18	16 4	14 40
16	23 18	22 29	21 39	20 47	19 53	18 55	17 53	16 43	15 24
17	23 30	22 43	21 56	21 8	20 17	19 22	18 23	17 17	16 3
18	23 40	22 55	22 11	21 25	20 37	19 46	18 50	17 47	16 37
19	23 48	23 5	22 24	21 40	20 55	20 6	19 13	18 14	17 7
20	23 55	23 14	22 35	21 54	21 10	20 24	19 33	18 38	17 34
21	24 1	23 22	22 45	22 6	21 24	20 39	19 51	18 58	17 58
22	24 6	23 29	22 53	22 16	21 36	20 53	20 8	19 17	18 20
23	24 11	23 36	23 1	22 26	21 47	21 7	20 23	19 34	18 39
24	24 15	23 43	23 8	22 34	21 57	21 18	20 36	19 50	18 57

Angles of Elevation for Milling Teeth in 70-degree Blank

No. of Teeth	Angle of Fluting Cutter								
	90	85	80	75	70	65	60	55	50
5	6° 25′	4° 42′	2° 57′	......	......	......	......	......	......
6	10 18	8 44	7 9	5° 32′	3° 48′	......	......	......	......
7	12 47	11 23	9 59	8 31	6 58	5° 21′	3° 33′	......	......
8	14 26	13 11	11 55	10 36	9 14	7 45	6 9	4° 23′	2° 21′
9	15 35	14 27	13 18	12 7	10 53	9 33	8 6	6 30	4 41
10	16 25	15 23	14 21	13 15	12 8	10 55	9 37	8 9	6 30
11	17 2	16 5	15 8	14 8	13 7	12 0	10 48	9 28	7 57
12	17 30	16 38	15 45	14 50	13 53	12 51	11 45	10 31	9 8
13	17 52	17 4	16 15	15 24	14 30	13 33	12 32	11 23	10 6
14	18 9	17 24	16 38	15 51	15 1	14 8	13 11	12 7	10 55
15	18 23	17 41	16 58	16 14	15 28	14 38	13 44	12 44	11 37
16	18 35	17 55	17 15	16 33	15 50	15 3	14 13	13 17	12 13
17	18 45	18 7	17 30	16 50	16 9	15 25	14 38	13 46	12 45
18	18 53	18 17	17 42	17 5	16 26	15 44	14 59	14 10	13 13
19	19 0	18 26	17 52	17 17	16 40	16 1	15 18	14 32	13 38
20	19 6	18 35	18 1	17 28	16 53	16 16	15 35	14 51	13 59
21	19 11	18 41	18 9	17 38	17 5	16 29	15 50	15 8	14 18
22	19 15	18 46	18 16	17 46	17 15	16 40	16 3	15 22	14 35
23	19 19	18 51	18 23	17 54	17 25	16 50	16 15	15 36	14 51
24	19 22	18 55	18 29	18 0	17 33	16 59	16 25	15 48	15 5

Angles of Elevation for Milling Teeth in 75-degree Blank

No. of Teeth	Angle of Fluting Cutter								
	90	85	80	75	70	65	60	55	50
5	4° 44′	3° 28′	2° 10′	......	......	......	......	......	......
6	7 38	6 29	5 19	4° 6′	2° 50′	1° 29′	......	......	......
7	9 29	8 27	7 24	6 17	5 10	3 57	2° 38′	1° 10′	......
8	10 44	9 48	8 51	7 50	6 51	5 45	4 34	3 14	1° 45′
9	11 36	10 46	9 54	9 0	8 5	7 5	6 0	4 49	3 27
10	12 14	11 28	10 40	9 52	9 1	8 7	7 8	6 3	4 49
11	12 42	12 0	11 16	10 32	9 45	8 56	8 2	7 1	5 54
12	13 4	12 25	11 45	11 4	10 21	9 35	8 45	7 49	6 47
13	13 21	12 45	12 8	11 29	10 50	10 7	9 21	8 29	7 31
14	13 34	13 0	12 26	11 50	11 13	10 33	9 50	9 2	8 7
15	13 45	13 13	12 41	12 7	11 33	10 55	10 15	9 30	8 39
16	13 54	13 24	12 54	12 22	11 50	11 14	10 37	9 54	9 7
17	14 2	13 33	13 5	12 35	12 5	11 31	10 56	10 16	9 31
18	14 8	13 41	13 14	12 46	12 17	11 45	11 12	10 34	9 51
19	14 13	13 48	13 22	12 55	12 28	11 58	11 26	10 50	10 10
20	14 18	13 54	13 29	13 4	12 38	12 9	11 39	11 5	10 27
21	14 22	13 59	13 36	13 12	12 46	12 19	11 50	11 17	10 41
22	14 25	14 3	13 41	13 18	12 53	12 28	12 0	11 29	10 54
23	14 28	14 7	13 46	13 24	13 0	12 36	12 9	11 40	11 6
24	14 31	14 11	13 50	13 29	13 7	12 44	12 18	11 50	11 18

Angles of Elevation for Milling Teeth in 80-degree Blank

No. of Teeth	Angle of Fluting Cutter								
	90	85	80	75	70	65	60	55	50
5	3° 7′	2° 17′	1° 26′	0° 43′	......	......	......	......	......
6	5 2	4 16	3 30	2 42	1° 52′	0° 58′	......	......	......
7	6 16	5 35	4 53	4 10	3 25	2 36	1° 45′	0° 46′	......
8	7 6	6 29	5 51	5 12	4 31	3 48	3 2	2 8	1° 8′
9	7 42	7 8	6 34	5 58	5 21	4 42	3 59	3 11	2 17
10	8 7	7 36	7 5	6 33	5 59	5 22	4 44	4 0	3 11
11	8 26	7 58	7 29	7 0	6 28	5 55	5 19	4 39	3 54
12	8 41	8 15	7 48	7 21	6 52	6 22	5 48	5 11	4 29
13	8 53	8 29	8 4	7 38	7 12	6 43	6 12	5 38	4 59
14	9 2	8 40	8 16	7 52	7 28	7 1	6 32	6 0	5 24
15	9 9	8 48	8 26	8 4	7 40	7 16	6 48	6 19	5 45
16	9 15	8 55	8 35	8 14	7 51	7 28	7 3	6 33	6 3
17	9 20	9 1	8 42	8 22	8 1	7 39	7 15	6 49	6 19
18	9 24	9 6	8 48	8 29	8 10	7 49	7 26	7 1	6 33
19	9 28	9 11	8 53	8 36	8 17	7 58	7 36	7 12	6 45
20	9 31	9 15	8 58	8 42	8 24	8 5	7 44	7 21	6 56
21	9 34	9 19	9 3	8 47	8 30	8 12	7 52	7 30	7 6
22	9 36	9 22	9 6	8 51	8 35	8 18	7 59	7 38	7 15
23	9 38	9 24	9 9	8 55	8 39	8 23	8 5	7 45	7 23
24	9 40	9 26	9 13	8 59	8 43	8 28	8 11	7 51	7 30

Angles of Elevation for Milling Teeth in 85-degree Blank

No. of Teeth	Angle of Fluting Cutter								
	90	85	80	75	70	65	60	55	50
5	1° 33′	1° 8′	......	......	......	......	......	......	......
6	2 30	2 7	1° 44′	1° 20′	0° 55′	......	......	......	......
7	3 7	2 46	2 26	2 4	1 42	1° 18′	0° 50′	......	......
8	3 32	3 13	2 55	2 35	2 15	1 53	1 29	1° 3′	0° 34′
9	3 50	3 33	3 16	2 58	2 40	2 20	1 59	1 35	1 8
10	4 3	3 48	3 32	3 16	2 59	2 41	2 21	1 59	1 35
11	4 13	3 59	3 44	3 30	3 14	2 57	2 39	2 19	1 57
12	4 20	4 7	3 53	3 40	3 25	3 10	2 53	2 35	2 15
13	4 26	4 14	4 1	3 48	3 35	3 21	3 6	2 48	2 30
14	4 30	4 19	4 7	3 55	3 43	3 29	3 15	2 59	2 42
15	4 34	4 23	4 12	4 1	3 50	3 37	3 24	3 9	2 52
16	4 37	4 27	4 17	4 6	3 56	3 44	3 30	3 17	3 1
17	4 40	4 30	4 21	4 11	4 1	3 50	3 37	3 24	3 9
18	4 42	4 33	4 24	4 15	4 5	3 55	3 43	3 30	3 16
19	4 44	4 35	4 27	4 18	4 9	3 59	3 48	3 36	3 22
20	4 46	4 37	4 29	4 21	4 12	4 3	3 52	3 41	3 28
21	4 47	4 39	4 31	4 23	4 15	4 6	3 56	3 45	3 33
22	4 48	4 41	4 33	4 25	4 18	4 9	3 59	3 49	3 37
23	4 49	4 42	4 35	4 27	4 20	4 12	4 2	3 53	3 41
24	4 50	4 43	4 36	4 29	4 22	4 14	4 5	3 56	3 45

Angles of Elevation of Dividing Head for Milling Teeth in Side Mills or End Mills with Large Number of Teeth

No. of Teeth	Angle of Fluting Cutter				
	45	50	60	70	80
25	75° 7′	77° 33′	81° 28′	84° 38′	87° 24′
26	75 44	78 4	81 49	84 51	87 30
27	76 17	78 32	82 8	85 3	87 36
28	76 49	78 58	82 26	85 14	87 42
29	77 17	79 21	82 42	85 24	87 46
30	77 44	79 43	82 57	85 34	87 51
32	78 32	80 23	83 24	85 51	87 59
34	79 14	80 59	83 48	86 6	88 7
36	79 51	81 29	84 9	86 19	88 13
38	80 24	81 58	84 29	86 31	88 19
40	80 53	82 22	84 45	86 42	88 24
42	81 20	82 44	85 0	86 51	88 29
44	81 44	83 4	85 14	87 0	88 33
46	82 7	83 23	85 27	87 8	88 37
48	82 26	83 39	85 38	87 16	88 40
50	82 45	83 55	85 49	87 22	88 43
52	83 3	84 9	85 59	87 28	88 46
54	83 17	84 22	86 8	87 34	88 49
56	83 31	84 34	86 16	87 39	88 52
58	83 46	84 46	86 24	87 44	88 54
60	83 58	84 57	86 31	87 49	88 56

Spline-Shaft Milling Cutter. — The most efficient method of forming splines on shafts is by hobbing, but special milling cutters may also be used. Since the cutter forms the space between adjacent splines, it must be made to suit the number of splines and the root diameter of the shaft. The cutter angle B equals 360 degrees divided by the number of splines. The following formulas are for determining the chordal width C at the root of the splines or the chordal width across the concave edge of the cutter. In these formulas, A = angle between center line of spline and a radial line passing through the intersection of the root circle and one side of the spline; W = width of spline; d = root diameter of splined shaft; C = chordal width at root circle between adjacent splines; N = number of splines.

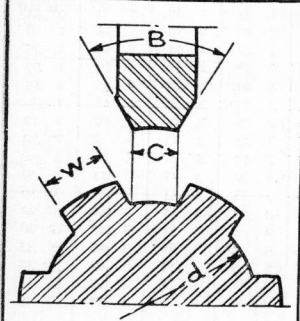

$$\operatorname{Sin} A = \frac{W}{d} \; ; \; C = \sin\left(\frac{180}{N} - A\right) \times d$$

Splines of involute form are often used in preference to the straight-sided type. Dimensions of the American Standard involute splines and hobs are given in the section on splines.

American Standard T-Slot Cutters

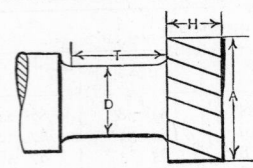

Approved by American Engineering Standards Committee, National Machine Tool Builders' Association, and American Society of Mechanical Engineers.

Width of Throat*†		Thickness of Cutter H		Diameter of Cutter A		Diameter of Neck D†	Length of Neck T
Standard	Nominal Bolt Size	Maximum	Minimum (Worn)	Maximum	Minimum (Worn)		
9/32	1/4	15/64	13/64	9/16	1/2	17/64	3/8
11/32	5/16	17/64	15/64	21/32	19/32	21/64	7/16
7/16	3/8	21/64	19/64	25/32	23/32	13/32	9/16
9/16	1/2	25/64	23/64	31/32	29/32	17/32	11/16
11/16	5/8	31/64	29/64	1 1/4	1 3/16	21/32	7/8
13/16	3/4	5/8	19/32	1 15/32	1 3/8	25/32	1 1/16
1 1/16	1	53/64	25/32	1 27/32	1 3/4	1 1/32	1 1/4
1 5/16	1 1/4	1 3/32	1 1/32	2 7/32	2 1/8	1 9/32	1 9/16
1 9/16	1 1/2	1 11/32	1 9/32	2 21/32	2 9/16	1 17/32	1 15/16

All dimensions in inches.

* The width of throat given in the table corresponds to the standard width for T-slots.

† In addition to the width of throat given, a secondary standard is recognized, having the width of throat the same as the nominal diameter of the T-bolt. This is to provide for the use, during the transition period, of this standard on machine tools where it is already established. If the narrower throat is used, the diameter of neck D should be reduced accordingly.

Inserted-Blade Cutters

Inserted-blade cutters are regularly furnished with high-speed steel blades. The side cutters have the blades set straight, while the face cutters have the blades set at an angle. Face milling cutters have a taper hole and keyway and will be furnished either right- or left-hand. Inserted-blade cutters with carbon steel blades are special. All dimensions in inches.

Side Milling Cutters			Face Milling Cutters			
Diameter	Width of Face	Size of Hole	Diameter	Cutting Faces of Blades		Number of B. & S. Taper Hole
				Width	Depth	
6	2	1 1/4	5 1/2	2 1/4	1 1/16	10
7	2	1 1/4	5 1/2	2 1/4	1 1/16	12
7	2	1 3/4	6 1/2	2 1/4	1 1/16	10
8	2	1 1/2	6 1/2	2 1/4	1 1/16	12
8	2	2	7 1/2	2 1/4	1 1/16	12
9	2	1 1/2	8 1/2	2 1/4	1 3/16	12
10	2	1 1/2	9 1/2	2 1/4	1 3/16	12

Concave, Convex, and Corner-rounding Cutters — American Standard

Concave   Convex   Corner-Rounding

Diameter of Circle* C			Cutter Diam. D	Thickness T ±.010	Diameter of Hole A		
Nom.	Max.	Min.			Nom.	Max.	Min.
Concave Cutters							
1/8	0.1280	0.1240	2	1/4	7/8	0.876	0.875
3/16	0.1905	0.1865	2	3/8	7/8	0.876	0.875
1/4	0.2530	0.2490	2	7/16	7/8	0.876	0.875
5/16	0.3155	0.3115	2 1/4	9/16	7/8	0.876	0.875
3/8	0.3780	0.3740	2 1/4	5/8	7/8	0.876	0.875
7/16	0.4405	0.4365	2 1/4	3/4	7/8	0.876	0.875
1/2	0.5040	0.4980	2 1/4	13/16	7/8	0.876	0.875
5/8	0.6290	0.6230	2 3/4	1	1	1.001	1.000
3/4	0.7540	0.7480	3	1 9/16	1	1.001	1.000
7/8	0.8790	0.8730	3 1/4	1 3/8	1	1.001	1.000
1	1.0050	0.9980	3 1/4	1 9/16	1	1.001	1.000
Convex Cutters							
1/8	0.1270	0.1230	2	1/8	7/8	0.876	0.875
3/16	0.1895	0.1855	2	3/16	7/8	0.876	0.875
1/4	0.2520	0.2480	2	1/4	7/8	0.876	0.875
5/16	0.3145	0.3105	2 1/4	5/16	7/8	0.876	0.875
3/8	0.3770	0.3740	2 1/4	3/8	7/8	0.876	0.875
7/16	0.4395	0.4355	2 1/4	7/16	7/8	0.876	0.875
1/2	0.5030	0.4970	2 1/4	1/2	7/8	0.876	0.875
5/8	0.6280	0.6220	2 3/4	5/8	1	1.001	1.000
3/4	0.7530	0.7470	3	3/4	1	1.001	1.000
7/8	0.8980	0.8720	3 1/4	7/8	1	1.001	1.000
1	1.0040	0.9960	3 1/4	1	1	1.001	1.000
Corner-rounding Cutters							
1/8*	0.1265	0.1245	2	1/4	7/8	0.876	0.875
1/4*	0.2520	0.2490	2 1/4	13/32	7/8	0.876	0.875
3/8*	0.3770	0.3740	3	9/16	1	1.001	1.000
1/2*	0.5025	0.4990	3 1/4	3/4	1	1.001	1.000
5/8*	0.6275	0.6240	3 1/2	15/16	1	1.001	1.000

* Radius R for corner-rounding cutters.

All dimensions in inches. Radial or hooked teeth optional with manufacturer. Corner-rounding cutters are made either right- or left-hand.

Formed Milling Cutters. — The spacing of the teeth in formed and eccentrically relieved cutters is much coarser than in ordinary milling cutters. The width of the space between the front of one tooth and the back of the next should be equal to about ½ of the width of the land. The grooves are milled with single-angle cutters varying from 30 to 45 degrees included angle. An angular cutter of 35 degrees included angle is satisfactory for most conditions. The most common of all formed cutters, outside of gear cutters, which form a class by themselves, are concave, convex and corner-rounding cutters, the latter being made in two types, single or double. The corner-rounding cutters should not be made with the rounded part a full quarter of a circle but the shape should merge into a tangent 5 degrees to a line perpendicular to the axis of the cutter.

Stagger-tooth Milling Cutters — American Standard

Cutter Diameter			Range of Face Widths	Hole Diameter		
Nom.	Max.	Min.		Nom.	Max.	Min.
2½	2.515	2.485	¼ to ½	⅞	0.876	0.875
3	3.015	2.985	³⁄₁₆ to ⅜	1	1.001	1.000
3	3.015	2.985	½ to ¾	1¼	1.251	1.250
4	4.015	3.985	¼ to ⅞	1¼	1.251	1.250
5	5.015	4.985	½ to ¾	1¼	1.251	1.250
6	6.015	5.985	⅜ to 1	1¼	1.251	1.250
8	8.015	7.985	⅜ to 1	1½	1.501	1.500

All dimensions in inches. Side teeth are not cutting teeth.

Metal Slitting Saws — American Standard

Cutter Diameter			Thickness Range	Hole Diameter		
Nom.	Max.	Min.		Nom.	Max.	Min.
2½	2.515	2.485	¹⁄₃₂ to ⅛	⅞	0.876	0.875
3	3.015	2.985	¹⁄₃₂ to ⁵⁄₃₂	1	1.001	1.000
4	4.015	3.985	¹⁄₃₂ to ³⁄₁₆	1	1.001	1.000
5*	5.015	4.985	¹⁄₁₆ to ³⁄₁₆	1*	1.001	1.000
6†	6.015	5.985	¹⁄₁₆ to ³⁄₁₆	1†	1.001	1.000
7**	7.015	6.985	¹⁄₁₆ to ³⁄₁₆	1**	1.001	1.000
8**	8.015	7.985	⅛ and ³⁄₁₆	1¼**	1.251	1.250

* ⅛-inch thickness made either with 1- or 1¼-inch hole.
† ⅛- and ³⁄₁₆- inch thicknesses made either with 1- or 1¼-inch hole.
** ⅛-inch thickness made either with 1- or 1¼-inch hole and ³⁄₁₆-inch thickness with 1¼-inch hole only.
All dimensions in inches.

Metal Slitting Cutters. — Thin cutters intended for cutting off or slitting purposes are termed metal slitting cutters. The sides of these cutters are ground to run true, but are made slightly thicker at the outside edge than at the hole or center, to provide clearance and prevent binding in the slot cut. A table is given showing the number of teeth used in these cutters for cutting steel. For brass and very deep slots the number of teeth should be only about two-thirds of the number of teeth given in the table. For light slotting, like screw slotting, etc., a cheaper grade of cutters with very fine teeth, not ground on the sides, is used. These are commonly termed screw slotting cutters. The number of teeth in these cutters for the most common diameters are as follows: 1¾ inch diameter, 52 teeth; 2 inches, 56 teeth; 2¼ inches, 60 teeth; 2½ inches, 64 teeth; 2¾ inches, 68 teeth; 3 inches, 72 teeth.

Number of Teeth in Metal Slitting Saws
(For Cutting Steel)

Diam. of Cutter	No. of Teeth	Diam. of Cutter	No. of Teeth	Diam. of Cutter	No. of Teeth	Diam. of Cutter	No. of Teeth	Diam. of Cutter	No. of Teeth	Diam. of Cutter	No. of Teeth
2½	30	3½	34	4½	38	5½	42	6½	46	7½	54
3	32	4	36	5	40	6	44	7	50	8	58

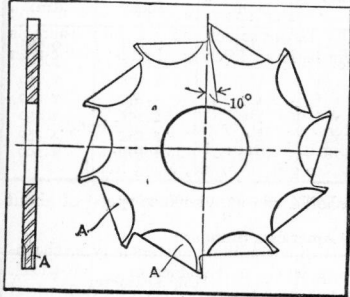

Saws for Copper. — Copper is one of the most difficult materials to cut with milling saws, and a special construction is necessary. One of the most successful types is shown in the accompanying engraving. The front of the tooth has a rake of 10 degrees and the metal is ground away on the sides between the teeth for clearance, as indicated at A. The number of teeth should be comparatively small. A pitch of about 1 inch, which would give 10 teeth in a 3-inch saw, gives good results.

Milling Cutters with Helical Teeth. — It is the general practice to cut the teeth straight on narrow cutters, up to about ¾ inch in width, and to cut the teeth helical or "spiral" on wider cutters. The angle between the helix and cutter axis should equal about 15 degrees. Cutters having helical teeth are generally used in preference to the type with straight or parallel teeth, especially for milling comparatively wide surfaces, because the former cut more smoothly. When the teeth are parallel to the axis, each tooth begins to cut along its entire width at the same time; hence, if a wide surface is being milled, a shock is produced as each tooth engages the metal. This difficulty is not experienced with helical teeth which, being at an angle, begin to cut at one side and continue across the work with a smooth shaving action. Helical cutters also require less power for driving and produce smoother surfaces.

Interlocking Cutters. — There are several methods of interlocking milling cutters which are made in sections. A simple method consists in milling a straight slot across the end of one cutter and providing the other cutter with a corresponding tongue fitting loosely in the slot. Ordinary side-mills are sometimes placed side by side with their hubs ground down so that the teeth of one of the cutters interlock into the spaces between the teeth of the other. Another method consists in cutting away two or more sectors on one end of each of the two cutters in such a manner that the remaining high sectors in one cutter fit loosely into the spaces cut away in the other section. The interlocking ends of some cutters are milled or planed off to produce an angular face, and a recess is provided in the cutter ends in which a washer is placed, against which the finished surfaces of the recess bear. Milling cutters are generally interlocked either (1) to maintain a standard width of cutter; (2) to enable the milling of two or more distinct widths with the same set of cutters; or (3) to enable long cutters to be made in sections, and still have a continuous tooth surface.

Cutter Grinding

Wheels for Sharpening Milling Cutters. — Grinding wheels for cutter sharpening should be of a medium-soft grade and not too fine — never finer than 60 grit. Fine wheels cut slowly and tend to burn the teeth. Wheels for sharpening cutters made of high-speed steels can be a little coarser than those used on carbon steel. If the wheel is too soft, it will wear rapidly, which makes it difficult to keep the cutter round while sharpening it. This difficulty can be overcome by using a wheel at least ¾-inch wide, instead of the ⅜- or ½-inch wheels commonly used. A wide soft wheel will last as long as a narrow one of harder grade, and being softer, it tends to eliminate the danger of burning. For sharpening ordinary milling cutters, a wide wheel will not be especially inconvenient, as generally there is plenty of room. The following "Aloxite" wheels have given good results for cutter sharpening operations:

> For carbon steel mills and cutters, 50 grit, O grade, D496 bond.
> For high-speed steel mills and cutters, 40 grit, O grade, D496 bond.
> For carbon-steel formed cutters, 50 grit, P grade, D495 bond.
> For high-speed steel formed cutters, 40 grit, P grade, D495 bond.

To obtain the best results, these wheels should run at a surface speed of about 5,000 feet per minute.

Form of Wheel for Cutter Grinding. — Ordinary milling cutters may be sharpened either by using the periphery of a disk wheel or the face of a cup-wheel. The latter grinds the lands of the teeth flat, whereas the periphery of a disk wheel leaves the teeth slightly concave. It has often been claimed that the cutter relieved with a disk wheel is inferior to the cutter relieved with the cup-wheel, owing to the smaller amount of metal directly back of the cutting edge. While the use of a cup-wheel theoretically possesses certain advantages over the disk type of wheel, actual tests indicate that longer life and higher rates of production are obtained with cutters relieved with the disk wheel. The conditions under which each cutter was tested were the same and the steel for the cutters was taken from the same bar. All cutters were given the same heat-treatment and one milling machine was used for all the tests. These tests proved that regardless of what combination of speeds and feeds was used, the result was practically always in favor of the cutter relieved with the disk wheel. In nearly all cases, from 20 to 30 per cent longer service, in inches milled, was obtained with cutters relieved with the disk wheel. The grinding wheels used, which proved to be of suitable grade and grain, were Norton 38–36–I silicate alundum for the disk wheel, and Norton 38–46–J alundum for the cup-wheel (Brown & Sharpe No. 50 shape). Great care was exercised in relieving the cutters so as not to burn the cutting edges.

Position of Tooth-rest on Cutter Grinder. — When grinding a cylindrical cutter having helical or "spiral" teeth, the tooth-rest should remain in a fixed position relative to the grinding wheel. The tooth being ground will then slide over the tooth-rest, thus causing the cutter to turn as it moves longitudinally, so that the edge of the helical tooth is ground to a uniform distance from the center, throughout its length. When grinding a straight-fluted cutter, it is also preferable to have the tooth-rest in a fixed position relative to the wheel, unless the cutter is quite narrow, because any warping of the cutter in hardening will result in inaccurate grinding, if the tooth-rest moves with the work. When the tooth-rest is fixed relative to the wheel, it should be somewhat wider than the wheel face so that the cutter will have a support before it reaches the wheel and also after it has been traversed past the wheel face. Narrow tooth-rests may be used when they are attached to the table, and remain fixed relative to the work.

Rotation of Wheel Relative to Cutter. — When grinding the teeth of cutters, reamers, etc., in a regular cutter grinding machine, the wheel can be revolved either against the cutting edge of the tooth as shown by arrow B (see illustration), or away from it, as indicated by arrow C. The cutter can be presented in either way, by swiveling the work around the stationary column of the machine, to either side of the wheel. By revolving the wheel against the tooth, as at B, a keen edge will be obtained without forming a burr, and there is also less danger of drawing the temper, thus enabling the grinding to be done more rapidly. Care must be taken, however, to hold the

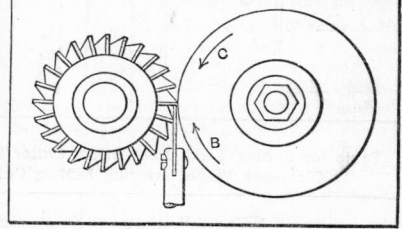

work securely against the tooth-rest as otherwise the wheel may draw the cutter away from the rest and score the tooth. There is also danger of the wheel being broken. Rotating the wheel as shown by arrow C is the safer method, as the wheel then holds the tooth against the rest. With the wheel reversed this way, a slight burr is left on the cutting edge, which should be removed with an oilstone.

Sharpening Angular Cutters. — In sharpening cutters of this type, the tooth-rest should be set exactly on the center as indicated at A (see illustration), so that

the cutter will be ground to the angle shown by the graduations on the machine. The angle for clearance, in this case, is obtained either by raising the wheel or lowering the swiveling head, depending upon the design of the machine. The tooth-rest should never be set below the center, as at B. Many machinists and toolmakers overlook this point, which is often the cause of angular cutters being inaccurate and unfit for close work.

Clearance Angle for Teeth. — Milling cutters usually have from 5 to 7 degrees of clearance. The practice in some shops, where special roughing and finishing cutters are used, is to give the roughing cutters a clearance of 7 degrees and finishing cutters, 5 degrees. Excessive clearance causes chattering when milling, and the teeth become dull quickly. The clearance angle is regulated, when grinding, by setting the center of the grinding wheel slightly above the center of the cutter, or by adjusting the tooth-rest slightly below the center. (See the accompanying tables.) The tooth-rest should always bear against the tooth that is being sharpened, and for cutters having helical teeth, it is attached to the wheel head so as to remain in a fixed position relative to the wheel.

Distance to Set Center of Wheel Above the Cutter Center (Disk Wheel)

Diam. of Emery Wheel	A for 5 Deg. Clearance	A for 7 Deg. Clearance	Diam. of Emery Wheel	A for 5 Deg. Clearance	A for 7 Deg. Clearance
2	3/32	1/8	4 1/4	3/16	17/64
2 1/4	3/32	9/64	4 1/2	13/64	9/32
2 1/2	7/64	5/32	4 3/4	13/64	19/64
2 3/4	1/8	11/64	5	7/32	5/16
3	1/8	3/16	5 1/4	15/64	21/64
3 1/4	9/64	13/64	5 1/2	15/64	11/32
3 1/2	5/32	7/32	5 3/4	1/4	23/64
3 3/4	5/32	15/64	6	17/64	3/8
4	11/64	1/4	.....	.....	......

Table for Setting Tooth Rest Below Cutter Center to Obtain 5 and 7 Degrees Clearance When Grinding Milling Cutter Teeth With Cup Wheel

Diam. of Cutter	A for 5 Deg. Clearance	A for 7 Deg. Clearance
1/4	0.011	0.015
3/8	0.015	0.022
1/2	0.022	0.030
5/8	0.028	0.037

Diam. of Cutter	A for 5 Deg. Clearance	A for 7 Deg. Clearance	Diam. of Cutter	A for 5 Deg. Clearance	A for 7 Deg. Clearance
3/4	0.033	0.045	3 1/2	0.154	0.210
7/8	0.037	0.052	3 3/4	0.165	0.225
1	0.044	0.060	4	0.176	0.240
1 1/8	0.050	0.067	4 1/2	0.198	0.270
1 1/4	0.055	0.075	5	0.220	0.300
1 1/2	0.066	0.090	5 1/2	0.242	0.330
1 3/4	0.077	0.105	6	0.264	0.360
2	0.088	0.120	6 1/2	0.286	0.390
2 1/4	0.099	0.135	7	0.308	0.420
2 1/2	0.110	0.150	7 1/2	0.330	0.450
2 3/4	0.121	0.165	8	0.352	0.480
3	0.132	0.180	9	0.396	0.540
3 1/4	0.143	0.195	10	0.440	0.600

Sharpening Formed Cutters. — Formed cutters should be ground radially or so that the faces of the teeth lie in planes passing through the axis of the cutter. The teeth should also have the same height to insure each tooth doing an equal amount of work. When setting up the grinder for formed cutters, the grinding side of the wheel should run true and be in line with the centers. If the wheel is set off center and the teeth are not ground radially, the cutter will not mill the desired shape. To insure grinding all the teeth to the same height or so that all cutting edges are at the same radial distance, a dial gage is sometimes used, having a point which bears against the formed surface or back of each tooth being ground. The cutter is adjusted so that the gage shows the same reading for each tooth; hence all the faces are ground to the same relative distance from that part of the formed surface which comes in contact with the gage.

REAMERS

Hand Reamers. — Hand reamers are made with both straight and helical flutes. The latter provide a shearing cut and are especially useful in reaming holes having keyways or grooves, as these are bridged over by the helical flutes, thus preventing binding or chattering. Hand reamers are made in both solid and expansion forms. The American standard dimensions for solid forms are given in the accompanying table. The expansion type is useful whenever, in connection with repair or other work, it is necessary to enlarge a reamed hole by a few thousandths of an inch. The expansion form is split through the fluted section and a slight amount of expansion is obtained by screwing in a tapering plug. The diameter increase may vary from 0.005 to 0.008 inch for reamers up to 1 inch diameter and from 0.010 to 0.012 inch for diameters between 1 and 2 inches. Hand reamers are tapered slightly on the end to facilitate starting them properly. The actual diameter of the shanks of commercial reamers may be from 0.002 to 0.005 inch under the reamer size. That part of the shank which is squared should be turned smaller in diameter than the shank itself, so that, when applying a wrench, no burr may be raised which may mar the reamed hole if the reamer is passed clear through it.

When fluting reamers, the cutter is so set with relation to the center of the reamer blank that the tooth gets a slight negative rake; that is, the cutter should be set *ahead* of the center, as shown in the illustration accompanying the table giving the amount to set the cutter ahead of the radial line. The amount is so selected that a tangent to the circumference of the reamer at the cutting point makes an angle of approximately 95 degrees with the front face of the cutting edge.

Amount to Set Cutter Ahead of Radial Line to Obtain Negative Front Rake

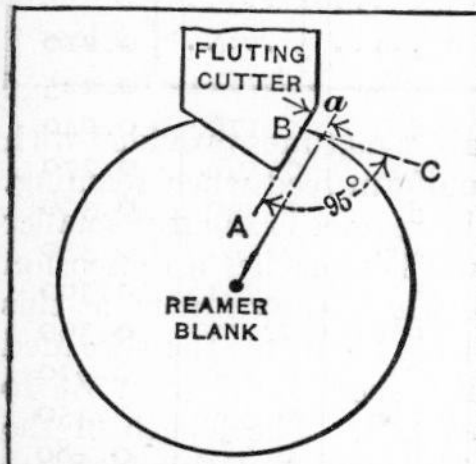

	Size of Reamer	Dimension *a*, Inches	Size of Reamer	Dimension *a*, Inches	Size of Reamer	Dimension *a*, Inches
	¼	0.011	⅞	0.038	2	0.087
	⅜	0.016	1	0.044	2¼	0.098
	½	0.022	1¼	0.055	2½	0.109
	⅝	0.027	1½	0.066	2¾	0.120
	¾	0.033	1¾	0.076	3	0.131

When fluting reamers, it is necessary to "break up the flutes"; that is, to space the cutting edges unevenly around the reamer. The difference in spacing should be very slight and need not exceed two degrees one way or the other. The manner in which the breaking up of the flutes is usually done is to move the index head to which the reamer is fixed a certain amount more or less than would be the case if the spacing were regular. A table is given showing the amount of this additional movement of the index crank for reamers with different numbers of flutes. When a reamer is provided with helical flutes, the angle of spiral should be such that the cutting edges make an angle of about 10 or at most 15 degrees with the axis of the reamer.

The relief of the cutting edges should be comparatively slight. An eccentric relief, that is, one where the land back of the cutting edge is convex, rather than flat, is used by one or two manufacturers, and is preferable for finishing reamers, as the reamer will hold its size longer. When hand reamers are used merely for removing stock, or simply for enlarging holes, the flat relief is better, because the reamer has a keener cutting edge. The width of the land of the cutting edges should be about 1/32 inch for a 1/4-inch, 1/16 inch for a 1-inch, and 3/32 inch for a 3-inch reamer.

Irregular Spacing of Teeth in Reamers

Number of flutes in reamer............	4	6	8	10	12	14	16
Index circle to use....	39	39	39	39	39	49	20
Before cutting........	Move Spindle the Number of Holes below More or Less than for Regular Spacing						
2d flute...........	8 less	4 less	3 less	2 less	4 less	3 less	2 less
3d flute...........	4 more	5 more	5 more	3 more	4 more	2 more	2 more
4th flute..........	6 less	7 less	2 less	5 less	1 less	2 less	1 less
5th flute..........	.....	6 more	4 more	2 more	3 more	4 more	2 more
6th flute..........	.....	5 less	6 less	4 less	4 less	1 less	2 less
7th flute..........	.....	.....	2 more	3 more	4 more	3 more	1 more
8th flute..........	.....	.....	3 less	2 less	3 less	2 less	2 less
9th flute..........	.....	.....	.....	5 more	2 more	1 more	2 more
10th flute.........	.....	.....	.....	1 less	2 less	3 less	2 less
11th flute.........	.....	.....	.....	.....	3 more	3 more	1 more
12th flute.........	.....	.....	.....	.....	4 less	2 less	2 less
13th flute.........	.....	.....	.....	.....	.....	2 more	2 more
14th flute.........	.....	.....	.....	.....	.....	3 less	1 less
15th flute.........	.....	.....	.....	.....	.....	.....	2 more
16th flute.........	.....	.....	.....	.....	.....	.....	2 less

Threaded-end Hand Reamers. — Hand reamers are sometimes provided with a thread at the extreme point in order to give them a uniform feed when reaming. The diameter on the top of this thread at the point of the reamer is slightly smaller than the reamer itself, and the thread tapers upward until it reaches a dimension of from 0.003 to 0.008 inch, according to size, below the size of the reamer; at this point the thread stops and a short neck about 1/16 inch wide separates the threaded portion from the actual reamer which is provided with a short taper from 3/16 to 7/16 inch long up to where the standard diameter is reached. The length of the threaded portion and the number of threads per inch for reamers of this kind are given in the accompanying table. The thread employed is a sharp V-thread.

Dimensions for Threaded-end Hand Reamers

Sizes of Reamers	Length of Threaded Part	No. of Threads per Inch	Diam. of Thread at Point of Reamer	Sizes of Reamers	Length of Threaded Part	No. of Threads per Inch	Diam. of Thread at Point of Reamer
			Full diameter				Full diameter
1/8 –5/16	3/8	32	−0.006	11/32 –11/2	9/16	18	−0.010
11/32–1/2	7/16	28	−0.006	117/32–2	9/16	18	−0.012
17/32–3/4	1/2	24	−0.008	21/32 –21/2	9/16	18	−0.015
25/32–1	9/16	18	−0.008	217/32–3	9/16	18	−0.020

American Standard Hand Reamers — Straight and Helical Flutes (ASA B5.14)

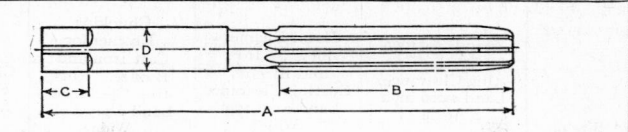

Reamer Diameter				Length Overall A	Flute Length B	Square Length C	Size of Square	No. of Flutes (Incl.)
Straight Flutes*		Helical Flutes						
Carbon Steel	High Speed	Carbon Steel	High Speed					
1/8	1/8	1/8	.....	3	1½	5/32	0.095	4 to 6
5/32	5/32	5/32	.....	3¼	1⅝	7/32	0.115	4 to 6
3/16	3/16	3/16	.....	3½	1¾	7/32	0.140	4 to 6
7/32	7/32	7/32	.....	3¾	1⅞	¼	0.165	4 to 6
¼	¼	¼	¼	4	2	¼	0.185	4 to 6
9/32	9/32	9/32	9/32	4¼	2⅛	¼	0.210	4 to 6
5/16	5/16	5/16	5/16	4½	2¼	5/16	0.235	4 to 6
11/32	11/32	11/32	11/32	4¾	2⅜	5/16	0.255	4 to 6
⅜	⅜	⅜	⅜	5	2½	⅜	0.280	4 to 6
13/32	13/32	13/32	13/32	5¼	2⅝	⅜	0.305	6 to 8
7/16	7/16	7/16	7/16	5½	2¾	7/16	0.330	6 to 8
15/32	15/32	15/32	15/32	5¾	2⅞	7/16	0.350	6 to 8
½	½	½	½	6	3	½	0.375	6 to 8
17/32	17/32	17/32	17/32	6¼	3⅛	½	0.400	6 to 8
9/16	9/16	9/16	9/16	6½	3¼	9/16	0.420	6 to 8
19/32	19/32	.....	19/32	6¾	3⅜	9/16	0.445	6 to 8
⅝	⅝	⅝	⅝	7	3½	⅝	0.470	6 to 8
21/32	21/32	.....	21/32	7⅜	3 11/16	⅝	0.490	6 to 8
11/16	11/16	11/16	11/16	7¾	3⅞	11/16	0.515	6 to 8
23/32	23/32	.....	23/32	8⅛	4 1/16	11/16	0.540	6 to 8
¾	¾	¾	¾	8⅜	4 3/16	¾	0.560	6 to 8
25/32	25/32	.....	25/32	8¾	4⅜	¾	0.585	8 to 10
13/16	13/16	13/16	13/16	9⅛	4 9/16	13/16	0.610	8 to 10
27/32	27/32	.....	27/32	9⅜	4 11/16	13/16	0.630	8 to 10
⅞	⅞	⅞	⅞	9¾	4⅞	⅞	0.655	8 to 10
29/32	29/32	.....	29/32	10	5	⅞	0.680	8 to 10
15/16	15/16	15/16	15/16	10¼	5⅛	15/16	0.705	8 to 10
31/32	31/32	.....	31/32	10⅝	5 5/16	15/16	0.725	8 to 10
1	1	1	1	10⅞	5 7/16	1	0.750	8 to 10
1 1/16	1 1/16	.....	1 1/16	11¼	5⅝	1	0.795	8 to 10
1⅛	1⅛	.....	1⅛	11⅝	5 13/16	1	0.845	8 to 10
1 3/16	1 3/16	.....	1 3/16	12	6	1	0.890	8 to 12
1¼	1¼	.....	1¼	12¼	6⅛	1	0.935	8 to 12
1 5/16	1 5/16	.....	1 5/16	12½	6¼	1	0.985	10 to 12
1⅜	1⅜	.....	1⅜	12⅝	6 5/16	1	1.030	10 to 12
1 7/16	1 7/16	.....	1 7/16	12⅞	6 7/16	1⅛	1.080	10 to 12
1½	1½	.....	1½	13	6½	1⅛	1.125	10 to 14

* Standard diameter range for straight-fluted carbon steel reamers also includes diameters advancing by 1/64ths up to ½ inch. For example: 9/64; 11/64; etc., up to 31/64. Hand reamers are tapered slightly on the end to facilitate proper starting. The nominal shank diameter D is the same as the reamer diameter.

Tolerances: For reamer diameters up to ¼ inch, inclusive, plus 0.0001 to 0.0004 inch; over ¼ to 1 inch inclusive, plus 0.0001 to 0.0005 inch; over 1 inch, plus 0.0002 to 0.0006 inch. Helical fluted reamers are regularly furnished with left hand helical flutes.

Reamers with threaded ends and all sizes and dimensions not listed are special.

Vertical Adjustment of Tooth-rest for Grinding Clearance on Reamers

Size of Reamer	Hand Reamer for Steel. Cutting Clearance Land 0.006 inch Wide		Hand Reamer for Cast Iron and Bronze. Cutting Clearance Land 0.025 inch Wide		Chucking Reamer for Cast Iron and Bronze. Cutting Clearance Land 0.025 inch Wide		Rose Chucking Reamers for Steel
	For Cutting Clearance	For Second Clearance	For Cutting Clearance	For Second Clearance	For Cutting Clearance	For Second Clearance	For Cutting Clearance on Angular Edge at End
½	0.012	0.052	0.032	0.072	0.040	0.080	0.080
⅝	0.012	0.062	0.032	0.072	0.040	0.090	0.090
¾	0.012	0.072	0.035	0.095	0.040	0.100	0.100
⅞	0.012	0.082	0.040	0.120	0.045	0.125	0.125
1	0.012	0.092	0.040	0.120	0.045	0.125	0.125
1⅛	0.012	0.102	0.040	0.120	0.045	0.125	0.125
1¼	0.012	0.112	0.045	0.145	0.050	0.160	0.160
1⅜	0.012	0.122	0.045	0.145	0.050	0.160	0.175
1½	0.012	0.132	0.048	0.168	0.055	0.175	0.175
1⅝	0.012	0.142	0.050	0.170	0.060	0.200	0.200
1¾	0.012	0.152	0.052	0.192	0.060	0.200	0.200
1⅞	0.012	0.162	0.056	0.196	0.060	0.200	0.200
2	0.012	0.172	0.056	0.216	0.064	0.224	0.225
2⅛	0.012	0.172	0.059	0.219	0.064	0.224	0.225
2¼	0.012	0.172	0.063	0.223	0.064	0.224	0.225
2⅜	0.012	0.172	0.063	0.223	0.068	0.228	0.230
2½	0.012	0.172	0.065	0.225	0.072	0.232	0.230
2⅝	0.012	0.172	0.065	0.225	0.075	0.235	0.235
2¾	0.012	0.172	0.065	0.225	0.077	0.237	0.240
2⅞	0.012	0.172	0.070	0.230	0.080	0.240	0.240
3	0.012	0.172	0.072	0.232	0.080	0.240	0.240
3⅛	0.012	0.172	0.075	0.235	0.083	0.240	0.240
3¼	0.012	0.172	0.078	0.238	0.083	0.243	0.245
3⅜	0.012	0.172	0.081	0.241	0.087	0.247	0.245
3½	0.012	0.172	0.084	0.244	0.090	0.250	0.250
3⅝	0.012	0.172	0.087	0.247	0.093	0.253	0.250
3¾	0.012	0.172	0.090	0.250	0.097	0.257	0.255
3⅞	0.012	0.172	0.093	0.253	0.100	0.260	0.255
4	0.012	0.172	0.096	0.256	0.104	0.264	0.260
4⅛	0.012	0.172	0.096	0.256	0.104	0.264	0.260
4¼	0.012	0.172	0.096	0.256	0.106	0.266	0.265
4⅜	0.012	0.172	0.096	0.256	0.108	0.268	0.265
4½	0.012	0.172	0.100	0.260	0.108	0.268	0.265
4⅝	0.012	0.172	0.100	0.260	0.110	0.270	0.270
4¾	0.012	0.172	0.104	0.264	0.114	0.274	0.275
4⅞	0.012	0.172	0.106	0.266	0.116	0.276	0.275
5	0.012	0.172	0.110	0.270	0.118	0.278	0.275

American Standard Rose Chucking and Fluted Chucking Reamers† — Straight and Taper Shanks‡ (ASA B5.14)

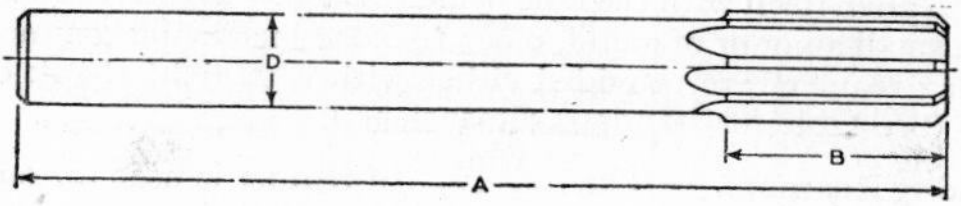

Reamer Diameter				Straight Shank Diameter *D*	Number of Taper Shank, American Standard*	Straight and Taper Shank	
Straight Shank		Taper Shank					
Rose Reamer	Fluted Reamer	Rose Reamer	Fluted Reamer			Overall Length *A*	Flute Length *B*
1/8	1/8	.....	.....	7/64	...	3 1/2	7/8
5/32	5/32	.....	.....	9/64	...	4	1
3/16	3/16	.....	.....	11/64	...	4 1/2	1 1/8
7/32	7/32	.....	.....	13/64	...	5	1 1/4
1/4	1/4	1/4	1/4	15/64	1	6	1 1/2
9/32	9/32	9/32	9/32	15/64	1	6	1 1/2
5/16	5/16	5/16	5/16	9/32	1	6	1 1/2
11/32	11/32	11/32	11/32	9/32	1	6	1 1/2
3/8	3/8	3/8	3/8	5/16	1	7	1 3/4
13/32	13/32	13/32	13/32	5/16	1	7	1 3/4
7/16	7/16	7/16	7/16	3/8	1	7	1 3/4
15/32	15/32	15/32	15/32	3/8	1	7	1 3/4
1/2	1/2	1/2	1/2	7/16	1	8	2
.....	17/32	.....	17/32	7/16	1	8	2
9/16	9/16	9/16	9/16	7/16	1	8	2
.....	19/32	.....	19/32	7/16	1	8	2
5/8	5/8	5/8	5/8	9/16	2	9	2 1/4
.....	21/32	.....	21/32	9/16	2	9	2 1/4
11/16	11/16	11/16	11/16	9/16	2	9	2 1/4
.....	23/32	.....	23/32	9/16	2	9	2 1/4
3/4	3/4	3/4	3/4	5/8	2	9 1/2	2 1/2
.....	25/32	.....	25/32	5/8	2	9 1/2	2 1/2
13/16	13/16	13/16	13/16	5/8	2	9 1/2	2 1/2
.....	27/32	.....	27/32	5/8	2	9 1/2	2 1/2
7/8	7/8	7/8	7/8	3/4	2	10	2 5/8
.....	29/32	.....	29/32	3/4	2	10	2 5/8
15/16	15/16	15/16	15/16	3/4	3	10	2 5/8
.....	31/32	.....	31/32	3/4	3	10	2 5/8
1	1	1	1	7/8	3	10 1/2	2 3/4
1 1/16	1 1/16	1 1/16	1 1/16	7/8	3	10 1/2	2 3/4
1 1/8	1 1/8	1 1/8	1 1/8	7/8	3	11	2 7/8
1 3/16	1 3/16	1 3/16	1 3/16	1	3	11	2 7/8
1 1/4	1 1/4	1 1/4	1 1/4	1	4	11 1/2	3
1 5/16	1 5/16	1 5/16	1 5/16	1	4	11 1/2	3
1 3/8	1 3/8	1 3/8	1 3/8	1	4	12	3 1/4
1 7/16	1 7/16	1 7/16	1 7/16	1 1/4	4	12	3 1/4
1 1/2	1 1/2	1 1/2	1 1/2	1 1/4	4	12 1/2	3 1/2

* See American Standard Self-Holding Taper Series. † High speed steel only.

‡ Fluted reamers are available with straight and helical flutes; Rose reamers have straight flutes only. Carbon steel reamers, and sizes and dimensions not listed are special. The lands on Rose reamers are cylindrically ground without radial relief, the reamer being designed for end cutting. Fluted reamers have a slight chamfer for end cutting and the relief is ground back of the cutting edge for the full length of the land.

Fluted Chucking Reamers. — Reamers of this type are used in turret lathes, screw machines, etc., for enlarging holes and finishing them smooth and to the required size. The best results are obtained with a floating type of holder which permits a reamer to align itself with the hole being reamed. These reamers are intended for removing a small amount of metal, 0.005 to 0.010 inch being common allowances. Fluted chucking reamers are provided either with a straight shank or a standard taper shank. (See table for standard dimensions.)

Rose Chucking Reamers. — The rose type of reamer is used for enlarging cored or other holes. The cutting edges at the end are ground to a 45-degree bevel. This type of reamer will remove considerable metal in one cut. The cylindrical part of the reamer has no cutting edges, but merely grooves cut for the full length of the reamer body, providing a way for the chips to escape and a channel for lubricant to reach the cutting edges. There is no relief on the cylindrical surface of the body part, but it is slightly back-tapered so that the diameter at the point with the beveled cutting edges is slightly larger than the diameter further back. The back-taper should not exceed 0.001 inch per inch. This form of reamer usually

Fluting Cutters for Reamers

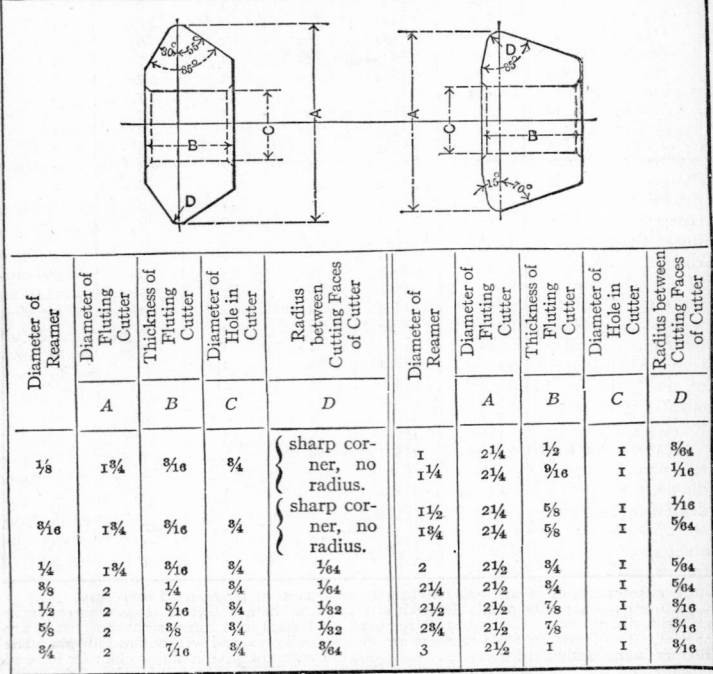

Diameter of Reamer	Diameter of Fluting Cutter	Thickness of Fluting Cutter	Diameter of Hole in Cutter	Radius between Cutting Faces of Cutter	Diameter of Reamer	Diameter of Fluting Cutter	Thickness of Fluting Cutter	Diameter of Hole in Cutter	Radius between Cutting Faces of Cutter
	A	B	C	D		A	B	C	D
1/8	1¾	3/16	¾	sharp corner, no radius.	1	2¼	½	1	3/64
					1¼	2¼	9/16	1	1/16
3/16	1¾	3/16	¾	sharp corner, no radius.	1½	2¼	5/8	1	1/16
					1¾	2¼	5/8	1	5/64
¼	1¾	3/16	¾	1/64	2	2½	¾	1	5/64
3/8	2	¼	¾	1/64	2¼	2½	¾	1	5/64
½	2	5/16	¾	1/32	2½	2½	7/8	1	3/16
5/8	2	3/8	¾	1/32	2¾	2½	7/8	1	3/16
¾	2	7/16	¾	3/64	3	2½	1	1	3/16

Dimensions of Formed Reamer Fluting Cutters

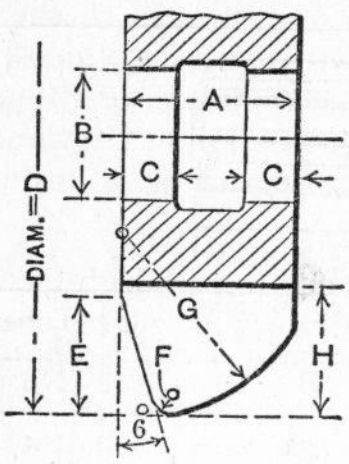

The making and maintenance of cutters of the formed type involves greater expense than the use of the angular cutters of which dimensions are given on the previous page; but the form of flute produced by the formed type of cutter is preferred by many reamer users. The claims made for the formed type of flute are that the chips can be more readily removed from the reamer, and that the reamer has greater strength and is less likely to crack or spring out of shape in hardening.

Size of Reamers used for	Number of Teeth in Reamer	Diam. of Cutter	Width of Cutter	Diam. of Hole	Width of Bearing	Length of Bevel	Radius	Radius	Depth of Tooth	Number of Teeth in Cutter
		D	*A*	*B*	*C*	*E*	*F*	*G*	*H*	
1/8–3/16	6	1 3/4	3/16	7/8	....	0.125	0.016	7/32	0.21	14
1/4–5/16	6	1 3/4	1/4	7/8	....	0.152	0.022	9/32	0.25	13
3/8–7/16	6	1 7/8	3/8	7/8	1/8	0.178	0.029	1/2	0.28	12
1/2–11/16	6–8	2	7/16	7/8	1/8	0.205	0.036	9/16	0.30	12
3/4–1	8	2 1/8	1/2	7/8	5/32	0.232	0.042	11/16	0.32	12
1 1/16–1 1/2	10	2 1/4	9/16	7/8	5/32	0.258	0.049	3/4	0.38	11
1 9/16–2 1/8	12	2 3/8	5/8	7/8	3/16	0.285	0.056	27/32	0.40	11
2 1/4–3	14	2 5/8	11/16	7/8	3/16	0.312	0.062	7/8	0.44	10

produces holes slightly larger than its size and it is, therefore, always made from 0.005 to 0.010 inch smaller than its nominal size, so that it may be followed by a fluted reamer for finishing. The grooves on the cylindrical portion are cut by a convex cutter having a width equal to from one-fifth to one-fourth the diameter of the rose reamer itself. The depth of the groove should be from one-eighth to one-sixth the diameter of the reamer. The teeth at the end of the reamer are milled with a 75-degree angular cutter; the width of the land of the cutting edge should be about one-fifth the distance from tooth to tooth. If an angular cutter is preferred to a convex cutter for milling the grooves on the cylindrical portion, because of the higher cutting speed possible when milling, an 80-degree angular cutter slightly rounded at the point may be used.

Cutters for Fluting Rose Chucking Reamers. — The cutters used for fluting rose chucking reamers on the end are 80-degree angular cutters for 1/4 and 5/16 inch diameter reamers; 75-degree angular cutters for 3/8 and 7/16 inch reamers; and 70-degree angular cutters for all larger sizes. The grooves on the cylindrical portion are milled with convex cutters of approximately the following sizes for given diameters of reamers: 5/32-inch convex cutter for 1/2-inch reamers; 5/16-inch cutter for 1-inch reamers; 3/8-inch cutter for 1 1/2-inch reamers; 13/32-inch cutters for 2-inch reamers; and 15/32-inch cutters for 2 1/2-inch reamers. The smaller sizes of reamers, from 1/4 to 3/8 inch in diameter, are often milled with regular double-angle reamer fluting cutters having a radius of 1/64 inch for 1/4-inch reamer, and 1/32 inch for 5/16- and 3/8-inch sizes.

American Standard Expansion Chucking Reamers — Straight and Taper Shanks*
(ASA B5.14)

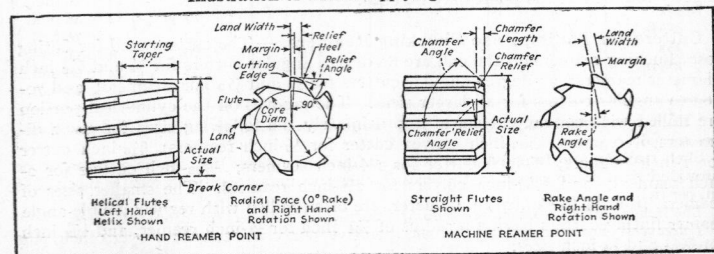

Diam. of Reamer	Length A	Flute Length B	Shank Diam. D	Taper Shank No.†	Diam. of Reamer	Length A	Flute Length B	Shank Diam. D	Taper Shank No.†
3/8	7	3/4	5/16	1	1 1/4	11 1/2	1 7/8	1	4
13/32	7	3/4	5/16	1	1 5/16	11 1/2	1 7/8	1	4
7/16	7	7/8	3/8	1	1 3/8	12	2	1	4
15/32	7	7/8	3/8	1	1 7/16	12	2	1 1/4	4
1/2	8	1	7/16	1	1 1/2	12 1/2	2 1/8	1 1/4	4
17/32	8	1	7/16	1	1 9/16	12 1/2	2 1/8	1 1/4	4
9/16	8	1 1/8	7/16	1	1 5/8	13	2 1/4	1 1/4	4
19/32	8	1 1/8	7/16	1	1 11/16	13	2 1/4	1 1/4	4
5/8	9	1 1/4	9/16	2	1 3/4	13 1/2	2 3/8	1 1/4	5
21/32	9	1 1/4	9/16	2	1 13/16	13 1/2	2 3/8	1 1/4	5
11/16	9	1 1/4	9/16	2	1 7/8	14	2 1/2	1 1/2	5
23/32	9	1 1/4	9/16	2	1 15/16	14	2 1/2	1 1/2	5
3/4	9 1/2	1 3/8	5/8	2	2	14	2 1/2	1 1/2	5
25/32	9 1/2	1 3/8	5/8	2	2 1/16	14 1/2	2 3/4	1 1/2	5
13/16	9 1/2	1 3/8	5/8	2	2 1/8	14 1/2	2 3/4	1 1/2	5
27/32	9 1/2	1 3/8	5/8	2	2 3/16	14 1/2	2 3/4	1 3/4	5
7/8	10	1 1/2	3/4	2	2 1/4	14 1/2	2 3/4	1 3/4	5
29/32	10	1 1/2	3/4	2	2 5/16	15	3	1 3/4	5
15/16	10	1 1/2	3/4	3	2 3/8	15	3	1 3/4	5
31/32	10	1 1/2	3/4	3	2 7/16	15	3	1 3/4	5
1	10 1/2	1 5/8	7/8	3	2 1/2	15	3	1 3/4	5
1 1/32	10 1/2	1 5/8	7/8	3	2 9/16	15 1/2	3 1/4	2	5
1 1/16	10 1/2	1 5/8	7/8	3	2 5/8	15 1/2	3 1/4	2	5
1 3/32	10 1/2	1 5/8	7/8	3	2 11/16	15 1/2	3 1/4	2	5
1 1/8	11	1 3/4	7/8	3	2 3/4	15 1/2	3 1/4	2	5
1 5/32	11	1 3/4	7/8	3	2 13/16	16	3 1/2	2	5
1 3/16	11	1 3/4	1	3	2 7/8	16	3 1/2	2	5
1 7/32	11	1 3/4	1	3	2 15/16	16	3 1/2	2	5
					3	16	3 1/2	2	5

* High speed steel only; carbon steel reamers, and sizes and dimensions not listed are special.

† See American Standard Self-Holding Taper Series.

The expansion feature of these reamers provides a means of adjustment which is important in reaming holes to close tolerances. When worn undersize, they may be expanded and reground to the original size.

Illustration of Terms Applying to Reamers

American Standard Shell Reamers — Straight and Helical Flutes* (ASA B5.14)

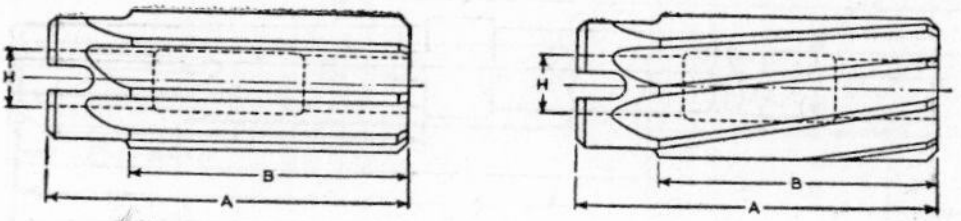

Diameter of Reamer	Length Overall *A*	Flute Length *B*	Hole Diameter Large End *H*	Arbor No.	Number of Flutes
3/4	2 1/4	1 1/2	3/8	4	8 to 10 incl.
13/16	2 1/2	1 3/4	1/2	5	8 to 10 incl.
7/8	2 1/2	1 3/4	1/2	5	8 to 10 incl.
15/16	2 1/2	1 3/4	1/2	5	8 to 10 incl.
1	2 1/2	1 3/4	1/2	5	8 to 10 incl.
1 1/16	2 3/4	2	5/8	6	8 to 12 incl.
1 1/8	2 3/4	2	5/8	6	8 to 12 incl.
1 3/16	2 3/4	2	5/8	6	8 to 12 incl.
1 1/4	2 3/4	2	5/8	6	8 to 12 incl.
1 5/16	3	2 1/4	3/4	7	8 to 12 incl.
1 3/8	3	2 1/4	3/4	7	8 to 12 incl.
1 7/16	3	2 1/4	3/4	7	8 to 12 incl.
1 1/2	3	2 1/4	3/4	7	10 to 14 incl.
1 9/16	3	2 1/4	3/4	7	10 to 14 incl.
1 5/8	3	2 1/4	3/4	7	10 to 14 incl.
1 11/16	3 1/2	2 1/2	1	8	10 to 14 incl.
1 3/4	3 1/2	2 1/2	1	8	12 to 14 incl.
1 13/16	3 1/2	2 1/2	1	8	12 to 14 incl.
1 7/8	3 1/2	2 1/2	1	8	12 to 14 incl.
1 15/16	3 1/2	2 1/2	1	8	12 to 14 incl.
2	3 1/2	2 1/2	1	8	12 to 14 incl.
2 1/16	3 3/4	2 3/4	1 1/4	9	12 to 16 incl.
2 1/8	3 3/4	2 3/4	1 1/4	9	12 to 16 incl.
2 3/16	3 3/4	2 3/4	1 1/4	9	12 to 16 incl.
2 1/4	3 3/4	2 3/4	1 1/4	9	12 to 16 incl.
2 5/16	3 3/4	2 3/4	1 1/4	9	14 to 16 incl.
2 3/8	3 3/4	2 3/4	1 1/4	9	14 to 16 incl.
2 7/16	3 3/4	2 3/4	1 1/4	9	14 to 16 incl.
2 1/2	3 3/4	2 3/4	1 1/4	9	14 to 16 incl.
2 9/16	4	3	1 1/2	10	14 to 16 incl.
2 5/8	4	3	1 1/2	10	14 to 16 incl.
2 11/16	4	3	1 1/2	10	14 to 16 incl.
2 3/4	4	3	1 1/2	10	14 to 16 incl.
2 13/16	4	3	1 1/2	10	14 to 18 incl.
2 7/8	4	3	1 1/2	10	14 to 18 incl.
2 15/16	4	3	1 1/2	10	14 to 18 incl.
3	4	3	1 1/2	10	14 to 18 incl.

* High speed steel only; carbon steel reamers and sizes and dimensions not listed are special.

Shell reamers are designed as a sizing or finishing reamer and are held on an arbor provided with driving lugs. The holes in these reamers are ground with a taper of 1/8 in. per ft.

The helical fluted reamers are regularly furnished with left-hand helical flutes.

Tolerances: For reamers up to 1 inch, inclusive, plus 0.0001 to 0.0005; over 1 inch, plus 0.0002 to 0.0006 inch.

American Standard Arbors for Shell Reamers—Straight and Taper Shanks

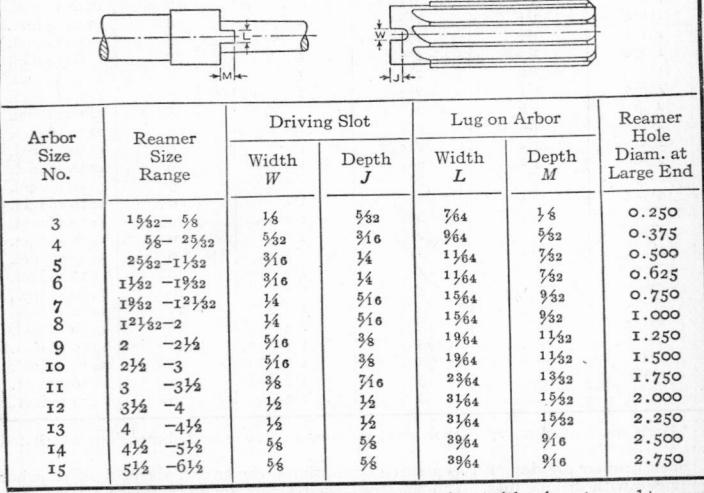

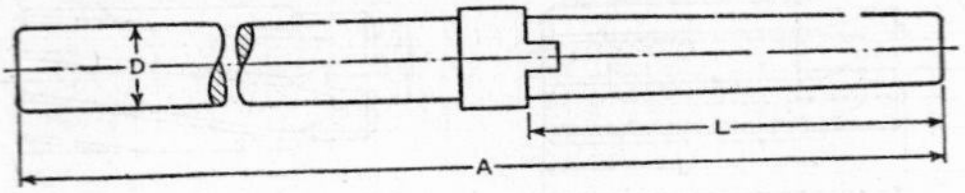

Arbor Size No.	Overall Length A	Approximate Length of Taper L	Reamer Size	Taper Shank No.*	Straight Shank Diam. D
4	9	2¼	¾	2	½
5	9½	2½	13/16 to 1	2	⅝
6	10	2¾	1 1/16 to 1¼	3	¾
7	11	3	1 5/16 to 1⅝	3	⅞
8	12	3½	1 11/16 to 2	4	1⅛
9	13	3¾	2 1/16 to 2½	4	1⅜
10	14	4	2 9/16 to 3	5	1⅝

* Taper shank number and taper same as Morse (see Morse Standard Taper Shanks). These arbors are designed to fit standard shell reamers (see table). End which fits reamer has taper of 0.125 inch per ft. Sizes and dimensions not listed are special.

American Standard Driving Slots and Lugs

Arbor Size No.	Reamer Size Range	Driving Slot		Lug on Arbor		Reamer Hole Diam. at Large End
		Width W	Depth J	Width L	Depth M	
3	15/32 – ⅝	⅛	5/32	7/64	⅛	0.250
4	⅝ – 25/32	5/32	3/16	9/64	5/32	0.375
5	25/32 – 1 1/32	3/16	¼	11/64	7/32	0.500
6	1 1/32 – 1 9/32	3/16	¼	11/64	7/32	0.625
7	1 9/32 – 1 21/32	¼	5/16	15/64	9/32	0.750
8	1 21/32 – 2	¼	5/16	15/64	9/32	1.000
9	2 – 2½	5/16	⅜	19/64	11/32	1.250
10	2½ – 3	5/16	⅜	19/64	11/32	1.500
11	3 – 3½	⅜	7/16	23/64	13/32	1.750
12	3½ – 4	½	½	31/64	15/32	2.000
13	4 – 4½	½	½	31/64	15/32	2.250
14	4½ – 5½	⅝	⅝	39/64	9/16	2.500
15	5½ – 6½	⅝	⅝	39/64	9/16	2.750

The hole in shell reamers has a taper of 0.125 inch per foot, with arbors tapered to correspond.

Shell reamer arbors are made slightly larger in diameter at the large end of the taper to permit a driving fit with the reamer.

American Standard Center Reamers and Machine Countersinks* (ASA B5.14)

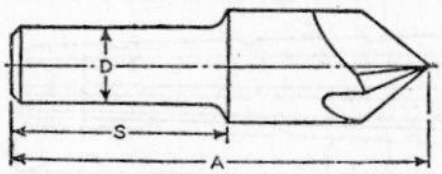

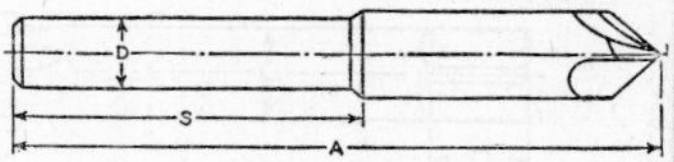

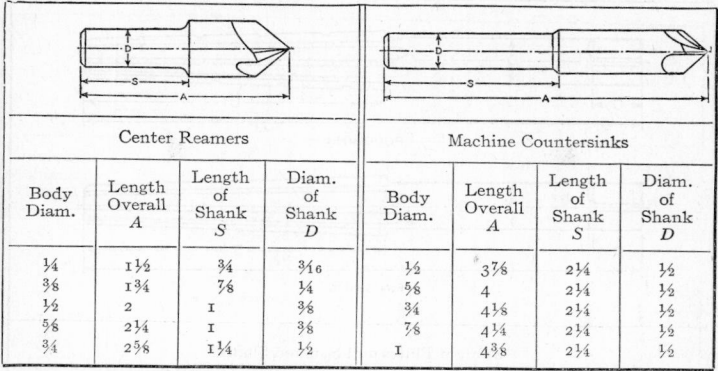

Center Reamers				Machine Countersinks			
Body Diam.	Length Overall *A*	Length of Shank *S*	Diam. of Shank *D*	Body Diam.	Length Overall *A*	Length of Shank *S*	Diam. of Shank *D*
1/4	1 1/2	3/4	3/16	1/2	3 7/8	2 1/4	1/2
3/8	1 3/4	7/8	1/4	5/8	4	2 1/4	1/2
1/2	2	1	3/8	3/4	4 1/8	2 1/4	1/2
5/8	2 1/4	1	3/8	7/8	4 1/4	2 1/4	1/2
3/4	2 5/8	1 1/4	1/2	1	4 3/8	2 1/4	1/2

* High speed steel and carbon steel; available with either 60 degree (common angle for lathe centers) or 82 degree (American Standard for countersunk machine and cap-screws) included angle.

Tolerances: All shank diameters minus 0.0005 to minus 0.002 inch.

Dimensions of Centers for Reamers and Arbors

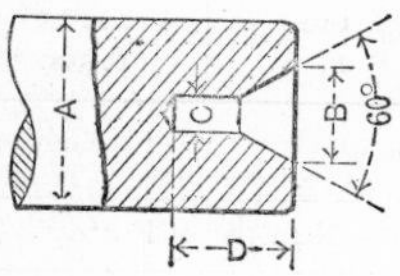

Diameter of Arbor	Largest Diameter of Center	Number of Drill	Depth of Hole	Diameter of Arbor	Largest Diameter of Center	Number of Drill	Depth of Hole	Diameter of Arbor	Largest Diameter of Center	Letter of Drill	Depth of Hole
A	*B*	*C*	*D*	*A*	*B*	*C*	*D*	*A*	*B*	*C*	*D*
				3/4	3/8	25	7/16	2 1/2	11/16	J	27/32
				13/16	13/32	20	1/2	2 5/8	45/64	K	7/8
				7/8	7/16	17	17/32	2 3/4	23/32	L	29/32
				15/16	15/32	12	9/16	2 7/8	47/64	M	29/32
				1	1/2	8	19/32	3	3/4	N	15/16
				1 1/8	33/64	5	5/8	3 1/8	49/64	N	31/32
				1 1/4	17/32	3	21/32	3 1/4	25/32	O	31/32
				1 3/8	35/64	2	21/32	3 3/8	51/64	O	1
				1 1/2	9/16	1	11/16	3 1/2	13/16	P	1
1/4	1/8	55	5/32	....	....	Letter	...	3 5/8	53/64	Q	1 1/16
5/16	5/32	52	3/16	1 5/8	37/64	A	23/32	3 3/4	27/32	R	1 1/16
3/8	3/16	48	7/32	1 3/4	19/32	B	23/32	3 7/8	55/64	R	1 1/16
7/16	7/32	43	1/4	1 7/8	39/64	C	3/4	4	7/8	S	1 1/8
1/2	1/4	39	5/16	2	5/8	E	3/4	4 1/4	29/32	T	1 1/8
9/16	9/32	33	11/32	2 1/8	41/64	F	25/32	4 1/2	15/16	V	1 3/16
5/8	5/16	30	3/8	2 1/4	21/32	G	13/16	4 3/4	31/32	W	1 1/4
11/16	11/32	29	13/32	2 3/8	43/64	H	27/32	5	1	X	1 1/4

American Standard Morse Taper Reamers* (ASA B5.14)

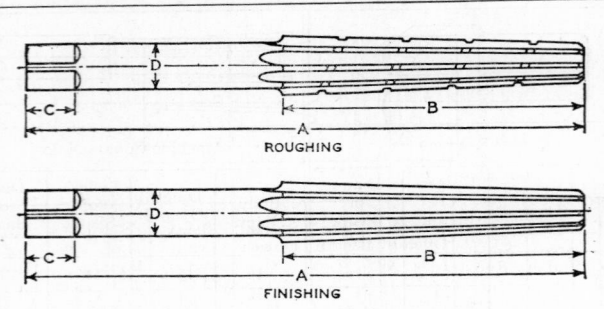

ROUGHING

FINISHING

Straight Flutes and Squared Shank[3]

Taper No.[1]	Small End Diam.[2]	Large End Diam.[2]	Length Overall A	Flute Length B	Square Length C	Shank Diam. D	Square Size
0	0.2503	0.3674	3¾	2¼	5/16	5/16	0.235
1	0.3674	0.5170	5	3	7/16	7/16	0.330
2	0.5696	0.7444	6	3½	5/8	5/8	0.470
3	0.7748	0.9881	7¼	4¼	7/8	7/8	0.655
4	1.0167	1.2893	8½	5¼	1	1⅛	0.845
5	1.4717	1.8005	9¾	6¼	1⅛	1½	1.125
6	2.1119	2.5550	12¼	8½	1½	2	1.500

Straight Flutes and Taper Shank[3]

Taper No.[1]	Small End Diam.[2]	Large End Diam.[2]	Length Overall A	Flute Length B	Taper Shank No.[4]	Number of Flutes[5] Roughing	Number of Flutes[5] Finishing
0	0.2503	0.3674	5¹¹⁄₃₂	2¼	0	4 to 6 incl.	4 to 6 incl.
1	0.3674	0.5170	6⁵⁄₁₆	3	1	4 to 6 incl.	6 to 8 incl.
2	0.5696	0.7444	7⅜	3½	2	4 to 6 incl.	6 to 8 incl.
3	0.7748	0.9881	8⅞	4¼	3	4 to 6 incl.	8 to 10 incl.
4	1.0167	1.2893	10⅞	5¼	4	4 to 8 incl.	8 to 10 incl.
5	1.4717	1.8005	13⅛	6¼	5	6 to 10 incl.	10 to 12 incl.
6	2.1119	2.5550	17¹³⁄₁₆	8½	6	6 to 12 incl.	12 to 14 incl.

* All standard Morse taper reamers available in high speed steel; straight flute, squared shank finishing reamers also available in carbon steel.
[1] Sizes No. 1 to 5 incl. have ASA standard taper (Morse).
[2] End diameters apply to finishing reamers.
[3] Finishing reamers also available with helical flute.
[4] See American Standard Self-Holding Taper Series.
[5] Number of flutes apply to both taper and squared shank reamers.
Tolerances: For squared shank diameters D, minus 0.0005 to minus 0.002 inch for all sizes.

American Standard Taper Pipe Reamers* (ASA B5.14)

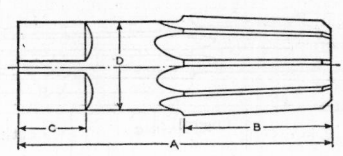

Nom. Size	Diameter		Length Overall A	Flute Length B	Square Length C	Shank Diameter D	Size of Square	No. of Flutes
	Large End	Small End						
1/8	0.362	0.316	2 1/8	3/4	3/8	0.4375	0.328	5 to 6 incl.
1/4	0.472	0.406	2 7/16	1 1/16	7/16	0.5625	0.421	5 to 6 incl.
3/8	0.606	0.540	2 9/16	1 1/16	1/2	0.7000	0.531	6 to 8 incl.
1/2	0.751	0.665	3 1/8	1 3/8	5/8	0.6875	0.515	6 to 8 incl.
3/4	0.962	0.876	3 1/4	1 3/8	11/16	0.9063	0.679	8 to 10 incl.
1	1.212	1.103	3 3/4	1 3/4	13/16	1.1250	0.843	8 to 10 incl.
1 1/4	1.553	1.444	4	1 3/4	15/16	1.3125	0.984	10 to 12 incl.
1 1/2	1.793	1.684	4 1/4	1 3/4	1	1.5000	1.125	10 to 12 incl.
2	2.268	2.159	4 1/2	1 3/4	1 1/8	1.8750	1.406	12 to 14 incl.

* Carbon steel and high speed steel.

These reamers are tapered 3/4 in. to the foot and are intended for reaming holes to be tapped with American Standard Taper Pipe Thread taps.

All sizes and dimensions not listed are special.

Brown & Sharpe Taper Reamers — Square Shank (ASA B5.14)

Taper Number*	Diam., Small End	Diam., Large End	Overall Length	Flute Length	Diam. of Shank	Size of Square	Number of Flutes
1	0.1974	0.3176	4 3/4	2 7/8	9/32	7/32	4 to 6
2	0.2474	0.3781	5 1/8	3 1/8	11/32	1/4	4 to 6
3	0.3099	0.4510	5 1/2	3 3/8	13/32	5/16	4 to 6
4	0.3474	0.5017	5 7/8	3 11/16	7/16	11/32	4 to 6
5	0.4474	0.6145	6 3/8	4	9/16	7/16	4 to 6
6	0.4974	0.6808	6 7/8	4 3/8	5/8	15/32	4 to 6
7	0.5974	0.8011	7 1/2	4 7/8	3/4	9/16	6 to 8
8	0.7474	0.9770	8 1/8	5 1/2	13/16	5/8	6 to 8
9	0.8974	1.1530	8 7/8	6 1/8	1	3/4	6 to 8
10	1.0420	1.3376	9 3/4	6 7/8	1 1/8	27/32	6 to 8
11	1.2474	1.5657	10 5/8	7 5/8	1 1/4	15/16	6 to 8
12	1.4974	1.8409	11 3/8	8 1/4	1 1/2	1 1/8	8 to 10

* Sizes number 1, 2, and 3 have ASA Standard Taper. Standard straight flute finishing reamers are carbon steel and high speed steel. Standard helical flute finishing reamers are high speed steel only.

These reamers are designed for use in reaming out Brown & Sharpe standard taper sockets.

American Standard Taper Pin Reamers* (ASA B5.14)

No. of Taper Pin Reamer	Diameter at Large End of Reamer	Diameter at Small End of Reamer	Overall Length of Reamer A	Length of Flute B	Length of Square C	Diameter of Shank D	Size of Square
7/0	0.0666	0.0497	$1\frac{13}{16}$	$1\frac{3}{16}$	$\frac{5}{32}$	$\frac{5}{64}$	0.060
6/0	0.0806	0.0611	$1\frac{5}{16}$	$1\frac{5}{16}$	$\frac{5}{32}$	$\frac{3}{32}$	0.070
5/0	0.0966	0.0719	$2\frac{3}{16}$	$1\frac{3}{16}$	$\frac{5}{32}$	$\frac{7}{64}$	0.080
4/0	0.1142	0.0869	$2\frac{5}{16}$	$1\frac{5}{16}$	$\frac{5}{32}$	$\frac{1}{8}$	0.095
3/0	0.1302	0.1029	$2\frac{5}{16}$	$1\frac{5}{16}$	$\frac{5}{32}$	$\frac{9}{64}$	0.105
2/0	0.1462	0.1137	$2\frac{9}{16}$	$1\frac{9}{16}$	$\frac{7}{32}$	$\frac{5}{32}$	0.115
0	0.1638	0.1287	$2\frac{15}{16}$	$1\frac{11}{16}$	$\frac{7}{32}$	$\frac{11}{64}$	0.130
1	0.1798	0.1447	$2\frac{15}{16}$	$1\frac{11}{16}$	$\frac{7}{32}$	$\frac{3}{16}$	0.140
2	0.2008	0.1605	$3\frac{3}{16}$	$1\frac{15}{16}$	$\frac{1}{4}$	$\frac{13}{64}$	0.150
3	0.2294	0.1813	$3\frac{11}{16}$	$2\frac{5}{16}$	$\frac{1}{4}$	$\frac{15}{64}$	0.175
4	0.2604	0.2071	$4\frac{1}{4}$	$2\frac{9}{16}$	$\frac{1}{4}$	$\frac{17}{64}$	0.200
5	0.2994	0.2409	$4\frac{5}{16}$	$2\frac{13}{16}$	$\frac{5}{16}$	$\frac{5}{16}$	0.235
6	0.3540	0.2773	$5\frac{7}{16}$	$3\frac{11}{16}$	$\frac{3}{8}$	$\frac{23}{64}$	0.270
7	0.4220	0.3297	$6\frac{5}{16}$	$4\frac{7}{16}$	$\frac{3}{8}$	$\frac{13}{32}$	0.305
8	0.5050	0.3971	$7\frac{3}{16}$	$5\frac{3}{16}$	$\frac{7}{16}$	$\frac{7}{16}$	0.330
9	0.6066	0.4805	$8\frac{5}{16}$	$6\frac{1}{4}$	$\frac{9}{16}$	$\frac{9}{16}$	0.420
10	0.7216	0.5799	$9\frac{5}{16}$	$6\frac{13}{16}$	$\frac{5}{8}$	$\frac{5}{8}$	0.470

* Commercial reamers may have (1) straight flutes; (2) "spiral" flutes or helical flutes of long lead; (3) helical flutes of comparatively short lead for machine reaming.

TWIST DRILLS AND COUNTERBORES

Twist drills are made with either straight or tapered shanks. The former are by far the more popular type in the smaller sizes because the price is comparatively low. The smaller sizes are parallel throughout their length whereas the larger sizes are ground with a "back taper" thus slightly reducing the drill body diameter nearest the shank. This feature is introduced to prevent binding when the drill is worn.

Straight Shank Drills: Straight shank drills have cylindrical shanks which may be of the same or of a different diameter than the body diameter of the drill and may be made with or without driving flats, tang, or grooves.

Taper Shank Drills: Taper shank drills are preferable to the straight shank type for drilling medium and large size holes. The taper on the shank conforms to one of the tapers in the ASA (Morse) Standard Series. The usual commercial range of taper shank drills is from ⅛ inch to 3½ inches in diameter. Taper shank drills are directly fitted into tapered holes in drilling machine spindles or driving sockets and generally have a driving tang.

American Standard Twist Drill Nomenclature

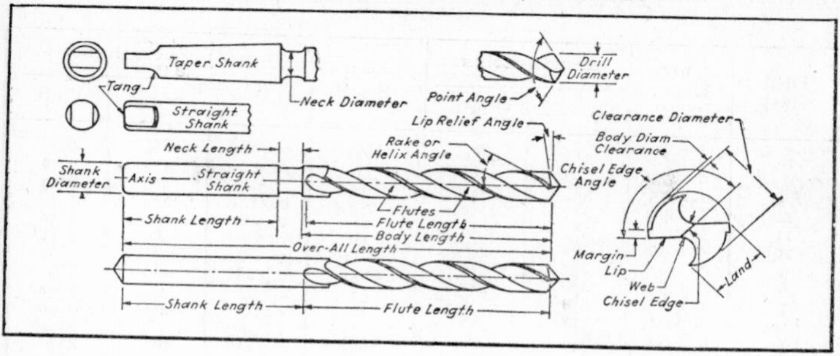

American Standard Straight Shank Twist Drills — From 0.0135 to 0.182 Inch, Inc.*

(ASA B5.12)

Drill Size	Drill Diam. Inches	Length-inches		Drill Size	Drill Diam. Inches	Length-inches	
		Overall	Flute			Overall	Flute
80	0.0135	3/4	3/16	44	0.086	2 1/8	1 1/8
79	0.0145	3/4	3/16	43	0.089	2 1/4	1 1/4
1/64	0.0156	3/4	3/16	42	0.0935	2 1/4	1 1/4
78	0.016	7/8	3/16	3/32	0.0938	2 1/4	1 1/4
77	0.018	7/8	3/16	41	0.096	2 3/8	1 3/8
76	0.020	7/8	3/16	40	0.098	2 3/8	1 3/8
75	0.021	1	1/4	39	0.0995	2 3/8	1 3/8
74	0.0225	1	1/4	38	0.1015	2 1/2	1 7/16
73	0.024	1 1/8	5/16	37	0.104	2 1/2	1 7/16
72	0.025	1 1/8	5/16	36	0.1065	2 1/2	1 7/16
71	0.026	1 1/4	3/8	7/64	0.1094	2 5/8	1 1/2
70	0.028	1 1/4	3/8	35	0.110	2 5/8	1 1/2
69	0.0292	1 3/8	1/2	34	0.111	2 5/8	1 1/2
68	0.031	1 3/8	1/2	33	0.113	2 5/8	1 1/2
1/32	0.0312	1 3/8	1/2	32	0.116	2 3/4	1 5/8
67	0.032	1 3/8	1/2	31	0.120	2 3/4	1 5/8
66	0.033	1 3/8	1/2	1/8	0.1250	2 3/4	1 5/8
65	0.035	1 1/2	5/8	**1/8**	**0.1250**	**5 1/8**	**2 3/4**
64	0.036	1 1/2	5/8	30	0.1285	2 3/4	1 5/8
63	0.037	1 1/2	5/8	29	0.136	2 7/8	1 3/4
62	0.038	1 1/2	5/8	28	0.1405	2 7/8	1 3/4
61	0.039	1 5/8	11/16	9/64	0.1406	2 7/8	1 3/4
60	0.040	1 5/8	11/16	**9/64**	**0.1406**	**5 3/8**	**3**
59	0.041	1 5/8	11/16	27	0.144	3	1 7/8
58	0.042	1 5/8	11/16	26	0.147	3	1 7/8
57	0.043	1 3/4	3/4	25	0.1495	3	1 7/8
56	0.0465	1 3/4	3/4	24	0.152	3 1/8	2
3/64	0.0469	1 3/4	3/4	23	0.154	3 1/8	2
55	0.052	1 7/8	7/8	5/32	0.1562	3 1/8	2
54	0.055	1 7/8	7/8	**5/32**	**0.1562**	**5 3/8**	**3**
53	0.0595	1 7/8	7/8	22	0.157	3 1/8	2
1/16	0.0625	1 7/8	7/8	21	0.159	3 1/4	2 1/8
52	0.0635	1 7/8	7/8	20	0.161	3 1/4	2 1/8
51	0.067	2	1	19	0.166	3 1/4	2 1/8
50	0.070	2	1	18	0.1695	3 1/4	2 1/8
49	0.073	2	1	11/64	0.1719	3 1/4	2 1/8
48	0.076	2	1	**11/64**	**0.1719**	**5 3/4**	**3 3/8**
5/64	0.0781	2	1	17	0.173	3 3/8	2 3/16
47	0.0785	2	1	16	0.177	3 3/8	2 3/16
46	0.081	2 1/8	1 1/8	15	0.180	3 3/8	2 3/16
45	0.082	2 1/8	1 1/8	14	0.182	3 3/8	2 3/16

* Boldface type indicates Long Length drills; all others, Short Length.

American Standard Straight Shank Twist Drills — From 0.185 to 0.500 Inch, Inc.*
(ASA B5.12)

Drill Size†	Drill Diam. Inches	Length-inches		Drill Size†	Drill Diam. Inches	Length-inches	
		Overall	Flute			Overall	Flute
13	0.185	3½	2 5/16	**19/64**	**0.2969**	**6⅜**	**4**
3/16	0.1875	3½	2 5/16	N	0.302	4⅜	3 1/16
3/16	**0.1875**	**5¾**	**3⅜**	5/16	0.3125	4½	3 3/16
12	0.189	3½	2 5/16	**5/16**	**0.3125**	**6⅜**	**4**
11	0.191	3½	2 5/16	O	0.316	4½	3 3/16
10	0.1935	3⅝	2 7/16	P	0.323	4⅝	3 5/16
9	0.196	3⅝	2 7/16	21/64	0.3281	4⅝	3 5/16
8	0.199	3⅝	2 7/16	**21/64**	**0.3281**	**6½**	**4⅛**
7	0.201	3⅝	2 7/16	Q	0.332	4¾	3 7/16
13/64	0.2031	3⅝	2 7/16	R	0.339	4¾	3 7/16
13/64	**0.2031**	**6**	**3⅝**	11/32	0.3438	4¾	3 7/16
6	0.204	3¾	2½	**11/32**	**0.3438**	**6½**	**4⅛**
5	0.2055	3¾	2½	S	0.348	4⅞	3½
4	0.209	3¾	2½	T	0.358	4⅞	3½
3	0.213	3¾	2½	23/64	0.3594	4⅞	3½
7/32	0.2188	3¾	2½	**23/64**	**0.3594**	**6¾**	**4¼**
7/32	**0.2188**	**6**	**3⅝**	U	0.368	5	3⅝
2	0.221	3⅞	2⅝	3/8	0.375	5	3⅝
1	0.228	3⅞	2⅝	**3/8**	**0.375**	**6¾**	**4¼**
A	0.234	3⅞	2⅝	V	0.377	5	3⅝
15/64	0.2344	3⅞	2⅝	W	0.386	5⅛	3¾
15/64	**0.2344**	**6⅛**	**3¾**	25/64	0.3906	5⅛	3¾
B	0.238	4	2¾	**25/64**	**0.3906**	**7**	**4⅜**
C	0.242	4	2¾	X	0.397	5⅛	3¾
D	0.246	4	2¾	Y	0.404	5¼	3⅞
E & ¼	0.250	4	2¾	13/32	0.4062	5¼	3⅞
E & ¼	**0.250**	**6⅛**	**3¾**	**13/32**	**0.4062**	**7**	**4⅜**
F	0.257	4⅛	2⅞	Z	0.413	5¼	3⅞
G	0.261	4⅛	2⅞	27/64	0.4219	5⅜	3 15/16
17/64	0.2656	4⅛	2⅞	**27/64**	**0.4219**	**7¼**	**4⅝**
17/64	**0.2656**	**6¼**	**3⅞**	7/16	0.4375	5½	4 1/16
H	0.266	4⅛	2⅞	**7/16**	**0.4375**	**7¼**	**4⅝**
I	0.272	4⅛	2⅞	29/64	0.4531	5⅝	4 3/16
J	0.277	4⅛	2⅞	**29/64**	**0.4531**	**7½**	**4¾**
K	0.281	4¼	2 15/16	15/32	0.4688	5¾	4 5/16
9/32	0.2812	4¼	2 15/16	**15/32**	**0.4688**	**7½**	**4¾**
9/32	**0.2812**	**6¼**	**3⅞**	31/64	0.4844	5⅞	4⅜
L	0.290	4¼	2 15/16	**31/64**	**0.4844**	**7¾**	**4¾**
M	0.295	4⅜	3 1/16	½	0.5000	6	4½
19/64	0.2969	4⅜	3 1/16	**½**	**0.5000**	**7¾**	**4¾**

* **Boldface type indicates Long Length drills, all others, Short Length.**

† Wire Gage sizes, Fractional sizes, Letter sizes.

Straight shank twist drills from 33/64 to 2 inches in diameter are not tabulated. Drills in this range are Long Length sizes and are standard in diameter increments of: 1/64 inch for drills of 33/64- to 1¼-inch diameter, 1/32 inch for drills of 1¼- to 1½-inch diameter, and 1/16 inch for drills of 1½- to 2-inch diameter.

Diameter Tolerances for American Standard Straight Shank Twist Drills

Drill Diameter-inches	Tolerance-inch
Up to 3/64 inclusive	Plus 0.0000 to minus 0.0006
Over 3/64 to ⅛ inclusive	Plus 0.0000 to minus 0.0008
Over ⅛ to ¼ inclusive	Plus 0.0000 to minus 0.0010
Over ¼ to ¾ inclusive	Plus 0.0000 to minus 0.0015
Over ¾ to 1½ inclusive	Plus 0.0000 to minus 0.0020
Over 1½ to 2 inclusive	Plus 0.0000 to minus 0.0025

American Standard Taper Shank Twist Drills — From 1/8 to 2 Inch, Inc. (ASA B5.12)

Drill Size (Inches)	Regular Shank*			Drill Size (Inches)	Regular Shank*		
	ASA Taper (Morse)	Overall Length (Inches)	Flute Length (Inches)		ASA Taper (Morse)	Overall Length (Inches)	Flute Length (Inches)
1/8	1	5 1/8	1 7/8	1 1/64	3	11 1/8	6 1/2
9/64	1	5 3/8	2 1/8	1 1/32	3	11 1/8	6 1/2
5/32	1	5 3/8	2 1/8	1 3/64	3	11 1/4	6 5/8
11/64	1	5 3/4	2 1/2	1 1/16	3	11 1/4	6 5/8
3/16	1	5 3/4	2 1/2	1 5/64	4	12 1/2	6 7/8
13/64	1	6	2 3/4	1 3/32	4	12 1/2	6 7/8
7/32	1	6	2 3/4	1 7/64	4	12 3/4	7 1/8
15/64	1	6 1/8	2 7/8	1 1/8	4	12 3/4	7 1/8
1/4	1	6 1/8	2 7/8	1 9/64	4	12 7/8	7 1/4
17/64	1	6 1/4	3	1 5/32	4	12 7/8	7 1/4
9/32	1	6 1/4	3	1 11/64	4	13	7 3/8
19/64	1	6 3/8	3 1/8	1 3/16	4	13	7 3/8
5/16	1	6 3/8	3 1/8	1 13/64	4	13 1/8	7 1/2
21/64	1	6 1/2	3 1/4	1 7/32	4	13 1/8	7 1/2
11/32	1	6 1/2	3 1/4	1 15/64	4	13 1/2	7 7/8
23/64	1	6 3/4	3 1/2	1 1/4	4	13 1/2	7 7/8
3/8	1	6 3/4	3 1/2	1 17/64	4	14 1/8	8 1/2
25/64	1	7	3 5/8	1 9/32	4	14 1/8	8 1/2
13/32	1	7	3 5/8	1 19/64	4	14 1/4	8 5/8
27/64	1	7 1/4	3 7/8	1 5/16	4	14 1/4	8 5/8
7/16	1	7 1/4	3 7/8	1 21/64	4	14 3/8	8 3/4
29/64	1	7 1/2	4 1/8	1 11/32	4	14 3/8	8 3/4
15/32	1	7 1/2	4 1/8	1 23/64	4	14 1/2	8 7/8
31/64	2	8 1/4	4 3/8	1 3/8	4	14 1/2	8 7/8
1/2	2	8 1/4	4 3/8	1 25/64	4	14 5/8	9
33/64	2	8 1/2	4 5/8	1 13/32	4	14 5/8	9
17/32	2	8 1/2	4 5/8	1 27/64	4	14 3/4	9 1/8
35/64	2	8 3/4	4 7/8	1 7/16	4	14 3/4	9 1/8
9/16	2	8 3/4	4 7/8	1 29/64	4	14 7/8	9 1/4
37/64	2	8 3/4	4 7/8	1 15/32	4	14 7/8	9 1/4
19/32	2	8 3/4	4 7/8	1 31/64	4	15	9 3/8
39/64	2	8 3/4	4 7/8	1 1/2	4	15	9 3/8
5/8	2	8 3/4	4 7/8	1 33/64	5	16 3/8	9 3/8
41/64	2	9	5 1/8	1 17/32	5	16 3/8	9 3/8
21/32	2	9	5 1/8	1 35/64	5	16 5/8	9 5/8
43/64	2	9 1/4	5 3/8	1 9/16	5	16 5/8	9 5/8
11/16	2	9 1/4	5 3/8	1 37/64	5	16 7/8	9 7/8
45/64	2	9 1/2	5 5/8	1 19/32	5	16 7/8	9 7/8
23/32	2	9 1/2	5 5/8	1 39/64	5	17	10
47/64	2	9 3/4	5 7/8	1 5/8	5	17	10
3/4	2	9 3/4	5 7/8	1 41/64	5	17 1/8	10 1/8
49/64	2	9 7/8	6	1 21/32	5	17 1/8	10 1/8
25/32	2	9 7/8	6	1 43/64	5	17 1/8	10 1/8
51/64	3	10 3/4	6 1/8	1 11/16	5	17 1/8	10 1/8
13/16	3	10 3/4	6 1/8	1 45/64	5	17 1/8	10 1/8
53/64	3	10 3/4	6 1/8	1 23/32	5	17 1/8	10 1/8
27/32	3	10 3/4	6 1/8	1 47/64	5	17 1/8	10 1/8
55/64	3	10 3/4	6 1/8	1 3/4	5	17 1/8	10 1/8
7/8	3	10 3/4	6 1/8	1 25/32	5	17 1/8	10 1/8
57/64	3	10 3/4	6 1/8	1 13/16	5	17 1/8	10 1/8
29/32	3	10 3/4	6 1/8	1 27/32	5	17 1/8	10 1/8
59/64	3	10 3/4	6 1/8	1 7/8	5	17 3/8	10 3/8
15/16	3	10 3/4	6 1/8	1 29/32	5	17 3/8	10 3/8
61/64	3	11	6 3/8	1 15/16	5	17 3/8	10 3/8
31/32	3	11	6 3/8	1 31/32	5	17 3/8	10 3/8
63/64	3	11	6 3/8	2	5	17 3/8	10 3/8
1	3	11	6 3/8				

* Some of the drill sizes listed are available with shanks smaller than regular, and some are available with shanks larger than regular.

Drill sizes from 2 to 3 1/2 inches diameter are not tabulated. Drills from 2 to 2 1/4 inch diameter are in 1/32 inch diameter increments; from 2 1/4 to 3 1/2, in 1/16 inch increments.

See page 1324 for drill diameter tolerances.

Automotive Series Straight Shank Twist Drills (ASA B5.12)

Diameter of Drill (Inches)	Letter, Fraction, No., or MM Size	Diam. of Shank		Short Length		Long Length	
		Max	Min	Overall Length	Flute Length	Overall Length	Flute Length
0.2500	1/4	0.2485	0.2475	4 1/2	3 1/8	6 1/2	4 5/16
0.2520	6.40 mm	0.2505	0.2495	4 1/2	3 1/8	6 1/2	4 5/16
0.2570	F	0.2550	0.2540	4 1/2	3 1/8	6 1/2	4 5/16
0.2610	G	0.2590	0.2580	4 1/2	3 1/8	6 1/2	4 5/16
0.2656	17/64	0.2636	0.2626	4 1/2	3 1/8	6 1/2	4 5/16
0.2720	I	0.2700	0.2690	4 1/2	3 1/8	6 3/4	4 1/2
0.2770	J	0.2750	0.2740	4 1/2	3 1/8	6 3/4	4 1/2
0.2812	9/32	0.2792	0.2782	4 3/4	3 3/8	6 3/4	4 1/2
0.2854	7.25 mm	0.2834	0.2824	4 3/4	3 3/8	6 3/4	4 1/2
0.2913	7.40 mm	0.2893	0.2883	4 3/4	3 3/8	6 3/4	4 1/2
0.2969	19/64	0.2949	0.2939	4 3/4	3 3/8	6 3/4	4 1/2
0.3020	N	0.3000	0.2990	4 3/4	3 3/8	7	4 11/16
0.3071	7.80 mm	0.3051	0.3041	4 3/4	3 3/8	7	4 11/16
0.3125	5/16	0.3105	0.3095	5	3 5/8	7	4 11/16
0.3160	O	0.3140	0.3130	5	3 5/8	7	4 11/16
0.3230	P	0.3210	0.3200	5	3 5/8	7	4 11/16
0.3281	21/64	0.3261	0.3251	5	3 5/8	7	4 11/16
0.3320	Q	0.3300	0.3290	5	3 5/8	7 1/4	4 15/16
0.3390	R	0.3370	0.3360	5	3 5/8	7 1/4	4 15/16
0.3438	11/32	0.3418	0.3408	5 1/4	3 7/8	7 1/4	4 15/16
0.3480	S	0.3460	0.3450	5 1/4	3 7/8	7 1/4	4 15/16
0.3543	9 mm	0.3523	0.3513	5 1/4	3 7/8	7 1/4	4 15/16
0.3594	23/64	0.3574	0.3564	5 1/4	3 7/8	7 1/4	4 15/16
0.3680	U	0.3660	0.3650	5 1/4	3 7/8	7 5/8	5 1/8
0.3750	3/8	0.3730	0.3720	5 5/8	4 1/8	7 5/8	5 1/8
0.3860	W	0.3840	0.3830	5 5/8	4 1/8	7 5/8	5 1/8
0.3906	25/64	0.3886	0.3876	5 5/8	4 1/8	7 5/8	5 1/8
0.3970	X	0.3950	0.3940	5 5/8	4 1/8	7 5/8	5 1/8
0.4062	13/32	0.4042	0.4032	5 5/8	4 1/8	7 5/8	5 1/8
0.4219	27/64	0.4199	0.4189	5 5/8	4 1/8	7 5/8	5 1/8
0.4375	7/16	0.4355	0.4345	6 1/8	4 7/16	8 1/8	5 7/16
0.4531	29/64	0.4511	0.4501	6 1/8	4 7/16	8 1/8	5 7/16
0.4688	15/32	0.4668	0.4658	6 1/8	4 7/16	8 1/8	5 7/16
0.4844	31/64	0.4824	0.4814	6 1/8	4 7/16	8 1/8	5 7/16
0.5000	1/2	0.4980	0.4970	6 1/8	4 7/16	8 1/8	5 7/16
0.5156	33/64	0.5131	0.5121	6 5/8	4 13/16	8 5/8	5 3/4
0.5312	17/32	0.5287	0.5277	6 5/8	4 13/16	8 5/8	5 3/4
0.5469	35/64	0.5444	0.5434	6 5/8	4 13/16	8 5/8	5 3/4
0.5625	9/16	0.5600	0.5590	6 5/8	4 13/16	8 5/8	5 3/4
0.5781	37/64	0.5756	0.5746	6 5/8	4 13/16	8 5/8	5 3/4
0.5938	19/32	0.5913	0.5903	7 1/8	5 3/16	9 1/8	6 1/8
0.6094	39/64	0.6069	0.6059	7 1/8	5 3/16	9 1/8	6 1/8
0.6250	5/8	0.6225	0.6215	7 1/8	5 3/16	9 1/8	6 1/8
0.6406	41/64	0.6381	0.6371	7 1/8	5 3/16	9 1/8	6 1/8
0.6562	21/32	0.6537	0.6527	7 1/8	5 3/16	9 1/8	6 1/8
0.6719	43/64	0.6694	0.6684	7 5/8	5 5/8	9 5/8	6 1/2
0.6875	11/16	0.6850	0.6840	7 5/8	5 5/8	9 5/8	6 1/2

Drill Diameter Tolerances.—*Automotive series,* plus 0.0000 to minus 0.0010 inch for 1/4 inch diameter drills, plus 0.0000 to minus 0.0015 inch for drills over 1/4 inch diameter. *American Standard Taper Shank* Drills, plus 0.0000 to: minus 0.0008 inch for 1/8 inch diameter drills, minus 0.0010 inch for drills over 1/8 to 1/4 inch diameter, minus 0.0015 inch for drills over 1/4 to 3/4 inch diameter, minus 0.0020 inch for drills over 3/4 to 1 1/2 inch diameter, minus 0.0025 inch for drills over 1 1/2 to 3 1/2 inch diameter. See also page 1322 for *Straight Shank* twist drill tolerances.

Steels for Twist Drills. — *Carbon Steel:* If the conditions are such that carbon steel drill speeds are sufficient for the purpose, high-speed-steel drills are not economical to use because the difference in performance as compared with the carbon steel tool does not compensate for the difference in price.

High-Speed Steel: For high surface speed drilling operations where carbon steels would fail by tempering, the properties of red hardness and abrasion resistance favor the use of high-speed steel.

Cobalt High-Speed Steel: These high-speed steel drills are capable of withstanding cutting speeds beyond the range of conventional high-speed-steel drills and have superior resistance to abrasion but are not to be compared with tungsten-carbide tipped tools.

Counterbores. — Counterbores for screw holes are generally made in sets. Each set contains three counterbores: one with the body of the size of the screw head and the pilot the size of the hole to admit the body of the screw; one with the body the size of the head of the screw and the pilot the size of the tap drill; and the third with the body the size of the body of the screw and the pilot the size of the tap drill. Counterbores are usually provided with four flutes cut on a right-hand spiral. The angle of the spiral is 15 degrees with the center line of the counterbore, which corresponds to a lead of the flute equal to about twelve times the diameter of the body of the counterbore. Counterbores for brass are fluted straight.

Small counterbores are often made with three flutes, but should then have the size plainly stamped on them before fluting, as they cannot afterwards be conveniently measured. The flutes should be deep enough to come below the surface of the pilot. The counterbore should be relieved on the end of the body only, and not on the cylindrical surface. To facilitate the relieving process, a small neck is turned between the guide and the body for clearance. The amount of clearance on the cutting edges is, for general work, from 4 to 5 degrees. The accompanying table gives dimensions for straight shank counterbores. The same dimensions, except for the shank part, may be used for Morse taper shank counterbores. The number of shank used for counterbores with bodies of different diameters is usually as follows: Up to ½ inch diameter body, No. 1 Morse taper shank; from 9/16 to 7/8 inch, No. 2; from 15/16 to 1⅜ inch, No. 3; from 1⁷/₁₆ to 2 inches, No. 4; from 2¹/₁₆ to 3 inches, No. 5 shank.

Counterbores With Interchangeable Cutters and Guides

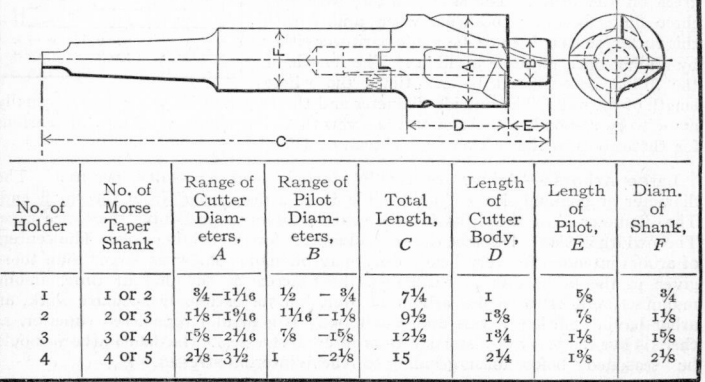

No. of Holder	No. of Morse Taper Shank	Range of Cutter Diameters, A	Range of Pilot Diameters, B	Total Length, C	Length of Cutter Body, D	Length of Pilot, E	Diam. of Shank, F
1	1 or 2	¾–1¹/₁₆	½ – ¾	7¼	1	⅝	¾
2	2 or 3	1⅛–1⁹/₁₆	¹¹/₁₆ –1⅛	9½	1⅜	⅞	1⅛
3	3 or 4	1⅝–2¹/₁₆	⅞ –1⅝	12½	1¾	1⅛	1⅝
4	4 or 5	2⅛–3½	1 –2⅛	15	2¼	1⅜	2⅛

Dimensions of Counterbores

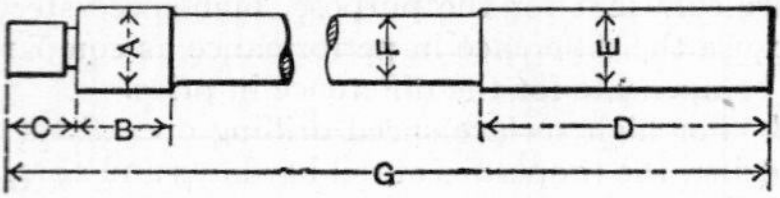

A	B	C	D	E	F	G	A	B	C	D	E	F	G
1/4	11/32	3/16	2 1/2	1/4	7/32	4 7/8	1 5/16	1 3/4	63/64	3 9/16	1 5/16	1 9/32	12 5/16
5/16	13/32	15/64	2 9/16	5/16	9/32	5 5/16	1 3/8	1 27/32	1 1/32	3 5/8	1 3/8	1 11/32	12 3/4
3/8	1/2	9/32	2 5/8	3/8	11/32	5 3/4	1 7/16	1 29/32	1 5/64	3 11/16	1 7/16	1 13/32	13 3/16
7/16	19/32	21/64	2 11/16	7/16	13/32	6 3/16	1 1/2	2	1 1/8	3 3/4	1 1/2	1 7/16	13 3/8
1/2	21/32	3/8	2 3/4	1/2	15/32	6 5/8	1 5/8	2 3/32	1 7/32	3 15/16	1 17/32	1 15/32	13 3/4
9/16	3/4	27/64	2 13/16	9/16	17/32	7 1/16	1 3/4	2 3/16	1 5/16	4 1/8	1 19/32	1 17/32	14 1/8
5/8	27/32	15/32	2 7/8	5/8	19/32	7 1/2	1 7/8	2 9/32	1 13/32	4 5/16	1 5/8	1 9/16	14 1/2
11/16	29/32	33/64	2 15/16	11/16	21/32	7 15/16	2	2 3/8	1 1/2	4 1/2	1 21/32	1 19/32	14 7/8
3/4	1	9/16	3	3/4	23/32	8 3/8	2 1/8	2 15/32	1 19/32	4 11/16	1 23/32	1 21/32	15 1/4
13/16	1 3/32	39/64	3 1/16	13/16	25/32	8 13/16	2 1/4	2 9/16	1 11/16	4 7/8	1 3/4	1 11/16	15 5/8
7/8	1 5/32	21/32	3 1/8	7/8	27/32	9 1/4	2 3/8	2 21/32	1 25/32	5 1/16	1 25/32	1 23/32	16
15/16	1 1/4	45/64	3 3/16	15/16	29/32	9 11/16	2 1/2	2 3/4	1 7/8	5 1/4	1 27/32	1 25/32	16 3/8
1	1 11/32	3/4	3 1/4	1	31/32	10 1/8	2 5/8	2 27/32	1 31/32	5 7/16	1 7/8	1 13/16	16 3/4
1 1/16	1 13/32	51/64	3 5/16	1 1/16	1 1/32	10 9/16	2 3/4	2 15/16	2 1/16	5 5/8	1 29/32	1 27/32	17 1/8
1 1/8	1 1/2	27/32	3 3/8	1 1/8	1 3/32	11	2 7/8	3 1/32	2 5/32	5 13/16	1 31/32	1 29/32	17 1/2
1 3/16	1 19/32	57/64	3 7/16	1 3/16	1 5/32	11 7/16	3	3 1/8	2 1/4	6	2	1 15/16	17 7/8
1 1/4	1 21/32	15/16	3 1/2	1 1/4	1 7/32	11 7/8	...	...	...	...	...	...	...

Hollow Mills. — A leading tool manufacturer's practice is as follows: The hole in hollow mills, from the cutting edges backwards, should be back tapered at the rate of 1/4 inch per foot for cutting steel and 3/8 inch per foot for cutting brass. Adjustable hollow mills are always provided with three flutes, cut straight, if the mill is to be used for brass, or cut on an angle not exceeding ten degrees, when the tool is used for steel. The cutters used for cutting the flutes are 55-degree, double-angle cutters, 12 degrees on one side and 43 degrees on the other. The land of a mill with only three flutes becomes too wide when milled with this cutter, so that it must be made narrower either by milling once more or by filing. The length of the fluted part should be 0.6 times the whole length of the mill. The outside diameter and the length of hollow mills are usually made to correspond to those of spring screw threading dies (see table of dimensions for these tools in the section on "Threading Dies").

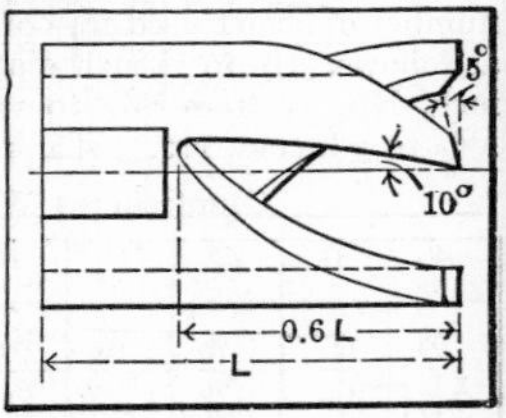

Lathe Arbors. — Arbors are usually tapered about 0.006 inch per foot. The diameter or nominal size *D* in the table is at a distance *F* from the small end. The diameter *G* of the drills for the centers conforms to Stub's steel wire gage. The "width of flat," listed in the last column, is for the driving dog. The centers of arbors intended for very heavy duty may be made somewhat larger than those given in the table. As to hardening, the practice at the present time, among manufacturers, is to harden arbors all over, but for extremely accurate work, an arbor having hardened ends and a soft body is generally considered superior, as there is less tendency of distortion from internal stresses. Hardened arbors should be "seasoned" before finish grinding to relieve internal stresses.

Proportions of Solid Lathe Arbors

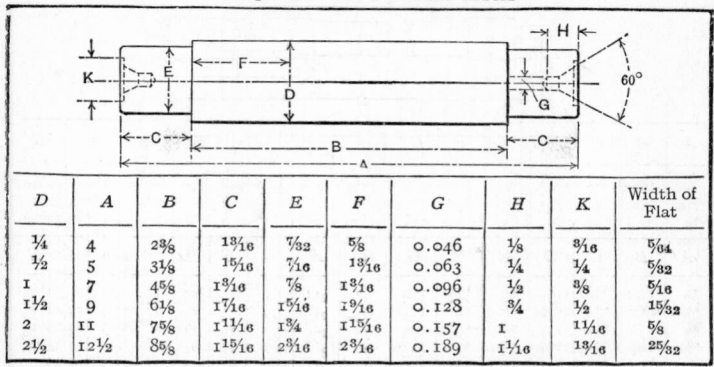

D	A	B	C	E	F	G	H	K	Width of Flat
1/4	4	2 3/8	1 3/16	7/32	5/8	0.046	1/8	3/16	5/64
1/2	5	3 1/8	15/16	7/16	13/16	0.063	1/4	1/4	5/32
1	7	4 5/8	1 3/16	7/8	1 3/16	0.096	1/2	3/8	5/16
1 1/2	9	6 1/8	1 7/16	1 5/16	1 9/16	0.128	3/4	1/2	15/32
2	11	7 5/8	1 11/16	1 3/4	1 15/16	0.157	1	11/16	5/8
2 1/2	12 1/2	8 5/8	1 15/16	2 3/16	2 3/16	0.189	1 1/16	13/16	25/32

Boring-bar Couplings

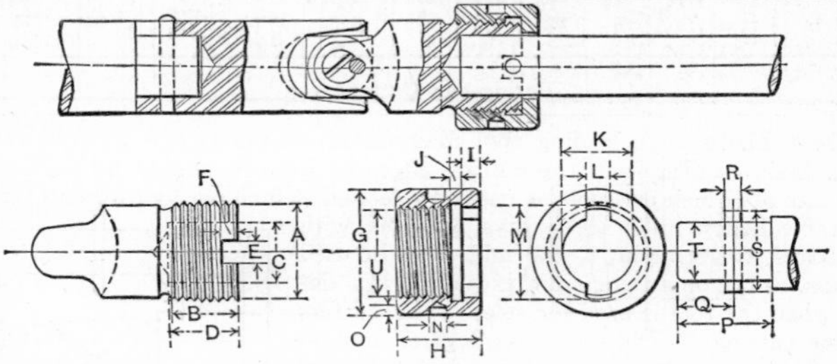

A	B	C	D	E	F	G	H	I	J	K	L	M
3/4	1/2	1/2	7/16	3/16	5/32	1	5/8	1/8	3/32	17/32	3/16	11/16
1	1/2	5/8	9/16	1/4	7/32	1 3/8	5/8	5/32	3/32	21/32	1/4	15/16
1 1/4	5/8	3/4	5/8	5/16	9/32	1 5/8	13/16	3/16	1/8	25/32	5/16	1 5/32
1 1/2	13/16	1	7/8	7/16	13/32	2	1 1/16	1/4	1/8	1 1/32	7/16	1 13/32
2 1/2	7/8	1 1/2	1 3/8	9/16	17/32	3	1 1/8	1/4	1/8	1 17/32	9/16	2 3/8
3	7/8	1 7/8	1 3/4	11/16	21/32	3 1/2	1 1/4	1/4	1/8	1 29/32	11/16	2 7/8

N	O	P	Q	R	S	T	U, Bore	Threads per Inch	Used for Bars
9/64	1/8	3/4	3/8	1/8	21/32	0.499	0.6610	16	3/8 to 1/2
11/64	5/32	7/8	15/32	3/16	7/8	0.624	0.9110	16	1/2 to 3/4
13/64	5/32	1 1/8	1/2	1/4	1 1/16	0.749	1.1615	12	3/4 to 1
15/64	3/16	1 3/8	11/16	3/8	1 5/16	0.999	1.4115	12	1 to 1 1/2
19/64	7/32	1 7/8	1 1/8	1/2	2 1/4	1.4985	2.4115	12	1 1/2 to 2
21/64	7/32	2 5/16	1 7/16	5/8	2 3/4	1.8735	2.9115	12	2 and over

Boring-bar Cutters — 1

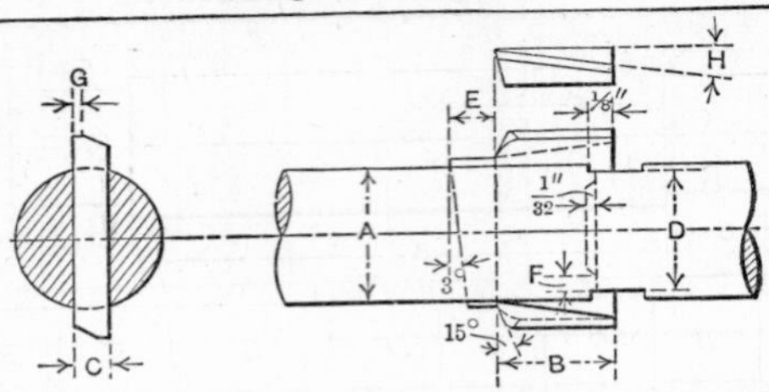

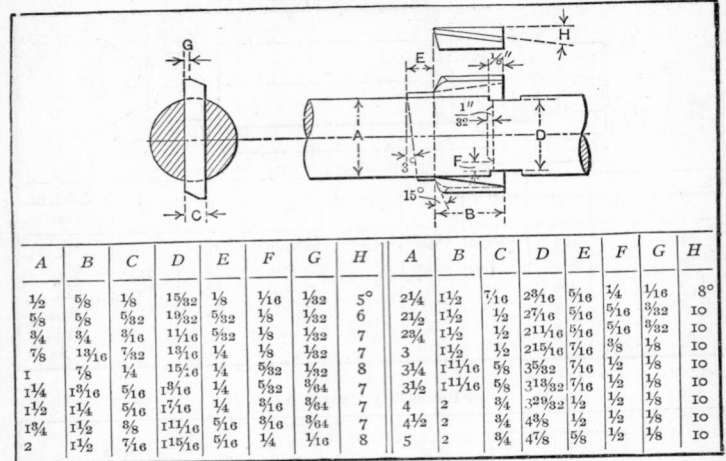

A	B	C	D	E	F	G	H	A	B	C	D	E	F	G	H
1/2	5/8	1/8	15/32	1/8	1/16	1/32	5°	2 1/4	1 1/2	7/16	2 3/16	5/16	1/4	1/16	8°
5/8	5/8	5/32	19/32	5/32	1/8	1/32	6	2 1/2	1 1/2	1/2	2 7/16	5/16	5/16	3/32	10
3/4	3/4	3/16	11/16	5/32	1/8	1/32	7	2 3/4	1 1/2	1/2	2 11/16	5/16	5/16	3/32	10
7/8	13/16	7/32	13/16	1/4	1/8	1/32	7	3	1 1/2	1/2	2 15/16	7/16	3/8	1/8	10
1	7/8	1/4	15/16	1/4	5/32	1/32	8	3 1/4	1 11/16	5/8	3 5/32	7/16	1/2	1/8	10
1 1/4	1 3/16	5/16	1 3/16	1/4	5/32	3/64	7	3 1/2	1 11/16	5/8	3 13/32	7/16	1/2	1/8	10
1 1/2	1 1/4	5/16	1 7/16	1/4	3/16	3/64	7	4	2	3/4	3 29/32	1/2	1/2	1/8	10
1 3/4	1 1/2	3/8	1 11/16	5/16	3/16	3/64	7	4 1/2	2	3/4	4 3/8	1/2	1/2	1/8	10
2	1 1/2	7/16	1 15/16	5/16	1/4	1/16	8	5	2	3/4	4 7/8	5/8	1/2	1/8	10

Boring-bar Cutters — 2

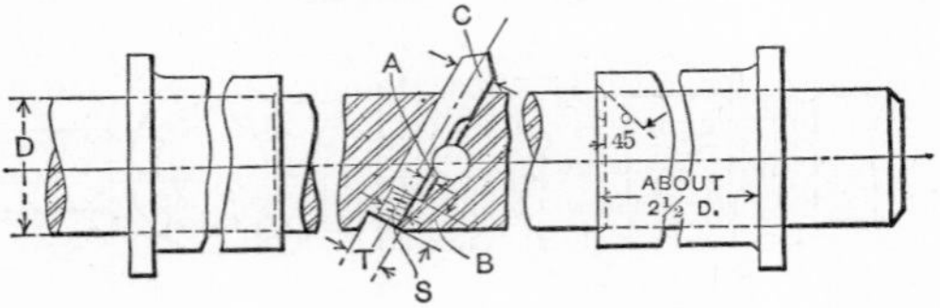

Diameter of Bar, D	Diameter of Cutter, C	Diameter of Pin	Depth of Flat, A	Diameter of Screw, S	Diameter T of Counter-bore	Length B of Thread	Diameter of Bar, D	Diameter of Cutter, C	Diameter of Pin	Depth of Flat, A	Diameter of Screw, S	Diameter T of Counterbore	Length B of Thread
3/8	1/8	1/16	1/64	1/16	1/8	5/64	1 1/2	3/8	9/32	3/64	5/16	3/8	3/8
7/16	1/8	3/32	1/64	1/16	1/8	5/64	1 5/8	7/16	5/16	3/64	5/16	3/8	3/8
1/2	1/8	3/32	1/64	1/16	1/8	5/64	1 3/4	7/16	5/16	3/64	3/8	7/16	1/2
9/16	1/8	1/8	1/32	1/8	5/32	1/8	1 7/8	1/2	11/32	1/16	3/8	7/16	1/2
5/8	3/16	1/8	1/32	1/8	5/32	1/8	2	1/2	3/8	1/16	7/16	1/2	9/16
11/16	3/16	5/32	1/32	1/8	3/16	5/32	2 1/8	9/16	13/32	1/16	7/16	1/2	9/16
3/4	3/16	5/32	1/32	1/8	3/16	5/32	2 1/4	9/16	13/32	1/16	1/2	9/16	5/8
13/16	1/4	5/32	1/32	3/16	1/4	3/16	2 3/8	5/8	7/16	5/64	1/2	9/16	5/8
7/8	1/4	5/32	1/32	3/16	1/4	3/16	2 1/2	5/8	15/32	5/64	9/16	5/8	11/16
15/16	1/4	3/16	1/32	3/16	1/4	1/4	2 5/8	11/16	1/2	5/64	9/16	5/8	11/16
1	1/4	3/16	1/32	3/16	1/4	1/4	2 3/4	11/16	1/2	5/64	5/8	11/16	3/4
1 1/8	5/16	7/32	1/32	1/4	5/16	5/16	2 7/8	3/4	17/32	3/32	5/8	3/4	7/8
1 1/4	5/16	1/4	3/64	1/4	5/16	5/16	3	3/4	9/16	3/32	5/8	3/4	7/8
1 3/8	3/8	1/4	3/64	1/4	5/16	5/16	...	...	...	...	...	...	...

Boring-bar Cutters — 3

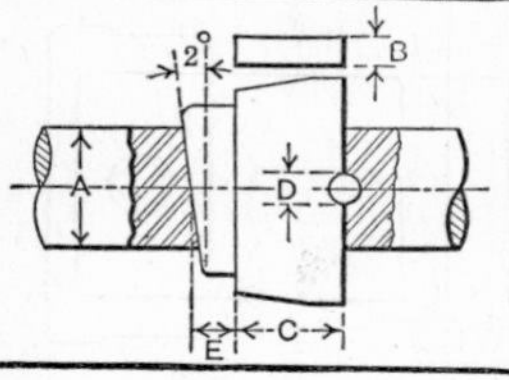

A	*B*	*C*	*D*	*E*
¾ to 1⁵⁄₁₆	¼	¾	³⁄₁₆	¼
1 to 1⅜	⁵⁄₁₆	¾	³⁄₁₆	¼
1½ to 2⅜	⅜	¾	¼	¼
2½ to 3	½	1	¼	⁵⁄₁₆
3⅛ and larger	⅝	1¼	⁵⁄₁₆	⅜

Boring Bars and Cutter Heads

Various methods of attaching cutters to boring-bars, and different designs of cutter-heads, are shown on the following pages. Many of the designs illustrated have been extensively used.

Fig. 1. A simple method of holding a flat cutter in a boring-bar. The cutter is held in a rectangular slot in the bar, by wedge *W*, tapered on one side to about 2 degrees; the cutter is centered by shoulders *S*.

Fig. 2. An excellent design in which the cutter is held and centered by a conical-ended screw *B*, which bears against a conical seat in the cutter. The screw end should have a taper of about 30 degrees included angle.

Fig. 3. Boring and facing cutter also held by a conical-ended screw which passes through a hole in the cutter. The hole is slightly offset so that the cutter will be forced back against its seat.

Fig. 4. Simple and inexpensive form of cutter made from drill rod and held by a taper pin which bears against a circular locating seat in the center.

Fig. 5. The cutter is secured by a fine threaded sleeve *B* and is centered by shoulders *S*. This form eliminates any tendency of springing the bar, and for that reason is sometimes preferred to wedges. The particular cutter shown in this bar is excellent for light finishing cuts. It has circular ends with slight clearance.

Fig. 6. A wedged cutter which is centered by pin *C*. The cutter is a plain rectangular piece of steel, except for the circular locating seat.

Fig. 7. The cutter is wedged by a piece of drill rod *W* having a tapering flat side, and is centered by the projecting shoulders *S*. The edge of the cutter against which the pin bears should be rounded, to locate the bearing in the center instead of on one corner. The cutter is solidly supported on the rear side.

Fig. 8. The clamping wedge is placed at right angles and engages a central notch in the cutter in order to bind and also center the latter. The objection to this design is that it requires two slots.

Fig. 9. Adjustable cutters made preferably of round steel flattened on one side for binding screws *B*. The adjusting screw *A* has a conical end which enters between the inner ends of the cutters.

Fig. 10. An inexpensive method of holding a cutter near the end of a bar.

Fig. 11. Boring and facing cutter clamped in its slot by an inclined screw *B*, which forces the flattened side of a hardened bushing against the cutter.

Fig. 12. Simple method of holding and adjusting single-ended cutter, adjustment being effected by screw *A*.

Fig. 13. A turret bar with tool held at an angle for boring blind holes, etc. Adjustments are effected by screw *A*.

Fig. 14. A modification of the type illustrated in Fig. 13.

Fig. 15. Cutter held by pin *B*, having a tapering flat side which bears against the flat side of the round cutter.

Types of Boring Bars

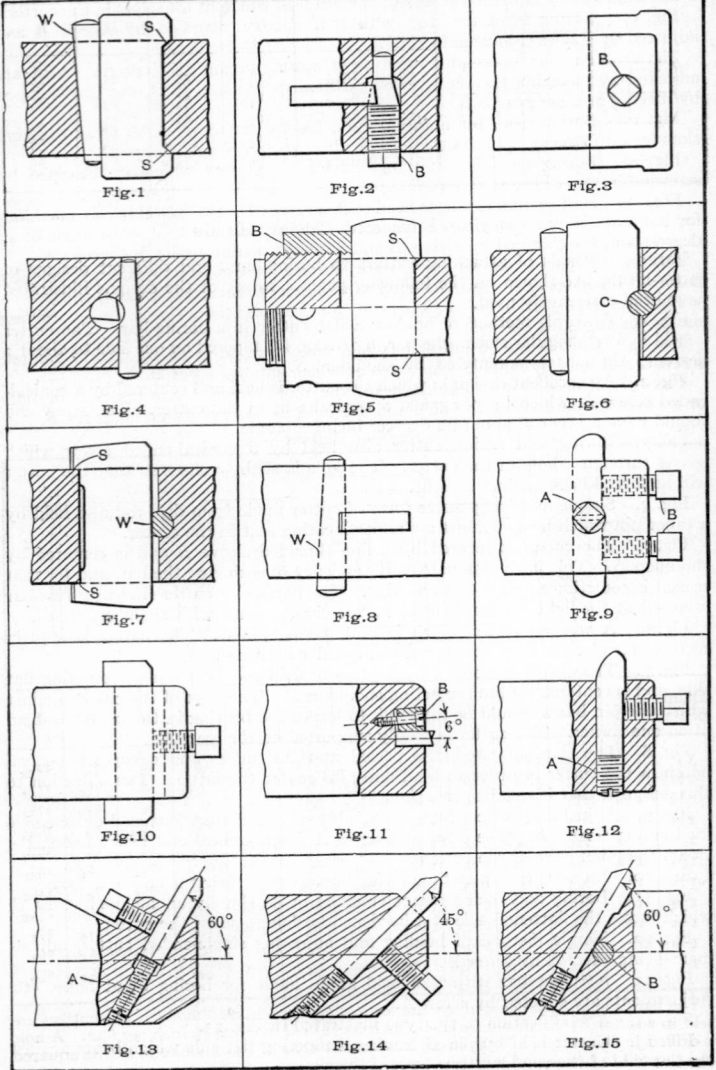

Fig.1   Fig.2   Fig.3
Fig.4   Fig.5   Fig.6
Fig.7   Fig.8   Fig.9
Fig.10   Fig.11   Fig.12
Fig.13   Fig.14   Fig.15

Fig. 16. Bar especially adapted for cast iron, having two cutters held by screws *B* and adjusted by hardened screws *C*, the heads of which fit into slots in the cutters.

Fig. 17. Boring head for steel with four cutters, clamped by screws *B* and adjusted by screws *C* located in ring *D*.

Fig. 18. Bar for brass and other light work, having two cutters which are adjusted by changing their lengthwise position in tapering slots, and are clamped by driving in taper pins *B*.

Fig. 19. Boring head for finishing cuts, having six tools which fit in tapering slots for adjustment. The cutters are held by screws *B* and clamps *D*.

Fig. 20. Boring head for finishing, having six cutters which are clamped by screwing in taper-headed screws *B*.

Fig. 21. Half-section of cutter-head such as is used in horizontal boring machines for holes of comparatively large diameter. The cutters are held at an angle of 45 degrees and are clamped by screws *B* and adjusted, within limits, by screws *A*.

Fig. 22. Type of bar for light work, having two cutters which are held by flattened bushings and screws inserted at an angle, to secure a wedging effect.

Fig. 23. Half-section of cutter-head for comparatively large holes having means for adjusting the tools.

Fig. 24. Cutters for boring and facing, which are adjusted by conical-pointed screw *C* and held by bolts *B*, the heads of which enter grooves *D*.

Fig. 25. Half-section of boring head, the tools of which are inserted in slots or grooves in the face of the disk and are held by slotted clamping posts *B*.

Boring-bar Cutters — 4

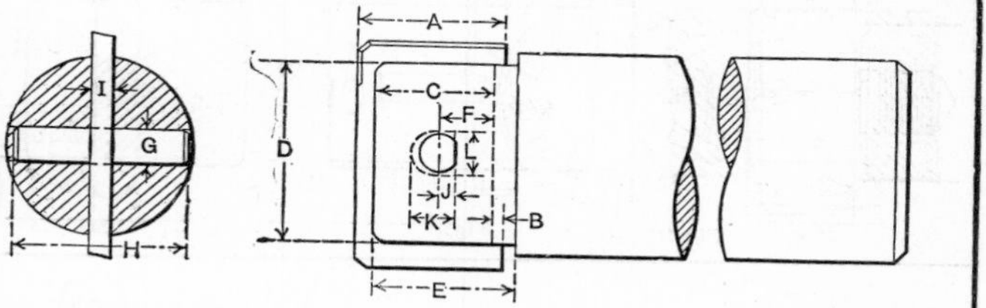

Diam. of Bar	*A*	*B*	*C*	*D*	*E*	*F*	*G*	*H*	*I*	*J*	*K*	*L*
3	1 7/8	1/16	1 5/8	2 7/8	1 3/4	3/4	9/16	2 3/4	1/2	1/8	5/8	19/32
2 3/4	1 3/4	1/16	1 1/2	2 5/8	1 5/8	11/16	1/2	2 1/2	7/16	1/8	9/16	17/32
2 1/2	1 5/8	1/16	1 3/8	2 3/8	1 1/2	11/16	1/2	2 1/4	3/8	1/8	9/16	17/32
2 1/4	1 1/2	1/16	1 1/4	2 1/8	1 3/8	5/8	7/16	2	3/8	1/8	1/2	15/32
2	1 1/2	1/16	1 1/4	1 7/8	1 3/8	5/8	7/16	1 7/8	3/8	1/8	1/2	15/32
1 3/4	1 3/8	1/16	1 1/8	1 5/8	1 1/4	9/16	3/8	1 5/8	5/16	3/32	7/16	13/32
1 1/2	1 1/4	1/16	1 1/8	1 3/8	1 1/4	9/16	5/16	1 3/8	5/16	3/32	3/8	11/32
1 3/8	1 1/4	1/16	1 1/16	1 5/16	1 3/16	17/32	5/16	1 1/4	1/4	3/32	3/8	11/32
1 1/4	1 1/8	1/16	15/16	1 3/16	1 1/16	15/32	1/4	1 1/8	1/4	3/32	5/16	9/32
1 1/8	1	1/16	13/16	1 1/16	15/16	13/32	1/4	1	1/4	3/32	5/16	9/32
1	7/8	1/16	11/16	15/16	13/16	11/32	1/4	7/8	1/4	3/32	5/16	9/32

The bars and cutters listed above are for machining "blind" holes. The cutters are held in position by hardened parallel pins having flats tapering 3/8 inch per foot. A hole is drilled in the cutter, a little larger in diameter than the pin, and one side is squared and tapered to correspond with the taper of the pin.

Types of Boring Bars

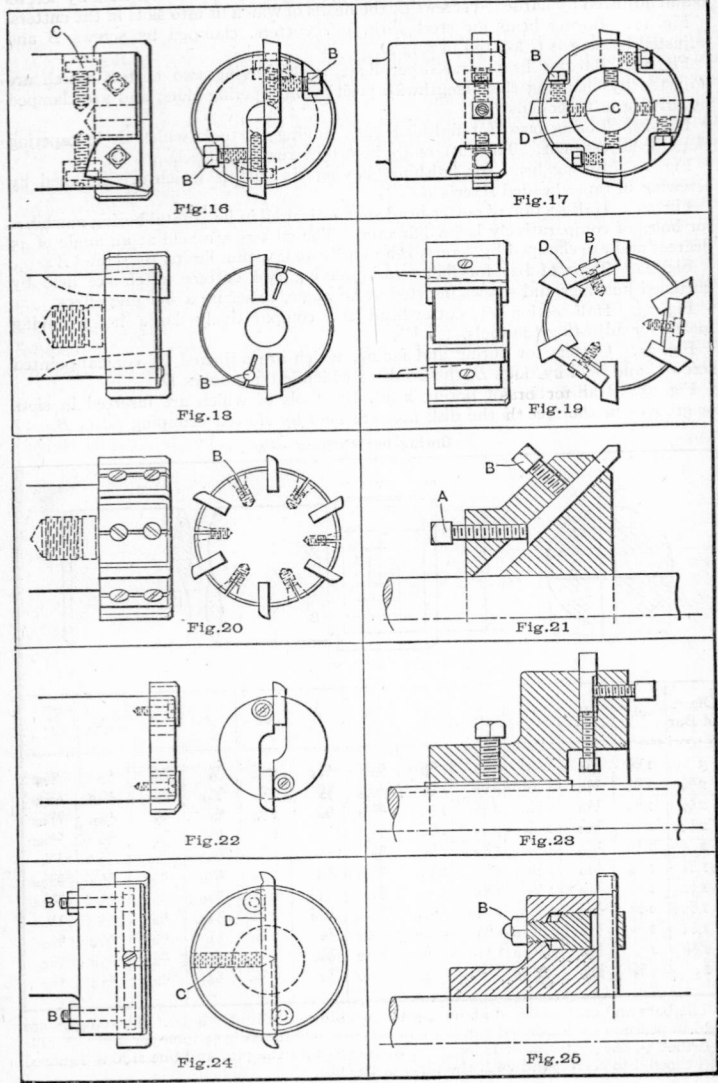

Fig.16

Fig.17

Fig.18

Fig.19

Fig.20

Fig.21

Fig.22

Fig.23

Fig.24

Fig.25

STANDARD TOOL SHANKS AND TOOL-POSTS

This American standard includes the preferred sizes of tool bits, tool shanks and tool-holders, and specifies important dimensions. Fig. 1 shows the single-screw tool-post used on most small lathes, and Fig. 2 illustrates a design for shapers and some light planers. A *tool-post ring collar* (Fig. 1) has a spherical seat and *rocker base* for supporting the tool and providing simple means of adjusting the height of the tool point. Shims may also be used for this purpose; or the ring collar may have diametrically spaced steps on the upper face to provide for adjustment.

Serrated wedges are sometimes used with square tool-posts on screw machines or with open-side tool-posts for obtaining vertical adjustment. An *adjustable collar and nut* fitted about the base of a round tool-post is sometimes used on screw machines. The *open-side tool-post* for lathes (Fig. 3) may have either a rocker base or a flat tool baseplate. The *four-way turret tool-post* (Fig. 4) used on manufacturing lathes, turret lathes and vertical boring mills is an indexing open-side type with either fixed base or rocker. The *strap-and-stud clamp type* of tool-holder (Fig. 5) is generally used on large lathes, boring mills, shapers, slotters, and planers. The studs in the case of a planer are attached (threaded or recessed) to the clapper (Fig. 6) or in sliding T-nuts (Fig. 5) and pass through the serrated tool baseplate against which the tool bears.

Table 1. Dimensions of Tool Shanks, Tool-Post Openings, and Lathe Center Height

Shank Section Figs. 1, 2, 4, and 5			Lathe Tool-Post Opening Figs. 1, 3, 4, and 5		
Max. *w*	Nominal *w* × *h*	Max. *h*	Min. *B*	Nominal *B* × *D*	Min. *D*
0.40	* 3/8 × 3/4	0.85	0.49	1/2 × 1 3/8	1.27
0.48	7/16 × 7/8	0.99	0.57	9/16 × 1 1/2	1.48
0.56	* 1/2 × 1	1.15	0.68	11/16 × 1 3/4	1.72
0.67	* 5/8 × 1 1/4	1.34	0.81	3/16 × 2	2.00
0.80	* 3/4 × 1 1/2	1.56	0.96	1 × 2 3/8	2.34
0.95	† 7/8 × 1 3/4	1.81	1.14	1 3/16 × 2 3/4	2.71
1.13	*1 × 2	2.11	1.35	1 3/8 × 3 1/8	3.16
1.34	†1 1/4 × 2 1/4	2.43	1.61	1 5/8 × 3 11/16	3.65
1.60	†1 1/2 × 2 3/4	2.86	1.91	1 7/8 × 4 1/4	4.29
Planer and Shaper Tool-Post Opening Figs. 1, 2, and 5			**Lathe Center Height Figs. 1 and 3**		
Min. *B*	Nominal *B* × *E*	Min. *E*	Max. *C*	Nominal *C*	Min. *C*
0.49	1/2 × 1 1/16	1.04	0.93	7/8	0.85
0.57	9/16 × 1 1/4	1.19	1.09	1	0.99
0.68	11/16 × 1 7/16	1.38	1.26	1 3/16	1.15
0.81	13/16 × 1 5/8	1.61	1.47	1 3/8	1.34
0.96	1 × 1 7/8	1.87	1.72	1 9/16	1.56
1.14	1 3/16 × 2 3/16	2.17	1.99	1 13/16	1.81
1.35	1 3/8 × 2 9/16	2.53	2.32	2 1/8	2.11
1.61	1 5/8 × 3	2.92	2.67	2 7/16	2.43
1.91	1 7/8 × 3 7/16	3.43	3.15	2 7/8	2.86

All dimensions are given in inches. * Size listed in Table 3. † Size listed in Table 4.

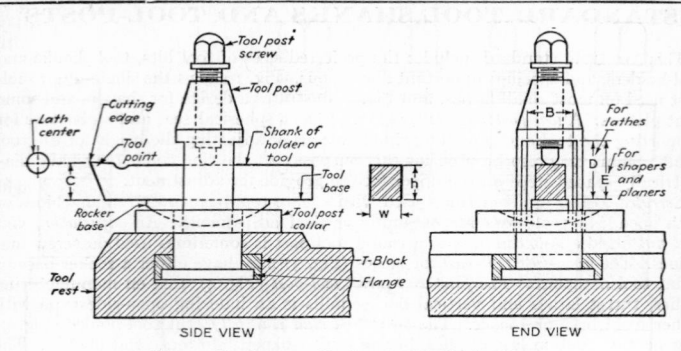

Fig. 1.   Single-screw Tool-post with Rocker Base

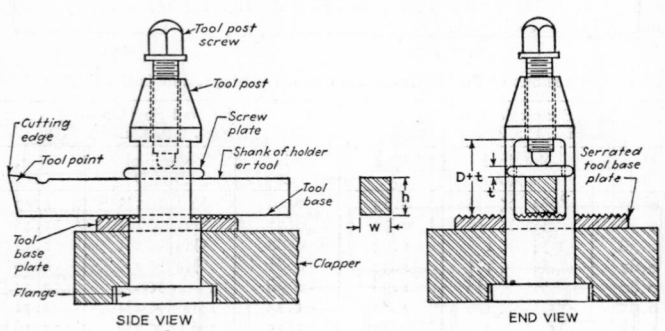

Fig. 2.   Single-screw Tool-post with Screw Plate and Serrated Base

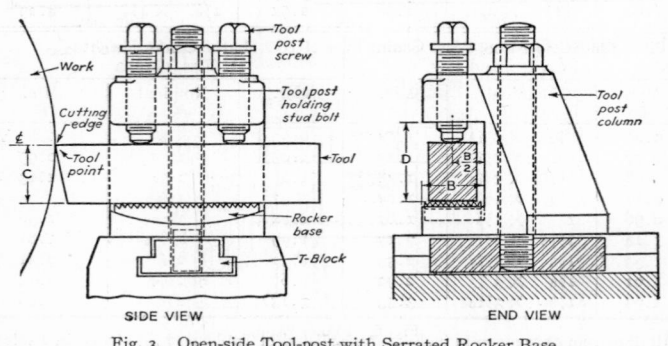

Fig. 3.   Open-side Tool-post with Serrated Rocker Base

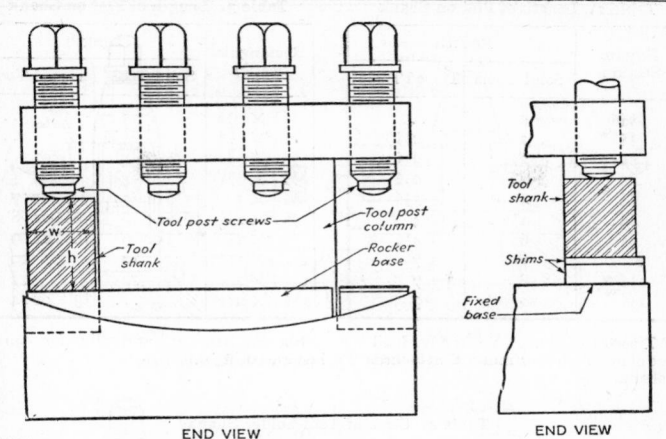

END VIEW   END VIEW

Fig. 4.   Four-way Open-side Tool-post

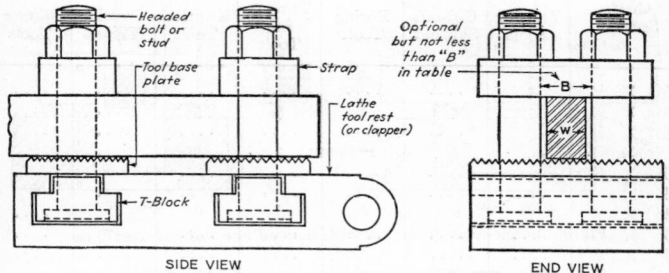

SIDE VIEW   END VIEW

Fig. 5.   Strap-and-stud Clamp Type of Tool-holder with Serrated Base

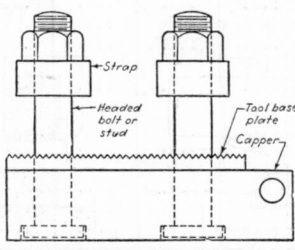

Fig. 6.   Planer Studs

Table 2. Length of Flat on Shank

Square Section	Length	
	Solid Tools	Tipped Tools*
3/16	2	....
1/4	2½	2¼
5/16	2½	2¼
3/8	3	2½
1/2	4	3½
5/8	4½	4
3/4	6	4½
1	7	7
1¼	8	7
1½	10	9

* Tipped tools have a relatively small piece of metal-cutting material attached to shank.

Table 3. Length of Flat on Shank

Rectangular Section	Length	
	Solid Tools	Tipped Tools
¼ × ½	4	...
5/16 × 5/8	4½	...
3/8 × 3/4	5	...
½ × ¾	5¼	5¼
½ × 1	†5½ or 7	†5½ or 7
5/8 × 1¼	†6½ or 8	†6½ or 8
¾ × 1½	†6½ or 9	†6½ or 9
1 × 1½	10	10
1 × 2	12	12
1½ × 2	...	†9 or 14

† Shorter lengths normally for turret lathes, boring mills, etc.

Table 4. Sizes of Tool-holder Shanks

Shank Cross Section	Length of Shank						
	Turning Tools	Cut-off, Side-cut	Boring Tools	Threading Tools	Knurling Tools	Carbide Tipped	Planer Tools
5/16 × ½	4	....	....	....	....	....	....
5/16 × ¾	4½	4½	*	5	5	....	....
5/16 × 7/8	5	....	....	....	....	....	....
3/8 × 7/8	....	5	*	5	5	....	....
3/8 × 15/16	....	....	....	....	....	6	....
½ × 1	....	....	....	....	....	....	6
½ × 1⅛	5	6	*	6	6	....	....
½ × 1¼	....	....	....	....	....	7	....
5/8 × 1¼	....	....	....	....	....	....	8½
5/8 × 1⅜	7	7	*	7	7	....	....
5/8 × 1½	....	....	....	....	....	8	....
¾ × 1½	....	....	....	....	....	....	10
¾ × 1⅝	8	8	*	....	....	....	....
¾ × 1¾	....	....	....	....	....	9	....
7/8 × 1¾	9	9	*	....	9	....	....
7/8 × 1⅞	....	....	....	....	....	10	....
1 × 2	11	....	*	....	....	....	....
1 × 2⅛	....	....	....	....	....	12	....
1⅛ × 1¾	....	....	....	....	....	....	13
1¼ × 2¼	13	....	....	....	....	....	....
1⅜ × 2	....	....	....	....	....	....	16
1⅞ × 2¼	....	....	....	....	....	....	19
2⅛ × 2¾	....	....	....	....	....	....	22

* Asterisks (*) indicate cross sections of shanks for boring tools. Lengths not specified.

Forming Tools

When curved surfaces or those of stepped, angular or irregular shape are required in connection with turning operations, especially on turret lathes and "automatics", forming tools are used. These tools are so made that the contour of the cutting edge corresponds to the shape required and usually they may be ground repeatedly without changing the shape of the cutting edge. There are two general classes of forming tools — the straight type and the circular type. The circular forming tool is generally used on small narrow forms, whereas the straight type is more suitable for wide forming operations. Some straight forming tools are clamped in a horizontal position upon the cut-off slide, whereas others are held in a vertical position in a special holder. A common form of holder for these vertical tools is one having a dovetail slot in which the forming tool is clamped; hence they are often called "dovetail forming tools." In many cases, two forming tools are used, especially when a very smooth surface is required, one being employed for roughing and the other for finishing.

There is an American standard for forming tool blanks. This standard (to be presented later in this section) covers both straight or dovetailed and the circular forms. Dimensions of the finished blanks are given excepting, of course, the formed part which must be shaped to suit whatever job the tool is to be used for. The American standard includes the important dimensions of holders for both straight and circular tools.

Dimensions of Steps on Straight or Dovetail Forming Tools. — The diagrams at the top of the accompanying table, illustrate a straight or "dovetail" forming tool. The upper or cutting face lies in the same plane as the center of the work and there is no rake. (Many forming tools have rake to increase the cutting efficiency and this type will be referred to later.) In making a forming tool, the various steps measured perpendicular to the front face (as at d) must be proportioned so as to obtain the required radial dimensions on the work. For example, if D equals the difference between two radial dimensions on the work, then

$$\text{Step } d = D \times \text{cosine front clearance angle}$$

Angles on Straight Forming Tools. — In making forming tools to the required shape or contour, any angular surfaces (like the steps referred to in the previous paragraph) are affected by the clearance angle. For example, assume that angle A on the work (see diagram at top of accompanying table) is 20 degrees. The angle on the tool in plane x-x, in that case, will be slightly less than 20 degrees. In making the tool, this modified or reduced angle is required because of the convenience in machining and measuring the angle square to the front face of the tool or in the plane x-x.

If the angle on the work is measured from a line parallel to the axis (as at A in diagram), then the reduced angle on the tool as measured square to the front face (or in plane x-x) is found as follows:

$$\tan \text{ reduced angle on tool} = \tan A \times \cos \text{ front clearance angle}.$$

If angle A on the work is larger than, say, 45 degrees, it may be given on the drawing as indicated at B. In this case, the angle is measured from a plane perpendicular to the axis of the work. When the angle is so specified, the angle on the tool in plane x-x may be found as follows:

$$\tan \text{ reduced angle on tool} = \frac{\tan B}{\cos \text{ clearance angle}}$$

Dimensions of Steps and Angles on Straight Forming Tools.

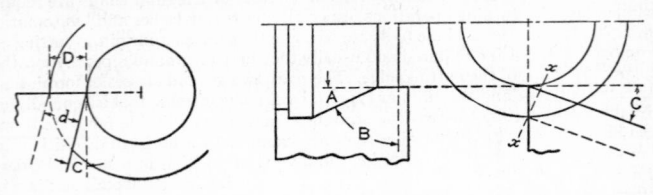

Upper section of table gives depth d of step on forming tool for a given dimension D which equals the actual depth of the step on the work, measured radially and along the cutting face of the tool (See diagram at left). First, locate depth D required on work; then find depth d on tool under tool clearance angle C. Depth d is measured perpendicular to front face of tool.

Radial Depth of Step D	Depth d of step on tool			Radial Depth of Step D	Depth d of step on tool		
	When $C = 10°$	When $C = 15°$	When $C = 20°$		When $C = 10°$	When $C = 15°$	When $C = 20°$
0.001	0.00098	0.00096	0.00094	0.040	0.03939	0.03863	0.03758
0.002	0.00197	0.00193	0.00187	0.050	0.04924	0.04829	0.04698
0.003	0.00295	0.00289	0.00281	0.060	0.05908	0.05795	0.05638
0.004	0.00393	0.00386	0.00375	0.070	0.06893	0.06761	0.06577
0.005	0.00492	0.00483	0.00469	0.080	0.07878	0.07727	0.07517
0.006	0.00590	0.00579	0.00563	0.090	0.08863	0.08693	0.08457
0.007	0.00689	0.00676	0.00657	0.100	0.09848	0.09659	0.09396
0.008	0.00787	0.00772	0.00751	0.200	0.19696	0.19318	0.18793
0.009	0.00886	0.00869	0.00845	0.300	0.29544	0.28977	0.28190
0.010	0.00984	0.00965	0.00939	0.400	0.39392	0.38637	0.37587
0.020	0.01969	0.01931	0.01879	0.500	0.49240	0.48296	0.46984
0.030	0.02954	0.02897	0.02819	....	....	....	....

Section of table below gives angles as measured in plane x-x perpendicular to front face of forming tool (See diagram on right). Find in first column the angle A required on work; then find reduced angle in plane x-x under given clearance angle C.

Angle A in Plane of Tool Cutting Face	Angle on tool in plane x-x			Angle A in Plane of Tool Cutting Face	Angle on tool in plane x-x		
	When $C = 10°$	When $C = 15°$	When $C = 20°$		When $C = 10°$	When $C = 15°$	When $C = 20°$
5°	4° 55'	4° 50'	4° 42'	50°	49° 34'	49° 1'	48° 14'
10	9 51	9 40	9 24	55	54 35	54 4	53 18
15	14 47	14 31	14 8	60	59 37	59 8	58 26
20	19 43	19 22	18 53	65	64 40	64 14	63 36
25	24 40	24 15	23 40	70	69 43	69 21	68 50
30	29 37	29 9	28 29	75	74 47	74 30	74 5
35	34 35	34 4	33 20	80	79 51	79 39	79 22
40	39 34	39 1	38 15	85	84 55	84 49	84 41
45	44 34	44 0	43 13	....	....	....	....

Table Giving Step Dimensions and Angles on Straight or Dovetailed Forming Tools. — The accompanying table "Dimensions of Steps and Angles on Straight Forming Tools" gives the required dimensions and angles within its range, direct or without calculation.

To Find Dimension of Step: The upper section of the table is used in determining the dimensions of steps. The radial depth of the step or the actual cutting depth D (see left-hand diagram) is given in the first column of the table. The columns which follow give the corresponding depths d for a front clearance angle of either 10, 15 or 20 degrees. To illustrate the use of the table, suppose a tool is required for turning the part shown in Fig. 1 which has diameters of 0.75, 1.25 and 1.75 inch, respectively. The difference between the largest and the smallest radius is 0.5 inch, which is the depth of one step. Assume that the clearance angle is 15 degrees. First, locate 0.5 in the column headed "Radial Depth of Step D"; then find depth d in the column headed "when $C = 15°$." As will be seen, this depth is 0.48296 inch. Prac-

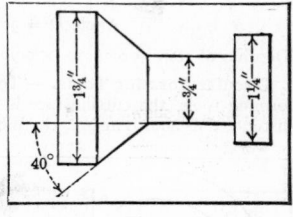

Fig. 1

tically the same procedure is followed in determining the depth of the second step on the tool. The difference in the radii in this case equals 0.25. Since this value is not given directly in the table, we first find the depth equivalent to 0.200 and then add to it the depth equivalent to 0.050. Thus, we have in this case 0.19138 + 0.04829 = 0.24147. In using this table, it is assumed that the top face of the tool is set at the height of the axis of the work.

To Find Angle: The lower section of the table applies to angles when they are measured relative to the axis of the work. The application of the table will again be illustrated by using the part shown in Fig. 1. The angle in this case is 40 degrees (which is also the angle in the plane of the cutting face of the tool). If the clearance angle is 15 degrees, then the angle measured in plane x-x square to the face of the tool is shown by the table to be 39° 1′ — a reduction of practically one degree.

Straight Forming Tools With Rake. — If a straight forming tool has rake, the depth x of each step (see Fig. 2), measured perpendicular to the front or clearance face, is affected not only by the clearance angle but by the rake angle F and the radii R and r of the steps on the work. First it is necessary to find three angles. These angles, which will be designated as A, B and C, are not shown on the drawing.

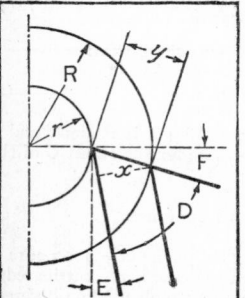

Fig. 2

Angle $A = 180°$ − rake angle F; $\sin B = \dfrac{r \sin A}{R}$;

angle $C = 180° - (A + B)$

$y = \dfrac{R \sin C}{\sin A}$; angle D of tool $= 90° - (E + F)$;

depth $x = y \sin D$

If the work has two or more shoulders, the depth x for other steps on the tool may be determined for each radius r. If the work has curved or angular forms, it is more practical to use a tool without rake because its profile, in the plane of the cutting face, duplicates that of the work.

Example: Assume that radius R equals 0.625 and radius r equals 0.375 inch so that the step on the work has a radial depth of 0.25 inch. The tool has a rake angle F of 10 degrees and a clearance angle E of 15 degrees. Then angle $A = 180 - 10 = 170$ degrees.

$$\sin B = \frac{0.375 \times 0.17365}{0.625} = 0.10419$$

Angle $B = 5° \; 59'$ nearly.   Angle $C = 180 - (170° + 5° \; 59') = 4° \; 1'$

$$\text{Dimension } y = \frac{0.625 \times 0.07005}{0.17365} = 0.25212$$

Angle $D = 90° - (15 + 10) = 65$ degrees.

Depth x of step $= 0.25212 \times 0.90631 = 0.2285$ inch.

Circular Forming Tools. — To provide sufficient periphery clearance on circular forming tools, the cutting face is off-set with relation to the center of the tool a distance C as shown in Fig. 3. Whenever a circular tool has two or more diameters,

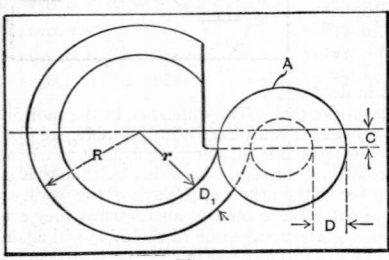

the difference in the radii of the steps on the tool will, therefore, not correspond exactly to the difference in the steps on the work. The form produced with the tool also changes, although the change is very slight, unless the amount of off-set C is considerable. Assume that a circular tool is required to produce the piece A having two diameters as shown. If the difference D_1 between the large and small radii of the tool were made equal to dimension D required on the work, D

Fig. 3

would be a certain amount over-size, depending upon the off-set C of the cutting edge. The following formulas can be used to determine the radii of circular forming tools for turning parts to different diameters:

Let R = largest radius of tool in inches; D = difference in radii of steps on work; C = amount cutting edge is off-set from center of tool; r = required radius in inches; then:

$$r = \sqrt{\left(\sqrt{R^2 - C^2} - D\right)^2 + C^2}. \tag{1}$$

If the small radius r is given and the large radius R is required, then:

$$R = \sqrt{\left(\sqrt{r^2 - C^2} + D\right)^2 + C^2}. \tag{2}$$

To illustrate, if D (Fig. 3) is to be ⅛ inch, the large radius R is 1⅛ inch, and C is ⁵⁄₃₂ inch, what radius r would be required to compensate for the off-set C of the cutting edge? Inserting these values in Formula (1):

$$r = \sqrt{\left(\sqrt{\left(1\tfrac{1}{8}\right)^2 - \left(\tfrac{5}{32}\right)^2} - \tfrac{1}{8}\right)^2 + \left(\tfrac{5}{32}\right)^2} = 1.0014 \text{ inch.}$$

The value of r is thus found to be 1.0014 inch; hence the diameter $= 2 \times 1.0014 = 2.0028$ inches instead of 2 inches, as would have been the case if the cutting edge had been exactly on the center-line. Formulas for circular tools used on different makes of screw machines can be simplified when the values R and C are constant for each size of machine. The accompanying table "Formulas for Circular Form-

Formulas for Circular Forming Tools
(For notation, see Fig. 3)

Make of Machine	Size of Machine	Radius R, Inches	Offset C, Inches	Radius r, Incnes
Brown & Sharpe	No. oo	0.875	0.125	$r = \sqrt{(0.8660 - D)^2 + 0.0156}$
	No. o	1.125	0.15625	$r = \sqrt{(1.1141 - D)^2 + 0.0244}$
	No. 2	1.50	0.250	$r = \sqrt{(1.4790 - D)^2 + 0.0625}$
	No. 6	2.00	0.3125	$r = \sqrt{(1.975 - D)^2 + 0.0976}$
Acme	No. 51	0.75	0.09375	$r = \sqrt{(0.7441 - D)^2 + 0.0088}$
	No. 515	0.75	0.09375	$r = \sqrt{(0.7441 - D)^2 + 0.0088}$
	No. 52	1.0	0.09375	$r = \sqrt{(0.9956 - D)^2 + 0.0088}$
	No. 53	1.1875	0.125	$r = \sqrt{(1.1809 - D)^2 + 0.0156}$
	No. 54	1.250	0.15625	$r = \sqrt{(1.2402 - D)^2 + 0.0244}$
	No. 55	1.250	0.15625	$r = \sqrt{(1.2402 - D)^2 + 0.0244}$
	No. 56	1.50	0.1875	$r = \sqrt{(1.4882 - D)^2 + 0.0352}$
Cleveland	¼″	0.625	0.03125	$r = \sqrt{(0.6242 - D)^2 + 0.0010}$
	⅜″	0.84375	0.0625	$r = \sqrt{(0.8414 - D)^2 + 0.0039}$
	⅝″	1.15625	0.0625	$r = \sqrt{(1.1546 - D)^2 + 0.0039}$
	⅞″	1.1875	0.0625	$r = \sqrt{(1.1859 - D)^2 + 0.0039}$
	1¼″	1.375	0.0625	$r = \sqrt{(1.3736 - D)^2 + 0.0039}$
	2″	1.375	0.0625	$r = \sqrt{(1.3736 - D)^2 + 0.0039}$
	2¼″	1.625	0.125	$r = \sqrt{(1.6202 - D)^2 + 0.0156}$
	2¾″	1.875	0.15625	$r = \sqrt{(1.8685 - D)^2 + 0.0244}$
	3¼″	1.875	0.15625	$r = \sqrt{(1.8685 - D)^2 + 0.0244}$
	4¼″	2.50	0.250	$r = \sqrt{(2.4875 - D)^2 + 0.0625}$
	6″	2.625	0.250	$r = \sqrt{(2.6131 - D)^2 + 0.0625}$

ing Tools" gives the standard values of R and C for circular tools used on different automatics. The formulas for determining the radius r (see column at right-hand side of table) contain a constant which represents the value of the expression $\sqrt{R^2 - C^2}$ in formula (1) on page **1340**.

The table "Constants for Determining Diameters of Circular Forming Tools" has been compiled to facilitate proportioning tools of this type. It gives constants for computing the various diameters of forming tools, when the cutting face of the tool is either ⅛, 3/16, ¼ or 5/16 inch below the horizontal center-line. As there is no standard distance for the location of the cutting face, the table has been prepared to correspond with distances commonly used. As an example, suppose the tool is required for a part having three diameters of 1.75, 0.75 and 1.25 inch, respectively, as shown in Fig. 1, and that the largest diameter of the tool is 3 inches and its cutting face is ¼ inch below the horizontal center-line. The first step would be to determine approximately the respective diameters of the forming tool and then correct these diameters by the use of the table. To produce the three diameters shown in Fig. 1, with a 3-inch forming tool, the tool diameters would be approximately 2, 3 and 2.5 inches, respectively. The first dimension (2 inches) is 1 inch less in diameter than that of the tool, and the necessary correction should be given in the column "Correction for Difference in Diameter"; but as the table is only extended to half-inch differences, it will be necessary to obtain this particular correction in two steps. On the line for 3-inch diameter and under corrections for ½ inch, we find 0.0085; then in line with 2½ and under the same heading, we find 0.0129; hence the total correction would be $0.0085 + 0.0129 = 0.0214$ inch. This correction is added to the approximate diameter, making the exact diameter of the first step $2 + 0.0214 = 2.0214$ inches. The next step would be computed in the same way, by noting on the 3-inch line the correction for ½ inch and adding it to the approximate diameter of the second step, giving an exact diameter of $2.5 + 0.0085 = 2.5085$ inches. Therefore, to produce the part shown in Fig. 1, the tool should have three steps of 3, 2.0214 and 2.5085 inches, respectively, provided the cutting face is ¼ inch below the center. All diameters are computed in this way, from the largest diameter of the tool.

The tables "Corrected Diameters of Circular Forming Tools" are especially applicable to tools used on Brown & Sharpe automatic screw machines. Directions for using these tables are given at the end of Table 4.

Circular Tools Having Top Rake. — Circular forming tools without top rake are satisfactory for brass, but tools for steel or other tough metals cut better when there is a rake angle of 10 or 12 degrees. For such tools the small radius r (see Fig. 3) for an outside radius R may be found by the formula:

$$r = \sqrt{P^2 + R^2 - 2\,PR\cos\theta}$$

To find the value of P proceed as follows: $\sin\phi$ = small rad. on work × sin rake angle ÷ large rad. on work. Angle β = rake angle $- \phi$. P = large rad. on work × $\sin\beta$ ÷ sin rake angle. Angle θ = rake angle $+ \delta$. $\sin\delta$ = vertical height C from center of tool to center of work ÷ R. It is assumed that the point of tool is to be set at same height as the work center.

Dimensions for Circular Cut-off Tools

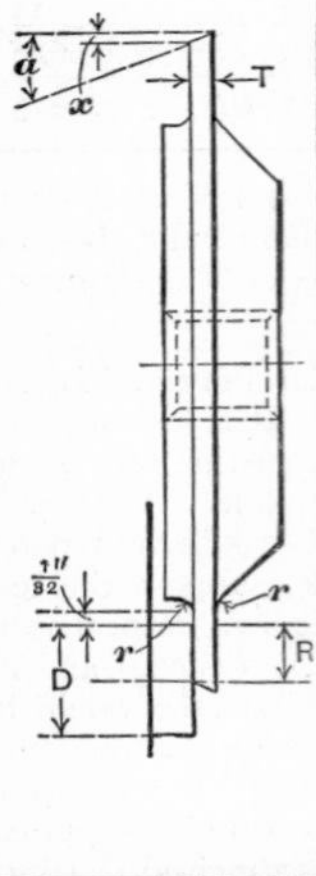

Diam. of Stock	Soft Brass, Copper a = 23 Deg.		Norway Iron, Machine Steel a = 15 Deg.		Drill Rod, Tool Steel a = 12 Deg.	
	T	x	T	x	T	x
1/16	0.031	0.013	0.039	0.010	0.043	0.009
⅛	0.044	0.019	0.055	0.015	0.062	0.013
3/16	0.052	0.022	0.068	0.018	0.076	0.016
¼	0.062	0.026	0.078	0.021	0.088	0.019
5/16	0.069	0.029	0.087	0.023	0.098	0.021
⅜	0.076	0.032	0.095	0.025	0.107	0.023
7/16	0.082	0.035	0.103	0.028	0.116	0.025
½	0.088	0.037	0.110	0.029	0.124	0.026
9/16	0.093	0.039	0.117	0.031	0.131	0.028
⅝	0.098	0.042	0.123	0.033	0.137	0.029
11/16	0.103	0.044	0.129	0.035	0.145	0.031
¾	0.107	0.045	0.134	0.036	0.152	0.032
13/16	0.112	0.047	0.141	0.038	0.158	0.033
⅞	0.116	0.049	0.146	0.039	0.164	0.035
15/16	0.120	0.051	0.151	0.040	0.170	0.036
1	0.124	0.053	0.156	0.042	0.175	0.037

The length of the blade equals radius of stock $R + x + r$ + 1/32 inch (for notation see illustration above); r = 1/16 inch for ⅜- to ¾-inch stock, and 3/32 inch for ¾- to 1-inch stock.

Constants for Determining Diameters of Circular Forming Tools

Diam. of Tool	Radius of Tool	Cutting Face 1/8 Inch Below Center			Cutting Face 3/16 Inch Below Center			Cutting Face 1/4 Inch Below Center			Cutting Face 5/16 Inch Below Center		
		Correction for 1/8 Inch Difference in Diam.	Correction for 1/4 Inch Difference in Diam.	Correction for 1/2 Inch Difference in Diam.	Correction for 1/8 Inch Difference in Diam.	Correction for 1/4 Inch Difference in Diam.	Correction for 1/2 Inch Difference in Diam.	Correction for 1/8 Inch Difference in Diam.	Correction for 1/4 Inch Difference in Diam.	Correction for 1/2 Inch Difference in Diam.	Correction for 1/8 Inch Difference in Diam.	Correction for 1/4 Inch Difference in Diam.	Correction for 1/2 Inch Difference in Diam.
1	0.500	....	....	....	....	....	....	....	....	....	....	....	....
1⅛	0.5625	0.0036	0.0065	....	0.0086	0.0154	....	0.0167	0.0296	....	0.0298	0.0519	....
1¼	0.625	0.0028	....	....	0.0067	....	....	0.0128	....	....	0.0221	....	....
1⅜	0.6875	0.0023	0.0042	0.0107	0.0054	0.0099	0.0253	0.0102	0.0185	0.0481	0.0172	0.0310	0.0829
1½	0.750	0.0019	....	....	0.0045	....	....	0.0083	....	....	0.0138	....	....
1⅝	0.8125	0.0016	0.0030	....	0.0037	0.0069	....	0.0069	0.0128	....	0.0114	0.0210	....
1¾	0.875	0.0014	....	....	0.0032	....	....	0.0058	....	....	0.0095	....	....
1⅞	0.9375	0.0012	0.0022	0.0052	0.0027	0.0051	0.0121	0.0050	0.0094	0.0223	0.0081	0.0152	0.0362
2	1.000	0.0010	....	....	0.0024	....	....	0.0044	....	....	0.0070	....	....
2⅛	1.0625	0.0009	0.0017	....	0.0021	0.0040	....	0.0038	0.0072	....	0.0061	0.0116	....
2¼	1.125	0.0008	....	....	0.0018	....	....	0.0034	....	....	0.0054	....	....
2⅜	1.1875	0.0007	0.0014	0.0031	0.0016	0.0031	0.0071	0.0029	0.0057	0.0129	0.0048	0.0092	0.0208
2½	1.250	0.0006	....	....	0.0015	....	....	0.0027	....	....	0.0043	....	....
2⅝	1.3125	0.0006	0.0011	....	0.0013	0.0026	....	0.0024	0.0046	....	0.0038	0.0073	....
2¾	1.375	0.0005	....	....	0.0012	....	....	0.0022	....	....	0.0035	....	....
2⅞	1.4375	0.0005	0.0009	0.0021	0.0011	0.0021	0.0047	0.0020	0.0038	0.0085	0.0032	0.0061	0.0135
3	1.500	0.0004	....	....	0.0010	....	....	0.0018	....	....	0.0029	....	....
3⅛	1.5625	0.0004	0.0008	....	0.0009	0.0018	....	0.0017	0.0032	....	0.0027	0.0051	....
3¼	1.625	0.0003	....	....	0.0008	....	....	0.0015	....	....	0.0024	....	....
3⅜	1.6875	0.0003	0.0007	0.0015	0.0008	0.0015	0.0033	0.0014	0.0028	0.0060	0.0023	0.0044	0.0095
3½	1.750	0.0003	....	....	0.0007	....	....	0.0013	....	....	0.0021	....	....
3⅝	1.8125	0.0003	0.0006	....	0.0007	0.0013	....	0.0012	0.0024	....	0.0019	0.0038	....
3¾	1.875	0.0002	....	....	0.0006	....	....	0.0011	....	....	0.0018	....	....

Corrected Diameters of Circular Forming Tools — 1

Length *c* on Tool	Number of B. & S. Automatic Screw Machine			Length *c* on Tool	Number of B. & S. Automatic Screw Machine		
	No. 00	No. 0	No. 2		No. 00	No. 0	No. 2
0.001	1.7480	2.2480	2.9980	0.058	1.6353	2.1352	2.8857
0.002	1.7460	2.2460	2.9961	0.059	1.6333	2.1332	2.8837
0.003	1.7441	2.2441	2.9941	0.060	1.6313	2.1312	2.8818
0.004	1.7421	2.2421	2.9921	0.061	1.6294	2.1293	2.8798
0.005	1.7401	2.2401	2.9901	0.062	1.6274	2.1273	2.8778
0.006	1.7381	2.2381	2.9882	1/16	1.6264	2.1263	2.8768
0.007	1.7362	2.2361	2.9862	0.063	1.6254	2.1253	2.8759
0.008	1.7342	2.2341	2.9842	0.064	1.6234	2.1233	2.8739
0.009	1.7322	2.2321	2.9823	0.065	1.6215	2.1213	2.8719
0.010	1.7302	2.2302	2.9803	0.066	1.6195	2.1194	2.8699
0.011	1.7282	2.2282	2.9783	0.067	1.6175	2.1174	2.8680
0.012	1.7263	2.2262	2.9763	0.068	1.6155	2.1154	2.8660
0.013	1.7243	2.2243	2.9744	0.069	1.6136	2.1134	2.8640
0.014	1.7223	2.2222	2.9724	0.070	1.6116	2.1115	2.8621
0.015	1.7203	2.2203	2.9704	0.071	1.6096	2.1095	2.8601
1/64	1.7191	2.2191	2.9692	0.072	1.6076	2.1075	2.8581
0.016	1.7184	2.2183	2.9685	0.073	1.6057	2.1055	2.8561
0.017	1.7164	2.2163	2.9665	0.074	1.6037	2.1035	2.8542
0.018	1.7144	2.2143	2.9645	0.075	1.6017	2.1016	2.8522
0.019	1.7124	2.2123	2.9625	0.076	1.5997	2.0996	2.8503
0.020	1.7104	2.2104	2.9606	0.077	1.5978	2.0976	2.8483
0.021	1.7085	2.2084	2.9586	0.078	1.5958	2.0956	2.8463
0.022	1.7065	2.2064	2.9566	5/64	1.5955	2.0954	2.8461
0.023	1.7045	2.2045	2.9547	0.079	1.5938	2.0937	2.8443
0.024	1.7025	2.2025	2.9527	0.080	1.5918	2.0917	2.8424
0.025	1.7005	2.2005	2.9507	0.081	1.5899	2.0897	2.8404
0.026	1.6986	2.1985	2.9488	0.082	1.5879	2.0877	2.8384
0.027	1.6966	2.1965	2.9468	0.083	1.5859	2.0857	2.8365
0.028	1.6946	2.1945	2.9448	0.084	1.5839	2.0838	2.8345
0.029	1.6926	2.1925	2.9428	0.085	1.5820	2.0818	2.8325
0.030	1.6907	2.1906	2.9409	0.086	1.5800	2.0798	2.8306
0.031	1.6887	2.1886	2.9389	0.087	1.5780	2.0778	2.8286
1/32	1.6882	2.1881	2.9384	0.088	1.5760	2.0759	2.8266
0.032	1.6867	2.1866	2.9369	0.089	1.5740	2.0739	2.8247
0.033	1.6847	2.1847	2.9350	0.090	1.5721	2.0719	2.8227
0.034	1.6827	2.1827	2.9330	0.091	1.5701	2.0699	2.8207
0.035	1.6808	2.1807	2.9310	0.092	1.5681	2.0679	2.8187
0.036	1.6788	2.1787	2.9290	0.093	1.5661	2.0660	2.8168
0.037	1.6768	2.1767	2.9271	3/32	1.5647	2.0645	2.8153
0.038	1.6748	2.1747	2.9251	0.094	1.5642	2.0640	2.8148
0.039	1.6729	2.1727	2.9231	0.095	1.5622	2.0620	2.8128
0.040	1.6709	2.1708	2.9211	0.096	1.5602	2.0600	2.8109
0.041	1.6689	2.1688	2.9192	0.097	1.5582	2.0581	2.8089
0.042	1.6669	2.1668	2.9172	0.098	1.5563	2.0561	2.8069
0.043	1.6649	2.1649	2.9152	0.099	1.5543	2.0541	2.8050
0.044	1.6630	2.1629	2.9133	0.100	1.5523	2.0521	2.8030
0.045	1.6610	2.1609	2.9113	0.101	1.5503	2.0502	2.8010
0.046	1.6590	2.1589	2.9093	0.102	1.5484	2.0482	2.7991
3/64	1.6573	2.1572	2.9076	0.103	1.5464	2.0462	2.7971
0.047	1.6570	2.1569	2.9073	0.104	1.5444	2.0442	2.7951
0.048	1.6550	2.1549	2.9054	0.105	1.5425	2.0422	2.7932
0.049	1.6531	2.1529	2.9034	0.106	1.5405	2.0403	2.7912
0.050	1.6511	2.1510	2.9014	0.107	1.5385	2.0383	2.7892
0.051	1.6491	2.1490	2.8995	0.108	1.5365	2.0363	2.7873
0.052	1.6471	2.1470	2.8975	0.109	1.5346	2.0343	2.7853
0.053	1.6452	2.1451	2.8955	7/64	1.5338	2.0336	2.7846
0.054	1.6432	2.1431	2.8936	0.110	1.5326	2.0324	2.7833
0.055	1.6412	2.1411	2.8916	0.111	1.5306	2.0304	2.7814
0.056	1.6392	2.1391	2.8896	0.112	1.5287	2.0284	2.7794
0.057	1.6373	2.1372	2.8877	0.113	1.5267	2.0264	2.7774

Corrected Diameters of Circular Forming Tools — 2

Length c on Tool	Number of B. & S. Automatic Screw Machine			Length c on Tool	Number of B. & S. Automatic Screw Machine		
	No. 00	No. 0	No. 2		No. 00	No. 0	No. 2
0.113	1.5267	2.0264	2.7774	0.171	1.4124	1.9119	2.6634
0.114	1.5247	2.0245	2.7755	11/64	1.4107	1.9103	2.6617
0.115	1.5227	2.0225	2.7735	0.172	1.4104	1.9099	2.6614
0.116	1.5208	2.0205	2.7715	0.173	1.4084	1.9080	2.6595
0.117	1.5188	2.0185	2.7696	0.174	1.4065	1.9060	2.6575
0.118	1.5168	2.0166	2.7676	0.175	1.4045	1.9040	2.6556
0.119	1.5148	2.0146	2.7656	0.176	1.4025	1.9021	2.6536
0.120	1.5129	2.0126	2.7637	0.177	1.4006	1.9001	2.6516
0.121	1.5109	2.0106	2.7617	0.178	1.3986	1.8981	2.6497
0.122	1.5089	2.0087	2.7597	0.179	1.3966	1.8961	2.6477
0.123	1.5070	2.0067	2.7578	0.180	1.3947	1.8942	2.6457
0.124	1.5050	2.0047	2.7558	0.181	1.3927	1.8922	2.6438
0.125	1.5030	2.0027	2.7538	0.182	1.3907	1.8902	2.6418
0.126	1.5010	2.0008	2.7519	0.183	1.3888	1.8882	2.6398
0.127	1.4991	1.9988	2.7499	0.184	1.3868	1.8863	2.6379
0.128	1.4971	1.9968	2.7479	0.185	1.3848	1.8843	2.6359
0.129	1.4951	1.9948	2.7460	0.186	1.3829	1.8823	2.6339
0.130	1.4932	1.9929	2.7440	0.187	1.3809	1.8804	2.6320
0.131	1.4912	1.9909	2.7420	3/16	1.3799	1.8794	2.6310
0.132	1.4892	1.9889	2.7401	0.188	1.3789	1.8784	2.6300
0.133	1.4872	1.9869	2.7381	0.189	1.3770	1.8764	2.6281
0.134	1.4853	1.9850	2.7361	0.190	1.3750	1.8744	2.6261
0.135	1.4833	1.9830	2.7342	0.191	1.3730	1.8725	2.6241
0.136	1.4813	1.9810	2.7322	0.192	1.3711	1.8705	2.6222
0.137	1.4794	1.9790	2.7302	0.193	1.3691	1.8685	2.6202
0.138	1.4774	1.9771	2.7282	0.194	1.3671	1.8665	2.6182
0.139	1.4754	1.9751	2.7263	0.195	1.3652	1.8646	2.6163
0.140	1.4734	1.9731	2.7243	0.196	1.3632	1.8626	2.6143
9/64	1.4722	1.9719	2.7231	0.197	1.3612	1.8606	2.6123
0.141	1.4715	1.9711	2.7224	0.198	1.3592	1.8587	2.6104
0.142	1.4695	1.9692	2.7204	0.199	1.3573	1.8567	2.6084
0.143	1.4675	1.9672	2.7184	0.200	1.3553	1.8547	2.6064
0.144	1.4655	1.9652	2.7165	0.201	....	1.8527	2.6045
0.145	1.4636	1.9632	2.7145	0.202	....	1.8508	2.6025
0.146	1.4616	1.9613	2.7125	0.203	....	1.8488	2.6006
0.147	1.4596	1.9593	2.7106	13/64	....	1.8486	2.6003
0.148	1.4577	1.9573	2.7086	0.204	....	1.8468	2.5986
0.149	1.4557	1.9553	2.7066	0.205	....	1.8449	2.5966
0.150	1.4537	1.9534	2.7047	0.206	....	1.8429	2.5947
0.151	1.4517	1.9514	2.7027	0.207	....	1.8409	2.5927
0.152	1.4498	1.9494	2.7007	0.208	....	1.8390	2.5908
0.153	1.4478	1.9474	2.6988	0.209	....	1.8370	2.5888
0.154	1.4458	1.9455	2.6968	0.210	....	1.8350	2.5868
0.155	1.4439	1.9435	2.6948	0.211	....	1.8330	2.5849
0.156	1.4419	1.9445	2.6929	0.212	....	1.8311	2.5829
5/32	1.4414	1.9410	2.6924	0.213	....	1.8291	2.5809
0.157	1.4399	1.9395	2.6909	0.214	....	1.8271	2.5790
0.158	1.4380	1.9376	2.6889	0.215	....	1.8252	2.5770
0.159	1.4360	1.9356	2.6870	0.216	....	1.8232	2.5751
0.160	1.4340	1.9336	2.6850	0.217	....	1.8212	2.5731
0.161	1.4321	1.9317	2.6830	0.218	....	1.8193	2.5711
0.162	1.4301	1.9297	2.6811	7/32	....	1.8178	2.5697
0.163	1.4281	1.9277	2.6791	0.219	....	1.8173	2.5692
0.164	1.4262	1.9257	2.6772	0.220	....	1.8153	2.5672
0.165	1.4242	1.9238	2.6752	0.221	....	1.8133	2.5653
0.166	1.4222	1.9218	2.6732	0.222	....	1.8114	2.5633
0.167	1.4203	1.9198	2.6713	0.223	....	1.8094	2.5613
0.168	1.4183	1.9178	2.6693	0.224	....	1.8074	2.5594
0.169	1.4163	1.9159	2.6673	0.225	....	1.8055	2.5574
0.170	1.4144	1.9139	2.6654	0.226	....	1.8035	2.5555

Corrected Diameters of Circular Forming Tools — 3

Length c on Tool	No. of B. & S. Machine No. 0	No. 2
0.227	1.8015	2.5535
0.228	1.7996	2.5515
0.229	1.7976	2.5496
0.230	1.7956	2.5476
0.231	1.7936	2.5456
0.232	1.7917	2.5437
0.233	1.7897	2.5417
0.234	1.7877	2.5398
15/64	1.7870	2.5390
0.235	1.7858	2.5378
0.236	1.7838	2.5358
0.237	1.7818	2.5339
0.238	1.7799	2.5319
0.239	1.7779	2.5300
0.240	1.7759	2.5280
0.241	1.7739	2.5260
0.242	1.7720	2.5241
0.243	1.7700	2.5221
0.244	1.7680	2.5201
0.245	1.7661	2.5182
0.246	1.7641	2.5162
0.247	1.7621	2.5143
0.248	1.7602	2.5123
0.249	1.7582	2.5104
0.250	1.7562	2.5084
0.251	1.7543	2.5064
0.252	1.7523	2.5045
0.253	1.7503	2.5025
0.254	1.7484	2.5005
0.255	1.7464	2.4986
0.256	1.7444	2.4966
0.257	1.7425	2.4947
0.258	1.7405	2.4927
0.259	1.7385	2.4908
0.260	1.7366	2.4888
0.261	1.7346	2.4868
0.262	1.7326	2.4849
0.263	1.7306	2.4829
0.264	1.7287	2.4810
0.265	1.7267	2.4790
17/64	1.7255	2.4778
0.266	1.7248	2.4770
0.267	1.7228	2.4751
0.268	1.7208	2.4731
0.269	1.7189	2.4712
0.270	1.7169	2.4692
0.271	1.7149	2.4673
0.272	1.7130	2.4653
0.273	1.7110	2.4633
0.274	1.7090	2.4614
0.275	1.7071	2.4594
0.276	1.7051	2.4575
0.277	1.7031	2.4555
0.278	1.7012	2.4535
0.279	1.6992	2.4516
0.280	1.6972	2.4496
0.281	1.6953	2.4477
9/32	1.6948	2.4472
0.282	1.6933	2.4457
0.283	1.6913	2.4438

Length c on Tool	No. of B. & S. Machine No. 0	No. 2
0.284	1.6894	2.4418
0.285	1.6874	2.4398
0.286	1.6854	2.4378
0.287	1.6835	2.4359
0.288	1.6815	2.4340
0.289	1.6795	2.4320
0.290	1.6776	2.4300
0.291	1.6756	2.4281
0.292	1.6736	2.4261
0.293	1.6717	2.4242
0.294	1.6697	2.4222
0.295	1.6677	2.4203
0.296	1.6658	2.4183
19/64	1.6641	2.4166
0.297	1.6638	2.4163
0.298	1.6618	2.4144
0.299	1.6599	2.4124
0.300	1.6579	2.4105
0.301	....	2.4085
0.302	....	2.4066
0.303	....	2.4046
0.304	....	2.4026
0.305	....	2.4007
0.306	....	2.3987
0.307	....	2.3968
0.308	....	2.3948
0.309	....	2.3929
0.310	....	2.3909
0.311	....	2.3890
0.312	....	2.3870
5/16	....	2.3860
0.313	....	2.3851
0.314	....	2.3831
0.315	....	2.3811
0.316	....	2.3792
0.317	....	2.3772
0.318	....	2.3753
0.319	....	2.3733
0.320	....	2.3714
0.321	....	2.3694
0.322	....	2.3675
0.323	....	2.3655
0.324	....	2.3636
0.325	....	2.3616
0.326	....	2.3596
0.327	....	2.3577
0.328	....	2.3557
21/64	....	2.3555
0.329	....	2.3538
0.330	....	2.3518
0.331	....	2.3499
0.332	....	2.3479
0.333	....	2.3460
0.334	....	2.3440
0.335	....	2.3421
0.336	....	2.3401
0.337	....	2.3381
0.338	....	2.3362
0.339	....	2.3342
0.340	....	2.3323

Length c on Tool	No. 2 B. & S Machine
0.341	2.3303
0.342	2.3284
0.343	2.3264
11/32	2.3250
0.344	2.3245
0.345	2.3225
0.346	2.3206
0.347	2.3186
0.348	2.3166
0.349	2.3147
0.350	2.3127
0.351	2.3108
0.352	2.3088
0.353	2.3069
0.354	2.3049
0.355	2.3030
0.356	2.3010
0.357	2.2991
0.358	2.2971
0.359	2.2952
23/64	2.2945
0.360	2.2932
0.361	2.2913
0.362	2.2893
0.363	2.2874
0.364	2.2854
0.365	2.2835
0.366	2.2815
0.367	2.2796
0.368	2.2776
0.369	2.2757
0.370	2.2737
0.371	2.2718
0.372	2.2698
0.373	2.2679
0.374	2.2659
0.375	2.2640
0.376	2.2620
0.377	2.2601
0.378	2.2581
0.379	2.2562
0.380	2.2542
0.381	2.2523
0.382	2.2503
0.383	2.2484
0.384	2.2464
0.385	2.2445
0.386	2.2425
0.387	2.2406
0.388	2.2386
0.389	2.2367
0.390	2.2347
25/64	2.2335
0.391	2.2328
0.392	2.2308
0.393	2.2289
0.394	2.2269
0.395	2.2250
0.396	2.2230
0.397	2.2211

Corrected Diameters of Circular Forming Tools — 4

Length c on Tool	No. 2 B. & S. Machine	Length c on Tool	No. 2 B. & S. Machine	Length c on Tool	No. 2 B. & S. Machine	Length c on Tool	No. 2 B. & S. Machine
0.398	2.2191	0.423	2.1704	0.449	2.1199	0.474	2.0713
0.399	2.2172	0.424	2.1685	0.450	2.1179	0.475	2.0694
0.400	2.2152	0.425	2.1666	0.451	2.1160	0.476	2.0674
0.401	2.2133	0.426	2.1646	0.452	2.1140	0.477	2.0655
0.402	2.2113	0.427	2.1627	0.453	2.1121	0.478	2.0636
0.403	2.2094	0.428	2.1607	$^{29}/_{64}$	2.1118	0.479	2.0616
0.404	2.2074	0.429	2.1588	0.454	2.1101	0.480	2.0597
0.405	2.2055	0.430	2.1568	0.455	2.1082	0.481	2.0577
0.406	2.2035	0.431	2.1549	0.456	2.1063	0.482	2.0558
$^{13}/_{32}$	2.2030	0.432	2.1529	0.457	2.1043	0.483	2.0538
0.407	2.2016	0.433	2.1510	0.458	2.1024	0.484	2.0519
0.408	2.1996	0.434	2.1490	0.459	2.1004	0.485	2.0500
0.409	2.1977	0.435	2.1471	0.460	2.0985	0.486	2.0480
0.410	2.1957	0.436	2.1452	0.461	2.0966	0.487	2.0461
0.411	2.1938	0.437	2.1432	0.462	2.0946	0.488	2.0441
0.412	2.1919	$^{7}/_{16}$	2.1422	0.463	2.0927	0.489	2.0422
0.413	2.1899	0.438	2.1413	0.464	2.0907	0.490	2.0403
0.414	2.1880	0.439	2.1393	0.465	2.0888	0.491	2.0383
0.415	2.1860	0.440	2.1374	0.466	2.0868	0.492	2.0364
0.416	2.1841	0.441	2.1354	0.467	2.0849	0.493	2.0344
0.417	2.1821	0.442	2.1335	0.468	2.0830	0.494	2.0325
0.418	2.1802	0.443	2.1315	$^{15}/_{32}$	2.0815	0.495	2.0306
0.419	2.1782	0.444	2.1296	0.469	2.0810	0.496	2.0286
0.420	2.1763	0.445	2.1276	0.470	2.0791	0.497	2.0267
0.421	2.1743	0.446	2.1257	0.471	2.0771	0.498	2.0247
$^{27}/_{64}$	2.1726	0.447	2.1237	0.472	2.0752	0.499	2.0228
0.422	2.1724	0.448	2.1218	0.473	2.0733	0.500	2.0209

Method of Using Tables for " Corrected Diameters of Circular Forming Tools." — These tables are especially applicable to the Brown & Sharpe automatic screw machines. The maximum diameter D of forming tools for these machines should be as follows: For No. 00 machine, 1¾ inch; for No. 0 machine, 2¼ inches; for No. 2 machine, 3 inches. To find the other diameters of the tool for any piece

Dimensions of Forming Tools for B. & S. Automatic Screw Machines

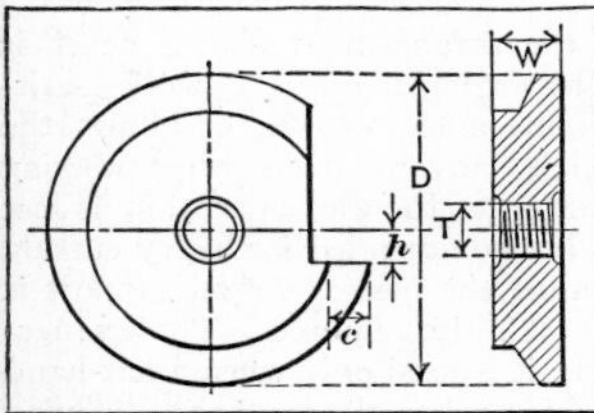

No. of Machine	Max. Diam., D	h	T	W
00	1¾	⅛	⅜–16	¼
0	2¼	⁵⁄₃₂	½–14	⁵⁄₁₆
2	3	¼	⅝–12	⅜
6	4	⁵⁄₁₆	¾–12	⅜

to be formed, proceed as follows: Subtract the smallest diameter of the work from that diameter of the work which is to be formed by the required tool diameter; divide the remainder by 2; locate the quotient obtained in the column headed "Length c on Tool," and opposite the figure thus located and in the column headed by the number of the machine used, read off directly the diameter to which the tool is to be made. The quotient obtained, which is located in the column headed "Length c on Tool," is the length c as shown in the illustration above.

Example: — A piece of work is to be formed on a No. o machine to two diameters, one being ¼ inch and one 0.550 inch; find the diameters of the tool. The maximum tool diameter is 2¼ inches. This will be the diameter which will cut the ¼ inch diameter of the work. To find the other diameter, proceed according to the rule given: 0.550 − ¼ = 0.300; 0.300 ÷ 2 = 0.150. In Table 2, opposite 0.150, we find that the required tool diameter is 1.9534 inch. These tables are for tools without rake.

Arrangement of Circular Tools. — When applying circular tools to automatic screw machines, their arrangement has an important bearing on the results obtained. The various ways of arranging the circular tools, with relation to the rotation of the spindle, are shown at *A*, *B*, *C* and *D*, in the illustration. These diagrams represent the view obtained when looking towards the chuck. The arrangement at *A* gives good results for long forming on brass, steel or gun-screw iron, for the reason that the pressure of the cut on the front tool is downward; the support is more rigid than when the forming tool is turned upside down on the front slide as shown at *B*; here the stock, turning up towards the tool, has a tendency to lift

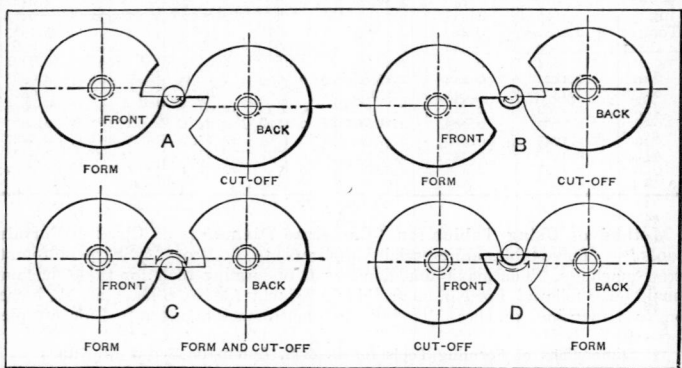

the cross-slide, causing chattering; therefore, the arrangement shown at *A* is recommended when a high finish is desired. The arrangement at *B* works satisfactorily for short steel pieces which do not require a high finish; it allows the chips to drop clear of the work, and is especially advantageous when making screws, when the forming and cut-off tools operate after the die, as no time is lost in reversing the spindle. The arrangement at *C* is recommended for heavy cutting on large work, when both tools are used for forming the piece; a rigid support is then necessary for both tools and a good supply of oil is also required. The arrangement at *D* is objectionable and should be avoided; it is used only when a left-hand thread is cut on the piece and when the cut-off tool is used on the front slide, leaving the heavy cutting to be performed from the rear slide. In all "cross-forming" work, it is essential that the spindle be kept in good condition, and that the collet or chuck have a parallel contact upon the bar which is being formed.

Speeds for Forming Tools. — Surface speeds for turning different materials with forming tools are given in the following table. These speeds correspond approximately to general practice, and are intended to serve as a guide. An ample supply of lard oil should be used and the tools kept in good condition.

Surface Speeds for Forming Tools

Material	Surface Speed, Feet per Minute	
	Carbon Steel	High-speed Steel
Brass rod....................................	175–200	225–300
Gun-screw iron.............................	75– 95	100–125
Norway iron and machine steel..................	55– 75	80–100
Drill rod and tool steel.........................	40– 55	60– 75

Feeds per Revolution for Forming Tools

Width of Forming Tool	Smallest Diameter of Part Formed					
	3/32	1/8	5/32	3/16	7/32	1/4
1/16	0.00075	0.0008	0.0009	0.001	0.0011	0.0012
3/32	0.0007	0.0008	0.0009	0.001	0.001	0.0013
1/8	0.00055	0.0007	0.0008	0.001	0.0009	0.0012
3/16	0.0003	0.0007	0.0008	0.0009	0.0009	0.0011
7/32	....	0.0005	0.0007	0.0009	0.0009	0.0011
1/4	....	0.0002	0.0007	0.0009	0.0009	0.001
5/16	....	....	0.0005	0.0008	0.0008	0.001
3/8	....	....	0.0002	0.0008	0.0008	0.0009
1/2	....	....	....	0.0008	0.0008	0.0009
5/8	....	....	....	0.0003	0.0005	0.0009
3/4	....	....	....	....	0.0002	0.0008
7/8	....	....	....	....	....	0.0005
1	....	....	....	....	....	0.0002

Width of Forming Tool	Smallest Diameter of Part Formed					
	5/16	3/8	1/2	5/8	3/4	7/8
1/16	0.0012	0.0012	0.0012	0.0012	0.0012	0.0012
3/32	0.0014	0.0015	0.0017	0.0019	0.002	0.0021
1/8	0.0014	0.0016	0.002	0.0023	0.0025	0.0025
3/16	0.0015	0.0016	0.0018	0.0019	0.0021	0.0022
7/32	0.0013	0.0015	0.0017	0.0018	0.002	0.0021
1/4	0.0012	0.0015	0.0016	0.0017	0.0018	0.002
5/16	0.0011	0.0013	0.0015	0.0016	0.0017	0.0018
3/8	0.001	0.0012	0.0012	0.0014	0.0016	0.0017
1/2	0.0009	0.001	0.0011	0.0013	0.0015	0.0016
5/8	0.0009	0.0009	0.001	0.0012	0.0014	0.0015
3/4	0.0008	0.0009	0.0009	0.0011	0.0013	0.0014
7/8	0.0006	0.0008	0.0009	0.001	0.0012	0.0013
1	0.0005	0.0008	0.0008	0.0009	0.001	0.0012

FORMING TOOLS

American Standard Forming Tool Blanks. — This standard covers both circular and dovetail forming tool blanks such as are commonly used on hand screw machines and on automatic screw machines. It also includes the mounting and clamping elements of the tool-holders used on these machines. The purpose of the standard is to provide interchangeability and also to permit a reduction in the number of forming tool blanks required. In order to establish a minimum number of blank sizes, the machines have been classified for reference purposes into six different groups of comparable stock capacities as shown by the accompanying Table 1. Each group of machines takes a definite size tool and the holders are provided with suitable mounting or clamping devices. The machine group numbers have been assigned arbitrarily to identify the size of the tool with the machines on which that size may be used. This standard is not intended to provide interchangeability of holders for various makes of machines except in connection with the mounting or clamp details.

Table 1. Machine Classifications for American Standard Forming Tool Blanks

Group Number	Type of Machine	Maximum Capacity*	Group Number	Type of Machine	Maximum Capacity*
1	No. 00 Brown & Sharpe	$3/8$	4	$1\frac{3}{4}$ Gridley	$1\frac{3}{4}$
	No. 19 Brown & Sharpe	$3/8$		$1\frac{3}{4}$ Greenlee	$1\frac{3}{4}$
	Index "0"	$7/16$		No. 4 Brown & Sharpe	$1\frac{7}{8}$
	$3/8$ Cleveland	$5/8$		2 Greenlee	2
2	$3/8$ Gridley	$3/8$		2 Gridley	2
	$1/2$ Davenport	$7/8$		No. 61 New Britain	$2\frac{1}{4}$
	$9/16$ Acme Gridley	$9/16$		2 Cleveland	$2\frac{1}{2}$
	No. 0 Brown & Sharpe	$5/8$		$2 \times 2\frac{3}{4}$ Cleveland	$3\frac{1}{4}$
	$5/8$ Cleveland	$3/4$		$2\frac{1}{4}$ Cleveland	$2\frac{1}{2}$
	$5/8 \times 7/8$ Cleveland	$1\frac{1}{16}$		$2\frac{1}{4} \times 2\frac{3}{4}$ Cleveland	$3\frac{1}{4}$
	No. 204 New Britain	$5/8$		$2\frac{1}{4}$ Gridley	$2\frac{1}{4}$
	No. 60 New Britain	1		$2\frac{1}{4}$ Greenlee	$2\frac{1}{4}$
	$7/8$ Greenlee	1		No. 42 New Britain	3
	$7/8 \times 1\frac{1}{4}$ Cleveland	$7/8$	5	No. 6 Brown & Sharpe	$2\frac{3}{8}$
3	$7/8$ Gridley	$7/8$		$2\frac{5}{8}$ Gridley	$2\frac{5}{8}$
	1 Acme Gridley	1		$2\frac{3}{4} \times 3\frac{3}{4}$ Cleveland	$3\frac{1}{4}$
	No. 2 Brown & Sharpe	$1\frac{1}{8}$		$2\frac{3}{4} \times 4$ Cleveland	$2\frac{3}{4}$
	$1\frac{1}{4}$ Gridley	$1\frac{1}{4}$		3 Gridley	3
	$1\frac{1}{4}$ Cleveland	$1\frac{1}{4}$		$3\frac{5}{16}$ Gridley	$3\frac{5}{16}$
	$1\frac{1}{4}$ Cleveland	$1\frac{3}{8}$	6	$3\frac{1}{4}$ Gridley	$3\frac{1}{4}$
	$1\frac{1}{4} \times 1\frac{1}{2}$ Cleveland	$1\frac{3}{4}$		$3\frac{1}{2}$ Gridley	$3\frac{1}{2}$
	$1\frac{1}{4} \times 1\frac{1}{2}$ Cleveland	$1\frac{1}{2}$		4 Gridley	4
	$1\frac{1}{4}$ Greenlee	$1\frac{1}{4}$		4 Cleveland	4
	$1\frac{3}{8}$ Gridley	$1\frac{3}{8}$		$4\frac{1}{4}$ Cleveland	$4\frac{1}{2}$
	$1\frac{1}{2}$ Greenlee	$1\frac{1}{2}$		$4\frac{1}{4}$ Cleveland	$4\frac{3}{4}$
	$1\frac{5}{8}$ Gridley	$1\frac{5}{8}$		$4\frac{1}{4}$ Gridley	$4\frac{3}{4}$
4	$1\frac{5}{8}$ Gridley	$1\frac{5}{8}$		$4\frac{1}{2}$ Gridley	$4\frac{1}{2}$
	$1\frac{5}{8}$ Acme Gridley	$1\frac{5}{8}$		5 Gridley	5
	No. 206 New Britain	$1\frac{5}{8}$		$5\frac{1}{2}$ Cleveland	$5\frac{1}{2}$
	No. 415 New Britain	$1\frac{5}{8}$		$6\frac{3}{4}$ Cleveland	$6\frac{3}{4}$
	No. 410 New Britain	...		$7\frac{3}{4}$ Cleveland	$7\frac{3}{4}$

* The group classification numbers apply to all machine models of the respective makes listed having the maximum capacities indicated. Dimensions in inches.

Table 2. American Standard Dimensions of Finished Blanks for Circular Forming Tools With Threaded Mounting Hole

The circular tool blanks in Table 2, which are provided with threaded mounting holes, are used for tools having nominal outside diameters of 1¾, 2¼, and 3 inches. For the larger blank diameters listed in Table 3, the mounting holes are unthreaded and counterbored. This method of mounting is for tool blanks having nominal outside diameters of 3½, 4, and 5 inches.

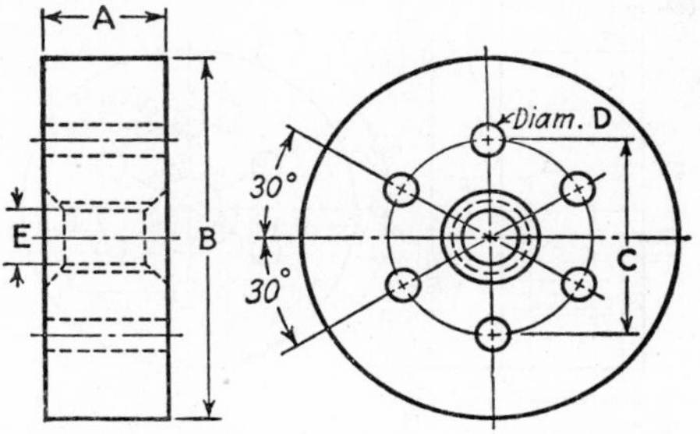

Group Number	Nominal Blank Size Notes 1, 2	Max. Diam. *B* Note 3	Max. Width *A* Note 3	Diam. Adjusting Hole Circle *C*	Diam. Adjusting Holes *D* Notes 4, 5, 6	Threaded Hole *E*	
						Diam. *E* Notes 7, 8	No. Threads per Inch
1	1¾ × ¼	1²⁵⁄₃₂	9/32	No pin hole		3/8	16
	1¾ × 3/8	1²⁵⁄₃₂	13/32			3/8	16
	1¾ × ½	1²⁵⁄₃₂	17/32			3/8	16
	1¾ × ¾	1²⁵⁄₃₂	25/32			3/8	16
	1¾ × 1	1²⁵⁄₃₂	1 1/32			3/8	16
2	2¼ × 3/8	2 9/32	13/32	1 3/8	3/16	½	13
	2¼ × ½	2 9/32	17/32	1 3/8	3/16	½	13
	2¼ × ¾	2 9/32	25/32	1 3/8	3/16	½	13
	2¼ × 1	2 9/32	1 1/32	1 3/8	3/16	½	13
	2¼ × 1¼	2 9/32	1 9/32	1 3/8	3/16	½	13
3	3 × ½	3 1/32	17/32	1½	3/16	5/8	11
	3 × ¾	3 1/32	25/32	1½	3/16	5/8	11
	3 × 1	3 1/32	1 1/32	1½	3/16	5/8	11
	3 × 1¼	3 1/32	1 9/32	1½	3/16	5/8	11
	3 × 1½	3 1/32	1 17/32	1½	3/16	5/8	11

All dimensions are given in inches.

(1) Blanks are designated by giving the nominal outside diameter and width.

(2) Blanks made of high-speed steel shall be stamped H.S.

(3) The tolerance on diameter *B* and width *A* is −1/64 inch.

(4) Six adjusting holes shall have a minimum depth of ¼ inch, greater depth or through holes being optional. Adjusting holes shall be equally spaced on the circle *C* and be slightly chamfered.

(5) Diameter of adjusting holes *D* shall be ± 0.002.

(6) Diameter *C* of location circle shall be ± 0.002.

(7) The threaded hole *E* shall be held within Class 2 tolerances (NC 2, ASA B1.1-1935). Both ends of threaded hole *E* shall be chamfered 35 degrees.

(8) Commercial blanks may not, in all cases, have the standard number of threads per inch listed in this table.

Table 3. American Standard Dimensions for Finished Blanks for Circular Forming Tools With Counterbored Mounting Hole

In obtaining circular forming tool blanks from commercial sources, the blank size is designated by giving the nominal outside diameter and nominal width. In the table below, the nominal diameter and width is $\frac{1}{32}$ inch less than the maximum diameter and width. For example, a forming tool having a maximum diameter of $3\frac{17}{32}$ inches and maximum width of $\frac{17}{32}$ inch would be designated as $3\frac{1}{2} \times \frac{1}{2}$.

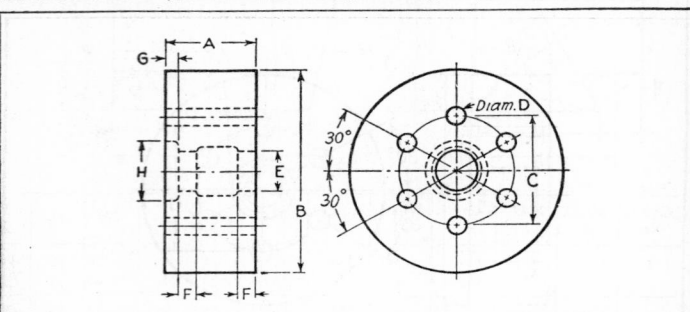

Group Number	Max. Diam. B Note 2	Max. Width A Note 2	Diam. Circle C Note 5	Diam. Holes D Notes 3,4	Mounting Hole Diam. E Note 6	Width F	Counterbore Diam. H Note 7	Counterbore Depth G
4	$3\frac{17}{32}$	$\frac{17}{32}$	$1\frac{7}{8}$	$\frac{1}{4}$	$\frac{3}{4}$	...	$1\frac{3}{32}$	$\frac{3}{16}$
	$3\frac{17}{32}$	$\frac{25}{32}$	$1\frac{7}{8}$	$\frac{1}{4}$	$\frac{3}{4}$	...	$1\frac{3}{32}$	$\frac{3}{16}$
	$3\frac{17}{32}$	$1\frac{5}{32}$	$1\frac{7}{8}$	$\frac{1}{4}$	$\frac{3}{4}$	...	$1\frac{3}{32}$	$\frac{7}{16}$
	$3\frac{17}{32}$	$1\frac{17}{32}$	$1\frac{7}{8}$	$\frac{1}{4}$	$\frac{3}{4}$	$\frac{5}{16}$	$1\frac{3}{32}$	$\frac{1}{4}$
	$3\frac{17}{32}$	$2\frac{5}{32}$	$1\frac{7}{8}$	$\frac{1}{4}$	$\frac{3}{4}$	$\frac{5}{16}$	$1\frac{3}{32}$	$\frac{3}{4}$
	$3\frac{17}{32}$	$2\frac{17}{32}$	$1\frac{7}{8}$	$\frac{1}{4}$	$\frac{3}{4}$	$\frac{5}{16}$	$1\frac{3}{32}$	$1\frac{1}{4}$
5	$4\frac{1}{32}$	$\frac{21}{32}$	$2\frac{1}{8}$	$\frac{5}{16}$	1	...	$1\frac{11}{32}$	$\frac{1}{4}$
	$4\frac{1}{32}$	$1\frac{5}{32}$	$2\frac{1}{8}$	$\frac{5}{16}$	1	...	$1\frac{11}{32}$	$\frac{1}{4}$
	$4\frac{1}{32}$	$1\frac{17}{32}$	$2\frac{1}{8}$	$\frac{5}{16}$	1	...	$1\frac{11}{32}$	$\frac{3}{4}$
	$4\frac{1}{32}$	$2\frac{5}{32}$	$2\frac{1}{8}$	$\frac{5}{16}$	1	$\frac{7}{16}$	$1\frac{11}{32}$	$\frac{1}{4}$
	$4\frac{1}{32}$	$2\frac{17}{32}$	$2\frac{1}{8}$	$\frac{5}{16}$	1	$\frac{7}{16}$	$1\frac{11}{32}$	$\frac{3}{4}$
	$4\frac{1}{32}$	$3\frac{5}{32}$	$2\frac{1}{8}$	$\frac{5}{16}$	1	$\frac{7}{16}$	$1\frac{11}{32}$	$1\frac{1}{4}$
6	$5\frac{1}{32}$	$\frac{21}{32}$	$2\frac{1}{8}$	$\frac{5}{16}$	1	...	$1\frac{11}{32}$	$\frac{1}{4}$
	$5\frac{1}{32}$	$1\frac{5}{32}$	$2\frac{1}{8}$	$\frac{5}{16}$	1	...	$1\frac{11}{32}$	$\frac{1}{4}$
	$5\frac{1}{32}$	$1\frac{17}{32}$	$2\frac{1}{8}$	$\frac{5}{16}$	1	...	$1\frac{11}{32}$	$\frac{3}{4}$
	$5\frac{1}{32}$	$2\frac{5}{32}$	$2\frac{1}{8}$	$\frac{5}{16}$	1	$\frac{7}{16}$	$1\frac{11}{32}$	$\frac{1}{4}$
	$5\frac{1}{32}$	$3\frac{5}{32}$	$2\frac{1}{8}$	$\frac{5}{16}$	1	$\frac{7}{16}$	$1\frac{11}{32}$	$1\frac{1}{4}$
	$5\frac{1}{32}$	$4\frac{5}{32}$	$2\frac{1}{8}$	$\frac{5}{16}$	1	$\frac{7}{16}$	$1\frac{11}{32}$	$2\frac{1}{4}$

All dimensions are given in inches.

(1) Blanks made of high-speed steel shall be stamped H.S.

(2) The tolerance on diameter B and width A is $-\frac{1}{64}$ inch.

(3) Six adjusting holes shall have a minimum depth of $\frac{1}{4}$ inch, greater depth or through holes being optional. Adjusting holes shall be equally spaced on the circle C and be slightly chamfered.

(4) Diameter of adjusting holes D shall be ± 0.002.

(5) Diameter C of location circle shall be ± 0.002.

(6) Bolt hole E shall have a tolerance of $+0.003$, -0.000 with 45 deg. chamfer at both ends.

(7) Diameter H shall have a slight radius at the bottom of counterbore.

Table 4. American Standard Finished Blanks for Dovetailed Forming Tools

Group No.	Max. A	Max. T	Length P	Width M	Height O	C	N	B	G	H	Y / X
1	1 1/32	2 9/32	1 1/2	0.732	9/32	1/4	0.834	5/32	5/16–18	3/8	1/8
	1 9/32	2 9/32	1 1/2	0.951	19/64	19/64	1.035	5/32	5/16–18	1/2	3/16
2	1 9/32	2 9/32	2	0.951	19/64	19/64	1.035	5/32	5/16–18	1/2	3/16
	1 17/32	2 9/32	2	0.951	19/64	19/64	1.035	5/32	5/16–18	1/2	3/16
	1 25/32	1 5/32	2	1.250	13/32	7/16	1.464	1/4	5/16–18	1/2	1/4
	2 25/32	1 5/32	2 7/16	2.000	33/64	1/2	2.771	1/2	7/16–14	3/8	5/16
3	1 25/32	1 5/32	2 7/16	1.250	13/32	7/16	1.464	1/4	5/16–18	1/2	1/4
	2 9/32	1 5/32	2 7/16	1.250	13/32	7/16	1.464	1/4	5/16–18	1/4	1/4
	2 25/32	1 5/32	2 7/16	1.250	13/32	7/16	1.464	1/4	5/16–18	1/4	1/4
4	2 25/32	2 17/32	2 5/8	1.614	35/64	1/2	2.349	1/2	5/16–18	1/2	1/4
	2 25/32	2 17/32	2 5/8	1.882	35/64	1/2	2.617	1/2	7/16–14	3/8	1/4
	3 1/32	2 17/32	2 5/8	1.882	35/64	1/2	2.617	1/2	7/16–14	3/8	1/4
5	2 25/32	1 9/32	2 7/16	2.000	33/64	1/2	2.771	1/2	7/16–14	3/8	5/16
	2 25/32	3 1/32	3	2.000	33/64	1/2	2.771	1/2	7/16–14	3/8	5/16
	3 1/32	3 1/32	3	2.000	33/64	1/2	2.771	1/2	7/16–14	3/8	5/16
	3 9/32	3 1/32	3	2.000	33/64	1/2	2.771	1/2	7/16–14	3/8	5/16
6	3 9/32	3 17/32	4	2.238	35/64	9/16	2.973	1/2	7/16–14	3/8	5/16
	3 17/32	3 17/32	4	2.883	43/64	5/8	3.815	5/8	7/16–14	3/8	5/16
	4 1/32	3 17/32	4	2.883	43/64	5/8	3.815	5/8	7/16–14	3/8	5/16
	4 17/32	3 17/32	4	2.883	43/64	5/8	3.815	5/8	7/16–14	3/8	5/16

Group No.	Width A	No. of Slots	J	K	L	S	
1	1 1/32	2	1/8	5/16	1/8	1/8	Tolerance for width of adjusting slot S is +0.003 − 0.000. Methods of adjustment are optional
1	1 9/32	2	1/8	5/16	1/8	1/8	
2	1 9/32	3	1/8	11/32	1/8	1/8	
2	1 25/32	3	1/8	11/32	1/8	1/8	
2	2 25/32	3	1/8	7/16	9/32	9/32	
3	1 25/32	3	1/8	7/16	9/32	9/32	

Min. width A and thickness T is 1/64″ less than max. Dovetail width M is to the theoretical sharp corners. Tolerance for measurement N over plugs B is +0.003, −0.003. Radius R is 1/32″ up to blank width 1 17/32″ inc. and 1/16″ for larger widths.

Table 5. Typical Circular Forming Tool-holder for Machines in Group No. 1

The circular forming tools for machines in group Nos. 1 to 3, inclusive (Tables 5 and 6), are held by a stud which enters a threaded hole in the center of the blank, and by an auxiliary clamp of the hook-bolt type as shown by plan views of the diagrams above the tables. Circular tools for machine group Nos. 4 to 6, inclusive (Table 7), are held by a bolt and nut in conjunction with a hook-bolt. Blanks for machines in group No. 1 (Table 5) have no adjusting pin-holes but a friction plate may be provided for use in adjusting the cutting edge to the center of the work. Holders for larger machines have positive means for adjusting the cutting edge of the tool to the center of the work.

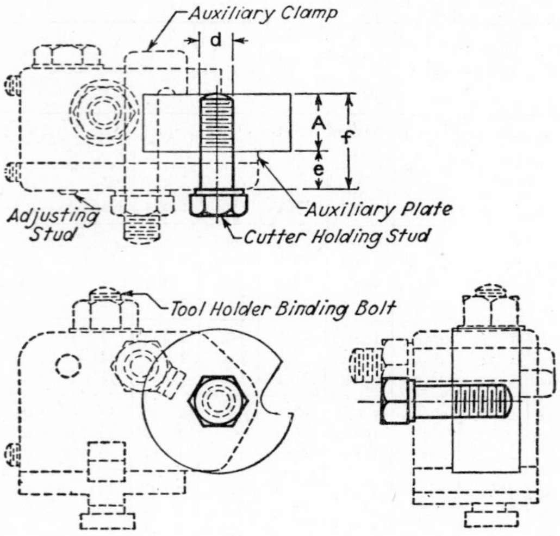

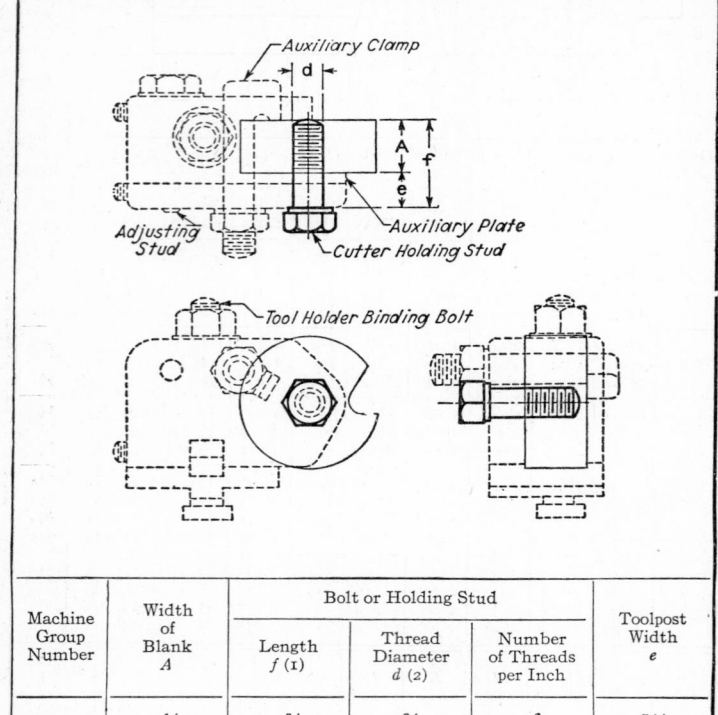

Machine Group Number	Width of Blank *A*	Bolt or Holding Stud: Length *f* (1)	Bolt or Holding Stud: Thread Diameter *d* (2)	Bolt or Holding Stud: Number of Threads per Inch	Toolpost Width *e*
	1/4	3/4	3/8	16	7/16
	3/8	7/8	3/8	16	7/16
1	1/2	1	3/8	16	7/16
	3/4	1 1/4	3/8	16	7/16
	1	1 1/2	3/8	16	7/16

All dimensions are given in inches.
Tolerance for dimensions not otherwise specified shall be held to ±0.010.
(1) Tolerance for length of bolt is ±1/32.
(2) Screw thread shall be made to Class 2 (NC 2, ASA B1.1–1935).

Table 6. Typical Circular Forming Tool-holder for Machines in Groups Nos. 2 and 3

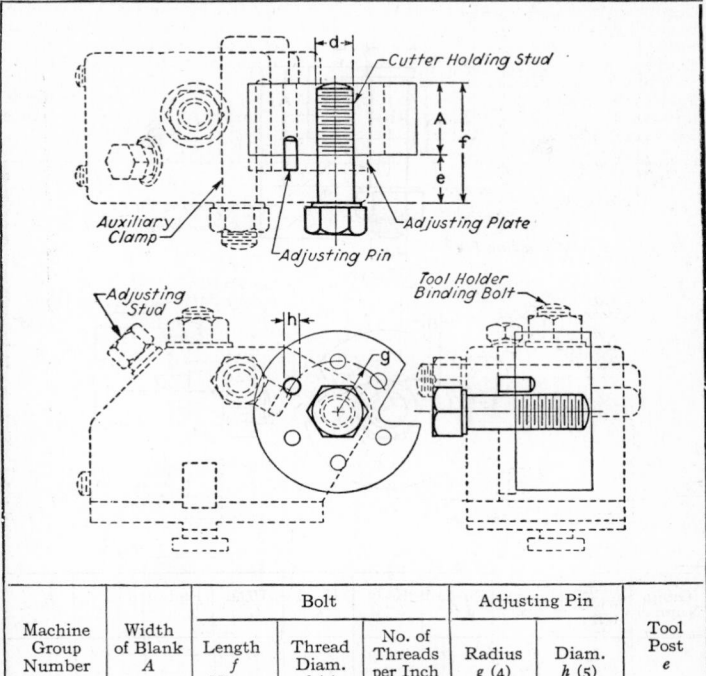

Machine Group Number	Width of Blank A	Bolt			Adjusting Pin		Tool Post e
		Length f Note 1	Thread Diam. d (2)	No. of Threads per Inch (3)	Radius g (4)	Diam. h (5)	
2	3/8	1 1/8	1/2	13	1 1/16	0.185	3/4
	1/2	1 1/4	1/2	13	1 1/16	0.185	3/4
	3/4	1 1/2	1/2	13	1 1/16	0.185	3/4
	1	1 3/4	1/2	13	1 1/16	0.185	3/4
	1 1/4	2	1/2	13	1 1/16	0.185	3/4
3	1/2	1 3/8	5/8	11	3/4	0.185	1 3/16
	3/4	1 5/8	5/8	11	3/4	0.185	1 3/16
	1	1 7/8	5/8	11	3/4	0.185	1 3/16
	1 1/4	2 1/8	5/8	11	3/4	0.185	1 3/16
	1 1/2	2 3/8	5/8	11	3/4	0.185	1 3/16

All dimensions are given in inches.
  Tolerances for dimensions not otherwise specified shall be held to ±0.010
  (1) Tolerance for length of bolt is ±1/32.
  (2) Screw thread d shall be made to Class 2 (NC 2, ASA B1.1-1935).
  (3) Commercial blanks may not, in all cases, have the standard number of threads per inch listed in this table.
  (4) Tolerance for the radius of the adjusting pin g is ±0.001.
  (5) Tolerance for the diameter of the pin is +0.000 − 0.001.

Table 7. Typical Circular Forming Tool-holder for Machines in Groups Nos. 4, 5, and 6

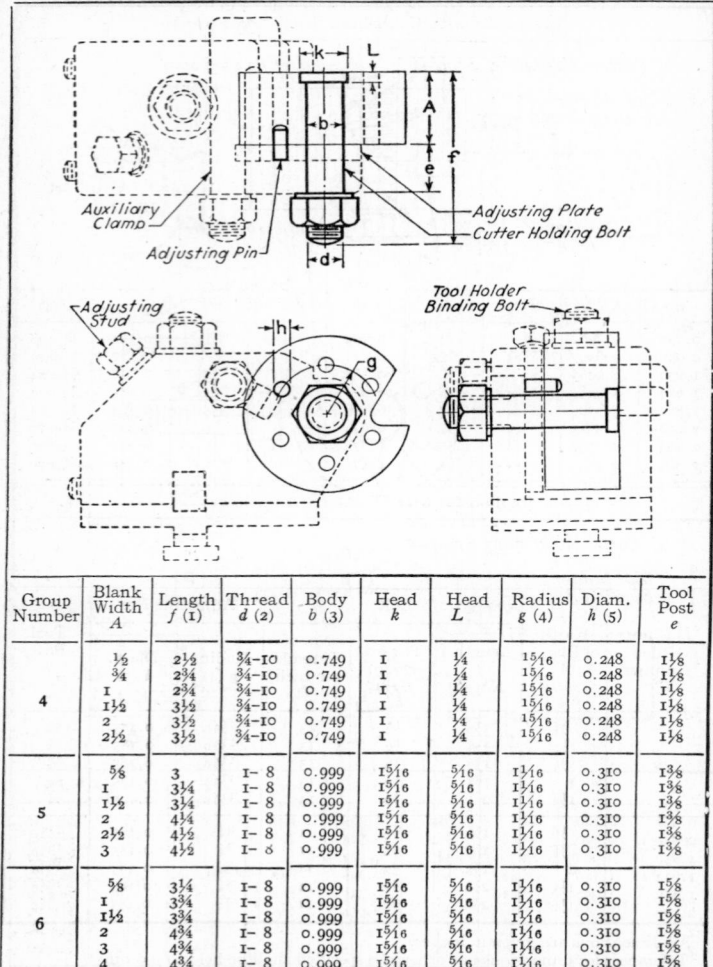

Group Number	Blank Width A	Length f (1)	Thread d (2)	Body b (3)	Head k	Head L	Radius g (4)	Diam. h (5)	Tool Post e
	½	2½	¾–10	0.749	1	¼	15⁄16	0.248	1⅛
	¾	2¾	¾–10	0.749	1	¼	15⁄16	0.248	1⅛
4	1	2¾	¾–10	0.749	1	¼	15⁄16	0.248	1⅛
	1½	3½	¾–10	0.749	1	¼	15⁄16	0.248	1⅛
	2	3½	¾–10	0.749	1	¼	15⁄16	0.248	1⅛
	2½	3½	¾–10	0.749	1	¼	15⁄16	0.248	1⅛
	⅝	3	1–8	0.999	15⁄16	5⁄16	1⅟16	0.310	1⅜
	1	3¼	1–8	0.999	15⁄16	5⁄16	1⅟16	0.310	1⅜
5	1½	3¼	1–8	0.999	15⁄16	5⁄16	1⅟16	0.310	1⅜
	2	4¼	1–8	0.999	15⁄16	5⁄16	1⅟16	0.310	1⅜
	2½	4½	1–8	0.999	15⁄16	5⁄16	1⅟16	0.310	1⅜
	3	4½	1–8	0.999	15⁄16	5⁄16	1⅟16	0.310	1⅜
	⅝	3¼	1–8	0.999	15⁄16	5⁄16	1⅟16	0.310	1⅝
	1	3¾	1–8	0.999	15⁄16	5⁄16	1⅟16	0.310	1⅝
6	1½	3¾	1–8	0.999	15⁄16	5⁄16	1⅟16	0.310	1⅝
	2	4¾	1–8	0.999	15⁄16	5⁄16	1⅟16	0.310	1⅝
	3	4¾	1–8	0.999	15⁄16	5⁄16	1⅟16	0.310	1⅝
	4	4¾	1–8	0.999	15⁄16	5⁄16	1⅟16	0.310	1⅝

Tolerance for dimensions not otherwise specified shall be held to ±0.010.
(1) Tolerance for length of bolt f is ±1⁄32.
(2) The screw thread d shall be made to Class 2 (NC 2, ASA B1.1–1935).
(3) The body of the screw b shall have tolerance of +0.000, −0.001.
(4) Tolerance for the radius of the adjusting pin g is ±0.001.
(5) Tolerance for the diameter of the adjusting pin h is +0.000, −0.001.

Table 8. Typical Dovetail Forming Tool-holders

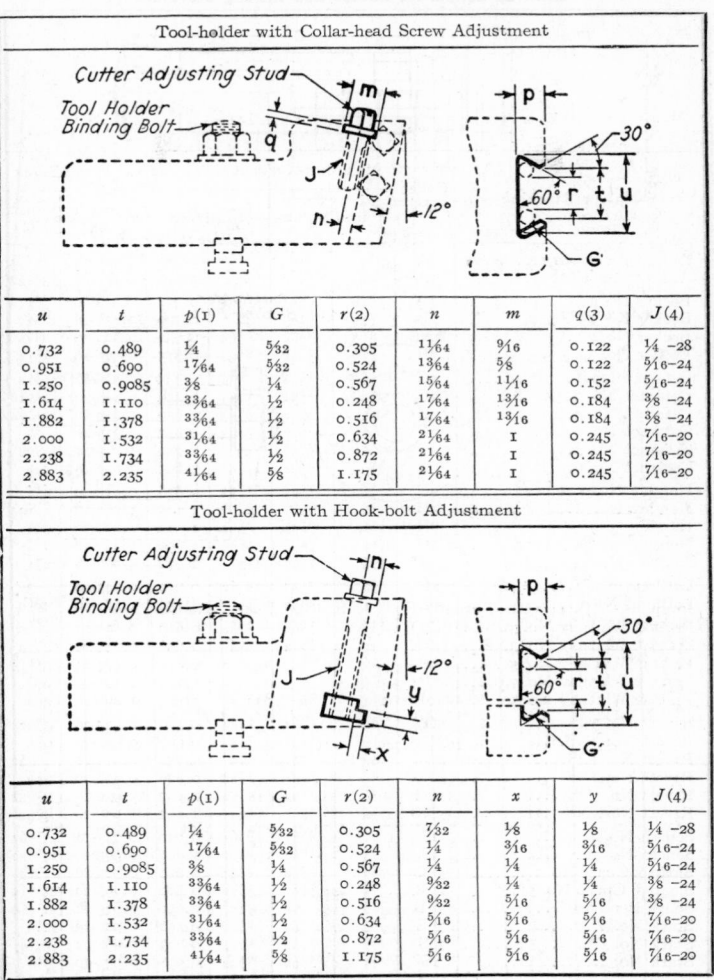

Tool-holder with Collar-head Screw Adjustment

u	t	$p(1)$	G	$r(2)$	n	m	$q(3)$	$J(4)$
0.732	0.489	¼	5⁄32	0.305	11⁄64	9⁄16	0.122	¼ –28
0.951	0.690	17⁄64	5⁄32	0.524	13⁄64	5⁄8	0.122	5⁄16–24
1.250	0.9085	3⁄8	¼	0.567	15⁄64	11⁄16	0.152	5⁄16–24
1.614	1.110	33⁄64	½	0.248	17⁄64	13⁄16	0.184	3⁄8 –24
1.882	1.378	33⁄64	½	0.516	17⁄64	13⁄16	0.184	3⁄8 –24
2.000	1.532	31⁄64	½	0.634	21⁄64	I	0.245	7⁄16–20
2.238	1.734	33⁄64	½	0.872	21⁄64	I	0.245	7⁄16–20
2.883	2.235	41⁄64	5⁄8	1.175	21⁄64	I	0.245	7⁄16–20

Tool-holder with Hook-bolt Adjustment

u	t	$p(1)$	G	$r(2)$	n	x	y	$J(4)$
0.732	0.489	¼	5⁄32	0.305	7⁄32	1⁄8	1⁄8	¼ –28
0.951	0.690	17⁄64	5⁄32	0.524	¼	3⁄16	3⁄16	5⁄16–24
1.250	0.9085	3⁄8	¼	0.567	¼	¼	¼	5⁄16–24
1.614	1.110	33⁄64	½	0.248	9⁄32	¼	¼	3⁄8 –24
1.882	1.378	33⁄64	½	0.516	9⁄32	5⁄16	5⁄16	3⁄8 –24
2.000	1.532	31⁄64	½	0.634	5⁄16	5⁄16	5⁄16	7⁄16–20
2.238	1.734	33⁄64	½	0.872	5⁄16	5⁄16	5⁄16	7⁄16–20
2.883	2.235	41⁄64	5⁄8	1.175	5⁄16	5⁄16	5⁄16	7⁄16–20

Tolerances for dimensions not otherwise specified shall be held to +0.010.
(1) Tolerance for the depth of dovetail p is ±0.003.
(2) Tolerance for the dovetail measured between plugs r is +0.002, −0.000.
(3) Tolerance for thickness of collar is +0.000, −0.002.
(4) The threads shall be made to Class 2 (NC-2, ASA B1.1—1935).

Draw-In Collets for Lathes and Milling Machines

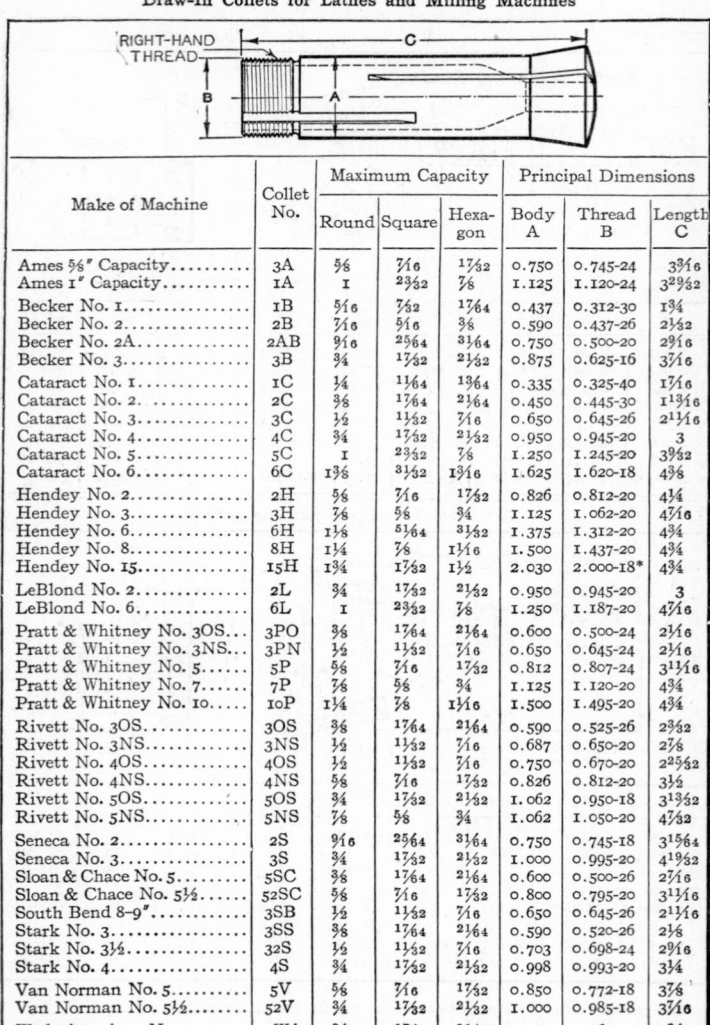

Make of Machine	Collet No.	Maximum Capacity			Principal Dimensions		
		Round	Square	Hexagon	Body A	Thread B	Length C
Ames 5/8" Capacity...........	3A	5/8	7/16	17/32	0.750	0.745-24	3 3/16
Ames 1" Capacity...........	1A	1	23/32	7/8	1.125	1.120-24	3 29/32
Becker No. 1...............	1B	5/16	7/32	17/64	0.437	0.312-30	1 3/4
Becker No. 2...............	2B	7/16	5/16	3/8	0.590	0.437-26	2 1/2
Becker No. 2A.............	2AB	9/16	25/64	31/64	0.750	0.500-20	2 9/16
Becker No. 3...............	3B	3/4	17/32	21/32	0.875	0.625-16	3 7/16
Cataract No. 1.............	1C	1/4	11/64	13/64	0.335	0.325-40	1 7/16
Cataract No. 2.............	2C	3/8	17/64	21/64	0.450	0.445-30	1 13/16
Cataract No. 3.............	3C	1/2	11/32	7/16	0.650	0.645-26	2 11/16
Cataract No. 4.............	4C	3/4	17/32	21/32	0.950	0.945-20	3
Cataract No. 5.............	5C	1	23/32	7/8	1.250	1.245-20	3 9/32
Cataract No. 6.............	6C	1 5/8	31/32	1 3/16	1.625	1.620-18	4 3/8
Hendey No. 2..............	2H	5/8	7/16	17/32	0.826	0.812-20	4 1/4
Hendey No. 3..............	3H	7/8	5/8	3/4	1.125	1.062-20	4 7/16
Hendey No. 6..............	6H	1 1/8	51/64	31/32	1.375	1.312-20	4 3/4
Hendey No. 8..............	8H	1 1/4	7/8	1 1/16	1.500	1.437-20	4 3/4
Hendey No. 15.............	15H	1 3/4	1 7/32	1 1/2	2.030	2.000-18*	4 3/4
LeBlond No. 2.............	2L	3/4	17/32	21/32	0.950	0.945-20	3
LeBlond No. 6.............	6L	1	23/32	7/8	1.250	1.187-20	4 7/16
Pratt & Whitney No. 3OS...	3PO	3/8	17/64	21/64	0.600	0.500-24	2 1/16
Pratt & Whitney No. 3NS...	3PN	1/2	11/32	7/16	0.650	0.645-24	2 1/16
Pratt & Whitney No. 5.....	5P	5/8	7/16	17/32	0.812	0.807-24	3 11/16
Pratt & Whitney No. 7.....	7P	7/8	5/8	3/4	1.125	1.120-20	4 3/4
Pratt & Whitney No. 10.....	10P	1 1/4	7/8	1 1/16	1.500	1.495-20	4 3/4
Rivett No. 3OS............	3OS	3/8	17/64	21/64	0.590	0.525-26	2 3/32
Rivett No. 3NS............	3NS	1/2	11/32	7/16	0.687	0.650-20	2 7/8
Rivett No. 4OS............	4OS	1/2	11/32	7/16	0.750	0.670-20	2 25/32
Rivett No. 4NS............	4NS	5/8	7/16	17/32	0.826	0.812-20	3 1/2
Rivett No. 5OS............	5OS	3/4	17/32	21/32	1.062	0.950-18	3 13/32
Rivett No. 5NS............	5NS	7/8	5/8	3/4	1.062	1.050-20	4 7/32
Seneca No. 2..............	2S	9/16	25/64	31/64	0.750	0.745-18	3 15/64
Seneca No. 3..............	3S	3/4	17/32	21/32	1.000	0.995-20	4 19/32
Sloan & Chace No. 5.......	5SC	3/8	17/64	21/64	0.600	0.500-26	2 7/16
Sloan & Chace No. 5 1/2......	52SC	5/8	7/16	17/32	0.800	0.795-20	3 11/16
South Bend 8-9"...........	3SB	1/2	11/32	7/16	0.650	0.645-20	2 11/16
Stark No. 3...............	3SS	3/8	17/64	21/64	0.590	0.520-26	2 1/8
Stark No. 3 1/2..............	32S	1/2	11/32	7/16	0.703	0.698-24	2 9/16
Stark No. 4...............	4S	3/4	17/32	21/32	0.998	0.993-20	3 3/4
Van Norman No. 5.........	5V	5/8	7/16	17/32	0.850	0.772-18	3 7/8
Van Norman No. 5 1/2........	52V	3/4	17/32	21/32	1.000	0.985-18	3 7/16
Wade American No. 5.......	5WA	3/4	17/32	21/32	0.970	0.965-20	3 3/8
Wade American No. 8.......	8WN	1	23/32	7/8	1.250	1.245-16	3 29/32

* This collet has a left-hand thread.

Draw-In Collets Used on Different Makes of Lathes and Milling Machines — 1

Make of Machine	Collet No.	Make of Machine	Collet No.
American 12″, 14″ and 16″ Lathes....	3H	Fay & Scott 14″, 16″, 18″, 20″ Lathes..	5NS
American 18″, 20″ and 24″ Lathes....	6H	Flather FMC—7″ Lathe..............	3C
Ames ⅝″ Capacity Bench Lathe.....	3A	Flather 13″ Lathe	4OS
Ames 1″ Capacity Bench Lathe......	1A	Flather 14″ and 16″ Cone-head	
Ames ⅝″ Capacity Bench Miller.....	3A	Lathes............................4NS	
Ames 1″ Capacity Bench Miller......	1A	Flather 18″ and 20″ Cone-head	
		Lathes............................5NS	
Becker No. 1 Vertical Miller........	1B	Flather 14″, 16″ and 20″ Geared-head	
Becker No. 2 Vertical Miller.........	2B	Lathes............................5NS	
Becker No. 2A Vertical Miller.......	2AB		
Becker No. 3 Vertical Miller........	3B	Greaves-Klusman 16″ and 18″ Lathes	3H
Boye & Emmes 14″, 16″ and 18″			
Lathes............................	6H	Hamilton 14″, 16″ and 18″ Lathes....	5C
Boye & Emmes 20″ and 24″ Lathes...	6C	Hardinge Bench Lathes and Millers	
Burke No. 0, 1, 2, 3, 4 and 5 Milling		(See Cataract)	
Machines.........................	3C	Hendey 12″ Cone Lathe.............	2H
		Hendey 12″ Geared Lathe......2H or 3H	
Carroll & Jamieson 13″, 14″ and 16″		Hendey 14″ Cone or Geared Lathes	
Lathes............................	3H	2H or 3H	
Carter & Hakes Milling Machine....	4OS	Hendey 16″ Cone or Geared Lathes	
Cataract No. 3 Bench Lathe		3H or 6H	
(½″ Capacity).....................	3C	Hendey 18″, 20″ and 24″ Cone or	
Cataract No. 4 Bench Lathe		Geared Lathes...............6H or 8H	
(¾″ Capacity)....................	4C	Hendey Centering Machine.........	2H
Cataract No. 5 Bench Lathe			
(1″ Capacity).....................	5C	Johnston 9½″ Lathe.................	3C
Cataract No. 3 Bench Miller........	3C		
Cataract No. 4 Bench Miller........	4C	LeBlond (Regal) 10″ Lathe..........	3C
Cataract No. 5 Bench Miller........	5C	LeBlond (Regal) 12″ and 14″ Lathes.	4NS
Cataract No. 3 Vertical Bench Miller.	3C	LeBlond (Regal) 16″ and 18″ Lathes.	6L
Cataract 9″ Quick-change Back-		LeBlond 12″, 14″, 16″ and 17″ Lathes.	2L
geared Lathe......................	5C	LeBlond No. 3—14″, 16″, 17″ and 18″	
Chard 16″, 18″ and 20″ Lathes......	6H	Lathes............................	3H
Chard 24″ and 28″ Lathes...........	8H	LeBlond No. 6—16″, 17″, 18″, 19″	
Cincinnati 14″ and 16″ Lathes......	3H	and 20″ Lathes....................	6L
Cincinnati 18″ and 20″ Lathes......	6H	Lehmann 16″ and 18″ Lathes........	5NS
Cisco 14″ Lathe....................	3H		
Cisco 16″, 18″ and 20″ Lathes........	8H	Monarch 9″, 10″, 11″ and 12″ O. S.	
Cushman Collet Chuck for Engine		Lathes...........................	2H
Lathes............................	15H	Monarch 14″ and 16″ Lathes.........	3H
		Monarch 18″ and 20″ Lathes.........	6H
Dalton B-4 Lathe...................	3C	Mueller 18″ Lathe..................	6H
Dalton B-6 Lathe................3C or 4C			
Davis 12″ and 14″ Lathes............	2H	Porter-Cable 9″ Production Lathe...	2H
Davis 16″ Lathe.....................	3H	Porter-Cable 12″ Carbo-Lathe.......	5C
Davis 18″ and 20″ Lathes............	6H	Porter-Cable (Mulliner) 12″ and 14″	
		Lathes............................	2H
Elgin ¾″ Capacity Bench Lathe.....	4C	Potter No. 3 Bench Lathe...........	3C

This table may be used to identify standard stock collets or to determine collet sizes for different types and makes of lathes and milling machines.

Draw-In Collets Used on Different Makes of Lathes and Milling Machines — 2

Make of Machine	Collet No.	Make of Machine	Collet No.
Potter No. 4 Bench Lathe...........	4C	Sidney Standard Pattern Lathes:	
Pratt & Whitney Bench Lathe		12″ Cone or Geared................	2H
	3PO or 3PN	14″ and 16″ Cone or Geared.......	3H
Pratt & Whitney 10″ Tool-room		18″ and 20″.....................	6H
Lathe...............................	5P	25″, 27″, 30″ and 36″..............	15H
Pratt & Whitney 13″ and 14″		Sidney Monotrol and Tritrol Lathes:	
Lathes...............................	7P	12″, 14″, 16″ and 18″.............	6H
Pratt & Whitney 16″ and 16-20″		18″ and 20″ (Heavy Pattern)......	8H
Lathes...............................	10P	24″, 30″ and 36″..............	15H
		Sloan & Chace No. 5 Bench	
Nebel Lathes (formerly Rahn-Lar-		Lathe............................	5SC
mon), 16″ and 18″, Series LN	8H	Sloan & Chace No. 5½ Bench	
Nebel Lathes, 18″, 20″, Series AA...	8H	Lathe............................	52SC
Nebel Lathes, 20″, 22″, Series B.....	8H	South Bend 8″ and 9″ Lathes........	3SB
Nebel Lathes, 24″, 26″, Series D	8H	South Bend 11″ Lathe..............	2S
		South Bend 13″ Lathe..............	4NS
Reed Prentice 18″ and 20″ Lathes....	6L	South Bend 15″ Lathe..............	4C
Reed Prentice Heavy-duty Lathes..	15H	South Bend 16″ Lathe..............	5NS
Rivett No. 3 Bench Lathe..........	3OS	South Bend 18″ Lathe..............	5C
Rivett No. 3 N.S. Bench Lathe......	3NS	South Bend 21″ Lathe..............	6H
Rivett No. 4 Bench Lathe..........	4OS	South Bend 24″ Lathe..............	6C
Rivett No. 504-4 N.S. Bench Lathe..	4NS	Springfield 14″ Lathe.........2H or 6H	
Rivett No. 608 Bench Lathe........	4NS	Springfield 16″ Lathe..........3H or 6H	
Rivett No. 5 Bench Lathe..........	5OS	Springfield 18″ and 20″ Lathes.......	6H
Rivett No. 505-606-705-5 N. S. Bench		Springfield 24″ and 26″ Lathes.......	8H
Lathes.............................	5NS	Stark No. 3 Bench Lathe............	3SS
Rivett No. 507 Bench Lathe........	4S	Stark No. 3½ Bench Lathe..........	32S
Rockford (Sundstrand) 9″, 15″ and		Stark No. 4 Bench Lathe............	4S
16″ Lathes.........................	3H	Stark Miller.......................	4S
Rockford (Economy) 12″ Lathe.....	2H		
Rockford (Economy) 14″ and 16″		Van Norman No. 5 Bench Lathe....	5V
Lathes...............................	3H	Van Norman No. 5½ Bench	
Rockford (Economy) 22″ Lathe.....	8H	Lathe............................	52V
		Van Norman Millers................	5V
Schaffner 11″ Lathe (Model "A")....	2H		
Sebastian 11″ Lathe (Old Model)....	2S	Wade American ¾″ Capacity Bench	
Sebastian (Viking) 12″, 14″, 16″ and		Lathe............................	5WA
18″ Lathes..........................	3H	Wade American 1″ Capacity Bench	
Sebastian (Viking) 20″ Lathe........	6H	Lathe............................	8WN
Sebastian (Gold Seal) 12″, 14″ and		Walcott 14″ Lathe..................	2H
16″ Lathes..........................	3H	Walcott 16″, 18″ and 20″ Lathes....	6H
Sebastian (Gold Seal) 18″ and 20″		Whitcomb Blaisdell 14″ Lathe.......	4C
Lathes...............................	6H	Whitcomb Blaisdell 16″ and 18″	
Seneca or Star 10″ and 12″ Lathes....	2S	Lathes..........................	3H
Seneca or Star 14″ Lathe...........	3S	Whitcomb Blaisdell 20″ Lathe.......	6H
Shepard Lathe.......................	4NS	Willard 13″ Lathe..................	3H
Shepard Lathe.......................	2H	Worcester 12″ Lathe................	2H
Shepard Lathe.......................	3H	Worcester 14″ Lathe................	3H

This table may be used to identify standard stock collets or to determine collet sizes for different types and makes of lathes and milling machines.

PUNCHES, DIES, AND PRESS WORK

Clearance between Punches and Dies. — The amount of clearance between a punch and die for blanking and perforating is governed by the thickness and kind of stock to be operated upon. For thin material such as tin, for example, the punch should be a close sliding fit, as, otherwise, the punching will have ragged edges, but for heavier stock there should be some clearance. The clearance between the punch and die in cutting heavy material, lessens the danger of breaking the punch and reduces the pressure required for the punching operation.

Meaning of the Term "Clearance." — There is a difference of opinion among diemakers as to the method of designating clearance. The prevailing practice of fifteen firms specializing in die work is as follows: Ten of these firms define clearance as the space between the punch and die on *one side*, or one-half the difference between the punch and die sizes. The remaining five firms consider clearance as the total difference between the punch and die sizes; for example, if the die is round, clearance equals die diameter minus punch diameter. The advantage of designating clearance as the space on each side is particularly evident in the case of dies of irregular form or of angular shape. While the practice of designating clearance as the difference between the punch and die diameters, may be satisfactory in the case of round dies, it leads to confusion when the dies are of special unsymmetrical forms. The term "clearance" should not be used in specifications without indicating clearly just what it means. According to the practice of one manufacturer of dies, the term "cutting clearance" is used to indicate the space between the punch and die on each side, and the term "die clearance" refers to the angular clearance provided below the cutting edge so that the parts will clear as they fall through the die. The term "clearance" as here used means the space on one side only; hence, for round dies, clearance equals die radius minus punch radius.

Clearances Generally Allowed. — For brass and soft steel, most dies are given a clearance on one side equal to the stock thickness multiplied by 0.05 or 0.06; but one-half of this clearance is preferred for some classes of work, and a clearance equal to the stock thickness multiplied by 0.10 may give the cleanest fracture for certain other operations such, for example, as punching holes in ductile steel boiler plate.

Where Clearance is Applied. — Whether clearance is deducted from the diameter of the punch or added to the diameter of the die depends upon the nature of the work. If a blank of given size is required, the die is made to that size and the punch is made smaller. Inversely, when holes of a given size are required, the punch is made to the diameter wanted and the die is made larger. Therefore, for blanking to a given size, the clearance is deducted from the size of the punch, and for perforating, the clearance is added to the size of the die.

Effect of Clearance on Working Pressure. — Clearance not only affects the smoothness of the fracture, but also the pressure required for punching or blanking. This pressure is greatest when the punch diameter is small compared to the thickness of the stock. In one test, for example, a punching pressure of about 32,000 pounds was required to punch ¾-inch holes into ⁵⁄₁₆-inch mild steel plate when the clearance was about 10 per cent. With a clearance of about 4½ per cent, the pressure increased to 33,000 pounds and a clearance of 2¾ per cent resulted in a pressure of 34,500 pounds.

Soft ductile metal requires more clearance than hard metal, although it has been common practice to increase the clearance for the harder metals. In punching holes in fairly hard steel, a clean fracture was obtained with a clearance of only 0.03 times stock thickness.

Angular Clearance for Dies. — The amount of angular clearance ordinarily given a blanking die varies from one to two degrees, although dies that are to be used for producing a comparatively small number of blanks are sometimes given a clearance angle of four or five degrees to facilitate making the die quickly. When a large number of blanks are required, a clearance of about one degree is used. There are two methods of giving clearance to dies: In one case the clearance extends to the top face of the die; in the other, there is a space about ⅛ inch below the cutting edge which is left practically straight, or having a very small amount of clearance. For very soft metal, such as soft, thin brass, the first method is employed, but for harder material, such as hard brass, steel, etc., it is better to have a very shallow clearance for a short distance below the cutting edge. When a die is made in this way, thousands of blanks can be cut with little variation in their size, as grinding the die face will not enlarge the hole to any appreciable extent.

Lubricants for Press Work. — Dies are often run without lubrication, but they will last longer if oiled slightly. The oil is applied to the stock either from a saturated felt-roller, brush or pad, or by coating one sheet thickly and then feeding it through the rolls. By the latter method, the rolls are coated with sufficient lubricant for a number of sheets, and a very thin coat is applied to the material so that the work does not have to be cleaned, as is sometimes necessary when a felt-roller or pad is used. Lard or sperm oil is used when punching iron, steel or copper. For drawing steel, the following mixture is recommended: 25 per cent flaked graphite; 25 per cent beef tallow; and 50 per cent lard oil. This mixture should be heated and the work dipped into it. Oildag mixed with heavy grease is also used for steel, and a thin mixture of grease (preferably tallow) and white lead has proved satisfactory. The following compound is also used for drawing sheet steel of a mild grade: Mix one pound of white lead, one quart of fish oil, three ounces of black lead, and one pint of water. These ingredients should be boiled until thoroughly mixed. For drawing brass and copper, a solution obtained by dissolving soap in hot water is often used. (Ivory soap has given good results.) The quantity of soap to use depends upon the thickness of the metal, a thin solution being preferable for thin stock. For cutting aluminum, use kerosene, and for drawing aluminum, use kerosene or vaseline of a cheap grade. Lard oil is also applied to aluminum when drawing deep shells. Aluminum should never be worked without a lubricant. For many classes of die work, no lubricant is required, especially when the metal is of a "greasy" nature, like tin plate, for instance.

Annealing Drawn Shells. — When drawing steel, iron, brass or copper, annealing is necessary after two or three draws have been made, as the metal is hardened by the drawing process. For steel and brass, anneal between every other reduction, at least. Tin plate or stock that cannot be annealed without spoiling the finish must ordinarily be drawn to size in one or two operations. Aluminum can be drawn deeper and with less annealing than the other commercial metals, provided the proper grade is used. In case it is necessary to anneal aluminum, this can be done by heating it in a muffle furnace, care being taken to see that the temperature does not exceed 700 degrees F.

Drawing Brass. — When drawing brass shells or cup-shaped articles, it is usually possible to make the depth of the first draw equal to the diameter of the shell. By heating brass to a temperature just below what would show a dull red in a dark room, it is possible to draw difficult shapes, otherwise almost impossible, and to get shapes with square corners.

Drawing Rectangular Shapes. — When square or rectangular shapes are to be drawn, the radius of the corners should be as large as possible, because it is in the corners that defects occur when drawing. Moreover, the smaller the radius, the less the depth which can be obtained in the first draw. The maximum depths which can be drawn with corners of a given radii are approximately as follows: With a radius of ³⁄₃₂ to ³⁄₁₆ inch, depth of draw, 1 inch; radius ³⁄₁₆ to ³⁄₈ inch, depth 1½ inch; radius ³⁄₈ to ½ inch, depth, 2 inches; radius ½ to ¾ inch, depth, 3 inches. These figures are taken from actual practice and can doubtless be exceeded slightly when using extra good metal. If the box needs to be quite deep and the radius is quite small, two or more drawing operations will be necessary.

When Punch and Die should be Hardened. — The blanking or cutting dies used on comparatively thin stock, such as tin, brass, aluminum, iron, steel, copper, zinc, etc., are ordinarily hardened and tempered to suit the work, and the punch is left quite soft, so that it can be "hammered up" to fit the die when worn. This practice is followed in some plants for all metals less than ¹⁄₁₆ inch thick which are not harder than iron or very mild steel. After the end of the punch has been upset by hammering, the punch and the die are oiled and forced together, which causes the hard die to shave the punch to a close fit. If the die is dull, it should be sharpened prior to this shearing operation. For some classes of work, the punch is made hard and the die soft. Both the punch and die should be hardened when they are to be used for blanking thick iron, steel, brass or other heavy metals.

Speeds and Pressures for Presses. — The speeds for presses equipped with cutting dies depend largely upon the kind of material being worked, and its thickness. For punching and shearing ordinary metals not over ¼ inch thick, the speeds usually range between 50 and 200 strokes per minute, 100 strokes per minute being a fair average. For punching metal over ¼ inch thick, geared presses with speeds ranging from 25 to 75 strokes per minute are commonly employed.

The cutting pressures required depend upon the shearing strength of the material, and the actual area of the surface being severed. For round holes the pressure required equals the circumference of the hole × the thickness of the stock × the shearing strength. To allow for some excess pressure, the tensile strength may be substituted for the shearing strength; the tensile strength for these calculations may be roughly assumed as follows: Mild steel, 60,000 pounds per square inch; wrought iron, 50,000 pounds; bronze, 40,000 pounds; copper, 30,000 pounds; aluminum, 20,000 pounds; zinc, 10,000 pounds; tin and lead, 5,000 pounds.

Pressure required for Punching. — The following approximate rule may be used for rapidly finding the pressure in tons required for punching circular holes in sheet steel: Multiply the diameter of the hole in inches by the thickness of the sheet steel and multiply this product by 80. The result is the pressure in tons required. To find the pressure required for punching holes in brass, multiply the diameter of the hole by the thickness, and multiply this product by 65.

Example: — What pressure is required for punching a hole 2 inches in diameter through ¼-inch steel stock? According to the rule, 2 × ¼ × 80 = 40 tons.

If a hole is not circular, use as a factor, instead of the diameter of the hole, one-third of the total length of the outline of the hole to be punched. For example, if a hole 1-inch square is to be punched through ¼-inch metal, the total outline (the four sides added together) is 4 inches. One-third of this is 1⅓, and the pressure in tons required equals 1⅓ × ¼ × 80 = 26⅔ tons.

Shut Height of Press. — The term "shut height" as applied to power presses, indicates the die space when the slide is at the bottom of its stroke and the slide connection has been adjusted upward as far as possible. The "shut height" is the distance from the lower face of the slide, either to the top of the bed or to the

Pressures Required for Punching

Pressure required to punch 0.25 per cent carbon steel of 65,000 pounds per square inch tensile strength. Circumference of hole × thickness of plate × 50,000 = pressure required in pounds, approximately.

Thickness of Plate, Inches	Diameter of Punch, Inches						
	$1\frac{1}{4}$	$1\frac{1}{8}$	1	$1\frac{5}{16}$	$\frac{7}{8}$	$1\frac{3}{16}$	$\frac{3}{4}$
	Pressure in Pounds						
$\frac{1}{8}$	24,600	22,100	19,600	18,400	17,200	16,000	14,700
$\frac{3}{16}$	36,800	33,100	29,500	27,600	25,800	24,000	22,100
$\frac{1}{4}$	49,100	44,200	39,300	36,800	34,400	32,000	29,500
$\frac{5}{16}$	61,400	55,200	49,100	46,000	42,900	39,900	36,800
$\frac{3}{8}$	73,600	66,300	58,900	55,200	51,500	47,900	44,200
$\frac{7}{16}$	85,900	77,300	68,700	64,400	60,100	55,900	51,500
$\frac{1}{2}$	98,200	88,400	78,500	73,600	68,700	63,800	58,900
$\frac{9}{16}$	110,400	99,400	88,400	82,800	77,300	71,800	66,200
$\frac{5}{8}$	122,700	110,400	98,200	92,000	85,900	79,800	73,600
$\frac{11}{16}$	135,000	121,400	108,000	101,200	94,500	87,800	81,000
$\frac{3}{4}$	147,300	132,500	117,800	110,400	103,100	95,800	88,400
$1\frac{3}{16}$	159,500	143,500	127,600	119,600	111,700	103,700	95,700
$\frac{7}{8}$	171,800	154,600	137,400	128,800	120,300	111,700	103,100
$1\frac{5}{16}$	184,100	165,600	147,200	138,000	128,800	119,700	......
1	196,400	176,700	157,100	147,200	137,400	......	......
$1\frac{1}{8}$	220,900	198,800	176,700	165,600	......	......	......
$1\frac{1}{4}$	245,400	220,900	196,400	......	......	......	......

Thickness of Plate, Inches	Diameter of Punch, Inches						
	$1\frac{1}{16}$	$\frac{5}{8}$	$\frac{9}{16}$	$\frac{1}{2}$	$\frac{7}{16}$	$\frac{3}{8}$	$\frac{5}{16}$	$\frac{1}{4}$
	Pressure in Pounds						
$\frac{1}{8}$	13,500	12,300	11,100	9,800	8,600	7,400	6,100	4,900
$\frac{3}{16}$	20,300	18,400	16,600	14,700	12,900	11,000	9,200	7,300
$\frac{1}{4}$	27,000	24,500	22,100	19,600	17,200	14,700	12,300	9,800
$\frac{5}{16}$	33,800	30,700	27,600	24,500	21,500	18,400	15,300	12,300
$\frac{3}{8}$	40,500	36,800	33,200	29,500	25,800	22,100	18,400	14,700
$\frac{7}{16}$	47,300	42,900	38,600	34,400	30,100	25,800	21,400	.....
$\frac{1}{2}$	54,000	49,100	44,200	39,300	34,400	29,600	......	.....
$\frac{9}{16}$	60,800	55,200	49,700	44,200	38,700	.....	......	.....
$\frac{5}{8}$	67,500	61,400	55,300	49,100	.....	.....	......	.....
$\frac{11}{16}$	74,300	67,500	60,900	.....	.....	.....	......	.....
$\frac{3}{4}$	81,000	73,600	......	.....	.....	.....	......	.....
$1\frac{3}{16}$	87,800	......	......	.....	.....	.....	......	.....

top of the bolster plate, there being two methods of determining it; hence, this term should always be accompanied by a definition explaining its meaning. According to one press manufacturer, the safest plan is to define "shut height" as the distance from the top of the bolster to the bottom of the slide, with the stroke down and the adjustment up, because most dies are mounted on bolster plates of standard thickness, and a misunderstanding which results in providing too much die space is less serious than having insufficient die space. It is believed that the expression

Standard Punches and Dies

Pratt & Whitney Co.

No. of Punch	Diam. A	B	C	D
2	$\frac{1}{8}$ to $\frac{3}{8}$	$1\frac{3}{32}$	$1\frac{7}{32}$	$1\frac{9}{32}$
3	$\frac{1}{8}$ to $\frac{9}{16}$	$1\frac{9}{32}$	$2\frac{3}{32}$	$1\frac{15}{32}$
4	$\frac{1}{4}$ to $\frac{13}{16}$	$2\frac{5}{32}$	$2\frac{9}{32}$	$1\frac{1}{2}$
5	$\frac{3}{8}$ to 1	$1\frac{1}{32}$	$1\frac{5}{32}$	$1\frac{15}{16}$
6	$\frac{9}{16}$ to $1\frac{1}{4}$	$1\frac{7}{32}$	$1\frac{3}{8}$	$2\frac{3}{8}$
7	$\frac{11}{16}$ to $1\frac{9}{16}$	$1\frac{17}{32}$	$1\frac{11}{16}$	$2\frac{11}{16}$
8	1 to $1\frac{3}{4}$	$1\frac{25}{32}$	$2\frac{1}{16}$	3
9	$1\frac{1}{2}$ to $2\frac{1}{4}$	$2\frac{9}{32}$	$2\frac{9}{16}$	3
10	2 to $2\frac{5}{8}$	$2\frac{21}{32}$	$2\frac{31}{32}$	3

No. of Die	Diam. Hole E	F	G
2	$\frac{1}{8}$ to $\frac{5}{16}$	$\frac{3}{4}$	$\frac{5}{8}$
3	$\frac{1}{8}$ to $\frac{9}{16}$	1	$\frac{3}{4}$
4	$\frac{1}{4}$ to $\frac{3}{4}$	$1\frac{1}{2}$	1
5	$\frac{1}{4}$ to 1	2	1
6	$\frac{1}{2}$ to $1\frac{1}{4}$	$2\frac{3}{8}$	$1\frac{1}{4}$
7	$\frac{3}{4}$ to $1\frac{9}{16}$	$2\frac{7}{8}$	$1\frac{1}{4}$

Richards

No. of Punch	Diam. A	B	C	D
0	$\frac{5}{32}$ to $\frac{13}{32}$	$1\frac{3}{32}$	$\frac{9}{16}$	$1\frac{1}{4}$
1	$\frac{9}{32}$ to $\frac{9}{16}$	$\frac{9}{16}$	$\frac{3}{4}$	$1\frac{1}{2}$
2	$\frac{9}{16}$ to $\frac{13}{16}$	$\frac{13}{16}$	1	$1\frac{1}{2}$
3	$\frac{11}{16}$ to $1\frac{1}{16}$	$1\frac{1}{16}$	$1\frac{1}{4}$	$1\frac{7}{8}$
3 S	$\frac{9}{32}$ to $\frac{9}{16}$	$1\frac{13}{16}$	1	$1\frac{7}{8}$
4	$\frac{15}{16}$ to $1\frac{5}{16}$	$1\frac{5}{16}$	$1\frac{1}{2}$	$2\frac{1}{4}$
4 S	$\frac{9}{16}$ to $1\frac{1}{16}$	$1\frac{1}{16}$	$1\frac{1}{4}$	$2\frac{1}{4}$
5	$1\frac{1}{16}$ to $1\frac{9}{16}$	$1\frac{9}{16}$	$1\frac{7}{8}$	$2\frac{5}{8}$
5 S	$\frac{11}{16}$ to $1\frac{5}{16}$	$1\frac{5}{16}$	$1\frac{1}{2}$	$2\frac{5}{8}$

No. of Die	Diam. Hole E	F	G
1	$\frac{1}{8}$ to $\frac{9}{16}$	$1\frac{1}{4}$	$\frac{3}{4}$
2	$\frac{1}{4}$ to $\frac{13}{16}$	$1\frac{5}{8}$	$\frac{7}{8}$
3	$\frac{3}{4}$ to $1\frac{1}{16}$	2	1
5	$\frac{15}{16}$ to $1\frac{9}{16}$	$2\frac{7}{8}$	$1\frac{1}{8}$
....	....	......	.....
....	....	......	.....

Cleveland Punch and Shear Works Co.

No. of Punch	Diam. A	B	C	D
6	$\frac{1}{8}$ to $\frac{7}{16}$	$\frac{9}{16}$	$\frac{3}{4}$	$2\frac{1}{8}$
11	$\frac{15}{32}$ to $\frac{11}{16}$	$\frac{3}{4}$	1	$2\frac{1}{8}$
16	$\frac{23}{32}$ to $1\frac{1}{16}$	$1\frac{1}{16}$	$1\frac{7}{32}$	$2\frac{1}{8}$
23	$1\frac{1}{16}$ to $1\frac{5}{16}$	$1\frac{5}{16}$	$1\frac{1}{2}$	$2\frac{1}{8}$
28	$1\frac{5}{16}$ to $1\frac{9}{16}$	$1\frac{9}{16}$	$1\frac{7}{8}$	$2\frac{5}{8}$
29	$1\frac{5}{16}$ to $1\frac{9}{16}$	$1\frac{9}{16}$	$1\frac{7}{8}$	$3\frac{3}{8}$
30	$1\frac{5}{16}$ to $2\frac{1}{16}$	$2\frac{1}{16}$	$2\frac{1}{4}$	$2\frac{5}{8}$
31	$1\frac{5}{16}$ to $2\frac{1}{16}$	$2\frac{1}{16}$	$2\frac{1}{4}$	$3\frac{3}{8}$
32	$2\frac{1}{16}$ to $2\frac{9}{16}$	$2\frac{9}{16}$	$2\frac{13}{16}$	$3\frac{3}{8}$

No. of Die	Diam. Hole E	F	G
42	$\frac{1}{8}$ to $\frac{9}{16}$	1	$\frac{7}{8}$
43	$\frac{1}{8}$ to $\frac{5}{8}$	$1\frac{1}{4}$	$\frac{7}{8}$
44	$\frac{1}{8}$ to $\frac{5}{8}$	$1\frac{5}{16}$	$\frac{3}{4}$
45	$\frac{1}{4}$ to $\frac{15}{16}$	$1\frac{1}{2}$	$\frac{7}{8}$
46	$\frac{1}{4}$ to $\frac{15}{16}$	$1\frac{1}{2}$	1
48	$\frac{1}{4}$ to $\frac{15}{16}$	$1\frac{9}{16}$	$2\frac{7}{32}$
55	$\frac{1}{4}$ to $1\frac{1}{16}$	$1\frac{13}{16}$	$1\frac{1}{8}$
60	$\frac{1}{2}$ to $1\frac{1}{4}$	2	$1\frac{1}{8}$
65	$\frac{5}{8}$ to $1\frac{5}{8}$	$2\frac{1}{2}$	$1\frac{1}{4}$

"shut height" was applied first to dies rather than to presses, the shut height of a die being the distance from the bottom of the lower section to the top of the upper section or punch, excluding the shank, and measured when the punch is in the lowest working position.

Diameters of Shell Blanks. — The diameters of blanks for drawing plain cylindrical shells can be obtained from the accompanying table, which gives a very close approximation for thin stock. The blank diameters given in this table are for sharp-cornered shells and are found by the following formula:

$$D = \sqrt{d^2 + 4\,dh}, \tag{1}$$

in which D = diameter of flat blank; d = diameter of finished shell; h = height of finished shell.

Example: — If the diameter of the finished shell is to be 1.5 inch, and the height, 2 inches, the trial diameter of the blank would be found as follows:

$$D = \sqrt{1.5^2 + 4 \times 1.5 \times 2} = \sqrt{14.25} = 3.78 \text{ inches.}$$

For a round-cornered cup, the following formula, in which r equals the radius of the corner, will give fairly accurate diameters, provided the radius does not exceed, say, ¼ the height of the shell:

$$D_{,} = \sqrt{d^2 + 4\,dh} - r. \tag{2}$$

These formulas are based on the assumption that the thickness of the drawn shell is the same as the original thickness of the stock, and that the blank is so proportioned that its area will equal the area of the drawn shell. This method of calculating the blank diameter is quite accurate for thin material, when there is only a slight reduction in the thickness of the metal incident to drawing; but when heavy stock is drawn and the thickness of the finished shell is much less than the original thickness of the stock, the blank diameter obtained from Formulas (1) or (2) will be too large, because when the stock is drawn thinner, there is an increase in area. When an appreciable reduction in thickness is to be made, the blank diameter can be obtained by first determining the "mean height" of the drawn shell by the following formula. This formula is only approximately correct, but will give results sufficiently accurate for most work:

$$M = \frac{ht}{T} \tag{3}$$

in which M = approximate mean height of drawn shell; h = height of drawn shell; t = thickness of shell; T = thickness of metal before drawing.

After determining the mean height, the blank diameter for the required shell diameter is obtained from the table previously referred to, the mean height being used instead of the actual height.

Example: — Suppose a shell 2 inches in diameter and 3¾ inches high is to be drawn, and that the original thickness of the stock is 0.050 inch, and thickness of drawn shell, 0.040 inch. To what diameter should the blank be cut? Using Formula (3) to obtain the mean height:

$$M = \frac{ht}{T} = \frac{3.75 \times 0.040}{0.050} = 3 \text{ inches.}$$

According to the table, the blank diameter for a shell 2 inches in diameter and 3 inches high is 5.29 inches. This formula is accurate enough for all practical purposes, unless the reduction in the thickness of the metal is greater than about one-fifth the original thickness. When there is considerable reduction, a blank calculated by this formula produces a shell that is too long. This, however, is an error in the right direction, as the edges of drawn shells are ordinarily trimmed.

If the shell has a rounded corner, the radius of the corner should be deducted from the figures given in the table. For example, if the shell referred to in the foregoing example had a corner of ¼-inch radius, the blank diameter would equal 5.29 − 0.25 = 5.04 inches.

Another formula which is sometimes used for obtaining blank diameters for shells, when there is a reduction in the thickness of the stock, is as follows:

$$D = \sqrt{a^2 + \left(a^2 - b^2\right)\frac{h}{t}} \qquad (4)$$

In this formula D = blank diameter; a = outside diameter; b = inside diameter; t = thickness of shell at bottom; h = depth of shell. This formula is based on the cubic contents of the drawn shell. It is assumed that the shells are cylindrical, and no allowance is made for a rounded corner at the bottom, or for trimming the shell after drawing. To allow for trimming, add the required amount to depth h. When a shell is of irregular cross-section, if its weight is known, the blank diameter can be determined by the following formula:

$$D = 1.1284 \sqrt{\frac{W}{wt}} \qquad (5)$$

in which D = blank diameter in inches; W = weight of shell; w = weight of metal per cubic inch; t = thickness of the shell.

In the construction of dies for producing shells, especially of irregular form, a common method of procedure is to make the drawing parts first. The actual blank diameter can then be determined by trial. One method is to cut a trial blank as near to size as can be estimated. The outline of this blank is then scribed on a flat sheet, after which the blank is drawn. If the finished shell shows that the blank is not of the right diameter, a new trial blank is cut either larger or smaller than the size indicated by the line previously scribed, this line acting as a guide. If a model shell is available, the blank diameter can also be determined as follows: First cut a blank somewhat large, and from the same material used for making the model; then, reduce the size of the blank until its weight equals the weight of the model.

Depth and Diameter Reductions of Drawn Shells. —The depth to which metal can be drawn in one operation depends upon the quality and kind of material, its thickness, the slant or angle of the dies, and the amount that the stock is thinned or "ironed" in drawing. A general rule for determining the depth to which cylindrical shells can be drawn in one operation is as follows: The depth or length of the first draw should never be greater than the diameter of the shell. If the shell is to have a flange at the top, it may not be practicable to draw as deeply as is indicated by this rule, unless the metal is extra good, because the stock is subjected to a higher tensile stress, owing to the larger blank which is necessary for forming the flange. According to another rule, the depth given the shell on the first draw should equal one-third the diameter of the blank. Ordinarily, it is possible to draw sheet steel of any thickness up to ¼ inch, so that the diameter of the first shell equals about six-tenths of the blank diameter. When drawing plain shells, the amount that the diameter is reduced for each draw must be governed by the quality of the metal and its susceptibility to drawing. The reduction for various thicknesses of metal is about as follows:

Approximate thickness of sheet steel	1/16	1/8	3/16	1/4	5/16
Possible reduction in diameter for each succeeding step, per cent	20	15	12	10	8

Diameters of Blanks for Drawn Shells

Diam. of Shell	Height of Shell																			
	¼	½	¾	1	1¼	1½	1¾	2	2¼	2½	2¾	3	3¼	3½	3¾	4	4½	5	5½	6
¼	0.56	0.75	0.90	1.03	1.14	1.25	1.35	1.44	1.52	1.60	1.68	1.75	1.82	1.89	1.95	2.01	2.14	2.25	2.36	2.46
½	0.87	1.12	1.32	1.50	1.66	1.80	1.94	2.06	2.18	2.29	2.40	2.50	2.60	2.69	2.78	2.87	3.04	3.21	3.36	3.50
¾	1.14	1.44	1.68	1.68	2.08	2.25	2.41	2.56	2.70	2.84	2.97	3.09	3.21	3.33	3.44	3.54	3.75	3.95	4.13	4.31
1	1.41	1.73	2.00	2.24	2.45	2.65	2.83	3.00	3.16	3.32	3.46	3.61	3.74	3.87	4.00	4.12	4.36	4.58	4.80	5.00
1¼	1.68	2.01	2.30	2.56	2.79	3.01	3.21	3.40	3.58	3.75	3.91	4.07	4.22	4.37	4.51	4.64	4.91	5.15	5.39	5.62
1½	1.94	2.29	2.60	2.87	3.12	3.36	3.57	3.78	3.97	4.15	4.33	4.50	4.66	4.82	4.98	5.12	5.41	5.68	5.94	6.18
1¾	2.19	2.56	2.88	3.17	3.44	3.68	3.91	4.13	4.34	4.53	4.72	4.91	5.08	5.26	5.41	5.58	5.88	6.17	6.45	6.71
2	2.45	2.83	3.16	3.46	3.74	4.00	4.24	4.47	4.69	4.90	5.10	5.29	5.48	5.66	5.83	6.00	6.32	6.63	6.93	7.21
2¼	2.70	3.09	3.44	3.75	4.04	4.31	4.56	4.80	5.03	5.25	5.46	5.66	5.86	6.05	6.23	6.41	6.75	7.07	7.39	7.69
2½	2.96	3.36	3.71	4.03	4.34	4.61	4.87	5.12	5.36	5.59	5.81	6.02	6.22	6.42	6.61	6.80	7.16	7.50	7.82	8.14
2¾	3.21	3.61	3.98	4.31	4.62	4.91	5.18	5.44	5.68	5.92	6.15	6.37	6.58	6.79	6.99	7.18	7.55	7.91	8.25	8.58
3	3.46	3.87	4.24	4.58	4.90	5.20	5.48	5.74	6.00	6.25	6.48	6.71	6.93	7.14	7.35	7.55	7.94	8.31	8.66	9.00
3¼	3.71	4.13	4.51	4.85	5.18	5.48	5.77	6.04	6.31	6.56	6.80	7.04	7.27	7.49	7.70	7.91	8.31	8.69	9.06	9.41
3½	3.97	4.39	4.77	5.12	5.45	5.77	6.06	6.34	6.62	6.87	7.12	7.36	7.60	7.83	8.05	8.26	8.67	9.07	9.45	9.81
3¾	4.22	4.64	5.03	5.39	5.73	6.05	6.35	6.64	6.91	7.18	7.44	7.69	7.92	8.16	8.38	8.61	9.03	9.44	9.83	10.20
4	4.47	4.90	5.29	5.66	6.00	6.32	6.63	6.93	7.21	7.48	7.75	8.00	8.25	8.49	8.72	8.94	9.38	9.80	10.20	10.58
4¼	4.72	5.15	5.55	5.92	6.27	6.60	6.91	7.22	7.50	7.78	8.05	8.31	8.56	8.81	9.04	9.28	9.72	10.15	10.56	10.96
4½	4.98	5.41	5.81	6.19	6.54	6.87	7.19	7.50	7.79	8.08	8.35	8.62	8.87	9.12	9.37	9.60	10.06	10.50	10.92	11.32
4¾	5.22	5.66	6.07	6.45	6.80	7.15	7.47	7.78	8.08	8.37	8.65	8.92	9.18	9.44	9.69	9.93	10.40	10.84	11.27	11.69
5	5.48	5.92	6.32	6.71	7.07	7.42	7.75	8.06	8.37	8.66	8.94	9.22	9.49	9.75	10.00	10.25	10.72	11.18	11.62	12.04
5¼	5.73	6.17	6.58	6.97	7.33	7.69	8.02	8.34	8.65	8.95	9.24	9.52	9.79	10.05	10.31	10.56	11.05	11.51	11.96	12.39
5½	5.98	6.42	6.84	7.23	7.60	7.95	8.29	8.62	8.93	9.23	9.53	9.81	10.08	10.36	10.62	10.87	11.37	11.84	12.30	12.74
5¾	6.23	6.68	7.09	7.49	7.86	8.22	8.56	8.89	9.21	9.52	9.81	10.10	10.38	10.66	10.92	11.18	11.69	12.17	12.63	13.08
6	6.48	6.93	7.35	7.75	8.12	8.49	8.83	9.17	9.49	9.80	10.10	10.39	10.68	10.95	11.23	11.49	12.00	12.49	12.96	13.42

For example, if a shell made of ⅟₁₆ inch stock is 3 inches in diameter after the first draw, it can be reduced 20 per cent on the next draw, and so on until the required diameter is obtained. These figures are based upon the assumption that the shell is annealed after the first drawing operation, and at least between every two of the following operations. Necking operations — that is, the drawing out of a short portion of the lower part of the cup into a long neck — may be done without such frequent annealings. In double-action presses, where the inside of the cup is supported by a bushing during drawing, the reductions possible may be increased to 30, 24, 18, 15 and 12 per cent, respectively. (The latter figures may also be used for brass in single-action presses.)

When a hole is to be pierced at the bottom of a cup and the remaining metal is to be drawn after the hole has been pierced or punched, always pierce from the opposite direction to that in which the stock is to be drawn after piercing. In extreme cases, it is necessary to machine the metal around the pierced hole in order to prevent the starting of cracks or flaws in the subsequent drawing operations.

The foregoing figures represent conservative practice and it is often possible to make greater reductions than are indicated by these figures, especially when using a good drawing metal. Taper shells require smaller reductions than cylindrical shells, because the metal tends to wrinkle if the shell to be drawn is much larger than the punch. The amount that the stock is "ironed" or thinned out while being drawn must also be considered, because a reduction in gage or thickness means greater pressure of the punch against the bottom of the shell; hence the amount that the shell diameter is reduced for each drawing operation must be lessened when much ironing is necessary. The extent to which a shell can be ironed in one drawing operation ranges between 0.002 and 0.004 inch per side, and should not exceed 0.001 inch on the final draw, if a good finish is required.

Allowances for Bending Sheet Metal. — In bending steel, brass, bronze or other metals, the problem is to find the length of straight stock required for each bend; then these lengths are added to the lengths of the straight sections to obtain the total length of the material before bending.

If L = length, in inches, of straight stock required before bending; T = thickness in inches; R = inside radius of bend in inches.

For 90-degree bends in soft brass and soft copper

$$\text{Table 1 or } L = (0.55 \times T) + (1.57 \times R) \tag{1}$$

For 90-degree bends in half-hard brass, half-hard copper and soft steel

$$\text{Table 2 or } L = (0.64 \times T) + (1.57 \times R) \tag{2}$$

For 90-degree bends in bronze, hard copper, cold-rolled steel and spring steel

$$\text{Table 3 or } L = (0.71 \times T) + (1.57 \times R) \tag{3}$$

Angle of Bend Other Than 90 Degrees: For angles other than 90 degrees, find length L, using tables or formulas, and multiply L by angle of bend, in degrees, divided by 90, to find length of stock before bending. In using this rule, note that *angle of bend* is the angle through which the material has actually been bent; hence, it is not in all cases the angle as given on a drawing. To illustrate, in Fig. 1 (see diagram), the angle on the drawing is 60 degrees, but the angle of bend A is 120 degrees (180 − 60 = 120); in Fig. 2, the angle of bend A is 60 degrees; in Fig. 3, angle A is 90 − 30 = 60 degrees. The Formulas (1), (2) and (3) are based upon extensive experiments of the Westinghouse Electric & Mfg. Co. They apply to parts bent with simple tools or on the bench, where limits of plus or minus ⅟₆₄ inch are specified. If a part has two or more bends of the same radius, it is, of course, only necessary to obtain the length required for one of the bends and then multiply by the number of bends, thus obtaining the total allowance for the bent sections.

Table 1. Lengths of Straight Stock Required for 90-Degree Bends in Soft Copper and Soft Brass

Radius R of Bend, Inches	Thickness T of Material, Inch												
	1/64	1/32	3/64	1/16	5/64	3/32	1/8	5/32	3/16	7/32	1/4	9/32	5/16
1/32	0.058	0.066	0.075	0.083	0.092	0.101	0.118	0.135	0.152	0.169	0.187	0.204	0.221
3/64	0.083	0.091	0.100	0.108	0.117	0.126	0.143	0.160	0.177	0.194	0.212	0.229	0.246
1/16	0.107	0.115	0.124	0.132	0.141	0.150	0.167	0.184	0.201	0.218	0.236	0.253	0.270
3/32	0.156	0.164	0.173	0.181	0.190	0.199	0.216	0.233	0.250	0.267	0.285	0.302	0.319
1/8	0.205	0.213	0.222	0.230	0.239	0.248	0.265	0.282	0.299	0.316	0.334	0.351	0.368
5/32	0.254	0.262	0.271	0.279	0.288	0.297	0.314	0.331	0.348	0.365	0.383	0.400	0.417
3/16	0.303	0.311	0.320	0.328	0.337	0.346	0.363	0.380	0.397	0.414	0.432	0.449	0.466
7/32	0.353	0.361	0.370	0.378	0.387	0.396	0.413	0.430	0.447	0.464	0.482	0.499	0.516
1/4	0.401	0.409	0.418	0.426	0.435	0.444	0.461	0.478	0.495	0.512	0.530	0.547	0.564
9/32	0.450	0.458	0.467	0.475	0.484	0.493	0.510	0.527	0.544	0.561	0.579	0.596	0.613
5/16	0.499	0.507	0.516	0.524	0.533	0.542	0.559	0.576	0.593	0.610	0.628	0.645	0.662
11/32	0.549	0.557	0.566	0.574	0.583	0.592	0.609	0.626	0.643	0.660	0.678	0.695	0.712
3/8	0.598	0.606	0.615	0.623	0.632	0.641	0.658	0.675	0.692	0.709	0.727	0.744	0.761
13/32	0.646	0.654	0.663	0.671	0.680	0.689	0.706	0.723	0.740	0.757	0.775	0.792	0.809
7/16	0.695	0.703	0.712	0.720	0.729	0.738	0.755	0.772	0.789	0.806	0.824	0.841	0.858
15/32	0.734	0.742	0.751	0.759	0.768	0.777	0.794	0.811	0.828	0.845	0.863	0.880	0.897
1/2	0.794	0.802	0.811	0.819	0.828	0.837	0.854	0.871	0.888	0.905	0.923	0.940	0.957
9/16	0.892	0.900	0.909	0.917	0.926	0.935	0.952	0.969	0.986	1.003	1.021	1.038	1.055
5/8	0.990	0.998	1.007	1.015	1.024	1.033	1.050	1.067	1.084	1.101	1.119	1.136	1.153
11/16	1.089	1.097	1.106	1.114	1.123	1.132	1.149	1.166	1.183	1.200	1.218	1.235	1.252
3/4	1.187	1.195	1.204	1.212	1.221	1.230	1.247	1.264	1.281	1.298	1.316	1.333	1.350
13/16	1.286	1.294	1.303	1.311	1.320	1.329	1.346	1.363	1.380	1.397	1.415	1.432	1.449
7/8	1.384	1.392	1.401	1.409	1.418	1.427	1.444	1.461	1.478	1.495	1.513	1.530	1.547
15/16	1.481	1.489	1.498	1.506	1.515	1.524	1.541	1.558	1.575	1.592	1.610	1.627	1.644
1	1.580	1.588	1.597	1.605	1.614	1.623	1.640	1.657	1.674	1.691	1.709	1.726	1.743
1 1/16	1.678	1.686	1.695	1.703	1.712	1.721	1.738	1.755	1.772	1.789	1.807	1.824	1.841
1 1/8	1.777	1.785	1.794	1.802	1.811	1.820	1.837	1.854	1.871	1.888	1.906	1.923	1.940
1 3/16	1.875	1.883	1.892	1.900	1.909	1.918	1.935	1.952	1.969	1.986	2.004	2.021	2.038
1 1/4	1.972	1.980	1.989	1.997	2.006	2.015	2.032	2.049	2.066	2.083	2.101	2.118	2.135

Table 2. Lengths of Straight Stock Required for 90-Degree Bends in Half-Hard Sheet Copper, Half-Hard Brass, and Soft Steel

Thickness T of Material, Inch

Radius R of Bend, Inches	1/64	1/32	3/64	1/16	5/64	3/32	1/8	5/32	3/16	7/32	1/4	9/32	5/16
1/32	0.059	0.069	0.079	0.089	0.099	0.109	0.129	0.149	0.169	0.189	0.209	0.229	0.249
3/64	0.084	0.094	0.104	0.114	0.124	0.134	0.154	0.174	0.194	0.214	0.234	0.254	0.274
1/16	0.108	0.118	0.128	0.138	0.148	0.158	0.178	0.198	0.218	0.238	0.258	0.278	0.298
3/32	0.157	0.167	0.177	0.187	0.197	0.207	0.227	0.247	0.267	0.287	0.307	0.327	0.347
1/8	0.206	0.216	0.226	0.236	0.246	0.256	0.276	0.296	0.316	0.336	0.356	0.376	0.396
5/32	0.255	0.265	0.275	0.285	0.295	0.305	0.325	0.345	0.365	0.385	0.405	0.425	0.445
3/16	0.304	0.314	0.324	0.334	0.344	0.354	0.374	0.394	0.414	0.434	0.454	0.474	0.494
7/32	0.354	0.364	0.374	0.384	0.394	0.404	0.424	0.444	0.464	0.484	0.504	0.524	0.544
1/4	0.402	0.412	0.422	0.432	0.442	0.452	0.472	0.492	0.512	0.532	0.552	0.572	0.592
9/32	0.451	0.461	0.471	0.481	0.491	0.501	0.521	0.541	0.561	0.581	0.601	0.621	0.641
5/16	0.500	0.510	0.520	0.530	0.540	0.550	0.570	0.590	0.610	0.630	0.650	0.670	0.690
11/32	0.550	0.560	0.570	0.580	0.590	0.600	0.620	0.640	0.660	0.680	0.700	0.720	0.740
3/8	0.599	0.609	0.619	0.629	0.639	0.649	0.669	0.689	0.709	0.729	0.749	0.769	0.789
13/32	0.647	0.657	0.667	0.677	0.687	0.697	0.717	0.737	0.757	0.777	0.797	0.817	0.837
7/16	0.696	0.706	0.716	0.726	0.736	0.746	0.766	0.786	0.806	0.826	0.846	0.866	0.886
15/32	0.735	0.745	0.755	0.765	0.775	0.785	0.805	0.825	0.845	0.865	0.885	0.905	0.925
1/2	0.795	0.805	0.815	0.825	0.835	0.845	0.865	0.885	0.905	0.925	0.945	0.965	0.985
9/16	0.893	0.903	0.913	0.923	0.933	0.943	0.963	0.983	1.003	1.023	1.043	1.063	1.083
5/8	0.991	1.001	1.011	1.021	1.031	1.041	1.061	1.081	1.101	1.121	1.141	1.161	1.181
11/16	1.090	1.100	1.110	1.120	1.130	1.140	1.160	1.180	1.200	1.220	1.240	1.260	1.280
3/4	1.188	1.198	1.208	1.218	1.228	1.238	1.258	1.278	1.298	1.318	1.338	1.358	1.378
13/16	1.287	1.297	1.307	1.317	1.327	1.337	1.357	1.377	1.397	1.417	1.437	1.457	1.477
7/8	1.385	1.395	1.405	1.415	1.425	1.435	1.455	1.475	1.495	1.515	1.535	1.555	1.575
15/16	1.482	1.492	1.502	1.512	1.522	1.532	1.552	1.572	1.592	1.612	1.632	1.652	1.672
1	1.581	1.591	1.601	1.611	1.621	1.631	1.651	1.671	1.691	1.711	1.731	1.751	1.771
1 1/16	1.679	1.689	1.699	1.709	1.719	1.729	1.749	1.769	1.789	1.809	1.829	1.849	1.869
1 1/8	1.778	1.788	1.798	1.808	1.818	1.828	1.848	1.868	1.888	1.908	1.928	1.948	1.968
1 3/16	1.876	1.886	1.896	1.906	1.916	1.926	1.946	1.966	1.986	2.006	2.026	2.046	2.066
1 1/4	1.973	1.983	1.993	2.003	2.013	2.023	2.043	2.063	2.083	2.103	2.123	2.143	2.163

Table 3. Lengths of Straight Stock Required for 90-Degree Bends in Hard Copper, Bronze, Cold-Rolled Steel, and Spring Steel

Radius R of Bend, Inches	Thickness T of Material, Inch												
	1/64	1/32	3/64	1/16	5/64	3/32	1/8	5/32	3/16	7/32	1/4	9/32	5/16
1/32	0.060	0.071	0.082	0.093	0.104	0.116	0.138	0.160	0.182	0.204	0.227	0.249	0.271
3/64	0.085	0.096	0.107	0.118	0.129	0.141	0.163	0.185	0.207	0.229	0.252	0.274	0.296
1/16	0.109	0.120	0.131	0.142	0.153	0.165	0.187	0.209	0.231	0.253	0.276	0.298	0.320
3/32	0.158	0.169	0.180	0.191	0.202	0.214	0.236	0.258	0.280	0.302	0.325	0.347	0.369
1/8	0.207	0.218	0.229	0.240	0.251	0.263	0.285	0.307	0.329	0.351	0.374	0.396	0.418
5/32	0.256	0.267	0.278	0.289	0.300	0.312	0.334	0.356	0.378	0.400	0.423	0.445	0.467
3/16	0.305	0.316	0.327	0.338	0.349	0.361	0.383	0.405	0.427	0.449	0.472	0.494	0.516
7/32	0.355	0.366	0.377	0.388	0.399	0.411	0.433	0.455	0.477	0.499	0.522	0.544	0.566
1/4	0.403	0.414	0.425	0.436	0.447	0.459	0.481	0.503	0.525	0.547	0.570	0.592	0.614
9/32	0.452	0.463	0.474	0.485	0.496	0.508	0.530	0.552	0.574	0.596	0.619	0.641	0.663
5/16	0.501	0.512	0.523	0.534	0.545	0.557	0.579	0.601	0.623	0.645	0.668	0.690	0.712
11/32	0.551	0.562	0.573	0.584	0.595	0.607	0.629	0.651	0.673	0.695	0.718	0.740	0.762
3/8	0.600	0.611	0.622	0.633	0.644	0.656	0.678	0.700	0.722	0.744	0.767	0.789	0.811
13/32	0.648	0.659	0.670	0.681	0.692	0.704	0.726	0.748	0.770	0.792	0.815	0.837	0.859
7/16	0.697	0.708	0.719	0.730	0.741	0.753	0.775	0.797	0.819	0.841	0.864	0.886	0.908
15/32	0.736	0.747	0.758	0.769	0.780	0.792	0.814	0.836	0.858	0.880	0.903	0.925	0.947
1/2	0.796	0.807	0.818	0.829	0.840	0.852	0.874	0.896	0.918	0.940	0.963	0.985	1.007
9/16	0.894	0.905	0.916	0.927	0.938	0.950	0.972	0.994	1.016	1.038	1.061	1.083	1.105
5/8	0.992	1.003	1.014	1.025	1.036	1.048	1.070	1.092	1.114	1.136	1.159	1.181	1.203
11/16	1.091	1.102	1.113	1.124	1.135	1.147	1.169	1.191	1.213	1.235	1.258	1.280	1.302
3/4	1.189	1.200	1.211	1.222	1.233	1.245	1.267	1.289	1.311	1.333	1.356	1.378	1.400
13/16	1.288	1.299	1.310	1.321	1.332	1.344	1.366	1.388	1.410	1.432	1.455	1.477	1.499
7/8	1.386	1.397	1.408	1.419	1.430	1.442	1.464	1.486	1.508	1.530	1.553	1.575	1.597
15/16	1.483	1.494	1.505	1.516	1.527	1.539	1.561	1.583	1.605	1.627	1.650	1.672	1.694
1	1.582	1.593	1.664	1.615	1.626	1.638	1.660	1.682	1.704	1.726	1.749	1.771	1.793
1 1/16	1.680	1.691	1.752	1.713	1.724	1.736	1.758	1.780	1.802	1.824	1.847	1.869	1.891
1 1/8	1.779	1.790	1.801	1.812	1.823	1.835	1.857	1.879	1.901	1.923	1.946	1.968	1.990
1 3/16	1.877	1.888	1.899	1.910	1.921	1.933	1.955	1.977	1.999	2.021	2.044	2.066	2.088
1 1/4	1.974	1.985	1.996	2.007	2.018	2.030	2.052	2.074	2.096	2.118	2.141	2.163	2.185

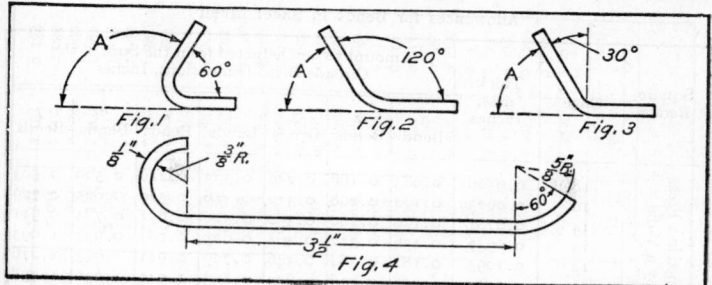

Example Showing Application of Formulas: Find the length before bending of the part illustrated by Fig. 4. Soft steel is to be used.

For bend at left-hand end (180-degree bend)

$$L = [(0.64 \times 0.125) + (1.57 \times 0.375)] \times \frac{180}{90} = 1.338$$

For bend at right-hand end (60-degree bend)

$$L = [(0.64 \times 0.125) + (1.57 \times 0.625)] \times \frac{60}{90} = 0.707$$

Total length before bending = 3.5 + 1.338 + 0.707 = 5.545 inches

Other Bending Allowance Formulas. — When bending sheet steel or brass, add from ⅓ to ½ of the thickness of the stock, for *each bend*, to the sum of the inside dimensions of the finished piece, to get the length of the straight blank. The harder the material the greater the allowance (⅓ of the thickness is added for soft stock and ½ of the thickness for hard material). The data given in the table, "Allowances for Bends in Sheet Metal," refer more particularly to the bending of sheet metal for counters, bank fittings and general office fixtures, for which purpose it is not absolutely essential to have the sections of the bends within very close limits. Absolutely accurate data for this work cannot be deduced, as the stock varies considerably as to hardness, etc. The figures given apply to sheet steel, aluminum, brass and bronze. Experience has demonstrated that for the semisquare corners, such as are formed in a V-die, the amount to be deducted from the sum of the outside bend dimensions, as shown in the accompanying illustration by the sum of the letters from a to e, is as follows: $X = 1.67\ BG$, where X = the amount to be deducted; B = the number of bends; and G = the decimal equivalent of the gage. The values of X for different gages and numbers of bends are given in the table. Its application may be illustrated by an example: A strip having two bends is to have outside dimensions of 2, 1½ and 2 inches, and is made of stock 0.125 inch thick. The sum of the outside dimensions is thus 5½ inches, and from the table the amount to be deducted is found to be 0.416; hence the blank will be 5.5 − 0.416 = 5.084 inches long.

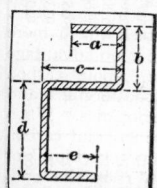

The lower part of the table applies to square bends which are either drawn through a block of steel made to the required shape, or else drawn through rollers in a draw-bench. The pressure applied not only gives a much sharper corner, but it also elongates the material more than in the V-die process. In this case, the deduction is $X = 1.33\ BG$.

Allowances for Bends in Sheet Metal

Square Bends	Gage	Thickness, Inches	Amount to be Deducted from the Sum of the Outside Bend Dimensions, Inches						
			1 Bend	2 Bends	3 Bends	4 Bends	5 Bends	6 Bends	7 Bends
Formed in a Press by a V-die	18	0.0500	0.083	0.166	0.250	0.333	0.416	0.500	0.583
	16	0.0625	0.104	0.208	0.312	0.416	0.520	0.625	0.729
	14	0.0781	0.130	0.260	0.390	0.520	0.651	0.781	0.911
	13	0.0937	0.156	0.312	0.468	0.625	0.781	0.937	1.093
	12	0.1093	0.182	0.364	0.546	0.729	0.911	1.093	1.276
	11	0.1250	0.208	0.416	0.625	0.833	1.041	1.250	1.458
	10	0.1406	0.234	0.468	0.703	0.937	1.171	1.406	1.643
Rolled or Drawn in a Draw-bench	18	0.0500	0.066	0.133	0.200	0.266	0.333	0.400	0.466
	16	0.0625	0.083	0.166	0.250	0.333	0.416	0.500	0.583
	14	0.0781	0.104	0.208	0.312	0.416	0.521	0.625	0.729
	13	0.0937	0.125	0.250	0.375	0.500	0.625	0.750	0.875
	12	0.1093	0.145	0.291	0.437	0.583	0.729	0.875	1.020
	11	0.1250	0.166	0.333	0.500	0.666	0.833	1.000	1.166
	10	0.1406	0.187	0.375	0.562	0.750	0.937	1.125	1.312

Drop-Forging Dies

Steel for Drop-forging Dies. — Practically all drop-forging dies are made of high-grade open-hearth steel. A 60-point carbon steel is mostly used, although steel as low as 40-point and as high as 85-point carbon is employed in some cases. A special hardening treatment is required for the low-carbon steel, which more than offsets the saving in price, and, except in special cases, there is no advantage in using high-carbon steels, owing to the expense. The average 60-point carbon steel die, if properly hardened, should last for from 15,000 to 40,000 forgings, and sometimes as many as 70,000 forgings can be made from one set of dies. When making dies for large forgings, it is often thought advisable to use 80-point carbon steel, and not harden the dies. This obviates the danger from "checking" or cracking in hardening, and the un-hardened steel is hard enough to resist the tendency to stretch. A steel that is quite high in carbon should always be used for dies that are intended for making forgings from tool steel or any other hard steel.

Allowance for Shrinkage. — When making dies for small cold-trimmed steel forgings, the proper allowance for shrinkage is 3/16 inch to the foot, or 0.015 inch to the inch. Such forgings are finished at a bright red heat and the rate of shrinkage is considerable. When making dies for hot-trimmed steel forgings of medium and large sizes, the shrinkage allowance is 1/8 inch to the foot, or 0.010 inch to the inch. Hot-trimmed forgings receive the finishing blow while comparatively cold, and shrink a smaller amount than the cold-trimmed forgings. The foregoing allowances are used for all dimensions of the die impression, such as depth, width or length. The shrinkage allowance for dies to be used in forging bronze or copper is practically the same as that for steel.

Draft Allowance. — The amount of draft in a drop-forging die varies from 3 to 10 degrees. If the die is for a thin forging of uniform section, 3 degrees is ample, but if the forging is deep and has narrow ribs which are apt to stick, at least 7 degrees is necessary. If a die is used for forging a piece that is ring-shaped or has an annular part, the central plug that forms the interior of the ring should have a draft of 10 degrees, because, as the forging cools while being worked, it tends to shrink around the plug and if the draft is insufficient, it will stick in the die. With the foregoing exception, most drop-forging dies have a 7-degree draft. For convenience in laying out, it is well to remember that a 7-degree taper is approximately equal to a ⅛-inch taper to the inch, and a 10-degree taper, 3/16 inch to the inch.

Locating Impression in the Die. — When laying out a drop-forging die, the impression should be located so that the heaviest end of the forging will be at the front of the die-block. This makes the forging easier to handle and also permits the use of a fairly large sprue. There should be at least 1½ inch left all around between the impression and the outside edge of the block. This also holds true for any part of the die, such as the edger, anvil or forming impression. If the forging has a hub or other projection that extends some distance from the main part on one side, the upper or top die should contain this deeper impression.

Obtaining Weight of Forging from Lead Proof. — After the upper and lower dies have been completed, shrinkage allowances and the general finish of the impressions are ordinarily tested by taking a "lead proof," and by weighing the lead, an approximate idea of the weight of the finished forging can be obtained. Roughly speaking, the finished forging will weigh two-thirds as much as the lead proof. The shrinkage of lead is practically the same as that of steel, so that the finished forging will also measure about the same as the one made of lead. In case of dies for eye-bolts and similar work, this rule must be disregarded, because the plugs that form the central opening will prevent the lead from shrinking naturally. When taking the lead proof, the die impressions are dusted with powdered chalk, and after the dies are clamped together, the molten lead is poured.

Amount of Flash for Drop-forging Dies. — Theoretically, there should be just enough forging metal in a die to fill the impression, and no more, but this is, of course, not practicable, as there is always some stock that must be disposed of after the impression is filled. To take care of this excess metal, dies are relieved all around the impression by milling a flat shallow recess about 1/64 inch deep and 5/8 inch wide. These dimensions are for dies of average size; in comparatively large dies this recess or "flash" would be a little deeper and wider. Both the upper and lower dies are flashed in this way. In addition, the upper die is "back-flashed," which means that there is a deeper recess, sometimes called the "gutter," milled around the impression at a distance of ¼ inch from the impression at every point. This back-flash is 3/64 inch deep and acts as a relief for the excess metal after it has been squeezed from the flash proper. Only the finishing impression is provided with a flash and back-flash.

The Break-down of Drop-forging Dies. — The width of section used as a break-down (also known as the edger or side cut) should be enough wider than the forging to give plenty of room for the work of forging. A forging 1 inch thick should have a break-down 1½ inch wide, and about the same proportions should be followed for forgings of other widths. The break-down should have a section corresponding with the gate and sprue of the die impression, but it should be made slightly longer, so that the forging will not be stretched when struck in the impression.

Hardening Drop-forging Dies. — Dies to be carbonized should always be packed for hardening in cast-iron or sheet-iron boxes containing a mixture of fresh bone and charcoal. The ordinary mixture is half bone and half charcoal. More bone gives greater hardness and more charcoal, less hardness, for a given heat; hence, the proportions should be varied according to requirements. The die should be packed face down on a one- or two-inch layer of this mixture and be settled so that the impression is filled. Sometimes the face is coated, before packing, with a thick paste of linseed oil and powdered bone-black, to protect the delicate edges from oxidation when in contact with the air. Fill the space between the sides of the die and the box with the bone and charcoal mixture, and cover over with a thick layer of wet clay paste to prevent the charcoal from burning out. Dies made of steel having less than 60-point carbon content should always be carbonized. Open-hearth steel dies containing 60-point carbon or over can be hardened without carbonizing.

Heating the Die. — An oil or gas furnace is recommended for heating, although a coal or coke-fired muffle furnace, capable of maintaining a temperature of at least 1600 degrees F., may be used, provided the temperature can be held constant. A temperature indicating device is necessary. The die should be put into the furnace as soon as the latter is lighted. If the correct quenching temperature for the steel is, say, 1500 degrees F., the furnace should be checked when the pyrometer indicates 1400 degrees, the die being allowed to "soak" at that heat for three or four hours. Then the heat should be slowly raised to 1500 degrees and held at that point one or two hours longer, according to the size of the die. Five hours is the minimum total time for heating, and seven or eight hours is much safer. A 60-point carbon die should be quenched between 1425 and 1450 degrees F.

Cooling the Heated Die. — When cooling, the face of the die should receive a sufficient flow of cold water to cause it to harden to the greatest possible depth. The back of the die should, at the same time, be cooled to make the shrinkage of the face and back equal, and to prevent warping. A good form of cooling tank is one having a large supply pipe extending up through the bottom for cooling the die face, and a smaller pipe above the tank to cool the back. Unless a jet of water under pressure is applied to the face of the die, the sunken parts of the impression will not harden equally with the face. Dies should not be cooled in a tank of still water, because steam forms in the die cavity which prevents the water from entering, thus causing the formation of soft spots. To overcome this, the water must be forced into the impression by pressure sufficient to overcome the resistance of the steam thus formed. Oil should not be used for hardening hammer dies, as its cooling action is not great enough to produce a sufficient depth of hardening. Hammer dies which are simply surface hardened will not withstand the heavy blows received in service. To secure a greater hardening effect, brine of about 40 per cent solution is used by some die-makers.

Tempering Dies. — Dies should be tempered and drawn as soon as they are cool enough to remove from the tank. The dies should be heated in an oil bath, and quenched in water or cool oil. Any high-grade cylinder oil of high flash-point is suitable. Low-grade oils smoke unpleasantly and will not stand high temperatures. The drawing temperature of die steels is about 450 degrees F., for average conditions. The corners of the die and the cut-off should be drawn to a purple color with the aid of a blow torch.

Dies for Bronze and Copper Forgings. — Dies for producing drop-forgings from bronze or copper differ from those used for steel or iron forgings principally in the matter of finish. Owing to the softness of copper and bronze, the metal is driven into very minute impressions in the surface of the dies; hence, these surfaces must be perfectly free from scratches, in order to insure a smooth finish on the work. Even though these metals are soft, the hammering necessary when forging is very hard on the dies, and to prevent them from dishing or spreading, tool steel is ordinarily used, unless the forgings are extra large and heavy. The shrinkage, draft and finish allowances on this class of drop-forging dies are practically the same as on dies for steel and iron.

Trimming Dies for Drop-forgings. — Hot-trimming dies are made of a special grade of steel known as hot-trimming die-stock. The objection to using ordinary tool steel for hot-trimming dies is that the edges of a hardened die check badly after the die has been used for a short time, and this checking is followed by a breaking away of the steel around the edges, thus rendering the die unfit for use. This special steel requires no hardening, and after the die is in use, the edges toughen and give better service than the best hardened tool steel. The usual form of punch for hot-trimming dies merely supports the forging while it is being pushed through. If the forging has a broad, flat top face, the punch need only be a little more than a flat piece that covers the forging and acts as a pusher. Such punches are commonly made of cast iron. Cold-trimming dies are made from good tool steel of from 1.00 to 1.25 per cent carbon, and hardened and drawn to a dark straw color. The punches for cold trimmers are also made of tool steel and are hardened and drawn to a very dark straw color. These punches are hardened to prevent them from upsetting at the edges. As with hot-trimming punches, the punch should fit the die loosely, but it should support the forging at every point while it is being pushed through the die. There are two instances in which trimming punches should fit the dies as closely as the average punching die for sheet metal work; first, when trimming forgings on which the fin comes at the corner of the forging; second, forgings that are formed all in one die, the other die being flat. In these two cases, unless the dies fit very well, there will be burrs at the trimmed edges.

BROACHES AND BROACHING

The Broaching Process. — The broaching process may be applied in machining holes or other internal surfaces and also to many flat or other external surfaces. Internal broaching is applied in forming either symmetrical or irregular holes, grooves, or slots in machine parts, especially when the size or shape of the opening, or its length in proportion to diameter or width, make other machining processes impracticable. Broaching originally was utilized for such work as cutting keyways, machining round holes into square, hexagonal, or other shapes, forming splined holes, and for a large variety of other internal operations. The development of broaching machines and broaches finally resulted in extensive application of the process to external, flat, and other surfaces. Most external or surface broaching is done on machines of vertical design, but horizontal machines are also used for some classes of work. The broaching process is very rapid, accurate, and it leaves a finish of good quality. It is employed extensively in automotive and other plants where duplicate parts must be produced in large quantities and frequently to given dimensions within small tolerances.

Types of Broaches. — A number of typical broaches and the operations for which they are intended are shown by the diagrams, Fig. 1. Broach *A* produces a round-cornered, square hole. Prior to broaching square holes, it is usually the practice to drill a round hole having a diameter *d* somewhat larger than the width of the square. Hence, the sides are not completely finished, but this unfinished part is not objectionable in most cases. In fact, this clearance space is an advantage during the broaching operation in that it serves as a channel for the broaching lubricant; moreover, the broach has less metal to remove. Broach *B* is for finishing

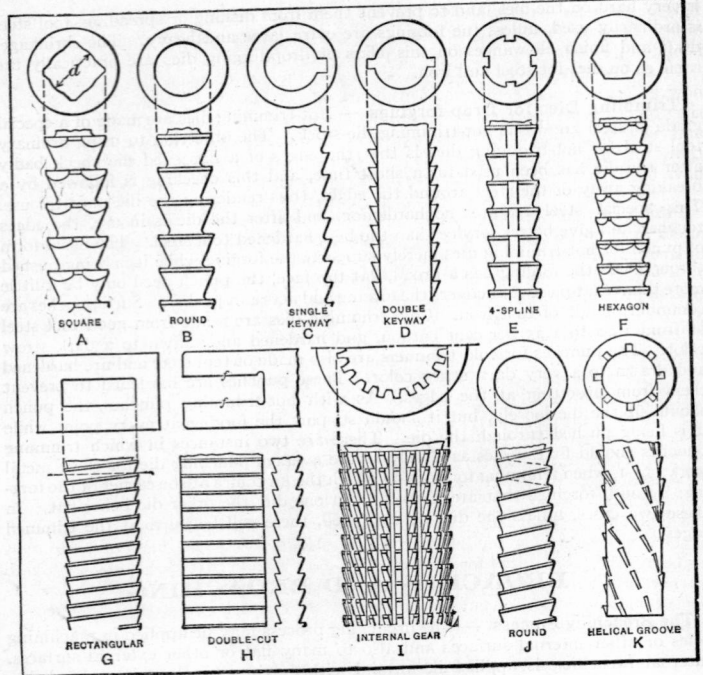

Fig. 1. Types of Broaches

round holes. Broaching is superior to reaming for some classes of work, because
the broach will hold its size for a much longer period, thus insuring greater accuracy.
Broaches C and D are for cutting single and double keyways, respectively. Broach
C is of rectangular section and, when in use, slides through a guiding bushing which
is inserted in the hole. Broach E is for forming four integral splines in a hub.
The broach at F is for producing hexagonal holes. Rectangular holes are finished
by broach G. The teeth on the sides of this broach are inclined in opposite directions, which has the following advantages: The broach is stronger than it would
be if the teeth were opposite and parallel to each other; thin work cannot drop
between the inclined teeth, as it tends to do when the teeth are at right angles,
because at least two teeth are always cutting; the inclination in opposite directions
neutralizes the lateral thrust. The teeth on the edges are staggered, the teeth on
one side being midway between the teeth on the other edge, as shown by the dotted
line. A double cut broach is shown at H. This type is for finishing, simultaneously,
both sides f of a slot, and for similar work. Broach I is the style used for forming
the teeth in internal gears. It is practically a series of gear-shaped cutters, the
outside diameters of which gradually increase toward the finishing end of the broach.
Broach J is for round holes but differs from style B in that it has a continuous
helical cutting edge. Some prefer this form because it gives a shearing cut. Broach

K is for cutting a series of helical grooves in a hub or bushing. In helical broaching, either the work or the broach is rotated to form the helical grooves as the broach is pulled through.

In addition to the typical broaches shown in Fig. 1, many special designs are now in use for performing more complex operations. Two surfaces on opposite sides of a casting or forging are sometimes machined simultaneously by twin broaches and, in other cases, three or four broaches are drawn through a part at the same time, for finishing as many duplicate holes or surfaces. Notable developments have been made in the design of broaches for external or " surface " broaching.

Pitch of Broach Teeth. — The pitch of broach teeth depends upon the depth of cut or chip thickness, length of cut, the cutting force required and power of the broaching machine. In the pitch formulas which follow

L = length, in inches, of layer to be removed by broaching.

d = depth of cut per tooth as shown by Table 1 (For internal broaches, d = depth of cut as measured on one side of broach or one-half difference in diameters of successive teeth in case of a round broach)

F = a factor. (For brittle types of material, F = 3 or 4 for roughing teeth, and 6 for finishing teeth. For ductile types of material, F = 4 to 7 for roughing teeth and 8 for finishing teeth.)

b = width in inches, of layer to be removed by broaching

P = pressure required in tons per square inch, of an area equal to depth of cut times width of cut, in inches (Table 2)

T = usable capacity, in tons, of broaching machine = 70 per cent of maximum tonnage

The minimum pitch shown by Formula (1) is based upon the receiving capacity of the chip space. The minimum, however, should not be less than 0.2 inch unless a smaller pitch is required for exceptionally short cuts to provide at least two teeth in contact simultaneously, with the part being broached. A reduction below 0.2 inch is seldom required in surface broaching but it may be necessary in connection with internal broaching.

$$\text{Minimum pitch} = 3\sqrt{LdF} \qquad (1)$$

Whether the minimum pitch may be used or not depends upon the power of the available machine. The factor F in the formula provides for the increase in volume as the material is broached into chips. If a broach has adjustable inserts for the finishing teeth, the pitch of the finishing teeth may be smaller than the pitch of the roughing teeth because of the smaller depth d of the cut. The higher value of F for finishing teeth prevents the pitch from becoming too small, so that the spirally curled chips will not be crowded into too small a space. The pitch of the roughing and finishing teeth should be equal for broaches without separate inserts (notwithstanding the different values of d and F) so that some of the finishing teeth may be ground into roughing teeth after wear makes this necessary.

$$\text{Allowable pitch} = \frac{dLbP}{T} \qquad (2)$$

If the pitch obtained by Formula (2) is larger than the minimum obtained by Formula (1), this larger value should be used because it is based upon the usable power of the machine. As the notation indicates, 70 per cent of the maximum tonnage T is taken as the usable capacity. The 30 per cent reduction is to provide a margin for the increase in broaching load resulting from the gradual dulling of the cutting edges. The procedure in calculating both minimum and allowable pitches will be illustrated by an example.

Table 1.   Designing Data for Surface Broaches

Material to be Broached	Depth of Cut per Tooth, Inch		Face Angle or Rake, Degrees	Clearance Angle, Degrees	
	Roughing*	Finishing		Roughing	Finishing
Steel, High Tensile Strength................	0.0015-0.002	0.0005	10-12	1.5-3	0.5-1
Steel, Medium Tensile Strength................	0.0025-0.005	0.0005	14-18	1.5-3	0.5-1
Cast Steel.................	0.0025-0.005	0.0005	10	1.5-3	0.5
Malleable Iron.............	0.0025-0.005	0.0005	7	1.5-3	0.5
Cast Iron, Soft............	0.006 -0.010	0.0005	10-15	1.5-3	0.5
Cast Iron, Hard...........	0.003 -0.005	0.0005	5	1.5-3	0.5
Zinc Die Castings.........	0.005 -0.010	0.0010	12 **	5	2
Cast Bronze..............	0.010 -0.025	0.0010	8	0	0
Wrought Aluminum Alloys	0.005 -0.010	0.0010	15 **	3	1
Cast Aluminum Alloys....	0.005 -0.010	0.0010	12 **	3	1
Magnesium Die Castings..	0.010 -0.015	0.0010	20 **	3	1

* The lower depth-of-cut values for roughing are recommended when work is not very rigid, the tolerance is small, a good finish is required, or length of cut is comparatively short.

** In broaching these materials, smooth surfaces for tooth and chip spaces are especially recommended.

Table 2.   Broaching Pressure P for Use in Pitch Formula (2)

Material to be Broached	Depth d of Cut per Tooth, Inch					Pressure P, Side-cutting Broaches
	0.024	0.010	0.004	0.002	0.001	
	Pressure P in Tons per Square Inch					
Steel, High Ten. Strength......	..	...	...	250	312	200- .004″ cut
Steel, Med. Ten. Strength......	..	...	158	185	243	143- .006″ cut
Cast Steel.....................	..	...	128	158	...	115- .006″ cut
Malleable Iron.................	..	...	108	128	...	100- .006″ cut
Cast Iron.....................	..	115	115	143	...	115- .020″ cut
Cast Brass...................	..	50	50	...	...	....
Brass, Hot Pressed............	..	85	85	...	...	....
Zinc Die Castings.............	..	70	70	...	...	....
Cast Bronze..................	35	35	...	...	...	....
Wrought Aluminum............	..	70	70	...	...	....
Cast Aluminum................	..	85	85	...	...	....
Magnesium Alloy..............	35	35	...	...	...	....

Example: Determine pitch of broach for cast iron when $L = 9$ inches; $d = 0.004$; and $F = 4$.

$$\text{Minimum pitch} = 3\sqrt{9 \times 0.004 \times 4} = 1.14$$

Next, apply Formula (2). Assume that $b = 3$ and $T = 10$; for cast iron and depth d of 0.004, $P = 115$ (Table 2). Then,

$$\text{Allowable pitch} = \frac{0.004 \times 9 \times 3 \times 115}{10} = 1.24$$

This pitch is safely above the minimum. If in this case the usable tonnage of an available machine were, say, 8 tons instead of 10 tons, the pitch as shown by Formula (2) might be increased to about 1.5 inches, thus reducing the number of teeth cutting simultaneously and, consequently, the load on the machine; or the cut per tooth might be reduced instead of increasing the pitch, especially if only a few teeth are in cutting contact, as might be the case with a short length of cut. If the usable tonnage in the preceding example were, say, 15, then a pitch of 0.84 would be obtained by Formula (2); hence the pitch in this case should not be less than the minimum of approximately 1.14 inches.

Depth of Cut per Tooth. — The term " depth of cut " as applied to surface of external broaches means the difference in the heights of successive teeth. This term, as applied to internal broaches for round, hexagonal or other holes, may indicate the total increase in the diameter of successive teeth; however, to avoid confusion, the term as here used means in all cases and regardless of the type of broach, the depth of cut as measured on one side.

In broaching free cutting steel, the Broaching Tool Institute recommends 0.003 to 0.006 inch depth of cut for surface broaching; 0.002 to 0.003 inch for multi-spline broaching; and 0.0007 to 0.0015 inch for round hole broaching. The accompanying

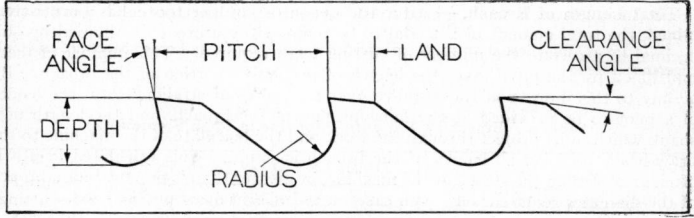

Terms Commonly Used in Broach Design

table contains data from a German source and applies specifically to surface broaches. All data relating to depth of cut are intended as a general guide only. While depth of cut is based primarily upon the machinability of the material, some reduction from the depth thus established may be required particularly when the work supporting fixture in surface broaching is not sufficiently rigid to resist the thrust from the broaching operation. In some cases, the pitch and cutting length may be increased to reduce the thrust force. Another possible remedy in surface broaching certain classes of work is to use a side-cutting broach instead of the ordinary depth cutting type. A broach designed for side cutting takes relatively deep narrow cuts which extend nearly to the full depth required. The side cutting section is followed by teeth arranged for depth cutting to obtain the required size and surface finish on the work. In general, small tolerances in surface broaching require a reduced cut per tooth to minimize work deflection resulting from the pressure of the cut.

Face Angle or Rake. — The face angle (see diagram) of broach teeth affects the chip flow and varies considerably for different materials. While there are some variations in practice, even for the same material, the angles given in the accompanying table are believed to represent commonly used values. Some broach designers increase the rake angle for finishing teeth in order to improve the finish on the work.

Clearance Angle. — The clearance angle (see illustration) for roughing steel varies from 1.5 to 3 degrees and for finishing steel from 0.5 to 1 degree. Some recommend the same clearance angles for cast iron and others, larger clearance angles varying from 2 to 4 or 5 degrees. Additional data will be found in Table 1.

Land Width. — The width of the land usually is about 0.25 × pitch. It varies, however, from about one-fourth to one-third of the pitch. The land width is selected so as to obtain the proper balance between tooth strength and chip space.

Depth of Broach Teeth. — The tooth depth as established experimentally and on the basis of experience, usually varies from about 0.37 to 0.40 of the pitch. This depth is measured radially from the cutting edge to the bottom of the tooth fillet.

Radius of Tooth Fillet. — The "gullet" or bottom of the chip space between the teeth should have a rounded fillet to strengthen the broach, facilitate curling of the chips, and safeguard against cracking in connection with the hardening operation. One rule is to make the radius equal to one-fourth the pitch. Another is to make it equal 0.4 to 0.6 the tooth depth. A third method preferred by some broach designers is to make the radius equal one-third of the sum obtained by adding together the land width, one-half the tooth depth, and one-fourth of the pitch.

Total Length of Broach. — After the depth of cut per tooth has been determined, the total amount of material to be removed by a broach is divided by this decimal to ascertain the number of cutting teeth required. This number of teeth multiplied by the pitch gives the length of the active portion of the broach. By adding to this dimension the distance over three or four straight teeth, the length of a pilot to be provided at the finishing end of the broach, and the length of a shank which must project through the work and the faceplate of the machine to the draw-head, the over-all length of the broach is found. This calculated length is often greater than the stroke of the machine, or greater than is practical for a broach of the diameter required. In such cases, a set of broaches must be used.

Chip Breakers. — The teeth of broaches frequently have rounded chip-breaking grooves located at intervals along the cutting edges. These grooves break up wide curling chips and prevent them from clogging the chip spaces, thus reducing the cutting pressure and strain on the broach. These chip-breaking grooves are on the roughing teeth only. They are staggered and applied to both round and flat or surface broaches. The grooves are formed by a round edged grinding wheel and usually vary in width from about 1/32 to 3/32 inch depending upon the size of broach. The more ductile the material, the wider the chip breaker grooves should be and the smaller the distance between them. Narrow slotting broaches may have the right- and left-hand corners of alternate teeth beveled to obtain chip-breaking action.

Shear Angle. — The teeth of surface broaches ordinarily are inclined so they are not at right angles to the broaching movement. The object of this inclination is to obtain a shearing cut which results in smoother cutting action and an improvement in surface finish. The shearing cut also tends to eliminate troublesome vibration. Shear angles for surface broaches are not suitable for broaching slots or any profiles that resist the outward movement of the chips. When the teeth are inclined, the fixture should be designed to resist the resulting thrusts unless it is practicable to incline the teeth of right- and left-hand sections in opposite directions to neutralize the thrust. The shear angle usually varies from 10 to 25 degrees.

Steels for Broaches. — High-speed steels are commonly used at the present time. The 18-4-2 or 18-4-3 types are more resistant to abrasion and wear than steels with a lower vanadium content although steels with one per cent vanadium or less are also used. A broach steel said to have very high resistance to wear and suitable for broaching steels having tensile strengths above 130,000 pounds per square inch, contains 10 per cent tungsten, 4 per cent chromium, 1.7 per cent vanadium, and 0.8 per cent carbon. The hardening heat recommended is 2250–2300 degrees F. and the tempering heat 1000–1040 degrees F. A steel of low tungsten content that is also recommended contains 2.5 per cent tungsten, 4 per cent chromium, 3 per cent vanadium, 2.5 per cent molybdenum, and 1.2–1.3 per cent carbon. The hardening heat is 1975–2050 degrees F. and the tempering heat 1060–1075 degrees F.

Cutting Oils for Broaching.— For broaching steel, a good grade of sulphur base oil is preferable, as a general rule. Cast iron may be broached dry but good results have also been obtained with a mixture of kerosene and soluble oil. Another mixture consists of one part soluble oil and twenty parts water.

Types of Broaching Machines. — Broaching machines may be divided into horizontal and vertical designs, and they may be classified further according to the method of operation, as, for example, whether a broach in a vertical machine is pulled up or pulled down in forcing it through the work. Horizontal machines usually pull the broach through the work in internal broaching but short rigid broaches may be pushed through. External surface broaching is also done on some machines of horizontal design, but usually vertical machines are employed for flat or other external broaching. Although parts usually are broached by traversing the broach itself, some machines are designed to hold the broach or broaches stationary during the actual broaching operation. This principle has been applied both to internal and surface broaching.

Vertical Duplex Type: The vertical duplex type of surface broaching machine has two slides or rams which move in opposite directions and operate alternately. While the broach connected to one slide is moving downward on the cutting stroke, the other broach and slide is returning to the starting position, and this returning time is utilized for reloading the fixture on that side; consequently, the broaching operation is practically continuous. Each ram or slide may be equipped to perform a separate operation on the same part when two operations are required.

Pull-up Type: Vertical hydraulically operated machines which pull the broach or broaches up through the work are used for internal broaching of holes of various shapes, for broaching bushings, splined holes, small internal gears, etc. A typical machine of this kind is so designed that all broach handling is down automatically.

Pull-down Type: The various movements in the operating cycle of a hydraulic pull-down type of machine equipped with an automatic broach-handling slide, are the reverse of the pull-up type. The broaches for a pull-down type of machine have shanks on each end, there being an upper one for the broach-handling slide and a lower one for pulling the broaches through the work.

Hydraulic Operation: Modern broaching machines, as a general rule, are operated hydraulically rather than by mechanical means. Hydraulic operation is efficient, flexible in the matter of speed adjustments, low in maintenance cost, and the "smooth" action required for fine precision finishing may be obtained. The hydraulic pressures required, which frequently are 800 to 1000 pounds per square inch, are obtained from a motor-driven pump forming part of the machine. Broaching machines for general use are so designed that the length of the stroke can be adjusted to suit the length of the broach. The cutting speeds of broaching machines may be varied for different materials and operations. These speeds frequently are between 20 and 30 feet per minute, and the return speeds often are double the cutting speed, or higher, to reduce the idle period.

FILES — HACK-SAW BLADES

Classes of Files. — Files are classified according to their shape or cross-section, and according to the pitch or spacing of the teeth and the nature of the cut. The cross-sections of file steel for all shapes in general use are shown in the illustration. The names of files made from steel of these sections are, referring to the numbers in the illustration: (1) hand; (2) flat; (3) mill; (4) pillar; (5) warding; (6) square; (7) round or "rat-tail"; (8) half-round; (9) three-square or triangular; (10) knife; (11) pit-saw; (12) crossing; (13) tumbler; (14) cross-cut; (15) feather-edge; (16) cant-saw; (17) cant-file; (18) cabinet; (19) shoe-rasp; (20) rasp. The blank for a "hand" file is parallel in thickness from the heel to the middle and tapered from the middle to the point, the latter being about one-half the thickness of the stock. The edges of the blank are usually parallel, but are sometimes drawn in slightly at the point. The "flat" file blank is parallel in both of its longitudinal sections from the heel to the middle and is tapered in both sections from the middle to the point, the thickness of the point being about two-thirds, and the width about one-half that of the stock. The "mill" file blank is parallel in thickness from the heel to the point and is usually tapered to about three-fourths the width of stock.

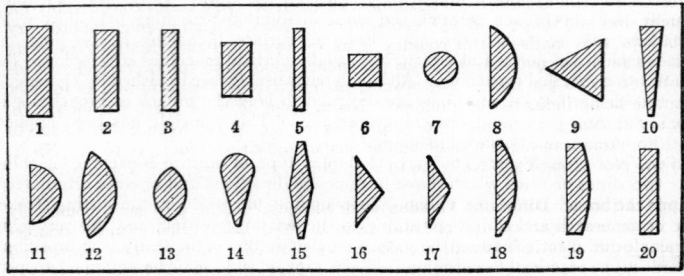

The mill file is also made blunt or of equal width and thickness throughout its length. The "warding" file is tapered in width from the heel to the point and is of uniform thickness. Aside from width, the "pillar" file is similar to the hand file; it is also made in narrow and extra-narrow patterns. The "three-square," "square" and "round" files are also made in slim and blunt forms. The slim form is of regular length but of smaller cross-section, and the blunt is of equal cross-section from the heel to the point, being either slim or regular. The "half-round" is not a full semi-circle, the arc being about one-third of a full circle. The "pit-saw" is a full half circle in section The "three-square," "cant-saw" and "cant-file" differ as to their angles, the former having equal angles (60 degrees) and equal sides; the cant-saw, 35-, 35- and 110-degree angles; and the cant-file, 30-, 30- and 120-degree angles. The well-known hand-saw file has the same section as the three-square type, but differs in that the edges are given the proper bluntness to insure durability; in the three-square files, the edges are left sharp, thus making them entirely unfit for filing saws.

File Teeth. — There are three general classifications of files according to the cut — single-cut, double-cut and rasp. The single-cut file (or "float," as the coarser cuts are sometimes called) has single rows of parallel teeth extending across the face at an angle of from 65 to 85 degrees with the axis of the file. This angle depends upon the form of the file and the nature of the work it is intended for. The double-cut file has two rows of teeth crossing each other. The angle of the first row is, for general work, from 40 to 45 degrees, and the second row, from 70 to 80 degrees. The angle of the first cut for double-cut finishing files is about 30 degrees and the second cut, from 80 to 87 degrees. The double cut gives a broken tooth, the surface of the file having a large number of small teeth inclining toward the point and resembling, in shape, the end of a diamond-pointed cold chisel. The second or "up-cut" is usually a little finer and not as deep as the first or "over-cut." Rasp teeth are round on top and disconnected, being formed by raising, with a punch, small portions of stock from the surface of the blank.

Coarseness of Cut. — Single- and double-cut files are further classified according to the spacing of the teeth. The names commonly used to designate the different grades of cut are "rough," "coarse," "bastard," "second-cut," "smooth," "dead-smooth" or "super-smooth." "Rough" files are usually single-cut, and the "dead-smooth," double-cut. The other grades are made in both double- and single-cuts. These degrees of coarseness are only comparable when files of the same length are considered, the number of teeth per inch of length decreasing as the length or size of the file increases. Some makers use a series of numbers to designate the cut or coarseness instead of names. The number of teeth per inch varies considerably for different sizes and shapes and on files of different makes. A fair average for ordinary machinists' files made in this country is as follows: Bastard-cut, from 20 to 25 teeth per inch; second-cut, 30 to 40 per inch; smooth, 50 to 60 per inch; dead-smooth, 70 to 80 per inch. The spacing of finer Grobet Swiss files is as follows, the grade being indicated by numbers: No. 0, from 40 to 70 teeth per inch; No. 1, 75 to 88; No. 2, 58 to 104; No 3, 100 to 130; No. 4, 120 to 160; No. 6, 200 to 220. For American-made files of similar shapes and sizes: No. 0, 35 to 60; No. 1, 55 to 75; No. 2, 80 to 95; No. 3, 90 to 120; No. 4, 125 to 135; No. 6, 160 to 200.

Application of Different Grades and Shapes. — The files most commonly used in general practice are 12- and 14-inch, "flat" and "half-round" double-and single-cut files in bastard, second-cut and smooth grades. The coarse and bastard cuts are generally used on coarser grades of work, and the second-cut and smooth, on comparatively fine work. The coarse and dead-smooth cuts are not often used in ordinary practice, although a rough single-cut is sometimes needed for soft material. The dead-smooth double-cut file is occasionally required for producing very fine surfaces. Single-cut mill files are commonly employed for lathe work. The mill-bastard is adapted to a large variety of lathe filing, and a mill second-cut is used on finer classes of work. The double-cut hand file with one "safe-edge" is used for finishing flat surfaces. The grade of cut is mostly bastard, although many second-cut and smooth are employed. The double-cut square-bastard in both taper and blunt forms is widely used for enlarging or truing rectangular slots, etc. Flat files are mostly double-cut bastard types, second-cut and smooth being used less frequently. Pillar files with one or both edges safe are useful on narrow work. Sharper files are required for cast iron and brass than for steel and wrought iron. Broad surfaces also require sharper files than narrow ones.

File Definitions. — The length of a file means the distance from the point to the heel and does not include the tang. The *heel* is that end of the file body adjacent to the handle. A *blunt* file is one having the same sectional shape from the point to the tang. An *equaling* file is similar in appearance to the blunt form, but has a very slight curvature from the point to the tang. The *back* is the convex side of the half-round, cabinet, pit-saw and similar forms. *Bellied* is the term used to describe a file having a fullness in the center. The coarse grades of single-cut files are sometimes called *floats*. *Safe-edge* means that the edge or side is smooth and without teeth, and may be presented to a surface that does not require filing. *Over-cut* is a term used to describe the first series of teeth on a double-cut file. *Up-cut* means the series of teeth superimposed on the over-cut series of a double-cut file. The term *superfine* (or *super*) cut is used by Lancashire file makers to designate the grade of cut known in this country as "dead-smooth." *Taper* is used to distinguish a file having tapering sides from one that is blunt or straight. Custom has also established this term as a short name for "three-square" or triangular hand-saw files.

Increment-cut Files. — The teeth of an "increment-cut" file are irregularly spaced, the method followed by a prominent concern being as follows: The rows of teeth are spaced progressively wider from the point towards the middle of the file, by regular increments of spacing, and progressively narrower from the middle towards the heel, by regular decrements of spacing. This spacing of the teeth is modified by introducing, while the teeth are being cut, a controllable irregularity as to the spacing, which is confined within maximum and minimum limits but is not a regular progressive increment or decrement. The successive rows are not exactly parallel, but are cut slightly angular with respect to each other, the angle or inclination being reversed during the operation of cutting, as may be required. It will be understood that the increments of spacing are very small. The theory is that if the teeth are equally spaced and have a uniform height and outline, the file will not cut so readily, the reason being that when so many teeth are in contact, considerable pressure is required to make them cut; but when the teeth are slightly irregular in height, a smaller number will be in contact and the pressure required will be correspondingly light. As the longer teeth wear down, the shorter ones will begin to work, although then the file will not cut so freely. File teeth are also formed by the increment-cut, so that they will produce smoother surfaces. If the teeth follow each other at regular intervals, they tend to drop into the cuts or furrows made by the preceding ones, causing chattering; the uneven teeth of hand and increment-cut files tend to prevent this chattering. The opinions of file makers differ regarding the foregoing advantages and objections.

File Testing. — The quality of files can be tested by a special machine (Herbert file-testing machine) which records the endurance and capacity for removing metal, by producing a curve or diagram on sectioned paper wound about a cylindrical drum connected with the file reciprocating mechanism, so as to make one revolution to 120,000 strokes of the file. On these diagrams, the horizontal distances represent the number of strokes made by the file being tested and the vertical distances, the number of cubic inches of metal removed. Tests show a remarkable difference in the quality of files, some being worn out after removing less than one cubic inch of iron, and cutting at the rate of only one cubic inch per 10,000 strokes; whereas, files of good quality remove 12½ cubic inches and cut at the rate of 5 cubic inches per 10,000 strokes. The difference in quality of two sides of the same file also varies greatly; in fact, the two sides are seldom equal in efficiency and durability. The files are tested until they slip over the surface of the test-bar without cutting, this condition being indicated by the curve taking a horizontal course. Tests which are stopped before this point is reached may give a false impression as to the relative merits of files. Thus, it may happen that two files cut equally well during the first 50,000 strokes, and if the tests were stopped at this point, the files would be considered equal in quality, but if they were continued, one file might cease cutting at 60,000 strokes and the other continue for 400,000 strokes, there being a great difference in the durability.

Application of Different Types of Files

Type of File	Character of Cut	Ordinary Use
Mill file, tapered or blunt	Single-cut, mostly bastard	Sharpening mill saws, mowing machine knives, etc. For lathe work, draw filing and, to some extent, for finishing brass and bronze.
Equaling file, mill sections, blunt	Double-cut, mostly bastard	General machine shop work (seldom used).
Flat file, taper	Double-cut, mostly bastard, but also second-cut and smooth	One of the most common files in use; not confined to any specific kind of work, but employed for a great variety of purposes.
Hand file, parallel sides, tapered in thickness	Double-cut, mostly bastard, but also second-cut, smooth and dead-smooth	Preferred by machinists for finishing flat surfaces. Its shape and safe-edge adapt it where a flat file could not be used.
Pillar file, parallel sides, tapered in thickness	Double-cut, same as " hand file " in coarseness	For general machine shop use on narrow work.
Square file, taper	Double-cut, bastard	Principally for enlarging openings of square or rectangular shape.
Square blunt file	Double-cut, bastard	For the rougher work in finishing or enlarging mortises or keyways when of considerable length.
Warding file, parallel in thickness, much taper on sides	Double-cut, mostly bastard	Used by jewelers and machinists, but more especially by locksmiths, for filing " wardnotches " in keys.
Round file, taper and blunt	Mostly bastard	For enlarging round holes and shaping curved surfaces (sometimes called "rat-tail" file).
Half-round, taper	Double-cut, mostly bastard, but also second-cut and smooth	Extensively used in machine shops on curved surfaces, etc.
Hook-tooth file, blunt	Single-cut, bastard	Principally for sharpening the teeth of cross-cut saws, called " hook-tooth " saws.

Application of Different Types of Files

Type of File	Character of Cut	Ordinary Use
Pit-saw file, blunt	Single-cut, second-cut	For filing teeth of what are known as pit and frame saws.
Three-square file, taper	Double-cut, mostly bastard	For filing acute angles, finishing corners, etc.
Hand-saw taper, tapered to a point	Single-cut, second-cut	Principally for sharpening hand saws.
Hand-saw taper	Double-cut, second-cut	Preferred by some for filing fine-toothed hand and hacksaws.
Slim hand-saw taper, three-square section	Single-cut, second-cut	Has largely superseded the regular hand-saw file, the advantage being a greater stroke.
Cant-saw file	Single-cut, bastard	Principally for filing cross-cut saws having M-shaped teeth.
Knife file, taper	Double-cut, mostly bastard	Quite generally used for various purposes to which the knife-shape is adapted.
Crossing file, double oval	Bastard, second-cut and smooth	Used as an engineer file.
Feather-edge file, blunt	Double-cut, bastard, second-cut and smooth	Used for practically the same purposes as knife file (seldom used).
Reaper file, several sections, all blunt	Single-cut, bastard	Principally for sharpening the knives of mowing and reaping machines.
Drill file	Cut only upon the edges	Especially adapted to extending or rounding the ends of slots, when a round file would be too frail.
Half-round wood-file	Double-cut, coarse	Ordinarily used by wood-workers, and sometimes on coarser kinds of brass work.
Cabinet file, wider and thinner than half-round	Double-cut, coarse bastard	For cabinet makers and wood-workers generally.

Results of File Tests. — The file testing machine has shown that the shape of the teeth has much more influence on the rate of cutting and the durability than the quality of the steel of which the file is made. The variations in the rate of cutting are more marked on cast iron than on steel. Of five files tested, all of which were worn out after making about 110,000 strokes, the following results were obtained: When filing cast iron, the best file, when new, cut at the rate of 14 cubic inches per 10,000 strokes, while the poorest file only cut a little over one-half cubic inch during the same number of strokes. When filing steel, a rate of 6 cubic inches per 10,000 strokes is rarely exceeded. The chief factors which affect the cutting efficiency of the file are the sharpness of the teeth; slope of front faces of the teeth, or rake; slope of the back faces of the teeth, or clearance; the temper; the angles of the two cuts relative to the axis of the file; the pitch or coarseness of the cut; and the ratio between the pitch or number of cuts per inch in the "up cut" and in the "over cut." The pitch or coarseness of the cut does not seem to influence the efficiency to any great extent. Very coarse files, however, are almost always inefficient, probably because of the difficulty of producing very large teeth that are, at the same time, sufficiently thin and sharp. On the other hand, very smooth files cut slower and do less work than those of somewhat coarser cut, although in some cases surprising results have been obtained from smooth files.

Toolmakers' Files. — Toolmakers' files can be obtained in sizes from 2 to 12 inches in length and in eleven cuts, designated by numbers. The first five numbers correspond approximately in fineness (number of teeth to the inch) to ordinary domestic files as follows: No. 000, same as "rough"; No. 00, same as "bastard"; No. 0, same as "second-cut"; No. 1, same as "smooth"; No. 2, same as "super-smooth." Toolmakers' files from No. 2 to No. 8 have no equivalent in ordinary files. The toolmakers' file is distinguished by its sharp outline, the teeth extending to the extreme points and edges. In width and thickness, these files are also more slender than common files, and somewhat lighter. The exact number of teeth per inch varies in both classes of files and with different makes of the same class. When ordering files of precision, the order should invariably specify toolmakers' files.

Height of Work for Filing. — For filing in a vise, the vise jaws should be level with the workman's elbows, which height varies from 40 to 44 inches from the floor; hence 42 inches is a good average height for a vise that is fixed permanently. If the work to be filed is small and delicate, requiring simply a movement of the arms, the vise should be higher so that the workman can stand erect and see the work to better advantage. If the parts to be filed are heavy, thus requiring considerable effort, the surface should preferably be below the elbow joint, as the operator stands further away from the work, and in a slightly stooping posture. Moreover, in this class of work, it is desirable to throw the weight of the body upon the file to make it cut.

Work Benches. — The height of work benches usually varies from 32 to 36 inches from the floor to the top of the bench, the height depending somewhat upon the nature of the work, lighter work being done on higher benches. For general purposes, the height should be about 34 inches. The width should be about 30 inches, and the top is ordinarily composed of heavy planks, 2 or 3 inches thick, in the front, and lighter 1-inch boards in the back. The thickness of the front planks is varied in accordance with the weight of the work for which the bench is intended. Maple and ash are considered the best woods for bench planking. The preferable position for benches, especially if used for fine accurate work, is the north side of the building, because the light on that side is more even throughout the day. The clearance space or gangway between the bench and the end of any projecting machine handles, handwheels, etc., should not be less than 2 feet 10 inches.

Table 1. Hack-Saw Blade Dimensions — Hand Frame Sizes

United States Department of Commerce, Simplified Practice Recommendation (R90-46)

Catalogue Dimensions, Inches			No. of Teeth per Inch	Actual Dimensions, Inches			
Edge Symbol, Length	Width	Thickness		Width Before Milling	Length Over-all	Center to Center of Pinholes	Pinhole Diameter
Carbon Type — Single Steel — Uniform Teeth							
S 10	½	0.025	18, 24, 32	0.500	10⅜	9⅞	5/32
S 12	½	0.025	14, 18, 24, 32	0.510	12⅜	11⅞	5/32
Standard Type — Single Steel — Starting Teeth							
DS 10	½	0.025	18, 24, 32	0.500	10⅜	9⅞	5/32
DS 12	½	0.025	14, 18, 24, 32	0.510	12⅜	11⅞	5/32
D 12	1	0.032	18, 24	1.000	12⅝	11⅞	7/32
Molybdenum Type — Single Steel — Welded and Composite Blade — Starting Teeth							
S 10	½	0.025	18, 24, 32	0.500	10⅜	9⅞	5/32
S 12	½	0.025	14, 18, 24, 32	0.510	12⅜	11⅞	5/32
18-4-1 Type — Single Steel — Welded and Composite — Starting Teeth							
S 10	½	0.025	18, 24, 32	0.500	10⅜	9⅞	5/32
S 12	½	0.025	14, 18, 24, 32	0.510	12⅜	11⅞	5/32
Broach Blades — Standard, Molybdenum, and 18-4-1 Types — Single Steel — Welded and Composite							
S 10	½	0.025	18 to 14	0.500	10⅜	9⅞	5/32
S 10	½	0.025	24 to 20	0.500	10⅜	9⅞	5/32
S 12	½	0.025	18 to 14	0.510	12⅜	11⅞	5/32
S 12	½	0.025	24 to 20	0.510	12⅜	11⅞	5/32

Hack-Saw Blade Definitions. — The following definitions apply in connection with the simplified practice recommendation R90-46. The types and sizes of hack-saw blades recommended for regular stock production are listed in Tables 1 and 2.

Carbon Type: Hack-saw blade made entirely of steel known in the industry as "ordinary steel," "straight carbon steel," or steel the properties of which are derived chiefly from the carbon content. This type does not contain substantial amounts of other alloying elements.

Standard Type: Hack-saw blade made entirely of steel known in the industry as "standard" or "tungsten alloy." It contains approximately and not more than 1¼ per cent tungsten and ¾ per cent molybdenum.

Molybdenum Type: All of blade or its tooth section is made of (1) steel containing not less than .60 per cent carbon or more than 3.0 per cent molybdenum; or (2) alloy steel containing not less than .60 per cent carbon, 6.0 per cent or less of tungsten, and over 3.0 per cent molybdenum. Other alloying elements may be present.

18-4-1 Type: All of blade or its tooth section contains not less than .55 per cent carbon and over 12.0 per cent tungsten. Other alloying elements may be present.

Single Steel: Entire blade is made of one type and piece of steel.

Welded and Composite: Blade is made of two or more pieces of steel joined together. Either molybdenum or 18-4-1 types are used for cutting edge or edges.

Uniform Teeth: Tooth spacing is uniform throughout tooth section.

Starting Teeth: Leading or forward 2½ inches of blade, have teeth of finer pitch than remainder of tooth section.

Broach Blade: Number of teeth per inch decreases from first to last tooth, no two teeth being spaced alike.

Tolerances. — *Thickness:* For Carbon and Standard Type blades +.001 −.003 inch; for Molybdenum and 18-4-1 Types ±.003 inch. *Width:* +0 −1/64 inch.

Blade Width. — The actual width is as given in Tables 1 and 2 with the following exceptions: Double edge power sizes, $+\frac{1}{4}$ inch. Welded and composite blades, $1\frac{1}{16}$ for catalogue widths of $\frac{5}{8}$ inch, $1\frac{3}{32}$ for catalogue widths of 1 inch, $1\frac{3}{8}$ for catalogue widths of $1\frac{1}{4}$ inches, $1\frac{5}{8}$ for catalogue widths of $1\frac{1}{2}$ inches, $2\frac{1}{8}$ for catalogue widths of 2 inches.

Symbols. — Symbol "S" means single-edge blade or blade with teeth on one edge only; Symbol "D" means double-edge blade or blade with teeth on both edges.

Table 2. Hack-Saw Blade Dimensions — Power Sizes

United States Department of Commerce, Simplified Practice Recommendation
(R90–46)

Catalogue Dimensions, Inches				No. of Teeth per Inch	Actual Dimensions, Inches			
Edge Symbol and Length (1)		Width	Thickness		Width Before Milling	Length Over-all	Center to Center of Pinholes	Pinhole Diameter
Molybdenum and 18-4-1 Types — Single Steel — Welded and Composite — Uniform Teeth								
S 12	S 12	$\frac{5}{8}$	0.032	14, 18	0.625	$12\frac{1}{2}$	$11\frac{7}{8}$	$\frac{3}{16}$
DS 12	S 12	1	.049	14	1.000	$12\frac{3}{4}$	$11\frac{7}{8}$	$\frac{9}{32}$
DS 12	S 12	1	.065	10	1.000	$12\frac{3}{4}$	$11\frac{7}{8}$	$\frac{9}{32}$
DS 14	S 14	1	.049	10, 14	1.000	$14\frac{3}{8}$	$13\frac{1}{2}$	$\frac{9}{32}$
DS 14	S 14	1	.065	10	1.000	$14\frac{3}{8}$	$13\frac{1}{2}$	$\frac{9}{32}$
DS 14	S 14	$1\frac{1}{4}$	.065	4, 6, 10	1.250	$14\frac{1}{2}$	$13\frac{1}{2}$	$\frac{9}{32}$
DS 14	S 14	$1\frac{1}{2}$	.072	4, 6	1.500	$14\frac{1}{2}$	$13\frac{1}{2}$	$\frac{9}{32}$
S 17	S 17	1	.049	14	1.000	$17\frac{3}{8}$	$16\frac{1}{2}$	$\frac{9}{32}$
S 17	S 17	1	.065	10	1.000	$17\frac{3}{8}$	$16\frac{1}{2}$	$\frac{9}{32}$
DS 17	S 17	$1\frac{1}{4}$	.065	4, 6, 10	1.250	$17\frac{1}{2}$	$16\frac{1}{2}$	$\frac{9}{32}$
S 18	S 18	1	.065	10	1.000	$18\frac{3}{8}$	$17\frac{1}{2}$	$\frac{9}{32}$
DS 18	S 18	$1\frac{1}{4}$	.065	4, 6, 10	1.250	$18\frac{1}{2}$	$17\frac{1}{2}$	$\frac{9}{32}$
DS 18	S 18	$1\frac{1}{2}$	.072	4, 6	1.500	$18\frac{1}{2}$	$17\frac{1}{2}$	$\frac{9}{32}$
DS 18	S 18	2	.072	4, 6	2.000	$18\frac{3}{4}$	$17\frac{1}{2}$	$\frac{9}{32}$
DS 21	S 21	2	.072	4, 6	2.000	$22\frac{1}{4}$	21	$\frac{9}{32}$
DS 21	S 21	2	.100	4	2.000	$22\frac{1}{4}$	21	$\frac{9}{32}$
DS 24	S 24	2	.072	4, 6	2.000	$25\frac{1}{4}$	24	$\frac{9}{32}$
DS 24	S 24	2	.100	4	2.000	$25\frac{1}{4}$	24	$\frac{9}{32}$
DS 24	S 24	2	.100	4	2.000	$25\frac{1}{4}$	24	$\frac{25}{64}$
DS 30	S 30	$2\frac{1}{2}$	.100	4	2.500	32	30	$\frac{25}{64}$
Coarse Tooth Molybdenum and 18-4-1 Types — Single Steel — Welded and Composite — Uniform Teeth								
....	S 14	$1\frac{1}{2}$	0.072	$\frac{3}{8}''$ (2)	$1\frac{9}{16}$	$14\frac{1}{2}$	$13\frac{1}{2}$	$\frac{9}{32}$
....	S 18	$1\frac{1}{2}$	.072	$\frac{3}{8}''$	$1\frac{9}{16}$	$18\frac{1}{2}$	$17\frac{1}{2}$	$\frac{9}{32}$
....	S 21	$1\frac{1}{2}$	.072	$\frac{3}{8}''$	$1\frac{9}{16}$	$22\frac{1}{4}$	21	$\frac{9}{32}$
....	S 21	2	.100	$\frac{3}{8}''$	$2\frac{1}{16}$	$22\frac{1}{4}$	21	$\frac{9}{32}$
....	S 24	$2\frac{1}{2}$	.100	$\frac{3}{8}''$	$2\frac{9}{16}$	$25\frac{1}{4}$	24	$\frac{9}{32}$
....	S 36	$4\frac{1}{2}$	.125	$\frac{3}{8}''$	$4\frac{1}{2}$	38	36	$\frac{1}{2}$
Broach Blades — Molybdenum and 18-4-1 Types — Single Steel — Welded and Composite								
....	S 12	1	0.065	10 to 6	1.000	$12\frac{3}{4}$	$11\frac{7}{8}$	$\frac{9}{32}$
....	S 14	1	.065	10 to 6	1.000	$14\frac{3}{8}$	$13\frac{1}{2}$	$\frac{9}{32}$
....	S 14	$1\frac{1}{4}$	.065	10 to 6	1.250	$14\frac{1}{2}$	$13\frac{1}{2}$	$\frac{9}{32}$

(1) The edge symbols in first column apply only to molybdenum blades in upper section.

(2) For coarse-tooth blades the $\frac{3}{8}$ inch is the pitch or point-to-point spacing. The producer may select $2\frac{1}{2}$ teeth per inch as an alternate standard.

Table 1. Compositions of Steels Used for Tools — Based on the Practice of the Westinghouse Electric & Mfg. Co.

The numbers in the first column are used to identify the steels listed in Table 2.

No.	Class of Steel	Chemical Composition, Per Cent (Upper Line, Minimum; Lower Line, Maximum)										
		C	Mn	P	S	Si	Ni	Cr	Va	W	Co	Mo
1	Carbon Steel for Tool Shanks	0.50 / 0.63	0.60 / 0.90	... / 0.04	... / ...	0.15 / ...	...	...	...	...	...	...
2	Tungsten High-Speed Steel	0.60 / 0.75	0.15 / 0.40	... / 0.03	... / 0.03	0.15 / 0.40	...	3.00 / 4.50	0.75 / 1.50	17.00 / 19.00	...	...
3	Carbon Tool Steel	1.00 / 1.10	0.15 / 0.35	... / 0.025	... / 0.025	0.10 / 0.35	...	...	...	...	...	...
4	Carbon Die Steel	0.80 / 0.90	... / 0.45	... / 0.025	... / 0.025	...	...	...	...	...	...	...
5	Carbon Steel Drill Rod *	1.20 / 1.35	0.15 / 0.35	... / 0.025	... / 0.025	0.10 / 0.25	...	...	...	...	...	...
	Carbon Steel Drill Rod †	1.15 / 1.30	0.15 / 0.35	... / 0.025	... / 0.025	0.10 / 0.25	...	...	...	...	...	...
	Carbon Steel Drill Rod ‡	1.10 / 1.25	0.15 / 0.35	... / 0.025	... / 0.025	0.10 / 0.25	...	...	...	...	...	...
6	Oil-Hardening Non-Deforming	0.85 / 0.95	1.05 / 1.25	... / 0.025	... / 0.025	0.20 / 0.35	...	0.40 / 0.60	... / 0.25	0.40 / 0.60	...	...
7	Low-Tungsten, Chrome-Vanadium	1.15 / 1.25	0.20 / 0.35	... / 0.025	... / 0.025	0.20 / 0.35	...	0.35 / 0.50	0.15 / 0.25	1.30 / 1.75	...	...
8	Chrome-Vanadium Steel	0.15 / 0.25	0.50 / 0.80	... / 0.04	... / 0.04	0.10 / 0.20	...	0.80 / 1.10	0.15 / 0.25	...	...	...
9	Alloy Die-Block Steel	0.50 / 0.60	0.50 / 0.80	... / 0.04	... / 0.04	0.20 / 0.39	1.25 / 1.75	0.60 / 0.80	... / 0.12	...	...	0.15 / 0.25
	Alloy Die-Block Steel	0.54 / 0.66	0.40 / 0.50	... / 0.03	... / 0.03	0.10 / 0.20	1.30 / 1.60	0.85 / 1.10	...	...	...	...

* Up to ¼ inch, inclusive,　† Over ¼ inch to ½ inch, inclusive,　‡ Over ½ inch.

Table 1 (*Continued*). Compositions of Steels Used for Tools — Based on the Practice of the Westinghouse Electric & Mfg. Co. The numbers in the first column are used to identify the steels listed in Table 2.

Chemical Composition, Per Cent (Upper Line, Minimum; Lower Line, Maximum)

No.	Class of Steel	C	Mn	P	S	Si	Ni	Cr	Va	W	Co	Mo
10	Carbon Die-Block Steel	0.55 / 0.65	0.50 / 0.70	…. / 0.04	…. / 0.04	0.15 / 0.30						
11	Chrome-Vanadium Steel	0.45 / 0.55	0.50 / 0.80	…. / 0.04	…. / 0.04			0.80 / 1.10	0.15 / 0.20			
12	Low-Tungsten Alloy	0.40 / 0.50	0.15 / 0.35	…. / 0.025	…. / 0.025	0.15 / 0.35		1.25 / 1.50	0.15 / 0.25	2.00 / 3.00		
13	Tungsten Fast-Finishing Steel	1.30 / 1.45	0.15 / 0.35	…. / 0.025	…. / 0.025	0.30 / 0.60		0.50		3.50 / 5.00		0.50
14	Tungsten-Chromium Hot-Work Steel	0.32 / 0.42	0.10 / 0.30	…. / 0.03	…. / 0.03	0.20 / 0.40		3.00 / 3.50	0.30 / 0.60	9.75 / 10.75		
		0.32 / 0.42	0.20 / 0.40	…. / 0.025	…. / 0.025	0.20 / 0.35		3.25 / 3.75	0.60 / 0.75	13.50 / 15.00		
15	High-Carbon High-Chromium	1.45 / 1.70	0.20 / 0.40	…. / 0.03	…. / 0.03	0.20 / 0.40		11.0 / 12.50	0.15		0.40 / 0.60	0.70 / 1.00
16	Cobalt High-Speed Steel	0.65 / 0.75	0.25 / 0.35	…. / 0.03	…. / 0.03	0.20 / 0.40		4.00 / 4.25	0.90 / 1.10	17.00 / 18.00	4.50 / 5.00	0.40 / 0.50
		0.70 / 0.80	0.40	…. / 0.04	…. / 0.025	0.50		4.00 / 5.00	1.50 / 2.25	17.50 / 19.50	7.50 / 10.00	1.00
17	Chrome-Vanadium	0.65 / 0.75	0.10 / 0.30	…. / 0.03	…. / 0.03	0.25 / 0.35		0.70 / 0.90	0.15 / 0.25			
18	Silicon-Molybdenum Steel	0.45 / 0.55	0.30 / 0.50	…. / 0.02	…. / 0.02	0.80 / 1.10						0.40 / 0.60

Table 2.　Steels Used for Different Types of Tools

(See Table 1 for compositions represented by the numbers)

Kind of Tool	No. or Symbol of Steel	Qualities Wanted in Tool	Hardness, Rockwell C	Remarks
Arbor nuts, milling machine	11	Fair hardness, great strength	46–52	Grind after hardening
Arbors, balancing	3	Very hard	63–66	Grind after hardening
Arbors, milling machine, large-shank	C-N₁	Fair hardness, great strength	46–52	Grind after hardening
Arbors, milling machine, small-shank	11	Fair hardness, great strength	46–52	Grind after hardening
Arbors, up to 1¼ inches diameter	3	Very hard	63–66	Grind after hardening
Broaches	2	Maximum hardness, normal distortion, best cutting edge	63–65	Grind after hardening
Broaches, push, short	3	Very hard, keen cutting edges	63–66	Grind after hardening
Bushings, guide	H-R₃	Hard wearing surface, normal distortion	Rock. Super. 90 min., 15 N. scale	Grind after hardening
Buttons, locating	5	Very hard	63–66	Grind after hardening
Centers, lathe	3	Very hard	63–66	Grind after hardening
Chisels, cold, cutting end of	12	Shock and wear resistance	50–54	Grind after hardening
Chisels, cold; for chipping semi-hard die parts	3	Fair hardness, reduced brittleness	57–60	Grind after hardening
Chisels, pneumatic, shank end of; hand hammer, end of	12	Shock and wear resistance	46–48	Finish to size before hardening

C-N₁, Chrome-nickel steel, with 0.30 to 0.40 per cent carbon,　　　　H-R₃, Hot-rolled steel, with from 0.08 to 0.25 per cent carbon.

Table 2 (*Continued*). Steels Used for Different Types of Tools
(See Table I for compositions represented by the numbers)

Kind of Tool	No. or Symbol of Steel	Qualities Wanted in Tool	Hardness, Rockwell C	Remarks
Clamps	11	Medium hardness	46-52	Finish to size before hardening
Collars, milling machine arbor, with hole over 1½ inches in diameter	8	Hard case, with semi-hard core, normal distortion, wear resisting	Rock. Super. 90 min. 15 N. scale	Grind after hardening
Collets, front end of spring, that can be ground in the hole	3	Very hard in hole, shank drawn to Rockwell C37-41	63-66	Grind hole after hardening
Collets, not ground in the hole; draw shank end to 50-55 Scleroscope	7	Hardness, wear resistance, minimum distortion	60-63	Rough-machine, strain-relieve, finish to size, and harden
Counterbore pilots	3	Very hard	63-66	Grind after hardening
Counterbores	2	Maximum hardness, normal distortion, best cutting edge	63-65	Grind after hardening
Cutters, drum; for woodwork	3	Toughness	50-54	Grind after hardening
Cutting tools for babbitt and non-ferrous metals	3	Very hard, keen cutting edges	63-66	Grind after hardening
Cutting tools that can be ground after hardening	2	Maximum hardness, normal distortion, best cutting edge	63-65	Grind after hardening
Cutting tools; when impractical to grind	2	Maximum hardness, with minimum distortion, and good cutting edge	63-65	Rough-machine, strain-relieve, and finish to size before hardening
Die-blocks; maximum depth of impression, ⅜ inch; for high production and close tolerances	9	High production capacity, hardness	52-55	Finish to size before hardening
Die-blocks; maximum depth of impression, ⅝ inch; for high production and close tolerances	9	High production capacity, hardness	47-50	Finish to size before hardening

Table 2 (*Continued*). **Steels Used for Different Types of Tools**

(See Table 1 for compositions represented by the numbers)

Kind of Tool	No. or Symbol of Steel	Qualities Wanted in Tool	Hardness, Rockwell C	Remarks
Die-blocks; maximum depth of impression, 3/4 inch; for normal production with liberal tolerances; for simple impressions where sturdy tools can be employed	9	Normal production capacity, medium hardness, low-cost upkeep	41–43	Blocks may be bought heat-treated and the impression finish-machined in heat-treated block
Die-blocks; maximum depth of impression, 1 inch; for high production and close tolerances	9	High production capacity, hardness	44–46	Finish to size before hardening
Die-blocks; maximum depth of impression, 3 inches; for normal production with liberal tolerances	9	Normal production capacity, medium hardness, low-cost upkeep	38–41	Blocks may be bought heat-treated and the impression finish-machined in heat-treated block
Die-blocks; very deep impressions; for plastic molds or drop-forgings, especially forgings that will be machined to size	9	Normal production capacity, medium hardness, low-cost upkeep	35–37	Blocks may be bought heat-treated and the impression finish-machined in heat-treated block
Die parts, frail, that can be ground; for hard, thin, ferrous materials, and other materials 3/16 inch thick and over	2	Reduced brittleness, normal distortion, and reduced hardening risks	57–60	Grind after hardening
Die parts, frail, that can be ground; for mill-annealed steel	2	Toughness, normal distortion	31–36	Grind after hardening
Die parts, frail; when impractical to grind; for mill-annealed steel	2	Toughness and minimum distortion	31–36	Finish to size before hardening
Die parts, frail; when impractical to grind; for hard, thin, ferrous materials, as well as other materials 3/16 inch thick and over	2	Reduced brittleness, minimum distortion and hardening risks	57–60	Rough-machine, strain-relieve and finish to size before hardening

Table 2 (*Continued*). **Steels Used for Different Types of Tools**

(See Table 1 for compositions represented by the numbers) ‖

Kind of Tool	No. or Symbol of Steel	Qualities Wanted in Tool	Hardness, Rockwell C	Remarks
Die parts, frail, where there is extreme risk of breakage or distortion in hardening; for soft, thin, ferrous materials	2	No distortion	28 max.	Finish to size, but do not harden
Die parts impractical to grind; for hard metals	15	Semi-hard	40–43	Finish to size before hardening
Die parts impractical to grind; for soft metals	15	Semi-hard	36–40	Finish to size before hardening
Die parts that can be ground, for hard metals	15	Semi-hard	40–43	Grind after hardening
Die parts that can be ground, for soft metals	15	Semi-hard, normal distortion	36–40	Grind after hardening
Die parts, medium hard, that can be ground; for ferrous material 1/16 inch thick and over; also for scaly iron and for steel with over 2.5 per cent silicon	2	Medium hardness, normal distortion	40–43	Grind after hardening
Die parts, medium hard; when impractical to grind; for ferrous materials 1/16 inch thick or over, for scaly iron and for steel with over 2½ per cent silicon	2	Medium hardness, minimum distortion and hardening risks	40–43	Finish to size before hardening
Die parts requiring surface hardness only	H-R₃	Surface hardness; hard surface approximately 0.004 inch thick	Rock. Super. 90 min. 15 N. scale	Finish to size before hardening; hard surface will not permit grinding; surface to be hardened must be machined
Die parts requiring surface hardness only; surface will not permit grinding	C-R₄	Surface hardness; hardened surface approximately 0.004 inch thick	Rock. Super. 90 min. 15 N. scale	Anneal before machining, finish to size before hardening

H-R₃, Hot-rolled steel, with from 0.08 to 0.25 per cent carbon.   C-R₄, Cold-rolled steel, with from 0.08 to 0.16 per cent carbon.

Table 2 (*Continued*). **Steels Used for Different Types of Tools**
(See Table 1 for compositions represented by the numbers)

Kind of Tool	No. or Symbol of Steel	Qualities Wanted in Tool	Hardness, Rockwell C	Remarks
Die parts, semi-hard, that can be ground; for steel with 2.5 per cent silicon or less, and for small blanking dies for steel	2	Semi-hard, normal distortion	36-40	Grind after hardening
Die parts, semi-hard; when impractical to grind; for steel with 2½ per cent silicon or less, and for small blanking dies for steel	2	Semi-hard, minimum distortion	36-40	Finish to size before hardening
Die parts with weak sections, that can be ground; for hard, thin, ferrous materials	2	Freedom from breakage, normal distortion, and reduced hardening risks	52-55	Grind after hardening
Die parts, with weak sections, when impractical to grind; for hard, thin, ferrous materials	2	Freedom from breakage, minimum distortion and hardening risks	52-55	Rough-machine, strain-relieve, and finish to size before hardening
Die strippers	H-R₄	Semi-hardness, machineability	29-33	Finish to size after hardening
Die strippers, compound, with stop lugs	17	Fair hardness, normal deformation	46-50	Finish to size and harden
Dies, bending and forming; for light materials	17	Maximum surface hardness, minimum distortion and breakage risks	63-66	Rough-machine, strain-relieve, finish to size, and harden
Dies, for copper, aluminum, and brass up to 0.020 inch thick for production of less than 50,000 pieces where tolerances are not close	H-R₃	Good cutting edges, minimum distortion, soft body	Rock. Super. 90 min. 15 N. scale	Largest dimension of punching not to be less than 3 inches
Dies for heavy fuller-board, fiber, and mica	H-R₃	Good cutting edges, minimum distortion, soft body	Rock. Super. 90 min. 15 N. scale	Largest dimension of punching not to be less than 3 inches

H-R₄ Hot-rolled steel, with from 0.30 to 0.45 per cent carbon.   H-R₃ Hot-rolled steel, with from 0.08 to 0.25 per cent carbon.

Table 2 (*Continued*). **Steels Used for Different Types of Tools**

(See Table I for compositions represented by the numbers)

Kind of Tool	No. or Symbol of Steel	Qualities Wanted in Tool	Hardness, Rockwell C	Remarks
Dies, for heavy plate materials	17	Hardness, wear resistance, normal deformation	54-57	Finish to size and harden
Dies for hot-pressing brass and copper alloys	14	Heat and wear resistance, minimum distortion	52-56	Rough-machine, strain-relieve, finish to size before hardening
Dies, for punching and shearing hot metals	14	Heat and wear resistance, normal distortion	52-56	Grind after hardening
Dies, for rivet holes in structural steel	11	Fair hardness, great strength	51-55	Finish to size before hardening
Dies, for small lots that can be ground	3	Hard, keen cutting edges	60-63	Grind after hardening
Dies impractical to grind; for hard, scaly, ferrous materials and non-ferrous materials of all thicknesses; for production between 5000 and 50,000 punchings	15	Hardness and toughness, minimum distortion, wear resistance	60-63	Rough-machine, strain-relieve, finish-machine, and harden
Dies impractical to grind; for quantities from 5000 to 50,000	7	Hardness, wear resistance, minimum distortion	60-63	Rough-machine, strain-relieve, finish to size, and harden
Dies that can be ground; for hard, scaly, ferrous materials and non-ferrous materials of all thicknesses; for production between 5000 and 50,000 punchings	15	Hardness and toughness, wear resistance, best quality cutting edge, normal distortion	60-63	Grind after hardening
Dies, semi-hard, for small production; for all metals, paper, etc.	3	Semi-hard	31-36	Grind after hardening
Dies, shaving, that can be ground after hardening; for all scaly iron and for steel with over 2.5 per cent silicon	2	Hardness, normal distortion, best edge for die work	60-63	Grind after hardening

Table 2 (*Continued*). Steels Used for Different Types of Tools

(See Table 1 for compositions represented by the numbers)

Kind of Tool	No. or Symbol of Steel	Qualities Wanted in Tool	Hardness, Rockwell C	Remarks
Dies, shaving; when impractical to grind; for all scaly iron, and for steel with over 2½ per cent silicon	2	Hardness, minimum distortion, and minimum hardening risk	60–63	Rough-machine, strain-relieve, and finish to size before hardening
Dies, straightening	17	Fair hardness, normal deformation	46–50	Finish to size and harden
Dies, straightening and sizing; for cold drop-forgings	17	Hardness, wear resistance, maintenance of shape and size	57–60	Finish to size and harden
Dies, thread-rolling	15	Hardness and toughness, minimum distortion, wear resistance	60–63	Rough-machine, strain-relieve, finish-machine, and harden
Dies, trimming; for cold drop-forgings	2	Hardness, minimum distortion, and minimum hardening risk	60–63	Rough-machine, strain-relieve, and finish to size before hardening
Dies, trimming; for cold drop-forgings	2	Hardness, normal distortion, best edge for die work	60–63	Grind after hardening
Dies, trimming; for hot forging	11	Medium ductility, maximum machineability, hardness	30–35	Finish to size after hardening
Dies, trimming; for large hot forgings	C-N₁	Medium ductility, maximum machineability, hardness	30–35	Rough-machine; if necessary, harden; and finish to size after hardening
Drifts, round taper	12	Shock and wear resistance	46–48	Finish to size before hardening
Drifts, small	5	Toughness	45–48	Grind after hardening

C-N, Chrome-nickel steel, with 0.30 to 0.40 per cent carbon.

Table 2 (*Continued*). **Steels Used for Different Types of Tools**

(See Table 1 for compositions represented by the numbers)

Kind of Tool	No. or Symbol of Steel	Qualities Wanted in Tool	Hardness, Rockwell C	Remarks
Drill bushings, from 0.339- to 1½-inch diameter hole	3	Very hard	63–66	Grind after hardening
Drill bushings, plain and slip	8	Hard case with semi-hard core, normal distortion, wear resisting	Rock. Super. 90 min. 15 N. scale	Grind after hardening
Drill bushings, screw type	7	Hardness, wear resistance, minimum distortion	60–63	Rough-machine, strain-relieve, finish to size, and harden
Drill bushings, small	5	Very hard	63–66	Grind after hardening
Drill plates, multiple-hole	7	Hardness, wear resistance, minimum distortion	60–63	Rough-machine, strain-relieve, finish to size, and harden
Gage pins	5	Very hard	63–66	Grind after hardening
Gages, large thread, plug, and ring	C-N₁	Medium ductility, maximum machineability, hardness	30–35	Rough-machine; if necessary, harden; and finish to size after hardening
Gages, plug and ring; for spline-shaft and holes	7	Hard, wear-resisting surface; permanence of size, shape, and form	60–63	Rough-machine, normalize, harden, draw, rough-grind, season, and finish-grind
Gages, plug, plain and taper; from 4 to 12 inches in diameter	8	Hard case, wear resisting; permanence of size, shape, and form	Rock. Super. 90 min. 15 N. scale	Rough-machine, strain-relieve, finish-machine, harden, draw, rough-grind, season, finish-grind, and lap
Gages, plug thread, over ⅜ inch in diameter, with threads finer than 24 per inch	11	Medium ductility, maximum machineability, hardness	30–35	Finish to size after hardening

C-N₁, Chrome-nickel steel, with 0.30 to 0.40 per cent carbon.

Table 2 (Continued). Steels Used for Different Types of Tools

(See Table I for compositions represented by the numbers)

Kind of Tool	No. or Symbol of Steel	Qualities Wanted in Tool	Hardness, Rockwell C	Remarks
Gages, plug thread; up to, but not including, ¼ inch diameter; all pitches; also gages ¼ to ⅜ inch diameter inclusive, with threads finer than 24 per inch	H-R₉	Hard surface approximately 0.003 inch thick, minimum distortion	Rock. Super. 90 min. 15 N. scale	Rough-machine, anneal, finish-machine, harden, and lap
Gages, plug thread, with 24 threads per inch or coarser, ¾ inch to 4 inches diameter	7	Hard, wear-resisting surface; permanence of size, shape, and form	60-63	Rough-machine, normalize, harden, draw, rough-grind, season, and finish-grind
Gages, plug thread, over 4 inches in diameter	11	Medium ductility, maximum machineability, hardness	30-35	Finish to size after hardening
Gages, ring	H-Rₓ	Hard wearing surface, minimum distortion	Rock. Super. 90 min. 15 N. scale	Anneal, rough-machine, strain-relieve, finish-machine to size, and harden
Gages, ring, plain and taper, with hole over 1½ inches in diameter	8	Hard case, wear resisting; permanence of size, shape, and form	Rock. Super. 90 min, 15 N. scale	Rough-machine, strain-relieve, finish-machine, harden, draw, rough-grind, season, finish-grind, and lap
Gages, sheet steel, up to ⅛ inch thick inclusive, requiring partial or complete hardening	SS₆	Hardness, wear resistance	63-66	Grind after hardening
Gages, solid, plain; straight and tapered plug	3	Wear-resisting surface, permanence of size, shape, and form	63-66	Machine, harden, draw, rough-grind, season, finish-grind, and lap
Gages, straight and tapered ring	3	Wear-resisting surface, permanence of size, shape and form	63-66	Rough-machine, anneal, finish-machine, harden, draw, rough-grind, season, finish-grind, and lap

H-R₈, Hot-rolled steel, with from 0.08 to 0.18 per cent carbon.   SS₆, Spring steel, with from 0.90 to 1.10 per cent carbon.

Table 2 (*Continued*).   **Steels Used for Different Types of Tools**

(See Table 1 for compositions represented by the numbers)

Kind of Tool	No. or Symbol of Steel	Qualities Wanted in Tool	Hardness, Rockwell C	Remarks
Gear hobs	7	Hardness, wear resistance, minimum distortion	60–63	Rough-machine, strain-relieve, finish to size, and harden
Gear hobs; when impractical to grind	2	Maximum hardness, with minimum distortion, and good cutting edge	63–65	Rough-machine, strain-relieve, and finish to size before hardening
Gears	11	Medium ductility, maximum machineability, hardness	30–35	Finish to size after hardening
Guide pins	H-R₃	Hard wearing surface, normal distortion	Rock. Super. 90 min. 15 N. scale	Grind after hardening
Jigs, welded, under 60 pounds in weight	H-R₄	Semi-hardness, machineability	29–33	Finish to size after hardening
Mandrels, lathe	3	Very hard	63–66	Grind after hardening
Milling cutter bodies, inserted teeth	11	Medium ductility, maximum machineability, hardness	30–35	Finish to size after hardening
Milling cutter bodies, inserted teeth	C-N₁	Medium ductility, maximum machineability, hardness	30–35	Rough-machine; if necessary, harden; and finish to size after hardening
Milling cutter teeth, inserted	2	Maximum hardness, normal distortion, best cutting edge	63–65	Grind after hardening
Milling cutters, backed-off form; when impractical to grind	2	Maximum hardness, with minimum distortion, and good cutting edge	63–65	Rough-machine, strain-relieve, and finish to size before hardening

H-R₃, Hot-rolled steel, with from 0.08 to 0.25 per cent carbon.   H-R₄, Hot-rolled steel, with from 0.30 to 0.45 per cent carbon.

C-N₁, Chrome-nickel steel, with 0.30 to 0.40 per cent carbon.

Table 2 *(Continued).*　**Steels Used for Different Types of Tools**

(See Table 1 for compositions represented by the numbers)

Kind of Tool	No. or Symbol of Steel	Qualities Wanted in Tool	Hardness, Rockwell C	Remarks
Milling cutters, dovetail	8	Hard case with semi-hard core, good wearing surface and cutting edge, minimum distortion	Rock. Super. 90 min. 15 N. Scale	Rough-machine, strain-relieve, finish-machine, and harden
Milling cutters; ground after hardening	2	Maximum hardness, normal distortion, best cutting edge	63-65	Grind after hardening
Mold parts for plastic materials; impractical to grind; where material is not pinched off	3	Case-hardened surface and semi-hard core, minimum distortion	Rock. Super. 90 min. 15 N. scale	Rough-machine, strain-relieve, and finish to size before hardening
Mold parts for plastics, ground after hardening	8	Hard case with semi-hard core, minimum distortion	Rock. Super. 90 min, 15 N. scale	Rough-machine, strain-relieve, finish to size, carburize, and harden
Molds, large, for molded materials	C-N1	Medium ductility, maximum machineability, hardness	30-35	Rough-machine; if necessary, harden; and finish to size after hardening
Molds, permanent	14	Heat and wear resistance, minimum distortion	52-56	Rough-machine, strain-relieve, finish to size before hardening
Nuts, clamping	11	Medium ductility, maximum machineability, hardness	30-35	Finish to size after hardening
Plungers; for bolt-heading machines	11	Fair hardness, great strength	46-52	Grind after hardening
Plungers, upsetting; for commutator bolts	11	Medium hardness	46-52	Finish to size before hardening

C-N, Chrome-nickel steel, with 0.30 to 0.40 per cent carbon.

Table 2 (*Continued*). **Steels Used for Different Types of Tools**
(See Table 1 for compositions represented by the numbers)

Kind of Tool	No. or Symbol of Steel	Qualities Wanted in Tool	Hardness, Rockwell C	Remarks
Plungers, upsetting; for nickel-steel shafts	11	Fair hardness, great strength	51–55	Finish to size before hardening
Punch backing plate for dies; over 5 inches in diameter	H-R₂	Fairly hard, normal distortion	44–48	Cut out by torch, anneal, machine, harden, and grind
Punches, center	3	Fair hardness, reduced brittleness	57–60	Grind after hardening
Punches, center, cutting end of	12	Shock and wear resistance	50–54	Grind after hardening
Punches, center, hammer end of	12	Shock and wear resistance	46–48	Finish to size before hardening
Punches for copper, aluminum, and brass up to 0.020 inch thick, for production of less than 50,000 pieces where tolerances are not too close	H-R₃	Semi-hard	36–40	Largest dimension of punching not to be less than 3 inches
Punches for heavy fuller-board, fiber, and mica	H-R₃	Good cutting edges, minimum distortion, soft body	Rock. Super. 90 min. 15 N. scale	Largest dimension of punching not to be less than 3 inches
Punches for heavy materials	3	Toughness	50–54	Grind after hardening
Punches for heavy plate materials	17	Hardness, wear resistance, normal deformation	54–57	Finish to size and harden
Punches for small production; for all metals, paper, etc.	3	Semi-hard	31–36	Grind after hardening
Punches for soft materials	3	Fair hardness, reduced brittleness	57–60	Grind after hardening
Punches, semi-hard	5	Toughness	45–48	Grind after hardening

H-R₂, Hot-rolled steel plate, with 0.30 to 0.45 per cent carbon.   H-R₃, Hot-rolled steel, with from 0.08 to 0.25 per cent carbon.

Table 2 (*Continued*).   **Steels Used for Different Types of Tools**

(See Table 1 for compositions represented by the numbers)

Kind of Tool	No. or Symbol of Steel	Qualities Wanted in Tool	Hardness, Rockwell C	Remarks
Punches, small piercing; under 1/64 inch in diameter	CS7	Hardness, shock and wear resistance	60-63	Grind after hardening
Punches, straight; for brass, copper, and insulation materials; shape impractical to grind	5	Reduction of brittleness	57-60	Finish to size before hardening
Punches, straight; ground after hardening; for brass, copper, and insulation materials	5	Reduction of brittleness	57-60	Grind after hardening
Reamers	2	Maximum hardness, normal distortion, best cutting edge	63-65	Grind after hardening
Reamers, hand	5	Very hard, keen cutting edge	63-66	Grind after hardening
Reamers, long; hand and line, and large taper	8	Hard case with semi-hard core, good wearing surface and cutting edge, minimum distortion	Rock. Super. 90 min. 15 N. scale	Rough-machine, strain-relieve, finish-machine, and harden
Rivet sets, cold	17	Hardness, wear resistance, normal deformation	46-60	Finish to size and harden
Rivet sets, large	11	Medium hardness	46-52	Finish to size before hardening
Rivet setting tools, forming end of	12	Shock and wear resistance	40-43	Finish to size before hardening
Saws, cutting-off, high-speed steel teeth for	2	Hard cutting end, with shank soft	61-63	Grind after hardening
Screwdrivers	12	Shock and wear resistance	46-48	Finish to size before hardening
Shear blades, small	3	Fair hardness, reduced brittleness	57-60	Grind after hardening

CS7, Carbon steel, No. 9 temper, with from 0.86 to 0.95 per cent carbon.

Table 2 (*Continued*). **Steels Used for Different Types of Tools**
(See Table 1 for compositions represented by the numbers)

Kind of Tool	No. or Symbol of Steel	Qualities Wanted in Tool	Hardness, Rockwell C	Remarks
Stamps, lettering and numbering	3	Fair hardness, reduced brittleness	57-60	Grind after hardening
Stripper fingers, long, thin	17	Fair hardness, normal deformation	46-50	Finish to size and harden
Taps, ground-thread	2	Maximum hardness, normal distortion, best cutting edge	63-65	Grind after hardening
Taps, not ground in thread	7	Hardness, wear resistance, minimum distortion	60-63	Rough-machine, strain-relieve, finish to size, and harden
Templets, sheet steel	SS₅	Hardness, wear resistance	63-66	Grind after hardening
Tool-holders	11	Medium ductility, maximum machineability, hardness	30-35	Finish to size after hardening
Tools requiring great pressure on small areas	17	Hardness, wear resistance, normal deformation	46-60	Finish to size and harden
V-blocks	H-R₃	Hard wearing surface, normal distortion	Rock. Super. 90 min. 15 N. scale	Grind after hardening
Vise jaws	H-R₃	Hard wearing surface, minimum distortion	Rock. Super. 90 min. 15 N. scale	Anneal, rough-machine, strain-relieve, finish-machine to size, and harden
Woodworking tools	3	Toughness	45-48	Grind after hardening
Wrenches, special	11	Medium ductility, maximum machineability, hardness	30-35	Finish to size after hardening

SS₅, Spring steel, with from 0.90 to 1.10 per cent carbon.   H-R₃, Hot-rolled steel, with from 0.08 to 0.25 per cent carbon.

Drawing Dies Cast from Iron Alloys. — Dies cast from nickel-chromium alloys and heat-treated have proved unusually successful in a number of sheet-metal stamping and drawing operations. The alloy compositions for this service have a nickel content of from 2 to 4 per cent and a chromium content of from 0.75 to 1 per cent. These nickel-chromium alloys can be easily heat-treated, possess a fine grain structure, take a high polish, and eliminate streaking of the metal being formed. Before heat-treatment, the Brinell hardness is between 250 and 300, and the tensile strength ranges from 40,000 to 50,000 pounds per square inch. After heat-treatment, the hardness is from 450 to 550 Brinell, and the tensile strength is between 30,000 and 40,000 pounds per square inch.

In most instances, it is possible to cast dies to such close dimensions that the male and female units will fit within small fractions of an inch even before being filed.

Haynes Stellite. — Haynes Stellite is an alloy of cobalt, chromium and tungsten and is non-ferrous or without iron in its composition. The hardness of this alloy is not materially affected by heat up to 1500 degrees F. and it is actually tougher at red heat than when cold. This important characteristic explains its wide application as a cutting tool material. Haynes Stellite works best when operated at high speed and with a comparatively light feed.

J-Metal: The cutting tool material known as J-Metal is an improved grade of Haynes Stellite. The use of J-Metal results either in higher cutting speeds or in greater production between tool grindings. J-Metal is adapted to various classes of machining operations on practically all kinds of machinable materials, excepting chilled cast iron and manganese steel. The hardness of J-Metal at room temperature is 600 Brinell or Rockwell C, 60–62. It is important to note that the hardness of J-Metal is practically unaffected at red heat and this red hardness is considerably greater than that of high-speed steel.

Haynes-Stellite — 2400: This is another cobalt-chromium-tungsten alloy. Cutting tools made of this material have greater edge strength and longer economic tool life at even higher speeds than tools made of J-Metal, without reduction of feed or depth of cut. In fact, the speeds and feeds recommended are from 10 to 50 per cent greater than those for J-Metal. This alloy may be used for roughing or finishing cast and forged steels, cast and malleable irons, nitrided, stainless and other alloy steels.

Carbide Tools. — Cemented or sintered carbides are used in the machine building and various other industries, chiefly for cutting tools but also for certain other tools or parts subject to considerable abrasion or wear. Carbide cutting tools, when properly selected to obtain the right combination of strength and hardness, are very effective in machining all classes of iron and steel, non-ferrous alloys, non-metallic materials, hard rubber, synthetic resins, slate, marble, and other materials which would quickly dull steel tools either because of hardness or abrasive action. Carbide cutting tools are not only durable, but capable of exceptionally high cutting speeds. There are different classes of sintered carbides, and various grades in each general class with different combinations of hardness and strength. They are applied to various types of tools for turning, milling, drilling, reaming, etc. Information about the particular grade or type of carbide tool for a given purpose should be obtained directly from the manufacturers. Data from practice on the allowable speeds and feeds will be found in that section of the handbook dealing with this subject.

Tungsten carbide is used extensively in cutting cast iron, non-ferrous metals which form short chips in cutting; plastics and various other non-metallic materials. A grade having a hardness of 87.5 Rockwell A might be used where a strong grade is required, as for roughing cuts, whereas for light high-speed finishing or other cuts, a hardness of about 92 might be preferable. When tungsten carbide is applied to steel, craters or chip cavities are formed back of the cutting edge; hence other carbides have been developed which offer greater resistance to abrasion.

Tungsten-titanium carbide (often called "titanium carbide") is adapted to cutting either heat-treated or unheat-treated steels, cast steel, or any tough material which might form chip cavities. It is also applicable to bronzes, monel metal, aluminum alloys, etc. *Tungsten-tantalum carbide* or "tantalum carbide" cutting tools are also applicable to steels, bronzes or other tough materials. A hardness of 86.8 Rockwell A is recommended by one manufacturer for roughing steel, whereas a grade for finishing might have a hardness ranging from 88.8 to 91.5 Rockwell A.

Graphitic Steel for Punches and Dies. — Graphitic steel contains approximately 1.50 per cent total carbon and around 1.00 per cent silicon, and in one form carries approximately 0.25 per cent molybdenum. It can readily be forged to shape from the "as rolled" condition, but before machining to shape it must always be normalized and annealed; this precipitates part of the total carbon in the form of free graphite, uniformly distributed throughout the steel, and develops the spheroidized pearlitic structure so well suited to good machining. Quenching develops a martensitic structure, the steel reacting in much the same manner as eutectoid tool steel. The resulting dies and punches show remarkable hardness and toughness, and are highly resistant to wear. For water-hardening uses, no molybdenum is added, this type of graphitic steel being known as "Graph-sil." When special toughness is required or freedom from distortion is essential, the oil-hardening "Graph-mo" is used.

Life of Graphitic Steel Dies. — Graphitic steel has now practically replaced all other types of steel used for dies and punches in the plant of the Timken Roller Bearing Co., Canton, Ohio. Every die or punch made from graphitic steel has shown from two to four times the life of the same part made from the steels formerly used. In many instances, as, for example, in a sizing die, from ten to thirty times the life has been secured. In one case, one of the dies formerly used, when examined after it had sized 10,000 pieces, was not found to be in anywhere nearly as good condition as a graphitic-steel die that had sized 309,000 pieces. Increased die and punch life alone was enough to justify the change, but combined with that, was the lower cost of the steel and the decrease in machining time. Graphitic steel can be machined practically as easily as gray cast iron, which means approximately a 30 to 50 per cent saving in machining time, as compared with the steel formerly used. A reduction of 80 per cent in die-dressing time is also effected.

Even greater is the saving that results from avoiding press shut-downs. The decrease in the number of dies and punches that must be kept in stock to assure continuous operation is also an important item. To all of these savings must be added the saving in production time gained by the capacity of the graphitic-steel dies and punches to stand up under high-speed heavy-duty service without requiring polishing or regrinding during a normal production run; and finally, the greater accuracy and improved appearance of the finished parts must be taken into consideration.

Steels for Dies, Punches and Shears Used on Hot Work. — In the selection of die steels for use in modern forging equipment, special consideration must be given to the resistance of the steel to heat, abrasion, and pressure. It is not possible to select a hot-work steel that will possess maximum ability to meet all of these service conditions. In one case, it will be necessary to select a steel having maximum resistance to heat and to abrasion. In another case, the capacity to withstand pressure, shock, and fatigue will be the governing factor.

Hot-work steels may be classified broadly as the tungsten (or molybdenum) type and the chromium type. The accepted usage of the term " hot-work steels," covers all steels used in manufacturing dies, shears, punches, etc., for use in forging machines, presses, hot trimmers, etc.

Tungsten steels may offer the best resistance to heat and abrasion. Molybdenum possesses heat-resisting properties similar to tungsten, and is sometimes used in analyses in place of tungsten in quantities equal to about one-half the tungsten content. Tungsten is an expensive element, but on jobs where dies operate at high temperatures, tungsten steels prove the most economical. Chromium is next to tungsten and molybdenum in heat-resisting qualities. Chromium steels are used largely in automatic hot-working machines where resistance to repeated impact and to heat are important.

The accompanying table gives the analyses for tungsten and chromium steels with broad limits. The compositions suggested are modified by steel makers to meet specific applications. No simple rule can be laid down for selecting a steel that will best meet the problems of a particular job. A thorough analysis of the job is the only sound basis for an intelligent solution of the problem. In the selection of hot-work steels for forging jobs, designers should not hesitate to draw upon the experience of the steel manufacturer.

Hot-Work Steels for Dies, Punches and Shears.

Analyses of Tungsten Steels Suitable for Hot-Work Dies				
Carbon	Tungsten	Chromium	Vanadium	Silicon
0.40–0.60	17.00–19.00	3.00–4.25	0.00–1.20	....
0.25–0.50	12.00–16.00	2.00–3.00	0.30–0.50	....
0.35–0.45	10.00–12.00	1.00–2.00	0.00–0.20	....
0.25–0.45	8.00–10.00	2.50–3.50	0.20–0.40	0.80–1.20
0.30–0.45	4.00– 6.00	5.00–6.00	0.20–0.40	....
0.50–0.60	2.00– 3.00	1.00–2.00	0.15–0.25	....

Analyses of Chromium Steels that Meet Certain Requirements of Hot-Work Dies					
Carbon	Chromium	Vanadium	Molybdenum	Silicon	Nickel
0.75–1.00	3.00–4.50	....	....	....	....
0.50–0.70	3.50–4.00	0.75–1.00	0.35–0.50	....	....
0.35–0.45	4.50–5.50	0.30–0.50	1.00–1.50	0.90–1.20	....
0.35–0.45	2.00–2.50	....	....	....	2.25–3.00

Dies can be maintained at a fairly even temperature by providing a large flow of liquid coolant, usually water. The application of a small stream of water may cause localized cooling and heat checking. Long slender punches have a tendency to warp when inadequate coolant is used. An air blast is a safer, although more expensive, method of removing scale and reducing heat.

The effect of abrasion on die life approaches that of heat. In high-speed presses and forging machines, abrasion surpasses heat in its effect on die life, since the dies of these fast machines do not operate at the high temperatures encountered with the slower machines. Abrasion is practically the limiting factor on die life when producing forgings to close tolerances. Tungsten steels, in addition to offering resistance to high temperatures, resist abrasion to a high degree. Lubricants, such as heavy oil or oil mixed with graphite, are often used to reduce abrasive action.

STANDARD TAPERS

Certain types of small tools and machine parts, such as twist drills, end mills, arbors, lathe centers, etc., are provided with taper shanks which fit into spindles or sockets of corresponding taper, thus providing not only accurate alignment between the tool or other part and its supporting member, but also more or less frictional resistance for driving the tool. There are several standards for "self-holding" tapers, but the Morse and the Brown & Sharpe are the standards most widely used by American manufacturers.

The name *self-holding* has been applied to the smaller tapers — like the Morse and the Brown & Sharpe — because, where the angle of the taper is only 2 or 3 degrees, the shank of a tool is so firmly seated in its socket that there is considerable frictional resistance to any force tending to turn or rotate the tool relative to the socket. The term "self-holding" is used to distinguish relatively small tapers from the larger or *self-releasing* type. A milling machine spindle having a taper of 3½ inches per foot is an example of a self-releasing taper. The included angle in this case is over 16 degrees and the tool or arbor requires a positive locking device to prevent slipping, but the shank may be released or removed more readily than one having a smaller taper of the self-holding type.

Morse Taper. — Dimensions relating to Morse standard taper shanks and sockets may be found in an accompanying table. The taper for different numbers of Morse tapers is slightly different, but it is approximately ⅝ inch per foot in most cases. The table gives the actual tapers, accurate to five decimal places. Morse taper shanks are used on a variety of tools, and exclusively on the shanks of twist drills.

Brown & Sharpe Taper. — This standard taper is used for taper shanks on tools such as end mills and reamers, the taper being approximately ½ inch per foot for all sizes except for taper No. 10, where the taper is 0.5161 inch per foot. Brown & Sharpe taper sockets are used for many arbors, collets, and machine tool spindles, especially milling machines and grinding machines. In many cases there are a number of different lengths of sockets corresponding to the same number of taper; all these tapers, however, are of the same diameter at the small end.

Jarno Taper. — The Jarno taper was originally proposed by Oscar J. Beale of the Brown & Sharpe Mfg. Co. This taper is based on such simple formulas that practically no calculations are required when the number of taper is known. The taper per foot of all Jarno taper sizes is 0.600 inch on the diameter. The diameter at the large end is as many eighths, the diameter at the small end is as many tenths, and the length as many half inches as are indicated by the number of the taper. For example, a No. 7 Jarno taper is ⅞ inch in diameter at the large end; ⁷⁄₁₀, or 0.700 inch at the small end; and ⁷⁄₂, or 3½ inches long; hence, diameter at large end = No. of taper ÷ 8; diameter at small end = No. of taper ÷ 10; length of taper = No. of taper ÷ 2. The Jarno taper is used on various machine tools, especially profiling machines and die-sinking machines. It has also been used for the headstock and tailstock spindles of some lathes.

American Standard Machine Tapers. — This standard includes a self-holding series (Tables 5, 7, 8, 9 and 10) and a steep taper series, Table 6. The self-holding taper series consists of 22 sizes which are listed in Table 5. The reference gage for the self-holding tapers is a plug gage. Table 11 gives the dimensions and tolerances for both plug and ring gages applying to this series. Tables 7 to 10 inclusive give the dimensions for self-holding taper shanks and sockets which are classified as to (1) means of transmitting torque from spindle to the tool shank, and (2) means of retaining the shank in the socket. The steep machine tapers consist of a preferred

Table 1. Morse Standard Taper Shanks

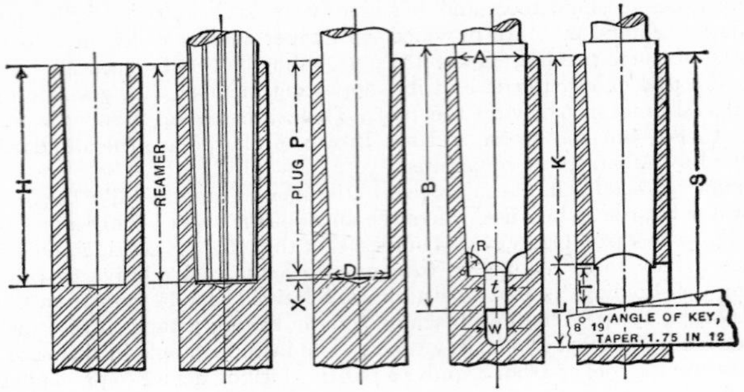

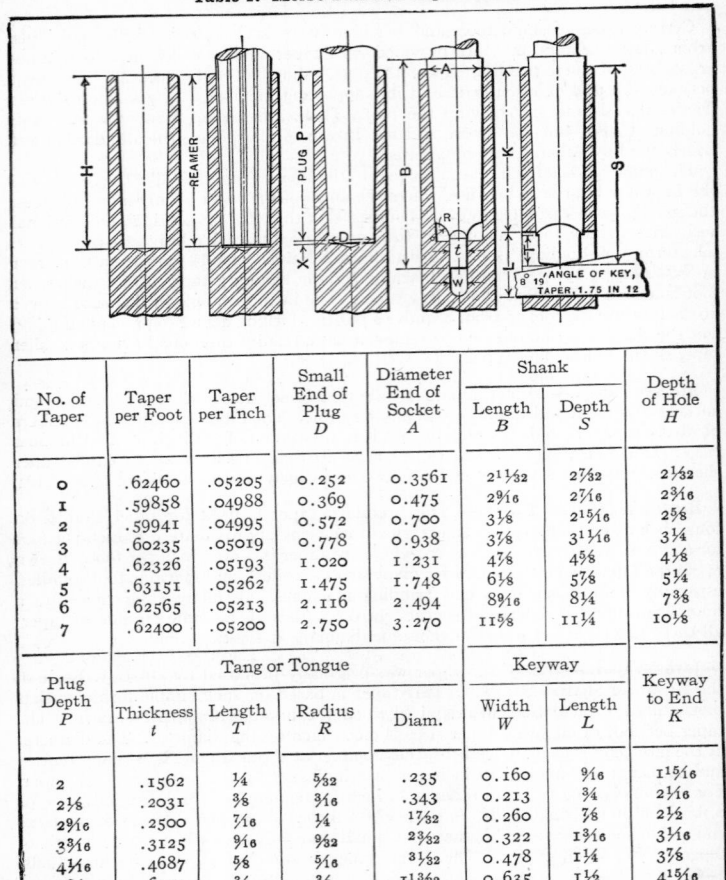

No. of Taper	Taper per Foot	Taper per Inch	Small End of Plug *D*	Diameter End of Socket *A*	Shank Length *B*	Shank Depth *S*	Depth of Hole *H*
0	.62460	.05205	0.252	0.3561	2 11/32	2 7/32	2 1/32
1	.59858	.04988	0.369	0.475	2 9/16	2 7/16	2 3/16
2	.59941	.04995	0.572	0.700	3 1/8	2 15/16	2 5/8
3	.60235	.05019	0.778	0.938	3 7/8	3 11/16	3 1/4
4	.62326	.05193	1.020	1.231	4 7/8	4 5/8	4 1/8
5	.63151	.05262	1.475	1.748	6 1/8	5 7/8	5 1/4
6	.62565	.05213	2.116	2.494	8 9/16	8 1/4	7 3/8
7	.62400	.05200	2.750	3.270	11 5/8	11 1/4	10 1/8

Plug Depth *P*	Tang or Tongue Thickness *t*	Tang or Tongue Length *T*	Tang or Tongue Radius *R*	Tang or Tongue Diam.	Keyway Width *W*	Keyway Length *L*	Keyway to End *K*
2	.1562	1/4	5/32	.235	0.160	9/16	1 15/16
2 1/8	.2031	3/8	3/16	.343	0.213	3/4	2 1/16
2 9/16	.2500	7/16	1/4	17/32	0.260	7/8	2 1/2
3 3/16	.3125	9/16	9/32	23/32	0.322	1 3/16	3 1/16
4 1/16	.4687	5/8	5/16	31/32	0.478	1 1/4	3 7/8
5 3/16	.6250	3/4	3/8	1 13/32	0.635	1 1/2	4 15/16
7 1/4	.7500	1 1/8	1/2	2	0.760	1 3/4	7
10	1.1250	1 3/8	3/4	2 5/8	1.135	2 5/8	9 1/2

series (bold-face type, Table 6) and an intermediate series (light-face type). A self-holding taper is defined as "a taper with an angle small enough to hold a shank in place ordinarily by friction without holding means. (Sometimes referred to as slow taper.)" A steep taper is defined as "a taper having an angle sufficiently large to insure the easy or self-releasing feature." The term "gage line" indicates the basic diameter at or near the large end of the taper.

Table 2. Dimensions of Morse Taper Sleeves

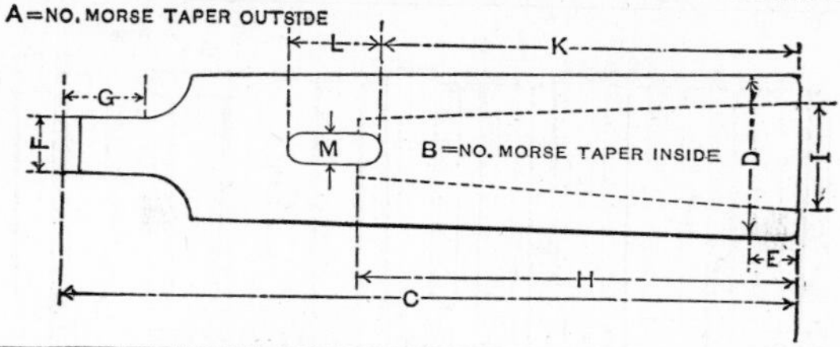

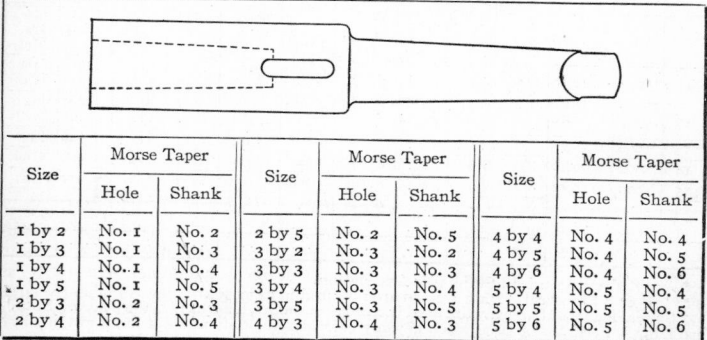

A	B	C	D	E	F	G	H	I	K	L	M
2	1	3⁹⁄₁₆	0.700	⅝	¼	⁷⁄₁₆	2³⁄₁₆	0.475	2¹⁄₁₆	¾	0.213
3	1	3¹⁵⁄₁₆	0.938	¼	⁵⁄₁₆	⁹⁄₁₆	2³⁄₁₆	0.475	2¹⁄₁₆	¾	0.213
3	2	4⁷⁄₁₆	0.938	¾	⁵⁄₁₆	⁹⁄₁₆	2⅝	0.700	2½	⅞	0.260
4	1	4⅞	1.231	¼	¹⁵⁄₃₂	⅝	2³⁄₁₆	0.475	2¹⁄₁₆	¾	0.213
4	2	4⅞	1.231	¼	¹⁵⁄₃₂	⅝	2⅝	0.700	2½	⅞	0.260
4	3	5⅜	1.231	¾	¹⁵⁄₃₂	⅝	3¼	0.938	3¹⁄₁₆	1³⁄₁₆	0.322
5	1	6⅛	1.748	¼	⅝	¾	2³⁄₁₆	0.475	2¹⁄₁₆	¾	0.213
5	2	6⅛	1.748	¼	⅝	¾	2⅝	0.700	2½	⅞	0.260
5	3	6⅛	1.748	¼	⅝	¾	3¼	0.938	3¹⁄₁₆	1³⁄₁₆	0.322
5	4	6⅝	1.748	¾	⅝	¾	4⅛	1.231	3⅞	1¼	0.478
6	1	8⅝	2.494	⅜	¾	1⅛	2³⁄₁₆	0.475	2¹⁄₁₆	¾	0.213
6	2	8⅝	2.494	⅜	¾	1⅛	2⅝	0.700	2½	⅞	0.260
6	3	8⅝	2.494	⅜	¾	1⅛	3¼	0.938	3¹⁄₁₆	1³⁄₁₆	0.322
6	4	8⅝	2.494	⅜	¾	1⅛	4⅛	1.231	3⅞	1¼	0.478
6	5	8⅝	2.494	⅜	¾	1⅛	5¼	1.748	4¹⁵⁄₁₆	1½	0.635
7	3	11⅝	3.270	⅜	1⅛	1⅜	3¼	0.938	3¹⁄₁₆	1³⁄₁₆	0.322
7	4	11⅝	3.270	⅜	1⅛	1⅜	4⅛	1.231	3⅞	1¼	0.478
7	5	11⅝	3.270	⅜	1⅛	1⅜	5¼	1.748	4¹⁵⁄₁₆	1½	0.635
7	6	12½	3.270	1¼	1⅛	1⅜	7⅜	2.494	7	1¾	0.760

Morse Taper Sockets — Hole and Shank Sizes

Size	Morse Taper		Size	Morse Taper		Size	Morse Taper	
	Hole	Shank		Hole	Shank		Hole	Shank
1 by 2	No. 1	No. 2	2 by 5	No. 2	No. 5	4 by 4	No. 4	No. 4
1 by 3	No. 1	No. 3	3 by 2	No. 3	No. 2	4 by 5	No. 4	No. 5
1 by 4	No. 1	No. 4	3 by 3	No. 3	No. 3	4 by 6	No. 4	No. 6
1 by 5	No. 1	No. 5	3 by 4	No. 3	No. 4	5 by 4	No. 5	No. 4
2 by 3	No. 2	No. 3	3 by 5	No. 3	No. 5	5 by 5	No. 5	No. 5
2 by 4	No. 2	No. 4	4 by 3	No. 4	No. 3	5 by 6	No. 5	No. 6

Table 3. Brown & Sharpe Taper Shanks

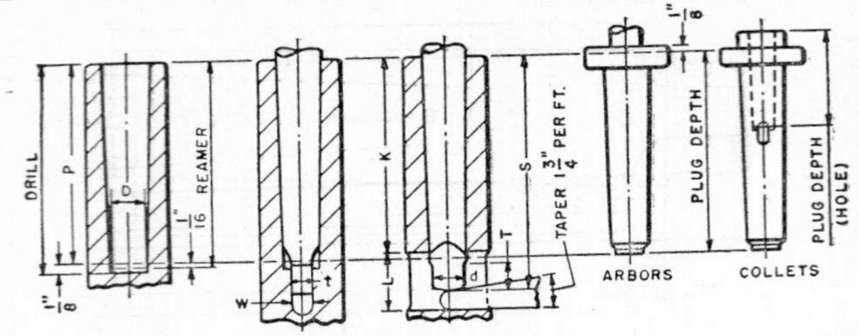

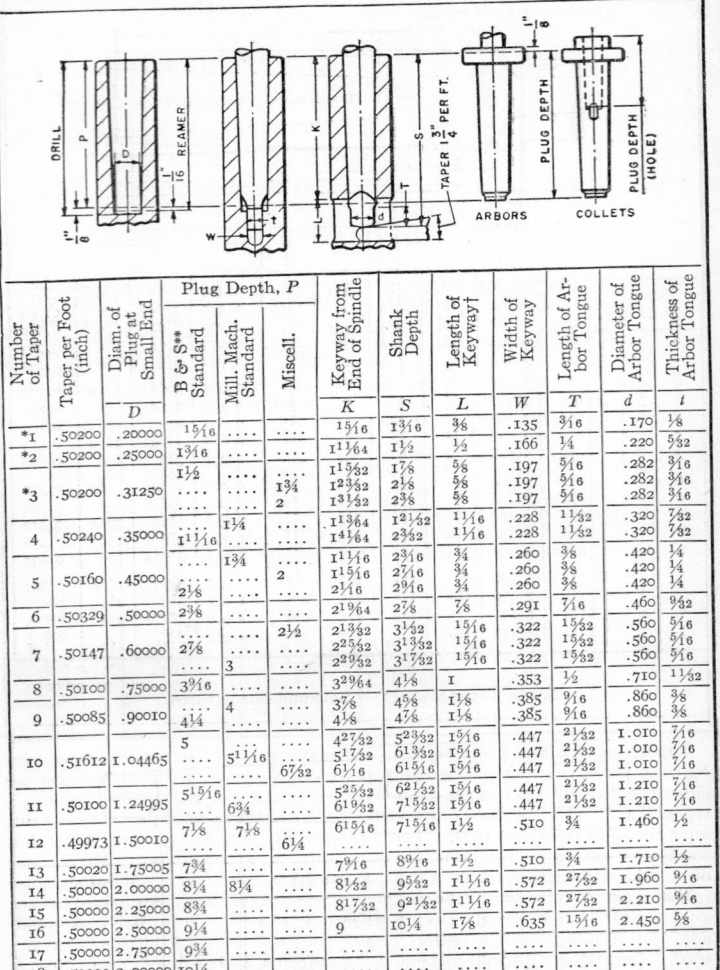

Number of Taper	Taper per Foot (inch)	Diam. of Plug at Small End	Plug Depth, P			Keyway from End of Spindle	Shank Depth	Length of Keyway†	Width of Keyway	Length of Arbor Tongue	Diameter of Arbor Tongue	Thickness of Arbor Tongue
			B & S** Standard	Mill. Mach. Standard	Miscell.							
		D				K	S	L	W	T	d	t
*1	.50200	.20000	15/16	....	....	15/16	1 3/16	3/8	.135	3/16	.170	1/8
*2	.50200	.25000	1 3/16	....	....	1 11/64	1 1/2	1/2	.166	1/4	.220	5/32
*3	.50200	.31250	1 1/2	....	....	1 15/32	1 7/8	5/8	.197	5/16	.282	3/16
			....	....	1 3/4	1 23/32	2 1/8	5/8	.197	5/16	.282	3/16
			....	....	2	1 31/32	2 3/8	5/8	.197	5/16	.282	3/16
4	.50240	.35000	....	1 1/4	....	1 13/64	1 21/32	1 1/16	.228	11/32	.320	7/32
			1 11/16	....	....	1 41/64	2 3/32	1 1/16	.228	11/32	.320	7/32
5	.50160	.45000	....	1 3/4	....	1 11/16	2 3/16	3/4	.260	3/8	.420	1/4
			....	....	2	1 15/16	2 7/16	3/4	.260	3/8	.420	1/4
			2 1/8	....	....	2 1/16	2 9/16	3/4	.260	3/8	.420	1/4
6	.50329	.50000	2 3/8	....	....	2 19/64	2 7/8	7/8	.291	7/16	.460	9/32
7	.50147	.60000	....	....	2 1/2	2 13/32	3 1/32	15/16	.322	15/32	.560	5/16
			2 7/8	....	....	2 25/32	3 13/32	15/16	.322	15/32	.560	5/16
			....	3	....	2 29/32	3 17/32	15/16	.322	15/32	.560	5/16
8	.50100	.75000	3 9/16	....	....	3 29/64	4 1/8	1	.353	1/2	.710	11/32
9	.50085	.90010	....	4	....	3 7/8	4 5/8	1 1/8	.385	9/16	.860	3/8
			4 1/4	....	....	4 1/8	4 7/8	1 1/8	.385	9/16	.860	3/8
10	.51612	1.04465	5	....	....	4 27/32	5 23/32	1 5/16	.447	21/32	1.010	7/16
			....	5 11/16	....	5 17/32	6 13/32	1 5/16	.447	21/32	1.010	7/16
			....	....	6 7/32	6 1/16	6 15/16	1 5/16	.447	21/32	1.010	7/16
11	.50100	1.24995	5 15/16	....	....	5 25/32	6 21/32	1 5/16	.447	21/32	1.210	7/16
			....	6 3/4	....	6 19/32	7 15/32	1 5/16	.447	21/32	1.210	7/16
12	.49973	1.50010	7 1/8	7 1/8	....	6 15/16	7 15/16	1 1/2	.510	3/4	1.460	1/2
			....	....	6 1/4	....	....	....	....	....	....	....
13	.50020	1.75005	7 3/4	....	....	7 9/16	8 9/16	1 1/2	.510	3/4	1.710	1/2
14	.50000	2.00000	8 1/4	8 1/4	....	8 1/32	9 5/32	1 11/16	.572	27/32	1.960	9/16
15	.50000	2.25000	8 3/4	....	....	8 17/32	9 21/32	1 11/16	.572	27/32	2.210	9/16
16	.50000	2.50000	9 1/4	....	....	9	10 1/4	1 7/8	.635	15/16	2.450	5/8
17	.50000	2.75000	9 3/4	....	....	....	....	....	....	....	....	....
18	.50000	3.00000	10 1/4	....	....	....	....	....	....	....	....	....

* Adopted by American Standards Association.
** " B & S Standard " Plug Depths are not used in all cases.
† Special lengths of keyway are used instead of standard lengths in some places. Standard lengths need not be used when keyway is for driving only and not for admitting key to force out tool.

Table 4. Jarno Taper Shanks

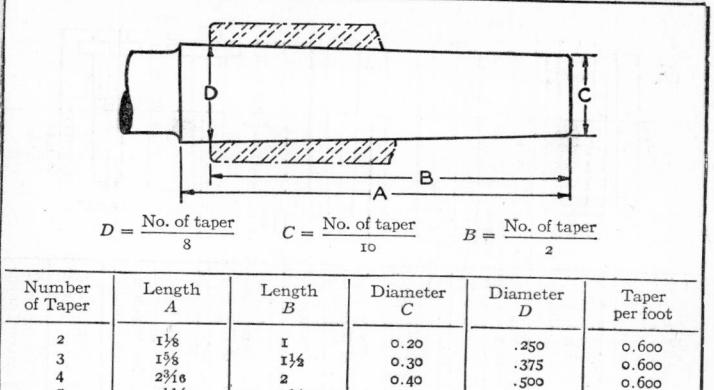

$$D = \frac{\text{No. of taper}}{8} \qquad C = \frac{\text{No. of taper}}{10} \qquad B = \frac{\text{No. of taper}}{2}$$

Number of Taper	Length A	Length B	Diameter C	Diameter D	Taper per foot
2	1⅛	1	0.20	.250	0.600
3	1⅝	1½	0.30	.375	0.600
4	2³⁄₁₆	2	0.40	.500	0.600
5	2¹¹⁄₁₆	2½	0.50	.625	0.600
6	3³⁄₁₆	3	0.60	.750	0.600
7	3¹¹⁄₁₆	3½	0.70	.875	0.600
8	4³⁄₁₆	4	0.80	1.000	0.600
9	4¹¹⁄₁₆	4½	0.90	1.125	0.600
10	5¼	5	1.00	1.250	0.600
11	5¾	5½	1.10	1.375	0.600
				1.500	
12	6¼	6	1.20		0.600
13	6¾	6½	1.30	1.625	0.600
14	7¼	7	1.40	1.750	0.600
15	7¾	7½	1.50	1.875	0.600
16	8⁵⁄₁₆	8	1.60	2.000	0.600
17	8¹³⁄₁₆	8½	1.70	2.125	0.600
18	9⁵⁄₁₆	9	1.80	2.250	0.600
19	9¹³⁄₁₆	9½	1.90	2.375	0.600
20	10⁵⁄₁₆	10	2.00	2.500	0.600

Tapers for Machine Tool Spindles. — Various standard tapers have been used for the taper holes in the spindles of machine tools requiring a taper hole for receiving either the shank of a cutter, an arbor, a center, or any tool or accessory requiring a tapering seat. The spindles of drilling machines and the taper shanks of twist drills are made to fit the Morse taper. For lathes, the Morse taper is generally used, but some lathes have either the Jarno, Brown & Sharpe, or a special taper. The practice of 33 lathe manufacturers is as follows: 20 use the Morse taper; 5, the Jarno; 3 use special tapers of their own; 2 use modified Morse (longer than the standard but the same taper); 2 use Reed (which is a short Jarno); 1 uses the Brown & Sharpe standard. For grinding machine centers Jarno, Morse and Brown & Sharpe tapers are used. Ten grinding machine manufacturers were divided as follows: 3 use Brown & Sharpe; 3 use Morse, and 4 use Jarno. The Brown & Sharpe taper has been extensively used for milling machine and dividing head spindles. The standard milling machine spindle adopted in 1927 by the milling machine manufacturers of the National Machine Tool Builders' Association, has a taper of 3½ inches per foot. This comparatively steep taper was adopted to insure easy release of arbors.

Table 5. American Standard Self-holding Tapers — Basic Dimensions

No. of Taper	Taper per Foot	Diam. at Gage Line (1) A	Means of Driving and Holding				Origin of Series
.239	0.50200	0.23922					Brown & Sharpe Taper Series
.299	0.50200	0.29968					
.375	0.50200	0.37525					
1	0.59858	0.47500					
2	0.59941	0.70000					
3	0.60235	0.93800					Morse Taper Series
4	0.62326	1.23100	Tang Drive With Shank Held in by Friction (See Table 7)	Tang Drive With Shank Held in by Key (See Table 8)	Key Drive With Shank Held in by Key (See Table 9)	Key Drive With Shank Held in by Draw-bolt (See Table 10)	
4½	0.62400	1.50000					
5	0.63151	1.74800					
6 (2)	0.62565	2.49400					
7 (2)	0.62400	3.27000					
200	0.750	2.000					
250	0.750	2.500					
300	0.750	3.000					
350	0.750	3.500					
400	0.750	4.000					¾ Inch per Foot Taper Series
450	0.750	4.500					
500	0.750	5.000					
600	0.750	6.000					
800	0.750	8.000					
1000	0.750	10.000					
1200	0.750	12.000					

All dimensions given in inches.
(1) See illustrations above Tables 7, 8, 9 and 10.
(2) These sizes are continued in the Tang Drive series for the present to meet special needs.

Table 6. American Standard Steep Machine Tapers

No. of Taper	Taper per Foot (1)	Diam. at Gage Line (2)	Length Along Axis	No. of Taper	Taper per Foot (1)	Diam. at Gage Line (2)	Length Along Axis
5	3.500	0.500	11⁄16	35	3.500	1.500	2¼
10	3.500	0.625	7⁄8	40	3.500	1.750	2¹¹⁄16
15	3.500	0.750	11⁄16	45	3.500	2.250	35⁄16
20	3.500	0.875	15⁄16	50	3.500	2.750	4
25	3.500	1.000	19⁄16	55	3.500	3.500	53⁄16
30	3.500	1.250	17⁄8	60	3.500	4.250	63⁄8

All dimensions given in inches.
(1) This taper corresponds to an included angle of 16°, 35′, 39.4″.
The tapers numbered 10, 20, 30, 40, 50, and 60 that are printed in heavy-faced type are designated as the "Preferred Series." The tapers numbered 5, 15, 25, 35, 45, and 55 that are printed in light-faced type are designated as the "Intermediate Series."
(2) The basic diameter at gage line is at or near large end of taper.

Table 7. American Standard Tang Drive with Shank Retained by Friction

No. of Taper	Diameter at Gage Line (1) A	Shank Length B	Exposed Length C	Tang Thickness E	Tang Length F	Tang Radius G
.239	0.23922	1 9/32	3/32	0.125	3/16	3/16
.299	0.29968	1 19/32	3/32	0.1562	1/4	3/16
.375	0.37525	1 31/32	3/32	0.1875	5/16	3/16
1	0.47500	2 9/16	1/8	0.2031	3/8	3/16
2	0.70000	3 1/8	3/16	0.250	7/16	1/4
3	0.93800	3 7/8	3/16	0.3125	9/16	9/32
4	1.23100	4 7/8	1/4	0.4687	5/8	5/16
4½	1.50000	5 3/8	1/4	0.5625	11/16	3/8
5	1.74800	6 1/8	1/4	0.625	3/4	3/8
6	2.49400	8 9/16	5/16	0.750	1 1/8	1/2
7	3.27000	11 5/8	3/8	1.125	1 3/8	3/4

No. of Taper	Tang Diameter H	Socket Depth K	Gage Line to Keyway M	Keyway Width N	Keyway Length O	Keyway to Tang P
.239	11/64	1 1/16	15/16	0.141	3/8	1/8
.299	7/32	1 5/16	1 11/64	0.172	1/2	11/64
.375	9/32	1 5/8	1 15/32	0.203	5/8	7/32
1	11/32	2 3/16	2 1/16	0.213	3/4	3/8
2	17/32	2 21/32	2 1/2	0.260	7/8	7/16
3	23/32	3 5/16	3 1/16	0.322	1 3/16	9/16
4	31/32	4 5/16	3 7/8	0.478	1 1/4	1/2
4½	1 13/64	4 5/8	4 5/16	0.573	1 3/8	9/16
5	1 13/32	5 5/16	4 15/16	0.635	1 1/2	9/16
6	2	7 13/32	7	0.760	1 3/4	1/2
7	2 5/8	10 5/32	9 1/2	1.135	2 5/8	7/8

All dimensions are in inches. (1) See Table 11 for plug gage dimensions.

Tolerances: For shank diameter A at gage line, +0.002 − 0.000; for hole diameter A + 0.000 − 0.002. For tang thickness E up to No. 5 inclusive, +0.000 − 0.006; larger than No. 5, +0.000 − 0.008. For width N of keyway up to No. 5 inclusive, +0.006 − 0.000; larger than No. 5, +0.008 − 0.000. For concentricity of tang E with center line of taper up to No. 5 inclusive, 0.0035; larger than No. 5, 0.005 (indicator reading). These concentricity tolerances also apply to the knockout keyway N. Tolerances for fractional dimensions are plus or minus 0.010, unless otherwise specified.

Table 8. American Standard Tang Drive with Shank Retained by Key

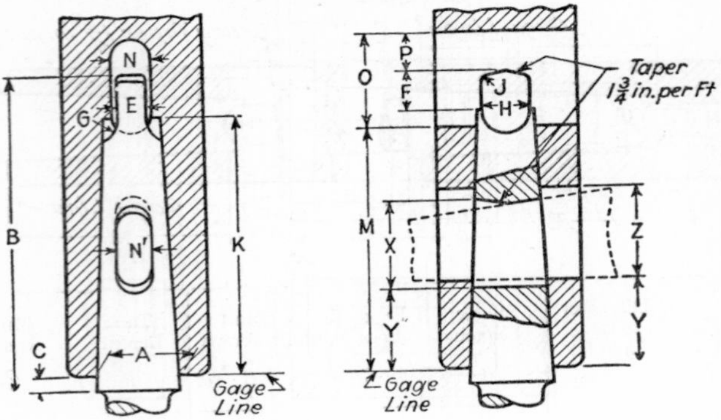

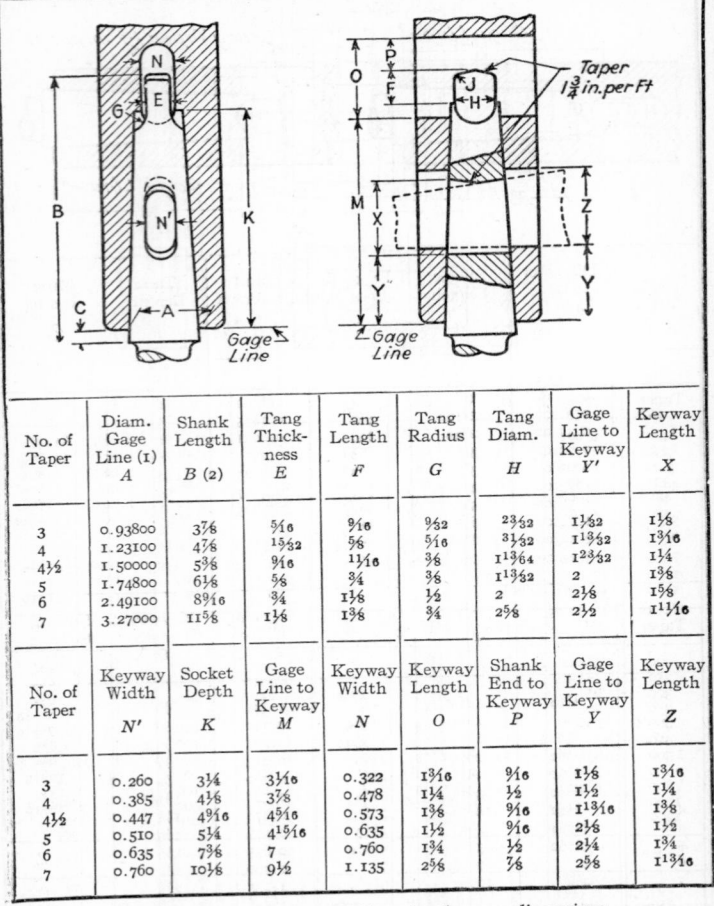

No. of Taper	Diam. Gage Line (1) *A*	Shank Length *B* (2)	Tang Thickness *E*	Tang Length *F*	Tang Radius *G*	Tang Diam. *H*	Gage Line to Keyway *Y′*	Keyway Length *X*
3	0.93800	3 7/8	5/16	9/16	9/32	23/32	1 1/32	1 1/8
4	1.23100	4 7/8	15/32	5/8	5/16	31/32	1 13/32	1 3/16
4 1/2	1.50000	5 3/8	9/16	11/16	3/8	1 13/64	1 23/32	1 1/4
5	1.74800	6 1/8	5/8	3/4	3/8	1 13/32	2	1 3/8
6	2.49100	8 9/16	3/4	1 1/8	1/2	2	2 1/8	1 5/8
7	3.27000	11 5/8	1 1/8	1 3/8	3/4	2 5/8	2 1/2	1 11/16

No. of Taper	Keyway Width *N′*	Socket Depth *K*	Gage Line to Keyway *M*	Keyway Width *N*	Keyway Length *O*	Shank End to Keyway *P*	Gage Line to Keyway *Y*	Keyway Length *Z*
3	0.260	3 1/4	3 1/16	0.322	1 3/16	9/16	1 1/8	1 3/16
4	0.385	4 1/8	3 7/8	0.478	1 1/4	1/2	1 1/2	1 1/4
4 1/2	0.447	4 9/16	4 5/16	0.573	1 3/8	9/16	1 13/16	1 3/8
5	0.510	5 1/4	4 15/16	0.635	1 1/2	9/16	2 1/8	1 1/2
6	0.635	7 3/8	7	0.760	1 3/4	1/2	2 1/4	1 3/4
7	0.760	10 1/8	9 1/2	1.135	2 5/8	7/8	2 5/8	1 13/16

All dimensions are in inches. (1) See Table 11 for plug gage dimensions.
(2) Exposed length *C* is the same as given in Table 7.

Tolerances: For shank diameter *A* at gage line, +0.002 − 0.000; for hole diameter *A* +0.000 − 0.002. For tang thickness *E* up to No. 5 inclusive, +0.000 − 0.006; larger than No. 5, +0.000 − 0.008. For width *N* of keyway up to No. 5 inclusive, +0.006 − 0.000; larger than No. 5, +0.008 − 0.000. For concentricity of tang *E* with center line of taper up to No. 5 inclusive, 0.0035; larger than No. 5, 0.005 (indicator reading). These concentricity tolerances also apply to the knockout keyway *N*. Tolerances for fractional dimensions are plus or minus 0.010, unless otherwise specified.

Table 9. American Standard Key Drive with Shank Retained by Key

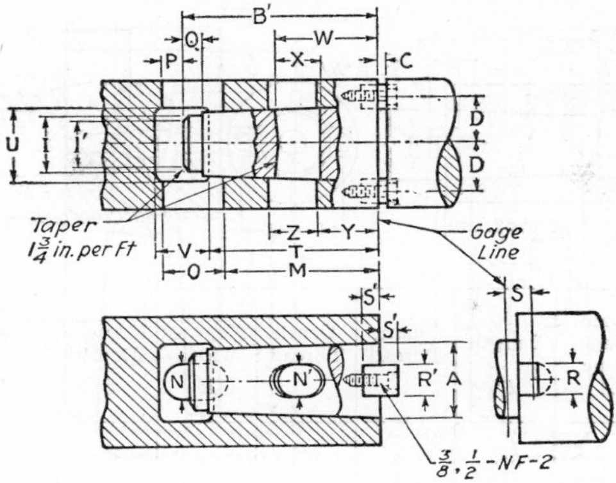

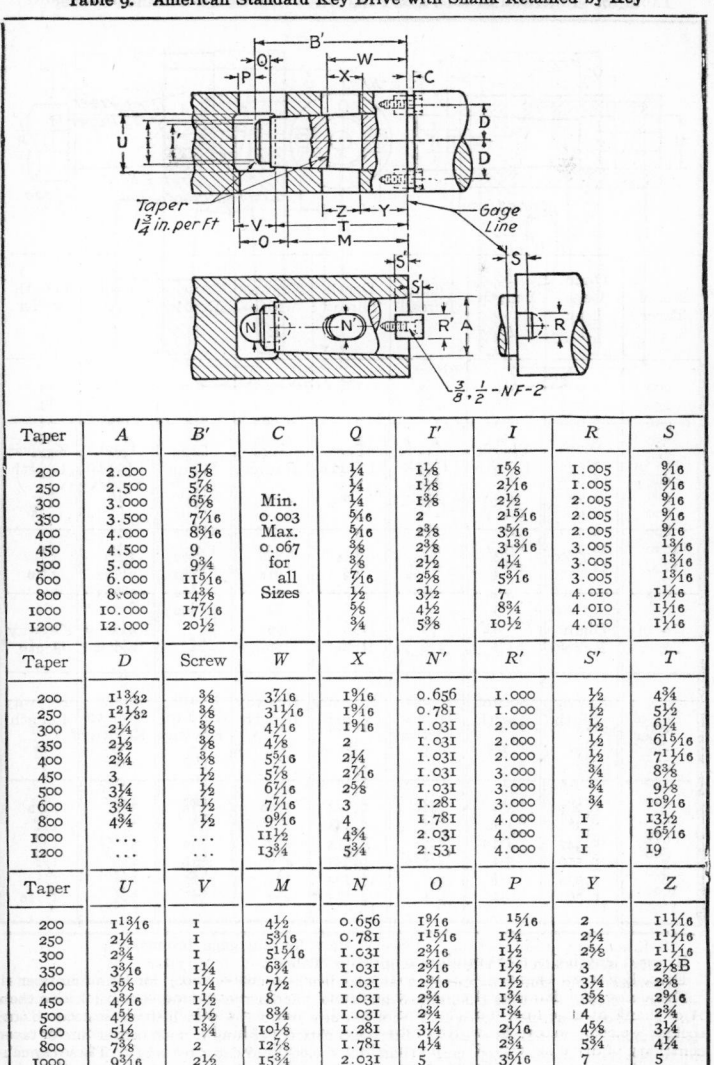

Taper	A	B′	C	Q	I′	I	R	S
200	2.000	5⅛		¼	1⅛	1⅝	1.005	9/16
250	2.500	5⅞		¼	1⅛	2 1/16	1.005	9/16
300	3.000	6⅝	Min.	¼	1⅜	2½	2.005	9/16
350	3.500	7 7/16	0.003	5/16	2	2 15/16	2.005	9/16
400	4.000	8 3/16	Max.	5/16	2⅜	3 5/16	2.005	9/16
450	4.500	9	0.067	⅜	2⅜	3 13/16	3.005	13/16
500	5.000	9¾	for	⅜	2½	4¼	3.005	13/16
600	6.000	11 5/16	all	7/16	2⅝	5 3/16	3.005	13/16
800	8.000	14⅜	Sizes	½	3½	7	4.010	1 1/16
1000	10.000	17 7/16		⅝	4½	8¾	4.010	1 1/16
1200	12.000	20½		¾	5⅜	10½	4.010	1 1/16
Taper	***D***	**Screw**	***W***	***X***	***N′***	***R′***	***S′***	***T***
200	1 13/32	⅜	3 7/16	1 9/16	0.656	1.000	½	4¾
250	1 21/32	⅜	3 11/16	1 9/16	0.781	1.000	½	5½
300	2¼	⅜	4 1/16	1 9/16	1.031	2.000	½	6¼
350	2½	⅜	4⅞	2	1.031	2.000	½	6 15/16
400	2¾	⅜	5 5/16	2¼	1.031	2.000	½	7 11/16
450	3	½	5⅞	2 7/16	1.031	3.000	¾	8⅜
500	3¼	½	6 7/16	2⅝	1.031	3.000	¾	9⅛
600	3¾	½	7 7/16	3	1.281	3.000	¾	10 9/16
800	4¾	½	9 9/16	4	1.781	4.000	1	13½
1000	...	...	11½	4¾	2.031	4.000	1	16 5/16
1200	...	...	13¾	5¾	2.531	4.000	1	19
Taper	***U***	***V***	***M***	***N***	***O***	***P***	***Y***	***Z***
200	1 13/16	1	4½	0.656	1 9/16	15/16	2	1 11/16
250	2¼	1	5 3/16	0.781	1 15/16	1¼	2¼	1 11/16
300	2¾	1	5 15/16	1.031	2 3/16	1½	2⅝	1 11/16
350	3 3/16	1¼	6¾	1.031	2 3/16	1½	3	2⅛B
400	3⅝	1¼	7½	1.031	2 3/16	1½	3¼	2⅜
450	4 3/16	1½	8	1.031	2¾	1¾	3⅝	2 9/16
500	4⅝	1½	8¾	1.031	2¾	1¾	4	2¾
600	5½	1¾	10⅛	1.281	3¼	2 1/16	4⅝	3¼
800	7⅜	2	12⅞	1.781	4¼	2¾	5¾	4¼
1000	9 3/16	2½	15¾	2.031	5	3 5/16	7	5
1200	11	3	18½	2.531	6	4	8¼	6

Table 10. American Standard Key Drive with Shank Retained by Draw-bolt

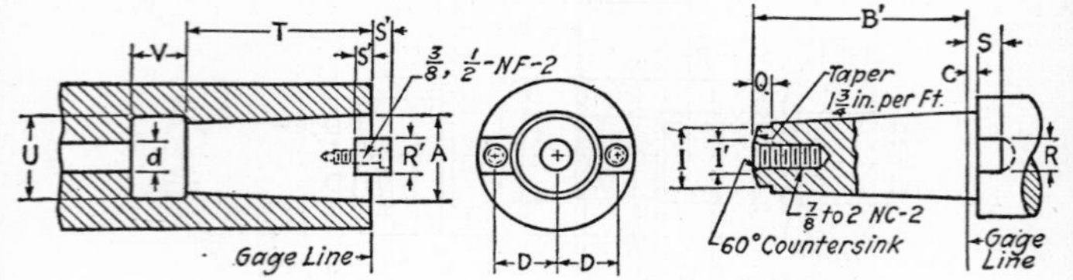

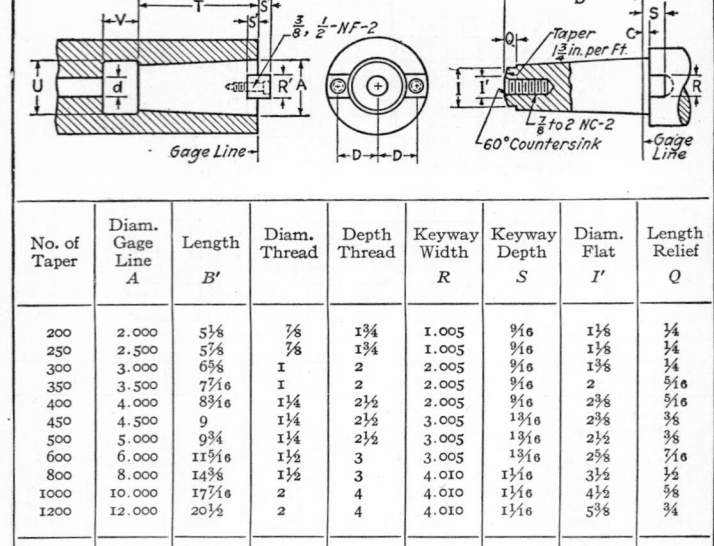

No. of Taper	Diam. Gage Line *A*	Length *B'*	Diam. Thread	Depth Thread	Keyway Width *R*	Keyway Depth *S*	Diam. Flat *I'*	Length Relief *Q*
200	2.000	5⅛	⅞	1¾	1.005	9/16	1⅛	¼
250	2.500	5⅞	⅞	1¾	1.005	9/16	1⅛	¼
300	3.000	6⅝	1	2	2.005	9/16	1⅜	¼
350	3.500	7 7/16	1	2	2.005	9/16	2	5/16
400	4.000	8 3/16	1¼	2½	2.005	9/16	2⅜	5/16
450	4.500	9	1¼	2½	3.005	13/16	2⅜	⅜
500	5.000	9¾	1¼	2½	3.005	13/16	2½	⅜
600	6.000	11 5/16	1½	3	3.005	13/16	2⅝	7/16
800	8.000	14⅜	1½	3	4.010	1 1/16	3½	½
1000	10.000	17 7/16	2	4	4.010	1 1/16	4½	⅝
1200	12.000	20½	2	4	4.010	1 1/16	5⅜	¾

No. of Taper	Diam. Relief *I*	Center of Screw *D*	Length to Relief *T*	Diam. Relief *U*	Depth Relief *V*	Draw Bolt Hole *d*	Keyway Width *R'*	Keyway Depth *S'*
200	1⅝	1 13/32	4¾	1 13/16	1	1	1.000	½
250	2 1/16	1 21/32	5½	2¼	1	1	1.000	½
300	2½	2¼	6¼	2¾	1	1⅛	2.000	½
350	2 15/16	2½	6 15/16	3 3/16	1¼	1⅛	2.000	½
400	3 5/16	2¾	7 11/16	3⅝	1¼	1⅜	2.000	½
450	3 13/16	3	8⅜	4 3/16	1½	1⅜	3.000	¾
500	4¼	3¼	9⅛	4⅝	1½	1⅜	3.000	¾
600	5 3/16	3¾	10 9/16	5½	1¾	1⅝	3.000	¾
800	7	4¾	13½	7⅜	2	1⅝	4.000	1
1000	8¾	...	16 5/16	9 3/16	2½	2¼	4.000	1
1200	10½	...	19	11	3	2¼	4.000	1

Exposed length *C* is 0.003 minimum and 0.067 maximum for all sizes.

Drive key screw sizes are ⅜–24 up to taper No. 400 inclusive and ½–20 for larger tapers.

Tolerances: For diameter *A* of hole at gage line, +0.000, −0.002 for all sizes; for diameter *A* of shank at gage line, +0.002, −0.000 for all sizes; for width of drive keyway *R'* in socket, +0.000, −0.001; for width of drive keyway *R* in shank, +0.001, −0.000; for concentricity of drive keyway *R* with centerline of spindle, 0.003, and for drive keyway *R'*, 0.001. Tolerances for fractional dimensions are plus or minus 0.010 unless otherwise specified.

Table 11.   American Standard Plug and Ring Gages for the Self-holding Taper Series

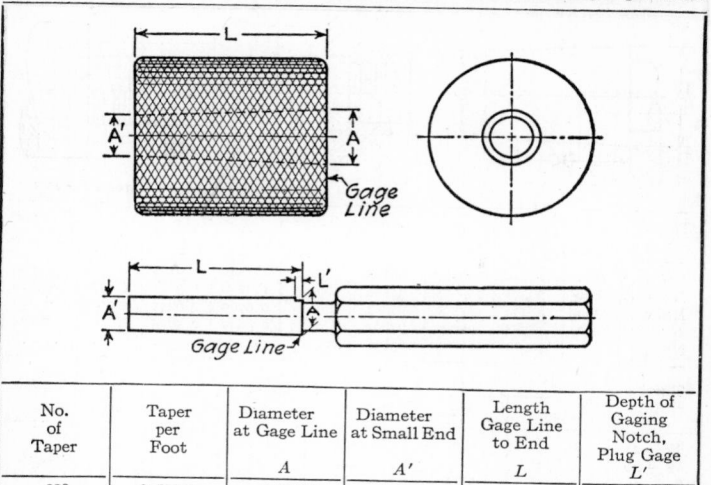

No. of Taper	Taper per Foot	Diameter at Gage Line A	Diameter at Small End A'	Length Gage Line to End L	Depth of Gaging Notch, Plug Gage L'
.239	0.50200	0.23922	0.20000	1 5/16	0.048
.299	0.50200	0.29968	0.25000	1 3/16	0.048
.375	0.50200	0.37525	0.31250	1 1/2	0.048
1	0.59858	0.47500	0.36900	2 1/8	0.040
2	0.59941	0.70000	0.57200	2 9/16	0.040
3	0.60235	0.93800	0.77800	3 3/16	0.040
4	0.62326	1.23100	1.02000	4 1/16	0.038
4 1/2	0.62400	1.50000	1.26600	4 1/2	0.038
5	0.63151	1.74800	1.47500	5 3/16	0.038
6	0.62565	2.49400	2.11600	7 1/4	0.038
7	0.62400	3.27000	2.75000	10	0.038
200	0.750	2.000	1.703	4 3/4	0.032
250	0.750	2.500	2.156	5 1/2	0.032
300	0.750	3.000	2.609	6 1/4	0.032
350	0.750	3.500	3.063	7	0.032
400	0.750	4.000	3.516	7 3/4	0.032
450	0.750	4.500	3.969	8 1/2	0.032
500	0.750	5.000	4.422	9 1/4	0.032
600	0.750	6.000	5.328	10 3/4	0.032
800	0.750	8.000	7.141	13 3/4	0.032
1000	0.750	10.000	8.953	16 3/4	0.032
1200	0.750	12.000	10.766	19 3/4	0.032

All dimensions in inches.

The taper per foot and diameter A at gage line are basic dimensions.   Dimensions in Column A are calculated for reference only.

Sizes No. 6 and 7 are continued in the Tang drive series for the present to meet special needs.

Plug Gage Tolerances: For diameters A and A', sizes 0.239 to No. 3 inclusive, +0.0001, −0.0000; sizes No. 4 to No. 300 inclusive, +0.00015, −0.00000; sizes No. 350 to No. 1200 inclusive, +0.0002, −0.0000.

Ring Gage Tolerances: For diameters A and A', sizes to No. 3 inclusive, −0.0001, +0.0000; sizes No. 4 to No. 300 inclusive, −0.00015, +0.00000; sizes No. 350 to No. 1200 inclusive, −0.0002, +0.0000.

Jacobs Tapers and Threads for Drill Chucks and Spindles

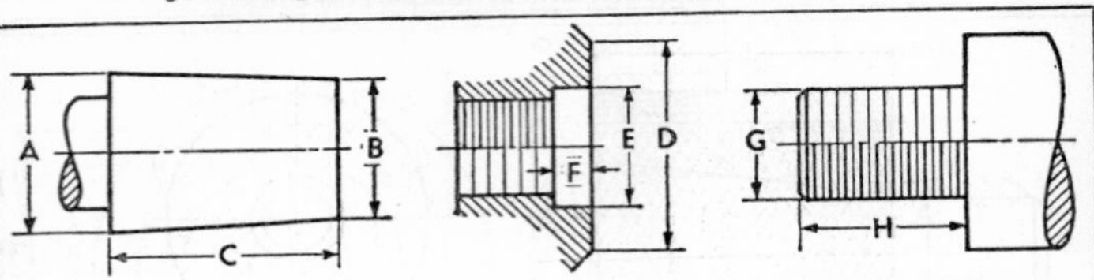

American Standard Thread Form

Taper Series	A	B	C	Taper per Ft.	Taper Series	A	B	C	Taper per Ft.
No. 0	.2500	.22844	.43750	.59145	No. 4	1.1240	1.0372	1.6563	.62886
No. 1	.3840	.33341	.65625	.92508	No. 5	1.4130	1.3161	1.8750	.62010
No. 2	.5590	.48764	.87500	.97861	No. 6	0.6760	0.6241	1.0000	.62292
No. 2(1)	.5490	.48784	.75000	.97861	No. 33	0.6240	0.5605	1.0000	.76194
No. 3	.8110	.74610	1.21875	.63898		......	......	......	......

Thread Size	Diameter D		Diameter E		Depth F	
	Max.	Min.	Max.	Min.	Max.	Min.
⅜ — 24	0.633	0.618	0.385	0.380	0.135	0.115
½ — 20	0.860	0.845	0.510	0.505	0.135	0.115
⅝ — 16	1.125	1.110	0.635	0.630	0.166	0.146
45⁄64 — 16	1.250	1.235	0.713	0.708	0.166	0.146
¾ — 16	1.250	1.235	0.760	0.755	0.166	0.146

Thread Size	Threaded Spindle		Plug Gage Pitch Diam.		Ring Gage Pitch Diam.	
	G (2)	H (3)	Go	Not Go	Go	Not Go
⅜ — 24	0.375	0.5625(4)	0.3479	0.3503	0.3465	0.3455
½ — 20	0.500	0.5625	0.4675	0.4701	0.4660	0.4650
⅝ — 16	0.625	0.6875	0.5844	0.5876	0.5825	0.5815
45⁄64 — 16	0.703	0.6875	0.6625	0.6657	0.6605	0.6595
¾ — 16	0.750	0.6875	0.7094	0.7126	0.7075	0.7065

Usual Chuck Capacities for Different Taper Series Numbers. — No. 0 taper, drill diameters, 0 — ⅛ inch; No. 1, 0 — ¼ inch; No. 2, 0 — ⅜ inch; No. 2 " Short," 0 — ¼ or 0 — 5⁄16 inch; No. 3, 0 — ½, ⅛ — ⅝, or 3⁄16 — ¾ inch; No. 4, ⅛ — ¾ inch; No. 5, ⅜ — 1 inch; No. 6, 0 — ½ inch; No. 33, 0 — ½ inch.
Usual Chuck Capacities for Different Thread Sizes. — Size ⅜ — 24, drill diameters 0 — ¼ or 0 — 5⁄16 inch; Size ½ — 20, drill diameters 0 — ¼, 0 — 5⁄16 or 0 — ⅜ inch; Sizes ⅝ — 16, 45⁄64 — 16, ¾ — 16, drill diameters 0 — 17⁄32, ⅛ — ⅝, or 3⁄16 — ¾ inch.

(1) These dimensions are for the No. 2 " short " taper. (2) All major screw thread diameters have a minus tolerance of 0.005 inch. (3) All dimensions H have a minus tolerance of 0.030 inch. (4) Length for No. I.B.S. chuck is 0.4375 inch.

Angle of Lathe Centers. — In the United States the standard included angle for the work-supporting ends of lathe centers is 60 degrees. This angle is increased to 75 degrees for some axle turning or other heavy-duty lathes. British standard lathe centers have an angle of either 60 or 75 degrees as specified by the purchaser. For lathes engaged in turning axles for railway rolling stock, the angle of 75 degrees has been adopted by the British Railway Companies. Experiments have shown that on lathe work at both high and low speeds the life of high-speed steel centers is approximately ten times that of carbon-steel centers.

Standard Tapers for Milling Machine Spindles

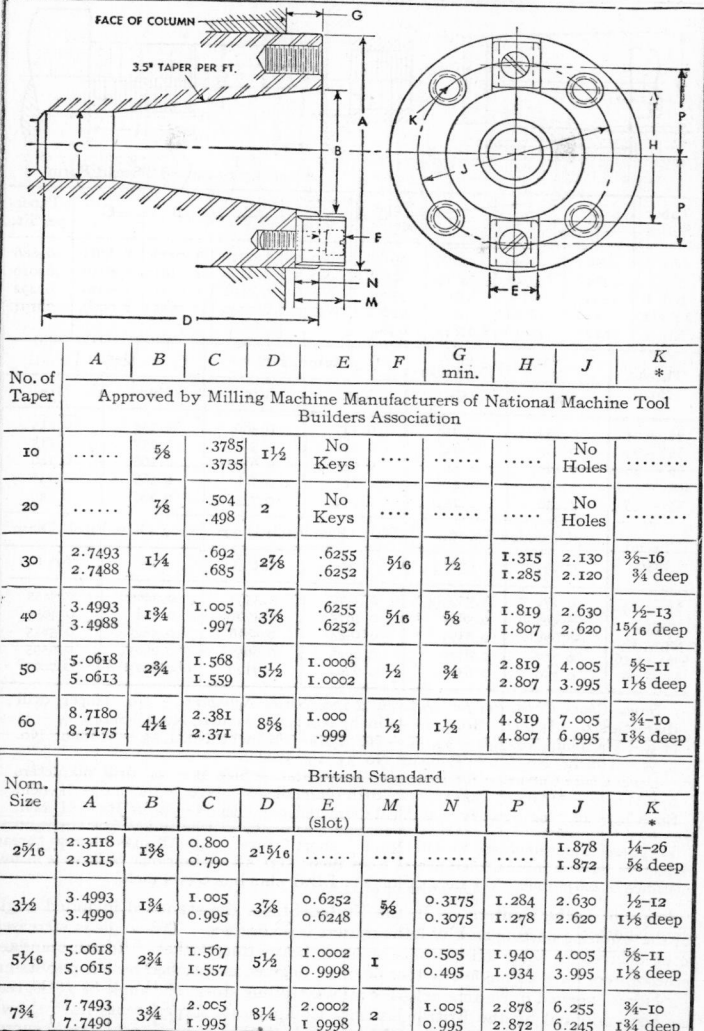

No. of Taper	A	B	C	D	E	F	G min.	H	J	K *
	Approved by Milling Machine Manufacturers of National Machine Tool Builders Association									
10	.....	5/8	.3785 .3735	1½	No Keys	....	......	.....	No Holes	....
20	.....	7/8	.504 .498	2	No Keys	....	......	.....	No Holes	....
30	2.7493 2.7488	1¼	.692 .685	2⅞	.6255 .6252	5/16	½	1.315 1.285	2.130 2.120	3/8-16 3/4 deep
40	3.4993 3.4988	1¾	1.005 .997	3⅞	.6255 .6252	5/16	5/8	1.819 1.807	2.630 2.620	½-13 15/16 deep
50	5.0618 5.0613	2¾	1.568 1.559	5½	1.0006 1.0002	½	¾	2.819 2.807	4.005 3.995	5/8-11 1⅛ deep
60	8.7180 8.7175	4¼	2.381 2.371	8⅝	1.000 .999	½	1½	4.819 4.807	7.005 6.995	3/4-10 1⅜ deep

Nom. Size	British Standard									
	A	B	C	D	E (slot)	M	N	P	J	K *
2 5/16	2.3118 2.3115	1⅜	0.800 0.790	2 15/16	......	....	......	.....	1.878 1.872	¼-26 5/8 deep
3½	3.4993 3.4990	1¾	1.005 0.995	3⅞	0.6252 0.6248	5/8	0.3175 0.3075	1.284 1.278	2.630 2.620	½-12 1⅛ deep
5 1/16	5.0618 5.0615	2¾	1.567 1.557	5½	1.0002 0.9998	1	0.505 0.495	1.940 1.934	4.005 3.995	5/8-11 1⅛ deep
7¾	7.7493 7.7490	3¾	2.005 1.995	8¼	2.0002 1.9998	2	1.005 0.995	2.878 2.872	6.255 6.245	3/4-10 1¾ deep

* Holes K in upper section of table have American standard thread form. Holes K of British Standard have Whitworth thread form. All dimensions are in inches.

Standard Arbors for Milling Machines

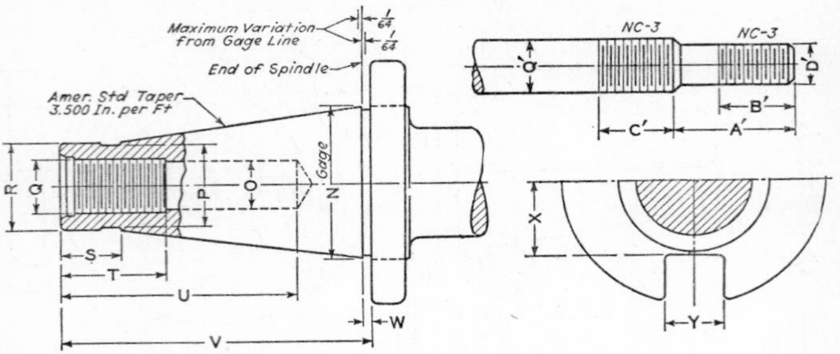

Size Number	Gage Diameter of Taper *N*	Clearance Hole Diameter *O*	Neck Diameter *P*	Thread Size Draw-in Bolt *Q*	Pilot Diameter *R*	Pilot Length *S*
30	1¼	27/64	41/64	½–13	0.675 0.673	13/16
40	1¾	17/32	15/16	⅝–11	0.987 0.985	1
50	2¾	⅞	1½	1–8	1.549 1.547	1
60	4¼	17/64	29/32	1¼–7	2.361 2.359	1¾

Size Number	Length of Perfect Threads *T*	Clearance Hole Depth *U*	Length *V*	Width of Clearance Groove *W*	Driving Slot Distance *X*	Driving Slot Width *Y*
30	1	2	2¾	1/16	0.640 0.625	0.630 0.640
40	1⅛	1 15/16	3¾	1/16	0.890 0.875	0.630 0.640
50	1¾	3½	5⅛	⅛	1.390 1.375	1.008 1.018
60	2¼	4¼	8 5/16	⅛	2.400 2.390	1.008 1.018

Dimensions of Draw-in Bolt End

Size Number	*A′*	*B′*	*C′*	*Q′*	*D′*
30	1 1/16	¾	¾	½–13	⅜–16
40	1 1/16	1 1/16	1⅛	⅝–11	½–13
50	1½	1¼	1⅜	1–8	⅝–11
60	1¾	1⅜	2	1¼–7	1–8

All dimensions are given in inches.

American Standard Taper Pins

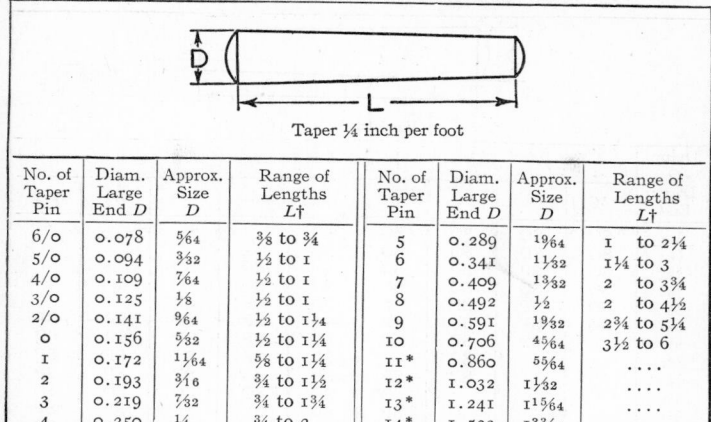

Taper ¼ inch per foot

No. of Taper Pin	Diam. Large End D	Approx. Size D	Range of Lengths L†	No. of Taper Pin	Diam. Large End D	Approx. Size D	Range of Lengths L†
6/0	0.078	5/64	3/8 to 3/4	5	0.289	19/64	1 to 2¼
5/0	0.094	3/32	½ to 1	6	0.341	11/32	1¼ to 3
4/0	0.109	7/64	½ to 1	7	0.409	13/32	2 to 3¾
3/0	0.125	1/8	½ to 1	8	0.492	½	2 to 4½
2/0	0.141	9/64	½ to 1¼	9	0.591	19/32	2¾ to 5¼
0	0.156	5/32	½ to 1¼	10	0.706	45/64	3½ to 6
1	0.172	11/64	5/8 to 1¼	11*	0.860	55/64	....
2	0.193	3/16	¾ to 1½	12*	1.032	1 1/32	....
3	0.219	7/32	¾ to 1¾	13*	1.241	1 15/64	....
4	0.250	¼	¾ to 2	14*	1.523	1 33/64	....

† These lengths L are suitable for use with the standard reamers listed on page 1320.
* Sizes Nos. 11 to 14 are special and their lengths are special.
Tolerance on diameter is +0.0013 − 0.0007 for all sizes.
To find diameter at small end of pin, multiply length L by 0.0208 and subtract product from large end diameter D.

Diameters at Small Ends of Standard Taper Pins

Pin Length in Inches	Pin Number and Small End Diam. for Given Length										
	0	1	2	3	4	5	6	7	8	9	10
¾	0.140	0.156	0.177	0.203	0.235	0.273	0.325	0.393	0.476	0.575	0.690
1	0.135	0.151	0.172	0.198	0.230	0.268	0.320	0.388	0.471	0.570	0.685
1¼	0.130	0.146	0.167	0.192	0.224	0.263	0.315	0.382	0.466	0.565	0.680
1½	0.125	0.141	0.162	0.187	0.219	0.258	0.310	0.377	0.460	0.560	0.675
1¾	0.120	0.136	0.157	0.182	0.214	0.252	0.305	0.372	0.455	0.554	0.669
2	0.114	0.130	0.151	0.177	0.209	0.247	0.299	0.367	0.450	0.549	0.664
2¼	0.109	0.125	0.146	0.172	0.204	0.242	0.294	0.362	0.445	0.544	0.659
2½	0.104	0.120	0.141	0.166	0.198	0.237	0.289	0.356	0.440	0.539	0.654
2¾	0.099	0.115	0.136	0.161	0.193	0.232	0.284	0.351	0.434	0.534	0.649
3	0.094	0.110	0.131	0.156	0.188	0.227	0.279	0.346	0.429	0.528	0.643
3¼	...	...	...	0.151	0.182	0.221	0.273	0.340	0.424	0.523	0.638
3½	...	...	...	0.146	0.177	0.216	0.268	0.335	0.419	0.518	0.633
3¾	...	...	...	0.141	0.172	0.211	0.263	0.330	0.414	0.513	0.628
4	...	...	...	0.136	0.167	0.206	0.258	0.326	0.409	0.508	0.623
4¼	...	...	...	0.131	0.162	0.201	0.253	0.321	0.403	0.502	0.617
4½	...	...	...	0.125	0.156	0.195	0.247	0.315	0.398	0.497	0.612
5	...	...	...	...	0.146	0.185	0.237	0.305	0.389	0.487	0.602
5½	...	...	...	...	...	...	...	0.294	0.377	0.476	0.591
6	...	...	...	...	...	...	...	0.284	0.367	0.466	0.581

British Standard Solid and Split Taper Pins
From Report No. 46, Part 3, 1935, of British Standard Institution

Taper on diameter ¼ inch per foot

Diam. D Large End	Length L in Inches								
	½	¾	1	1¼	1½	1¾	2	2¼	2½
1/16	SO	SO	SO	SO	SO				
5/64	SO	SO	SO	SO	SO				
3/32	SO	SO	SO	SO	SO	SO	SO		
7/64	SO	SO	SO	SO	SO	SO	SO		
1/8	SO	SP	SP	SP	SP	SP	SP		
5/32	SO	SP	SP	SP	SP	SP	SP	SP	SP
3/16		SO	SP	SP	SP	SP	SP	SP	SP
7/32			SO	SP	SP	SP	SP	SP	SP
1/4			SO	SP	SP	SP	SP	SP	SP
9/32					SO	SO	SO	SO	SO
5/16					SO	SP	SP	SP	SP
11/32						SO	SO	SO	SO
3/8							SO	SP	SP
7/16								SO	SP
1/2									SO

Diam. D Large End	Length L								
	2¾	3	3¼	3½	4	4½	5	5½	6
3/16	SP	SP	SP	SP	SP				
7/32	SP	SP	SP	SP	SP	SP			
1/4	SP	SP	SP	SP	SP	SP	SP		
9/32	SO	SO	SO	SO	SO	SO	SO	SO	
5/16	SP	SP	SP	SP	SP	SP	SP	SP	SP
11/32	SO	SO	SO	SO	SO	SO	SO	SO	SO
3/8	SP	SP	SP	SP	SP	SP	SP	SP	SP
7/16	SP	SP	SP	SP	SP	SP	SP	SP	SP
1/2	SP	SP	SP	SP	SP	SP	SP	SP	SP
9/16		SO	SO	SO	SP	SP	SP	SP	SP
5/8			SO	SO	SP	SP	SP	SP	SP

Dimensions in inches. All diameters and lengths marked either SO (meaning solid) or SP (split) are standard for *solid* taper pins. Only the diameters and lengths marked SP are standard for *split* taper pins. These split pins are split (not sawn) at the small end for a length of not less than 20 per cent of the pin length. The diameters at the large end have a plus or minus tolerance of 0.002 inch.

The steel used for solid and split taper pins must contain 0.12 to 0.20 per cent carbon; silicon, 0.20 per cent maximum; manganese, 0.40 to 0.80 per cent; sulphur, 0.05 per cent maximum; phosphorus, 0.05 per cent maximum. The minimum hardness is 120 Brinell or the equivalent Rockwell number.

Solid taper pins, when cold, must withstand bending at the middle of the length to an angle of 180 degrees around a circle having a diameter equal to the mean pin diameter, without showing signs of fracture. Split taper pins, when cold, must withstand opening up for two-thirds of the length of the split, the wings being bent backward to an angle of 180 degrees and closed upon the pin without showing signs of fracture.

Straight Knurls. — It is important to select a suitable angle for the teeth for knurling different materials. A blunt knurl will work better on soft materials than one with a more acute angle. The following angles are satisfactory:

Brass and hard copper.......90 deg.   Norway iron and machine steel.....70 deg.
Gun-screw iron.............80 deg.   Drill rod and tool steel............60 deg.

When laying out a set of cams for knurling operations, it is necessary to know the depth of the knurl teeth. This depth can be obtained direct from the table, " Depth of Teeth in Knurls."

Concave Knurls. — The radius of a concave knurl should not be the same as the radius of the piece to be knurled. If the knurl and the work are of the same radius, the material compressed by the knurl will be forced down on the shoulder D and spoil the appearance of the work. A design of concave knurl is shown in the accompanying illustration, and all the important dimensions are designated by

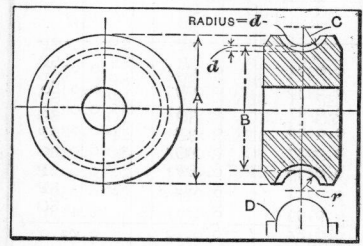

letters. To find these dimensions, the pitch of the knurl required must be known, and also, approximately, the throat diameter B. This diameter must suit the knurl holder used, and be such that the circumference contains an even number of teeth with the required pitch. When these dimensions have been decided upon, all the other unknown factors can be found by the following formula: Let R = radius of piece to be knurled; r = radius of concave part of knurl; C = radius of cutter or hob for cutting the teeth in the knurl; B = diameter over concave part of knurl (throat diameter); A = outside diameter of knurl; d = depth of tooth in knurl; P = pitch of knurl (number of teeth per inch circumference); p = circular pitch of knurl; then, $r = R + \frac{1}{2}d$; $C = r + d$; $A = B + 2r - (3d + 0.010$ inch).

As the depth of the tooth is usually very slight, the throat diameter B will be accurate enough for all practical purposes for calculating the pitch, and it is not necessary to take into consideration the pitch circle. For example, assume that the pitch of a knurl is 32, that the throat diameter B is 0.5561 inch, that the radius R of the piece to be knurled is 1/16 inch, and that the angle of the teeth is 90 degrees; find the dimensions of the knurl. Using the notation given:

$$p = \frac{1}{P} = \frac{1}{32} = 0.03125 \text{ inch;}$$

$$d = 0.0156 \text{ inch (see table "Depth of Teeth in Knurls");}$$

$$r = \frac{1}{16} + \frac{0.0156}{2} = 0.0703 \text{ inch;}$$

$$C = 0.0703 + 0.0156 = 0.0859 \text{ inch;}$$

$$A = 0.5561 + 0.1406 - (0.0468 + 0.010) = 0.6399 \text{ inch.}$$

Speeds and Feeds for Knurling. — When the knurl has been designed, the next thing to consider, before laying out the cams, is the speed and feed for knurling. As a general rule, a knurl can be worked at the same speed as the circular forming and cut-off tools. It is good practice to feed the knurl gradually to the center of the work, starting to feed when the knurl touches the work and then pass off the center of the work with a quick rise on the cam. The knurl should also dwell for a certain number of revolutions, depending on its pitch and the nature of the material.

The feed required for knurling is governed by the nature of the material being knurled, the diameter of the material, and the width and pitch of the knurl. The surest and most practical way to find the feed required is by experimenting. The results of different experiments are given in the table "Feeds for Cross-slide Knurling." These feeds are applicable only when knurling from the cross-slide.

Depth of Teeth in Knurls

P = number of teeth in one inch of circumference;
p = circular pitch;
α = included angle of teeth;
d = depth of teeth in knurl.

P	p	$\alpha = 90°$ d	$\alpha = 80°$ d	$\alpha = 70°$ d	$\alpha = 60°$ d
16	0.0625	0.0312	0.0371	0.0445	0.0540
18	0.0555	0.0277	0.0330	0.0395	0.0480
20	0.0500	0.0250	0.0297	0.0357	0.0433
22	0.0454	0.0227	0.0260	0.0324	0.0393
24	0.0416	0.0208	0.0247	0.0297	0.0360
26	0.0384	0.0192	0.0228	0.0274	0.0332
28	0.0357	0.0178	0.0212	0.0254	0.0308
30	0.0333	0.0166	0.0199	0.0237	0.0287
32	0.0312	0.0156	0.0185	0.0222	0.0270
34	0.0294	0.0147	0.0175	0.0209	0.0254
36	0.0277	0.0138	0.0164	0.0197	0.0239
38	0.0263	0.0131	0.0156	0.0187	0.0226
40	0.0250	0.0125	0.0148	0.0178	0.0216
42	0.0238	0.0119	0.0142	0.0169	0.0206
44	0.0227	0.0113	0.0134	0.0161	0.0195
46	0.0217	0.0108	0.0128	0.0154	0.0187
48	0.0208	0.0104	0.0124	0.0148	0.0180
50	0.0200	0.0100	0.0119	0.0142	0.0173
52	0.0192	0.0096	0.0114	0.0137	0.0166
54	0.0185	0.0092	0.0109	0.0131	0.0159
56	0.0178	0.0089	0.0106	0.0127	0.0154
58	0.0172	0.0086	0.0102	0.0122	0.0148
60	0.0166	0.0083	0.0099	0.0118	0.0143
62	0.0161	0.0080	0.0096	0.0114	0.0138

Turret Knurling. — Definite information cannot be given for feeds for knurling from the turret, as it is impossible to take into consideration all the various conditions under which a knurl will be operated. When two knurls are employed for spiral and diamond knurling, the knurls can be operated at a higher rate of feed for producing a spiral than they can for producing a diamond knurl. The reason for this is that in the first case the two knurls work in the same groove, whereas in the latter case they work independently of each other. For end knurling, when the knurl only has to be fed in to the depth of the tooth, the feed varies from that used for spiral or diamond knurling. The diameter of the work is also a determining factor. The table "Feeds for Turret Knurling" is applicable particularly to spiral and diamond knurling, but can also be used as a guide for bevel or end knurling. The diameter of the work or its strength to resist the torsional stress resulting from the knurling operation is not taken into consideration, and allowance should be made for this when using the feeds given. The feeds to be used for backing the knurls off the work should be as follows: For brass, screw stock and machine steel, twice the feeds given in the table; for tool steel, three times the feeds given in the table.

Feeds for Cross-slide Knurling

Diameter of Stock, Inches	Width of Knurl, Inches							
	1/16	1/8	3/16	1/4	5/16	3/8	7/16	1/2
	Feed per Revolution, Inches							
1/16	0.0010	0.0005	.....	.....	.....	.....	.....	.....
1/8	0.0014	0.0009	0.0005	.....	.....	.....	.....	.....
3/16	0.0018	0.0012	0.0010	0.0005	.....	.....	.....	.....
1/4	0.0022	0.0016	0.0014	0.0010	0.0005	.....	.....	.....
5/16	0.0026	0.0020	0.0018	0.0013	0.0010	0.0005	.....	.....
3/8	0.0030	0.0025	0.0022	0.0017	0.0015	0.0010	0.0005	.....
7/16	0.0034	0.0029	0.0026	0.0021	0.0018	0.0015	0.0010	0.0005
1/2	0.0039	0.0032	0.0030	0.0025	0.0022	0.0020	0.0014	0.0008
9/16	0.0042	0.0036	0.0034	0.0029	0.0028	0.0024	0.0017	0.0012
5/8	0.0046	0.0040	0.0038	0.0033	0.0031	0.0028	0.0020	0.0016
11/16	0.0050	0.0045	0.0042	0.0037	0.0034	0.0031	0.0023	0.0020
3/4	0.0054	0.0049	0.0048	0.0041	0.0038	0.0034	0.0026	0.0023
13/16	0.0059	0.0052	0.0052	0.0045	0.0042	0.0037	0.0029	0.0026
7/8	0.0062	0.0058	0.0055	0.0049	0.0045	0.0040	0.0033	0.0029
15/16	0.0068	0.0062	0.0058	0.0052	0.0048	0.0042	0.0037	0.0032
1	0.0070	0.0065	0.0060	0.0055	0.0050	0.0045	0.0040	0.0035

Revolutions Required for Knurling. — The depth of the tooth and the feed per revolution govern the number of revolutions required for knurling. If R is the radius of the stock, d is the depth of the tooth, c is the distance the knurl travels from the point of contact to the center of the work, at the feed required for knurling and r = radius of knurl; then

$$c = \sqrt{(R + r)^2 - (R - d + r)^2}.$$

If radius of stock R = 5/32 inch, depth of tooth d = 0.0156 inch and radius of knurl r = 0.3125 inch, then $c = \sqrt{(0.1562 + 0.3125)^2 - (0.1562 - 0.0156 + 0.3125)^2}$ = 0.120 inch = rise required. Assume that it is required to find the number of revolutions to knurl a piece of brass 5/16 inch in diameter with a knurl 1/8 inch wide of 32 pitch. The included angle of the tooth for knurling brass is 90 degrees, the circular pitch is 0.0312 and, referring to the table "Depth of Teeth in Knurls," the depth is found to be 0.0156. The distance c (as determined in the previous example) is 0.120 inch; then referring to the table "Feeds for Cross-slide Knurling," the feed per revolution for a knurl 1/8 inch wide, knurling 5/16 inch stock, is 0.002 inch; therefore, the total revolutions required = 0.120 ÷ 0.002 = 60 revolutions. In some cases the feeds given in this table can be increased 50 per cent with satisfactory results.

Knurls for Knurling in the Lathe. — The knurls commonly used for lathe work have spiral teeth and ordinarily there are three classes known as coarse, medium and fine. The medium pitch is generally used. The teeth of coarse knurls have a spiral angle of 36 degrees and the pitch of the knurled cut (measured parallel to the axis of the work) should be about 8 per inch. For medium knurls, the spiral angle is 29½ degrees and the pitch, measured as before, is 12 per inch. For fine knurls, the spiral angle is 25¾ degrees and the pitch, 20 per inch. The knurls should be about ¾ inch in diameter and ⅜ inch wide; when made to these dimensions, coarse knurls have 34 teeth, medium, 50 teeth, and fine knurls 80 teeth. To prevent forming a double set of projections when knurling, feed the knurl in with considerable pressure at the start, and then partially relieve the pressure before engaging the power feed. Use oil when knurling.

Feeds for Turret Knurling

Pitch of Knurl	Feed per Revolution				Pitch of Knurl	Feed per Revolution			
	Brass Rod	Gun-screw Iron	Ma-chine Steel	Tool Steel		Brass Rod	Gun-screw Iron	Ma-chine Steel	Tool Steel
16	0.0100	0.0080	0.0060	0.0040	40	0.0158	0.0128	0.0086	0.0058
18	0.0105	0.0084	0.0063	0.0042	42	0.0164	0.0132	0.0088	0.0059
20	0.0110	0.0088	0.0065	0.0044	44	0.0168	0.0136	0.0090	0.0061
22	0.0115	0.0092	0.0068	0.0046	46	0.0173	0.0140	0.0092	0.0062
24	0.0118	0.0096	0.0070	0.0048	48	0.0178	0.0143	0.0094	0.0063
26	0.0123	0.0100	0.0072	0.0050	50	0.0182	0.0145	0.0098	0.0064
28	0.0128	0.0103	0.0074	0.0051	52	0.0185	0.0148	0.0103	0.0065
30	0.0135	0.0106	0.0076	0.0052	54	0.0189	0.0150	0.0108	0.0066
32	0.0140	0.0110	0.0078	0.0053	56	0.0193	0.0153	0.0111	0.0067
34	0.0145	0.0115	0.0080	0.0054	58	0.0195	0.0156	0.0115	0.0068
36	0.0150	0.0120	0.0082	0.0056	60	0.0198	0.0158	0.0118	0.0069
38	0.0153	0.0125	0.0084	0.0057	62	0.0200	0.0160	0.0120	0.0070

Cams for Threading. — The tables "Spindle Revolutions and Cam Rise for Threading" give the revolutions required for threading various lengths and pitches and the corresponding rise for the cam lobe. To illustrate the use of these tables, suppose a set of cams is required for threading a screw to the length of ⅜ inch in a B. & S. machine. Assume that the spindle speed is 2400 revolutions per minute; the number of revolutions to complete one piece, 400; time required to make one piece, 10 seconds; pitch of the thread, 1/32 inch or 32 threads per inch. By referring to the table, under 32 threads per inch, and opposite ⅜ inch (length of threaded part), the number of revolutions required is found to be 15 and the rise required for the cam, 0.413 inch.

Cams of this type are often cut on a circular milling attachment. When this method is employed, the number of minutes the attachment should be revolved for each 0.001 inch rise, is first determined. As 15 revolutions are required for threading and 400 for completing one piece, that part of the cam surface required for the actual threading operation equals 15 ÷ 400 = 0.0375, which is equivalent to 810 minutes of the circumference. As the total rise, in this case, through an arc of 810 minutes is 0.413 inch, the number of minutes for each 0.001 inch rise equals 810 ÷ 413 = 1.96, or, approximately, two minutes. If the attachment is graduated to read to five minutes, the cam will be fed laterally 0.0025 inch each time it is turned five minutes.

Spindle Revolutions and Cam Rise for Threading — 1

Number of Threads per Inch

First Line: Revolutions of Spindle for Threading.   Second Line: Rise on Cam for Threading.

Length of Threaded Portion		14	16	18	20	24	28	30	32	36	40	48	56	64	72	80
1/16	Rev.	…	…	…	…	3.00	5.00	5.00	5.00	5.50	5.50	6.00	8.00	8.50	9.00	9.50
	Rise	…	…	…	…	0.106	0.157	0.147	0.138	0.134	0.121	0.110	0.129	0.120	0.113	0.107
1/8	Rev.	…	3.50	3.50	4.00	4.50	6.50	7.00	7.00	7.00	8.00	9.00	11.50	12.50	13.50	14.50
	Rise	…	0.186	0.165	0.170	0.159	0.204	0.205	0.193	0.171	0.176	0.165	0.185	0.176	0.169	0.163
3/16	Rev.	4.00	4.50	5.00	5.50	6.00	8.50	8.50	9.00	10.00	10.50	12.00	15.00	16.50	18.00	19.50
	Rise	0.243	0.239	0.236	0.234	0.213	0.267	0.249	0.248	0.244	0.231	0.220	0.241	0.232	0.225	0.219
1/4	Rev.	5.00	5.50	6.00	6.50	7.50	10.00	10.50	11.00	12.00	13.00	15.00	18.50	20.50	22.50	24.50
	Rise	0.304	0.292	0.283	0.276	0.266	0.314	0.308	0.303	0.293	0.286	0.275	0.297	0.288	0.281	0.276
5/16	Rev.	6.00	6.50	7.00	8.00	9.00	12.00	12.50	13.00	14.50	15.50	18.00	22.00	24.50	27.00	29.50
	Rise	0.364	0.345	0.330	0.340	0.319	0.377	0.367	0.358	0.354	0.341	0.330	0.354	0.345	0.338	0.332
3/8	Rev.	7.00	7.50	8.50	9.00	10.50	13.50	14.50	15.00	16.50	18.00	21.00	25.50	28.50	31.50	34.50
	Rise	0.425	0.398	0.401	0.383	0.372	0.424	0.425	0.413	0.403	0.396	0.385	0.410	0.401	0.394	0.388
7/16	Rev.	7.50	8.50	9.50	10.50	12.00	15.50	16.00	17.00	19.00	20.50	24.00	29.00	32.50	36.00	39.50
	Rise	0.455	0.451	0.448	0.446	0.425	0.487	0.469	0.468	0.464	0.451	0.440	0.466	0.457	0.450	0.444
1/2	Rev.	8.50	9.50	10.50	11.50	13.50	17.00	18.00	19.00	21.00	23.00	27.00	32.50	36.50	40.50	44.50
	Rise	0.516	0.504	0.496	0.489	0.478	0.534	0.528	0.523	0.513	0.506	0.495	0.522	0.513	0.506	0.501
9/16	Rev.	9.50	10.50	11.50	13.00	15.00	19.00	20.00	21.00	23.50	25.50	30.00	36.00	40.50	45.00	49.50
	Rise	0.577	0.558	0.543	0.553	0.531	0.597	0.587	0.578	0.574	0.561	0.550	0.579	0.570	0.563	0.559
5/8	Rev.	10.50	11.50	13.00	14.00	16.50	20.50	22.00	23.00	25.50	28.00	33.00	39.50	44.50	49.50	54.50
	Rise	0.637	0.611	0.614	0.595	0.584	0.644	0.645	0.633	0.623	0.616	0.605	0.635	0.626	0.619	0.613
11/16	Rev.	11.00	12.50	14.00	15.50	18.00	22.50	23.50	25.00	28.00	30.50	36.00	43.00	48.50	54.00	59.50
	Rise	0.668	0.664	0.661	0.659	0.638	0.707	0.689	0.688	0.684	0.671	0.660	0.691	0.682	0.675	0.679
3/4	Rev.	12.00	13.50	15.00	16.50	19.50	24.00	25.50	27.00	30.00	33.00	39.00	46.50	52.50	58.50	64.50
	Rise	0.728	0.717	0.708	0.701	0.691	0.754	0.748	0.743	0.733	0.726	0.715	0.747	0.738	0.731	0.726

Spindle Revolutions and Cam Rise for Threading — 2

Number of Threads per Inch

First Line: Revolutions of Spindle for Threading. Second Line: Rise on Cam for Threading

Length of Threaded Portion	14	16	18	20	24	28	30	32	36	40	48	56	64	72	80
13/16	13.00 / 0.789	14.50 / 0.770	16.00 / 0.755	18.00 / 0.765	21.00 / 0.744	26.00 / 0.817	27.50 / 0.807	29.00 / 0.798	32.50 / 0.794	35.50 / 0.781	42.00 / 0.770	50.00 / 0.804	56.50 / 0.795	63.00 / 0.788	69.50 / 0.782
7/8	14.00 / 0.850	15.50 / 0.823	17.50 / 0.826	19.00 / 0.808	22.50 / 0.797	27.50 / 0.864	29.50 / 0.865	31.00 / 0.853	34.50 / 0.843	38.00 / 0.836	45.00 / 0.825	53.50 / 0.860	60.50 / 0.851	67.50 / 0.844	74.50 / 0.838
15/16	14.50 / 0.880	16.50 / 0.876	18.50 / 0.873	20.50 / 0.871	24.00 / 0.850	29.50 / 0.927	31.00 / 0.909	33.00 / 0.908	37.00 / 0.904	40.50 / 0.891	48.00 / 0.880	57.00 / 0.916	64.50 / 0.907	72.00 / 0.900	79.50 / 0.894
1	15.50 / 0.941	17.50 / 0.929	19.50 / 0.920	21.50 / 0.914	25.50 / 0.903	31.00 / 0.974	33.00 / 0.968	35.00 / 0.963	39.00 / 0.953	43.00 / 0.946	51.00 / 0.918	60.50 / 0.972	68.50 / 0.963	76.50 / 0.956	84.50 / 0.951
1 1/8	17.50 / 1.062	19.50 / 1.035	22.00 / 1.038	24.00 / 1.020	28.50 / 1.009	34.50 / 1.083	37.00 / 1.084	39.00 / 1.073	43.50 / 1.061	48.00 / 1.056	57.00 / 1.045	67.50 / 1.084	76.50 / 1.076	85.50 / 1.069	94.50 / 1.063
1 1/4	19.00 / 1.153	21.50 / 1.142	24.00 / 1.133	26.50 / 1.126	31.50 / 1.115	38.00 / 1.193	40.50 / 1.187	43.00 / 1.183	48.00 / 1.171	53.00 / 1.166	63.00 / 1.155	74.50 / 1.197	84.50 / 1.188	94.50 / 1.181	104.5 / 1.176
1 3/8	21.00 / 1.275	23.50 / 1.248	26.50 / 1.251	29.00 / 1.233	34.50 / 1.211	41.50 / 1.303	44.50 / 1.304	47.00 / 1.293	52.50 / 1.281	58.00 / 1.276	69.00 / 1.265	81.50 / 1.310	92.50 / 1.301	103.5 / 1.294	……
1 1/2	22.50 / 1.366	25.50 / 1.354	28.50 / 1.345	31.50 / 1.339	37.50 / 1.328	45.00 / 1.413	48.00 / 1.406	51.00 / 1.403	57.00 / 1.391	63.00 / 1.386	75.00 / 1.375	88.50 / 1.422	100.5 / 1.413	……	……
1 5/8	24.50 / 1.487	27.50 / 1.460	31.00 / 1.463	34.00 / 1.445	40.50 / 1.434	48.50 / 1.523	52.00 / 1.524	55.00 / 1.513	61.50 / 1.501	68.00 / 1.496	81.00 / 1.485	95.50 / 1.535	……	……	……
1 3/4	26.00 / 1.578	29.50 / 1.566	33.00 / 1.558	36.50 / 1.551	43.50 / 1.540	52.00 / 1.633	55.50 / 1.626	59.00 / 1.623	66.00 / 1.610	73.00 / 1.606	87.00 / 1.595	102.5 / 1.647	……	……	……
1 7/8	28.00 / 1.700	31.50 / 1.673	35.50 / 1.676	39.00 / 1.658	46.50 / 1.646	55.50 / 1.743	59.50 / 1.743	63.00 / 1.733	70.50 / 1.720	78.00 / 1.716	93.00 / 1.705	……	……	……	……
2	29.50 / 1.791	33.50 / 1.779	37.50 / 1.770	41.50 / 1.764	49.50 / 1.752	59.00 / 1.853	63.00 / 1.846	67.00 / 1.843	75.00 / 1.830	83.00 / 1.826	99.00 / 1.815	……	……	……	……

Practical Points on Cam and Tool Design. — The following general rules are given to aid in designing cams and special tools for automatic screw machines, and apply particularly to B. & S. machines:

1. Use the highest spindle speeds that the various tools will stand.

2. Use the arrangement of circular tools best suited for the class of work. (See paragraph: "Arrangement of Circular Tools.")

3. Decide on the quickest and best method of arranging the operations before designing the cams.

4. Do not use turret tools for forming when the cross-slide tools can be used to better advantage.

5. Do not use a circular cut-off tool without top rake when cutting Norway iron, machine steel, etc.

6. Make the shoulder on the circular cut-off tool large enough so that the clamping screw will grip firmly.

7. When chips clinging to the work are objectionable, the circular forming tool should be turned upside down and placed on the rear cross-slide.

8. Do not use too narrow a cut-off blade.

9. Allow 0.005 to 0.010 inch for the circular tools to approach the work and 0.003 to 0.005 inch for the cut-off tool to pass the center.

10. When cutting off work large in diameter, the feed of the cut-off tool should be increased until near the end of the cut where the piece breaks off. After it breaks off, the feed should again be increased until the tool has passed the center.

11. When a thread is cut up to a shoulder, the piece should be grooved or necked to make allowance for the lead on the die. This requires an extra projection on the forming tool and also an extra amount of rise on the cam.

12. Use circular forming and cut-off tools made from high-speed steel when cutting Norway iron, machine steel, etc.

13. Use a fine feed and high spindle speed for all cutting tools.

14. Allow sufficient clearance for tools to pass one another.

15. Always make a diagram of the cross-slide tools in position on the work when difficult operations are to be performed; it is also necessary to make a diagram of the tools held in the turret.

16. Do not drill a hole the depth of which is more than 2½ times the diameter of the drill, but use two or more drills as required. If there are not sufficient holes in the turret, drop the drill back clear of the hole, and advance it into the hole again.

17. Do not run a drill at a slow speed.

18. When the turret tools operate farther in than the face of the chuck, see that they will clear the chute when revolving the turret.

19. See that the body of all turret tools will clear the side of the chute when revolving the turret.

20. Do not use a box-tool for a roughing cut. Use a hollow mill.

21. Do not use a box-tool with solid supports. Use solid supports only on cold-drawn or finished stock.

22. The rise on the thread lobe should be reduced so that the spindle will reverse when the die or tap holder is drawn out.

23. When threading Norway iron, machine steel, etc., if the spindle speed used for the other tools is too high for threading, use a special threading attachment.

24. When bringing another tool into position after a threading operation, allow clearance before revolving the turret.

25. Make provision to revolve the turret rapidly, especially when pieces are being made in from three to five seconds and when only a few tools are used in the turret.   It is sometimes convenient to use two sets of tools.

26. When using a belt-shifting attachment for threading, clearance should be allowed, as it requires extra time to shift the belt.

27. When laying out a set of cams for operating on a piece which requires to be slotted, cross-drilled or burred, allowance should be made on the lead cam so that the transferring arm can descend and ascend to and from the work without coming in contact with any of the turret tools.

28. Always allow a vacant hole in the turret when it is necessary to use the transferring arm.

29. Use standard tools whenever possible.

30. When designing special tools allow as much clearance as possible. Do not make them so that they will just clear each other, as a slight inaccuracy in the dimensions will then often cause trouble.

31. When designing special tools having intricate movements, avoid springs as much as possible, and use positive actions.

Stock for Screw Machine Products. — The amount of stock required for the production of 1000 pieces on the automatic screw machine can be obtained directly from the table "Stock required for Screw Machine Products." To use this table, add to the length of the work the width of the cut-off tool blade; then the number of feet of material required for 1000 pieces can be found opposite the figure thus obtained, in the column headed "Feet per 1000 Parts." Screw machine stock usually comes in bars 10 feet long, and in compiling this table an allowance was made for chucking on each bar.

The table can be extended by using the following formula, in which F = number of feet required for 1000 pieces; L = length of piece in inches; W = width of cut-off tool blade in inches.

$$F = (L + W) \times 84.$$

The amount to add to the length of the work, or the width of the cut-off tool, is given in the following, which is standard in a number of machine shops:

Diameter of Stock, Inches	Width of Cut-off Tool Blade, Inches
0.000–0.250	0.045
0.251–0.375	0.062
0.376–0.625	0.093
0.626–1.000	0.125
1.000–1.500	0.156

It is sometimes convenient to know the weight of a certain number of pieces, when estimating the price. The weight of round bar stock can be found by means of the following formulas, in which W = weight in pounds; D = diameter of stock in inches; F = length in feet:

For brass stock: $W = D^2 \times 2.86 \times F.$
For steel stock: $W = D^2 \times 2.675 \times F.$
For iron stock: $W = D^2 \times 2.65 \times F.$

Stock Required for Screw Machine Products

The table gives the amount of stock, in feet, required for 1000 pieces, when the length of the finished part plus the thickness of the cut-off tool blade is known. Allowance has been made for chucking. To illustrate, if length of cut-off tool and work equals 0.140 inch, 11.8 feet of stock is required for the production of 1000 parts.

Length of Piece and Cut-off Tool	Feet per 1000 Parts	Length of Piece and Cut-off Tool	Feet per 1000 Parts	Length of Piece and Cut-off Tool	Feet per 1000 Parts	Length of Piece and Cut-off Tool	Feet per 1000 Parts
0.050	4.2	0.430	36.1	0.810	68.1	1.380	116.0
0.060	5.0	0.440	37.0	0.820	68.9	1.400	117.6
0.070	5.9	0.450	37.8	0.830	69.7	1.420	119.3
0.080	6.7	0.460	38.7	0.840	70.6	1.440	121.0
0.090	7.6	0.470	39.5	0.850	71.4	1.460	122.7
0.100	8.4	0.480	40.3	0.860	72.3	1.480	124.4
0.110	9.2	0.490	41.2	0.870	73.1	1.500	126.1
0.120	10.1	0.500	42.0	0.880	73.9	1.520	127.7
0.130	10.9	0.510	42.9	0.890	74.8	1.540	129.4
0.140	11.8	0.520	43.7	0.900	75.6	1.560	131.1
0.150	12.6	0.530	44.5	0.910	76.5	1.580	132.8
0.160	13.4	0.540	45.4	0.920	77.3	1.600	134.5
0.170	14.3	0.550	46.2	0.930	78.2	1.620	136.1
0.180	15.1	0.560	47.1	0.940	79.0	1.640	137.8
0.190	16.0	0.570	47.9	0.950	79.8	1.660	139.5
0.200	16.8	0.580	48.7	0.960	80.7	1.680	141.2
0.210	17.6	0.590	49.6	0.970	81.5	1.700	142.9
0.220	18.5	0.600	50.4	0.980	82.4	1.720	144.5
0.230	19.3	0.610	51.3	0.990	83.2	1.740	146.2
0.240	20.2	0.620	52.1	1.000	84.0	1.760	147.9
0.250	21.0	0.630	52.9	1.020	85.7	1.780	149.6
0.260	21.8	0.640	53.8	1.040	87.4	1.800	151.3
0.270	22.7	0.650	54.6	1.060	89.1	1.820	152.9
0.280	23.5	0.660	55.5	1.080	90.8	1.840	154.6
0.290	24.4	0.670	56.3	1.100	92.4	1.860	156.3
0.300	25.2	0.680	57.1	1.120	94.1	1.880	158.0
0.310	26.1	0.690	58.0	1.140	95.8	1.900	159.7
0.320	26.9	0.700	58.8	1.160	97.5	1.920	161.3
0.330	27.7	0.710	59.7	1.180	99.2	1.940	163.0
0.340	28.6	0.720	60.5	1.200	100.8	1.960	164.7
0.350	29.4	0.730	61.3	1.220	102.5	1.980	166.4
0.360	30.3	0.740	62.2	1.240	104.2	2.000	168.1
0.370	31.1	0.750	63.0	1.260	105.9	2.100	176.5
0.380	31.9	0.760	63.9	1.280	107.6	2.200	184.9
0.390	32.8	0.770	64.7	1.300	109.2	2.300	193.3
0.400	33.6	0.780	65.5	1.320	110.9	2.400	201.7
0.410	34.5	0.790	66.4	1.340	112.6	2.500	210.1
0.420	35.3	0.800	67.2	1.360	114.3	2.600	218.5

JIGS AND FIXTURES

Material for Jig Bushings. — Bushings are generally made of a good grade of tool steel to insure hardening at a fairly low temperature and to lessen the danger of fire cracking. They can also be made from machine steel, which will answer all practical purposes, provided the bushings are properly casehardened to a depth of about 1/16 inch. Sometimes bushings for guiding tools may be made of cast iron, but only when the cutting tool is of such a design that no cutting edges come within the bushing itself. For example, bushings used simply to support the smooth

Table 1. American Standard Renewable Wearing Bushings — Slip and Fixed Types

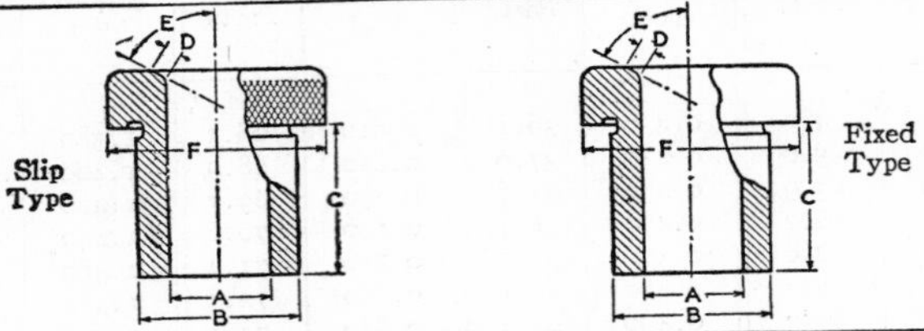

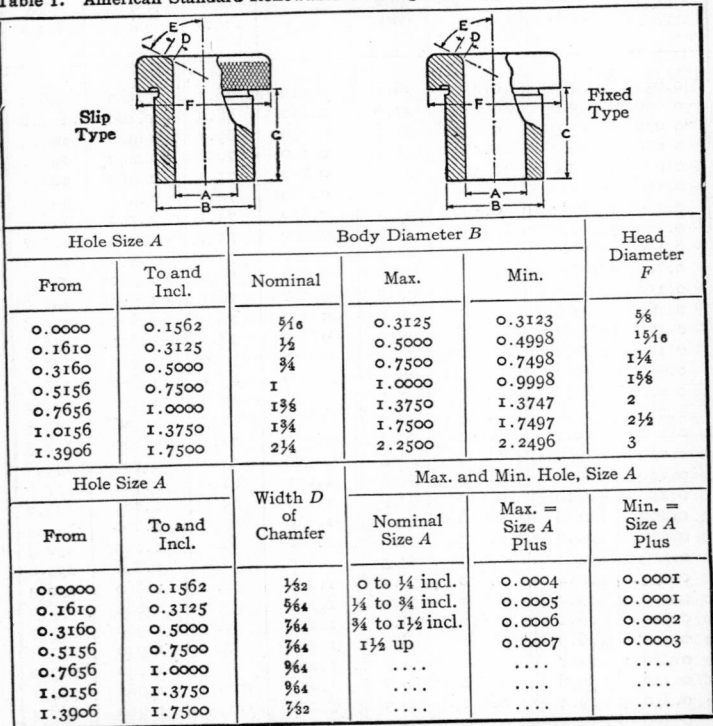

Hole Size *A*		Body Diameter *B*			Head Diameter *F*
From	To and Incl.	Nominal	Max.	Min.	
0.0000	0.1562	5/16	0.3125	0.3123	5/8
0.1610	0.3125	1/2	0.5000	0.4998	15/16
0.3160	0.5000	3/4	0.7500	0.7498	1 1/4
0.5156	0.7500	1	1.0000	0.9998	1 5/8
0.7656	1.0000	1 3/8	1.3750	1.3747	2
1.0156	1.3750	1 3/4	1.7500	1.7497	2 1/2
1.3906	1.7500	2 1/4	2.2500	2.2496	3

Hole Size *A*		Width *D* of Chamfer	Max. and Min. Hole, Size *A*		
From	To and Incl.		Nominal Size *A*	Max. = Size *A* Plus	Min. = Size *A* Plus
0.0000	0.1562	1/32	0 to 1/4 incl.	0.0004	0.0001
0.1610	0.3125	5/64	1/4 to 3/4 incl.	0.0005	0.0001
0.3160	0.5000	7/64	3/4 to 1 1/2 incl.	0.0006	0.0002
0.5156	0.7500	7/64	1 1/2 up	0.0007	0.0003
0.7656	1.0000	9/64	....	....	....
1.0156	1.3750	9/64	....	....	....
1.3906	1.7500	7/32	....	....	....

All dimensions given in inches. Tolerance on fractional dimensions where not otherwise specified shall be ±0.010 inch. The head design shall be in accordance with the manufacturer's practice. The angle of chamfer, *E*, shall be 59 deg ± 1 deg and a slight radius shall be provided at the intersection of this chamfer with the hole, *A*. Head of slip type is usually knurled. When renewable wearing bushings are to be used with liner bushings of the head type, the length under head, *C*, should be increased over the jig plate thickness by the thickness of the liner bushing head. Hole sizes conform to the American Standard for Twist Drills.

Table 2.   American Standard Press Fit Wearing Bushings — Headless and Head Types

Hole Diam. A*		Diam. B, Unfinished			Diam. B, Finished		Width Chamfer D
From	To Incl.	Nom.	Max.	Min.	Max.	Min.	
0.0156	0.0625	5/32	0.166	0.161	0.1578	0.1575	1/32
0.0630	0.0995	13/64	0.213	0.208	0.2046	0.2043	1/32
0.1024	0.1378	1/4	0.260	0.255	0.2516	0.2513	1/32
0.1406	0.1875	5/16	0.327	0.322	0.3141	0.3138	1/32
0.1910	0.2500	13/32	0.421	0.416	0.4078	0.4075	1/16
0.2520	0.3125	1/2	0.520	0.515	0.5017	0.5014	5/64
0.3160	0.4219	5/8	0.645	0.640	0.6267	0.6264	3/32
0.4375	0.5000	3/4	0.770	0.765	0.7518	0.7515	7/64
0.5156	0.6250	7/8	0.895	0.890	0.8768	0.8765	7/64
0.6406	0.7500	1	1.020	1.015	1.0018	1.0015	7/64
0.7656	1.0000	1 3/8	1.395	1.390	1.3772	1.3768	9/64
1.0156	1.3750	1 3/4	1.770	1.765	1.7523	1.7519	9/64
1.3906	1.7500	2 1/4	2.270	2.265	2.2525	2.2521	7/32

Hole A From	To and Incl.	C Short	C Med.	C Long	Diam. F	Height G	Hole Size A above Nominal
0.0156	0.0625	5/16	....	1/2	1/4	3/32	+.0001 to +.0004
0.0630	0.0995	5/16	....	1/2	5/16	3/32	+.0001 to +.0004
0.1024	0.1378	5/16	....	1/2	3/8	3/32	+.0001 to +.0004
0.1406	0.1875	5/16	1/2	3/4	7/16	1/8	+.0001 to +.0004
0.1910	0.2500	5/16	1/2	3/4	17/32	5/32	+.0001 to +.0004
0.2520	0.3125	5/16	1/2	3/4	5/8	5/32	+.0001 to +.0005
0.3160	0.4219	1/2	3/4	1	13/16	7/32	+.0001 to +.0005
0.4375	0.5000	1/2	3/4	1	15/16	7/32	+.0001 to +.0005
0.5156	0.6250	3/4	1	1 3/8	1 1/8	1/4	+.0001 to +.0005
0.6406	0.7500	3/4	1	1 3/8	1 1/4	5/16	+.0001 to +.0005
0.7656	1.0000	3/4	1	1 3/8	1 5/8	3/8	+.0001 to +.0005
1.0156	1.3750	1	1 3/8	1 3/4	2	3/8	+.0002 to +.0006
1.3906	1.7500	1	1 3/8	1 3/4	2 1/2	3/8	+.0003 to +.0007

* Hole sizes A conform to the American Standard for twist drill sizes. The body diameter, B, for unfinished bushings is larger than the nominal diameter in order to provide grinding stock for fitting to jig plate holes. Tolerance on fractional dimensions where not otherwise specified shall be ±0.010 inch. The length, C, is the overall length for the headless type and the length underhead for the head type. The head design shall be in accordance with the manufacturer's practice. The angle of chamfer, E, shall be 59 deg ± 1 deg and a slight radius shall be provided at the intersection of this chamfer with the hole, A.

surface of a boring-bar or the shank of a reamer might, in some instances, be made of cast iron, but hardened steel bushings should always be used for guiding drills, reamers, taps, etc., when the cutting edges come in direct contact with the guiding surfaces. If the outside diameter of the bushing is very large, as compared with the diameter of the cutting tool, the cost of the bushing can sometimes be reduced by using an outer cast-iron body and inserting a hardened tool steel bushing.

Renewable Bushings. — Renewable wearing bushings to guide the tool are for use in liners which in turn are installed in the jig. They are used where the bushing will wear out or become obsolete before the jig or where several bushings are to be interchangeable in one hole. Renewable wearing bushings are divided into

Table 3.   American Standard Liner Bushings — Headless and Head Types

Range of Hole Size in Renewable Wearing Bushings*		Inside Diameter A of Liner Bushing			Body Diameter B Unfinished		
From	To and Incl.	Nom.	Max.	Min.	Nom.	Max.	Min.
0.0000	0.1562	$\frac{5}{16}$	0.3129	0.3126	$\frac{1}{2}$	0.520	0.515
0.1610	0.3125	$\frac{1}{2}$	0.5005	0.5002	$\frac{3}{4}$	0.770	0.765
0.3160	0.5000	$\frac{3}{4}$	0.7506	0.7503	1	1.020	1.015
0.5156	0.7500	1	1.0007	1.0004	$1\frac{3}{8}$	1.395	1.390
0.7656	1.0000	$1\frac{3}{8}$	1.3760	1.3756	$1\frac{3}{4}$	1.770	1.765
1.0156	1.3750	$1\frac{3}{4}$	1.7512	1.7508	$2\frac{1}{4}$	2.270	2.265
1.3906	1.7500	$2\frac{1}{4}$	2.2515	2.2510	$2\frac{3}{4}$	2.770	2.765

Range of Hole Size in Renewable Wearing Bushings*		Body Diameter B Finished		Jig Plate Thickness C			Head Diam. F
From	To and Incl.	Max.	Min.	Short	Medium	Long	Max.
0.0000	0.1562	0.5017	0.5014	$\frac{5}{16}$	$\frac{1}{2}$	$\frac{3}{4}$	$\frac{5}{8}$
0.1610	0.3125	0.7518	0.7515	$\frac{5}{16}$	$\frac{1}{2}$	$\frac{3}{4}$	$\frac{15}{16}$
0.3160	0.5000	1.0018	1.0015	$\frac{1}{2}$	$\frac{3}{4}$	1	$1\frac{1}{4}$
0.5156	0.7500	1.3772	1.3768	$\frac{3}{4}$	1	$1\frac{3}{8}$	$1\frac{5}{8}$
0.7656	1.0000	1.7523	1.7519	$\frac{3}{4}$	1	$1\frac{3}{8}$	2
1.0156	1.3750	2.2525	2.2521	1	$1\frac{3}{8}$	$1\frac{3}{4}$	$2\frac{1}{4}$
1.3906	1.7500	2.7526	2.7522	1	$1\frac{3}{8}$	$1\frac{3}{4}$	3

* For detail dimensions of renewable wearing bushings see Table 1. Hole sizes A conform to the American Standard for Twist Drills.

Minimum body diameter, B for unfinished bushings, is 0.015 to 0.020 inch larger than nominal diameter to provide grinding stock for fitting to jig plate holes. Tolerance on fractional dimensions where not otherwise specified shall be ±0.010 inch. The head design shall be in accordance with the manufacturer's practice. The length, C, is the overall length for the headless type and the length under head for the head type.

two classes, "Fixed" and "Slip." Fixed renewable bushings are installed in the liner with the intention of leaving them in place until worn out. Slip renewable bushings are interchangeable in a given size of liner and, to facilitate removal, they are usually made with a knurled head. (For standard dimensions, see Table 1.)

Press Fit Bushings. — Press fit wearing bushings to guide the tool are for installation directly in the jig without the use of a liner and are employed principally where the bushings are used for short production runs and will not require replacement. They are intended also for short center distances. (See Table 2.)

Liner Bushings. — Liner bushings are provided with and without heads and are permanently installed in a jig to receive the renewable wearing bushings. They are sometimes called "master bushings." (See Table 3.)

Jig Plate Thickness. — The American Standard lengths of the press fit portion of jig bushings, given in the tables, are based on standardized or uniform jig plate thicknesses of 5/16, 1/2, 3/4, 1, 1 3/8, and 1 3/4 inches.

Threaded Bushings. — Some removable bushings are threaded on the outside and made to fit a tapped hole in the jig. The lower part of a screw bushing is usually turned straight and ground, in order to center the bushing in the hole in the jig, and the head is either knurled or milled hexagon for a wrench. Screw bushings are not only used to guide the cutting tools but also serve to locate and clamp the work.

Hardening Jig Bushings. — When hardening bushings made of tool steel they should be brought to an even red heat in a clean fire; the heating should never be hurried. Gas furnaces are excellent for heating, but a clean charcoal fire will answer the purpose. As soon as the bushing has been brought to an even red heat, it should be dipped in water just warm enough to take off the chill. Heat bushing to a "sizzling" heat, and leave it in the air to cool.

Allowances for Grinding and Lapping Jig Bushings

Oper-ation	Diameter of Bushings in Inches					
	1/2	1	1 1/2	2	2 1/2	3
A	0.008	0.010	0.013	0.016	0.020	0.025
B	0.0005	0.0005	0.0007	0.0008	0.0009	0.001
C	0.008	0.010	0.013	0.016	0.020	0.025
D	0.0005	0.0005	0.0007	0.0008	0.0009	0.001

A — Grind outside; B — Lap outside after grinding; C — Grind inside; D — Lap inside after grinding.

Knurled-Head Thumb-Screws

	A	B	C	D	E
	1/2	5/32	1/2	1/8	3/4
	9/16	5/32	5/8	5/32	15/16
	5/8	3/16	3/4	3/16	1 1/8
	11/16	7/32	7/8	1/4	1 5/16
	3/4	1/4	1	5/16	1 1/2
	7/8	5/16	1 1/8	3/8	1 3/4

Wing-nuts for Jigs. — Star Handwheels. — Wing-nuts are used on hook bolts or swiveling eye-bolts, when a comparatively light pressure is required. The thumb- or wing-nut is preferable to a knurled nut, as it gives a better grip and makes it possible to tighten the bolt more firmly. The dimensions of an excellent design of handwheel for use on jigs, etc., are given in an accompanying table. These wheels have a rather long stem or hub which provides a good length of thread and brings the grip or handle far enough from the jig body to prevent the fingers or knuckles from striking it. The "star" design of handle also permits a good grip. By having the casting solid, these handwheels can be tapped out for any size thread, or a plain hole can be drilled when it is desired to attach the handles to round stock.

Dimensions of Wing or Thumb Nuts

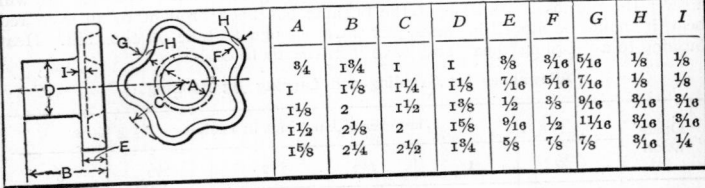

	A	B	C	D	E	F	G
	3/16	5/8	13/16	5/16	3/8	7/16	1/8
	1/4	3/4	1 1/2	15/32	1/2	17/32	5/32
	5/16	3/4	1 1/2	15/32	1/2	17/32	5/32
	3/8	13/16	1 3/4	17/32	9/16	5/8	5/32
	7/16	7/8	2	21/32	5/8	11/16	3/16
	1/2	1 1/16	2 1/2	3/4	13/16	7/8	3/16

Star Handwheels for Jigs

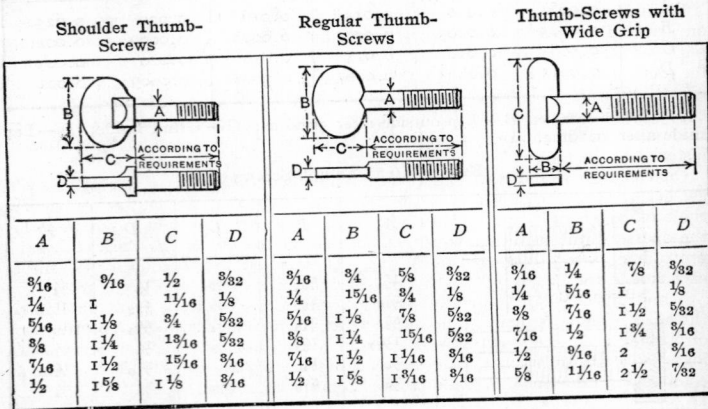

	A	B	C	D	E	F	G	H	I
	3/4	1 3/4	1	1	3/8	3/16	5/16	1/8	1/8
	1	1 7/8	1 1/4	1 1/8	7/16	5/16	7/16	1/8	1/8
	1 1/8	2	1 1/2	1 3/8	1/2	3/8	9/16	3/16	3/16
	1 1/2	2 1/8	2	1 5/8	9/16	1/2	11/16	3/16	3/16
	1 5/8	2 1/4	2 1/2	1 3/4	5/8	7/8	7/8	3/16	1/4

Shoulder Thumb-Screws				Regular Thumb-Screws				Thumb-Screws with Wide Grip			
A	B	C	D	A	B	C	D	A	B	C	D
3/16	9/16	1/2	3/32	3/16	3/4	5/8	3/32	3/16	1/4	7/8	3/32
1/4	1	11/16	1/8	1/4	15/16	3/4	1/8	1/4	5/16	1	1/8
5/16	1 1/8	3/4	5/32	5/16	1 1/8	7/8	5/32	3/8	7/16	1 1/2	5/32
3/8	1 1/4	13/16	5/32	3/8	1 1/4	15/16	5/32	7/16	1/2	1 3/4	3/16
7/16	1 1/2	15/16	3/16	7/16	1 1/2	1 1/16	3/16	1/2	9/16	2	3/16
1/2	1 5/8	1 1/8	3/16	1/2	1 5/8	1 3/16	3/16	5/8	11/16	2 1/2	7/32

Collar-head Screws

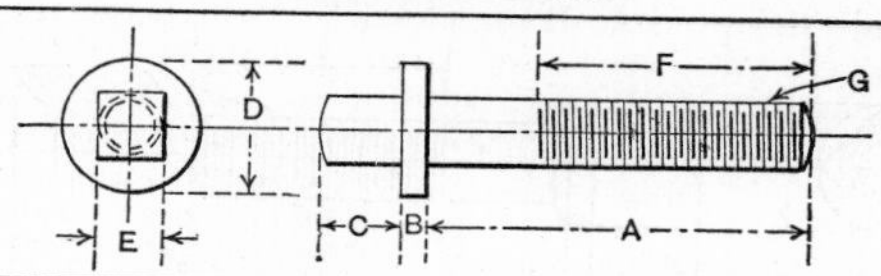

A	*B*	*C*	*D*	*E*	*F*	Diameter *G* and Threads per Inch
5/8	1/16	3/16	5/16	3/16	1/2	No. 10 — 32
7/8	1/16	3/16	5/16	3/16	5/8	No. 10 — 32
1 1/8	1/16	3/16	5/16	3/16	7/8	No. 10 — 32
1 3/8	1/16	3/16	5/16	3/16	1	No. 10 — 32
1 5/8	1/16	3/16	5/16	3/16	1 1/4	No. 10 — 32
7/8	3/32	1/4	7/16	1/4	5/8	No. 14 — 24
1 1/8	3/32	1/4	7/16	1/4	7/8	No. 14 — 24
1 3/8	3/32	1/4	7/16	1/4	1	No. 14 — 24
1 5/8	3/32	1/4	7/16	1/4	1 1/4	No. 14 — 24
1 7/8	3/32	1/4	7/16	1/4	1 7/16	No. 14 — 24
7/8	1/8	5/16	9/16	5/16	5/8	5/16 — 18
1 1/4	1/8	5/16	9/16	5/16	1	5/16 — 18
1 5/8	1/8	5/16	9/16	5/16	1 1/4	5/16 — 18
2	1/8	5/16	9/16	5/16	1 1/2	5/16 — 18
1	1/8	3/8	11/16	3/8	3/4	3/8 — 16
1 3/4	1/8	3/8	11/16	3/8	1 5/16	3/8 — 16
2 1/2	1/8	3/8	11/16	3/8	1 7/8	3/8 — 16
1 3/8	3/16	7/16	3/4	7/16	1	7/16 — 14
2 1/8	3/16	7/16	3/4	7/16	1 5/8	7/16 — 14
2 1/2	3/16	7/16	3/4	7/16	1 7/8	7/16 — 14
1 3/4	3/16	1/2	7/8	1/2	1 5/16	1/2 — 13
2 1/2	3/16	1/2	7/8	1/2	1 7/8	1/2 — 13
3 1/4	3/16	1/2	7/8	1/2	2 3/8	1/2 — 13

Clamping Screws, Screw Bushings and Studs. — Collar-head screws are used on jigs and fixtures in conjunction with clamps, straps and latches for clamping purposes (see table for dimensions). Rocking collar-screws are used with clamps for rough work, since they adapt themselves to any irregularities of the work and give a full bearing on the clamps in any position the work may assume.

Shoulder-screws are used for fastening clamping blocks, latches, or any parts that must move through a limited distance while still remaining permanently fastened to the tool.

Quarter-turn thumb-screws may be rapidly manipulated and are especially of use in box jigs. An objection to this type of screw is that the wear takes place on the boss on which it acts. Half-turn thumb-screws are also used in box jigs when the quarter-turn thumb-screw cannot be used on account of the work or bushing protruding through the end of the jig. These screws are used in pairs, one on each side of the jig cover.

Screw bushings are generally avoided when accurate work is required, as a threaded bushing is likely to be out of true. Sometimes, however, no other type of bushing is adapted for the work in hand. (See table of "Aligning Screw Bushings.") Studs are used in jig design for locating work with holes in it. The accompanying table shows a recommended form of collar stud.

Rocking Collar-screws

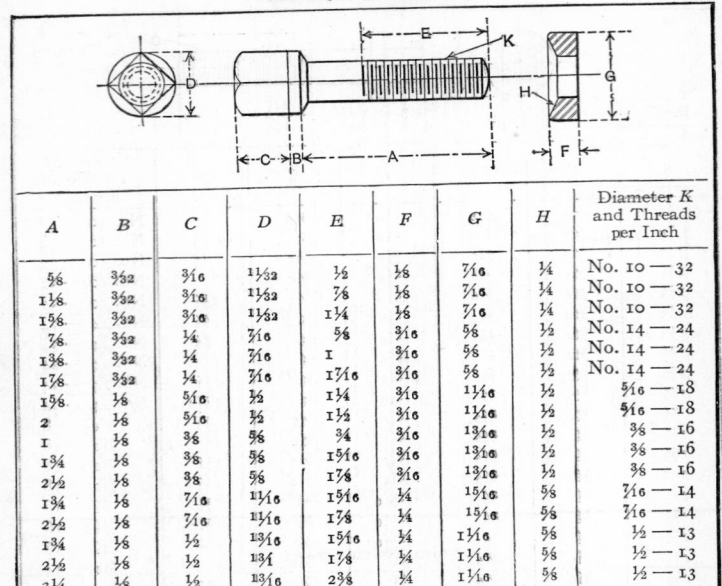

A	B	C	D	E	F	G	H	Diameter K and Threads per Inch
5/8	3/32	3/16	11/32	1/2	1/8	7/16	1/4	No. 10 — 32
1 1/8	3/32	3/16	11/32	7/8	1/8	7/16	1/4	No. 10 — 32
1 5/8	3/32	3/16	11/32	1 1/4	1/8	7/16	1/4	No. 10 — 32
7/8	3/32	1/4	7/16	5/8	3/16	5/8	1/2	No. 14 — 24
1 3/8	3/32	1/4	7/16	1	3/16	5/8	1/2	No. 14 — 24
1 7/8	3/32	1/4	7/16	1 7/16	3/16	5/8	1/2	No. 14 — 24
1 5/8	1/8	5/16	1/2	1 1/4	3/16	11/16	1/2	5/16 — 18
2	1/8	5/16	1/2	1 1/2	3/16	11/16	1/2	5/16 — 18
1	1/8	3/8	5/8	3/4	3/16	13/16	1/2	3/8 — 16
1 3/4	1/8	3/8	5/8	1 5/16	3/16	13/16	1/2	3/8 — 16
2 1/2	1/8	3/8	5/8	1 7/8	3/16	13/16	1/2	3/8 — 16
1 3/4	1/8	7/16	11/16	1 9/16	1/4	15/16	5/8	7/16 — 14
2 1/2	1/8	7/16	11/16	1 7/8	1/4	15/16	5/8	7/16 — 14
1 3/4	1/8	1/2	13/16	1 9/16	1/4	1 1/16	5/8	1/2 — 13
2 1/2	1/8	1/2	1 3/4	1 7/8	1/4	1 1/16	5/8	1/2 — 13
3 1/4	1/8	1/2	1 13/16	2 3/8	1/4	1 1/16	5/8	1/2 — 13

Shoulder-screws

A	B	C	D		E	Diameter F and Threads per inch
0.249	1/2	1/8	1/2	to 3/4	7/16	No. 10 — 32
0.249	1/2	1/8	3/16	to 7/16	5/16	No. 10 — 32
0.3115	5/8	5/32	3/16	to 1/2	3/8	No. 14 — 24
0.3115	5/8	5/32	9/16	to 7/8	1/2	No. 14 — 24
0.374	3/4	5/32	1/4	to 7/16	3/8	No. 14 — 24
0.374	3/4	5/32	1/2	to 11/16	1/2	No. 14 — 24
0.4365	13/16	5/32	3/8	to 9/16	1/2	5/16 — 18
0.4365	13/16	5/32	7/8	to 1 1/8	3/4	5/16 — 18
0.499	7/8	3/16	3/8	to 9/16	1/2	3/8 — 16
0.499	7/8	3/16	15/16	to 1 1/4	3/4	3/8 — 16
0.5615	1	3/16	1/2	to 3/4	5/8	7/16 — 14
0.5615	1	3/16	1 1/4	to 1 1/2	7/8	7/16 — 14
0.6235	1 1/8	1/4	1/2	to 5/8	3/4	1/2 — 13
0.6235	1 1/8	1/4	1 1/8	to 1 5/8	7/8	1/2 — 13
0.686	1 1/4	1/4	1 1/8	to 1 3/4	1	1/2 — 13
0.7485	1 3/8	5/16	3/4	to 1 1/8	7/8	5/8 — 11
0.7485	1 3/8	5/16	1 1/4	to 2	1 1/8	5/8 — 11

Quarter-turn Thumb-screws

A	B	C	D	E	Diameter F and Threads per Inch
7/16	1/2	1 1/16	3/16	5/16	No. 10 — 32
5/8	1/2	1 1/16	3/16	1/2	No. 10 — 32
7/8	1/2	1 1/16	3/16	5/8	No. 10 — 32
1 3/8	1/2	1 1/16	3/16	1	No. 10 — 32
5/8	9/16	1 3/16	1/4	1/2	No. 14 — 24
1 1/8	9/16	1 3/16	1/4	7/8	No. 14 — 24
1 5/8	9/16	1 3/16	1/4	1 1/4	No. 14 — 24
5/8	5/8	1	5/16	1/2	5/16 — 18
1 1/4	5/8	1	5/16	1	5/16 — 18
2	5/8	1	5/16	1 1/2	5/16 — 18
3/4	1 1/16	1 3/16	3/8	9/16	3/8 — 16
1	1 1/16	1 3/16	3/8	3/4	3/8 — 16
1 3/4	1 1/16	1 3/16	3/8	1 5/16	3/8 — 16
2 1/2	1 1/16	1 3/16	3/8	1 7/8	3/8 — 16
1	3/4	1 5/16	7/16	3/4	7/16 — 14
1 3/4	3/4	1 5/16	7/16	1 5/16	7/16 — 14
2 1/2	3/4	1 5/16	7/16	1 1/4	7/16 — 14
1 3/4	3/4	1 5/16	1/2	1 5/16	1/2 — 13
2 1/2	3/4	1 5/16	1/2	1 1/4	1/2 — 13
3 1/4	3/4	1 5/16	1/2	1 5/8	1/2 — 13

Half-turn Thumb-screws

A	B	C	D	E	F	Diameter G and Threads per Inch
7/16	1/2	3/16	1 1/16	5/16	3/4	No. 10 — 32
5/8	1/2	3/16	1 1/16	1/2	3/4	No. 10 — 32
7/8	1/2	3/16	1 1/16	5/8	3/4	No. 10 — 32
1 3/8	1/2	3/16	1 1/16	1	3/4	No. 10 — 32
5/8	9/16	3/16	1 3/16	1/2	7/8	No. 14 — 24
1 1/8	9/16	3/16	1 3/16	7/8	7/8	No. 14 — 24
1 5/8	9/16	3/16	1 3/16	1 1/4	7/8	No. 14 — 24
5/8	5/8	3/16	1	1/2	1	5/16 — 18
1 1/4	5/8	3/16	1	1	1	5/16 — 18
2	5/8	3/16	1	1 1/2	1	5/16 — 18
3/4	1 1/16	1/4	1 3/16	9/16	1 1/4	3/8 — 16
1	1 1/16	1/4	1 3/16	3/4	1 1/4	3/8 — 16
1 3/4	1 1/16	1/4	1 3/16	1 5/16	1 1/4	3/8 — 16
2 1/2	1 1/16	1/4	1 3/16	1 7/8	1 1/4	3/8 — 16
1	3/4	1/4	1 5/16	3/4	1 3/8	7/16 — 14
1 3/4	3/4	1/4	1 5/16	1 5/16	1 3/8	7/16 — 14
2 1/2	3/4	1/4	1 5/16	1 1/4	1 3/8	7/16 — 14
1 3/4	3/4	1/4	1 5/16	1 5/16	1 1/2	1/2 — 13
2 1/2	3/4	1/4	1 5/16	1 1/4	1 1/2	1/2 — 13
3 1/4	3/4	1/4	1 5/16	1 5/8	1 1/2	1/2 — 13

Aligning Screw Bushings

	B	D	E	F	Diameter G and Threads per Inch
	7/8	1/8	5/16	1 1/16	1/2 — 13
	1	5/32	5/16	7/8	5/8 — 11
	1 1/4	3/16	5/16	1	3/4 — 10
	1 1/2	3/16	7/16	1 1/4	1 — 14
	1 7/8	1/4	1/2	1 5/8	1 1/4 — 12
	2 1/4	1/4	5/8	2	1 1/2 — 12
	2 3/4	1/4	3/4	2 3/8	1 3/4 — 8
	3 1/4	1/4	7/8	2 3/4	2 — 8

A and C, according to requirements

Collar Studs — Hardened and Ground

	A	B	C	D	E	F
	0.251	0.249	1/2	1/2	3/16	1/4 — 5/8
	0.3135	0.3115	9/16	1/2	3/16	5/16 — 11/16
	0.376	0.374	5/8	5/8	3/16	3/8 — 3/4
	0.4385	0.4365	11/16	5/8	3/16	7/16 — 13/16
	0.501	0.499	3/4	5/8	1/4	1/2 — 7/8
	0.5635	0.5615	7/8	5/8	1/4	1/2 — 7/8
	0.626	0.624	1	3/4	1/4	1/2 — 1 1/16
	0.6885	0.6865	1 1/8	3/4	1/4	5/8 — 1 3/16
	0.751	0.749	1 1/4	7/8	1/4	5/8 — 1 3/8

Hand Nuts

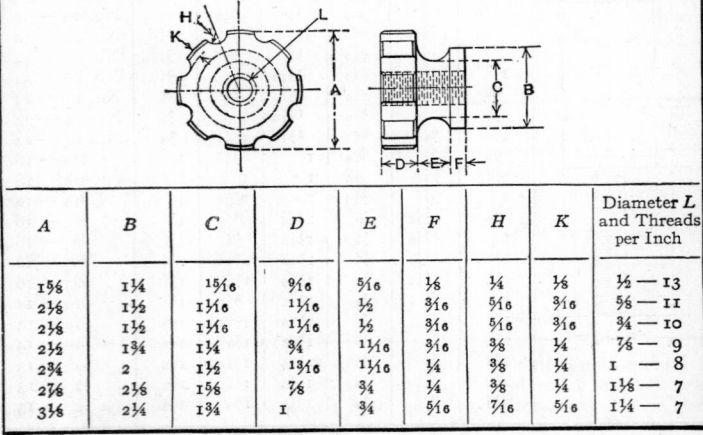

A	B	C	D	E	F	H	K	Diameter L and Threads per Inch
1 5/8	1 1/4	15/16	9/16	5/16	1/8	1/4	1/8	1/2 — 13
2 1/8	1 1/2	1 1/16	11/16	1/2	3/16	5/16	3/16	5/8 — 11
2 1/8	1 1/2	1 1/16	11/16	1/2	3/16	5/16	3/16	3/4 — 10
2 1/2	1 3/4	1 1/4	3/4	11/16	3/16	3/8	1/4	7/8 — 9
2 3/4	2	1 1/2	13/16	11/16	1/4	3/8	1/4	1 — 8
2 7/8	2 1/8	1 5/8	7/8	3/4	1/4	3/8	1/4	1 1/8 — 7
3 1/8	2 1/4	1 3/4	1	3/4	5/16	7/16	5/16	1 1/4 — 7

Dimensions of Jig-Screw Latches

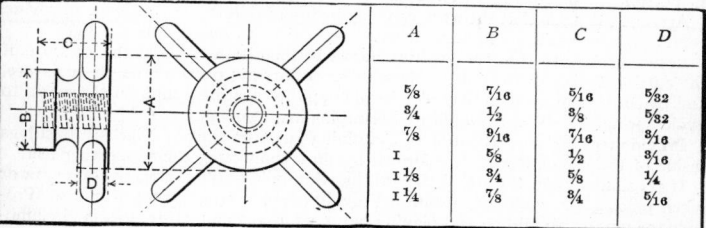

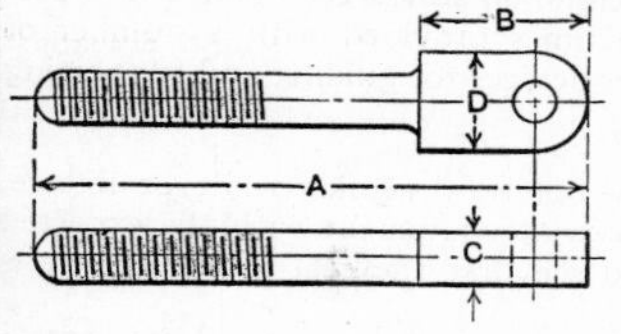

	A	B	C	D
	1¼	⅜	⅛	5/16
	1¾	⅝	5/32	⅜
	2⅜	¾	3/16	7/16
	2⅞	⅞	¼	½
	3½	1	5/16	⅝
	4⅛	1¼	⅜	¾

Dimensions of Latch Nuts

	A	B	C	D
	⅝	7/16	5/16	5/32
	¾	½	⅜	5/32
	⅞	9/16	7/16	3/16
	1	⅝	½	3/16
	1⅛	¾	⅝	¼
	1¼	⅞	¾	5/16

Standard Jig Feet

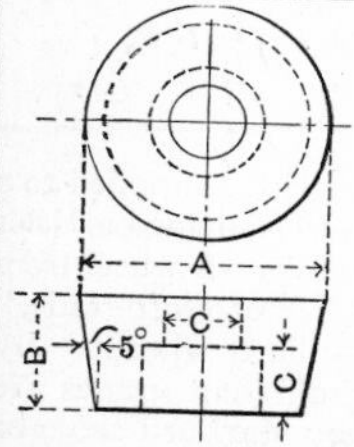

	A	B	C	A	B	C
	⅜	3/16	⅛	13/16	13/32	7/32
	7/16	7/32	9/64	¾	⅜	¼
	½	¼	5/32	⅞	7/16	9/32
	9/16	9/32	11/64	1	½	5/16
	⅝	5/16	3/16	......	......	......

Screws for Jig Feet

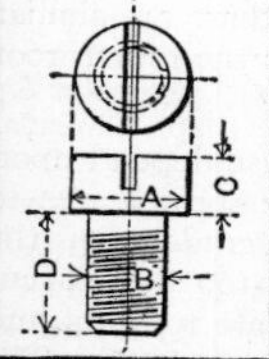

	A	B	C	D	A	B	C	D
	0.160	⅛	0.110	9/32	0.299	7/32	0.192	7/16
	0.191	9/64	0.123	5/16	0.343	¼	0.219	15/32
	0.213	5/32	0.137	11/32	0.386	9/32	0.246	½
	0.233	11/64	0.150	⅜	0.426	5/16	0.273	17/32
	0.256	3/16	0.164	13/32	....	....	....	....

Definition of Jig and Fixture. — The distinction between a jig and fixture is not easy to define, but, as a general rule, it is as follows: A jig either holds or is held on the work, and, at the same time, contains guides for the various cutting tools, whereas a fixture holds the work while the cutting tools are in operation, but does not contain any special arrangements for guiding the tools. A fixture, therefore, must be securely held or fixed to the machine on which the operation is performed — hence the name. A fixture is sometimes provided with a number of gages and stops, but not with bushings or other devices for guiding and supporting the cutting tools.

Pointers on Jig and Fixture Design. — Before designing a jig or fixture, compare the cost of production when using present equipment with the expected cost when using the proposed equipment, and see that the cost of the fixture is not in excess of the expected gain.

Before laying out a jig or fixture, decide upon the locating points and outline a clamping arrangement. Make the clamping and binding devices as quick-acting as possible. For rough castings, make some of the locating points adjustable.

Arrange the jig so that the work can only be inserted in the correct way. Provide handles whenever they will make it more convenient to manipulate the jig.

Locate clamps so that they will be in the best position to resist the pressure of the cutting tools. If possible, make all clamps integral parts of the jig or fixture, and place the clamps as nearly as possible opposite bearing points on the work, to avoid springing. Avoid complicated clamping arrangements.

Provide feet opposite all surfaces containing guide bushings. Place all bushings inside of the geometrical figure formed by lines connecting the supporting feet.

If possible, design the jig so that all locating points are visible to the operator when placing the work in position. Provide holes for the escape of chips. Provide tongues on all milling and planing fixtures for engaging table slots, and clamping lugs on jigs or fixtures which must be securely held to the machine while in use.

GRINDING, POLISHING AND LAPPING

Cylindrical Grinding

Grade and Grain of Grinding Wheels. — The term "grade," as applied to a grinding wheel, refers to the tenacity with which the bond holds the cutting particles or abrasive grains in place, and not to the hardness of the abrasive. A wheel from which the abrasive grains can easily be dislodged is called "soft," or of "soft grade," and one which holds the grains securely is referred to as a "hard wheel." By varying the amount and composition of the bond, wheels of different grades are obtained. The grain or coarseness of a wheel is designated by standard sieve or screen numbers. The wire diameters and tolerances for both wire diameters and openings are standardized. The screen number differs somewhat from the actual number of meshes per inch in most cases. For example a No. 10 screen has 9.2 meshes per inch; a No. 100 screen has 101 meshes per inch, and there are similar slight variations. The openings in successive screen sizes vary by the fourth root of 2, every screen being 1.189 times the size of the preceding one.

Selection of Wheels for Grinding. — The grade and grain to use depend upon the kind of material to be ground, its degree of hardness and the surface area in contact with the wheel. Theoretically, a wheel is of the proper grade when the bond is just hard enough to hold the abrasive until it becomes too dull to cut effectively; then, because of the increased friction, the dull grains are torn out and new points come into action, so that the wheel automatically sharpens itself. The harder the stock being ground, the more quickly the grains are dulled; hence, as a general rule, the harder the material, the softer the wheel, and *vice versa*, although some very soft materials, such as brass, are ground with a soft wheel which crumbles easily and does not become "loaded" or clogged with metal. When a hard wheel is used for grinding hard material, the grains become dulled, but are not dislodged as rapidly as they should be; consequently, the periphery of the wheel is worn smooth and becomes glazed, and excessive pressure is required to make the wheel cut. Any undue pressure tends to distort the work, and this tendency is increased by the heat generated. If the surface of the wheel becomes loaded with chips and burns the work, even when plenty of water is used, it is too hard. A highly polished surface is sometimes obtained at the expense of accuracy by using hard wheels that require so much pressure to make them grind that the work is distorted. In order to secure accuracy, as well as the most economical results, the wheel must cut freely and without perceptible pressure. The area of the surface in contact with the wheel also affects the grade. For a given material the wheel should be softer, as the area increases. Definite information on the selection of grinding wheels suitable for different classes of work may be obtained from various grinding wheel manufacturers.

The grain or coarseness of the wheel depends upon the hardness of the material, its composition and the finish required. Generally speaking, coarse wheels are better adapted to most work, because the larger grains permit deeper cuts to be taken. The quality of the finish (except when grinding brass or other soft metals) depends more on the depth of cut and condition of the wheel face than on the fineness of the abrasive material. In fact, very fine surfaces can be obtained with a comparatively coarse wheel, provided there is the proper relation between the grade and surface speeds of the wheel and work. When rough grinding, the cutting particles are constantly worn away or dislodged, so that the face of the wheel is kept rough or sharp, and the ground surface is also comparatively rough; after the wheel face has been trued with a diamond, light finishing cuts in conjunction with a reduced work speed will give a smooth finish. When grinding brass or soft bronze, the grain of the wheel must be as fine as the finish desired; that is, it is not practicable to use a coarse wheel for finishing these metals. Bronzes containing manganese or phosphor permit the use of coarser wheels.

Mounting Grinding Wheels. — Grinding wheels should fit freely on their spindles but without unnecessary play. If a wheel is forced on the spindle, there is danger of starting cracks. The diameter of the flanges should be one-half the wheel diameter (never less than one-third), and the flanges should be relieved or recessed to secure an annular bearing at their circumference. The inner flange should be keyed or shrunk on the spindle. Compressible washers of blotting paper or rubber should be placed between the wheel and the flanges, to distribute the clamping pressure evenly. The flanges should be clamped just tight enough to hold the wheel firmly. Wheels should be carefully inspected, and be tapped lightly before mounting, as new wheels occasionally burst when first brought up to speed, because of hidden cracks resulting from rough handling in transit.

Glazed and Loaded Wheels. — A wheel is glazed when the cutting particles have become dull, or worn down even with the bond, which latter is so hard that the abrasive grains are not dislodged when too dull to cut effectively. Glazing may indicate either that the wheel is too hard for the work, or that the wheel speed is too high. The remedy for glazing is to decrease the speed or use a softer wheel. A wheel is " loaded " when the pores or interstices between the cutting particles are partly or entirely clogged with the material being ground. Loading prevents the wheel from cutting and causes excessive heat to be generated. If a wheel becomes loaded, the bond may be too hard or the speed too slow. The remedy for loading is to increase the speed or use a softer wheel.

Speed of Grinding Wheel and Work. — The peripheral speed of a grinding wheel is usually somewhere between 5500 and 6000 feet per minute, but speeds varying from 5000 to 7000 feet per minute are employed. As the wheel diminishes in size, it appears to get softer. This is because the grit of a small wheel is in contact with the work oftener, owing to the increased number of revolutions necessary for the same surface speed. There are a number of factors, such as the kind of material, finish desired, etc., which determine the proper *work* speed; hence, the speed must be varied to suit conditions. A surface speed of 25 feet per minute might be suitable for rough grinding a certain piece of steel, but it would not give the best results for another steel part of different composition. Twenty-five feet per minute is a fair average for rough grinding soft steel when using comparatively soft, free-cutting wheels; for finishing with the same wheel, the speed would ordinarily be reduced about 25 per cent. When harder and more compact wheels are used, the speed is increased for finishing. It is the modern practice, when rough grinding, to use a fairly coarse wheel of soft enough grade to cut freely, and a comparatively slow work speed in conjunction with a coarse side feed of the wheel or work. This method of grinding is employed when using large machines which have sufficient driving power to enable broad cuts to be taken and are rigid enough to prevent excessive vibration. With small light grinders, it is not always feasible to use a coarse side feed, owing to the lack of rigidity and driving power. The depth of the cut, or amount that the wheel is fed inward at each reversal, must also be governed, to some extent, by the power and rigidity of the machine.

Allowance for Grinding. — The amount of stock that can be economically removed by grinding depends primarily upon the size and power of the grinding machine. For ordinary commercial grinding, in connection with manufacturing operations, the work is generally reduced in a lathe to somewhere between 1/64 and 1/32 inch of the required diameter. When the diameter has been rough turned to this dimension, it is more economical to remove the stock by grinding than by taking a light finishing cut in the lathe, provided a grinder of sufficient power is available.

Table of Grinding Wheel Speeds

Diameter of Wheel, Inches	Rev. per Min. for Surface Speed of 4000 Feet	Rev. per Min. for Surface Speed of 5000 Feet	Rev. per Min. for Surface Speed of 6000 Feet	Diameter of Wheel, Inches	Rev. per Min. for Surface Speed of 4000 Feet	Rev. per Min. for Surface Speed of 5000 Feet	Rev. per Min. for Surface Speed of 6000 Feet
1	15279	19099	22918	28	546	683	819
2	7639	9549	11459	30	509	637	764
3	5093	6366	7639	32	477	596	716
4	3820	4775	5730	34	449	561	674
5	3056	3820	4584	36	424	531	637
6	2546	3183	3820	38	402	503	603
7	2183	2728	3274	40	382	478	573
8	1910	2387	2865	42	364	455	546
10	1528	1910	2292	44	347	434	521
12	1273	1592	1910	46	332	415	498
14	1091	1364	1637	48	318	397	477
16	955	1194	1432	50	306	383	459
18	849	1061	1273	52	294	369	441
20	764	955	1146	54	283	354	425
22	694	868	1042	56	273	341	410
24	637	796	955	58	264	330	396
26	586	733	879	60	255	319	383

If the work is turned too close to the finished size, the cost of turning becomes excessive. On the other hand, too large an allowance means that stock is being ground that could be removed to better advantage by rough turning.

Standard Grinding Wheel Markings. — This American standard applies to grinding wheels and other bonded abrasives, segments, bricks, sticks, hones, rubs and other shapes which are for removing material, or producing a desired surface or dimension. The standard does not apply to diamond wheels or to specialties such as sharpening stones. This is a standard system of *markings only*. Symbols, arranged in uniform sequence, indicate the most essential characteristics of a grinding wheel. Wheels bearing the same standard markings if made by different manufacturers may not, and probably will not, have the same grinding action.

Sequence of Markings. — The marking consists of six parts which are written in the order or sequence shown below.

1	2	3	4	5	6
Abrasive Type	Grain Size	Grade	Structure	Bond Type	Manufacturer's Record

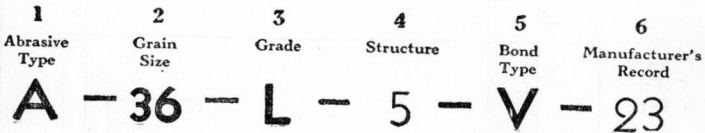

A — 36 — L — 5 — V — 23

This is a sample or typical marking. The meaning of each letter and number in this or other markings is indicated by the following complete list.

1. *Abrasive Letters:* The letter (A) is used for aluminum oxide and (C) for silicon carbide. The manufacturer may designate some particular type in either of these broad classes, by using his own symbol as a prefix (Example, 38A).

2. *Grain Size:* The grain sizes commonly used and varying from coarse to fine are indicated by the following numbers: 10, 12, 14, 16, 20, 24, 30, 36, 46, 54, 60, 70, 80, 90, 100, 120, 150, 180, 220. The following additional sizes are used occasionally: 240, 280, 320, 400, 500, 600. The wheel manufacturer may add to the regular grain number an additional symbol to indicate a special grain combination.

3. *Grade:* Grades are indicated by letters of the alphabet from A to Z in all bonds or processes. Wheel grades from A to Z range from soft to hard.

4. *Structure:* The use of a structure symbol is optional. The structure is indicated by Nos. 1 to 15 (or higher, if necessary) with progressively higher numbers indicating less density and a wider grain spacing or "more open" structure.

5. *Bond or Process:* Bonds are indicated by the following letters: V, vitrified; S, silicate; E, shellac or elastic; R, rubber; B, resinoid (synthetic resins); O, oxychloride.

6. *Manufacturer's Record.* The sixth position may be used for manufacturer's private factory records; this is optional.

Marking Small Wheels. — Wheels too small to permit complete marking may have grain and grade marking only; or marking on wheel may be omitted and a complete marking placed on tags or labels accompanying each container.

Diamond Wheel Markings. — Manufacturers of diamond wheels use markings which are as close to the standard adopted for other wheels as is practicable. A complete diamond wheel marking consists of seven symbols as follows: (1) D for diamond; (2) grit size number; (3) grade letter — sometimes omitted; (4) diamond concentration number — 25 for low, 50 for medium, 100 for high; (5) bond letter — B for resinoid, M for metal, V for vitrified; (6) **bond mo**dification symbol — sometimes omitted; (7) depth of diamond section.

Standard Types of Grinding Wheels — 1
Approved by Grinding Wheel Manufacturers Association of United States and Canada.

Number and Type	Shape of Cross-section
No. 1 Straight Type	
No. 2 Cylinder Type	
No. 4 Tapered two sides	
No. 5 Recessed one side	
No. 6 Straight Cup Type	

Dimensions of each type are given in tables following; see type number.

Standard Types of Grinding Wheels — 2

Types 3, 8, 9, 10 and 14 eliminated by revisions in 1927 and 1928

Number and Type	Shape of Cross-section
No. 7 Recessed two sides	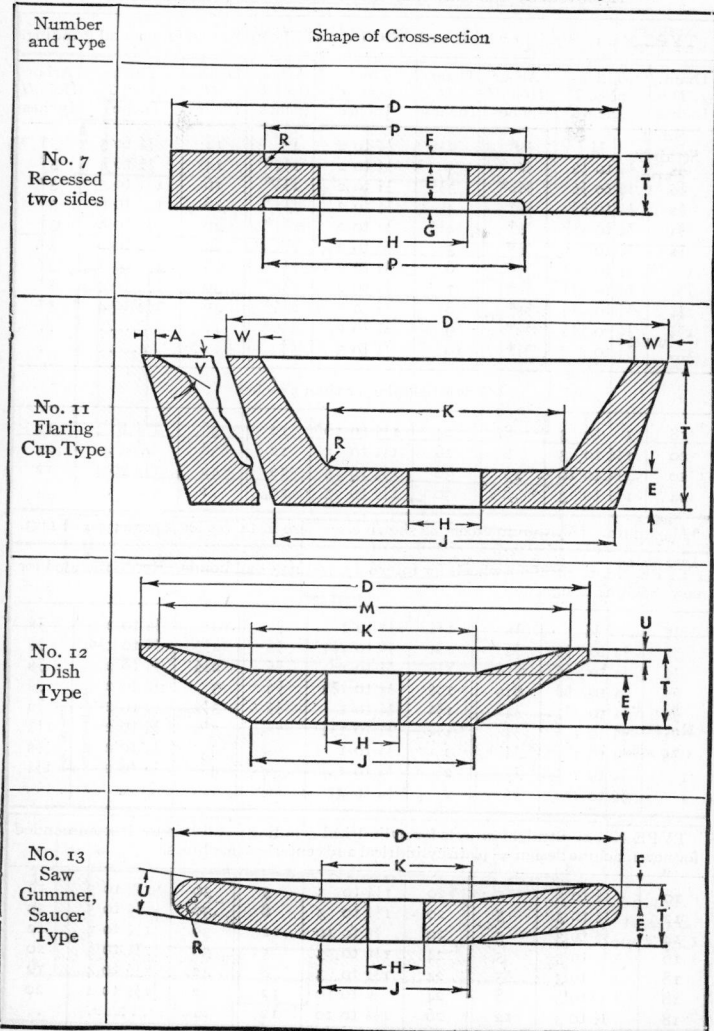
No. 11 Flaring Cup Type	
No. 12 Dish Type	
No. 13 Saw Gummer, Saucer Type	

Dimensions of each type are given in tables following; see type number

Grinding Wheel Dimensions

Approved by the Grinding Wheel Manufacturers Association

TYPE No. 1: Straight wheels with vitrified and silicate bonds, for general grinding.

Diam., D Inches	Thickness, T Inches	Arbor Hole, H Inches	Diam., D Inches	Thickness, T Inches	Arbor Hole, H Inches	Diam., D Inches	Thickness, T Inches	Arbor Hole, H Inches
¼	¼	⅛*	2½	¼ to 2	1*	12	¼ to 3	5†
⅜	¼ to ½	3⁄16*	3	¼ to 2	1¼*	14	½ to 4	5†
½	¼ to ½	5⁄16*	3½	¼ to 2	1¼*	16	1 to 5	5†
⅝	¼ to ⅝	⅜*	4	¼ to 2	1½*	18	1 to 6	5†
¾	¼ to 1	½*	4½	¼ to 2	1¾*	20	1¼ to 8	5†
⅞	¼ to 1	½*	5	¼ to 2	2*	24	1¼ to 8	5†
1	¼ to 1	⅝*	6	¼ to 2	2½*	26	1½ to 4	5†
1¼	¼ to 1¼	⅝*	7	¼ to 2	2½*	30	1½ to 4	5†
1½	¼ to 1½	⅝*	8	¼ to 2	2½*	36	1½ to 4	5†
1¾	¼ to 1½	⅝*	9	¼ to 2	2½*	..	....	..
2	¼ to 2	¾*	10	¼ to 3	5†	..	....	..

Arbor holes larger than 5 inches

18	1 to 3	8	24	1¼ to 10	12	36	1¼ to 4	12
20	1¼ to 3	8	26	1¼ to 5	12	36	2, 3, 4	24
20	1¼ to 10	12	30	1¼ to 5	12	42	1½ to 4	12
24	1¼ to 3	8	30	1¼ to 5	20	..	....	..

* Maximum.   † Maximum except as shown elsewhere in tables on pages 1452 and 1453.

TYPE No. 1: Straight wheels for internal grinding — all bonds. Recommended for new machine design.

¼	¼	⅛	1¼	¼ to 1	⅜	2	¼ to 2	⅞
⅜	¼ to ½	⅛	1¼	¼ to 1¼	⅝	2½	¼ to 1½	⅝
½	¼ to ½	3⁄16	1½	¼ to 1	⅜	2½	¼ to 2	⅞
⅝	¼ to ⅝	3⁄16	1½	¼ to 1½	⅝	3	¼ to 2	⅞
⅝	¼ to ⅝	¼	1¾	¼ to 1	½	3½	¼ to 2	⅞
¾	¼ to 1	¼	1¾	¼ to 1½	⅝	3½	¼ to 2	1¼
⅞	¼ to 1	¼	2	¼ to 1	⅜	4	¼ to 2	⅞
1	¼ to 1	¼	2	¼ to 1	½	4	¼ to 2	1¼
1	¼ to 1	⅜	2	¼ to 2	⅝	...	....	...

TYPE No. 1: Straight wheels for cylindrical grinding — all bonds. Recommended for new machine design — plain cylindrical and centerless machines.

10	¼ to 3	5	20	1¼ to 3	5	30	1¼ to 5	12
12	¼ to 3	5	20	1¼ to 3	8	30	1¼ to 5	20
14	½ to 3	5	20	¾ to 10	12	36	1¼ to 4	12
16	1 to 3	5	24	1¼ to 3	5	36	1¼ to 4	20
18	1 to 3	5	24	1¼ to 3	8	42	1½ to 4	12
18	1 to 3	8	24	¾ to 10	12	42	1½ to 4	20
18	¾ to 3	12	26	1¼ to 10	12	..	....	..

For minimum arbor hole sizes refer to page 1458.

Grinding Wheel Dimensions (*Continued*)

TYPE No. 1: Straight wheels with organic bonds, for general grinding.

Diam., *D* Inches	Thickness, *T* Inches	Arbor Hole, *H* Inches	Diam., *D* Inches	Thickness, *T* Inches	Arbor Hole, *H* Inches	Diam., *D* Inches	Thickness, *T* Inches	Arbor Hole, *H* Inches
1	1/8 to 3/4	5/8	6	1/32 to 1½	2½	18	3/4 to 4	5
1½	1/8 to 3/4	5/8	7	1/16 to 1½	2½	20	1 to 4	5
2	1/32 to 1	3/4	8	1/16 to 1½	2½	24	1½ to 4	5
2½	1/32 to 1	1	10	3/32 to 2	5	30	1½ to 4	5
3	1/32 to 1	1¼	12	3/32 to 4	5	36	2½ to 4	5
4	1/32 to 1½	1½	14	3/32 to 4	5	..	......	.
5	1/32 to 1½	2	16	1/8 to 4	5	..	......	.
Arbor holes larger than 5 inches								
16	2 to 3	6	20	3/4 to 10	12	30	1¼ to 5	12
18	1 to 3	8	24	1¼ to 3	8	30	1¼ to 5	20
18	3/4 to 1½	12	24	3/4 to 10	12	36	1¼ to 5	12
20	1¼ to 3	8	26	1¼ to 10	12	42	1½ to 4	12

TYPE No. 1: Straight wheels for tool grinding — all bonds. Recommended for new machine design.

20	2½, 3	8	26	2½, 3	12	36	3, 4	24
24	2½, 3	12	30	2½, 3, 4	12	..	....	..

TYPE No. 1: Straight wheels with organic bonds, for high-speed snagging. Recommended for new machine design.

16	2, 2½, 3	6	20	2, 2½, 3	8	30	3, 4	12
18	2, 2½, 3	8	24	2 to 4	12	36	3, 4	12

For minimum arbor hole sizes refer to page 1458.

TYPE No. 2: Cylinder wheels for general grinding — all bonds.

Diam., *D* Inches	Thickness, *T* Inches	Wall Thickness, *W*	Diam., *D* Inches	Thickness, *T* Inches	Wall Thickness, *W*	Diam., *D* Inches	Thickness, *T* Inches	Wall Thickness, *W*
8	4	1	16	4	3	18	6	2
10	4	1	16	5	1¼	18	6	4
10	4	1¼	16	5	1½	20	4	4
10	4	1½	16	6	2	20	6	2
12	4	1¼	16	6	3	20	6	2½
12	4	1½	16	8	2	20	6	4
14	4	1¼	18	4	2	24	6	2½
14	4	1½	18	4	4	30	6	2
14	5	1½	18	5	1¼	30	6	3
16	4	1½	18	5	1½	..	.	...
16	4	2	18	5	4	..	.	...

Grinding Wheel Dimensions (*Continued*)

TYPE No. 5: Wheels recessed on one side, for general grinding — all bonds.

Diam., D Inches	Thick-ness, T Inches	Arbor Hole, H Inches	Recess P	Recess F	Diam., D Inches	Thick-ness, T Inches	Arbor Hole, H Inches	Recess P	Recess F
3/8	1/4	1/8	1/4	1/8	3	3/4	7/8	1 3/4	3/8
1/2	1/4	1/8	1/4	1/8	3	1	7/8	1 5/8	1/2
5/8	1/4	1/8	1/4	1/8	3	1	7/8	1 3/4	3/8
3/4	1/4	1/8	1/4	1/8	3	1 1/4	7/8	2 5/16	5/8
3/4	3/8	1/4	7/16	1/8	3 1/2	3/4	7/8	1 3/4	3/8
7/8	1/4	1/8	1/4	1/8	3 1/2	1	7/8	1 3/4	5/8
7/8	3/8	1/4	7/16	1/8	3 1/2	1 1/4	7/8	1 3/4	5/8
7/8	3/8	5/16	7/16	1/8	4	3/4	7/8	1 5/8	1/4
1	1/4	1/8	1/4	1/8	4	3/4	7/8	1 3/4	3/8
1	3/8	1/4	7/16	1/8	4 1/2	3/4	7/8	1 3/4	3/8
1	3/8	5/16	7/16	1/8	12	1 1/2	5	7 1/2	1/2
1	5/8	3/8	5/8	1/4	14	1 1/2	5	7 1/2	1/2
1	3/4	3/8	5/8	1/4	14	1 1/2	5	9	1/2
1 1/4	3/8	1/4	7/16	1/8	14	2 1/2	5	8	1/2
1 1/4	3/8	5/16	7/16	1/8	14	2 1/2	5	9	1/2
1 1/4	5/8	3/8	5/8	1/4	14	3	5	8	1
1 1/2	3/8	1/4	7/16	1/8	14	3	5	9	1
1 1/2	3/8	5/16	7/16	1/8	14	3 1/2	5	8	1 1/2
1 1/2	5/8	3/8	5/8	1/4	14	4	5	8	2
1 1/2	3/4	3/8	5/8	1/4	14	4	5	9	2
1 1/2	1	3/8	5/8	1/4	18	2 1/2	5	8 1/2	1/2
1 3/4	3/4	3/8	1	3/8	18	3	5	8 1/2	1
2	3/8	5/16	7/16	1/8	18	3 1/2	5	8 1/2	1 1/2
2	5/8	3/8	5/8	1/4	18	4	5	8 1/2	2
2	3/4	7/8	1 1/4	1/4	20	2 1/2	5	8 1/2	1/2
2	1	3/8	5/8	1/4	20	3	5	8 1/2	1
2 1/2	3/4	7/8	1 3/4	1/4	20	3 1/2	5	8 1/2	1 1/2
2 1/2	3/4	7/8	1 3/4	3/8	20	4	5	8 1/2	2
2 1/2	1	7/8	1 3/4	1/4	24	2 1/2	5	10 1/2	1/2
2 1/2	1 1/4	7/8	1 3/4	5/8	24	3	5	10 1/2	1
2 3/4	1	7/8	1 3/4	3/8	24	3 1/2	5	10 1/2	1 1/2
2 3/4	1 1/4	7/8	1 3/4	5/8	24	4	5	10 1/2	2
3	3/4	7/8	1 5/8	1/4	....	...	.	.....	...

TYPE No. 5: Wheels recessed on one side, for cylindrical grinding — all bonds. Recommended for new machine design.

Diam., D Inches	Thick-ness, T Inches	Arbor Hole, H Inches	Recess P	Recess F	Diam., D Inches	Thick-ness, T Inches	Arbor Hole, H Inches	Recess P	Recess F
14	2 1/2	5	8	1/2	20	2 1/2	5	8 1/2	1/2
14	3	5	8	1	20	3	5	8 1/2	1
14	3 1/2	5	8	1 1/2	20	3 1/2	5	8 1/2	1 1/2
14	4	5	8	2	20	4	5	8 1/2	2
18	2 1/2	5	8 1/2	1/2	24	2 1/2	5	10 1/2	1/2
18	3	5	8 1/2	1	24	3	5	10 1/2	1
18	3 1/2	5	8 1/2	1 1/2	24	3 1/2	5	10 1/2	1 1/2
18	4	5	8 1/2	2	24	4	5	10 1/2	2

Grinding Wheel Dimensions (*Continued*)

TYPE No. 4: Wheels tapered two sides, for general grinding — all bonds. For new installations, a taper of ¾ inch per ft. only is recommended in accordance with American Standard Safety Code.

Diam., D Inches	Face Width, U Inches	Arbor Hole, H Inches	Diam., D Inches	Face Width, U Inches	Arbor Hole, H Inches	Diam., D Inches	Face Width, U Inches	Arbor Hole, H Inches
10	1		16	2½		24	2	
10	1½		16	3		24	2½	
12	1½		18	1		24	3	
12	2		18	1½		24	3½	
12	2½	As ordered	18	2	As ordered	24	4	As ordered
14	1		18	2½		26	2½	
14	1½		18	3		26	3	
14	2		20	2		26	4	
16	1		20	2½		30	2½	
16	1½		20	3		30	3	
16	2		20	3½		30	4	

TYPE No. 6: Straight cup wheels for general grinding — all bonds.

Diam., D Inches	Thickness, T	Max. Arbor Hole, H	Straight Face Thickness of Wall, W	Thickness at Hole, E	Bevel Face Width of Flat, A	Angle of Bevel, V
2½	1½	¾	⅜	⅜	⅛	30°
3	1½	1	⅜	⅜	⅛	30°
3½	1¾	1¼	⅜	⅜	⅛	30°
4	1½	1¼	⅜	⅜	⅛	30°
5	1½	1½	⅜	⅜	⅛	30°
6	1½	1½	⅜	⅜	......	......
7	2	1½	½	½	⅛	30°
6	3	1½	1	1	......	......
6	4	1½	1	1	......	......
8	4	2	1	1	......	......
8	5	2	1	1	......	......
8	6	2	1	1	......	......
10	4	2½	1	1	......	......
10	4	2½	1¼	1¼	......	......
10	4	2½	1½	1½	......	......
12	4	2½	1¼	1¼	......	......
12	4	2½	1½	1½	......	......
12	5	2½	1½	1½	......	......
12	6	2½	1¾	1¾	......	......
14	4	3	1¼	1¼	......	......
14	4	3	1½	1½	......	......
14	5	3	1¼	1¼	......	......
14	6	3	1½	1½	......	......
16	5	3	2	2	......	......

Grinding Wheel Dimensions (*Continued*)

TYPE No. 7: Wheels recessed on two sides, for general grinding — all bonds.

Diam., D Inches	Thickness, T Inches	Recess Diam., P Inches	Recess Depth, F Inches	Recess Depth, G Inches	Diam., D Inches	Thickness, T Inches	Recess Diam., P Inches	Recess Depth, F Inches	Recess Depth, G Inches
12	1½	7½	3/16	7/16	24	2½	14¼	9/16	9/16
12	1½	7½	½	½	24	2¾	15¼	5/8	5/8
14	1½	7½	3/16	7/16	24	2¾	14¼	9/16	9/16
14	2	7½	3/16	7/16	24	3	15¼	1 1/16	1 1/16
14	2	7½	3/16	15/16	24	3	14¼	13/16	13/16
14	4	8	½	½	24	3¼	14¼	13/16	13/16
14	5	8	1	1	24	3½	15¼	13/16	13/16
14	6	8	1	2	24	4	14¼	13/16	13/16
18	2	11	½	3/8	26	2¼	15¼	5/8	5/8
18	2½	11	3/8	5/8	26	2¼	14¼	9/16	9/16
18	3	11	½	3/4	26	2½	15¼	5/8	3/8
20	2¼	15¼	½	½	26	2½	14¼	9/16	9/16
20	2¼	14¼	9/16	9/16	26	2¾	15¼	5/8	5/8
20	2½	15¼	5/8	9/16	26	2¾	14¼	9/16	9/16
20	2½	14¼	9/16	9/16	26	3	15¼	5/8	7/8
20	2¾	15¼	5/8	5/8	26	3	14¼	13/16	13/16
20	2¾	14¼	9/16	9/16	30	2¼	15¼	5/8	1/8
20	3	15¼	1 1/16	1 1/16	30	2¼	14¼	9/16	9/16
20	3	14¼	13/16	13/16	30	2½	15¼	5/8	3/8
20	3¼	14¼	13/16	13/16	30	2½	14¼	9/16	9/16
20	3½	14¼	13/16	13/16	30	2¾	15¼	5/8	5/8
20	4	14¼	13/16	13/16	30	2¾	14¼	9/16	9/16
24	2¼	15¼	½	½	30	3	15¼	5/8	7/8
24	2¾	14¼	9/16	9/16	30	3	14¼	13/16	13/16
24	2½	15¼	5/8	9/16	..	...	....	....	....

When diameter D is 12 or 14 inches, arbor hole, H is 5 inches; when D is 18 inches, H is 8 inches; when D is 20 to 30 inches, H is 12 inches.

TYPE No. 7: Wheels recessed on two sides, for cylindrical grinding — all bonds. Recommended for new machine design.

Diam., D Inches	Thickness, T Inches	Recess Diam., P Inches	Recess Depth, F Inches	Recess Depth, G Inches	Diam., D Inches	Thickness, T Inches	Recess Diam., P Inches	Recess Depth, F Inches	Recess Depth, G Inches
14	2½	8	9/16	9/16	26	2½	14¼	9/16	9/16
14	3	8	13/16	13/16	26	3	14¼	13/16	13/16
18	2½	11	9/16	9/16	26	3½	14¼	13/16	13/16
18	3	11	13/16	13/16	26	4	14¼	13/16	13/16
20	2½	11	9/16	9/16	30	2½	14¼	9/16	9/16
20	3	11	13/16	13/16	30	3	14¼	13/16	13/16
20	2½	14¼	9/16	9/16	30	3½	14¼	13/16	13/16
20	3	14¼	13/16	13/16	30	4	14¼	13/16	13/16
24	2½	14¼	9/16	9/16	36	2½	14¼	9/16	9/16
24	3	14¼	13/16	13/16	36	3	14¼	13/16	13/16
24	3½	14¼	13/16	13/16	36	3½	14¼	13/16	13/16
24	4	14¼	13/16	13/16	36	4	14¼	13/16	13/16

When diameter D is 14 inches, arbor hole, H is 5 inches; when D is 18 inches, H is 8 inches; when D is 20 inches, H is 8 or 12 inches; when D is 24 to 36 inches, H is 12 inches.

Grinding Wheel Dimensions (Continued)

TYPE No. 11: Flaring cup wheels for general grinding—all bonds.

			Straight Face				Bevel Face	
Diam., D Inches	Thickness, T Inches	Max. Arbor Hole, H Inches	Wall, W Inches	Thickness at Hole, E Inches	Outside Flat Diam., J Inches	Inside Flat Diam., K Inches	Flat, A Inches	Angle of Bevel, V Inches
3	1¼	¾	¼	⅜	2¼	1⅝	⅛	30°
3¼	1¼	¾	¼	⅜	2⅛	1½	⅛	30°
3½	1½	1¼	¼	⅜	2¾	2¼	⅛	30°
4	1½	1½	¼	½	3	2⅝	⅛	30°
4½	2	1½	¼	½	3¾	3⅛	⅛	30°
5	1¾	1½	¼	½	3¾	3⅛	⅛	30°
6	2	2	⅜	½	4½	3¾	⅛	30°
7	2	2	¾	½	5	3¾	.....	.....

TYPE No. 12: Dish wheels for general grinding — all bonds.

Diam., D Inches	Thickness, T Inches	Max. Arbor Hole, H Inches	Thickness at Hole, E Inches	Diam. of Flats, K, J Inches	Width of Edge, U Inches	Diam., M Inches
3	½	¾	$\frac{5}{16}$	1½	$\frac{1}{16}$	2¾
3½	½	¾	$\frac{5}{16}$	1¾	$\frac{3}{32}$	3⅛
4	½	1	$\frac{5}{16}$	2	$\frac{3}{32}$	3⅝
4½	½	1	$\frac{5}{16}$	2¼	⅛	4
5	½	1¼	$\frac{5}{16}$	2½	⅛	4½
6	½	1½	$\frac{5}{16}$	3	⅛	5¼
6	¾	1½	⅜	3	⅛	5¼
8	¾	2	½	4	⅛	7
8	1	2	½	4	⅛	7

TYPE No. 13: Saucer wheels for saw gumming — all bonds.

Diam., D Inches	Thickness, T Inches	Max. Arbor Hole, H Inches	Thickness, E and U Inches	Diam., D Inches	Thickness, T Inches	Max. Arbor Hole, H Inches	Thickness, E and U Inches
6	½	1¼	¼	10	1	1½	¾
6	⅝	1¼	⅜	10	1⅛	1½	⅞
6	¾	1¼	½	10	1¼	1½	1
6	⅞	1¼	⅝	10	1⅜	1½	1⅛
6	1	1¼	¾	10	1½	1½	1¼
8	½	1¼	¼	12	⅝	2	⅜
8	⅝	1¼	⅜	12	¾	2	½
8	¾	1¼	½	12	⅞	2	⅝
8	⅞	1¼	⅝	12	1	2	¾
8	1	1¼	¾	12	1⅛	2	⅞
8	1⅛	1¼	⅞	12	1¼	2	1
8	1¼	1¼	1	12	1⅜	2	1⅛
10	⅝	1½	⅜	12	1½	2	1¼
10	¾	1½	½	12	1⅝	2	1⅜
10	⅞	1½	⅝	12	1¾	2	1½

When diameter D is 6 or 8 inches, flat diameters J and K are 3 inches; when D is 10 inches, J and K are 3½ inches; when D is 12 inches, J and K are 4 inches.

Minimum Diameters of Grinding Wheel Arbor Holes

Wheel Diam., Inches	Wheel Thickness								
	¼	⅜	½	⅝	¾	1	1¼	1½	1¾
	Min. Arbor Hole Diam.								
6	½	½	½	½	½	½	⅝	⅝	¾
7	½	½	½	½	⅝	⅝	⅝	¾	¾
8	⅝	⅝	⅝	⅝	⅝	⅝	¾	¾	¾
9	⅝	⅝	⅝	⅝	¾	¾	¾	¾	1
10	¾	¾	¾	¾	¾	¾	¾	¾	1
12	¾	¾	¾	¾	¾	1	1	1	1
14	⅞	⅞	⅞	⅞	1	1	1¼	1¼	1¼
16	.....	.....	.....	.....	1¼	1¼	1¼	1¼	1¼
18	.....	.....	.....	.....	1¼	1¼	1¼	1½	1½
20	.....	.....	.....	.....	.....	1½	1½	1½	1½
24	.....	.....	.....	.....	.....	1½	1½	1½	1¾
26	.....	.....	.....	.....	.....	.....	1½	1½	1¾
30	.....	.....	.....	.....	.....	.....	....	1¾	1¾
36	.....	.....	.....	.....	.....	.....	....	....	2

Wheel Diam., Inches	Wheel Thickness								
	2	2¼	2½	2¾	3	3¼	3½	4	4½
	Min. Arbor Hole Diam.								
6	¾	¾	¾	¾	¾	¾	¾	1	1
7	¾	¾	¾	¾	1	1	1	1	1
8	1	1	1	1	1	1	1	1¼	1¼
9	1	1	1	1	1¼	1¼	1¼	1¼	1¼
10	1	1	1¼	1¼	1¼	1¼	1¼	1¼	1½
12	1	1	1¼	1¼	1¼	1¼	1¼	1½	1½
14	1¼	1¼	1¼	1¼	1½	1½	1½	1½	1½
16	1¼	1½	1½	1½	1½	1½	1¾	1¾	1¾
18	1½	1½	1½	1½	1½	1¾	1¾	1¾	1⅞
20	1½	1½	1½	1¾	1¾	1¾	1⅞	1⅞	1⅞
24	1¾	1¾	1¾	1¾	1¾	2	2	2	2
26	1¾	1¾	1¾	2	2	2	2	2¼	2¼
30	2	2	2	2	2	2¼	2¼	2½	2½
36	2¼	2¼	2¼	2½	2½	2½	2¾	2¾	3

The nine types of grinding wheels retained in the Simplified Practice Recommendation (R45–39) are representative of practically all wheels used on the standard makes of grinding machines. This classification of grinding wheels will greatly simplify the stocking of wheels wherever a quantity is kept on hand, and it will also enable the user to identify accurately a grinding wheel in ordering, by giving the type number and the complete dimensions designated for the cross-section of that type. (See preceding tables.)

Abrasive Grain Sizes and United States Standard Sieve Series

Approved by Abrasive Grain Association and Grinding Wheel Manufacturers Association

Allowable Size Limits for Aluminum Oxide and Silicon Carbide Abrasives for Polishing Uses and Grinding-wheels.

Grit No.	100% Must Pass Sieve No. Below	Control Sieve No.	Control Sieve Opening Inch	Max. % of Over-size on Control Sieve	Min. Through Control Sieve and Retained %	Min. On Sieve No.	Cumulative Min. Through Control Sieve and Retained %	Cumulative On Sieve No.	Max. of 3% to Pass Sieve No.
10	7	8	0.0937	15	45	10	80	10 and 12	14
12	8	10	0.0787	15	45	12	80	12 and 14	16
14	10	12	0.0661	15	45	14	80	14 and 16	18
16	12	14	0.0555	15	45	16	80	16 and 18	20
20	14	16	0.0469	15	45	18	80	18 and 20	25
24	16	20	0.0331	20	45	25	75	25 and 30	35
30	18	25	0.0280	20	45	30	75	30 and 35	40
36	20	30	0.0232	20	45	35	75	35 and 40	45
46	30	40	0.0165	20	45	45	75	45 and 50	60
54	35	45	0.0138	20	45	50	75	50 and 60	70
60	40	50	0.0117	30	45	60	70	60 and 70	80
70	50	60	0.0098	15	45	70	70	70 and 80	100
80	60	70	0.0083	15	40	80	70	80 and 100	120
90	70	80	0.0070	15	40	100	70	100 and 120	140
100	80	100	0.0059	15	30	120	65	120 and 140	200
120	100	120	0.0049	15	40	140	60	140 and 170	230
150	100	140	0.0041	15	40	170 and 200	75	170, 200 and 230	270
180	120	170	0.0035	15	40	200 and 230	65	200, 230 and 270	....
220	140	200	0.0029	15	40	230 and 270	60	230, 270 and 325	....

United States Standard Sieve Series

U.S. Standard Sieve Series No.	Sieve Opening mm	Sieve Opening Inch	Sieve Wire Diam. Inch
4	4.76	0.187	0.050
5	4.00	0.157	0.044
6	3.36	0.132	0.040
7	2.83	0.111	0.036
8	2.38	0.0937	0.0331
10	2.00	0.0787	0.0299
12	1.68	0.0661	0.0272
14	1.41	0.0555	0.0240
16	1.19	0.0469	0.0213
18	1.00	0.0394	0.0189
20	0.84	0.0331	0.0165
25	0.71	0.0280	0.0146
30	0.59	0.0232	0.0130
35	0.50	0.0197	0.0114
40	0.42	0.0165	0.0098
45	0.35	0.0138	0.0087
50	0.297	0.0117	0.0074
60	0.250	0.0098	0.0064
70	0.210	0.0083	0.0055
80	0.177	0.0070	0.0047
100	0.149	0.0059	0.0040
120	0.125	0.0049	0.0034
140	0.105	0.0041	0.0029
170	0.088	0.0035	0.0025
200	0.074	0.0029	0.0021
230	0.062	0.0024	0.0018
270	0.053	0.0021	0.0016
325	0.044	0.0017	0.0014

To illustrate, take grit No. 10. All material must pass through the coarsest sieve, termed the "control sieve" — in this case the No. 7. Through the next to the coarsest sieve — in this case the No. 8 — all material may pass, but not more than 15 per cent may be retained on it. At least 45 per cent must pass through No. 8, and be retained on No. 10 sieve, but it is permissible to have 100 per cent pass through No. 8, and remain on No. 10 sieve, the requirement being that the grain passing through No. 8, and retained on No. 10 and No. 12 must add to at least 80 per cent; consequently, if 45 per cent passed through No. 8 sieve and was retained on No. 10 sieve, then at least 35 per cent must be retained on the No. 12 sieve. Not more than 3 per cent is permitted to pass through the No. 14 sieve.

GRINDING

Standard Shapes of Mounted Wheels and Points — 1

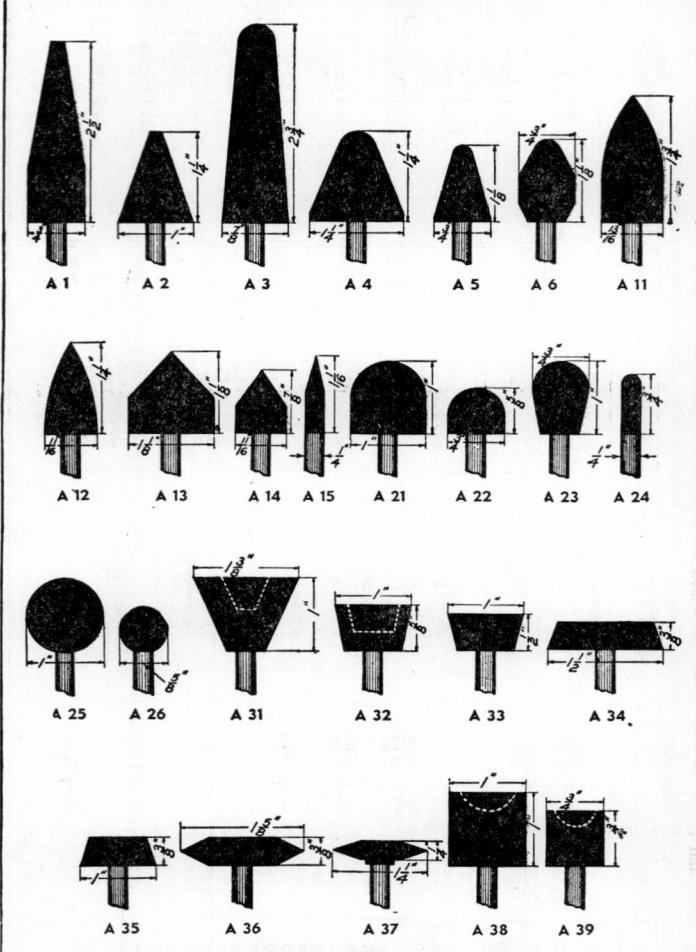

The maximum speeds of mounted vitrified wheels and points of average grade range from about 38,000 to 152,000 R.P.M. for diameters of 1 inch down to ¼ inch. However, the safe operating speed usually is limited by the critical speed (speed at which vibration or whip tends to become excessive) which varies according to wheel or point dimensions, spindle diameter, and overhang.

Standard Shapes of Mounted Wheels and Points — 2

B 41   B 42   B 43   B 44   B 45   B 46   B 47   B 51   B 52   B 53   B 54   B 55

B 61   B 62   B 63   B 64   B 65   B 71   B 72   B 73   B 74

B 81   B 82   B 83   B 84   B 91   B 92   B 93   B 94   B 95   B 96   B 97

B 98   B 101   B 102   B 103   B 104   B 105   B 106   B 111   B 112   B 113

B 114   B 115   B 121   B 122   B 123   B 124   B 131   B 132   B 133   B 134   B 135   B 136

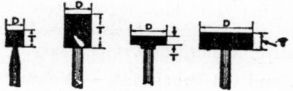

Group W

Abrasives for Grinding. — The commercial abrasive materials for grinding wheels are both natural and artificial. Emery and corundum are natural abrasives; materials like alundum, carborundum, crystolon, aloxite, adamite and carbolite are produced artificially. *Emery* is a very tough and durable abrasive, but contains iron and other non-cutting elements, and is little used in automatic grinding machines. *Corundum* is purer than emery and contains a much larger percentage of crystalline alumina, which is the element in both abrasives that does the cutting. *Carborundum*, which is a trade name for carbide of silicon, is a product of the electric furnace. The principal materials used in the manufacture of carborundum are coke and sand. The coke is used to supply the carbon, and the sand, the silicon. *Alundum* is also made in the electric furnace by the fusion of a mineral called bauxite, which was considered infusible until the invention of the electric process. Bauxite is a soft earth and somewhat resembles light yellow clay. Chemically, it is the purest form of aluminum oxide found in nature. *Aloxite* consists essentially of aluminum oxide. It is a product of the electric furnace, and is made by heating an ore containing this oxide with certain ingredients which are added to remove the impurities.

Vitrified Grinding Wheels. — The wheels most generally used in automatic grinding machines are bonded by the vitrified process. Vitrified wheels are porous and free cutting and are not affected by water, acids, oils, heat or cold. The bond is composed of suitable clays and fluxes, which are mixed with the abrasive in power-driven mixing kettles. The wheels, after being molded, are baked or burned continuously for a period of 100 hours or more, the time depending upon the size of the wheels. During this baking process the temperature is gradually raised until the clay is partially melted and vitrified. The wheels are then allowed to cool slowly for a week, care being taken to prevent sudden temperature changes. As the cooling takes place, the clay crystallizes and binds the abrasive grains firmly together.

The Silicate Process. — Silicate of soda is the principal ingredient in the bond of silicate grinding wheels or those made by the silicate process. The abrasive grains are first mixed with the bond in special machines, and the mixture is then tamped into molds. After the wheels are molded, they are dried and baked in special ovens from which all fire gases are excluded. This causes a chemical reaction which hardens or sets the bond. The temperature of the ovens is much lower than is required in connection with the vitrified process. Some shapes of silicate wheels are molded under hydraulic pressure. This method is employed for disk wheels and very hard wheels. Silicate wheels can be made in large sizes and can be produced in a comparatively short time. Vitrified wheels are rarely made larger than 36 inches in diameter, 30 inches being the maximum size with some manufacturers; silicate wheels are made as large as 60 inches in diameter. Silicate wheels are especially adapted for grinding operations in which it is important to have the lowest possible wheel wear compatible with cool cutting.

Elastic Wheels. — Very thin grinding wheels are made by the elastic process. Shellac is the principal ingredient in the bond and the wheels are baked at a low temperature to set the shellac. Wheels made by this process are strong and have considerable elasticity, so that very thin elastic wheels can be safely used; wheels ⅟₃₂ inch thick are manufactured. These wheels are used principally for fine grinding, cutting off stock, or wherever a thin wheel is necessary.

Vulcanite, Celluloid, and Oil Processes. — Vulcanite wheels are bonded with vulcanized rubber. Very hard, tough, thin wheels can be produced by this process, but they are expensive. Wheels made by the celluloid process have a bond of celluloid, as the name implies. The abrasive grains are mixed with the celluloid, and this mixture is rolled into sheets from which the wheels are cut. After seasoning for several months, the wheels are ready to finish. With the oil process, an oxidizing oil is mixed with the grains. This mixture is then formed into wheels by compressing it into molds with a hydraulic press. Oil wheels are similar in action to elastic wheels but are less dependable as to grade and uniformity. These three processes are only used to a limited extent.

Truing a Grinding Wheel. — The only satisfactory method of truing the wheels used in automatic grinding machines is by the use of a diamond tool. This tool should be rigidly clamped to the machine and the wheel should revolve at the speed required for grinding. The diamond tool should be held with the point quite close to the supporting clamp, in order to reduce vibration and give a smooth accurate wheel surface. Diamond tools usually have round shanks to permit clamping them in different positions, so that the wear on the diamond will not be confined to one or two points. When truing the wheel, light cuts should be taken and water be used to keep the diamond cool.

Diamond Tools. — The diamonds used in tools for truing grinding wheels are of two kinds, the carbon or black diamond and bort. The black diamond rarely has any visible crystallization; its color varies, but is often a very dark purple-brown. Bort is a semi-transparent stone — an imperfect "brilliant." It is not as hard as a black diamond, and is considerably lower in price. For truing soft wheels, bort may be more economical than the more expensive stones, but, as a general rule, the black diamond is cheaper in the long run.

Setting Diamonds. — The diamonds used for truing grinding wheels are usually set in the end of a soft-steel rod. A hole is drilled in the end, just a little deeper than the length of the stone and of the same diameter as the thickest part. The diamond is then fixed in place by carefully peening the metal over it, by using a small set. The end of the rod is then ground away to expose part of the diamond. Diamonds are also brazed in position: First drill a hole a little deeper than the greatest dimension of the diamond. The drilling should be done without lubricant, as oil of any kind tends to prevent the spelter from flowing smoothly. This being done, the hole should be closed in slightly — just enough to make it out of round. The molten spelter is now poured into the hole, filling it completely, and the diamond, held in a pair of tweezers, is pushed into the liquid spelter in the hole, until it strikes the bottom. After the spelter has cooled, the end of the rod in which the diamond is located can be shaped in the customary manner. The fact that the hole is closed in slightly, prevents the core of spelter from working out of the end of the rod.

Wheels for Surface Grinding. — Comparatively soft wheels are used on vertical spindle surface grinders and other types using cup wheels. This is because of the relatively large contact area between the wheel and work, and also because there is not the same clearance as in other grinding operations. Owing to the large contact area between the wheel and work, the selection of wheels of the proper grade for surface grinding is of particular importance, for if a wheel is a little too soft it will wear rapidly, and one that is a little too hard will fill and glaze.

Wheels for Internal Grinding. — When selecting wheels of the proper grain and grade for internal grinding, the following points should be considered: Diameter of hole; speed of wheel-spindle; kind of work; whether the hole is plain or keyseated; nature of material; stiffness of machine; rigidity of wheel-spindle; and whether the cut is for roughing or finishing. As regards the diameter of the hole, there are several points to consider. If the hole is below ¾ or 1 inch in diameter, the wheel should be as large as possible so that it will last longer. The wheel is usually ordered of the same diameter or larger than the hole to be ground and then is trued until it enters the hole. By using a wheel which is only slightly smaller than the hole, the arc of contact of the wheel and work is large, and, consequently, a much softer wheel must be used than if the wheel were small in relation to the diameter of the hole. When a hole is plain, a softer wheel should be used than if the hole were keyseated. Slots or keyseats have a shaving action on the wheel-face and quickly tear out the grains; hence, for keyseated work, a harder wheel should be used than on plain hole work, and it should also have a wider face. The greater the rigidity of the machine, the softer the grade and coarser the grain of the wheel should be. The rigid machine also has the advantage of removing the stock with rapidity and without chatter marks. In commercial grinding a wheel is generally selected which will be fairly suitable for both roughing and finishing to avoid changing wheels.

Centerless Grinding

In centerless grinding the work is supported on a work-rest and between the grinding wheel and a regulating wheel which usually is made of material similar to that of the grinding wheel. The work-rest is equipped with suitable guides for receiving and supporting the work. The grinding wheel forces the work downward against the work-rest and also against the regulating wheel. The latter imparts a uniform rotation to the work which has the same peripheral speed as the regulating wheel, the speed of which is adjustable.

Through-feed Method of Grinding. — There are three general methods of centerless grinding which may be described as through-feed, in-feed, and end-feed methods. The through-feed method is applied to straight cylindrical parts. The work is given an axial movement by the regulating wheel and passes between the grinding and regulating wheels from one side to the other. The rate of feed depends upon the diameter and speed of the regulating wheel and its inclination which is adjustable. It may be necessary to pass the work between the wheels more than once, the number of passes depending upon such factors as the amount of stock to be removed, the roundness and straightness of the unground work, and the limits of accuracy required.

In-feed Method of Centerless Grinding. — When parts have shoulders, heads or some part larger than the ground diameter, the in-feed method usually is employed. This method is similar to the "plunge cut" form grinding on a center type of grinder. The length of the section or sections to be ground in any one operation is limited by the width of the wheel. As there is no axial feeding movement, the regulating wheel is set with its axis approximately parallel to that of the grinding wheel, there being a slight inclination to keep the work tight against the end stop.

End-feed Method of Grinding. — The end-feed method is applied only to taper work. The grinding wheel, regulating wheel, and the blade or work-rest are set in a fixed relation to each other and the work is fed in from the front mechanically or manually to a fixed end stop. Either the grinding or regulating wheel, or both, are dressed to the proper taper.

Automatic Centerless Grinding. — The grinding of relatively small parts may be done automatically by equipping the machine with a magazine, gravity chute, or hopper feed, provided the shape of the part will permit using these feeding mechanisms.

Internal Centerless Grinding. — Internal grinding machines based upon the centerless principle utilize the outside diameter of the work as a guide for grinding the bore which is concentric with the outer surface. In addition to straight and tapered bores, interrupted and "blind" holes can be ground by the centerless

Centerless Grinding Production Data*

Class of Work	Material	Limits, Size Within	Finish	Stock Removed	No. of Cuts	Net Production per Hour
Through-feed method of grinding — short cylindrical parts						
Piston-pin	Steel, H.†	.0001	Excellent	.012 to .015	6	250 to 300
Chain roller pin	Steel, H.	.0005	Excellent	.005 to .008	1	3000
Short shaft 1″ dia.× 6″ long	Steel, Case H.	.0005	Commercial	.010	3	300
Automobile piston	Cast I. or Al.	.0004	Good	.005	3	175
Through-feed method — medium and long bars						
Bar, 2½″ dia.×18 ft. long	Steel, O.H. or Bessemer	.001	Commercial	.005 to .007	2	90 to 120 ft.
Bar, 1″ dia.×18 ft. long	Steel, O.H. or Bessemer	.0005	Good Commercial	.005 to .010	2	200 to 250 ft.
Bar, ½″ dia.×18 ft. long	Drill rod, high car.	.0005	Good Commercial	.005 to .010	2	250 to 300 ft.
Through-feed method — rings or disks						
Ball-bearing race, 1″ dia.	Steel, H.†	.0004	Excellent	.015	3	850
Roller-bearing cup, 5″ dia.	Steel, H.	.0004	Excellent	.020	6	340
Roller-bearing cup, 8.375″ dia.	Steel, H.	.0006	Excellent	.030	8	120
Disk roller 3/16″ dia. ×3/16″ long	Steel, H.	.0001	Excellent	.005	1	8000
Plain in-feed grinding						
Shackle bolt .43″ dia.	Steel, Case H.	.001	Commercial	.008 to .012	1	700
Bolt, .74″ dia.×5½″ long	Steel, Case H.	.001	Commercial	.010 to .015	2	300
Valve tappet .625″ dia.	Steel, H.	.0002	Excellent	.012	2	350
Rivet	Steel	.001	Commercial	.020 to .030	1	100
Automatic magazine feed						
Trip staff .082″ dia.	Steel	.0002	Excellent	.002 to .004	1	2700
Twist drill 3/16″ dia.	Steel, H.S.	.0003	Excellent	.005 to .010	2	420
Poppet-valve stem	Steel, heat-tr.	.0005	Excellent	.010 to .012	2	350

* Compiled by Cincinnati Grinders Inc.
† (H) means hardened.

method. When two or more grinding operations must be performed on the same part, such as roughing and finishing, the work can be rechucked in the same location as often as required.

Rates of Production in Centerless Grinding. — Rates of production vary widely according to the character of the work, the material, the accuracy and finish required, and other factors. As a general rule, parts ground by the through-feed method require two passes and from 0.010 to 0.015 inch of stock is removed; however, when an extra-fine finish and extreme accuracy are essential, as for piston-pins, etc., the number of passes is increased. Most work is ground either by the through-feed or in-feed methods. The rate of production with the through-feed method depends chiefly upon the amount of stock to be removed, whereas, with the in-feed method, the production rate is limited to a considerable extent by the time required for loading and unloading. The accompanying table contains production data from actual practice, applying to these different methods of grinding. These production figures, compiled by Cincinnati Grinders Inc., are intended as a general guide only.

Roll Grinding

A number of causes of roll grinding troubles are listed in the following, in order of frequency:

Chatter, Bouncing, or Hammering. — 1. Wheel-spindle: Poor fit; end play; spring, internal stresses (from overloading); insufficient heating of bearings.

2. Spindle drive: Whipping belt; uneven thickness of belt or belt splices; vibration of motor, if integrally mounted; uneven speed.

3. Vibration: Machine vibration; building or foundation vibration; uneven traverse drive through rack and pinion.

4. Roll drive: Uneven gear action; uneven pressure of driving pins; faceplate out of true; driving pins not parallel with work axis; worn thrust bearings.

5. Wheel: Grading too hard; face too wide for grading of wheel; out of balance; not trued; wheel sides not true with face; glazing; wheel not tight on mounting.

6. Work mounting: Poorly designed rests; poorly fitted centers; loose centers or neck rests; centers too loose or too tight; faulty lubrication.

7. Operation: Too high spindle speed; work speed too slow or too fast; lack of lubrication of neck rests or centers; dull wheel due to poor dressing.

Scratches and Fish-tails. — 1. Coolant: Lack of filtration of machine coolant or city water; improper cleaning of guards after dressing or changing to finer wheels; gummy coolants; coolants that disintegrate wheel bound.

2. Dressing: Wheel grains only partially removed because of dull diamond; ragged wheel edges; dressing sludge left in wheel guard; wheel face and sides not properly cleaned after dressing.

3. Hammering: Wheel grains loosened by hammering of wheel on work.

4. Loose dirt: Dirt in air; dirt resting or dropping on roll.

Diamond Marks. — 1. Diamond: Too sharp, cracked, or broken; wrong angle (horizontal or vertical); lack of rigidity; dull diamond which presses in grains or bond of the wheel.

2. Traverse: Too fast for dressing; uneven hand feed; dressing at same traverse rate and direction as on work.

3. Dressing Feed: Too deep.

Traverse Marks. — 1. Wheel: Corners not rounded off; dragging edge from faulty dressing; spring in spindle; feed too deep on finishing cuts.

2. Traverse: Too fast.

3. Work Speed: Too high (should be slightly changed with each pass to break up pattern; this may be accomplished with traverse instead).

Wheel Marks. — 1. Wheels: Too big a gap between grits used; final wheel too coarse or too soft.

2. Dressing: Too coarse.

3. Operation: Lack of "finishing out" on all wheels.

Loading or Glazing of Wheel. — 1. Wheel: Too hard, either from grading or manipulation.

2. Dressing: Stone too dull; dressing too fine; dressing intervals too far apart.

3. Coolant: Too gummy or dirty.

Work out of Round. — 1. Roll supports: Rests or centers not in good condition.

2. Neck rests: Not round; infrequent grinding.

3. Temperature: Elongation of roll from temperature change, and resistance of centers to this elongation; distortion of roll.

4. Drive: Roll wabble due to poor drive.

Work out of Parallel. — 1. Grinder: Worn ways; improper setting of tailstock; centers not concentric with bodies.

2. Dressing: Dressing off center line; location of dresser causing dressing action different from that found in grinding.

3. Temperature: Roll not at room temperature.

Burning. — 1. Wheel: Too hard in effect.

2. Operation: Wheel fed to work too rapidly.

Grading. — When the wheel effect is too hard, it may be caused by the following: (a) Wheel speed too high; (b) work speed too low; (c) traverse too low; (d) wheel feed too light; (e) wheel face too wide; (f) wheel diameter too great; (g) coolant too thick; (h) dressing too dull; (i) wheel or belt slippage.

Polishing and Buffing

The terms "polishing" and "buffing" are sometimes applied to similar classes of work in different plants, but according to approved usage of the terms, there is the following distinction: Polishing is any operation performed with wheels having abrasive glued to the working surfaces, whereas, buffing is done with wheels having the abrasive applied loosely instead of imbedding it into glue; moreover, buffing is not so harsh an operation as ordinary polishing, and it is commonly utilized for obtaining very fine surfaces having a "grainless finish."

Polishing Wheels. — The principal materials from which polishing wheels are made are wood, leather, canvas, cotton cloth, felt, paper, walrus or sea-horse hide, sheepskin, impregnated rubber, canvas composition, and wool. Leather and canvas are the materials most commonly used in polishing wheel construction. Bull-neck leather wheels are made of oak tanned bullneck leather cut into disks of uniform thickness and cemented together. Wooden wheels covered with leather to which emery or some other abrasive is glued, are employed extensively for polishing flat surfaces, especially when good edges must be maintained. Canvas wheels are made in various ways; wheels having disks that are cemented together are very hard and used for rough, coarse work, whereas those having sewed disks are made of varying densities by sewing together a larger or smaller number of disks into sections and gluing them. Wheels in which the disks are held together by sewing and which are not stiffened by the use of glue, usually require metal side plates to support the canvas disks. Muslin wheels are made from sewed buffs glued together, but the outer edges of a wheel frequently are left open or free from glue to provide an open face of any desired depth. Wool felt wheels are flexible and resilient, and the density may be varied by sewing two or more disks together and then cementing these to form a wheel. Solid wheels made of Spanish or Mexican felt are quite popular for fine finishing but have little value as general utility wheels. Paper wheels are made from strawboard paper disks and are cemented together under pressure to form a very hard wheel for rough work. Softer wheels are similarly made from felt paper. Walrus leather or sea-horse hide may be used for fine polishing, but these wheels are expensive. The "compress" canvas wheel is commonly used in place of walrus wheels. This compress type of wheel has a cushion of polishing material formed by pieces of leather, canvas, felt, or whatever material is used, which are held in a crosswise radial position by two side plates attached to the wheel hub. This cushion of polishing material may be varied in density to suit the requirements; it may readily be shaped to conform to the curvature of the work and this shape can be maintained. Sheepskin polishing wheels and also paper wheels are used very little at the present time.

Polishing Operations and Abrasives. — Polishing operations on such parts as chisels, hammers, screwdrivers, wrenches, and other parts which are given a fine finish but are not plated, usually require four operations which are "roughing," "dry fining," "greasing" and "coloring." The roughing is frequently regarded as a solid grinding wheel job. Sometimes there are two steps to the greasing operation — rough and fine greasing. For some hardware, such as the cheaper screwdrivers, wrenches, etc., the operations of roughing and dry fining are considered sufficient. For knife blades and cutlery the roughing operation is performed with solid grinding wheels and the polishing is known as fine or blue glazing, but these terms are never used when referring to the polishing of hardware parts, plumbers' supplies, etc. A term used in finishing German silver, white metal, and similar materials is "sand-buffing," which, in distinction from the ordinary buffing operation that is used only to produce a very high finish, actually removes considerable metal, as in rough polishing or flexible grinding. For sand-buffing, rotten-stone and pumice are loosely applied.

For the finer finishing and coloring work, emery is employed quite generally in preference to artificial abrasives. The abrasive numbers used for roughing ordinarily range from 60 to 80; for dry fining from 90 to 120; and for finishing from 150 to one of the "flour" grades.

Buffing Wheels. — Buffing wheels, as defined by the Metal Finishers' Equipment Association, are wheels manufactured from disks (either whole or pieced) of bleached or unbleached cotton or woolen cloth, and they are used as the agent for carrying abrasive powders, such as tripoli, crocus, rouge, lime, etc., which are mixed with waxes or greases as a bond. There are two main classes of buffs known as the "pieced-sewed" buffs, which are made from various weaves and weights of cloths, and the "full disk" buffs which are made from the best sheeting and shirting. Bleached cloth is harder and stiffer than unbleached cloth, and is used for the faster cutting buffs. Coarsely woven unbleached cloth is recommended for highly colored work on soft metals, while the finer woven unbleached cloths are better adapted for the harder metals. A stiff buff when working at the usual speed is not suitable for "cutting down" soft metal or for use on light plated ware, but is used on the harder metals and for heavy nickel-plated articles.

Speed of Polishing Wheels. — The proper speed for polishing is governed to some extent by the nature of the work, but for ordinary operations the polishing wheel, according to one manufacturer, should have a peripheral speed of about 7500 feet per minute. If run at a lower rate of speed, the work tends to tear the polishing material from the wheel too readily, and the work is not as good in quality. Another manufacturer recommends the following speeds: Muslin, felt or sea-horse polishing wheels having wood or iron centers should be run at peripheral speeds varying from 3000 to 7000 feet per minute. It is rarely necessary to exceed 6000 feet per minute, and for most purposes 4000 feet per minute is sufficient. If the wheels are kept in good condition, in perfect balance, and are suitably mounted on substantial buffing lathes, they are safe for speeds within the limits given.

Grain Numbers of Emery. — The numbers commonly used in designating the different grains of emery, corundum and other abrasives are 10, 12, 14, 16, 18, 20, 24, 30, 36, 40, 46, 54, 60, 70, 80, 90, 100, 120, 150, 180 and 200, ranging from coarse to fine. These numbers represent the number of meshes per linear inch in the grading sieve. An abrasive finer than No. 200 is known as "flour" and the degree of fineness is designated by the letters CF, F, FF, FFF, FFFF and PCF or SF, ranging from coarse to fine. The methods of grading flour-emery adopted by different manufacturers do not exactly agree, the letters differing somewhat for the finer grades.

Grades of Emery Cloth. — The coarseness of emery cloth is indicated by letters and numbers corresponding to the grain number of loose emery. The letters and numbers for grits ranging from fine to coarse are as follows: FF, F, 120, 100, 90, 80, 70, 60, 54, 46, 40. For large work roughly filed, use coarse cloth such as Nos. 46 or 54, and then finer grades to obtain the required polish. If the work has been carefully filed, a good polish can be obtained with Nos. 60 and 90 cloth, and a brilliant polish by finishing with No. 120 and flour-emery.

Mixture for Cementing Emery Cloth to a Lapping Wheel. — Use 4½ pounds of rosin; 3 pounds of paraffine; 9 ounces of vaseline; melt the ingredients and mix them thoroughly. Heat the surface of the lapping wheel and spread on the mixture; then rub the emery cloth down so as to exclude all air from between the surface of the wheel and cloth. The surface of the lapping wheel should be clean before the cement is applied.

Exhaust Systems for Grinding, Polishing and Buffing Wheels

Defects in Exhaust Systems. — The principal defects in the exhaust systems for grinding, polishing and buffing wheels are as follows: 1. Making the suction duct too small and, not infrequently, of the same size throughout its length. 2. Running the branch pipes into the main suction pipe at right angles, and sometimes at the bottom of the main. 3. Providing a fan too small for the service. 4. Using a discharge pipe too small for the fan. 5. Using a cyclone separator or dust separator too small for the system. The result of such mistakes in the design of exhaust systems is that the suction is entirely inadequate for carrying off the dust, which then clogs the pipes and spreads about the room.

Branch Pipe Specifications. — The following specifications for the design, construction and operation of exhaust systems conform to Section 81 of the New York State Labor Law: The diameter of branch pipes leading from the wheel hoods to the main suction duct must conform to the sizes given in the accompanying table, "Diameters of Branch Pipes for Grinding and Polishing Wheel Exhaust Systems." In case the grinding wheel is thicker than is given in this table, or if a disk instead of a regular wheel is used, it must have a branch pipe not smaller than is required for the grinding surface given. Buffing wheels six inches or less in diameter, used for jewelry work, may have a three-inch branch pipe. The thickness given for buffing wheels applies to the thickness of the wheel at the center. In case the wheel is thicker than is given in this table, it must have a branch pipe no smaller than is called for by its grinding surface. Branch pipes must not be smaller than the sizes specified, throughout their entire length. All branch pipes must enter the main suction duct at an angle not exceeding forty-five degrees and should be inclined in the direction of the air flow at the junction with the main. Branch pipes must not project into the main duct. All laps in piping must be made in the direction of the air flow. All bends, turns or elbows, whether in main or branch pipes, must be made with a radius in the throat equal to at least one and one-half times the diameter of the pipe to which they are connected.

Diameters of Suction Ducts for Exhaust Systems

The table gives the diameter in inches of the main suction duct at any point for any number of uniform-size branch pipes when the area of the main at any point is made equal to the combined areas of the branch pipes preceding that point, plus twenty per cent.

Number of Branch Pipes	Diameter of Branch Pipes, Inches								
	3	3½	4	4½	5	5½	6	6½	7
	Area of each Branch Pipe in Square Inches								
	7.07	9.62	12.566	15.9	19.635	23.758	28.274	33.183	38.485
	Area of each Branch Pipe plus 20 per cent (Square Inches)								
	8.484	11.544	15.08	19.08	23.562	28.51	33.93	39.82	46.182
1	3⅜	3⅞	4⅜	5	5½	6	6⅝	7⅛	7¾
2	4¾	5½	6¼	7	7¾	8⅝	9¼	10⅛	10⅞
3	5¾	6⅝	7⅝	8⅝	9½	10½	11½	12⅜	13¼
4	6⅝	7¾	8¾	9⅞	11	12⅛	13⅛	14¼	15⅜
5	7⅜	8⅝	9⅞	11	12¼	13½	14¾	16	17⅛
6	8⅛	9½	10¾	12⅛	13½	14¾	16⅛	17½	18¾
7	8¾	10¼	11⅝	13⅛	14½	16	17½	18⅞	20¼
8	9⅜	10⅞	12⅜	14	15½	17⅛	18⅝	20⅛	21¾
9	9⅞	11½	13⅛	14⅞	16½	18⅛	19¾	21⅜	23
10	10½	12⅛	13⅞	15⅝	17⅜	19⅛	20¾	22½	24¼
11	11	12¾	14⅝	16⅜	18¼	20	21⅞	23⅝	25½
12	11½	13⅜	15¼	17⅛	19	20⅞	22¾	24¾	26⅝
13	11⅞	13⅞	15⅞	17⅞	19¾	21¾	23¾	25¾	27¾
14	12⅜	14⅜	16½	18½	20½	22⅝	24⅝	26¾	28¾
15	12¾	14⅞	17	19⅛	21¼	23⅜	25½	27⅝	29¾
16	13¼	15⅜	17⅝	19¾	22	24⅛	26⅜	28½	30¾
17	13⅝	15⅞	18⅛	20⅜	22⅝	24⅞	27⅛	29⅜	31⅝
18	14	16⅜	18⅝	21	23¼	25⅝	27⅞	30¼	32⅝
19	14⅜	16¾	19⅛	21½	23⅞	26¼	28¾	31⅛	33½
20	14¾	17⅛	19⅝	22⅛	24½	27	29½	31⅞	34⅜
21	15⅛	17⅝	20⅛	22⅝	25⅛	27⅝	30⅛	32¾	35⅛
22	15½	18	20⅝	23⅛	25¾	28⅜	30⅞	33½	36
23	15¾	18½	21⅛	23¾	26⅜	29	31½	34¼	36¾
24	16⅛	18⅞	21½	24¼	26⅞	29⅝	32¼	34⅞	37⅝
25	16½	19¼	22	24¾	27½	30⅛	32⅞	35⅝	38⅜
26	16¾	19⅝	22⅜	25⅛	28	30¾	33½	36⅜	39⅛
27	17⅛	20	22⅞	25⅝	28½	31⅜	34⅛	37	39⅞
28	17½	20⅜	23¼	26⅛	29	32	34¾	37¾	40⅝
29	17¾	20¾	23⅝	26⅝	29½	32½	35½	38⅜	41⅜
30	18	21	24	27	30	33	36	39	42

Area of Fan Inlet and Main Suction Duct. — The inlet of the fan or exhauster should be at least twenty per cent greater in area than the sum of the areas of all the branch pipes, and such increase should be carried proportionately throughout the entire length of the main suction duct; that is, the area of the main at any given point should be at least twenty per cent greater than the combined areas of all branch pipes entering it between that point and the closed end of the system. If such increase is made greater than twenty per cent, the area of the main at any point (except that proportion of it between the branch pipe nearest the fan, and the fan) should bear approximately the same ratio to the combined areas of the branches between that point and the closed end of the system, as the area of the main at the branch nearest the fan bears to the combined areas of all the branches. (This provision is made to permit the use of a fan having a larger inlet area than the area of the main at the branch pipe nearest to the fan, if desired.) The table, "Diameters of Suction Ducts for Exhaust Systems," gives the sizes of main suction ducts.

Diameters of Branch Pipes for Grinding and Polishing Wheel Exhaust Systems

Emery or Other Grinding Wheels				Buffing, Polishing or Rag Wheels			
Diameter of Wheel, Inches	Max. Thickness of Wheel	Max. Grinding Surface, Square Inches	Min. Diameter of Branch Pipe, Inches	Diameter of Wheel, Inches	Max. Thickness of Wheel	Max. Grinding Surface, Square Inches	Min. Diameter of Branch Pipe, Inches
Up to 6	1	19	3	Up to 6	1	19	3½
7– 9	1½	43	3½	7–12	1½	57	4
10–16	2	101	4	13–16	2	101	4½
17–19	3	180	4½	17–20	3	189	5
20–24	4	302	5	21–24	4	302	5½
25–30	5	472	6	25–30	5	472	6½

Suction and Discharge Pipe Sizes. — The area of the discharge pipe from the fan should be as large or larger than the area of the fan inlet, throughout its entire length. In the main trunk lines, both suction and discharge should be provided with suitable "clean-out doors" not over ten feet apart, and the end of the main suction duct should be blanked off with a removable cap.

Suction Head. — Sufficient static suction head should be maintained in each branch pipe within one foot of the hood, to produce a difference in level of two inches of water between the two sides of a U-shaped tube. The test is to be made by placing one end of a rubber tube over a small hole made in the pipe, the other end of the tube being connected to one side of the U-shaped water-gage. All branch pipes must be open and unobstructed while test is made.

In addition to the foregoing specifications, which are compulsory under the New York law, a number of recommendations are given in the following which are designed to make exhaust systems more efficient and durable.

Arrangement of Suction and Discharge Pipes. — In the case of undershot wheels (the top of the wheel running towards the operator, which is almost invariably the direction of rotation of both emery and buffing wheels), the main suction duct should be back of and below the wheels, and as close to them as practicable. Sometimes it is preferable to fasten the suction duct to the ceiling of the floor below. Both the main suction and discharge pipes should be short and have as few bends as possible to avoid frictional losses. If one or the other must be of considerable length, it is better to place the fan quite close to the nearest branch pipe which enters the large end of the main, as a long discharge pipe is preferable to a long suction pipe. Avoid any pockets or low places in the ducts where dust might accumulate. The main suction duct should be enlarged between every branch pipe entering it, and in no case should it receive more than two branches in a section of uniform area. All enlargements in the size of the main suction duct should be made by tapering it and not by an abrupt change of diameter.

Arrangement of Branch Pipes. — Branch pipes should enter the main at the top or sides — never at the bottom. Two branches should never enter a main directly opposite each other. Each branch pipe should be equipped with a shut-off damper or "blast gate" which may be closed, if desired, when the wheel is not in use. Not more than twenty-five per cent of the blast gates should be closed at one time, because the air velocity in the main duct may drop too low and let the dust accumulate on the bottom. The lower part of the wheel hood should extend far enough beneath the front of the wheel, so that the dust will enter it and not fall outside. This should be done even though it is necessary to leave considerable space between the wheel and the lower part of the hood to prevent interference with the work. Branch pipes should join with the hood as near as possible at the point where the dust will naturally be thrown into them by the wheels; this is very important. A screen across the mouth of the branch pipe, where it enters the hood, is objectionable, because it obstructs the passage of material and the ravelings from buffing wheels, with the result that within a short time the draft is entirely cut off. It is good practice to use a trap at the junction of the hood and branch pipe, provided it is cleaned out regularly and not allowed to fill with dust. It will catch the heavier particles and so take some wear off the fan. All bends, turns or elbows, whether in main or branch pipes, should be made with a radius in the throat equal to twice the diameter of the pipe to which they are connected, wherever space permits. Elbows should be made of metal one or two gages heavier than the pipe to which they are connected, as the wear on them is much greater.

The Cyclone Separator. — The size of the cyclone separator or dust collector is governed by the operating conditions, light dusts requiring a larger separator than heavy dusts. The separator should have an inlet area at least as large as the area of the fan discharge pipe. For light buffing dusts, lint, etc., the air outlet from the top of the separator should be large enough so that the velocity of the discharge will not exceed 300 to 480 feet per minute. A separator should then be selected having other dimensions in proportion. The air outlet should be provided with a canopy or elbow to exclude the weather, but should be otherwise unobstructed. There should be ample clearance in the separator for the accumulation or storage of dust, which should never be allowed to pile up as high as the bottom of the separator.

Emery and buffing wheel exhaust systems should be kept separate, owing to the danger of sparks from the former setting fire to the lint dust in the latter. The withdrawal of air from a room by an exhaust system naturally tends to create a slight vacuum, and for this reason, inlets for air, at least equal to the sum of the areas of the branch pipes, should be left open.

Grindstones and Oilstones

Grindstones. — Most of the grindstones used in this country come from Huron, Mich.; Berea, Ohio; or from Grindstone Island, Nova Scotia. All of these localities produce several grades. Most Berea stones are rather coarse; those from Nova Scotia are of all grades. Grindstones are natural sand-stones, and the cutting material is oxide of silicon (SiO_2), or quartz sand, as it is commonly called. Grindstones are softer when wet than when dry, and they should never be left standing with one side in the water, because when the stone is again used, this side will be worn away faster than the other. The large, rapidly revolving stones used in connection with some manufacturing operations, for producing smooth surfaces, are hacked around the periphery to make them cut faster. A hack, which somewhat resembles an adz, should have an edge that is a little longer than one-half the width of the stone. When hacking, the tool is held at a slight angle while cutting around one-half the face of the stone; the angle of the hack is then changed for finishing the other half, the cuts being about 1¼ inch apart. As the stone wears away, this operation is repeated. The high spots are hacked closely to increase the wear and keep the stone true.

Speeds for Grindstones.

The proper speed for a grindstone depends upon its use. For grinding machinists' tools, the peripheral speed should range from 800 to 1000 feet per minute, and for carpenters' tools, from 500 to 600 feet per minute. When grindstones are used for smoothing surfaces preliminary to polishing operations, they are run at much higher speeds. One prominent cutlery concern operates Huron stones at 4300 feet per minute, and soft stones at approximately 3600 feet per minute. The maximum speed is, of course, limited by the strength of the stone. It is difficult to determine what the safe maximum speed is, because stones from the same quarry vary in strength. Some Sheffield grinders run their stones at 4500 feet per minute, and others limit the speed to 2500 feet per minute. According to some authorities, the speeds given in the table "Maximum Speeds for Grindstones" should not be exceeded unless the stone is very hard and strong. The number of revolutions given in this table, for various diameters, corresponds to a peripheral speed of approximately 3400 feet per minute.

Maximum Speeds for Grindstones

Diameter of Stone	Revolutions per Minute	Diameter of Stone	Revolutions per Minute	Diameter of Stone	Revolutions per Minute
3 feet	365	4 feet 6 inches	240	6 feet	180
3 feet 6 inches	308	5 feet	216	6 feet 6 inches	166
4 feet	270	5 feet 6 inches	196	7 feet	154

Tests made in the Sheffield district show that the strength of a wet grindstone is considerably less than one in a dry condition. The water which soaks into the stone not only reduces its tensile strength, but also increases the weight and centrifugal stress for the same peripheral speed. This reduction of strength in the case of a wet grindstone was found in some cases to be as much as 40 or 50 per cent. For example, a stone of one-square-inch section broke under a stress of 146 pounds when dry, but when soaked in water over night, another piece of the same stone broke at only 80 pounds per square inch. In another test, the figures were 186 and 116 pounds for the dry and wet stones, respectively.

Doubtless some of the speeds given as permissible for grindstones are excessive, except for very strong stones. The following figures are the result of a careful investigation, and are given as the *safe* maximum speed for Ohio and Huron grindstones, which are the two varieties most widely used. The velocity for Ohio stones should never exceed 3000 feet per minute and, ordinarily, should not be higher than 2500 feet per minute. Huron stones may be run at 3500 feet per minute, but it is safer to limit them to 3000 feet per minute. If the variety of the stone is not known, the speed should be limited to 2500 feet per minute.

Mounting Grindstones. — Many grindstone failures have resulted from improper mounting, rather than from too high a speed. The use of wooden wedges has been the principal source of trouble. These are either driven in too tight or become wet after being inserted, so that cracks are started in the corners of the square hole in the stone. These cracks extend outward and so weaken the stone that rupture is frequently the result. The tendency for cracks to start can be overcome by a proper method of mounting. It is good practice to fill the central space around the arbor with cement or lead after the stone is centered. Wooden wedges should never be used. The stone should be supported by flanges of generous proportions, and wooden washers from ½ to 1 inch in thickness (or a double thickness of leather or rubber) should be inserted between the flanges and the stone to compensate for surface inequalities.

Oilstones. — The natural oilstones commonly used are the Washita and Arkansas. The Washita is a coarser and more rapidly cutting stone then the Arkansas, and is generally considered the most satisfactory for sharpening woodworkers' tools. There are various grades of Washita rock, varying from the perfect crystallized and porous whetstone grit, to vitreous flint and hard sandstone. The sharpness of the grit of any Washita stone depends entirely upon the character of its crystallization. The best whetstones are porous and uniform in texture and are composed entirely of silica crystals. The poorer grades are less porous, making them vitreous or "glassy." They may also have hard spots or sand holes, or contain grains of sand among the crystals. For general work, a soft, free-grit, quick-cutting stone is required, although a fine-grit medium-hard stone is sometimes preferable. Washita stones are sometimes white in color, but frequently streaked more or less with a yellow or red tinge. They are found in the spurs of the Ozark mountains of Arkansas.

The Arkansas stones are of finer grain and appear like white marble. They are excellent for sharpening delicate instruments, producing keen, smooth edges. The Arkansas stone is harder, more transparent and more compact than the Washita, has an exceedingly sharp grit, and will both cut and polish very hard metals. This rock is quarried with difficulty, for it is so badly cracked, seamed and streaked with quartz that only a small portion of sound, pure rock can be obtained of sufficient size and quality for whetstones. The Arkansas stone is used more frequently in machine shops than the Washita. The "soft Arkansas" is a grade between the regular Arkansas and the Washita stone. It is not quite so fine grained and hard as the regular Arkansas, but cuts faster and is better for some purposes. The soft grade is especially adapted for sharpening the tools of wood-carvers, patternmakers, etc.

The Turkey oilstone is well-known throughout the world, and until the introduction of the Washita was the leading oilstone for sharpening mechanics' tools. It is quarried in the interior of Asia Minor, and is a very fine close-grained stone, containing from 70 to 75 per cent silica, closely blended with from 20 to 25 per cent calcite. It has exceptional abrading qualities, but is found in small pieces and contains so many seams and flaws as to make it difficult to procure a real good stone of sufficient size to be serviceable.

The Hindostan is a fine-gritted sandstone quarried in Indiana. It is much softer than the Washita or other oilstones commonly used, and wears away much faster. It is very sharp-gritted, however, and cuts steel rapidly, imparting a medium coarse edge. This kind of stone may be used with oil or water.

Many artificial oilstones are now used for various classes of work. These are commonly furnished in three grits: viz., fine, medium and coarse, and in all required shapes. Coarse stones are used for sharpening large and very dull tools, nicked tools, machine knives, and for general use where fast cutting is required without regard to fine finish. Medium stones are used for sharpening mechanics' tools in general especially those used by carpenters and in wood-working establishments. The medium grit gives a medium fine edge, well suited for working soft wood, cloth, leather, rubber and paper cutting machine or hand knives. Fine stones are used by machinists and engravers, die workers, instrument makers, cabinet makers, and all users of tools requiring a very fine, keen edge. Some artificial stones have one medium and one coarse face, thus combining two stones in one.

Truing Surfaces of Oilstones. — Oilstones which have uneven surfaces can be trued by the following method: Secure a cast-iron block having a true surface, and cover the surface with loose emery mixed with water; then place the oilstone upon the cast-iron block and grind it true. This method is applicable to either coarse oilstones or fine razor hones. Stones of special shape may be formed by planing a groove of corresponding shape in the cast-iron block and drawing the stone through the groove, using emery and water as an abrasive.

Care of Oilstones. — Oilstones should be properly cared for: first, in order to retain the original life and sharpness of the grit; second, to keep the surface flat and even; third, to prevent glazing. The following instructions are given by the Pike Mfg. Co.: An oilstone should be kept clean and moist; allowing it to remain dry a long time, or exposing it to the air, tends to harden it. A new stone should be soaked in oil for several days before using (with the exception of Pike India and Pike Crystolon). If the stone is kept in a dry place, it should be placed in a box having a closed cover, and a few drops of fresh, clean oil should be placed on it. To restore an even flat surface on an oilstone, grind it on the side of a grindstone, or rub it down with sand-stone or an emery brick.

An oilstone can be prevented from glazing by the proper use of oil or water. Either oil or water will prevent the particles of steel that are cut away from the tool being sharpened from filling the surface of the stone. Plenty of water should be used on all coarse-grained natural stones; on medium- or fine-grained natural stones, such as Arkansas or Washita, as well as on all artificial stones, oil should be used invariably, as water is not thick enough to keep the steel particles out of the pores. To further prevent glazing, dirty oil should always be wiped off the stone as soon as possible after using. This is very important, for if the oil is left on the stone, it dries in, carrying steel dust with it. Cotton waste is one of the best things for cleaning a stone. If a stone does become glazed or gummed up, cleaning with gasoline or ammonia will usually restore its cutting qualities; but if this treatment is not effective, scour the stone with loose emery or a piece of sand-paper fastened to a flat board.

Laps and Lapping

Material for Laps. — Laps are usually made of soft cast iron, copper, brass or lead. In general, the best material for laps to be used on very accurate work is soft, close-grained cast iron. If the grinding, prior to lapping, is of inferior quality, or an excessive allowance has been left for lapping, copper laps may be preferable. They can be charged more easily and cut more rapidly than cast iron, but do not produce as good a finish. Whatever material is used, the lap should be softer than the work, as, otherwise, the latter will become charged with the abrasive and cut the lap, the order of the operation being reversed. A common and inexpensive form of lap for holes is made of lead which is cast around a tapering steel arbor. The arbor usually has a groove or keyway extending lengthwise, into which the lead flows, thus forming a key that prevents the lap from turning. When the lap has worn slightly smaller than the hole and ceases to cut, the lead is expanded or stretched a little by the driving in of the arbor. When this expanding operation has been repeated two or three times, the lap usually must be trued or replaced with a new one, owing to distortion.

The tendency of lead laps to lose their form is an objectionable feature. They are, however, easily molded, inexpensive, and quickly charged with the cutting abrasive. A more elaborate form for holes is composed of a steel arbor and a split cast-iron or copper shell which is sometimes prevented from turning by a small dowel pin. The lap is split so that it can be expanded to accurately fit the hole being operated upon. For hardened work, some toolmakers prefer copper to either cast iron or lead. For holes varying from ¼ to ½ inch in diameter, copper or brass is sometimes used; cast iron is used for holes larger than ½ inch in diameter. The arbors for these laps should have a taper of about ¼ or ⅜ inch per foot. The length of the lap should be somewhat greater than the length of the hole, and the thickness of the shell or lap proper should be from ⅛ to ⅙ its diameter.

External laps are commonly made in the form of a ring, there being an outer ring or holder and an inner shell which forms the lap proper. This inner shell is made of cast iron, copper, brass or lead. Ordinarily the lap is split and screws are provided in the holder for adjustment. The length of an external lap should at least equal the diameter of the work, and might well be longer. Large ring laps usually have a handle for moving them across the work.

Laps for Flat Surfaces. — Laps for producing plane surfaces are made of cast iron. In order to secure accurate results, the lapping surface must be a true plane. A flat lap that is used for roughing or "blocking down" will cut better if the surface is scored by narrow grooves. These are usually located about ½ inch apart and extend both lengthwise and crosswise, thus forming a series of squares similar to those on a checker-board. An abrasive of No. 100 or 120 emery and lard oil can be used for charging the roughing lap. For finer work, a lap having an unscored surface is used, and the lap is charged with a finer abrasive. After a lap is charged, all loose abrasive should be washed off with gasoline, for fine work, and when lapping, the surface should be kept moist, preferably with kerosene. Gasoline will cause the lap to cut a little faster, but it evaporates so rapidly that the lap soon becomes dry and the surface caked and glossy in spots. Loose emery should not be applied while lapping, for if the lap is well charged with abrasive in the beginning, is kept well moistened and not crowded too hard, it will cut for a considerable time. The pressure upon the work should be just enough to insure constant contact. The lap can be made to cut only so fast, and if excessive pressure is applied it will become "stripped" in places. The causes of scratches are: Loose abrasive on the lap; too much pressure on the work, and poorly graded abrasive. To produce a perfectly smooth surface free from scratches, the lap should be charged with a very fine abrasive.

Grading Abrasives for Lapping. — For high-grade lapping, abrasives can be evenly graded as follows: A quantity of flour-emery or other abrasive is placed in a heavy cloth bag, which is gently tapped, causing very fine particles to be sifted through. When a sufficient quantity has been obtained in this way, it is placed in a dish of lard or sperm oil. The largest particles will then sink to the bottom and in about one hour the oil should be poured into another dish, care being taken not to disturb the sediment at the bottom. The oil is then allowed to stand for several hours, after which it is poured again, and so on, until the desired grade is obtained.

Charging Laps. — To charge a flat cast-iron lap, spread a very thin coating of the prepared abrasive over the surface and press the small cutting particles into the lap with a hard steel block. There should be as little rubbing as possible. When the entire surface is apparently charged, clean and examine for bright spots; if any are visible, continue charging until the entire surface has a uniform gray appearance. When the lap is once charged, it should be used without applying more abrasive until it ceases to cut. If a lap is over-charged and an excessive amount of abrasive is used, there is a rolling action between the work and lap which results in inaccuracy. The surface of a flat lap is usually finished true, prior to charging, by scraping and testing with a standard surface-plate, or by the well-known method of scraping-in three plates together, in order to secure a plane surface. In any case, the bearing marks or spots should be uniform and close together. These spots can be blended by covering the plates evenly with a fine abrasive and rubbing them together. While the plates are being ground in, they should be carefully tested and any high spots which may form should be reduced by rubbing them down with a smaller block.

To charge cylindrical laps for internal work, spread a thin coating of prepared abrasive over the surface of a hard steel block, preferably by rubbing lightly with a cast-iron or copper block; then insert an arbor through the lap and roll the latter over the steel block, pressing it down firmly to imbed the abrasive into the surface of the lap. For external cylindrical laps, the inner surface can be charged by rolling-in the abrasive with a hard steel roller that is somewhat smaller in diameter than the lap. The taper cast-iron blocks which are sometimes used for lapping taper holes can also be charged by rolling-in the abrasive, as previously described; there is usually one roughing and one finishing lap, and when charging the former, it may be necessary to vary the charge in accordance with any error which might exist in the taper.

Rotary Diamond Lap. — This style of lap is used for accurately finishing very small holes, which, because of their size, cannot be ground. While the operation is referred to as lapping, it is, in reality, a grinding process, the lap being used the same as a grinding wheel. Laps employed for this work are made of mild steel, soft material being desirable because it can be charged readily. Charging is usually done by rolling the lap between two hardened steel plates. The diamond dust and a little oil is placed on the lower plate, and as the lap revolves, the diamond is forced into its surface. After charging, the lap should be washed in benzine. The rolling plates should also be cleaned before charging with dust of a finer grade. It is very important not to force the lap when in use, especially if it is a small size. The lap should just make contact with the high spots and gradually grind them off. If a diamond lap is lubricated with kerosene, it will cut freer and faster. These small laps are run at very high speeds, the rate depending upon the lap diameter. Soft work should never be ground with diamond dust because the dust will leave the lap and charge the work.

When using a diamond lap, it should be remembered that such a lap will not produce sparks like a regular grinding wheel; hence, it is easy to crowd the lap and "strip" some of the diamond dust. To prevent this, a sound intensifier or "harker" should be used. This is placed against some stationary part of the grinder spindle, and indicates when the lap touches the work, the sound produced by the slightest contact being intensified.

Grading Diamond Dust. — The grades of diamond dust used for charging laps are designated by numbers, the fineness of the dust increasing as the numbers increase. The diamond, after being crushed to powder in a mortar, is thoroughly mixed with high-grade olive oil. This mixture is allowed to stand five minutes and then the oil is poured into another receptacle. The coarse sediment which is left is removed and labeled No. 0, according to one system. The oil poured from No. 0 is again stirred and allowed to stand ten minutes, after which it is poured into another receptacle and the sediment remaining is labeled No. 1. This operation is repeated until practically all of the dust has been recovered from the oil, the time that the oil is allowed to stand being increased as shown by the following table, in order to obtain the smaller particles that require a longer time for precipitation:

To obtain No. 1 — 10 minutes.	To obtain No. 4 — 2 hours.
To obtain No. 2 — 30 minutes.	To obtain No. 5 — 10 hours.
To obtain No. 3 — 1 hour.	To obtain No. 6 — until oil is clear.

The No. 0 or coarse diamond which is obtained from the first settling is usually washed in benzine, and re-crushed unless very coarse dust is required. This No. 0 grade is sometimes known as "ungraded" dust. In some places the time for settling, in order to obtain the various numbers, is greater than that given in the table.

Cutting Properties of Laps and Abrasives. — In order to determine the cutting properties of abrasives when used with different lapping materials and lubricants, a series of tests was conducted, the results of which were given in a paper by W. A. Knight and A. A. Case, presented before the American Society of Mechanical Engineers. In connection with these tests, a special machine was used, the construction being such that quantitative results could be obtained with various combinations of abrasive, lubricant, and lap material. These tests were confined to surface lapping.

It was not the intention to test a large variety of abrasives, three being selected as representative; namely, Naxos emery, carborundum, and alundum. Abrasive No. 150 was used in each case, and seven different lubricants, five different pressures, and three different lap materials were employed. The lubricants were lard oil, machine oil, kerosene, gasoline, turpentine, alcohol, and soda water.

These tests indicated throughout that there is, for each different combination of lap and lubricant, a definite size of grain that will give the maximum amount of cutting. With all the tests, except when using the two heavier lubricants, some reduction in the size of the grain below that used in the tests (No. 150) seemed necessary before the maximum rate of cutting was reached. This reduction, however, was continuous and soon passed below that which gave the maximum cutting rate.

Cutting Qualities with Different Laps. — The surfaces of the steel and cast-iron laps were finished by grinding. The hardness of the different laps, as determined by the scleroscope was, for cast-iron, 28; steel, 18; copper, 5. The total amount ground from the test-pieces with each of the three laps showed that, taking the whole number of tests as a standard, there is scarcely any difference between the steel and cast iron, but that copper has somewhat better cutting qualities, although, when comparing the laps on the basis of the highest and lowest values obtained with each lap, steel and cast iron are as good for all practical purposes as copper, when the proper abrasive and lubricant are used.

Wear of Laps. — The wear of laps depends upon the material from which they are made and the abrasive used. The wear on all laps was about twice as fast with carborundum as with emery, while with alundum the wear was about one and one-fourth times that with emery. On an average, the wear of the copper lap was about three times that of the cast-iron lap. This is not absolute wear, but wear in proportion to the amount ground from the test-pieces.

Lapping Abrasives. — As to the qualities of the three abrasives tested, it was found that carborundum usually began at a lower rate than the other abrasives, but, when once started, its rate was better maintained. The performance gave a curve that was more nearly a straight line. The charge or residue as the grinding proceeded remained cleaner and sharper and did not tend to become pasty or muck-like, as is so frequently the case with emery. When using a copper lap, carborundum shows but little gain over the cast-iron and steel laps, whereas, with emery and alundum, the gain is considerable.

Effect of Different Lapping Lubricants. — The action of the different lubricants was found to depend upon the kind of abrasive and the lap material.

Lard and Machine Oil. — The test showed that lard oil, without exception, gave the higher rate of cutting, and that, in general, the initial rate of cutting is higher with the lighter lubricants, but falls off more rapidly as the test continues. The lowest results were obtained with machine oil, when using an emery-charged, cast-iron lap. When using lard oil and a carborundum-charged steel lap, the highest results were obtained.

Gasoline and Kerosene. — On the cast-iron lap, gasoline was superior to any of the lubricants tested. Considering all three abrasives, the relative value of gasoline, when applied to the different laps, is as follows: Cast iron, 127; copper, 115; steel, 106. Kerosene, like gasoline, gives the best results on cast iron and the poorest on steel. The values obtained by carborundum were invariably higher than those obtained with emery, except when using gasoline and kerosene on a copper lap.

Turpentine and Alcohol. — Turpentine was found to do good work with carborundum on any lap. With emery, turpentine did fair work on the copper lap, but, with the emery on cast-iron and steel laps, it was distinctly inferior. Alcohol gives the lowest results with emery on the cast-iron and steel laps.

Soda Water. — Soda water gives medium results with almost any combination of lap and abrasives, the best work being on the copper lap and the poorest, on the steel lap. On the cast-iron lap, soda water is better than machine or lard oil, but not so good as gasoline or kerosene. Soda water when used with alundum on the copper lap, gave the highest results of any of the lubricants used with that particular combination.

Lapping Pressures. — Within the limits of the pressures used, that is, up to 25 pounds per square inch, the rate of cutting was found to be practically proportional to the pressure. The higher pressures of 20 and 25 pounds per square inch are not so effective on the copper lap as on the other materials.

Wet and Dry Lapping. — With the "wet method" of using a surface lap, there is a surplus of oil and abrasive on the surface of the lap. As the specimen being lapped is moved over it, there is more or less movement or shifting of the abrasive particles. With the "dry method," the lap is first charged by rubbing or rolling the abrasive into its surface. All surplus oil and abrasive are then washed off, leaving a clean surface, but one that has embedded uniformly over it small particles of the abrasive. It is then like the surface of a very fine oilstone and will cut away hardened steel that is rubbed over it. While this has been termed the dry method, in practice, the lap surface is kept moistened with kerosene or gasoline.

Experiments on dry lapping were carried out on the cast-iron, steel, and copper laps used in the previous tests, and also on one of tin made expressly for the purpose. Carborundum alone was used as the abrasive and a uniform pressure of 15 pounds per square inch was applied to the specimen throughout the tests. In dry lapping, much depends upon the manner of charging the lap. The rate of cutting decreased much more rapidly after the first 100 revolutions than with the wet method. Considering the amounts ground off during the first 100 revolutions, and the best result obtained with each lap taken as the basis of comparison, it was found that with a tin lap, charged by rolling No. 150 carborundum into the surface, the rate of cutting, when dry, approached that obtained with the wet method. With the other lap materials, the rate with the dry method was about one-half that of the wet method.

Summary of Lapping Tests. — The initial rate of cutting does not greatly differ for different abrasives. There is no advantage in using an abrasive coarser than No. 150. The rate of cutting is practically proportional to the pressure. The wear of the laps is in the following proportions: cast iron, 1.00; steel, 1.27; copper, 2.62. In general, copper and steel cut faster than cast iron, but, where permanence of form is a consideration, cast iron is the superior metal. Gasoline and kerosene are the best lubricants to use with a cast-iron lap. Machine and lard oil are the best lubricants with copper or steel laps. They are least effective on a cast-iron lap.

Honing Process

The hone-abrading process for obtaining cylindrical forms with precise dimensions and surfaces of fine quality, is applied to the surfaces of cylinder or other bores, bearings, pin holes, etc., and also to some external cylindrical surfaces. In honing, several desirable results are combined in the process. These include (1) generating a true cylindrical form by the rapid economical removal of metal necessary to eliminate whatever inaccuracies may have remained from a previous or preliminary machining operation; (2) obtaining a true cylindrical form of given diameter within extremely small dimensional limits (0.0002 to 0.0003 inch on many classes of work); (3) securing a final surface finish of practically any desired quality or degree of smoothness needed for precision work.

The honing tool contains abrasive stones or sticks which vary as to width, length, and thickness. These abrasive stones, as applied to a cylindrical bore, are expanded to bear evenly against it with a pressure that is varied to suit requirements. The honing machine imparts combined rotary and reciprocating motions to the hone which is self-centering in the bore. A true cylindrical form is generated by these combined motions in conjunction with positively controlled expansion and equalized pressure of the honing tool. The cutting action of the hone is also under control to secure the required surface quality. Honing pressures may be controlled either hydraulically or mechanically to obtain the required pressure cycle.

The amount of metal removed by honing varies for different classes of work and also depends upon the accuracy of the preceding operation. For example, from 0.001 to 0.003 inch may be removed from a ground hole; 0.003 to 0.005 inch from a reamed hole, and 0.005 to 0.010 inch from a bored hole. These figures are merely by way of illustration, and much larger amounts up to about 0.080 inch of stock, can be removed. In general, stock removal from bore diameters may be at rates of 0.009 to 0.012 inch per minute on cast iron, and 0.005 to 0.008 inch per minute on steel of 60 to 65 Rockwell C. These rates apply to lengths equal to three or four times the diameter. Stock has been removed from long parts such as gun barrels, at the rate of 65 cubic inches per hour. An ample and continuous supply of clarified coolant should be supplied in honing. The kind of coolant depends upon the material to be honed.

High-Speed Balancing

Static Balancing. — There are several methods of testing the standing or static balance of a circular part. A simple method that is sometimes used for flywheels, etc., is illustrated by the diagram, Fig. 1. An accurate shaft is inserted through the bore of the finished wheel, which is then mounted on carefully leveled "parallels" A. If the wheel is in an unbalanced state, it will turn until the heavy side is downward. When it will stand in any position as the result of counter-balancing and reducing the heavy portions, it is said to be in standing or static balance. Another test which is used for disk-shaped parts is shown in Fig. 2. The disk D is mounted on a vertical arbor attached to an adjustable cross-slide B. The latter is carried by a table C, which is supported by a knife-edged bearing. A pendulum having an adjustable screw-weight W at the lower end, is suspended from cross-slide B. To test the static balance of disk D, slide B is adjusted until pointer E of the pendulum coincides with the center of a stationary scale F. Disk D is then turned halfway around without moving the slide, and if the indicator remains stationary, it shows that the disk is in balance for this particular position. The test is then repeated for ten or twelve other positions, and the heavy sides are reduced, usually by drilling out the required amount of metal. There are several other devices for testing the static balance which are designed on this same principle.

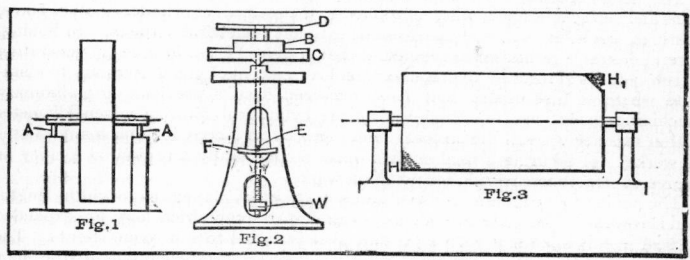

Fig.1   Fig.2   Fig.3

Running Balance. — A cylindrical body may be in perfect static balance and not be in a balanced state when rotating at high speed. If the rotating part is in the form of a thin disk, static balancing, if carefully done, may be accurate enough for high speeds, but if the rotating part is long in proportion to its diameter, and the unbalanced portions are at opposite ends or in different planes, the balancing must be done so as to counteract the centrifugal force of these heavy parts when they are rotating rapidly. This is known as a running balance or dynamic balancing. To illustrate, if a heavy section is located at H (Fig. 3), and another correspondingly heavy section at H_1, one may exactly counter-balance the other when the cylinder is stationary, and this static balance may be sufficient for a part rigidly mounted and rotating at a comparatively slow speed; but when the speed is very high, as in the case of turbine rotors, etc., the heavy masses H and H_1, being in different planes, are in an unbalanced state owing to the effect of centrifugal force, which results in excessive strains and injurious vibrations. Theoretically, to obtain a perfect running balance, the exact position of the heavy sections should be located and the balancing effected either by reducing their weight or by adding counter-weights opposite each section and in the same plane at the proper radius; but if the rotating part is rigidly mounted on a stiff shaft, a running balance that is sufficiently accurate for practical purposes can be obtained by means of comparatively few counter-balancing weights located with reference to the unbalanced parts.

Balancing Machines. — Several types of machines have been developed for testing the running or dynamic balance of machine parts. Some balancing machines are designed primarily for wheels, disks and comparatively narrow face parts, whereas others are arranged to test various classes of work, such as crankshafts, rotors of generators and motors, pulleys, spindles, etc. Balancing machines are widely used, particularly when rotative speeds are high and the requirements are exacting in regard to vibration.

CUTTING SPEEDS AND FEEDS

Cutting Speeds for Turning. — The cutting speed is governed principally by the hardness of the metal to be turned; the kind of steel of which the turning tool is made; the shape of the tool and its heat-treatment; the feed and depth of cut; the cooling medium used, if any; the power of the machine; and its design and condition. The table "Cutting Speeds and Feeds for Turning Tools" gives the speeds for a given depth of cut and feed when turning hard, medium and soft steel or cast iron. This table is based upon the results of the experiments conducted by Mr. F. W. Taylor, and it is assumed that a tool made of a good grade of high-speed steel, properly heat-treated and correctly ground, is used. It will be noted that the cutting speed is much slower for cast iron than for steel. Cast iron is cut with less pressure or resistance than soft steel, but the slower speed required for cast iron is probably due to the fact that the pressure of the chip is concentrated closer to the cutting edge, combined with the fact that cast iron wears the tool faster than steel. The speeds given are higher than those ordinarily used, and, in many cases, a slower rate would be necessary to prevent chattering, or because of some other limiting condition. Ordinary machine steel is generally turned at a speed varying between 90 and 150 feet per minute. For ordinary gray cast iron, the speed usually varies from 75 to 100 feet per minute; for annealed tool steel, from 50 to 60 feet per minute; for soft yellow brass, from 150 to 225 feet per minute; for hard bronze, from 50 to 100 feet per minute, the speed depending upon the composition of the alloy. These speeds are for high-speed steel cutting tools. They are intended as a general guide only. Most high-speed steel cutting tools are made from steel containing about 0.70 per cent carbon, 4 per cent chromium, 1 per cent vanadium, and 18 per cent tungsten. This high-tungsten low-vanadium steel is comparatively easy to harden. Cobalt-tungsten high-speed steels are used by some manufacturers, and good grades are particularly adapted for heavy cutting. Tests to determine the comparative durability of tungsten and cobalt-tungsten steels indicate that cobalt steels last two to three times longer between grinding. These cobalt steels require very careful forging, and from ½ to ⅟₁₆ inch should be ground off after hardening to remove a relatively soft outer layer. Their scleroscope hardness should be 80 to 90.

The cutting speed is limited by the durability of the turning tool or the length of time it will turn effectively without regrinding. The hardness of the metal being turned, combined with the quality of the tool, are the two factors, aside from the speed, which largely govern the time that the tool can be used before regrinding is necessary. The experiments of Mr. Taylor led to the conclusion that, as a rule, it is not economical to use roughing tools at a speed so slow as to cause them to last more than 1½ hours, without being reground; hence, the speeds given in the table previously referred to are based upon this length of time between grindings. Sometimes the work speed cannot be as high as the tool will permit, because of the chattering that often results when a machine is old or not massive enough to absorb the vibrations. The radius of the tool point or "nose" also affects the cutting speed and durability. Tests made in cast iron and steel showed that durability increased as the radius increased.

Speeds for Haynes Stellite Cutting Tools. — Haynes Stellite alloys consist essentially of cobalt, chromium, and tungsten, and contain no iron excepting a very small amount in the raw materials. An important property of these alloys is their high degree of "red hardness," which means that they can remain hard while at a red heat. There are several grades differing as to strength and ductility, thus adapting these alloys to a variety of applications. Stellite No. 3 is one grade adapted to metal cutting and especially for machining cast iron and malleable iron; it is also applicable to certain operations on steel.

Cutting Speeds and Feeds for Turning Tools*

Steel — Standard 7/8-inch Tool   Cast Iron — Standard 7/8-inch Tool

Depth of Cut in Inches	Feed in Inches	Speed in Feet per Minute for a Tool which is to last 1½ Hour before Re-grinding			Depth of Cut in Inches	Feed in Inches	Speed in Feet per Minute for a Tool which is to last 1½ Hour before Re-grinding		
		Soft Steel	Medium Steel	Hard Steel			Soft Cast Iron	Medium Cast Iron	Hard Cast Iron
3/32	1/64	476	238	108	3/32	1/16	122	61.2	35.7
	1/32	325	162	73.8		1/8	86.4	43.2	25.2
	1/16	222	111	50.4		3/16	70.1	35.1	20.5
	3/32	177	88.4	40.2	1/8	1/32	156	77.8	45.4
1/8	1/64	420	210	95.5		1/16	112	56.2	32.8
	1/32	286	143	65.0		1/8	79.3	39.7	23.2
	1/16	195	97.6	44.4		3/16	64.3	32.2	18.8
	1/8	133	66.4	30.2	3/16	1/32	137	68.6	40.1
3/16	1/64	352	176	80.0		1/16	99.4	49.7	29.0
	1/32	240	120	54.5		1/8	70.1	35.0	20.5
	1/16	164	82	37.3		3/16	56.8	28.4	16.6
	1/8	112	56	25.5	1/4	1/32	126	62.9	36.7
1/4	1/64	312	156	70.9		1/16	90.8	45.4	26.5
	1/32	213	107	48.4		1/8	64.1	32.0	18.7
	1/16	145	72.6	33.0		3/16	52	26.0	15.2
	3/32	116	58.1	26.4	3/8	1/32	111	55.4	32.3
3/8	1/64	264	132	60.0		1/16	80	40.0	23.4
	1/32	180	90.2	41.0		1/8	56.4	28.2	16.5
	1/16	122	61.1	27.8	1/2	1/32	104	52.1	30.4
1/2	1/64	237	118	53.8		1/16	75.2	37.6	22.0
	1/32	162	80.8	36.7		1/8	43.1	21.6	12.6

Steel — Standard 5/8-inch Tool   Cast Iron — Standard 5/8-inch Tool

Depth of Cut	Feed	Soft Steel	Medium Steel	Hard Steel	Depth of Cut	Feed	Soft Cast Iron	Medium Cast Iron	Hard Cast Iron
1/16	1/64	548	274	125	3/32	1/32	160	80.0	46.6
	1/32	358	179	81.6		1/16	110	55.0	32.2
	1/16	235	117	53.3		1/8	75.4	37.7	22.0
3/32	1/64	467	234	106	1/8	1/32	148	74.0	43.3
	1/32	306	153	69.5		1/16	104	51.8	32.0
	1/16	200	100	45.5		1/8	69.6	34.8	20.3
	3/32	156	78	35.5	3/16	1/64	183	91.6	68.0
1/8	1/64	417	209	94.8		1/32	135	67.5	39.4
	1/32	273	136	62.0		1/16	94	47.0	27.4
	1/16	179	89.3	40.6		1/8	64.3	32.2	18.8
	3/32	140	69.8	31.7	1/4	1/64	171	85.7	50.1
3/16	1/64	362	181	82.2		1/32	126	63.2	36.9
	1/32	236	118	53.8		1/16	87.8	43.9	25.6
	1/16	155	77.4	35.2		3/32	70.4	35.2	20.6
1/4	1/64	328	164	74.5	3/8	1/64	156	77.8	45.4
	1/32	215	107	48.8		1/32	116	57.8	33.8
3/8	1/64	286	143	65.0		1/16	79.7	39.9	23.3

* Cutting speeds for tools of a good grade of high-speed steel, properly ground and heat-treated.

The most efficient cutting speed for a given material and machine should be determined by tests under manufacturing conditions. For milling ordinary castings, try speeds around 100 feet per minute. If the castings are hard, much lower speeds may be necessary. For turning ordinary cast iron, try speeds from 125 to 150 feet per minute depending upon the depth of cut, rate of feed, and machinability of the metal. For yellow brass, try speeds from 250 to 300 feet per minute. Here are a few examples from practice which may be useful as a general guide:

Operation: milling rough cylinder blocks on a line-type milling machine; cutting speed, 110 feet per minute; feed, 10.5 inches per minute; depth of cut, ⅛ inch.

Operation: milling cylinder blocks on a drum-type milling machine; cutting speed, 120 feet per minute; feed, 18 inches per minute; depth of cut, ⅛ inch.

Operation: light-milling manifolds on a vertical mill; cutting speed, 148 feet per minute; feed, 15¼ inches per minute; depth of cut, ⅛ inch.

Operation: boring cylinder blocks. Note: Cutting speeds in a number of different plants range from 52 to 104 feet per minute, and feeds from 4½ to 8½ inches per minute.

Operation: turning bronze; cutting speed, 130 feet per minute.

Haynes Stellite J-Metal: A special grade of Stellite for cutting cast iron, semi-steel, and steel has been given the name of "J-metal." Tests conducted in actual production operations have shown that this metal, with the same feed and depth of cut used for turning cast iron and semi-steel with Grade 3 Stellite cutters, will operate at a maximum speed 50 per cent greater than was formerly possible for the most efficient results. At this higher speed, the number of pieces per grind equals that normally obtained at slower speeds. At the same speed, feed, and depth of cut, J-metal shows an increase in cutting life of at least 100 per cent over Grade 3 Stellite, and a ratio of 4 to 1 over the number of pieces formerly obtained per grind. The metal shows the same superiorities over standard Stellite in steel cutting operations.

Cutting Speeds for Cemented-carbide Tools. — All cutting speeds given in this handbook are intended as a general guide only. This is especially true of data on cutting alloys which belong in the cemented-carbide group. The data given for these comparatively new cutting materials represent what has been done under manufacturing conditions, but the figures, in some cases, may be far below the maximum speeds possible. The latter can only be determined by actual test with a given machine and material; and there is a wide range of maximum cutting speeds, even for the same cutting alloy and material, due to the influence of vibrations which may result from lack of adequate work and tool support.

In turning cast iron, cutting speeds of 200 to 350 feet per minute are commonly employed, and it may be possible, under very favorable conditions, to increase these speeds two or three times. On the contrary, a reduction in some of the speeds here recommended may be necessary due to such factors as lack of rigidity and hard cutting qualities of the material. Brass and the softer grades of bronze may be turned at speeds of from 400 to 500 feet per minute, and possibly at much higher speeds, depending upon the alloy and the rate of feed. Speeds for cast aluminum alloys ordinarily vary from 500 to 6000 or 8000 feet a minute, although lower speeds may be necessary if the alloy is high in silicon or highly abrasive. Cemented-carbide tools, however, may be applied successfully to abrasive materials. Marble, for example, has been turned at a speed of 400 feet a minute. These alloys have been used successfully for hard rubber, fiber, non-metallic gear materials, etc. Although cemented-carbide tools are particularly adapted to machining cast iron, semi-steel, malleable iron, brass, bronze, aluminum alloys, and the more special materials previously mentioned, they have also been developed for machining steel.

Cutting Speeds and Feeds for Cemented-carbide Tools

Examples from Practice. Tantalum-carbide tools were used for materials marked with asterisks (*) Column 2. Tungsten carbide was used for all other examples. These speeds and feeds are intended as a general guide only. The rigidity of the machine and tool support, interrupted cuts, and other factors result in wide variations in practice.

Machining Operation	Kinds of Material	Cutting Speed, Ft. per Min.	Depth of Cut, Inch	Rate of Feed		
				Per Rev.	Inches per Min.	Inch per Tooth
Turning	Cast Iron	250	¼	0.070	...	...
	Cast Iron	210	⅜	0.062	...	...
	Cast Iron (1)	260	3/16	0.015	...	...
	Cast Iron (2)	150	¼–¾	0.050	...	...
	Semi-Steel (3)	280	⅛	0.012	...	...
	Semi-Steel	300	...	...	...	...
	*Semi-Steel	225	...	0.028	...	...
	*Semi-Steel	286	5/32	0.015	...	...
	*Chilled C.I.	62	⅝	.....	...	...
	*S.A.E. 52100	185	⅛–5/16	0.020	...	...
	*Tool Steel 1.10%	140	½	0.020	...	...
	Silicon Steel	500	...	...	...	...
	Carbon Steel 0.90%	500	...	...	...	...
	Bronze	400	...	0.020	...	...
	Bronze	425	3/16	0.024	...	...
	Bronze	550	⅛	0.031	...	...
	Brass Casting (4)	458	3/32	0.108	...	...
	Cast Aluminum	1000	...	...	...	...
	Aluminum Alloy	570	⅛	0.031	...	...
Face Milling	Cast Iron	226	1/16	...	24¾	0.014
	Cast Iron	276	1/16	...	24¾	0.012
	Cast Iron	205	⅛	...	14½	0.009
	Cast Iron	280	3/32	...	32½	...
	Cast Iron	288	⅛	...	26	...
	Cast Iron	307	⅛	...	21	0.009
	Cast Iron	370	⅛	...	52½	0.012
	Cast Iron (5)	227	⅛	...	11	...
	Cast Iron (5)	235	⅛	...	9.3	...
	Cast Iron (5)	236	⅛	...	23	...
	Cast Iron	225	...	...	32	...
	*S.A.E. 1020	375	1/16	...	42	...
	Cast Aluminum	1285	⅛	...	80	0.008
End Milling	Cast Iron	263	⅛	...	38	0.007
	Cast Iron	214	⅛	...	38	0.009
	Cast Iron	273	...	...	38	0.006
Boring	Cast Iron	250	...	...	...	...
	Brass	350	...	...	...	...
	Aluminum	1500	...	...	...	...

(1) Interrupted cut. (2) Much higher speed possible for lighter cut. (3) 9 to 17 hours between tool grindings. (4) Six days between tool grindings. (5) These milling cutters used from 16 to 19 hours without sharpening.

Cutting Speeds and Feeds for Cemented-carbide Milling Cutters

Material to be Milled	Roughing, Feet per Minute		Finishing
	Over ⅛-inch depth of cut	Under ⅛-inch depth of cut	Under ¹⁄₁₆-inch depth of cut
Cast Iron, soft...............	200– 250	250– 325	300– 400
Cast Iron, medium..........	150– 200	200– 250	250– 300
Cast Iron, hard.............	100– 125	125– 175	150– 250
†Malleable Iron..............	225– 300	250– 350	350– 450
†*Cast Steel	100– 200	150– 250	200– 300
†*Low-carbon Steel, soft........	150– 200	175– 250	200– 350
†*Low-carbon Steel, medium	100– 150	150– 225	175– 250
†*Low-carbon Steel, hard.......	75– 100	100– 150	150– 200
Yellow Brass...............	300– 400	350– 500	400– 600
Ordinary Bronze............	200– 300	250– 350	350– 500
‡Aluminum..................	**	**	**

RECOMMENDED FEEDS IN INCH PER TOOTH PER CUTTER REVOLUTION

Material to be Milled	Roughing Depth ⅛–³⁄₁₆ inch	Semi-finishing Depth ¹⁄₁₆–⅛ inch	Finishing Depth ¹⁄₁₆ inch or under
Cast Iron.....................	0.008–0.010	0.009–0.014	0.006–0.008
Malleable Iron................	0.008–0.010	0.009–0.014	0.006–0.008
Brass........................	0.010–0.012	0.012–0.016	0.008–0.010
Bronze.......................	0.010–0.012	0.012–0.016	0.008–0.010
Aluminum....................	0.004–0.007	0.005–0.007	0.003–0.006
Steel........................	0.004–0.008	0.005–0.009	0.003–0.006

† Use Coolant.   * Tantalum Carbide Cutters.

** Cutting speeds for turning or milling aluminum alloys with carbide cutters, may range from 500 to 15000 ft. per min. or even higher (in some "high cycle" milling) depending upon the machinability of the alloy and the maximum speed of available equipment. As a general rule, the highest speed obtainable may be employed, with the possible exception of alloys having a high silicon content.

Note: The feed in inches per minute equals the feed per tooth per revolution multiplied by the number of cutter teeth multiplied by R.P.M.

Example: Find the feed in inches per minute and the speed in R.P.M. for a 5-inch cutter having 10 teeth. The depth of cut is ⅛ inch and the operation rough-milling soft cast iron.

The table indicates that a speed of about 250 feet per minute applies in this case. Divide 250 by the circumference of the cutter in feet to obtain the revolutions per minute. Thus, 250 ÷ 1.31 feet = 191 R.P.M.

The table shows a recommended feed per tooth from 0.008 to 0.010 inch. Next multiply the "teeth per minute" by 0.008 thus obtaining a table feed of 15.3 inches per minute. (The "teeth per minute" is obtained by multiplying the number of cutter teeth by the number of revolutions per minute.) In this example we have 0.008 × 10 × 191 = 15.3.

Cutting Speeds for Rigidly Mounted Tungsten-Carbide Tools

Material	Depth of Cut, Inch						
	1/32	1/16	3/32	1/8	5/32	3/16	1/4
	Cutting Speed, Feet per Minute						
Cast Iron, Soft, Brinell up to 185.............	330	310	290	275	260	245	225
Cast Iron, Medium, Brinell up to 205..........	270	260	240	220	210	190	170
Malleable Iron..........	350	330	310	300	285	275	250
Yellow Brass............	750	700	650	600	550	520	450
Ordinary Bronze........	450	420	390	370	350	330	300
Cast Aluminum.........	1500	1400	1300	1200	1125	1050	900

If the machine is in good condition, the tool is of ample size and rigidly mounted with practically no overhang, and the part itself is of solid design, it will then be possible to use the cutting speeds listed in the table which covers materials most commonly used. Generally speaking, carbide tools operate from two to four times faster than high-speed steel tools.

Typical Average Speeds, Feeds and Depths of Cut for Tantalum-Carbide Tools

Material Machined — Straight Cutting	Speed in Feet per Minute	Feed per Rev. in Inches	Depth of Cut, in Inches
Aluminum, Die-Cast (94 Al 6Si)...	1400 to 3500	0.002 to 0.020	0.062 to 0.125
Beryllium Bronze, Hardened.....	150 to 300	0.008 to 0.040	up to 3/8
Brass, Common Yellow..........	300 to 1000	0.008 to 0.040	up to 1 1/4
Gray Cast Iron up to 200 Brinell ...	165 to 400	0.040 to 0.080	0.040 to 3/8
Gray Cast Iron, 200 to 400 Brinell.	130 to 260	0.008 to 0.080	0.040 to 3/8
Cast Iron, Malleable..............	250 to 400	0.008 to 0.080	0.040 to 1/2
Cast Iron, Copper Silicon........	175 to 350	0.008 to 0.070	0.040 to 3/8
Chilled Cast Iron, 78 Scleroscope..	15 to 40	0.125 to 0.320	0.040 to 3/16
Armature Copper.................	800 to 1200	0.008 to 0.040	0.008 to 1/4
Electrode Carbon.................	150 to 300	0.020 to 3/8	0.040 to 1 1/2
Bakelite, Durez, etc..............	600 to 1000	0.012 to 0.050	0.004 to 1/4
Paper Calender Rolls.............	300 to 800	0.012 to 0.050	0.008 to 1/4
Steel, Soft S.A.E. 1015	200 to 1000	0.008 to 0.040	0.003 to 1/2
Steel, about 190 Brinell..........	200 to 1000	0.008 to 0.040	0.003 to 1/2
Steel, about 250 Brinell.........	175 to 600	0.008 to 0.040	0.003 to 3/8
Steel, S.A.E. 6150, 350 Brinell ...	175 to 300	0.008 to 0.040	0.003 to 1/4
Steel, Cast, 0.60 C, 0.60 Mn.......	175 to 300	0.010 to 0.040	0.050 to 3/8
Steel, Stainless, 460 Brinell........	175 to 400	0.004 to 0.040	0.003 to 1/4
Steel, Stainless 18–8.............	125 to 400	0.004 to 0.040	0.003 to 1/4
Steel, S.A.E. 4150, 325 Brinell	100 to 200	0.004 to 0.025	0.003 to 1/4
Steel, 0.50 C, 0.80 Mn, 0.60 Mo, 477 Br.	85 to 125	0.004 to 0.040	0.003 to 1/8
Steel, 2.50 Mn, 0.45 C............	100 to 175	0.004 to 0.040	0.003 to 3/16

While rather wide limits are given in this table, the higher speeds, in general, apply to the lighter, and the slower speeds to the heavier cuts. The speeds are dependent also upon the type of machine tools available and the rigidity of tool and work at the higher speeds.

The function of tantalum carbide is to resist the "cratering" action of chips. This resistance is due to certain fundamental differences between tantalum carbide and tool materials containing chiefly tungsten. The frictional resistance of tantalum carbide against metals is very low.

Feeds and Speeds for Carbide Tools on "Automatics." — Carbide-tipped tools give excellent results in machining both carbon and alloy steels. The following information is from the Carboloy Company.

Cutting Speeds: Too low a cutting speed will shorten the tool life and give an unsatisfactory finish on the work. The right cutting speed will produce a bright, smooth finish and prolong the tool life.

For turning, boring, and facing with ordinary single-point tools on various grades of steel, the cutting speed will depend upon the depth of cut, feed, and hardness of the metal to be cut. The usual range is from 200 to 350 surface feet per minute.

Feed per Revolution: Too fine a feed on rough-turning operations increases wear of the tool tip and makes chip disposal more difficult. Heavier feeds produce stiffer chips, which break more readily and can be handled more easily. When fine feeds are necessary, a carbide grade that has a high degree of wear resistance is recommended. Obviously, the choice of feed depends upon the type of tool used, the rigidity of the work, and the character of the steel being machined. Feeds from 0.010 to 0.020 inch per revolution are common for single-point or roller turner tools.

Form tools require fine feeds to prevent chatter. Feeds from 0.0025 to 0.005 inch per revolution are generally used, but on some steels feeds up to 0.010 inch are possible. A harder grade of carbide is generally used for form tools to resist the abrasion caused by fine feeds.

If the power available is insufficient, the feed may have to be decreased and a harder grade of carbide used. The depth of cut can also be reduced, but the speed should not be cut below the minimum for carbide tools.

Cutting Off: In cutting off, if the work has a hole drilled in the center, so that the tool does not have to cut to a dead center, little trouble is likely to be experienced; but when such operations are performed on solid steel parts with carbide tools, a built-up edge is frequently formed on the edge of the tool, causing dulling and flaking of the cutting edge. In some instances, it has been found possible to start a cut with a carbide cut-off tool and complete it with a high-speed steel tool.

The weight and the length of the piece being cut off must also be considered, as the "drop" may tend to cramp the tool and break the tip. If the piece being cut off has a hole in the center, a supporting bar may be fed into the hole to prevent the drop. If the work-piece has no hole, a V-guide can be fed under the work to support it and prevent cramping, or a guide with a hole fitting the outside of the work can be used to steady the overhanging piece.

For most types of steel cut in automatic screw machines, the rake angle of the carbide tool in the direction of the feed should be between 4 and 8 degrees on the chip-breaker surface. Rake angles up to 10 and even 15 degrees on the chip-breaker surface may be necessary when certain types of low-carbon, nickel-alloy, Nitralloy, stainless, and high-speed steels are to be cut.

Chip-breaker: Careful grinding of chip-breakers on carbide tools controls the dangerous ribbon chips which tend to wind around the tool-block and work. Chip curlers should be ground at an angle that will deflect the chip and cause it to clear the tool-holder or block. A chip-breaker should be ground at an angle to the side cutting edge to deflect the chip against the shoulder of the work and thus break it.

Cutting Fluid: The high cutting speeds used with carbide tools make the cooling quality of the cutting fluid an important item. Soft-soap base solubles help prevent rust, and cool the work effectively. Straight cutting oils are not usually recommended. An ample flow of coolant is necessary. The cutting fluid should be supplied through pipes at least $\frac{3}{8}$ inch in diameter, and the tank should be large enough to keep the coolant temperature reasonably low.

If there is any noticeable chatter, look for the following causes: Too light a tool section; too fine a feed; too large a nose radius; improperly ground tool; excessive tool overhand; a dull tool; or unsatisfactory support of the work.

Average Cutting Speeds and Feeds for Turning, Facing, and Boring with Haynes Stellite J-Metal

Type of Cut	Cutting Speed, Feet per Minute	Feed per Rev., In.	Cutting Speed, Feet per Minute	Feed per Rev., In.	Cutting Speed, Feet per Minute	Feed per Rev., In.
	Hard Cast Iron		Medium Cast Iron		Malleable Iron	
Rough-Turn......	60-90	0.020-0.062	100-150	0.020-0.125	125-175	0.020-0.035
Finish-Turn.......	150-175	0.020-0.035	150-175	0.020-0.050	150-200	0.020-0.035
Rough-Face.......	60-90	0.020-0.062	100-150	0.020-0.125	125-175	0.020-0.035
Finish-Face.......	150-175	0.020-0.035	150-175	0.020-0.050	150-200	0.020-0.035
Rough-Bore.......	60-90	0.020-0.062	80-150	0.020-0.125	100-175	0.020-0.035
Finish-Bore.......	100-150	0.020-0.035	125-175	0.020-0.050	150-200	0.020-0.035

Type of Cut	Steel Castings		S.A.E. No. 3115		Cold-Rolled Stock	
Rough-Turn......	60-125	0.015-0.030	125-175	0.020-0.030	200-300	0.020-0.035
Finish-Turn.......	125-200	0.010-0.020	150-200	0.010-0.020	300-400	0.010-0.020
Rough-Face.......	60-125	0.015-0.030	125-175	0.020-0.030	200-300	0.020-0.035
Finish-Face.......	125-200	0.010-0.020	150-200	0.010-0.020	300-400	0.010-0.020
Rough-Bore.......	60-125	0.015-0.030	125-175	0.015-0.030	200-300	0.015-0.030
Finish-Bore.......	125-200	0.010-0.020	150-200	0.010-0.020	200-350	0.010-0.020

Definite rules covering speeds and feeds for all materials and operations cannot be given because of variations in the hardness of the material being machined, the finish desired, the condition of the machine, the condition of the fixture, and the production requirements; however, the figures in the table will make it possible to estimate for general purposes what may be expected of J-Metal in turning, facing, and boring operations. The figures apply to dry machining. Cutting speeds may be increased 30 per cent if a coolant is used.

Speeds and Feeds for Drilling. — Drill speeds, in revolutions per minute, decrease as the drill diameter increases, but the peripheral speed should be practically constant for all diameters and for a given material. The feed should increase as the drill diameter increases. The speed is governed not only by the composition of the material to be drilled, but by the design and condition of the drilling machine, the shape and degree of sharpness of the drill point, and the quality of steel in the drill itself. There is no general agreement among the makers of high-speed twist drills as to what the cutting speed should be for ordinary shop practice. Some decrease the peripheral speed with the increase of drill diameter, others recommend the reverse, but most manufacturers advise a constant peripheral speed.

Drilling Speeds and Feeds for Different Materials. — The Cleveland Twist Drill Co. recommends the following speeds and feeds as a guide, until more definite data can be obtained in actual practice: Start at a moderate speed and feed. For carbon-steel twist drills, start at a peripheral speed of 30 feet per minute for machinery steel, 35 to 50 feet per minute for cast iron, 60 to 120 feet per minute for brass. For high-speed steel drills, start at a peripheral speed of 70 to 100 feet per minute for machinery steel, 70 to 150 feet per minute for cast iron, 50 to 70 feet per minute for alloy steel, 200 to 300 feet per minute for brass; see also the table on page 1491. The feeds are governed by the size of the drill and the material drilled. The general rule is to use a feed of 0.001 to 0.002 inch per revolution for drills smaller than 1/8 inch; 0.002 to 0.004 for drills 1/8 to 1/4 inch; 0.004 to 0.007 for drills 1/4 to 1/2 inch; 0.007 to 0.015 for drills 1/2 to 1 inch; and 0.015 to 0.025 for drills larger than

1 inch. The feeds for alloy and hard steels should generally be less than given in the foregoing, while cast iron, brass and aluminum may usually be drilled with a heavier feed. To maintain the speeds and feeds recommended, it will be necessary to use some good cutting compound.

A drill split up the web is evidence of too much feed or insufficient lip clearance at the center due to improper grinding. The rapid wearing away of the extreme outer corners of the cutting edges indicates that the speed is too high. The best results will be obtained when the effect of the work on the tool is somewhere between these conditions. A drill chipping or breaking out at the cutting edges indicates that either the feed is too heavy or the drill has been ground with too much lip clearance.

High Speed and Light Feed for Drilling. — A drill tempered to give maximum results drilling hard steel might be too brittle to work well in softer and tougher materials. Commercial twist drills are tempered for average conditions to give good results in either hard or soft material. In most cases, better results are obtained with a comparatively light feed and a high speed. For automatic machines, when the holes do not exceed two drill diameters in depth, and a flood of oil is used, high speeds and light feeds are especially recommended. For deeper holes, slower speeds and heavier feeds should be used in order to facilitate getting rid of the chips. Drills for automatic machines should, if possible, be ground so as to sever the chip in a small compact roll.

Nothing will "check" a high-speed drill quicker than to turn a stream of cold water on it after it has become heated while in use. It is equally bad to plunge it in cold water after the point has been heated in grinding. The small checks or cracks resulting from this practice will eventually chip out and cause rapid wear or breakage.

Insufficient speed in drilling small holes with hand feed greatly increases the risk of breakage, especially at the moment the point of the drill is breaking through the farther side of the work. This is due to the operator's inability to correctly gage the feed when the drill is running too slow.

Speeds for Tapping. — The speeds for tapping cast iron with high-speed steel taps, usually range from 70 to 90 feet per minute. The softer grades of steel, such as Bessemer, open-hearth, and screw stock may be tapped at speeds of 40 to 70 feet per minute under suitable conditions, and tough alloy steels at 20 to 40 feet per minute. Owing to the numerous alloys designated as brass, it is difficult to give speed data for them but, in general, the speeds for tapping brass may about double the speeds recommended for soft steel. The speeds for taps are usually somewhat less than for dies, as the former do not cut as freely nor discharge chips as readily; cooling compounds may also be applied to dies more effectively.

Speeds and Feeds for Thread Milling. — When milling screw threads, the surface speed of the blank may not exceed 2 or 3 inches per minute if the thread is of coarse pitch, and especially if the material is tough, whereas, when the pitches are finer and the material softer, the surface speed may be increased to 6 or 8 inches per minute for steel, and be two or three times faster for softer materials. The speed of the milling cutter usually varies from 100 to 125 feet per minute, with slower and faster speeds according to conditions. For instance, a speed of 100 feet per minute might be satisfactory for machine steel, whereas for tool steel, the speed might be reduced to about 70 feet per minute. The design of the machine and the general type may affect the speeds and feeds somewhat, and the steel used for the cutters is another important factor. In milling lead-screws or other accurate screws, it is preferable to feed rather slowly so that the stock may be thoroughly cooled, in order to avoid errors due to expansion and contraction.

Drilling Speeds for High-speed and Carbon Steel Drills*

Drill Diam., Inches	High-speed Steel Drills							
	Bronze, Brass, 300 Feet	Cast Iron, Annealed, 150 Feet	Cast Iron, Hard, 70 Feet	Mild Steel, 100 Feet	Drop Forgings, 60 Feet	Mal. Iron, 90 Feet	Tool Steel, 50 Feet	Cast Steel, 40 Feet
	Revolutions Per Minute							
1/16	....	9170	4278	6111	3660	....	3056	2440
1/8	9170	4584	2139	3056	1830	2745	1528	1220
3/16	6112	3056	1426	2037	1210	1830	1019	807
1/4	4585	2292	1070	1528	915	1375	764	610
5/16	3660	1833	856	1222	732	1138	611	490
3/8	3056	1528	713	1019	610	915	510	407
7/16	2614	1310	611	873	522	784	437	348
1/2	2287	1146	535	764	458	688	382	305
5/8	1830	917	428	611	366	569	306	245
3/4	1525	764	357	509	305	458	255	203
7/8	1307	655	306	436	261	392	218	174
1	1143	573	267	382	229	349	191	153
1 1/4	915	458	214	306	183	275	153	122
1 1/2	762	382	178	255	153	212	127	102
1 3/4	654	327	153	218	131	196	109	87
2	571	287	134	191	115	172	95	77

Drill Diam., Inches	Carbon Steel Drills							
	Bronze, Brass, 150 Feet	Cast Iron, Annealed, 70 Feet	Cast Iron, Hard, 30 Feet	Mild Steel, 30 Feet	Drop Forgings, 25 Feet	Mal. Iron, 35 Feet	Tool Steel, 25 Feet	Cast Steel, 20 Feet
	Revolutions Per Minute							
1/16	9170	4278	1833	1833	1528	2139	1528	1220
1/8	4585	2139	917	917	764	1069	764	610
3/16	3056	1426	611	611	510	713	510	407
1/4	2287	1070	458	458	382	535	382	305
5/16	1830	856	367	367	306	428	306	245
3/8	1525	713	306	306	255	357	255	203
7/16	1307	611	262	262	218	306	218	174
1/2	1143	535	229	229	191	268	191	153
5/8	915	428	183	183	153	214	153	122
3/4	762	357	153	153	127	178	127	102
7/8	654	306	131	131	109	153	109	87
1	571	267	115	115	95	134	95	77
1 1/4	458	214	92	92	76	107	76	61
1 1/2	381	178	76	76	64	89	64	51
1 3/4	327	153	65	65	54	76	54	44
2	286	134	57	57	48	67	48	39

* Based upon recommendations of the Cleveland Twist Drill Co.

Speeds and Feeds for Drilling Monel, Nickel, and Inconel *

Monel and Nickel

Drill Size, Inches	Speed, Feet per Minute	R.P.M.	Feed per Rev., Inches	Drill Size, Inches	Speed, Feet per Minute	R.P.M.	Feed per Rev., Inches
1/16	50	3055	0.0015	15/16	40	165	0.012
3/32	50	2100	0.0020	1	40	150	0.013
1/8	50	1525	0.0025	1 1/8	40	135	0.014
3/16	50	1020	0.003	1 1/4	40	120	0.015
1/4	60	920	0.0035	1 3/8	40	115	0.015
5/16	60	735	0.004	1 1/2	40	102	0.015
3/8	60	610	0.0045	1 5/8	40	100	0.016
7/16	60	525	0.005	1 3/4	40	85	0.016
1/2	60	460	0.0055	1 7/8	40	80	0.016
9/16	60	405	0.006	2	40	75	0.016
5/8	60	365	0.007	2 1/4	40	65	0.016
11/16	60	335	0.008	2 1/2	40	60	0.016
3/4	60	305	0.009	2 3/4	40	55	0.016
13/16	40	190	0.010	3	40	50	0.016
7/8	40	175	0.011	..	..	..	..

Inconel

Drill Size, Inches	Speed, Feet per Minute	R.P.M.	Feed per Rev., Inches	Drill Size, Inches	Speed, Feet per Minute	R.P.M.	Feed per Rev., Inches
1/16	40	2445	0.0015	15/16	30	120	0.012
3/32	40	1645	0.0020	1	30	115	0.013
1/8	40	1220	0.0025	1 1/8	30	100	0.014
3/16	40	815	0.003	1 1/4	30	90	0.015
1/4	45	685	0.0035	1 3/8	30	80	0.015
5/16	45	550	0.004	1 1/2	30	75	0.015
3/8	45	460	0.0045	1 5/8	30	70	0.016
7/16	45	395	0.005	1 3/4	30	65	0.016
1/2	45	345	0.0055	1 7/8	30	60	0.016
9/16	45	305	0.006	2	30	57	0.016
5/8	45	275	0.007	2 1/4	30	50	0.016
11/16	45	250	0.008	2 1/2	30	45	0.016
3/4	45	230	0.009	2 3/4	30	42	0.016
13/16	30	140	0.010	3	30	38	0.016
7/8	30	130	0.011	..	..	..	..

K-Monel (Unhardened)

Drill Size, Inches	Speed, Feet per Minute	R.P.M.	Feed per Rev., Inches	Drill Size, Inches	Speed, Feet per Minute	R.P.M.	Feed per Rev., Inches
1/16	25	1525	0.001	7/8	20	90	0.008
3/32	25	1050	0.0015	15/16	20	85	0.008
1/8	25	765	0.002	1	20	75	0.009
3/16	25	510	0.0025	1 1/8	20	67	0.009
1/4	30	460	0.003	1 1/4	20	60	0.010
5/16	30	370	0.0035	1 3/8	20	57	0.010
3/8	30	305	0.004	1 1/2	20	54	0.010
7/16	30	265	0.0045	1 5/8	20	50	0.011
1/2	30	230	0.005	1 3/4	20	43	0.011
9/16	30	205	0.0055	1 7/8	20	40	0.011
5/8	30	185	0.006	2	20	38	0.012
11/16	30	170	0.0065	2 1/4	20	32	0.012
3/4	30	155	0.007	2 1/2	20	30	0.012
13/16	20	95	0.0075	2 3/4	20	27	0.012

* International Nickel Co., Inc.

Cutting Speeds and Equivalent R.P.M. for Drills of Number and Letter Sizes

Size No.	Cutting Speed, Feet per Minute										
	30'	40'	50'	60'	70'	80'	90'	100'	110'	130'	150'
	Revolutions per Minute for Number Sizes										
1	503	670	838	1005	1173	1340	1508	1675	1843	2179	2513
2	518	691	864	1037	1210	1382	1555	1728	1901	2247	2593
4	548	731	914	1097	1280	1462	1645	1828	2010	2376	2741
6	562	749	936	1123	1310	1498	1685	1872	2060	2434	2809
8	576	768	960	1151	1343	1535	1727	1919	2111	2495	2879
10	592	790	987	1184	1382	1579	1777	1974	2171	2566	2961
12	606	808	1010	1213	1415	1617	1819	2021	2223	2627	3032
14	630	840	1050	1259	1469	1679	1889	2099	2309	2728	3148
16	647	863	1079	1295	1511	1726	1942	2158	2374	2806	3237
18	678	904	1130	1356	1582	1808	2034	2260	2486	2930	3380
20	712	949	1186	1423	1660	1898	2135	2372	2610	3084	3559
22	730	973	1217	1460	1703	1946	2190	2433	2676	3164	3649
24	754	1005	1257	1508	1759	2010	2262	2513	2764	3267	3769
26	779	1039	1299	1559	1819	2078	2338	2598	2858	3378	3898
28	816	1088	1360	1631	1903	2175	2447	2719	2990	3534	4078
30	892	1189	1487	1784	2081	2378	2676	2973	3270	3864	4459
32	988	1317	1647	1976	2305	2634	2964	3293	3622	4281	4939
34	1032	1376	1721	2065	2409	2753	3097	3442	3785	4474	5162
36	1076	1435	1794	2152	2511	2870	3228	3587	3945	4663	5380
38	1129	1505	1882	2258	2634	3010	3387	3763	4140	4892	5645
40	1169	1559	1949	2339	2729	3118	3508	3898	4287	5067	5846
42	1226	1634	2043	2451	2860	3268	3677	4085	4494	5311	6128
44	1333	1777	2221	2665	3109	3554	3999	4442	4886	5774	6662
46	1415	1886	2358	2830	3301	3773	4244	4716	5187	6130	7074
48	1508	2010	2513	3016	3518	4021	4523	5026	5528	6534	7539
50	1637	2183	2729	3274	3820	4366	4911	5457	6002	7094	8185
52	1805	2406	3008	3609	4211	4812	5414	6015	6619	7820	9023
54	2084	2778	3473	4167	4862	5556	6251	6945	7639	9028	10417
Size	Revolutions per Minute for Letter Sizes										
A	491	654	818	982	1145	1309	1472	1636	1796	2122	2448
B	482	642	803	963	1124	1284	1445	1605	1765	2086	2407
C	473	631	789	947	1105	1262	1420	1578	1736	2052	2368
D	467	622	778	934	1089	1245	1400	1556	1708	2018	2329
E	458	611	764	917	1070	1222	1375	1528	1681	1968	2292
F	446	594	743	892	1040	1189	1337	1486	1635	1932	2229
G	440	585	732	878	1024	1170	1317	1463	1610	1903	2195
H	430	574	718	862	1005	1149	1292	1436	1580	1867	2154
I	421	562	702	842	983	1123	1264	1404	1545	1826	2106
J	414	552	690	827	965	1103	1241	1379	1517	1793	2068
K	408	544	680	815	951	1087	1223	1359	1495	1767	2039
L	395	527	659	790	922	1054	1185	1317	1449	1712	1976
M	389	518	648	777	907	1036	1166	1295	1424	1683	1942
N	380	506	633	759	886	1012	1139	1265	1391	1644	1897
O	363	484	605	725	846	967	1088	1209	1330	1571	1813
P	355	473	592	710	828	946	1065	1183	1301	1537	1774
Q	345	460	575	690	805	920	1035	1150	1266	1496	1726
R	338	451	564	676	789	902	1014	1127	1239	1465	1690
S	329	439	549	659	769	878	988	1098	1207	1427	1646
T	320	426	533	640	746	853	959	1066	1173	1387	1600
U	311	415	519	623	727	830	934	1038	1142	1349	1557
V	304	405	507	608	709	810	912	1013	1114	1317	1520
W	297	396	495	594	693	792	891	989	1088	1286	1484
X	289	385	481	576	672	769	865	962	1058	1251	1443
Y	284	378	473	567	662	756	851	945	1040	1229	1418
Z	277	370	462	555	647	740	832	925	1017	1202	1387

For fractional drill sizes, use table on page 1516.

Speeds and Feeds For Milling, Drilling and Turning *

Speeds in Feet per Minute at Largest Diameter — Figures given in Body of Table

Material to be Machined. For materials marked (†) use a cooling compound. For those marked (‡) use lard oil or similar coolant.	Milling						Drilling		Turning						
	Carbon Steel Cutter		High-speed Steel Cutter		Stellite No. 3		Carbon Steel Drill	High-speed Steel	Carbon Steel Tool		High-speed Steel Tool		Stellite Tools		
	Rough.	Fin.	Rough.	Fin.	Rough.	Fin.			Rough.	Fin.	Rough.	Fin.	Stell. No.	Rough.	Fin.
Malleable	60	75	90	100	135	170	50	70	90	100	130	150	2	200	240
Cast Iron { Machine Castings	40	50	60	70	90	110	35	50	60	75	90	110	2	135	160
Med. Hard Castings	20	25	30	40	45	55	16	25	30	35	45	50	3	70	85
Hard Castings	10	12	15	20	22	27	8	12	15	18	22	25	3	35	42
Steel Castings †	30	35	45	55	65	80	25	35	45	55	65	80	2	100	120
Steel up to 0.30 % C. { Soft. Mach. St. †	60	75	90	110	135	170	50	70	90	110	130	160	1	200	240
Medium †	40	50	60	70	90	100	35	50	60	70	90	100	1	135	160
Fairly Hard †	25	35	40	50	55	80	20	30	35	45	50	65	1	80	95
Tool Steel, well annealed ‡	25	35	40	50	55	80	20	30	35	45	50	65	2	80	95
Cr. Ni. Steel, annealed ‡	25	35	40	50	55	80	20	30	35	45	50	65	2	80	95
Brass — Yellow	75	95	110	150	170	200	60	90	110	150	160	220	3	250	300
Bronze	40	50	60	70	90	100	35	50	66	70	90	100	3	135	160
Aluminum	460	550	700	900	1000	1200	350	550	700	900	1000	1300	3	1500	1800

Feeds. { The feed for rough-milling should be all that the machine, work, fixture and tool will withstand — the feed for roughing is usually too low. The feeds for finishing are, with spiral mills, about 0.005 inch per tooth per revolution; with face mills, about 0.010 inch per tooth per revolution. The drilling feeds per revolution are, for ⅛ inch diameter, 0.002 inch; ¼ inch diameter, 0.006 inch; ½ inch diameter, 0.007 inch; ¾ inch diameter, 0.010 inch. The feeds for rough-turning should be all that machine and work will withstand. Finishing feed depends upon finish required and kind of material and tool.

* These speeds and feeds were compiled by the Kempsmith Mfg. Co. as representing conservative, modern practice. They are intended only as a general guide, and when all conditions are favorable, may often be increased considerably; or, in the case of hard materials, they must sometimes be less than those given. The speeds for tools of simple form which are easy to grind and replace, such as lathe tools, etc., should be much higher than the speeds for tools, such as milling cutters, which are more difficult to grind and must last longer between the sharpening periods to secure greater economy. The speeds should be reduced for tools used in machines of the automatic class, because such tools, as a rule, require more time for resetting in the working position.

Torque, Thrust and Horsepower Required for Drilling

Material and Heat-treatment	Hardness of Material			Drill Diam., Inches	Feed, Inch per Rev.	Drill Speed, R.P.M.	Torque, Pounds-Feet	Thrust in Pounds	H.P. at Drill Point
	Brinell No.	Rock-well B Scale	Sclero-scope						
Cast Iron (Regular) No Heat-treatment	143	76	30	½	0.009	446	6.0	500	0.51
				⅝	0.011	364	10.0	621	0.70
				¾	0.012	302	15.6	760	0.90
				1	0.013	230	27.7	1006	1.22
				1¼	0.015	179	43.3	1270	1.49
				1½	0.015	153	63.0	1517	1.85
Steel S.A.E. 1020 No Heat-treatment	137	84	29	½	0.009	442	11.5	626	0.97
				⅝	0.011	368	19.4	732	1.34
				¾	0.012	298	29.2	910	1.67
				1	0.013	228	54.0	1415	2.35
				1¼	0.015	176	87.9	1900	2.96
				1½	0.015	150	120.0	2150	3.46
Steel S.A.E. 1045 Normalized at 1600 F. Annealed at 1475 F.	159	82	28	½	0.009	445	11.0	636	0.94
				⅝	0.011	368	19.6	762	1.38
				¾	0.012	298	29.1	959	1.66
				1	0.013	228	54.0	1490	2.45
				1¼	0.015	176	93.0	2000	3.13
				1½	0.015	150	127.0	2300	3.77
Steel S.A.E. 1095 (Tool Steel) Annealed	154	85	25	½	0.009	445	15.4	852	1.31
				⅝	0.011	363	24.8	1067	1.72
				¾	0.012	298	37.4	1566	2.14
				1	0.013	225	74.0	2575	3.19
				1¼	0.015	176	114.8	3327	3.86
				1½	0.015	150	167.2	3983	4.78
Steel S.A.E. 2320 Annealed at 1600 F.	163	85.5	25	½	0.009	446	11.0	618	0.94
				⅝	0.011	368	18.7	728	1.32
				¾	0.012	298	27.7	1027	1.58
				1	0.013	228	51.3	1615	2.23
				1¼	0.015	176	86.1	2058	2.90
				1½	0.015	151	118.0	2506	3.54
Steel S.A.E. 3135 Normalized at 1575 F. Annealed at 1500 F.	192	88.5	29	½	0.009	446	10.4	647	0.89
				⅝	0.011	371	17.5	813	1.25
				¾	0.012	298	26.3	1200	1.50
				1	0.013	228	50.8	1683	2.21
				1¼	0.015	176	88.0	2100	2.96
				1½	0.015	151	117.0	2600	3.38
Steel S.A.E. 3250 Normalized at 1650 F. Annealed at 1475 F.	207	92.5	30	½	0.009	445	12.4	728	1.06
				⅝	0.011	369	20.5	875	1.45
				¾	0.012	298	31.9	1363	1.82
				1	0.013	227	59.0	2137	2.57
				1¼	0.015	179	109.4	2988	3.76
				1½	0.015	150	143.1	3225	4.13
Steel S.A.E. 6150 Normalized at 1650 F. Annealed at 1550 F.	187	86.5	29	½	0.009	444	14.0	725	1.19
				⅝	0.011	368	22.3	838	1.57
				¾	0.012	299	34.3	1269	1.97
				1	0.013	228	62.4	1862	2.72
				1¼	0.015	175	110.8	2430	3.71
				1½	0.015	149	143.3	3000	4.10

Data from paper by O. W. Boston and C. J. Oxford, presented before the American Society of Mechanical Engineers. In making these tests, sharp twist drills were used and a coolant consisting of one part of soluble oil and sixteen parts of water.

Approximate Pressures in Pounds Required for Feeding Drills

Drill Diam., Inches	Feed per Revolution, Inches						
	0.004	0.006	0.008	0.010	0.012	0.014	0.016
	Feeding Pressures for Cast Iron						
1/16	75	125	150	200	235	275	325
1/8	100	150	200	250	300	350	400
1/4	135	200	275	325	400	460	525
3/8	175	250	325	410	500	575	650
1/2	200	300	400	500	590	685	780
5/8	250	350	475	580	700	810	925
3/4	275	400	540	675	800	925	1050
7/8	300	450	600	750	900	1035	1190
1	350	500	675	825	1000	1150	1325
Diam.	Pressures for 30 Per Cent Semi-steel						
1/16	75	110	150	......	......	......	......
1/8	100	150	210	265	310	......	......
1/4	160	235	315	390	465	535	610
3/8	210	310	410	505	605	700	800
1/2	265	375	500	625	740	860	975
5/8	315	450	600	725	875	1025	1160
3/4	350	525	675	850	1000	1175	1330
7/8	375	575	750	925	1125	1300	1475
1	430	630	830	1030	1230	1430	1630
Diam.	S.A.E. 0.20 Per Cent Carbon Steel (1020) — 28 Scleroscope						
1/16	60	90	110	125	......	......	......
1/8	110	150	190	225	260	......	......
1/4	200	275	350	415	480	550	625
3/8	300	400	500	600	700	800	900
1/2	390	525	650	775	915	1050	1175
5/8	475	650	800	975	1135	1300	1460
3/4	575	775	960	1150	1350	1575	1750
7/8	675	900	1125	1350	1575	1800	......
1	760	1025	1275	1550	1800	......	......
Diam.	S.A.E. Nickel-chromium Steel (3140) — 45 Scleroscope						
1/16	100	125	160	190	......	......	......
1/8	150	200	250	290	325	......	......
1/4	300	375	450	575	600	690	760
3/8	425	550	660	775	890	1000	1125
1/2	550	700	860	1000	1160	1325	1450
5/8	675	875	1050	1250	1425	1625	1800
3/4	800	1025	1250	1475	1700	......	......
7/8	925	1175	1450	1700	......	......	......
1	1050	1325	1600	......	......	......	......

Factor of safety of 1.5 should be allowed for increase in pressure when drills become dull; the pressures given are for sharp drills having normal points.

Cutting Speeds and Feeds for Turret Lathes

Material	Cutting Speeds (Ft. per Min.) for Roughing Cuts		Feeds per Revolution for Roughing Cuts	
	H.S. Steel Cobalt (18-4-1)	Carbide	Ram Type Machine	Saddle Type Machine
Cast Iron..................	50 to 60	180 to 200	0.016 to 0.025	0.032 to 0.060
Semi-steel (hard)..........	40 to 50	140 to 160	0.016 to 0.025	0.032 to 0.060
Malleable iron*...........	80 to 100	250 to 300	0.016 to 0.025	0.032 to 0.060
Steel Casting (0.35% carbon)*....................	45 to 60	150 to 180	0.010 to 0.020	0.018 to 0.030
Brass (85-5-5)	200 to 300	600 to 1000	Maximum	Maximum
Bronze (80-10-10)*..........	110 to 150	600	0.016 to 0.030	0.016 to 0.050
Aluminum**..............	400	800	***	***
SAE 1020 (Coarse feed)*...	60 to 80	300	0.020 to 0.030	0.024 to 0.044
SAE 1020 (Fine feed)*.....	100 to 120	450	0.007 to 0.020	0.010 to 0.030
SAE 1035*...............	75 to 90	250	0.020 to 0.030	0.024 to 0.044
S.A.E. 1050*.............	60 to 80	200	0.012 to 0.020	0.025 to 0.090
SAE 1118 (old X-1315)*....	175 to 200	400 to 500	0.010 to 0.015	0.010 to 0.015
SAE 2317 (old 2315)*	90 to 110	300	0.012 to 0.020	0.025 to 0.090
SAE 3150*................	50 to 60	200	0.012 to 0.020	0.025 to 0.090
SAE 4150*................	60 to 80	200	0.012 to 0.020	0.025 to 0.090

* The asterisk indicates that a water soluble oil lubricant is used.
** The double asterisk indicates that a kerosene lubricant is used.
*** Fine feeds to produce good finish.
Note: These speeds and feeds (obtained from Warner & Swazey Co.) are intended as a general guide only and are subject to change because of variations in materials, type of machine and its condition, type of cutting tool and method of mounting, cutting fluid used, if any, and method of holding work.

Cutting Speeds for Stainless Steels. — The physical properties of stainless steels vary considerably; consequently, there is a corresponding variation in cutting speed data. The chips of free-cutting grades are short and brittle. The chips of other stainless steels are tough and stringy and slower speeds should be employed. The cutting speeds which follow are based upon data of the Rustless Iron & Steel Corporation and apply to single-point turning tools. The speeds in all cases are in surface feet per minute.

Straight Chromium Hardenable Steels. — These speeds are recommended for annealed or cold drawn steels (200 to 240 Brinell). Carbide Tools: 100 to 200 for roughing; 150 to 400 for finishing. High Cobalt or Cast Alloys: 60 to 150 for roughing; 80 to 200 for finishing. Tungsten or Molybdenum H.S.S.: 40 to 100 for roughing; 60 to 150 for finishing.

Steels in this group can be hardened and tempered to provide a wide range of mechanical properties.

Straight Chromium Non-Hardenable Steels (Annealed or Cold Drawn). — Carbide Tools: 140 to 200 for roughing; 150 to 400 for finishing. High Cobalt or Cast Alloys: 100 to 150 for roughing; 100 to 200 for finishing. Tungsten or Molybdenum H.S.S.: 60 to 100 for roughing; 80 to 150 for finishing.

Chromium-Nickel Steels (Annealed or Cold Drawn). — Carbide Tools: 130 to 250 for roughing; 150 to 400 for finishing.   High Cobalt or Cast Alloys: 100 to 150 for roughing; 100 to 200 for finishing.   Tungsten or Molybdenum H.S.S.: 60 to 120 for roughing; 100 to 140 for finishing.

Cutting Speeds for Threading Dies. — When conducting tests to determine the most economical speed for threading dies, it is preferable to begin with a relatively slow speed and increase it as much as the die will stand without excessive dulling.   As dies are not sharpened so easily as some other forms of cutting tools, this should be considered when determining the speed.   See table below.

Cutting Speeds for Threading Dies — High-Speed Steel Chasers

Material to be Threaded	Threads per Inch			
	4 to 7	8 to 14	16 to 24	28 up
	Surface Speeds — Ft. per Min.			
Steel Screw Stock	20	30	40	50
Carbon Steel 1040–1095....	15	20	25	30
Alloy Steels...............	8	10	15	20
Brass Rod................	50	100	150	200
Aluminum Rod..........	50	100	150	200
Bronze....................	40	80	100	150
Monel Metal.............	8	10	15	20
Stainless Steel...........	8	10	15	20

Th'd Dia.	Surface Speeds and Equivalent R.P.M.											
	8	10	15	20	25	30	40	50	80	100	150	200
¼	122	153	229	306	382	458	611	764	1222	1528	2292	3056
⅜	81	102	153	204	255	306	407	509	815	1019	1528	2036
½	61	76	115	153	191	229	306	382	611	764	1146	1528
⅝	49	61	92	122	153	184	244	306	489	611	917	1224
¾	41	51	76	102	127	153	204	255	407	509	762	1016
⅞	35	44	65	87	109	131	175	218	349	437	657	876
1	31	38	57	76	95	115	153	191	306	382	573	764
1⅛	27	34	51	68	85	102	136	170	272	340	510	680
1¼	24	30	46	61	76	92	122	153	244	306	458	612
1⅜	22	28	42	56	69	83	111	139	222	278	417	556
1½	20	25	38	51	64	76	102	127	204	255	382	508
1⅝	19	23	35	47	59	70	94	118	188	235	351	468
1¾	17	22	33	44	55	65	87	109	175	218	327	436
1⅞	16	20	31	41	51	61	81	102	163	204	306	408
2	15	19	29	38	48	57	76	95	153	191	287	382

Hacksaw Speeds. — The following hacksaw speeds are given on the authority of a leading manufacturer: The total amount of travel of the cutting blade in feet per minute, including forward and return strokes, should be as follows: For mild steel, 130; for annealed tool steel, 90; and for unannealed tool steel, 60 feet per minute.   Thus in the case of a 6-inch stroke, for example, the revolutions per minute of the driving crank should be 130 for mild steel, 90 for annealed tool steel, and 60 for unannealed tool steel.   All of these steels are cut with the use of a cutting compound.   Bronze can ordinarily be cut at the same speed as mild steel when a suitable compound is used.   Brass heats the blade very rapidly if cut dry, and must be cut with a cooling compound adapted to brass.   It also fills up the teeth of the saw if not used with the right kind of compound, but with a suitable compound, it may be cut at the same speed as machine steel.

Tool Life Between Successive Grindings. — In establishing cutting speeds, the "life" of a tool between grindings, or the time elapsing before it requires sharpening, is an important factor. The time required for tool-sharpening and replacement should be considered. For example, a simple lathe tool is more readily ground and replaced than a tool such as might be found on an automatic screw machine. In the case of a lathe, cutting speeds for rough turning usually are established so that the tool life between grindings will not be less than 30 or 40 minutes and not longer than $1\frac{1}{2}$ hours, whereas cutting speeds for "automatics" usually permit operating continuously for several hours. A common method of increasing the tool life, especially on automatics, is to use exceptionally durable cutting tools such as cobalt high-speed steels and carbide tools.

Ratio of Feed to Depth of Cut. — Tests have shown that a cutting speed representing a certain "tool life," does not remain constant for a given area of cut because it is affected by the relation between the depth of the cut and the feeding movement. In turning, if the depth of cut is doubled and the feed reduced one-half, the cutting speed usually can be increased 25 to 40 per cent. This increase is due to the fact that there is a narrower chip and twice as much cutting edge in contact with the work; consequently, the cooling area for conducting away the heat is larger. If the cutting speed is increased 25 per cent by doubling the depth of cut and reducing the feed one-half, the cubic inches of metal removed in a given time will also be increased 25 per cent. Tests have demonstrated that a depth of cut for turning, equal to 8 times the feed, is a desirable ratio. The depth ordinarily varies from 5 to 10 times the feed in taking roughing cuts.

Planing Speeds. — The speeds for planing cast iron and steel usually vary from 30 to 55 feet per minute on the cutting stroke, with a return speed three to four times as great. A general idea of planer speeds may be obtained from the following figures, given by the Cincinnati Planer Co., and representing the practice in some of the best machine shops: Cast iron, roughing, 45 to 55 ft. per min.; cast iron, finishing, 30 to 40 ft. per min.; steel castings, roughing, and finishing, 30 to 40 ft. per min.; mild steel forgings, roughing 45 to 55 ft. per min. and finishing 30 to 40 ft. per min.; bronze and brass, roughing, 150 to 200 ft. per min. and finishing, 100 to 150 ft. per min.; aluminum, roughing, 200 to 300 ft. per min. Planing speeds are lower than cutting speeds for turning because in planing it seldom is practicable to use an ample supply of cutting fluid. The net or actual cutting speeds for various combinations of forward and return speeds are given in the table, "Actual Cutting Speeds of Planers." The upper half of this table shows how many feet per minute the planer actually cuts, and the lower half gives the same data in feet per hour. A slight increase in the forward speed has a much greater effect on the net cutting speed and rate of production than a comparatively high increase of the return speed. To illustrate, when the cutting speed is 30 feet per minute and the return speed, 90 feet per minute, a planer tool actually cuts 22.5 feet per minute. If the return speed is increased to 150 feet per minute, the net cutting speed is increased to 25 feet — a gain of 2.5 feet for a return-speed increase of approximately 66 per cent. If the cutting speed is increased to 35 feet (the return speed remaining at 90), the net cutting speed is increased to approximately 25 feet per minute, as before, but with a cutting speed increase of only about 16 per cent. Hence, it is important to have the cutting speed as high as conditions will permit.

Feeds for Planing. — The feed of a planing tool varies widely for different kinds of material and classes of work; it is also governed by the depth of cut, the nature of the cut (whether roughing or finishing), and by the rigidity of the work when clamped in position for planing. Feeds ordinarily vary from $\frac{1}{16}$ to $\frac{1}{8}$ inch for rough-planing steel, and from $\frac{1}{8}$ to $\frac{3}{16}$ inch for roughing cast iron. When taking light finishing cuts in cast iron, a broad tool having a flat edge is commonly used and the feed ordinarily varies from ¼ to ½ inch per stroke. When planing large rigid castings, a feed as coarse as ¾ or 1 inch per stroke is often employed.

Actual Cutting Speeds of Planers

Cutting Speed, Feet per Minute	Return Speed, Feet per Minute							
	50	60	70	80	90	100	120	150
	Actual Number of Feet Traversed on Cutting Strokes per Minute							
20	14.3	15.0	15.5	16.0	16.4	16.7	17.1	17.6
25	16.7	17.6	18.4	19.0	19.6	20.0	20.7	21.4
30	18.7	20.0	21.0	21.8	22.5	23.1	24.0	25.0
35	20.6	22.0	23.3	24.3	25.2	25.9	27.1	28.4
40	22.2	24.0	25.4	26.7	27.7	28.6	30.0	31.6
45	23.7	25.7	27.4	28.8	30.0	31.0	32.7	34.6
50	25.0	27.3	29.2	30.8	32.1	33.3	35.3	37.5
	Actual Number of Feet Traversed on Cutting Strokes per Hour							
20	857	900	933	960	981	1000	1028	1058
25	1000	1058	1105	1142	1173	1200	1241	1285
30	1125	1200	1260	1309	1350	1384	1440	1500
35	1235	1321	1400	1460	1512	1555	1625	1702
40	1333	1440	1527	1600	1661	1714	1800	1894
45	1421	1542	1643	1728	1800	1862	1964	2076
50	1500	1636	1750	1846	1928	2000	2117	2250

Speeds and Feeds for Gear Cutting. — The variations in speed and feed, owing to limiting conditions, are probably greater for gear cutting than for most other machining operations. The important factors governing the speed and feed, aside from the design and condition of the machine, are the pitch of the gear to be cut, the hardness of the metal, the kind of steel used for making the cutter, the form and condition of the cutter, the rigidity of the gear blank when mounted for cutting, the accuracy and finish required for the gear, and the cutting lubricant used in the case of steel gears. The following speeds are given by Gould & Eberhardt as a fair average for cutting medium grades of cast iron and steel, when using carbon and high-speed steel cutters:

Material	Carbon Steel Cutters			High-speed Steel Cutters		
	Min.	Average	Max.	Min.	Average	Max.
Cast Iron, Feet per Minute.......	35	45	60	60	70	80
Steel, Feet per Minute..........	25	30	40	45	50	55

While these figures are based upon gear-cutting practice, they are merely intended to serve as a guide until the most economical speed for a given case can be determined by actual tests. More specific data on speeds and feeds are given in the table "Speeds and Feeds for Gear Cutting." This table applies to machines of the rotary-cutter type and covers diametral pitches varying from 1 to 20. The feeds and speeds listed are for cast iron and steel gears of medium grade, with suitable variations for carbon or high-speed steel cutters. The first column gives the maximum capacity of the machine, in diametral pitch; it will be noted that the values vary somewhat for a gear of given pitch, for machines of different capacity. For example, when a cast-iron gear of 6 diametral pitch is cut on a machine having a capacity of 3 diametral pitch, the feed per minute is given as 4.5 inches; but when the same pitch is cut on a larger machine of 2 diametral pitch capacity, the feed can be increased to 11.5 inches per minute, high-speed steel cutters being used in each case.

Feeds for Given Pitch and Material. — The tables "Feeds for Gear Cutting" contain practical data on the feeds to use for different materials and pitches. The data in the table apply to high-speed steel cutters and are intended as a general guide only. The feeds listed vary according to diametral pitch, kind of material and nature of cut. The shearing-tooth cutter for roughing, referred to in the tables, is an ordinary gear cutter having faces of alternate teeth ground at an angle of 11 degrees, so that the teeth have rake and cut similar to a side turning tool. Cast-iron gears up to 2½ diametral pitch can usually be finished in one cut with a rotary formed cutter. Cast-iron gears coarser than 2 diametral pitch should, as a rule, have the teeth roughened or "blocked out" prior to finishing.

Feeds for Hobbing. — The feeds for hobbing usually vary from about 0.020 to 0.200 inch per revolution of the gear. Gould & Eberhardt recommend the following feeds for hobbing spur gears. The figures give the movement of the hob per revolution of the gear.

Material	Feed, Inches	Material	Feed, Inches	Material	Feed, Inches
Tool Steel......	0.010	Soft Steel.......	0.040	Roughing Soft Steel..........	0.080
Tough Steel....	0.020	Average Cast Iron..........	0.050	Roughing Average Cast Iron...	0.100
Average Steel...	0.030	Soft Cast Iron ..	0.060	Roughing Soft Cast Iron.......	0.150

When hobbing helical gears, the feed depends somewhat upon the angle of the teeth. For angles varying from 0 to 36 degrees the feed should be about the same as for spur gears; for angles from 36 to 48 degrees, the feed should equal ⅘ of that for spur gears; from 48 to 60 degrees, ⅔ of the spur gear feed; from 60 to 70 degrees, ½ of the spur gear feed; for angles above 70 degrees, ⅓ of the spur gear feed. The feed is diminished in the case of helical gears, because when the hob is set to conform to the helix angle, the feed of the cutter, per revolution, is increased by the turning movement of the gear blank necessary for generating the helical teeth.

Speeds and Feeds for Gear Cutting *

Capacity of Machine	Diam. Pitch	Cutter		R.P.M.		Cutting Speed, Feet per Min.		Feed per Min.		No. of Cuts	
		Diam.	No. of Teeth	Cast Iron	Steel	Cast Iron	Steel	Cast Iron	Steel	Cast Iron	Steel
				High-speed Steel Cutters							
1 D.P. for Cast Iron 1¼ D.P. for Steel	1.00	8.00	13	27.5	22.5	58	47.5	3.5	2.8	2	2
	1.25	7.25	14	33.5	22.5	64	43.5	4.5	2.8	2	2
	1.50	7.25	14	33.5	22.5	64	43.5	4.5	2.8	2	2
	1.75	6.25	10	40.5	27.5	67	45.5	4.5	2.8	2	2
	2.00	6.25	11	40.5	27.5	67	45.5	4.5	3.5	2	2
	2.25	6.25	11	40.5	27.5	67	45.5	4.5	3.5	1	2
	2.50	6.25	14	40.5	27.5	67	45.5	5.6	3.5	1	2
	2.75	5.25	12	49.5	33.5	69	46.5	6.9	4.5	1	2
	3.00	5.25	12	49.5	33.5	69	46.5	6.9	4.5	1	2
	4.00	5.25	16	49.5	33.5	69	46.5	8.5	5.6	1	2
	5.00	5.25	18	49.5	33.5	69	46.5	11.0	6.9	1	2
	6.00	4.25	16	60.5	40.5	68	45.5	11.0	6.9	1	2
				High-speed Steel Cutters							
2 D.P. for Cast Iron 3 D.P. for Steel	2.00	6.25	11	38	26.5	63	44	4	2.7	2	3
	2.25	6.25	11	38	26.5	63	44	4	2.7	2	2
	2.50	6.25	14	38	26.5	63	44	6	4	1	2
	2.75	5.25	12	48	33	67	46	6	4	1	2
	3.00	5.25	12	48	33	67	46	6	4	1	2
	4.00	5.25	16	48	33	67	46	7.3	6	1	2
	5.00	5.25	18	48	33	67	46	9	6	1	2
	6.00	4.25	16	60.5	38	68	43	11.5	7.3	1	2
	7.00	4.25	18	60.5	38	68	43	11.5	7.3	1	2
	8.00	4.25	20	60.5	38	68	43	14.5	9.1	1	1
	10.00	4.25	22	60.5	38	68	43	14.5	9.1	1	1
	12.00	4.25	24	60.5	38	68	43	14.5	9.1	1	1
				High-speed Steel Cutters							
3 D.P. for Cast Iron 4 D.P. for Steel	3.00	4.75	11	46.5	39	59	49	3.5	2.6	1	2
	4.00	4.00	12	55.5	46.5	59	49	4.5	3.5	1	2
	5.00	3.50	12	55.5	46.5	51.5	43	4.5	3.5	1	2
	6.00	3.50	13	55.5	46.5	51.5	43	4.5	3.5	1	2
	7.00	3.50	14	55.5	46.5	51.5	43	5.8	4.5	1	2
	8.00	3.50	16	55.5	46.5	51.5	43	5.8	4.5	1	1
	10.00	3.50	18	55.5	46.5	51.5	43	7.6	5.8	1	1
	12.00	3.50	18	55.5	46.5	51.5	43	7.6	5.8	1	1
	14.00	2.875	16	79	55.5	60	40.5	10.0	7.6	1	1
	16.00	2.875	18	79	55.5	60	40.5	10.0	7.6	1	1
	18.00	2.875	18	79	55.5	60	40.5	10.0	7.6	1	1
	20.00	2.875	20	79	55.5	60	40.5	10.0	7.6	1	1

* Compiled by Gould & Eberhardt.

Feeds for Gear Cutting

Compiled by the Cincinnati Gear Cutting Machine Co. The gears are assumed to be of substantial design, and the belts on the machine to be in good condition. For steel gears, a lard oil lubricant is used. For teeth coarser than $1\frac{3}{4}$ diametral pitch, feeds are not given for finishing in one cut, because satisfactory results cannot be obtained with a single cut on the No. 7 machine.

For *High-speed Steel Cutters* with a peripheral speed on cast iron of 55 feet per minute and 80 feet per minute on steel.

Diametral Pitch of Gear	Cast-iron Gears	Soft Steel Gears	High-carbon Steel	Nickel-steel Alloy	Cast-iron Gears	Soft Steel Gears	High-carbon Steel	Nickel-steel Alloy	Arrows Indicate Range of Different Sizes of Machines
	Feed, Inches per Min., when Finishing in One Cut				Feed, Inches per Min. for Roughing Cut, leaving 0.010 to 0.030 Inch for Finishing				
1	....	....	....	....	2	$1\frac{5}{8}$	$1\frac{5}{8}$	$1\frac{1}{4}$	
$1\frac{1}{4}$	....	....	....	....	$2\frac{1}{2}$	2	2	$1\frac{5}{8}$	
$1\frac{1}{2}$	....	....	....	....	$3\frac{3}{8}$	$2\frac{1}{16}$	$2\frac{1}{16}$	$2\frac{1}{16}$	
$1\frac{3}{4}$	$2\frac{1}{16}$	$2\frac{1}{16}$	$2\frac{1}{16}$	$1\frac{11}{16}$	$4\frac{3}{8}$	$3\frac{3}{8}$	$3\frac{3}{8}$	$2\frac{11}{16}$	
2	$3\frac{1}{8}$	$2\frac{1}{2}$	$2\frac{1}{2}$	$1\frac{15}{16}$	$5\frac{1}{8}$	4	4	$3\frac{1}{8}$	
$2\frac{1}{2}$	$3\frac{1}{8}$	$2\frac{1}{2}$	$2\frac{1}{2}$	$1\frac{15}{16}$	$5\frac{1}{8}$	4	4	$3\frac{1}{8}$	
3	$3\frac{7}{16}$	$2\frac{1}{2}$	$2\frac{1}{2}$	2	$5\frac{7}{16}$	$4\frac{1}{4}$	$4\frac{1}{4}$	$3\frac{7}{16}$	
4	$3\frac{7}{16}$	$2\frac{1}{2}$	$2\frac{1}{2}$	2	$5\frac{7}{16}$	$4\frac{1}{4}$	$4\frac{1}{4}$	$3\frac{7}{16}$	
5	$3\frac{7}{16}$	$2\frac{1}{2}$	$2\frac{1}{2}$	2	$5\frac{7}{16}$	$4\frac{1}{2}$	$4\frac{1}{4}$	$3\frac{7}{16}$	No. 3
6	$4\frac{1}{4}$	$3\frac{7}{16}$	$3\frac{7}{16}$	$2\frac{1}{2}$	$5\frac{7}{16}$	$4\frac{1}{4}$	$4\frac{1}{4}$	$3\frac{7}{16}$	No. 4
7	$4\frac{1}{4}$	$3\frac{7}{16}$	$3\frac{7}{16}$	$2\frac{1}{2}$	$5\frac{7}{16}$	$4\frac{1}{4}$	$4\frac{1}{4}$	$3\frac{7}{16}$	No. 5
8	$4\frac{1}{4}$	$3\frac{7}{16}$	$3\frac{7}{16}$	$2\frac{1}{2}$	$5\frac{7}{16}$	$4\frac{1}{4}$	$4\frac{1}{4}$	$3\frac{7}{16}$	No. 6
9	$5\frac{7}{16}$	$4\frac{1}{4}$	$4\frac{1}{4}$	$3\frac{7}{16}$	$6\frac{13}{16}$	$5\frac{7}{16}$	$5\frac{7}{16}$	$4\frac{1}{4}$	No. 7
10	$5\frac{7}{16}$	$4\frac{1}{4}$	$4\frac{1}{4}$	$3\frac{7}{16}$	$6\frac{13}{16}$	$5\frac{7}{16}$	$5\frac{7}{16}$	$4\frac{1}{4}$	
	When using Shearing Tooth Cutter for Roughing Cut				Finishing Cut				
1	$2\frac{1}{2}$	2	2	$1\frac{5}{8}$	$2\frac{11}{16}$	$2\frac{11}{16}$	$2\frac{11}{16}$	$2\frac{1}{16}$	
$1\frac{1}{4}$	$3\frac{5}{16}$	$2\frac{1}{2}$	$2\frac{1}{2}$	2	$3\frac{5}{16}$	$3\frac{5}{16}$	$3\frac{5}{16}$	$2\frac{11}{16}$	
$1\frac{1}{2}$	$4\frac{3}{8}$	$4\frac{3}{8}$	$3\frac{3}{8}$	$3\frac{3}{8}$	$4\frac{3}{8}$	$4\frac{3}{8}$	$4\frac{3}{8}$	$3\frac{3}{8}$	
$1\frac{3}{4}$	$5\frac{9}{16}$	$5\frac{9}{16}$	$4\frac{3}{8}$	$4\frac{1}{16}$	$5\frac{9}{16}$	$5\frac{9}{16}$	$5\frac{9}{16}$	$4\frac{3}{8}$	
2	$6\frac{9}{16}$	$6\frac{9}{16}$	$5\frac{1}{8}$	$4\frac{1}{16}$	$6\frac{9}{16}$	$6\frac{9}{16}$	$6\frac{9}{16}$	$5\frac{1}{8}$	
$2\frac{1}{2}$	$6\frac{9}{16}$	$6\frac{9}{16}$	$5\frac{1}{8}$	$4\frac{1}{16}$	$6\frac{9}{16}$	$6\frac{9}{16}$	$6\frac{9}{16}$	$5\frac{1}{8}$	
3	$8\frac{1}{2}$	$8\frac{1}{2}$	$6\frac{13}{16}$	$5\frac{7}{16}$	$6\frac{13}{16}$	$6\frac{13}{16}$	$6\frac{13}{16}$	$5\frac{7}{16}$	No. 3
4	$8\frac{1}{2}$	$8\frac{1}{2}$	$6\frac{13}{16}$	$5\frac{7}{16}$	$6\frac{13}{16}$	$6\frac{13}{16}$	$6\frac{13}{16}$	$6\frac{13}{16}$	No. 4
5	$8\frac{1}{2}$	$8\frac{1}{2}$	$6\frac{13}{16}$	$5\frac{7}{16}$	$6\frac{13}{16}$	$6\frac{13}{16}$	$6\frac{13}{16}$	$6\frac{13}{16}$	No. 5
6	$8\frac{1}{2}$	$8\frac{1}{2}$	$6\frac{13}{16}$	$5\frac{7}{16}$	$6\frac{13}{16}$	$6\frac{13}{16}$	$6\frac{13}{16}$	$6\frac{13}{16}$	No. 6
7	$8\frac{1}{2}$	$8\frac{1}{2}$	$6\frac{13}{16}$	$5\frac{7}{16}$	$6\frac{13}{16}$	$6\frac{13}{16}$	$6\frac{13}{16}$	$6\frac{13}{16}$	No. 7
8	$10\frac{5}{8}$	$10\frac{5}{8}$	$8\frac{1}{2}$	$8\frac{1}{2}$	$6\frac{13}{16}$	$6\frac{13}{16}$	$6\frac{13}{16}$	$6\frac{13}{16}$	
9	$10\frac{5}{8}$	$10\frac{5}{8}$	$8\frac{1}{2}$	$8\frac{1}{2}$	$8\frac{1}{2}$	$8\frac{1}{2}$	$8\frac{1}{2}$	$8\frac{1}{2}$	
10	$10\frac{5}{8}$	$10\frac{5}{8}$	$8\frac{1}{2}$	$8\frac{1}{2}$	$8\frac{1}{2}$	$8\frac{1}{2}$	$8\frac{1}{2}$	$8\frac{1}{2}$	

Hollow Milling, Drilling, Reaming, Threading and Knurling

Hollow Mills. — For roughing cuts, especially in brass, a hollow mill gives satisfactory results. The accompanying table gives the proportions of hollow mills and cutting angles for various materials. In applying these hollow mills for roughing machine screws or other small screws, use a mill having a diameter *A* that will leave from 0.005 to 0.015 inch for finishing, the allowance depending upon the size of the screw. In making these hollow mills, they should be reamed out tapering from the rear to give clearance to the blades. A taper of from ⅛ to ³⁄₁₆ inch per foot is usually satisfactory. For steel, the cutting edge is set about ¹⁄₁₀ off the diameter ahead of the center, but for brass, it should be on the center-line.

Speeds for External Cutting Tools. — The following speeds are applicable to external cutting tools, such as box-tool cutters, hollow mills, etc. These speeds are intended for average conditions on the materials specified.

Material	Surface Speed, Feet per Minute	
	Carbon Steel	High-speed Steel
Brass (ordinary quality).....................	170–180	250–270
Gun-screw iron................................	70– 80	100–120
Norway iron and machine steel..................	60– 70	90–100
Drill rod and tool steel........................	35– 40	50– 60

Centering Tools. — When drilling holes which are less than ³⁄₁₆ inch in diameter in the automatic screw machine, it is always advisable, especially if the hole passes through the work, to use a starting or centering tool. The included angle of the cutting edges on the centering tool should be less than the angle of the drill which is to follow, as otherwise the point of the drill will start to cut before the body of the drill is properly supported, and the drill may not start concentric with the work. The included angle of the point which has been found suitable for centering tools varies from 90 to 100 degrees, 90 degrees being preferable for brass and 100 degrees for steel. When the material is quite hard, a centering tool having a double angle is sometimes used. The point has an included angle of 118 degrees, while the remaining part of the cutting edge has an included angle of 90 degrees. This strengthens the point of the tool and, at the same time, a center is formed that supports the body of the drill before the point begins to cut. The table "Length of Point on Twist Drills and Centering Tools" was compiled to facilitate determining the rise on the cam necessary for the centering operation. Feeds which have been found satisfactory for general work are given in the table "Feeds for Centering Tools."

Feeds for Centering Tools

Diameter in Inches	Feed in Inches per Revolution		
	Brass Rod	Machine Steel	Tool Steel
¼	0.004	0.003	0.002
⁵⁄₁₆	0.004	0.004	0.003
⅜	0.005	0.0045	0.004
½	0.0055	0.005	0.0045
¾	0.006	0.005	0.005
1	0.0065	0.005	0.0055

Proportions of Hollow Mills

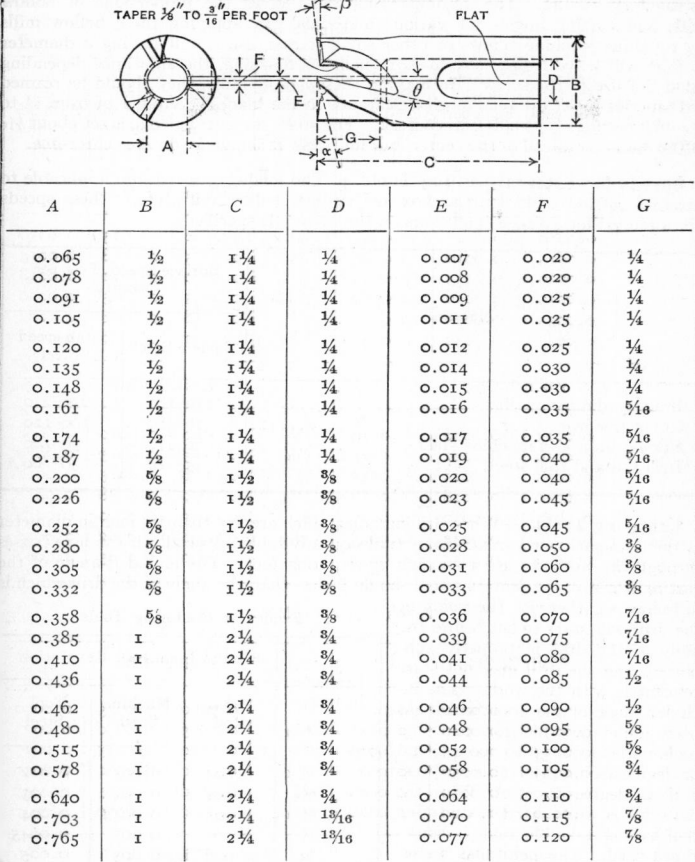

A	B	C	D	E	F	G
0.065	½	1¼	¼	0.007	0.020	¼
0.078	½	1¼	¼	0.008	0.020	¼
0.091	½	1¼	¼	0.009	0.025	¼
0.105	½	1¼	¼	0.011	0.025	¼
0.120	½	1¼	¼	0.012	0.025	¼
0.135	½	1¼	¼	0.014	0.030	¼
0.148	½	1¼	¼	0.015	0.030	¼
0.161	½	1¼	¼	0.016	0.035	5⁄16
0.174	½	1¼	¼	0.017	0.035	5⁄16
0.187	½	1¼	¼	0.019	0.040	5⁄16
0.200	⅝	1½	⅜	0.020	0.040	5⁄16
0.226	⅝	1½	⅜	0.023	0.045	5⁄16
0.252	⅝	1½	⅜	0.025	0.045	5⁄16
0.280	⅝	1½	⅜	0.028	0.050	⅜
0.305	⅝	1½	⅜	0.031	0.060	⅜
0.332	⅝	1½	⅜	0.033	0.065	⅜
0.358	⅝	1½	⅜	0.036	0.070	7⁄16
0.385	1	2¼	¾	0.039	0.075	7⁄16
0.410	1	2¼	¾	0.041	0.080	7⁄16
0.436	1	2¼	¾	0.044	0.085	½
0.462	1	2¼	¾	0.046	0.090	½
0.480	1	2¼	¾	0.048	0.095	⅝
0.515	1	2¼	¾	0.052	0.100	⅝
0.578	1	2¼	¾	0.058	0.105	¾
0.640	1	2¼	¾	0.064	0.110	¾
0.703	1	2¼	13⁄16	0.070	0.115	⅞
0.765	1	2¼	13⁄16	0.077	0.120	⅞

Cutting Angles for Hollow Mills

Angle	Brass Rod	Machine Steel	Tool Steel
α	8 degrees	15 degrees	10 degrees
β	8 degrees	5 degrees	3 degrees
θ	. . . .	15 degrees	10 degrees

Feeds for Swing Tools and Hollow Mills
(High-speed or Carbon Steel Tools)

Feeds for Swing Tools

Smallest Diam. of Stock	Brass Rod, Feed per Revolution	Machine Steel, Feed per Revolution	Tool Steel, Feed per Revolution	Smallest Diam. of Stock	Brass Rod, Feed per Revolution	Machine Steel, Feed per Revolution	Tool Steel, Feed per Revolution
1/32-inch Chip				**1/8-inch Chip**			
1/16	0.0010	0.0008	0.0005	3/8	0.0020	0.0015	0.0010
1/8	0.0015	0.0010	0.0008	7/16	0.0025	0.0018	0.0015
3/16	0.0020	0.0015	0.0010	1/2	0.0030	0.0020	0.0018
1/4	0.0030	0.0020	0.0015	9/16	0.0035	0.0025	0.0020
5/16	0.0035	0.0025	0.0018	5/8	0.0038	0.0028	0.0022
3/8	0.0040	0.0030	0.0020	11/16	0.0042	0.0030	0.0025
1/16-inch Chip				**3/16-inch Chip**			
1/4	0.0025	0.0020	0.0010	1/2	0.0020	0.0010	0.0008
5/16	0.0030	0.0022	0.0013	9/16	0.0025	0.0013	0.0010
3/8	0.0035	0.0025	0.0015	5/8	0.0028	0.0015	0.0012
7/16	0.0040	0.0028	0.0018	11/16	0.0030	0.0018	0.0015
1/2	0.0045	0.0030	0.0020	3/4	0.0035	0.0020	0.0018
9/16	0.0050	0.0032	0.0025	13/16	0.0038	0.0022	0.0020
5/8	0.0060	0.0035	0.0028	7/8	0.0040	0.0025	0.0020

Feeds for Hollow Mills

Smallest Diam. of Stock	Brass Rod, Feed per Revolution	Machine Steel, Feed per Revolution	Tool Steel, Feed per Revolution	Smallest Diam. of Stock	Brass Rod, Feed per Revolution	Machine Steel, Feed per Revolution	Tool Steel, Feed per Revolution
1/16-inch Chip				**3/16-inch Chip**			
3/16	0.0045	0.0030	0.0015	1/2	0.0060	0.0045	0.0020
1/4	0.0050	0.0040	0.0018	9/16	0.0065	0.0050	0.0023
5/16	0.0055	0.0045	0.0020	5/8	0.0070	0.0055	0.0025
3/8	0.0060	0.0050	0.0025	11/16	0.0080	0.0060	0.0030
7/16	0.0070	0.0050	0.0028	3/4	0.0090	0.0065	0.0035
1/2	0.0080	0.0060	0.0030	13/16	0.0100	0.0070	0.0040
1/8-inch Chip				**1/4-inch Chip**			
3/8	0.0070	0.0050	0.0030	5/8	0.0050	0.0035	0.0015
7/16	0.0075	0.0055	0.0035	11/16	0.0055	0.0040	0.0018
1/2	0.0080	0.0060	0.0040	3/4	0.0060	0.0050	0.0020
9/16	0.0090	0.0065	0.0050	13/16	0.0070	0.0055	0.0025
5/8	0.0110	0.0075	0.0060	7/8	0.0080	0.0060	0.0030
11/16	0.0130	0.0090	0.0070	......	......	......	......
3/4	0.0150	0.0110	0.0080	......	......	......	......

Length of Point on Twist Drills and Centering Tools

Size of Drill	Decimal Equivalent	Length of Point, Angle = 90°	Length of Point, Angle = 118°	Size of Drill	Decimal Equivalent	Length of Point, Angle = 90°	Length of Point, Angle = 118°	Size or Diam. of Drill	Decimal Equivalent	Length of Point, Angle = 90°	Length of Point, Angle = 118°	Diam. of Drill	Decimal Equivalent	Length of Point, Angle = 90°	Length of Point, Angle = 118°
60	0.0400	0.020	0.012	37	0.1040	0.052	0.031	14	0.1820	0.091	0.055	3/8	0.3750	0.188	0.113
59	0.0410	0.021	0.012	36	0.1065	0.054	0.032	13	0.1850	0.093	0.056	25/64	0.3906	0.195	0.117
58	0.0420	0.021	0.013	35	0.1100	0.055	0.033	12	0.1890	0.095	0.057	13/32	0.4063	0.203	0.122
57	0.0430	0.022	0.013	34	0.1110	0.056	0.033	11	0.1910	0.096	0.057	27/64	0.4219	0.211	0.127
56	0.0465	0.023	0.014	33	0.1130	0.057	0.034	10	0.1935	0.097	0.058	7/16	0.4375	0.219	0.131
55	0.0520	0.026	0.016	32	0.1160	0.058	0.035	9	0.1960	0.098	0.059	29/64	0.4531	0.227	0.136
54	0.0550	0.028	0.017	31	0.1200	0.060	0.036	8	0.1990	0.100	0.060	15/32	0.4688	0.234	0.141
53	0.0595	0.030	0.018	30	0.1285	0.065	0.039	7	0.2010	0.101	0.060	31/64	0.4844	0.242	0.145
52	0.0635	0.032	0.019	29	0.1360	0.068	0.041	6	0.2040	0.102	0.061	1/2	0.5000	0.250	0.150
51	0.0670	0.034	0.020	28	0.1405	0.070	0.042	5	0.2055	0.103	0.062	33/64	0.5156	0.258	0.155
50	0.0700	0.035	0.021	27	0.1440	0.072	0.043	4	0.2090	0.105	0.063	17/32	0.5313	0.266	0.159
49	0.0730	0.037	0.022	26	0.1470	0.074	0.044	3	0.2130	0.107	0.064	35/64	0.5469	0.273	0.164
48	0.0760	0.038	0.023	25	0.1495	0.075	0.045	2	0.2210	0.111	0.067	9/16	0.5625	0.281	0.169
47	0.0785	0.040	0.024	24	0.1520	0.076	0.046	1	0.2280	0.114	0.068	37/64	0.5781	0.289	0.173
46	0.0810	0.041	0.024	23	0.1540	0.077	0.046	15/64	0.2344	0.117	0.070	19/32	0.5938	0.297	0.178
45	0.0820	0.041	0.025	22	0.1570	0.079	0.047	1/4	0.2500	0.125	0.075	39/64	0.6094	0.305	0.183
44	0.0860	0.043	0.026	21	0.1590	0.080	0.048	17/64	0.2656	0.133	0.080	5/8	0.6250	0.313	0.188
43	0.0890	0.045	0.027	20	0.1610	0.081	0.048	9/32	0.2813	0.141	0.084	41/64	0.6406	0.320	0.192
42	0.0935	0.047	0.028	19	0.1660	0.083	0.050	19/64	0.2969	0.148	0.089	21/32	0.6563	0.328	0.197
41	0.0960	0.048	0.029	18	0.1695	0.085	0.051	5/16	0.3125	0.156	0.094	43/64	0.6719	0.336	0.202
40	0.0980	0.049	0.029	17	0.1730	0.087	0.052	21/64	0.3281	0.164	0.098	11/16	0.6875	0.344	0.206
39	0.0995	0.050	0.030	16	0.1770	0.089	0.053	11/32	0.3438	0.171	0.103	23/32	0.7188	0.359	0.216
38	0.1015	0.051	0.030	15	0.1800	0.090	0.054	23/64	0.3594	0.180	0.108	3/4	0.7500	0.375	0.225

Speeds for Drilling. — When drilling in automatic screw machines designed for high speeds, the best results are generally obtained by giving the drills light feeds and high peripheral velocities. High-speed steel drills are adapted to drilling Norway iron, machine steel, tool steel, etc., and ordinary carbon steel drills are used for brass and similar materials, when the surface speed does not exceed that given in the following:

Material	Surface Speed, Feet per Minute	
	Carbon Steel	High-speed Steel
Brass (ordinary quality)......................	160–180	....
Gun-screw iron...............................	60– 70	100–125
Norway iron and machine steel.................	50– 60	80–100
Drill rod and tool steel.......................	30– 40	50– 60

Feeds for Drilling. — Feeds for high-speed and ordinary carbon steel twist drills are given in the table "Feeds for Twist Drills used in Automatic Screw Machines." These feeds are for general work and can be increased in some cases. For general practice, it is more satisfactory to use rather light feeds, as a straighter hole can be produced than when the drill is forced. Drills from ⅛ inch to ³⁄₁₆ inch in diameter are capable of standing the heaviest feeds in proportion to their diameter, and when a hole does not pass through the work, a ⅛-inch drill has been fed as much as 0.016 inch per revolution when drilling brass. Feeds as heavy as this are not recommended, because concentric holes cannot be produced when the drill is forced to such an extent.

Feeds for Twist Drills Used in Automatic Screw Machines
(High-speed and Carbon Steel Drills)

Drill Size	Feed per Revolution			Drill Size	Feed per Revolution		
	Brass Rod	Machine Steel	Tool Steel		Brass Rod	Machine Steel	Tool Steel
70	0.00070	0.00060	0.00050	⁹⁄₃₂	0.0058	0.0052	0.0042
65	0.00075	0.00065	0.00055	⁵⁄₁₆	0.0059	0.0055	0.0043
60	0.00080	0.00070	0.00060	¹¹⁄₃₂	0.0060	0.0058	0.0045
56	0.00120	0.00100	0.00080	⅜	0.0062	0.0060	0.0048
¹⁄₁₆	0.00180	0.00150	0.00100	¹³⁄₃₂	0.0065	0.0062	0.0050
⁵⁄₆₄	0.00250	0.00200	0.00120	⁷⁄₁₆	0.0068	0.0065	0.0052
³⁄₃₂	0.00250	0.00230	0.00150	¹⁵⁄₃₂	0.0070	0.0068	0.0055
⁷⁄₆₄	0.00300	0.00250	0.00180	½	0.0070	0.0070	0.0058
⅛	0.00320	0.00280	0.00200	¹⁷⁄₃₂	0.0072	0.0072	0.0059
⁹⁄₆₄	0.00350	0.00300	0.00230	⁹⁄₁₆	0.0075	0.0075	0.0060
⁵⁄₃₂	0.00380	0.00320	0.00250	¹⁹⁄₃₂	0.0078	0.0078	0.0062
¹¹⁄₆₄	0.00400	0.00350	0.00280	⅝	0.0080	0.0079	0.0063
³⁄₁₆	0.00420	0.00400	0.00300	²¹⁄₃₂	0.0082	0.0080	0.0064
¹³⁄₆₄	0.00450	0.00420	0.00320	¹¹⁄₁₆	0.0085	0.0082	0.0065
⁷⁄₃₂	0.00480	0.00450	0.00350	¾	0.0090	0.0083	0.0068
¹⁵⁄₆₄	0.00500	0.00480	0.00380	¹³⁄₁₆	0.0095	0.0085	0.0069
¼	0.00550	0.00500	0.00400	⅞	0.0100	0.0088	0.0070

Counterboring. — As a rule, more trouble is experienced in using counterbores on automatic machines than with any other cutting tool. This is probably due to the fact that counterbores are generally improperly made for the work on which they are to operate. Generally speaking, there are several reasons for the unsuccessful working of counterbores, some of which may be summed up as follows: 1. Too many cutting edges, not allowing enough chip space and also not providing for sufficient lubrication. 2. Too much cutting surface in contact with the work. 3. Insufficient clearance on the periphery of the teeth. 4. Improper location of the cutting edges relative to the center. 5. Improper method of holding the counterbore. 6. Improper grinding of the cutting edges. 7. Too weak a cross-section. 8. The use of a feed and speed in excess of what the tool will stand.

For work in automatic machines, where the counterbore cannot be withdrawn when it plugs up with chips and seizes in the work, the tool should not have more than three cutting teeth. The periphery of the teeth should be backed off eccentrically, and the body of the counterbore should taper towards the back. The amount of taper generally varies from 0.020 to 0.040 inch per foot. The relation of the cutting edge to the center has an important bearing on the efficiency of the tool. For deep counterboring, where the difference between the diameter of the teat and the body of the counterbore is great, the cutting edge should never be located ahead of the center; often, if it is located a little behind the center, better results are obtained; but this rule is only general, as the material to a considerable extent governs the location of the cutting edges. It is advisable to have the cutting edge ahead of the center when the counterbore is to be used as a facing tool, or for counterboring brass, provided it is not required to enter the work to a depth greater than its diameter. For general work, the cutting edges should be radial. Straight flutes are suitable for either brass or steel, but for steel, it is better to have the teeth cut spirally, the spiral being sufficient to give a rake of from 10 to 15 degrees. If the difference between the diameter of the pilot and the body of the counterbore is not very great, and if the counterbore must extend into the work to a depth greater than its diameter, the cutting edge should be back of the center, that is, to the rear of the radial line parallel to the cutting face. When the counterbore has to remove considerable material or enter the work to a depth greater than its diameter, it is generally advisable to rough out the hole to the diameter of the body of the counterbore with a three-fluted drill; then the counterbore is used only for squaring up the bottom of the hole. This method is especially advisable when counterboring machine or tool steel.

Speeds for Counterbores. — The surface speed at which a counterbore can be worked is slightly less than the surface speed used for drilling. The surface speeds given below are recommended for counterbores made from carbon and high-speed steel.

Material	Surface Speed, Feet per Minute	
	Carbon Steel	High-speed Steel
Brass (ordinary quality)........................	150–160	180–200
Gun-screw iron................................	50– 60	80– 90
Norway iron and machine steel..................	40– 50	70– 80
Drill rod and tool steel.........................	30– 35	45– 50

Feeds for Counterbores. — The method of holding a counterbore when applying it to the work, and the strength of the cross-section in proportion to the width of the chip being removed, governs, to a considerable extent, the amount of feed. The material being cut and the depth to which the counterbore penetrates into the work also have an important bearing on the rate of feed. These conditions should be taken into consideration when using the feeds given in the table "Feeds for Counterboring in Automatic Screw Machines." These feeds are for counterbores having three cutting edges; if there is but one cutting edge, the feed should be decreased from 40 to 50 per cent, and for two cutting edges, from 15 to 20 per cent. The feeds given in this table apply only when the counterbore penetrates from one-half to three-quarters of its diameter into the work. When the counterbore penetrates to a greater distance, the feed should be decreased from 15 to 25 per cent. It is good practice to always drop the counterbore back after it has penetrated to a depth equal to half its diameter, to remove the chips and to cool and lubricate it.

Feeds for Counterboring in Automatic Screw Machines
(High-speed and Carbon Steel Tools)

Diam. of Counter-bore	Feed per Revolution			Diam. of Counter-bore	Feed per Revolution		
	Brass Rod	Machine Steel	Tool Steel		Brass Rod	Machine Steel	Tool Steel
	Chip Width, 1/32 Inch				Chip Width, 1/8 Inch		
1/8	0.0025	0.0018	0.0015	1/2	0.0050	0.0042	0.0025
3/16	0.0030	0.0023	0.0020	9/16	0.0052	0.0045	0.0030
1/4	0.0035	0.0030	0.0025	5/8	0.0055	0.0048	0.0032
5/16	0.0045	0.0040	0.0030	11/16	0.0058	0.0050	0.0035
3/8	0.0050	0.0045	0.0035	3/4	0.0060	0.0055	0.0040
7/16	0.0060	0.0050	0.0038	13/16	0.0065	0.0058	0.0045
1/2	0.0075	0.0052	0.0040	7/8	0.0070	0.0060	0.0050
Diam.	Chip Width, 1/16 Inch			Diam.	Chip Width, 3/16 Inch		
1/4	0.0030	0.0028	0.0020	9/16	0.0045	0.0035	0.0025
5/16	0.0035	0.0030	0.0025	5/8	0.0048	0.0038	0.0028
3/8	0.0040	0.0035	0.0028	11/16	0.0050	0.0040	0.0030
7/16	0.0045	0.0038	0.0030	3/4	0.0055	0.0043	0.0032
1/2	0.0050	0.0040	0.0035	13/16	0.0060	0.0045	0.0035
9/16	0.0055	0.0045	0.0038	7/8	0.0065	0.0048	0.0038
5/8	0.0060	0.0050	0.0040	15/16	0.0070	0.0050	0.0040
Diam.	Chip Width, 3/32 Inch			Diam.	Chip Width, 1/4 Inch		
3/8	0.0040	0.0032	0.0020	11/16	0.0040	0.0030	0.0020
7/16	0.0045	0.0035	0.0025	3/4	0.0042	0.0032	0.0022
1/2	0.0050	0.0040	0.0030	13/16	0.0045	0.0035	0.0025
9/16	0.0055	0.0045	0.0035	7/8	0.0048	0.0038	0.0030
5/8	0.0060	0.0050	0.0040	15/16	0.0050	0.0040	0.0032
11/16	0.0070	0.0055	0.0045	1	0.0050	0.0045	0.0035
7/8	0.0075	0.0060	0.0050	......	......	......	......

Reaming. — When reaming holes in automatic screw machines, it is advisable not to leave any more material to be removed by the reamer than is absolutely necessary. For general work, the following allowances will give good results for reamers ranging in diameter from ⅛ to ⅜ inch. For reamers over ⅜ inch diameter, a drill ¹⁄₆₄ inch less in diameter is generally used; this would leave from 0.012 to 0.015 inch to remove, as the drill will cut slightly larger than its nominal size.

Diameter of reamer in inches	⅛	³⁄₁₆	¼	⁵⁄₁₆	⅜
Diameter of hole before reaming	0.120	0.182	0.242	0.302	0.368

Various reasons for the inefficient working of reamers are as follows: 1. Chattering, which results when the teeth are evenly spaced. 2. Chips clinging to the teeth, owing to high peripheral velocities and insufficient clearance. 3. Enlarged and tapered holes, due to holding the reamer rigidly instead of "floating." The floating type of holder should always be used when reaming deep holes. There are various methods adopted to prevent reamers from chattering, but the unequal spacing of the teeth has been found the most satisfactory and inexpensive. For machine reamers varying from ⅛ to ¼ inch, three cutting edges are sometimes used, but the difficulty of measuring the diameter limits their use. As a general rule, four and six cutting edges are used on reamers varying from ⅛ inch to ⅜ inch, and eight to twelve cutting edges on reamers varying from ⅜ inch to ⅞ inch.

Speeds for Reaming. — The surface speeds used for reaming should be slightly less than for counterboring, as the reamer generally penetrates to a greater depth and has more cutting edges in contact with the work. When a good supply of lard oil is used, the following surface speeds will be found satisfactory:

Material	Surface Speed, Feet per Minute	
	Carbon Steel	High-speed Steel
Brass (ordinary quality).........................	120–125	150–160
Gun-screw iron..................................	35– 40	65– 75
Norway iron and machine steel..................	30– 35	50– 60
Drill rod and tool steel..........................	20– 25	30– 40

Feeds for Reaming in Automatic Screw Machines
(High-speed and Carbon Steel Tools)

Diam. of Reamer	Feed per Revolution			Diam. of Reamer	Feed per Revolution		
	Brass Rod	Machine Steel	Tool Steel		Brass Rod	Machine Steel	Tool Steel
⅛	0.007	0.004	0.002	⁹⁄₁₆	0.014	0.010	0.009
³⁄₁₆	0.008	0.004	0.003	⅝	0.015	0.011	0.010
¼	0.009	0.005	0.004	¹¹⁄₁₆	0.016	0.012	0.011
⁵⁄₁₆	0.010	0.006	0.005	¾	0.017	0.013	0.011
⅜	0.011	0.007	0.006	¹³⁄₁₆	0.018	0.014	0.012
⁷⁄₁₆	0.012	0.008	0.007	⅞	0.020	0.015	0.012
½	0.013	0.009	0.008	......	......	......	......

Feeds for Reaming. — The feeds for reaming, given in the table "Feeds for Reaming in Automatic Screw Machines" will be found suitable when the amount of material removed does not exceed that given in the preceding paragraph on "Reaming." When reaming thin tubing, especially of brass, the feed should be decreased somewhat.

Speeds for Recessing Tools. — The surface speeds of recessing tools can be slightly greater than those used for counterboring, on account of the light feeds and small amount of cutting surface in contact with the work. As a rule, the following surface speeds can be used with satisfactory results:

Material	Surface Speed, Feet per Minute	
	Carbon Steel	High-speed Steel
Brass (ordinary quality)........................	170–180	200–225
Gun-screw iron..................................	60– 70	90–100
Norway iron and machine steel	45– 55	75– 85
Drill rod and tool steel.........................	35– 40	50– 60

Box-tool Cutters. — Box-tool cutters are applied to the work either radially, as shown at A and B (see accompanying illustration), or tangentially, as at C and D. Generally, in automatic screw machine practice, the cutter is set radially for turning brass and, when held in this way, the cutting angles are approximately as given in the illustration. Tool A is for roughing and tool B for finishing, the cutting face of the latter being ground parallel for a short distance y equal to approximately one-fifth of the diameter being turned. For steel turning, the cutter should be set tangentially to the work as shown at C and D. The end of tool C should be ground to approximately the following angles:

Cutting Angles for Machine Steel

$a = 10$ degrees;
$b = 10$ degrees;
$c = 8$ to 10 degrees;
$d = 70$ to 72 degrees.

Cutting Angles for Tool Steel

$a = 8$ degrees;
$b = 8$ degrees;
$c = 8$ to 10 degrees;
$d = 72$ to 74 degrees.

The form of tool shown at C is commonly used for roughing cuts, but will not produce an absolutely square shoulder. For finishing cuts, the tool is ground as shown at D, which produces a square shoulder. The cutting angles for tool D are as follows:

Cutting Angles for Machine Steel

$e =$ from 10 to 12 degrees;
$f =$ from 15 to 18 degrees;
$g =$ from 60 to 65 degrees.

Cutting Angles for Tool Steel

$e =$ from 8 to 10 degrees;
$f =$ from 8 to 10 degrees;
$g =$ from 70 to 74 degrees.

While the cutting face on the tool shown at D is straight, it is usually advisable, especially when cutting machine steel and Norway iron, to give more "lip" to the tool as shown by the dotted line h. The cutting edge of a radial cutter for rough turning brass rod is set above the horizontal center-line of the work, an amount equal to about 0.02 times the diameter being turned. If the stock is rough or of irregular shape, the cutter should precede the support by an amount equal to from 0.010 to 0.020 inch, but when the bar is cylindrical and has a finished surface, the support for roughing cuts should precede the tool. The face of a tangent cutter should be set back a distance x (see illustration at D) equal to about ⅛ the diameter being turned, for tool steel, and ¹⁄₁₀ the diameter, for machine steel. Sometimes, it is also advisable, especially when cutting machine steel, to elevate the tool from the horizontal an angle of from 1 to 2 degrees, to increase the clearance.

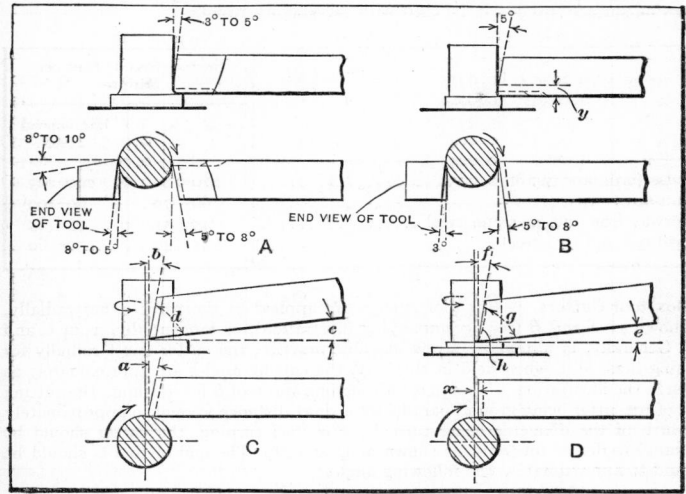

Diagrammatical Views of Different Methods of Application of Box-tool Cutters in Automatic Screw Machine Practice

Size of Steel for Box-tool Cutters. — For special conditions, the tool is sometimes made of rectangular section but ordinarily square stock is used. The square sections recommended for box-tool cutters are as follows:

Largest diameter of work, in inches:	¼	⅜	½	¾	1
Square section of tool, in inches:	³⁄₁₆	¼	⁵⁄₁₆	⅜	⁷⁄₁₆

Automatic Screw Machine Tapping. — Tapping on the automatic screw machine presents certain difficulties. There is a tendency for the chips to clog and break the tap at the moment of reversal, as the chips then lodge back of the cutting edges and tend to prevent the tap from reversing. Taps for screw machine work should have a liberal chip space, the flutes being as deep and the lands as narrow as possible. The cutting edges are, in general, radial. The tap drill diameters listed in the tables found on pages 1158 and 1159 are for screw threads of the American or U. S. standard form. These sizes may be used for all classes of work and material. The thread obtained has approximately three-fourths of the full depth which is ample for strength.

Feeds for Box-tools
(High-speed or Carbon Steel Tools)

Roughing Box-tools

Smallest Diam. of Stock	Brass Rod, Feed per Revolution	Machine Steel, Feed per Revolution	Tool Steel, Feed per Revolution	Smallest Diam. of Stock	Brass Rod, Feed per Revolution	Machine Steel, Feed per Revolution	Tool Steel, Feed per Revolution
1/32-inch Chip				1/8-inch Chip			
1/16	0.0020	0.0015	0.0010	3/8	0.0045	0.0030	0.0020
1/8	0.0030	0.0020	0.0015	7/16	0.0050	0.0035	0.0025
3/16	0.0040	0.0030	0.0020	1/2	0.0060	0.0040	0.0030
1/4	0.0050	0.0040	0.0025	9/16	0.0070	0.0050	0.0035
5/16	0.0060	0.0045	0.0030	5/8	0.0085	0.0060	0.0040
3/8	0.0075	0.0050	0.0035	3/4	0.0100	0.0070	0.0050
1/16-inch Chip				3/16-inch Chip			
1/4	0.0045	0.0030	0.0020	1/2	0.0040	0.0025	0.0015
5/16	0.0060	0.0040	0.0025	9/16	0.0045	0.0030	0.0018
3/8	0.0090	0.0060	0.0030	5/8	0.0050	0.0032	0.0020
7/16	0.0105	0.0070	0.0040	11/16	0.0055	0.0035	0.0023
1/2	0.0120	0.0080	0.0050	3/4	0.0060	0.0040	0.0025
9/16	0.0135	0.0090	0.0060	13/16	0.0070	0.0045	0.0028
5/8	0.0150	0.0100	0.0075	7/8	0.0075	0.0050	0.0030

Finishing Box-tools

Smallest Diam. of Stock	Brass Rod	Machine Steel	Tool Steel	Smallest Diam. of Stock	Brass Rod	Machine Steel	Tool Steel
0.005-inch Chip				0.020-inch Chip			
1/32	0.0020	0.0020	0.0018	3/8	0.0040	0.0040	0.0025
1/16	0.0030	0.0030	0.0020	7/16	0.0045	0.0045	0.0030
3/32	0.0045	0.0045	0.0025	1/2	0.0050	0.0050	0.0035
1/8	0.0060	0.0060	0.0030	9/16	0.0060	0.0060	0.0035
3/16	0.0070	0.0070	0.0040	5/8	0.0070	0.0070	0.0040
1/4	0.0080	0.0080	0.0050	11/16	0.0075	0.0075	0.0045
5/16	0.0100	0.0100	0.0060	3/4	0.0080	0.0080	0.0050
3/8	0.0120	0.0120	0.0080	13/16	0.0090	0.0090	0.0050
0.010-inch Chip				0.030-inch Chip			
1/4	0.0070	0.0070	0.0035	1/2	0.0040	0.0040	0.0020
5/16	0.0080	0.0080	0.0040	9/16	0.0045	0.0045	0.0022
3/8	0.0085	0.0085	0.0045	5/8	0.0050	0.0050	0.0025
7/16	0.0090	0.0090	0.0050	11/16	0.0055	0.0055	0.0028
1/2	0.0095	0.0095	0.0055	3/4	0.0060	0.0060	0.0030
9/16	0.0100	0.0100	0.0060	13/16	0.0070	0.0070	0.0035
5/8	0.0100	0.0100	0.0065	7/8	0.0080	0.0080	0.0040

Rules for Calculating Cutting Speeds. — To find the number of revolutions required for a given cutting speed, in feet per minute: *Multiply the given cutting speed by 12, and divide the product by the circumference (in inches) of the turned part.*

To find the cutting speed in feet per minute for a given number of revolutions and diameter: *Multiply the revolutions per minute by the circumference, and divide the product by 12.*

Expressing these rules as formulas:

$$N = \frac{C \times 12}{3.1416\,D} \qquad\qquad C = \frac{3.1416\,DN}{12}$$

in which N = revolutions per minute; C = cutting speed in feet per minute; and D = diameter in inches.

To find the time, in minutes, required to take one complete cut over a part to be turned, when the feed per revolution, the total length of the cut, and the number of revolutions per minute are given: *Divide the total length of the cut by the product of the number of revolutions per minute and the feed per revolution.*

If L = total length of cut in inches; N = revolutions per minute; F = feed per revolution in inches; and T = time required to take one complete cut, in minutes; then:

$$T = \frac{L}{N \times F}$$

Speeds for Metal-cutting Saws. — The following speeds and feeds for metal-cutting saws are recommended by Henry Disston & Sons, Inc. Speeds and feeds vary over a wide range depending upon the kind of machine as well as the size, shape, and kind of metal to be cut; hence, the following speeds are intended as a general guide only.

Solid-tooth Circular Saws. — Low-carbon steel: Speed, 60–90 feet per minute; feed, 3–6 inches per minute. Tool and alloy steel: Speed, 40–60 feet per minute; feed, ½–2½ inches per minute. Cast iron: Speed, 60–70 feet per minute; feed, 5 inches per minute. Brass: Speed, 500–800 feet per minute; feed, 80 inches per minute. Copper: Speed, 600–700 feet per minute; feed, 60 inches per minute. Aluminum: Speed, 800–1000 feet per minute; feed, 90 inches per minute.

"Hot saws" for sawing hot metal (structural shapes, rails, billets, etc., in rolling mills) should operate at speeds of 22,000 to 25,000 feet per minute.

Inserted-tooth Metal-cutting Saws. — Generally speaking, an inserted-tooth saw is not recommended smaller than 18 inches in diameter, although smaller sizes are made. Small saws usually are applied to work requiring fine or relatively fine teeth which are impossible when the teeth are of the inserted type. The following speeds are not suitable for all compositions but represent general practice. Steel: Speed, 40 feet per minute; feed, 2½–10 inches per minute. Cast iron: Speed, 40 feet per minute; feed, 5 inches per minute. Brass: Speed, 500 feet per minute; feed, 80 inches per minute. Copper: Speed, 750 feet per minute; feed, 60 inches per minute. Aluminum: Speed, 1200 feet per minute; feed, 90 inches per minute.

Metal-cutting Band Saws. — The speeds which follow apply to Disston "hard-edge" saws which have milled teeth. Aluminum sheets: Speed of blade, 1000–3000 feet per minute. Bakelite: Speed, 800–1000 feet per minute. Brass sheets and tubing: Speed, 700–1500 feet per minute. Carbon tool steel: Speed, 100–150 feet per minute. Cast iron: Speed, 100–150 feet per minute. Cold-rolled steel: Speed, 150–200 feet per minute. High-speed steel: Speed, 90–125 feet per minute. Malleable iron: Speed, 150–200 feet per minute. Hard rubber: Speed, 150–200 feet per minute. Slate: Speed, 100–150 feet per minute. The number of saw teeth per inch recommended for these different materials ranges from 8 to 14, and the saw user should be guided by the recommendations of the manufacturer.

Revolutions per Minute for Various Cutting Speeds and Diameters

Diameter, Inches	Cutting Speed, Feet per Minute											
	40	50	60	70	80	90	100	120	140	160	180	200
	Revolutions per Minute											
¼	611	764	917	1070	1222	1376	1528	1834	2139	2445	2750	3056
5⁄16	489	611	733	856	978	1100	1222	1466	1711	1955	2200	2444
3⁄8	408	509	611	713	815	916	1018	1222	1425	1629	1832	2036
7⁄16	349	437	524	611	699	786	874	1049	1224	1398	1573	1748
½	306	382	459	535	611	688	764	917	1070	1222	1375	1528
9⁄16	272	340	407	475	543	611	679	813	951	1086	1222	1358
5⁄8	245	306	367	428	489	552	612	736	857	979	1102	1224
11⁄16	222	273	333	389	444	500	555	666	770	888	999	1101
¾	203	254	306	357	408	458	508	610	711	813	914	1016
13⁄16	190	237	284	332	379	427	474	569	664	758	853	948
7⁄8	175	219	262	306	349	392	438	526	613	701	788	876
15⁄16	163	204	244	285	326	366	407	488	570	651	733	814
1	153	191	229	267	306	344	382	458	535	611	688	764
1 1⁄16	144	180	215	251	287	323	359	431	503	575	646	718
1 1⁄8	136	170	204	238	272	306	340	408	476	544	612	680
1 3⁄16	129	161	193	225	258	290	322	386	451	515	580	644
1 ¼	123	153	183	214	245	274	306	367	428	490	551	612
1 5⁄16	115	146	175	204	233	262	291	349	407	466	524	582
1 3⁄8	111	139	167	195	222	250	278	334	389	445	500	556
1 7⁄16	106	133	159	186	212	239	265	318	371	424	477	530
1 ½	102	127	153	178	204	230	254	305	356	406	457	508
1 9⁄16	97.6	122	146	171	195	220	244	293	342	390	439	488
1 5⁄8	93.9	117	141	165	188	212	234	281	328	374	421	468
1 11⁄16	90.4	113	136	158	181	203	226	271	316	362	407	452
1 ¾	87.3	109	131	153	175	196	218	262	305	349	392	436
1 7⁄8	81.5	102	122	143	163	184	204	244	286	326	367	408
2	76.4	95.5	115	134	153	172	191	229	267	306	344	382
2 1⁄8	72.0	90.0	108	126	144	162	180	216	252	288	324	360
2 ¼	68.0	85.5	102	119	136	153	170	204	238	272	306	340
2 3⁄8	64.4	80.5	96.6	113	129	145	161	193	225	258	290	322
2 ½	61.2	76.3	91.7	107	122	138	153	184	213	245	275	306
2 5⁄8	58.0	72.5	87.0	102	116	131	145	174	203	232	261	290
2 ¾	55.6	69.5	83.4	97.2	111	125	139	167	195	222	250	278
2 7⁄8	52.8	66.0	79.2	92.4	106	119	132	158	185	211	238	264
3	51.0	63.7	76.4	89.1	102	114	127	152	178	203	228	254
3 1⁄8	48.8	61.0	73.2	85.4	97.6	110	122	146	171	195	219	244
3 ¼	46.8	58.5	70.2	81.9	93.6	105	117	140	164	188	211	234
3 3⁄8	45.2	56.5	67.8	79.1	90.4	102	113	136	158	181	203	226
3 ½	43.6	54.5	65.5	76.4	87.4	98.1	109	131	153	174	196	218
3 5⁄8	42.0	52.5	63.0	73.5	84.0	94.5	105	126	147	168	189	210
3 ¾	40.8	51.0	61.2	71.4	81.6	91.8	102	122	143	163	184	205
3 7⁄8	39.4	49.3	59.1	69.0	78.8	88.6	98.5	118	138	158	177	197
4	38.2	47.8	57.3	66.9	76.4	86.0	95.6	115	134	153	172	191
4 ¼	35.9	44.9	53.9	62.9	71.8	80.8	89.8	108	126	144	162	180
4 ½	34.0	42.4	51.0	59.4	67.9	76.3	84.8	102	119	136	153	170
4 ¾	32.2	40.2	48.2	56.3	64.3	72.4	80.4	96.9	113	129	145	161
5	30.6	38.2	45.9	53.5	61.1	68.8	76.4	91.7	107	122	138	153
5 ¼	29.1	36.4	43.6	50.9	58.2	65.4	72.7	87.2	102	116	131	145
5 ½	27.8	34.7	41.7	48.6	55.6	62.5	69.4	83.3	97.2	111	125	139
5 ¾	26.6	33.2	39.8	46.5	53.1	59.8	66.4	80.0	93.0	106	120	133
6	25.5	31.8	38.2	44.6	51.0	57.2	63.6	76.3	89.0	102	114	127
6 ¼	24.4	30.6	36.7	42.8	48.9	55.0	61.1	73.3	85.5	97.7	110	122
6 ½	23.5	29.4	35.2	41.1	47.0	52.8	58.7	70.4	82.2	93.9	106	117
6 ¾	22.6	28.3	34.0	39.6	45.3	50.9	56.6	67.9	79.2	90.6	102	113
7	21.8	27.3	32.7	38.2	43.7	49.1	54.6	65.5	76.4	87.4	98.3	109
7 ¼	21.1	26.4	31.6	36.9	42.2	47.4	52.7	63.2	73.8	84.3	94.9	105
7 ½	20.4	25.4	30.5	35.6	40.7	45.8	50.9	61.1	71.0	81.4	91.6	102
7 ¾	19.7	24.6	29.5	34.4	39.4	44.3	49.2	59.0	68.9	78.7	88.6	98.4
8	19.1	23.9	28.7	33.4	38.2	43.0	47.8	57.4	66.9	76.5	86.0	95.6

Revolutions per Minute for Various Cutting Speeds and Diameters

Diameter, Inches	Cutting Speed, Feet per Minute											
	225	250	275	300	325	350	375	400	425	450	500	550
	Revolutions per Minute											
1/4	3438	3820	4202	4584	4966	5348	5730	6112	6493	6875	7639	8403
5/16	2750	3056	3362	3667	3973	4278	4584	4889	5195	5501	6112	6723
3/8	2292	2546	2801	3056	3310	3565	3820	4074	4329	4584	5093	5602
7/16	1964	2182	2401	2619	2837	3056	3274	3492	3710	3929	4365	4802
1/2	1719	1910	2101	2292	2483	2675	2866	3057	3248	3439	3821	4203
9/16	1528	1698	1868	2037	2207	2377	2547	2717	2887	3056	3396	3736
5/8	1375	1528	1681	1834	1987	2139	2292	2445	2598	2751	3057	3362
11/16	1250	1389	1528	1667	1806	1941	2084	2223	2362	2501	2779	3056
3/4	1146	1273	1401	1528	1655	1783	1910	2038	2165	2292	2547	2802
13/16	1058	1175	1293	1410	1528	1646	1763	1881	1998	2116	2351	2586
7/8	982	1091	1200	1310	1419	1528	1637	1746	1855	1965	2183	2401
15/16	917	1019	1120	1222	1324	1426	1528	1630	1732	1834	2038	2241
1	859	955	1050	1146	1241	1337	1432	1528	1623	1719	1910	2101
1 1/16	809	899	988	1078	1168	1258	1348	1438	1528	1618	1798	1977
1 1/8	764	849	933	1018	1103	1188	1273	1358	1443	1528	1698	1867
1 3/16	724	804	884	965	1045	1126	1206	1287	1367	1448	1609	1769
1 1/4	687	764	840	917	993	1069	1146	1222	1299	1375	1528	1681
1 5/16	654	727	800	873	946	1018	1091	1164	1237	1309	1455	1601
1 3/8	625	694	764	833	903	972	1042	1111	1181	1250	1389	1528
1 7/16	598	664	730	797	863	930	996	1063	1129	1196	1329	1461
1 1/2	573	636	700	764	827	891	955	1018	1082	1146	1273	1400
1 9/16	550	611	672	733	794	855	916	978	1039	1100	1222	1344
1 5/8	528	587	646	705	764	822	881	940	999	1057	1175	1293
1 11/16	509	566	622	679	735	792	849	905	962	1018	1132	1245
1 3/4	491	545	600	654	709	764	818	873	927	982	1091	1200
1 13/16	474	527	579	632	685	737	790	843	895	948	1054	1159
1 7/8	458	509	560	611	662	713	764	815	866	917	1019	1120
1 15/16	443	493	542	591	640	690	739	788	838	887	986	1084
2	429	477	525	573	620	668	716	764	811	859	955	1050
2 1/8	404	449	494	539	584	629	674	719	764	809	899	988
2 1/4	382	424	468	509	551	594	636	679	721	764	849	933
2 3/8	362	402	442	482	522	563	603	643	683	724	804	884
2 1/2	343	382	420	458	496	534	573	611	649	687	764	840
2 5/8	327	363	400	436	472	509	545	582	618	654	727	800
2 3/4	312	347	381	416	451	486	520	555	590	625	694	763
2 7/8	299	332	365	398	431	465	498	531	564	598	664	730
3	286	318	350	381	413	445	477	509	541	572	636	700
3 1/8	274	305	336	366	397	427	458	488	519	549	611	672
3 1/4	264	293	323	352	381	411	440	470	499	528	587	646
3 3/8	254	283	311	339	367	396	424	452	481	509	566	622
3 1/2	245	272	300	327	354	381	409	436	463	490	545	600
3 5/8	237	263	289	316	342	368	395	421	447	474	527	579
3 3/4	229	254	280	305	331	356	382	407	433	458	509	560
3 7/8	221	246	271	295	320	345	369	394	419	443	493	542
4	214	238	262	286	310	334	358	382	405	429	477	525
4 1/4	202	224	247	269	292	314	337	359	383	404	449	494
4 1/2	191	212	233	254	275	297	318	339	360	382	424	466
4 3/4	180	201	221	241	261	281	301	321	341	361	402	442
5	171	191	210	229	248	267	286	305	324	343	382	420
5 1/4	163	181	199	218	236	254	272	290	308	327	363	399
5 1/2	156	173	190	208	225	242	260	277	294	312	347	381
5 3/4	149	166	182	199	215	232	249	265	282	298	332	365
6	143	159	174	190	206	222	238	254	270	286	318	349
6 1/4	137	152	168	183	198	213	229	244	259	274	305	336
6 1/2	132	146	161	176	190	205	220	234	249	264	293	322
6 3/4	127	141	155	169	183	198	212	226	240	254	283	311
7	122	136	149	163	177	190	204	218	231	245	272	299
7 1/4	118	131	144	158	171	184	197	210	223	237	263	289
7 1/2	114	127	139	152	165	178	190	203	216	229	254	279
7 3/4	111	123	135	148	160	172	185	197	209	222	246	271
8	107	119	131	143	155	167	179	191	203	215	238	262

Speeds for Turning Unusual Materials. — *Slate*, on account of its peculiarly stratified formation, is rather difficult to turn, but if handled carefully, can be machined in an ordinary lathe. The cutting speed should be about the same as for cast iron. A sheet of fiber or pressed paper should be interposed between the chuck or steadyrest jaws and the slate, to protect the latter. Slate rolls must not be centered and run on the tailstock. A satisfactory method of supporting a slate roll having journals at the ends is to bore a piece of lignum vitæ to receive the turned end of the roll, and center it for the tailstock spindle.

Rubber can be turned at a peripheral speed of 200 feet per minute, although it is much easier to grind it with an abrasive wheel that is porous and soft. For cutting a rubber roll in two, the ordinary parting tool should not be used, but a tool shaped like a knife; such a tool severs the rubber without removing any material.

Gutta percha can be turned as easily as wood, but the tools must be sharp and a good soap-and-water lubricant used.

Copper can be turned easily at 200 feet per minute.

Lime-stone such as is used in the construction of pillars for balconies, etc., can be turned at 150 feet per minute, and the formation of ornamental contours is quite easy. *Marble* is a treacherous material to turn. It should be cut with a tool such as would be used for brass, but at a speed suitable for cast iron. It must be handled very carefully to prevent flaws in the surface.

The foregoing speeds are for high-speed steel tools. Tools tipped with tungsten carbide are adapted for cutting various non-metallic products which cannot be machined readily with steel tools, such as slate, marble, synthetic plastic materials, etc. In drilling slate and marble, use flat drills; and for plastic materials, tungsten-carbide-tipped twist drills. Cutting speeds ranging from 75 to 150 feet per minute have been used for drilling slate (without coolant) and a feed of 0.025 per revolution for drills ¾ and 1 inch in diameter.

Machinability of Metals. — The machinability of a metal, or its resistance to cutting, may depend not only upon the hardness, but also upon properties not indicated by a hardness test. In cutting steels, the allowable cutting speed for a given tool life between grindings, is, as a general rule, inversely proportional to the hardness *of a given steel*. To illustrate, tests in turning an alloy steel with a high-speed steel tool showed a cutting speed of 70 feet per minute when the hardness of the steel was 180 Brinell; the cutting speed had to be reduced to about 35 feet per minute when the hardness was increased to 360 Brinell, the life between tool grindings for these tests being 20 minutes in each case. The machinability of other steels of the same hardness might vary. For example, the tests just referred to showed more or less variation in the cutting speeds for steels of the same hardness, but having different compositions or properties. Thus, while there is a constant relationship between the hardness of a steel and its tensile strength, there is not the same constant relationship between steel hardness and machinability as applied to different steels. In one test a high-speed steel turning tool lasted 20 minutes between successive grindings when cutting chromium-vanadium steel of 300 Brinell at 30 feet per minute, whereas a 3½ per cent nickel steel of the same hardness permitted a cutting speed of about 45 feet per minute for a tool life of 20 minutes. To cite another example, the cutting speed during a 20-minute interval between grinds was 170 feet per minute for nickel-chromium steel of 280 Brinell and 210 feet per minute for chromium-vanadium steel of the same hardness.

Relation Between Cast-Iron Hardness and Machinability: Although the allowable cutting speed of a given steel is approximately in inverse proportion to the hardness, the machinability of cast iron may not be changed by increasing the hardness and may even be improved. For example, it was found more difficult to machine a plain cast iron of about 170 Brinell than a nickel-chromium cast iron of

240 Brinell. In another case, plain iron of 160 Brinell was more difficult to machine than a cast iron of about 200 Brinell containing less silicon and 1.25 per cent nickel. As the foregoing examples show, there is no fixed relationship between the hardness and machinability of plain and alloy cast irons

Relation Between Tensile Strength and Hardness: The following simple rules show the approximate relationship between tensile strength and hardness as determined both by the Brinell and Rockwell tests. Brinell hardness = tensile strength × 0.002 approximately. Rockwell hardness (C scale) = tensile strength × 0.0002 approximately.

Tool Grinding

Tool Contour. — Tools for turning, planing, etc., are made in straight, bent, offset, and other forms to locate the cutting edges in convenient positions for operating on differently located surfaces. The contour or shape of the cutting edge may also be varied to suit different classes of work. Tool shapes, however, are not only related to the kind of operation, but, in the case of roughing tools particularly, the contour may have a decided effect upon the cutting efficiency of the tool. To illustrate, an increase in the side cutting-edge angle of a roughing tool, or in the nose radius, tends to permit higher cutting speeds because the chip will be thinner for a given feed rate. Such changes, however, may result in chattering or vibrations unless the work and the machine are rigid; hence, the most desirable contour may be a compromise between the ideal form and one that is needed to meet practical requirements.

Terms and Definitions. — The terms and definitions relating to single-point tools vary somewhat in different plants, but the following are in general use.

Single-point Tool: This term is applied to tools for turning, planing, boring, etc., which have a cutting edge at one end. This cutting edge may be formed on one end of a solid piece of steel, or the cutting part of the tool may consist of an insert or tip which is held to the body of the tool either by brazing, welding, or by mechanical means.

Shank: The shank is the main body of the tool. If the tool is an inserted cutter type, the shank supports the cutter or bit. (See diagram, Fig. 1.)

Nose: This is a general term sometimes used to designate the cutting end but usually it relates more particularly to the rounded tip of the cutting end.

Face: The surface against which the chips bear, as they are severed in turning or planing operations, is called the face.

Flank: The flank is that end surface that is adjacent to the cutting edge and below it when the tool is in a horizontal position as for turning.

Base: The base is that surface of the tool shank which bears against the supporting tool-holder or block.

Clearance Angle: The clearance angle relates to the end or side surfaces which are below the cutting edge. The nominal clearance angle is measured from a plane that is perpendicular to the base of the tool shank. The effective clearance angle of a turning tool may be greater or less than the nominal clearance angle, depending upon the position of the tool relative to the axis of the work.

Relief Angle: Clearance may consist of two angles (as shown by the diagram, Fig. 1) to reduce the amount of end surface adjacent to the cutting edge and the amount of grinding required in sharpening the tool. In such cases, the angle of that surface which is adjacent to the cutting edge may be called the relief angle — end relief or side relief angle, depending upon the location of the surface.

Lip Angle: Lip angle is the angle between the tool face and the ground end surface or flank adjacent to the cutting edge. If the tool has side and back rake, the lip angle should be measured in whatever plane it is smallest.

Cutting Angle: The true cutting angle equals the lip angle plus the relief angle. In turning, it is the angle between the face of the tool and a line tangent to the machined surface at the cutting point. The true cutting angle depends upon the position of a turning tool relative to the axis of the work.

Rake: A metal-cutting tool is said to have "rake" when the tool face or surface against which the chips bear as they are being severed, is inclined for the purpose either of increasing or diminishing the keenness or bluntness of the cutting end. Rake is obtained by grinding the face so that it slopes away from the main cutting edge or that part of the cutting edge which normally does the cutting. The tool shown in Fig. 1 has rake. If the face of this tool did not incline but was parallel with the base of the tool, there would be no rake, the rake angle being zero.

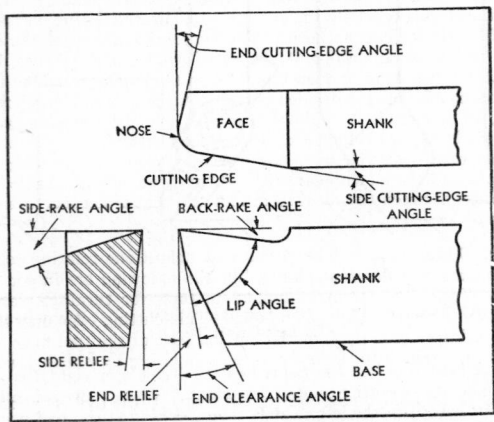

Fig. 1. Terms Applied to Single-point Turning Tools

Rake Angle: The nominal rake angle is an angle between the tool face and a plane parallel to the base of the tool. *Back rake angle* is measured in the direction of the tool shank and *side rake angle* in a direction at right angles to the tool shank. The actual or effective rake of a turning tool depends upon its position relative to the axis of the work. To illustrate, if the tool is clamped in its holder with the point below the centers (or below a horizontal plane intersecting the axis of the work) the effective rake will be reduced.

Positive Rake: If the inclination of the tool face is such as to make the cutting end keener or more acute than when the rake angle is zero, the rake is said to be "positive." Most tools for turning or planing steel or cast iron have positive rake.

Negative Rake: If the inclination of the tool face makes the cutting end less keen or more blunt than when the rake angle is zero, the rake is said to be "negative." Negative rake increases the strength of the cutting end and is sometimes required in cutting exceptionally hard materials or when the tool is subjected to severe shocks as in taking interrupted cuts. Negative rake carbide tools may also be used effectively in high-speed turning and milling.

Back Rake: When a tool is given rake by inclining the face away from the end or nose or in the direction of the shank, it is said to have back rake. When a cutting edge inclines downward toward the point, the term "negative back rake" is often used. This might also be thought of as *front rake* or the opposite of back rake. Tools are given front rake to provide a shearing action for interrupted cuts. Such tools usually have positive side rake; hence they do not have *true* negative rake.

Side Rake: When a tool is given rake by inclining the face away from a cutting edge located on one side, it is said to have side rake. The inclination for side rake is approximately at right angles to the shank.

Straight Tool: A straight tool has the point on the end of a straight shank (see diagram A, Fig. 2).

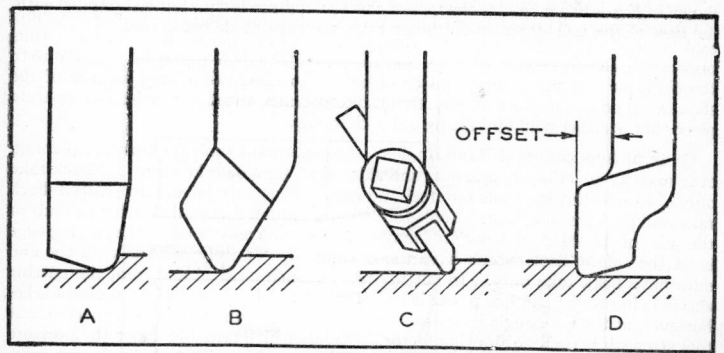

Fig. 2. (A) Straight Tool. (B) Left-Bent Tool. (C) Right-Bent Tool. (D) Left-Offset Tool

Bent Tool: A bent tool has the point bent to the left or right (see diagrams B and C), to make its operation more convenient. These tools are called left-bent tools if the point is bent to the left as at B, when looking at the tool from the point end with the face upward and the shank pointing away and vice versa.

Offset Tool: An offset tool has the point at either side of, but parallel to, the shank. It is known as a right-offset tool if the point is offset to the right of the shank when looking at the tool from the point end with the face upward and the shank pointing away. Diagram D illustrates a left-offset tool.

Right-hand and Left-hand Tools: According to the most generally accepted definition, a right-hand tool has the main cutting edge on the right-hand side when viewed from the point end with the face up, and vice versa for a left-hand tool. A right-hand tool, when used in a lathe, cuts from the right-hand end of the work, or, in facing operations, on the right-hand side of a flange, shoulder or shaft end, whereas the opposite is true of a left-hand tool. These definitions, while not universally accepted, conform with the standard terms adopted by the American Standards Association.

Right-Cut Tool: A right-cut single-point tool is one which, when viewed from the point end of the tool, with the face up, has the cutting edge on the right side, like tool A, Fig. 2.

Left-Cut Tool: A left-cut tool has the cutting edge on the left when looking at the point end with the face upward. (Diagram D.)

End-Cut Tool: An end-cut single-point tool is one having its principal cutting edge on the end.

Tipped Tool: This term designates the type of tool having a small tip of either high-speed steel or special cutting material permanently fixed to the shank, as by brazing or welding. The cutting edge is formed on this tip.

Tool Bit: The term "bit" is commonly applied to the cutting tools which are inserted in a tool shank or holder (as at C, Fig. 2), so designed that the bit may readily be removed either for sharpening or for replacing with another form.

Nominal Size: The size of a tool of square or rectangular section, according to the American Standard for single-point tools, is expressed by giving the width of the shank, the height of the shank, and the total tool length, in the order named. For example, the size might be ¾ × 1½ × 12 inches. This same method of designation is used for a tool-bit holder, and the size of the bit is added.

Chip-Breaker: A groove formed in or on a shoulder formed on the face of a turning tool back of the cutting edge, for the purpose of breaking up the chips and thus preventing the formation of long continuous chips which would be dangerous to the operator and also bulky and cumbersome to handle. A chip-breaker of the shoulder type may be formed directly on the tool face or it may consist of a separate piece that is either held by brazing or by clamping.

General Application of Rake Angles. — Single-point tools for turning, planing, etc., may have (1) both back rake and side rake; (2) side rake only; (3) back rake only. Rough-turning tools for steel and cast iron usually have both positive back rake and positive side rake. Tools formed and ground especially for facing ends or the sides of shoulders, flanges, etc., may have side rake only because the cutting edge is on the side. Tools which have the cutting edge entirely or chiefly on the end may have back rake only. In cutting metals, such as steel and iron, the cutting action is improved and less power is required when using tools having positive rake; however, as the rake angle increases, the cutting end of the tool is weakened so that tool strength becomes a limiting factor. Metals which crumble under the pressure of the tool, such as cast brass, may be machined readily with tools having no rake. Tools for cutting iron and steel, which require exceptional strength because of the hardness of the metal, may have little or no rake and in some cases negative rake is preferable. Carbide turning tools having negative rake angles up to 4 degrees, or more, have proved effective in turning at high-speeds and with feeds ranging from 0.015 to 0.030 inch per revolution. Carbide tools for planing usually have negative rake to better withstand the impact or shock at the beginning of each cut. See table of rake and clearance angles.

Clearance or Relief Angle. — In order that the cutting edge may work without interference, the edge must be ground with a certain clearance angle which should be just enough to permit the tool to cut freely. A clearance angle of 8 or 10 degrees is about right for lathe turning tools intended for general work. Tools for turning brass or other soft metals, especially when considerable hand manipulation is required, should have a clearance of 12 or 14 degrees, so that the tool can easily be fed into the metal. Excessive clearance weakens the cutting edge and may cause it to crumble under the pressure of the cut.

Side Cutting-edge Angle. — This angle (see Fig. 1), which is also known as the *lead angle,* may range from zero to 15 or 20 degrees for rough-turning tools. Tools for ordinary rough-turning should preferably have a side cutting-edge angle of from 10 to 20 degrees, 15 degrees being a fair average. The advantages are as follows: (1) When a turning or planing tool begins cutting at a square end or corner, the thrust or load on the tool is back near its support and the load is applied more gradually; (2) the chip thickness is less for a given amount of feed when there is a side cutting angle because of the angular position of the cutting edge; (3) when the cut extends to the end of a bar in turning, the final section of metal is removed gradually and cannot be pushed off in the form of a ring or hoop.

Rake and Clearance Angles for Rough-Turning Tools

These average values are intended as a general guide only

Rake and Clearance	Cast Iron	Low-carbon Steel	High-carbon Steel	Alloy Steels	Soft Brass	Aluminum	Copper
	Angles for High-speed Steel Tools						
Back Rake (1)....	6–8	8–12	4–6	5–8	0	25–50	10–12
Side Rake........	10–12	14–18	8–10	10–15	0	10–20	20–25
Clearance (2).....	6–9	8–10	6–8	6–8	10–15	7–10	6–8
	Angles for Sintered Carbide Tools (3)						
Back Rake (1)....	0–6	4–6	4–6	4–6	0	25	4
Side Rake........	8–10	10–14	6–10	6–10	0	15	20
Clearance (2).....	5–7	6–8	5–7	5–7	8–10	7–10	8–10

1. For interrupted cuts, the back rake may be "negative," the inclination of the cutting edge being downward toward the tool point.

2. The end- and side-clearance angles usually are the same.

3. These positive rake angles for carbide tools are typical of conventional practice; however, effective results have been obtained by employing negative rake usually varying from zero to minus 4 degrees, in conjunction with exceptionally high cutting speeds and with feeds varying from 0.015 to 0.030 inch per revolution.

If a tool is to leave a square shoulder at the end of the cut, the cutting edge is in line with the shank or without a cutting edge angle.

End Cutting-edge Angle. — Tools for turning or planing which are designed to do most of the cutting along the side have an end cutting-edge angle (see Fig. 1). This angle serves to bring the nose or rounded corner into contact with the work, and not only provides clearance, but facilitates feeding the tool inward as when taking a deeper cut. This end angle ordinarily ranges from 8 to 15 degrees. Angles up to 20 or 30 degrees may be required in special cases, as, for example, when the tool must be plunged into the cut.

Chip-breakers. — Many steel turning tools are equipped with chip-breaking devices to prevent the formation of long continuous chips in connection with the turning of steel at the high speeds made possible by high-speed steel and especially sintered carbide tools. Long steel chips are dangerous to the operator, cumbersome to handle, and they may twist around the tool and cause damage. Broken chips not only occupy less space, but permit a better flow of coolant to the cutting edge and reduce the amount of heat transferred from the chips to the tool. Several different forms of chip-breakers are illustrated in Fig. 3.

Angular Shoulder Type: The angular shoulder type shown at A is one of the commonly used forms. As the enlarged sectional view shows, the chip-breaking shoulder is located back of the cutting edge. The angle a between the shoulder and cutting edge may vary from 6 to 15 degrees or more, 8 degrees being a fair average. The ideal angle, width W and depth G, depends upon the speed and feed, the depth of cut, and the material. As a general rule, width W at the end of the tool, varies from 3/32 to 7/32 inch, and the depth G may range from 1/64 to 1/16 inch. The shoulder radius equals depth D. If the tool has a large nose radius, the corner of the shoulder at the nose end may be beveled off, as illustrated at B, to prevent it from coming into contact with the work. The width K for type B should equal approximately 1.5 times the nose radius.

Parallel Shoulder Type: Diagram C illustrates the type which has a chip-breaking shoulder that is parallel with the cutting edge. With this form, the chips are likely

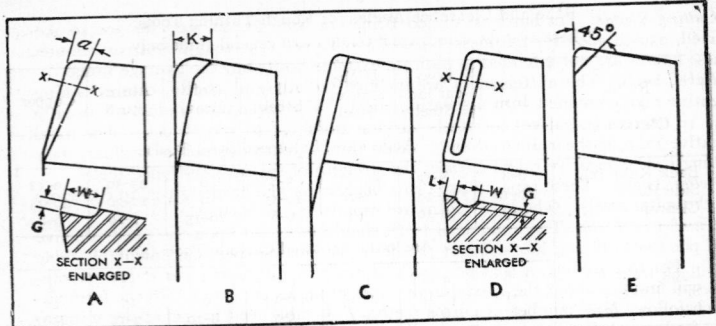

Fig. 3.   Different Forms of Chip-breakers for Turning Tools

to come off in short curled sections.   The parallel form may also be applied to straight tools which do not have a side cutting-edge angle.   The tendency with this parallel shoulder form is to force the chips against the work and thus cause breakage.

Groove Type: This type (diagram D) consists of a groove that is ground into the face of the tool.   Between the groove and the cutting edge, there is a land L. Under ideal conditions, this width L, the groove width W, and the groove depth G, would be varied according to the feed, depth of cut and material.   For average use, L is about $\frac{1}{32}$ inch; G, $\frac{1}{32}$ inch; and W, $\frac{1}{16}$ inch.   There are differences of opinion concerning the relative merits of the groove type and the shoulder type. Both types have proved satisfactory when properly proportioned for a given class of work.

Chip-breaker for Light Cuts: Diagram E illustrates a form of chip-breaker that is sometimes used on tools for finishing cuts having a maximum depth of about $\frac{1}{32}$ inch.   This is a shoulder type having an angle of 45 degrees and a maximum width of about $\frac{1}{16}$ inch.   It is important in grinding all chip-breakers to give the chip-bearing surfaces a fine finish, such as would be obtained by honing.   This greatly increases the life of the tool.

Planing Tools. — Many of the principles which govern the shape of turning tools also apply in the grinding of tools for planing.   The amount of rake depends upon the hardness of the material, and the direction of the rake should be away from the *working part* of the cutting edge.   The angle of clearance should be about 4 or 5 degrees for planer tools, which is less than for lathe tools.   This small clearance is allowable because a planer tool is held about square with the platen, whereas a lathe tool, the height and inclination of which can be varied, may not always be clamped in the same position.

Carbide Tools: Carbide tools for planing usually have negative rake.   Round-nose and square-nose end-cutting tools should have a "negative back rake" (or front rake) of 2 or 3 degrees.   Side cutting tools may have a negative back rake of 10 degrees, a negative side rake of 5 degrees, and a side cutting-edge angle of 8 degrees.

Milling Cutters with Negative Rake. — Milling cutters having carbide-tipped teeth and negative rake are very efficient, particularly in milling alloy and heat-treated steels.   The negative-rake principle has been applied effectively to many operations such as plain face milling, face or straddle milling to a shoulder, slotting operations, etc.

Cutting Speeds: For hardness of 300 Brinell or less, 500 to 700; for 300 to 400 Brinell, 250 to 500; for hardnesses above 400 Brinell, 150 to 350 feet per minute. These figures are not intended to indicate extreme limits but the average range.

Rake Angle: The cutter teeth are inclined radially and axially, thus obtaining negative rake combined with a shearing effect. The inclination radially is usually 5 to 10 degrees (negative) for steels varying from 325 to 500 Brinell. The axial negative rake or shear angle usually varies from 8 to 10 degrees for ordinary face milling. The negative rake increases the strength of the carbide-tipped teeth.

Relief Angles: These range from 2 to 4 degrees for the harder steels to 6 degrees for the softer steels. The land widths are usually $\frac{3}{64}$ to $\frac{1}{16}$ inch.

Number of Teeth: The number of teeth should be based upon the most effective feed per tooth, taking into account the desirable cutting speed and available table feed. For face milling, a feed per tooth of 0.005 to 0.008 inch per cutter revolution will produce about the maximum number of pieces per grind. In the formulas which follow, N = number of cutter teeth; T = table feed in inches per minute; F = feed per tooth in inches; R = revolutions per minute:

$$N = T \div (R \times F); \quad F = T \div (R \times N); \quad T = R \times N \times F$$

Dry Milling: Negative rake milling is done without a coolant. If the chips stick to the cutting edges, an air blast may be used to remove them.

Twist Drill Grinding. —
The cutting end of a drill should conform to the following requirements: The two cutting edges should incline at the proper angle α

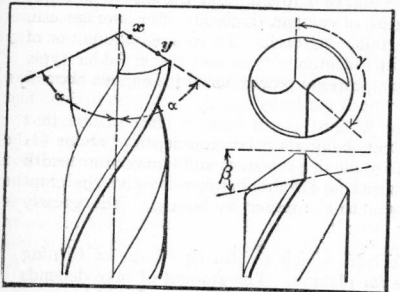

with the axis (see illustration); each edge should have the *same* inclination and be of the same length; the angle of clearance, β, back of the cutting edge should be sufficient to permit the drill to cut freely; and the clearance should be the same on both sides and increase toward the point or center of the drill.

Angle of Cutting Edge. — The angle α of the cutting edge should be about 59 degrees, as measured from the axis, although there is a difference of opinion regarding this angle. As the angle is decreased, the pressure required for feeding a drill through the metal diminishes, but the length of each cutting edge is increased with the result that more power is required to turn the drill. An included angle of 118 degrees (59 degrees between the cutting edge and axis) is thought by some authorities to equalize the thrust and torsion to best advantage, while others advocate more acute angles. A spotting drill should have an included angle of 100 degrees, so that the body of the drill following will be properly supported before the point begins to cut.

Clearance Angle. — The clearance angle β is very important, and the splitting of drills through the web is often an indication of insufficient clearance, especially at the drill point. If the end of a drill conforms exactly to the conical shape of the bottom of a hole, it will not cut, because the lack of clearance prevents the cutting edges from sinking into the metal. Theoretically, the clearance should be just enough to permit the drill to cut freely, because excessive clearance weakens the cutting edges. One prominent drill concern advocates an angle β of 12 degrees at the periphery of the drill, with a gradual increase towards the center until the straight line formed by the end or point of the drill is at an angle γ of approximately 135 degrees, as shown by the plan view. When soft metal is to be drilled, and heavier feeds are possible, the angle of clearance may be increased to 15 degrees, whereas, for hard material, such as tool steel, the amount of clearance is diminished, because a finer feed must be used and a strong cutting edge is required.

Sharpening Carbide Tools: — Carbide tools should be sharpened before dulling becomes excessive and there is pitting or crumbling of the edges. One method of determining when tools need resharpening is by periodic inspection. Another method is to determine either the amount of production which can be obtained before excessive dulling occurs, or the equivalent period of time. This production figure or time interval then indicates the allowable tool life between successive grindings of tools used on a given machine and class of work. Usually, sharpening should not require the removal of more than 0.005 to 0.010 inch of carbide. Since carbide tool grinding procedure varies more or less in different plants, the recommendations of forty prominent machinery and abrasive manufacturers were obtained and are presented in the following summary.

General Procedure in Carbide Tool Grinding: — The general procedure depends upon the kind of grinding operation required. If the operation is merely to resharpen a dull tool, a diamond wheel of fine grit ordinarily is used. If the tool is new or is a "standard design" and changes in shape are necessary, the general practice is to use vitrified silicon carbide wheels for roughing, and diamond wheels for finishing, although silicon carbide wheels of comparatively fine grain are sometimes used for finishing. A final operation commonly designated as lapping, may or may not be employed for obtaining extra-fine finish.

Wheel Speeds: — The speed of silicon carbide wheels usually is about 5000 feet per minute. The speeds of diamond wheels generally range from 5000 to 6000 feet per minute.

Offhand Grinding. — In grinding single-point tools (excepting chip breakers) the common practice is to hold the tool by hand, press it against the wheel face and traverse it continuously across the wheel face while the tool is supported on the machine rest or table which is adjusted to the required angle. This is known as "offhand grinding" to distinguish it from the machine grinding of cutters as in regular cutter grinding practice. The selection of wheels adapted to carbide tool grinding is very important.

Silicon Carbide Wheels: — The green colored silicon carbide wheels generally are preferred to the dark gray or gray-black variety, although the latter are sometimes used.

Grain or Grit Sizes: — For roughing, a grain size of 60 is very generally used. For finish grinding with silicon carbide wheels, a finer grain size of 100 or 120 is common. A silicon carbide wheel such as C60-I-7V may be used for grinding both the steel shank and carbide tip. However, for under-cutting steel shanks up to the carbide tip, it may be advantageous to use an aluminum oxide wheel suitable for high speed steel grinding.

Grade: — According to the standard system of marking, different grades from soft to hard are indicated by letters from A to Z. For carbide tool grinding fairly soft grades such as G, H, I and J are used. The usual grades for roughing are I or J and for finishing H, I and J. The grade should be such that a sharp free-cutting wheel will be maintained without excessive grinding pressure. Harder grades than those indicated tend to overheat and crack the carbide.

Structure: — The common structure numbers for carbide tool grinding are 7 and 8. The larger cup-wheels (10 to 14 inches) may be of the porous type and be designated as 12P. The standard structure numbers range from 1 to 15 with progressively higher numbers indicating less density and more open wheel structure.

Diamond Wheels: — Wheels with diamond-impregnated grinding faces, are fast and cool cutting and have a very low rate of wear. They are used extensively both for resharpening and for finish grinding of carbide tools when preliminary roughing is required. Diamond wheels are also adapted for sharpening multi-tooth cutters such as milling cutters, reamers, etc., which are gound in a cutter grinding machine.

Resinoid bonded wheels are commonly used for grinding chip breakers, milling cutters, reamers or other multi-tooth cutters. They are also applicable to precision grinding of carbide dies, gages, and various external, internal and surface grinding operations. Fast, cool cutting action is characteristic of these wheels.

Metal bonded wheels are often used for offhand grinding of single-point tools especially when durability or long life and resistance to grooving of the cutting face, are considered more important than the rate of cutting. *Vitrified bonded* wheels are used both for roughing of chipped or very dull tools and for ordinary resharpening and finishing. They provide rigidity for precision grinding, a porous structure for fast cool cutting, sharp cutting action and durability.

Diamond Wheel Grit Sizes: — For roughing with diamond wheels a grit size of 100 is the most common both for offhand and machine grinding. Grit sizes of 120 and 150 are frequently used in offhand grinding of single point tools (1) for resharpening, (2) for a combination roughing and finishing wheel and (3) for chip-breaker grinding. Grit sizes of 220 or 240 are used for ordinary finish grinding all types of tools (offhand and machine) and also for cylindrical, internal and surface finish grinding. Grits of 320 and 400 are used for "lapping" to obtain very fine finishes, and for hand hones. A grit of 500 is for lapping to a mirror finish on such work as carbide gages and boring or other tools for exceptionally fine finishes.

Diamond Wheel Grades: — Diamond wheels are made in several different grades to better adapt them to different classes of work. The grades vary for different types and shapes of wheels. Standard Norton grades are H, J and L for resinoid bonded wheels, grade N for metal bonded wheels and grades J, L, N and P for vitrified wheels. Harder and softer grades than standard may at times be used to advantage.

Diamond Concentration: — The relative amount (by carat weight) of diamond in the diamond section of the wheel is known as the "diamond concentration." Concentrations of 100 (high), 50 (medium) and 25 (low) ordinarily are supplied. A concentration of 50 represents one-half the diamond content of 100 (if the depth of the diamond is the same in each case) and 25 equals one-fourth the content of 100 or one-half the content of 50 concentration.

100 Concentration: — Recommended (especially in grit sizes up to about 220) for general machine grinding of carbides, and for grinding cutters and chip breakers. Vitrified and metal bonded wheels usually have 100 concentration.

50 Concentration: — In the finer grit sizes of 220, 240, 320, 400 and 500, a 50 concentration is recommended for offhand grinding with resinoid bonded cup-wheels.

25 Concentration: — A low concentration of 25 is recommended for offhand grinding with resinoid bonded cup-wheels with grit sizes of 100, 120 and 150.

Depth of Diamond Section: — The radial depth of the diamond section usually varies from $\frac{1}{16}$ to $\frac{1}{4}$ inch. The depth varies somewhat according to the wheel size and type of bond.

Dry Versus Wet Grinding of Carbide Tools: — In using silicon carbide wheels, grinding should be done either absolutely dry or with enough coolant to flood the wheel and tool. Satisfactory results may be obtained either by the wet or dry method. However, dry grinding is the most prevalent usually because, in wet grinding, operators tend to use an inadequate supply of coolant to obtain better visibility of the grinding operation and avoid getting wet; hence checking or cracking in many cases is more likely to occur in wet grinding than in dry grinding.

Wet Grinding with Silicon Carbide Wheels: — One advantage commonly cited in connection with wet grinding is that an ample supply of coolant permits using wheels about one grade harder than in dry grinding thus increasing the wheel life. Plenty of coolant also prevents thermal stresses and the resulting cracks, and there is less tendency for the wheel to load. A dust exhaust system also is unnecessary.

Wet Grinding with Diamond Wheels: — In grinding with diamond wheels the general practice is to use a coolant to keep the wheel face clean and promote free cutting. The amount of coolant may vary from a small stream to a coating applied to the wheel face by a felt pad.

Coolants for Carbide Tool Grinding: — In grinding either with silicon carbide or diamond wheels a coolant that is used extensively consists of water plus a small amount either of soluble oil, sal soda, or soda ash to prevent corrosion. One prominent manufacturer recommends for silicon carbide wheels about 1 ounce of soda ash per gallon of water and for diamond wheels kerosene. The use of kerosene is quite general for diamond wheels and usually it is applied to the wheel face by a felt pad. Another coolant recommended for diamond wheels consists of 80 per cent water and 20 per cent soluble oil.

Peripheral Versus Flat Side Grinding: — In grinding single point carbide tools with silicon carbide wheels, the roughing preparatory to finishing with diamond wheels may be done either by using the flat face of a cup-shaped wheel (side grinding) or the periphery of a "straight" or disk-shaped wheel. Even where side grinding is preferred, the periphery of a straight wheel may be used for heavy roughing

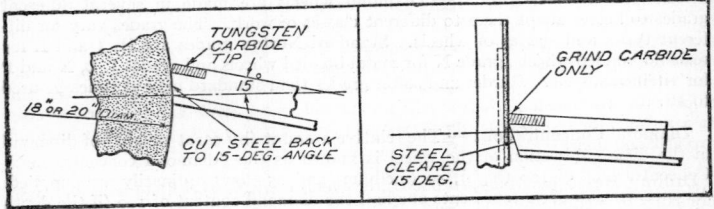

as in grinding back chipped or broken tools (see left-hand diagram). Reasons for preferring peripheral grinding include faster cutting with less danger of localized heating and checking especially in grinding broad surfaces. The advantages usually claimed for side grinding are that proper rake or relief angles are easier to obtain and the relief or land is ground flat. The diamond wheels used for tool sharpening are designed for side grinding. (See right-hand diagram.)

Lapping Carbide Tools: — Carbide tools may be finished by lapping, especially if an exceptionally fine finish is required on the work as, for example, tools used for precision boring or turning non-ferrous metals. If the finishing is done by using a diamond wheel of very fine grit (such as 240, 320 or 400), the operation is often called "lapping." A second lapping method is by means of a power-driven lapping disk charged with diamond dust, Norbide powder, or silicon carbide finishing compound. A third method is by using a hand lap or hone usually of 320 or 400 grit. In many plants the finishes obtained with carbide tools meet requirements without a special lapping operation. In all cases any feather edge which may be left on tools should be removed and it is good practice to bevel the edges of roughing tools at 45 degrees to leave a chamfer 0.005 to 0.010 inch wide. This is done by hand honing and the object is to prevent crumbling or flaking off at the edges when hard scale or heavy chip pressure is encountered.

Hand Honing: — Hand honing of carbide tools at the machine or while tools are in use, is done frequently to defer removal for grinding. The consensus of opinion seems to be that hand honing "between grinds" is desirable *if correctly done by an experienced workman* so as not to change relief angles or round over the cutting edges. However, since hand honing by the machine operator is difficult to control and since many operators are incapable of proper honing, the preference in many plants is to avoid honing.

Chip Breaker Grinding: — For this operation a straight diamond wheel is used on a universal tool and cutter grinder, a small surface grinder, or a special chip-breaker grinder. A resinoid bonded wheel of the grade J or N commonly is used and the tool is held rigidly in an adjustable holder or vise. The width of the diamond wheel usually varies from ⅛ to ¼ inch. A vitrified bond may be used for wheels as thick as ¼ inch, and a resinoid bond for relatively narrow wheels.

Summary of Miscellaneous Points: — In grinding a single-point carbide tool, traverse it across the wheel face continuously to avoid localized heating. This traverse movement should be quite rapid in using silicon carbide wheels and comparatively slow with diamond wheels. A hand traversing and feeding movement, whenever practicable, is generally recommended because of greater sensitivity. In grinding, maintain a constant, moderate pressure. Never cool a hot tool by dipping it in a liquid, as this may crack the tip. Wheel rotation should preferably be *against* the cutting edge or from the front face toward the back. If the grinder is driven by a reversing motor, opposite sides of a cup wheel can be used for grinding right- and left-hand tools and with rotation against the cutting edge. If it is necessary to grind the top face of a single-point tool, this should precede the grinding of the side and front relief, and top-face grinding should be minimized to maintain the tip thickness. In machine grinding with a diamond wheel, limit the feed per traverse to 0.001 inch for 100 to 120 grit; 0.0005 inch for 150 to 240 grit; and 0.0002 inch for 320 grit and finer.

Drilling Holes in Glass. — There are several methods of drilling holes in glass. For holes of medium and large size, use brass or copper tubing, having an outside diameter equal to the size of hole required. Revolve the tube at a peripheral speed of about 100 feet per minute, and use carborundum (80 to 100 grit) and light machine oil between the end of the pipe and the glass. Insert the abrasive under the drill with a thin piece of soft wood, to avoid scratching the glass. The glass should be supported by a felt or rubber cushion, not much larger than the hole to be drilled. If practicable, it is well to drill about halfway through and then turn the glass over and drill down to meet the first cut. Any fin that may be left in the hole can be removed with a round second-cut file wet with turpentine. For comparatively small holes, a solid drill is often used. Use steel rod or an old three-cornered file, grinding the end to a long tapering triangular shaped point. Grip the drill in a chuck and rotate rapidly. Use a mixture of turpentine and camphor as a lubricant. Holes up to ½ inch in diameter can be drilled in glass with a flat drill which has been hardened in sulphurous acid, a mixture of turpentine and camphor being used as a lubricant.

Cutting Fluids for Machining Operations

The function of a cutting fluid varies somewhat for different metal-cutting operations, but, in general, the fluid serves to prevent excessive heating of the tool and work (especially when removing metal rapidly in taking roughing cuts) and by reducing friction and heat generation, prevent excessive tool wear and, in many cases, warpage of the work by localized heating. In screw machine or turret lathe work and in certain other cases, improvement in surface finish is also an important function of the cutting fluid. Washing away chips is another function, especially in deep-hole drilling, grinding, milling, and cutting-off operations with power-driven saws. In selecting the cutting fluid, protection of machined surfaces against corrosion may be an important factor; on some machine tools, the fluid is selected to perform both the usual function of a cutting fluid and, at the same time, serve as a lubricant for machine slides located near the cutting tools. Many different kinds of cutting fluids have been used. In general, if *cooling* effect is required chiefly, an oil-and-water emulsion is used, but if lubrication of chip bearing surfaces must be combined with cooling, then some mineral oil combination is employed. Between these extremes there are many border-line cases, and, consequently, differences of opinion. There are no fixed rules or formulas for selecting cutting oils, except the rule of actual test with a given tool or operation and material. The following general types of cutting fluids are utilized chiefly in modern machine shop practice.

Emulsifying or Soluble Oils. — Soluble oils are extensively used for machining operations, particularly when an inexpensive cooling medium meets practical requirements. When an emulsifying oil is mixed with water, an emulsion is formed rather than a solution, but the name "soluble oil" has been generally accepted because the oil apparently dissolves or goes into solution with the water. To obtain a mixture of oil and water, an emulsifying agent is required and soap has proved to be very effective. The emulsion formed contains an infinite number of minute and invisible oil particles which give the mixture a milky or creamy white color. The proportions of the mixture should be determined by test. If the mixture is too weak, it may cause corrosion of both work and machine. The mixture may range from 1 part soluble oil to 5 parts water up to 1 part soluble oil and 50 or even 100 parts water. Soluble oils are easily mixed; but since the emulsion is of the oil-in-water type, it should always be prepared by pouring the *oil* into the water instead of pouring the water into the oil. The emulsification is aided at temperatures somewhat above 40 degrees F., but the use of boiling water may have a reverse tendency. Agitation or stirring increases the emulsifying tendency unless too violent when there may be a reverse tendency. Even though a soluble oil may serve readily with hard water, it may be desirable to soften the water for obtaining one of the leaner mixtures or to eliminate scum formation. To prevent corrosion when a soluble oil is used, there should be sufficient air circulation to evaporate the water from the machined surface, thus leaving the oil to form a protective coating. In other words, if rapid drying is prevented either by lack of air circulation or by high humidity, rusting is likely to occur.

Paste Compounds: Emulsions may be formed by mixing paste compounds with water. A paste made of saponified mineral oil with a high soap content has the consistency of grease. Paste compounds are not used as extensively as soluble oils but they are often applied particularly in connection with grinding operations. These paste compounds do not emulsify with water as readily as the soluble oils and this is particularly true with hard water. Hot water and steam may be required in some cases to obtain the best mixing results.

Straight Cutting Oils. — Straight cutting oils may be either in the mineral class or in the fatty or animal class such as the lard oil.

Straight Mineral Oils: The chief use of mineral oils in connection with machining processes is for blending with base cutting oils for obtaining whatever properties are required for different machining operations. Straight mineral oils are applicable to light machining operations especially on non-ferrous metals or in machining free-cutting steel, particularly if both cooling and lubricating effects are required. The low viscosity grades are preferable because of their cooling and penetrating properties. Straight mineral oils are sometimes used on automatics in preference to an emulsion which might interfere with proper lubrication of adjacent machine slides or other parts.

Straight Fatty Oils: Straight fatty oils have in the past been used quite extensively, especially for the heavier machining operations, but certain objectionable features have resulted in the substitution of other cutting fluids. The cost of a fatty oil such as lard oil is not only high but a straight animal oil tends to become rancid and produce an objectionable odor. Bacteria breed in such oils and cause skin troubles among machine operators. Sulphurized cutting oils have supplanted the fatty oils to a considerable degree, for machining operations requiring chip lubrication. Fatty oils, however, may be used in cases where a sulphurized mineral oil would tarnish the machined parts unless some preventive treatment is applied.

Mineral Lard Oil. — Mixtures of mineral oil and lard oil may be used to obtain a cutting fluid having greater lubricating value than a straight mineral oil and much lower cost than a straight lard oil. They may be used when the chip pressures are moderate. The proportion of lard oil and mineral oil depends upon the character of the machining operation and the need for both cooling and lubricating effects. For light machining, straight mineral oil may be satisfactory; for heavier duty or where the metal is removed at comparatively high rate, the mineral oil may contain from 10 to 40 per cent of lard oil. As a general rule, the percentage of lard oil is increased with the hardness of the stock to be machined. The No. 1 or prime lard oil is the most commonly used animal fatty oil. There are, however, synthetic fatty oils which are used in conjunction with mineral oils to obtain the so-called mineral lard oils. Mineral lard oils are frequently used in connection with automatic screw machine practice. The Saybolt viscosity (which is controlled by the mineral oil) generally varies from 150 to 225 seconds at 100 degrees F. for the blended oil.

Sulphurized and Chlorinated Cutting Oils. — The oils in these two general classes are especially useful when there is high chip-bearing pressure as in machining alloy or other tough steels. The sulphurized and chlorinated base oils are blended with mineral oils and produce metallic oxides or a *metallic*-film lubrication instead of fluid-film lubrication, as a result of the heat generated by the cutting tool. While mineral oils may contain natural sulphur, it has little or no value in cutting oils. There are two methods of adding sulphur. The sulphur may be cooked in and bonded with a fatty oil such as lard or sperm oil, thus obtaining a compound or "sulphur base" which is added to the mineral oil. The transparent oils are produced by this method, and the required viscosity is obtained by blending the base with a mineral oil. A second method is to add the sulphur direct to the mineral oil by the application of heat. The result is a dark or opaque oil which is suitable where work visibility is not required as in pipe threading and miscellaneous roughing operations. Chlorine, like sulphur, is added to mineral oils to obtain cutting fluids suitable for high chip-bearing pressures.

Aqueous Solutions. — When the function of a cutting fluid is merely to cool the work and possibly wash away chips, water containing some alkali has often been used, although these aqueous solutions have been replaced quite largely by modern cutting fluids. They do not, of course, provide the lubricating film that is important for many classes of work and they also cause corrosion of both work and the machine. These aqueous solutions may contain carbonate of soda, borax, caustic soda, etc.   Lard oil and soft soap may also be used to improve the properties.   An inexpensive mixture for turning, milling, etc., is made in the following proportions: 1 pound of sal-soda (carbonate of soda), 1 quart of lard oil, 1 quart of soft soap, and enough water to make 10 or 12 gallons.   This mixture is boiled for one-half hour, preferably by passing a steam coil through it.   If the solution should have an objectionable smell, this can be eliminated by adding about 2 pounds of unslaked lime.

Cutting Fluids for Different Materials and Operations. — The selection of a cutting fluid depends upon machinability of the metal and various other factors; hence the following recommendations are intended as a general guide only.

Steels: See information relating to different classes of cutting fluids.   If a soluble oil is suitable, use 1 part oil and 10 to 20 parts water.   Mineral-oil or mineral-lard-oil combinations may be used in preference to soluble oils when the latter tend to corrode the work.   When steel is so tough that the pressure on the tool is very high, a sulphurized oil is preferable to an emulsion.   In cutting hard steels, an oil containing a small amount of chlorine may be preferable.   Sulphur-base cutting oils are also used for low- or medium-carbon steels when visibility of the machined surface is essential.

Brass: For machining brass rod in automatics, soluble oils and mineral lard oils are commonly used.   A cutting oil may be preferred to an emulsion because it not only serves as a cutting fluid but provides lubrication for adjacent slides or other machine bearings near the cutting area.   Common proportions for an emulsion are: soluble oil 1 part and water 20 to 25 parts.   Mineral lard oil may contain from 5 to 10 per cent of lard oil.   Cast brass is usually machined dry.

Monel Metal: In turning Monel metal, an emulsion gives a slightly longer tool life than a sulphurized mineral oil, but the latter aids in chip breakage which frequently is desirable.

Aluminum Alloys: Many different cutting fluids have been recommended such as (1) from 90 per cent kerosene and 10 per cent mineral oil to 50 per cent kerosene and 50 per cent mineral oil; (2) soluble oil emulsion with 15 per cent kerosene; (3) 50 per cent kerosene, 40 per cent lard oil and 10 per cent chlorinated solvent.   (See also Machining Aluminum.)

Cast Iron: While cast iron ordinarily is machined dry, a soluble oil emulsion may be used to avoid an excessive amount of dust around the machine.

Turning: For turning steel, soluble oil emulsions, mineral lard oils and sulphurized cutting oils are used, depending upon the character of the turning operation and the toughness of the steel and resulting chip pressures.   For additional information, see classes of oils mentioned.

Milling: Soluble oils, mineral lard oils and sulphurized oils are used, depending upon the machinability of the metal.   Soluble oils usually consist of 1 part oil and 10 to 25 parts water.

Drilling: For light or ordinary drilling in steel, use soluble oil emulsion consisting of 1 part oil and 25 to 50 parts water; for heavy-duty drilling, use a sulphurized cutting oil of 100 to 200 Saybolt viscosity at 100 degrees F., containing ½ to 2 per cent active sulphur.

Tapping: For soft or ductile steel, use a sulphurized cutting oil containing 2 to 4 per cent active sulphur, and for the harder steels a chlorinated cutting oil.

Thread Cutting: For steel, use either 1 part soluble oil and 15 parts water or a sulphurized cutting oil containing 2 to 4 per cent active sulphur with Saybolt viscosity varying from 125 to 300 at 100 degrees F.   For copper alloys, use a sulphurized oil of 75 to 100 Saybolt viscosity at 100 degrees F. containing ½ to 1 per cent active sulphur.   For aluminum and magnesium alloys, use a sulphurized oil of 35 to 50 Saybolt viscosity at 100 degrees F.   These are general recommendations only.

Cutting Fluids Recommended for Machining Operations — 1

Soluble Oils. — Types of oils or paste compounds which form emulsions when mixed with water: Soluble oils are used extensively in machining both ferrous and non-ferrous metals when the cooling quality is paramount and the chip-bearing pressure is not excessive. Care should be taken in selecting the proper soluble oil for precision grinding operations. Grinding coolants should be free from fatty materials that tend to load the wheel, thus affecting the finish on the machined part. Soluble coolants should contain rust preventive constituents to prevent corrosion.

Base Oils. — Various types of highly sulphurized and chlorinated oils containing in-organic, animal, or fatty materials. This "base stock" usually is "cut back" or blended with a lighter oil, unless the chip-bearing pressures are high, as in cutting alloy steel, in which case the base stock may be used straight. Base oils usually have a viscosity range of from 300 to 900 seconds at 100 degrees F.

Mineral Oils. — This group includes all types of oils extracted from petroleum such as paraffin oil, mineral seal oil, and kerosene. Mineral oils are often blended with base stocks, but they are generally used in the original form for light machining operations on both free-machining steels and non-ferrous metals. The coolants in this class should be of a type that has a relatively high flash point. Care should be taken to see that they are nontoxic, so that they will not be injurious to the operator. The heavier mineral oils (paraffin oils) usually have a viscosity of about 100 seconds at 100 degrees F. Mineral seal oil and kerosene have a viscosity of 35 to 60 seconds at 100 degrees F.

Material to be Cut	Turning	Milling
Aluminum (Note 1—See notes on next page)	Mineral Oil with 10 Per Cent Fat (or) Soluble Oil	Soluble Oil (96 Per Cent Water) (or) Mineral Seal Oil (or) Mineral Oil
Alloy Steels (Note 2)	25 Per Cent Sulphur base Oil* with 75 Per Cent Mineral Oil	10 Per Cent Lard Oil with 90 Per Cent Mineral Oil
Brass	Mineral Oil with 10 Per Cent Fat	Soluble Oil (96 Per Cent Water)
Tool Steels and Low-carbon Steels	25 Per Cent Lard Oil with 75 Per Cent Mineral Oil	Soluble Oil
Copper	Soluble Oil	Soluble Oil
Monel Metal	Soluble Oil	Soluble Oil
Cast Iron (Note 3)	Dry	Dry
Malleable Iron	Soluble Oil	Soluble Oil
Bronze	Soluble Oil	Soluble Oil
Magnesium (Note 5)	10 Per Cent Lard Oil with 90 Per Cent Mineral Oil	Mineral Seal Oil

Cutting Fluids Recommended for Machining Operations — 2

Material to be Cut	Drilling	Tapping
Aluminum (Note 4)	Soluble Oil (75 to 90 Per Cent Water) (or) 10 Per Cent Lard Oil with 90 Per Cent Mineral Oil	Lard Oil (or) Sperm Oil (or) Wool Grease (or) 25 Per Cent Sulphur-base Oil* Mixed with Mineral Oil
Alloy Steels (Note 2)	Soluble Oil	30 Per Cent Lard Oil with 70 Per Cent Mineral Oil
Brass	Soluble Oil (75 to 90 Per Cent Water) (or) 30 Per Cent Lard Oil with 70 Per Cent Mineral Oil	10 to 20 Per Cent Lard Oil with Mineral Oil
Tool Steels and Low-carbon Steels	Soluble Oil	25 to 40 Per Cent Lard Oil with Mineral Oil (or) 25 Per Cent Sulphur-base Oil* with 75 Per Cent Mineral Oil
Copper	Soluble Oil	Soluble Oil
Monel Metal	Soluble Oil	25 to 40 Per Cent Lard Oil Mixed with Mineral Oil (or) Sulphur-base Oil* Mixed with Mineral Oil
Cast Iron (Note 3)	Dry	Dry (or) 25 Per Cent Lard Oil with 75 Per Cent Mineral Oil
Malleable Iron	Soluble Oil	Soluble Oil
Bronze	Soluble Oil	20 Per Cent Lard Oil with 80 Per Cent Mineral Oil
Magnesium (Note 5)	60-second Mineral Oil	20 Per Cent Lard Oil with 80 Per Cent Mineral Oil

Note 1. In machining aluminum, several varieties of coolants may be used. For rough machining, where the stock removal is sufficient to produce heat, water soluble mixtures can be used with good results to dissipate the heat. Other oils that may be recommended are straight mineral seal oil; a 50-50 mixture of mineral seal oil and kerosene; a mixture of 10 per cent lard oil with 90 per cent kerosene; and a 100-second mineral oil cut back with mineral seal oil or kerosene.

Note 2. The sulphur-base oil referred to contains 4½ per cent sulphur compound. Base oils are usually dark in color. As a rule, they contain sulphur compounds resulting from a thermal or catalytic refinery process. When so processed, they are more suitable for industrial coolants than when they have had such compounds as flowers of sulphur added by hand. The adding of sulphur compounds by hand to the coolant reservoir is of temporary value only, and the non-uniformity of the solution may affect the machining operation.

Note 3. A soluble oil or low-viscosity mineral oil may be used in machining cast iron to prevent excessive metal dust.

Note 4. Sulphurized oils ordinarily are not recommended for tapping aluminum; however, for some tapping operations they have proved very satisfactory, although the work should be slushed in a solvent right after machining to prevent discoloration.

Note 5. When machining magnesium, use an anhydrous non-acid oil. Water solubles or emulsions should never be used because water would intensify an accidental chip fire.

Grinding: Soluble oil emulsions or emulsions made from paste compounds are used extensively, although mineral oils are preferred in some cases to improve the quality of the ground surface. For cylindrical grinding, use 1 part soluble oil and from 70 to 80 parts water; for centerless grinding, use 1 part oil to 50 parts water. Mineral oils are used with vitrified wheels but are not recommended for wheels with rubber or shellac bonds.

Broaching: For steel, use a heavy mineral oil such as sulphurized oil of 300 to 500 Saybolt viscosity at 100 degrees F. to provide both adequate lubricating effect and a dampening of the shock loads. Soluble oil emulsions may be used for the lighter broaching operations.

Cutting Fluids for use with Carbide Tools. — Both soluble oils and sulphurized or chlorinated oils are used with carbide tools. A soluble oil emulsion, if supplied in sufficient quantity, is excellent as a cooling medium, but in some cases the lubricating effect of a cutting oil is desirable. If oil is objectionable because of smoking, a larger volume may be required. Some contend that sulphurized and chlorinated oils tend to weaken the binder or brazing materials and thus loosen the carbide tips; but other observers believe that the binder is affected by fatigue or by the high temperatures.

Application of Cutting Fluids. — Cutting fluids should be applied where the cutting action is taking place and at the highest possible velocity without causing splashing. As a general rule, it is preferable to supply from 3 to 5 gallons per minute for each single-point tool on a machine such as a turret lathe or automatic. The temperature of the cutting fluid should be kept below 110 degrees F. If the volume of fluid used is not sufficient to maintain the proper temperature, means of cooling it should be provided.

Cutting Fluids for Machining Magnesium. — In machining magnesium, it is the general but not invariable practice in the United States to use a cutting fluid, whereas, in England, magnesium usually is machined dry except in cases where heat generated by high cutting speeds would not be dissipated rapidly enough without a cutting fluid. This condition may exist when, for example, small tools without much heat-conducting capacity are employed on automatics.

The cutting fluid for magnesium should be an anhydrous oil having, at most, a very low acid content. Various mineral-oil cutting fluids are used for magnesium. To secure adequate cooling, the supply of fluid should be large (4 to 5 gallons per minute) and the viscosity low; however, to avoid too low a flash point, a compromise between cooling capacity and flash point is necessary. *Soluble oils or emulsions should never be used for machining magnesium.* Compressed air may be preferable to a fluid because it leaves the chips or swarf clean and dry.

A cutting fluid serves primarily to cool the work and also eliminate a possible fire hazard, especially when dull tools are operated at high speeds with fine feeds. Even when using sharp tools, the cut should not be less than 0.001 inch because fine chips are more likely to become ignited at high speeds. While a variety of mineral oils may be used, the following properties are recommended: Specific gravity 0.79 to 0.86; viscosity (Saybolt) at 100 degrees F., up to 55 seconds; flash point, minimum value (closed cup), 160 degrees F.; saponification No., 16 (max.); free acid (max.) 0.2 per cent. Oil-water emulsions, while good coolants, are objectionable because water will greatly intensify any accidental chip fire.

Machining Magnesium. — Magnesium alloys are readily machined and with relatively low power consumption per cubic inch of metal removed. The usual practice is to employ high cutting speeds with relatively coarse feeds and deep cuts. Exceptionally fine finishes can be obtained so that grinding to improve the finish usually is unnecessary. The horsepower normally required in machining magnesium varies from 0.15 to 0.30 per cubic inch per minute. While this value is low, especially in comparison with power required for cast iron and steel, the total amount of power for machining magnesium usually is high because of the exceptionally rapid rate at which metal is removed.

Carbide tools are recommended for maximum efficiency, although high-speed steel frequently is employed. Tools should be designed so as to dispose of chips readily or without excessive friction, by employing polished chip-bearing surfaces, ample chip spaces, large clearances, and small contact areas. *Keen-edged tools should always be used.*

Feeds and Speeds for Magnesium: Speeds ordinarily range up to 5000 feet per minute for rough- and finish-turning, up to 3000 feet per minute for rough-milling, and up to 9000 feet per minute for finish-milling. For rough-turning, the following combinations of speed in feet per minute, feed per revolution, and depth of cut are recommended: Speed 300 to 600 feet per minute — feed 0.030 to 0.100 inch, depth of cut 0.5 inch; speed 600 to 1000 — feed 0.020 to 0.080, depth of cut 0.4; speed 1000 to 1500 — feed 0.010 to 0.060, depth of cut 0.3; speed 1500 to 2000 — feed 0.010 to 0.040, depth of cut 0.2; speed 2000 to 5000 — feed 0.010 to 0.030, depth of cut 0.15.

Lathe Tool Angles for Magnesium: The true or actual rake angle resulting from back and side rakes usually varies from 10 to 15 degrees. Back rake varies from 10 to 20, and side rake from 0 to 10 degrees. Reduced back rake may be employed to obtain better chip breakage. The back rake may also be reduced to from 2 to 8 degrees on form tools or other broad tools to prevent chatter.

Parting Tools: For parting tools, the back rake varies from 15 to 20 degrees, the front end relief 8 to 10 degrees, the side relief measured perpendicular to the top face 8 degrees, the side relief measured in the plane of the top face from 3 to 5 degrees.

Milling Magnesium: In general, the coarse-tooth type of cutter is recommended. The number of teeth or cutting blades may be one-third to one-half the number normally used; however, the two-blade fly-cutter has proved to be very satisfactory. As a rule, the land relief or primary peripheral clearance is 10 degrees followed by secondary clearance of 20 degrees. The lands should be narrow, the width being about 3/64 to 1/16 inch. The rake, which is positive, is about 15 degrees.

For rough-milling and speeds in feet per minute up to 900 — feed, inch per tooth, 0.005 to 0.025, depth of cut up to 0.5; for speeds 900 to 1500 — feed 0.005 to 0.020, depth of cut up to 0.375; for speeds 1500 to 3000 — feed 0.005 to 0.010, depth of cut up to 0.2.

Drilling Magnesium: If the depth of a hole is less than five times the drill diameter, an ordinary twist drill with highly polished flutes may be used. The included angle of the point may vary from 70 degrees to the usual angle of 118 degrees. The relief angle is about 12 degrees. The drill should be kept sharp and the outer corners rounded to produce a smooth finish and prevent burr formation. For deep hole drilling, use a drill having a helix angle of 40 to 45 degrees with large polished flutes of uniform cross-section throughout the drill length to facilitate the flow of chips. A pyramid-shaped "spur" or "pilot point" at the tip of the drill will reduce the "spiraling or run-off."

Drilling speeds vary from 300 to 2000 feet per minute with feeds per revolution ranging from 0.015 to 0.050.

Reaming Magnesium: Reamers up to 1 inch in diameter should have four flutes; larger sizes six flutes. These flutes may be either parallel with the axis or have a negative helix angle of 10 degrees. The positive rake angle varies from 5 to 8 degrees, the relief angle from 4 to 7 degrees, and the clearance angle from 15 to 20 degrees.

Tapping Magnesium: Standard taps may be used unless Class 3 or Class 4 tolerances are required, in which case the tap should be designed for magnesium.

A high-speed steel concentric type with a ground thread is recommended. The concentric form, which eliminates the radial thread relief, prevents jamming of chips while the tap is being backed out of the hole. The positive rake angle at the front may vary from 10 to 25 degrees and the "heel rake angle" at the back of the tooth from 3 to 5 degrees. The chamfer extends over two to three threads. For holes up to ¼ inch in diameter, two-fluted taps are recommended; for sizes from ½ to ¾ inch, three flutes; and for larger holes, four flutes. Tapping speeds ordinarily range from 75 to 200 feet per minute, and mineral oil cutting fluid should be used.

Threading Dies for Magnesium: Threading dies for use on magnesium should have about the same cutting angles as taps. Narrow lands should be used to provide ample chip space. Either solid or self-opening dies may be used. The latter type is recommended when maximum smoothness is required. Threads may be cut at speeds up to 1000 feet per minute.

Grinding Magnesium: As a general rule, magnesium is ground dry. The highly inflammable dust should be formed into a sludge by means of a spray of water or low-viscosity mineral oil. Accumulations of dust or sludge should be avoided. For surface grinding, when a fine finish is desirable, a low-viscosity mineral oil may be used.

Machining Aluminum. — Some of the alloys of aluminum have been machined successfully without any lubricant or cutting compound, but in order to obtain the best results, some form of lubricant is desirable. For many purposes, a soluble cutting oil is good.

Tools for aluminum and its alloys should have appreciably more side and top rake than the tools for cutting steel. The front clearance of a tool most suitable for machining aluminum and its alloys should be about 8 degrees, the top rake from 30 to 50 degrees, making the total angle of the cutting edge from 35 to 55 degrees. A side rake of from 10 to 20 degrees will materially assist in the cutting action.

In all cases it is essential that the cutting edges of the tools be keen, smooth, and free from grinding wheel scratches, burrs, or wire edges. Keen tool edges are best obtained by finish-grinding on a fine or very fine abrasive wheel, followed by hand-stoning with a fine or very fine oilstone.

Parting tools for machining aluminum and its alloys should have from 12 to 20 degrees top rake and be stoned so that their cutting edges are keen and smooth. With such tools, the front clearance angle should be decreased to about 3 or 4 degrees. Facing tools should be ground so as to have a side rake similar in amount to that indicated for the top rake of the outside turning tools.

High-carbon steel tools ground to the thin cutting edges necessary for aluminum soon fail because of brittleness. High-speed steel tools give much better results, except when used for machining aluminum alloys containing appreciable amounts of silicon. For the high-silicon alloys use cemented tungsten-carbide tools.

Milling cutters, straddle mills, end-mills, and similar cutters work to best advantage in machining aluminum and its alloys if they are of the coarse-tooth spiral type and have a considerable amount of top rake on their cutting edges. Face milling cutters with inserted teeth are satisfactory for machining aluminum. Such cutters should be designed so that the inserted teeth have appreciable top and side rake.

Excellent threads may be chased in even the softest aluminum in an engine lathe, using a single-pointed threading tool with considerable top and side rake. The tool must be ground so as to give the required thread contour. Hand and machine taps will produce smooth and accurate threads in aluminum if they are of the spiral-fluted ground-thread type. Experience has shown that such taps should have a right-hand spiral flute when intended to cut a right-hand thread, and the spiral angle should be similar to that used in an ordinary twist drill. Satisfactory taps for use in aluminum have been made by chasing threads on annealed high-carbon twist drills followed by rehardening and grinding.

Machining Plastics. — Molded plastic parts do not require machining, as a general rule, unless the tolerances are exceptionally small or there are undercuts, angular holes, or other openings difficult or impracticable to reproduce in a mold. It is common practice, however, to machine laminated phenolic plastics and also cast phenolic plastics, as well as sheet, bar, and tube stock such as is commonly used for making parts such as pinions or gears. The machining characteristics of different plastics vary somewhat so that the general recommendations given may require some modification to obtain the best results for a given class of work. Although plastics are poor conductors of heat, they usually are machined dry or without a cutting fluid. In some cases, either an air jet, water, or a soap solution is used. The maximum speed at which a cutting tool can operate without excessive heating should be determined by actual test.

Turning and Boring Plastics: Tools of high-speed steel, Stellite and carbide are commonly used in machining plastics. The general practice in turning and boring is similar to that for brass so far as the feed and speed are concerned. Speeds usually vary from 250 to 500 feet per minute for high-speed steel tools and from 500 to 1500 for Stellite and carbide tools. According to the Haynes Stellite Co., hot-set molded parts require tools having less clearance and more rake than those used for steel or other metals. The cold-set acetate and polystyrene molded parts should be turned with tools having no rake and plenty of clearance. Parts molded of "Vinylite" plastic can usually be machined satisfactorily with ordinary metal-cutting tools, provided the front and side clearances are about double those required for machine steel.

Cutting Off Plastics: Tools for cutting off should have greater front and side clearances than for steel. The cutting speed should be about half that employed for a turning operation.

Drilling Plastics: Standard twist drills may be used for small holes up to ⅛ or ³⁄₁₆ inch, but for larger sizes particularly, it is preferable to use the commercial high-speed steel drills designed especially for plastics. These drills are made both in wire gage and fractional sizes. They have relatively large flutes to provide greater space for chips, and polished flutes are preferable. For large-quantity production, carbide-tipped drills are recommended. Extra clearance back of the edges of the flutes tends to reduce friction and heating. Frequent removal of the drill may be necessary, especially in drilling comparatively deep holes. A feed of 0.007 to 0.015 inch per revolution is a common range. Drilling speeds usually vary from 150 to 300 feet per minute. With carbide-tipped drills, the speeds may be as high as 12,000 to 15,000 R.P.M. The drill point should have an included angle of 55 to 60 degrees for thin sections and 90 degrees for the thicker sections. The clearance angle usually is 15 degrees. To avoid excessive heating and aid in chip removal, an air jet may be directed into the hole. In some cases, a soap solution is effective as a cutting fluid. If the drill-spindle movement is cam-operated, design the cam to advance the drill tip slowly at the beginning or for about 0.010 inch, then continue at the full rate of speed and allow a dwell of about 2 to 5 revolutions at the bottom of the hole; then withdraw the drill rapidly.

Tapping and Threading Plastics: For tapping small holes in hot- or cold-set molded parts, a high-speed steel nitrided chromium-plated tap is recommended. The rake may vary from 0 to 5 degrees negative. The size of the hole should allow for about three-fourths of the standard thread depth. Small holes generally are tapped dry. If a coolant is used, water is preferable to oil. Tapping speeds usually vary from 40 to 55 per minute. Threaded brass inserts or bushings are often used, in which case they may be tapped either before or after insertion. In cutting a 60-degree thread, such as the American standard, use a tool that is ground to cut on one side only and feed it in at an angle of 30 degrees by setting the compound rest at this angle.

Drill Jigs for Plastics: In the design of jigs for drilling, close-fitting drill bushing should be avoided. They may increase not only the friction on the drill but also the tendency of the chips to plug up the drill flutes. If the operation is such that a drill bushing is absolutely essential, a floating leaf or templet should be employed. When using a templet, the hole should be spotted with the templet in place, using the drill size corresponding to the final hole size; then the templet should be removed and the hole completed. Pilot holes should be avoided, except in special instances when the hole is to be reamed or counterbored.

Sawing Hot-set Molded Parts: The sawing of molded hot-set parts is done chiefly on circular and band saws. Band saws are to be recommended at times for straight cutting because they run cooler than circular saws. Band saw manufacturers advocate saw teeth set to clear, some advocating one-half the thickness of the blade on each side so that saws give a width of cut double their thickness. Narrower saws and more set are needed for cutting curves than for straight cuts. Band saws just soft enough to permit filing are recommended, but saws must be kept sharp. Dull saws cause chipping and might result in saw breakage. Sawing is usually done dry but some recommend water for cooling. Saw teeth should have little set and eight to nine teeth per inch. The speed is 1800 to 2500 feet per minute.

Sawing Cold-set Molded Parts: Sawing of cold-set polystyrene or cellulose acetate can be done with circular saws having nine to twelve teeth per inch for thin sheets and six teeth per inch for thickness over ¼ inch. Saws six to nine inches in diameter are run at speeds of 3000 to 3600 R.P.M. and should be hollow ground. They usually are ½2 to ⅟16 inch thick. The use of a water spray gives a cleaner cut. One large saw manufacturer recommends that pieces be cut with a stream of water running in the kerf while the saw is cutting. This applies to both circular and band saws; otherwise, the cold-set type of material will fuse. The circular saws recommended are 14 inches, 12 and 9 gage, 130 teeth, 10 degrees rake to be operated at 3000 R.P.M. and made of a special alloy steel stock.

For band sawing, manufacturers suggest a band saw which is 19 to 20 gage, having twenty points to the inch and hardened and tempered. The saw should be operated at 4000 to 4500 feet per minute.

Milling Hot-set and Cold-set Molded Parts: Milling of molded parts is not as a rule feasible, but where it is required, milling speeds and feeds of the range used for brass are recommended. A speed of 400 feet with carbon steel cutters and 1200-1600 feet is recommended with carbide cutters. Single and double bladed fly cutters are sometimes used at high speed with fine cuts. Where little material has to be removed, a high-speed woodworking shaper with a carbide tipped tool can be used to advantage. It is desirable and may be necessary to use an air blast to assure proper chip removal from the milling cutter. Wherever possible it is recommended that spiral milling cutters be used, and that the number of teeth in the cutter head be such that at least two of them are in contact with the work at all times.

The same general rules that apply to turning, facing, and boring operations also hold for milling Vinyl molded parts. Standard cutters can be used, but higher speeds are feasible if extra clearances are ground on the cutter blades.

Machining Non-metallic Gear Blanks. —

Laminated phenolic plastics are extensively used for non-metallic gears and pinions. A non-metallic pinion should preferably be used in conjunction with either a hardened steel or a cast-iron gear, thus providing a durable and comparatively noiseless drive. Small- or medium-sized gears may be formed by molding, provided the quantity is large enough to warrant the cost of a mold. Most non-metallic gears, however, are machined from blanks cut from laminated phenolic plastics which have physical properties superior to the molded gears. These blanks may be cut either by punching in a die, by shearing, or by sawing. An efficient method of producing small blanks is to punch them from thin sheet stock. If necessary, the face width of the gear or pinion may be increased by riveting together two or more of these blanks. Gear blanks may also be cut either from a laminated plastic bar or thick tube. Before cutting the gear teeth, the blanks are machined, as by grinding, to obtain a concentric blank of the required diameter. The larger gears are sawed from sheet stock and then turned to size. Gear blanks which are ready for the gear-cutting operation are supplied by manufacturers of laminated plastic materials. The gear teeth are cut with standard gear-cutting equipment. Metal reinforcing end plates and bushings are commonly employed in connection with laminated gears.

Punching Operations: Most grades of laminated phenolics can be punched either hot or cold. The die must be kept sharp, however, in order to produce good results. The minimum clearance between individual punchings, and also between punchings and the edge of the material strips, should be about three times the thickness of the material. For hot punching or shearing, the material is heated in a steam or electric oven, designed to give a uniform temperature throughout the heating chamber. The material is left in the oven just long enough to be uniformly heated to oven temperature. Further heating causes brittleness. Temperatures of 100 to 120 degrees C. (212 to 248 degrees F.) are recommended. The heating time ranges from five minutes for $\frac{1}{16}$-inch material to thirty minutes for $\frac{1}{4}$-inch material.

Dies for punching laminated plastics are designed the same as for punching metal, except that smaller clearances are allowed between punch and die. In cold punching, this clearance is small, approaching a "sliding fit." The strippers are close fitting and backed with strong springs.

Because these plastic materials expand after being compressed in a die, blanks will be larger than the die diameter and holes will be smaller. On hot punchings, allowance should be made for shrinkage of the material after punching. This shrinkage varies with the grade of material, thickness of piece, and the temperature of the material during the punching operation. For very small holes and blanks, allowances for shrinkage are often neglected, while for large pieces and accurate work, they must be carefully considered. As an example, suppose a 1-inch diameter hole is to be punched hot in $\frac{3}{32}$-inch thick stock; this would require a die of 1.009 inches and a punch of 1.007 inches in diameter. If this piece is punched cold, however, the die should be 1.005 inches in diameter and the punch 1.003 inches in diameter.

Shearing Laminated Plastics: Shears suitable for thin metal sheet are used for cutting laminated plastics. The knife must be kept sharp. In trimming paper-base grades cold, clean-cut edges are obtained with thicknesses of $\frac{1}{32}$ inch and under, and when trimmed hot, up to $\frac{1}{8}$ inch. Fabric-base grades are trimmed cold up to $\frac{1}{16}$ inch, and hot up to $\frac{1}{8}$ inch. Greater thicknesses can be sheared if the condition of the edge is not important.

Sawing Plastics: Material up to 1 inch thick may be cut with a 12- to 16-inch circular saw at about 3000 R.P.M., and material 1 inch thick and over, with a 16-inch saw at about 2400 R.P.M. A saw used for roughing cuts has bevel teeth, seven to the inch, while a smooth saw, with no set — similar to that for metal — is used for finishing cuts. For use on all thick material, the saws should be hollow-ground to prevent binding. The smaller the projection of the saw above the material or the sawing table, the better will be the sawed edges. A thin sheet of plastic or other material placed under the piece to be sawed, is of advantage when extreme smoothness of cut is desired.

A band saw is used for sawing round blanks from plate stock. The usual band saw is of the bevel-tooth type, with some set, and has three to seven teeth per inch. It is run at 3000 feet per minute.

Machining Zinc Alloy Die-Castings. — Machining of zinc alloy die-castings is mostly done without a lubricant. For particular work, especially deep drilling and tapping, a lubricant such as lard oil and kerosene (about half and half) or a 50–50 mixture of kerosene and machine oil may be used to advantage. A mixture of turpentine and kerosene has been found effective on certain difficult jobs.

In drilling, standard carbon steel drills are used for shallow holes and high-speed drills of the high-spiral type are recommended for deep holes. The standard 118-degree angle of point between cutting edges is recommended. A lip clearance of 12 degrees is satisfactory for most drilling, but in some cases may be increased up to 15 degrees. Flutes that are larger than normal offer the advantage of providing plenty of chip clearance. Straight flute drills have been found useful in enlarging existing holes. Peripheral speeds of from 200 to 300 feet per minute are generally found satisfactory for high-speed steel drills and about half this speed for carbon steel drills.

Threading: Button or acorn dies are satisfactory for threading small diameters of work. Either radial or tangent type chasers may be employed for the larger diameters. For radial type chasers, one manufacturer recommends a 10-degree radial hook for straight threads, a 7-degree radial hook for tapered threads; and a surface speed of 50 feet per minute for 3½ to 7½ threads per inch, 100 feet per minute for 8 to 11 threads per inch, and 200 feet per minute for 12 to 32 threads per inch. In using tangent type chasers with zinc alloys, the cutting edge must be on or very near the center to avoid rapid wearing of the chasers just behind the cutting edge. A 5-degree positive rake is recommended.

Reaming: In reaming, tools with six straight flutes are commonly used, although tools with eight flutes irregularly spaced have been found to yield better results by one manufacturer. Many standard reamers have a land that is too wide for best results. A land about 0.015 inch wide is recommended but this may often be ground down to around 0.007 or even 0.005 inch to obtain freer cutting, less tendency to loading, and reduced heating.

Turning: Tools of high-speed steel are commonly employed although the application of Stellite and carbide tools, even on short runs, is feasible. For steel or Stellite, a positive top rake of from 0 to 20 degrees and an end clearance of about 15 degrees is commonly recommended. Where side cutting is involved, a side clearance of about 4 degrees minimum is recommended. With carbide tools, the end clearance should not exceed 6 to 8 degrees and the top rake should be from 5 to 10 degrees positive. For boring, facing, and other lathe operations, rake and clearance angles are about the same as for tools used in turning.

Machining Monel, Nickel, and Nickel Alloys. — Lathe roughing tools usually have a back rake of 6 to 8 degrees, a side rake of 10 to 15 degrees, and a clearance of 8 to 12 degrees. Broad nose finishing tools have a back rake of 20 to 25 degrees and a front clearance of 12 to 15 degrees.

The most satisfactory high-speed tool steel for machining high nickel materials is the 18–4–1 tungsten high-speed steel. A modification of this steel having an added high cobalt and low molybdenum content is also satisfactory. This latter type is better for the machining of castings than the regular high-speed steel. Stellite, tungsten carbide, and tantalum carbide tools may prove to be superior to these high-speed steel tools where the nature of the work and the condition of the machine permit their use. Carbon tool steels are not satisfactory because of the high heat generated in machining high-nickel materials.

A sulphurized or water soluble oil is recommended for rough- and finish-turning. A sulphurized oil is also recommended for milling, threading, tapping, boring, reaming, and broaching. Speeds and feeds for the drilling of Monel, nickel, and Inconel are given in the section on cutting speeds and feeds.

PRINCIPLES OF IRON AND STEEL MANUFACTURE

Iron Ore. — Iron ore is an oxide of iron containing, ordinarily, from 35 to 65 per cent of iron, and, in addition, oxygen, phosphorus, sulphur, silica (sand) and other impurities. If the ore contains less than 40 per cent iron, it must first be concentrated, and if less than 25 per cent iron, it is not considered a commercial product, owing to the excessive cost of smelting. At the present time, the ores mined in this country average slightly over 50 per cent iron, although the "Lake" ores sometimes contain over 60 per cent.

Pig Iron. — When iron ore is charged in a blast furnace, mixed with limestone as a flux, and melted down with either charcoal, coke or anthracite coal as fuel, the resulting metal is what is commercially known as pig iron. It contains about 93 per cent of pure iron, from 3 to 5 per cent of carbon, and some silicon, phosphorus, sulphur, etc. Pig iron is used in foundries for the manufacture of iron castings by simply re-melting it in a cupola and without materially changing its chemical composition. Pig iron is classified: (1) according to the method of manufacture; (2) its intended use; (3) its composition. The methods of manufacture produce: (1) coke pig iron, which is smelted with coke and always with a hot blast; (2) charcoal pig, which is smelted with charcoal and either a hot or cold blast; (3) anthracite pig, smelted with anthracite coal mixed with coke, using a hot blast. Classifications according to intended use are: (1) Bessemer pig, used for the Bessemer and acid open-hearth processes of making steel; (2) basic pig, used for the basic process; (3) malleable pig, used for malleable cast-iron castings; (4) foundry pig, used for foundry work; (5) forge pig, an inferior grade used for puddling and some classes of foundry work. The grading according to composition was formerly done by breaking the pig and examining the fracture; the modern method is by chemical analysis. In this country pig iron is usually sold in tons of 2240 pounds.

Classes of Steel. — The word steel is applied to many mixtures which differ greatly from each other in their chemical as well as physical qualities. The ingredient that exerts the most influence on steel is carbon. High-grade razor steel contains about 1.25 per cent of carbon, spring steel 1 per cent, steel rails from 0.50 to 0.75 per cent, and soft steel boiler plate may have as little as 0.062 per cent of carbon. Steel which is very low in carbon can easily be welded, but it cannot be hardened; when the carbon is above 0.33 per cent, welding is more difficult and can be done only by the use of borax or some other flux, or by the electric or thermit processes. Steel with carbon above 0.75 per cent can readily be hardened. In tool steel, other ingredients than carbon are sometimes used to influence its hardness, such as nickel, manganese, chromium, tungsten, etc., the last named playing an important part in so-called "high-speed steels," that is, tool steels that will cut metal at a high speed without losing their temper or hardness. Pig iron and cast iron contain about 4 per cent of carbon, and wrought iron only a trace of it, while steel is between these two extremes; hence, in the manufacture of steel it is important to get the right proportion of carbon. One method is to burn the carbon out of pig iron, as in the Bessemer and open-hearth process, and the other method is to add carbon to wrought iron, as in the crucible process.

Bessemer Process. — In the Bessemer process of making steel, the molten pig iron is put into a large pear-shaped vessel, called the "converter," and the impurities are oxidized and removed by blowing air up through the molten mass. The molten iron (from 10 to 15 tons at a time) is poured into the converter while the latter is in a horizontal position; then the compressed air is turned into the blast box at the bottom, as the converter rises to a vertical position. A "blow" generally lasts about nine or ten minutes. The metal in the converter is then practically liquid wrought iron. The converter is again turned to a horizontal position, the blast is shut off, and a certain amount of spiegeleisen or ferro-manganese is added in a liquid form to give the steel the proper amount of carbon and manganese to make it suitable for the purpose desired. The liquid steel is then poured out into "ingot molds," and the resulting ingots, while still hot, are rolled into blooms, billets, or rails without any additional re-heating, except a short period in the "soaking pits."

Open-hearth Process. — The open-hearth process, sometimes called "the Siemens-Martin process," is a method of producing steel by removing the impurities contained in a bath of iron lying on the hearth of a regenerative furnace, the hearth being open or exposed to the action of the flame.

In 1912 the open-hearth furnace produced approximately twice as much steel as the Bessemer converter and since then the open-hearth process has been gaining steadily. Now, a large percentage of the total tonnage is made by the open-hearth process. Better grades of structural steel are made in the open-hearth furnace, and the process produces a more uniform and reliable steel than the Bessemer, as the operations are under better control.

Tool Steel. — Tool steel, as the term is used in the machine-building industry, may be defined in a general way as any steel that is suitable for making cutting or certain other classes of tools. Tool steel contains a sufficient amount of carbon so that it will harden if heated above a certain temperature and rapidly cooled. The

Percentage of Carbon in Carbon Steel Tools

Name of Tool Machinists' Tools	Carbon, Per Cent	Name of Tool Blacksmiths' Tools	Carbon, Per Cent
Turning and Planing Tools....	1.15	Cold Chisel.............	0.75
Chipping Chisels.............	0.85	Hot Chisel.............	0.85
Saw Arbor..................	0.75	Hot Punch.............	0.85
Lathe Center...............	1.05	Flatter.................	0.85
Chuck Jaw..................	0.85	Anvil Facing............	0.75
Milling Cutters..............	1.15	Hammer................	0.75
Twist Drills.................	1.15	Miscellaneous	
Ordinary Files..............	1.25		
Machinists' Hammer..........	0.95	Rivet Set...............	0.70
Mandrel....................	1.05	Roll Expander..........	1.05
Pliers.....................	0.75	Beading Tool...........	0.80
Reamer Blades..............	1.10	Threading Dies........	1.05
Hand Reamers..............	1.05	Wire Drawing Dies	1.40
Saw for Steel....	1.60	Drop-forging Dies.......	0.70
Screw Driver...............	0.65	Pipe Cutter............	1.15
Taps......................	1.10	Circular Saw............	0.85
Vise Jaws..................	0.75	Band Saw..............	0.75
Wrenches..................	0.75	Ball Bearing Races......	1.15
		Crowbar...............	0.75

The above table is intended as an approximate guide in selecting steels for various purposes. Average figures are given; the percentage of carbon might vary 0.05 per cent either way, in most cases, without seriously affecting the quality of the tool.

crucible process formerly was used for making all the high-grade tool steel used for metal-cutting tools and, consequently, the terms " tool steel " and " crucible steel " are often used interchangeably, but at the present time the electric furnace is used extensively for producing tool steel.

Open-hearth Tool Steel. — Open-hearth tool steel is used for a large variety of tools and implements which ordinarily are made from steels containing about 0.65 to 0.85 per cent carbon. These tools include hammers, sledges, pliers, wood-working tools, stone cutters' tools, picks, bars, axes, cheap knives, blacksmith tools, forging dies, agricultural implements, and numerous other products. The extensive use of open-hearth steel in the agricultural field accounts for the name " agricultural tool steel."

Electric Steel. — The most important uses of electric furnaces in steel plants and foundries are for making special alloy steels, tool steel, and for melting the steel used in making steel castings. Electric furnaces are also used for melting the ferro-alloys which are added to " special steels." Electric furnaces permit of very close control of the composition of steel, and alloy additions may be made in the furnace itself rather than in the ladle.

Types of Steel. — *Killed steel* is a type of steel from which there is only a slight evolution of gases during solidification of the metal after pouring into molds. This type of steel has more uniform chemical composition and properties as compared to other types; there are, however, some variations in composition from surface to center and from top to bottom of the ingot.

Rimmed steels are characterized by marked differences in chemical composition across the section and from top to bottom of the ingot. They have an outer rim that is lower in carbon, phosphorus and sulphur than the average composition of the whole ingot and an inner portion or core that is higher than the average in those elements. The typical structure of the rimmed steel ingot results from a marked gas evolution during solidification of the outer rim.

Semi-killed steels are characterized by variable degrees of uniformity of composition and have properties intermediate between those of killed and rimmed steels.

Capped steels have characteristics similar to those of rimmed steel but to a degree intermediate between those of rimmed and semi-killed steels.

Temper of Steels. — Temper numbers indicate certain degrees of strength, hardness and ductility produced in steel strip by cold rolling and by the use of thermal treatment in conjunction with cold rolling.

No. 1 (Hard Temper) is strip intended for flat work not requiring ability to with-stand cold forming.

No. 2 (Half Hard Temper) is moderately stiff strip which can be bent 90 degrees across the direction of rolling around a radius equal to the thickness.

No. 3 (Quarter Hard Temper) is medium soft strip suitable for limited bending, forming, and drawing and can be bent 180 degrees across the direction of rolling and 90 degrees in the direction of rolling around a radius equal to the thickness.

No. 4 (Skin Rolled Temper) is soft, ductile strip suitable for fairly deep drawing where surface disturbances such as stretcher strains are objectionable. It may be bent flat upon itself in any direction. *Skin-rolled*, *planish rolled*, and *pinch passed* are equivalent terms with respect to temper.

No. 5 (Dead Soft Temper) is soft ductile strip produced without definite control of stretcher straining and fluting. It is suitable for difficult drawing applications where such surface disturbances are not objectionable and may be bent flat upon itself in any direction.

SAE Standard Steels — Compositions, Applications, and Heat-treatments

The standard steel compositions of the Society of Automotive Engineers, Inc., given in the accompanying table, are considered adequate for practically all parts made of ferrous materials that are necessary for the production of automotive apparatus, and include grades that have been found commercially available and technically adequate for the service required of such parts. Definite applications of SAE steels are not specified as the selection of a proper steel for a given part must depend upon an intimate knowledge of a number of important factors, such as the availability and price of the material, the detailed design of the part and the severity of the service to be imposed, whether the part is to be forged or machined and its machineability; hence only general applications are indicated. (See following text and tables.)

Specifications Number for Steels. — A numeral index system is used for SAE steel specifications, which makes it possible to use specification numerals on shop drawings and blueprints that are partially descriptive of the kind of material covered by such numbers. The first figure indicates the class to which the steel belongs: thus " 1 — " indicates a carbon steel; " 2 — " a nickel steel, etc. In the case of the alloy steels, the second figure generally indicates the approximate percentage of the predominant alloying element. Usually the last two or three figures indicate the average carbon-content in " points," or hundredths of 1 per cent. Thus " 2340 " indicates a nickel steel of approximately 3 per cent nickel (3.25 to 3.75), and 0.40 per cent carbon (0.38 to 0.43). See table of basic numerals. In some instances, in order to avoid confusion, it has been found necessary to depart from this system of identifying the approximate alloy composition of a steel by varying the second and third digits of the number. An instance of such departure is the steel numbers selected for several of the corrosion- and heat-resisting alloys.

Applications and Heat-treatments. — In applying the detailed heat-treatments (see tables, " Typical Heat-treatments for SAE Steels "), it is recommended, in order to obtain uniform physical properties, that the final quench be made from the lowest temperature that will develop the maximum physical properties, bearing in mind that with thinner sections lower temperatures are required than with thicker sections. It is important to bear in mind when using the information on heat-treatments, that it is based on the tests and experience of steel manufacturers and consumers and is intended only as a guide in selecting the proper steels and their heat-treatment. The notes on heat-treatments and physical properties are not to be considered in any way a part of the standard specifications for SAE steels. They are added solely for the information of users of the steels and the guidance of purchasers in the selection of proper materials for different purposes. They should not be incorporated in the customer's specifications when ordering steel.

Variations in the effect of the usual forms of heat-treatment may be due to personnel, variations in the steel composition or manufacture, and to changes in local conditions such as control and precision of heat-treating equipment. In order to minimize the effects of such variations, steel users should keep each heat of steel separate in the stock-room and during processing so that the necessary adjustments of treatment can be made.

Water and Brine Quenching: When selecting a steel, the user should always keep in mind the importance of obtaining the desired strength and hardness without the necessity of resorting to drastic forms of quenching. Water and brine quenching may be considered as drastic treatments when applied to carbon and simple alloy steels containing more than 0.35 per cent carbon. Oil quenching minimizes distortion, whereas water and brine accentuate it. Improperly applied drastic quenching may lead to serious cracking or spalling. Frequently the necessity for drastic heat-treatment can be avoided by proper control of hardenability. Such procedure is especially important in the case of parts of intricate shape and with sudden changes in section. This caution is not intended to condemn the practice of water or brine quenching in all cases, as there are frequent instances where the production of suitable parts can be obtained in no other manner. It is intended as a warning to the uninitiated to go slowly until the necessary experience and skill have been acquired.

Carburizing. — The process of carburizing as considered in these notes refers to the various dry or pack hardening methods as well as to the newer processes utilizing gases and molten baths as the carburizing medium. The procedure after carburizing is usually divided into two methods: (1) Quench direct; (2) Cool slowly or in box.

The first method refers to removal of the work from the furnace or from the carburizing box and quenching the parts while they are at or slightly below the carburizing temperature or by quenching from gas carburizing furnaces. The second method is to allow the work to cool slowly without any quenching, in the box or container or in a cooling chamber provided in the furnace. The relative value of these two methods is dependent upon the type of steel treated, the method of carburizing, the kind of furnace installation and the physical results desired. Tempering of parts after carburizing, cyaniding and activated bath treatments is sometimes omitted in commercial practice but is included in the accompanying recommendations as being in accord with good heat treating practice. Parts carburized in activated baths should be treated similarly to other carburized work and may be given any of the hardening treatments shown under the specific steels.

Jominy Hardenability Test. — The Jominy end-quench test is a standard method of determining and designating *hardenability* of steel. This test may be used in comparing the hardenability either of successive heats of steel, or of steels of different compositions. The probable hardness of steel for new parts, when production experience is not available, may also be predicted, provided cooling rates occurring during quenching are known.

The Jominy test consists in water-quenching one end of a test bar which is held vertically with the lower end ½ inch above a ½-inch round quenching orifice. The quenching water has a temperature of 40 to 85 degrees F. When the test bar is not in position, this column of water must rise to a free height of 2½ inches above the opening. The test bar (except for shallow-hardening steels) has a diameter of 1 inch and a length of either 3 or 4 inches, depending upon the method of suspending it vertically in the quenching fixture. All decarburization must be removed from the test bar in machining it to the standard diameter and the bar must be normalized. Preparatory to quenching, the test bar is heated to the specified hardening temperature and held at this temperature for 30 minutes. The heated specimen remains in the fixture for at least 10 minutes, and the surrounding air must be free from currents during cooling. The fixture must be dry at the beginning of each test, and the time between removal of the specimen from the furnace and the beginning of the quench shall not be more than 5 seconds.

Two flats 180 degrees apart are ground not less than 0.015 inch deep along the entire length of the test bar. Then Rockwell C hardness measurements are made at 1/16-inch intervals along these flat surfaces. To illustrate the method of recording the result, assume that a test bar hardened above Rockwell C 50 to a distance of 1½ inches (24/16) from the quenched end. This result would be indicated by the marking $J_{50} = 24$. Similarly, a hardness of Rockwell C 30 out 5/16 inch from the end would be designated by $J_{30} = 5$. The last figure in each case equals the distance from the end of the test bar in sixteenths of an inch.

Chemical Compositions of SAE Standard Steels — 1

These compositions are applicable either to open-hearth or electric furnace steels. For the latter, the maximum phosphorus and sulphur content is 0.025 per cent. The nominal chemical limits or ranges in the compositions on pages 1, 2, 3 and 4 of this table are subject to standard variations in check analysis. New SAE numbers without prefixes are now used to replace numbers such as X1015, X1020, etc.

SAE Number	AISI Number*	Carbon C	Manganese Mn	Phosphorus P (Max.)	Sulphur S (Max.)
CARBON STEELS					
1006	C1006	0.08 max.	0.25–0.40	0.040	0.050
1008	C1008	0.10 max.	0.25–0.50	0.040	0.050
1010	C1010	0.08–0.13	0.30–0.60	0.040	0.050
1015	C1015	0.13–0.18	0.30–0.60	0.040	0.050
1016	C1016	0.13–0.18	0.60–0.90	0.040	0.050
1017	C1017	0.15–0.20	0.30–0.60	0.040	0.050
1018	C1018	0.15–0.20	0.60–0.90	0.040	0.050
1019	C1019	0.15–0.20	0.70–1.00	0.040	0.050
1020	C1020	0.18–0.23	0.30–0.60	0.040	0.050
1021	C1021	0.18–0.23	0.60–0.90	0.040	0.050
1022	C1022	0.18–0.23	0.70–1.00	0.040	0.050
1024	C1024	0.19–0.25	1.35–1.65	0.040	0.050
1025	C1025	0.22–0.28	0.30–0.60	0.040	0.050
1026	C1026	0.22–0.28	0.60–0.90	0.040	0.050
1027	C1027	0.22–0.29	1.20.1.50	0.040	0.050
1030	C1030	0.28–0.34	0.60–0.90	0.040	0.050
1033	C1033	0.30–0.36	0.70–1.00	0.040	0.050
1034	C1034	0.32–0.38	0.50–0.80	0.040	0.050
1035	C1035	0.32–0.38	0.60–0.90	0.040	0.050
1036	C1036	0.30–0.37	1.20–1.50	0.040	0.050
1038	C1038	0.35–0.42	0.60–0.90	0.040	0.050
1039	C1039	0.37–0.44	0.70–1.00	0.040	0.050
1040	C1040	0.37–0.44	0.60–0.90	0.040	0.050
1041	C1041	0.36–0.44	1.35–1.65	0.040	0.050
1042	C1042	0.40–0.47	0.60–0.90	0.040	0.050
1043	C1043	0.40–0.47	0.70–1.00	0.040	0.050
1045	C1045	0.43–0.50	0.60–0.90	0.040	0.050
1046	C1046	0.43–0.50	0.70–1.00	0.040	0.050
1049	C1049	0.46–0.53	0.60–0.90	0.040	0.050
1050	C1050	0.48–0.55	0.60–0.90	0.040	0.050
1052	C1052	0.47–0.55	1.20–1.50	0.040	0.050
1055	C1055	0.50–0.60	0.60–0.90	0.040	0.050
1060	C1060	0.55–0.65	0.60–0.90	0.040	0.050
1062	C1062	0.54–0.65	0.85–1.15	0.040	0.050
1064	C1064	0.60–0.70	0.50–0.80	0.040	0.050
1065	C1065	0.60–0.70	0.60–0.90	0.040	0.050
1066	C1066	0.60–0.71	0.85–1.15	0.040	0.050
1070	C1070	0.65–0.75	0.60–0.90	0.040	0.050
1074	C1074	0.70–0.80	0.50–0.80	0.040	0.050
1078	C1078	0.72–0.85	0.30–0.60	0.040	0.050
1080	C1080	0.75–0.88	0.60–0.90	0.040	0.050
1085	C1085	0.80–0.93	0.70–1.00	0.040	0.050
1086	C1086	0.82–0.95	0.30–0.50	0.040	0.050
1090	C1090	0.85–0.98	0.60–0.90	0.040	0.050
1095	C1095	0.90–1.03	0.30–0.50	0.040	0.050
FREE-CUTTING STEELS					
Bessemer † 1111	B1111	0.13 max.	0.60–0.90	0.07–0.12	0.08–0.15
† 1112	B1112	0.13 max.	0.70–1.00	0.07–0.12	0.16–0.23
† 1113	B1113	0.13 max.	0.70–1.00	0.07–0.12	0.24–0.33

* American Iron and Steel Institute.

† Because of the nature of the process, acid bessemer steels are not furnished with specified silicon content.

Chemical Compositions of SAE Standard Steels — 2

SAE Number	AISI Number*	Carbon C	Manganese Mn	Phosphorus P (Max.)	Sulphur S
FREE-CUTTING STEELS (Continued)					
Open Hearth					
1109	C1109	0.08–0.13	0.60–0.90	0.040	0.08–0.13
1114	C1114	0.10–0.16	1.00–1.30	0.040	0.08–0.13
1115	C1115	0.13–0.18	0.60–0.90	0.040	0.08–0.13
1116	C1116	0.14–0.20	1.10–1.40	0.040	0.16–0.23
1117	C1117	0.14–0.20	1.00–1.30	0.040	0.08–0.13
1118	C1118	0.14–0.20	1.30–1.60	0.040	0.08–0.13
1119	C1119	0.14–0.20	1.00–1.30	0.040	0.24–0.33
1120	C1120	0.18–0.23	0.70–1.00	0.040	0.08–0.13
1126	C1126	0.23–0.29	0.70–1.00	0.040	0.08–0.13
1132	C1132	0.27–0.34	1.35–1.65	0.040	0.08–0.13
1137	C1137	0.32–0.39	1.35–1.65	0.040	0.08–0.13
1138	C1138	0.34–0.40	0.70–1.00	0.040	0.08–0.13
1140	C1140	0.37–0.44	0.70–1.00	0.040	0.08–0.13
1141	C1141	0.37–0.45	1.35–1.65	0.040	0.08–0.13
1144	C1144	0.40–0.48	1.35–1.65	0.040	0.24–0.33
1145	C1145	0.42–0.49	0.70–1.00	0.040	0.04–0.07
1146	C1146	0.42–0.49	0.70–1.00	0.040	0.08–0.13
1151	C1151	0.48–0.55	0.70–1.00	0.040	0.08–0.13

SAE Number	AISI Number*	Carbon C	Manganese Mn	Nickel Ni	Chromium Cr	Phos. P (Max.)	Sulphur S (Max.)
MANGANESE STEELS†							
1320	1320	0.18–0.23	1.60–1.90	....	....	0.040	0.040
1330	1330	0.28–0.33	1.60–1.90	....	....	0.040	0.040
1335	1335	0.33–0.38	1.60–1.90	....	....	0.040	0.040
1340	1340	0.38–0.43	1.60–1.90	....	....	0.040	0.040
NICKEL STEELS†							
2317	2317	0.15–0.20	0.40–0.60	3.25–3.75	....	0.040	0.040
2330	2330	0.28–0.33	0.60–0.80	3.25–3.75	....	0.040	0.040
2340	2340	0.38–0.43	0.70–0.90	3.25–3.75	....	0.040	0.040
2345	2345	0.43–0.48	0.70–0.90	3.25–3.75	....	0.040	0.040
2512	E2512	0.09–0.14	0.45–0.60	4.75–5.25	....	0.025	0.025
2515	2515	0.12–0.17	0.40–0.60	4.75–5.25	....	0.040	0.040
2517	E2517	0.15–0.20	0.45–0.60	4.75–5.25	....	0.025	0.025
NICKEL–CHROMIUM STEELS†							
3115	3115	0.13–0.18	0.40–0.60	1.10–1.40	0.55–0.75	0.040	0.040
3120	3120	0.17–0.22	0.60–0.80	1.10–1.40	0.55–0.75	0.040	0.040
3130	3130	0.28–0.33	0.60–0.80	1.10–1.40	0.55–0.75	0.040	0.040
3135	3135	0.33–0.38	0.60–0.80	1.10–1.40	0.55–0.75	0.040	0.040
3140	3140	0.38–0.43	0.70–0.90	1.10–1.40	0.55–0.75	0.040	0.040
3141	3141	0.38–0.43	0.70–0.90	1.10–1.40	0.70–0.90	0.040	0.040
3145	3145	0.43–0.48	0.70–0.90	1.10–1.40	0.70–0.90	0.040	0.040
3150	3150	0.48–0.53	0.70–0.90	1.10–1.40	0.70–0.90	0.040	0.040
3310	E3310	0.08–0.13	0.45–0.60	3.25–3.75	1.40–1.75	0.025	0.025
3316	E3316	0.14–0.19	0.45–0.60	3.25–3.75	1.40–1.75	0.025	0.025

* American Iron and Steel Institute. The letter E, where used, indicates an electric furnace steel. AISI number without prefix indicates steel is predominately open hearth.
† Silicon content 0.20–0.35 per cent.

Chemical Compositions of SAE Standard Steels — 3

SAE Number	AISI Number*	Carbon C	Manganese Mn	Nickel Ni	Chromium Cr	Moly. Mo
MOLYBDENUM STEELS†						
4017	4017	0.15-0.20	0.70-0.90	......	......	0.20-0.30
4023	4023	0.20-0.25	0.70-0.90	......	......	0.20-0.30
4024	4024	0.20-0.25	0.70-0.90	......	......	0.20-0.30
4027	4027	0.25-0.30	0.70-0.90	......	......	0.20-0.30
4028	4028	0.25-0.30	0.70-0.90	......	......	0.20-0.30
4032	4032	0.30-0.35	0.70-0.90	......	......	0.20-0.30
4037	4037	0.35-0.40	0.70-0.90	......	......	0.20-0.30
4042	4042	0.40-0.45	0.70-0.90	......	......	0.20-0.30
4047	4047	0.45-0.50	0.70-0.90	......	......	0.20-0.30
4053	4053	0.50-0.56	0.75-1.00	......	......	0.20-0.30
4063	4063	0.60-0.67	0.75-1.00	......	......	0.20-0.30
4068	4068	0.63-0.70	0.75-1.00	......	......	0.20-0.30
4119	......	0.17-0.22	0.70-0.90	......	0.40-0.60	0.20-0.30
4125	......	0.23-0.28	0.70-0.90	......	0.40-0.60	0.20-0.30
4130	4130	0.28-0.33	0.40-0.60	......	0.80-1.10	0.15-0.25
4137	4137	0.35-0.40	0.70-0.90	......	0.80-1.10	0.15-0.25
4140	4140	0.38-0.43	0.75-1.00	......	0.80-1.10	0.15-0.25
4145	4145	0.43-0.48	0.75-1.00	......	0.80-1.10	0.15-0.25
4150	4150	0.48-0.53	0.75-1.00	......	0.80-1.10	0.15-0.25
4317	4317	0.15-0.20	0.45-0.65	1.65-2.00	0.40-0.60	0.20-0.30
4320	4320	0.17-0.22	0.45-0.65	1.65-2.00	0.40-0.60	0.20-0.30
4340	4340	0.38-0.43	0.60-0.80	1.65-2.00	0.70-0.90	0.20-0.30
4608	4608	0.06-0.11	0.25-0.45	1.40-1.75	......	0.15-0.25
4615	4615	0.13-0.18	0.45-0.65	1.65-2.00	......	0.20-0.30
4617	......	0.15-0.20	0.45-0.65	1.65-2.00	......	0.20-0.30
4620	4620	0.17-0.22	0.45-0.65	1.65-2.00	......	0.20-0.30
X4620	......	0.18-0.23	0.50-0.70	1.65-2.00	......	0.20-0.30
4621	4621	0.18-0.23	0.70-0.90	1.65-2.00	......	0.20-0.30
4640	4640	0.38-0.43	0.60-0.80	1.65-2.00	......	0.20-0.30
4812	4812	0.10-0.15	0.40-0.60	3.25-3.75	......	0.20-0.30
4815	4815	0.13-0.18	0.40-0.60	3.25-3.75	......	0.20-0.30
4817	4817	0.15-0.20	0.40-0.60	3.25-3.75	......	0.20-0.30
4820	4820	0.18-0.23	0.50-0.70	3.25-3.75	......	0.20-0.30
CHROMIUM STEELS †						
5045	5045	0.43-0.48	0.70-0.90	......	0.55-0.75	......
5046	5046	0.43-0.50	0.75-1.00	......	0.20-0.35	......
5115	......	0.13-0.18	0.70-0.90	......	0.70-0.90	......
5120	5120	0.17-0.22	0.70-0.90	......	0.70-0.90	......
5130	5130	0.28-0.33	0.70-0.90	......	0.80-1.10	......
5132	5132	0.30-0.35	0.60-0.80	......	0.75-1.00	......
5135	5135	0.33-0.38	0.60-0.80	......	0.80-1.05	......
5140	5140	0.38-0.43	0.70-0.90	......	0.70-0.90	......
5145	5145	0.43-0.48	0.70-0.90	......	0.70-0.90	......
5147	5147	0.45-0.52	0.70-0.95	......	0.85-1.15	......
5150	5150	0.48-0.53	0.70-0.90	......	0.70-0.90	......
5152	5152	0.48-0.55	0.70-0.90	......	0.90-1.20	......
5160	5160	0.55-0.65	0.75-1.00	......	0.70-0.90	......
50100	E50100	0.95-1.10	0.25-0.45	......	0.40-0.60	......
51100	E51100	0.95-1.10	0.25-0.45	......	0.90-1.15	......
52100	E52100	0.95-1.10	0.25-0.45	......	1.30-1.60	......

* American Iron and Steel Institute. The letter E, where used, indicates an electric furnace steel. AISI number without prefix indicates steel is predominately open hearth.
† Silicon content 0.20-0.35 per cent except for SAE 4608 which is 0.25 per cent max. Maximum sulphur and phosphorus contents are 0.040 per cent each except for SAE 4024 and 4028 which have 0.035 to 0.050 per cent sulphur, and SAE 50100, 51100 and 52100 which have 0.025 per cent, max. sulphur and phosphorus.

Chemical Compositions of SAE Standard Steels — 4

SAE Number	AISI Number*	Carbon C	Manganese Mn	Silicon Si	Chromium Cr	Vanadium V Min.
CHROMIUM VANADIUM STEEL**						
6150	6150	0.48–0.53	0.70–0.90	0.20–0.35	0.80–1.10	0.15
SILICON MANGANESE STEELS**						
9254	......	0.50–0.60	0.50–0.80	1.20–1.60	0.50–0.80	......
9255	9255	0.50–0.60	0.70–0.95	1.80–2.20	......	......
9260	9260	0.55–0.65	0.70–1.00	1.80–2.20	......	......
9261	9261	0.55–0.65	0.75–1.00	1.80–2.20	0.10–0.25	......
9262	9262	0.55–0.65	0.75–1.00	1.80–2.20	0.25–0.40	......

SAE Number	AISI Number*	Carbon C	Manganese Mn	Nickel Ni	Chromium Cr	Moly. Mo
TRIPLE ALLOY STEELS**						
8615	8615	0.13–0.18	0.70–0.90	0.40–0.70	0.40–0.60	0.15–0.25
8617	8617	0.15–0.20	0.70–0.90	0.40–0.70	0.40–0.60	0.15–0.25
8620	8620	0.18–0.23	0.70–0.90	0.40–0.70	0.40–0.60	0.15–0.25
8622	8622	0.20–0.25	0.70–0.90	0.40–0.70	0.40–0.60	0.15–0.25
8625	8625	0.23–0.28	0.70–0.90	0.40–0.70	0.40–0.60	0.15–0.25
8627	8627	0.25–0.30	0.70–0.90	0.40–0.70	0.40–0.60	0.15–0.25
8630	8630	0.28–0.33	0.70–0.90	0.40–0.70	0.40–0.60	0.15–0.25
8632	8632	0.30–0.35	0.70–0.90	0.40–0.70	0.40–0.60	0.15–0.25
8635	8635	0.33–0.38	0.75–1.00	0.40–0.70	0.40–0.60	0.15–0.25
8637	8637	0.35–0.40	0.75–1.00	0.40–0.70	0.40–0.60	0.15–0.25
8640	8640	0.38–0.43	0.75–1.00	0.40–0.70	0.40–0.60	0.15–0.25
8641	8641	0.38–0.43	0.75–1.00	0.40–0.70	0.40–0.60	0.15–0.25
8642	8642	0.40–0.45	0.75–1.00	0.40–0.70	0.40–0.60	0.15–0.25
8645	8645	0.43–0.48	0.75–1.00	0.40–0.70	0.40–0.60	0.15–0.25
8647	8647	0.45–0.50	0.75–1.00	0.40–0.70	0.40–0.60	0.15–0.25
8650	8650	0.48–0.53	0.75–1.00	0.40–0.70	0.40–0.60	0.15–0.25
8653	8653	0.50–0.56	0.75–1.00	0.40–0.70	0.50–0.80	0.15–0.25
8655	8655	0.50–0.60	0.75–1.00	0.40–0.70	0.40–0.60	0.15–0.25
8660	8660	0.55–0.65	0.75–1.00	0.40–0.70	0.40–0.60	0.15–0.25
8719	8719	0.18–0.23	0.60–0.80	0.40–0.70	0.40–0.60	0.20–0.30
8720	8720	0.18–0.23	0.70–0.90	0.40–0.70	0.40–0.60	0.20–0.30
8735	8735	0.33–0.38	0.75–1.00	0.40–0.70	0.40–0.60	0.20–0.30
8740	8740	0.38–0.43	0.75–1.00	0.40–0.70	0.40–0.60	0.20–0.30
8745	8745	0.43–0.48	0.75–1.00	0.40–0.70	0.40–0.60	0.20–0.30
8750	8750	0.48–0.53	0.75–1.00	0.40–0.70	0.40–0.60	0.20–0.30
9310	E9310	0.08–0.13	0.45–0.65	3.00–3.50	1.00–1.40	0.08–0.15
9315	E9315	0.13–0.18	0.45–0.65	3.00–3.50	1.00–1.40	0.08–0.15
9317	E9317	0.15–0.20	0.45–0.65	3.00–3.50	1.00–1.40	0.08–0.15
9437	9437	0.35–0.40	0.90–1.20	0.30–0.60	0.30–0.50	0.08–0.15
9440	9440	0.38–0.43	0.90–1.20	0.30–0.60	0.30–0.50	0.08–0.15
9442	9442	0.40–0.45	1.00–1.30	0.30–0.60	0.30–0.50	0.08–0.15
9445	9445	0.43–0.48	1.00–1.30	0.30–0.60	0.30–0.50	0.08–0.15

* American Iron and Steel Institute.   The letter E, where used, indicates an electric furnace steel.   AISI number without prefix indicates steel is predominately open hearth.
** Maximum sulphur and phosphorus contents 0.040 per cent each, except for SAE 8641 which has 0.040 to 0.060 per cent sulphur and SAE 9310, 9315 and 9317, which have 0.025 per cent each of sulphur and phosphorus.   Except for silicon-manganese steels, silicon content is 0.20–0.35 per cent.

Chemical Compositions of SAE Standard Steels — 5

SAE Number	AISI Number*	Carbon C	Manganese Mn	Nickel Ni	Chromium Cr	Moly. Mo
TRIPLE ALLOY STEELS** (Continued)						
9747	9747	0.45-0.50	0.50-0.80	0.40-0.70	0.10-0.25	0.15-0.25
9763	9763	0.60-0.67	0.50-0.80	0.40-0.70	0.10-0.25	0.15-0.25
9840	9840	0.38-0.43	0.70-0.90	0.85-1.15	0.70-0.90	0.20-0.30
9845	9845	0.43-0.48	0.70-0.90	0.85-1.15	0.70-0.90	0.20-0.30
9850	9850	0.48-0.53	0.70-0.90	0.85-1.15	0.70-0.90	0.20-0.30

SAE Number†	AISI Type*	Carbon C	Manganese Mn Max.	Chromium Cr	Nickel Ni	Other Elements
WROUGHT CHROMIUM NICKEL AUSTENITIC STEELS†† (Not capable of heat treatment)						
30301	301	0.08-0.15	2.00	16.00-18.00	6.00-8.00	....
30302	302	0.08-0.15	2.00	17.00-19.00	7.00-10.00	
30303F	303	0.15 max.	2.00	17.00-19.00	8.00-10.00	P, S, Se, Min. 0.07; Zr, Mo, Max. 0.60
30304	304	0.08 max.	2.00	18.00-20.00	8.00-11.00	....
30305	305	0.12 max.	2.00	17.00-19.00	10.00-13.00	....
30309	309	0.20 max.	2.00	22.00-24.00	12.00-15.00	....
30310	310	0.25 max.	2.00	24.00-26.00	19.00-22.00	
30316	316	0.08 max.	2.00	16.00-18.00	10.00-14.00	Mo 2.00-3.00
30317	317	0.08 max.	2.00	18.00-20.00	11.00-15.00	Mo 3.00-4.00
30321	321	0.08 max.	2.50	17.00-19.00	8.00-12.00	Min. Ti = 5 × C
30325	325	0.25 max.	0.60-0.90	7.00-10.00	19.00-23.00	Cu 1.00-1.50
30347	347	0.08 max.	2.50	17.00-19.00	9.00-13.00	Min. Cb = 10 × C
WROUGHT STAINLESS CHROMIUM IRONS AND STEELS††						
51410	410	0.15 max.	1.00	11.50-13.50	....	....
51414	414	0.08-0.15	1.00	11.50-13.50	1.25-2.50	....
51416F	416	0.15 max.	1.25	12.00-14.00	....	P, S, Se, Min. 0.07; Zr, Mo, Max. 0.60
51420	420	0.30-0.40	1.00	12.00-14.00	....	....
51420F	....	0.30-0.40	1.25	12.00-14.00	....	P, S, Se, Min. 0.07; Zr, Mo, Max. 0.60
51430	430	0.12 max.	1.00	14.00-18.00	....	....
51430F	....	0.12 max.	1.25	14.00-18.00	....	P, S, Se, Min. 0.07; Zr, Mo, Max. 0.60
51431	431	0.20 max.	1.00	15.00-17.00	1.25-2.50	....
51440A	440A	0.60-0.75	1.00	16.00-18.00	....	Max. Mo 0.75
51440B	440B	0.75-0.95	1.00	16.00-18.00	....	Max. Mo 0.75
51440C	440C	0.95-1.20	1.00	16.00-18.00	....	Max. Mo 0.75
51440F	....	0.95-1.20	1.25	16.00-18.00	....	P, S, Se, Min. 0.07; Zr, Mo, Max. 0.75
51442	442	0.20 max.	1.00	18.00-23.00	....	....
51446	446	0.25 max.	1.00	23.00-27.00	1.00 max.	....
51501	501	Over 0.10	1.00	4.00-6.00	....	....

* American Iron and Steel Institute.

** Maximum sulphur and phosphorus contents 0.040 per cent each and silicon content 0.20-0.35 per cent.

† The letters A, B, and C indicate three types of steel differing only in carbon content. The letter F indicates a free machining steel.

†† Maximum phosphorus content is 0.04 per cent and maximum sulphur content is 0.03 per cent except for SAE 51442 which has 0.035 per cent sulphur, max.; SAE 30303F, 51416F, 51420F, 51430F and 51440F, for which see Other Elements column; and SAE 30325, not specified. Maximum silicon content is 1.00 per cent except for SAE 30310, 30321 and 30347 which have 1.50 per cent, and SAE 30325 which has 1.00-2.00 per cent.

Carbon Steels. — *SAE steels 1006, 1008, 1010, 1015:* These steels are the lowest carbon steels of the plain carbon type, and are selected where cold formability is the primary requisite. They are produced both as rimmed and killed steels (see page 1544). Rimmed steel is used for sheet, strip, rod, and wire where excellent surface finish or good drawing qualities are required, such as body and fender stock, hoods, lamps, oil pans, and other deep drawn and formed products. It is also used for cold heading wire for tacks, and rivets and low carbon wire products. Killed steel (usually aluminum killed or special killed) is used for difficult stampings or where non-aging properties are needed. Killed steels (usually silicon killed) should be used in preference to rimmed steel for forging or heat treating applications.

These steels have relatively low tensile values and should not be selected where much strength is desired. Within the carbon range of the group, strength and hardness will increase with increase in carbon and/or with cold work, but such increases in strength are at the sacrifice of ductility or the ability to withstand cold deformation. Where cold rolled strip is used the proper temper designation should be specified to obtain the desired properties (see page 1544).

When under 0.15 carbon, the steels are susceptible to serious grain growth, causing brittleness, which may occur as the result of a combination of critical strain (from cold work) followed by heating to certain elevated temperatures. If cold worked parts formed from these steels are to be later heated to temperatures in excess of 1100 degrees F., the user should exercise care to avoid trouble from this cause. When this condition develops it can be overcome by heating the parts to a temperature well in excess of the upper critical point, or at least 1750 degrees F.

Steels in this group, being nearly pure iron or ferritic in structure, do not machine freely and should be avoided for cut screws and operations requiring broaching or smooth finish on turning. The machinability of bar, rod and wire products is improved by cold drawing. Steels in this group are readily welded.

SAE 1016, 1017, 1018, 1019, 1020, 1021, 1022, 1023, 1024, 1025, 1026, 1027, 1030: Steels in this group, due to the carbon range covered, have increased strength and hardness, and reduced cold formability compared to the lowest carbon group. For heat treating purposes they are known as carburizing or case hardening grades. When uniform response to heat treatment is required, or for forgings, killed steel is preferred; for other uses, semi-killed or rimmed steel may be indicated, depending on the combination of properties desired. Rimmed steels can ordinarily be supplied up to 0.25 carbon.

Selection of one of these steels for carburizing applications depends on the nature of the part, the properties desired, and the processing practice preferred. Increase in carbon gives greater core hardness with a given quench, or permits the use of thicker sections. Increase in manganese improves the hardenability of both the core and case; in carbon steels this is the only change in composition that will increase case hardenability. The higher manganese variants also machine much better. For carburizing applications SAE 1016, 1018, and 1019 are widely used for thin sections or water quenched parts. SAE 1022 and 1024 are used for heavier sections or where oil quenching is desired, and SAE 1024 is sometimes used for such parts as transmission and rear axle gears. SAE 1027 is used for parts given a light case to obtain satisfactory core properties without drastic quenching. SAE 1025 and 1030, while not usually regarded as carburizing types, are sometimes used in this manner for larger sections or where greater core hardness is needed.

For cold formed or headed parts the lowest manganese grades (SAE 1017, 1020, and 1025) offer the best formability at their carbon level. SAE 1020 is used for fan blades and some frame members, and SAE 1020 and 1025 are widely used for low strength bolts. The next higher manganese types (SAE 1018, 1021, and 1026) provide increased strength.

All of these steels may be readily welded or brazed by the common commercial methods. SAE 1020 is frequently used for welded tubing. These steels are used for numerous forged parts, the lower carbon grades where high strength is not essential. Forgings from the lower carbon steels usually machine better in the as forged condition without annealing, or after normalizing.

SAE 1030, 1033, 1034, 1035, 1036, 1038, 1039, 1040, 1041, 1042, 1043, 1045, 1046, 1049, 1050, 1052: These steels, of the medium carbon type, are selected for uses where higher mechanical properties are needed and are frequently further hardened and strengthened by heat treatment or by cold work. These grades are ordinarily produced as killed steels.

Steels in this group are suitable for a wide variety of automotive type applications. The particular carbon and manganese level selected is affected by a number of factors. Increase in the mechanical properties required in section thickness, or in depth of hardening, ordinarily indicates either higher carbon or manganese or both. The heat treating practice preferred, particularly the quenching medium, has a great effect on the steel selected. In general, any of the grades over 0.30 carbon may be selectively hardened by induction or flame methods.

The lower carbon and manganese steels in this group find usage for certain types of cold formed parts. SAE 1030 is used for shift and brake levers, SAE 1034 and 1035 are used in the form of wire and rod for cold upsetting such as bolts, and SAE 1038 for bolts and studs. In practically all cases the parts cold formed from these steels are heat treated prior to use. Stampings are usually limited to flat parts or simple bends. The higher carbon SAE 1038, 1040, and 1042 are frequently cold drawn to specified physical properties for use without heat treatment for some applications, such as cylinder head studs.

All of this group of steels are used for forgings, the selection being governed by the section size and the physical properties desired after heat treatment. Thus SAE 1030 and 1035 are used for shifter forks and many small forgings where moderate properties are desired, but the deeper hardening SAE 1036 is used for more critical parts where a higher strength level and more uniformity is essential, such as some front suspension parts. Forgings such as connecting rods, steering arms, truck front axles, axle shafts, and tractor wheels are commonly made from the SAE 1038 to 1045 group. Larger forgings at similar strength levels need more carbon and perhaps more manganese. Examples are crankshafts from SAE 1046 and 1052. These steels are also used for small forgings where high hardness after oil quenching is desired. Suitable heat treatment is necessary on forgings from this group to provide machinability. These steels are also widely used for parts machined from bar stock, the selection following an identical pattern to that described for forgings. They are used both with and without heat treatment, depending on the application and the level of properties needed. As a class they are considered good for normal machining operations. It is also possible to weld these steels by most commercial methods, but precautions should be taken to avoid cracking from too rapid cooling.

SAE 1055, 1060, 1062, 1064, 1065, 1066: Steels in this group are of the high carbon type, having more carbon than is required to achieve maximum as quenched hardness. They are used for applications where the higher carbon is needed to improve wear characteristics for cutting edges, to make springs, and for special purposes. Selection of a particular grade is affected by the nature of the part, its end use, and the manufacturing methods available.

SAE 1070, 1074, 1078, 1080, 1085, 1086, 1090, 1095: In general, cold forming methods are not practical on this group of steels, being limited to flat stampings and springs coiled from small diameter wire. Practically all parts from these steels are heat treated before use, with some variations in heat treating methods to obtain optimum properties for the particular application.

Uses in the spring industry include SAE 1065 for pretempered wire and SAE 1066 for cushion springs of hard drawn wire, SAE 1064 may be used for small washers and thin stamped parts, SAE 1074 for light flat springs formed from annealed stock, and SAE 1080 and 1085 for thicker flat springs. SAE 1085 is also used for heavier coil springs. Valve spring wire and music wire are special products.

Due to good wear properties when properly heat treated, the high carbon steels find wide usage in the farm implement industry. SAE 1070 has been used for plow beams, SAE 1074 for plow shares, and SAE 1078 for such parts as rake teeth, scrapers, cultivator shovels and plow shares. SAE 1085 has been used for scraper blades, disks, and for spring tooth harrows. SAE 1086 and 1090 find use as mower and binder sections, twine holders, and knotter disks.

Free Cutting Steels. — *SAE 1111, 1112, 1113:* This class of steels is intended for those uses where easy machining is the primary requirement. They are characterized by a higher sulphur content than comparable carbon steels. This results in some sacrifice of cold forming properties, weldability, and forging characteristics. In general the uses are similar to those for carbon steels of similar carbon and manganese content.

These steels are commonly known as Bessemer screw stock, and are considered the best machining steels available, machinability improving within the group as sulphur increases. They are used for a wide variety of machined parts. While of excellent strength in the cold drawn condition, they have an unfavorable property of cold shortness and are not commonly used for vital parts. These steels may be cyanided or carburized but when uniform response to heat treating is necessary, open hearth steels are recommended.

SAE 1109, 1114, 1115, 1116, 1117, 1118, 1119, 1120, 1126: Steels in this group are used where a combination of good machinability and more uniform response to heat treatment is needed. The lower carbon varieties are used for small parts which are to be cyanided or carbonitrided. SAE 1116, 1117, 1118, and 1119 carry more manganese for better hardenability, permitting oil quenching after case hardening heat treatments in many instances. The higher carbon SAE 1120 and 1126 provide more core hardness when this is needed.

SAE 1132, 1137, 1138, 1140, 1141, 1144, 1145, 1146, 1151: This group of steels has characteristics comparable to carbon steels of the same carbon level, except for changes due to higher sulphur as noted previously.

They are widely used for parts where a large amount of machining is necessary, or where threads, splines or other operations offer special tooling problems. SAE 1137, for example, is widely used for nuts and bolts and studs with machined threads. The higher manganese SAE 1132, 1137, 1141, and 1144 offer greater hardenability, the higher carbon types being suitable for oil quenching for many parts. All of these steels may be selectively hardened by induction or flame heating if desired.

Carburizing Grades of Alloy Steels. *Properties of the Case:* The properties of carburized and hardened cases depend upon the carbon and alloy content, the structure of the case, and the degree and distribution of residual stresses. The carbon content of the case depends upon the details of the carburizing process, and the response of iron and the alloying elements present, to carburization. The original carbon content of the steel has little or no effect upon the carbon content produced in the case. The hardenability of the case therefore depends upon the alloy content of the steel and the final carbon content produced by carburizing, but not upon the initial carbon content of the steel.

With complete carbide solution the effect of alloying elements upon the hardenability of the case, will in general be the same as the effect of these elements upon the hardenability of the core. As an exception to this, any element which inhibits carburizing may reduce the hardenability of the case. It is also true that some elements which raise the hardenability of the core may tend to produce more retained austenite and consequently somewhat lower hardness in the case.

Alloy steels are frequently used for case hardening because the required surface hardness can be obtained by moderate speeds of quenching. This may mean less distortion than would be encountered with water quenching. It is usually desirable to select a steel which will attain a minimum surface hardness of 58 or 60 Rockwell C after carburizing and oil quenching. Where section sizes are large, a high hardenability alloy steel may be necessary, while for medium and light sections, low hardenability steels will suffice.

In general, the case hardening alloy steels may be divided into two classes so far as the hardenability of the case is concerned. Only the general type of steel (SAE 3300-4100, etc.) is given. As the original carbon content of the steel has no effect upon the carbon content of the case, the last two digits in the specification numbers are not meaningful so far as the case is concerned.

(a) — *High Hardenability Case.* — *SAE 2500, 3300, 4300, 4800, 9300*

As these are high alloy steels, both the case and the core have high hardenability. These types of steel are used particularly for carburized parts having thick sections, such as bevel drive pinions and heavy gears. Good case properties can be obtained by oil quenching. These steels are likely to have retained austenite in the case after carburizing and quenching, consequently special precautions or treatments, such as refrigeration, may be required.

(b) — *Medium Hardenability Case.* — *SAE 1300, 2300, 4000, 4100, 4600, 5100, 8600, 8700*

Carburized cases of these steels have medium hardenability which means that their hardenability is intermediate between that of plain carbon steel and the higher alloy carburizing steels just described. In general, these steels can be used for average size case hardened automotive parts such as gears, pinions, piston pins, ball studs, universal crosses, crankshafts, etc. Satisfactory case hardness should be produced in most cases by oil quenching.

Core Properties: The core properties of case hardened steels depend upon both carbon and alloy content of the steel. Each of the general types of alloy case hardening steel is usually made with two or more carbon contents so as to produce different hardenability in the core.

The most desirable hardness for the core depends upon the design and functioning of the individual part. In general, where high compressive loads are encountered, relatively high core hardness is beneficial in supporting the case. Low core hardnesses may be desirable where great toughness is essential.

The case hardening steels may be divided into three general classes depending upon hardenability of the core.

(a) — *Low Hardenability Core.* — *SAE 4017, 4023, 4024, 4027[1], 4028[1], 4608, 4615, 4617[1], 8615[1], 8617[1]*

(b) — *Medium Hardenability Core.* — *SAE 1320, 2317, 2512, 2515[1], 3115, 3120, 4032, 4119, 4317, 4620, 4621, 4812, 4815[1], 5115, 5120, 8620, 8622, 8720, 9420*

(c) — *High Hardenability Core.* — *SAE 2517, 3310, 3316, 4320, 4817, 4820, 9310, 9315, 9317*

Heat Treatments: In general, all of the alloy carburizing steels are made fine grain and most are suitable for direct quenching from the carburizing temperature. Several other types of heat treatment involving single and double quenching are also used for most of these steels. (See tables of Typical Heat Treatments for SAE Steels.)

---

[1] Borderline classifications might be considered in the next higher hardenability group.

Directly Hardenable Grades of Alloy Steels. — These steels may be considered in five groups on the basis of approximate mean carbon content of the SAE specification. In general, the last two figures of the specification agree with the mean carbon content. Consequently the heading " .30–.37 Mean Carbon Content of SAE Specification " includes steels such as SAE 1330, 3135, and 4137.

Mean Carbon Content of SAE Specification	Common Applications
(a) — .30–.37 per cent	Heat treated parts requiring moderate strength and great toughness.
(b) — .40–.42 per cent	Heat treated parts requiring higher strength and good toughness.
(c) — .45–.50 per cent	Heat treated parts requiring fairly high hardness and strength with moderate toughness.
(d) — .50–.62 per cent	Springs and hand tools.
(e) — 1.02 per cent	Ball and roller bearings.

It is necessary to deviate from the above plan in the classification of the carbon molybdenum steels. When carbon molybdenum steels are used, it is customary to specify higher carbon content for any given application than would be specified for other alloy steels, due to the low alloy content of these steels. For example, SAE 4063 is used for the same applications as SAE 4140, 4145 and 5150. Consequently in the following discussion, the carbon molybdenum steels have been shown in the groups where they belong on the basis of applications rather than carbon content.

For the present discussion, steels of each carbon content are divided into two or three groups on the basis of hardenability. Transformation ranges and consequently heat treating practices vary somewhat with different alloying elements even though the hardenability is not changed.

.30–.37 Mean Carbon Content of SAE Specification. — These steels are frequently used for water quenched parts of moderate section size and for oil quenched parts of small section size. Typical applications of these steels are connecting rods, steering arms and steering knuckles, axle shafts, bolts, studs, screws, and other parts requiring strength and toughness where section size is small enough to permit obtaining the desired physical properties with the customary heat treatment.

Steels falling in this classification may be subdivided into two groups on the basis of hardenability:

(a) — Low Hardenability: SAE 1330, 1335, 4037, 4042, 4130, 5130, 5132, 8630

(b) — Medium Hardenability: SAE 2330, 3130, 3135, 4137, 5135, 8632, 8635, 8637, 8735, 9437

.40–.42 Mean Carbon Content of SAE Specification. — In general, these steels are used for medium and large size parts requiring high degree of strength and toughness. The choice of the proper steel depends upon the section size and the mechanical properties which must be produced. The low and medium hardenability steels are used for average size automotive parts such as steering knuckles, axle shafts, propeller shafts, etc. The high hardenability steels are used particularly for large axles and shafts for large aircraft parts.

These steels are usually considered as oil quenching steels, although some large parts made of the low and medium hardenability classifications may be quenched in water under properly controlled conditions.

These steels may be divided into three groups on the basis of hardenability:

(a) — Low Hardenability: SAE 1340, 4047, 5140, 9440

(b) — Medium Hardenability: SAE 2340, 3140, 3141, 4053, 4063, 4140, 4640, 8640, 8641, 8642, 8740, 8742, 9442

(c) — High Hardenability: SAE 4340, 9840

.45–.50 Mean Carbon Content of SAE Specification. — These steels are used primarily for gears and other parts requiring fairly high hardness as well as strength and toughness. Such parts are usually oil quenched and a minimum of 90 per cent martensite in the as quenched condition is desirable.

(a) — Low Hardenability: SAE 5045, 5046, 5145, 9747, 9763

(b) — Medium Hardenability: SAE 2345, 3145, 3150, 4145, 5147, 5150, 8645, 8647, 8650, 8745, 8747, 8750, 9445, 9845

(c) — High Hardenability: SAE 4150, 9850

.50–.62 Mean Carbon Content of SAE Specification. — These steels are used primarily for springs and hand tools. The hardenability necessary depends upon the thickness of the material and the quenching practice.

(a) — Medium Hardenability: SAE 4068, 5150, 5152, 6150, 8650, 9254, 9255, 9260, 9261

(b) — High Hardenability: SAE 8653, 8655, 8660, 9262

1.02 Mean Carbon Content of SAE Specification. — *SAE 50100, 51100, 52100*
These are straight chromium electric furnace steels used primarily for the races and balls or rollers of anti-friction bearings. They are also used for other parts requiring high hardness and wear resistance. The compositions of the three steels are identical, except for a variation in chromium, with a corresponding variation in hardenability.

(a) — Low Hardenability: SAE 50100

(b) — Medium Hardenability: SAE 51100, 52100

Resulphurized Steel. — Some of the alloy steels, SAE 4024, 4028 and 8641, are made resulphurized so as to give better machinability at a relatively high hardness. In general, increased sulphur results in decreased transverse ductility, notched impact toughness, and weldability.

Chromium Nickel Austenitic Steels (*Not capable of heat treatment*). —

SAE 30301: This steel is capable of attaining high tensile strength and ductility by moderate or severe cold working. It is used largely in the cold rolled or cold drawn condition in the form of sheet, strip and wire. Its corrosion resistance is good but not equal to SAE 30302.

SAE 30302: This is the most widely used of the general purpose austenitic chromium nickel stainless steels. It is used for deep drawing largely in the annealed condition. It can be worked to high tensile strengths but with slightly lower ductility than SAE 30301.

SAE 30303F: This is a free machining type recommended for the manufacture of parts produced on automatic machines. Caution must be used in forging this steel.

SAE 30304: This is similar to SAE 30302 but somewhat superior in corrosion resistance and having superior welding properties for certain types of equipment.

SAE 30305: Similar to SAE 30304 but capable of lower hardness. Has greater ductility with slower work hardening tendency.

SAE 30309: This steel has high heat resisting qualities and is resistant to oxidation at temperatures up to about 1800 deg. F.

SAE 30310: This steel has the highest heat resisting properties of any of the chromium nickel steels listed herewith and is used to resist oxidation at temperatures up to about 1900 deg. F.

SAE 30316: This steel is recommended for use in parts where unusual resistance to chemical or salt water corrosion is necessary. It has superior creep strength at elevated temperatures.

SAE 30317: This steel is similar to SAE 30316 but has the highest corrosion resistance of all these alloys in many environments.

SAE 30321: This steel is recommended for use in the manufacture of welded structures where heat treatment after welding is not feasible. It is also recommended for use where temperatures up to 1600 deg. F. are encountered in service.

SAE 30325: Used for such parts as heat control shafts.

SAE 30347: This steel is similar to SAE 30321 with the following additional statement. This columbium alloy is sometimes preferred to titanium because less columbium is lost in the welding operation.

Stainless Chromium Irons and Steels. — *SAE 51410:* This is a general purpose stainless steel capable of heat treatment to show good physical properties. It is used for general stainless applications, both in the heat treated and annealed condition but it is not as resistant to corrosion as SAE 51430 in either the annealed or heat treated condition.

SAE 51414: This is a corrosion and heat resisting nickel-bearing chromium steel with somewhat better corrosion resistance than SAE 51410. It will attain slightly higher mechanical properties when heat treated than SAE 51410. It is used in the form of tempered strip or wire, and in bars and forgings for heat treated parts.

SAE 51416F: This is a free machining grade for the manufacture of parts produced in automatic screw machines.

SAE 51420: This steel is capable of heat treating to a relatively high hardness. It will harden to a maximum of approximately 500 Brinell. It has its maximum corrosion resisting qualities only in the fully hardened condition. It is used for cutlery, hardened pump shafts, etc.

SAE 51420F: This is similar to SAE 51420 except for its free machining properties.

SAE 51430: This is a steel of a high chromium type not capable of heat treatment and is recommended for use in parts of moderate draw. Corrosion and heat resistance are superior to SAE 51410.

SAE 51430F: This is similar to SAE 51430 except for its free machining properties.

SAE 51431: This is a nickel bearing chromium steel designed for heat treatment to high mechanical properties. Its corrosion resistance is superior to other hardenable steels.

SAE 51440A: A hardenable chromium steel with greater quenched hardness than SAE 51420 and greater toughness than SAE 51440B and 51440C. Maximum corrosion resistance is obtained in the fully hardened and polished condition.

SAE 51440B: A hardenable chromium steel with greater quenched hardness than SAE 51440A. Maximum corrosion resistance is obtained in the fully hardened and polished condition. Capable of hardening to 50–60 Rockwell C depending upon carbon content.

SAE 51440C: This steel has the greatest quenched hardness and wear resistance upon heat treatment of any corrosion or heat resistant steel.

SAE 51440F: The same as SAE 51440C, except for its free machining characteristics.

SAE 51442: A corrosion and heat resisting chromium steel with corrosion resisting properties slightly better than SAE 51430 and with good scale resistance up to 1600 deg. F.

SAE 51446: A corrosion and heat resisting steel with maximum amount of chromium consistent with commercial malleability. Used principally for parts which must resist high temperatures in service without scaling. Resists oxidation up to 2000 deg. F.

SAE 51501: Used for its heat and corrosion resistance and good mechanical properties at temperatures up to approximately 1000 deg. F.

General Applications of SAE Steels

These applications are intended as a general guide only since the selection may depend upon the exact character of the service, cost of material, machinability when machining is required, or other factors. When more than one steel is recommended for a given application, information on the characteristics of each steel listed will be found in the section beginning on page 1552.

Application	SAE No.	Application	SAE No.
Adapters....................	1145	Chain pins, transmission ..	4320
Agricultural steel........	1070	" " "	4815
" "	1080	" " "	4820
Aircraft forgings.........	4140	Chains, transmission.....	3135
Axles, front or rear.......	1040	" "	3140
" " "	4140	Clutch disks..............	1060
Axle shafts..............	1045	" "	1070
" "	2340	" "	1085
" "	2345	Clutch springs...........	1060
" "	3135	Coil springs.............	4063
" "	3140	Cold-headed bolts.......	4042
" "	3141	Cold-heading steel.......	30905
" "	4063	Cold-heading wire or rod..	rimmed*
" "	4340	" " "	1035
Ball-bearing races........	52100	Cold-rolled steel.........	1070
Balls for ball bearings.....	52100	Connecting-rods........	1040
Body stock for cars.......	rimmed*	" "	3141
Bolts, anchor............	1040	Connecting-rod bolts.....	3130
Bolts and screws.........	1035	Corrosion resisting.......	51710
Bolts, cold-headed.......	4042	" "	30805
Bolts, connecting-rod.....	3130	Covers, transmission......	rimmed*
Bolts, heat-treated........	2330	Crankshafts..............	1045
Bolts, heavy-duty........	4815	" "	1145
" " "	4820	" "	3135
Bolts, steering-arm.......	3130	" "	3140
Brake levers..............	1030	" "	3141
" "	1040	Crankshafts, Diesel engine.	4340
Bumper bars.............	1085	Cushion springs..........	1060
Cams, free-wheeling......	4615	Cutlery, stainless........	51335
" " "	4620	Cylinder studs...........	3130
Camshafts................	1020	Deep-drawing steel.......	rimmed*
" "	1040	" " "	30905
Carburized parts.........	1020	Differential gears........	4023
" "	1022	Disks, clutch............	1070
" "	1024	" "	1060
" "	1320	Ductile steel.............	30905
" "	2317	Fan blades..............	1020
" "	2515	Fatigue resisting........	4340
" "	3310	" "	4640
" "	3115	Fender stock for cars.....	rimmed*
" "	3120	Forgings, aircraft........	4140
" "	4023	Forgings, carbon steel.....	1040
" "	4032	" " "	1045
" "	1117	Forgings, heat-treated.....	3240
" "	1118	" " "	5140

* The "rimmed" and "killed" steels listed are in the SAE 1008, 1010 and 1015 group. See general description of these steels.

General Applications of SAE Steels

These applications are intended as a general guide only since the selection may depend upon the exact character of the service, cost of material, machinability when machining is required, or other factors. When more than one steel is recommended for a given application, information on the characteristics of each steel listed will be found in the section beginning on page 1552.

Application	SAE No.	Application	SAE No.
Forgings, heat-treated....	6150	Key stock...............	1030
Forgings, high-duty.......	6150	"　　"	2330
Forgings, small or medium.	1035	"　　"	3130
Forgings, large...........	1036	Leaf springs.............	1085
Free-cutting carbon steel..	1111		9260
"　　"　　"　　"	1113	Levers, brake............	1030
Free-cutting chro.-ni. steel.	30615	"　　"	1040
Free-cutting mang. steel...	1132	Levers, gear shift........	1030
"　　"　　"　　" ...	1137	Levers, heat-treated......	2330
Gears, carburized........	1320	Lock-washers...........	1060
"　　"	2317	Mower knives...........	1085
"　　"	3115	Mower sections.........	1070
"　　"	3120	Music wire.............	1085
"　　"	3310	Nuts...................	3130
"　　"	4119	Nuts, heat-treated.......	2330
"　　"	4125	Oil-pans, automobile......	rimmed*
"　　"	4320	Pinions, carburized......	3115
"　　"	4615	"　　"	3120
"　　"	4620	"　　"	4320
"　　"	4815	Piston-pins.............	3115
"　　"	4820	"　　"	3120
Gears, heat-treated.......	2345	Plow beams.............	1070
Gears, car and truck.....	4027	Plow disks.............	1080
"　　"　　"　　"	4032	Plow shares...........	1080
Gears, cyanide-hardening..	5140	Propeller shafts........	2340
Gears, differential........	4023	"　　"	2345
Gears, high duty........	4640	"　　"	4140
"　　"　　"　　"	6150	Races, ball-bearing.......	52100
Gears, oil-hardening......	3145	Ring gears.............	3115
"　　"　　"	3150	"　　"	3120
"　　"　　"　　"	4340	"　　"	4119
"　　"　　"　　"	5150	Rings, snap...........	1060
Gears, ring..............	1045	Rivets.................	rimmed*
"　　"	3115	Rod and wire...........	killed*
"　　"	3120	Rod, cold-heading.......	1035
"　　"	4119	Roller bearings..........	4815
Gears, transmission.......	3115	Rollers for bearings......	52100
"　　"	3120	Screws and bolts.........	1035
"　　"	4119	Screw stock, Bessemer....	1111
Gears, truck and bus.....	3310	"　　"　　"	1112
"　　"　　"　　"	4320	"　　"　　"	1113
Gear shift levers........	1030	Screw stock, open hearth...	1115
Harrow disks...........	1080	Screws, heat-treated......	2330
"　　"	1095	Seat springs.............	1095
Hay-rake teeth..........	1095	Shafts, axle.............	1045

* The "rimmed" and "killed" steels listed are in the SAE 1008, 1010 and 1015 group. See general description of these steels.

General Applications of SAE Steels

These applications are intended as a general guide only since the selection may depend upon the exact character of the service, cost of material, machinability when machining is required, or other factors. When more than one steel is recommended for a given application, information on the characteristics of each steel listed will be found in the section beginning on page 1552.

Application	SAE No.	Application	SAE No.
Shafts, cyanide-hardening..	5140	Steel, cold-heading.......	30905
Shafts, heavy-duty.......	4340	Steel, free-cutting carbon..	11111
" " "	6150	" " " " ..	1113
" " "	4615	Steel, free-cutting chro.-ni..	30615
" " "	4620	Steel, free-cutting mang...	1132
Shafts, oil-hardening......	5150	" " " " ...	0000
Shafts, propeller.........	2340	Steel, minimum distortion.	4615
" "	2345	" " " .	4620
" "	4140	" " " .	4640
Shafts, transmission......	4140	Steel, soft ductile	30905
Sheets and strips.........	rimmed*	Steering arms............	4042
Snap rings..............	1060	Steering-arm bolts........	3130
Spline shafts............	1045	Steering knuckles........	3141
" "	1320	Steering-knuckle pins.....	4815
" "	2340	" " "	4820
" "	2345	Studs...................	1040
" "	3115	"	1111
" "	3120	Studs, cold-headed.......	4042
" "	3135	Studs, cylinder..........	3130
" "	3140	Studs, heat-treated.......	2330
" "	4023	Studs, heavy-duty........	4815
Spring clips.............	1060	" " "	4820
Springs, coil.............	1095	Tacks..................	rimmed*
" "	4063	Thrust washers..........	1060
" "	6150	Thrust washers, oil-harden.	5150
Springs, clutch..........	1060	Transmission shafts......	4140
Springs, cushion........	1060	Tubing.................	1040
Springs, leaf............	1085	Tubing, front axle........	4140
" "	1095	Tubing, seamless.........	1030
" "	4063	Tubing, welded..........	1020
" "	4068	Universal joints..........	1145
" "	9260	Valve springs............	1060
" "	6150	Washers, lock............	1060
Springs, hard-drawn coiled.	1066	Welded structures........	30705
Springs, oil-hardening.....	5150	Wire and rod............	killed*
Springs, oil-tempered wire.	1066	Wire, cold-heading.......	rimmed*
Springs, seat............	1095	" " "	1035
Springs, valve...........	1060	Wire, hard-drawn spring..	1045
Spring wire..............	1045	" " " " ...	1055
Spring wire, hard-drawn...	1055	Wire, music.............	1085
Spring wire, oil-tempered..	1055	Wire, oil-tempered spring..	1055
Stainless irons...........	51210	Wrist-pins, automobile....	1020
" "	51710	Yokes..................	1145
Steel, cold-rolled.........	1070		

* The "rimmed" and "killed" steels listed are in the SAE 1008, 1010 and 1015 group. See general description of these steels.

Strength and Hardness Data — SAE Steels — 1

Draw. Temp. Deg. F.	Tensile Strength Pounds Sq. In.	Yield Point Pounds Sq. In.	Brinell Hardness when Quenched in		Rockwell Hardness when Quenched in	
			Water	Oil	Water	Oil
SAE 1035 Quenched in water and in oil at 1525 to 1575 degrees F.						
800	96,000*	65,000*	212	197	B96	B93
900	93,000*	63,000*	202	192	B94	B92
1,000	90,000*	60,000*	192	187	B92	B91
1,100	88,000*	56,000*	187	183	B91	B90
1,200	86,000*	53,000*	183	179	B90	B89
1,300	83,000*	51,000*	174	170	B88	B87
SAE 1045 Quenched in water and in oil at 1475 to 1525 degrees F.						
800	115,000*	80,000*	248	235	C24	B99
900	110,000*	75,000*	235	229	B99	B98
1,000	106,000*	70,000*	229	223	B98	B97
1,100	103,000*	67,000*	217	212	B96	B96
1,200	100,000*	65,000*	212	207	B96	B95
1,300	95,000*	62,000*	197	192	B93	B92
SAE 2330 Normalized at 1625 to 1725 degrees F. Quenched in water at 1450 to 1550 degrees F.						
800	152,000	126,000	302	...	C32	...
900	136,000	110,000	277	...	C29	...
1,000	121,000	95,000	235	...	B99	...
1,100	107,000	80,000	217	...	B96	...
1,200	95,000	66,000	187	...	B91	...
1,300	83,000	55,000	166	...	B86	...
SAE 2340 Normalized at 1625 to 1725 degrees F. Quenched in oil at 1425 to 1475 degrees F.						
800	165,000	147,000	...	331	...	C35
900	147,000	127,000	...	302	...	C32
1,000	130,000	108,000	...	248	...	C24
1,100	115,000	90,000	...	229	...	C21
1,200	103,000	75,000	...	217	...	B96
1,300	93,000	63,000	...	183	...	B90
SAE 3130 Normalized at 1650 to 1750 degrees F. Quenched in water at 1500 to 1550 degrees F.						
800	165,000	142,000	311	...	C33	...
900	145,000	123,000	277	...	C29	...
1,000	125,000	105,000	248	...	C24	...
1,100	110,000	90,000	217	...	B96	...
1,200	100,000	76,000	202	...	B94	...
1,300	93,000	66,000	187	...	B91	...
SAE 3140 Normalized at 1600 to 1700 degrees F. Quenched in oil at 1475 to 1525 degrees F.						
800	175,000	152,000	...	331	...	C35
900	155,000	133,000	...	302	...	C32
1,000	138,000	115,000	...	269	...	C28
1,100	123,000	100,000	...	248	...	C24
1,200	110,000	85,000	...	223	...	C20
1,300	103,000	70,000	...	217	...	B96

* Tensile strength and yield point data apply to oil quenching.

Strength and Hardness Data — SAE Steels — 2

Draw. Temp. Deg. F.	Tensile Strength Pounds Sq. In.	Yield Point Pounds Sq. In.	Brinell Hardness when Quenched in		Rockwell Hardness when Quenched in	
			Water	Oil	Water	Oil

SAE 3240 Normalized at 1625 to 1725 degrees F.
Quenched in oil at 1475 to 1525 degrees F.

Draw. Temp. Deg. F.	Tensile Strength Pounds Sq. In.	Yield Point Pounds Sq. In.	Water	Oil	Water	Oil
800	200,000	180,000	...	388	...	C41
900	175,000	152,000	...	341	...	C36
1,000	155,000	132,000	...	321	...	C34
1,100	136,000	115,000	...	285	...	C30
1,200	123,000	100,000	...	255	...	C25
1,300	110,000	87,000	...	229	...	C21

SAE 4140 Normalized at 1650 to 1750 degrees F.
Quenched in oil at 1525 to 1625 degrees F.

Draw. Temp. Deg. F.	Tensile Strength Pounds Sq. In.	Yield Point Pounds Sq. In.	Water	Oil	Water	Oil
800	180,000	155,000	...	363	...	C38
900	170,000	145,000	...	352	...	C37
1,000	156,000	132,000	...	321	...	C34
1,100	142,000	116,000	...	293	...	C31
1,200	125,000	100,000	...	255	...	C25
1,300	110,000	85,000	...	223	...	C20

SAE 4340 Normalized at 1625 to 1725 degrees F.
Quenched in oil at 1475 to 1550 degrees F.

Draw. Temp. Deg. F.	Tensile Strength Pounds Sq. In.	Yield Point Pounds Sq. In.	Water	Oil	Water	Oil
800	210,000	190,000	...	415	...	C44
900	195,000	175,000	...	401	...	C42
1,000	178,000	156,000	...	363	...	C38
1,100	160,000	138,000	...	331	...	C35
1,200	140,000	119,000	...	285	...	C30
1,300	120,000	95,000	...	241	...	C23

SAE 4640 Normalized at 1650 to 1700 degrees F.
Quenched in oil at 1450 to 1500 degrees F.

Draw. Temp. Deg. F.	Tensile Strength Pounds Sq. In.	Yield Point Pounds Sq. In.	Water	Oil	Water	Oil
800	178,000	147,000	...	363	...	C38
900	158,000	130,000	...	321	...	C34
1,000	142,000	115,000	...	293	...	C31
1,100	128,000	103,000	...	262	...	C26
1,200	120,000	93,000	...	241	...	C23
1,300	115,000	88,000	...	229	...	C21

SAE 5140 Normalized at 1625 to 1725 degrees F.
Quenched in oil at 1500 to 1600 degrees F.

Draw. Temp. Deg. F.	Tensile Strength Pounds Sq. In.	Yield Point Pounds Sq. In.	Water	Oil	Water	Oil
800	180,000	160,000	...	363	...	C38
900	160,000	140,000	...	331	...	C35
1,000	140,000	120,000	...	293	...	C31
1,100	125,000	102,000	...	255	...	C25
1,200	111,000	87,000	...	223	...	C20
1,300	100,000	78,000	...	202	...	B94

These tables give conservative physical properties that may be expected of standard test specimens (0.505 by 2 inches) machined from rolled bars 1½ inches diameter or square. Hardness readings were taken at a depth equal to one-half radius of bar and are not comparable with surface hardness readings on heat-treated bars. The strength and hardness data are not part of the SAE steel specifications.

Corrosion-resistant Steels. — Many different terms and trade names have been applied to corrosion-resistant steels. "Stainless Steel" is a term commonly used to indicate any or all rustless steels or iron alloys designed to resist atmospheric corrosion, the attack of hot or cold acids, and scaling at elevated temperatures. However, "Stainless Steel" is strictly a trade name, originally applied to cutlery steels containing no more than 0.70 per cent carbon and from 9 to 16 per cent chromium which were patented in 1916 by the English metallurgist Brearley, and the genuine "Stainless Steel" produced in this country is a straight chrome-iron alloy made under patents owned by the American Stainless Steel Co., Pittsburgh, Pa.

Applications. — The applications of stainless steels may be divided broadly into two groups: (1) Where corrosion resistance is required, including resistance to high-temperature oxidation; (2) where unusual mechanical properties of hardness, strength, toughness or ductility are required, including resistance to wear and abrasion. Corrosion-resistant steels cover a wide range of compositions and physical properties. The common applications include cutlery; surgical and dental instruments; poppet valves for internal-combustion engines; turbine blades; pump shafts; architectural trim; polished parts of automobiles; chemical, dairy, laundry, and oil equipment, etc. The chromium content commonly ranges from 10 or 12 to 18 or 20 per cent, some steels having less and some more than these minimum or maximum values. The "18–8" stainless steel often referred to is a steel having about 18 per cent chromium and 8 per cent nickel.

Stainless Steel with Free Machining Qualities. — The high-chromium stainless steel alloys first produced were extremely difficult to machine, and grinding and polishing operations were also difficult and expensive. By producing this steel with a high sulphur content or by the addition of selenium, free machining qualities can be obtained. Such stainless steels contain approximately 0.10 per cent carbon, 18 per cent chromium, 8 per cent nickel, and 0.30 per cent sulphur (or 0.25 per cent selenium instead of sulphur). They can be machined in automatic screw machines with regular tools at speeds equal to, or closely approximating, those used for ordinary Bessemer screw stock. These materials can also be easily drilled, tapped, and threaded with dies. Wire and tubing can be cold-drawn by simply using the lime coat and lubricants regularly employed for drawing ordinary steel.

Characteristics of 18–8 Stainless Steel. — The chrome-nickel stainless steel known as 18–8 is made to have a tensile strength of from 90,000 to 100,000 pounds per square inch in the annealed state. The elongation varies from 60 to 70 per cent. Cold-working will increase the tensile strength to from 120,000 to 125,000 pounds per square inch. Because of the high feeding pressure required for drilling 18–8 stainless steels, a specially heat-treated high-speed drill with a heavy web section has been introduced. The web should be thinned at the point and a sulphur-base oil used as a cutting fluid.

General Properties of Alloy Steels. — Alloy or "special" steels are combinations of iron and carbon with some other element, such as nickel, chromium, tungsten, vanadium, manganese and molybdenum. All of these metals give certain distinct properties to the steel, but in all cases the principal quality is the increase in hardness and toughness.

Nickel steel usually contains from 3 to 3.5 per cent nickel (ordinarily not over 5 per cent), and from 0.20 to 0.40 per cent carbon. This steel is used for armor plate, ammunition, bridge construction, rails, etc. One of the reasons why nickel steel is adapted for armor plate is that it does not crack when perforated by a projectile. The Krupp steel used for armor plate contains approximately 3.5 per cent nickel, 1.5 per cent chromium and 0.25 per cent carbon. The advantages claimed for nickel steel for railroad rails are its increased resistance to abrasion and high elastic limit. On sharp curves, it has been estimated that a nickel steel rail will outlast four ordinary rails.

Chromium steel is well adapted for armor-piercing projectiles, owing to its hardness, toughness and stiffness, and is extensively used for this purpose. Chromium steel is also used in the construction of safes and for castings subjected to unusually severe stresses, such as those used in rock-crushing machinery, etc. The percentage of chromium used in chromium steels varies over quite a wide range in the low-chromium and high-chromium steels.

Tungsten steel is largely employed for high-speed metal cutting tools and magnet steels. It has also been used in the manufacture of armor plate and armor-piercing projectiles, in which case it is combined either with nickel or chromium or with both of these metals. The property that tungsten imparts to steel is that of hardening in the air, after heating to the required temperature. This steel usually contains from 5 to 15 per cent tungsten (although the percentage is sometimes as high as 24 per cent) and from 0.4 to 2 per cent carbon.

Vanadium steels ordinarily contain from 0.16 to 0.25 per cent vanadium. The effect of vanadium is to increase the tensile strength and elastic limit, and it gives the steel the valuable property of resisting, to an unusual degree, repeated stresses. Vanadium steel is especially adapted for springs, car axles, gears subjected to severe service, and for all parts which must withstand constant vibration and varying stresses.

Manganese steel (also known as Hadfield manganese steel) contains about 12 per cent manganese and from 0.8 to 1.25 per cent carbon. If there is only 1.5 per cent manganese, the steel is very brittle, and additional manganese increases this brittleness until the quantity has reached 4 to 5.5 per cent, when the steel can be pulverized under the hammer. With a further increase of manganese, the steel becomes ductile and very hard, these qualities being at their highest degree when the manganese content is 12 per cent. The ductility of the steel is brought out by sudden cooling, the process being opposite that employed for carbon steel.

Molybdenum steels have properties similar to tungsten steels, except that a smaller quantity of molybdenum than of tungsten is required to secure similar results.

TESTING THE HARDNESS OF METALS

Brinell Hardness Test. — The Brinell test for determining the hardness of metallic materials consists in applying a known load to the surface of the material to be tested through a hardened steel ball of known diameter. The diameter (or depth) of the resulting permanent impression in the metal is measured. The Brinell hardness number is taken as the quotient of the applied load divided by the area of the surface of the impression, which is assumed to be spherical. Thus

$$\text{Brinell number} = \frac{\text{load on indenting tool in kilograms}}{\text{surface area of indentation in square millimeters}}$$

Brinell's original assumption was that the area of the indentation is always directly proportional to the load. Investigation has shown, however, that the Brinell number is not directly proportional to the load because of a number of factors which vary more or less with different materials.

If the steel ball were not deformed under the applied load and if the impression were truly spherical, then the above formula would be a general one, and any combination of applied load and size of ball could be used. The impression, however, is not quite a spherical surface since there must always be some deformation of the steel ball and some recovery of form of the metal in the impression; hence for a standard Brinell test, the size and characteristics of the ball and the magnitude of the applied load must be standardized. A standard ball 10 millimeters in diameter and a load of 3000 kilograms for hard metals and 500 kilograms for soft metals is standard practice. For extremely soft metals a load of 100 kilograms is sometimes used.

The load should be applied for at least 10 seconds in the case of iron and steel, and at least 30 seconds in testing other metals. A period of 2 minutes has been recommended for magnesium and magnesium alloys.

Due to the error introduced by flattening of the standard steel ball for hardnesses above about 400 Brinell, better determinations of such materials can be made with a Hultgren Ball up to about 600 Brinell or a tungsten carbide ball for higher values. It will be noted from Table 1 that hardness values obtained respectively by the use of these three balls begin to differ above 432 Brinell.

Rockwell Hardness Test. — The Rockwell hardness tester is essentially a machine that measures hardness by determining the depth of penetration of a penetrator into the specimen under certain fixed conditions of test. The penetrator may be either a steel ball or a diamond sphero-conical penetrator. The hardness number is related to the depth of indentation and the number is higher the harder the material. A minor load of 10 kg. is first applied which causes an initial penetration; the dial is set at zero on the black-figure scale, and the major load is applied. This major load is customarily 60 kg. or 100 kg. when a steel ball is used as a penetrator, but other loads may be used when found necessary. The ball penetrator is ⅟₁₆ inch in diameter normally; but other penetrators of larger diameter, such as ⅛ inch, may be employed for soft metals. When a diamond sphero-conical penetrator is employed the load usually is 150 kg. Experience decides the best combination of load and penetrator for use. After the major load is applied and removed, according to standard procedure, the reading is taken while the minor load is still applied.

The Rockwell Hardness Scales. — The various Rockwell scales and their applications are shown in the table below. The type of penetrator and load used with each are shown in Tables 1 and 2 which give comparative hardness values for different hardness scales.

Scale	Testing Application
A	For tungsten carbide and other extremely hard materials. Also for thin, hard sheets.
B	For materials of medium hardness such as low and medium carbon steels in the annealed condition.
C	For materials harder than Rockwell B-100.
D	Where somewhat lighter load is desired than on C scale, as on case hardened pieces.
E	For very soft materials such as bearing metals.
F	Same as E scale but using ⅟₁₆-inch ball.
G	For metals harder than tested on B scale.
H & K	For softer metals.
15-N; 30-N; 45-N	Where shallow impression or small area is desired. For hardened steel and hard alloys.
15-T; 30-T; 45-T	Where shallow impression or small area is desired for materials softer than hardened steel.

Shore's Scleroscope. — The scleroscope is an instrument which measures the hardness of the work in terms of elasticity. A diamond-tipped hammer is allowed to drop from a known height on the metal to be tested. As this hammer strikes the metal, it rebounds, and the harder the metal, the greater the rebound. The extreme height of the rebound is recorded, and an average of a number of readings taken on a single piece will give a good indication of the hardness of the work. The surface smoothness of the work affects the reading of the instrument. The readings are also affected by the contour and mass of the work and the depth of the case, in carburized work, the soft core of light-depth carburizing, pack-hardening, or cyanide hardening, absorbing the force of the hammer fall and decreasing the rebound. The hammer weighs about 40 grains, the height of the rebound of hardened steel is in the neighborhood of 100 on the scale, or about 6¼ inches, while the total fall is about 10 inches or 255 millimeters.

Vickers Hardness Test. — The Vickers test is similar in principle to the Brinell test. The standard Vickers penetrator is a square-based diamond pyramid having an included point angle of 136 degrees. The numerical value of the hardness number equals the applied load in kilograms divided by the area of the pyramidal impression. A smooth, firmly supported, flat surface is required. The load, which usually is applied for 30 seconds, may either be 5, 10, 20, 30, 50 or 120 kilograms. The 50-kilogram load is usually employed. The hardness number is based upon the diagonal length of the square impression. The Vickers test, which is considered very accurate, may, with proper load regulation, be applied to thin sheets as well as to larger sections.

Knoop Hardness Numbers. — The Knoop hardness test is applicable to extremely thin metal, plated surfaces, exceptionally hard and brittle materials, very shallow carburized or nitrided surfaces, or whenever the applied load must be kept below 3600 grams. The Knoop indentor is a diamond ground to an elongated pyramidal form and it produces an indentation having long and short diagonals with a ratio of approximately 7 to 1. The longitudinal angle of the indentor is 172 degrees 30 minutes and the transverse angle 130 degrees. The Tukon Tester in which the Knoop indentor is used is fully automatic under electronic control. The Knoop hardness number equals load in kilograms divided by the projected area of indentation in square millimeters. The indentation number corresponding to the long diagonal and for a given load, may be determined from a table computed for a theoretically perfect indentor. The load, which may be varied from 25 to 3600 grams, is applied for a definite period and always normal to the surface tested. Lapped plane surfaces free from scratches are required.

Monotron Hardness Indicator. — With this instrument, a diamond-ball impressor point ¾ mm. in diameter is forced into the material to a depth of 9/5000 inch and the pressure required to produce this constant impression indicates the hardness. One of two dials shows the pressure in kilograms and pounds, and the other shows the depth of the impression in millimeters and inches. Readings in Brinell numbers may be obtained by means of a scale designated as $M - 1$.

Keep's Test. — With this apparatus a standard steel drill is caused to make a definite number of revolutions, while it is pressed with standard force against the specimen to be tested. The hardness is automatically recorded on a diagram on which a dead soft material gives a horizontal line, while a material as hard as the drill itself gives a vertical line, intermediate hardness being represented by the corresponding angle between 0 and 90 degrees.

Table 1. Comparative Hardness Scales for Steel — 1

Rockwell C-Scale Hardness Number	Diamond Pyramid Hardness Number Vickers	Brinell Hardness Number 10-mm. Ball, 3000-kg. Load			Rockwell Hardness Number		Rockwell Superficial Hardness Number Superficial Brale Penetrator			Shore Scleroscope Hardness Number
		Standard Ball	Hultgren Ball	Tungsten Carbide Ball	A-Scale 60-kg. Load Brale Penetrator	D-Scale 100-kg. Load Brale Penetrator	15-N Scale 15-kg. Load	30-N Scale 30-kg. Load	45-N Scale 45-kg. Load	
68	940	....	....	....	85.6	76.9	93.2	84.4	75.4	97
67	900	....	....	....	85.0	76.1	92.9	83.6	74.2	95
66	865	....	....	....	84.5	75.4	92.5	82.8	73.3	92
65	832	....	....	739	83.9	74.5	92.2	81.9	72.0	91
64	800	....	....	722	83.4	73.8	91.8	81.1	71.0	88
63	772	....	....	705	82.8	73.0	91.4	80.1	69.9	87
62	746	....	....	688	82.3	72.2	91.1	79.3	68.8	85
61	720	....	....	670	81.8	71.5	90.7	78.4	67.7	83
60	697	....	613	654	81.2	70.7	90.2	77.5	66.6	81
59	674	....	599	634	80.7	69.9	89.8	76.6	65.5	80
58	653	....	587	615	80.1	69.2	89.3	75.7	64.3	78
57	633	....	575	595	79.6	68.5	88.9	74.8	63.2	76
56	613	....	561	577	79.0	67.7	88.3	73.9	62.0	75
55	595	....	546	560	78.5	66.9	87.9	73.0	60.9	74
54	577	....	534	543	78.0	66.1	87.4	72.0	59.8	72
53	560	....	519	525	77.4	65.4	86.9	71.2	58.6	71
52	544	500	508	512	76.8	64.6	86.4	70.2	57.4	69
51	528	487	494	496	76.3	63.8	85.9	69.4	56.1	68
50	513	475	481	481	75.9	63.1	85.5	68.5	55.0	67
49	498	464	469	469	75.2	62.1	85.0	67.6	53.8	66
48	484	451	455	455	74.7	61.4	84.5	66.7	52.5	64
47	471	442	443	443	74.1	60.8	83.9	65.8	51.4	63
46	458	432	432	432	73.6	60.0	83.5	64.8	50.3	62
45	446	421	421	421	73.1	59.2	83.0	64.0	49.0	60
44	434	409	409	409	72.5	58.5	82.5	63.1	47.8	58
43	423	400	400	400	72.0	57.7	82.0	62.2	46.7	57
42	412	390	390	390	71.5	56.9	81.5	61.3	45.5	56
41	402	381	381	381	70.9	56.2	80.9	60.4	44.3	55
40	392	371	371	371	70.4	55.4	80.4	59.5	43.1	54
39	382	362	362	362	69.9	54.6	79.9	58.6	41.9	52
38	372	353	353	353	69.4	53.8	79.4	57.7	40.8	51
37	363	344	344	344	68.9	53.1	78.8	56.8	39.6	50
36	354	336	336	336	68.4	52.3	78.3	55.9	38.4	49
35	345	327	327	327	67.9	51.5	77.7	55.0	37.2	48
34	336	319	319	319	67.4	50.8	77.2	54.2	36.1	47
33	327	311	311	311	66.8	50.0	76.6	53.3	34.9	46
32	318	301	301	301	66.3	49.2	76.1	52.1	33.7	44
31	310	294	294	294	65.8	48.4	75.6	51.3	32.5	43
30	302	286	286	286	65.3	47.7	75.0	50.4	31.3	42
29	294	279	279	279	64.7	47.0	74.5	49.5	30.1	41
28	286	271	271	271	64.3	46.1	73.9	48.6	28.9	41
27	279	264	264	264	63.8	45.2	73.3	47.7	27.8	40

Note: The values in this table shown in bold faced type correspond to those shown in American Society for Testing Materials Specification E48–43T.

Table 1. Comparative Hardness Scales for Steel — 2

Rockwell C-Scale Hardness Number	Diamond Pyramid Hardness Number Vickers	Brinell Hardness Number 10-mm. Ball, 3000-kg. Load			Rockwell Hardness Number		Rockwell Superficial Hardness Number Superficial Brale Penetrator			Shore Scleroscope Hardness Number
		Standard Ball	Hultgren Ball	Tungsten Carbide Ball	A-Scale 60-kg. Load Brale Penetrator	D-Scale 100-kg. Load Brale Penetrator	15-N Scale 15-kg. Load	30-N Scale 30-kg. Load	45-N Scale 45-kg. Load	
26	272	258	258	258	63.3	44.6	72.8	46.8	26.7	38
25	266	253	253	253	62.8	43.8	72.2	45.9	25.5	38
24	260	247	247	247	62.4	43.1	71.6	45.0	24.3	37
23	254	243	243	243	62.0	42.1	71.0	44.0	23.1	36
22	248	237	237	237	61.5	41.6	70.5	43.2	22.0	35
21	243	231	231	231	61.0	40.9	69.9	42.3	20.7	35
20	238	226	226	226	60.5	40.1	69.4	41.5	19.6	34
(18)	230	219	219	219	....	....	....	....	....	33
(16)	222	212	212	212	....	....	....	....	....	32
(14)	213	203	203	203	....	....	....	....	....	31
(12)	204	194	194	194	....	....	....	....	....	29
(10)	196	187	187	187	....	....	....	....	....	28
(8)	188	179	179	179	....	....	....	....	....	27
(6)	180	171	171	171	....	....	....	....	....	26
(4)	173	165	165	165	....	....	....	....	....	25
(2)	166	158	158	158	....	....	....	....	....	24
(0)	160	152	152	152	....	....	....	....	....	24

Note: The values shown in this table in boldfaced type correspond to those shown in American Society for Testing Materials Specification E48–43T.

Values in ( ) are beyond the normal range and are given for information only.

Comparison of Hardness Scales. — Tables 1 and 2 show comparisons of various hardness scales. All such tables are based on the assumption that the metal tested is homogeneous to a depth several times that of the indentation. To the extent that the metal being tested is not homogeneous, errors are introduced because different loads and different shapes of penetrators meet the resistance of metal of varying hardness, depending on the depth of indentation. Another source of error is introduced in comparing the hardness of different materials as measured on different hardness scales. This arises from the fact that in any hardness test, metal that is severely cold-worked actually supports the penetrator and different metals, different alloys, and different analyses of the same type of alloy have different cold-working properties. In spite of the possible inaccuracies introduced by such factors, it is of considerable value to be able to compare hardness values in a general way.

The data shown in Table 1 are based upon extensive tests on carbon and alloy steels mostly in the heat-treated condition, but have been found to be reliable on constructional alloy steels and tool steels in the as-forged, annealed, normalized, quenched and tempered conditions, providing they are homogeneous. These hardness comparisons are not as accurate for special cases such as high manganese steel, 18–8 stainless steel and other austenitic steels, nickel base alloys, as well as constructional alloy steels and nickel base alloys in the cold-worked condition.

The data shown in Table 2 are for hardness measurements of unhardened steel, steel of soft temper, grey and malleable cast iron, and most non-ferrous metals. Again these hardness comparisons are not as accurate for annealed metals of high Rockwell B hardness such as austenitic stainless steel, nickel and high nickel alloys and cold-worked metals of low B-scale hardness such as aluminum and the softer alloys.

Table 2. Comparative Hardness Scales for Unhardened Steel, Soft-temper Steel, Grey and Malleable Cast Iron, and Non-ferrous Alloys* — 1

Rockwell Hardness Number			Rockwell Superficial Hardness Number			Rockwell Hardness Number			Brinell Hardness Number	
Rockwell B scale 1/16" Ball Penetrator — 100 kg. Load	Rockwell F scale 1/16" Ball Penetrator — 60 kg. Load	Rockwell G scale 1/16" Ball Penetrator — 150 kg. Load	Rockwell Superficial 15-T scale 1/16" Ball Penetrator — 15 kg. Load	Rockwell Superficial 30-T scale 1/16" Ball Penetrator — 30 kg. Load	Rockwell Superficial 45-T scale 1/16" Ball Penetrator — 45 kg. Load	Rockwell E scale 1/8" Ball Penetrator — 100 kg. Load	Rockwell K scale 1/8" Ball Penetrator — 150 kg. Load	Rockwell A scale "Brale" Penetrator — 60 kg. Load	Brinell Scale 10 mm Standard Ball — 500 kg. Load	Brinell Scale 10 mm. Standard Ball — 3000 kg. Load
100	....	82.5	93.0	82.0	72.0	...	....	61.5	201	240
99	....	81.0	92.5	81.5	71.0	....	....	61.0	195	234
98	....	79.0	....	81.0	70.0	....	....	60.0	189	228
97	....	77.5	92.0	80.5	69.0	....	....	59.5	184	222
96	....	76.0	....	80.0	68.0	....	....	59.0	179	216
95	....	74.0	91.5	79.0	67.0	....	....	58.0	175	210
94	....	72.5	....	78.5	66.0	....	....	57.5	171	205
93	....	71.0	91.0	78.0	65.5	....	....	57.0	167	200
92	....	69.0	90.5	77.5	64.5	....	100	56.5	163	195
91	....	67.5	....	77.0	63.5	....	99.5	56.0	160	190
90	....	66.0	90.0	76.0	62.5	....	98.5	55.5	157	185
89	....	64.0	89.5	75.5	61.5	....	98.0	55.0	154	180
88	....	62.5	....	75.0	60.5	....	97.0	54.0	151	176
87	....	61.0	89.0	74.5	59.5	....	96.5	53.5	148	172
86	....	59.0	88.5	74.0	58.5	....	95.5	53.0	145	169
85	....	57.5	....	73.5	58.0	....	94.5	52.5	142	165
84	....	56.0	88.0	73.0	57.0	....	94.0	52.0	140	162
83	....	54.0	87.5	72.0	56.0	....	93.0	51.0	137	159
82	....	52.5	....	71.5	55.0	....	92.0	50.5	135	156
81	....	51.0	87.0	71.0	54.0	....	91.0	50.0	133	153
80	....	49.0	86.5	70.0	53.0	....	90.5	49.5	130	150
79	....	47.5	....	69.5	52.0	....	89.5	49.0	128	147
78	....	46.0	86.0	69.0	51.0	....	88.5	48.5	126	144
77	....	44.0	85.5	68.0	50.0	....	88.0	48.0	124	141
76	....	42.5	....	67.5	49.0	....	87.0	47.0	122	139
75	99.5	41.0	85.0	67.0	48.5	....	86.0	46.5	120	137
74	99.0	39.0	....	66.0	47.5	....	85.0	46.0	118	135
73	98.5	37.5	84.5	65.5	46.5	....	84.5	45.5	116	132
72	98.0	36.0	84.0	65.0	45.5	....	83.5	45.0	114	130
71	97.5	34.5	....	64.0	44.5	100	82.5	44.5	112	127
70	97.0	32.5	83.5	63.5	43.5	99.5	81.5	44.0	110	125
69	96.0	31.0	83.0	62.5	42.5	99.0	81.0	43.5	109	123
68	95.5	29.5	....	62.0	41.5	98.0	80.0	43.0	107	121
67	95.0	28.0	82.5	61.5	40.5	97.5	79.0	42.5	106	119
66	94.5	26.5	82.0	60.5	39.5	97.0	78.0	42.0	104	117
65	94.0	25.0	....	60.0	38.5	96.0	77.5	....	102	116
64	93.5	23.5	81.5	59.5	37.5	95.5	76.5	41.5	101	114
63	93.0	22.0	81.0	58.5	36.5	95.0	75.5	41.0	99	112
62	92.0	20.5	....	58.0	35.5	94.5	74.5	40.5	98	110
61	91.5	19.0	80.5	57.0	34.5	93.5	74.0	40.0	96	108
60	91.0	17.5	....	56.5	33.5	93.0	73.0	39.5	95	107
59	90.5	16.0	80.0	56.0	32.0	92.5	72.0	39.0	94	106

* See note at end of table.

Table 2 Comparative Hardness Scales for Unhardened Steel, Soft-temper Steel, Grey and Malleable Cast-iron, and Non-ferrous Alloys* — 2

Rockwell Hardness Number			Rockwell Superficial Hardness Number			Rockwell Hardness Number				Brinell
Rockwell B scale 1/16" Ball Penetrator 100 kg. Load	Rockwell F scale 1/16" Ball Penetrator 60 kg. Load	Rockwell G scale 1/16" Ball Penetrator 150 kg. Load	Rockwell Superficial 15-T scale 1/16" Ball Penetrator 15 kg. Load	Rockwell Superficial 30-T scale 1/16" Ball Penetrator 30 kg. Load	Rockwell Superficial 45-T scale 1/16" Ball Penetrator 45 kg. Load	Rockwell E scale 1/8" Ball Penetrator 100 kg. Load	Rockwell H scale 1/8" Ball Penetrator 60 kg. Load	Rockwell K scale 1/8" Ball Penetrator 150 kg. Load	Rockwell A scale "Brale" Penetrator 60 kg. Load	Brinell Scale 10-mm. Standard Ball — 500 kg. Load
58	90.0	14.5	79.5	55.0	31.0	92.0	....	71.0	38.5	92
57	89.5	13.0	....	54.5	30.0	91.0	....	70.5	38.0	91
56	89.0	11.5	79.0	54.0	29.0	90.5	....	69.5	....	90
55	88.0	10.0	78.5	53.0	28.0	90.0	....	68.5	37.5	89
54	87.5	8.5	....	52.5	27.0	89.5	....	68.0	37.0	87
53	87.0	7.0	78.0	51.5	26.0	89.0	....	67.0	36.5	86
52	86.5	5.5	77.5	51.0	25.0	88.0	....	66.0	36.0	85
51	86.0	4.0	....	50.5	24.0	87.5	....	65.0	35.5	84
50	85.5	2.5	77.0	49.5	23.0	87.0	....	64.5	35.0	83
50	85.5	2.5	77.0	49.5	23.0	87.0	....	64.5	35.0	83
49	85.0	1.0	76.5	49.0	22.0	86.5	....	63.5	....	82
48	84.5	....	....	48.5	20.5	85.5	....	62.5	34.5	81
47	84.0	....	76.0	47.5	19.5	85.0	....	61.5	34.0	80
46	83.0	....	75.5	47.0	18.5	84.5	....	61.0	33.5	..
45	82.5	....	....	46.0	17.5	84.0	....	60.0	33.0	79
44	82.0	....	75.0	45.5	16.5	83.5	....	59.0	32.5	78
43	81.5	....	74.5	45.0	15.5	82.5	....	58.0	32.0	77
42	81.0	....	....	44.0	14.5	82.0	....	57.5	31.5	76
41	80.5	....	74.0	43.5	13.5	81.5	....	56.5	31.0	75
40	79.5	....	73.5	43.0	12.5	81.0	....	55.5	....	..
39	79.0	....	....	42.0	11.0	80.0	....	54.5	30.5	74
38	78.5	....	73.0	41.5	10.0	79.5	....	54.0	30.0	73
37	78.0	....	72.5	40.5	9.0	79.0	....	53.0	29.5	72
36	77.5	....	....	40.0	8.0	78.5	100	52.0	29.0	..
35	77.0	....	72.0	39.5	7.0	78.0	99.5	51.5	28.5	71
34	76.5	....	71.5	38.5	6.0	77.0	99.0	50.5	28.0	70
33	75.5	....	....	38.0	5.0	76.5	....	49.5	....	69
32	75.0	....	71.0	37.5	4.0	76.0	98.5	48.5	27.5	..
31	74.5	....	....	36.5	3.0	75.5	98.0	48.0	27.0	68
30	74.0	....	70.5	36.0	2.0	75.0	....	47.0	26.5	67
29	73.5	....	70.0	35.5	1.0	74.0	97.5	46.0	26.0	..
28	73.0	....	....	34.5	....	73.5	97.0	45.0	25.5	66
27	72.5	....	69.5	34.0	....	73.0	96.5	44.5	25.0	..
26	72.0	....	69.0	33.0	....	72.5	....	43.5	24.5	65
25	71.0	....	....	32.5	....	72.0	96.0	42.5	....	64
24	70.5	....	68.5	32.0	....	71.0	95.5	41.5	24.0	..
23	70.0	....	68.0	31.0	....	70.5	....	41.0	23.5	63
22	69.5	....	....	30.5	....	70.0	95.0	40.0	23.0	..
21	69.0	....	67.5	29.5	....	69.5	94.5	39.0	22.5	62
20	68.5	....	....	29.0	....	68.5	....	38.0	22.0	..
19	68.0	....	67.0	28.5	....	68.0	94.0	37.5	21.5	61
18	67.0	....	66.5	27.5	....	67.5	93.5	36.5	....	..

* See note at end of table.

Table 2. Comparative Hardness Scales for Unhardened Steel, Soft-temper Steel, Grey and Malleable Cast Iron, and Non-ferrous Alloys* — 3

(Compiled by Wilson Mechanical Instrument Co.)

Rockwell Hardness Number			Rockwell Superficial Hardness Number			Rockwell Hardness Number				Brinell
Rockwell B scale 1/16" Ball Penetrator 100 kg. Load	Rockwell F scale 1/16" Ball Penetrator 60 kg. Load	Rockwell G scale 1/16" Ball Penetrator 150 kg. Load	Rockwell Superficial 15-T scale 1/16" Ball Penetrator 15 kg. Load	Rockwell Superficial 30-T scale 1/16" Ball Penetrator 30 kg. Load	Rockwell Superficial 45-T scale 1/16" Ball Penetrator 45 kg. Load	Rockwell E scale 1/8" Ball Penetrator 100 kg. Load	Rockwell H scale 1/8" Ball Penetrator 60 kg. Load	Rockwell K scale 1/8" Ball Penetrator 150 kg. Load	Rockwell A scale "Brale" Penetrator 60 kg. Load	Brinell Scale 10-mm. Standard Ball — 500 kg. Load
17	66.5	....	....	27.0	....	67.0	93.0	35.5	21.0	60
16	66.0	....	66.0	26.0	....	66.5	....	35.0	20.5	..
15	65.5	....	65.5	25.5	....	65.5	92.5	34.0	20.0	59
14	65.0	....	....	25.0	....	65.0	92.0	33.0	....	..
13	64.5	....	65.0	24.0	....	64.5	91.5	32.0	....	58
12	64.0	....	64.5	23.5	....	64.0	91.0	31.5	....	..
11	63.5	....	....	23.0	....	63.5	90.5	30.5	....	57
10	63.0	....	64.0	22.0	....	62.5	....	29.5	....	..
9	62.0	....	....	21.5	....	62.0	90.0	29.0	....	..
8	61.5	....	63.5	20.5	....	61.5	89.5	28.0	....	56
7	61.0	....	63.0	20.0	....	61.0	....	27.0	....	..
6	60.5	....	....	19.5	....	60.5	89.0	26.0	....	55
5	60.0	....	62.5	18.5	....	60.0	88.5	25.5	....	..
4	59.5	....	62.0	18.0	....	59.0	88.0	24.5	....	..
3	59.0	....	....	17.0	....	58.5	....	23.5	....	54
2	58.0	....	61.5	16.5	....	58.0	87.5	23.0	....	..
1	57.5	....	61.0	16.0	....	57.5	87.0	22.0	....	..
	57.0	....	....	15.0	....	57.0	....	21.0	....	53

* Not applicable to annealed metals of high B-scale hardness such as austenitic stainless steels, nickel and high-nickel alloys nor to cold-worked metals of low B-scale hardness such as aluminum and the softer alloys.

Turner's Sclerometer. — In making this test a weighted diamond point is drawn, once forward and once backward, over the smooth surface of the material to be tested. The hardness number is the weight in grams required to produce a standard scratch.

Mohs's Hardness Scale. — Hardness, in general, is determined by what is known as Mohs's scale, a standard for hardness which is mainly applied to non-metallic elements and minerals. In this hardness scale there are ten degrees or steps, each designated by a mineral, the difference in hardness of the different steps being determined by the fact that any member in the series will scratch any of the preceding members. This scale is as follows:

1. Talc; 2. gypsum; 3. calcite; 4. fluor spar; 5. apatite; 6. orthoclase; 7. quartz; 8. topaz; 9. sapphire or corundum; 10. diamond.

These minerals, arbitrarily selected as standards, are successively harder, from talc, the softest of all minerals, to diamond, the hardest. This scale, which is now universally used for non-metallic minerals, is, however, not applied to metals.

Relation Between Hardness and Tensile Strength. — The approximate relationship between the hardness and tensile strength is shown by the following formula in which B = Brinell hardness number.

Tensile strength = $B \times 515$ (for Brinell numbers up to 175).

Tensile strength = $490 \times B$ (for Brinell numbers larger than 175).

These formulas give the tensile strength in pounds per square inch and apply to steels. This definite relationship between hardness and tensile strength does not apply to non-ferrous metals with the possible exception of certain aluminum alloys.

Hardness of Heat-treated Steel — 1

Tests showing both Rockwell and Brinell hardness numbers

Kind of Steel	Drawn to — Deg. F.	Chemical Composition, Per Cent					Hardness	
		C	Mn	Si	P	S	Brinell 3000 kg.	Rockwell C
Carbon Steel Quenched in Brine at 1420 Deg. F.	0	0.80	0.20	0.25	0.001	0.015	724	67.5
	340	0.80	0.20	0.25	0.001	0.015	678	64.5
	450	0.80	0.20	0.25	0.001	0.015	627	60.8
	505	0.80	0.20	0.25	0.001	0.015	599	58.1
	610	0.80	0.20	0.25	0.001	0.015	557	55.3
	755	0.80	0.20	0.25	0.001	0.015	476	49.3
	855	0.80	0.20	0.25	0.001	0.015	427	45.3
	915	0.80	0.20	0.25	0.001	0.015	389	42.2
	1000	0.80	0.20	0.25	0.001	0.015	333	36.7
	1050	0.80	0.20	0.25	0.001	0.015	310	33.9
	1175	0.80	0.20	0.25	0.001	0.015	250	25.0
	1250	0.80	0.20	0.25	0.001	0.015	221	19.1
	0	1.20	0.20	0.25	0.001	0.015	755	68.4
	310	1.20	0.20	0.25	0.001	0.015	686	67.1
	450	1.20	0.20	0.25	0.001	0.015	631	62.7
	550	1.20	0.20	0.25	0.001	0.015	587	58.6
	665	1.20	0.20	0.25	0.001	0.015	529	54.3
	755	1.20	0.20	0.25	0.001	0.015	491	51.9
	850	1.20	0.20	0.25	0.001	0.015	439	47.7
	980	1.20	0.20	0.25	0.001	0.015	352	40.5
	1050	1.20	0.20	0.25	0.001	0.015	313	34.7
	1110	1.20	0.20	0.25	0.001	0.015	295	32.5
	1175	1.20	0.20	0.25	0.001	0.015	259	26.5
	1300	1.20	0.20	0.25	0.001	0.015	224	19.9

	Deg. F.	C	Mn	P	S	Ni	Brinell	R_c
Nickel Steel, 3½ per cent, Quenched in Water at 1600 Deg. F.	0	0.15	0.49	0.029	0.020	3.46	394	41.9
	950	0.15	0.49	0.029	0.020	3.46	224	20.8
	1250	0.15	0.49	0.029	0.020	3.46	183	10.9
	0	0.35	0.76	0.010	0.020	3.44	516	53.0
	350	0.35	0.76	0.010	0.020	3.44	488	47.9
	650	0.35	0.76	0.010	0.020	3.44	387	39.9
	950	0.35	0.76	0.010	0.020	3.44	285	30.4
	1250	0.35	0.76	0.010	0.020	3.44	212	17.5

	Deg. F.	C	Mn	P	S	Cr	Brinell	R_c
Chrom. St. Quenched in Oil at 1500 F.	950	1.01	0.22	0.026	0.024	1.33	345	37.3
	1250	1.01	0.22	0.026	0.024	1.33	284	30.1

	Deg. F.	C	Mn	Si	V	Cr	Brinell	R_c
High Chromium Steel* Quenched in Oil at 1750 F.	0	2.20	0.20	0.30	0.80	12	748	68.0
	310	2.20	0.20	0.30	0.80	12	703	65.2
	550	2.20	0.20	0.30	0.80	12	628	60.9
	850	2.20	0.20	0.30	0.80	12	574	56.3
	1000	2.20	0.20	0.30	0.80	12	538	54.3

* The high chromium steel contains 0.50% cobalt.

Hardness of Heat-treated Steel — 2
Tests showing both Rockwell and Brinell hardness numbers

Kind of Steel	Drawn to — Deg. F.	Chemical Composition, Per Cent					Hardness	
		C	Mn	Si	V	Cr	Brinell 3000 kg.	Rockwell C
High Chromium Steel* Quenched in Oil at 1750 F.	1050	2.20	0.20	0.30	0.80	12	506	51.9
	1130	2.20	0.20	0.30	0.80	12	456	48.1
	1175	2.20	0.20	0.30	0.80	12	433	45.4
	1235	2.20	0.20	0.30	0.80	12	401	42.8
	1265	2.20	0.20	0.30	0.80	12	377	40.7
	1300	2.20	0.20	0.30	0.80	12	342	36.8
	1330	2.20	0.20	0.30	0.80	12	330	35.1
	1380	2.20	0.20	0.30	0.80	12	301	32.1
	1440	2.20	0.20	0.30	0.80	12	269	26.9
	Deg. F.	C	Mn	P	Ni	Cr	Brinell	R_c
Chromium Nickel Steel Quenched in Oil at 1550 F.	0	0.30	0.70	0.035	2.14	0.82	469	47.5
	350	0.30	0.70	0.035	2.14	0.82	472	48.0
	650	0.30	0.70	0.035	2.14	0.82	423	42.8
	950	0.30	0.70	0.035	2.14	0.82	321	34.2
	1250	0.30	0.70	0.035	2.14	0.82	253	25.1
	Deg. F.	C	Mn	Si	V	Cr	Brinell	R_c
Chromium Vanadium Steel Quenched in Brine at 1475 F.	0	0.90	0.20	0.25	0.20	0.80	709	66.1
	310	0.90	0.20	0.25	0.20	0.80	671	63.4
	450	0.90	0.20	0.25	0.20	0.80	627	59.3
	550	0.90	0.20	0.25	0.20	0.80	578	56.6
	665	0.90	0.20	0.25	0.20	0.80	538	53.6
	755	0.90	0.20	0.25	0.20	0.80	502	51.0
	850	0.90	0.20	0.25	0.20	0.80	456	47.1
	915	0.90	0.20	0.25	0.20	0.80	420	44.6
	980	0.90	0.20	0.25	0.20	0.80	401	42.9
	1050	0.90	0.20	0.25	0.20	0.80	354	38.2
	1110	0.90	0.20	0.25	0.20	0.80	325	34.7
	1175	0.90	0.20	0.25	0.20	0.80	290	31.0
	1215	0.90	0.20	0.25	0.20	0.80	259	26.2
	1300	0.90	0.20	0.25	0.20	0.80	236	22.3
	1330	0.90	0.20	0.25	0.20	0.80	224	20.4
	Deg. F.	C	Mn	Cr	V	W	Brinell	R_c
High-speed Steel† Quenched in Oil at 2330 F.	0	0.68	0.20	4	1	18	709	66.2
	1100	0.68	0.20	4	1	18	698	63.3
	1200	0.68	0.20	4	1	18	657	60.7
	1235	0.68	0.20	4	1	18	611	57.3
	1265	0.68	0.20	4	1	18	547	53.0
	1300	0.68	0.20	4	1	18	500	49.9
	1330	0.68	0.20	4	1	18	444	45.5
	1360	0.68	0.20	4	1	18	403	42.7
	1420	0.68	0.20	4	1	18	368	39.0
	1480	0.68	0.20	4	1	18	313	33.8

* The high chromium steel contains 0.50% cobalt.
† The high-speed steel contains 0.32% silicon.

IRON AND STEEL CASTINGS

The different classes of cast iron include gray cast iron, white cast iron, chilled cast iron, and malleable cast iron. Cast iron primarily is an alloy of iron and carbon. It usually contains from 2½ to 3½ per cent carbon and varying amounts of silicon, manganese, phosphorous, and sulphur. The carbon in most castings is in two forms: free carbon or graphite represents one form and combined carbon or cementite the other. The physical properties of castings depend primarily upon the relative amounts of these two forms of carbon.

Gray Cast Iron. — Gray cast iron may easily be cast into any desirable form and it may also be machined readily. As the name indicates, the fracture is gray in color. The total carbon content usually ranges from 3 to 3½ per cent. According to one estimate, over 95 per cent of all iron castings are the gray iron type.

White Cast Iron. — When nearly all of the carbon in a casting is in the combined form, it is known as "white cast iron" because it has a silvery-white fracture. Such cast iron is very hard and also brittle, the ductility being practically zero. Many gray iron castings have wear-resisting surfaces of white cast iron. These are designated by the term "chilled cast iron" because such castings are produced in molds having metal chills for cooling the molten metal rapidly, thus forming cementite and white cast iron.

Alloy Cast Iron. — This term designates castings containing alloying elements such as nickel, chromium, molybdenum, and copper in sufficient amounts to appreciably change the physical properties. These elements may be added either to increase the strength or to obtain special properties such as higher wear resistance, corrosion resistance, or heat resistance. Alloy cast irons are used extensively for such parts as automotive cylinders, pistons, piston rings, crankcases, brake drums; for certain machine tool castings, for certain types of dies, for parts of crushing and grinding machinery, and for applications where the casting must resist scaling at high temperatures. Machinable alloy cast irons having tensile strengths up to 70,000 pounds per square inch or even higher may be produced.

Nickel-Chromium Cast Iron. — A corrosion- and heat-resistant cast iron having the same coefficient of expansion as plain cast iron at elevated temperatures consists of 28 to 32 per cent nickel, 4 to 5 per cent chromium, and the remainder cast iron. It is very tough, is machineable, and maintains its properties without deterioration at high temperatures. The hardness is from 140 to 240 Brinell, and the tensile strength is approximately 30,000 pounds per square inch. This metal is intended for use in contact with plain cast iron or steel,— for example, as a liner or insert — where it will attain a higher temperature than its surroundings, and must pass through the heating and cooling cycles without becoming separated from the base metal that surrounds it. Examples of its application are bushings and liners for pumps and compressors that handle hot liquids or vapors and automobile-engine valve-seat inserts.

Malleable-iron Castings. — Malleable iron is produced by the annealing or graphitization of "white iron" castings. Malleable castings are used for many industrial applications where strength, ductility, machinability, and resistance to shock are important factors. In manufacturing these castings, the usual procedure is to produce first a hard brittle white iron from a charge of pig iron and scrap. These hard white-iron castings are then placed in annealing pots and the graphitization (malleabilizing) of the castings is accomplished by means of a suitable heat treatment. During this annealing period the temperature is slowly increased to 1550 or 1600 degrees F., and this temperature is maintained from 48 to 60 hours, after which it is slowly reduced. This malleabilizing process is applicable to sections at least 4 inches thick, graphitization occurring throughout the entire section.

Physical Properties of Malleable Iron. — The average values of the tensile strength, yield point, and elongation of malleable iron, based upon approximately twenty thousand tests made by seventeen investigators, are as follows: Tensile strength (pounds per square inch) 54,000; yield point, 36,000; elongation in 2 inches, 18 per cent. The average ultimate shearing strength is about 48,000; the modulus of elasticity in tension, 25,000,000; and, in shear, 12,500,000 pounds per square inch. The average chemical composition is as follows: Carbon, 1.00 to 2.00; silicon, 0.60 to 1.10; manganese, under 0.30; phosphorus, under 0.20; sulphur, 0.06 to 0.15 per cent.

Meehanite Castings. — Castings produced by the Meehanite controlled process may have various combinations of physical properties to meet different requirements. In addition to a number of general engineering types, there are heat-resisting, wear-resisting and corrosion-resisting Meehanite castings. These castings may be produced in a cupola, open hearth or electric furnace, but the cupola is the most widely used.

Physical Properties. — The general engineering types have minimum tensile strengths ranging from 30,000 to 55,000 pounds per square inch, and compressive strengths from 120,000 to 200,000 pounds per square inch. Some types of Meehanite are adapted to heat-treatment, thus increasing the tensile strength to 75,000 pounds per square inch or higher. The tensile strengths of heat-resisting types vary from 27,000 to 40,000 pounds per square inch, and the compressive strengths from 130,000 to 162,000 pounds per square inch. The corrosion-resisting types of Meehanite castings have a minimum tensile strength of 42,000 pounds per square inch and a compressive strength of 160,000 pounds per square inch.

Applications. — Meehanite castings have a wide range of applications. Because of their uniform solidity and density, they are applicable not only for complex sections but for various classes of pressure castings used with water, oil, steam, gas, and other substances. These castings are also used for cylinders and rams of hydraulic presses; for locomotive parts subject to wear such as pistons, cylinder liners, packing rings, cross-head shoes, air compressor parts, grate bars, etc.; truck and trailer brake-drums; gears, retorts, rolls, conveyor chains, parts requiring resistance to corrosion growth, etc. The resistance to growth of Meehanite under either continuous high temperatures or alternating high and low temperatures has established it as an essential material in many industrial furnace and high-temperature applications.

In pumping machinery in gravel, cement, mining, crude oil, and chemical plants, the resistance of this metal to abrasion and corrosion is one of its most valuable characteristics. The wear resisting property of Meehanite has given it an important place in the making of dies for forming, drawing, and stamping metal.

Welding. — Meehanite castings may be welded by means of the electric arc, using a steel or alloy rod or special cast-iron rod. They may also be welded by gas, using a cast-iron Meehanite or bronze rod.

Steel Castings. — Steel castings are especially adapted for machine parts that must withstand shocks or heavy loads. They are stronger than either wrought iron, cast iron, or malleable iron and are very tough. The steel used for making steel castings may be produced either by the Bessemer, open-hearth, electric, or crucible processes. The raw materials used are steel scrap, pig iron, and iron ore, the materials and their proportions varying according to the process and the type of furnace used. Steel for comparatively small castings may be made by the

Bessemer or crucible furnaces, whereas for large castings, the open-hearth furnace is preferable. The electric furnace is now used considerably, some of the larger sizes being employed in conjunction with open-hearth furnaces and Bessemer converters which partially refine the charge. Steel castings are used for such parts as cylinder covers, cross-heads, cross-head guides, bearing caps, bedplates, stern-posts for ships, rudder frames, gun mounts, locomotive side frames, etc. They are of special importance in ship construction and for various classes of railway equipment.

There are two very general classes of steel castings — namely, the carbon steel and the alloy steel. The carbon steel castings may have a carbon content ranging from 0.05 to 1.70; manganese, from 0.50 to 1.00; silicon, from 0.20 to 0.75; phosphorus, 0.05 maximum; and sulphur, 0.06 maximum. Low-carbon steels (containing less than 0.20 per cent carbon) may have a tensile strength ranging from 40,000 to 70,000 pounds per square inch. High-carbon steels containing more than 0.40 per cent carbon may have a tensile strength ranging from 70,000 to 120,000 pounds per square inch. The medium-carbon cast steels with a carbon content varying from 0.20 to 0.40 may have a tensile strength varying from 60,000 to 80,000 pounds per square inch. Alloy cast steels contain special elements, such as chromium, nickel, molybdenum, tungsten, etc. These various alloys, in conjunction with suitable heat-treatments, make it possible to secure steel castings having a wide range of physical properties.

Manganese Steel Castings. — The metal for manganese steel castings is refined in a Bessemer converter from which it is poured into a ladle in which the proper quantity of ferromanganese has been previously placed. Manganese steel castings are generally allowed to cool in the mold, and are then annealed for from 3 to 26 hours at temperatures ranging from 1800 to 2000 degrees F. Unannealed manganese steel castings are exceptionally brittle and almost glass hard. After the heat-treatment, they are tough and ductile with a tensile strength of about 90,000 pounds and an elastic limit of about 60,000 pounds per square inch.

Semi-steel Castings. — What is commonly known as "semi-steel" and less frequently as "toughened cast iron" is produced by adding soft steel or wrought-iron scrap to the charge in a cupola. The semi-steel castings obtained from this mixture are cast in the same manner as ordinary castings. The mixture or charge for making semi-steel castings usually contains about 20 per cent of steel scrap, although any amount up to about 70 per cent may be used. Semi-steel castings have less total carbon than ordinary cast iron, there seldom being more than 3 per cent. The fine grain of semi-steel is due to the low percentage and fineness of the graphitic carbon. Semi-steel is commonly used for large gears, for the tables, saddles, slides, etc., of machine tools, and for parts requiring a good appearance.

Seasoning Castings to Prevent Warpage after Machining. — Castings, such as machine beds, etc., may warp out of shape gradually after planing or milling, especially if considerable metal is removed from one side only, thus relieving the internal strains unequally. There are several methods of "seasoning" castings to avoid excessive warpage.

1. Leave castings in the mold until throughly cold.

2. If equipment is available for heating casting, heat to 1050 degrees F. (low red) for a period of one hour per inch of wall thickness; then cool slowly in furnace. This may be done after rough machining. Some additional improvement may be obtained by reheating, but, ordinarily, this is not required.

3. Machine extra surfaces (as on the under side of a bed) in order to neutralize the strains on both sides of casting.

4. Suspend casting from crane and pound with wooden blocks, thus setting up strain-relieving vibrations (metal hammers would cause peening).

5. Store castings several months after rough-machining. This method may be objectionable because of the time required.

Firebrick

Melting Points of Firebricks. — According to the United States Bureau of Standards, the melting points of firebricks are as follows: The most common firebrick will melt at a temperature ranging from 2830 to 3140 degrees F.; bauxite brick, from 2950 to 3245 degrees; silica brick, from 3090 to 3100 degrees; chromite brick, at 3720 degrees; and magnesia brick, at 4950 degrees. These melting points, which represent the lowest temperature at which a small piece of the brick could be distinctly seen to flow, were determined in an electric vacuum furnace, the temperature being measured with an optical pyrometer.

The heat conductivity of firebrick is six times as great at 3000 degrees F. as at 200 degrees F.

General Information about Firebrick. — To obtain the best results from brick work, observe the following precautions: All firebrick should be kept in a dry place, as moisture, especially in cold weather, will greatly injure any brick. Use good fireclay equal in refractory qualities to the brick itself. Apply thin with dipped joints and rub the brick to make a brick-to-brick joint. Warm up slowly to expel moisture. Remember that fireclay bricks contract, and silica, chromium and magnesia bricks expand under high temperatures. All furnaces in which silica brick is used should be heated and cooled slowly and uniformly. From 250 to 350 pounds of fireclay or silica cement are enough to lay up one thousand brick. Finely ground fireclay should be used for laying up fireclay brick, and silica cement for silica brick. For estimating on firebrick work, use the following figures:

One square foot of 4½-inch wall requires 7 bricks; 1 square foot of 9-inch wall requires 14 bricks; 1 square foot of 13½-inch wall requires 21 bricks; a cubic foot of brick work requires seventeen 9-inch straight bricks; 1 cubic foot of fireclay brick work weighs 150 pounds; 1 cubic foot of silica brick work weighs 130 pounds; 1000 bricks (closely stacked) occupy 56 cubic feet; 1000 bricks (loosely stacked) occupy 72 cubic feet. For estimating on red brick work, figure on 9 cubic feet of sand and three bushels of lime for laying 1000 bricks.

Cement for High Temperatures. — As a binder for a cement to stand high heat (1475 degrees F.), use sodium silicate (water glass) diluted with rain water until a specific gravity of 20 degrees on the Baume hydrometer is obtained. Sand or quartz may be used in the cement to give the proper consistency.

Methods of Cleaning Castings

Pickling Solutions. — The pickling solutions used for removing scale from castings and forgings preparatory to milling or other machining operations are usually composed of dilute sulphuric acid or oil of vitriol, although hydrofluoric acid is sometimes used. A sulphuric acid bath is commonly made of one part acid and from four to ten parts water. The acid should be poured into the water while the latter is being stirred, but *the water should never be added to the acid*, as this may suddenly generate steam which may cause an explosion. Such an accident would be likely to throw the concentrated acid over the workman and cause serious burns. Sulphuric acid will not attack the sand or black oxide of iron which forms the scale upon castings, but it soaks through and attacks the iron beneath the scale and finally dissolves a sufficient amount to loosen the scale. Then the castings should be washed, preferably with hot water; if the castings are small, it is good practice after washing to immerse them in a soda solution to neutralize any acid that may remain.

A hydrofluoric acid pickling solution is preferable in some respects to the sulphuric acid solution, but it is more dangerous and must be handled carefully. Hydrofluoric acid is commonly sold in three grades, the first containing 30 per cent acid, the second 48 per cent, and the third 52 per cent, the balance of the solution being water. The 30 per cent solution is the one commonly used for pickling castings. The pickling bath should contain one gallon of the 30 per cent solution to from twenty to twenty-five gallons of water. If less water is used, the pickling can be done more rapidly, but by using slightly more water, the acid can be used for a longer period. Hydrofluoric acid attacks and dissolves the sand and the black oxide of iron. A bath can be used repeatedly by adding one-third the original quantity of acid before immersing a new lot of castings. Hydrofluoric acid cannot be kept in a crock, jug or glass receptacle and must be placed in a lead carboy, except when diluted, in which case it can be kept in wooden tubs or barrels. When handling concentrated hydrofluoric acid, a workman should always use rubber gloves, and if any acid comes into contact with the hands, it should be washed off at once with water and dilute ammonia.

Solutions for Cleaning Brass Castings. — A solution commonly used for pickling brass castings is made by mixing three parts of sulphuric acid and two parts of nitric acid, and adding to each quart of the mixture about a handful of common salt. This solution must be kept in an earthenware crock or in a vitrified receptacle, and the bath must be large enough to dip the castings into it. The following proportions are also used for cleaning brass castings: 1. Two parts nitric acid; one part sulphuric acid. 2. For a bright dip: One part nitric acid; one part sulphuric acid.

Recovering Copper from Dipping Acids. — Some copper is dissolved when dipping brass castings in acid to clean them. In order to recover this copper, run the acid liquids from the washing tanks into a large wooden vat containing milk of lime, and stir thoroughly. The lime neutralizes the acids and precipitates the sulphuric acid as sulphate of calcium. This acid is neutralized first, then the nitric acid is acted upon, and nitrate of calcium is produced. The clear liquid contains nitrate of calcium and nitrate of copper. Run this solution through any kind of scrap iron. The iron removes the copper from the solution, dissolving and taking the place of the copper. The copper settles at the bottom of the tank as a slush. At intervals, the copper may be taken out of the vat, dried and melted into ingots. All of the copper may be recovered if the supply of scrap iron is kept up.

Soda Cleaning Solution. — The solution used in soda kettles for removing oil or grease from machine parts should contain about one-half pound of sal-soda to each gallon of water. If old paint is to be removed, the solution should consist of about one-quarter pound of caustic soda to each gallon of water. As caustic soda is a strong alkali, care should be taken to prevent it from getting onto the hands. These solutions should be heated to the boiling point before immersing the parts to be cleaned; then the work will dry quickly after being removed, and will not rust. A wire basket or perforated bucket is convenient for washing small pieces. The time required for cleaning depends somewhat upon the nature of the grease and to what extent it has dried and hardened.

Dipping Solution to Preserve Iron Castings. — Mix 100 pounds of dry lamp black to a paste, with benzine. Then make a mixture of 5 gallons lamp black paste, 2 gallons turpentine japan, 1 gallon boiled oil, 1 to 2 gallons cheap varnish.

For very good work, add to the above 12½ pounds of refined lamp black ground in japan. Dilute the mixture with turpentine until it is as thin as water, and clean the castings before dipping.

The Sand Blast. — To obtain good results with a sand blast, it is necessary to provide an ample supply of air. The table "Cubic Feet of Free Air for Sand-blast Nozzles" gives the amount of air required for nozzles of different diameter and different air pressures. The pressure that should be used depends upon the nature of the work. For cleaning light castings, such as stove castings, etc., use from 5 to 10 pounds; for medium- and heavy-grade iron castings, 15 to 20 pounds;

Cubic Feet of Free Air for Sand-blast Nozzles

Nozzle Diameter, Inches	Air Gage Pressures, Pounds per Square Inch					
	5	10	15	20	25	30
	Cubic Feet of Free Air per Minute					
¼	14.4	21.8	26.7	30.8	34.5	40.0
⅜	34.6	49.0	60.0	69.0	77.0	90.0
½	61.6	87.0	107.0	123.0	138.0	161.0
⅝	96.5	136.0	167.0	193.0	216.0	252.0
¾	133.0	196.0	240.0	277.0	310.0	362.0
⅞	189.0	267.0	326.0	378.0	422.0	493.0

for steel castings, 30 to 75 pounds; for buildings and steel structures, 5 to 30 pounds, depending upon the height. The air piping connecting the receiver and the sand blast should not be less in diameter than the air connection of the sand blast; but if the distance between the receiver and the sand blast is over 75 feet, the piping should be larger than the air connection of the sand blast, to allow for the loss of pressure from friction. It is not that the sand blast will require all of this air, but the most satisfactory results are obtained by having a "backing of air" behind the jets. The piping should also be protected from condensation, if the lines are long, and moisture must be kept from the sand to insure proper working. The sand should be sharp, clean quartz or silica, sifted through a screen of the proper mesh and dried long enough beforehand to be cold when used. When using a ¼-inch nozzle, the sand should be passed through a No. 8 mesh screen. With a ½-inch nozzle, much coarser sand can be used. A coarse sand will be found effective for general work in the foundry, especially for cleaning steel castings.

Pattern Materials — Shrinkage, Draft and Finish Allowances

Woods for Patterns. — Woods commonly used for patterns are white pine, mahogany, cherry, maple, birch, white wood and fir. For most patterns, white pine is considered superior because it is easily worked, readily takes glue and varnish, and is fairly durable. For medium- and small-sized patterns, especially if they are to be extensively used, a harder wood is preferable. Mahogany is often used for patterns of this class, although many prefer cherry. As mahogany has a close grain, it is not as susceptible to atmospheric changes as a wood of coarser grain. Mahogany is superior in this respect to cherry, but is more expensive. In selecting cherry, never use young timber. Maple and birch are employed quite extensively, especially for turned parts, as they take a good finish. White wood is sometimes substituted for pine, but it is inferior to the latter in being more susceptible to atmospheric changes.

Selection of Wood. — It is very important to select wood for patterns that is well seasoned; that is, it should either be kiln dried or kept one or two years before using, the time depending upon the size of the lumber. During the seasoning or drying process the moisture leaves the wood cells and the wood shrinks, the shrinkage being almost entirely across the grain rather than in a lengthwise direction. Naturally, after this change takes place, the wood is less liable to warp, although it will absorb moisture in damp weather. Patterns also tend to absorb moisture from the damp sand of molds, and to minimize troubles from this source they are covered with varnish. Green or water-soaked lumber should not be put in a drying room, because the ends will dry out faster than the rest of the log, thus causing cracks. In a log there is what is called the "sap wood" and the "heart wood." The outer layers form the sap wood which is not as firm as the heart wood and is more likely to warp; hence, it should be avoided, if possible.

Pattern Varnish. — Patterns intended for repeated use are varnished to protect them against moisture, especially when in the damp molding sand. The varnish used should dry quickly to give a smooth surface that readily draws from the sand. Yellow shellac varnish is generally used. It is made by dissolving gum shellac in grain alcohol. Wood alcohol is sometimes substituted, but is inferior. The color of the varnish is commonly changed for covering core prints, in order to readily distinguish the prints from the body of the pattern. Black shellac varnish (which is the color generally used) is made by the addition of lamp black. This should be of good quality and free from grit. Red varnish can be made by adding Chinese vermilion. All coloring powders should be well pulverized. At least three coats of varnish should be applied to patterns, the surfaces being rubbed down with sand paper after applying the preliminary coats, in order to obtain a smooth surface.

Glue for Patterns. — There are many qualities of glue both in the liquid, sheet and pulverized form. Animal glue in the sheet or flake form is generally used for pattern work. As a rule, the best quality is of amber color and the flakes are rather thin. Where glue is used in small quantities, the pulverized form has the advantage of being quickly prepared. Freshly made glue is the strongest and, if of good quality, can be drawn out into thin threads. Whenever practicable, glued joints should be reinforced by nails or screws. A joint to be glued should be accurately fitted because glue does not get a grip unless the parts are in close contact.

Before applying glue, clean the surfaces of sand paper dust or other foreign material, so that the glue can enter the pores of the wood. This is very important. If the end grain must be glued, first apply a sizing coat to fill the openings among the fibers. When the sizing coat is dry, apply a second coat to the surface and unite. If the preliminary coat is not applied, the open end grain is liable to absorb the glue so rapidly as to weaken the joint. The hot glue should be thin enough to spread easily. It can be thicker, however, for pine than for wood of closer grain, like mahogany, because (aside from the quality of the glue) the holding or binding property depends upon the extent to which the glue enters the pores of the wood. All glued joints should be firmly pressed together with clamps immediately after applying the glue. The latter should be given plenty of time in which to set; ten or twelve hours in a dry place should be sufficient.

Shrinkage Allowance. — The shrinkage allowances ordinarily made on patterns to compensate for the contraction of castings in cooling are as follows: Cast iron, $3/32$ to $1/8$ inch per foot; common brass, $3/16$ inch per foot; yellow brass, $7/32$ inch per foot; bronze, $5/32$ inch per foot; aluminum, $1/8$ to $5/32$ inch per foot; steel casting, $3/16$ inch per foot. The amount of shrinkage, in any case, depends to some extent upon the shape and size of the casting. A plain casting that is long in proportion to its width will contract differently from one that is more compact, even though both castings have the same weight and were cast from the same material. A heavy iron casting may shrink only $\frac{1}{10}$ inch per foot or even less, whereas a lighter casting of the same material may shrink $\frac{1}{8}$ inch per foot. A cylindrical or column-shaped casting will contract more in a lengthwise direction than radially. Hence, when making patterns for rather large castings of this kind, the allowance should be about $\frac{1}{10}$ inch lengthwise and from $\frac{1}{20}$ to $\frac{1}{16}$ inch per foot radially. For pipes or other hollow castings, the lateral shrinkage is very much less than for solid castings or those having thick walls. The patternmakers' shrink rule has graduations which are longer than standard measurement, to give the allowance directly.

A general rule for columns of comparatively small diameter but great length, such as are used for building purposes, is to allow $\frac{1}{8}$ inch per foot for shrinkage lengthwise and make no allowance on the diameter. The "one-tenth" shrinkage rule is the standard (for cast iron) in most machine pattern-shops. Although this is not the proper allowance for all forms of casting, the adoption of a standard eliminates the confusion that would follow the use of a number of rules for different classes of work. There can be no fixed rule governing shrinkage allowance, as it is largely a question of local conditions and practice.

Draft for Patterns. — The draft or the amount of taper given to patterns to facilitate withdrawing them from the mold, depends somewhat upon the size and shape of the pattern. A general rule is to taper each side $\frac{1}{8}$ inch for each foot of surface to be drawn. The average amount for small patterns is about $\frac{1}{16}$ inch per foot, although in some cases it can be less, but, as a rule, there should be at least $\frac{1}{32}$ inch draft. The draft slopes away from the pattern "face" which is usually upper-most in the mold when the pattern is drawn. Some patterns do not require draft because none of the surfaces are at right angles to the face. In some cases, very small patterns are made without draft.

Finish Allowance. — The amount added to a pattern to allow for machining the casting varies widely. It depends upon the method of machining, the size of the casting, and the importance of having a clean surface, free from flaws or defective spots. If castings are to be finished from the rough upon disk grinders, very little allowance is necessary; in fact, the molder may rap a pattern enough to allow for the finish. On small castings to be finished by milling or planing about $\frac{1}{8}$ inch is usually allowed for the machining operation, whereas large castings for engine beds, flywheels, pump cylinders, etc., often have an allowance of $\frac{3}{4}$ to 1 inch.

Standard Pattern Colors. — The color markings described in the following are recommended as standard for foundry patterns and core-boxes of wood construction. These standard colors have been accepted by the Bureau of Standards, the American Foundrymen's Association, the Steel Founders' Society of America, the Malleable Iron Research Institute, and by numerous other associations as well as prominent manufacturers.

(1) Surfaces to be left *unfinished* are to be painted *black*.

(2) Surfaces to be *machined* are to be painted *red*.

(3) *Seats of and for loose pieces* are to be marked by *red stripes on a yellow background*.

(4) *Core prints* and *seats for loose core prints* are to be painted *yellow*.

(5) *Stop-offs* are to be indicated by *diagonal black stripes on a yellow base*.

The colors may be obtained by mixing suitable inexpensive pigments with varnish or shellac to produce the type of coating desired.

Metal Patterns. — Metal patterns are especially adapted to molding machine practice, owing to their durability and superiority in retaining the required shape. The original master pattern is generally made of wood, the casting obtained from the wood pattern being finished to make the metal pattern. The materials commonly used are brass, cast iron, aluminum and steel. Brass patterns should have a rather large percentage of tin, as this gives a good surface for the casting. Cast iron is generally used for patterns of large size, as it is cheaper than brass and more durable. Cast-iron patterns are largely used on molding machines. Aluminum patterns are light but they shrink considerably. White metal is sometimes used when it is necessary to avoid shrinkage. The gates for the mold may be cast or made of sheet brass. Some patterns are made of vulcanized rubber, especially for light match-board work.

Obtaining Weight of Casting from Pattern Weight. — To obtain the approximate weight of a casting, multiply the weight of the pattern by the factor given in the accompanying table. For example, if the weight of a white-pine pattern is 4 pounds, what is the weight of a solid cast-iron casting obtained from that pattern? Casting weight = $4 \times 16 = 64$ pounds. If the casting is cored, fill the core-boxes with dry sand, and multiply the weight of the sand by one of the following factors: For cast iron, 4; for brass, 4.65; for aluminum, 1.4. Then subtract the product of the sand weight and the factor just given from the weight of the solid casting, to obtain the weight of the cored casting. As the weight of

Factors for Obtaining Weight of Casting from Pattern Weight

Pattern Material	Factors				
	Cast Iron	Aluminum	Copper	Zinc	Brass, 70% Copper, 30% Zinc
White pine...............	16.00	5.70	19.60	15.00	19.00
Mahogany, Honduras	12.00	4.50	14.70	11.50	14.00
Cherry...................	10.50	3.80	13.00	10.00	12.50
Cast iron................	1.00	0.35	1.22	0.95	1.17
Aluminum	2.85	1.00	3.44	2.70	3.30

wood varies considerably, the results obtained by the use of the table are only approximate, the factors being based on the average weight of the woods listed. For metal patterns, the results are more accurate.

Branch Pipes for Exhausting Shavings from Wood Working Machines. — The sizes of branch pipes, given in the accompanying table, are correct for pipes not exceeding twenty feet in length. Where branch pipes contain a number of elbows, or exceed twenty feet in length, the area should be proportionately increased. Where the work is light and the branch pipes short, smaller connections than those given can sometimes be used. The area of the main duct should be equal to, or slightly larger than, the sum of the areas of the connecting branches. This proportion should be carefully maintained. If the main pipe is too small, the suction will be impaired, and if it is too large, the velocity of the air may be reduced to such an extent that the material being exhausted will settle in the bottom of the pipe, thereby reducing the area. If the main pipe is unusually long (exceeding 100 feet) the area should be increased from 10 to 20 per cent. Avoid abrupt turns in the piping, and never enter branch pipes at right angles to the main pipe, but always connect them at an angle of from 30 to 45 degrees. Branch pipes should never enter the main at the bottom but always at the side, and two pipes should not enter directly opposite each other.

Branch Pipes for Exhausting Shavings from Wood Working Machines

Type of Machine	Diam. of Branch Pipe, Inches	Type of Machine	Diam. of Branch Pipe, Inches
Saws:		Planer knives:	
Rip, Cut-off, Split — 18 inches diam. or less	4	Length of knife, 24 inches	6
		Length of knife, 30 inches	7
Swing, Bracket, Groove — 18 to 24 inches diam.	5	Matcher heads, each	5
		Door tenoner	5
		Sash tenoner	5
Heavy cut-off, 24 to 42 inches diameter	6	Sticker machines, each head	4
Band	4	Sand drum, 24 inches long	4
Band resaw, ¾ to 1 inch	5	Sand drum, 30 inches long	5
Band resaw, 1½ to 2½ ins.	6	Floor sweep-up	6
Planer knives:		Heavy timber planer, each head	7
Length of knife, 5 inches	4	Diagonal planer for doors	7
Length of knife, 10 inches	5	Diagonal planer for doors, with sand drum	8
Length of knife, 14 inches	6		

Speed of Circular Saws for Wood

Size of Saw, Ins.	Rev. per Min.	Size of Saw, Ins.	Rev. per Min.	Size of Saw, Ins.	Rev. per Min.	Size of Saw, Ins.	Rev. per Min.	Size of Saw, Ins.	Rev. per Min.
8	4500	20	1800	32	1125	44	840	56	650
10	3600	22	1650	34	1050	46	800	58	625
12	3000	24	1500	36	1000	48	750	60	600
14	2600	26	1400	38	950	50	725	64	550
16	2200	28	1300	40	900	52	700	68	525
18	2000	30	1200	42	870	54	675	72	500

Extrusion of Metals

The Extrusion Process. — By means of the extrusion process, certain fairly plastic metals are formed into various shapes by forcing the metal, which is usually heated, under high pressure through an aperture of the shape to be produced. In this manner, a continuous bar or pipe of the cross-section of the aperture or die is produced. Many different non-ferrous alloys are used in connection with the extrusion process. These include various compositions of bronze and brass, aluminum alloys, copper, tin, etc., the alloy depending, of course, upon the application. The S.A.E. standard aluminum compositions Nos. 260, 24, 282, and 281 are used for extruded shapes, as well as in the form of sheets, bars, rods, and wire. The advantages of the extrusion process are that it permits parts of unusual cross-section to be produced cheaply. On account of the high pressure under which the metal is extruded, its structure becomes more compact and its strength is increased. The surfaces are smooth and free from flaws and other defects. The dimensions of the extruded shapes can be gaged with accuracy, so that they can be used directly with no or very little additional finishing. The extruded bar may be passed through a drawing die if a special degree of accuracy is required.

Extruded Shapes. — Extruded bars, rods and sections are produced in a large variety of standard and special shapes. These include, in addition to the common shapes, many more or less special cross-sections for producing small pinions, ratchet wheels, segment gears, and many other parts, with machining in many cases reduced to a cutting-off operation. The extrusion process is not restricted to solid bars and rods as it is applied in producing various hollow forms in bronze, brass and other compositions. The structural shapes for aluminum alloys include S.A.E. standards for equal, unequal and bulb angles; shallow, deep and bulb channels; tees and zees. Many extruded sections are employed for art metal work. The extrusion process is often used instead of rolling because it is much simpler and less expensive to provide extrusion tools for a new section or special shape than to provide rolls. These special shapes may be odd sizes of so-called standard sections or they may be sections that are nearly standard but are changed slightly.

Extruding Blooms for Aluminum Tubing. — An important class of extruded products includes those sections on which further work is to be done, such as tube blooms and sheet slabs, as well as rectangular billets. Practically all drawn aluminum tubing is made from extruded blooms. The principal reason for this is that the bloom that goes on to the draw- or push-bench must be as nearly perfect in finish and dimensions as it is possible to make it. Extrusion seems to be the only practical method of obtaining these results. It is possible to pierce aluminum-alloy billets, but the extruded blooms are much more nearly perfect, resulting in lower scrap losses and a better finished product.

Extruding Alloys Difficult to Roll. — Another class of extruded products consists of those made from alloys that cannot be rolled. Certain aluminum-magnesium alloys are so brittle in the hot cast condition that they break up badly on rolling, but can be extruded without great difficulty. On account of its very desirable physical properties, one of these alloys is used to a considerable extent for drawing fine wire. It has been found to be almost impossible to roll cast ingots of this alloy; hence billets about $1\frac{1}{2}$ inches square are extruded, and then put on the rod mill, where they are rolled without great difficulty.

While it is true that certain alloys can be extruded with less difficulty than they can be rolled, this is not true of all alloys. Pure aluminum can be rolled and extruded more easily than any of its alloys. Those alloys of the duralumin class, containing about 4 per cent copper, require about three times as much power to roll as pure aluminum. In color and surface finish, extruded products are quite superior to rolled shapes. This is very important when aluminum is used for decorative purposes, particularly for architectural work.

Extruding Collapsible Tubes. — The collapsible tubes used for tooth paste, artists' paints, etc., are extruded from disks or slugs of pure tin containing about one-half of one per cent copper to harden the metal slightly. These tubes are formed by forcing the slightly lubricated metal through a small annular space between a punch and die, using a pressure of 50 to 100 tons, depending upon the size of the tube.

Die-Casting

Die-casting is a method of producing finished castings by forcing molten metal into a suitable mold, which is arranged to open after the metal has solidified so that the casting can be removed. The die-casting process makes it possible to secure accuracy and uniformity in castings, and machining costs are either eliminated altogether or are greatly reduced. The greatest advantage of the die-casting process is due to the fact that parts are accurately and, usually, completely finished when taken from the dies. When the dies are properly made, castings may be accurate within 0.001 inch or even less and a limit of 0.002 and 0.003 inch can be maintained easily on many classes of work.

Die-castings are extensively used in the manufacture of such products as cash registers, meters, time-controlling devices, small housings, washing machines, and parts for a great variety of mechanisms. Lugs and gear teeth are cast in place and both external and internal screw threads can be cast. Holes can be formed within about 0.001 inch of size and the most accurate bearings require only a finish-reaming operation. Figures and letters may be cast sunken or in relief on wheels for counting or printing devices, and owing to numerous developments, many shapes which formerly were believed too intricate for die-casting are now produced successfully by this process.

As to the limitations of the die-casting process it may be mentioned that the cost of dies is high, and, therefore, die-casting is applicable only when a large number of duplicate parts are required. The stronger and harder metals cannot be die-cast so that the process is not applicable for casting parts which must necessarily be made of iron or steel, although special alloys have been developed for die-casting which have considerable tensile and compressive strength.

Alloys Used for Die-Casting. — The alloys used in modern die-casting practice may be divided into six main classifications as follows: (1) Zinc-base alloys; (2) tin-base alloys; (3) lead-base alloys; (4) aluminum-base alloys; (5) copper-base or brass and bronze alloys; and (6) magnesium-base alloys.

Zinc-base Die-casting Alloys. — The alloys in this group are produced by alloying zinc with aluminum and copper. S.A.E. alloy No. 903 contains aluminum 3.5 to 4.3; copper, maximum, 0.10; magnesium, 0.03 to 0.08 per cent; iron, maximum, 0.10; cadmium, maximum, 0.005; tin, maximum, 0.005; lead, maximum, 0.007 and the remainder zinc. S.A.E. alloy No. 921 contains aluminum, 3.5 to 4.5; copper, 2.5 to 3.5; magnesium, 0.02 to 0.10; iron, lead, cadmium and tin, the same as No. 903 and the remainder, zinc. S.A.E. No. 925 contains copper 0.75 to 1.25; magnesium, 0.02 to 0.08; tin, 0.002; aluminum, iron, lead and cadmium, the same as No. 903 and the remainder, zinc. Alloy No. 921 has been largely replaced by alloys 903 and 925 because the latter possess greater permanence of properties and dimensions. Alloy No. 925 is much stronger and harder than alloy No. 903 but at elevated temperatures is subject to growth in dimensions and loss of impact strength and in this respect is inferior to No. 903.

Tin-base Alloys. — In this group tin is alloyed with copper, antimony, and lead. S.A.E. Alloy No. 10 contains, as the principal ingredients, in percentages, tin, 90; copper, 4 to 5; antimony, 4 to 5; lead, maximum, 0.35. This high-quality babbitt mixture is used for main-shaft and connecting-rod bearings or bronze-backed bearings in the automotive and aircraft industries. S.A.E. No. 110 contains tin, 87.75; antimony, 7.0 to 8.5; copper, maximum, 2.25 to 3.75 and other constituents the same as No. 10. S.A.E. No. 11, which contains a little more copper and antimony and about 4 per cent less tin than No. 10, is also used for bearings or other applications requiring a high-class tin-base alloy. These tin-base compositions are used chiefly for automotive bearings but they are also used for different classes of die-castings, especially for milking machines, soda fountains, syrup pumps, and similar apparatus requiring resistance against the action of acids, alkalies and moisture.

Lead-base Alloys. — These alloys are employed usually where a cheap non corrosive metal is needed and strength is relatively unimportant. Such alloy are used for parts which must withstand the action of strong mineral acids and for parts of X-ray apparatus. S.A.E. Composition No. 13 contains (in percentages) lead, 86; antimony, 9.25 to 10.75; tin, 4.5 to 5.5 per cent. S.A.E. Specification No. 14 contains less lead and more antimony and copper. The lead content is 76; antimony, 14 to 16; and tin, 9.25 to 10.75 per cent. These alloys, Nos. 13 and 14, are inexpensive owing to the high lead content and may be used for bearings which are large and subjected to light service. They are also suitable for some die-castings, but should not be substituted for an alloy with a high tin content.

Aluminum-base Alloys. — Aluminum die-castings are used for many parts requiring lightness, strength, and resistance to corrosion. These alloys will take and hold a high polish, and are used for vacuum cleaners and other household utensils, camera parts, motor and instrument housings, etc. There are many compositions limited practically to two general groups, namely, the aluminum-copper and the aluminum-silicon alloys. S.A.E. Alloy No. 312 (generally known as No. 12) is an inexpensive general-purpose alloy, and has been used in the United States more than any other aluminum casting alloy. The main elements, in addition to aluminum, are: Copper, 7 to 9; iron, maximum, 2.5; and silicon, 1 to 2 per cent. The tensile strength should be about 33,000 pounds per square inch. A typical aluminum-silicon alloy contains, in addition to aluminum: Silicon, 12; iron, 2, maximum; copper, 0.60 maximum. The tensile strength is about 30,000 to 33,000 pounds per square inch. S.A.E. Alloy No. 305 contains 11 to 13 per cent silicon, and is especially resistant to salt-water corrosion. These alloys because of their fluidity are adapted for thin-walled castings or for complicated castings consisting of both thin and heavy sections. The tensile strength of ¼-inch round test bars cast to size should be about 33,000 pounds per square inch, with an elongation of 1.5 per cent.

Copper-base Alloys. — In producing die-castings, the use of alloys having relatively high melting temperatures naturally presents difficulties not occurring with lower melting points, especially in regard to the life of the die-casting dies. Thus, in casting copper-base alloys, it has been necessary to develop special alloy steels and casting methods. The well-known plunger type and "gooseneck" types of die-casting machines are not suitable for brass or bronze alloys. The latter, when cast, are handled in small charges and forced into the die at an unusual speed and pressure. Zinc, for instance, is cast at pressures of 800 to 1000 pounds per square inch; aluminum, at from 400 to 500; and brass, at about 20,000 pounds per square inch. A typical copper-base alloy contains (in percentages) about 57 to 59 copper, 40 to 42 zinc, and 0.5 to 1.5 tin, and the tensile strength is around 65,000 to 75,000 pounds per square inch.

Magnesium-base Alloys. — Magnesium alloy die-castings are used where extreme lightness or a high strength-weight ratio is required. S.A.E. alloy No. 501 is a widely used composition and combines good mechanical properties with good casting characteristics. It contains: Aluminum, 8.3 to 9.7; manganese, min., 0.13; zinc, 0.4 to 1.0; silicon, max., 0.5; copper, max., 0.05; nickel, max., 0.03; other impurities, max., 0.3 per cent and the remainder, magnesium. Typical physical properties are a tensile strength of 31,000 pounds per square inch and a yield strength of 20,000 pounds per square inch.

Dies for Die-casting Machines. — The dies or molds of die-casting machines are generally made of steel although cast-iron and also non-metallic materials of a refractory nature have been used, the latter being intended especially for bronze or brass castings, which, owing to their comparatively high melting temperatures, would injure ordinary steel dies. The steel most generally used is a low-carbon steel. Chromium-vanadium and tungsten steels have been employed when dies must withstand relatively high temperatures.

The making of these dies requires considerable skill and experience. They must be so designed that the metal will rapidly flow to all parts of the impression and at the same time allow the air to escape through very small grooves cut into the parting of the die, as otherwise blow-holes or air-pockets will result. In order to secure solid castings, the gates and vents must be located with reference to the particular shape to be cast. Shrinkage is another important feature, especially on accurate work. The amount usually varies from 0.002 to 0.007 inch per inch, but to determine the exact shrinkage allowance for an alloy containing three or four metals is difficult except by experiment.

Die-casting Bearing Metals in Place. — Practically all the metals that are suitable for bearings can be conveniently die-cast in place. Automobile connecting-rods are an example of work to which this process has been applied successfully. In this case, after the bearings are cast in place, they are finished by reaming. The best metals for the bearings, and those that also can be die-cast most readily, are the babbitts containing about 85 per cent tin with the remainder copper and antimony. These metals should not contain over 9 per cent copper. The copper constitutes the hardening element in the bearing. A recommended composition for a high-class bearing metal is 85 per cent tin, 10 per cent antimony, and 5 per cent copper. The antimony may vary from 7 to 10 per cent and the copper from 5 to 8 per cent. As bearing metals with so high a percentage of tin are expensive, a number of bearing metals have been developed containing a high percentage of lead. One of these metals contains from 95 to 98 per cent lead which has been treated in the electric furnace. After die-casting, the metal becomes harder upon seasoning a few days. In die-casting bearings, the work is located from the bolt holes which are drilled previous to die-casting. It is important that the bolt holes be accurately drilled with relation to the remainder of the machined surfaces.

Precision Investment Casting

This highly developed process is capable of great casting accuracy and also the formation of intricate contours. The process may be utilized when metals are too hard to machine or otherwise fabricate; when it is the only practical method of producing a part; or when it is more economical than any other method of obtaining work of the quality required. Precision investment casting is especially applicable in producing either exterior or interior contours of intricate form with surfaces so located that they could not be machined readily if at all. This process provides efficient, accurate means of producing such parts as turbine blades, airplane or other parts which have high melting points and must withstand exceptionally high temperatures, and many other products. The accuracy and finish of precision investment castings may either eliminate machining entirely or reduce it to a minimum. The quantity that may be produced economically, may range from a few to thousands of duplicate parts.

Materials Which May Be Cast. — The precision investment process may be applied to a wide range of both ferrous and non-ferrous alloys. In industrial applications these include aluminum, and bronze alloys, stellite, Hastelloys, stainless and other alloy steels, and iron castings especially where thick and thin sections are encountered. In producing investment castings, it is possible to control the process in various ways so as to change the porosity or density of castings, obtain hardness variations in different sections, and vary the corrosion resistance and strength by special alloying.

General Procedure in Making Investment Castings. — Precision investment casting is similar in principle to the " lost wax " process which has long been used in manufacturing jewelry, ornamental pieces, dentures, inlays, and other items required in dentistry. When this process is employed, both the pattern and mold used in producing the casting are destroyed after each casting operation, but they may both be replaced readily. The " dispensable pattern " (or cluster of duplicate patterns) is first formed in a permanent mold or die and then is used to form the cavity in the mold or " investment " in which the casting (or castings) is made. The investment or casting mold consists of a refractory material contained within a reinforcing steel flask. The pattern is made of wax, plastic, or a mixture of the two. The material used is evacuated from the investment to form a cavity (without parting lines) for receiving the metal to be cast. Evacuation of the pattern (by the application of sufficient heat to melt and vaporize it) and the use of a master mold or die for reproducing it quickly and accurately in making duplicate castings, are distinguishing features of this casting process. Modern applications of the process include many developments such as variations in the preparation of molds, patterns, investments, etc., as well as in the casting procedure. Application of the process requires specialized knowledge and experience.

Master Mold for Making Dispensable Patterns. — Duplicate patterns for each casting operation are made by injecting the wax or other pattern material into the master mold or die which usually is made either of carbon steel or of a soft metal alloy. Rubber, alloy steels, and other materials are used in some cases. The mold cavity commonly is designed to form a cluster of patterns for multiple casting. The mold cavity is not, as a rule, an exact duplicate of the part to be cast because it is necessary to allow for shrinkage and perhaps to compensate for distortion which might affect the accuracy of the cast product. In producing master molds, there is considerable variation in practice. One general method is to form the cavity by machining; another is by pouring a molten alloy around a master pattern which usually is made of monel metal or of a high alloy stainless steel. Unless the cavity is machined, a master pattern is required. Sometimes, a sample of the product itself may be used as a master pattern, when, for example, a slight reduction in size due to shrinkage is not objectionable. The dispensable pattern material, which may consist of waxes, plastics, or a combination of these materials, is injected into the mold either by pressure, by gravity, or by the centrifugal method. The mold is made in sections to permit removal of the dispensable pattern. The mold while in use may be kept at the correct temperature either by electrical means, by using steam, or a water jacket.

Shrinkage Allowances for Patterns. — The shrinkage allowance varies considerably for different materials. In casting accurate parts, experimental preliminary casting operations may be necessary to determine the required shrinkage allowance and possible effects of distortion. Shrinkage allowances, in inches per inch, usually average about 0.022 for steel, 0.012 for gray iron, 0.016 for brass, 0.012 to 0.022 for bronze, 0.014 for aluminum, and 0.058 for magnesium alloys.

Investment Materials. — The investment materials which surround the dispensable pattern are made according to various formulas which may be simple or complex. The investment is in liquid form and the degree of liquidity depends chiefly upon the intricacy of the pattern forms. The investment must be fluid enough to enter such places as small holes, form sharp contours, threads, etc., and fill completely every part of the investment cavity. The accuracy of the product and its surface finish may be affected by the liquidity of the investment material. Porosity is another factor. If it is excessive, the finish will be marred but there should be enough porosity to permit escape of air when the molten metal enters the cavity. The procedure in " investing " or applying the investment materials, varies according to these materials, the kind of metal to be cast and properties required in the casting. The hardening or setting up of the investment material may merely involve standing for a given time or hardening may be at a controlled temperature.

Evacuation of the Pattern. — In cases where heat is applied to control investment hardening or setting up, this heat may also result in evacuating most of the pattern material; however, complete evacuation is essential and methods are employed to remove all traces of the pattern. Evacuation may require closely regulated temperature and the use of boiling water, low pressure steam, or the application of a vacuum to the sprue bottom.

Casting Operations. — The temperature of the flask for casting may range all the way from a chilled condition up to 2000 degrees F. or higher, depending upon the metal to be cast, the size and shape of the casting or cluster, and the desired metallurgical conditions. Metals while being cast are nearly always subjected to centrifugal force or other pressure. The procedure is governed by the kind of alloy, the size of investment cavity, and its contours or shape.

Investment Removal. — The investments surrounding the casting or cluster is removed by destroying it. The investment may be soluble in water but those used for ferrous castings are broken by using pneumatic tools, hammers, or by shot or abrasive blasting and tumbling to remove all of the particles. Gates, sprues and runners may be removed from the castings by an abrasive cutting wheel or a band saw. The shape of the cluster and machinability of the material are factors governing the selection of the method.

Accuracy of Investment Castings. — The accuracy of precision investment castings may, in general, compare favorably with many machined parts. The over-all tolerance varies with the size of the work, the kind of metal, and the skill and experience back of the casting operations. Under normal conditions, the tolerances may vary from plus or minus 0.005 or 0.006 inch per inch, down to 0.0015 to 0.002 inch per inch, and even smaller tolerances are possible on very small dimensions. In some cases where tolerances applying to a lengthwise dimension must be smaller than would be normal for the casting process, the casting gate may be at one end to permit controlling the length by a grinding operation when the gate is removed.

Casting Milling Cutters by Investment Method. — Possible applications of precision investment casting in tool manufacture and in other industrial applications, are indicated by its use in producing high-speed steel milling cutters of various forms and sizes. Thousands of these cutters have been precision cast in the Ford plant. Removal of the risers, sand-blasting to improve the appearance, and grinding the cutting edges are the only machining operations required. The bore is used as cast. Numerous tests have shown that the life of these cutters compares favorably with high-speed steel cutters made in the usual way.

Casting Weights and Sizes. — Investment castings may vary in weight from a fractional part of an ounce up to 25 pounds or more. Although the range of weights representing the practice of different firms specializing in investment casting may vary from about ½ pound up to 10 or 20 pounds, a practical limit of 3 or 4 pounds is common. The length of investment castings ordinarily does not exceed 5 or 6 inches but much longer parts may be cast. While it is possible to cast sections having a thickness of only a few thousandths of an inch, the preferable minimum thickness, as a general rule, is about 0.020 inch for alloys of high castability and 0.040 inch for alloys of low castability.

Metal Spraying Process

In the application of this process, a metal spraying " gun " is used to deposit either ferrous or non-ferrous metals upon metallic or other surfaces. The object may be to build up worn or under-sized parts, provide wear-resisting or corrosion-resisting surfaces, correct defective castings, etc. Non-ferrous metals may be applied to ferrous metals, or vice-versa, and metallic coatings may also be applied to non-metallic materials such as glass, porcelain, stone, brick, concrete, or leather. Any metal obtainable in wire form may be utilized and in some cases, the material to be sprayed is in the form of rods. The wire is fed automatically through the nozzle of the gun; then gas, oxygen, and compressed air serve to melt and blow the atomized metal against the surface to be coated. As the metal impinges against the surface at high velocity, it solidifies and forms a homogeneous bond with the surface. The gas used may be acetylene; propane, or natural, gas; butane, or coal, gas. Any desired thickness of metal may be deposited and the metals include steels ranging from low to high carbon content, various brass and bronze compositions, babbitt metal, tin, zinc, lead, nickel, copper, and aluminum. The movement of the spray gun, in covering a given surface, is either controlled mechanically or by hand. In enlarging worn or under-size shafts, spindles, etc., it is common practice to clamp the gun in a lathe tool-holder and use the feed mechanism to traverse the gun at a uniform rate while the metal is being deposited upon the rotating work-piece. The spraying operation may be followed by machining or grinding to obtain a more precise dimension. Cold drawn steel or brass shafts or rods may be covered with high-carbon steel, stainless steel, or monel metal to provide wear or corrosion resisting surfaces. Pitted valve seats may be resurfaced, blow holes in castings filled, parts zinc coated to prevent corrosion, under-sized bores reduced, and there are numerous other applications of the metal spraying process.

FORGE SHOP EQUIPMENT

Blacksmiths' Anvils. — The quality of an anvil can generally be judged by its ring, a good anvil giving out a clear, sharp sound when struck with a hammer. If soft or defective, the sound will be dull. A good anvil so mounted that it gives out a full volume of sound is easier to work upon than one having a dead ring. Anvils ordinarily vary in weight from 150 to 300 pounds. A mistake is often made in selecting anvils that are too light for the service required. A 300-pound anvil is suitable for almost any kind of machine blacksmithing, and, if of this weight or heavier, it will not move around while in use or need to be strapped to its block. The square hole in the face of an anvil for receiving the cutting and forming tools is called the "hardie hole," and the small round hole near it is called the "pritchel hole." Anvils are usually made with a wrought-iron body to which is welded a hardened steel face.

Setting the Anvil. — The height of an anvil should be such that when standing beside it the knuckles of the hands will just reach the top surface or face. A solid oak block set endwise in the ground is often used as a foundation, but a cast-iron mounting block is preferable as it can easily be moved. The casting should have a fairly broad base, and a pocket at the top for receiving the anvil; a flat block of wood is provided to act as a cushion. An anvil should not be strapped rigidly to its foundation, as this checks the vibration which tends to keep the face free from scales, and renders a high-grade wrought-iron anvil little better than one made of cast iron. When a wooden block is used under the anvil, it is necessary to drive in a few spikes to keep the anvil in place, but these should be so placed that they do not bear directly upon or bind against the corners.

Steam Hammer Rating. — The capacity of a steam hammer or its rating is the weight of the ram and its attached parts, such as the piston and rod. The steam pressure behind the piston is not considered as far as the rating is concerned. For example, a 1000-pound hammer has reciprocating parts of that weight. The steam pressures for operating hammers usually vary from 75 to 100 pounds per square inch.

Capacity of Steam Hammers. — The capacity of a steam hammer or the proper size to use for working iron and steel of a given cross-sectional area can be determined approximately by the following rule: Multiply the area of the largest cross-section to be worked by 80, if of steel, or 60, if of iron, and the product will be the required rating of the hammer in pounds. For example, the capacity of a hammer for working steel billets 5 inches square would be determined as follows: 5 × 5 = 25; and 25 × 80 = 2000, which is the rating of the hammer in pounds. A hammer rated according to this rule is an economical size to use, although it can, of course, be employed for heavier work.

Power for Operating Steam Hammers. — The boiler horsepower for operating a steam hammer depends upon the service required and the number of hammers in use. Ordinarily, the boiler capacity can be less where there are a number of hammers, because all of the hammers are rarely, if ever, used at the same time; consequently, there is a reserve power; but with a single hammer, especially when in constant service, the boiler capacity should be proportionately greater. For average conditions, the boiler horsepower can be determined approximately by the following rule: Divide the rated capacity of the hammer in pounds by 100, and the quotient will be the boiler horsepower required for continuous operation. For example, if the hammer is rated at 2000 pounds, the boiler horsepower would equal 2000 ÷ 100 = 20 H.P. This rule is also applicable in cases where the hammer is not used continually, by estimating the amount of idle time and making suitable allowance, but the boiler capacity must not be reduced to such an extent that there is a decided diminution in the pressure during the working period.

For foundations for steam hammers, see section on "Machinery and Hammer Foundations."

Board Drop-hammers. — This type of hammer is generally considered superior to the steam hammer for producing drop-forgings of small and medium size. When the work is heavy and requires a great deal of "breaking down" or drawing, or even when the forgings are light, but have thin sections that cool quickly, thus requiring sharp, rapid blows, the steam hammer will usually give better results than a "board drop." The capacity of most of the board drop-hammers in use varies from 800 to 1500 pounds; the steam hammers found in drop-forging plants usually range from 2000 to 5000 pounds capacity, for handling average work. It does not seem practicable to build board drops larger than 3000 pounds falling weight, and where the forgings are heavy enough to require a capacity over 1500 or 2000 pounds, steam hammers are usually preferred. The latter type is also preferred in some forge shops for all classes of work. It is generally conceded that the cost of operation and repairs is greater for steam hammers, but the latter has a greater output for a given capacity.

The power required for operating board drop-hammers varies considerably with the nature of the work. Very little power is required at the point of "pick up,"

Dimensions of Flat-jawed Tongs

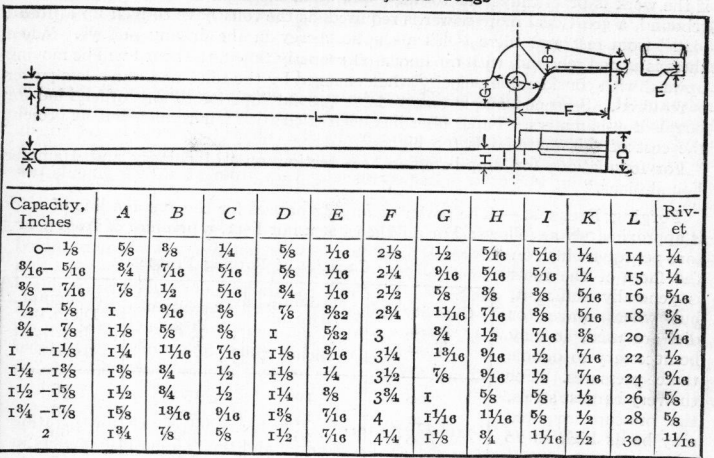

Capacity, Inches	A	B	C	D	E	F	G	H	I	K	L	Rivet
0- 1/8	5/8	3/8	1/4	5/8	1/16	2 1/8	1/2	5/16	5/16	1/4	14	1/4
3/16 - 5/16	3/4	7/16	5/16	5/8	1/16	2 1/4	9/16	5/16	5/16	1/4	15	1/4
3/8 - 7/16	7/8	1/2	5/16	3/4	1/16	2 1/2	5/8	3/8	3/8	5/16	16	5/16
1/2 - 5/8	1	9/16	3/8	7/8	3/32	2 3/4	11/16	7/16	3/8	5/16	18	3/8
3/4 - 7/8	1 1/8	5/8	3/8	1	5/32	3	3/4	1/2	7/16	3/8	20	7/16
1 - 1 1/8	1 1/4	11/16	7/16	1 1/8	3/16	3 1/4	13/16	9/16	1/2	7/16	22	1/2
1 1/4 - 1 3/8	1 3/8	3/4	1/2	1 1/8	1/4	3 1/2	7/8	9/16	1/2	7/16	24	9/16
1 1/2 - 1 5/8	1 1/2	3/4	1/2	1 1/4	3/8	3 3/4	1	5/8	5/8	1/2	26	5/8
1 3/4 - 1 7/8	1 5/8	13/16	9/16	1 3/8	7/16	4	1 1/16	11/16	5/8	1/2	28	5/8
2	1 3/4	7/8	5/8	1 1/2	7/16	4 1/4	1 1/8	3/4	11/16	1/2	30	11/16

Dimensions of Goose-neck Tongs

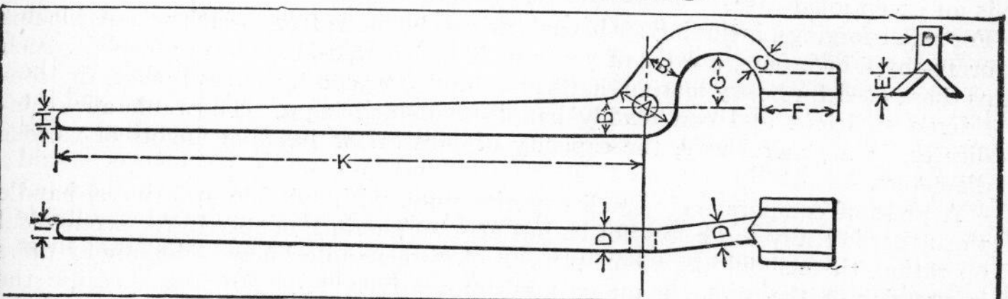

Capacity, Inches	A	B	C	D	E	F	G	H	I	K	Rivet
1/4 - 5/16	5/8	1/2	7/16	5/16	1/8	1	1/2	5/16	1/4	14	1/4
3/8 - 7/16	3/4	9/16	1/2	5/16	3/16	1 1/8	9/16	5/16	1/4	16	5/16
1/2 - 5/8	7/8	5/8	9/16	3/8	1/4	1 1/4	5/8	3/8	5/16	18	3/8
3/4 - 7/8	1	3/4	5/8	7/16	3/8	1 1/2	3/4	3/8	5/16	20	7/16
1 - 1 1/8	1 1/8	7/8	11/16	1/2	1/2	1 3/4	7/8	3/8	5/16	20	1/2
1 1/4 - 1 3/8	1 1/4	1	3/4	9/16	5/8	2	1	7/16	3/8	22	1/2
1 1/2 - 1 3/4	1 3/8	1 1/8	7/8	5/8	3/4	2 1/8	1 1/8	1/2	3/8	24	9/16
1 7/8 - 2 1/8	1 3/8	1 3/16	15/16	11/16	1	2 1/4	1 1/4	1/2	3/8	26	5/8
2 1/4 - 2 1/2	1 1/2	1 1/4	1	3/4	1 1/8	2 1/2	1 1/2	9/16	7/16	28	5/8
2 5/8 - 2 7/8	1 1/2	1 5/16	1 1/16	3/4	1 1/4	2 3/4	1 3/4	9/16	7/16	30	3/4
3 - 3 1/4	1 5/8	1 3/8	1 1/8	3/4	1 1/2	3	2	5/8	1/2	32	3/4
3 1/2 - 3 3/4	1 3/4	1 1/2	1 1/4	3/4	1 3/4	3 1/4	2 1/4	5/8	1/2	34	3/4
4 - 4 1/4	2	1 5/8	1 5/16	13/16	2	3 1/4	2 1/2	11/16	9/16	36	3/4
4 1/2 - 4 3/4	2 1/8	1 5/8	1 5/16	13/16	2 1/8	3 1/4	2 3/4	11/16	9/16	38	3/4
5	2 1/4	1 3/4	1 3/8	7/8	2 1/4	3 1/2	3 1/4	3/4	5/8	40	7/8

if the work is practically "die to die;" but when the work is soft and there is no rebound, a great deal more power is required, as the rolls have to pick up a "dead load" from rest and there is little kinetic energy in the driving pulleys. When there is a good rebound, with the knock-off properly timed, the board will be moving upward with considerable velocity when engaged by the rolls, and much less power is required. Seasoned maple boards have proved superior to any other kind for board drop-hammers. Paper fiber has been tried with fair results, but at present the cost of this material is too high.

For foundations for drop-hammers, see section on "Machinery and Hammer Foundations."

Forging Presses. — The power of forging presses for the average line of work is approximately as follows: For mild steel at a fair heat, a pressure of from 3 to 5 tons per square inch on the faces of the tools is generally sufficient, but when swages or dies are used, it may be necessary to double these pressures. For the very hardest steels, the pressure required may be as high as 10 or even 15 tons per square inch, but this is an exceptional case.

Capacity of Forging Presses

Capacity of Press, Tons	Maximum Diam. of Ingots, Inches	Capacity of Press, Tons	Maximum Diam. of Ingots, Inches
300	10	1500	36
500	14	2000	48
800	20	3000	60
1200	27	4000	72

For small forgings, including such parts as can be made from 8-inch square blooms or 12- by 6-inch flats, a press of 300 tons is sufficient, and for larger forgings, such as those used for heavy marine shafts and cranks, a 3000-ton press is generally considered sufficient and can readily handle a 60-inch ingot. The table above indicates, in a general way, the capacity of presses for handling ingots of various diameters.

A press of comparatively small capacity may, with suitable appliances, handle work that is really too heavy for it, but at some sacrifice of speed; for economical operation, there should be ample power. As is generally known, the forging press is superior to the steam hammer for comparatively large forgings, because the hammer tends to spread the surface metal without acting upon the center of the ingot to the required degree. With a press, the forging action goes right to the center of the ingot, as evidenced by the bulging that takes place at the sides, and if there is a cavity in the ingot, forging under the press closes it, whereas a hammer by spreading the surface metal, may tend to enlarge it. As forgings diminish in size, the difference in favor of the press is less marked. Owing to the recent increase in the operating speed of forging presses, however, they now compete with power hammers in the forging of comparatively light work, and the range of presses has been greatly extended.

Air Pressures and Pipe Sizes for Forges. — Blacksmiths' forges require air pressures varying from 1½ to 6 ounces per square inch. Small forges with the blower close to them are adequately supplied with 1½ ounce pressure. If the blower is some distance away and a long discharge pipe with many bends leads to the forge, even though the latter be small, it may be necessary to carry 3 ounces pressure or more, to overcome the friction in the air ducts. Large forges usually require from 3 to 6 ounces pressure. The table, "Air Pressures and Pipe Sizes for Forges," gives the diameters of discharge mains for various tuyere sizes and number of forges.

Air Pressures and Pipe Sizes for Forges*

Diam. Forge Tuyere, Inches	Number of Forges Supplied by Blower									
	1	2	3	4	5	6	7	8	9	10
	Diameter Discharge Main at Blower, Inches									
¾	1½	1½	2	2	2½	2½	3	3	3	3
1	1½	2	2½	3	3	3½	3½	4	4	4
1¼	2	2½	3	3½	4	4	4½	5	5	5
1½	2	3	3½	4	4½	5	6	6	6	6
1¾	2½	3½	4	4½	5	6	6	7	7	7
2	3	4	4½	5	6	7	7	8	8	8
2¼	3	4	5	6	7	7	8	9	9	9
2½	3½	5	6	7	8	8	9	9	10	10
2¾	4	5	6	7	8	9	10	10	11	11
3	4	6	7	8	9	10	11	11	12	12
3½	4½	7	8	9	10	11	12	13	14	14
4	6	8	9	11	12	13	14	15	16	17

* American Blower Co.

The Cold Swaging Process. — Cold swaging is a method of reducing or forming steel or other material while cold, by drawing to a point or reducing the diameter, as may be required. This is performed by a machine that causes the work to be struck a large number of successive blows by a pair of dies shaped to give the required form. This process is principally applied to the reduction of wires, rods and tubes, and is the only method by which rolled or plated stock can be reduced without destroying the plating or coating. For this reason, it is largely employed for jewelers' work. It is also extensively used for pointing rods or tubes which are to be drawn. The process is used in the manufacture of needles, bicycle spokes, button hooks, crochet needles, etc.

Forging Machines. — Some forging machines are intended especially for bolt and rivet heading, and others for more general work. The form or shape into which a part is forged is governed by dies of the required shape and also by a heading tool or plunger which bends or upsets the heated bar of metal and forces it into the die impression. The die may have a single impression, or two or three impressions may be required in order to forge the part by successive operations.

Dies for Bolt and Rivet Forging Machines. — Bolt and rivet dies used in forging machines are, as a rule, made from steel containing from 0.60 to 0.80 per cent carbon and are hardened and drawn. The heading tool, which must be tougher than the dies, is generally made from steel containing from 0.40 to 0.50 per cent carbon, and is drawn considerably more than the forming dies.

Dies and Tools Used in Hot-pressed Center-feed Nut Machines. — The dies used in hot-pressed center-feed nut machines are usually made from chilled iron castings, the dies being ground to size. It is claimed that dies made from this material will last fully eight times as long as those made from ordinary carbon steel, but as it is somewhat difficult to obtain the proper amount of chill, many manufacturers use a good grade of open-hearth crucible steel instead. A crucible steel which is found to give good results contains from 0.90 to 1.10 per cent carbon. In many cases, vanadium alloy steel is used for dies for nut forging machines. The composition of vanadium steel for dies varies. Two grades of vanadium tool steel are recommended for forging machine dies by the American Vanadium Co., of Pittsburgh, Pa. One is composed of carbon, 0.50 per cent; chromium, from 0.80 to 1.10 per cent; manganese, from 0.40 to 0.60 per cent; vanadium, not less than 0.16 per cent; silicon, not more than 0.20 per cent. The heat-treatment recommended for this steel is as follows: Heat to 1550 degrees F. and quench in oil; then re-heat to from 1425 to 1450 degrees F., and quench in water, submerging the face of the die only.

The second kind of vanadium tool steel recommended has the following analysis: Carbon, from 0.65 to 0.75 per cent; manganese, from 0.40 to 0.60 per cent; vanadium, not less than 0.16 per cent; silicon, not more than 0.20 per cent. The heat-treatment for this steel should be as follows: Heat to 1525 degrees F. and quench in water, with only the face of the die submerged. Ordinary carbon tool steel dies should be drawn to a light straw color.

Bulldozer Dies. — Many of the tools or dies used on bulldozers are made of cast iron, in order to reduce the cost, and those parts of the dies which are subjected to wear are faced with hardened steel plates which may readily be replaced, if necessary. Whenever hot punching or cutting is done, high-speed self-hardening steel should be used for the working members of the tool.

Helve Hammers. — Power hammers of the helve type are adapted especially for relatively light forging operations, particularly when a rapid succession of blows is required. Ordinary helve hammers are usually built in sizes ranging from 15 to 200 pounds, this rating being based upon the weight of the hammer head. Some "upright helve" hammers are made in sizes up to 500 pounds.

Vertical Power Hammers. — Vertical power hammers of the crank- and pneumatically-operated types are used for general forging operations, especially on the lighter classes of work. Power hammers of the vertical type usually range in size from 25 pounds up to 500 pounds.

Efficiency of Forging Hammers. — The Heim method for determining the efficiency of forging hammers is based on the results of numerous tests conducted by allowing an ordinary drop-hammer to fall a predetermined distance upon a pure lead cylinder, the height of which is 1.5 times its diameter. The diameters of the cylinders which have been adopted for use in testing various sizes of hammers

Table 1. Dimensions of Lead Plugs Used for Testing Various Sizes of Hammers

Falling Weight of Hammer		Diameter of Lead Cylinder *		Falling Weight of Hammer		Diameter of Lead Cylinder *	
Pounds	Kilograms	Inches	Millimeters	Pounds	Kilograms	Inches	Millimeters
66	30	1.18	30	330	150	2.36	60
110	50	1.38	35	506	230	2.76	70
165	75	1.57	40	770	350	3.15	80
220	100	1.97	50	1100	500	3.54	90

* Height equals 1.5 × diameter.

Table 2. Values of Factors Used in Calculating Power of Hammers

A	0.10	0.15	0.20	0.25	0.30	0.35	0.40	0.45	0.50	0.55	0.60
B	1.01	1.63	2.31	3.08	3.94	4.90	5.97	7.17	8.52	10.03	11.73

(with regard to their falling weight) are given in Table I. The following formula gives the number of foot-pounds of work done by one blow of the hammer:

Work = $36.75\ D^3\ [8.85\ A + 13.12\ (A^2 + A^4)]$ foot-pounds, where D = diameter of lead cylinder; $A = (H - H_1) \div H$; H = original height of cylinder; H_1 = height of cylinder after being struck by the hammer.

If the expression inside the brackets in the formula is designated by B, the formula may be expressed in the following form:

$$Work = 36.75\ D^3 B$$

After the lead cylinder has been struck by the hammer, the value of A is calculated and the number of foot-pounds of work developed by the hammer is then obtained by taking the value of B from Table II and substituting in the formula.

Example: — Suppose a 100-kilogram (220-pound) hammer striking 180 blows per minute is allowed to strike a lead cylinder, the original dimensions of which are 50 millimeters (1.97 inch) in diameter by 75 millimeters (2.95 inches) high. After the blow has been struck, the resulting height of the cylinder is 48 millimeters (1.90 inch). From the preceding formula:

$$A = \frac{2.95 - 1.90}{2.95} = 0.35 \qquad B = 4.9, \text{ from Table II}$$

Substituting the values of D and B in the formula for the work done by one blow of the hammer:

$36.75 \times 1.97^3 \times 4.9 = 1376$ foot-pounds = work done by one blow.

$\dfrac{1376 \times 180}{60} = 4128$ foot-pounds = work done per second.

The maximum power required to drive the hammer is 10.3 horsepower. As one horsepower is equivalent to 550 foot-pounds of work per second, the amount of power consumed by the hammer per second is: $10.3 \times 550 = 5665$ foot-pounds. The efficiency of the hammer is found to be:

$$\text{Efficiency} = \frac{\text{useful work}}{\text{power supplied}} = \frac{4128}{5665} = 72 \text{ per cent.}$$

The Heim formula and method of testing may be applied to all types of hammers, but, when used on steam hammers, the test must be made while the hammer is running continuously and not when set to deliver a single blow.

Machinery and Hammer Foundations

The materials commonly used are concrete, stone, brick, and wood in conjunction with concrete for machines subjected to considerable vertical shock. The principal characteristics of these materials are briefly as follows: Concrete is an ideal foundation material, as it becomes practically one solid piece and is much cheaper than a masonry foundation. Stone, in addition to being strong and durable, has great vibration-absorbing power, but is quite costly. Brick is not so durable as stone, but is cheaper and available everywhere. In building a foundation, provision should be made for the foundation bolts, when these are necessary. Sometimes the bolts are set permanently in the foundation, or they may be placed in pipes and have pockets at the lower ends, thus permitting adjustment or removal, if necessary. The bolts are usually located in the proper position by making a wooden templet in which holes are bored to coincide with the holes in the machine base. The inclination of the sides of a foundation should vary from $1\frac{1}{2}$ to 3 inches per foot from the vertical. The foundation pit should be excavated below the frost line of the locality.

Concrete Foundations. — The timber used for making the forms in which concrete foundations are molded should be about 1 inch thick, dressed on the inner side to give a smooth surface. The form should be braced externally about every 2½ feet, and internally about every foot in height. As the form is being filled, the inside braces can be removed. If pocket molds are used for the lower ends of the bolts, they should be soaked in water two or three hours before using, to prevent their swelling and sticking in the concrete. Do not use concrete that has been mixed over twenty minutes. Ram with rammers weighing about 1 pound per square inch of face area, the ramming being continued until water just shows at the

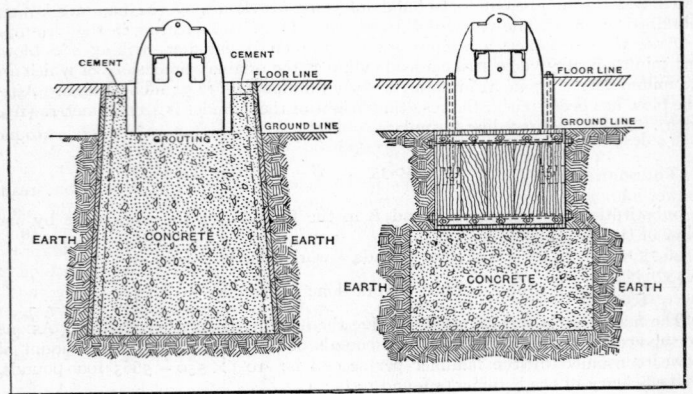

Fig. 1   Fig. 2

surface. Put down the concrete in layers about 6 inches thick and work it onto the form with a shovel, to obtain a smooth, even surface. The foundation may be partly filled with stones about the size of a man's head, placed approximately one foot apart and not less than one foot from the foundation surfaces. These stones should be wet before laying. If the work is stopped at night before completion, make grooves in the surface and when starting the next day, sprinkle and dust over with dry cement. As soon as the concrete has set, remove the form, as it is much easier to patch when the cement is somewhat "green." Foundations are sometimes "slushed" instead of being rammed. In this case, the concrete is mixed just wet enough so that it cannot be piled up. It is then dumped into the molds and worked in them to prevent air bubbles. The first method gives a more homogeneous structure as there is no chance for the broken stones to settle. When the machine is in position, the space around the foundation bolts may be filled with liquid cement, lead or melted sulphur.

Drop-hammer Foundations. — The following drop-hammer foundations are recommended by the E. W. Bliss Company:

Concrete Foundation: Excavate a hole from 10 to 14 feet deep and from 8 to 12 feet square; build up a block of concrete with tapering sides, as shown in Fig. 1, having a top about 6 to 12 inches wider, all around, than the base of the anvil. Place the anvil in position and wedge it level; then run a thin mixture of concrete under the anvil and allow it to set. Next move the wedges and build up a wall of concrete from 4 to 6 inches thick around the anvil. (See illustration.) This will make the use of bolts unnecessary and the anvil will set solid and will not be likely to shift. Solid concrete makes an excellent foundation that does not deteriorate, as is the case with timber when subjected to dampness from the earth or atmospheric moisture. Another advantage is that it is almost impervious to sparks or hot pieces of metal.

Timber-concrete Foundations: Excavate a hole somewhat larger than the anvil or base of the hammer. At the bottom lay a bed of concrete from 1 to 2 feet thick, as shown in Fig. 2. On this concrete bed place, endwise, Georgia pine timbers 12 by 12 inches by 6 to 8 feet long. These should be securely strapped together by steel bands on the outside fastened with through bolts. The timber base should preferably be a little larger than the anvil. To preserve the timbers coat them with oil of tar or creosote. The tops of the timbers should be adzed off evenly to obtain a level surface for the anvil. Another method of making a foundation of this kind, for small and medium sized hammers, is to put the timbers upon a foot or more of gravel rammed down on a hard-pan bottom. When the timbers, which are also placed endwise and bolted, are in position, the space around the sides is filled with gravel tightly rammed.

Foundation for Steam Hammer. — To secure the greatest efficiency from steam power hammers, the foundations on which they are mounted must be solid. Concrete resting upon hard-pan has given better results than the combination of heavy wooden beams and concrete often used. When making solid concrete foundations, there should be several inches of cement placed over the concrete, and a cushion of wood, at least 3 inches thick, between the cement and base of the anvil, to give the necessary resiliency and prevent the concrete from being pulverized by the impact of the blows. In the front and rear of the hammer there should be openings down to the level of the anvil base, so that it can be leveled or adjusted by wedging and grouting with cement, in case it should sag or get out of alignment with the upper parts of the hammer. These openings can be covered with hatches set level with the floor.

Machine and Forge Shop Floor Materials

Machine shop floors are commonly made of wood or concrete. Probably there is no floor for the machine shop as good as one made of selected hard maple, properly laid and supported, as it wears smoothly and evenly. Concrete, however, has its advantages, the most important of which is its fire-resisting qualities. There are few objections to a wooden floor, and from the standpoint of health it is generally considered superior to concrete. Where there is much heat, or large quantities of moisture or chemicals in bulk, wooden floors should not be used. In certain classes of store-rooms, or where there is a likelihood of considerable moisture, as in wash rooms, concrete floors are considered superior to wood.

Concrete and Wooden Floors. — The following information on shop floors and their materials is abstracted from a paper by Mr. L. C. Wason read before the American Society of Mechanical Engineers. While the factor of cost is apt to be considered first, very often the maintenance and adaptability for the particular service required is of first importance. The initial cost of a granolithic floor surface is at no disadvantage compared with a wooden floor, as the cost of such a surface laid in the best manner is about equal to the cost of seven-eighths maple flooring. In addition, the granolithic surface is fire-proof and will not decay or disintegrate as the result of moisture, which is one of the weak points of the wooden floor. On the other hand, a wooden floor is more easily repaired than a granolithic surface. In making a comparison between wooden and granolithic floors, it is also necessary to consider the workmanship. With a maple top floor, the wearing quality depends comparatively little on the skill of the one who lays the floor, but with a granolithic finish, the work must be done carefully and intelligently. Among the objections to the granolithic surface, one of the most prominent is the bad effect of a concrete floor upon the health and comfort of the workmen. This is not due to the hardness of the floor, but rather to its heat conductivity. When a workman stands for hours on a concrete floor, the heat of the body is conducted to the floor quite rapidly, which tends to disarrange the circulation and cause physical ailments, such as rheumatism, etc. For men working steadily at machines, and usually in one position, this objectionable feature can be overcome by the use of insulating foot-boards or wooden gratings upon which to stand.

The dust produced by the wear of some granolithic surfaces has proved harmful to delicate machinery, whereas a wooden floor does not of itself produce a dust capable of any appreciable abrasive action. It is possible, however, by gluing battleship linoleum to concrete floors, to obtain many of the advantages of a wooden surface. Linoleum is also an effective insulation against the loss of bodily heat.

High resistance to wear and practically complete dustlessness can be secured in a granolithic surface if properly made. To secure a durable and practically dustless floor, proceed as follows: Do not use sand, as sand grains are quickly broken by abrasion and form dust. The granolithic finish should contain the highest possible proportion of tough stone aggregate. Use stone suitable for macadam road, and of a size that will pass through a half-inch round mesh screen, but use nothing smaller than that passed by a 20-mesh screen. Mix the concrete dry, and of a consistency for making blocks, so that considerable tamping will be required to bring enough water to the surface for troweling. Finally, do the troweling before the mortar sets. Prolonged troweling of a wet mixture brings to the top the "laitance" of the concrete, which is the part incapable of a true set. A top layer of laitance is therefore porous and wears down quickly. Even the fine particles of good cement should not be brought to the surface, as they form a layer which is weakly bonded to the rest of the concrete and wears away rapidly, appearing in the air as dust.

To Prevent Dust on Concrete Floors. — The Aberthaw Construction Co. of Boston, contracting engineers specializing in concrete, recommends the following method of curing a dusty concrete floor: Have the surface entirely dry; then paint it with a mixture of boiled linseed oil thinned with gasoline. Apply several coats, until the oil shows glossy on the top. The theory of this is that the linseed oil, having been boiled, has lost most of its volatile components and is practically permanent. The gasoline thins this down enough so that it will strike into the pores. A little experimenting will show the proper proportions. The thinner it is, the more coats will be required and the deeper it will strike in. A floor that is causing serious trouble from dust can often be cured with very little trouble and expense in this way.

Floors for Forge Shops. — There is considerable difference in opinion as to the best material for blacksmith shop flooring. Wood is too inflammable, bricks crack and break from the heat, cement or concrete has the same objectionable features, and asphalt is out of the question. Perhaps nothing is superior to or cheaper than dirt mixed with ashes. If kept moist by sprinkling at least once a day, it is more comfortable to stand upon than the other materials mentioned. It is easily repaired and leveled in case holes are worn in it, and is not affected by dropping heavy or hot pieces upon it. The space between the walls and forges, however, may be covered with concrete to facilitate the handling of such appliances as portable surface-plates and vises.

WELDING METHODS

Classes of Welds. — Welds are classified according to the way the ends are formed prior to making the weld. The different welds ordinarily made in hand-forging practice are the scarf weld, butt weld, lap weld, cleft or split weld and jump weld. These welds are shown by the accompanying illustration. It will be seen that the surfaces, in most instances, are rounded or crowned. This is done so that when the heated ends are brought together they will unite first in the center. Any slag or dirt which may have adhered to the heated surfaces will then be forced out as the welding proceeds from the center outward. When making a lap weld, the hammering should begin at the center in order to work all the slag out, as the faces in this case are not rounded.

Welding Heat. — When two pieces of wrought iron or mild steel are heated until they become soft and plastic and will stick together when one is pressed or hammered against the other, they have reached what is commonly known as a welding heat. The quality of the weld depends largely upon the welding heat. If the ends to be heated are not hot enough, they will not stick together; inversely, if the work remains in the fire too long, it becomes overheated and burned, which greatly injures the metal. Iron which has been overheated has a rough, spongy appearance and

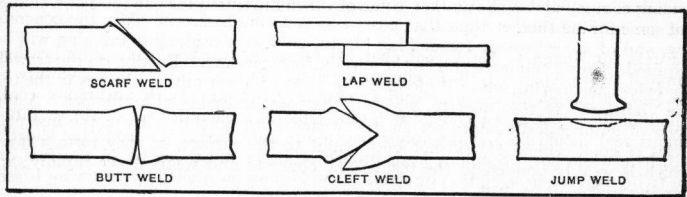

Different Kinds of Welds

is brittle. The danger of burning is increased when the air blast is too strong and the fire is oxidizing. It is important to heat the work slowly to secure a uniform temperature throughout the ends to be heated. With rapid heating, the outside may be raised to the welding temperature, while the interior is much below it; consequently, the weld will be defective.

Fire for Welding. — When heated iron comes into contact with the air it absorbs oxygen, thus forming a scale or oxide of iron on the surface, which prevents the formation of a good weld. A fire for heating parts to be welded should have a fairly thick bed between the tuyere and the work, so that the oxygen in the air blast will be consumed before it reaches the parts being heated. When there is only a thin bed of fuel beneath the work, or if too strong a blast is used, the excess of oxygen will pass through and oxidize the iron. The hotter the iron, the greater the formation of scale. The surface being heated can be given an additional protection by covering it with some substance that will exclude the air. (See "Fluxes for Welding.") Ordinarily, the air blast for a forge fire should have a pressure varying from 3 to 5 ounces per square inch. (See "Air Pressures and Pipe Sizes for Forges.")

Fluxes for Welding. — When iron is being heated preparatory to welding, the heated surfaces are oxidized to some extent or covered with oxide of iron, which forms a black scale when the hot iron comes into contact with the air. If this scale is not removed, it will cause a defective weld. Wrought iron can be heated to a high enough temperature to melt this oxide so that the latter is forced out from between the surfaces by the hammer blows; but when welding machine steel, and especially tool steel, a temperature high enough to melt the oxide would burn the steel, and it is necessary to use what is called a flux. This is a substance, such as sand or borax, having a melting temperature below the welding temperature of the work, and it is sprinkled upon the heated ends when they have reached about a yellow heat. The flux serves two purposes: It melts and covers the heated surfaces, thus protecting them from oxidation, and, when molten, aids in dissolving any oxide that may have formed, the oxide melting at a lower temperature when combined with the flux. Wrought iron can be welded in a clean, well-kept fire without using a flux of any kind, except when the material is very thin. The fluxes commonly used are fine clean sand and borax. When borax is used, it will give better results if burned. This can be done by heating it in a crucible until reduced to the liquid state. It should then be poured onto a flat surface to form a sheet; when cold, it can easily be broken up and pulverized. The borax powder can be used plain or it can be mixed with an equal quantity of fine clean sand and about 25 per cent iron (not steel) filings. For tool steel, a flux made of one part sal-ammoniac and twelve parts borax is recommended. When pieces are put together previous to welding, as in split welds, or when taking a second heat (usually termed a "wash"), a flux that will flow easily should be used. There are many welding compounds on the market, some of which are suited for one class of welding and some for another.

Fuels for Forge. — Coke, coal, charcoal, oil and gas are used as fuels for heating iron and steel preparatory to forging or welding. For general work, a coke fire is the best, although bituminous coal is extensively used. With anthracite coal, it is difficult to get a hot enough fire, especially on a small forge. Coke or bituminous coal should be low in sulphur, because sulphur makes the iron "hot short" or brittle while hot. Sulphur, lead, bronze or brass must not be in the fuel or fire to be used for heating iron or steel. A weld may be spoiled by throwing brass filings into a fire before heating the work.

Machine Welding. — There are three common types of welds that can be made satisfactorily in a forging machine, simple examples of which are shown in the accompanying illustration.

Lap-welding: This is one of the most successful methods that can be used in joining pieces together in a forging machine, whenever requirements will permit. There are several applications of this type of welding: Two pieces can be joined together (as shown in the illustration) or several pieces can be welded together in one block. Machine lap-welding is also employed for enlarging the diameter of a bar, this being accomplished by welding a U-shaped piece of rectangular stock to the end, and then upsetting the mass into the shape desired. An end plunger is used to upset the bar after the latter is securely held between the opposing faces of the gripping dies.

Pin-welding: In order to make a pin weld, the end of the bar is reduced and inserted in a hole in the part to which it is to be joined (see illustration). The reduced end is usually made from one-quarter to one-half the diameter of the original bar. The U-shaped piece, or other part which is to be joined to it, is generally made thicker where the weld is made, in order to strengthen the weld. The welding operation is effected by a plunger in the ram of the machine, which upsets the "pin" and at the same time forms the joint.

Butt-welding: This method of machine welding is not as common as the other two methods referred to, but is satisfactory when properly applied. To make a butt weld, it is not necessary to prepare the stock beforehand, although the pieces should have practically the desired shape. The weld is effected by a plunger having a pointed end which is forced through the forward member to be joined, thus closely pressing together the material and insuring a solid weld (see illustration). This method of welding is not considered as practicable as pin-welding, but when properly handled, it is satisfactory for many classes of work. Wrought iron is welded in a forging machine without using any flux, but the parts to be joined must be clean and free from scale. As a rule, compressed air is used to remove the

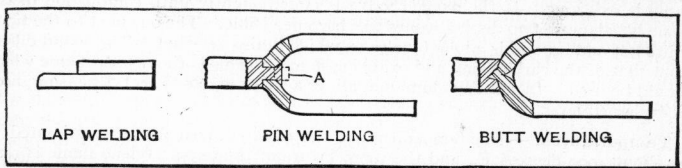

LAP WELDING   PIN WELDING   BUTT WELDING

scale formed by oxidization. A small jet of air is directed against the work just before the machine is operated. For welding steel having a comparatively high carbon content, it is necessary to use a flux to make a satisfactory weld. (See "Fluxes for Welding.")

Autogenous or Gas Welding

Autogenous welding is usually defined as a process of uniting metals by fusing them together without compression or hammering and also without using a flux or adding new material to form the joint. When using a high-temperature gas flame, such as is obtained with an oxy-acetylene torch, additional material (in the form of a rod or wire) is ordinarily fused between the parts to be welded and a flux may also be used; hence, the term "autogenous welding" which has been commonly used to designate this method, is not strictly accurate and for this reason the expression "gas welding" is also used to indicate the welding of metals by means of a high-temperature gas flame.

Many different metals can be welded with an oxy-acetylene torch, although in the practical application of this method it is essential to distinguish between classes of work that can be welded on a commercial basis and work which should be done only to meet an emergency and which, under ordinary conditions, might be done more cheaply by other methods.

Welding Torch. — The intense local heat required for welding metal by the gas process is obtained by the combustion of a mixture of gases such as oxygen and acetylene or oxygen and hydrogen. The torch is a simple device, consisting of a handle, two needle valves, tubes for the oxygen and for the acetylene, a head and a tip. The acetylene is admitted under lower pressure than the oxygen, and regulators on the storage tanks serve to control the working pressure of both gases. The mixing of the acetylene and oxygen gases takes place in the head of the torch, where the oxygen meets cross currents of the acetylene gas. The diameter of the holes in the tip and the pressures of the respective gases determine the quality of the mixture. The diameters of the holes are graded and the tips are numbered to correspond. These tips are interchangeable, different sizes being required.

Adjusting the Torch. — Before using the welding torch, it is essential to regulate the acetylene and oxygen gas pressures with reference to the thickness of metal to be welded. The oxygen and acetylene must also be adjusted to obtain a *neutral flame*, which will neither oxidize (burn) the metal nor carbonize it. When a white cone appears at the tip and beyond the cone there is a white envelope of flame with a long blue streamer flame, the combustion is unbalanced. There is insufficient oxygen and an excess of carbon in the flame. Now, if the oxygen needle valve is opened full, the white-hot cone at the tip will be very short and surrounded by a blue-white envelope. Combustion is now unbalanced because of the excess of oxygen, which combines with all of the acetylene gas available while the remainder tends to attack the metal. Combustion is accompanied by a roaring sound, and the flame is oxidizing. If the oxygen valve is closed slightly until combustion in the flame is balanced, two distinct cones will become visible. The one next to the tip is white hot and beyond is a long blue cone, which is also very hot. The sound differs from that of the carbonizing and oxidizing flames. This is the neutral flame which should be used. In welding aluminum alloys a slight excess of acetylene is required as explained later.

Temperatures. — The temperature of the oxy-hydrogen flame is estimated to be about 4000 degrees F., and the temperature of the oxy-acetylene flame is estimated to be about 5400 degrees F. by some authorities and as high as 6300 degrees F. by others. The exact temperatures are not known. With the oxy-acetylene flame the number of British thermal units per cubic foot is approximately five times greater than is obtained with the oxy-hydrogen flame.

Size of Torch Tip to Use. — The proper size of tip to use for welding depends upon the thickness of metal and the rate at which the heat is dissipated. Sometimes the rate of conduction and radiation is affected by the location of the parts to be welded. Welders are advised to use as large a tip as possible without overheating the metal, in order to weld faster and use less gas. If the flame is too small for the thickness of the metal to be welded, the heat will be radiated too rapidly.

Preparing Joint for Welding. — When material is only about 1/16 to 1/8 inch thick, it can be welded successfully when the edges are square, but when thicker plates are to be welded, it is necessary to bevel the edges to obtain the best results, as otherwise the heat of the flame suitable for welding will not penetrate and cause perfect fusion beyond a depth of, say, from 1/8 to 3/16 inch; hence, when material is thicker than about 1/8 inch, the edges are beveled and the V-shaped channel thus formed is filled by using adding material. The edges of steel and iron plate should be beveled to an angle of 45 degrees, so that when the plates are placed together, the included angle of the V-shaped channel is about 90 degrees. (See accompanying illustration.) The angle may be smaller for brass and bronze when the work is done by experienced men. If the plates are quite thick, it is preferable to bevel and weld on both sides, the bevel extending into the center of the plate from each side.

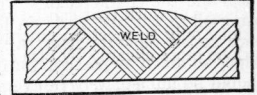

When it is necessary to weld thick material from one side only, it is advisable to reduce the included angle to about 60 degrees. Aluminum need not be beveled as much as steel, and if the plates are 1/4 inch thick or less, beveling is not necessary when a welding iron or spud is employed to break up the oxide, although experience is required to work successfully in this manner.

Provision for Expansion and Contraction. — As a general rule, 1 or 2 per cent of the length of the weld is allowed for expansion and contraction when welding two plates of steel together, especially if the weld is long. For example, if the joint is 12 inches long, the pieces should be laid so that they are 1/4 inch farther apart at one end than at the end where the welding is begun; thus, there is a tapering space between them. After the parts are "tacked" together and as the welding proceeds, the molten metal cools and contracts. This contraction causes the welded section to act like a hinge, and the unwelded ends draw closer together. It is often difficult to provide for expansion and contraction when welding castings.

Welding Rods or Adding Materials. — Mild steel should be welded with a welding rod or wire that is low in carbon. A welding rod having the composition of pure Swedish iron is preferable. The use of commercial steel wire is not recommended. Cast-iron welding rods should be made from a fine grade of cast iron, high in silicon and low in manganese and sulphur. The best rods are cast in metal molds, which insure density of metal and freedom from blow-holes and sand. Cast aluminum welding rods are used on aluminum castings and the drawn rods or wire are preferable for welding rolled aluminum sheets. Brass and bronze are welded with cast welding rods and drawn bronze rods. Brass wire is not suitable as it contains too much zinc which burns out, leaving the welding material defective. The diameter of the rod or wire should be chosen with reference to the thickness of the joint and the size of the tip and flame. A small wire should not be used for welding a heavy plate.

General Procedure when Welding. — To become proficient in the art of autogenous welding requires experience and practice, but a knowledge of some of the fundamental principles will enable the operator to make more rapid progress. It is advisable to begin by welding thin strips of iron or steel not over ⅛ inch in thickness. Such light metals can be welded without the addition of a filling-in material. The torch should be given a semicircular or zig-zag motion. This movement tends to blend the metal and reduces the liability of overheating. The beveled surfaces of thicker materials are heated by a semicircular movement of the flame, care being taken to melt them to a soft, plastic state without burning the metal. Wherever fusion occurs, new metal should be added from a "welding rod," the composition of which is suitable for the work in hand. The surface should be thoroughly fused before adding metal from the welding stick, and the latter should be held close to, or in contact with, the puddle of molten metal. The heat is then radiated from the puddle to the welding rod, whereas if the metal were allowed to drop through the flame, it might be burned to an injurious extent.

Pre-heating Castings. — As a general rule, it is necesary to pre-heat all cast-iron parts before welding, although some parts of very simple form may be welded without pre-heating. The source of heat for pre-heating depends upon local conditions and the character of work. Oil burners, charcoal fires, or pre-heating stoves using oil or gas are used. A hard-wood charcoal fire is sometimes used in preference to oil blow-torches. All pre-heated parts should be covered with asbestos paper as much as possible during pre-heating and welding, and the welded section should be immediately protected from radiation and rapid cooling after welding.

Welding Cast Iron. — It is highly important to pre-heat all cast iron before welding except possibly very simple parts, as explained in the preceding paragraph. The metal should be covered as soon as the weld is finished and be allowed to cool slowly. If the metal is more than ¼ inch thick, the edges should be beveled at an angle of about 45 degrees on each side. For comparatively heavy welds, it is well to leave three small points of contact for aligning the broken parts in their original position. To make the weld, the flame should be passed for some distance around the fracture and then be directed on it until the metal is cherry-red. When this occurs, have an assistant throw on a little scaling powder, and when the metal begins to run, add cast iron from the cast-iron "welding stick," which should be of specially refined material. Powder should be added only when the metal does not flow well, as little as possible being used. Never attempt to re-weld pieces that have been previously welded or brazed, without first cutting away all of the old metal.

Welding Steel. — Steel less than ⅛ inch thick can be welded without the addition of any welding metal. If the thickness exceeds ⅛ inch, the edges should be beveled or chamfered. It is very important not to add the welding material until the edges are fused or molten at the place where the weld is being made. In no case should the flame be held at one point until a foam is produced, as this is an indication that the metal is being burned. Do not hold the flame steadily in the center of the weld, but give it a semicircular or zig-zag motion with an uplifting movement at each revolution, the object being to drive the molten metal toward the center of the weld. When welding a crack located in the middle of a heavy steel sheet, begin by chamfering the metal on each side of the fracture at an angle of 45 degrees, the slope extending to the bottom; then apply the welding torch to the sheet beyond the end of the crack, until there is sufficient expansion to open the crack perceptibly. The weld should then be made, and, as a rule, it will be found that the expansion will compensate for the contraction when cooling. No flux is required when welding low-carbon steel, because the oxide melts at a lower temperature than the fusing point of the metal. Flux may be used on the higher carbon steels to prevent oxidation.

Aluminum Welding. — The successful welding of aluminum alloy castings by the oxy-acetylene process, depends a great deal upon the success achieved in breaking down the aluminum oxide, the forming of which is intensified as soon as the oxy-acetylene torch flame comes in contact with the metal. It is this oxide film that prevents the proper flow of the metal at the welding temperatures and that has been the cause of many failures in aluminum welds.

Cleaning Surfaces. — The surfaces to be joined must be thoroughly cleaned and the material near the surfaces to be welded must also be clean, as otherwise the impurities near the joint will invariably set up auto-corrosion in the weld. Oily machine parts should be allowed to remain for a few seconds in a hot 10 per cent caustic soda solution, after which, the castings should be thoroughly washed and scrubbed in plenty of clean hot water. It is often advisable first to wash the oily castings with gasoline to remove the greater part of the grease and dirt.

Joint Beveling. — After the work is cleaned, a V-shaped groove is filed or chipped along the crack or seam to the bottom to permit the metal to be melted the full depth of the work. However, aluminum alloy castings up to ¼ inch in thickness can be welded with the torch flame without beveling the joints.

Preheating. — In welding aluminum and aluminum alloy castings, it is necessary to preheat and anneal the work in order to prevent too rapid expansion and contraction of the metal. Preheating also conserves gas, increases the rate of welding, and prevents warping. Great care, however, must be exercised to avoid exceeding a temperature of 750 and 840 degrees F., respectively, when preheating and reheating or annealing the work. At higher temperatures a piece of work may be rendered useless by deformation. During the preheating of castings of complex shape or castings that vary greatly in thickness, the casting should be covered with sheet asbestos to keep the temperature as uniform as possible. The asbestos should not be removed during the welding operation, except as it is necessary to effect the weld.

Welding Procedure. — A puddling rod, made from a piece of mild steel rod ³⁄₁₆ or ¼ inch in diameter and flattened on one end like a flat scraper, is used in welding to scrape and agitate the metal at the moment of melting in order to break up the oxide and allow the molten metal to flow together. It is necessary to wipe the puddling rod frequently to prevent it from becoming coated with oxide, and care must be taken not to allow it to reach a red heat, as otherwise oxide of iron will be formed on it which might result in a defective weld. The oxide formed in the course of melting aluminum offers considerable resistance to the welding flame, and it must be eliminated to effect a homogeneous weld. This is best done by employing an aluminum alloy welding flux which dissolves and deoxidizes the layer of oxide adjacent to the joint to be welded, at the temperature at which the aluminum reaches a molten state.

The welding material, usually a rod or broken aluminum part, should be of as pure aluminum as it is possible to obtain and the end of the rod should be kept in the molten bath while welding. For aluminum alloy castings, the welding material should be of approximately the same composition as the alloy to be welded.

Flame Adjustment. — In making a weld, the torch flame should be so adjusted that it will furnish a slight excess of acetylene, and it is essential to avoid contact of the white-hot bulb or cone with the metal that is about to become molten, because the hot temperature in this part of the flame tends to produce holes in the metal which are often difficult to repair. The correct distance varies according to the size of torch tip employed, but in general, the distance should be from ¼ to ¾ inch. After welding, the casting should be reheated evenly and allowed to cool very slowly. When the casting is cold, it should be thoroughly washed in hot water to remove all traces of the flux, which would otherwise continue to produce a chemical action on the metal that would result in harmful corrosion.

Aluminum Welding Fluxes. — The oxide formed in the course of melting aluminum offers considerable resistance to the welding flame. It does not always rise to the surface, especially if the work is thick, yet it must be eliminated to effect a homogeneous weld. This is done by employing a flux which dissolves and deoxidizes the layer of oxide adjacent to the joint to be welded, at the temperature at which the aluminum reaches a molten state. Another function of a flux is to protect the fused metal from contact with the air.

An example of a good flux for aluminum and aluminum alloys with a melting point of approximately 1110 degrees F. is one containing a mixture of lithium chloride, potassium chloride, potassium bisulphate, and potassium fluoride.

When castings that have sand on their surface are to be welded, a flux that will remove the sand must be used. If the sand is not removed, it is in part reduced, resulting in silicon being passed into the metal — a condition that often reduces the strength of the weld an appreciable amount. A flux that is adapted for use under these conditions is composed of potassium chloride or fluorspar. This flux will prevent silicon from entering the alloy.

The flux may be applied in paste form to the surfaces to be welded, or the parts may be heated and the powdered flux sprinkled over the joint, or the end of the welding rod may be heated and dipped into the flux, which readily adheres to it in the form of a thin varnish; the last method is the safest and best.

Welding Brass. — In many cases it is preferable to braze rather than to weld brass parts. When the oxy-acetylene torch is used for brass, adjust the flame until there is a single cone, as for steel welding. Keep the point of the white flame slightly away from the weld, according to the thickness of the piece, so that the heat will not be sufficient to burn the copper in the brass or volatilize the zinc. If a white smoke appears, remove the flame, as this indicates excessive heat. A little borax should be used as a flux. For brass welding, it is advisable to use a tip about one size larger than for the same thickness of steel. As the weld is really cast brass, it will not have the strength of rolled sheet brass. Do not breathe the fumes while welding brass.

Welding Copper. — The purest copper wire obtainable should be used as a filler when welding copper and great care should be taken to prevent oxidation. Use the same kind of flame as for steel, but a much larger tip for corresponding dimensions, because of the great radiating property of copper. Pre-heating is necessary when a large piece of copper is to be welded, as otherwise so much heat from the torch will be dissipated by radiation that little will be left for fusing the metal. Copper will weld at about 1930 degrees F.; hence, the flame need not have so high a temperature as for steel and it must not be concentrated on so small a surface. On account of the radiation, however, the total quantity of heat must be greater. Welded copper has the strength of cast copper, but can be rendered more tenacious by hammering. The radiation of heat from copper can be considerably lessened by covering it with asbestos sheets while heating. To weld copper to steel, first raise the steel to a white heat (the welding point); then put the copper into contact with it and the two metals will fuse together. When the copper begins to flow, withdraw the flame slightly to prevent burning. Ordinary borax may be used as a flux for copper welding.

Welding High-speed Steel to Machine Steel. — Compression welding can be employed advantageously for welding small high-speed drills which require carbon steel shanks of special length. A jig made to hold the carbon steel shank and the high-speed steel drill in line should be employed, and the ends set about ⅛ inch apart. When the ends have been heated by the torch to the welding temperature, or until the ends are in a pasty condition, the drill is given a smart rap with a wooden mallet and driven against the steel shank, thus producing a butt or compression weld. This method is most successful for lengthening small twist drills with the oxy-acetylene torch.

Welding Cast Iron to Steel. — To weld cast iron to steel, cast-iron rods are used as welding material. The steel must be first heated to the melting point, as cast iron melts at a lower temperature. A very little scaling powder should be used. Pre-heating the cast iron and steel is generally recommended when the joint exceeds three or four inches in length, especially if adjacent parts are thin and likely to crack.

Welding Steel Castings. — As steel castings vary in carbon content, no fixed rule can be laid down for welding them; but, in general, they offer no serious difficulty to welding provided approved welding rods are used. This statement applies to castings whose carbon content is not more than 0.25 per cent. Steel castings containing carbon much in excess of 0.25 or 0.30 per cent may require the use of special welding rods such as those containing nickel. Nickel welding rods give good results on certain grades of steel castings, railway track steel, switch points and other steel products having comparatively high carbon content.

Welding Malleable Iron. — Welding of malleable iron with the oxy-acetylene torch is not recommended, the reason being that the welded joint is necessarily weaker than the malleable iron due to the changes in physical structure produced by the high temperature. Brazing with an approved bronze rod is recommended. A brazed joint in malleable iron will generally be nearly, if not quite, as strong as the original material. Brazing can be effected at a temperature that causes little change in the malleable characteristics.

Welding Tool Steel. — Welding tool steel of the higher carbon contents, with the oxy-acetylene torch, is not generally recommended. The carbon content is changed and the weld produced may be valueless for tool purposes. However, a skilled welder can produce welds in high-carbon steel under proper conditions with fair success and if properly heat-treated they may give satisfaction under some conditions of use.

Welding Alloy Steels. — The alloy steels such as vanadium, chrome-nickel, etc., used in motor car construction may be welded successfully with adding material containing vanadium or nickel. The welds should be heat-treated afterwards in order to restore the joint portion to the physical condition of the part before welding

Efficiency of Joints Welded by Oxy-Acetylene Process. — In order to determine the strength of joints in mild steel plates welded by the oxy-acetylene process, a series of tests was made at the Univerity of Illinois. These tests included (1) static load in tension, (2) repeated load (bending) and (3) impact in tension (in a drop-testing machine). The principal object of the tests was to compare the strength of the welded joints with the strength of the original plate. This ratio of strength is defined as the *efficiency of the joint.* The efficiency may be computed by either of two methods. The first method for obtaining the joint efficiency consists in comparing the strength of a test piece containing the welded joint, with the strength of a test piece of equal width cut from the same plate, no allowance being made for the additional thickness of the joint due to the addition of filler material. The second method for obtaining the *efficiency of the joint material* is based on the intensity of stress at the yield point or rupture both for the joint and the plate, as computed from the load and dimensions of the cross-section. The tests were made on joints welded by skilled workmen and in a shop especially fitted for oxy-acetylene welding. For joints made without subsequent treatment after welding, the joint efficiency for static tension was about 100 per cent for plates ½ inch thick or less; the efficiency decreased for thicker plates. For static tension tests the efficiency of the material in the joints may vary from 75 to 85 per cent, depending upon the skill of the operator. For repeated stress tests, the joint efficiency was about 100 per cent for plates ½ inch thick or less. Hammering or drawing the weld while hot, increases the strength. The impact tests showed that oxy-acetylene welded joints are decidedly weaker under shock than is the original material.

Cutting Metals with an Oxidizing Flame

The oxy-hydrogen and oxy-acetylene flames are especially adapted to cutting metals. When iron or steel is heated to a high temperature, it has a great affinity for oxygen and readily combines with it to form different oxides, which causes the metal to be disintegrated and burned with great rapidity. The metal cutting or burning torch operates on this principle. A torch tip is designed to pre-heat the metal, which is then burned or oxidized by a jet of pure oxygen. The kerf or path left by the flame is suggestive of a saw cut when the cutting torch has been properly adjusted and used. The traversing motion of the torch along the work may be controlled either by hand or mechanically.

The Cutting Torch. — The ordinary cutting torch consists of a heating jet using oxygen and acetylene, oxygen and hydrogen, or, in fact, any other gas which, when combined with oxygen, will produce sufficient heat. By the use of this heating jet, the metal is first brought to a sufficiently high temperature, and an auxiliary jet of pure oxygen is then turned onto the red-hot metal, when the action just referred to takes place. Some cutting torches have a number of pre-heating flame ports surrounding the central oxygen port, so that a pre-heating flame will precede the oxygen regardless of the way in which the torch is moved. This arrangement has been used to advantage in mechanically guided torches. The rate of cutting varies with the thickness of the steel, the size of the tip and the oxygen pressure.

Adjustment and Use of Cutting Torch. — When using the cutting torch for the cutting of steel plate, the pre-heating flame first comes into contact with the edge of the plate and quickly raises it to a white hot temperature, and then the oxygen valve is opened by pulling a trigger on the torch and, as the pure oxygen comes into contact with the heated metal, the latter is burned or oxidized.

Metals that can be Cut. — Metals such as wrought iron and steels of comparatively low carbon content can be cut readily with the cutting torch. High carbon steels may be cut successfully if pre-heated to a temperature that depends some-what on the carbon content. The higher the carbon content, the greater the degree of pre-heating. A black heat is sufficient for ordinary tool steel, but a low red may be required for some of the alloy tool steels. Brass and bronze plates have been cut by interposing them between steel plates.

Cutting Stainless Steel. — Stainless steel can be cut readily by the flux-injection method. The elements which give stainless steel their desirable properties produce oxides which reduce the operation to a slow melting away process when the conventional oxy-acetylene cutting equipment is used. By injecting a suitable flux directly into the stream of cutting oxygen before it enters the torch, the obstructing oxides are removed. A portable flux feeding unit is designed to inject a predetermined amount of the flux powder. The rate of flux flow is accurately regulated by a vibrator type of dispenser with rheostat control. The flux-injection method is applicable either to machine cutting or to a hand controlled torch. The operating procedure and speed of cutting are practically the same as in cutting mild steel.

Cutting Cast Iron. — The cutting of cast iron with the oxy-acetylene torch is practicable although it cannot be cut as readily as steel. The ease of cutting seems to depend largely on the physical character of the cast iron, very soft cast iron being more difficult to cut than harder varieties. The cost is much higher than that for cutting the same thickness of steel, because of the larger pre-heating flame necessary and the larger oxygen consumption. In spite of this, however, this method is economical in many cases. The slag from a cast iron cut contains considerable melted cast iron, while in the case of steel, the slag is practically free from particles of the metal. This indicates that cast iron cutting is partly a melting operation. Increased speed and decreased cost can often be obtained by feeding a steel rod, about ¼ inch in diameter, into the top of the cut, just beneath the torch tip. This furnishes a large amount of slag which flows over the cut and increases the temperature of the cast iron. Special tips are used owing to the amount of heat and oxygen required.

Mechanically Guided Torches. — Cutting torches used for cutting openings in plates or blocks or for cutting parts to some definite outline, often are guided mechanically. Torches guided by pantograph mechanisms are especially adapted for tracing the outline to be cut from a pattern or drawing. Other designs are preferable for straight-line cutting and one type is designed for circular cutting.

Cutting Steel Castings. — When cutting steel castings, care should be taken to prevent burning pockets in the metal when the flame strikes a blow-hole. If a blow-hole is penetrated, the molten oxide will splash into the cavity and the flame will be diverted. The presence of the blow-hole is generally indicated by excessive sparks. The operator should immediately move the torch back along the cut and direct it at an angle so as to strike the metal beneath the blow-hole and burn it away if possible beyond the cavity, when cutting in the normal position may be resumed.

Thickness of Metal that can be Cut. — The maximum thickness of metal that can be cut by these high-temperature flames depends largely upon the gases used and the pressure of the oxygen, which may be as high as 150 pounds per square inch; the thicker the metal the higher the pressure required. When using the oxy-acetylene flame, it might be practicable to cut iron or steel up to 12 or 14 inches in thickness, whereas, the oxy-hydrogen flame has been used to cut steel plates 24 inches thick. The oxy-hydrogen flame will cut thicker material principally because it is longer than the oxy-acetylene flame and can penetrate to the full depth of the cut, thus keeping all the oxide in a molten condition so that it can easily be blown out by the oxygen cutting jet. A mechanically guided torch will cut thick material more satisfactorily than a hand-guided torch, because the flame is directed straight into the cut and does not wabble, as it tends to do when the torch is held by hand. With any flame, the cut is less accurate and the kerf wider, as the thickness of the metal increases. When cutting light material, the kerf might be $\frac{1}{16}$ inch wide, whereas, for heavy stock it might be $\frac{1}{4}$ or $\frac{3}{8}$ inch wide.

Welding with Thermit

Thermit Process. — This process of welding metals is effected by pouring superheated thermit steel around the parts to be united. Thermit is a mixture of finely divided aluminum and iron oxide. This mixture is placed in a crucible and the steel is produced by igniting the thermit in one spot by means of a special powder, which generates the intense heat necessary to start the chemical reaction. When the reaction is once started, it continues throughout the entire mass, the oxygen of the iron being taken up by the aluminum (which has a strong affinity for it), producing aluminum oxide (or slag) and superheated thermit steel. Ordinarily, the reaction requires from 35 seconds to one minute, depending upon the amount of thermit used. As soon as it ceases, the steel sinks to the bottom of the crucible and is tapped into a mold surrounding the parts to be welded. As the temperature of the steel is about 4000 to 4500 degrees F., it fuses and amalgamates with the broken sections, thus forming a homogeneous weld.

It is necessary to pre-heat the sections to be welded before pouring, to prevent chilling the steel. The principal steps of the welding operation are, to clean the sections to be welded, remove enough metal at the fracture to provide for a free flow of thermit steel, align the broken members and surround them with a mold to retain the steel, pre-heat by means of a gasoline torch to prevent chilling the steel, ignite the thermit and tap the molten steel into the mold. This process is especially applicable to the welding of large sections. It has been extensively used for welding locomotive frames, broken motor casings, rudder- and stern-posts of ships, crankshafts, spokes of driving wheels, connecting rods, and heavy repair work in general. One of the great advantages of the thermit process is that broken parts can usually be welded in place. For example, locomotive frames are welded by simply removing parts that would interfere with the application of a suitable mold. Thermit is also used for pipe welding, rail welding, and in foundry practice, to prevent the "piping" of ingots.

Composition of Thermit Steel. — An average analysis of thermit steel is as follows: Carbon, 0.20 to 0.30 per cent; manganese, 0.50 to 0.60 per cent; silicon, 0.25 to 0.50 per cent; sulphur, 0.03 to 0.04 per cent; phosphorus, 0.03 to 0.04 per cent; aluminum, 0.07 to 0.18 per cent. The tensile strength is about 65,000 pounds per square inch and the elastic limit about 34000 pounds per square inch.

Electric Welding

Electric welding processes are utilized extensively in joining both ferrous and non-ferrous metals in connection with the assembly of parts in manufacturing, in producing liquid- or gas-type joints, and for a large variety of miscellaneous operations. The following summary deals with important developments in electric welding processes, their characteristic features, and general applications.

Resistance Welding. — In welding metals by the resistance method, heat is generated within the metals by their resistance to the passage of electric current. This current may range from a few thousand to several hundred thousand amperes, depending upon the thickness of the stock. The transformer of the welder converts the commercial voltage down to a low voltage which usually is less than 30 and to a large current volume.

The current required for welding decreases as the electrical resistance of metal increases. Stainless steel, monel metal, and silicon bronzes require less current than ordinary steel because they have higher resistance. Copper and silver are difficult to weld because of their low resistance and the difficulty in obtaining electrodes to carry the large volume of current. Aluminum, which has two-thirds the conductivity of copper, may be welded readily although considerable current is required. There are two general methods of resistance welding. One is known as spot welding and the other as butt welding.

Spot Welding. — Spot welding is commonly employed to join sheets of metal by fusing them at various points. A typical application consists in clamping two or more sheets or pieces to be welded, between two copper or copper alloy welding tips or electrodes; then when current of sufficient strength passes from one electrode to another, the fusing or welding occurs. In addition to ordinary steel, coated and plated steels such as tin plate, terne plate, galvanized and zinc plated steel can be spot welded successfully. In the case of chromium plated steel, however, there is likely to be objectionable marring of the chromium plate which is too thin to permit subsequent finishing. Commercial aluminum alloys in either sheet or extruded form may be spot welded, provided the thickness is not excessive. High welding current values and a comparatively brief welding period are essential. On alternating-current aluminum welding machines, duration of the welding current may be controlled by electronic equipment. The electrode's shape must result in a high concentration of current. The welding tips used for magnesium alloys are similar to those employed for aluminum.

Projection Welding. — This method is a form of spot welding and it is so named because projections or embossed areas on one or both parts to be welded, make contact and localize the current flow and heating. Circular projections usually are employed. Projection welding is especially useful in welding stampings because the projecting areas may be formed in the die. Copper and brass are not adapted to projection welding. In some cases, however, dissimilar metals may be welded, such as steel to brass, aluminum or bronze. Ordinary spot welding is preferable to projection welding for thin steel sheets.

Seam Welding. — When this method is employed, the welding is done between two rotating circular electrodes. The seam consists of a series of spots. If the spacing is such that the spots overlap, a liquid- or gas-tight joint may be formed. The term "stitch" welding is sometimes used to indicate spot welding when there are spaces between the welds. Terne plate, tin plate, galvanized iron, and, in fact, most coated as well as uncoated steels, may be seam welded satisfactorily. Stainless steels, especially the 18-8 type, weld readily. When aluminum is seam welded, roller electrodes are employed. Otherwise the equipment is similar to the alternating-current spot-welding equipment.

Butt-Welding. — This method is employed extensively in end-to-end joining, as in forming continuous strips, bars or tubes, and also in welding ring-shaped or circular parts. There are also miscellaneous applications of end or butt welding. In what is known as *"upset" butt welding*, the ends to be welded are forced together and the current in passing through the end surfaces where resistance is highest, causes fusion. This method has largely been supplanted by *flash welding*, which is used extensively and is so named because of the flashing action between the parts being welded. These parts may either make very light contact or there may be a small air gap between them. The flashing is accompanied by fusion, and welding is completed by the application of pressure. A stock length allowance is required to compensate for the "burn off" and "push up." The pressure between parts may range from 5000 to 25,000 pounds per square inch, depending upon the alloy being welded. Flash welding is applicable to practically all steels and alloys in common use.

Percussive Welding. — This resistance process is confined to butt welded joints. An intensive discharge of electrical energy occurs either simultaneously with or slightly before the application of high pressure or a sudden hammer-like blow. The joining of pieces of wire, rod or tubing to each other or to flat surfaces, especially when the metals are dissimilar, represent typical applications of percussive welding.

Arc Welding.
— Arc welding is a fusion process so that pressure is not required. In *metal arc welding*, an electric arc between the "base metal" and the melting electrode, fuses adjacent edges of the base metal and supplies filler metal. The arc is maintained by moving or feeding the melting electrode toward the base metal. This may be done either manually or automatically. The weld metal may consist of either of a mixture of filler and base metals or it may contain filler metal only. In *carbon arc* and *atomic hydrogen welding*, the filler metal (in wire or rod form) may or may not have a manual or automatic feeding movement and be welded simultaneously with the base metal. Unless filler metal is employed, the weld metal consists of base metal only.

Unshielded and Shielded Welding Processes. — If the molten metal in a weld is not protected in some manner, oxidation and the absorption of nitrogen from the air may seriously affect the physical properties of the weld; hence, a number of methods of protecting the molten metal have been developed. When such protection is employed, the welding is known as a *"shielded" process*. The primary reason for this shielding is to obtain weld metal having the same physical properties as the base metal. If there is no protection or only partial protection, this is known as an *unshielded process*. The real distinction between a shielded and an unshielded process is in the physical properties of the weld itself. The unshielded process is suitable for many applications although it should not be employed for butt joints or for parts subjected to high residual or other stresses or to fatigue or impact stresses. Welds obtained by an unshielded process may have adequate tensile strength but lack the required ductility and resistance to fatigue and impact. The following terms relate to different shielded processes:

Covered Electrode Welding — This term includes all processes whereby shielding is the result of combustion, vaporization, and melting of different ingredients in whatever covering is applied to the wire core of the electrode.

Taper Shielded Welding — This term includes all processes utilizing a ribbon or cord which is fed independently and automatically into the zone of the arc. The functioning is similar to that of the coverings on the covered electrodes.

Gas Shielded Welding — The arc zone in these gas shielded processes is surrounded by a reducing or inert gas which is supplied from an independent source.

Flux Shielded Welding — These processes, as the name implies, utilize a flux (in the form of a paste or powder) which is placed in the joint ahead of the arc and is either partially or entirely melted and vaporized as the welding proceeds.

Currents Used for Resistance Welding. — Both shielded and unshielded processes utilize alternating and direct currents and covered electrodes for either alternating or direct currents or both are obtainable. In atomic hydrogen and double carbon-arc welding, alternating current is used. When only one carbon electrode is employed in a carbon arc process, a direct current with straight polarity is used, the work being the positive pole and the electrode the negative pole. The electrode is the negative pole. There is no carbon pick-up in the weld and the electrode is consumed at a relatively low rate.

When "magnetic blow" causes arc instability, alternating current usually is preferable. Direct current may be preferable for certain types of bare and covered non-ferrous electrodes or in making ferrous welds in horizontal, vertical and overhead positions.

Arc Welding Equipment. — In selecting welding equipment, the type, size and rating should be based upon the character of the work. The following general types are applicable to a wide range of arc welding processes:

Either variable-voltage or constant-voltage, direct-current generators and motor generators; direct-current arc rectifiers; variable-voltage alternating-current transformers; variable-voltage alternating-current rotating motor generators, frequency changes, phase changes, or combinations. The constant-voltage direct-current equipment may be designed for either single or multiple operation.

Variable Voltage. — The variable voltage or constant energy, direct-current and alternating-current equipment is designed to prevent the sputtering and extinction of the arc when the welder is inexperienced, and it also aids the experienced welder. The electrical energy delivered remains approximately constant within the range of voltage variation likely to occur in manual welding.

Constant Voltage. — Direct-current equipment of this type is designed to supply constant voltage to a welding system. Thus, current for a number of different welding operators may be obtained from this system. The amount of current in the arc may be controlled by adjustable resistance. Where a number of low current arcs are grouped in a limited area, multiple operation is advantageous.

Maintaining Arc Length Automatically. — Maintaining an arc length that is practically constant is essential in metallic arc welding. To accomplish this, the welding electrodes must be moved forward or toward the arc at whatever rate is required to compensate for the electrode loss as metal is deposited in the joint. In manual operation, maintaining the arc length depends upon the skill and experience of the operator. Automatic operation results in greater uniformity of arc length which tends toward more uniform welding. Other advantages of automatic control may be summarized as follows: A comparatively inexperienced welder can produce satisfactory welds; much higher currents can be used so that better fusion is possible; the rate of welding speed is relatively high; welding wire losses in the form of stub ends are eliminated; and continuous welds without intermediate craters are obtained. Bare or light-coated types of electrodes are used generally in automatic metallic arc welding because the current can be conducted readily into the electrode. If shielded arc welding is to be done, automatic special electrodes and attachments are employed.

Fully Automatic Arc Welding Equipment. — Arc welding apparatus that is fully automatic, controls not only the arc length but the movement of the work past the welding head or *vice versa*. The work usually is moved for the circumferential welding of tank seams or other cylindrical vessels, and the welding head usually is moved for welding the longitudinal seams of tanks, ship plates, and in welding light metal structures which may require support by jigs or clamps. If the path of the seam is irregular, as is often the case, it may be impracticable to design the welder so that the electrode will follow an irregular seam automatically. In such cases, the electrode is guided along the seam manually and only the arc is maintained automatically. Such a welder may be classed as *semi-automatic.*

Types of Joints. — The type of joint depends upon the structure being welded, the plate thickness, and the electrode used. Groove and fillet joints of all the common types may be employed. Single V-grooves are generally used in conjunction with electrodes of the bare and lightly-coated types. In welding with a shielded arc, the

U-form of groove is frequently used. Grooves of uniform width throughout their length are essential, especially when electrode is moved automatically along the seam. If the electrode moves along the seam at a uniform rate, variations in the groove width are liable to result in lack of uniformity in the weld. Even when the operator attempts to regulate the speed in order to compensate for those sections of the groove which are either too wide or too narrow, the results are not always satisfactory. In welding straight seams or circular seams, deviations from either a straight line or circle, as the case may be, should also be avoided so that adjustments of the welding head will not be necessary.

Application of Automatic Carbon Arc Welding. — Automatic shielded carbon arc welding is adapted to the welding of duplicate parts such as tanks, boilers, barrels, ship and barge work, etc. This method is applicable to the various steels, including stainless steels of the 18-8, 25-12, and 25-20 types. It is also applicable to copper, copper alloys, aluminum, and aluminum alloys.

Submerged Melt or "Unionmelt" Welding Process. — In welding by this fully automatic electric process, a special granulated material (or welding composition known as "Unionmelt") is laid automatically along the seam so that it covers constantly the end of the bare metal electrode; consequently, the entire welding action occurs beneath this material and without visible arc sparks, spatter, smoke, or flash. The movement of the welding head is accompanied by continuous feeding of the bare welding rod from a reel and the granulated material or Unionmelt is deposited progressively along the seam a few inches in front of the rod. The welding head performs the triple function of depositing the Unionmelt, feeding the welding rod into the welding zone, and transmitting the welding current to the rod. Several types of welding heads have been designed for different classes of work. Since only part of the Unionmelt is fused during the welding, the unfused material is picked up, usually by a suction cleaner, and returned to the hopper for reuse. The welding voltage, current, speed, and rod feed are all regulated automatically by electrical controls.

Any source of single-phase alternating current or direct current at an open-circuit voltage of about 85 to 100, can be used for the welding current. Alternating current is most frequently used.

Molten metal from the electrode is thoroughly mixed with the melted base metal to form the weld and the molten weld metal is covered by a liquid blanket of molten Unionmelt. The welds are characterized by unusual strength, ductility, shock resistance, uniformity, density, and corrosion resistance. In fact, the physical properties equal and are often superior to those of the base metal. The Unionmelt normally does not enter into the weld metal; special alloying elements, however, can be introduced into the weld metal by means of this material. The ratio of rod to plate that is fused in the weld is about 1 to 1.7.

General Application of the Process. — Unionmelt welding is especially advantageous for repetitive work and where welds can be made with the surface of the welding puddle approximately horizontal. The process is used extensively for such work as fabricating ships, barges, railroad cars, tanks, pipes, pressure vessels of all types, and many other classes of work.

This process has been applied successfully to welding low-carbon and medium-carbon steels, high-strength steels, stainless and other alloy steels. It has also been used for welding nickel, Monel, Everdur, and other non-ferrous metals.

Welds may be made in one pass which, because of the thickness of the material, would require two or more passes by other methods. The welding speed is another important feature. For example, butt welds can be made at 10 to 12 inches per minute in one-inch steel plate and at 5 to 6 inches per minute in two-inch plate.

Standard Arc and Gas Welding Symbols — 1

The welding symbols which follow are a standard of the American Welding Society. The *joint* of the weld is the basis of reference. A complete welding symbol consists of an arrow connecting with a reference line on one or both sides of which will be found the basic symbol or symbols and dimensional figures, indicating the type and size of weld. The locations of all symbols and figures relative to the reference line, are standardized as shown by examples to follow. The arrow points to the joint or to that member which is to be grooved when the groove is in one part only. There is always an "arrow" (or "near") side of the joint to which the arrow points, and an "opposite" (or "far") side.

Symbols Indicating Type of Weld								Field Weld	Weld all Around	Flush
Bead	Fillet	Square Groove	V Groove	Bevel Groove	U Groove	J Groove	Plug & Slot			

LOCATION OF SYMBOL INDICATING TYPE OF WELD

Symbol showing type of weld is always placed along reference line in general location indicated by dotted lines.

If weld symbol has one side or line which is perpendicular to reference line, always draw symbol with this line on left-hand side as shown for fillet weld (first diagram), for bevel groove weld (second diagram), and for J-groove weld (third diagram).

For welds on "arrow" (or "near") side of joint, place symbol on near side of reference line, with that part of symbol representing *joint face* toward observer (or beneath a horizontal reference line) as shown by first diagram.

For welds on "other" (or "far") side of joint, show symbol on far side of reference line, with *joint face* away from observer (or above a horizontal reference line) as shown by second diagram.

For welds on both sides of joint, show symbols on both sides of reference line (third diagram).

If joints have more than one type of weld, show symbol for each type. First diagram shows V weld on one side and bead on the other.

Show side from which square groove weld is made by location of bead or flush symbols. Second diagram: Square-groove weld with bead on "arrow" (or "near") side. Third diagram: Square-groove weld flush on both sides.

LOCATION OF SYMBOLS FOR GENERAL INSTRUCTIONS

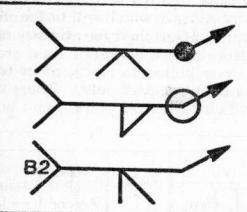

Black dot field-weld symbol usually indicates work erected in field; however, erecting shop may be classed as "field" by some manufacturers. Diagram shows standard location of dot.

Circle means "weld all around." Diagram shows circle at standard location.

Specification reference symbol is placed in tail of arrow to identify specification for filler metal etc. which may be given elsewhere on drawing. Tail may be omitted when there is no reference symbol.

METHODS OF INDICATING DIMENSIONS OF WELD

If vertical reference lines are used, place symbols and figures in position for reading from right-hand side of drawing.

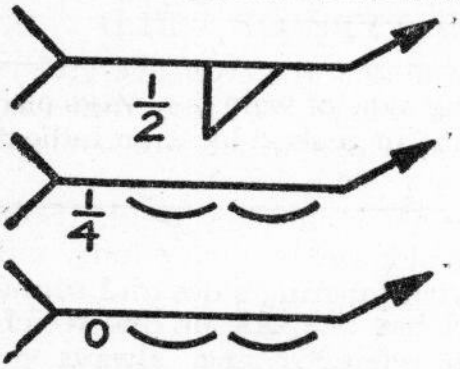

Size is shown at left of symbol. First diagram: ½-inch fillet weld. Size equals length of side and face of weld is assumed to have 45-degree angle unless otherwise specified. Second diagram: ¼-inch bead welds used in building up surfaces (size is minimum height of pad). Third diagram: Zero mark shows that minimum height of pad is not specified.

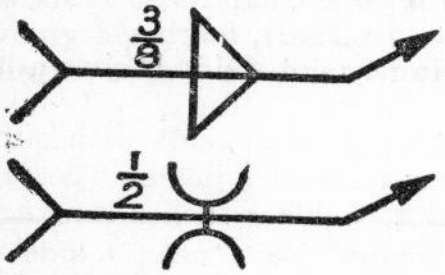

When *duplicate* welds are on both sides of joint, show size of weld on one side only. First diagram: ⅜-inch fillet weld on both sides. Second diagram: ½-inch U weld on both sides.

If weld sizes are not duplicate on "arrow side" and "other" side of joint, show dimensions on both sides. Diagram: ⅞-inch V weld on arrow (or near) side of joint; ⅜-inch V weld on other (or far) side.

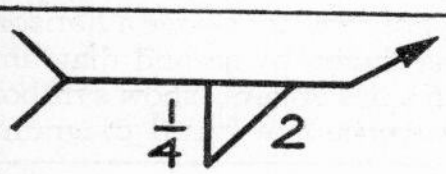

Show length of weld at right of symbol. Diagram shows ¼-inch fillet weld 2 inches long.

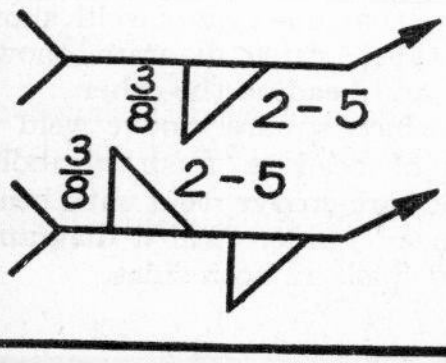

For intermittent welding, last figure at right shows distances between centers of "increments" or welded sections. First diagram: ⅜-inch fillet weld, 2-inch increments, 5 inches pitch or distance between centers of increments. Second diagram: (Weld symbols are staggered to show that intermittent welds are also staggered or not opposite each other). Two staggered ⅜-inch fillet welds, 2-inch increments, and 5 inches pitch.

Standard Arc and Gas Welding Symbols — 3

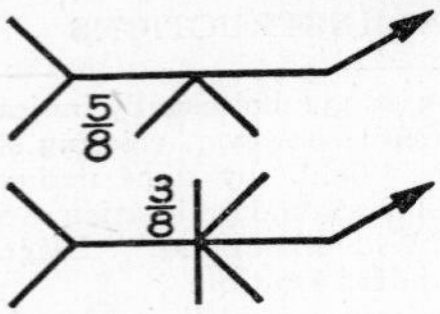

	Total depth of V and bevel-groove welds is assumed to equal thickness of welded part when depth dimension is not given. When depth of V and bevel-groove welds is less than thickness of part to be welded, depth is given. First diagram: V weld 5/8-inch deep. Second diagram: Bevel-groove weld 3/8 inch deep on both sides.
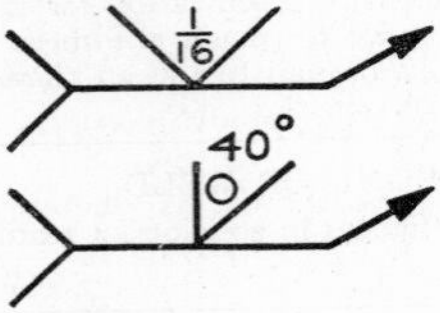	Show root opening of V and bevel-groove welds inside symbol when specification is required. If included angle of either V or bevel-groove weld is not user's standard and must be specified, place as shown. First diagram: V-weld with 1/16 inch root opening. Second diagram: 40° bevel-groove weld, no root opening.
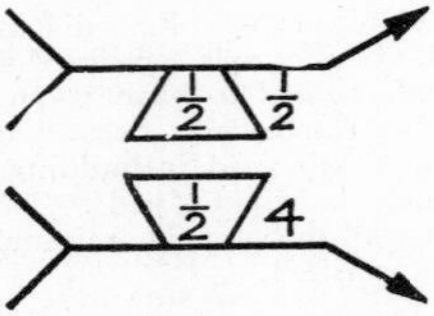	To show size of plug and slot welds, give root opening and root length. (These dimensions are equal for plug welds which are conical in form.) First diagram: 1/2-inch plug weld. Second diagram: 1/2-inch slot weld 4 inches long. (Slot weld is oblong with tapering sides and rounded ends.)
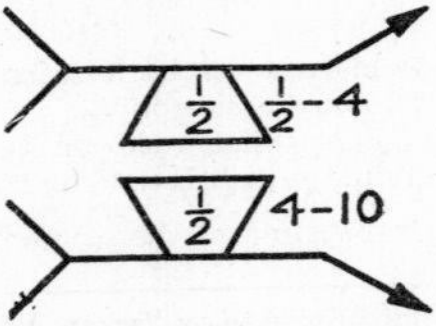	Pitch of row of plug or slot welds is shown by last figure at right. First diagram: 1/2-inch plug welds with pitch or center-to-center spacing of 4 inches. Second diagram: 1/2-inch slot welds 4 inches long and 10 inches pitch.
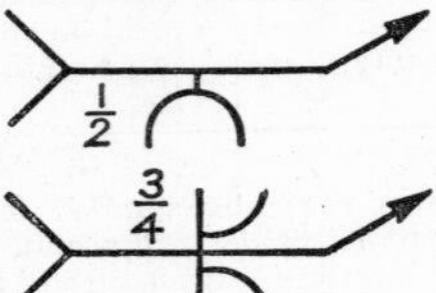	For U and J groove welds having user's standard proportions but incomplete penetration, show size or depth of single groove before welding. First diagram: 1/2-inch U weld. Second diagram: 3/4-inch J welds on both sides.
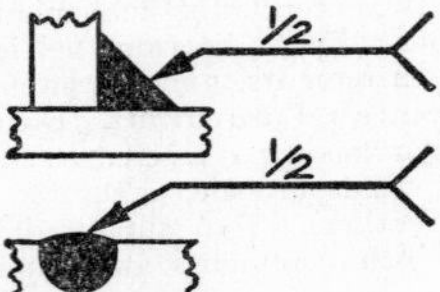	If cross-sectional shape of weld is shown on drawing, size of weld may be given without basic weld symbol. First diagram: 1/2-inch fillet weld. Second diagram: 1/2-inch U weld.

Standard Welding Definitions. — The following revised definitions were issued in 1945 by National Electrical Manufacturers Association.

Weld: A weld is a localized consolidation of metals by a welding process.

Fusion Welding: Fusion welding is a group of processes in which metals are welded together by bringing them to the molten state at the surfaces to be joined, with or without the addition of filler metal, without the application of mechanical pressure or blows.

Arc Welding: Arc welding is a non-pressure (fusion) welding process wherein the welding heat is obtained from an arc either between the base metal or weld metal and an electrode or between two electrodes.

Carbon Arc Welding: Carbon arc welding is an arc-welding process wherein one or more carbon or graphite electrodes are used with or without the use of filler metal.

Shielded Carbon Arc Welding: Shielded carbon arc welding is a carbon arc-welding process wherein the arc and molten weld metal are protected from the atmosphere by a shielding medium.

Metal Arc Welding: Metal arc welding is an arc-welding process wherein the electrode supplies the filler metal in the weld.

Shielded Metal Arc Welding: Shielded metal arc welding is a metal arc-welding process wherein the arc and weld metal are protected from the atmosphere by a shielding medium.

Atomic Hydrogen Welding: Atomic hydrogen welding is an alternating-current arc-welding process wherein the welding heat is obtained from an arc between two suitable electrodes in an atmosphere of hydrogen.

Manual Welding: Manual welding is welding wherein the arc is controlled or the torch is manipulated by hand.

Semi-automatic Welding: Semi-automatic welding is welding wherein the feed of filler metal is automatically controlled, the manipulation of the welding unit being controlled by hand.

Automatic Welding: Automatic welding is welding with equipment which automatically controls the entire welding operation, including feed, speed, oscillation, interruption, etc.

Carbon Arc Cutting: Carbon arc cutting is the process of severing metals by melting with the heat of the carbon arc.

Metal Arc Cutting: Metal arc cutting is the process of severing metals by melting with the heat of the metal arc.

Base (Parent) Metal: Base metal is the metal which is to be welded (or cut).

Weld Metal: Weld metal is the metal resulting from the fusion of the base metal or the base metal and the filler metal.

Filler Metal: Filler metal is the material that is added to the base metal to produce the weld in some forms of the fusion welding process.

Flux: Flux is the material used in welding to prevent the formation of oxides, nitrides or other undesirable inclusions in the weld and to eliminate those which have formed. In metal arc welding it is also employed to aid in the retention of the various elements of the electrode and to retard the rate of cooling of the weld metal.

Arc-welding Electrode: An arc-welding electrode is a wire or metal rod or a carbon (or other suitable material) rod, used as one (or both) of the terminals in an electrode circuit for the purpose of producing a welding arc.

Carbon-arc Electrode: A carbon-arc electrode is a carbon or graphite rod through which current is conducted between the electrode holder and the arc.

Metal-arc Electrode: A metal-arc electrode is a wire or rod, either lightly coated or covered, through which current is conducted between the electrode holder and the arc to provide filler metal.

(See also *Lightly Coated Electrodes* and *Heavily Covered Electrodes*, under Welding Electrode Standards.)

Electrode Holder: An electrode holder is a device used in the arc-welding process for mechanically holding the electrode and conducting the electric current from the electrode lead terminal to the electrode.

Filter Lens: A filter lens is a colored glass used in goggles, helmets and shields to exclude harmful light rays.

Welding Electrode Standards. — The electrode standards of the National Electrical Manufacturers Association (adopted in 1945) include two general classes of electrodes designated as "Lightly Coated" and "Heavily Covered"; in addition, there are seven types of electrodes identified by letters A to G and distinguished by their general applications.

Lightly Coated Electrodes: Electrodes with a thin coating designed to control welding characteristics. These are divided into two classes which are as follows:

1. Electrodes (formerly known as bare electrodes) with the coating applied either during or prior to the drawing operation.
2. Electrodes with coatings applied after the drawing process. Included herein are washed, sprayed, brushed, tumbled, dipped or otherwise made light coatings.

B. Heavily Covered Electrodes: Electrodes which have a relatively thick covering material serving the dual purpose of stabilizing the arc and improving the properties of the weld metal. Extrusion, wrapping, dipping or combinations of these or other means are included in this classification.

A. Mild-steel Electrodes: Ferrous electrodes designed primarily for welding mild steel with weld-tensile strengths, in general, not exceeding 75,000 pounds per square inch.

B. High-tensile Electrodes: Steel electrodes whose alloys are added to give tensile strength above 75,000 pounds per square inch in weld metal.

C. Hard-surfacing Electrodes: Electrodes which produce a weld metal to resist either wear, abrasion or impact.

D. Electrodes for Welding Cast Iron: 1. Ferrous electrodes having a mild steel or cast iron core principally used for the welding of cast iron. 2. Non-ferrous electrodes principally used for the welding of cast iron.

E. Corrosion Resisting Chromium and Chromium-Nickel Steel (Stainless) Welding Electrodes: All ferrous electrodes containing chromium in excess of 4 per cent as a principal alloying element and with or without the addition of nickel.

F. Non-ferrous Electrodes: Electrodes producing a weld deposit of essentially non-ferrous elements excepting chromium and nickel.

G. Miscellaneous Electrodes: All electrodes of a type or for purposes not defined under types A to F, inclusive.

Diameters and Lengths of Electrodes

| Electrode Diameter (Inches) | Length (Inches) | | | Electrode Diameter (Inches) | Length (Inches) | | |
| | End Grip | | | | End Grip | | |
	Mild-steel Electrodes	Corrosion and Scale Resisting Alloy Electrodes	Center Grip All Types		Mild-steel Electrodes	Corrosion and Scale Resisting Alloy Electrodes	Center Grip All Types
1/16	9	9	18	3/16	14 or 18	14	..
5/64	9	9	18	7/32	18	..	..
3/32	12 or 14	9	18	1/4	18	14	..
1/8	14	14	..	5/16	18	18	..
5/32	14	14	..	3/8	18	18	..

Strength of Joints Welded by Electric Arc Process. — An extensive series of tests to determine the strength of arc-welded joints in steel plates for ship construction (containing about 0.15 per cent carbon) showed the following results:

The ultimate strength of small welded specimens was over 100 per cent of the strength of the unwelded steel plate for thicknesses of ½ inch and averaged 90 per cent for plates ¾ and 1 inch thick. Up to the point of fracture, the extensions of the welded specimens are not sensibly different from those of similar unwelded material. At stresses greater than the elastic limit, the welded material is less ductile than mild steel and the ultimate elongation of a welded specimen, measured on a length of 8 inches, is only 10 per cent, as compared with 25 or 30 per cent for mild steel. Welded specimens are not capable of being bent without fracture over a given radius for more than 80 degrees with ¼-inch plate, and the bend is reduced to about 20 degrees in the case of 1-inch plate. Unwelded material under the same conditions can be bent to 180 degrees.

Butt welds have a tensile strength of from 90 to 95 per cent in welded plate. Lap welds with fillets on both edges have a tensile strength of from 70 to 80 per cent of the unwelded material. While the tensile strength of large butt welds is about the same as the unwelded material, it was thought that greater reliability of workmanship could be obtained with joints that are either lapped or strapped. It was found that the lap joint is about as strong as the riveted lap joint, and will withstand more trying conditions than the riveted lap joint.

Soldering and Brazing

Solders. — Solders for joining metallic surfaces or edges are almost invariably composed of an alloy of two or more metals. The solder used must have a lower melting point than the metals to be joined by it, but the fusing point should approach, as nearly as possible, that of the metals to be joined so that a more tenacious joint is effected. Solders may be divided into two general classes, hard and soft. The former fuses at a red heat; the latter, at a comparatively low temperature. These solders are also subdivided into a variety of classes such as brass, silver, gold, copper, tin, plumbers' solder and others — the name, in most cases, designating the application.

Soft Solders. — Soft solders consist chiefly of lead and tin, although other metals are occasionally added to lower the melting point. Lead-tin alloys melt at a lower temperature, with an increase in the percentage of tin, up to a certain point, but when the tin exceeds 67 per cent, the melting point rises gradually to the melting point of tin, as shown by the table "Melting Temperatures of Lead-tin Alloys." This table also gives the Brinell hardness test. The results show that the hardest alloy contains 66 per cent of tin and 34 per cent of lead. Soft solders are termed "common," "medium" and "fine," according to the tin content, those containing the most lead being the cheapest and having the highest melting temperatures.

Fine solder is largely used for soldering britannia metal, brass and tin-plate articles. It is also used for soldering cast iron, steel, copper and many alloys. The soft solder called "common" is used by plumbers for ordinary work; this solder contains two parts of lead to one part of tin. The best soft solders are made from pure lead and pure tin. Antimony is an objectionable impurity as it renders the solder less fluid when melted and tends to prevent perfect adhesion of the surfaces. Zinc also has an injurious effect on soft solder, causing it to flow sluggishly. Aluminum acts in a similar way. A small percentage of phosphorus renders soft solder very "lively"; that is, the solder has a tendency to run freely. Too much phosphorus is injurious, and if added to thin the solder it should be in the form of phosphor-tin. One or two ounces of five per cent phosphor-tin to one hundred pounds of solder is generally sufficient.

Melting Temperatures of Lead-tin Alloys

Percentage		Melting Temp., Deg. F.	Brinell Hardness Test	Percentage		Melting Temp., Deg. F.	Brinell Hardness Test
Tin	Lead			Tin	Lead		
0	100	618.8	3.9	60	40	368.6	14.6
10	90	577.4	10.1	66	34	356.0	16.7
20	80	532.4	12.16	70	30	365.0	15.8
30	70	491.0	14.5	80	20	388.4	15.2
40	60	446.0	15.8	90	10	419.0	13.3
50	50	401.0	15.0	100	0	450.0	4.1

Melting Temperatures of Copper-zinc Alloys

Percentage		Melting Temp., Deg. F.	Percentage		Melting Temp., Deg. F.	Percentage		Melting Temp., Deg. F.
Copper	Zinc		Copper	Zinc		Copper	Zinc	
100	0	1980	71	29	1746	41	59	1544
96	4	1967	66.4	33.6	1684	35	65	1501
86	14	1890	63	37	1666	33	67	1477
80	20	1846	60	40	1634	29	71	1467
76	24	1796	50	50	1616	24	76	1364
72	28	1756	48	52	1598	20	80	1301

Hard Soldering and Brazing. — Hard solder is used for joining such metals as copper, silver and gold, and alloys such as brass, German silver, gun metal, etc., which require a strong joint and often a solder the color of which is near that of the metal to be joined. The hard soldering of copper, iron, brass, etc., is generally known as brazing, and the solder as spelter. The operations of hard soldering and brazing are identical, and the two terms are often used interchangeably. According to common usage, however, there is the following distinction. Brazing is generally understood to mean the joining of metals by a film of brass, whereas hard soldering (which is the term used by jewelers) ordinarily means that "silver solder" is used as the uniting medium. (See "Silver Solders.") For hard soldering or brazing, a red heat is necessary, and borax is used as a flux to protect the metal from oxidation, and to dissolve the oxides formed. Heating cannot be done with a soldering iron, but should be effected by a blowpipe, blowtorch, gas forge or a coke or charcoal fire.

As a greater degree of heat is required to melt spelter than soft solder, brazed work will withstand more heat without breaking or weakening than parts which are soldered. The chief advantage of a brazed joint, however, lies in its superior strength. Before work is assembled for brazing, it should be carefully cleaned; the parts are then fastened together in the position they are to occupy when joined. Usually the pieces are secured by pinning, but sometimes wire, bolts or clamps are used for holding the parts together. If practicable, they should be secured in such a way that the work can be turned over during the process of brazing without disturbing the relation of the parts, thus affording a better chance to apply the flux and spelter.

Composition of Brazing Alloys

Percentage				Characteristics	Color
Copper	Zinc	Tin	Lead		
58	42	....	....	Very strong	Reddish-yellow
53	47	....	....	Strong	Reddish-yellow
48	52	....	....	Medium	Reddish-yellow
54.5	43.5	1.5	0.5	Medium	Reddish-yellow
34	66	....	....	Easily fusible	White
44	50	4	2	Easily fusible	Gray
55	26	15	4	White solder	White

Soft and Hard Solders for Various Metals

Metal to be Soldered	Flux	Soft Solder		
		Tin	Lead	Other Constituents*
Aluminum........	Stearin........................	70	....	Zn 25, Al 3, P-tin 2
Brass..........	Chloride of zinc, rosin, or chloride of ammonia..............	66	34	......
Gun metal.....		63	37	......
Copper..........		60	40	......
Lead............	Tallow or rosin..................	33	67	......
Block tin........	Chloride of zinc..............	99	1	......
Tinned steel.....	Chloride of zinc or rosin........	64	36	......
Galvanized steel...	Hydrochloric acid..............	58	42	......
Zinc............	Hydrochloric acid..............	55	45	......
Pewter..........	Gallipoli oil..................	25	25	Bi 50
Iron and steel.....	Chloride of ammonia..........	50	50	......
Gold............	Chloride of zinc..............	67	33	......
Silver............	Chloride of zinc..............	67	33	......
Bismuth..........	Chloride of zinc..............	33	33	Bi 34

* Zn = zinc.   Al = aluminum.   P-tin = phosphor-tin.   Bi = bismuth.

Metal to be Soldered	Flux	Hard Solder			
		Copper	Zinc	Silver	Gold
Brass, soft........	Borax..............	22	78	......	......
Brass, hard.......	Borax..............	45	55	......	......
Copper..........	Borax..............	50	50	......	......
Gold............	Borax..............	22	......	11	67
Silver............	Borax..............	20	10	70	......
Cast iron........	Cuprous oxide.....	55	45	......	......
Iron and steel.....	Borax..............	64	36	......	......

Fluxes for Soldering. — As two pieces to be soldered must be thoroughly alloyed with the material used as a solder, the temperature must be raised and maintained at such a point that inter-penetration can take place completely. It is necessary that the surfaces to be joined be perfectly clean, and means must be provided to prevent oxidation during soldering, oxides tending to prevent interfusion. This is accomplished by using a coating of some substance that melts at the fusing temperature of the solder, and thus excludes the air. The coating should have a solvent action on the oxide, thus keeping the metal clean and enabling the metal and solder to unite thoroughly. The fluxes generally used are rosin, sal-ammoniac, zinc chloride and borax. The flux is added first and the solder melted by means of a flame or soldering iron, the latter first having been smoothed with a file and then properly tinned. Rosin and chloride of zinc are fluxes commonly used for soft soldering tin (tinned iron) brass, etc. For hard soldering or brazing, use burnt or calcined borax, or boracic acid in powdered form. In all cases where zinc chloride is used as a flux, the article should be cleaned after soldering to prevent subsequent corrosion of the metal.

Alloys for Brazing Solders. — The alloys or "spelters" used for brazing are composed of copper-zinc alloys. The melting point of these alloys depends upon the percentage of zinc. As the proportion of zinc increases, the melting point is lowered, as shown by the table "Melting Temperatures of Copper-zinc Alloys." The fusing point of the spelter should be as close as possible to that of the article to be brazed, as a more tenacious joint is thereby secured. An easily fusible spelter may be made of two parts zinc to one part copper, but the joint will be weaker than when an alloy more difficult to fuse is employed. A spelter that is readily fused may be made of 44 per cent copper, 50 per cent zinc, 4 per cent tin and 2 per cent lead. Alloys containing much lead should be avoided, since lead does not transfuse with brass and thus decreases the strength of the joint. A hard solder for the richer alloys of copper and zinc may be produced from 53 parts copper and 47 parts zinc. Copper and iron have a much higher melting point than brass, thus allowing the use of a richer copper alloy. Tin is often added as one of the ingredients, but it should be sparingly used, because it increases the brittleness of the solder. The addition of tin to brass lightens the color, giving it a gray tint. A variety of different brazing alloys and their characteristics are given in the table "Composition of Brazing Alloys."

Silver Solders. — Silver solder is a hard solder containing silver, copper and zinc or brass. The composition of silver solders varies considerably according to the nature of the work. A silver solder extensively used by jewelers contains 70 parts silver and 30 parts copper. Silver coins can be used for small work. Silver soldering is employed for uniting comparatively small parts requiring a strong joint. The heating is usually effected by a blowpipe, and borax or powdered boracic acid may be used as a flux. The flux should be applied before heating, if possible.

A hard solder of low fusing point, that is used extensively by one of the largest electrical companies, is composed of 34.36 per cent copper; 49.24 per cent silver; and 16.40 per cent zinc. Borax is used as a flux.

Solders for German silver are generally made of the same materials as those which compose the alloy to be soldered, but in such proportions that the melting point is lower. In some cases, silver solder is used for uniting German silver articles, and German silver solder is also used for soldering articles of iron and steel on account of its high melting point and tenacity. German silver solder is known under different names, as argentan, arguzoid, etc. It is rendered moderately fusible by an addition of zinc to the copper and nickel. If the solder is too brittle, this is an indication of too much zinc, which defect can be remedied by adding the requisite amount of copper and nickel. For soldering alloys composed of from 16 to 22 per cent nickel, the following proportions may be used as a solder: Copper 47 per cent; nickel 11 per cent; and zinc 42 per cent.

Dip Brazing. — The principal difference between "dip brazing" and ordinary brazing is that with the former method the work is immersed into the molten spelter until the parts are heated sufficiently to be united by it. This method is extensively employed in bicycle manufacture as it is more economical for duplicate work.

Brazing Band-saws. — Band-saws are joined by lap brazing, silver solder being generally used. The lap is formed by beveling the ends to a sharp edge for a length of about ⅜ inch for saws up to ¾ inch wide, and ½ inch for saws from ¾ to 1½ inch wide. After a flux (such as borax) has been applied to the joint, the ends are clamped together. The solder is sometimes melted into the joint from the edges, or it may be applied between the two surfaces. A convenient method is as follows: Pound a piece of silver, about the size of a dime, until quite thin; then clamp it between the surfaces to be brazed after applying damp, powdered borax. When the heat is applied and the silver melts, clamp the beveled ends of the saw tightly together. The heating should be localized as much as possible. For a flux, use lump borax and pulverize it as used.

Cleaning Surfaces to be Brazed. — Before brazing iron or steel, the surfaces should be thoroughly cleaned, either by filing, grinding or by the use of a sand blast. Brass or bronze parts can be cleaned by dipping in a solution of one-third nitric acid and two-thirds sulphuric acid. This same solution can be used to remove the scale after brazing.

Aluminum Solder. — A thoroughly reliable aluminum solder that is used by a large electrical concern is composed of 75.5 parts (by weight) of tin; 18 parts of zinc; and 2.5 parts of aluminum. No flux is needed. It is advisable to slightly heat the parts to be soldered. Another aluminum solder is composed of 80 per cent tin and 20 per cent zinc, stearic acid being used as a flux.

Sweating. — When parts are soldered together by heating them sufficiently to melt the solder, instead of using a soldering iron, the operation is often known as sweating. Brass boxes for engine connecting-rods are usually sweated together prior to machining, in order to hold the two halves in alignment while finishing the sides and boring. The finished surfaces forming the joint between the brasses are first tinned or covered with solder. This is done by heating the brasses enough to melt the solder, then applying a flux (such as sal-ammoniac), and finally the solder. After tinning, the brasses are again heated if the solder has hardened; they are then put together and allowed to cool. The halves are separated after machining by heating them until the solder melts.

Brazing High-speed Steel Tips to Carbon Steel Shanks. — A method which is used in a large manufacturing plant is as follows: A seat is formed in the tool shank to receive the tip. A welding compound or flux is used in welding the tip to the shank. The flux is placed on the seat of the shank and the tip is then put on top of the flux in the desired position. The tool is placed in the preheating chamber of the furnace and heated to 1550 — 1600 degrees F., allowing sufficient time for complete penetration of the heat. The tool is then removed from the preheating chamber and the tip is pressed firmly to the seat of the shank to insure a close contact between the two pieces. Then the tool is placed in the main furnace chamber and heated rapidly to a temperature of approximately 2250 to 2400 degrees F., depending upon the kind of material used for the tip and its hardening requirements. The tool is next removed from the furnace and sufficient pressure applied to the tip to insure perfect cohesion. The press used for this purpose should be equipped with a pivoted pressure shoe and this shoe must be preheated to prevent cracking of the tip.

The hardening is accomplished at the same time as the tipping operation when tools are tipped with low-cobalt high-speed and high-cobalt high-speed steel. Tools that cannot be ground after hardening are often heated in barium chloride or some similar salt bath. After the pressing and welding operation, the tool is cooled to room temperature under an air blast or quenched in oil. It is advisable to maintain the oil quenching bath at a temperature of 150 to 200 degrees F. After the tipping operation, the tool should be reheated uniformly in an open furnace to a temperature of 1050 to 1150 degrees F. and allowed to cool in air. The hardened tools should have a minimum Rockwell C hardness of 63. Tips are cut from bar stock according to dimensions on standard detail drawings. The material generally used for the shanks of tools tipped with the cutting materials regularly employed contains 0.50 to 0.63 per cent carbon; 0.60 to 0.90 per cent manganese; 0.04 per cent phosphorus; and 0.15 per cent silicon.

Brazing Carbide Tips to Steel Shanks. — Sintered carbide tips or blanks are attached to steel shanks by brazing. Shanks usually are made of low-alloy steels having carbon contents ranging from 0.40 to 0.60 per cent. One prominent manufacturer of carbide tools recommends the following shank steels in the order listed: (1) High-silicon steel containing approximately 0.55 carbon, 0.85 manganese, 0.30 vanadium, 2.10 silicon, 0.25 chromium, and maximum sulphur and phosphorus contents of 0.025; (2) S.A.E. 2340 steel; (3) any low-alloy steel having 0.40 to 0.60 carbon.

Shank Preparation: The carbide tip usually is inserted into a milled recess or seat, but some prefer to omit the recess and braze the tip to the top of the shank. When a recess is used, the bottom should be flat to provide a firm even support for the tip. The corner radius of the seat should preferably be somewhat smaller than the radius on the tip to avoid contact and insure support along each side of the recess.

Cleaning: All surfaces to be brazed must be absolutely clean. Surfaces of the tip may be cleaned by grinding lightly or by sand-blasting. Cleaning with carbon tetrachloride is also recommended.

Brazing Materials and Equipment: The brazing metal may be copper, naval brass such as Tobin bronze, or silver solder. A flux such as borax is used to protect the clean surfaces and prevent oxidation. Heating may be done either in a furnace or by means of an oxy-acetylene torch or an oxy-hydrogen torch. Copper brazing usually is done in a furnace, although an oxy-hydrogen torch with excess hydrogen is sometimes used. An oxy-acetylene torch usually is employed for silver brazing or soldering.

Brazing Procedure: One method of brazing with a torch is to first place a thin sheet material, such as copper foil, around and beneath the carbide tip, the top of which is covered with flux. The flame is applied to the under side of the tool shank, and, when the materials melt, the tip is pressed firmly into its seat with tongs or with the end of a rod. If the brazing material is in the form of wire or rod, this may be used to coat or tin the surfaces of the recess after the flux melts and runs freely. The tip is then inserted, flux is applied to the top, and the heating is continued until the coatings melt and run freely. A firm which supplies carbide tips with nickel-coated surfaces ready for silver soldering, suggests the following procedure: The tip, after coating with flux, is placed in the recess and the shank end is heated. Then a small piece of silver solder, having a melting point of 1325 degrees F., is placed on top of the tip. When this solder melts, it runs over the nickel-coated surfaces while the tip is held firmly into its seat. In all carbide tip brazing, the brazed tool should be cooled slowly to avoid cracking due to unequal contraction between the steel and carbide. To insure slow cooling, the tool may be buried in powdered charcoal, graphite, asbestos, mica, or lime.

Braze Hardening. — This copper-brazing method is applicable in tipping lathe, planer or similar tools with molybdenum steel tips. First clean the tip and end of the shank by immersion in carbon tetrachloride. Cover end of shank with commercial powdered copper brazing flux; then insert the tool partly in the muffle of the furnace (electric or gas). When the flux melts, withdraw the tool and place the tip in position with the copper sheet or foil below and also above the tip. Add more flux and preheat the tip to about 1500 degrees F. Then move the tip end in and heat the tool uniformly to the full hardening temperature; then withdraw it from the furnace and force out the excess copper or flux either with tongs or a press. When the copper solidifies, quench the tip end in oil to below 200 degrees F. This operation, which usually requires less than twenty minutes, brazes and hardens the tip. The final step is to temper the tipped tool at 1050 degrees F.

Previously hardened high-speed steel tips may be attached to shanks by silver brazing. It is possible to braze the hardened tip and temper it simultaneously. This braze-tempering method is suitable for tools not subject to heavy roughing cuts. Tools which are braze-hardened, may be used for either roughing or finishing cuts because copper will withstand much higher temperatures than silver solder; moreover, the tool shank is hardened considerably by the braze-hardening method, whereas, in braze tempering, the shank is relatively unhardened.

Hard-Facing. — Hard-facing is the process of welding on to parts or surfaces a coating, edge or point of a metal highly capable of resisting abrasion and wear. In other words, a metal surface, which, due to its use, may normally be worn away rapidly is protected by a layer of special alloy. The process can be applied equally well to new parts or to old worn parts. In many instances, if hard-facing is employed, the metal for the part itself can be selected primarily to withstand shock and fatigue without regard to wear resistance. This often effects a considerable saving in the first cost of the part.

Hard-Facing Materials. — Hard-facing materials may be divided into three general classes: The first comprises alloys having an iron base and containing such elements as chromium, tungsten, manganese, silicon and sometimes cobalt and nickel. The second class is composed of non-ferrous alloys, and the third class consists of the so-called diamond substitutes which are essentially tungsten carbide.

Hard-facing materials of the first class are generally used only under conditions of moderate abrasive wear or severe impact. This class is represented by Hascrome, a self-hardening chromium-manganese-iron alloy. Deposits of Hascrome have a tensile strength of 40,000 and a compressive strength of 177,000 pounds per square inch. Deposits made by the oxy-acetylene process have a hardness of 240 to 500 Brinell, depending upon the amount of excess acetylene in the flame and upon the rate of cooling. Slow cooling makes Hascrome harder than does quenching. Arc-welded deposits have a hardness of 240 to 400 Brinell, depending on the rate of cooling. Hascrome has the property of work hardening under impact, a property similar to that of manganese steel.

The second class (non-ferrous alloys) is represented by Haynes Stellite. This cobalt-chromium-tungsten alloy combines excellent welding properties with maximum wear resistance. When cold, Haynes Stellite is almost as hard as hardened steel and it has the unique property of retaining its original hardness practically unimpaired at the high surface heats developed by friction — and even at a red heat. Haynes Stellite welding rod is available in different grades which vary in regard to physical properties such as hardness, abrasion resistance, shock resistance, etc. All possess to a marked degree the quality of red hardness which is so essential in a wear-resistant alloy.

In the third class (diamond substitutes), Haystellite, a cast tungsten carbide, is recommended. It approaches the diamond in hardness but possesses considerable toughness. It cannot be applied, like welding rods, by melting with the oxy-acetylene flame. It is, therefore, used in the form of small castings of uniform size and shape which are held in place by a binding material. Composite rod consists of various screen sizes of sharp, irregular-shaped grains of Haystellite uniformly distributed in a binding material. These rods are applied quickly and easily with the oxy-acetylene flame like ordinary hard-facing materials.

Chromium Plating. — Chromium plating is an electrolytic process of depositing chromium on metals either as a protection against corrosion or to increase the surface wearing qualities. The value of chromium-plating plug and ring gages has probably been more thoroughly demonstrated than any other one application of this treatment. Chromium-plated gages not only wear longer, but when worn, the chromium may be removed and the gage replated and reground to size.

In general, chromium-plated tools have operated well, giving greatly improved performance on nearly all classes of materials, such as brass, bronze, copper, nickel, aluminum, cast iron, steel, plastics, asbestos compositions, and similar materials. Increased cutting life has been obtained with chromium-plated drills, taps, reamers, files, broaches, tool tips, saws, thread chasers, and the like. Dies for stamping, drawing, hot-forging, die-casting, and for molding plastic materials have shown greatly increased life after being plated with hard chromium.

Special care is essential in grinding and lapping tools preparatory to plating the cutting edges, because the chromium deposit is influenced materially by the grain structure and hardness of the base metal. The thickness of the plating may vary from 0.0001 to 0.001 or 0.002 inch, the thicker platings being used to build up undersize tools such as taps and reamers. Procedure followed by Westinghouse in the hard chromium-plating of tools, as well as parts salvaged by depositing chromium to increase diameters, is as follows: (1) Degrease with solvent; (2) mount the tools on racks; (3) clean in an anodic alkali bath held at a temperature of 82 degrees C. for from three to five minutes; (4) rinse in boiling water; (5) immerse in a 20 per cent hydro-chloric acid solution for two to three seconds; (6) rinse in cold water; (7) rinse in hot water; (8) etch in a reverse-current chromic acid bath for two to five minutes; (9) place work immediately in the chromium-plating bath; and (10) remove hydrogen embrittlement, if necessary, by immersing the plated tools for two hours in an oil bath maintained at 177 degrees C.

Chromium has a very low coefficient of friction. The static coefficient of friction for steel on chromium-plated steel is 0.17, and the sliding coefficient of friction is 0.16. This compares with static coefficient of friction for steel on steel of 0.30 and a sliding coefficient of friction of 0.20. The static coefficient of friction for steel on babbitt is 0.25, and the sliding coefficient of friction 0.20, whereas for chromium-plated steel on babbitt, the static coefficient of friction is 0.15, and the sliding coefficient of friction 0.13. These figures apply to highly polished bearing surfaces. Articles that are to be chromium-plated in order to resist frictional wear should be highly polished before plating so that full advantage can be taken of the low coefficient of friction that is characteristic of chromium. Chromium resists attack by almost all organic and inorganic compounds, except muriatic and sulphuric acids. The melting point of chromium is 2930 degrees F., and it remains bright up to 1200 degrees F. Above this temperature, it forms a light adherent oxide, which does not readily become detached. For this reason, chromium has been used successfully for protecting articles that must resist high temperatures, even above 2000 degrees F

HEAT-TREATMENT—STANDARD STEELS

Heat-Treating Definitions. — This glossary of heat-treating terms has been adopted by the American Foundrymen's Association, the American Society for Metals, the American Society for Testing Materials and the Society of Automotive Engineers. Since it is not intended to be a specification but is strictly a set of definitions, temperatures have purposely been omitted.

Aging: A change in a metal by which its structure recovers from an unstable condition produced by quenching (quench aging) or by cold working (strain aging). The change in structure consists in precipitation, often submicroscopic, and is marked by a change in physical properties. Aging which takes place slowly at room temperature may be accelerated by a slight increase in temperature. See also *Stress Relieving*.

Annealing: A process involving heating and cooling applied usually to induce softening. The term is also used to cover treatments intended to remove stresses; alter mechanical or physical properties; produce a definite microstructure; remove gases. Certain specific heat treatments of iron-base alloys covered by the term annealing are black annealing, blue annealing, box annealing, bright annealing, full annealing, graphitizing, malleablizing, process annealing.

Annealing, Black: A process of box annealing iron-base alloy sheets after hot rolling, shearing and pickling. The process does not impart a black color to the product if properly done. The name originated in the appearance of the hot-rolled material before pickling and annealing.

Annealing, Blue: A process of softening iron-base alloys in the form of hot-rolled sheet, in which the sheet is heated in the open furnace to a temperature within the transformation range and cooled in air; the formation of a bluish oxide on the surface is incidental.

Annealing, Box: A process of annealing which, to prevent oxidation, is carried out in a suitable closed metal container with or without packing material. The charge is usually heated slowly to a temperature below, but sometimes above or within, the transformation temperature range and cooled slowly. It is also called *Close Annealing* or *Pot Annealing*.

Annealing, Bright: A process of annealing which is usually carried out in a controlled furnace atmosphere so that surface oxidation is reduced to a minimum and the surface remains relatively bright.

Annealing, Flame: A process in which the surface of an iron-base alloy is softened by localized heat applied by a high-temperature flame.

Annealing, Full: A softening process in which an iron-base alloy is heated to a temperature above the transformation range and, after being held for a proper time at this temperature, is cooled slowly to a temperature below the transformation range. The objects are ordinarily allowed to cool slowly in the furnace, although they may be removed from the furnace and cooled in some medium which assures a slow rate of cooling.

Annealing, Inverse: A heat treatment, analogous to *Precipitation Hardening*, applied to cast iron usually to increase its hardness and strength.

Annealing, Process: — A process commonly applied in the sheet and wire industries, in which an iron-base alloy is heated to a temperature close to, but below, the lower limit of the transformation range and subsequently cooled. This process is applied for the purpose of softening for further cold working.

Austempering: A trade name for a patented heat treating process consisting in quenching an iron-base alloy from a temperature above the transformation range in a medium having a suitably high rate of heat abstraction, and maintaining the alloy, until transformation is complete, at a temperature which is below that of pearlite formation and above that of martensite formation. The temperature for austenite transformation is chosen on the basis of the properties desired.

Bluing: A treatment of the surface of iron-base alloys, usually in the form of sheet or strip, on which, by the action of air or steam at a suitable temperature, a thin blue oxide film is formed on the initially scale-free surface, as a means of improving appearance and resistance to corrosion. This term is also used to denote a heat treatment of springs after fabrication, to reduce the internal stress created by coiling and forming.

Brunorizing: The trade name for a special treatment applied to steel rails which, after cooling to a temperature below the transformation range, are reheated to a temperature slightly above that range, and then are allowed to cool in the air, the ends of the rails being partially quenched by jets of compressed air.

Burnt: A term applied to a metal permanently damaged by being heated to a temperature close to the melting point. The damage may involve melting of some constituent or penetration by, and reaction of the metal with, a gas such as oxygen, or by segregation of component elements of the metal.

Carburizing: A process in which carbon is introduced into a solid iron-base alloy by heating above the transformation temperature range while in contact with a carbonaceous material which may be a solid, liquid or gas. Carburizing is frequently followed by quenching to produce a hardened case. The term carbonizing is sometimes used erroneously in place of carburizing.

Case: (1) The surface layer of an iron-base alloy which has been suitably altered in composition and can be made substantially harder than the interior or core by a process of case hardening. (2) The term case is also used to designate the hardened surface layer of a piece of steel that is large enough to have a distinctly softer core or center.

Cementation: The process of introducing elements into the outer layer of metal objects by means of high-temperature diffusion.

Controlled Cooling: A term used to describe a process by which a steel object is cooled from an elevated temperature, usually from the final hot forming operation in a predetermined manner of cooling to avoid hardening, cracking, or internal damage.

Core: (1) The interior portion of an iron-base alloy which after case hardening is substantially softer than the surface layer or case. (2) The term core is also used to designate the relatively soft central portion of certain hardened tool steels.

Critical Range or *Critical Temperature Range:* Synonymous with *Transformation Range*, which is preferred.

Cyaniding: A process of case hardening an iron-base alloy by the simultaneous absorption of carbon and nitrogen by heating in a cyanide salt. Cyaniding is usually followed by quenching to produce a hard case.

Decarburization: The loss of carbon from the surface of an iron-base alloy as the result of heating in a medium which reacts with the carbon.

Drawing: Drawing, or drawing the temper, is synonymous with *Tempering*, which is preferable.

Graphitizing: An annealing process applied to certain iron-base alloys, such as cast iron or some steels with high carbon and silicon contents, by which the combined carbon is wholly or in part transformed to graphitic or free carbon. See *Temper Carbon*.

Hardening: Any process of increasing hardness of metal by suitable treatment, usually involving heating and cooling.

Hardening, Age: See *Aging*

Hardening, Case: A process of surface hardening involving a change in the composition of the outer layer of an iron-base alloy followed by appropriate thermal treatment. Typical case-hardening processes are *Carburizing*, *Cyaniding*, *Carbo-Nitriding* and *Nitriding*.

Hardening, Flame: A process of heating the surface layer of an iron-base alloy above the transformation temperature range by means of a high-temperature flame, followed by quenching.

Hardening, Precipitation: A process of hardening an alloy in which a constituent precipitates from a supersaturated solid solution. See also *Aging.*

Hardening, Secondary: An increase in hardness following the normal softening that occurs during the tempering of certain alloy steels.

Heating, Differential: A heating process by which the temperature is made to vary throughout the object being heated so that on cooling different portions may have such different physical properties as may be desired.

Heating, Induction: A process of local heating by electrical induction.

Heat Treatment: A combination of heating and cooling operations applied to a metal or alloy in the solid state to obtain desired conditions or properties. Heating for the sole purpose of hot working is excluded from the meaning of this definition.

Heat Treatment, Solution: A treatment in which an alloy is heated to a suitable temperature and held at this temperature for a sufficient length of time to allow a desired constituent to enter into solid solution, followed by rapid cooling to hold the constituent in solution. The material is then in a supersaturated, unstable state, and may subsequently exhibit *Age Hardening.*

Homogenizing: A high-temperature heat-treatment process intended to eliminate or to decrease chemical segregation by diffusion.

Malleablizing: A process of annealing white cast iron in which the combined carbon is wholly or in part transformed to graphitic or free carbon, and, in some cases, part of the carbon is removed completely. See *Temper Carbon.*

Nitriding: A process of case hardening in which an iron-base alloy of special composition is heated in an atmosphere of ammonia or in contact with nitrogenous material. Surface hardening is produced by the absorption of nitrogen without quenching.

Nitriding, Carbo: A process of case hardening an iron-base alloy by the simultaneous absorption of carbon and nitrogen by heating in a gaseous atmosphere of suitable composition, followed by either quenching or cooling slowly as required.

Normalizing: A process in which an iron-base alloy is heated to a temperature above the transformation range and subsequently cooled in still air at room temperature.

Overheated: A metal is said to have been overheated if, after exposure to an unduly high temperature, it develops an undesirably coarse grain structure but is not permanently damaged. The structure damaged by overheating can be corrected by suitable heat treatment or by mechanical work or by a combination of the two. In this respect it differs from a *Burnt* structure.

Patenting: A process of heat treatment applied to medium or high carbon steel in wire making prior to the wire drawing or between drafts. It consists in heating to a temperature above the transformation range, followed by cooling to a temperature below that range in air or in a bath of molten lead or salt maintained at a temperature appropriate to the carbon content of the steel and the properties required of the finished product.

Preheating: (1) A general term used to describe a heating applied preliminary to some further thermal or mechanical treatment. (2) A term specifically applied to tool steel to describe a process in which the steel is heated slowly and uniformly to a temperature below the hardening temperature and is then transferred to a furnace in which the temperature is substantially above the preheating temperature.

Quenching: A process of rapid cooling from an elevated temperature, by contact with liquids, gases or solids.

Quenching, Differential: A quenching process by which only certain desired portions of the object are quenched and hardened.

Quenching, Hot: A process of quenching iron-base alloys in a medium, the temperature of which is substantially higher than atmospheric temperature.

Quenching, Pot: A process of quenching carburized parts directly from the carburizing box or pot.

Sandberg Sorbitic Treatment: A treatment in which carbon steel objects are moderately hardened, either wholly or in part. It consists in cooling the parts to be hardened through the transformation range at a moderately rapid rate by the application of jets of air, steam, or atomized water and then allowing the residual heat in the object to effect a tempering operation.

Soaking: Prolonged heating of a metal at a selected temperature.

Spheroidizing: Any process of heating and cooling steel that produces a rounded or globular form of carbide in the structure.

Stress Relieving: A process to reduce internal residual stresses in a metal object by heating the object to a suitable temperature and holding for a proper time at that temperature. This treatment may be applied to relieve stresses induced by casting, quenching, normalizing, machining, cold working or welding. Stress relieving is sometimes termed *Aging.*

Temper Carbon: The free or graphitic carbon which comes out of solution usually in the form of rounded nodules in the structure during *Graphitizing* or *Malleablizing.*

Tempering: A process of reheating hardened or normalized steel to a temperature below the transformation temperature range, followed by any desired rate of cooling.

Transformation Range: In ferrous alloys the transformation range on heating is the temperature interval within which austenite forms. The transformation range on cooling is the temperature interval in which austenite disappears. Distinction must be made between the two ranges. They may overlap but never coincide. The limiting temperatures of the ranges depend on the composition of the alloy and, particularly for the cooling, on the rate of change of temperature.

Structure of Fully Annealed Carbon Steel.—In carbon steel that has been fully annealed, there are normally present, apart from such impurities as phosphorus and sulphur, two constituents: the element iron in a form metallurgically known as *ferrite* and the chemical compound iron carbide in the form metallurgically known as *cementite.* This latter constituent consists of 6.67 per cent carbon and 93.33 per cent iron. A certain proportion of these two constituents will be present as a mechanical mixture. This mechanical mixture, the amount of which depends upon the carbon content of the steel, consists of alternate bands or layers of ferrite and cementite. Under the microscope it frequently has the appearance of mother-of-pearl and hence has been named *pearlite.* Pearlite contains about 0.85 per cent carbon and 99.15 per cent iron, neglecting impurities. A fully annealed steel containing 0.85 per cent carbon would consist entirely of pearlite. Such a steel is known as *eutectoid* steel and has a laminated structure characteristic of a eutectic alloy. Steel which has less than 0.85 per cent carbon (*hypo-eutectoid* steel) has an excess of ferrite above that required to mix with the cementite present to form pearlite, hence both ferrite and pearlite are present in the fully annealed state. Steel having a carbon content greater than 0.85 per cent (*hyper-eutectoid* steel) has an excess of cementite over that required to mix with the ferrite to form pearlite, hence both cementite and pearlite are present in the fully annealed state. The structural constitution of carbon steel in terms of ferrite, cementite, pearlite and austenite for different carbon contents and at different temperatures is shown by the accompanying diagram.

Effect of Heating Fully Annealed Carbon Steel.—When carbon steel in the fully annealed state is heated above the lower critical point, which is some tempera-

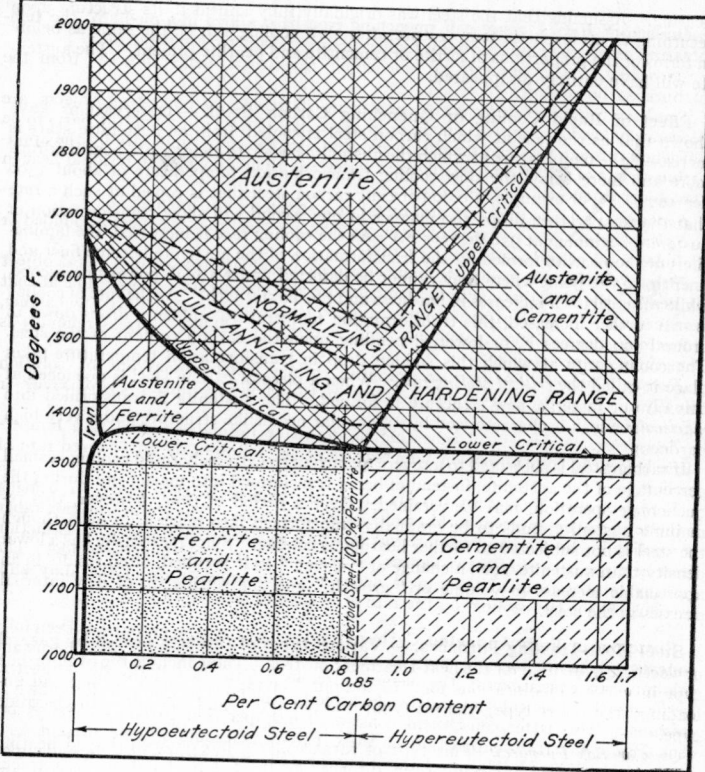

ture in the range of 1335 to 1355 degrees F. (depending upon the carbon content), the alternate bands or layers of ferrite and cementite which make up the pearlite begin to merge into each other. This process continues until the pearlite is thoroughly "dissolved," forming what is known as *austenite*. If the temperature of the steel continues to rise and there is present, in addition to the pearlite, any excess ferrite or cementite, this also will begin to dissolve into the austenite until finally only austenite will be present. The temperature at which the excess ferrite or cementite is completely dissolved in the austenite is called the *upper critical point*. This temperature varies with the carbon content of the steel much more widely than the lower critical point (see diagram).

Effect of Slow Cooling Carbon Steel. — If carbon steel which has been heated to the point where it consists entirely of austenite is slowly cooled, the process of transformation which took place during the heating will be reversed but the upper and lower critical points will occur at somewhat lower temperatures than they do on heating. Assuming that the steel was originally fully annealed, its structure upon returning to atmospheric temperature after slow cooling will be the same as before in terms of the proportions of ferrite or cementite and pearlite present. The austenite will have entirely disappeared.

Effect of Rapid Cooling or Quenching Carbon Steel. — Observations have shown that as the rate at which carbon steel is cooled from an austenitic state is increased, the temperature at which the austenite begins to change into pearlite drops more and more below the slow cooling transformation temperature of about 1300 degrees F. (For example, a 0.80 per cent carbon steel that is cooled at such a rate that the temperature drops 500 degrees in one second will show transformation of austenite beginning at 930 degrees F.) As the cooling rate is increased, the laminations of the pearlite formed by the transformation of the austenite become finer and finer up to the point where they cannot be detected under a high power microscope, while the steel itself increases in hardness and tensile strength. As the rate of cooling is still further increased, this transformation temperature suddenly drops down to around 500 degrees F. or lower, depending upon the carbon content of the steel. The cooling rate at which this sudden drop in transformation temperature takes place is called the *critical cooling rate.* When a piece of carbon steel is quenched at this rate or faster, a new structure is formed. The austenite is transformed into *martensite* which is characterized by an angular needlelike structure and a very high hardness.

If carbon steel is subjected to a severe quench or to extremely rapid cooling, a small percentage of the austenite, instead of being transformed into martensite during the quenching operation, may be retained. Over a period of time, however, this remaining austenite tends to be gradually transformed into martensite even though the steel is not subjected to further heating or cooling. Since martensite has a lower density than austenite, such a change or " ageing " as it is called, often results in an appreciable increase in volume or " growth " and the setting up of new internal stresses in the steel.

Steel Heat-Treating Furnaces. — Various types of furnaces heated by gas, oil or electricity, are used for the heat-treatment of steel. These include the oven or box type in various modifications for " in-and-out " or for continuous loading and unloading; the retort type; the pit type; the pot type; and the salt-bath electrode type.

Oven or Box Furnaces: This type of furnace has a box or oven-shaped heating chamber. The " in-and-out " oven furnaces are loaded by hand or by a track-mounted car which, when rolled into the furnace, forms the bottom of the heating chamber. The car type is used where heavy or bulky pieces must be handled. Some oven type furnaces are provided with a full muffle or a semi-muffle which is an enclosed refractory chamber into which the parts to be heated are placed. The full-muffle, being fully enclosed, prevents any flames or burning gases from coming in contact with the work and permits a special atmosphere to be used to protect or condition the work. The semi-muffle, which is open at the top, protects the work from direct impingement of the flame although it does not shut the work off from the hot gases. In the direct-heat type oven furnace, the work is open to the flame. In the electric oven furnace, a retort is provided if gas atmospheres are to be employed to confine the gas and prevent it from attacking the heating elements. Where muffles are used, they must be replaced periodically and a greater amount of fuel is required than in a direct-heat type of oven furnace.

For continuous loading and unloading, there are several types such as rotary hearth car; roller-, furnace belt-, walking-beam or pusher-conveyor; and a continuous-kiln type through which track-mounted cars are run. In the continuous type of furnace, the work may pass through several zones maintained at different temperatures for preheating, heating, soaking, and cooling.

Retort Furnace: This is a vertical type of furnace provided with a cylindrical metal retort into which the parts to be heat-treated are suspended either individually, if large enough, or in a container of some sort. The use of a retort permits special gas atmospheres to be employed for carburizing, nitriding, etc.

Pit Type Furnace: This is a vertical furnace arranged for the loading of parts in a metal basket. The parts are heated by convection, the basket, when lowered into place, fitting into the furnace chamber in such a way as to provide a dead-air space to prevent direct heating.

Pot Type Furnace: This furnace is used for the immersion method of heat-treating small parts. A cast-alloy pot is employed to hold a bath of molten lead or salt in which the parts are placed for heating.

Salt Bath Electrode Furnace: In this type of electric furnace, heating is accomplished by means of electrodes suspended directly in the salt bath. The patented grouping and design of electrodes provide an electromagnetic action which results in an automatic stirring action throughout the bath. This tends to produce an even temperature throughout.

Hardening

Basic Steps in Hardening. — The operation of hardening steel consists fundamentally of two steps. The first step is to heat the steel to some temperature above (usually at least 100 degrees F. above) its transformation point so that it becomes entirely austenitic in structure. The second step is to quench the steel at some rate faster than the critical rate (which depends on the carbon content, the amounts of alloying elements present other than carbon, and the grain size of the austenite) to produce a martensitic structure. The hardness of a martensitic steel depends upon its carbon content and ranges from about 460 Brinell at 0.20 per cent carbon to about 710 Brinell above 0.50 carbon. In comparison, ferrite has a hardness of about 90 Brinell, pearlite about 240 Brinell, and cementite around 550 Brinell.

Critical Points of Decalescence and Recalescence. — The critical or transformation point at which pearlite is transformed into austenite as it is being heated is also called the *decalescence point*. If the temperature of the steel was observed as it passed through the decalescence point, it would be noted that it would continue to absorb heat without appreciably rising in temperature, although the immediate surroundings were hotter than the steel. Similarly, the critical or transformation point at which austenite is transformed back into pearlite upon cooling is called the *recalescence point*. When this point is reached, the steel will give out heat so that its temperature instead of continuing to fall, will momentarily increase.

The recalescent point is lower than the decalescence point by anywhere from 85 to 215 degrees F., and the lower of these points does not manifest itself unless the higher one has first been fully passed. These critical points have a direct relation to the hardening of steel. Unless a temperature sufficient to reach the decalescence point is obtained, so that the pearlite is changed into austenite, no hardening action can take place; and unless the steel is cooled suddenly before it reaches the recalescence point, thus preventing the changing back again from austenite to pearlite, no hardening can take place. The critical points vary for different kinds of steel and must be determined by tests in each case. It is the variation in the critical points that makes it necessary to heat different steels to different temperatures when hardening.

Hardening Temperatures. — The maximum temperature to which a steel is heated before quenching to harden it is called the hardening temperature. Hardening temperatures vary for different steels and different classes of service, although, in general, it may be said that the hardening temperature for any given steel is above the lower critical point of that steel. Just how far above this point the hardening temperature lies for any particular steel depends on three factors: (1) The chemical composition of the steel; (2) the amount of excess ferrite (if the steel has less than 0.85 per cent carbon content) or the amount of excess cementite (if the steel has more than 0.85 per cent carbon content) that is to be dissolved in the austenite; and (3) the maximum grain size permitted, if desired.

The general range of full hardening temperatures for carbon steels is shown by the diagram. This range is merely indicative of general practice and is not intended to represent absolute hardening temperature limits. It can be seen that for steels of less than 0.85 per cent carbon content, the hardening range is above the upper critical point — that is, above the temperature at which all of the excess ferrite has been dissolved in the austenite. On the other hand, for steels of more than 0.85 per cent carbon content, the hardening range lies somewhat below the upper critical point. This indicates that in this hardening range some of the excess cementite still remains undissolved in the austenite. If steel of more than 0.85 per cent carbon content were heated above the upper critical point and then quenched, the resulting grain size would be excessively large.

At one time it was considered desirable to heat steel only to the minimum temperature at which it would fully harden, one of the reasons being to avoid grain growth that takes place at higher temperature. It is now realized that no such rule as this can be applied generally since there are factors other than hardness which must be taken into consideration. For example, in many cases toughness can be impaired by too low a temperature just as much as by too high a temperature. It is true, however, that too high hardening temperatures result in warpage, distortion, increased scale, and decarburization.

Hardening Temperatures for Carbon Tool Steels. — The best hardening temperatures for any given tool steel are dependent upon the type of tool and the intended class of service. Wherever possible, the specific recommendations of the tool steel manufacturer should be followed. General recommendations for hardening temperatures of carbon tool steels based on carbon content are as follows: For steel of 0.65 to 0.80 per cent carbon content, 1450 to 1550 degrees F.; for steel of 0.80 to 0.95 per cent carbon content, 1410 to 1460 degrees F.; for steel of 0.95 to 1.10 per cent content, 1390 to 1430 degrees F.; and for steels of 1.10 per cent and over carbon content, 1380 to 1420 degrees F. For a given hardening temperature range, the higher temperatures tend to produce deeper hardness penetration and increased compressional strength while the lower temperatures tend to result in shallower hardness penetration but increased resistance to splitting or bursting stresses.

Determining Hardening Temperatures. — A hardening temperature can be specified directly or it may be specified indirectly as a certain temperature rise above the lower critical point of the steel. Where the temperature is specified directly, a pyrometer of the type which indicates the furnace temperature or a pyrometer of the type which indicates the work temperature may be employed. If the pyrometer shows furnace temperature, care must be taken to allow sufficient time for the work to reach the furnace temperature after the pyrometer indicates that the required hardening temperature has been attained. If the pyrometer indicates work temperature, then, where the work-piece is large, time must be allowed for the interior of the work to reach the temperature of the surface which is the temperature indicated by the pyrometer.

Where the hardening temperature is specified as a given temperature rise above the critical point of the steel, a pyrometer which indicates the temperature of the work should be used. The critical point, as well as the given temperature rise, can be more accurately determined with this type of pyrometer. As the work is heated, its temperature, as indicated by the pyrometer, rises steadily until the lower critical or decalescence point of the steel is reached. At this point, the temperature of the work ceases to rise and the pyrometer indicating or recording pointer remains stationary or fluctuates slightly. After a certain elapsed period, depending upon the rate at which heat is furnished to the work, the internal changes in structure of the steel which take place at the lower critical point are completed and the temperature of the work again begins to rise. Since a small fluctuation in temperature may occur in the interval during which structural changes are taking place, for uniform practice the critical point may be considered as the temperature at which the pointer first becomes stationary.

Heating Steel in Liquid Baths. — The liquid baths commonly used for heating steel tools preparatory to hardening are molten lead, sodium cyanide, barium chloride, a mixture of barium and potassium chloride and other metallic salts. The molten substance is retained in a crucible or pot and the heat required may be obtained from gas, oil, or electricity. The principal advantages of heating baths are as follows: No part of the work can be heated to a temperature above that of the bath; the temperature can be easily maintained at whatever degree has proved, in practice, to give the best results; the submerged steel can be heated uniformly, and the finished surfaces are protected against oxidation.

Salt Baths. — Molten baths of various salt mixtures or compounds are used extensively for heat-treating operations such as hardening and tempering; they are also utilized for annealing ferrous and non-ferrous metals. Commercial salt-bath mixtures are available which meet a wide range of temperature and other metallurgical requirements. For example, there are neutral baths for heating tool and die steels without carburizing the surfaces; baths for carburizing the surfaces of low-carbon steel parts; baths adapted for the usual tempering temperatures of, say, 300 to 1100 degrees F.; and baths which may be heated to temperatures up to approximately 2400 degrees F. for hardening high-speed steels. Salt baths are also adapted for local or selective hardening, the type of bath being selected to suit the requirements. For example, a neutral bath may be used for annealing the ends of tubing or other parts, or an activated cyanide bath for carburizing the ends of shafts or other parts. Surfaces which are not to be carburized are protected by copper plating. When the work is immersed, the unplated parts are subjected to the carburizing action.

Baths may consist of a mixture of sodium, potassium, barium, and calcium chlorides or nitrates of sodium, potassium, barium, and calcium in varying proportions, to which sodium carbonate and sodium cyanide are sometimes added to prevent decarburization. Various proportions of these salts provide baths of different properties. Potassium cyanide is seldom used as sodium cyanide costs less. The specific gravity of a salt bath is not as high as that of a lead bath; consequently the work may be suspended in a salt bath and does not have to be held below the surface as in a lead bath.

The Lead Bath. — The lead bath is extensively used, but is not adapted to the high temperatures required for hardening high-speed steel, as it begins to vaporize at about 1190 degrees F. As the temperature increases, the lead volatilizes and gives off poisonous vapors; hence, lead furnaces should be equipped with hoods to carry away the fumes. Lead baths are generally used for temperatures below 1500 or 1600 degrees F. They are often employed for heating small pieces which must be hardened in quantities. It is important to use pure lead that is free from sulphur. The work should be pre-heated before plunging it into the molten lead.

Defects in Hardening. — Uneven heating is the cause of most of the defects in hardening. Cracks of a circular form, from the corners or edges of a tool, indicate uneven heating in hardening. Cracks of a vertical nature and dark-colored fissures indicate that the steel has been burned and should be put on the scrap heap. Tools which have hard and soft places have been either unevenly heated, unevenly cooled, or "soaked," a term used to indicate prolonged heating. A tool not thoroughly moved about in the hardening fluid will show hard and soft places, and have a tendency to crack. Tools which are hardened by dropping them to the bottom of the tank, sometimes have soft places, owing to contact with the floor or sides.

Scale on Hardened Steel. — The formation of scale on the surface of hardened steel is due to the contact of oxygen with the heated steel; hence, to prevent scale, the heated steel must not be exposed to the action of the air. When using an oven heating furnace, the flame should be so regulated that it is not visible in the heating chamber. The heated steel should be exposed to the air as little as possible, when transferring it from the furnace to the quenching bath. An old method of preventing scale and retaining a fine finish on dies used in jewelry manufacture, small taps, etc. is as follows: Fill the die impression with powdered boracic acid and place near the fire until the acid melts; then add a little more acid to insure covering all the surfaces. The die is then hardened in the usual way. If the boracic acid does not come entirely off in the quenching bath, immerse the work in boiling water. Dies hardened by this method are said to be as durable as those heated without the acid.

Hardening or Quenching Baths. — The purpose of a quenching bath is to remove heat from the steel being hardened at a rate that is faster than the critical cooling rate. Generally speaking, the more rapid the rate of heat extraction above the cooling rate, the higher will be the resulting hardness. To obtain the different rates of cooling required by different classes of work, baths of various kinds are used. These include plain or fresh water, brine, caustic soda solutions, oils of various classes, oil-water emulsions, baths of molten salt or lead for high-speed steels and air cooling for some high-speed steel tools when a slow rate of cooling is required. To minimize distortion and cracking where such tendencies are present, without sacrificing depth of hardness penetration, a quenching medium should be selected that will cool rapidly at the higher temperatures and more slowly at the lower temperatures, i.e., below 750 degrees F. Oil quenches in general meet this requirement.

Oil Quenching Baths: Oil is used very extensively as a quenching medium as it results in a good proportion of hardness, toughness, and freedom from warpage when used with standard steels. Oil baths are used extensively for alloy steels. Various kinds of oils are employed such as prepared mineral oils and vegetable, animal and fish oils, either singly or in combination. Prepared mineral quenching oils are widely used because they have good quenching characteristics, are chemically stable, do not have an objectionable odor, and are relatively inexpensive. Special compounded oils of the soluble type are used in many plants instead of such oils as fish oil, linseed oil, cottonseed oil, etc. The soluble properties enable the oil to form an emulsion with water.

Oil cools steel at a slower rate than water, but the rate is fast enough for alloy steel. Oils have different cooling rates, however, and this rate may vary through the initial and final stages of the quenching operation. Faster cooling in the initial stage and slower cooling at lower temperatures is preferable because there is less danger of cracking the steel. The temperature of quenching oil baths should range ordinarily between 90 and 130 degrees F. A fairly constant temperature may be maintained either by circulating the oil through cooling coils or by using a tank provided with a cold water jacket.

A good quenching oil should possess a flash and fire point sufficiently high to be safe under the conditions used and 350 degrees F. should be about the minimum point. The specific heat of the oil regulates the hardness and toughness of the quenched steel; and the greater the specific heat, the higher will be the hardness produced. Specific heats of quenching oils vary from o.20 to o.75, the specific heats of fish, animal and vegetable oils usually being from o.2 to o.4, and of soluble and mineral oils from o.5 to o.7. The efficient temperature range for quenching oil is from 90 to 140 degrees F.

Quenching in Water.—Many carbon tool steels are hardened by immersing them in a bath of fresh water, but water is not an ideal quenching medium. Contact between the water and work and the cooling of the hot steel is impaired by the formation of gas bubbles or an insulating vapor film especially in holes, cavities or pockets. The result is uneven cooling and in some cases excessive strains which may cause the tool to crack; in fact, there is greater danger of cracking in a fresh water bath than in one containing salt water or brine.

In order to secure more even cooling and reduce danger of cracking, either rock salt (8 or 9 per cent) or caustic soda (3 to 5 per cent) may be added to the bath in order to eliminate or prevent the formation of a vapor film or gas pockets, thus promoting rapid early cooling. Brine is commonly used and ¾ pound of rock salt per gallon of water is equivalent to about 8 per cent of salt. Brine is not inherently a more severe or drastic quenching medium than plain water, although it may seem to be because the brine makes better contact with the heated steel and, consequently, cooling is more effective. In still bath quenching, a slow up-and-down movement of the tool is preferable to a violent swishing around.

The temperature of water-base quenching baths should preferably be kept around 70 degrees F., but 70 to 90 or 100 degrees F. is a safe range. The temperature of the hardening bath has a great deal to do with the hardness obtained. The higher the temperature of the quenching water, the more nearly does its effect approach that of oil; and if boiling water is used for quenching, it will have an effect even more gentle than that of oil — in fact, it would leave the steel nearly soft. Parts of irregular shape are sometimes quenched in a water bath that has been warmed somewhat to prevent sudden cooling and cracking.

When water is used, it should be " soft " as unsatisfactory results will be obtained with " hard " water. Any contamination of water-base quenching liquids by soap tends to decrease their rate of cooling. A water bath having 1 or 2 inches of oil on the top is sometimes employed to advantage for quenching tools made of high-carbon steel as the oil through which the work first passes reduces the sudden quenching action of the water.

The bath should be amply large to dissipate the heat rapidly and the temperature should be kept about constant so that successive pieces will be cooled at the same rate. Irregularly shaped parts should be immersed so that the heaviest or thickest section enters the bath first. After immersion, the part to be hardened should be agitated in the bath; the agitation reduces the tendency of the formation of a vapor coating on certain surfaces, and a more uniform rate of cooling is obtained. The work should never be dropped to the bottom of the bath until quite cool.

Flush or Local Quenching by Pressure-spraying: When dies for cold heading, drawing, extruding, etc., or other tools, require a hard working surface and a relatively soft but tough body, the quenching may be done by spraying water under pressure against the interior or other surfaces to be hardened. Special spraying fixtures are used to hold the tool and apply the spray where the hardening is required. The pressure-spray prevents the formation of gas pockets previously referred to in connection with the fresh water quenching bath; hence fresh water is effective for flush quenching and there is no advantage in using brine.

Quenching in Molten Salt Bath. — A molten salt bath may be used in preference to oil for quenching high-speed steel. The object in using a liquid salt bath for quenching (instead of an oil bath) is to obtain maximum hardness with minimum cooling stresses and distortion which might result in cracking expensive tools, especially if there are irregular sections. The temperature of the quenching bath may be around 1100 or 1200 degrees F. Quenching is followed by cooling to room temperature and then the tool is tempered or drawn in a bath having a temperature range of 950 to 1100 degrees F. In many cases, the tempering temperature is about 1050 degrees F.

Tanks for Quenching Baths. — The main point to be considered in a quenching bath is to keep it at a uniform temperature, so that successive pieces quenched will be subjected to the same heat. The next consideration is to keep the bath agitated, so that it will not be of different temperatures in different places; if thoroughly agitated and kept in motion, as is the case with the bath shown in Fig. 1, it is not even necessary to keep the pieces in motion in the bath, as steam will not be likely to form around the pieces quenched. Experience has proved that if a piece is held still in a thoroughly agitated bath, it will come out much straighter than if it has been moved around in an unagitated bath. This is an important consideration, especially when hardening long pieces. It is, besides, no easy matter to keep heavy and long pieces in motion unless it be done by mechanical means.

In Fig. 1 is shown a water or brine tank for quenching baths. Water is forced by a pump or other means through the supply pipe into the intermediate space between the outer and inner tank. From the intermediate space it is forced into the inner tank through holes as indicated. The water returns to the storage tank by overflowing from the inner tank into the outer one and then through the overflow pipe as indicated. In Fig. 3 is shown another water or brine tank of a more common type. In this case the water or brine is pumped from the storage tank and continuously returned to it. If the storage tank contains a large volume of water, there is no need of a special means for cooling. Otherwise, arrangements must be made for cooling the water after it has passed through the tank. The bath is agitated by the force with which the water is pumped into it. The holes at A are drilled at an angle, so as to throw the water toward the center of the tank. In Fig. 2 is shown an oil quenching tank in which water is circulated in an outer surrounding tank for keeping the oil bath cool. Air is forced into the oil bath to keep it agitated. Fig. 4 shows the ordinary type of quenching tank cooled by water forced through a coil of pipe. This can be used for either oil, water or brine. Fig. 5 shows a similar type of quenching tank, but with two coils of pipe. Water flows through one of these and steam through the other. By this means it is possible to keep the bath at a constant temperature.

Interrupted Quenching. — *Austempering, martempering,* and *isothermal quenching* are three methods of interrupted quenching that have been developed to obtain greater toughness and ductility for given hardnesses and to avoid the difficulties of quench cracks, internal stresses, and warpage, frequently experienced when the conventional method of quenching steel directly and rapidly from above the transformation point to atmospheric temperature is employed. In each of these three methods, quenching is begun when the work has reached some temperature above the transformation point and is conducted at a rate faster than the critical rate. The rapid cooling of the steel is interrupted, however, at some temperature above that at which martensite begins to form. The three methods differ in the temperature range at which interruption of the rapid quench takes place, the length of time that the steel is held at this temperature, and whether the subsequent cooling to atmospheric temperature is rapid or slow, and is or is not preceded by a tempering operation.

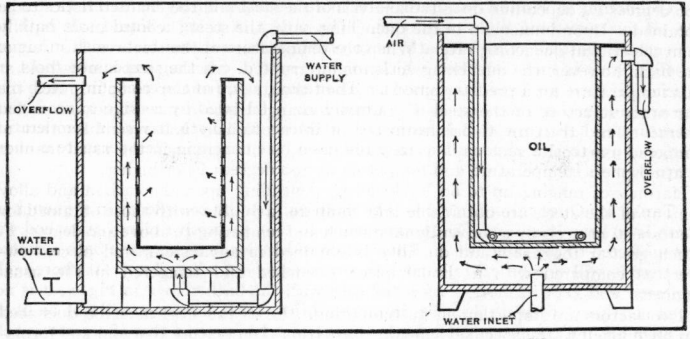

Fig. 1.

Fig. 2

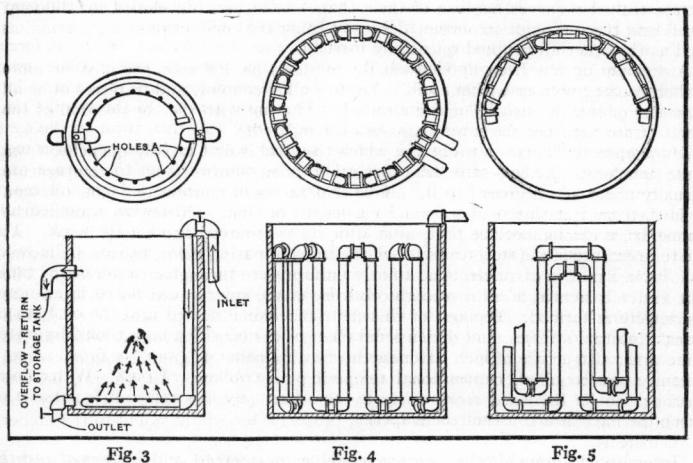

Fig. 3   Fig. 4   Fig. 5

One of the reasons for maintaining the steel at a constant temperature for a definite period of time is to permit the inside sections of the piece to reach the same temperature as the outer sections so that when transformation of the structure does take place, it will occur at about the same rate and period of time throughout the piece. In order to maintain the constant temperature required in interrupted quenching, a quenching arrangement for absorbing and dissipating a large quantity of heat without increase in temperature is needed. Molten salt baths equipped for water spray or air cooling around the exterior of the bath container have been used for this purpose.

Austempering: This is a patented heat-treating process in which steels are quenched in a bath maintained at some constant temperature in the range of 350 to

800 degrees F., depending upon the analysis of the steel and the characteristics to be obtained. Upon immersion in the quenching bath, the steel is cooled more rapidly than the critical quenching rate. When the temperature of the steel reaches that of the bath, however, the quenching action is interrupted. If the steel is now held at this temperature for a predetermined length of time, say, from 10 to 60 minutes, the austenitic structure of the steel is gradually changed into a new structure, called *bainite*. The structure of bainite is accicular (needlelike) and resembles that of tempered martensite such as is usually obtained by quenching in the usual manner to atmospheric temperature and tempering at 400 degrees F. or higher.

Hardnesses ranging up to 60 Rockwell C, depending upon the carbon and alloy content of the steel, are obtainable and compare favorably with those obtained for the respective steels by a conventional quench and tempering to above 400 degrees F. Much greater toughness and ductility is obtained in an austempered piece, however, as compared with a similar piece quenched and tempered in the usual manner.

Two factors are important in austempering. First, the steel must be quenched rapidly enough to the specified sub-transformation temperature to avoid any formation of pearlite, and second, it must be held at this temperature until the transformation from austenite to bainite is completed. Time and temperature transformation curves (called S-curves because of their shape) have been developed for different steels and these provide important data governing the conduct of austempering, as well as the other interrupted quenching methods.

Austempering has been applied chiefly to steels having 0.60 per cent or more carbon content with or without additional low alloy content, and to pieces of small diameter or section, usually under 1 inch but varying with the composition of the steel. Case hardened parts may also be austempered.

Martempering: This is a process in which the steel is first rapidly quenched from some temperature above the transformation point down to some temperature (usually about 400 degrees F.) just above that at which martensite begins to form. It is then held at this temperature for a length of time sufficient to equalize the temperature throughout the part, after which it is removed and cooled in air. As the temperature of the steel drops below the transformation point, martensite begins to form in a matrix of austenite at a fairly uniform rate throughout the piece. The soft austenite acts as a cushion to absorb some of the stresses which develop as the martensite is formed. Because of this fact, the difficulties presented by quench cracks, internal stresses, and dimensional changes are largely avoided, while at the same time, a structure of high hardness can be obtained. If greater toughness and ductility are required, conventional tempering may follow. In general, heavier sections can be hardened more easily by the martempering process than by the austempering process. The martempering process is especially suited to the higher alloyed steels.

Isothermal Quenching: This process resembles austempering in that the steel is first rapidly quenched from above the transformation point down to a temperaure which is above that at which martensite begins to form and is held at this temperature until the austenite is completely transformed into bainite. The constant temperature to which the piece is quenched and then maintained is usually 450 degrees F. or above. The process differs from austempering in that after transformation to a bainite structure has been completed, the steel is immersed in another bath and is brought up to some higher temperature, depending upon the characteristics desired, and is maintained at this temperature for a definite period of time, followed by cooling in air. Thus, tempering to obtain the desired toughness or ductility takes place immediately after the structure of the steel has changed to bainite and before it is cooled to atmospheric temperature.

Tempering

The object of *tempering* or *drawing* is to reduce the brittleness in hardened steel and to remove the internal strains caused by the sudden cooling in the quenching bath. The tempering process consists in heating the steel by various means to a certain temperature and then cooling it. When steel is in a fully hardened condition, its structure consists largely of *martensite*. On reheating to a temperature of from about 300 to 750 degrees F., a softer and tougher structure known as *troostite* is formed. If the steel is reheated to a temperature of from 750 to 1290 degrees F., a structure known as *sorbite* is formed which has somewhat less strength than troostite but much greater ductility.

Tempering Temperatures. — If steel is heated in an oxidizing atmosphere a film of oxide forms on the surface which changes color as the temperature increases. These oxide colors (see table) have been used extensively in the past as a means of gaging the correct amount of temper; but since these colors are affected to some extent by the composition of the metal, the method is not dependable.

The availability of reliable pyrometers in combination with tempering baths of oil, salt or lead make it possible to heat the work uniformly and to a given temperature within close limits.

Suggested temperatures for tempering various tools are given in the accompanying table.

Tempering in Oil. — Oil baths are extensively used for tempering tools (especially in quantity), the work being immersed in oil heated to the required temperature, which is indicated by a thermometer. It is important that the oil have a uniform temperature throughout and that the work be immersed long enough to acquire this temperature. Cold steel should not be plunged into a bath heated for tempering, owing to the danger of cracking it. The steel should either be preheated to about 300 degrees F., before placing it in the bath, or the latter should be at a comparatively low temperature before immersing the steel, and then be heated to the required degree. A temperature of from 650 to 700 degrees F. can be obtained with heavy tempering oils; for higher temperatures, either a bath of nitrate salts or a lead bath is generally used.

In tempering, the best method is to immerse the pieces to be tempered in the oil before starting to heat the latter. They are then heated with the oil. After the pieces tempered are taken out of the oil bath, they should immediately be dipped in a tank of caustic soda, and after that in a tank of hot water. This will remove all oil which might adhere to the tools. The following tempering oil has given satisfactory results: mineral oil, 94 per cent; saponifiable oil, 6 per cent; specific gravity, 0.920; flash point, 550 degrees F.; fire test, 625 degrees F.

Tempering in Salt Baths. — Molten salt baths may be used for tempering or drawing operations. Nitrate baths are particularly adapted for the usual drawing temperature range of, say, 300 to 1100 degrees F. Tempering in an oil bath usually is limited to temperatures of 500 to 600 degrees, and some heat-treating specialists recommend the use of a salt bath for temperatures above 350 or 400 degrees, as it is considered more efficient and economical. Tempering in a bath (salt or oil) has several advantages, such as ease in controlling the temperature range and maintenance of a uniform temperature. The work is also heated much more rapidly in a molten bath. While a gas- or oil-fired muffle or semi-muffle furnace may be used for tempering, a salt bath or oil bath is preferable. A salt bath is recommended for tempering high-speed steel, although furnaces may also be used. The bath or furnace temperature should be increased gradually, say, from 300 to 400 degrees up to the tempering temperature which may range from 1050 to 1150 degrees F. for high-speed steel.

Tempering in a Lead Bath. — The lead bath is commonly used for heating steel in connection with tempering, as well as for hardening. The bath is first heated to the temperature at which the steel should be tempered; the pre-heated work is then placed in the bath long enough to acquire this temperature, after which it is removed and cooled. As the melting temperature of pure lead is about 620 degrees F., tin is commonly added to it to lower the temperature sufficiently for tempering. Reductions in temperature can be obtained by varying the proportions of lead and tin, as shown by the table, "Temperatures of Lead Bath Alloys."

Temperatures of Lead Bath Alloys

Parts Lead	Parts Tin	Melting Temp., Deg. F.	Parts Lead	Parts Tin	Melting Temp., Deg. F.	Parts Lead	Parts Tin	Melting Temp., Deg. F.
200	8	560	39	8	510	19	8	460
100	8	550	33	8	500	17	8	450
75	8	540	28	8	490	16	8	440
60	8	530	24	8	480	15	8	430
48	8	520	21	8	470	14	8	420

To Prevent Lead from Sticking to Steel. — To prevent hot lead from sticking to parts heated in it, mix common whiting with wood alcohol, and paint the part that is to be heated. Water can be used instead of alcohol, but in that case the paint must be thoroughly dry, as otherwise the moisture will cause the lead to "fly." Another method is to make a thick paste according to the following formula: Pulverized charred leather, 1 pound; fine wheat flour, 1½ pounds; fine table salt, 2 pounds. Coat the tool with this paste and heat slowly until dry, then proceed to harden. Still another method is to heat the work to a blue color, or about 600 degrees F., and then dip it in a strong solution of salt water, prior to heating in the lead bath. The lead is sometimes removed from parts having fine projections or teeth, by using a stiff brush just before immersing in the cooling bath. This is necessary to prevent the formation of soft spots.

Tempering in Sand. — The sand bath is used for tempering certain classes of work. One method is to deposit the sand on an iron plate or in a shallow box which has burners beneath it. With this method of tempering, tools such as boiler punches, etc., can be given a varying temper by placing them endwise in the sand. As the temperature of the sand bath is higher toward the bottom, a tool can be so placed that the color of the lower end will be a deep dark blue when the middle portion is a very dark straw, and the working end or top a light straw color, the hardness gradually increasing from the bottom up.

Double Tempering. — In tempering high-speed steel tools, it is common practice to repeat the tempering operation or "double temper" the steel. This is done by heating the steel to the tempering temperature (say 1050 degrees F.) and holding it at that temperature for two hours. It is then cooled to room temperature, reheated to 1050 degrees F. for another two-hour period, and again cooled to room temperature. After the first tempering operation, some untempered martensite remains in the steel. This martensite is not only tempered by a second tempering operation but is relieved of internal stresses, thus improving the steel for service conditions. The hardening temperature for the higher alloy steels may affect the hardness after tempering. For example, molybdenum high-speed steel when heated to 2100 degrees F. had a hardness of 61 Rockwell C after tempering whereas a temperature of 2250 degrees F. resulted in a hardness of 64.5 Rockwell C after tempering.

Temperatures as Indicated by the Color of Plain Carbon Steel

Degrees Centigrade	Degrees Fahrenheit	Color of Steel	Degrees Centigrade	Degrees Fahrenheit	Color of Steel
221.1	430	Very pale yellow	265.6	510	Spotted red-brown
226.7	440	Light yellow	271.1	520	Brown-purple
232.2	450	Pale straw-yellow	276.7	530	Light purple
237.8	460	Straw-yellow	282.2	540	Full purple
243.3	470	Deep straw-yellow	287.8	550	Dark purple
248.9	480	Dark yellow	293.3	560	Full blue
254.4	490	Yellow-brown	298.9	570	Dark blue
260.0	500	Brown-yellow	337.8	640	Light blue

Tempering Temperatures for Various Plain Carbon Steel Tools

Degrees F.	Class of Tool
495 to 500	Taps ½ inch or over, for use on automatic screw machines.
495 to 500	Nut taps ½ inch and under.
515 to 520	Taps ¼ inch and under, for use on automatic screw machines.
525 to 530	Thread dies to cut thread close to shoulder.
500 to 510	Thread dies for general work.
495	Thread dies for tool steel or steel tube.
525 to 540	Dies for bolt threader threading to shoulder.
460 to 470	Thread rolling dies.
430 to 435	Hollow mills (solid type) for roughing on automatic screw machine.
485	Knurls.
450	Twist drills for hard service.
450	Centering tools for automatic screw machine.
430	Forming tools for automatic screw machine.
430 to 435	Cut-off tools for automatic screw machine.
440 to 450	Profile cutters for milling machine.
430	Formed milling cutters.
435 to 440	Milling cutters.
430 to 440	Reamers.
460	Counterbores and countersinks.
480	Cutters for tube or pipe-cutting machine.
460 and 520	Snaps for pneumatic hammers — harden full length, temper to 460 degrees, then bring point to 520 degrees.

Annealing, Spheroidizing, and Normalizing

Annealing of steel is a heat-treating process in which the steel is heated to some elevated temperature, usually in or near the critical range, is held at this temperature for some period of time, and is then cooled, usually at a slow rate. Spheroidizing and normalizing may be considered as special cases of annealing.

The *full annealing* of carbon steel consists in heating it slightly above the *upper* critical point for hypo-eutectoid steels (steels of less than 0.85 per cent carbon content) and slightly above the *lower* critical point for hyper-eutectoid steels (steels of more than 0.85 per cent carbon content), holding it at this temperature until it is uniformly heated and then slowly cooling it to 1000 degrees F. or below. The resulting structure is layer-like or lamellar in character due to the pearlite which is formed during the slow cooling. Annealing is employed (1) to soften steel for machining, cutting, stamping, etc., or for some particular service; (2) to alter ductility, toughness, electrical or magnetic characteristics or other physical properties; (3) to refine the crystal structure; (4) to produce grain reorientation; or (5) to relieve stresses and hardness resulting from cold working.

The *spheroidizing* of steel, according to the American Society of Metals, is " any process of heating and cooling that produces a rounded or globular form of carbide.' High-carbon steels are spheroidized to improve their machinability especially in continuous cutting operations such as are performed by lathes and screw machines. In low-carbon steels, spheroidizing may be employed to meet certain strength requirements before subsequent heat-treatment. Spheroidizing also tends to increase resistance to abrasion.

The *normalizing* of steel consists in heating it to some temperature above that used for annealing, usually about 100 degrees F. above the upper critical range, and then cooling it in still air at room temperature. Normalizing is intended to put the steel into a uniform, unstressed condition of proper grain size and refinement so that it will properly respond to further heat-treatments. It is particularly important in the case of forgings which are to be later heat-treated. Normalizing may or may not (depending upon the composition) leave steel in a sufficiently soft state for machining with available tools. In some cases, annealing for machinability is preceded by normalizing and the combined treatment — frequently called a *double anneal* — produces a better result than a simple anneal.

Annealing Practice. — For carbon steels, the following annealing temperatures are recommended by the American Society of Testing Materials: Steels of less than 0.12 per cent carbon content, 1600 to 1700 degrees F.; steels of 0.12 to 0.29 per cent carbon content, 1550 to 1600 degrees F.; steels of 0.30 to 0.49 per cent carbon content, 1500 to 1550 degrees F.; and for 0.50 to 1.00 per cent carbon steels, from 1450 to 1500 degrees F. Slightly lower temperatures are satisfactory for steels having more than 0.75 per cent manganese content. Heating should be uniform to avoid the formation of additional stresses. In the case of large work-pieces, the heating should be slow enough so that the temperature of the interior does not lag too far behind that of the surface.

It has been found that in annealing steel, the higher the temperature to which it is heated to produce an austenitic structure, the greater the tendency of the structure to become lamellar (pearlitic) in cooling. On the other hand, the closer the austenitizing temperature to the critical temperature, the greater is the tendency of the annealed steel to become spheroidal.

Rate of Cooling: After heating the steel to some temperature within the annealing range, it should be cooled slowly enough to permit the development of the desired softness and ductility. In general, the slower the cooling rate, the greater the resulting softness and ductility. Steel of a high carbon content should be cooled more slowly than steel of a low carbon content; also the higher the alloy content, the slower is the cooling rate usually required. Where extreme softness and ductility are not required, the steel may be cooled in the annealing furnace to some temperature well below the critical point, say, to about 1000 degrees F. and then removed and cooled in air.

Annealing by Constant Temperature Transformation. — It has been found that steel which has been heated above the critical point so that it has an austenitic structure can be transformed into a lamellar (pearlitic) or a spheroidal structure by holding it for a definite period of time at some constant sub-critical temperature. In other words, it is feasible to anneal steel by means of a constant-temperature transformation as well as by the conventional continuous cooling method. When the constant-temperature transformation method is employed, the steel, after being heated to some temperature above the critical and held at this temperature until it is austenitized, is cooled as rapidly as feasible to some relatively high sub-critical transformation temperature. The selection of this temperature is governed by the desired microstructure and hardness required and is taken from a transformation time and temperature curve (often called a TTT curve.) As drawn for a particular steel, such a curve shows the length of time required to transform that steel from an austenitic state at various sub-critical temperatures. After being held at the selected sub-critical temperature for the required length of time, the steel is cooled to room temperature,— again, as rapidly as feasible. This rapid cooling down to the selected transformation temperature and then down to room temperature has a negligible effect on the structure of the steel and makes possible in many instances a considerable saving in time over the conventional slow cooling method of annealing.

The softest condition in steel can be developed by heating it to a temperature usually less than 100 degrees F. above the lower critical point and then cooling it to some temperature, usually less than 100 degrees below the critical point, where it is held until the transformation is completed. Certain steels require a very lengthy period of time for transformation of the austenite when held at a constant temperature within this range. For such steels a practical procedure is to allow most of the transformation to take place in this temperature range where a soft product is formed and then to finish the transformation at a lower temperature where the time for the completion of the transformation is short.

Spheroidizing Practice. — A common method of spheroidizing steel consists in heating it to or slightly below the lower critical point, holding it at this temperature for a period of time, and then cooling it slowly to about 1000 degrees F. or below. The length of time at which the steel is held at the spheroidizing temperature largely governs the degree of spheroidization. High-carbon steel may be spheroidized by subjecting it to a temperature that alternately rises and falls between a point within and a point without the critical range. Tool steel may be spheroidized by heating to a temperature slightly above the critical range and then, after being held at this temperature for a period of time, cooling without removal from the furnace.

Normalizing Practice. — When using the lower carbon steels, simple normalizing is often sufficient to place the steel in its best condition for machining and will lessen distortion in carburizing or hardening. In the medium and higher carbon steels, combined normalizing and annealing constitutes the best practice. For unimportant parts, the normalizing may be omitted entirely or annealing practiced only when the steel is otherwise difficult to machine. Both processes are recommended in the following heat-treatments (for S. A. E. steels) as representing the best metallurgical practice. The temperatures recommended for normalizing and annealing have been made indefinite in many instances because of the many different types of furnace used in various plants and the difference in results desired.

Casehardening

In order to harden low-carbon steel it is necessary to increase the carbon content of the surface of the steel so that a thin outer " case " can be hardened by heating the steel to the hardening temperature and then quenching it. The process, therefore, involves two separate operations. The first is the *carburizing* operation for impregnating the outer surface with sufficient carbon, and the second operation is that of heat-treating the carburized parts so as to obtain a hard outer case and, at the same time, give the " core " the required physical properties. The term " casehardening " is ordinarily used to indicate the complete process of carburizing and hardening.

Carburization. — Carburization is the result of heating iron or steel to a temperature below its melting point in the presence of a solid, liquid, or gaseous material which decomposes so as to liberate carbon when heated to the temperature used. In this way, it is possible to obtain by the gradual penetration, diffusion, or absorption of the carbon by the steel, a " zone " or " case " of higher carbon content at the outer surfaces than that of the original object. When a carburized object is rapidly cooled or quenched in water, oil, brine, etc., from the proper temperature, this case becomes hard, leaving the inside of the piece soft, but of great toughness.

Use of Carbonaceous Mixtures. — When carburizing materials of the solid class are used, the casehardening process consists in packing steel articles in metal boxes or pots, with a carbonaceous compound surrounding the steel objects. The boxes or pots are sealed and placed in a carburizing oven or furnace maintained usually at a heat of from about 1650 to 1700 degrees F. for a length of time depending upon the extent of the carburizing action desired. The carbon from the carburizing compound will then be absorbed by the steel on the surfaces desired, and the low-carbon steel is converted into high-carbon steel at these portions, while the internal sections and the insulated parts of the object retain practically their original low-carbon content. The result is a steel of a dual structure, a high-carbon and a low-carbon steel in the same piece. The carburized steel may now be heat-treated by heating and quenching, in much the same way as high-carbon steel is hardened, in order to develop the properties of hardness and toughness; but as the steel is, in reality, two steels in one, one high-carbon and one low-carbon, the correct heat-treatment after carburizing includes two distinct processes, one suitable for the high-carbon portion or the " case," as it is generally termed, and one suitable for the low-carbon portion or core. The method of heat-treatment varies according to the kind of steel used. Usually an initial heating and slow cooling is followed by reheating to 1400–1450 degrees F., quenching in oil or water, and a final tempering. More definite information is given in the following section on S.A.E. steels.

Carburizers: There are many commercial carburizers on the market in which the materials used as the generator may be hard and soft wood charcoal, animal charcoal, coke, coal, beans and nuts, bone and leather, or various combinations of these. The energizers may be barium, cyanogen, and ammonium compounds, various salts, soda ash, or lime and oil hydrocarbons.

Pack-Hardening. — When cutting tools, gages, and other parts made from high-carbon steels, are heated for hardening while packed in some carbonaceous material in order to protect delicate edges, corners or finished surfaces, the process usually is known as pack-hardening. Thus, the purpose is to protect the work, prevent scale formation, insure uniform heating, and minimize the danger of cracking and warpage. The work is packed, as in carburizing, and in the same type of receptacle. Common hardwood charcoal often is used, especially if it has had an initial heating to eliminate shrinkage and discharge its more impure gases. The lowest temperature required for hardening should be employed for pack-hardening — usually 1400 to 1450 degrees F. for carbon steels. Pack-hardening has also been applied to high-speed steels, but modern developments in heat-treating salts have made it possible to harden high-speed steel without decarburization, injury to sharp edges, or marring the finished surfaces. See paragraph on Salt Baths.

Cyanide Hardening. — When low-carbon steel requires a very hard outer surface but does not need high shock-resisting qualities, the cyanide hardening process may be employed to produce what is known as superficial hardness. This superficial hardening is the result of carburizing a very thin outer skin (which may be only a few thousandths inch thick) by immersing the steel in a bath containing sodium cyanide. The temperatures usually vary from 1450 to 1650 degrees F. and he percentage of sodium cyanide in the bath extends over a wide range, depending pon the steel used and properties required.

Nitriding Process. — Nitriding is a process for surface hardening certain alloy teels by heating the steel in an atmosphere of nitrogen (ammonia gas) at approximately 950 degrees F. The steel is then cooled slowly. Finish machined surfaces ardened by nitriding are subject to minimum distortion. The physical properties, uch as toughness, high impact strength, etc., can be imparted to the core by previous heat-treatments and are unaffected by drawing temperatures up to 950 legrees F. The "Nitralloy" steels suitable for this process may readily be machined in the heat-treated as well as in the annealed state, and they forge as easily s alloy steels of the same carbon content. Certain heat-treatments must be applied prior to nitriding, the first being annealing to relieve rolling, forging, or machining trains. Parts or sections not requiring heat-treating should be machined or ground to the exact dimensions required. Close tolerances must be maintained n finish machining, but allowances for growth due to adsorption of nitrogen should be made, and this usually amounts to about 0.0005 inch for a case depth of 0.02 inch. Parts requiring heat-treatment for definite physical properties are forged or cut rom annealed stock; heat-treated for the desired physical properties, rough machined, normalized, and finish machined. If quenched and drawn parts are normalized afterwards, the drawing and normalizing temperatures should be alike. The normalizing temperature may be below but should never be above the drawing temperature.

Liquid Carburizing. — Activated liquid salt baths are now used extensively for carburizing. Sodium cyanide and other salt baths are used. The salt bath is heated by electrodes immersed in it, the bath itself acting as the conductor and resistor. One or more groups of electrodes, with two or more electrodes per group, may be used. The heating is accompanied by a stirring action to insure uniform temperature and carburizing activity throughout the bath. The temperature may be controlled by a thermocouple immersed in the bath and connecting with a pyrometer designed to provide automatic regulation. The advantages of liquid baths include rapid action; uniform carburization; minimum distortion; and elimination of the packing and unpacking required when carbonaceous mixtures are used. In selective carburizing, the portions of the work which are not to be carburized are copper plated and the entire piece is then immersed in an activated cyanide bath. The copper inhibits any carburizing action on the plated parts, and this method offers a practical solution for selectively carburizing any portion of a steel part.

Gas Carburizing. — When carburizing gases are used, the mixture varies with the type of case and quality of product desired. The gaseous hydrocarbons most widely used are methane (natural gas), propane, and butane. These carbon bearing gases are mixed with air, with manufactured gases of several types, with flue gas, or with other specially prepared "diluent" gases. It is necessary to maintain a continuous fresh stream of carburizing gases to the carburizing retort or muffle, as well as to remove the spent gases from the muffle continuously, in order to obtain the correct mixture of gases inside the muffle. A slight pressure is maintained on the muffle to exclude foreign gases.

The horizontal rotary type of gas carburizing furnace has a retort or muffle which revolves slowly. This type is adapted to small parts such as ball and roller bearings, chain links, small axles, bolts, etc. With this type of furnace very large pieces such as gears, for example, may be injured by successive shocks due to tumbling within the rotor.

The vertical pit type of gas carburizer has a stationary rotor which is placed vertically in a pit. The work, instead of circulating in the gases as with the rotary type, is stationary and the gases circulate around it. This type is applicable to long large shafts or other parts or shapes that cannot be rolled in a rotary type of furnace. There are three types of continuous gas furnaces which may be designated as (1) direct quench and manually operated, (2) direct quench and mechanically operated and (3) cooling-zone type. Where production does not warrant using a large continuous type furnace, a horizontal muffle furnace of the batch type may be used, especially if the quantities of work are varied and the production not continuous.

Casehardening Steels. — A low-carbon steel containing, say, from 0.15 to 0.20 per cent of carbon is suitable for casehardening. In addition to straight-carbon steels, the low-carbon alloy steels are employed. The alloys add to casehardened parts the same advantageous properties which they give to other classes of steel. Various steels for casehardening will be found in the section on S.A.E. steels.

To Clean Work after Casehardening. — To clean work, especially if knurled where dirt is likely to stick into crevices after casehardening, wash it in caustic soda (1 part soda to 10 parts water). In making this solution, the soda should be put into hot water gradually, and the mixture stirred until the soda is thoroughly dissolved. A still more effective method of cleaning is to dip the work into a mixture of 1 part sulphuric acid and 2 parts water. Leave the pieces in this mixture about three minutes; then wash them off immediately in a soda solution.

Flame Hardening. — This method of hardening is especially applicable to the selective hardening of large steel forgings or castings which must be finish-machined prior to heat-treatment, or which because of size or shape cannot be heat-treated by using a furnace or bath. An oxy-acetylene torch is used to heat quickly the surface to be hardened; this surface is then quenched to secure a hardened layer which may vary in depth from a mere skin to ¼ inch and with hardness ranging from 400 to 700 Brinell. A multi-flame torch-head may be equipped with quenching holes or a spray nozzle back of the flame. This is not a carburizing or a case-hardening process as the torch is only a heating medium. Most authorities recommend tempering or drawing of the hardened surface at temperatures between 200 and 350 degrees F. This treatment may be done in a standard furnace, an oil bath, or with a gas flame. It should follow the hardening process as close as possible. Medium-carbon and many low-alloy steels are suitable for hardening. Plain carbon steels ranging from 0.35 to 0.60 per cent carbon will give hardnesses of from 400 to 700 Brinell. Steels in the 0.40 to 0.45 per cent carbon range are preferred, as they have excellent core properties and produce hardnesses of from 400 to 500 Brinell without checking or cracking. Higher carbon steels will give greater hardnesses, but extreme care must be taken to prevent cracking. This requires careful control of the quenching operation.

Spinning Method of Flame Hardening: This method is employed on circular objects that can be rotated or spun past a stationary flame. It may be subdivided according to the speed of rotation, as, first, where the part is rotated slowly in front of a stationary flame and the quench is applied immediately after the flame. This method is used on large circular pieces such as track wheels and bearing surfaces. There will be a narrow band of material with lower hardness between adjacent torches if more than one path of the flame is required to harden the surface. There will also be an area of lower hardness where the flame is extinguished. A second method is applicable to small rollers or pinions. The work is spun at a speed of 50 to 150 R.P.M. in front of the flame until the entire piece has reached the proper temperature; then it is quenched as a unit by a cooling spray or ejecting into a cooling bath.

The Progressive Method: With this method the torch travels along the face of the work while the work remains stationary. It is used to harden lathe ways, gear teeth, and track rails.

The Stationary or Spot-hardening Method: When this method is employed, the work and torch are both stationary. When the spot to be hardened reaches the quenching temperature, the flame is removed and the quench applied.

The Combination Method: This is a combination of the spinning and progressive methods. It is used for long bearing surfaces. The work rotates slowly past the torch as the torch travels longitudinally across the face of the work at the rate of the torch width per revolution of the work.

The equipment for the stationary method of flame-hardening consists merely of an acetylene torch, an oxy-acetylene supply, and a suitable means of quenching; but when the other methods are employed, work-handling tools are essential and specially designed torches are desirable. A lathe is ideally suited for the spinning or combination hardening method, while a planer is adapted for progressive hardening. Production jobs, such as the hardening of gears, require specially designed machines. These machines reduce handling and hardening time, as well as assuring consistent results.

Induction Hardening. — The hardening of steel by means of induction heating and subsequent quenching in either liquid or air, is particularly applicable to parts which require localized hardening or controlled depth of hardening and to irregularly shaped parts, such as cams which require uniform surface hardening around their contour. Advantages offered by induction hardening are: (1) a short heating cycle which may range from a fraction of a second to several seconds (heat energy can be induced in a piece of steel at the rate of 100 to 250 B.T.U. per square inch per minute by induction heating, as compared with a rate of 3 B.T.U. per square inch per minute for the same material at room temperature when placed in a furnace with a wall temperature of 2000 degrees F.); (2) absence of tendency to produce oxidation or decarburization; (3) exact control of depth and area of hardening; (4) close regulation of degree of hardness obtained by automatic timing of heating and quenching cycles; (5) minimum amount of warpage or distortion; and (6) possibility of substituting carbon steels for higher cost alloy steels.

The principal advantage of induction hardening to the designer lies in its application to localized zones. Thus, specific areas in a given part can be heat treated separately to the respective hardnesses required. Parts can be designed so that the stresses at any given point in the finished piece can be relieved by local heating. Parts can be designed in which welded or brazed assemblies are built up prior to heat treating with only internal surfaces or projections requiring hardening.

Types of Induction Heating Equipment. — Induction heating is secured by placing the metal part inside or close to an " applicator " coil of one or more turns, through which alternating current is passed. The coil, formed to suit the general class of work to be heated, is usually made of copper tubing through which water is passed to prevent overheating of the coil itself. In most cases, the work piece is held either in a fixed position or is rotated slowly within or close to the applicator coil. Where the length of work is too great to permit heating in a fixed position, progressive heating may be employed. Thus, a rod or tube of steel may be fed through an applicator coil of one or more turns so that the heating zone travels progressively along the entire length of the work piece.

The frequency of the alternating current used and the type of generator employed to supply this current to the applicator coil depend upon the character of the work to be done. There are three types of equipment used commercially to produce high-frequency current for induction heating: (1) motor generator sets which deliver current at frequencies of approximately 1000, 2000, 3000, and 10,000 cycles;

(2) spark gap oscillator units which produce frequencies ranging from 80,000 to 300,000 cycles; and (3) vacuum tube oscillator sets, which produce currents at frequencies ranging from 350,000 to 15,000,000 cycles or more.

Depth of Heat Penetration. — Generally speaking, the higher the frequency used, the shallower the depth of heat penetration. For heating clear through, for deep hardening and for large work pieces, low power concentrations and low frequencies are usually employed. For very shallow and closely controlled depths of heating, as in surface hardening, and in localized heat treating of small work pieces, currents at high frequencies are employed.

For example, a ½-inch round bar of hardenable steel will be heated through its entire structure quite rapidly by an induced current of 2000 cycles. After quenching, the bar would show through hardness with a decrease in hardness from surface to center. The same piece of steel could be readily heated and surface hardened to a depth of 0.100 inch with current at 9600 cycles, and to an even shallower depth with current at 100,000 cycles. A ¼-inch bar, however, would not reach a sufficiently high temperature at 2000 cycles to permit hardening but at 9600 cycles through hardening would be accomplished, while current at over 100,000 cycles would be needed for surface hardening.

Types of Steel for Induction Hardening. — Most of the standard types of steels can be hardened by induction heating, providing the carbon content is sufficient to produce the desired degree of hardness by quenching. Thus, low carbon steels with a carburized case, medium and high carbon steels (both plain and alloy), and cast iron with a portion of the carbon in combined form, may be used for this purpose. In the case of alloy steels, induction heating should be limited primarily to the shallow hardening type, i.e., those of low alloy content, otherwise the severe quench usually required may result in a highly-stressed surface with consequent reduced load-carrying capacity and danger of cracking.

Through Hardening, Annealing and Normalizing by Induction. — For through hardening, annealing and normalizing by induction, low power concentrations are desirable to prevent too great a temperature differential between surface and interior of the work. A satisfactory rate of heating is obtained when the total power input to the work is slightly greater than the radiation losses at the desired temperature. If possible, as low a frequency should be used as is consistent with good electrical coupling. A number of applicator coils may be connected in a series so that several work pieces can be heated simultaneously, thus reducing the power input to each. Widening the spacing between work and applicator coil also will reduce the amount of power delivered to the work.

Induction Surface Hardening. — As indicated in " Depth of Heat Penetration," currents at much higher frequencies are required in induction surface hardening than in through hardening by induction. In general, the smaller the work piece, the thinner the section, or the shallower the depth to be hardened, the higher will be the frequency required. High power concentrations are also needed to make possible a short heating period so that an undue amount of heat will not be conducted to adjacent or interior areas, where a change in hardness is not desired. Generators of large capacity and applicator coils of but a few turns, or even a single turn, provide the necessary concentration of power in the localized area to be hardened.

Induction heating of internal surfaces, such as the interior of a hollow cylindrical part or the inside of a hole, can be accomplished readily with applicator coils shaped to match the cross-section of the opening which may be round, square, eliptical, etc. If the internal surface is of short length, a multiturn applicator coil extending along its entire length may be employed. Where the power available is insufficient to heat the entire internal surface at once, progressive heating is used. For this purpose an applicator coil of few turns — often but a single turn — is employed, and either coil or work is moved so that the heated zone passes progressively from one end of the hole or opening to the other. For bores of small diameter, a hairpin shaped applicator, extending the entire length of the hole, may be employed and the work rotated about the axis of the hole to insure even heating.

Quenching After Induction Heating. — After induction heating, quenching may be by immersion in a liquid bath (usually oil), by liquid spray (usually water), or by self-quenching. (The term " self-quenching " is used when there is no quenching medium and hardening of the heated section is due chiefly to rapid absorption of heat by the mass of cool metal adjacent to it.) Quenching by immersion offers the advantage of even cooling and is particularly satisfactory for through heated parts. Spray quenching may be arranged so that the quenching ring and applicator coil are in the same or adjacent units, permitting the quenching cycle to follow immediately the heating cycle without removal of the work from the holding fixture. Automatic timing to a fraction of a second may also be employed for both heating and quenching with this arrangement to secure the exact degree of hardness desired. Self-quenching is applicable only in thin-surface hardening where the mass of adjacent cool metal in the part is great enough to conduct the heat rapidly out of the surface layer which is being hardened. It has been recommended that for adequate self quenching, the mass of the unheated section should be at least ten times that of the heated shell. It has been found difficult to use the self-quenching technique to produce hardened shells of much more than about 0.060 inch thickness. Close to this limit, self-quenching can only be accomplished with the easily hardenable steels. By using a combination of self-quench and liquid quench, however, it is possible to produce hardened shells on work too thin to self-quench completely. In general, self-quenching is confined chiefly to relatively small parts and simple shapes.

Induction Hardening of Gear Teeth. — Several advantages are claimed for the induction hardening of gear teeth. One advantage is that the gear teeth can be completely machined, including shaving, when in the soft-annealed or normalized condition, and then hardened, since when induction heating is used, distortion is held to a minimum. Another advantage claimed is that bushings and inserts can be assembled in the gears before hardening. A wide lattitude in choice of built-up webs and easily-machined hubs is afforded since the hardness of neither web nor hub is affected by the induction hardening operation although slight dimensional changes may occur in certain designs. Regular carbon steels can be used in place of alloy steels for a wide variety of gears, and a steel with a higher carbon content can frequently be substituted for a carburizing steel so that the carburizing operation can be eliminated. Another saving in time is the elimination of cleaning after hardening.

In heating spur gears teeth by induction, the gear is usually placed inside a circular unit which combines the applicator coil and quenching ring. An automatic timing device controls both the heating and quenching cycles. During the heating cycle, the gear is rotated at 25 to 35 R.P.M. to insure uniform heating.

In hardening bevel gears, the applicator coil is wound to conform to the face angle of the gear. In some spiral-bevel gears, there is a tendency to obtain more heat on one side of the tooth than on the other. In some sizes of spiral-bevel gears this can be overcome by applying slightly more heat to insure hardening of the concave side. In some forms of spiral-bevel gears, it has been the practice to carburize that part of the gear surface which is to be hardened, after the teeth have been rough-cut. This is followed by the finish-cutting operation, after which the teeth can be induction heated, using a long enough period to heat the entire tooth. When the gear is quenched only the carburized surface will become hardened.

Approximate Compositions and Heat-treating Characteristics of Tool and Die Steels

Type of Tool Steel	Chemical Composition†								Non-Warping Prop.	Safety in Hardening	Resistance to Decarb.	Depth of Hardening	Hardening Temp. Range, Deg. F.
	C	Mn	Si	Cr	V	W	Mo	Co					
Water Hardening													
.80 Carbon	.70-.85	*	*	*					Poor	Fair	Best	Shallow	1420-1450
.90 Carbon	.85-.95	*	*	*					Poor	Fair	Best	Shallow	1420-1450
1.00 Carbon	.95-1.10	*	*	*					Poor	Fair	Best	Shallow	1420-1450
1.20 Carbon	1.10-1.30	*	*	*					Poor	Fair	Best	Shallow	1420-1500
.90 Carbon-V	.85-.95	*	*	*	.15-.35				Poor	Fair	Best	Shallow	1420-1500
1.00 Carbon-V	.95-1.10	*	*	*	.15-.35				Poor	Fair	Best	Shallow	1420-1500
1.00 Carbon-VV	.90-1.10	*	*	*	.35-.50				Poor	Fair	Best	Shallow	1420-1500
Oil Hardening													
Low Manganese	.90	1.20	.25	.50	.20[1]				Good	Good	Good	Deep	1450-1500
High Manganese	.90	1.60	.25	.35[1]	.20[1]		.30[1]		Good	Good	Good	Deep	1420-1450
High Carbon-High Chromium‡	2.15	.35	.35	12.00	.80[1]	.75[1]	.80[1]		Good	Good	Fair	Through	1750-1800
Chromium	1.00	.35	.25	1.40			.40		Fair	Good	Good	Deep	1525-1550
Molybdenum Graphitic	1.45	.65	1.00				.25		Good	Good	Good	Deep	1450-1550
Air Hardening													
High Carbon-High Chromium	1.50	.40	.40	12.00	.80[1]		.90		Best	Best	Fair	Through	1850-1900
5 Per Cent Chromium Air Hard.	1.00	.60	.25	5.25	.40[1]		1.10	.60[1]	Best	Best	Good	Through	1725-1775
High Carbon-High Chromium-Cobalt	1.50	.40	.40	12.00	.80[1]		.90	3.10	Best	Best	Fair	Through	1850-1900
Shock Resisting													
Chromium-Tungsten	.50	.25	.35	1.40	.20	2.25	.40[1]		Fair	Good	FG[4]	Deep	1650-1800
Silicon-Molybdenum	.50	.40	1.00		.25[1]		.50		Poor[2]	Poor[2]	Poor	Deep	1550-1575[5]
Silicon-Manganese	.55	.80	2.00	.30[1]	.25[1]		.40[1]		Poor[2]	Poor[3]	Poor	Deep	1550-1600[6]
Hot Work													
Chromium-Molybdenum-Tungsten	.35	.30	1.00	5.00	.25[1]	1.25	1.50		Good	Good	Fair	Through	1850-1900
Chromium-Molybdenum-V	.35	.30	1.00	5.00	.40		1.50		Good	Good	Fair	Through	1825-1875
Chromium-Molybdenum-VV	.35	.30	1.00	5.00	.90		1.50		Good	Good	Fair	Through	1825-1875
Tungsten	.32	.30	.20	3.25	.40	9.00			Good	Good	Fair	Through	2100-2150

Approximate Compositions and Heat-treating Characteristics of Tool and Die Steels (*Continued*)

Type of Tool Steel	Chemical Composition†								Non-Warping Prop.	Safety in Hardening	Resistance to Decarb.	Depth of Hardening	Hardening Temp. Range, Deg. F.
	C	Mn	Si	Cr	V	W	Mo	Co					
High Speed													
Tungsten, 18-4-1	.70	.30	.30	4.10	1.10	18.00	..	..	Good	Good	Good	Through	2300-2375
Tungsten, 18-4-2	.80	.30	.30	4.10	2.10	18.50	.80	..	Good	Good	Good	Through	2300-2375
Tungsten, 18-4-3	1.05	.30	.30	4.10	3.25	18.50	.70	..	Good	Good	Good	Through	2300-2375
Cobalt-Tungsten, 14-4-2-5	.80	.30	.30	4.10	2.00	14.00	.80	5.00	Good	Fair	Poor	Through	2350-2400
Cobalt-Tungsten, 18-4-1-5	.75	.30	.30	4.10	1.00	18.00	.80	5.00	Good	Fair	Poor	Through	2300-2375
Cobalt-Tungsten, 18-4-2-8	.80	.30	.30	4.10	1.75	18.50	.80	8.00	Good	Fair	Poor	Through	2300-2400
Cobalt-Tungsten, 18-4-2-12	.80	.30	.30	4.10	1.75	20.00	.80	12.00	Good	Fair	Poor	Through	2350-2400
Molybdenum, 8-2-1	.80	.30	.30	4.00	1.15	1.50	8.50	..	Good	Fair	Poor	Through	2150-2250
Molybdenum-Tungsten, 6-6-2	.83	.30	.30	4.10	1.99	6.25	5.00	..	Good	Fair	Fair	Through	2200-2250
Molybdenum-Tungsten, 6-6-3	1.15	.30	.30	4.10	3.25	5.75	5.25	..	Good	Fair	Fair	Through	2175-2250
Cobalt-Molybdenum-Tungsten, 6-6-2-8	.85	.30	.30	4.10	2.00	6.00	5.00	8.00	Good	Fair	Poor	Through	2225-2275

† C = carbon; Mn = manganese; Si = silicon; Cr = chromium; V = vanadium; W = tungsten; Mo = molybdenum; Co = cobalt.
‡ This steel may have 0.50 per cent nickel as an optional element. The steel has been found to give satisfactory application either with or without the element present.

* Carbon tool steels are normally supplied in four grades of quality: special, extra, standard, and commercial. On special and extra grades, limits on manganese, silicon, and chromium are not generally required if Shepherd hardenability limits are specified. On standard and commercial grades, manganese and silicon are limited to 0.35 per cent maximum each. Chromium is limited to 0.15 per cent manganese for the standard grade and 0.20 per cent maximum for the commercial grade. The total of manganese, silicon, and chromium is not to exceed 0.75 per cent for either the standard or commercial grade.

[1] Optional element. Steels have found satisfactory application either with or without the element present. In the case of silicon manganese steel listed under Shock Resisting Steels, if chromium, vanadium and molybdenum are not present, then hardenability will be affected.
[2] Poor when water quenched, fair when oil quenched.
[3] Poor when water quenched, good when oil quenched.
[4] FG means fair to good.
[5] Temperature given is for water quenching. For oil quenching, a temperature range of 1600 to 1625 degrees F. is recommended.
[6] Temperature given is for water quenching. For oil quenching, a temperature range of 1600 to 1675 degrees F. is recommended.

Table 1. Typical Heat Treatments for SAE Carbon Steels

				Carburizing Grades				
SAE No.	Normalize Deg. F.	Carburize Deg. F.	Cool *	Reheat Deg. F.	Cool *	2nd Reheat Deg. F.	Cool *	Temper[3] Deg. F.
1010 to 1022	....	1650–1700	A	....	..	....	..	250–400
	....	1650–1700	B	1400–1450	A	....	..	250–400
	....	1650–1700	C	1400–1450	A	....	..	250–400
	....	1650–1700	C	1650–1700	B	1400–1450	A	250–400
	....	1500–1650[1]	B	....	..	....	..	Optional
	....	1350–1575[2]	D	....	..	....	..	Optional
1024	1650–1750[4]	1650–1700	E	....	..	....	..	250–400
	....	1350–1575[2]	D	....	..	....	..	Optional
1025 1026 1027	....	1650–1700	A	....	..	....	..	250–400
	....	1500–1650[1]	B	....	..	....	..	Optional
	....	1350–1575[2]	D	....	..	....	..	Optional
1030	....	1500–1650[1]	B	....	..	....	..	Optional
	....	1350–1575[2]	D	....	..	....	..	Optional
1111 1112 1113	....	1500–1650[1]	B	....	..	....	..	Optional
	....	1350–1575[2]	D	....	..	....	..	Optional
1109 to 1120	....	1650–1700	A	....	..	....	..	250–400
	....	1650–1700	B	1400–1450	A	....	..	250–400
	....	1650–1700	C	1400–1450	A	....	..	250–400
	....	1650–1700	C	1650–1700	B	1400–1450	A	250–400
	....	1500–1650[1]	B	....	..	....	..	Optional
	....	1350–1575[2]	D	....	..	....	..	Optional
1126	....	1500–1650[1]	B	....	..	....	..	Optional
	....	1350–1575[2]	D	....	..	....	..	Optional

		Heat Treating Grades			
SAE Number	Normalize Deg. F.	Anneal	Harden Deg. F.	Quench *	Temper Deg. F.
1025 & 1030	....	....	1575–1650	A	
1033 to 1035			1525–1575	B	
1036	1600–1700	....	1525–1575	B	
			1525–1575	B	
1038 to 1040	1600–1700	....	1525–1575	B	
			1525–1575	B	
1041	1600–1700 and/or	1400–1500	1475–1550	E	To Desired Hardness
1042 to 1050	1600–1700		1475–1550	B	
1052 & 1055	1550–1650 and/or	1400–1500	1475–1550	E	
1060 to 1074	1550–1650 and/or	1400–1500	1475–1550	E	
1078	....	1400–1500[5]	1450–1500	A	
1080 to 1090	1550–1650 and/or	1400–1500[5]	1450–1500	E[6]	
1095	....	1400–1500[5]	1450–1500	F	
	....	1400–1500[5]	1500–1600	E	
1132 & 1137	1600–1700 and/or	1400–1500	1525–1575	B	
1138 & 1140	....	....	1500–1550	B	
	1600–1700		1500–1550	B	
1141 & 1144	....	1400–1500	1475–1550	E	
	1600–1700	1400–1500	1475–1550	E	
1145 to 1151	....	....	1475–1550	B	
	1600–1700		1475–1550	B	

* Symbols: A = Water or Brine; B = Water or oil; C = Cool slowly; D = Air or Oil; E = Oil; F = Water, Brine or Oil.

[1] Activated or cyanide baths; may be given refining heat as in other processes.

[2] Carbonitriding atmospheres; may be given refining heat as in other processes.

[3] Even where tempering temperatures are shown, tempering is not mandatory on many applications. It is usually employed for partial stress relief, and improves resistance to grinding cracks.

[4] Normalizing temperatures at least 50 deg. F. above the carburizing temperature are sometimes recommended where minimum heat treat distortion is of vital importance.

[5] Slow cooling produces a spheroidal structure in these high carbon steels which is sometimes required for machining purposes.

[6] May be water or brine quenched by special techniques such as partial immersion or time quenched, otherwise they are subject to quench cracking.

Table 2. Typical Heat Treatments for SAE Alloy Steels

SAE No.	Normalize[1]	Cycle Anneal[3]	Carburized Deg. F.	Cool *	Reheat Deg. F.	Cool *	Temper[8] Deg. F
					Carburizing Grades		
1320	yes	...	1650–1700	E	1400–1450[6]	E	250–350
	yes	...	1650–1700	E	1475–1525[7]	E	250–350
	yes	...	1650–1700	C	1400–1450[6]	E	250–350
	yes	...	1650–1700	C	1500–1550[7]	E	250–350
	yes	...	1650–1700	E[5]	....	..	250–350
	yes	...	1500–1650[4]	E	....	..	250–350
2317	yes	yes	1650–1700	E	1375–1425[6]	E	250–350
	yes	yes	1650–1700	E	1450–1500[7]	E	250–350
	yes	yes	1650–1700	C	1375–1425[6]	E	250–350
	yes	yes	1650–1700	C	1475–1525[7]	E	250–350
	yes	yes	1650–1700	E[5]	....	..	250–350
	yes	yes	1450–1650[4]	E	....	..	250–350
2512 to 2517	yes[2]	...	1650–1700	C	1325–1375[6]	E	250–350
	yes[2]	...	1650–1700	C	1425–1475[7]	E	250–350
3115 & 3120	yes	...	1650–1700	E	1400–1450[6]	E	250–350
	yes	...	1650–1700	E	1475–1525[7]	E	250–350
	yes	...	1650–1700	C	1400–1450[6]	E	250–350
	yes	...	1650–1700	C	1500–1550[7]	E	250–350
	yes	...	1650–1700	E[5]	....	..	250–350
	yes	...	1500–1650[4]	E	....	..	250–350
3310 & 3316	yes[2]	...	1650–1700	E	1400–1450[6]	E	250–350
	yes[2]	...	1650–1700	C	1475–1500[7]	E	250–350
4017 to 4032	yes	yes	1650–1700	E[5]	....	..	250–350
4119 & 4125	yes	...	1650–1700	E[5]	....	..	250–350
4317 & 4320 / 4608 to 4621	yes	yes	1650–1700	E	1425–1475[6]	E	250–350
	yes	yes	1650–1700	E	1475–1525[7]	E	250–350
	yes	yes	1650–1700	C	1425–1475[6]	E	250–350
	yes	yes	1650–1700	C	1475–1525[7]	E	250–350
	yes	yes	1650–1700	E[5]	....	..	250–350
	yes	yes	1650–1700	E[5]	....	..	250–350
	yes	...	1500–1650[4]	E	....	..	250–350
4812 to 4820	yes[2]	yes	1650–1700	E	1375–1425[6]	E	250–350
	yes[2]	yes	1650–1700	E	1450–1500[7]	E	250–350
	yes[2]	yes	1650–1700	C	1375–1425[6]	E	250–350
	yes[2]	yes	1650–1700	C	1450–1500[7]	E	250–350
	...	...	1650–1700	E[5]	....	..	250–350
5115 & 5120	yes	...	1650–1700	E	1425–1475[6]	E	250–350
	yes	...	1650–1700	E	1500–1550[7]	E	250–350
	yes	...	1650–1700	C	1425–1475[6]	E	250–350
	yes	...	1650–1700	C	1500–1550[7]	E	250–350
	yes	...	1500–1650[4]	E	....	..	250–350
8615 to 8625 / 8720	yes	yes	1650–1700	E	1475–1525[6]	E	250–350
	yes	yes	1650–1700	E	1525–1575[7]	E	250–350
	yes	yes	1650–1700	C	1475–1525[6]	E	250–350
	yes	yes	1650–1700	C	1525–1575[7]	E	250–350
	yes	yes	1650–1700	E[5]	....	..	250–350
	yes	yes	1500–1650[4]	E	....	..	250–350
9310 to 9317	yes[2]	...	1650–1700	E	1400–1450[6]	E	250–350
	yes[2]	...	1650–1700	C	1500–1525	E	250–350

* Symbols: C = Cool slowly; E = Oil.

[1] Normalizing temperatures should not be less than 50 degrees F. higher than the carburizing temperature. Follow by air cooling.

[2] After normalizing, reheat to temperatures of 1000–1200 degrees F. and hold approximately 4 hours.

[3] Where cycle annealing is desired, heat to normalizing temperature — hold for uniformity — cool rapidly to 1000–1250 degrees F.; hold 1 to 3 hours, then air or furnace cool to obtain a structure suitable for machining and finish.

[4] This treatment is for activated or cyanide baths, and parts may be given refining heats as indicated for other heat treating processes.

[5] This treatment applicable to fine-grained steels only. When fine-grained steels are employed, a second reheat is often unnecessary.

[6] This treatment when case hardness only is paramount.

[7] This treatment when core hardness is paramount.

[8] Tempering treatment is optional. Tempering is generally employed for partial stress relief and improved resistance to cracking from grinding operations.

Table 2 *(Continued).* **Typical Heat Treatments for SAE Alloy Steels**

		Directly Hardenable Grades			
SAE No.	Normalize Deg. F.	Anneal Deg. F.	Harden Deg. F.	Quench *	Temper Deg. F.
1330	.... and/or	....	1525–1575	B	To desired hardness
	1600–1700 and/or	1500–1600	1525–1575	B	To desired hardness
1335 & 1340	....	....	1500–1550	E	To desired hardness
	1600–1700 and/or	1500–1600	1525–1575	E	To desired hardness
2330	....	....	1450–1500	E	To desired hardness
	1600–1700 and/or	1400–1500	1450–1500	E	To desired hardness
2340 & 2345	....	....	1425–1475	E	To desired hardness
	1600–1700 and/or	1400–1500	1425–1475	E	To desired hardness
3130	1600–1700	....	1500–1550	B	To desired hardness
3135 to 3141	....	....	1500–1550	E	To desired hardness
	1600–1700 and/or	1450–1550	1500–1550	E	To desired hardness
3145 & 3150	....	....	1500–1550	E	To desired hardness
	1600–1700 and/or	1450–1500	1500–1550	E	To desired hardness
4037 & 4042	....	1525–1575	1500–1575	E	Gears, 350–450 / To desired hardness
4047 & 4053	....	1450–1550	1500–1575	E	To desired hardness
4063 & 4068	....	1450–1550	1475–1550	E	To desired hardness
4130	1600–1700 and/or	1450–1550	1600–1650	B	To desired hardness
4137 & 4140	1600–1700 and/or	1450–1550	1550–1600	E	To desired hardness
4145 & 4150	1600–1700 and/or	1450–1550	1500–1600	E	To desired hardness
4340	1600–1700 and draw 1100–1225		1475–1525	E	To desired hardness
4640	1600–1700 and/or	1450–1550	1450–1500	E	To desired hardness
	1600–1700 and/or	1450–1500	1450–1500	E	Gears, 350–450
5045 & 5046	1600–1700 and/or	1450–1550	1475–1500	E	250–300
5130 & 5132	1650–1750 and/or	1450–1550	1500–1550	G	To desired hardness
5135 to 5145	1650–1750 and/or	1450–1550	1500–1550	E	To desired hardness / Gears, 350–400
5147 to 5152	1650–1750 and/or	1450–1550	1475–1550	E	To desired hardness / Gears, 350–400
50100 / 51100 / 52100	....	1350–1450	1425–1475	H	To desired hardness
	....	1350–1450	1500–1600	E	To desired hardness
6150	1650–1750 and/or	1550–1650	1600–1650	E	To desired hardness
9254 to 9262	....	....	1500–1650	E	To desired hardness
8627 to 8632	1600–1700 and/or	1450–1550	1550–1650	B	To desired hardness
8635 to 8641	1600–1700 and/or	1450–1550	1525–1575	E	To desired hardness
8642 to 8653	1600–1700 and/or	1450–1550	1500–1550	E	To desired hardness
8655 to 8660	1650–1750 and/or	1450–1550	1475–1550	E	To desired hardness
8735 & 8740	1600–1700 and/or	1450–1550	1525–1575	E	To desired hardness
8745 & 8750	1600–1700 and/or	1450–1550	1500–1550	E	To desired hardness
9437 & 9440	1600–1700 and/or	1450–1550	1550–1600	E	To desired hardness
9442 to 9747	1600–1700 and/or	1450–1550	1500–1600	E	To desired hardness
9840	1600–1700 and/or	1450–1550	1500–1550	E	To desired hardness
9845 & 9850	1600–1700 and/or	1450–1550	1500–1550	E	To desired hardness

	Heat Treating Grades — Chromium-Nickel Austenitic Steels				
SAE No.	Normalize	Anneal[9]	Harden Deg. F.	Quenching Medium	Temper
30301 to 30347	....	1800–2100	....	Water or Air	....

* Symbols: B = Water or oil; E = Oil; G = Water, caustic solution or oil; H = Water.

[9] Quench to produce full austenitic structure using water or air in accordance with thickness of section. Annealing temperatures given cover process and full annealing as now used by industry, the lower end of the range being used for process annealing.

Table 2 (Continued). Typical Heat Treatments for SAE Alloy Steels

		Heat Treating Grades — Stainless Chromium Irons and Steels				
SAE No.*	Normalize	Sub-critical Anneal, Deg. F.	Full Anneal Deg. F.	Harden Deg. F.	Quenching Medium	Temper Deg. F.
51410	....	1300–1350[10]	1550–1650[11]	 1750–1850	Oil or air	To desired hardness
51414	....	1200–1250[10]	....	 1750–1850	Oil or air	To desired hardness
51416	....	1300–1350[10]	1550–1650[11]	 1750–1850	Oil or air	To desired hardness
51420 51420F	....	1350–1450[10]	1550–1650[11]	 1800–1850	Oil or air	To desired hardness
51430 51430F	.....	1400–1500[12] 1250–1500[12]	....	....	....	....
51431	.....	1150–1225[10]	....	1800–1900	Oil or air	To desired hardness
51440A 51440B 51440C 51440F	.....	1350–1440[10]	1550–1650[11]	1850–1950	Oil or air	To desired hardness
51442	.....	1400–1500[12]	....	....	....	....
51446	.....	1500–1650[12]	....	....	....	....
51501	.....	1325–1375[10]	1525–1600[11]	1600–1700	Oil or air	To desired hardness

* Suffixes A, B and C denote three types of steel differing in carbon content only. Suffix F denotes a free machining steel.

[10] Usually air cooled, but may be furnace cooled.

[11] Cool slowly in furnace.

[12] Cool rapidly in air.

Heat-Treating High-Speed Steels

Cobaltcrom Steel. — This is a tungstenless alloy steel or high-speed steel which contains approximately 1.5 per cent carbon, 12.5 per cent chromium, and 3.5 per cent cobalt. Tools such as dies, milling cutters, etc., made from cobaltcrom steel can be cast to shape in suitable molds, the teeth of cutters being formed so that it is necessary only to grind them.

Before the blanks can be machined, they must be annealed; this operation is performed by pack-annealing at the temperature of 1800 degrees F., for a period of from three to six hours, according to the size of the castings being annealed. The following directions are given for the hardening of blanking and trimming dies, milling cutters, and similar tools made from cobaltcrom steel: Heat slowly in a hardening furnace to about 1830 degrees F., and hold the temperature at this point until the tools are thoroughly soaked. Then reduce the temperature about 50 degrees, withdraw the tools from the furnace, and allow them to cool in the atmosphere. As soon as the red color disappears from the cooling tool, place it in quenching oil until cold. The slight drop of 50 degrees in temperature while the tool is still in the hardening furnace is highly important in order to obtain proper results. The steel will be injured if the tool is heated above 1860 degrees F. In cooling milling cutters or other rotary tools, it is suggested that they be suspended on a wire to insure a uniform rate of cooling.

Tools that are subjected to shocks or vibration, such as pneumatic rivet sets, shear blades, etc., should be heated slowly to 1650 degrees F., after which the temperature should be reduced to about 1610 degrees F., at which point the tool should be removed from the furnace and permitted to cool in the atmosphere. There is no appreciable scaling present in the hardening of cobaltcrom steel tools.

Preheating Tungsten High-Speed Steel. — Tungsten high-speed steel must be hardened at a very high temperature; consequently, tools made from such steel are seldom hardened without at least one preheating stage to avoid internal strain. This applies especially to milling cutters, taps, and other tools having thin teeth and thick bodies and to forming tools of irregular shape and section. The tools should be heated slowly and carefully to a temperature somewhat below the critical point of the steel, usually in the range of 1500 to 1600 degrees F. By so limiting the preheating temperature, the operation is not unduly sensitive and the tool may be safely left in the furnace until it reaches a uniform temperature throughout its length and cross section.

A single stage of preheating is customary for tools that are simple in form and are not more than from 1 to 1½ inches in thickness. For large, intricate tools, two stages of preheating are frequently used. The first brings the tool up to a temperature of about 1100 to 1200 degrees F., and the second raises its temperature to 1550 to 1600 degrees F. A preheating time of 5 minutes for each ¼ inch in tool thickness has been recommended for a furnace temperature of 1600 degrees F. This is where a single stage of preheating is used and the furnace capacity is sufficient for maintaining practically constant temperature when the tools are changed. To prevent undue chilling, it is common practice to insert a single tool or a small lot in the hardening furnace as often as a tool or lot is removed, rather than to insert a full charge of cold metal at one time.

Preheating is usually done in a simple type of oven furnace heated by gas, electricity, or oil. Atmospheric control is seldom used, although in the case of 18-4-1 steel a slightly reducing atmosphere (2 to 6 per cent carbon monoxide) has been found to produce the least amount of scale and will result in a better surface after final hardening.

Hardening of Tungsten High-Speed Steel. — All tungsten high-speed steels must be heated to a temperature close to their fusion point to develop their maximum efficiency as metal-cutting tools. This requires a hardening temperature ranging from 2200 to 2500 degrees F. The effect of changes in the hardening temperature on the cutting efficiency of several of the more common high-speed steels are shown in Table 1. The figures given are ratios, the value 1.00 for each steel being assigned to the highest observed cutting speed for that steel. The figures for different steels therefore cannot be directly compared with each other, except to note changes in the point of maximum cutting efficiency.

The figures in the table refer to tools heated in an oven type furnace in which a neutral atmosphere is maintained. The available data indicate that a steel reaches its best cutting qualities at a temperature approximately 50 degrees F. lower than the figures in the table if it is hardened in a bath type furnace. It is, however, desirable, in any case, to use a hardening temperature approximately 50 degrees lower than that giving maximum cutting qualities, in order to avoid possibility of overheating the tool.

Length of Time for Heating: The cutting efficiency of a tool is affected by the time that it is kept at the hardening temperature, almost as much as by the hardening temperature itself. It has been common practice to heat a tool for hardening until a " sweat " appeared on its surface. This sweat is presumably a melting of the oxide film on the surface of a tool heated in an oxidizing atmosphere. It does not show when the tool is heated in an inert atmosphere. This method of determining the proper heating time is at best an approximation and indicates only the temperature on the outside of the tool rather than the condition of the interior. As such, it cannot be relied upon to give consistent results.

The only safe method is to heat the tool for a definite predetermined time, based on the size and the thickness of metal which the heat must penetrate to reach the

Table 1.   Relation of Hardening Temperature to Cutting Efficiency

Hardening Temperature, Degrees F.	Typical Analyses of High-Speed Steels			
	18-4-1	14-4-2	18-4-1 Cobalt	14-4-2 Cobalt
2200	0.86	0.83	0.84	0.85
2250	0.88	0.88	0.86	0.88
2300	0.90	0.93	0.90	0.91
2350	0.95	0.98	0.94	0.94
2400	0.99	0.98	0.98	0.98
2450	1.00	...	0.99	1.00
2500	0.98	...	1.00	0.97

Table 2.   Length of Heating Time for Through Hardening

High-Speed Steel Tool Thickness, in Inches	Time in Furnace at High Heat, in Minutes	High-Speed Steel Tool Thickness, in Inches	Time in Furnace at High Heat, in Minutes	High-Speed Steel Tool Thickness, in Inches	Time in Furnace at High Heat, in Minutes
¼	2	1½	7	5	18
½	3	2	8	6	20
¾	4	3	12	8	25
1	5	4	15	10	30

interior. The values given in Table 2 are based on a series of experiments to determine the relative cutting efficiency of a group of tools hardened in an identical manner, except for variations in the time the tools were kept at the hardening temperature. The time given is based on that required to harden throughout a tool resting on a conducting hearth; the tool receives heat freely from three sides, on its large top surface and its smaller side surfaces. (The table does not apply to a disk lying flat on the hearth.) In the case of a tool having a projecting cutting edge, such as a tap, the thickness or depth of the projection portion on which the cutting edge is formed should be used in referring to the table.

The time periods given in Table 2 are based on complete penetration of the hardening. For very thick tools, the practical procedure is to harden to a depth sufficient to produce an adequate cutting edge, leaving the interior of the tool relatively soft.

Where atmosphere control is not provided, it will be found impracticable in many cases to use both the temperature for maximum cutting efficiency, given in Table 1, and the heating time, given in Table 2, because abnormal scaling, grain growth, and surface decarburization of the tool will result. The principal value of an accurate control of the furnace atmosphere appears to lie in the fact that its use makes possible the particular heat-treatment that produces the best structure in the tool without destruction of the tool surface or grain.

Quenching Tungsten High-Speed Steel. — High-speed steel is usually quenched in oil. The oil bath offers a convenient quench; it calls for no unusual care in handling and brings about a uniform and satisfactory rate of cooling, which does not vary appreciably with the temperature of the oil. Some authorities believe it desirable to withdraw the tool from the oil bath for a few seconds after it has reached a dull red. It is also believed desirable to move the tool around in the quenching oil, particularly immediately after it has been placed in it, to prevent the formation of a gas film on the tool. Such a film is usually a poor conductor of heat and slows up the rate of cooling.

Salt Bath: Quenching in a lead or salt bath at from 1000 to 1200 degrees F. has the advantage that cooling of the tool from hardening to room temperature is accomplished in two stages, thus reducing the possibility of setting up internal strains which may tend to crack the tool. The quenching temperature is sufficiently below the lower critical point for a tool so quenched to be allowed to cool to room temperature in still air. This type of quench is particularly advantageous for tools of complicated section which would easily develop hardening cracks. The salt quench has the advantage that the tool sinks and requires only a support, while the same tool will float in the lead bath and must be held under the surface. It is believed that the lead quench gives a somewhat higher matrix hardness, and is of advantage for tools that tend to fail by nose abrasion. Tools treated as described are brittle unless given a regular tempering treatment, as the 1100-degree F. quenching temperature is not a substitute for later tempering at the same temperature, after the tool has cooled to room temperature.

Air Cooling: Many high-speed steel tools are quenched in air, either in a stream of dry compressed air or in still air. Small sections harden satisfactorily in still air, but heavier sections should be subjected to air under pressure. One advantage of air cooling is that the tool can be kept straight and free from distortion, although it is likely that there will be more scale on a tool thus quenched than when oil, lead, or salt is used. Thin flat tools, which must be kept straight and flat, can be cooled advantageously between steel plates.

Straightening High-Speed Tools when Quenching. — The final straightness required in a tool must be considered when it is quenched. When a number of similar tools are to be hardened, a jig can be used to advantage for holding the tools while quenching. When long slender tools are quenched without holders, they frequently warp and must be straightened later. The best time for this straightening is during the first few minutes after the tools have been quenched, as the steel is then quite pliable and may be bent without difficulty. The straightening must be done at once, as the tools become hard in a few minutes.

Anneal Before Rehardening. — Tools that are too soft after hardening must be annealed before rehardening. A quick anneal, such as previously described, is all that is required to put such a tool into the proper condition for rehardening. This treatment is absolutely essential. In the case of milling cutters and forming tools of irregular section, a full anneal should be used.

Tempering or Drawing Tungsten High-Speed Steel. — The tempering or drawing temperature for high-speed steel tools usually varies from 900 to 1200 degrees F. This temperature is higher for turning and planing tools than for such tools as milling cutters, forming tools, etc. If the temperature is below 800 degrees F., the tool is likely to be too brittle. The general idea is to temper tools at the highest temperature likely to occur in actual service. Since this temperature ordinarily would not be known, the general practice is to temper at whatever temperature experience with that particular steel and tool has proved to be the best. The furnace used for tempering usually is kept at a temperature of from 1000 to 1100 degrees F. for ordinary high-speed steels and from 1200 to 1300 degrees F. for steels of the cobalt type. These furnace temperatures apply to tools of the class used on lathes and planers. Such tools, in service, frequently heat to the point of visible redness. Milling cutters, forming tools, or any other tools for lighter duty, may be tempered as low as 850 or 900 degrees F. When the tool has reached the temperature of the furnace it should be held at this temperature for from one to several hours until it has been heated evenly throughout. It should then be allowed to cool gradually in the air and in a place that is dry and free from air drafts. In tempering, the tool should not be quenched, as this tends to produce strains which may result later in cracks.

Annealing Tungsten High-Speed Steel. — The following method of annealing high-speed steel has been used extensively. Use an iron box or pipe of sufficient size to allow at least one-half inch of packing between the pieces of steel to be annealed and the sides of the box or pipe. It is not necessary that each piece of steel be kept separate from every other piece, but only that the steel be prevented from touching the sides of the annealing pipe or box. Pack carefully with powdered charcoal, fine dry lime or mica (preferably charcoal), and cover with an air-tight cap, or lute with fire clay; heat slowly to 1600 to 1650 degrees F. and keep at this heat from 2 to 8 hours, depending upon the size of the pieces to be annealed. A piece 2 by 1 by 8 inches requires about three hours. Cool as slowly as possible, and do not expose to the air until cold as cooling in air is likely to cause partial hardening. A good way is to allow the box or pipe to remain in the furnace until cold.

Hardening Molybdenum High-Speed Steels. — In Table 3 are given the compositions of several molybdenum high-speed steels which are widely used for general

Table 3. Composition of Molybdenum High-Speed Steels

Element	Molybdenum-Tungsten		Molybdenum-Vanadium	Tungsten-Molybdenum
	Type Ia (Per Cent)	Type Ib* (Per Cent)	Type II (Per Cent)	Type III (Per Cent)
Carbon	0.70–0.85	0.76–0.82	0.70–0.90	0.75–0.90
Tungsten	1.25–2.00	1.60–2.30	....	5.00–6.00
Chromium	3.00–5.00	3.70–4.20	3.00–5.00	3.50–5.00
Vanadium	0.90–1.50	1.05–1.35	1.50–2.25	1.25–1.75
Molybdenum	8.00–9.50	8.00–9.00	7.50–9.50	3.50–5.50
Cobalt	See footnote	4.50–5.50	See footnote	See footnote

*Cobalt may be used in any of these steels in varying amounts up to 9 per cent, and the vanadium content may be as high as 2.25 per cent. When cobalt is used in Type III the vanadium content may be as high as 2.25 per cent. When cobalt is used in Type III steel, this steel becomes susceptible to decarburization. As an illustration of the use of cobalt, Type Ib steel is included. This is steel T10 in the U. S. Navy Specification 46S37, dated November 1, 1939.

commercial tool applications. The general method of hardening molybdenum high-speed steels resembles that used for 18-4-1 tungsten high-speed steel except that the hardening temperatures are lower and more precautions must be taken to avoid decarburization, especially on tools made from Type I or Type II steels, when the surface is not ground after hardening. Either salt baths or atmosphere controlled furnaces are recommended for hardening molybdenum high-speed steel.

The usual method is to preheat uniformly in a separate furnace to 1250 to 1550 degrees F. and then transfer to a high-heat furnace maintained at some temperature in the hardening temperature range given in Table 4. Single point cutting tools, in general, should be hardened at the upper end of the temperature range indicated by Table 4. Slight grain coarsening is not objectionable in such tools when they are properly supported in service and are not subjected to chattering; however, when

Table 4. Heat-Treatment of Molybdenum High-Speed Steels

Heat-Treating Operation	Molybdenum-Tungsten	Molybdenum-Vanadium	Tungsten-Molybdenum
	Types Ia and Ib* (Temp., in Deg. F.)	Type II (Temp., in Deg. F.)	Type III (Temp., in Deg. F.)
Forging	1850–2000	1850–2000	1900–2050
Not below	1600	1600	1600
Annealing	1450–1550	1450–1550	1450–1550
Strain Relief	1150–1350	1150–1350	1150–1350
Preheating	1250–1500	1250–1500	1250–1550
Hardening†	2150–2250*	2150–2250	2175–2275
Salt	2150–2225	2150–2225	2150–2250
Tempering	950–1100	950–1100	950–1100

*Under similar conditions Type Ib steel requires a slightly higher hardening heat than Type Ia.
†The higher side of the hardening range should be used for large sections, and the lower side for small sections.

these tools are used for intermittent cuts, it is better to use the middle of the temperature range. All other cutting tools, such as drills, countersinks, taps, milling cutters, reamers, broaches, form tools, etc., should be hardened in the middle of the range shown. For certain tools, such as slender taps, cold punches, blanking and trimming dies, etc., where greater toughness to resist shocks is required, the lower end of the hardening temperature range should be used.

Molybdenum high-speed steels can be pack-hardened following the same practice as is used for tungsten high-speed steels, but keeping on the lower side of the hardening range (approximately 1850 degrees F.). Special surface treatments such as nitriding by immersion in molten cyanide that are used for tungsten high-speed steels are also applicable to molybenum high-speed tools.

When heated in an open fire or in furnaces without atmosphere control, these steels do not sweat like 18–4–1 steels; consequently, determining the proper time in the high-heat chamber is a matter of experience. This time approximates that used with 18–4–1 steels, although it may be slightly longer when the lower part of the hardening range is used. Much can be learned by preliminary hardening of test pieces and checking up on the hardness fracture and structure. It is difficult to give the exact heating time, as this is affected by temperature, type of furnace, size and shape, and furnace atmosphere. Rate of heat transfer is most rapid in salt baths, and slowest in controlled-atmosphere furnaces with high carbon-monoxide content.

Quenching and Tempering of Molybdenum High-speed Tools. — Quenching may be done in oil, air, or molten bath. To reduce the possibility of breakage and undue distortion of intricately shaped tools, it is advisable to quench in a molten bath at approximately 1100 degrees F. The tool also may be quenched in oil and removed while still red, or at approximately 1100 degrees F. The tool is then cooled in air to room temperature, and tempered immediately to avoid cracking.

When straightening is necessary, it should be done after quenching and before cooling to room temperature prior to tempering.

To temper, the tools should be reheated slowly and uniformly to 950 to 1100 degrees F. For general work, 1050 degrees F. is most common. The tools should be held at this temperature at least one hour. Two hours is a safer minimum, and four hours is maximum. The time and temperature depend on the hardness and toughness required. Where tools are subjected to more or less shock, multiple temperings are suggested.

Protective Coatings for Molybdenum Steels. — Borax may be applied by sprinkling it lightly over the steel when the latter is heated in a furnace to a slow temperature (1200 to 1400 degrees F.). Small tools may be rolled in a box of borax before heating. Another method more suitable for finished tools is to apply the borax or boric acid in the form of a supersaturated water solution. In such cases, the tools are immersed in the solution at 180 to 212 degrees F., or it may be applied with a brush or spray. Pieces so treated are heated as usual, taking care in handling to insure good adherence. Special protective coatings or paints, when properly applied, have been found extremely useful. They do not fuse or run at the temperatures used, and therefore do not affect the furnace hearth. When applying these coatings, it is necessary to have a surface free from scale or grease to insure good adherence. They may be sprayed or brushed on, and usually one thin coat is sufficient. Heavy coats tend to pit the surface of the tool and also are difficult to remove. Tools covered with these coatings should be allowed to dry before they are charged into the preheat furnace. After hardening and tempering, the coating can be easily removed by light blasting with sand or steel shot. When tools are lightly ground, these coatings come off immediately.

Nitriding High-speed Steel Tools. — Nitriding as applied to high-speed steel is for the purpose of increasing tool life by producing a very hard skin or case, the thickness of which ordinarily is from 0.001 to 0.002 inch. Nitriding is done after the tool has been fully heat-treated and finish ground. (The process differs entirely from that which is applied to certain alloy steels in order to surface harden them by heating in an atmosphere of nitrogen or ammonia gas.) The temperature of the high-speed steel nitriding bath, which is a mixture of sodium and potassium cyanides, is equal to or slightly lower than the tempering temperature. For ordinary tools, this temperature usually varies from about 1025 to 1050 degrees F.; but if the tools are exceptionally fragile, the range may be reduced to 950 or 1000 degrees F. Accurate temperature control is essential to prevent exceeding the final tempering temperature. The nitriding time may vary from 10 or 15 minutes to 30 minutes or longer, as determined by experiment. The shorter periods are applied to tools for iron or steel, or any shock-resisting tools, and the longer periods are for tools used in machining non-ferrous metals and plastics. This nitriding process is applied to tools such as hobs, reamers, taps, box-tools, form tools, milling cutters, etc. Nitriding may increase tool life 50 to 200 per cent, or more, but it should always be preceded by correct heat-treatment.

Nitriding Bath Mixtures and Temperatures: A mixture of 60 per cent sodium cyanide and 40 per cent potassium cyanide is commonly used. This mixture has a melting point of 925 degrees F. which is gradually reduced to 800 degrees F. as the cyanate content of the bath increases. A more economical mixture of 70 per cent sodium cyanide and 30 per cent potassium cyanide may be used if the operating temperature of the bath is only 1050 degrees F. Nitriding bath temperature should not exceed 1100 degrees F. because higher temperatures accelerate the formation of carbonate at the expense of the essential cyanide. A third mixture suitable for nitriding consists of 55 per cent sodium cyanide, 25 per cent potassium chloride and 20 per cent sodium carbonate. This mixture melts at 930 degrees F.

Equipment for Hardening High-speed Steel. — Equipment for hardening high-speed steel consists of a hardening furnace capable of maintaining a temperature of 2350 to 2450 degrees F.; a preheating furnace capable of maintaining a temperature of 1700 to 1800 degrees F., and of sufficient size to hold a number of pieces of the work; a tempering (drawing) furnace capable of maintaining a temperature of 1000 to 1200 degrees F. as a general rule; and a water-cooled tank of quenching oil.

High-speed steels usually are heated for hardening either in some type of electric furnace or in a gas-fired furnace of the muffle type. The small furnaces used for high-speed steel seldom are oil-fired. It is desirable to use automatic temperature control and, where an oven type of furnace is employed, a controlled atmosphere is advisable because of the variations in cutting qualities caused by hardening under uncontrolled conditions. Some furnaces in both electric and fuel-fired types are equipped with a salt bath suitable for high-speed steel hardening temperatures. Salt baths have the advantage of providing protection against the atmosphere during the heating period. A type of salt developed for commercial use is water-soluble, so that all deposits from the hardening bath may be removed by immersion in water after quenching in oil or salt, or after air-cooling. One type of electric furnace heats the salt bath internally by electrodes immersed in it. The same type is also applied to various heat-treating operations, such as cyanide hardening, liquid carburizing, tempering, and annealing.

An open-forge fire has many disadvantages, especially in hardening cutters or other tools that cannot be ground all over after hardening. The air blast decarburizes the steel and lack of temperature control makes it impossible to obtain uniform results. Electric and gas furnaces provide continuous uniform heat, and the temperature may be regulated accurately, especially when pyrometers are used. In shops equipped with only one furnace for carbon steel and one for high-speed steel, the tempering can be done in the furnace used for hardening carbon steel after the preheating is finished and the steel has been removed for hardening.

Heating High-speed Steel for Forging. — Care should be taken not to heat high-speed steel for forging too abruptly. In winter, the steel may be extremely cold when brought into the forge shop. If the steel is put directly into the hot forge fire, it is likely to develop cracks which will show up later in the finished tool. It should, therefore, be warmed gradually before heating for forging.

Sub-zero Treatment of Steel

The sub-zero treatment consists in subjecting the steel, after hardening and either before or after tempering, to a sub-zero temperature (which usually ranges from −100 degrees F. to −120 degrees F.) and for a period of time varying with the size or volume of the tool, gage or other part. Commercial equipment is available for obtaining these low temperatures.

The sub-zero treatment is employed by most gage manufacturers in order to stabilize precision gages and prevent subsequent changes in size or form. Sub-zero treatment is also applied to some high-speed steel cutting tools. The object in this case is to increase the durability or life of the tools; however, up to the present time the results of tests by metallurgists and tool engineers often differ considerably and in some instances are contradictory. Methods of procedure also vary, especially in regard to the order and number of operations in the complete heat-treating and cooling cycle.

Changes Resulting From Sub-zero Treatment. — When steel is at the hardening temperature, it contains a solid solution of carbon and iron known as *austenite*. When the steel is hardened by sudden cooling, most of the austenite which is relatively soft, tough and ductile even at room temperatures, is transformed to martensite which is a hard and strong constituent. If all of the austenite were changed to martensite upon reaching room temperature, this would be an ideal hardening operation, but many steels retain some austenite. In general, the higher the carbon and alloy contents and the higher the hardening temperature, the greater the tendency to retain austenite. When steel is cooled to sub-zero temperatures, the stability of the retained austenite is reduced so that it is more readily transformed. To obtain more complete transformation the sub-zero treatment may be repeated. The ultimate transformation of austenite to martensite may take place in carbon steel without the aid of sub-zero treatment, but this natural transformation might require six months or longer, whereas by refrigeration this change occurs in a few hours.

The thorough, uniform heating which is always recommended in heat-treating operations should be accompanied by thorough, uniform cooling when the sub-zero treatment is applied. To insure uniform cooling, the sub-zero cooling period should be increased for the larger tools and it may range from two to six hours. The tool or other part is sometimes surrounded by one or more layers of heavy wrapping or asbestos paper to delay the cooling somewhat and insure uniformity. After the cooling cycle is started, it should continue without interruption.

In some cases, the sub-zero treatment may cause cracking. Normally the austenite in steel provides a cushioning effect which may prevent cracking or breakage resulting from treatments involving temperature and dimensional changes; but, if this cushioning effect is removed, particularly at very low temperatures as in sub-zero treatments, there may be danger of cracking especially in the case of tools having large or irregular sections and sharp corners offering relatively low resistance to stresses. This is one reason why sub-zero treatments may differ in regard to the cooling and tempering cycle.

Stabilizing Dimensions of Gages or Precision Parts by Sub-zero Cooling. —
Transformation of austenite into martensite is accompanied by an increase in volume; consequently, the transformation of austenite which may naturally occur over a period of months or years, tends to change the dimensions and form of steel parts, and such changes may be serious in the case of precision gages, close-fitting machine parts, etc. To prevent such changes, the sub-zero treatment has proved effective. Gage-blocks, for example, may be stabilized by hardening followed by repeated cycles of chilling and tempering, to transform a large percentage of the austenite into martensite.

Order of Operations for Stabilizing Precision Gages: If precision gages, sine-bars, etc., are heat-treated in the ordinary manner and then are finished without some stabilizing treatment, dimensional changes and warpage are liable to occur. Sub-zero cooling provides a practical and fairly rapid method of obtaining the necessary stabilization by transforming the austenite into martensite. In stabilization treatments of this kind, tempering is the final operation. One series of treatments which has been recommended after hardening and rough-grinding is as follows:

(a) Cool to −120 degrees F. (This cooling period may require from one to six hours, depending on the size and form of the gage.)

(b) Place gage in boiling water for two hours (oil or salt bath may also be used). Note: Steps (a) and (b) may be repeated from two to six times, depending on the size and form of the gage. These repeated cycles will eventually transform practically all of the austenite into martensite. Two or three cooling and drawing operations usually are sufficient for such work as thread gages and gage-blocks.

(c) Follow with regular tempering or drawing operation and finish gage by lapping.

Series of Stabilizing Treatments for Chromium Steel: The following series of treatments has proved successful in stabilizing precision gage-blocks made from S.A.E. 52100 chromium steel.

(a) Preheat to 600 degrees F. and then heat to 1575 degrees F. for a period of four minutes.

(b) Quench in oil at 85 degrees F. (Uniform quenching is essential)

(c) Temper at 275 degrees F. for one hour.

(d) Cool in tempering furnace to room temperature.

(e) Continue cooling in atmosphere of industrial refrigerator for six hours with temperature of atmosphere at −120 degrees F.

(f) Allow gage-blocks to return to room temperature and again temper.

Note: The complete treatment consists of six sub-zero cooling periods, each followed by a tempering operation. The transformation to martensite is believed to be complete even after the fifth cooling period. The hardness is about 66 Rockwell C. Transformation is checked by magnetic tests based upon the magnetism of martensite and the non-magnetic qualities of austenite.

Stabilizing Dimensions of Close-fitting Machine Parts. — Sub-zero treatment will always cause an increase in size. Machine parts subjected to repeated and perhaps drastic changes in temperature, as in aircraft, may eventually cause trouble due to growth or warpage as the austenite gradually changes to martensite. In some instances, the sizes of close-fitting moving parts have increased sufficiently to cause seizure. Such treatment, for example, may be applied to precision bearings made from S.A.E. 52100 or alloy carburizing steels for stabilizing or aging them. *Time* aging of 52100 steels after hardening has been found to cause changes as large as .0025 inch in medium size sections. A practical remedy is to apply the sub-zero treatment before the final grinding or other machining operation.

Sub-zero Treatment of Carburized Parts to Improve Physical Properties. — The sub-zero treatment has been applied to carburized machine parts. In the case of carburized gears, for example, the amount of retained austenite may be sufficient to reduce the life of the gears. In one case, the Rockwell hardness was increased from 55 C to 65 C without loss of impact resistance qualities; in fact, impact and fatigue resistance may be increased in some cases.

Application of Sub-zero Treatments to High-speed Steel. — The sub-zero treatment has been applied to such tools as milling cutters, hobs, taps, broaches and drills. It is applicable to different classes of high-speed steels, such as the 18–4–1 tungsten, 18–4–14 cobalt, and the molybdenum high-speed steels. This *cold* treatment is applied preferably in conjunction with the heat-treatment, both being combined in a continuous cycle of operations. The general procedure is either to harden the steel, cool it to a sub-zero temperature, and then temper; or, especially if there is more than one tempering operation, the first one may *precede* sub-zero cooling. The cooling and tempering cycle may be repeated two or more times. The number and order of the operations, or the complete cycle, may be varied to suit the class of work and, to minimize the danger of cracking, particularly if the tool has large or irregular sections, sharp corners or edges, or a high cobalt content. A sub-zero treatment of some kind with a final tempering operation for stress relief, is intended to increase strength and toughness without much loss in hardness; consequently, if there is greater strength at a given hardness, tools subjected to sub-zero treatment can operate with a higher degree of hardness than those heat-treated in the ordinary manner, or, if greater toughness is preferred, this can be obtained by tempering to the original degree of hardness.

Order of Cooling and Tempering Periods for High-speed Steel. — The order or cycle for the cooling and tempering periods has not been standardized. The methods which follow have been applied to high-speed steel tools. They are given as examples of procedure and are subject to possible changes due to subsequent developments. The usual ranges of preheating and hardening temperatures are given; but for a particular steel, the recommended temperatures should be obtained from the manufacturer.

1. *Double Sub-zero Treatment:* (For rugged simple tool forms without irregular sections, sharp corners or edges where cracks might develop during the sub-zero treatment).

(a) Preheat to from 1400 to 1600 degrees F. (double preheating is preferable, the first preheating ranging from 700 to 1000 degrees F.).

(b) Heat to the hardening temperature. (Note: Tests indicate that the effect of sub-zero treatment on high-speed steel may be influenced decidedly by the hardening temperature. If this temperature is near the lower part of the range, the results are unsatisfactory. Effective temperatures for ordinary high-speed steels appear to range from 2300 to 2350 degrees F.)

(c) Quench in oil, salt, lead or air, down to a temperature of 150–200 degrees F. (Note: One method is to quench in oil; a second method is to quench in oil to about 200–225 degrees F. and then air-cool; a third method is to quench in salt bath at 1050–1100 degrees F. and then air-cool.)

(d) Cool in refrigerating unit to temperature of −100 to −120 degrees F. *right after quenching.* (Note: Tests have shown that a delay of one hour has a detrimental effect, and in ten hours the efficiency of the sub-zero treatment is reduced 50 per cent. This is due to the fact that the austenite becomes more and more stabilized when the sub-zero treatment is delayed; consequently, the austenite is more difficult to transform into martensite.) This refrigerating period usually varies from two to six hours, depending on the size of the tool. Remove tool from refrigerating unit and allow to return to room temperature.

(e) Temper to required hardness for a period of two and one-half to three hours. The tempering temperature usually varies from a minimum of 1000 to 1100 degrees F. for ordinary high-speed steels. Tests indicate that if this first tempering is less than two and one-half hours at 1050 degrees F., there will not be sufficient precipitation of carbides at the tempering temperature to allow complete transformation of the retained austenite on cooling, whereas more than three hours causes some loss both in room temperature hardness, hot hardness, strength, and toughness.

(f) Repeat sub-zero treatment, step (d).

(g) Repeat tempering operation, step (e). (Note: The time for the second tempering operation is sometimes reduced to about one-half the time required for the first tempering.)

2. *Single Sub-zero Treatment:* This is the same as procedure No. 1 except that a second sub-zero cooling is omitted; hence the cycle consists of hardening, sub-zero cooling, and double tempering. Procedure No. 3 which follows also has one sub-zero cooling period in the cycle, but this *follows* the first tempering operation.

3. *Tempering Followed by Sub-zero Treatment:* (For tools having irregular sections, sharp corners or edges where cracks might develop if the hardening operation were followed immediately by sub-zero cooling.)

(a) and (b) Preheat and heat for hardening.

(c) Quench as described under Procedure No. 1.

(d) Temper to required hardness.

(e) Cool to sub-zero temperature −100 to −120 degrees F. and then allow tool to return to room temperature.

(f) Repeat tempering operation.

Sub-zero Treatment Applied to Finished Cutting Tools. — Stock cutters or other tools which have been heat-treated in the usual manner (without sub-zero cooling) and finished by grinding, have subsequently been subjected to the sub-zero treatment with beneficial results. The increase in cutting efficiency or the life between grindings, as determined by tests with different tools, have varied from about 25 per cent up to several hundred per cent. Hardening and tempering without sub-zero cooling tends to stabilize whatever austenite is retained; hence the sub-zero treatment of stock tools is not likely to increase the tool durability to the same degree as when this treatment is included in with the heat-treating process; moreover, the improvement in tool life is not so pronounced in the case of stock tools which have been double-tempered.

Pyrometers

Pyrometers are of great value in connection with the heat-treatment of steel, as they make it possible to determine high temperatures accurately; moreover, the temperature, when heating for hardening, can be regulated to conform with the temperature that has given the best results in practice.

Thermo-electric Pyrometer. — The most commonly used pyrometers are of the *thermo-electric* type. In this type, temperature variations are determined by the measurement of an electric current generated by the action of heat on the junction of two dissimilar metals. The thermo-couple, consisting of two pieces of dissimilar metals, is placed at some point within the furnace and is connected by wires with a meter which may be close to the furnace or in some other part of the plant.

Resistance Pyrometer. — The variation in electric conductivity due to changes in temperature is the principle upon which the *resistance pyrometer* is based. This type is very accurate for temperatures below 1600 degrees F., but should not be used continuously for higher temperatures. The maximum temperature is about 3200 degrees F.

Radiation Pyrometer. — Radiation pyrometers measure radiated heat and are adapted for very high temperatures. The Féry radiation pyrometer is practically a reflecting telescope having a concave mirror which focuses the radiant heat of the object upon the " hot " junction of a small thermo-couple. No part of the instrument is inserted in the high heat to be measured. If the temperature of a furnace is to be measured, the tube is either held on a tripod or in the hand, and is pointed toward the door of the furnace. The temperature can then be read off on the indicator.

Optical Pyrometers. — There are several classes of *optical pyrometers*. One type indicates the temperature by heating the filament of an electric lamp to the same color as that of the incandescent body, the temperature of which is required. The current then being consumed is indicated by a milliammeter, and the corresponding temperature is determined. There are several other types of optical pyrometers. These pyrometers may be used to estimate the highest temperatures, and may be used for temperatures above 3000 degrees F., both in laboratory and industrial work.

Pyrometers of Automatic Control Type. — The pyrometer that automatically controls furnace temperatures is so arranged that the moving element of the instrument not only indicates the temperature by its position relative to a scale, but by combined mechanical and electrical apparatus, controls the temperature, within certain limits, by regulating the heat supply. The pyrometer can be set for any temperature desired within certain maximum and minimum limits and may be applied to furnaces heated either by gas, oil, or electricity.

Indicating Pyrometers. — Many of the pyrometers used in heat-treating plants may be designated as the " indicating " type, since the temperature variations are shown by the position of a hand or pointer relative to a graduated scale. The indicating instrument may be located close to the furnace or in some central station or controlling room. When it is by the furnace, the furnace operator controls the temperature either according to his experience with similar work, or possibly by reference to data previously recorded. This is a common method in small plants, but where a large heat-treating department is installed, a centralized system of control is quite general.

Recording Pyrometers. — A recording pyrometer is provided with some kind of marking device which traces either a continuous or a dotted line upon a chart graduated with reference to temperature and time. By referring to one of these charts, the temperature at any period within the range of the chart is shown graphically. Where a heat-treating plant contains two or more furnaces, a pyrometer may be installed that will record automatically on a chart temperature variations in each furnace to which it is connected. This type of pyrometer is generally used when the heat-treating process requires a half hour or more for its completion. When four, six, or eight records are needed, these may be printed on the chart in different colors to avoid confusion.

Calibration of Pyrometers. — Pyrometers should occasionally be compared with a standard pyrometer or be calibrated in some other way. A satisfactory way of calibrating pyrometers is by using the " freezing points " of melted salts. Pure common salt (NaCl) is melted in a pure graphite crucible. When the salt has been raised to a temperature of 100 to 200 degrees F. above its melting point, the bare welded end of the thermo-couple is inserted to a depth of 2 or 3 inches. The crucible is then removed from the furnace and allowed to cool. The pointer on the meter will drop gradually until the salt begins to freeze or solidify; then the pointer will stop until the salt is frozen. The freezing point of pure salt is taken at 800 degrees C. (1472 deg. F.). After calibrating and before being further used, the couple end should be washed in hot water to remove all traces of the salt, as otherwise the couple will deteriorate rapidly, especially when heated considerably above the melting point of salt in an open furnace. When calibrating pyrometers, care should be taken that the zero setting of the meter agrees with the cold end of the couple, which is always kept away from the heat and generally at the temperature of the outside air. The following table gives data from the Bureau of Standards on certain substances which may be used for calibrating pyrometers.

Water boils at	100 deg. C.	(212 deg. F.)
Tin freezes at	231.9 deg. C.	(449.4 deg. F.)
Zinc freezes at	419.4 deg. C.	(786.9 deg. F.)
Common salt freezes at	800 deg. C.	(1472 deg. F.)
Copper freezes at	1083 deg. C.	(1981.4 deg. F.)

Standard samples of metals of certified melting points can also be purchased from the National Bureau of Standards for use in checking thermocouple pyrometers. These include tin, zinc, aluminum, copper and lead.

Seger Temperature Cones. — The " sentinel " pyrometer or Seger temperature cones are in the form of triangular pyramids (about 3 inches high), composed of metallic and mineral substances which fuse at certain temperatures. They are made in series, each successive cone having a fusing temperature that differs slightly from the one above or below in the scale; that is, if the series were placed in a furnace and the temperature gradually raised, one cone after another would melt as its melting point was reached. These cones are sometimes used in pairs to determine the mini-

Baumé Gravity and Corresponding Specific Gravities, Weights per Gallon and Calorific Value of Fuel Oil

Kind of Oil	Baumé or A.P.I.*	Specific Gravity	Pounds per Gallon	Calculated Btu per Pound	Calculated Btu per Gallon
	14	0.9722	8.10	18,810	152,361
	15	0.9655	8.05	18,850	151,743
	16	0.9589	7.99	18,890	150,931
	17	0.9523	7.94	18,930	150,304
	18	0.9459	7.88	18,970	149,484
Mexico, California, Texas and Kansas Crude Fuel Oil	19	0.9395	7.83	19,010	148,848
	20	0.9333	7.78	19,050	148,209
	21	0.9271	7.73	19,090	147,506
	22	0.9210	7.68	19,130	146,918
	23	0.9150	7.63	19,170	146,267
	24	0.9090	7.58	19,210	145,612
	25	0.9032	7.54	19,250	145,145
	26	0.8974	7.49	19,290	144,482
	27	0.8917	7.44	19,330	143,815
	28	0.8860	7.39	19,370	143,144
Kansas, Indian Territory and Illinois Crudes, Penn. Fuel, California Refined Fuel Oil	29	0.8805	7.34	19,410	142,469
	30	0.8750	7.29	19,450	141,790
	31	0.8695	7.25	19,490	141,303
	32	0.8641	7.21	19,530	140,811
	33	0.8588	7.16	19,570	140,121
	34	0.8536	7.12	19,610	139,623
	35	0.8484	7.07	19,650	138,926
	36	0.8433	7.03	19,690	138,421
	37	0.8383	6.99	19,730	137,913
Ohio, Penn. and West Virginia Crude, California and Kansas Refined	38	0.8333	6.95	19,770	137,402
	39	0.8284	6.91	19,810	136,887
	40	0.8235	6.87	19,850	136,370
	41	0.8187	6.83	19,890	135,849
	42	0.8139	6.80	19,930	135,524
	43	0.8092	6.76	19,970	134,997
	44	0.8045	6.72	20,010	134,467
	45	0.8000	6.68	20,050	133,934
	46	0.7954	6.64	20,090	133,398
Kerosene and Gasoline	47	0.7909	6.60	20,130	132,858
	48	0.7865	6.57	20,170	132,517
	49	0.7821	6.53	20,210	131,971
	50	0.7777	6.49	20,250	131,423

*Degrees Baumé is numerically the same as degrees A. P. I. (American Petroleum Institute).

mum and maximum temperatures for a given process, one cone being selected for the lowest and another for the highest temperature required. Tests have shown that this method for determining temperatures is reliable within 35 degrees F.

Melting Temperatures of Seger Cones

No. of Cone	Melting Temp., Deg. F.	No. of Cone	Melting Temp., Deg. F.	No. of Cone	Melting Temp., Deg. F.	No. of Cone	Melting Temp., Deg. F.	No. of Cone	Melting Temp., Deg. F.
010	1743	01	2066	9	2390	18	2714	27	3038
09	1778	1	2102	10	2426	19	2750	28	3074
08	1814	2	2138	11	2462	20	2786	29	3110
07	1850	3	2174	12	2498	21	2822	30	3146
06	1886	4	2210	13	2534	22	2858	31	3182
05	1922	5	2246	14	2570	23	2894	32	3218
04	1958	6	2282	15	2606	24	2930	33	3254
03	1994	7	2318	16	2642	25	2966	....	....
02	2030	8	2354	17	2678	26	3002	....	....

Judging Temperatures by Color. — The color method of judging temperatures is not dependable but the accompanying table may be used as a general guide (see also table of tempering temperatures in following section " Tempering.") The U. S. Bureau of Standards states that skilled observers may vary as much as 100 degrees F. in their estimation of relatively low temperatures by color; beyond 2200 degrees F., it is practically impossible to make estimations with any certainty.

Temperatures as Indicated by Color of Steel

Degrees Centigrade	Degrees Fahrenheit	Color of Steel	Degrees Centigrade	Degrees Fahrenheit	Color of Steel
400	752	Red heat, visible in the dark	800	1472	Dull cherry-red
			900	1652	Cherry-red
474	885	Red heat, visible in the twilight	1000	1832	Bright cherry-red
			1100	2012	Orange-red
525	975	Red heat, visible in the daylight	1200	2192	Orange-yellow
			1300	2372	Yellow-white
581	1077	Red heat, visible in the sunlight	1400	2552	White welding heat
			1500	2732	Brilliant white
700	1292	Dark red	1600	2912	Dazzling white (bluish-white)

Characteristics of Fuel Oils. — The calorific values in B.T.U. per pound of oil, as given in the table, " Baumé Gravity and Corresponding Specific Gravities, Weights per Gallon and Calorific Value of Fuel Oil," were determined by the formula: B.T.U. = $18650 + 40$ (No. of Degrees Baumé — 10). Sixty-four samples of petroleum oils, ranging from heavy crude oil to gasoline, and representing the products of the principal oil fields of the United States, were examined for calorific power by combustion in oxygen in the Atwater Mahler bomb calorimeter with results ranging from 18,572 to 21,120 B.T.U. per pound. In general, the decrease in calorific power with increase in specific gravity was fairly regular, so that the relation between the two may be expressed, approximately, by means of a simple formula. When the calorific powers calculated from the densities by means of this formula were compared with those actually determined, it was found that in one-ninth of the cases the difference was greater and in eight-ninths it was less than one per cent; in only one-thirtieth was it greater than two per cent, and in no case was it as great as 3 per cent; hence, the calorific value of commercially pure petroleum oils can be determined from the density with sufficient accuracy for most practical purposes.

Commercial Fuel Oils. — Commercial fuel oils are available in different grades, the characteristics of which are given in the accompanying table.

A.P.I. Gravity, Weight and Combustion Data for Commercial Fuel Oils

Grade of Oil	Appr. Gravity A.P.I. at 60° F.*	Weight Lbs. per Gal. at 60° F.	Flash Point, Deg. F.		App. Heat Content B.T.U. per Gal.
			Min.	Max.	
No. 1 Light domestic fuel oil-distillate	40° to 38°	6.89 to 6.97	100° or legal	165°	136,000 to 139,000
No. 2 Medium domestic fuel oil-distillate	36° to 32°	7.05 to 7.14	110° or legal	190°	139,500 to 140,500
No. 3 Heavy domestic fuel oil-distillate	32° to 28°	7.23 to 7.41	110° or legal	200°	141,000 to 143,500
No. 4 Light industrial fuel oil	26° to 24°	7.51 to 7.60	150°	....	144,000 to 145,500
No. 5 Medium industrial fuel oil	22° to 18°	7.70 to 7.90	150°	....	146,000 to 148,500
No. 6 Heavy industrial fuel oil	16° to 14°	8.01 to 8.12	150°	....	149,000 to 152,000

*Degrees A.P.I. (American Petroleum Institute) gravity is numerically the same as degrees Baumé.

Flash Point and Fire Test. — The distinction between the "flash point" and, the "fire test" of an oil is as follows: The flash point is the temperature at which the amount of vapor given off is sufficient to form an inflammable or explosive mixture with the air over the surface of the oil, so that the gaseous mixture ignites and burns with a momentary flash when a flame is applied. As the temperature of the oil rises, more vapor is given off, and when the production of vapor is rapid enough to maintain a continuous flame, the oil takes fire and burns. The temperature at which this occurs is called the fire test, firing point or burning point of the oil.

Heat-treatment of Non-Ferrous Alloys

The solution and precipitation methods of heat-treatment may be applied to certain non-ferrous alloys such as wrought aluminum and also to some of the magnesium or Dowmetal alloys.

Wrought Aluminum Alloys. — The wrought alloys of aluminum may be divided into two classes depending upon the manner in which their harder tempers are produced. One class comprises the alloys in which strain-hardening, by definite amounts of cold work following the last annealing operation, produces the varying degrees of strength and hardness. The alloys in the other class depend primarily upon heat-treatment processes to develop their higher mechanical properties. While there is a wide range of tensile properties in both classes of alloys, the highest combinations of strength and ductility available in the widest range of products are to be found in the heat-treated alloys. In the aluminum alloys which respond to heat-treatment, the alloying constituents which give the increased strength and hardness are substances which are more soluble in solid aluminum at high temperatures than at low temperatures.

Solution Heat-treatment. — The first step in heat-treatment, frequently called the "solution heat-treatment," consists in heating the alloy to some temperature below the melting point, usually in the range of 900 to 1000 degrees F. for aluminum alloys, to put as much as possible of the alloying constituent into solid solution. The alloy is held at this temperature for some period of time, usually from 20 to 60 minutes for aluminum alloys, according to the thickness of the piece. This permits the entire piece to reach a uniform temperature and the dissolving of the alloying elements in the solid solution to take place throughout. In effect, the alloying constituent has been dissolved in the aluminum and dispersed as completely as when sugar is dissolved in water. The alloy is then quenched and — in contrast to steel after quenching — is in a relatively soft condition.

Precipitation Heat-treatment. — After quenching, the alloy undergoes an aging process which, if carried out at elevated temperatures, is called a "precipitation heat-treatment," because during this stage some of the alloying constituent which is held in solid solution precipitates from the solid solution in the form of extremely fine particles. This precipitation may occur spontaneously at room temperature, as is the case in the so-called "natural aging" of certain alloys, or it may require a "precipitation heat-treatment" or "artificial aging" at about 300 degrees F., in the case of certain other alloys to produce increased hardness and tensile strength.

Heat-treatment of Dowmetal Alloys. — Dowmetal castings may be used as cast or in a heat-treated condition. Heat-treatment is not required for general use. However, when increased tensile strength, ductility and toughness are required, without change of yield strength or hardness, castings are "solution heat-treated." This solution heat-treatment is performed in specially designed ovens at temperatures varying from 500 to 800 degrees F., depending upon the alloy, and is followed by air-cooling. Castings so treated are in the best condition for shock resistance. If castings require high yield strength but are not subject to shock, they are solution heat-treated and aged. This aging or precipitation is done at about 350 degrees F.

Heat-treatment of Copper Alloys. — Precipitation hardening of copper alloys is useful in producing materials which have high strength and high electrical conductivity. Beryllium copper which has been precipitation hardened may have a tensile strength ranging up to 200,000 pounds per square inch.

BRASS, BRONZE, ALUMINUM AND OTHER ALLOYS

Cast Brass and Bronze. — The following information on S.A.E. Standard Brass and Bronze Castings includes typical applications of the different alloys in the automotive industry, the composition in percentage, and physical properties based upon standard test bars cast to size with only a minimum amount of machining to remove the fin gate. Standard specimens of wrought material are taken parallel to the direction of rolling and all rods, bars and shapes are tested in full size when practicable.

Red Brass Castings. — **S.A.E. Standard No. 40.** — Red brass is used for water-pump impellers, fittings for gasoline and oil lines, small bushings, small miscellaneous castings. This is a free-cutting brass with good casting and finished properties.

Composition of No. 40: Copper, 84 to 86; tin, 4 to 6; lead, 4 to 6; zinc, 4 to 6; iron, max., 0.25; nickel, max., 0.75; phosphorus, max., 0.05; aluminum, 0.00; sulphur, max., 0.05; antimony, max., 0.25; other impurities, max., 0.15 per cent.

Physical Properties: Tensile strength, 26,000 pounds per square inch; yield point, 12,000 pounds per square inch; elongation in 2 inches (or proportionate gage length), 15 per cent.

Yellow Brass Castings — **S.A.E. Standard No. 41.** — Yellow brass is used for radiator parts, fittings for water-cooling systems, battery terminals, miscellaneous castings. This alloy is intended for commercial castings when cheapness and good machining properties are essential.

Composition of No. 41: Copper, 62 to 67; lead, 1.50 to 3.50; tin, max., 1; iron, max., 0.75; nickel, max., 0.25; phosphorus, max., 0.03; aluminum, max., 0.30; sulphur, max., 0.05; antimony, max., 0.15; other impurities, max., 0.15 per cent; zinc, remainder.

Physical Properties: Tensile strength, 20,000 pounds per square inch; elongation in 2 inches (or proportionate gage length), 15 per cent.

Manganese Bronze Castings — **S.A.E. Standard No. 43.** — This alloy is intended for castings requiring strength and toughness. It is used for such automotive parts as gear-shifter forks; counters, spiders; brackets and similar fittings; parts for starting motors; landing-gear and tail-skid castings for airplanes.

Composition of No. 43: Copper, 55 to 60; zinc, 38 to 42; tin, max., 1.50; manganese, max., 3.50; aluminum, max., 1.50; iron, max., 2; lead, max., 0.40 per cent.

Physical Properties: Tensile strength, 65,000 pounds per square inch; elongation in 2 inches (or proportionate gage length), 25 per cent.

High Tensile Manganese Bronze Castings — **S.A.E. Standard No. 430.** — This alloy is intended for use in castings where high strength and toughness are required such as marine propellers, shafts and gears.

Composition of No. 430: Copper, 60 to 68; iron, 2 to 4; aluminum, 3 to 6; manganese, 2.5 to 5; tin, max., 0.50; lead, max., 0.20, and nickel, max., 0.50 per cent; zinc, remainder.

Physical Properties: This alloy is manufactured in two grades, distinguished by chemical composition: Grade A being in the lower, and Grade B in the higher range of manganese, aluminum and iron content. Tensile strength, Grade A, 90,000, and Grade B, 110,000 pounds per square inch; elongation in 2 inches, Grade A, 20, and Grade B, 12 per cent.

Cast Brass to be Brazed — **S.A.E. Standard No. 44.** — This brass is used for water-pipe fittings which are to be brazed. It begins to melt at about 1830 degrees F. and is entirely melted at approximately 1870 degrees F. The alloy or spelter used for brazing must have a lower melting temperature. Silver solder may be used.

Composition of No. 44: Copper, 83 to 86; zinc, 14 to 17; lead, max., 0.50; iron, max., 0.15 per cent.

Brazing Solder — S.A.E. Standard No. 45. — This solder begins to melt at approximately 1560 degrees F. and is entirely melted at about 1600 degrees F. It may be used by melting in a crucible under a flux of borax, with or without the addition of boric acid. The part to be brazed is dipped into the melted solder. When used in powdered form, this solder, mixed with a flux, is applied to the material and then melted either by means of a brazing torch or by using a furnace.

Composition of No. 45: Copper, 48 to 52; lead, max., 0.50; iron, max., 0.10 per cent; zinc, remainder.

Hard Bronze Castings — S.A.E. Standard No. 62. — This is a strong general utility bronze suitable for severe working conditions and heavy pressures. Typical applications include gears; bearings; bushings for severe service; valve guides; valve-tappet guides; camshaft bearings; fuel pump, timer and distributor parts; connecting-rod bushings; piston-pins; rocker lever; steering sector and hinge bushings; starting-motor parts.

Composition of No. 62: Copper, 86 to 89; tin, 9 to 11; lead, max., 0.20; iron, max., 0.06; zinc, 1 to 3 per cent.

Physical Properties: Tensile strength, 30,000 pounds per square inch; yield point, 15,000 pounds per square inch; elongation in 2 inches (or proportionate gage length), 14 per cent.

Leaded Gun Metal Castings — S.A.E. Standard No. 63. — This general-utility bronze combines strength with fair machining qualities. It is especially good for bushings subjected to heavy loads and severe working conditions. It is also used for fittings subjected to moderately high water or oil pressures.

Composition of No. 63: Copper, 86 to 89; tin, 9 to 11; phosphorus, max., 0.25; zinc and other impurities, max., 0.50; lead, 1 to 2.50 per cent.

Physical Properties: Tensile strength, 30,000 pounds per square inch; yield point, 12,000 pounds per square inch; elongation in 2 inches (or proportionate gage length), 10 per cent.

Phosphor Bronze Castings — S.A.E. Standard No. 64. — This alloy is excellent when anti-friction qualities are important and where resistance to wear and scuffing are desired. It is used for such parts as wrist-pins, piston-pins, valve rocker-arm bushings, fuel and water-pump bushings, steering-knuckle bushings, aircraft control bushings.

Properties of No. 64: Copper, 78.50 to 81.50; tin, 9 to 11; lead, 9 to 11; phosphorus, 0.05 to 0.25; zinc, max., 0.75; other impurities, max., 0.25 per cent.

Physical Properties: Tensile strength, 25,000 pounds per square inch; yield point, 12,000 pounds per square inch; elongation in 2 inches (or proportionate gage length), 8 per cent.

Phosphor Gear Bronze Castings — S.A.E. Standard No. 65. — This bronze is not used regularly but it may be employed for gears and worm wheels where the requirements are severe and a very hard bronze is necessary.

Properties of No. 65: Copper, 88 to 90; tin, 10 to 12; phosphorus, 0.10 to 0.30; nickel, max., 0.05; lead, zinc, and other impurities, max., 0.50 per cent.

Physical Properties: Tensile strength, 35,000 pounds per square inch; yield point, 20,000 pounds per square inch; elongation in 2 inches (or proportionate gage length), 10 per cent.

Bronze Backing for Lined Bearings — S.A.E. Standard No. 66. — This is an inexpensive but suitable alloy for bronze-backed bearings of connecting-rods or main engine bearings.

Composition: Copper, 83 to 86; tin, 4.50 to 6; lead, 8 to 10; zinc, max., 2; other impurities, max., 0.25 per cent.

Physical Properties: Tensile strength, 25,000 pounds per square inch; yield point, 12,000 pounds per square inch; elongation in 2 inches, 8 per cent.

Bronze Bearing Castings — S.A.E. Standard No. 660. — This composition is widely used for bronze bearings. Typical applications in the automotive industry include such parts as spring bushings, torque tube bushings, steering-knuckle bushings, piston-pin bushings, thrust washers, etc.

Composition of No. 660: Copper, 81 to 85; tin, 6.50 to 7.50; lead, 6 to 8; zinc, 2 to 4; iron, max., 0.20; antimony, max., 0.20; other impurities, max., 0.50 per cent.

Physical Properties: Tensile strength, 30,000 pounds per square inch; yield point, 14,000 pounds per square inch; elongation in 2 inches, 18 per cent.

Cast Aluminum Bronze — S.A.E. Standard No. 68. — This alloy has considerable strength, resistance to corrosion, hardness equal to manganese bronze, and good bearing qualities under certain conditions. It is used for worm-wheels, gears, valve guides, valve seats, and forgings.

Composition of No. 68: Copper, (Grade A) 87 to 89, (Grade B) 89.50 to 90.50; aluminum, (Grade A) 7 to 9, (Grade B) 9.50 to 10.50; iron, (Grade A) 2.50 to 4, (Grade B) not over 1; tin, max., (Grade A) 0.5, (Grade B) 0.2; total other impurities, (Grade A), 1, (Grade B) 0.5 per cent.

Physical Properties: Tensile strength, (Grades A and B) as cast, 65,000 pounds per square inch; tensile strength, (Grade B) as heat-treated, quenched and drawn, 80,000 pounds per square inch; yield point, (Grades A and B) as cast, 25,000 pounds per square inch; yield point, (Grade B) as heat-treated, 50,000 pounds per square inch. Elongation in 2 inches, (Grade A) as cast, 20 per cent; (Grade B) 15 per cent; (Grade B) as heat-treated, 4 per cent.

Wrought Copper and Copper Alloys

The alloys in this group include commercial brass sheets, wrought aluminum bronze, naval brass or Tobin bronze, and other S.A.E. standard compositions.

Commercial Brass Sheet — S.A.E. Standard No. 70. — There are three grades designated as A, B and C. Grades A and B are used for deep drawing. As this brass is used for many purposes requiring properties not indicated by ordinary physical test data, it is often advisable to obtain from the manufacturer brass having an anneal or temper adapted to actual requirements.

Temper of Sheet Brass: The tempers are designated as Quarter Hard (1); Half Hard (2); Three-Quarter Hard (3); Hard (4); Extra Hard (6); Spring (8); Extra Spring (10). The numbers following each temper designation represent the amount of reduction in B. & S. gage numbers when the brass sheets are rolled. The greater the reduction, the harder the brass.

Composition of No. 70: Copper, (Grade A) 68.50 to 71.50, (Grade B) 66 to 69, (Grade C) 64.50 to 67.50; lead, max., (Grade A) 0.05, (Grade B) 0.07, (Grade C) 0.30, iron, max., (Grade A) 0.05, (Grade B) 0.04, (Grade C) 0.05 per cent; zinc (Grades A, B and C) remainder.

Physical Properties: The ultimate tensile strength (pounds per square inch) varies from 49,000 min. in the quarter-hard temper to 104,000 max. in the extra-spring temper for Grade A and from 49,000 min. in the quarter-hard temper to 98,500 max. in the extra spring temper for Grades B and C as shown in table.

Hardness and Ultimate Strength of No. 70 Sheet Brass by Tempers

Temper of Commercial Brass Sheet (S.A.E. No. 70) and Equivalent Reduction in B. & S. Gage Numbers		Rockwell Hardness Numbers				Ultimate Strength Pounds per Square Inch	
		B Scale 1/16" Ball-100 kg. Load		Superficial 30-T Scale 1/16" Ball-30 kg. Load			
Temper	Gage Nos.	Min.	Max.	Min.	Max.	Min.	Max.
Grade A							
Quarter Hard	1	40	65	43	60	49,000	59,000
Half Hard	2	60	77	56	68	56,500	66,500
Three-Quarter Hard	3	72	82	65	72	64,000	74,000
Hard	4	79	86	70	74	71,000	81,000
Extra Hard	6	85	91	74	77	82,500	91,500
Spring	8	89	93	76	78	90,500	99,500
Extra Spring	10	91	95	77	79	95,000	104,000
Grades B and C							
Quarter Hard	1	40	65	43	60	49,000	59,000
Half Hard	2	57	74	54	66	55,000	65,000
Three-Quarter Hard	3	70	80	65	71	62,000	72,000
Hard	4	76	84	68	73	68,000	78,000
Extra Hard	6	83	89	73	76	79,000	88,500
Spring	8	87	92	75	78	86,000	95,000
Extra Spring	10	88	93	76	79	89,500	98,500

The hardness numbers equivalent to such temper designations as "quarter hard," "half hard," etc., vary over a wide range as shown by the table above. The hardness number represented by a given temper designation depends not only upon the kind of annealing and thickness of a given material, but may be affected decidedly by the composition or type of alloy. "Quarter hard" red brass sheet (S.A.E. No. 79), for example, may have a Rockwell hardness varying from 50 to 95 which differs considerably from the minimum and maximum numbers given in the table above opposite "quarter hard."

Hardness tests of the indentation type, such as Rockwell or Brinell, are generally used for thin materials; however, if the sheet is very thin, the test may be for comparison only with other sheets of the same composition and thickness. When the penetration is deep relative to the thickness, there may be an apparent decrease of hardness due to the flow or punching-through of the material because of lack of lateral support; however,when the penetration is even greater relative to thickness, there may be an apparent *increase* in hardness due to the pressure of the penetrator on the anvil of the instrument.

Wrought Aluminum Bronze — S.A.E. Standard No. 701. — This alloy has great strength, high resistance to corrosion, and a hardness equal to manganese bronze. It has good bearing and anti-friction properties and is used for gears, forgings, hot-forged valve seats and bushings for internal-combustion engines. The 10 per cent alloy can be heat-treated in a manner similar to steel. The physical properties improve somewhat by heating and quenching.

Composition of No. 701: Copper, 88 to 95; aluminum, 4.5 to 10; iron, max., 4; other additions including nickel, tin and manganese, max., 2; other impurities including zinc and lead, max., 0.25 per cent.

Physical Properties: The ultimate strength (pounds per square inch) of rods and bars varies from 72,000 to 80,000; and plates, sheets and strips, from 50,000 to 60,000. The yield point of rods and bars (pounds per square inch) varies from

35,000 to 40,000; and plates, sheets and strips, from 20,000 to 24,000. This material must withstand cold bending without fracture through an angle of 120 degrees around a pin, the radius of which is equal to the diameter or thickness of the material.

Copper Sheet — S.A.E. Standard No. 71. — Copper sheet is used for so many different purposes that it is often advisable to consult the manufacturer regarding the anneal or temper required to obtain definite properties.

Composition of No. 71: Copper, min., 99.50 per cent.

Physical Properties: Tensile strength, soft temper with thicknesses ranging from 0.005 to 0.375 inch, 36,000 to 37,000 pounds per square inch, max.; hard copper with thicknesses from 0.072 to 0.375 inch, 35,000 to 40,000 pounds per square inch, min. Elongation of the soft grade varies from 20 to 25 per cent, and of the hard grade, from 8 to 15 per cent.

Free-cutting Brass Rod — S.A.E. Standard No. 72. — Rods of this composition are used for miscellaneous small screw machine parts, pins, nuts, screws, valve disks, valve caps, etc.

Composition of No. 72: Copper, 60 to 63; lead, 2.50 to 3.75; iron, max., 0.15; other impurities, max., 0.50 per cent; zinc, remainder.

Naval Brass (Tobin Bronze) Rod — S.A.E. Standard No. 73. — This alloy is used for applications requiring a stronger, tougher, and less corrodible material than commercial brass rod.

Composition of No. 73: Copper, 59 to 62; tin, 0.50 to 1.50; iron, max., 0.10; lead, max., 0.30; other impurities, max., 0.10 per cent; zinc, remainder.

Physical Properties: Minimum tensile strength in pounds per square inch varies from 54,000 to 62,000, depending upon the diameter of the rod; yield point, from 22,000 to 31,000; elongation, from 25 to 40 per cent. Hot-pressed forgings should have an ultimate strength of 54,000, a yield point of 22,000 pounds per square inch, with an elongation in 2 inches of 25 per cent.

Copper Tubing — S.A.E. Standard No. 75. — This is a general purpose material having a minimum copper content of 99.9 per cent.

Physical Properties: Expanding test: A hardened and ground taper pin, having an included angle of 60 degrees shall be capable of being driven into one end of the tube until the diameter of tubes ¾ inch and under is expanded 40 per cent, and of tubes over ¾ inch is expanded 30 per cent without rupture. This test shall be made on annealed tubes only. For light drawn temper the tensile strength is 36,000 to 50,000 pounds per square inch and the hardness 25 to 50 Rockwell B. For hard drawn temper the minimum tensile strength is 50,000 pounds per square inch and the minimum hardness, 50 Rockwell B.

Phosphor Bronze Strips — S.A.E. Standard No. 77. — This specification covers bronze strip up to 0.080 inch thick and includes different tempers in two grades designated as A and B. The tempers are: Half Hard (2); Hard (4); Extra Hard (6); Spring (8). The numbers following the temper designations indicate the reductions during rolling in B. & S. gage numbers. These phosphor bronze strips are used for various kinds of springs. Grade A spring temper is generally used for flat springs formed with easy bends across the grain. Grade B, extra hard temper, is usually employed for flat springs with easy bends either across or with the grain. Grade B, hard temper, is generally used for clips or contact springs with difficult bends. Grade A is also used for friction plates in clutches, and for thrust washers.

Composition of No. 77: Tin, (Grade A) 3.8 to 5.8, (Grade B) 7 to 9; phosphorus, (Grade A) 0.03 to 0.35, (Grade B) 0.03 to 0.25; zinc, max., (Grades A and B) 0.30 to

0.20; iron, max., (Grades A and B) 0.10; lead, max., (Grade A) 0.5, (Grade B) 0.2; antimony, max., (Grades A and B), 0.1; nickel, max., (Grade B), 0.15 per cent and copper, (Grades A and B), the remainder. Total copper, tin and phosphorus, min., 99.50 per cent.

Physical Properties: Minimum tensile strength, Grade A, half hard, 55,000; hard, 72,000; extra hard, 84,000; spring, 91,000 pounds per square inch. Grade B, half hard, 69,000; hard, 85,000; extra hard, 97,000 and spring, 105,000 pounds per square inch.

Red Brass Sheet — S.A.E. Standard No. 79. — This alloy in the quarter hard temper is used in the manufacture of radiators and lamp shells, and there are two grades designated as A and B.

Composition of No. 79: Copper, (Grade A) 84 to 86, (Grade B) 79 to 81; lead, max., (Grade A) 0.05, (Grade B) 0.05; iron, max., (Grade A) 0.05, (Grade B) 0.05; zinc, (Grades A and B) remainder.

Physical Properties: Ultimate tensile strength, pounds per square inch, (Grade A) quarter hard, 44,000 to 54,000; (Grade B) quarter hard, 48,000 to 58,000.

Wires and Rods

Brass Wire — S.A.E. Standard No. 80. — This wire is used for making springs. Grade A is intended for severe service, and Grade B for ordinary conditions. Permissible variations in the specified diameter are as follows: Sizes over 0.050 inch, plus or minus 1 per cent; sizes 0.050 to 0.025 inch, plus or minus 0.0005 inch; sizes under 0.025 inch, plus or minus 0.00025 inch.

Composition of No. 80: Copper, (Grade A) 70 to 74, (Grade B) 64 to 68; lead, max., (Grades A and B) 0.10; iron, max., (Grade A) 0.06, (Grade B) 0.07 per cent; zinc, (Grades A and B) remainder.

Physical Properties: This wire shall have a tensile strength of at least 100,000 pounds per square inch, and it should be capable of being bent through an angle of 180 degrees around a wire of the same diameter without breaking.

Phosphor Bronze Wire — S.A.E. Standard No. 81. — This wire is intended primarily for springs. Permissible variations in the specified diameter are as follows: Sizes over 0.050 inch, plus or minus 1 per cent; sizes 0.050 to 0.025 inch, plus or minus 0.0005 inch; sizes under 0.025 inch, plus or minus 0.00025 inch.

Composition of No. 81: Tin, 4 to 6; phosphorus, 0.03 to 0.40; zinc, max., 0.20; iron, max., 0.10; lead, max., 0.10 per cent; copper, remainder.

Physical Properties: Minimum tensile strength varies from 100,000 to 130,000 pounds per square inch, depending upon the diameter, the strength in pounds per square inch decreasing as the diameter increases. This wire should withstand any bend through an angle of 180 degrees flat back on itself without fracture on the outside of the bent portion.

Brass Wire — S.A.E. Standard No. 82. — Wire conforming to this specification is suitable for brazing and torch welding. This wire should be soft annealed and the surface should be clean and free from scale or other foreign matter.

Composition of No. 82: Copper, 59 to 62; lead, max., 0.30; iron, max., 0.06 per cent; zinc, remainder.

Soft or Annealed Copper Wire — S.A.E. Standard No. 83. — This wire is used for various electrical purposes. The electric resistivity shall be determined by resistance measurements at a temperature of 20 degrees centigrade (68 degrees F.), and it shall not exceed 891.58 pounds per mile-ohm. For the purpose of calculating weights, cross sections, etc., the specific gravity of copper be taken as 8.89 at 20 degrees centigrade. Permissible variations in the nominal diameter are as follows: Sizes 0.010 inch and larger, plus or minus 1 per cent; sizes under 0.010 inch, plus or minus 0.1 mil (0.0001 inch).

Physical Properties: Tensile strength varies from 36,000 to 40,000 pounds per square inch, depending upon the diameter. The elongation in 10 inches varies from 20 to 35 per cent, the latter applying to diameters from 0.289 inch to 0.460 inch, inc.

Brass Rod — S.A.E. Standard No. 88. — This specification applies to rods capable of being forged readily while hot and easily machined. These rods may be produced by hot-rolling or extrusion, and may be finished by cold-drawing, if necessary, to meet requirements as to size.

Composition of No. 88: Copper, 58.50 to 61.50; lead, 1.50 to 2.50; iron, max., 0.15; tin, max., 0.15; nickel, max., 0.15; zinc, remainder. Total elements named, min., 99.90 per cent.

Physical Properties: Hot-pressed forgings should have an ultimate strength of 45,000 and a yield point of 18,000 pounds per square inch. The elongation in 2 inches is 25 per cent.

Cast Aluminum Alloys

The S.A.E. standard cast aluminum alloys, like the wrought alloys, are of two types. *Type 1:* Improvement in the physical properties of Type 1 results from alloying only. *Type 2:* The properties of Type 2 that result from alloying, are further improved by heat-treatment.

The mechanical properties shown in these specifications are the values that should be obtained from standard test specimens separately cast in sand under conditions that duplicate, as closely as possible, the conditions of solidification of the casting and tested without machining except to adapt the ends to the grips of the testing equipment. In the case of alloys that are poured in permanent metal molds, the test bars should also be poured in a metal test bar mold.

In the design of patterns for the production of aluminum alloy sand castings, a shrinkage of 0.156 (5/32) inch per foot is usually allowed, although this value may vary slightly, depending upon the form and size of the casting. The producer of castings should be consulted concerning the design of the pattern so that the best results may be obtained with the alloy that is to be used.

S.A.E. Standard No. 300, Type 2 Alloy. — This alloy is of a composition which can be made almost entirely from scrap materials and, when the iron content approaches the maximum permitted, requires that special molding conditions be satisfied in order to secure sound castings. It is being used extensively for gasoline engine pistons. A "stabilizing" heat treatment (aging of as cast material) is recommended in order to minimize changes in dimensions and mechanical properties as a result of service at elevated temperatures.

Composition of No. 300: Copper, 6 to 8; iron, max. 1.5; silicon, 5-6; manganese, max. 0.75; magnesium, 0.15 to 0.5; zinc, 1.0; other elements, 1.25 per cent total; remainder, aluminum.

Physical Properties: Tensile strength, 27,000 pounds per square inch and Brinell hardness (500 kg. 10 mm.), 100.

S.A.E. Standard No. 310, Type 1 Alloy. — This is a general purpose alloy which develops high mechanical properties and a good ductility when aged for several weeks at room temperature or for a short time at a slightly elevated temperature. Within the first two weeks after casting, or before artificial aging, the alloy has a high ductility, permitting severe cold deformation. Since the alloy does not require a high-temperature solution heat-treatment, it can be used as an alternate for S.A.E. No. 38 alloy if heat-treating facilities are not available. The alloy has good casting properties and can be machined easily.

Composition of No. 310: Copper, maximum 0.2; iron, maximum 1.0; silicon, magnesium, maximum 0.25; magnesium, 0.4–0.6; zinc, 4.8–5.7; titanium, 0.1–0.3; chromium, 0.4–0.6; other elements, maximum 0.05 per cent each; remainder, aluminum.

Physical Properties: Tensile strength, 30,000 pounds per square inch and elongation in 2 inches, 3 per cent minimum.

S.A.E. Standard No. 320, Type 1 Alloy.

This alloy is used for carburetor cases, cast pipe fittings, and other castings requiring high resistance to corrosion. It has good mechanical properties and is easily machined.

Composition of No. 320: Magnesium, 3.2 to 4.3; manganese, max., 0.60; iron, max., 0.4; silicon, max., 0.3; copper. max., 0.10; zinc max., 0.05; all elements other than aluminum, magnesium and manganese, max., 0.6 per cent; titanium, max., 0.2; aluminum, remainder.

Physical Properties: Tensile strength, 22,000 pounds per square inch minimum; elongation in 2 inches, 6 per cent minimum; specific gravity, about 2.64 (less than that of pure aluminum).

S.A.E. Standard No. 321, Type 2 Alloy.

This alloy is used for automobile engine pistons because of its low coefficient of expansion compared with other aluminum alloys, its hardness and resistance to wear, and its good mechanical properties at elevated temperatures. The pistons are as a rule cast in permanent metal molds but this alloy may also be used for sand castings and for other applications similar to those for Nos. 34 and 39.

Composition of No. 321: Silicon, 11.0 to 13.0; magnesium, 0.7 to 1.3; manganese, max., 0.05; nickel, 2.0 to 3.0; copper, 0.5 to 1.5; iron, max., 1.3; zinc, max., 0.1; other impurities, max., 0.2 per cent; aluminum, remainder.

S.A.E. Standard No. 322, Type 2 Alloy.

This alloy is used for water-cooled cylinder heads for automotive or aircraft engines and for similar applications requiring sound leak-proof castings produced either in sand or permanent metal molds. This alloy has excellent foundry characteristics and resistance to corrosion.

Composition of No. 322: Silicon, 4.5 to 5.5; copper, 1.0 to 1.5; magnesium, 0.4 to 0.6; iron, max., 0.5; manganese, max., 0.1; zinc, max., 0.05; titanium, max., 0.2; other impurities, max., 0.2 per cent; aluminum, remainder.

Physical Properties: This alloy can be heat-treated to improve its mechanical properties. The minimum tensile strength ranges from 27,000 to 36,000 pounds per square inch, depending upon heat-treatment, and the elongation in 2 inches, from 2 to 4 per cent minimum.

S.A.E. Standard No. 323, Type 2 Alloy.

This alloy has excellent foundry characteristics and resistance to corrosion. It is commonly used for high-strength castings which are too intricate to permit using alloy No. 38. It is also preferred where high corrosion resistance is necessary.

Composition of No. 323: Silicon, 6.5 to 7.5; magnesium, 0.2 to 0.4; iron, max., 0.5; copper, max., 0.2; zinc, max., 0.05; titanium, max., 0.2; other impurities, max., 0.05 per cent; aluminum, remainder.

Physical Properties: Tensile strength, 23,000 to 30,000 pounds per square inch minimum, depending upon heat-treatment; elongation in 2 inches, from 3 to 5 per cent minimum.

S.A.E. Standard No. 324, Type 2 Alloy.

This alloy is used for castings requiring a maximum ratio of strength to weight. It is used for some aircraft fittings, truck parts, and especially where service conditions are severe.

Composition of No. 324: Magnesium, 9.5 to 11.3; copper, max., 0.20; iron, max., 0.30; silicon, max., 0.20; other impurities, max., 0.20 per cent; aluminum, remainder.

Physical Properties: Minimum tensile strength, 42,000 pounds per square inch; elongation in 2 inches, 12 per cent minimum; specific gravity, about 2.55 compared with 2.70 for pure aluminum.

S.A.E. Standard No. 325, Type 2 Alloy. — This alloy was developed to provide castings having physical properties approaching those of S.A.E. No. 38, but which could not be made from alloy ingot produced entirely from available classes of scrap.

Composition of No. 325: Copper, 3.0–4.5; iron, maximum 1.2; silicon, maximum 2.5; manganese, maximum 0.5; magnesium, maximum 0.05; zinc, maximum 0.5; titanium, maximum 0.2; nickel, maximum 0.3; other elements, maximum 0.3 per cent each; and remainder, aluminum.

Physical Properties: Tensile strength, 27,000 pounds per square inch and elongation in 2 inches, 3 per cent.

S.A.E. Standard No. 33, Type 1 Alloy. — This is widely used as a general casting alloy and for such parts as crankcases, oil-pans, differential carriers, transmission cases, camshaft housings, cylinder heads for water-cooled automobile engines.

Composition of No. 33: Copper, 6.0 to 8.0; zinc, max., 2.2; magnesium, max., 0.05; manganese, max., 0.3; iron, max., 1.05; silicon, max., 1.0 to 3.0; aluminum, remainder. Total, all elements other than aluminum, max., 13.5 per cent.

Physical Properties: Minimum tensile strength, 19,000 pounds per square inch; elongation in 2 inches, ordinarily from 1 to 2½ per cent; specific gravity, from 2.83 to 2.86. If cast in permanent molds, the minimum tensile strength will be about 23,000 pounds per square inch.

S.A.E. Standard No. 34, Type 2 Alloy. — This alloy has been used chiefly for pistons of automobile engines (like No. 321). It is also used for camshaft bearings, valve tappet guides, and other parts requiring hardness and resistance to wear. It is used principally for permanent mold castings but is also cast in sand. Air-cooled cylinder heads for aircraft engines and valve guides and piston sleeves for Diesel engines are other examples of applications.

Composition of No. 34: Copper, 9.2 to 10.8; iron, max., 1.50; iron plus silicon, max., 2.0; magnesium, 0.15 to 0.35; manganese, max., 0.3; zinc, max., 0.2; other impurities, max., 0.3 per cent; aluminum, remainder.

Physical Properties: Minimum tensile strength, from 26,000 to 34,000 pounds per square inch for permanent mold castings. The sand cast alloy should have a tensile strength of at least 23,000 pounds per square inch, and this may be increased by heat-treatment to a minimum of 30,000 pounds per square inch.

S.A.E. Standard No. 35, Type 1 Alloy. — This alloy is used for general casting purposes, particularly for large intricate castings having both thin and heavy sections, or for castings which must be leak-proof under pressure. It has good resistance to salt spray corrosion. It is used for automobile body parts, manifolds, instruments, and a variety of parts not requiring the higher mechanical properties of a type 2 alloy.

Composition of No. 35: Silicon, 4.5 to 6.0; copper, max., 0.4; iron, max., 0.8; zinc, max., 0.2; titanium, max., 0.2; manganese, max., 0.3; magnesium, max., 0.05; other impurities, max., 0.3 per cent; aluminum, remainder.

Physical Properties: Minimum tensile strength, 17,000 pounds per square inch for sand castings, and 21,000 pounds per square inch for metal mold castings; elongation, 2½ to 3 per cent; specific gravity, 2.65 to 2.66.

S.A.E. Standard No. 37, Intermediate Alloy. — Applications of this alloy are similar to those of No. 35 which it surpasses in mechanical properties. It has good foundry characteristics and resistance to salt spray corrosion.

Composition of No. 37: Silicon, 12.0 to 13.0; iron, max., 0.8; copper, max., 0.15; zinc, max., 0.1; manganese, max., 0.2; magnesium, max., 0.05; other impurities, max., 0.2 per cent; aluminum, remainder.

Physical Properties: Minimum tensile strength, 24,000 pounds per square inch; elongation in 2 inches, 5 per cent minimum.

S.A.E. Standard No. 38, Type 2 Alloy. —

This alloy is used for windshield frames; fire engine, motor coach and aircraft engine crankcases; and a variety of other parts in both motor vehicle and aircraft assemblies where high strength and light weight are essential. It has good resistance to salt spray corrosion and is extensively used in the manufacture of outboard motors and for certain castings used on ships.

Composition of No. 38: Copper, 4.0 to 5.0; silicon, max., 1.2; iron, max., 1.0; manganese, max., 0.05; magnesium, max., 0.03; zinc, max., 0.05; titanium, max., 0.2; other impurities, max., 0.05 per cent; aluminum, remainder.

Physical Properties: One of three heat-treatments may be applied, depending upon properties required. Minimum tensile strength ranges from 29,000 to 36,000 pounds per square inch, depending upon heat-treatment; the elongation in 2 inches ranges from 3 to 6 per cent. The specific gravity is about 2.77.

S.A.E. Standard No. 39, Type 2 Alloy. —

This alloy is used for pistons and cylinder heads of aircraft engines and for other castings subjected to elevated temperatures. It may be used as cast but usually is heat-treated to develop higher physical properties or to relieve casting strains and stabilize dimensions at elevated temperatures.

Composition of No. 39: Copper, 3.5 to 4.5; nickel, 1.7 to 2.3; magnesium, 1.2 to 1.8; iron, max., 1.0; silicon, max., 0.7; other impurities, max., 0.3 per cent; aluminum, remainder.

Physical Properties: Minimum tensile strength for sand castings, 23,000 pounds per square inch which may be increased to 32,000 by heat-treatment. If cast in permanent molds, the minimum tensile strength is 26,000 pounds per square inch which may be increased to 40,000 by heat-treatment. Specific gravity is about 2.73 to 2.77, the higher values being for permanent mold castings.

Wrought Aluminum Alloys

S.A.E. standard specifications for wrought alloys as given in the following indicate fabricated forms which are regularly manufactured. Type 1 indicates an improvement in the physical properties resulting from alloying only. Type 2 indicates that the properties resulting from alloying are further improved by heat-treatment.

S.A.E. Standard No. 201, Type 1 Alloy. —

This alloy is manufactured in the form of sheets, plates, bars, rods and wire, and in the standard size of tubing specified for aircraft fuel and oil lines. The sheets are used for aircraft gasoline tanks. engine cowling, and other moderately stressed parts and for panels, roof sheets, etc., in truck and bus construction.

Composition of No. 201: Magnesium, 2.2 to 2.8; chromium, 0.15 to 0.35; aluminum, min. 96.1 per cent.

Physical Properties: In sheet form the tensile strength in the "soft" to "hard" tempers ranges from 31,000 to 39,000 pounds per square inch min.; the elongation in 2 inches varies from 3 to 4 per cent in the hard temper, and from 15 to 20 per cent in the soft temper, depending upon the thickness. The yield strength in the soft temper is approximately 14,000 pounds per square inch; in the harder tempers it averages 75 to 85 per cent of the ultimate tensile strength. The shearing strength ranges from 18,000 to 24,000 pounds per square inch for soft to hard tempers.

Table 1. Aluminum Alloy Temper Designations

Meanings of Symbols: –F, *As fabricated* (not heat-treated or intentionally strain hardened); –O, *Annealed, recrystallized* (wrought products only); –H, *Strain hardened* (–H1, plus one or more digits — *strain hardened only;* –H2, plus one or more digits — *strain hardened then partially annealed;* –H3, plus one or more digits — *strain hardened then stabilized;* –W, *Solution heat treated — unstable temper;* –T, *Treated to produce stable tempers other than* –F, –O, or –H (–T2, annealed — cast products only; –T3, *Solution heat-treated then cold worked;* –T4, *solution heat-treated;* –T5, *artificially aged only;* –T6, *solution heat-treated then artificially aged;* –T7, *solution heat-treated then stabilized;* –T8, *solution heat-treated, cold worked, artificially aged;* –T9, *solution heat-treated, artificially aged, cold worked;* –T10, *artificially aged then cold worked.*)

Alloy	Old Temper	Flat Sheet (10)	Coiled Sheet (10)	Plate (10)	All Forms (11)	Extrusions (10)	Extrusions (11)	Wire Rod Bar (10)	Tubing (10)	Tubing (11)	Forgings (10)	Rivets (10)	Rivets (11)
11S	–W							–T4					
	–T3							–T3					
	–T8							–T8					
14S and 14S[9]	–W	–T3	–T4	–T4	–T4	–T4	–T42	–T4			–T4		
	–T	–T6	–T6	–T6	–T6	–T6	–T62	–T6			–T6		
	–T	..	..	..	..	..	..	..			–T61[4]		
17S	–T											–T4	–T3[5]
	–T					–T4						..	–T31[6]
	..					..							–T41[7]
A17S	–T											–T4	–T3[5]
18S	–T										–T61[4]		
24S and 24S[9]	–T	–T3	–T4	–T4	–T4	–T4	–T42	–T4	–T3	–T4		–T4	–T31[6]
	–RT	–T36	–T36	–T36	–T36	..	..	–T36	..	..		..	..
	–T80	..	–T6	..	–T6	..	..	..				..	..
	–T81	–T81		..		..							
	–T86	–T86		–T86									
25S	–T										–T6		
32S	–T										–T6		
A51S	–W										–T4		
	–T										–T6		
53S	–W					–T4	–T4				–T4	–T4	–T4
													–T41[7]
	–T					–T6	–T6				–T6	–T6	–T6
	–T5					–T5	..				..		
	–T61					..						–T61	–T61
61S	–W	–T4	–T4	–T4	–T4	–T4	–T4		–T4	–T4			
	–T	–T6	–T6	–T6	–T6	–T6	–T6		–T6	–T6	–T6	–T6	–T6
	–T5	..	..	..	..	–T5	..		..	..	..	..	..
	–T62	..	..	..	..	–T62	..		..	..	..	..	..
	–T81	..						–T81	..				
63S	–T					–T6	–T6						
	–T5					–T5	–T5						
75S	–W	–W[8]	–W[8]	–W[8]	–W[8]	–W[8]	–W[8]						
75S[9]	–T	–T6	–T6	–T6*	–T6	–T6	–T6	–T6					

1. Products listed also available in –O and –F tempers.   2. Forgings also available in –F temper.   3. For extruded tubing, see under extrusions.   4. Boiling water quench.   5. Driven cold after full natural aging.   6. Driven cold immediately after solution heat-treatment, or when refrigerated to defer natural aging.   7. Driven hot, at solution heat-treating temperature — any temper.   8. To be specific, time of natural aging must be stated; for example, 75S–W (2 hr.), 75S–W (2 mo.).   9. "Alclad" available only in the form of sheet and plate.   10. Heat-treatment by "Alcoa."   11. Heat-treatment by customer.

Table 2. Aluminum Alloy Temper Designations

The temper symbols or designations as revised by the Aluminum Company of America are given on this and the preceding page. The temper designation, where required, follows the alloy designation and is separated from it by a dash as in the previous system. A letter indicates the basic temper which may be defined more specifically by the addition of one or more digits. Temper designations for sand castings and permanent mold castings have not been changed. The meanings of symbols are given in Table 1.

Non-heat-treatable Alloys[1]

Alloy	Old T.	New Temper Designation		
2S and 3S	¼H, ½H, ¾H, H, Ex. H'd.[9]	-H12, -H14, -H16, -H18, -H19	-H22, -H24, -H26, -H28, ..	
4S, 52S and 56S	¼H, ½H, ¾H, H, Ex. H'd.[9]			-H32, -H34, -H36, -H38, -H39

Alloy	Old Temper	New Temper Designation			
		Flat Sheet[10]	Coiled Sheet[10]	Plate[10]	See Note 2
14S, 14S[12]	-W, -T	-T3, -T6	-T4, -T6	-T4, -T6	-T4, -T6
24S and 24S[12]	-T, -RT, -T80, -T81, -T86	-T3, -T36, .., -T81, -T86	-T4, .., -T6, .., ..	-T4, -T36, .., .., -T86	-T4, .., -T6, .., ..
61S	-W, -T	-T4, -T6	-T4, -T6	-T4, -T6	-T4, -T6
75S, 75S[12]	-W, -T	-W14, -T6	-W14, -T6	-W14, -T6	-W14, -T6

Alloy	Wire, Rod, Bar[13]		Alloy	Forgings	
	Old T.	New T.[10]		Old Temper	New Temper[10]
11S	-W, -T3, -T8	-T4, -T3, -T8	14S	-W, -T, -T	-T4, -T6, -T61[4]
14S	-W, -T	-T4, -T6	18S	-T	-T61[4]
17S	-T	-T4	25S	-T	-T6
24S	-T, -RT	-T4, -T36	32S	-T	-T6
61S	-W, -T, -T81	-T4, -T6, -T81	A51S	-W, -T	-T4, -T6
75S	-T	-T6	53S	-W, -T	-T4, -T6

Rivets[1]

Alloy	Old T.	New Temper	
17S	-T, -T, ..	-T4[10], ..	T3[5], -T31[6], -T41[7]
A17S	-T	-T4	-T3[5]
24S	-T	-T4	-T31[6]
53S	-W, -T, -T61	-T4, -T6, -T61	-T4, -T41[7], -T6, -T61
61S	-T	-T6	-T6

Tubing[1,8]

Alloy	Old T.	New Temper	
24S	-T	-T3[10]	-T41[11]
61S	-W, -T	-T4[10], -T61[10]	-T41[11], -T61[11]

Extrusions[1]

Alloy	Old T.	New Temper	
14S	-W, -T	-T4[10], -T61[10]	-T42[11], -T62[11]
24S	-T	-T4[10]	-T42[11]
53S	-W, -T, -T5	-T4[10], -T61[10], -T5[10]	-T41[11], -T61[11], ..
61S	-W, -T, -T5, -T62	-T4[10], -T61[10], -T5[10], -T62[10]	-T41[11], -T61[11], .., ..
63S	-T, -T5	-T61[10], -T5[10]	-T61[11], -T5[11]
75S	-W, -T	-W10,14 T6[10],	-W11,14, -T611

Example: -H22 to -H28 means *strain hardened and then partially annealed*, as indicated by the general symbol -H2 above Table 1.

1. Also available in -O and -F tempers. 2. All forms heat-treated by customer. 3. Forgings also available in -F temper. 4. Boiling water quench. 5. Driven cold after full natural aging. 6. Driven cold immediately after solution heat-treatment or when refrigerated to defer natural aging. 7. Driven hot at solution heat-treating temperature — any temper. 8. For extruded tubing, see Extrusions. 9. Extra hard, non-standard. 10. Heat-treated by "Alcoa." 11. Heat-treated by customer. 12. "Alclad." 13. Also in -O and -F tempers and rolled or extruded structural shapes. 14. To be specific, time of natural aging must be stated as 75S-W (2 mo.).

S.A.E. Standard No. 24, Type 2 Alloy. — This alloy, in the form of sheets, plates, tubing, bars, rods, wire, rivets, and in rolled and extruded shapes, is replacing No. 26 to an increasing extent in the construction of aircraft because of its high physical properties.

Composition of No. 24: Copper, 3.7 to 4.9; magnesium, 1.2 to 1.8; manganese, 0.3 to 0.9; aluminum, min., 92.0 per cent.

Physical Properties: In the form of sheets, the tensile strength varies from 35,000 for soft temper to 62,000 pounds per square inch for heat-treated sheets, and the elongation in 2 inches from 12 to 18 per cent. The yield strength of a heat-treated sheet is about 40,000 pounds per square inch minimum.

S.A.E. Standard No. 25, Type 1 Alloy. — This specification applies to commercially pure aluminum sheets and strips. These aluminum sheets have excellent forming qualities and can readily be spun, stamped, or drawn into desired shapes. Aluminum of commercial purity is manufactured in practically all forms, such as bars, rods, wire, tubing, extruded shapes, etc.

Composition of No. 25: Aluminum, min., 99.0 per cent.

Physical Properties: The tensile strength of flat sheets varies from about 14,000 to 22,000 pounds per square inch minimum, depending upon the temper. The elongation in the hard temper varies from 1 to 4 per cent, and in the soft from 15 to 30 per cent, depending upon the thickness. In the soft temper, the yield strength is about 5000 pounds per square inch, and in the harder temper from 80 to 95 per cent of the ultimate tensile strength.

S.A.E. Standard No. 26, Type 2 Alloy. — This alloy is commonly known as duralumin, dural, or 17S. It is commercially available in sheets, tubing, bars, wire, etc., and in both rolled and extruded forms, including standard structural shapes. It is used for bolts and nuts, machine screws, wood screws, rivets, forgings, screw machine products, fuel and lubrication tube fittings, etc.

Composition of No. 26: Copper, 3.5 to 4.5; magnesium, 0.2 to 0.75; manganese, 0.4 to 1.0; aluminum, min., 92.0 per cent.

Physical Properties: The minimum tensile strength of heat-treated sheets and plates is about 58,000 pounds per square inch; the yield strength, 34,000 pounds per square inch; and elongation from 6 to 18 per cent. Bars, rods, wire and structural shapes have a minimum tensile strength of 55,000 pounds per square inch and a yield strength of 32,000 pounds per square inch minimum. In the annealed condition, the tensile strength should not exceed 35,000 pounds per square inch. In the heat-treated temper the shearing strength is about 36,000 pounds per square inch.

S.A.E. Standard No. 260, Type 2 Alloy. — This alloy has been used principally for the production of high-strength forgings and is rapidly replacing S.A.E. Nos. 26 and 27 for such uses. It is also available in the form of extruded sections.

Composition of No. 260: Copper, 3.9 to 5.0; iron, maximum 1.0; silicon, 0.5 to 1.2; manganese, 0.4 to 1.2; magnesium, 0.2 to 0.75; zinc, maximum 0.25; chromium, maximum 0.10; titanium, maximum 0.15; other elements, maximum 0.05 each and 0.15 per cent total; and remainder aluminum.

Physical Properties: Minimum tensile strength for forgings up to 4-inch thickness is 65,000 pounds per square inch, and for extrusions from 60,000 to 68,000 pounds per square inch depending upon thickness. Minimum elongation in 2 inches for forgings is 10 per cent and for extrusions, 7 per cent.

S.A.E. Standard No. 27, Type 2 Alloy. — This alloy is especially adapted to forging because of its excellent hot-working properties. The forgings in common use include connecting-rods for automotive engines, crankcases, airplane propellers, automobile hardware, miscellaneous fittings. This alloy in the form of sheets and plates is used less than the S.A.E. Nos. 24 and 26.

Composition of No. 27: Copper, 3.9 to 5.0; manganese, 0.5 to 1.1; silicon, 0.5 to 1.1; aluminum, min., 92.0 per cent.

Physical Properties: The minimum tensile strength for forgings is about 55,000, and the yield strength 30,000 pounds per square inch. The elongation in 2 inches is 16 per cent. The shearing strength is about 35,000 pounds per square inch for the heat-treated condition.

S.A.E. Standard No. 270, Type 2 Alloy. — This alloy finds its principal usage in the production of forged pistons for high output gasoline engines and in similar forgings requiring a relatively high strength at elevated temperatures.

Composition of No. 270: Copper, 3.5 to 4.5; iron, max. 1.0; silicon, max. 0.9; manganese, max. 0.2; magnesium, 0.45 to 0.9; zinc, max. 0.25; chromium, max. 0.10; titanium, max. 0.15; nickel, 1.7 to 2.3; other elements, max. 0.05 each and 0.15 total; remainder, aluminum.

Physical Properties: Tensile strength 55,000 pounds per square inch and elongation in 2 inches, 10 per cent.

S.A.E. Standard No. 280, Type 2 Alloy. — This alloy can readily be formed hot, and is therefore used in the manufacture of complicated forgings not readily produced from alloys Nos. 26 or 27.

Composition of No. 280: Magnesium, 0.45 to 0.9; silicon, 0.6 to 1.2; chromium, max., 0.25 and aluminum, min. 96.3 per cent.

Physical Properties: This alloy has a minimum tensile strength of 44,000 pounds per square inch; a minimum yield strength of 34,000 pounds per square inch and an elongation in 2 inches of 14 per cent.

S.A.E. Standard No. 281, Type 2 Alloy. — This alloy has good mechanical properties, especially yield strength, and is capable of being formed more severely in the heat-treated (*T*) temper than the other Type 2 alloys. In the quenched (*W*) temper even more difficult forming can be done and the resulting shape can then be aged artificially to produce the heat-treated (*T*) temper. This alloy is used in the form of sheet and plate in bus and truck construction and also finds some use in aircraft and aircraft engines in the form of both tubing and sheet.

Composition of No. 281: magnesium, 0.8 to 1.2; silicon, 0.4 to 0.8; copper, 0.15 to 0.40; chromium, max., 0.35; titanium, max., 0.15; manganese, max., 0.15 and aluminum, 96.0 per cent.

Physical Properties: In the form of sheet, plate and tubing this alloy has the following properties: in the quenched temper (*W*) a minimum tensile strength of 30,000 pounds per square inch and a minimum yield strength of 35,000 pounds per square inch and in the soft temper (*O*) a maximum tensile strength of 22,000 pounds per square inch.

S.A.E. Standard No. 29, Type 1 Alloy. — This alloy is used instead of commercially pure aluminum when somewhat greater strength and hardness are required. The forming qualities are nearly the equal of commercial aluminum except for deep drawing and spinning. In the form of sheets, it is used for aircraft tanks and automobile body panels, although harder alloys are finding increasing use for these purposes.

Composition of No. 29: Manganese, 1.0 to 1.5; copper, max., 0.2; aluminum, min., 97.0 per cent.

Physical Properties: The tensile strength of flat sheets varies from 19,000 to 27,000 pounds per square inch for soft to hard tempers. Elongation in the hard temper varies from 1 to 4 per cent, and in the soft temper from 20 to 25 per cent. In the soft temper, the yield strength is about 5000 pounds per square inch, and in the harder tempers from 85 to 95 per cent of the ultimate tensile strength.

Magnesium Alloys

Pure magnesium is a relatively soft, silver-white metal. In its pure state it does not possess sufficient strength for many commercial uses. When alloyed with certain other metals, chiefly aluminum, manganese and zinc, a wide range of useful properties is obtained. Some of these alloys are characterized by their strength, others by their toughness, and still others by their thermal conductivity. The chief characteristic is extreme lightness, the average specific gravity being only 1.80.

Compositions of Dowmetal Alloys. — Some magnesium alloys are designated by the trade name "Dowmetal." Dowmetal alloys are available for sand and permanent mold castings, die-castings, press and hammer forgings, extruded shapes, plates, sheets and strips Their compositions vary more or less for different applications. The nominal compositions of these alloys are given in the accompanying table.

Nominal Compositions of Dowmetal Alloys *

Element	Dowmetal Alloy							
	C	FS-1	G	H	J-1	M	O-1	R
	Composition, Per Cent							
Aluminum........	9.0	3.0	10.0	6.0	6.5	....	8.5	9.0
Manganese.......	0.1	0.3	0.1	0.2	0.2	1.5	0.2	0.2
Zinc............	2.0	1.0	....	3.0	1.0	....	0.5	0.6
Magnesium	88.9	95.7	89.9	90.8	92.3	98.5	90.8	90.2

* Note: These compositions vary slightly depending on the application of the alloy. Other elements, such as silicon, copper, nickel and iron, present in small amounts as impurities, not shown.

Applications of Dowmetal Alloys. — Recommendations for the use of various Dowmetal alloys in the form of castings, forgings, extruded shapes and rolled forms are given below.

Sand Castings: Dowmetal C and Dowmetal H are most commonly used for sand castings. Where pressure tightness is the governing factor especially in thin walled castings, Dowmetal C is preferred. Where high strength is the important factor, Dowmetal H is indicated. Both alloys can be heat-treated for improvement of various properties. Dowmetal M has casting characteristics inferior to those of Dowmetals C and H but it does have good welding characteristics and is used for such applications as tank fittings where castings must be welded into place.

Permanent Mold Castings: Dowmetal C is most widely used for permanent mold castings because of its combination of good casting characteristics, mechanical properties and corrosion resistance. Dowmetal G has better casting characteristics than Dowmetal C but its corrosion resistance and mechanical properties are slightly inferior. Dowmetal H does not have as good foundry characteristics as C and G, hence it is used only for special applications.

Die-castings: Dowmetal R is the magnesium alloy most widely used for die-castings. It possesses a desirable combination of good casting characteristics and good mechanical properties. Special alloys are available for die-castings if specific properties are required.

Forgings: The most widely used Dowmetal alloys for forging are J-1 and O-1, due to their superior mechanical properties. Dowmetal O-1 is used where maximum strength is required, whereas Dowmetal J-1 is indicated where greater formability and weldability are desired. Dowmetal O-1 can be heat-treated for improved mechanical properties. Dowmetal M is used where maximum formability and weldability are desired and strength is not of paramount importance.

Extruded Shapes: Dowmetals FS-1, J-1, M and O-1 are available as extruded materials. The alloys are made in all forms of extrusions with the exception that Dowmetal O-1 is not available as tubing. Dowmetal J-1 is a general-purpose extrusion alloy of improved strength. Dowmetal M is a moderate strength alloy with the best weldability and hot formability. Dowmetal O-1 has the highest strength in the extruded condition and is heat treatable.

Sheet, Plate, and Strip: Dowmetals FS-1, J-1 and M are available as rolled magnesium products. Each alloy is available in the annealed condition, denoted by the letter "*a*" following the alloy designation, or in the hard rolled condition denoted by the letter "*h*". Dowmetal J-1 is also available as plate in the as rolled condition designated as J-1r. Dowmetal J-1 has the best mechanical properties of the rolled alloys and is used in applications where strength is most important. Where better formability is desired along with good shear and tensile strengths, Dowmetal FS-1 is used. Dowmetal M is used where maximum weldability and formability, low cost, and moderate strength are desired.

Physical Properties of Dowmetal Alloys. — The physical properties of the various Dowmetal alloys varies with their composition and condition, i.e., whether as cast, heat-treated, aged, stabilized, etc. The range in tensile strengths of these alloys is given below.

Casting Alloys: In the cast condition ultimate tensile strengths range from 14,000 to 29,000 pounds per square inch and yield strengths from 4500 to 14,000 pounds per square inch. In the heat-treated condition ultimate tensile strengths range from 33,000 to 40,000 pounds per square inch and ultimate strengths from 12,000 to 23,000 pounds per square inch.

Forging Alloys: The ultimate tensile strengths range from 36,000 to 50,000 pounds per square inch and the yield strengths from 23,000 to 34,000 pounds per square inch.

Extruded Alloys: For bars and rods the ultimate tensile strengths range from 38,000 to 50,000 pounds per square inch and the yield strengths from 26,000 to 34,000 pounds per square inch.

For shapes, the ultimate tensile strength ranges from 34,000 to 49,000 pounds per square inch and the yield strength from 20,000 to 32,000 pounds per square inch. For tubing the ultimate tensile strength ranges from 33,000 to 40,000 pounds per square inch and the yield strength is 21,000 pounds per square inch.

Rolled Alloys: In the annealed condition the ultimate tensile strength ranges from 33,000 to 43,000 pounds per square inch and the yield strength from 15,000 to 26,000 pounds per square inch. In the hard rolled condition the ultimate tensile strength ranges from 37,000 to 47,000 pounds per square inch and the yield strength from 29,000 to 34,000 pounds per square inch. In the as rolled condition the ultimate tensile strength of the J-1 alloy is 43,000 pounds per square inch and the yield strength 28,000 pounds per square inch.

Heat-treatment of Dowmetal Alloys. — Dowmetal castings may be used as cast or in a heat-treated condition. Heat-treatment is not required for general use. However, when increased tensile strength, ductility and toughness are required, without change of yield strength or hardness, castings are "solution heat-treated." This solution heat-treatment is performed in specially designed ovens at temperatures varying from 630 to 785 degrees F., depending upon the alloy, and is followed by air-cooling. Castings so treated are in the best condition for shock resistance. If castings require high yield strength but are not subject to shock, they are solution heat-treated and aged. This aging or "precipitation" is done at about 350 degrees F.

S.A.E. Cast Magnesium Alloys

S.A.E. Standard No. 50 Alloy. — This alloy is used for most commercial applications. It is used in the "as cast," "heat treated," or "heat treated and aged" condition as may be required.

Composition of No. 50: Aluminum, 5.3 to 6.7; manganese, min., 0.15; zinc, 2.5 to 3.5; silicon, max., 0.5; copper, max., 0.05; nickel, max., 0.03; other impurities, max., 0.3 per cent and the remainder, magnesium.

Physical Properties: For sand castings as in the "as cast," "heat treated" and "heat treated and aged" conditions the minimum tensile strengths are respectively: 24,000, 30,000 and 32,000 pounds per square inch; the minimum yield strengths are respectively: 10,000, 10,000 and 16,000 pounds per square inch and the elongations in 2 inches are respectively: 4, 6 and 2 per cent.

S.A.E. Standard No. 500 Alloy. — This is a sand casting alloy to be used particularly where maximum pressure tightness is required. It may be used in the "as cast," "heat treated" or "heat treated and aged" condition as may be required.

Composition of No. 500: Aluminum 8.3 to 9.7; manganese, min., 0.10; zinc, 1.7 to 2.3; silicon, max., 0.5; copper, max., 0.05; nickel, max., 0.03; other impurities, max., 0.3 per cent and the remainder, magnesium.

Physical Properties: For sand castings in the "as cast," "heat treated" and "heat treated and aged" conditions, the minimum tensile strengths are respectively: 20,000, 30,000 and 32,000 pounds per square inch; the yield strengths are respectively: 10,000, 10,000 and 17,000 pounds per square inch and the elongations in 2 inches are respectively: 1, 6 and 1 per cent.

S.A.E. Wrought Magnesium Alloys

S.A.E. Standard No. 51 Alloy. — This alloy is used where maximum salt water resistance and weldability are desired. It is used in the annealed temper for applications requiring maximum formability, such as aircraft tanks and wheel fairings.

Composition of No. 51: Manganese, min., 1.20; silicon, max., 0.3; copper, max., 0.05; nickel, max., 0.03; other impurities, max., 0.3 per cent and the remainder, magnesium.

Physical Properties: Standard tensile test specimens machined from plate or sheet stock in thicknesses between 0.016 inch and 0.025 inch have a minimum tensile strength of 32,000 pounds per square inch in the hard rolled temper, a maximum tensile strength of 35,000 pounds per square inch in the annealed temper and an elongation in 2 inches of 4 per cent in the hard rolled temper and 12 per cent in the annealed temper.

S.A.E. Standard No. 510 Alloy. — This alloy is generally used where moderate formability and mechanical properties are required.

Composition of No. 510: Aluminum, 3.3 to 4.7; manganese, min., 0.20; zinc, max., 0.3; silicon, max., 0.5; copper, max., 0.05; nickel, max., 0.03; other impurities, max., 0.3 per cent and the remainder, magnesium.

Physical Properties: Standard tensile test specimens machined from plate or sheet stock in thicknesses between 0.16 and 0.125 inch have a tensile strength of 36,000 pounds per square inch, minimum in the hard rolled temper and 38,000 pounds per square inch, maximum in the annealed temper; a yield strength of 25,000 pounds per square inch in the hard rolled temper and an elongation in 2 inches of 4 per cent in the hard rolled temper and 10 per cent in the annealed temper.

S.A.E. Standard No. 511 Alloy. — This alloy is used where high mechanical properties are required. It is available in the hard rolled and annealed tempers.

Composition of No. 511: Aluminum 5.8 to 7.2; manganese, min., 0.15; zinc, max., 0.3; silicon, max., 0.5; copper, max., 0.05; nickel, 0.03; other impurities, 0.3 per cent and the remainder, magnesium.

Physical Properties: Standard tension test specimens machined from plate or sheet stock in thicknesses between 0.016 inch and 0.125 inch have tensile strength of 39,000 pounds per square inch, minimum in the hard rolled temper and 42,000 pounds per square inch, maximum in the annealed temper; a yield strength of 28,000 pounds per square inch in the hard rolled temper and an elongation in 2 inches of 3 per cent in the hard rolled temper and 10 per cent in the annealed temper.

S.A.E. Standard No. 52 Alloy. — This is a general purpose alloy with moderate strength and fair weldability. It is especially suited for the production of thin wall tubing and other sections requiring good extrusion characteristics.

Composition of No. 52: Aluminum, 2.4 to 3.0; manganese, min., 0.20; zinc, 0.7 to 1.3; silicon, max., 0.5; copper, max., 0.05; nickel, max., 0.03; other impurities, max., 0.3 per cent and the remainder magnesium.

Physical Properties: Standard test specimens machined from solid bar stock and structural shapes have a minimum tensile strength of 37,000 pounds per square inch in extruded bars up to 1½ inches and 34,000 pounds per square inch in structural shapes; a yield strength of 25,000 pounds per square inch in the former and 17,000 pounds per square inch in the latter and an elongation in 2 inches of 12 per cent in the former and 10 per cent in the latter.

S.A.E. Standard No. 520 Alloy. — This alloy is used for extruded bars, rods and shapes with good strength and fair weldability.

Composition of No. 520: Aluminum, 5.8 to 7.2; manganese, min., 0.15; zinc, 0.4 to 1.0; silicon, max., 0.5; iron, max., 0.05; nickel, max., 0.03; other impurities, max., 0.3 per cent and the remainder, magnesium.

Physical Properties: Standard tension test specimens machined from solid bar stock and structural shapes have a minimum tensile strength of 40,000 pounds per square inch in extruded bars up to 1½ inches and 38,000 pounds per square inch in structural shapes; a yield strength of 26,000 pounds per square inch in the former and 23,000 pounds per square inch in the latter and an elongation in 2 inches of 12 per cent in the former and 10 per cent in the latter.

S.A.E. Standard No. 522 Alloy. — This is an extrusion alloy used for applications requiring maximum weldability.

Composition of No. 522: Manganese, min. 1.2; silicon, max. 0.3; copper, max. 0.05; nickel, max. 0.03; and calcium, 0.3 per cent; remainder, magnesium.

Physical Properties: Tensile strength is 30,000 pounds per square inch for extruded bars, ¼ inch to 1½ inches; 29,000 pounds per square inch for structural shapes and 28,000 pounds per square inch for hollow shapes. Elongation in 2 inches is 3 per cent for extruded bars, ¼ inch to 1½ inches and 2 per cent for structural and hollow shapes.

S.A.E. Standard Nos. 53, 531, 532 and 533 Alloys. — These are forging alloys. Nos. 53 and 533 are suitable for hammer forging. The former has somewhat better physical properties but the latter may be readily welded and contains no tin. No.

533 may also be press forged. Hammer forgings are normally more economical than press forgings but can only be used for applications involving moderate stresses. Press forging alloys Nos. 531 and 532 are used in applications involving higher stresses. No. 532 is stronger than No. 531 but more difficult to forge and is usually employed only for comparatively simple forgings requiring highest physical properties.

Composition of No. 53: Aluminum, 3.0 to 4.0; manganese, min. 0.2; zinc, max. 0.3; silicon, max. 0.3; copper, max. 0.3; nickel, max. 0.005; iron, max. 0.005 and tin, 4.0 to 6.0 per cent; remainder, magnesium.

Composition of No. 531: Aluminum, 5.8 to 7.2; manganese, minimum 0.15; zinc, 0.4 to 1.5; silicon, maximum 0.3; copper, max. 0.05; nickel, maximum 0.005 and iron, maximum 0.005 per cent; remainder, magnesium.

Composition of No. 532: Aluminum, 7.8 to 9.2; manganese, minimum 0.12; zinc, 0.2 to 0.8; silicon, maximum 0.3; copper, maximum 0.05; nickel, maximum 0.005 and iron, maximum 0.005 per cent; remainder, magnesium.

Composition of No. 533: Manganese, minimum 1.2; silicon, maximum 0.3; copper, maximum 0.05 and nickel, maximum 0.03 per cent; remainder, magnesium.

Physical Properties: In the as forged condition, No. 53 has a minimum tensile strength of 36,000; No. 531, 38,000; No. 532, 42,000; and No. 533, 30,000 pounds per square inch. Nos. 53 and 531 have a yield strength of 22,000; No. 532, 26,000; and No. 533, 18,000 pounds per square inch. No. 53 has a minimum elongation in 2 inches of 7; No. 531, 6; No. 532, 5; and No. 533, 3 per cent.

Miscellaneous Alloys

Beryllium Copper. — By alloying with copper, small amounts of beryllium and nickel, an alloy is obtained having high tensile strength, high fatigue limit and hardness, and also with relatively high electrical and thermal conductivity, depending upon the heat-treatment. This alloy has many applications in the electrical and aircraft industries or wherever strength, corrosion resistance, conductivity, non-

Compositions of Miscellaneous Alloys — Approximate Proportions

Alloys	Antimony	Bismuth	Copper	Iron	Lead	Nickel	Silver	Tin	Zinc
Brass, common yellow...	....	....	61.6	....	2.9	....	....	0.2	35.3
Brass, to be rolled.......	....	....	32	....	....	....	....	1.5	10
Brass castings, common..	....	....	20	....	....	....	....	2.5	1.25
Gun metal...............	....	....	8	....	....	....	....	1	....
Copper flanges...........	....	....	9	....	....	....	....	0.26	1
Bronze statuary..........	....	....	91.4	....	1.37	....	....	1.7	5.53
German silver*..........	....	....	....	....	....	....	....	....	....
Britannia metal.........	50	25	....	....	....	....	....	25	....
Chinese white copper.....	....	....	20.2	....	....	15.8	....	1.3	12.7
Pattern letters...........	15	15	....	....	70	....	....	....	....
Bell metal...............	....	....	4	....	....	....	....	1	....
Chinese gongs...........	....	....	40.5	....	....	....	....	9.2	....
White metal, ordinary...	28.4	....	3.7	....	....	....	....	14.2	3.7
Spelter..................	....	....	1	....	....	....	....	....	1
Type metal..............	1	....	....	....	3-7	....	....	....	....

* Nickel silver or German silver usually contains 17 to 19% nickel, 55 to 65% copper and the remainder zinc. There are various compositions.

Miscellaneous Lead-Tin-Antimony and Tin-Antimony-Copper Alloys

Name of Metal	Lead, Per Cent	Tin, Per Cent	Antimony, Per Cent	Copper, Per Cent	Zinc, Per Cent
Electrotype metal	93	3	4	....	....
Linotype metal	85	3	12	....	....
Stereotype metal	82	6	12	....	....
Bearing, French R.R.	80	12	8	....	....
Type metal	77.5	6.5	16	....	....
Metallic packing, French R.R.	76	14	10	....	....
Bearing, American R.R.	73.5	8	18.5	....	....
Piston packing, French R.R.	73	12	15	....	....
Bearing, French R.R.	70	20	10	....	....
Stereotype, Mackenzie metal	70	13	17	....	....
Type	70	10	18	2	....
Bearing, American R.R.	68	21	11	....	....
Stereotype	68	17	15	....	....
Type	63.2	12	24	0.8	....
Type	60	35	5	....	....
Type, common	60	10	30	....	....
Solder	60	39	1	....	....
Type	55.5	40	4.5	....	....
Type, best	50	25	25	....	....
Bearing, American R.R., No. 2	46	36.5	16.5	1	....
Hoyle's metal	42	46	12	....	....
Bearing, French R.R.	42	42	16	....	....
Bearing, Italian R.R.	37	38	25	....	....
Stereotype	35	60	5	....	....
White metal	33	54	10.6	2.4	....
English Britannia	....	94	5	1	....
English Britannia	....	85.5	9.7	1.8	3
English Britannia, sheet	....	90.6	7.8	1.6	....
English Britannia, cast	....	90.6	9.2	0.2	....
Bearing, Russian R.R.	....	90	8	2	....
Pewter	1.8	89.4	7	1.8	....
Queen's metal	....	88.5	7.1	3.5	0.9
Queen's metal (Footnote)	....	88.5	7	3.5	*
Jacoby metal	....	85	10	5	....
German Britannia	....	84	9	2	5
German Britannia	....	72	24	4	....
French, car bearings	....	83.3	11.2	5.5	....
Bearing, German R.R.	....	83	11	6	....
Britannia, Baumgartel	....	81.9	16.3	1.8	....
Bearing, Swiss R.R.	....	80	10	10	....
Britannia, Ashberry	....	77.8	19.4	2.8	....
Britannia, Ashberry	....	77.8	19.4	....	2.8
Bearing, German	....	76	17	7	....
Bearing, Karmarsch	....	71.4	7.2	21.4	....
Bearing, Karmarsch	....	70.8	19.7	9.5	....
Minofor, Britannia	....	68.5	18.2	3.3	10
Bearing, G. W. R., England	....	67	11	22	....
Bearing, French R.R.	....	67	22	11	....

*Bismuth, 1 per cent.

magnetic and non-sparking properties are essential. Beryllium copper is obtainable in the form of sheets or plates, strips, rods, wire, and tubes.

Composition: The patented composition follows: Beryllium, 2 to 2.25 per cent; nickel, 0.25 to 0.50 per cent; iron, usually less than 0.1 per cent; copper, remainder.

Heat-treatment: Alloys containing less than 1 per cent beryllium do not respond to heat-treatment. Alloys are slightly heat-treatable when the beryllium content ranges from 1 to 1.6 per cent, and they respond readily to heat-treatment when the beryllium content is 1.6 to 2.75 per cent. To harden and strengthen beryllium copper, it is only necessary to hold it at a temperature of 275 degrees C. (527 degrees F.) for a length of time depending upon the properties required. The heat-treated alloy may be allowed to cool gradually or it may be quenched in water. The heating period is about 3½ hours to attain maximum hardness and tensile strength, whereas, for better ductility and longer fatigue life, the heating time is reduced to 1½ or 2 hours. Under some conditions, the heat-treating temperature may be as low as 250 degrees C. or as high as 300 degrees C.

Mechanical Properties: Soft annealed beryllium copper sheet has a tensile strength of about 70,000 pounds per square inch, and this may be increased to about 175,000 by average heat-treatment. By cold-working and heat-treating, the strength may be increased to about 195,000 pounds per square inch.

The hardness of beryllium copper sheets 0.050 inch thick is about 110 Brinell for soft annealed sheets and 340 Brinell when average heat-treatment is applied. The specific gravity is 8.23. The foregoing data apply to an alloy containing 2 to 2.25 per cent beryllium.

Monel. — Monel is a nickel-copper alloy that is extensively used especially where a combination of high strength, toughness and corrosion resistance are essential. This alloy is unique in that the nickel and copper in it are refined from the ore without separation; hence Monel has been called a " natural alloy." Monel is more resistant to corrosion than either of its principal constituents, which are nickel and copper. It is used in various forms such as cold-drawn rods and bars, hot-rolled and forged rods and bars, cold-drawn wire, hot-rolled plate and standard cold-rolled sheets, cold-drawn seamless tubing, and different grades of castings.

Applications of Monel: As Monel metal possesses excellent resistance to corrosion either by natural waters (hard and soft) or salt water, it has been widely used for

Mechanical Properties of Monel

Form	Tensile Strength Lb. per Sq. In.	Yield Strength 0.2% Set, Lb. per Sq. In.	Elongation in 2 In., %
Cold-drawn Rod and Bar, Annealed...	70,000- 85,000	25,000-35,000	50-35
Cold-drawn Rod and Bar, as Drawn...	85,000-125,000	60,000-95,000	35-15
Hot-rolled Rod and Bar..............	80,000- 95,000	40,000-65,000	45-30
Forged Rod and Bar..................	80,000-110,000	60,000-85,000	40-20
Cold-drawn Wire, Annealed..........	70,000- 85,000	25,000-35,000	.....
Cold-drawn Wire, Regular Temper.....	110,000-140,000	....	.....
Cold-drawn Wire, Spring Temper......	140,000-175,000	....	.....
Hot-rolled Plate, as Rolled..........	80,000-110,000	40,000-90,000	55-25
Hot-rolled Plate, Annealed..........	70,000- 85,000	25,000-45,000	60-50
Standard Cold-rolled Sheet..........	65,000- 80,000	25,000-35,000	40-25
Cold-drawn Tubing, Annealed........	65,000- 80,000	25,000-35,000	35-25
Cold-drawn Tubing, as Drawn.......	90,000-105,000	60,000-75,000	20-15
Castings, Regular...................	60,000- 80,000	30,000-40,000	40-20
Castings, Grade " H "...............	70,000- 90,000	45,000-65,000	20-10
Castings, Grade " S "...............	90,000-115,000	70,000-90,000	3-1

parts of water meters, pumps, propeller shafts, propellers, pump shafts and pump impellers, condenser tubes and bolts, domestic hot-water storage tanks and heaters, etc. Monel offers good resistance to corrosion by all acids except those of a highly oxidizing character. It also offers useful resistance to corrosion by all the common organic acids and is practically free from corrosion by neutral and alkaline organic compounds. Monel is practically completely resistant to most alkaline solutions.

Approximate Composition. — There are various grades or types of Monel, depending upon the application and properties required. The nickel content varies from 65 to 67; copper, 29 to 30; iron, 0.9 to 1.5; silicon, 0.25 to 3; manganese, 0.3 to 1; carbon, 0.15 to 0.2 per cent. The composition known as *K*-Monel is practically the same as the other grades excepting that it contains about 2.75 per cent aluminum. *K*-Monel is ordinarily used when, in addition to high corrosion resistance, it is essential to have higher hardness and even greater strength than obtainable with the other alloys. *KR*-Monel is a free machining alloy with properties similar to *K*-Monel. It is produced in rod and wire forms and is adapted to automatic screw machine work. *KR*-Monel, like *K*-Monel, is non-magnetic.

Hardness of Monel. — The Brinell hardness (3000 Kg.) for cold-drawn rods and bars varies from 120 to 220; for hot-rolled rods and bars, from 130 to 170; for forged rods and bars, from 130 to 215; for hot-rolled plates as rolled, from 150 to 230, and annealed, from 125 to 170. Monel castings vary from 125 to 325.

Composition Brass or Ounce Metal. — This alloy, which is commonly used for parts subjected to hydrostatic pressures up to 350 pounds per square inch, is known commercially as composition metal 85-5-5-5 or ounce metal. The composition, according to A.S.T.M. standard specifications, follows: Copper, 84 to 86; tin, 4 to 6; lead, 4 to 6; zinc, 4 to 6; iron, 0.25; nickel, 1; and phosphorus, 0.05 per cent. The minimum tensile strength is given as 30,000, and yield point is 14,000 pounds per square inch. The elongation in 2 inches is 20 per cent.

Everdur. — This alloy, which contains copper, silicon and manganese in varying proportions, has the strength of mild steel and the corrosion-resisting properties of copper. The following mechanical properties relate to a wrought alloy containing 96 per cent of copper, 3 per cent of silicon, and 1 per cent of manganese. The tensile strength of soft rods and bars, in pounds per square inch, is about 50,000, and hard rods and bars, from 60,000 to 90,000; yield point for soft rods and bars is about 15,000, and for hard rods and bars, from 25,000 to 65,000 depending upon the diameter. Everdur is also made in the form of plates, sheets, strips, tubing, and it may be either hot- or cold-rolled.

Everdur possesses excellent welding characteristics and is readily welded by the oxy-acetylene, metallic or carbon arc, and resistance methods. Everdur welding rod shows excellent adherence to steel when applied by the carbon or metallic arc. Everdur sheet metal is especially suitable for water heating and storage tanks of welded construction.

Brass and Bronze Alloys that can be Welded. — Non-ferrous alloys like any other metal, must meet three basic requirements in order to be considered good welding materials: First, the welding power requirements must be reasonable; second, the welds must be satisfactory from a metallurgical and a physical point of view; and third, the life of the welding points or rolls must not be too short.

Pure or 100 per cent copper is poor in weldability, and so is brass containing 95 per cent copper and only 5 per cent zinc. With an increase in the zinc content of brass to 10 per cent, the weldability ranges from poor to fair. Brass containing 85 per cent copper and 15 per cent zinc is fair in weldability, whereas with a copper content of 80 per cent and a zinc content of 20 per cent, the weldability ranges from fair to good. As the copper content decreases below this percentage and the zinc content increases, the weldability becomes good.   A bronze alloy containing 95 per cent copper and 5 per cent tin is fair in weldability.   Commercial bronze with an analysis of 90 per cent copper and 10 per cent tin possesses good welding properties, while the weldability of 85 per cent copper and 15 per cent tin is very good.

Acid-resisting Alloy. — The following alloy is claimed to possess exceptional qualities with regard to its ability to resist the action of acids: Nickel, 66.6 per cent; chromium, 18 per cent; copper, 8.5 per cent; tungsten, 3.3 per cent; aluminum, 2 per cent; manganese, 1 per cent; titanium, 0.2 per cent; boron, 0.2 per cent and lithium, 0.2 per cent. This alloy is difficult to cast because it contracts considerably at the point of solidification.   It can be drawn into wire and is easy to work.

Norbide. — Norbide or Norton Boron Carbide is a compound of boron and carbon which is said to be the hardest material ever produced for commercial use. The hardness is considerably greater than that of silicon carbide and is next to the diamond.   Norbide in powdered form may be used for many lapping jobs in place of diamond dust.   For example, it has proved successful in grinding and lapping dies, cutting tools, and other parts made of cemented tungsten carbide and tantalum carbide.   In the molded form, Norbide offers high resistance to abrasion and may be used where an extremely hard smooth wear-resisting material is required.   One important application is in linings for the nozzles used in pressure or sand blasting. Norbide is produced in the electric furnace from carbon and boric acid.

Phos-Copper. — This is a brazing alloy that melts at approximately 1300 degrees F.   It may be substituted for expensive silver solders and is particularly useful for applications where strength or gas- and liquid-tight joints are required.   One application is on refrigerator parts where leakproof joints are essential.   This alloy possesses high tensile strength and excellent penetration; it is self-fluxing for most applications, has high ductility, high resistance to fatigue and corrosion, high electrical conductivity, and unusual fluidity at the brazing temperature.

Nichrome. — Nichrome is an alloy composed of nickel and chromium, which is practically non-corrosive and far superior to nickel in its ability to withstand high temperatures.   Its melting point is about 1550 degrees C. (about 2800 degrees F.). Nichrome is not injured by oxidation of the exposed surface at high temperatures, and it is very strong even when heated red hot.   The strength of a nichrome casting, when cold, varies from 45,000 to 50,000 pounds per square inch.   At a temperature of 1800 degrees F., nichrome has a tensile strength of about 30,000 pounds.

Bakelite. — This is a synthetic organic substance resulting from the chemical condensation of phenol and formaldehyde.   It may be used in either the liquid or solid form.   As a liquid it is used for impregnating porous materials, for enameling under heat and pressure and as a binding agent for molded compounds.   Solid bakelite is unaffected by water, steam, oils and almost all chemicals.   The solid substance does not melt or soften at ordinary machine temperatures and is destroyed only at temperatures in the vicinity of 300 degrees C.   It is easily and accurately molded.

Kirksite. — This is a zinc-base alloy, in both cast and rolled forms, that is especially useful in the aircraft or other industries for making low-cost sheet metal forming, blanking and trimming dies.   Even large forming or cutting dies may be made readily.   Forming dies are cast to shape and little or no machining or hand work is required.   Kirksite can be remelted repeatedly.   It is not intended to replace steel or cast-iron dies but is for use when the total production or manufacturing conditions justify a low-cost die construction.   Melting point, 717 degrees F., tensile strength, 37,800 pounds per square inch sand cast, and 62,000 rolled.   Rolled Kirksite is applied to blanking or trimming dies.

Powdered Metal Process

This is a process by means of which metal parts in large quantities can be made by the compressing and sintering of various powdered metals such as brass, bronze and iron. The compressing of the metal powder into the shape of the part to be made is done by accurately formed dies and punches in special types of presses known as briquetting machines. The "green" compressed pieces are then sintered in an atmosphere controlled furnace at high temperatures, causing the metal powder to be bonded together into a solid mass. A subsequent sizing or pressing operation and supplementary heat treatments may also be employed in some cases. The physical properties of the final product are usually comparable to those of cast or wrought products of the same composition. Using closely controlled conditions, steel of high hardness and tensile strength has also been made by this process.

Any desired porosity from 5 to 50 per cent can be obtained in the final product. Large quantities of porous bronze and iron bearings which are impregnated with oil for self-lubrication, have been made by this process. Other porous powder metal products are being used for the filtering of liquids and gases. Where continuous porosity is desired in the final product, the voids between particles are kept connected or open by mixing one per cent of zinc stearate or other finely powdered metallic soap throughout the metal powder before briquetting and then boiling this out in a low temperature baking before the piece is sintered.

The dense type of powdered metal products include refractory metal wire and sheet, cemented carbide tools, and electrical contact materials (products which could not be made as satisfactorily by other processes) and gears or other complex shapes which might also have been made by die-casting or the precise machining of wrought or cast metal.

Advantages of Powdered Metal Process. — This process is advantageous when irregular curves, eccentrics, radial projections, or recesses are required. Where a part has irregular holes, keyways, flat sides, splines or square holes that are not easily machined, powdered metal parts may solve the problem. Tapered holes and counterbores are easily produced. Axial projections can be formed but the permissible size depends on the extent to which the powder will flow into the die recesses. Projections not more than one-quarter the length of the part are practicable. Slots, grooves, blind holes, and recesses of varied depths are also obtainable.

Limiting Factors in Powdered Metal Process. — The number and variety of shapes which may be obtained are limited by the lack of plastic flow of powders, i.e., the difficulty with which they can be made to flow around corners. Tolerances in diameter usually cannot be held closer than 0.001 inch and tolerances in length are limited to 0.005 inch. This difference in diameter and length tolerances may be due to the elasticity of the powder and spring of the press.

Factors Affecting Design of Briquetting Tools. — High-speed steel is recommended for dies and punches and oil-hardening steel for strippers and knock-outs. One manufacturer specifies dimensional tolerances of 0.0002 inch and super-finished surfaces for these tools. Because of the high pressures employed and the abrasive character of certain refractory materials used in some powdered metal compositions, there is frequently a tendency toward severe wear of dies and punches. In such cases, carbide inserts, chrome plating, or highly resistant die steels are employed. With regard to the shape of the die, corner radii, fillets, and bevels should be used to avoid sharp corners. Feather edges, threads, and reentrant angles are usually impractical. The making of punches and dies is particularly exacting because allowances must be made for change in dimensions due to growth after briquetting and shrinkage or growth during sintering.

Etching and Etching Fluids

Etching Fluids for Different Metals. — A common method of etching names or simple designs upon steel is to apply a thin, even coating of beeswax or some similar substance which will resist acid; then mark the required lines or letters in the wax with a sharp-pointed scriber, thus exposing the steel (where the wax has been removed by the scriber point) to the action of an acid, which is finally applied. To apply a very thin coating of beeswax, place the latter in a silk cloth, warm the piece to be etched, and rub the pad over it. Regular coach varnish is also used instead of wax, as a "resist."

An etching fluid ordinarily used for carbon steel consists of nitric acid, 1 part; water, 4 parts. It may be necessary to vary the amount of water, as the exact proportion depends upon the carbon in the steel and whether it is hard or soft. For hard steel, use nitric acid, 2 parts; acetic acid, 1 part. For high-speed steel, nickel or brass, use nitro-hydrochloric acid (nitric, 1 part; hydrochloric, 4 parts). For high-speed steel it is sometimes better to add a little more nitric acid. For etching bronze, use nitric acid, 100 parts; muriatic acid, 5 parts. For brass, nitric acid, 16 parts; water, 160 parts; dissolve 6 parts potassium chlorate in 100 parts of water; then mix the two solutions and apply.

A fluid which may be used either for producing a frosted effect or for deep etching (depending upon the time it is allowed to act) is composed of 1 ounce sulphate of copper (blue vitriol); ¼ ounce alum; ½ teaspoonful of salt; 1 gill of vinegar, and 20 drops of nitric acid. For aluminum, use a solution composed of alcohol, 4 ounces; acetic acid, 6 ounces; antimony chloride, 4 ounces; water, 40 ounces.

Various acid-resisting materials are used for covering the surfaces of steel rules, etc., prior to marking off the lines on a graduating machine. When the graduation lines are fine and very closely spaced, as on machinists' scales which are divided into hundredths or sixty-fourths, it is very important to use a thin resist that will cling to the metal and prevent any under-cutting of the acid; the resist should also enable fine lines to be drawn without tearing or crumbling as the tool passes through it. One resist that has been extensively used is composed of about 50 per cent of asphaltum, 25 per cent of beeswax, and, in addition, a small percentage of Burgundy pitch, black pitch, and turpentine. A thin covering of this resisting material is applied to the clean polished surface to be graduated and, after it is dry, the work is ready for the graduating machine. For some classes of work, paraffin is used for protecting the surface surrounding the graduation lines which are to be etched. The method of application consists in melting the paraffin and raising its temperature high enough so that it will flow freely; then the work is held at a slight angle and the paraffin is poured on its upper surface. The melted paraffin forms a thin protective coating.

Coloring Metals

General Requirements in the Coloring of Metal Surfaces. — Copper is more susceptible to coloring processes and materials than any of the other metals, and hence the alloys containing large percentages of copper are readily given various shades of yellow, brown, red, blue, purple, and black. Alloys with smaller percentages of copper (or none at all) can be given various colors, but not as easily as if copper were the principal ingredient, and the higher the copper content, the more readily can the alloy be colored. The shades, and even the colors, can be altered by varying the density of the solution, its temperature and the length of time the object is immersed. They can also be altered by finishing the work in different ways. If a cotton buff is used, one shade will be produced; a scratch brush will produce another, etc. Thus to color work the same shade as that of a former lot, all the data in connection with these operations must be preserved so they can be repeated with exactness.

Cleaning Metals for Coloring. — Metal surfaces to be colored chemically must first be thoroughly cleaned. To remove grease from small parts, dip in benzine, ether or some other solvent for the grease. Boil large pieces in a solution of one part caustic soda and ten parts water. For zinc, tin or britannia metal, do not use caustic soda, but a bath composed of one part carbonate of soda or potash and ten parts water. After boiling, wash in clean water. Do not touch the clean surfaces with the fingers, but handle the objects by the use of tongs or wires.

Pickling Solutions or Dips for Coloring. — The grease removal should be followed by chemical cleansing, which principally serves the purpose of removing the greenish or brownish films which form on copper, brass, bronze, etc. The composition of the bath or mixture for pickling varies for different metals. For copper and its alloys, a mixture of 100 parts concentrated sulphuric acid (66 degrees Baumé) and 75 parts nitric acid (40 degrees Baumé) is sometimes used. If the metal is to be given a luster instead of a mat or dull finish, add about 1 part common salt to 100 parts of the pickling solution, by weight. A better dip for a mat surface consists of 90 parts nitric acid (36 degrees Baumé), 45 parts concentrated sulphuric acid, 1 part salt, and from 1 to 5 parts of sulphate of zinc, by weight. The composition of copper-zinc alloys will produce different color tones in the same dip and will affect the results of chemical coloring. After pickling, washing in water is necessary.

Another good method of removing these films is to soak the work in a pickle composed of spent aquafortis until a black scale is formed, and then dip it for a few minutes into a solution of 64 parts water, 64 parts commercial sulphuric acid, 32 parts aquafortis, and 1 part hydrochloric acid. After that the work should be thoroughly rinsed several times with distilled water.

Coloring Brass. — Polished brass pieces can be given various shades from golden yellow to orange by immersing them for a certain length of time in a solution composed of 5 parts, by weight, of caustic soda, 50 parts water and 10 parts copper carbonate. When the desired shade is reached, the work must be well washed with water and dried in sawdust. Golden yellow may be produced as follows: Dissolve 100 grains lead acetate in 1 pint of water and add a solution of sodium hydrate until the precipitate which first forms is re-dissolved; then add 300 grains red potassium ferro-cyanide. With the solution at ordinary temperatures, the work will assume a golden yellow, but heating the solution darkens the color, until at 125 degrees F. it has changed to a brown.

To Produce a Rich Gold Color. — Brass can be given a rich gold color by boiling it in a solution composed of 2 parts, by weight, of saltpeter, 1 part common salt, 1 part alum, 24 parts water and 1 part hydrochloric acid. Another method is to apply a mixture of 3 parts alum, 6 parts saltpeter, 3 parts sulphate of zinc, and 3 parts common salt. After applying this mixture the work is heated over a hot plate until it becomes black, after which it is washed with water, rubbed with vinegar, and again washed and dried.

White Colors or Coatings. — The white color or coating that is given to such brass articles as pins, hooks and eyes, buttons, etc., can be produced by dipping them in a solution made as follows: Dissolve 2 ounces fine-grain silver in nitric acid, then add 1 gallon distilled water, and put this into a strong solution of sodium chloride. The silver will precipitate in the form of chloride, and must be washed until all traces of the acid are removed. Testing the last rinse water with litmus paper will show when the acid has disappeared; then mix this chloride of silver with an equal amount of potassium bitartrate (cream of tartar), and add enough water to give it the consistency of cream. The work is then immersed in this solution and stirred around until properly coated, after which it is rinsed in hot water and dried in sawdust.

Silvering. — A solution for silvering, that is applicable to such work as gage or clock dials, etc., can be made by grinding together in a mortar 1 ounce of very dry chloride of silver, 2 ounces cream of tartar, and 3 ounces common salt, then add enough water to obtain the desired consistency and rub it onto the work with a soft cloth. This will give brass or bronze surfaces a dead-white thin silver coating, but it will tarnish and wear if not given a coat of lacquer. The ordinary silver lacquers that can be applied cold are the best. Before adding the water, the mixture, as it leaves the mortar, can be kept a long time if put in very dark colored bottles, but if left in the light it will decompose.

To Give Brass a Green Tint. — One solution that will produce the verde antique, or rust green, is composed of 3 ounces crystallized chloride of iron, 1 pound ammonium chloride, 8 ounces verdigris, 10 ounces common salt, 4 ounces potassium bitartrate and 1 gallon of water. If the objects to be colored are large, the solution can be put on with a brush. Several applications may be required to give the desired depth of color. Small work should be immersed and the length of time it remains in the solution will govern the intensity of the color.

Blackening Brass. — There are many different processes and solutions for blackening brass. Trioxide of arsenic, white arsenic or arsenious acid are different names for the chemical that is most commonly used. It is the cheapest chemical for producing black on brass, copper, nickel, German silver, etc., but has a tendency to fade, especially if not properly applied, although a coat of lacquer will preserve it a long time. A good black can be produced by immersing the work in a solution composed of 2 ounces white arsenic, 5 ounces cyanide of potassium, and 1 gallon of water. This should be boiled in an enamel or agate vessel, and used hot. Another cheap solution is composed of 8 ounces of sugar of lead, 8 ounces hyposulphite of soda and 1 gallon of water. This must also be used hot and the work afterwards lacquered to prevent fading. When immersed, the brass first turns yellow, then blue and then black, the latter being a deposit of sulphide of lead.

Preservation of Color. — After a part has been given the desired color, it is usually washed in water and then dried with clean sawdust. The colored surfaces of alloys are commonly protected and preserved by coating with a colorless lacquer, such as japan lacquer. Small parts are coated by dipping, and large ones by rubbing the lacquer on. The lacquer is hard after drying, and insoluble in most fluids; hence, it can be washed without injury.

Niter Process of Bluing Steel. — The niter process of bluing iron and steel is as follows: The niter or nitrate of potash (often called saltpeter) is melted in an iron pot and heated to about 600 degrees F. The parts to be blued are cleaned and polished and then immersed in the molten niter until a uniform color of the desired shade has been obtained. This requires only a few seconds. The articles are then removed and allowed to cool, after which the adhering niter is washed off in water. Parts which will not warp may be immersed immediately after removing from the niter bath. After cleaning, dry in sawdust, and then apply some suitable oil, such as linseed, to prevent rusting. To secure uniform coloring, a pyrometer should be used to gage the temperature of the niter, because a higher heat than 600 degrees F. will produce a dark color, whereas a lower heat will give a lighter shade.

Bluing Steel by Heat-treatment. — Polished steel parts can be given a blue color by heating in hot sand, wood ashes, or pulverized charcoal. Place the substance in an iron receptacle and stir constantly, while heating, in order to heat uniformly. Heat just hot enough to char a pine stick. The parts to be blued must be absolutely free from grease. They are placed in the heated substance until the desired color is obtained. Further coloring is then checked by immersing in oil. Small parts are sometimes heated by a Bunsen burner or by laying upon a heated plate. For a light blue color, heat in sand or wood ashes, and for a dark blue, use pulverized charcoal. The quality of the color depends largely upon the fineness of the finish. Still another method of coloring by heat is to immerse the parts in a molten bath of potassium nitrate and sodium nitrate. The coloring is then checked by plunging the work into boiling water.

Blue-black Finish. — To obtain a blue-black finish on small steel parts, use a mixture of 16 parts, by weight, of saltpeter and 2 parts of black oxide of manganese. This mixture is heated to a temperature of 750 degrees F. and the objects are immersed in it. The oxide of manganese is deposited on the work and must, therefore, be frequently replenished in the mixture.

Black Finish. — To obtain a black rust-protecting finish on hardened parts, temper, after hardening, in "heavy" cylinder oil; then immediately place the part with the oil on it in an oven having a temperature of from 300 to 350 degrees F. Remove the work in from 5 to 8 minutes, when the black finish is baked onto it.

Gun Metal Finish. — Several different chemical solutions have been used successfully for giving steel a gun metal finish or black color. Among these are the following: 1. Bismuth chloride, one part; copper chloride, one part; mercury chloride, two parts; hydrochloric acid, six parts; and water, fifty parts. 2. Ferric chloride, one part; alcohol, eight parts; and water, eight parts. 3. Copper sulphate, two parts; hydrochloric acid, three parts; nitric acid, seven parts; and perchloride of iron, eighty-eight parts. Other solutions have been prepared from nitric ether, nitric acid, copper sulphate, iron chloride, alcohol and water and from nitric acid, copper sulphate, iron chloride and water. The method of applying these and finishing the work is practically the same in all cases.

The surface is given a very thin coating with a soft brush or sponge that has been well squeezed, and is then allowed to dry. The work is then put in a closed retort to which steam is admitted and maintained at a temperature of about 100 degrees F., until the parts are covered with a slight rust. They are then boiled in clean water for about fifteen minutes and allowed to dry. A coating of black oxide will cover the surface, and this is scratch brushed. After brushing, the surface will show a grayish black. By repeating the sponging, steaming and brushing operations several times, a shiny black lasting surface will be obtained. For the best finishes, these operations are repeated as many as eight times.

Another process employs a solution of mercury chloride and ammonium chloride which is applied to the work three times and dried each time. A solution of copper sulphate, ferric chloride, nitric acid, alcohol and water is then applied three times and dried as before. A third solution of ferrous chloride, nitric acid and water is applied three times, and the work is boiled in clean water and dried each time. Finally, a solution of potassium chloride is applied and the work boiled and dried three times. The work is then scratch brushed and given a thin coating of oil. Ordnance for the French Government is treated in this way. The above methods are applicable to hardened and tempered steels, as a temperature of 100 degrees F. does not affect the hardness of the steel. For steels that will stand 600 degrees temperature without losing the desired hardness, better and much cheaper methods have been devised.

The American Gas Furnace Co. has developed a process employing a furnace with a revolving retort. The work is charged in this, together with well-burnt bone.

A chemical solution that gasifies when it enters the furnace is then injected into this retort while the work is heated to the proper temperature. This solution has been named "Carbonia." The color does not form a coating on the outside, as with the other processes, but a thin layer of the metal itself is turned to the proper color. By varying the temperature of the furnace, the time the work is in it, and the chemical, different colors can be produced from light straw to brown, blue, purple and black, or gun metal finish. Rough or sand-blasted surfaces will have a frosted appearance, while smooth polished surfaces will have a shiny brilliant appearance.

Browning Iron and Steel. — A good brown color can be obtained as follows: Coat the steel with ammonia and dry it in a warm place; then coat it with muriatic or nitric acid and dry it in a warm place; then place the steel in a solution of tannin or gallic acid and again dry it. The color can be deepened by placing the work near the fire, but it should be withdrawn the minute the desired shade is reached or it will turn black.

To Produce a Bronze Color. — A bronze-like color can be produced by exposing iron or steel parts to the vapors of heated *aqua regia*, dipping them in melted vaseline, and then heating them until the vaseline begins to decompose, when it is wiped off with a soft cloth. Another method of producing this bronze-brown color is to slightly heat the work, evenly cover the surfaces with a paste of antimony chloride (known as "bronzing salt"), and let the object stand until the desired color is obtained. The paste can be made more active by adding a little nitric acid.

To Produce a Gray Color. — A gray color on steel can be obtained by immersing the work in a heated solution of ten grains of antimony chloride, ten grains of gallic acid, 400 grains of ferric chloride and five fluid ounces of water. The first color to appear is pale blue, and this passes through the darker blues to the purple and, finally, to the gray. If immersed long enough, the metal will assume the gray color, but any of the intermediate colors may be produced. When used cold, this is also one of the bronzing solutions.

Mottled Coloring. — Mottled colors on steel can be produced by heating the objects to a good cherry-red for several minutes in cyanide of potassium, then pouring the cyanide off, and placing the receptacle containing the work back on the fire for five minutes. The contents are then quickly dumped into clean water. To heighten the colors, boil afterward in water and oil.

Coppering Solution. — A coppering solution for coating finished surfaces in order that lay-out lines may be more easily seen, is composed of the following ingredients: To 4 ounces of distilled water (or rain water) add all the copper sulphate (blue vitriol) it will dissolve; then add 10 drops of sulphuric acid. Test by applying to a piece of steel, and, if necessary, add four or five drops of acid. The surface to be coppered should be polished and free from grease. Apply the solution with clean waste, and, if a bright copper coating is not obtained, add a few more drops of the solution; then scour the surface with fine emery cloth, and apply rapidly a small quantity of fresh solution.

White Coatings for Laying Out Lines. — Powdered chalk or whiting mixed with alcohol is commonly used for coating finished metal surfaces preparatory to laying out lines for machining operations. Alcohol is preferable to water, because it will dry quicker and does not tend to rust the surface. This mixture can be applied with a brush and is more convenient than a coppering solution for general work. For many purposes, the surface can be coated satisfactorily by simply rubbing dry chalk over it.

MATERIALS

The Elements. — All matter is made up of one or more elements, each of which is a substance that cannot be separated into substances different from itself by ordinary chemical means.   Ninety-two different elements have been recognized.

The Elements — Symbols, Atomic Numbers and Weights, Melting Points

Name of Element	Symbol	Atomic Number	Atomic Weight*	Melting Point Deg. C.	Name of Element	Symbol	Atomic Number	Atomic Weight*	Melting Point Deg. C.
Actinium	Ac	89	....	....	Mercury	Hg	80	200.61	−38.87
Alabamine	Ab	85	....	....	Molybdenum	Mo	42	95.95	2620
Aluminum	Al	13	26.97	**659.7**	Neodymium	Nd	60	144.27	840
Antimony	Sb	51	121.76	**630.5**	Neon	Ne	10	20.183	−248.67
Argon	A	18	39.944	−189.2	Nickel	Ni	28	58.69	**1455**
Arsenic	As	33	74.91	814	Nitrogen	N	7	14.008	−209.86
Barium	Ba	56	137.36	850	Osmium	Os	76	190.2	2700
Beryllium	Be	4	9.02	1350	Oxygen	O	8	16.000	−218.4
Bismuth	Bi	83	209.00	271.3	Palladium	Pd	46	106.7	**1553**
Boron	B	5	10.82	2300	Phosphorus	P	15	30.98	44.1
Bromine	Br	35	79.916	−7.2	Platinum	Pt	78	195.23	**1773.5**
Cadmium	Cd	48	112.41	320.9	Polonium	Po	84	....	....
Calcium	Ca	20	40.08	810	Potassium	K	19	39.096	62.3
Carbon	C	6	12.01	>3500	Praseodymium	Pr	59	140.92	940
Cerium	Ce	58	140.13	640	Protoactinium	Pa	91	231	....
Cesium	Cs	55	132.91	28.5	Radium	Ra	88	226.05	960
Chlorine	Cl	17	35.457	−101.6	Radon	Rn	86	222	−110
Chromium	Cr	24	52.01	1615	Rhenium	Re	75	186.31	3000
Cobalt	Co	27	58.94	1480	Rhodium	Rh	45	102.91	1985
Columbium	Cb	41	92.91	1950	Rubidium	Rb	37	85.48	38.5
Copper	Cu	29	63.57	**1083**	Ruthenium	Ru	44	101.7	2450
Dysprosium	Dy	66	162.46	....	Samarium	Sm	62	150.43	>1300
Erbium	Er	68	167.2	....	Scandium	Sc	21	45.10	1200
Europium	Eu	63	152.0	....	Selenium	Se	34	78.96	220
Fluorine	F	9	19.000	−223	Silicon	Si	14	28.06	1420
Gadolinium	Gd	64	156.9	....	Silver	Ag	47	107.880	**960.5**
Gallium	Ga	31	69.72	29.75	Sodium	Na	11	22.997	97.5
Germanium	Ge	32	72.60	958.5	Strontium	Sr	38	87.63	800
Gold	Au	79	197.2	**1063**	Sulphur	S	16	32.06	113–119
Hafnium	Hf	72	178.6	1700	Tantalum	Ta	73	180.88	2850
Helium	He	2	4.003	<−272.2	Tellurium	Te	52	127.61	452
Holmium	Ho	67	163.5	....	Terbium	Tb	65	159.2	....
Hydrogen	H	1	1.0080	−259.14	Thallium	Tl	81	204.39	303.5
Illinium	Il	61	....	....	Thorium	Th	90	232.12	1845
Indium	In	49	114.76	155	Thulium	Tm	69	169.4	....
Iodine	I	53	126.92	113.5	Tin	Sn	50	118.70	**231.89**
Iridium	Ir	77	193.1	2350	Titanium	Ti	22	47.90	1800
Iron	Fe	26	55.85	1535	Tungsten	W	74	183.92	3370
Krypton	Kr	36	83.7	−157	Uranium	U	92	238.07	<1850
Lanthanum	La	57	138.92	826	Vanadium	V	23	50.95	1710
Lead	Pb	82	207.21	**327.4**	Virginium	Vi	87	....	....
Lithium	Li	3	6.940	186	Xenon	Xe	54	131.3	−112
Lutecium	Lu	71	174.99	1800	Ytterbium	Yb	70	173.04	1800
Magnesium	Mg	12	24.32	651	Yttrium	Y	39	88.92	1490
Manganese	Mn	25	54.93	1260	Zinc	Zn	30	65.38	**419.47**
Masurium	Ma	43	....	....	Zirconium	Zr	40	91.22	1900

Melting points shown in bold face type are often used as reference standards.   Melting points of commercial metals vary due to slight impurities.
* The values given are International atomic weights as of 1940.

Specific Gravity and Properties of Metals

Metal or Composition	Chemical Symbol	Specific Gravity	Weight per Cubic Inch, Pound	Weight per Cubic Foot, Pounds	Melting Point, Deg. F.	Linear Expansion per Unit Length per Deg. F.	Temp., Deg. F.*	Electric Conductivity Silver = 100
Aluminum	Al	2.70	0.0975	168.5	1220	0.0001244	68	63.0
Antimony	Sb	6.618	0.2390	413.0	1167	0.00000755	68	3.59
Barium	Ba	3.78	0.1365	235.9	1562	.....	.....	30.61
Bismuth	Bi	9.781	0.3532	610.3	520	0.0000077	68	1.40
Boron	B	2.535	0.0916	158.2	4172	.....	.....	.....
Brass: 80C., 20Z.	.....	8.60	0.3105	536.6	1823	.....	.....	.....
70C., 30Z.	.....	8.44	0.3048	526.7	1706	0.0001	76 to 212	.....
60C., 40Z.	.....	8.30	0.3018	521.7	1652	.....	.....	.....
50C., 50Z.	.....	8.20	0.2961	511.7	1616	.....	.....	.....
Bronze: 90C., 10T.	.....	8.78	0.3171	547.9	1841	0.0001	.....	.....
Cadmium	Cd	8.648	0.3123	539.6	610	.....	.....	24.38
Calcium	Ca	1.54	0.0556	96.1	1490	.....	.....	21.77
Chromium	Cr	6.93	0.2502	432.4	2939	.....	.....	16.00
Cobalt	Co	8.71	0.3145	543.5	2696	0.0000683	68	16.93
Copper	Cu	8.89	0.3210	554.7	1981	0.0000900	68	97.61
Gold	Au	19.3	0.6969	1204.3	1945	0.0000778	68	76.61
Iridium	Ir	22.42	0.8096	1399.0	4262	0.0000361	68	13.52
Iron, cast	Fe	7.03–7.73	0.254–0.279	438.7–482.4	1990–2300	0.0000555	68	14.57
Iron, wrought	Fe	7.80–7.90	0.282–0.285	486.7–493.0	2750	0.0000661	68	8.42
Lead	Pb	11.342	0.4096	707.7	621	0.0000163	212	.....
Magnesium	Mg	1.741	0.0628	108.6	1204	0.0001444	68–212	39.44
Manganese	Mn	7.3	0.2636	455.5	2300	0.0001294	68	15.75
Mercury (68° F.)	Hg	13.546	0.4892	845.3	−38	.....	.....	1.75
Molybdenum	Mo	10.2	0.3683	636.5	4748	0.0000294	68	17.60
Nickel	Ni	8.8	0.3178	549.1	2651	0.0000700	68	12.89
Platinum	Pt	21.37	0.7717	1333.5	3224	0.0000496	68	14.43
Potassium	K	0.870	0.0314	54.3	144	.....	.....	19.62
Silver	Ag	10.42–10.53	0.376–0.380	650.2–657.1	1761	0.0001025	68	100.00
Sodium	Na	0.9712	0.0351	60.6	207	.....	.....	31.98
Steel, Carbon	.....	.....	0.283–0.284	489.0–490.8	2500	0.00000633	68	12.00
Tantalum	Ta	16.6	0.5998	1035.8	5162	0.00000361	68	54.63
Tellurium	Te	6.25	0.2257	390.0	846	.....	.....	0.001
Tin	Sn	7.29	0.2633	454.9	449	0.0001496	64–212	14.39
Titanium	Ti	4.5	0.1621	280.1	3272	.....	.....	13.73
Tungsten	W	18.6–19.1	0.672–0.690	1161–1192	6098	0.0000239	32–212	14.00
Uranium	U	18.7	0.6753	1166.9	<3362	.....	.....	16.47
Vanadium	V	5.6	0.2022	394.4	3110	.....	.....	4.95
Zinc	Zn	7.04–7.16	0.254–0.259	439.3–446.8	788	0.00017	68	29.57

*Temperature given for each metal is that at which expansion coefficient shown in previous column was determined

Melting Points of Alloys of Low Fusing Point

Bismuth	Lead	Tin	Cadmium	Melting Point, Degrees F.	Bismuth	Lead	Tin	Melting Point, Degrees F.
50.0	25.0	12.5	12.5	149	20.0	40.0	40.0	293
50.1	26.6	13.3	10.0	158	19.0	38.0	43.0	298
38.4	30.8	15.4	15.4	160	18.1	36.2	45.7	304
27.5	27.5	10.5	34.5	167	17.3	34.6	48.1	311
50.0	34.5	9.3	6.2	171	16.6	33.2	50.2	316
50.0	25.0	25.0	....	187	16.0	36.0	48.0	311
50.0	31.2	18.8	....	201	15.3	38.8	45.9	309
55.6	....	33.3	11.1	203	14.8	40.2	45.0	307
50.0	....	25.0	25.0	203	14.0	43.0	43.0	309
47.0	35.5	17.5	....	208	13.7	44.8	41.5	320
42.1	42.1	15.8	....	226	13.3	46.6	40.1	329
40.0	40.0	20.0	....	235	12.8	49.0	38.2	342
36.5	36.5	27.0	....	243	12.5	50.0	37.5	352
33.3	33.4	33.3	....	253	11.7	46.8	41.5	333
30.8	38.4	30.8	....	266	11.4	45.6	43.0	329
28.5	43.0	28.5	....	270	11.2	44.4	44.4	320
25.0	50.0	25.0	....	300	10.8	43.2	46.0	318
23.5	47.0	29.5	....	304	10.5	42.0	47.5	320
22.2	44.4	33.4	....	289	10.2	41.0	48.8	322
21.0	42.0	37.0	....	289	10.0	40.0	50.0	324

Weights of American Woods, in Pounds per Cubic Foot

(United States Department of Agriculture)

Species	Green	Airdry	Species	Green	Airdry
Alder, red	46	28	Hickory, pecan	62	45
Ash, black	52	34	Hickory, true	63	51
Ash, commercial white	48	41	Honeylocust	61	..
Ash, Oregon	46	38	Larch, western	48	36
Aspen	43	26	Locust, black	58	48
Basswood	42	26	Maple, bigleaf	47	34
Beech	54	45	Maple, black	54	40
Birch	57	44	Maple, red	50	38
Birch, paper	50	38	Maple, silver	45	33
Cedar, Alaska	36	31	Maple, sugar	56	44
Cedar, eastern red	37	33	Oak, red	64	44
Cedar, northern white	28	22	Oak, white	63	47
Cedar, southern white	26	23	Pine, lodgepole	39	29
Cedar, western red	27	23	Pine, northern white	36	25
Cherry, black	45	35	Pine, Norway	42	34
Chestnut	55	30	Pine, ponderosa	45	28
Cottonwood, eastern	49	28	Pines, southern yellow:		
Cottonw'd, northern black	46	24	Pine, loblolly	53	36
Cypress, southern	51	32	Pine, longleaf	55	41
Douglas fir, coast region	38	34	Pine, shortleaf	52	36
Douglas fir, Rocky Mt. reg.	35	30	Pine, sugar	52	25
Elm, American	54	35	Pine, western white	35	27
Elm, rock	53	44	Poplar, yellow	38	28
Elm, slippery	56	37	Redwood	50	28
Fir, balsam	45	25	Spruce, eastern	34	28
Fir, commercial white	46	27	Spruce, Engelmann	39	23
Gum, black	45	35	Spruce, Sitka	33	28
Gum, red	50	34	Sycamore	52	34
Hemlock, eastern	50	28	Tamarack	47	37
Hemlock, western	41	29	Walnut, black	58	38

Specific gravity is a number indicating how many times a certain volume of a material is heavier than an equal volume of water. As the density of water differs slightly at different temperatures, it is the usual custom to make comparisons on the basis that the water has a temperature of 62 degrees F. The weight of one cubic inch of pure water at 62 degrees F. is 0.0361 pound. If the specific gravity of any material is known, the weight of a cubic inch of the material can, therefore, be found by multiplying its specific gravity by 0.0361.

Example: — The specific gravity of cast iron is 7.2. Find the weight of 5 cubic inches of cast iron.

$$7.2 \times 0.0361 \times 5 = 1.2996 \text{ pound.}$$

To find the weight per cubic foot of a material, the specific gravity of which is known, multiply the specific gravity by 62.355.

If the weight of a cubic inch of a material is known, the specific gravity is found by dividing the weight per cubic inch by 0.0361.

Example: — The weight of a cubic inch of gold is 0.697 pound. Find the specific gravity.

$$0.697 \div 0.0361 = 19.31.$$

If the weight per cubic foot of a material is known, the specific gravity is found by multiplying this weight by 0.01604.

Average Specific Gravity of Miscellaneous Substances

Substance	Sp. Gr.	Weight per Cubic Foot, Lbs.	Substance	Sp. Gr.	Weight per Cubic Foot, Lbs.
Asbestos.............	2.8	175	Gypsum.............	2.2	137
Asphaltum...........	1.4	87	Ice..................	0.9	56
Borax...............	1.75	109	Ivory................	1.85	115
Brick, common.......	1.8	112	Limestone...........	2.6	163
Brick, fire...........	2.3	144	Marble..............	2.7	169
Brick, hard..........	2.0	125	Masonry.............	2.4	150
Brick, pressed.......	2.15	134	Mica................	2.8	175
Brickwork, in mortar ..	1.6	100	Mortar..............	1.5	94
Brickwork, in cement..	1.8	112	Phosphorus..........	1.8	112
Cement, Portland (set)	3.1	194	Plaster of Paris.......	1.8	112
Chalk...............	2.6	163	Quartz...............	2.6	163
Charcoal.............	0.4	25	Salt, common.........	2.1	131
Coal, anthracite.......	1.5	94	Sand, dry............	1.6	100
Coal, bituminous......	1.27	79	Sand, wet............	2.0	125
Concrete.............	2.2	137	Sandstone...........	2.3	144
Earth, loose..........	1.2	75	Slate................	2.8	175
Earth, rammed.......	1.6	100	Soapstone...........	2.7	169
Emery...............	4.0	250	Soil, common black....	2.0	125
Glass................	2.6	163	Sulphur.............	2.0	125
Granite..............	2.65	166	Trap................	3.0	187
Gravel...............	1.75	109	Tile.................	1.8	112

The weight per cubic foot is calculated on the basis of the specific gravity, and considers the material solidly packed. With many substances this is practically impossible, and a cubic foot of ordinary anthracite coal, for example, does not weigh more than from 55 to 65 pounds, due to the air spaces between the pieces of coal.

Specific Gravity of Liquids. — The specific gravity of liquids is the number which indicates how much a certain volume of the liquid weighs compared with an equal volume of water, the same as in the case of solid bodies. The density of liquids is also often expressed in degrees on the hydrometer, an instrument for determining the density of liquids, provided with graduations made to an arbitrary scale. The hydrometer consists of a glass tube with a bulb at one end containing air, and arranged with a weight at the bottom so as to float in an upright position in the liquid, the density of which is to be measured. The depth to which the hydrometer sinks in the liquid is read off on the graduated scale. The most commonly used hydrometer is the Baumé. The value of the degrees on the Baumé scale differs according to whether the liquid is heavier or lighter than water. The specific gravity for liquids heavier than water equals 145 ÷ (145 − degrees Baumé). For liquids lighter than water, the specific gravity equals 140 ÷ (130 + degrees Baumé).

Specific Gravity of Gases. — The specific gravity of gases is the number which indicates their weight in comparison with that of an equal volume of air. The specific gravity of air is 1, and the comparison is made at 32 degrees F.

Specific Gravity of Gases
(At 32 degrees F.)

Gas	Sp. Gr.	Gas	Sp. Gr.	Gas	Sp. Gr.
Air................	1.000	Ether vapor......	2.586	Marsh gas......	0.555
Acetylene..........	0.920	Ethylene.........	0.967	Nitrogen........	0.971
Alcohol vapor.......	1.601	Hydrofluoric acid.	2.370	Nitric oxide.....	1.039
Ammonia...........	0.592	Hydrochloric acid.	1.261	Nitrous oxide...	1.527
Carbon dioxide....	1.520	Hydrogen........	0.069	Oxygen.........	1.106
Carbon monoxide....	0.967	Illuminating gas..	0.400	Sulphur dioxide..	2.250
Chlorine...........	2.423	Mercury vapor...	6.940	Water vapor....	0.623

1 cubic foot of air at 32 degrees F. and atmospheric pressure weighs 0.0807 pound.

Average Weights and Volumes of Fuels
Anthracite coal, 1 cubic foot = 55 to 65 pounds.

    1 ton (2240 pounds) = 34 to 41 cubic feet.

Bituminous coal, 1 cubic foot = 50 to 55 pounds.

    1 ton (2240 pounds) = 41 to 45 cubic feet.

Charcoal, 1 cubic foot = 18 to 18.5 pounds.

    1 ton (2240 pounds) = 120 to 124 cubic feet.

Coke 1 cubic foot = 28 pounds.

    1 ton (2240 pounds) = 80 cubic feet.

The average weight of a bushel of charcoal is 20 pounds; of a bushel of coke, 40 pounds; of a bushel of anthracite coal, 67 pounds; and of a bushel of bituminous coal, 60 pounds.

Weight of Wood. — The weight of seasoned wood per cord is approximately as follows, assuming about 70 cubic feet of *solid wood* per cord: Beech, 3300 pounds; chestnut, 2600 pounds; elm, 2900 pounds; maple, 3100 pounds; poplar, 2200 pounds; white pine, 2200 pounds; red oak, 3300 pounds; white oak, 3500 pounds.

Weight per Foot of Wood, Board Measure. — The following is the weight in pounds of various kinds of woods, commercially known as dry timber, per foot board measure: White oak, 4.16; white pine, 1.98; Douglas fir, 2.65; short-leaf yellow pine, 2.65; red pine, 2.60; hemlock, 2.08; spruce, 2.08; cypress, 2.39; cedar, 1.93; chestnut, 3.43; Georgia yellow pine, 3.17; California spruce, 2.08.

Specific Gravity of Liquids

Liquid	Sp. Gr.	Liquid	Sp. Gr.	Liquid	Sp. Gr.
Acetic acid...........	1.06	Fluoric acid....	1.50	Petroleum oil...	0.82
Alcohol, commerical...	0.83	Gasoline......	0.70	Phosphoric acid.	1.78
Alcohol, pure........	0.79	Kerosene......	0.80	Rape oil........	0.92
Ammonia.............	0.89	Linseed oil....	0.94	Sulphuric acid...	1.84
Benzine.............	0.69	Mineral oil....	0.92	Tar.............	1.00
Bromine.............	2.97	Muriatic acid..	1.20	Turpentine oil...	0.87
Carbolic acid........	0.96	Naphtha.......	0.76	Vinegar........	1.08
Carbon disulphide.....	1.26	Nitric acid....	1.50	Water..........	1.00
Cotton-seed oil......	0.93	Olive oil......	0.92	Water, sea......	1.03
Ether, sulphuric.......	0.72	Palm oil.......	0.97	Whale oil.......	0.92

Degrees on Baumé's Hydrometer Converted into Specific Gravity

Deg. Baumé	Specific Gravity		Deg. Baumé	Specific Gravity		Deg. Baumé	Specific Gravity	
	Liquids Heavier than Water	Liquids Lighter than Water		Liquids Heavier than Water	Liquids Lighter than Water		Liquids Heavier than Water	Liquids Lighter than Water
0	1.000	......	27	1.229	0.892	54	1.593	0.761
1	1.007	......	28	1.239	0.886	55	1.611	0.757
2	1.014	......	29	1.250	0.881	56	1.629	0.753
3	1.021	......	30	1.261	0.875	57	1.648	0.749
4	1.028	......	31	1.272	0.870	58	1.667	0.745
5	1.036	......	32	1.283	0.864	59	1.686	0.741
6	1.043	......	33	1.295	0.859	60	1.706	0.737
7	1.051	......	34	1.306	0.854	61	1.726	0.733
8	1.058	......	35	1.318	0.849	62	1.747	0.729
9	1.066	......	36	1.330	0.843	63	1.768	0.725
10	1.074	1.000	37	1.343	0.838	64	1.790	0.721
11	1.082	0.993	38	1.355	0.833	65	1.813	0.718
12	1.090	0.986	39	1.368	0.828	66	1.836	0.714
13	1.099	0.979	40	1.381	0.824	67	1.859	0.710
14	1.107	0.972	41	1.394	0.819	68	1.883	0.707
15	1.115	0.966	42	1.408	0.814	69	1.908	0.704
16	1.124	0.959	43	1.422	0.809	70	1.933	0.700
17	1.133	0.952	44	1.436	0.805	71	1.959	0.696
18	1.142	0.946	45	1.450	0.800	72	1.986	0.693
19	1.151	0.940	46	1.465	0.796	73	2.014	0.689
20	1.160	0.933	47	1.480	0.791	74	2.042	0.686
21	1.169	0.927	48	1.495	0.787	75	2.071	0.683
22	1.179	0.921	49	1.510	0.782	76	2.101	0.679
23	1.189	0.915	50	1.526	0.778	77	2.132	0.676
24	1.198	0.909	51	1.542	0.773	78	2.164	0.673
25	1.208	0.903	52	1.559	0.769	79	2.197	0.669
26	1.219	0.897	53	1.576	0.765	80	2.230	0.666

Weights of Non-Ferrous Metal Sheets — 1

American Wire or Brown & Sharpe Gage No.	Thickness, Inch	Approximate Weight, Pounds per Square Foot				
		Copper*	Yellow Brass	Tobin Bronze	5 Per Cent Phosphor-Bronze	Everdur 1010
0000	0.4600	21.33	20.27	20.14	21.20	20.40
000	0.4096	18.99	18.05	17.93	18.88	18.17
00	0.3648	16.92	16.07	16.41	16.81	16.18
0	0.3249	15.06	14.32	14.23	14.98	14.41
1	0.2893	13.41	12.75	12.67	13.33	12.83
2	0.2576	11.94	11.35	11.28	11.87	11.43
3	0.2294	10.64	10.11	10.04	10.57	10.17
4	0.2043	9.473	9.002	8.943	9.414	9.061
5	0.1819	8.434	8.015	7.963	8.382	8.068
6	0.1620	7.512	7.138	7.092	7.465	7.185
7	0.1443	6.691	6.358	6.317	6.649	6.400
8	0.1285	5.958	5.662	5.625	5.921	5.699
9	0.1144	5.304	5.041	5.008	5.272	5.074
10	0.1019	4.725	4.490	4.461	4.696	4.519
11	0.0907	4.206	3.997	3.971	4.180	4.023
12	0.0808	3.747	3.560	3.537	3.723	3.584
13	0.0720	3.338	3.173	3.152	3.318	3.193
14	0.0641	2.972	2.825	2.807	2.954	2.843
15	0.0571	2.648	2.516	2.500	2.631	2.532
16	0.0508	2.355	2.238	2.223	2.341	2.253
17	0.0453	2.100	1.996	1.983	2.087	2.009
18	0.0403	1.869	1.776	1.764	1.857	1.787
19	0.0359	1.665	1.582	1.572	1.654	1.592
20	0.0320	1.484	1.410	1.401	1.475	1.419
21	0.0285	1.321	1.256	1.248	1.314	1.264
22	0.0253	1.178	1.119	1.112	1.170	1.127
23	0.0226	1.048	0.9958	0.9893	1.041	1.002
24	0.0201	0.9320	0.8857	0.8799	0.9263	0.8915
25	0.0179	0.8300	0.7887	0.7836	0.8248	0.7939
26	0.0159	0.7373	0.7006	0.6960	0.7327	0.7052
27	0.0142	0.6584	0.6257	0.6216	0.6544	0.6298
28	0.0126	0.5842	0.5552	0.5516	0.5806	0.5588
29	0.0113	0.5240	0.4979	0.4947	0.5207	0.5012
30	0.0100	0.4637	0.4406	0.4377	0.4608	0.4435
31	0.0089	0.4127	0.3922	0.3897	0.4102	0.3947
32	0.0080	0.3709	0.3525	0.3502	0.3686	0.3548
33	0.0071	0.3292	0.3129	0.3109	0.3272	0.3149
34	0.0063	0.2921	0.2776	0.2758	0.2903	0.2794
35	0.0056	0.2597	0.2468	0.2452	0.2581	0.2484
36	0.0050	0.2318	0.2203	0.2189	0.2304	0.2218
37	0.0045	0.2087	0.1983	0.1970	0.2074	0.1996
38	0.0040	0.1855	0.1763	0.1752	0.1844	0.1774
39	0.0035	0.1623	0.1542	0.1532	0.1613	0.1552
40	0.0031	0.1437	0.1366	0.1357	0.1429	0.1375

* Copper sheets can also be obtained in fractional-inch thicknesses varying by sixteenths of an inch from 1/16 to 2 inches.

Weights of Non-Ferrous Metal Sheets — 2

American Wire or Brown & Sharpe Gage No.	Thickness, Inch	Approximate Weight, Pounds per Square Foot				
		S.A.E. Aluminum Alloys Nos. 26 and 27	S.A.E. Aluminum Alloy No. 28	Aluminum Commercially Pure (99 to 99.4 Per Cent)	Nickel Silver 18%*	Nickel Silver 20%–30%
0000	0.4600	6.680	6.410	6.490	20.93	21.20
000	0.4096	5.950	5.710	5.780	18.64	18.88
00	0.3648	5.290	5.090	5.140	16.60	16.81
0	0.3249	4.720	4.530	4.580	14.78	14.97
1	0.2893	4.200	4.030	4.080	13.16	13.33
2	0.2576	3.738	3.591	3.632	11.72	11.87
3	0.2294	3.329	3.198	3.234	10.44	10.57
4	0.2043	2.964	2.848	2.880	9.296	9.414
5	0.1819	2.640	2.536	2.565	8.277	8.382
6	0.1620	2.351	2.258	2.284	7.372	7.466
7	0.1443	2.094	2.012	2.034	6.566	6.649
8	0.1285	1.865	1.792	1.812	5.847	5.921
9	0.1144	1.660	1.595	1.613	5.206	5.272
10	0.1019	1.479	1.420	1.437	4.637	4.696
11	0.0907	1.316	1.264	1.279	4.127	4.179
12	0.0808	1.172	1.126	1.139	3.677	3.724
13	0.0720	1.045	1.004	1.015	3.276	3.318
14	0.0641	0.930	0.894	0.904	2.917	2.954
15	0.0571	0.829	0.796	0.805	2.598	2.631
16	0.0508	0.737	0.708	0.716	2.312	2.341
17	0.0453	0.657	0.631	0.639	2.061	2.087
18	0.0403	0.585	0.562	0.568	1.834	1.857
19	0.0359	0.5210	0.5010	0.5060	1.634	1.655
20	0.0320	0.4640	0.4460	0.4510	1.456	1.474
21	0.0285	0.4140	0.3970	0.4020	1.297	1.313
22	0.0253	0.3671	0.3527	0.3567	1.156	1.171
23	0.0226	0.3280	0.3150	0.3186	1.028	1.041
24	0.0201	0.2917	0.2802	0.2834	0.9146	0.9262
25	0.0179	0.2597	0.2495	0.2524	0.8145	0.8248
26	0.0159	0.2307	0.2216	0.2242	0.7235	0.7327
27	0.0142	0.2060	0.1980	0.2002	0.6462	0.6544
28	0.0126	0.1828	0.1756	0.1776	0.5734	0.5807
29	0.0113	0.1640	0.1575	0.1593	0.5142	0.5207
30	0.0100	0.1451	0.1394	0.1410	0.4550	0.4608
31	0.0089	0.1296	0.1245	0.1259	0.4050	0.4101
32	0.0080	0.1154	0.1108	0.1121	0.3640	0.3686
33	0.0071	0.1027	0.0987	0.0998	0.3231	0.3272
34	0.0063	0.0914	0.0878	0.0888	0.2867	0.2903
35	0.0056	0.0814	0.0782	0.0791	0.2548	0.2580
36	0.0050	0.0726	0.0697	0.0705	0.2275	0.2304
37	0.0045	0.0646	0.0620	0.0627	0.2048	0.2074
38	0.0040	0.0576	0.0553	0.0560	0.1820	0.1843
39	0.0035	0.0512	0.0492	0.0498	0.1593	0.1613
40	0.0031	0.0456	0.0438	0.0443	0.1411	0.1429

* Multiply weights in this column by 0.9905 for 10 per cent nickel-silver and by 0.9937 for 15 per cent nickel-silver.

Weights of Magnesium Alloy Sheets and Plates — 1

Weights are for Dowmetal M (S.A.E. No. 51). See also *Note 2* at end of table.

Thickness, Inch	American or B. & S. Gage No.	Weight, Pounds per Square Foot	Standard Widths, Inches	Standard Lengths, Inches				
				60	72	96	120	144
				Weights in Pounds				
0.016	26	0.147	24	1.47	1.76	....	....	....
0.018	25	0.166	24	1.66	1.99	....	....	....
0.020	24	0.184	24	1.84	2.21	2.94	....	....
			30	2.30	2.76	....	....	....
0.023	23	0.212	24	2.12	2.54	3.39	....	....
			30	2.65	3.18	....	....	....
0.025	22	0.230	24	2.3	2.76	3.68	....	....
			30	2.87	3.45	....	....	....
0.028	21	0.258	24	2.58	3.10	4.13	....	....
			30	3.22	3.87	....	....	....
0.032	20	0.295	24	2.95	3.54	4.72	5.9	....
			30	3.69	4.42	5.90	7.38	....
			36	4.42	5.31	7.08	....	....
0.036	19	0.332	24	3.32	3.98	5.31	6.64	....
			30	4.15	4.98	6.64	8.30	....
			36	4.98	5.98	7.97	....	....
0.040	18	0.369	24	3.69	4.43	5.90	7.38	....
			30	4.61	5.53	7.38	9.22	....
			36	5.53	6.64	8.85	11.1	....
0.045	17	0.415	24	4.15	4.98	6.64	8.30	....
			30	5.19	6.22	8.30	10.4	....
			36	6.22	7.47	9.96	12.5	....
0.051	16	0.470	24	4.70	5.64	7.52	9.40	11.3
			30	5.87	7.05	9.40	11.7	14.1
			36	7.05	8.46	11.3	14.1	16.9
			42	8.22	9.87	13.2	16.4	19.7
0.057	15	0.525	24	5.25	6.30	8.4	10.5	12.6
			30	6.57	7.88	10.5	13.1	15.8
			36	7.88	9.45	12.6	15.8	18.9
			42	9.19	10.1	14.7	18.4	22.1
0.064	14	0.590	24	5.9	7.07	9.45	11.8	14.2
			30	7.38	8.85	11.8	14.7	17.7
			36	8.85	10.6	14.2	17.7	21.2
			42	10.3	12.4	16.5	20.6	24.8
0.072	13	0.662	24	6.54	7.85	10.5	13.1	15.7
			30	8.17	9.80	13.1	16.3	19.6
			36	9.80	11.8	15.7	19.6	23.5
			42	11.4	13.7	18.3	22.9	27.4
0.081	12	0.746	24	7.46	8.96	11.9	14.9	17.9
			30	9.34	11.2	14.9	18.6	22.4
			36	11.2	13.4	17.9	22.4	26.8
			42	13.0	15.7	20.9	26.1	31.3
			48	14.9	17.9	23.9	29.8	35.8
0.091	11	0.838	24	8.38	10.1	13.4	16.8	20.1
			30	10.5	12.6	16.8	20.9	25.1
			36	12.6	15.1	20.1	25.1	30.2
			42	14.7	17.6	23.5	29.3	35.2
			48	16.8	20.1	26.8	33.5	40.2
0.102	10	0.940	24	9.4	11.3	15.0	18.8	22.6
			30	11.7	14.1	18.8	23.5	28.2
			36	14.1	16.9	22.6	28.2	33.8
			42	16.4	19.7	26.3	32.9	39.4
			48	18.8	22 6	30 0	37.6	45.1

Weights of Magnesium Alloy Sheets and Plates — 2

Thickness, Inch	American or B. & S. Gage No.	Weight, Pounds per Square Foot	Standard Widths, Inches	Standard Lengths, Inches				
				60	72	96	120	144
				Weights in Pounds				
0.114	9	1.05	24	10.5	12.6	16.8	21.0	25.2
			30	13.1	15.7	21.0	26.2	31.5
			36	15.7	18.9	25.2	31.5	37.8
			42	18.4	22.1	29.4	36.7	44.1
			48	21.0	25.2	33.6	42.0	50.4
0.128	8	1.18	24	11.8	14.2	18.9	23.6	28.3
			30	14.7	17.7	23.6	29.4	35.4
			36	17.7	21.2	28.3	35.4	42.5
			42	20.6	24.8	33.0	41.3	49.5
			48	23.6	28.3	37.8	47.2	56.6
0.156	5⁄32	1.44	24	14.4	17.3	23.1	28.8	34.6
			30	18.0	21.6	28.8	36.0	43.2
			36	21.6	25.9	34.6	43.2	51.9
			42	25.2	30.2	40.3	50.4	60.5
			48	28.8	34.6	46.1	57.6	69.1
0.188	3⁄16	1.73	24	17.3	20.8	27.7	34.6	41.5
			30	21.6	25.9	34.6	43.3	51.9
			36	25.9	31.2	41.5	51.9	62.3
			42	30.3	36.4	48.4	60.5	72.6
			48	34.6	41.5	55.4	69.2	82.5
0.219	7⁄32	2.02	24	20.2	24.2	32.3	40.4	48.5
			30	25.2	30.3	40.4	50.5	60.6
			36	30.3	36.4	48.5	60.6	72.7
			42	35.4	42.4	56.6	70.7	84.9
			48	40.4	48.5	64.7	80.8	....
0.250	1⁄4	2.30	24	23.0	27.6	36.8	46.0	55.2
			30	28.8	34.5	46.0	57.5	69.0
			36	34.5	41.4	55.2	69.0	82.8
			42	40.3	48.3	54.4	80.5	....
			48	46.0	55.2	73.6	92.0	....
0.313	5⁄16	2.88	24	28.8	34.6	46.1	57.6	69.1
			30	36.0	43.2	57.6	72.0	86.4
			36	43.2	51.8	69.1	86.4	....
			42	50.4	60.5	80.6	....	....
			48	57.6	69.1	92.2	....	....
0.375	3⁄8	3.46	24	34.6	41.5	55.4	69.2	83.0
			30	43.3	51.9	69.2	86.5	....
			36	51.9	62.3	83.0	....	....
			42	60.6	72.7	....	....	....
			48	69.2	83.0	....	....	....
0.437	7⁄16	4.03	24	40.3	48.4	64.5	....	....
			30	50.4	60.5	80.6	....	....
			36	60.5	72.5	....	....	....
			42	70.5	84.6	....	....	....
			48	80.6	....	....	....	....
0.500	1⁄2	4.61	24	46.1	55.3	73.8	92.2	....
			30	57.6	69.2	92.2	....	....
			36	69.2	83.0	....	....	....
			42	80.7	....	....	....	....
			48	92.2	....	....	....	....

Note 1: Sheet is defined as rolled metal up to 0.250 inch thickness. Material 0.250 inch thick and over is designated as plate.

Note 2: The weights in this table are for Dowmetal M(S.A.E. No. 51). To obtain comparable weights for Dowmetal FS-1 (S.A.E. No. 510), multiply the weights shown by 1.005. For Dowmetal J-1 (S.A.E. No. 511), multiply the weights shown by 1.022.

Weight of Brass, Aluminum, and Copper Rods and Bars, Pounds per Foot*

Diam. or Size*	BRASS			ALUMINUM		COPPER		
	Round	Hex.*	Square	Round	Hex.*	Round	Hex.*	Square
1/8	0.045	0.049	0.057	0.015	.....	0.047	0.052	0.060
5/32	0.070	0.077	0.090	0.023	.....	.....	.....	.....
3/16	0.101	0.112	0.129	0.034	0.037	0.107	0.118	0.136
7/32	0.138	0.152	0.176	0.046	0.051	.....	.....	.....
1/4	0.181	0.199	0.230	0.060	0.066	0.190	0.209	0.242
9/32	0.229	0.252	0.291	0.076	.....	.....	.....	.....
5/16	0.282	0.311	0.360	0.093	0.103	0.296	0.327	.377
11/32	0.342	0.377	0.435	0.113	0.125	.....	.....	.....
3/8	0.407	0.448	0.518	0.135	0.149	0.427	0.471	.543
7/16	0.554	0.611	0.705	0.184	0.203	0.581	0.640	0.740
1/2	0.723	0.798	0.922	0.240	0.264	0.759	0.837	0.966
9/16	0.916	1.010	1.166	0.304	0.335	0.960	1.06	1.22
5/8	1.130	1.246	1.439	0.375	0.414	1.19	1.31	1.51
1 1/16	1.368	1.509	1.742	0.454	0.501	1.43	1.58	1.83
3/4	1.628	1.795	2.073	0.540	0.595	1.71	1.88	2.17
1 3/16	1.911	2.107	2.433	0.633	0.700	2.00	2.21	2.55
7/8	2.216	2.444	2.822	0.735	0.811	2.32	2.56	2.96
1 5/8	2.544	2.806	3.240	0.844	0.930	2.67	2.94	3.40
1	2.89	3.19	3.68	0.961	1.06	3.04	3.35	3.86
1 1/16	3.26	3.60	4.16	1.08	1.20	3.43	3.78	4.36
1 1/8	3.66	4.04	4.66	1.22	1.34	3.84	4.24	4.89
1 3/16	4.08	4.50	5.19	1.35	1.49	4.28	4.72	5.45
1 1/4	4.52	4.98	5.76	1.50	1.65	4.74	5.23	6.04
1 5/16	4.98	5.50	6.35	1.66	1.82	5.23	5.76	6.66
1 3/8	5.47	6.03	6.97	1.81	2.00	5.74	6.33	7.31
1 7/16	5.98	6.59	7.61	1.99	2.18	6.27	6.92	7.98
1 1/2	6.51	7.18	8.29	2.16	2.38	6.83	7.53	8.69
1 9/16	7.06	7.79	8.99	2.34	2.58	7.41	8.17	9.43
1 5/8	7.64	8.43	9.73	2.54	2.80	8.01	8.84	10.2
1 11/16	8.24	9.09	10.49	2.74	.....	8.64	9.53	11.0
1 3/4	8.86	9.77	11.29	2.98	3.25	9.29	10.2	11.8
1 13/16	9.51	10.48	12.11	3.15	.....	9.97	11.0	12.7
1 7/8	10.18	11.22	12.96	3.37	3.73	10.7	11.8	13.6
1 15/16	10.86	11.98	13.83	3.60	.....	11.4	12.6	14.5
2	11.58	12.76	14.74	3.84	4.23	12.1	13.4	15.5
2 1/16	.....	.....	.....	4.09	.....	.....	.....	.....
2 1/8	13.07	14.41	16.64	4.34	.....	13.7	15.1	17.4
2 3/16	.....	.....	.....	4.59	.....	.....	.....	.....
2 1/4	14.65	16.16	18.66	4.86	.....	15.4	16.9	19.6
2 5/16	.....	.....	.....	5.13	.....	.....	.....	.....
2 3/8	16.33	18.00	20.79	5.41	.....	17.1	18.9	21.8
2 7/16	.....	.....	.....	5.70	.....	.....	.....	.....
2 1/2	18.09	19.95	23.04	6.00	.....	19.0	20.9	24.2
2 9/16	.....	.....	.....	6.30	.....	.....	.....	.....
2 5/8	19.95	21.99	25.40	6.62	.....	20.9	23.1	26.6
2 3/4	21.89	24.14	27.88	7.26	.....	23.0	25.3	29.2
2 7/8	23.93	26.38	30.47	7.94	.....	25.1	27.7	31.9
3	26.05	28.73	33.17	8.64	.....	27.3	30.1	34.8

* Weights per foot are based upon the following weights per cubic inch: Brass (free-cutting) 0.307; aluminum alloy (screw machine stock) 0.1018; copper, 0.322 lb. per cu. in. Size of hexagon equals distance across flats.

Areas and Weights of Magnesium Alloy Rods and Bars

Round Bars			Square Bars			Hexagonal Bars		
Diameter, Inches	Area, Square Inches	Weight, Pounds per Foot	Width, Inches	Area, Square Inches	Weight, Pounds per Foot	Width Across Flats, Inches	Area, Square Inches	Weight, Pounds per Foot
1/8	0.012	0.009	1/8	0.016	0.012	1/4	0.054	0.041
3/16	0.028	0.022	3/16	0.035	0.027	5/16	0.084	0.064
1/4	0.049	0.038	1/4	0.063	0.048	3/8	0.122	0.094
5/16	0.077	0.059	5/16	0.098	0.075	7/16	0.166	0.127
3/8	0.110	0.084	3/8	0.141	0.108	1/2	0.216	0.166
7/16	0.150	0.115	7/16	0.191	0.147	9/16	0.274	0.210
1/2	0.196	0.151	1/2	0.250	0.192	5/8	0.338	0.259
9/16	0.248	0.190	9/16	0.316	0.243	11/16	0.409	0.314
5/8	0.307	0.236	5/8	0.391	0.300	3/4	0.487	0.374
11/16	0.371	0.285	11/16	0.473	0.363	13/16	0.571	0.438
3/4	0.442	0.339	3/4	0.563	0.432	7/8	0.663	0.509
13/16	0.518	0.398	13/16	0.660	0.507	15/16	0.761	0.584
7/8	0.601	0.462	7/8	0.766	0.588	1	0.865	0.665
15/16	0.690	0.530	15/16	0.879	0.675	1 1/16	0.977	0.750
1	0.785	0.603	1	1.00	0.768	1 1/8	1.09	0.837
1 1/16	0.887	0.681	1 1/16	1.13	0.868	1 3/16	1.22	0.937
1 1/8	0.994	0.763	1 1/8	1.27	0.975	1 1/4	1.35	1.04
1 3/16	1.11	0.852	1 3/16	1.41	1.08	1 5/16	1.49	1.14
1 1/4	1.23	0.945	1 1/4	1.56	1.20	1 3/8	1.64	1.26
1 5/16	1.35	1.04	1 5/16	1.72	1.32	1 7/16	1.79	1.37
1 3/8	1.48	1.14	1 3/8	1.89	1.45	1 1/2	1.95	1.50
1 7/16	1.62	1.24	1 7/16	2.07	1.59	1 9/16	2.11	1.62
1 1/2	1.77	1.36	1 1/2	2.25	1.73	1 5/8	2.28	1.75
1 9/16	1.92	1.47	1 9/16	2.44	1.87	1 11/16	2.46	1.89
1 5/8	2.07	1.59	1 5/8	2.64	2.03	1 3/4	2.65	2.03
1 11/16	2.24	1.72	1 11/16	2.85	2.19	1 13/16	2.84	2.18
1 3/4	2.40	1.84	1 3/4	3.06	2.38	1 7/8	3.04	2.33
1 13/16	2.58	1.98	1 13/16	3.29	2.53	1 15/16	3.25	2.50
1 7/8	2.76	2.12	1 7/8	3.52	2.70	2	3.46	2.66
1 15/16	2.95	2.26	1 15/16	3.75	2.88	2 1/8	3.91	3.00
2	3.14	2.41	2	4.00	3.07	2 1/4	4.38	3.36
2 1/8	3.55	2.73	2 1/8	4.52	3.47	2 3/8	4.88	3.75
2 1/4	3.98	3.06	2 1/4	5.06	3.89	2 1/2	5.41	4.15
2 3/8	4.43	3.40	2 3/8	5.64	4.33	2 5/8	5.96	4.58
2 1/2	4.91	3.77	2 1/2	6.25	4.80	2 3/4	6.54	5.02
2 5/8	5.41	4.15	2 5/8	6.89	5.29	2 7/8	7.14	5.48
2 3/4	5.94	4.56	2 3/4	7.56	5.81	3	7.79	5.98
2 7/8	6.48	4.98	2 7/8	8.25	6.34	3 1/4	9.14	7.02
3	7.07	5.43	3	9.00	6.91	3 1/2	10.6	8.14
3 1/8	7.67	5.89	3 1/8	9.77	7.50	3 3/4	12.2	9.35
3 1/4	8.29	6.37	3 1/4	10.6	8.14	4	13.8	10.6
3 3/8	8.95	6.87	3 3/8	11.4	8.75	4 1/2	17.5	13.4
3 1/2	9.62	7.39	3 1/2	12.2	9.37	5	21.6	16.6
3 5/8	10.3	7.91	3 5/8	13.1	10.1	5 1/2	26.2	20.1
3 3/4	11.0	8.45	3 3/4	14.0	10.8	6	31.1	23.9
3 7/8	11.8	9.06	3 7/8	15.0	11.5	6 1/2	36.6	28.1
4	12.6	9.68	4	16.0	12.3	7	42.4	32.6
4 1/4	14.2	10.9	4 1/4	18.1	13.9	....	....	....
4 1/2	15.9	12.2	4 1/2	20.2	15.5	....	....	....
4 3/4	17.7	13.6	4 3/4	22.6	17.3	....	....	....
5	19.6	15.1	5	25.0	19.5	....	....	....
5 1/2	23.8	18.3	5 1/2	30.2	23.2	....	....	....
6	28.3	21.7	6	36.0	27.6	....	....	....
....	....	....	....	*....	....	....	....	....

Note: Weights in table are for Dowmetal M (S.A.E. No. 522). For weights of Dowmetal Fs-1 (S.A.E. No. 52) multiply weights shown by 1.005; for Dowmetal J-1 (S.A.E. No. 520) and Dowmetal O-1, multiply by 1.022; for pure magnesium, multiply by 0.989.

Pounds of Round Brass Rod per Thousand Pieces — r*

Length, Inches†	Diameter of Stock, Inches															
	1/16	3/32	1/8	5/32	3/16	7/32	1/4	9/32	5/16	11/32	3/8	13/32	7/16	15/32	1/2	17/32
1/32	0.03	0.07	0.12	0.19	0.3	0.4	0.5	0.6	0.7	0.9	1.1	1.3	1.5	1.7	1.9	2.2
1/16	0.06	0.13	0.24	0.36	0.6	0.8	1.0	1.1	1.4	1.7	2.1	2.4	2.8	3.3	3.7	4.2
3/32	0.09	0.19	0.36	0.55	0.8	1.0	1.4	1.7	2.2	2.6	3.1	3.7	4.3	4.9	5.6	6.3
1/8	0.12	0.26	0.48	0.73	1.0	1.4	1.8	2.3	2.9	3.5	4.2	4.9	5.7	6.6	7.5	8.5
5/32	0.15	0.33	0.59	0.92	1.3	1.8	2.3	2.9	3.6	4.4	5.3	6.2	7.2	8.2	9.4	10.6
3/16	0.18	0.39	0.71	1.1	1.5	2.1	2.8	3.5	4.4	5.3	6.3	7.4	8.6	9.9	11.2	12.7
7/32	0.21	0.46	0.83	1.2	1.8	2.5	3.2	4.1	5.1	6.2	7.4	8.7	10.1	11.5	13.1	14.8
1/4	0.24	0.52	0.95	1.4	2.1	2.8	3.7	4.7	5.8	7.1	8.4	9.9	11.5	13.2	15.0	17.0
9/32	0.27	0.59	1.1	1.6	2.3	3.2	4.2	5.3	6.6	8.0	9.5	11.2	13.0	14.8	16.9	19.1
5/16	0.30	0.66	1.2	1.8	2.6	3.6	4.7	5.9	7.3	8.9	10.6	12.4	14.4	16.5	18.8	21.2
11/32	0.33	0.72	1.3	2.0	2.9	3.9	5.1	6.5	8.1	9.7	11.6	13.6	15.8	18.8	20.7	23.3
3/8	0.36	0.79	1.5	2.2	3.1	4.3	5.6	7.1	8.8	10.6	12.7	14.9	17.3	19.8	22.5	25.5
13/32	0.39	0.85	1.6	2.3	3.4	4.7	6.0	7.7	9.5	11.5	13.7	16.1	18.7	21.5	24.4	27.6
7/16	0.42	0.92	1.7	2.5	3.7	5.0	6.5	8.3	10.3	12.4	14.8	17.4	20.2	23.1	26.3	29.7
15/32	0.45	0.99	1.8	2.7	3.9	5.4	7.0	8.9	11.0	13.3	15.9	18.6	21.6	24.8	28.2	31.8
1/2	0.48	1.0	1.9	2.8	4.2	5.7	7.5	9.5	11.7	14.2	16.9	19.9	23.1	26.4	30.1	34.0
17/32	0.51	1.1	2.1	3.1	4.5	6.1	8.0	10.1	12.5	15.1	18.0	21.1	24.5	28.1	31.9	36.1
9/16	0.54	1.1	2.2	3.3	4.7	6.5	8.4	10.7	13.2	16.0	19.0	22.4	26.0	29.7	33.8	38.2
19/32	0.57	1.2	2.3	3.4	5.0	6.8	8.9	11.3	14.0	16.9	20.1	23.6	27.4	31.4	35.7	40.3
5/8	0.60	1.3	2.4	3.6	5.2	7.2	9.4	11.9	14.7	17.8	21.2	24.9	28.9	33.1	37.6	42.5
21/32	0.63	1.3	2.5	3.8	5.5	7.6	9.8	12.5	15.4	18.6	22.2	26.1	30.3	34.7	39.5	44.6
11/16	0.66	1.4	2.6	4.0	5.8	7.9	10.3	13.1	16.2	19.5	23.3	27.4	31.7	36.4	41.4	46.7
23/32	0.69	1.5	2.8	4.2	6.0	8.3	10.8	13.7	16.9	20.4	24.3	28.6	33.2	38.0	43.2	48.8
3/4	0.72	1.5	2.9	4.4	6.3	8.6	11.3	14.3	17.6	21.3	25.4	29.8	34.6	39.7	45.1	51.0
25/32	0.75	1.6	3.0	4.6	6.6	9.0	11.7	14.9	18.4	22.2	26.5	31.1	36.1	41.3	47.0	53.1
13/16	0.78	1.7	3.1	4.7	6.8	9.4	12.2	15.5	19.1	23.1	27.5	32.3	37.5	43.0	48.9	55.2
27/32	0.81	1.7	3.2	4.9	7.1	9.7	12.7	16.1	19.8	24.0	28.6	33.6	39.0	44.6	50.8	57.3
7/8	0.84	1.8	3.4	5.1	7.4	10.1	13.1	16.7	20.6	24.9	29.6	34.8	40.4	46.3	52.6	59.5

* Multiply given weight by 1.273 for square stock, 1.103 for hexagonal stock, and 1.055 for octagonal stock.
† Length selected should allow for waste due to cutting off, etc.

Pounds of Round Brass Rod per Thousand Pieces —2*

Diameter of Stock, Inches

Length, Inches†	1/16	3/32	1/8	5/32	3/16	7/32	1/4	9/32	5/16	11/32	3/8	13/32	7/16	15/32	1/2	17/32
29/32	0.87	1.9	3.5	5.3	7.6	10.6	13.6	17.3	21.3	25.8	30.7	36.1	41.9	47.9	54.5	61.6
15/16	0.90	1.9	3.6	5.5	7.9	10.8	14.1	17.9	22.1	26.7	31.8	37.3	43.3	49.6	56.4	63.7
31/32	0.93	2.0	3.7	5.7	8.2	11.2	14.6	18.5	22.8	27.5	32.8	38.6	44.7	51.3	58.3	65.8
1	0.96	2.1	3.7	5.8	8.4	11.5	15.0	19.1	23.5	28.4	33.9	39.8	46.2	52.9	60.2	68.0
1 1/16	1.0	2.2	4.0	6.2	9.0	12.3	16.0	20.3	25.0	30.2	36.0	42.3	49.1	56.2	63.9	72.2
1 1/8	1.0	2.3	4.2	6.6	9.5	13.0	16.9	21.5	26.5	32.0	38.1	44.8	52.0	59.5	67.7	76.5
1 3/16	1.1	2.5	4.4	6.9	10.0	13.7	17.8	22.7	28.0	33.8	40.2	47.3	54.9	62.8	71.5	80.7
1 1/4	1.2	2.6	4.7	7.3	10.6	14.4	18.8	23.9	29.4	35.6	42.4	49.8	57.8	66.2	75.2	85.0
1 5/16	1.2	2.7	4.9	7.7	11.1	15.2	19.7	25.1	30.9	37.3	44.5	52.2	60.6	69.5	79.0	89.2
1 3/8	1.3	2.9	5.1	8.0	11.6	15.9	20.7	26.3	32.4	39.1	46.6	54.7	63.5	72.8	82.8	93.5
1 7/16	1.3	3.0	5.4	8.4	12.1	16.6	21.6	27.5	33.9	40.9	48.7	57.2	66.4	76.1	86.5	97.7
1 1/2	1.4	3.1	5.6	8.8	12.7	17.3	22.6	28.7	35.3	42.7	50.8	59.7	69.3	79.4	90.3	102.0
1 9/16	1.5	3.3	5.9	9.2	13.2	18.1	23.5	29.9	36.8	44.5	53.0	62.2	72.2	82.7	94.1	106.0
1 5/8	1.5	3.4	6.1	9.5	13.7	18.8	24.4	31.0	38.3	46.2	55.1	64.7	75.1	86.0	97.8	110.0
1 11/16	1.6	3.5	6.3	9.9	14.3	19.5	25.4	32.2	39.7	48.0	57.2	67.2	78.0	89.3	101.0	114.0
1 3/4	1.6	3.6	6.6	10.3	14.8	20.2	26.3	33.4	41.2	49.8	59.3	69.7	80.9	92.6	105.0	119.0
1 13/16	1.7	3.8	6.8	10.6	15.3	20.9	27.3	34.6	42.7	51.6	61.4	72.2	83.8	95.9	109.0	123.0
1 7/8	1.8	3.9	7.0	11.0	15.9	21.7	28.2	35.8	44.2	53.4	63.6	74.7	86.7	99.3	112.0	127.0
1 15/16	1.8	4.0	7.3	11.4	16.4	22.4	29.2	37.0	45.6	55.1	65.7	77.1	89.5	102.0	116.0	131.0
2	1.9	4.2	7.5	11.7	16.9	23.1	30.1	38.2	47.1	56.9	67.8	79.6	92.4	105.0	120.0	136.0
2 1/8	2.0	4.4	8.0	12.5	18.0	24.6	32.0	40.6	50.1	60.5	72.0	84.6	98.2	112.0	127.0	144.0
2 1/4	2.1	4.7	8.4	13.2	19.1	26.0	33.9	43.0	53.0	64.0	76.3	89.6	104.0	119.0	135.0	153.0
2 3/8	2.2	5.0	8.9	13.9	20.1	27.5	35.7	45.4	56.0	67.6	80.5	94.6	109.0	125.0	143.0	161.0
2 1/2	2.4	5.2	9.4	14.7	21.2	28.9	37.6	47.8	58.9	71.2	84.8	99.6	115.0	132.0	150.0	170.0
2 5/8	2.5	5.5	9.9	15.4	22.2	30.4	39.5	50.2	61.9	74.7	89.0	104.0	121.0	139.0	158.0	178.0
2 3/4	2.6	5.8	10.3	16.2	23.3	31.8	41.4	52.6	64.8	78.3	93.2	109.0	127.0	145.0	165.0	187.0
2 7/8	2.7	6.0	10.8	16.9	24.3	33.3	43.3	55.0	67.8	81.8	97.5	114.0	132.0	152.0	173.0	195.0
3	2.8	6.3	11.3	17.6	25.4	34.7	45.2	57.4	70.7	85.4	101.0	119.0	138.0	158.0	180.0	204.0

* Multiply given weight by 1.273 for square stock, 1.103 for hexagonal stock, and 1.055 for octagonal stock.

† Length selected should allow for waste due to cutting off, etc.

Pounds of Round Brass Rod per Thousand Pieces — 3*

Diameter of Stock, Inches

Length, Inches†	9/16	19/32	5/8	11/16	3/4	13/16	7/8	15/16	1	1 1/16	1 1/8	1 3/16	1 1/4	1 5/16	1 3/8	1 1/2
1/32	2.4	2.7	3.0	3.6	4.3	5.0	5.8	6.7	7.6	8.5	9.6	10.7	11.8	13.0	14.0	17.0
1/16	4.7	5.3	5.9	7.1	8.5	9.9	11.5	13.2	15.0	17.0	19.0	21.2	23.6	26.0	28.0	34.0
3/32	7.1	7.9	8.8	10.7	12.7	14.9	17.3	19.8	22.6	25.5	28.6	31.8	35.4	39.0	43.0	51.0
1/8	9.5	10.6	11.8	14.2	17.0	19.9	23.1	26.4	30.1	34.0	38.1	42.5	47.2	52.0	57.0	68.0
5/32	11.9	13.3	14.7	17.8	21.2	24.9	28.9	33.1	37.7	42.5	47.7	53.1	59.0	65.0	71.0	85.0
3/16	14.2	15.9	17.7	21.4	25.5	29.8	34.6	39.7	45.2	51.0	57.2	63.7	70.8	78.0	85.0	102.0
7/32	16.6	18.6	20.6	24.9	29.7	34.8	40.4	46.3	52.7	59.5	66.7	74.4	82.6	91.0	100.0	119.0
1/4	19.0	21.2	23.6	28.5	34.0	39.8	46.2	52.9	60.3	68.0	76.3	85.0	94.4	104.0	113.0	136.0
9/32	21.4	23.9	26.5	32.1	38.2	44.8	52.0	59.5	67.8	76.5	85.8	95.6	106.0	117.0	128.0	153.0
5/16	23.8	26.6	29.5	35.7	42.5	49.8	57.8	66.2	75.4	85.0	95.4	106.0	118.0	130.0	142.0	170.0
11/32	26.1	29.2	32.4	39.2	46.7	54.7	63.5	72.8	82.9	93.5	104.0	116.0	129.0	143.0	156.0	187.0
3/8	28.5	31.9	35.4	42.8	51.0	59.7	69.3	79.4	90.4	102.0	114.0	127.0	141.0	156.0	170.0	204.0
13/32	30.9	34.5	38.3	46.4	55.2	64.7	75.1	86.0	98.0	110.0	124.0	138.0	153.0	169.0	184.0	221.0
7/16	33.3	37.2	41.3	49.9	59.5	69.7	80.9	92.6	105.0	119.0	133.0	148.0	165.0	182.0	199.0	238.0
15/32	35.7	39.9	44.2	53.5	63.7	74.6	86.7	99.3	113.0	127.0	143.0	159.0	177.0	195.0	213.0	255.0
1/2	38.0	42.5	47.2	57.1	68.0	79.6	92.4	105.0	120.0	136.0	152.0	170.0	188.0	208.0	227.0	272.0
17/32	40.4	45.2	50.1	60.6	72.2	84.6	98.2	112.0	128.0	144.0	162.0	180.0	200.0	221.0	241.0	289.0
9/16	42.8	47.8	53.1	64.2	76.5	89.6	104.0	119.0	135.0	153.0	171.0	191.0	212.0	234.0	256.0	306.0
19/32	45.2	50.5	56.0	67.8	80.7	94.6	109.0	125.0	143.0	161.0	181.0	201.0	224.0	247.0	270.0	323.0
5/8	47.6	53.2	59.0	71.4	85.0	99.6	115.0	132.0	150.0	170.0	190.0	212.0	236.0	260.0	284.0	340.0
21/32	49.9	55.8	61.9	74.9	89.2	104.0	121.0	139.0	158.0	178.0	200.0	223.0	247.0	273.0	298.0	357.0
11/16	52.3	58.5	64.9	78.5	93.5	109.0	127.0	145.0	165.0	187.0	209.0	233.0	259.0	286.0	313.0	374.0
23/32	54.7	61.1	67.8	82.1	97.7	114.0	132.0	152.0	173.0	195.0	219.0	244.0	271.0	299.0	327.0	391.0
3/4	57.1	63.8	70.8	85.6	102.0	119.0	138.0	158.0	180.0	204.0	228.0	255.0	283.0	312.0	341.0	408.0
25/32	59.5	66.5	73.7	89.2	106.0	124.0	144.0	165.0	188.0	212.0	238.0	265.0	295.0	325.0	355.0	425.0
13/16	61.8	69.1	76.7	92.8	110.0	129.0	150.0	172.0	196.0	221.0	248.0	276.0	306.0	338.0	369.0	442.0
27/32	64.2	71.8	79.6	96.4	114.0	134.0	156.0	178.0	203.0	229.0	257.0	287.0	318.0	351.0	384.0	459.0
7/8	66.6	74.4	82.6	100.0	119.0	139.0	161.0	185.0	211.0	238.0	267.0	297.0	330.0	364.0	398.0	476.0

* Multiply given weight by 1.273 for square stock, 1.103 for hexagonal stock, and 1.055 for octagonal stock.

† Length selected should allow for waste due to cutting off, etc.

Pounds of Round Brass Rod per Thousand Pieces — 4*

Length, Inches†	9/16	19/32	5/8	11/16	3/4	13/16	7/8	15/16	1	1 1/16	1 1/8	1 3/16	1 1/4	1 5/16	1 3/8	1 1/2
29/32	69.0	77.1	85.5	103.0	123	144	167	191	218	246	276	308	342	377	412	493
15/16	71.4	79.8	88.5	107.0	127	149	173	198	226	255	286	318	354	390	426	510
31/32	73.7	82.4	91.4	110.0	131	154	179	205	233	263	295	329	365	403	441	527
1	76.1	85.1	94.4	114.0	136	159	184	211	241	272	305	340	377	416	455	544
1 1/16	80.9	90.4	100.0	121.0	144	169	196	225	256	289	324	361	401	442	483	578
1 1/8	85.5	95.7	106.0	128.0	153	179	208	238	271	306	343	382	424	468	512	612
1 3/16	90.4	101.0	112.0	135.0	161	189	219	251	286	323	362	403	448	494	540	646
1 1/4	95.2	106.0	118.0	142.0	170	199	231	264	301	340	381	425	472	520	569	680
1 5/16	99.9	111.0	123.0	149.0	178	209	242	278	316	357	400	446	495	546	597	714
1 3/8	104.0	117.0	129.0	157.0	187	219	254	291	331	374	419	467	519	572	626	748
1 7/16	109.0	122.0	135.0	164.0	195	229	265	304	346	391	438	488	542	598	654	782
1 1/2	114.0	127.0	141.0	171.0	204	239	277	317	361	408	457	510	566	624	683	816
1 9/16	119.0	133.0	147.0	178.0	212	249	289	331	377	425	477	531	590	650	711	850
1 5/8	123.0	138.0	153.0	185.0	221	259	300	344	392	442	496	552	613	676	739	884
1 11/16	128.0	143.0	159.0	192.0	229	268	312	357	407	459	515	574	637	702	768	918
1 3/4	133.0	148.0	165.0	199.0	238	278	323	370	422	476	534	595	660	728	796	952
1 13/16	138.0	154.0	171.0	207.0	246	288	335	383	437	493	553	616	684	754	825	986
1 7/8	142.0	159.0	177.0	214.0	255	298	346	397	452	510	572	637	708	780	853	1020
1 15/16	147.0	164.0	182.0	221.0	263	308	358	410	467	527	591	659	731	806	882	1054
2	152.0	170.0	188.0	228.0	272	318	369	423	482	544	610	680	755	832	910	1088
2 1/8	161.0	180.0	200.0	242.0	289	338	393	450	512	578	648	722	802	884	967	1156
2 1/4	171.0	191.0	212.0	257.0	306	358	416	476	542	612	686	765	849	936	1024	1224
2 3/8	180.0	202.0	224.0	271.0	323	378	439	503	573	646	725	807	896	988	1081	1292
2 1/2	190.0	212.0	236.0	285.0	340	398	462	529	603	680	763	850	944	1040	1138	1360
2 5/8	199.0	223.0	247.0	299.0	357	418	485	556	633	714	801	892	991	1092	1195	1428
2 3/4	209.0	234.0	259.0	314.0	374	438	508	582	663	748	839	935	1038	1144	1252	1496
2 7/8	218.0	244.0	271.0	328.0	391	458	531	609	693	782	877	977	1085	1196	1309	1564
3	228.0	255.0	283.0	342.0	408	478	554	635	723	816	915	1020	1132	1248	1366	1632

* Multiply given weight by 1.273 for square stock, 1.103 for hexagonal stock, and 1.055 for octagonal stock.
† Length selected should allow for waste due to cutting off, etc.

Weights per Thousand of Square Brass Blanks — 1

In estimating costs for press work, the material cost is the most important item. To illustrate the use of the tables, assume that a 6⅝ inch round blank is required and that the estimate is to be based upon a blank 6⅞ inches square, there being a ¼-inch margin allowance. If brass of No. 22 B & S gage is to be used, the weight in pounds per thousand square blanks is found in the table under No. 22 gage and opposite the square blank size of 6⅞. This table is based upon the following formula:

Weight per thousand = blank area × thickness × 0.306 × 1000.

To obtain weight of sheet steel blanks multiply figure in table by 0.928.

For sheet aluminum, multiply by 0.32. For sheet copper, multiply by 1.051. For circular blanks, multiply by 0.7854.

Square Blanks		B. & S. Gage Numbers and Decimal Equivalents						
Sizes, Inches	Areas, Sq. In.	No. 16 0.05082	No. 17 0.04526	No. 18 0.04030	No. 19 0.03589	No. 20 0.03196	No. 21 0.02846	No. 22 0.02535
½	0.25	3.89	3.46	3.08	2.75	2.44	2.18	1.94
⅝	0.39	6.07	5.41	4.82	4.29	3.82	3.40	3.03
¾	0.56	8.71	7.79	6.94	6.18	5.50	4.90	4.36
⅞	0.77	11.97	10.60	9.44	8.41	7.49	6.67	5.94
1	1.00	15.55	13.85	12.33	10.98	9.78	8.71	7.76
1⅛	1.27	19.69	17.53	15.61	13.90	12.38	11.03	9.82
1¼	1.56	24.29	21.63	19.26	17.15	15.28	13.60	12.12
1⅜	1.89	29.41	26.19	23.32	20.77	18.49	16.47	14.67
1½	2.25	34.99	31.16	27.75	24.71	22.00	19.59	17.45
1⅝	2.64	41.07	36.58	32.57	29.00	25.83	23.00	20.49
1¾	3.06	47.62	42.41	37.76	33.63	29.95	26.67	23.75
1⅞	3.52	54.68	48.70	43.36	38.61	34.39	30.62	27.27
2	4.00	62.20	55.40	49.33	43.93	39.12	34.84	31.03
2⅛	4.52	70.23	62.54	55.69	49.60	44.17	39.33	35.03
2¼	5.06	78.72	70.11	62.42	55.59	49.51	44.08	39.27
2⅜	5.64	87.72	78.13	69.56	61.95	55.17	49.13	43.76
2½	6.25	97.19	86.56	77.07	68.64	61.12	54.43	48.48
2⅝	6.89	107.15	95.44	84.98	75.68	67.39	60.01	53.45
2¾	7.56	117.60	104.73	93.25	83.05	73.95	65.86	58.62
2⅞	8.27	128.54	114.48	101.93	90.78	80.84	71.99	64.12
3	9.00	139.96	124.65	110.99	98.84	88.02	78.38	69.81
3⅛	9.77	151.87	135.25	120.43	107.25	95.51	85.05	75.76
3¼	10.56	164.22	146.25	130.22	115.97	103.27	91.96	81.91
3⅜	11.39	177.13	157.75	140.46	125.09	111.39	99.19	88.35
3½	12.25	190.50	169.66	151.06	134.53	119.80	106.68	95.02
3⅝	13.14	204.34	181.98	162.04	144.31	128.51	114.43	101.93
3¾	14.06	218.65	194.72	173.39	154.41	137.50	122.44	109.06
3⅞	15.02	233.57	208.02	185.22	164.95	146.89	130.81	116.51
4	16.00	248.81	221.59	197.31	175.72	156.48	139.34	124.11
4⅛	17.02	264.68	235.72	209.89	186.92	166.45	148.22	132.03
4¼	18.06	280.85	250.12	222.71	198.34	176.62	157.28	140.09
4⅜	19.14	297.64	265.08	236.03	210.20	187.18	166.69	148.47
4½	20.25	314.91	280.45	249.72	222.39	198.04	176.35	157.08
4⅝	21.39	332.63	296.24	263.78	234.91	209.19	186.28	165.92

Weights per Thousand of Square Brass Blanks — 2

Square Blanks		B. & S. Gage Numbers and Decimal Equivalents						
Sizes, Inches	Areas, Sq. In.	No. 16 0.05082	No. 17 0.04526	No. 18 0.04030	No. 19 0.03589	No. 20 0.03196	No. 21 0.02846	No. 22 0.02535
4¾	22.56	350.83	312.45	278.20	247.76	220.63	196.47	175.00
4⅞	23.77	369.65	329.20	293.13	261.05	232.46	207.01	184.39
5	25.00	388.77	346.24	308.30	274.56	244.49	217.72	193.93
5⅛	26.26	408.37	363.69	323.83	288.40	256.82	228.69	203.70
5¼	27.56	428.58	381.69	339.86	302.67	269.53	240.01	213.79
5⅜	28.89	449.27	400.11	356.27	317.28	282.54	251.60	224.10
5½	30.25	470.42	418.95	373.04	332.22	295.84	263.44	234.65
5⅝	31.64	492.03	438.20	390.18	347.48	309.43	275.55	245.43
5¾	33.06	514.11	457.87	407.69	363.08	323.32	287.91	256.45
5⅞	34.52	536.82	478.09	425.69	379.11	337.60	300.62	267.78
6	36.00	559.83	498.58	443.94	395.36	352.07	313.52	279.26
6⅛	37.52	583.47	519.64	462.70	412.06	366.94	326.75	291.05
6¼	39.06	607.42	540.96	481.68	428.97	382.00	340.16	302.99
6⅜	40.64	631.99	562.85	501.16	446.32	397.45	353.92	315.25
6½	42.25	657.03	585.14	521.02	464.00	413.19	367.95	327.74
6⅝	43.89	682.53	607.86	541.24	482.01	429.23	382.23	340.46
6¾	45.56	708.50	630.99	561.84	500.36	445.57	396.77	353.41
6⅞	47.27	735.09	654.67	582.92	519.14	462.29	411.66	366.68
7	49.00	762.00	678.63	604.26	538.13	479.21	426.73	380.10
7⅛	50.76	789.36	703.00	625.96	557.46	496.42	442.06	393.75
7¼	52.56	817.36	727.93	648.16	577.23	514.02	457.73	407.71
7⅜	54.39	845.81	753.28	670.73	597.33	531.92	473.67	421.91
7½	56.25	874.74	779.04	693.66	617.76	550.11	489.87	436.34
7⅝	58.14	904.13	805.21	716.97	638.51	568.60	506.33	451.00
7¾	60.06	933.99	831.80	740.65	659.60	587.37	523.05	465.89
7⅞	62.02	964.47	858.95	764.82	681.12	606.54	540.12	481.10
8	64.00	995.26	886.57	789.24	702.87	625.90	557.36	496.45

Square Blank Sizes, Inches	B. & S. Gage Numbers and Decimal Equivalents							
	No. 23 0.02257	No. 24 0.02010	No. 25 0.01790	No. 26 0.01594	No. 27 0.01420	No. 28 0.01264	No. 29 0.01126	No. 30 0.01003
½	1.73	1.54	1.37	1.22	1.09	0.97	0.86	0.77
⅝	2.70	2.40	2.14	1.91	1.70	1.51	1.35	1.20
¾	3.88	3.46	3.08	2.74	2.44	2.18	1.94	1.73
⅞	5.29	4.71	4.19	3.73	3.33	2.96	2.64	2.35
1	6.91	6.15	5.48	4.88	4.35	3.87	3.45	3.07
1⅛	8.74	7.79	6.93	6.18	5.50	4.90	4.36	3.89
1¼	10.79	9.61	8.56	7.62	6.79	6.04	5.38	4.79
1⅜	13.06	11.63	10.36	9.22	8.22	7.31	6.52	5.80
1½	15.54	13.84	12.32	10.97	9.78	8.70	7.75	6.91
1⅝	18.24	16.24	14.47	12.88	11.48	10.21	9.10	8.11
1¾	21.15	18.83	16.77	14.94	13.31	11.84	10.55	9.40
1⅞	24.28	21.63	19.26	17.15	15.28	13.60	12.11	10.79
2	27.63	24.60	21.91	19.51	17.38	15.47	13.78	12.28
2⅛	31.19	27.78	24.74	22.03	19.62	17.47	15.56	13.86
2¼	34.96	31.13	27.73	24.69	22.00	19.58	17.44	15.54
2⅜	38.96	34.70	30.90	27.51	24.51	21.82	19.44	17.31

Weights per Thousand of Square Brass Blanks — 3

Square Blank Sizes, Inches	No. 23 0.02257	No. 24 0.02010	No. 25 0.01790	No. 26 0.01594	No. 27 0.01420	No. 28 0.01264	No. 29 0.01126	No. 30 0.01003
2½	43.17	38.44	34.23	30.49	27.16	24.17	21.53	19.18
2⅝	47.59	42.38	37.71	33.61	29.94	26.65	23.74	21.15
2¾	52.23	46.51	41.42	36.88	32.86	29.25	26.06	23.21
2⅞	57.09	50.84	45.28	40.32	35.92	31.97	28.48	25.37
3	62.16	55.36	49.00	43.90	39.11	34.81	31.01	27.62
3⅛	67.45	60.07	53.49	47.64	42.44	37.77	33.65	29.97
3¼	72.93	64.95	57.84	51.51	45.89	40.84	36.39	32.51
3⅜	78.67	70.06	62.39	55.56	49.49	44.06	39.25	34.96
3½	84.60	75.34	67.10	59.75	53.23	47.38	42.21	37.60
3⅝	90.75	80.82	71.97	64.09	57.10	50.82	45.27	40.33
3¾	97.10	86.48	77.01	68.58	61.09	54.38	48.44	43.15
3⅞	103.73	92.38	82.27	73.26	65.26	58.09	51.75	46.10
4	110.50	98.41	87.64	78.04	69.52	61.89	55.13	49.11
4⅛	117.55	104.68	93.23	83.02	73.96	65.83	58.64	52.24
4¼	124.73	111.08	98.92	88.09	78.47	69.85	62.23	55.43
4⅜	132.19	117.72	104.84	93.36	83.17	74.03	65.95	58.74
4½	139.86	124.55	110.92	98.77	87.99	78.32	69.77	62.15
4⅝	147.73	131.56	117.16	104.33	92.94	82.73	73.70	65.65
4¾	155.81	138.76	123.57	110.04	98.03	87.26	77.73	69.24
4⅞	164.17	146.20	130.20	115.94	103.29	91.94	81.90	72.95
5	172.66	153.77	136.94	121.94	108.63	96.70	86.14	76.73
5⅛	181.36	161.51	143.84	128.09	114.10	101.57	90.48	80.60
5¼	190.34	169.51	150.96	134.43	119.75	106.60	94.96	84.59
5⅜	199.53	177.69	158.24	140.92	125.53	111.74	99.54	88.67
5½	208.92	186.06	165.69	147.55	131.44	117.00	104.23	92.84
5⅝	218.52	194.60	173.30	154.33	137.48	122.38	109.02	97.11
5¾	228.33	203.34	181.08	161.25	143.65	127.87	113.91	101.47
5⅞	238.41	212.32	189.08	168.38	150.00	133.52	118.94	105.95
6	248.63	221.42	197.19	175.60	156.43	139.24	124.04	110.49
6⅛	259.13	230.77	205.51	183.01	163.03	145.12	129.28	115.16
6¼	269.76	240.24	213.95	190.52	169.72	151.08	134.58	119.88
6⅜	280.68	249.96	222.60	198.23	176.59	157.19	140.03	124.73
6½	291.80	259.86	231.42	206.08	183.58	163.42	145.57	129.67
6⅝	303.12	269.95	240.40	214.08	190.71	169.76	151.23	134.71
6¾	314.66	280.22	249.55	222.23	197.97	176.22	156.98	139.83
6⅞	326.47	290.74	258.92	230.57	205.40	182.83	162.87	145.08
7	338.41	301.38	268.39	239.00	212.91	189.52	168.83	150.39
7⅛	350.57	312.20	278.03	247.59	220.56	196.33	174.90	155.79
7¼	363.00	323.28	287.89	256.37	228.38	203.29	181.10	161.32
7⅜	375.64	334.53	297.92	265.39	236.34	210.37	187.40	166.93
7½	388.49	345.97	308.10	274.37	244.42	217.57	193.81	172.64
7⅝	401.54	357.60	318.46	283.59	252.63	224.88	200.32	178.44
7¾	414.80	369.41	328.97	292.95	260.97	232.30	206.94	184.33
7⅞	428.34	381.46	339.71	302.51	269.49	239.88	213.69	190.35
8	442.01	393.64	350.55	312.17	278.09	247.54	220.52	196.43

Weight of Round Steel Bars per Running Inch

Diam. of Bar, Ins.	Weight per In., Lbs.	Diam. of Bar, Ins.	Weight per In., Lbs.	Diam. of Bar, Ins.	Weight per In., Lbs.	Diam. of Bar, Ins.	Weight per In., Lbs.	Diam. of Bar, Ins.	Weight per In., Lbs.
1/64	0.00005	2	0.89	5	5.56	8	14.3	14	43.6
1/32	0.00022	2 1/16	0.94	5 1/16	5.70	8 1/8	14.7	14 1/8	44.3
1/16	0.00087	2 1/8	1.00	5 1/8	5.84	8 1/4	15.1	14 1/4	45.1
3/32	0.0020	2 3/16	1.06	5 3/16	5.98	8 3/8	15.6	14 3/8	45.9
1/8	0.0035	2 1/4	1.13	5 1/4	6.13	8 1/2	16.1	14 1/2	46.7
5/32	0.0054	2 5/16	1.19	5 5/16	6.27	8 5/8	16.5	14 5/8	47.5
3/16	0.0078	2 3/8	1.25	5 3/8	6.42	8 3/4	17.0	14 3/4	48.4
7/32	0.0106	2 7/16	1.33	5 7/16	6.57	8 7/8	17.5	14 7/8	49.2
1/4	0.0139	2 1/2	1.39	5 1/2	6.72	9	18.0	15	50.0
9/32	0.0176	2 9/16	1.46	5 9/16	6.88	9 1/8	18.5	15 1/8	50.8
5/16	0.0217	2 5/8	1.53	5 5/8	7.03	9 1/4	19.0	15 1/4	51.7
11/32	0.0263	2 11/16	1.61	5 11/16	7.19	9 3/8	19.5	15 3/8	52.5
3/8	0.0313	2 3/4	1.68	5 3/4	7.35	9 1/2	20.1	15 1/2	53.4
13/32	0.0367	2 13/16	1.76	5 13/16	7.51	9 5/8	20.6	15 5/8	54.3
7/16	0.0425	2 7/8	1.84	5 7/8	7.67	9 3/4	21.1	15 3/4	55.1
15/32	0.0488	2 15/16	1.92	5 15/16	7.84	9 7/8	21.7	15 7/8	56.0
1/2	0.0556	3	2.00	6	8.00	10	22.2	16	56.9
17/32	0.0627	3 1/16	2.08	6 1/16	8.17	10 1/8	22.8	16 1/8	57.8
9/16	0.0703	3 1/8	2.17	6 1/8	8.34	10 1/4	23.4	16 1/4	58.7
19/32	0.0784	3 3/16	2.26	6 3/16	8.51	10 3/8	23.9	16 3/8	59.6
5/8	0.0868	3 1/4	2.35	6 1/4	8.68	10 1/2	24.5	16 1/2	60.5
21/32	0.0957	3 5/16	2.44	6 5/16	8.86	10 5/8	25.1	16 5/8	61.4
11/16	0.105	3 3/8	2.53	6 3/8	9.03	10 3/4	25.7	16 3/4	62.4
23/32	0.115	3 7/16	2.63	6 7/16	9.21	10 7/8	26.3	16 7/8	63.3
3/4	0.125	3 1/2	2.72	6 1/2	9.39	11	26.9	17	64.2
25/32	0.136	3 9/16	2.82	6 9/16	9.57	11 1/8	27.5	17 1/8	65.2
13/16	0.147	3 5/8	2.92	6 5/8	9.76	11 1/4	28.1	17 1/4	66.1
27/32	0.158	3 11/16	3.02	6 11/16	9.94	11 3/8	28.8	17 3/8	67.1
7/8	0.170	3 3/4	3.13	6 3/4	10.1	11 1/2	29.4	17 1/2	68.1
29/32	0.182	3 13/16	3.23	6 13/16	10.3	11 5/8	30.0	17 5/8	69.0
15/16	0.195	3 7/8	3.34	6 7/8	10.5	11 3/4	30.7	17 3/4	70.0
31/32	0.21	3 15/16	3.45	6 15/16	10.7	11 7/8	31.3	17 7/8	71.0
1	0.22	4	3.56	7	10.9	12	32.0	18	72.0
1 1/16	0.25	4 1/16	3.67	7 1/16	11.1	12 1/8	32.7	18 1/8	73.0
1 1/8	0.28	4 1/8	3.78	7 1/8	11.3	12 1/4	33.4	18 1/4	74.0
1 3/16	0.31	4 3/16	3.90	7 3/16	11.5	12 3/8	34.0	18 3/8	75.0
1 1/4	0.35	4 1/4	4.01	7 1/4	11.7	12 1/2	34.7	18 1/2	76.1
1 5/16	0.38	4 5/16	4.13	7 5/16	11.9	12 5/8	35.4	18 5/8	77.1
1 3/8	0.42	4 3/8	4.25	7 3/8	12.1	12 3/4	36.1	18 3/4	78.1
1 7/16	0.46	4 7/16	4.38	7 7/16	12.3	12 7/8	36.8	18 7/8	79.2
1 1/2	0.50	4 1/2	4.50	7 1/2	12.5	13	37.6	19	80.2
1 9/16	0.54	4 9/16	4.63	7 9/16	12.7	13 1/8	38.3	19 1/8	81.3
1 5/8	0.59	4 5/8	4.75	7 5/8	12.9	13 1/4	39.0	19 1/4	82.4
1 11/16	0.63	4 11/16	4.88	7 11/16	13.1	13 3/8	39.8	19 3/8	83.4
1 3/4	0.68	4 3/4	5.01	7 3/4	13.3	13 1/2	40.5	19 1/2	84.5
1 13/16	0.73	4 13/16	5.15	7 13/16	13.6	13 5/8	41.3	19 5/8	85.6
1 7/8	0.78	4 7/8	5.28	7 7/8	13.8	13 3/4	42.0	19 3/4	86.7
1 15/16	0.83	4 15/16	5.42	7 15/16	14.0	13 7/8	42.8	19 7/8	87.8

Weights of Square and Round Steel Bars in Pounds per Lineal Foot

Diam. of Round or Side of Square, Inches	Weight in Pounds		Diam. of Round or Side of Square, Inches	Weight in Pounds		Diam. of Round or Side of Square, Inches	Weight in Pounds	
	Square Bar	Round Bar		Square Bar	Round Bar		Square Bar	Round Bar
1/16	0.013	0.010	2 1/16	14.46	11.36	5	85.00	66.76
3/32	0.030	0.023	2 1/8	15.35	12.06	5 1/8	89.30	70.14
1/8	0.053	0.042	2 3/16	16.27	12.78	5 1/4	93.71	73.60
5/32	0.083	0.065	2 1/4	17.21	13.52	5 3/8	98.23	77.15
3/16	0.120	0.094	2 5/16	18.18	14.28	5 1/2	102.9	80.78
7/32	0.163	0.128	2 3/8	19.18	15.06	5 5/8	107.6	84.49
1/4	0.212	0.167	2 7/16	20.20	15.87	5 3/4	112.4	88.29
9/32	0.269	0.211	2 1/2	21.25	16.69	5 7/8	117.4	92.17
5/16	0.332	0.261	2 9/16	22.33	17.53	6	122.4	96.13
11/32	0.402	0.316	2 5/8	23.43	18.40	6 1/8	127.6	101.8
3/8	0.478	0.376	2 11/16	24.56	19.29	6 1/4	132.8	104.3
13/32	0.561	0.441	2 3/4	25.71	20.19	6 3/8	138.2	108.5
7/16	0.651	0.511	2 13/16	26.90	21.12	6 1/2	143.7	112.8
15/32	0.747	0.587	2 7/8	28.10	22.07	6 5/8	149.2	117.2
1/2	0.850	0.668	2 15/16	29.34	23.04	6 3/4	154.9	121.7
17/32	0.960	0.754	3	30.60	24.03	6 7/8	160.7	126.2
9/16	1.076	0.845	3 1/16	31.89	25.05	7	166.6	130.8
19/32	1.199	0.941	3 1/8	33.20	26.08	7 1/8	172.6	135.6
5/8	1.328	1.043	3 3/16	34.55	27.13	7 1/4	178.7	140.4
21/32	1.464	1.150	3 1/4	35.92	28.21	7 3/8	184.9	145.2
11/16	1.607	1.262	3 5/16	37.31	29.30	7 1/2	191.3	150.2
23/32	1.756	1.380	3 3/8	38.73	30.42	7 5/8	197.7	155.3
3/4	1.913	1.502	3 7/16	40.18	31.55	7 3/4	204.2	160.4
25/32	2.076	1.628	3 1/2	41.65	32.71	7 7/8	210.9	165.6
13/16	2.245	1.763	3 9/16	43.15	33.89	8	217.6	170.9
27/32	2.420	1.900	3 5/8	44.68	35.09	8 1/8	224.5	176.3
7/8	2.603	2.044	3 11/16	46.23	36.31	8 1/4	231.4	181.8
29/32	2.792	2.192	3 3/4	47.82	37.55	8 3/8	238.5	187.3
15/16	2.988	2.347	3 13/16	49.42	38.81	8 1/2	245.7	192.9
31/32	3.192	2.508	3 7/8	51.05	40.10	8 5/8	252.9	198.6
1	3.400	2.670	3 15/16	52.71	41.40	8 3/4	260.3	204.4
1 1/16	3.838	3.015	4	54.40	42.73	8 7/8	267.8	210.3
1 1/8	4.303	3.380	4 1/16	56.11	44.07	9	275.4	216.3
1 3/16	4.795	3.766	4 1/8	57.85	45.44	9 1/8	283.1	222.3
1 1/4	5.313	4.172	4 3/16	59.62	46.83	9 1/4	290.9	228.5
1 5/16	5.857	4.600	4 1/4	61.41	48.24	9 3/8	298.8	234.7
1 3/8	6.428	5.049	4 5/16	63.23	49.66	9 1/2	306.9	241.0
1 7/16	7.026	5.518	4 3/8	65.08	51.11	9 5/8	315.0	247.4
1 1/2	7.650	6.008	4 7/16	66.95	52.58	9 3/4	323.2	253.8
1 9/16	8.301	6.519	4 1/2	68.85	54.07	9 7/8	331.6	260.4
1 5/8	8.978	7.051	4 9/16	70.78	55.59	10	340.0	267.0
1 11/16	9.682	7.604	4 5/8	72.73	57.12	10 1/4	357.2	280.6
1 3/4	10.41	8.178	4 11/16	74.71	58.67	10 1/2	374.9	294.4
1 13/16	11.17	8.773	4 3/4	76.71	60.25	10 3/4	392.9	308.6
1 7/8	11.95	9.388	4 13/16	78.74	61.85	11	411.4	323.1
1 15/16	12.76	10.02	4 7/8	80.80	63.46	11 1/2	449.7	353.2
2	13.60	10.68	4 15/16	82.89	65.10	12	489.6	384.5

Weight in Pounds per Foot and per Inch of Hexagon Steel Bars

Width across Flats, Inches	Weight in Pounds		Width across Flats. Inches	Weight in Pounds		Width across Flats, Inches	Weight in Pounds	
	Per Running Foot	Per Running Inch		Per Running Foot	Per Running Inch		Per Running Foot	Per Running Inch
1/4	0.195	0.016	3/4	1.66	0.138	1 9/16	7.17	0.597
9/32	0.23	0.019	13/16	1.91	0.159	1 5/8	7.76	0.647
5/16	0.29	0.024	7/8	2.25	0.187	1 11/16	8.37	0.697
11/32	0.36	0.030	29/32	2.40	0.200	1 3/4	9.00	0.750
3/8	0.43	0.036	15/16	2.58	0.215	1 7/8	10.32	0.860
13/32	0.50	0.042	1	2.94	0.245	2	11.78	0.982
7/16	0.56	0.047	1 1/16	3.33	0.277	2 1/8	13.30	1.108
15/32	0.64	0.053	1 3/32	3.52	0.293	2 1/4	14.91	1.242
1/2	0.73	0.061	1 1/8	3.73	0.311	2 3/8	16.61	1.384
17/32	0.82	0.068	1 3/16	4.15	0.346	2 1/2	18.40	1.533
9/16	0.93	0.077	1 1/4	4.60	0.383	2 5/8	20.29	1.691
19/32	1.10	0.092	1 5/16	5.07	0.422	2 3/4	22.27	1.856
5/8	1.15	0.096	1 3/8	5.57	0.464	3	26.50	2.208
11/16	1.40	0.117	1 7/16	6.07	0.506	3 1/4	31.10	2.592
23/32	1.52	0.127	1 1/2	6.62	0.552	3 1/2	36.07	3.006

Weights of Steel Plates. — For obtaining the weights of steel plates in pounds, the accompanying table may be used. First, multiply the length of the plate in inches by its breadth, and then this product by the constant C given in the table opposite the thickness of the plate.

Thickness	C	Thickness	C	Thickness	C	Thickness	C
3/16	0.0531	3/8	0.1062	9/16	0.1594	3/4	0.2125
1/4	0.0708	7/16	0.1240	5/8	0.1771	7/8	0.2479
5/16	0.0885	1/2	0.1417	11/16	0.1948	1	0.2833

Example: — Find the weight per square foot of area of steel plate, 7/16 inch thick.

$$12 \times 12 \times 0.1240 = 17.856 \text{ pounds.}$$

Weights of Hot-pressed Hexagon Nuts

Size of Bolt	Thickness of Nut	Width across Flats	Weight of 100 Nuts, Pounds	Size of Bolt	Thickness of Nut	Width across Flats	Weight of 100 Nuts, Pounds	Size of Bolt	Thickness of Nut	Width across Flats	Weight of 100 Nuts, Pounds
1/4	1/4	1/2	1.3	5/8	5/8	1 1/4	19.1	1 1/8	1 1/4	2	96
5/16	5/16	5/8	2.4	5/8	3/4	1 1/4	22.9	1 1/4	1 3/8	2 1/4	134
3/8	3/8	3/4	4.1	3/4	3/4	1 3/8	27.2	1 3/8	1 1/2	2 1/2	180
7/16	7/16	7/8	6.8	3/4	7/8	1 1/2	39.0	1 1/2	1 5/8	2 3/4	235
1/2	1/2	7/8	7.1	7/8	7/8	1 5/8	44.0	1 5/8	1 3/4	3	300
1/2	1/2	1	9.8	7/8	1	1 5/8	50.0	1 3/4	1 7/8	3 1/4	370
9/16	9/16	1 1/8	14.0	1	1	1 3/4	57.0	1 7/8	2	3 1/2	460
5/8	5/8	1 1/8	14.7	1	1 1/8	1 3/4	64.0	2	2	3 1/2	450

Weights of Flat Rolled Steel per Lineal Foot in Pounds

U. S. St'd Gage for Plate	Width of Flat Steel, Inches						
	⅛	3⁄16	¼	5⁄16	⅜	7⁄16	½
0000000	0.2126	0.3189	0.4252	0.5315	0.6378	0.7441	0.8504
000000	0.1992	0.2998	0.3984	0.4980	0.5976	0.6972	0.7968
00000	0.1860	0.2790	0.3720	0.4650	0.5580	0.6510	0.7440
0000	0.1728	0.2592	0.3456	0.4320	0.5184	0.6048	0.6912
000	0.1594	0.2391	0.3188	0.3985	0.4782	0.5579	0.6376
00	0.1462	0.2193	0.2924	0.3655	0.4386	0.5117	0.5848
0	0.1328	0.1992	0.2656	0.3320	0.3984	0.4648	0.5312
1	0.1196	0.1794	0.2392	0.2990	0.3588	0.4186	0.4784
2	0.1130	0.1695	0.2260	0.2825	0.3390	0.3955	0.4520
3	0.1062	0.1593	0.2124	0.2655	0.3186	0.3717	0.4248
4	0.0996	0.1494	0.1992	0.2490	0.2988	0.3486	0.3984
5	0.0930	0.1395	0.1860	0.2325	0.2790	0.3255	0.3720
6	0.0864	0.1296	0.1728	0.2160	0.2592	0.3024	0.3456
7	0.0798	0.1197	0.1596	0.1995	0.2394	0.2793	0.3192
8	0.0730	0.1095	0.1460	0.1825	0.2190	0.2555	0.2920
9	0.0664	0.0996	0.1328	0.1660	0.1992	0.2324	0.2656
10	0.0598	0.0897	0.1196	0.1495	0.1794	0.2093	0.2392
11	0.0532	0.0798	0.1064	0.1330	0.1596	0.1862	0.2128
12	0.0466	0.0699	0.0932	0.1165	0.1398	0.1631	0.1864
13	0.0398	0.0597	0.0796	0.0995	0.1194	0.1393	0.1592
14	0.0332	0.0498	0.0664	0.0830	0.0996	0.1162	0.1328
15	0.0298	0.0447	0.0596	0.0745	0.0894	0.1043	0.1192
16	0.0266	0.0399	0.0532	0.0665	0.0798	0.0931	0.1064
17	0.0240	0.0360	0.0480	0.0600	0.0720	0.0840	0.0960
18	0.0212	0.0318	0.0424	0.0530	0.0636	0.0742	0.0848
19	0.0186	0.0279	0.0372	0.0465	0.0558	0.0651	0.0744
20	0.0160	0.0240	0.0320	0.0400	0.0480	0.0560	0.0640
21	0.0146	0.0219	0.0292	0.0365	0.0438	0.0511	0.0584
22	0.0133	0.0201	0.0268	0.0335	0.0402	0.0469	0.0536
23	0.0120	0.0180	0.0240	0.0300	0.0360	0.0420	0.0480
24	0.0106	0.0159	0.0212	0.0265	0.0318	0.0371	0.0424
25	0.0094	0.0141	0.0188	0.0235	0.0282	0.0329	0.0376
26	0.0080	0.0120	0.0160	0.0200	0.0240	0.0280	0.0320
27	0.0074	0.0111	0.0148	0.0185	0.0222	0.0259	0.0296
28	0.0066	0.0099	0.0132	0.0165	0.0198	0.0231	0.0264
29	0.0060	0.0090	0.0120	0.0150	0.0180	0.0210	0.0240
30	0.0054	0.0081	0.0108	0.0135	0.0162	0.0189	0.0212
31	0.0046	0.0069	0.0092	0.0115	0.0138	0.0161	0.0184
32	0.0044	0.0066	0.0088	0.0110	0.0132	0.0154	0.0176
33	0.0040	0.0060	0.0080	0.0100	0.0120	0.0140	0.0160
34	0.0036	0.0054	0.0072	0.0090	0.0108	0.0126	0.0144
35	0.0034	0.0051	0.0068	0.0085	0.0102	0.0119	0.0136
36	0.0030	0.0045	0.0060	0.0075	0.0090	0.0105	0.0120
37	0.0028	0.0042	0.0056	0.0070	0.0084	0.0098	0.0112
38	0.0026	0.0039	0.0052	0.0065	0.0078	0.0091	0.0104

Weights of Flat Rolled Steel Per Lineal Foot in Pounds (Continued)

U. S. St'd Gage for Plate	Width of Flat Steel, Inches							
	9/16	5/8	11/16	3/4	13/16	7/8	1	2
0000000	0.9567	1.0630	1.1693	1.2756	1.3819	1.4882	1.7008	3.4016
000000	0.8964	0.9960	1.0956	1.1952	1.2948	1.3944	1.5936	3.1872
00000	0.8370	0.9300	1.0230	1.1160	1.2090	1.3020	1.4880	2.9760
0000	0.7776	0.8640	0.9500	1.0368	1.1232	1.2096	1.3824	2.7648
000	0.7173	0.7970	0.8767	0.9564	1.0361	1.1158	1.2752	2.5504
00	0.6579	0.7310	0.8041	0.8772	0.9505	1.0234	1.1696	2.3392
0	0.5976	0.6640	0.7300	0.7968	0.8632	0.9296	1.0624	2.1248
1	0.5382	0.5980	0.6578	0.7176	0.7774	0.8372	0.9568	1.9136
2	0.5085	0.5650	0.6215	0.6780	0.7345	0.7910	0.9040	1.8080
3	0.4779	0.5310	0.5841	0.6372	0.6903	0.7434	0.8496	1.6992
4	0.4482	0.4980	0.5478	0.5976	0.6474	0.6972	0.7968	1.5936
5	0.4185	0.4650	0.5115	0.5580	0.6045	0.6510	0.7440	1.4880
6	0.3888	0.4320	0.4752	0.5184	0.5616	0.6048	0.6912	1.3824
7	0.3591	0.3990	0.4389	0.4788	0.5187	0.5586	0.6384	1.2768
8	0.3285	0.3650	0.4015	0.4380	0.4745	0.5110	0.5840	1.1680
9	0.2988	0.3320	0.3652	0.3984	0.4316	0.4648	0.5312	1.0624
10	0.2691	0.2990	0.3289	0.3588	0.3887	0.4186	0.4784	0.9568
11	0.2394	0.2660	0.2926	0.3192	0.3458	0.3724	0.4256	0.8512
12	0.2097	0.2330	0.2563	0.2796	0.3029	0.3262	0.3728	0.7456
13	0.1791	0.1990	0.2189	0.2388	0.2587	0.2786	0.3184	0.6368
14	0.1494	0.1660	0.1826	0.1992	0.2158	0.2324	0.2656	0.5312
15	0.1341	0.1490	0.1639	0.1788	0.1937	0.2086	0.2384	0.4768
16	0.1197	0.1330	0.1463	0.1596	0.1729	0.1862	0.2128	0.4256
17	0.1080	0.1200	0.1320	0.1440	0.1560	0.1680	0.1920	0.3840
18	0.0954	0.1060	0.1166	0.1272	0.1378	0.1484	0.1696	0.3392
19	0.0837	0.0930	0.1023	0.1116	0.1209	0.1302	0.1488	0.2976
20	0.0720	0.0800	0.0880	0.0960	0.1040	0.1120	0.1280	0.2560
21	0.0657	0.0730	0.0803	0.0876	0.0949	0.1022	0.1168	0.2336
22	0.0603	0.0670	0.0737	0.0804	0.0871	0.0938	0.1072	0.2144
23	0.0540	0.0600	0.0660	0.0720	0.0780	0.0840	0.0960	0.1920
24	0.0477	0.0530	0.0583	0.0636	0.0689	0.0742	0.0848	0.1696
25	0.0423	0.0470	0.0517	0.0564	0.0611	0.0658	0.0752	0.1504
26	0.0360	0.0400	0.0440	0.0480	0.0520	0.0560	0.0640	0.1280
27	0.0333	0.0370	0.0407	0.0444	0.0481	0.0518	0.0592	0.1184
28	0.0297	0.0330	0.0363	0.0396	0.0429	0.0462	0.0528	0.1056
29	0.0270	0.0300	0.0330	0.0360	0.0390	0.0420	0.0480	0.0960
30	0.0243	0.0270	0.0297	0.0324	0.0351	0.0378	0.0432	0.0864
31	0.0207	0.0230	0.0253	0.0276	0.0299	0.0322	0.0368	0.0736
32	0.0198	0.0220	0.0242	0.0264	0.0286	0.0308	0.0352	0.0704
33	0.0180	0.0200	0.0220	0.0240	0.0260	0.0280	0.0320	0.0640
34	0.0162	0.0180	0.0198	0.0216	0.0234	0.0252	0.0288	0.0576
35	0.0153	0.0170	0.0187	0.0204	0.0221	0.0238	0.0272	0.0544
36	0.0135	0.0150	0.0165	0.0180	0.0195	0.0210	0.0240	0.0480
37	0.0126	0.0140	0.0154	0.0168	0.0182	0.0196	0.0224	0.0448
38	0.0117	0.0130	0.0143	0.0156	0.0169	0.0182	0.0208	0.0416

Weights of Flat Rolled Steel per Lineal Foot in Pounds (*Continued*)

U. S. St'd Gage for Plate	Width of Flat Steel, Inches							
	3	4	5	6	7	8	9	10
0000000	5.1024	6.8032	8.504	10.204	11.905	13.606	15.307	17.008
000000	4.7808	6.3744	7.968	9.561	11.155	12.748	14.342	15.936
00000	4.4640	5.9520	7.440	8.928	10.416	11.904	13.392	14.880
0000	4.1472	5.5296	6.912	8.294	9.676	11.059	12.441	13.824
000	3.8256	5.1008	6.376	7.651	8.926	10.201	11.476	12.752
00	3.5088	4.6784	5.848	7.017	8.187	9.356	10.526	11.696
0	3.1872	4.2496	5.312	6.374	7.436	8.499	9.561	10.624
1	2.8704	3.8272	4.784	5.740	6.697	7.654	8.611	9.568
2	2.7120	3.6160	4.520	5.424	6.328	7.232	8.136	9.040
3	2.5488	3.3984	4.248	5.097	5.947	6.796	7.646	8.496
4	2.3904	3.1872	3.984	4.780	5.577	6.374	7.171	7.968
5	2.2320	2.9760	3.720	4.464	5.208	5.952	6.696	7.440
6	2.0736	2.7648	3.456	4.147	4.838	5.529	6.220	6.912
7	1.9152	2.5536	3.192	3.830	4.468	5.107	5.745	6.384
8	1.7520	2.3360	2.920	3.504	4.088	4.672	5.256	5.840
9	1.5936	2.1248	2.656	3.187	3.718	4.249	4.780	5.312
10	1.4352	1.9136	2.392	2.870	3.348	3.827	4.305	4.784
11	1.2768	1.7024	2.128	2.553	2.979	3.404	3.830	4.256
12	1.1184	1.4912	1.864	2.236	2.609	2.982	3.355	3.728
13	0.9552	1.2736	1.592	1.910	2.228	2.547	2.865	3.184
14	0.7968	1.0624	1.328	1.593	1.859	2.124	2.390	2.656
15	0.7152	0.9536	1.192	1.430	1.668	1.907	2.145	2.384
16	0.6384	0.8512	1.064	1.276	1.489	1.702	1.915	2.128
17	0.5760	0.7680	0.960	1.152	1.344	1.536	1.728	1 920
18	0.5088	0.6786	0.848	1.027	1.187	1.357	1.526	1.696
19	0.4464	0.5952	0.744	0.892	1.041	1.190	1.319	1.488
20	0.3840	0.5120	0.640	0.768	0.896	1.024	1.152	1.280
21	0.3504	0.4672	0.584	0.700	0.817	0.934	1.051	1.168
22	0.3216	0.4288	0.536	0.643	0.750	0.857	0.964	1.072
23	0.2880	0.3840	0.480	0.576	0.672	0.768	0.864	0.960
24	0.2544	0.3392	0.424	0.508	0.593	0.678	0.763	0.848
25	0.2256	0.3008	0.376	0.451	0.526	0.601	0.676	0.752
26	0.1920	0.2560	0.320	0.384	0.448	0.512	0.596	0.640
27	0.1776	0.2368	0.296	0.355	0.414	0.473	0.532	0.592
28	0.1584	0.2112	0.264	0.316	0.369	0.422	0.475	0.528
29	0.1440	0.1920	0.240	0.288	0.336	0.384	0.432	0.480
30	0.1272	0.1768	0.216	0.259	0.302	0.353	0.388	0.432
31	0.1104	0.1472	0.184	0.220	0.257	0.297	0.331	0.368
32	0.1056	0.1408	0.176	0.211	0.246	0.281	0.316	0.352
33	0.0960	0.1280	0.160	0.192	0.224	0.256	0.288	0.320
34	0.0864	0.1152	0.144	0.172	0.201	0.230	0.259	0.288
35	0.0816	0.1088	0.136	0.163	0.190	0.217	0.244	0.272
36	0.0720	0.0960	0.120	0.148	0.168	0.192	0.216	0.240
37	0.0674	0.0896	0.112	0.134	0.156	0.179	0.201	0.224
38	0.0624	0.0832	0.104	0.124	0.145	0.166	0.187	0.208

Weights of Flat Rolled Steel per Lineal Foot in Pounds (*Continued*)

U. S. St'd Gage for Plate	Width of Flat Steel, Inches							
	11	12	13	14	15	16	18	20
0000000	18.708	20.409	22.110	23.811	25.512	27.212	30.614	34.016
000000	17.529	19.123	20.716	22.310	23.904	25.497	28.684	31.872
00000	16.368	17.856	19.344	20.832	22.320	23.808	26.784	29.760
0000	15.206	16.588	17.971	19.353	20.736	22.118	24.883	27.648
000	14.027	15.302	16.577	17.852	19.128	20.403	22.953	25.504
00	12.865	14.035	15.204	16.374	17.544	18.713	21.052	23.392
0	11.686	12.748	13.811	14.873	15.936	16.998	19.123	21.248
1	10.524	11.481	12.438	13.395	14.352	15.308	17.222	19.136
2	9.944	10.848	11.752	12.656	13.560	14.464	16.272	18.080
3	9.345	10.195	11.044	11.894	12.744	13.593	15.292	16.992
4	8.764	9.561	10.358	11.155	11.952	12.748	14.342	15.936
5	8.184	8.928	9.672	10.416	11.160	11.804	13.392	14.880
6	7.603	8.294	8.985	9.676	10.368	11.059	12.441	13.824
7	7.022	7.660	8.299	8.937	9.576	10.214	11.491	12.768
8	6.424	7.008	7.592	8.176	8.760	9.344	10.512	11.680
9	5.843	6.374	6.905	7.436	7.968	8.499	9.561	10.624
10	5.262	5.740	6.219	6.697	7.176	7.654	8.611	9.568
11	4.681	5.107	5.532	5.958	6.384	6.809	7.660	8.512
12	4.100	4.473	4.846	5.219	5.592	5.964	6.710	7.456
13	3.502	3.820	4.139	4.457	4.776	5.094	5.731	6.368
14	2.921	3.187	3.452	3.718	3.984	4.249	4.780	5.312
15	2.622	2.860	3.099	3.337	3.576	3.814	4.291	4.768
16	2.340	2.553	2.766	2.979	3.192	3.404	3.830	4.256
17	2.112	2.304	2.496	2.688	2.880	3.072	3.456	3.840
18	1.865	2.055	2.204	2.374	2.544	2.714	3.056	3.392
19	1.636	1.785	1.934	2.083	2.232	2.380	2.638	2.976
20	1.408	1.536	1.664	1.792	1.920	2.048	2.304	2.560
21	1.284	1.401	1.518	1.635	1.752	1.868	2.102	2.336
22	1.179	1.286	1.393	1.500	1.608	1.715	1.929	2.144
23	1.056	1.152	1.248	1.344	1.440	1.536	1.728	1.920
24	0.932	1.017	1.102	1.187	1.272	1.356	1.526	1.696
25	0.827	0.902	0.977	1.052	1.128	1.203	1.353	1.504
26	0.704	0.768	0.832	0.896	0.960	1.024	1.192	1.380
27	0.651	0.710	0.769	0.828	0.888	0.947	1.065	1.184
28	0.580	0.633	0.686	0.739	0.792	0.844	0.950	1.056
29	0.528	0.576	0.624	0.672	0.720	0.768	0.864	0.960
30	0.475	0.518	0.561	0.604	0.648	0.707	0.777	0.864
31	0.404	0.441	0.478	0.515	0.552	0.594	0.662	0.736
32	0.387	0.422	0.457	0.492	0.528	0.563	0.633	0.714
33	0.352	0.384	0.416	0.448	0.480	0.512	0.576	0.640
34	0.316	0.345	0.374	0.403	0.432	0.460	0.518	0.576
35	0.299	0.326	0.359	0.380	0.408	0.435	0.489	0.544
36	0.264	0.296	0.312	0.336	0.360	0.384	0.432	0.480
37	0.246	0.279	0.291	0.313	0.336	0.358	0.403	0.448
38	0.228	0.249	0.270	0.291	0.312	0.332	0.374	0.416

Weight of Flat Rolled Steel Bars in Pounds per Lineal Foot

(One cubic foot of rolled steel weighs 489.6 pounds.)

Width of Bar, Inches

Thickness of Bar, Ins.	¼	½	¾	1	1¼	1½	1¾	2	2¼	2½	2¾	3	3¼	3½	3¾	4	4¼	4½
1/16	0.053	0.106	0.159	0.21	0.27	0.32	0.37	0.42	0.48	0.53	0.58	0.64	0.69	0.74	0.80	0.85	0.90	0.96
1/8	0.106	0.212	0.319	0.42	0.53	0.64	0.74	0.85	0.96	1.06	1.17	1.27	1.38	1.49	1.59	1.70	1.81	1.91
3/16	0.159	0.319	0.478	0.64	0.80	0.96	1.12	1.28	1.43	1.59	1.75	1.91	2.07	2.23	2.39	2.55	2.71	2.87
1/4	0.213	0.425	0.638	0.85	1.06	1.28	1.49	1.70	1.91	2.13	2.34	2.55	2.76	2.98	3.19	3.40	3.61	3.83
5/16	0.266	0.531	0.797	1.06	1.33	1.59	1.86	2.13	2.39	2.66	2.92	3.19	3.45	3.72	3.98	4.25	4.52	4.78
3/8	0.319	0.638	0.956	1.28	1.59	1.91	2.23	2.55	2.87	3.19	3.51	3.83	4.14	4.46	4.78	5.10	5.42	5.74
7/16	0.372	0.744	1.12	1.49	1.86	2.23	2.60	2.98	3.35	3.72	4.09	4.46	4.83	5.21	5.58	5.95	6.32	6.69
1/2	0.425	0.850	1.28	1.70	2.13	2.55	2.98	3.40	3.83	4.25	4.68	5.10	5.53	5.95	6.38	6.80	7.22	7.65
9/16	0.478	0.956	1.43	1.91	2.39	2.87	3.35	3.83	4.30	4.78	5.26	5.74	6.22	6.69	7.17	7.65	8.13	8.61
5/8	0.531	1.06	1.59	2.13	2.66	3.19	3.72	4.25	4.78	5.31	5.84	6.38	6.91	7.44	7.97	8.50	9.03	9.56
11/16	0.584	1.17	1.75	2.34	2.92	3.51	4.09	4.68	5.26	5.84	6.43	7.01	7.60	8.18	8.77	9.35	9.93	10.52
3/4	0.638	1.28	1.91	2.55	3.19	3.83	4.46	5.10	5.74	6.38	7.01	7.65	8.29	8.93	9.56	10.20	10.84	11.48
13/16	0.691	1.38	2.07	2.76	3.45	4.14	4.83	5.53	6.22	6.91	7.60	8.29	8.98	9.67	10.36	11.05	11.74	12.43
7/8	0.744	1.49	2.23	2.98	3.72	4.46	5.21	5.95	6.69	7.44	8.18	8.93	9.67	10.41	11.16	11.90	12.64	13.39
15/16	0.797	1.59	2.39	3.19	3.98	4.78	5.58	6.38	7.17	7.97	8.77	9.56	10.36	11.16	11.95	12.75	13.55	14.34
1	0.850	1.70	2.55	3.40	4.25	5.10	5.95	6.80	7.65	8.50	9.35	10.20	11.05	11.90	12.75	13.60	14.45	15.30
1 1/16	0.903	1.81	2.71	3.61	4.52	5.42	6.32	7.23	8.13	9.03	9.93	10.84	11.74	12.64	13.55	14.45	15.35	16.26
1 1/8	0.956	1.91	2.87	3.83	4.78	5.74	6.69	7.65	8.61	9.56	10.52	11.48	12.43	13.39	14.34	15.30	16.26	17.21
1 3/16	1.01	2.02	3.03	4.04	5.05	6.06	7.07	8.08	9.08	10.09	11.10	12.11	13.12	14.13	15.14	16.15	17.16	18.17
1 1/4	1.06	2.12	3.19	4.25	5.31	6.38	7.44	8.50	9.56	10.63	11.69	12.75	13.81	14.88	15.94	17.00	18.06	19.13
1 5/16	1.12	2.23	3.34	4.46	5.58	6.69	7.81	8.93	10.04	11.16	12.27	13.39	14.50	15.62	16.73	17.85	18.97	20.08
1 3/8	1.17	2.34	3.50	4.68	5.84	7.01	8.18	9.35	10.52	11.69	12.86	14.03	15.19	16.36	17.53	18.70	19.87	21.04
1 7/16	1.22	2.44	3.66	4.89	6.11	7.33	8.55	9.78	11.00	12.22	13.44	14.66	15.88	17.11	18.33	19.55	20.77	21.99
1 1/2	1.27	2.55	3.82	5.10	6.38	7.65	8.93	10.20	11.48	12.75	14.03	15.30	16.58	17.85	19.13	20.40	21.68	22.95
1 9/16	1.33	2.66	3.98	5.31	6.64	7.97	9.30	10.63	11.95	13.28	14.61	15.92	17.27	18.59	19.92	21.25	22.58	23.91
1 5/8	1.38	2.76	4.14	5.53	6.91	8.29	9.67	11.05	12.43	13.81	15.19	16.53	17.96	19.34	20.72	22.10	23.48	24.86
1 11/16	1.43	2.87	4.30	5.74	7.17	8.61	10.04	11.48	12.91	14.34	15.78	17.21	18.65	20.08	21.52	22.95	24.38	25.82
1 3/4	1.49	2.97	4.46	5.95	7.44	8.93	10.41	11.90	13.39	14.88	16.36	17.85	19.34	20.83	22.31	23.80	25.29	26.78
1 13/16	1.54	3.08	4.62	6.16	7.70	9.24	10.78	12.33	13.87	15.41	16.95	18.49	20.03	21.57	23.11	24.65	26.19	27.73
1 7/8	1.59	3.19	4.78	6.38	7.97	9.56	11.16	12.75	14.34	15.94	17.53	19.13	20.72	22.31	23.91	25.50	27.09	28.69
1 15/16	1.65	3.29	4.94	6.59	8.23	9.88	11.53	13.18	14.82	16.47	18.12	19.76	21.41	23.06	24.70	26.35	28.00	29.64
2	1.70	3.40	5.10	6.80	8.50	10.20	11.90	13.60	15.30	17.00	18.70	20.40	22.10	23.80	25.50	27.20	28.90	30.60

Weight of Flat Rolled Steel Bars in Pounds per Lineal Foot

(One cubic foot of rolled steel weighs 489.6 pounds.)

Width of Bar, Inches

Thickness of Bar, Ins.	4¾	5	5¼	5½	5¾	6	6½	7	7½	8	8½	9	9½	10	10½	11	11½	12
1/16	1.01	1.06	1.11	1.17	1.22	1.27	1.38	1.49	1.59	1.70	1.81	1.91	2.02	2.12	2.23	2.34	2.44	2.55
1/8	2.02	2.12	2.23	2.34	2.44	2.55	2.76	2.97	3.18	3.40	3.61	3.82	4.04	4.25	4.46	4.67	4.89	5.10
3/16	3.03	3.19	3.35	3.51	3.67	3.83	4.14	4.46	4.78	5.10	5.42	5.74	6.06	6.38	6.69	7.01	7.33	7.65
1/4	4.04	4.25	4.46	4.68	4.89	5.10	5.53	5.95	6.38	6.80	7.23	7.65	8.08	8.50	8.93	9.35	9.78	10.20
5/16	5.05	5.31	5.58	5.84	6.11	6.38	6.91	7.44	7.97	8.50	9.03	9.56	10.09	10.63	11.16	11.69	12.22	12.75
3/8	6.06	6.38	6.69	7.01	7.33	7.65	8.29	8.93	9.56	10.20	10.84	11.48	12.11	12.75	13.39	14.03	14.66	15.30
7/16	7.07	7.44	7.81	8.18	8.55	8.93	9.67	10.41	11.16	11.90	12.64	13.39	14.13	14.88	15.62	16.36	17.11	17.85
1/2	8.08	8.50	8.93	9.35	9.78	10.20	11.05	11.90	12.75	13.60	14.45	15.30	16.15	17.00	17.85	18.70	19.55	20.40
9/16	9.08	9.56	10.04	10.52	11.00	11.48	12.43	13.39	14.34	15.30	16.26	17.21	18.17	19.13	20.08	21.04	21.99	22.95
5/8	10.10	10.63	11.16	11.69	12.22	12.75	13.81	14.88	15.94	17.00	18.06	19.13	20.19	21.25	22.31	23.38	24.44	25.50
11/16	11.10	11.69	12.27	12.86	13.44	14.03	15.19	16.36	17.53	18.70	19.87	21.04	22.21	23.38	24.54	25.71	26.88	28.05
3/4	12.11	12.75	13.39	14.03	14.67	15.30	16.58	17.85	19.13	20.40	21.68	22.95	24.23	25.50	26.78	28.05	29.33	30.60
13/16	13.12	13.81	14.50	15.19	15.89	16.58	17.96	19.34	20.72	22.10	23.48	24.86	26.24	27.63	29.01	30.39	31.77	33.15
7/8	14.13	14.88	15.62	16.36	17.11	17.85	19.34	20.83	22.31	23.80	25.29	26.78	28.26	29.75	31.24	32.73	34.21	35.70
15/16	15.15	15.94	16.73	17.53	18.33	19.13	20.72	22.31	23.91	25.50	27.09	28.69	30.28	31.88	33.47	35.06	36.66	38.25
1	16.15	17.00	17.85	18.70	19.55	20.40	22.10	23.80	25.50	27.20	28.90	30.60	32.30	34.00	35.70	37.40	39.10	40.80
1 1/16	17.16	18.06	18.97	19.87	20.77	21.68	23.48	25.29	27.09	28.90	30.71	32.51	34.32	36.13	37.93	39.74	41.54	43.35
1 1/8	18.17	19.13	20.08	21.04	22.00	22.95	24.86	26.78	28.69	30.60	32.51	34.43	36.34	38.25	40.16	42.08	43.99	45.90
1 3/16	19.18	20.19	21.20	22.21	23.22	24.23	26.24	28.26	30.28	32.30	34.32	36.34	38.36	40.38	42.39	44.41	46.43	48.45
1 1/4	20.19	21.25	22.31	23.38	24.44	25.50	27.63	29.75	31.88	34.00	36.13	38.25	40.38	42.50	44.63	46.75	48.88	51.00
1 5/16	21.20	22.31	23.43	24.54	25.66	26.78	29.01	31.24	33.47	35.70	37.93	40.16	42.39	44.63	46.86	49.09	51.32	53.55
1 3/8	22.21	23.38	24.54	25.71	26.88	28.05	30.39	32.73	35.06	37.40	39.74	42.08	44.41	46.75	49.09	51.43	53.76	56.10
1 7/16	23.22	24.44	25.66	26.88	28.10	29.33	31.77	34.21	36.66	39.10	41.54	43.99	46.43	48.88	51.32	53.76	56.21	58.65
1 1/2	24.23	25.50	26.78	28.05	29.33	30.60	33.15	35.70	38.25	40.80	43.35	45.90	48.45	51.00	53.55	56.10	58.65	61.20
1 9/16	25.23	26.56	27.89	29.22	30.55	31.88	34.53	37.19	39.84	42.50	45.16	47.81	50.47	53.13	55.78	58.44	61.09	63.75
1 5/8	26.24	27.63	29.01	30.39	31.77	33.15	35.91	38.68	41.44	44.20	46.96	49.73	52.49	55.25	58.01	60.78	63.54	66.30
1 11/16	27.25	28.69	30.12	31.56	32.99	34.43	37.29	40.16	43.03	45.90	48.77	51.64	54.51	57.38	60.24	63.11	65.98	68.85
1 3/4	28.26	29.75	31.24	32.73	34.21	35.70	38.68	41.65	44.63	47.60	50.58	53.55	56.53	59.50	62.48	65.45	68.43	71.40
1 13/16	29.27	30.81	32.35	33.89	35.43	36.98	40.06	43.14	46.22	49.30	52.38	55.46	58.54	61.63	64.71	67.79	70.87	73.95
1 7/8	30.28	31.88	33.47	35.06	36.66	38.25	41.44	44.63	47.81	51.00	54.19	57.38	60.56	63.75	66.94	70.13	73.31	76.50
1 15/16	31.29	32.94	34.58	36.23	37.88	39.53	42.82	46.11	49.41	52.70	55.99	59.29	62.58	65.88	69.17	72.46	75.76	79.05
2	32.30	34.00	35.70	37.40	39.10	40.80	44.20	47.60	51.00	54.40	57.80	61.20	64.60	68.00	71.40	74.80	78.20	81.60

Areas and Weights of Fillets of Steel, Cast Iron and Brass

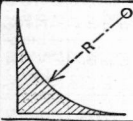

Calculations are based on the following weights:

Steel.........489.6 pounds per cubic foot.
Cast iron.....450 pounds per cubic foot.
Cast brass....504 pounds per cubic foot.

Radius R, Inches	Area, Square Inches	Weight of Steel		Weight of Cast Iron		Weight of Cast Brass	
		Per Foot	Per Inch	Per Foot	Per Inch	Per Foot	Per Inch
1/4	0.0134	0.0455	0.0038	0.0418	0.0035	0.0469	0.0040
5/16	0.0209	0.0712	0.0059	0.0655	0.0054	0.0733	0.0061
3/8	0.0302	0.1027	0.0085	0.0945	0.0078	0.1058	0.0088
7/16	0.0411	0.1397	0.0116	0.1285	0.0107	0.1439	0.0120
1/2	0.0536	0.1825	0.0152	0.1679	0.0140	0.1880	0.0157
9/16	0.0679	0.2310	0.0192	0.2125	0.0177	0.2380	0.0200
5/8	0.0834	0.2847	0.0237	0.2619	0.0218	0.2932	0.0244
11/16	0.1014	0.3447	0.0287	0.3171	0.0264	0.3550	0.0300
3/4	0.1207	0.4105	0.0342	0.3777	0.0315	0.4228	0.0352
13/16	0.1416	0.4817	0.0401	0.4432	0.0369	0.4962	0.0414
7/8	0.1643	0.5580	0.0465	0.5134	0.0428	0.5747	0.0479
15/16	0.1886	0.6405	0.0534	0.5893	0.0491	0.6597	0.0550
1	0.2146	0.7300	0.0608	0.6716	0.0559	0.7519	0.0626
1 1/8	0.2716	0.9250	0.0771	0.8510	0.0709	0.9527	0.0794
1 1/4	0.3353	1.140	0.0950	1.049	0.0874	1.174	0.0979
1 3/8	0.4057	1.200	0.1000	1.104	0.0920	1.236	0.1030
1 1/2	0.4828	1.642	0.1368	1.511	0.1259	1.691	0.1410
1 5/8	0.5668	1.930	0.1608	1.776	0.1479	1.988	0.1657
1 3/4	0.6572	2.235	0.1862	2.056	0.1713	2.302	0.1920
1 7/8	0.7545	2.565	0.2137	2.360	0.1970	2.642	0.2202
2	0.8585	2.917	0.2431	2.684	0.2237	3.005	0.2504
2 1/8	0.9692	3.292	0.2743	3.029	0.2502	3.391	0.2826
2 1/4	1.086	3.695	0.3079	3.399	0.2832	3.806	0.3172
2 3/8	1.210	4.115	0.3429	3.786	0.3155	4.238	0.3532
2 1/2	1.341	4.560	0.3800	4.195	0.3496	4.697	0.3914
2 5/8	1.478	5.030	0.4192	4.628	0.3857	5.181	0.4317
2 3/4	1.623	5.507	0.4589	5.066	0.4222	5.672	0.4727
2 7/8	1.774	6.027	0.5022	5.545	0.4621	6.208	0.5017
3	1.931	6.565	0.5471	5.940	0.4950	6.762	0.5635
3 1/8	2.096	7.125	0.5937	6.555	0.5462	7.339	0.6116
3 1/4	2.267	7.700	0.6417	7.084	0.5903	7.931	0.6609
3 3/8	2.444	8.300	0.6917	7.636	0.6363	8.549	0.7124
3 1/2	2.629	8.925	0.7438	8.211	0.6926	9.193	0.7661
3 5/8	2.820	9.575	0.7979	8.809	0.7341	9.862	0.8220
3 3/4	3.018	10.27	0.8523	9.448	0.7873	10.58	0.8817
3 7/8	3.222	10.97	0.9142	10.09	0.8408	11.30	0.9417
4	3.434	11.65	0.9709	10.72	0.8933	12.00	1.000
4 1/4	3.876	13.15	1.096	12.10	1.008	13.54	1.130
4 1/2	4.346	14.77	1.231	13.59	1.132	15.21	1.270
4 3/4	4.842	16.45	1.371	15.13	1.261	16.94	1.412
5	5.365	18.25	1.521	16.79	1.400	18.80	1.570

Tin Plate Base Weight and Thickness

Base * Weight, Lbs., and Symbols	Weight per Sq. Ft.	Approx. Thickness, Inch	Base Weight, Lbs., and Symbols	Weight per Sq. Ft.	Approx. Thickness, Inch	Base Weight, Lbs., and Symbols	Weight per Sq. Ft.	Approx. Thickness, Inch
55	0.253	0.006	128–IXL	0.588	0.015	255–7 X	1.125	0.028
60	0.276	0.007	135–IX	0.620	0.015	268–D 4 X	1.230	0.031
65	0.298	0.007	139–DC	0.638	0.016	275–8 X	1.263	0.032
70	0.321	0.008	155–2 X	0.712	0.018	295–9 X	1.355	0.034
75	0.344	0.009	175–3 X	0.804	0.020	315–10 X	1.447	0.036
80	0.367	0.009	180–DX	0.827	0.021	335–11 X	1.539	0.038
85	0.390	0.010	195–4 X	0.895	0.022	355–12 X	1.631	0.041
90	0.413	0.010	210–D 2 X	0.964	0.024	375–13 X	1.722	0.043
95	0.436	0.011	215–5 X	0.988	0.025	395–14 X	1.814	0.045
100–ICL	0.459	0.011	235–6 X	1.08	0.027	415–15 X	1.906	0.048
107–IC	0.491	0.012	240–D 3 X	1.10	0.027	435–16 X	1.998	0.050

* Weight of standard " base box " containing 112 sheets, 14 × 20 inches.

Sheet Zinc Gage

(Matthiessen & Hegeler Zinc Co.)

Gage No.	Thickness, Inches	Gage No.	Thickness, Inches	Gage No.	Thickness, Inches	Gage No.	Thickness, Inches
1	0.002	8	0.016	15	0.040	22	0.090
2	0.004	9	0.018	16	0.045	23	0.100
3	0.006	10	0.020	17	0.050	24	0.125
4	0.008	11	0.024	18	0.055	25	0.250
5	0.010	12	0.028	19	0.060	26	0.375
6	0.012	13	0.032	20	0.070	27	0.500
7	0.014	14	0.036	21	0.080	28	1.000

American "Russia-Iron" Gage

Gage No.	Thickness, Ins.	Gage No.	Thickness, Ins.	Gage No.	Thickness, Ins.	Gage No.	Thickness, Ins.	Gage No.	Thickness, Ins.
7	0.015	9	0.017	11	0.020	13	0.024	15	0.027
8	0.016	10	0.018	12	0.021	14	0.025	16	0.030

Weight in Pounds per Square Foot of Zinc Plate

Gage No.	Weight in Pounds per Sq. Foot	Gage No.	Weight in Pounds per Sq. Foot	Gage No.	Weight in Pounds per Sq. Foot	Gage No.	Weight in Pounds per Sq. Foot
1	0.07	8	0.60	15	1.50	22	3.37
2	0.15	9	0.67	16	1.68	23	3.75
3	0.22	10	0.75	17	1.87	24	4.70
4	0.30	11	0.90	18	2.06	25	9.40
5	0.37	12	1.05	19	2.25	26	14.00
6	0.45	13	1.20	20	2.62	27	18.75
7	0.52	14	1.35	21	3.00	28	37.50

Table giving Number of Pieces in One Pound, when Weight of One Hundred Pieces is Known

Example: — 100 pieces weigh 11 pounds 5 ounces. From the table, there are then 8.84 pieces in one pound.

Ounces	Pounds								
	0	1	2	3	4	5	6	7	8
0	......	100.00	50.00	33.33	25.00	20.00	16.67	14.29	12.50
1	1600.00	94.12	48.48	32.65	24.61	19.75	16.49	14.16	12.40
2	800.00	88.88	47.06	32.00	24.24	19.51	16.33	14.03	12.31
3	533.33	84.21	45.71	31.37	23.88	19.27	16.16	13.91	12.21
4	400.00	80.00	44.44	30.77	23.52	19.05	16.00	13.79	12.12
5	320.00	76.19	43.24	30.19	23.19	18.82	15.84	13.67	12.03
6	266.66	72.73	42.11	29.63	22.86	18.60	15.69	13.56	11.94
7	228.57	69.57	41.03	29.09	22.53	18.39	15.53	13.44	11.85
8	200.00	66.67	40.00	28.57	22.22	18.18	15.38	13.33	11.76
9	177.78	64.00	39.02	28.07	21.92	17.98	15.24	13.22	11.68
10	160.00	61.54	38.09	27.58	21.62	17.78	15.09	13.11	11.59
11	145.45	59.26	37.21	27.12	21.33	17.58	14.95	13.01	11.51
12	133.33	57.14	36.36	26.67	21.05	17.39	14.81	12.90	11.43
13	123.08	55.17	35.56	26.23	20.78	17.20	14.68	12.80	11.35
14	114.29	53.33	34.78	25.81	20.51	17.02	14.54	12.70	11.27
15	106.67	51.61	34.04	25.40	20.25	16.84	14.41	12.60	11.19

Ounces	Pounds								
	9	10	11	12	13	14	15	16	17
0	11.11	10.00	9.09	8.33	7.69	7.14	6.66	6.25	5.88
1	11.03	9.94	9.04	8.29	7.65	7.11	6.64	6.23	5.86
2	10.96	9.88	8.99	8.25	7.62	7.08	6.61	6.20	5.84
3	10.89	9.82	8.94	8.20	7.58	7.04	6.59	6.17	5.82
4	10.81	9.76	8.89	8.16	7.54	7.01	6.56	6.15	5.80
5	10.74	9.69	8.84	8.12	7.51	6.98	6.53	6.13	5.78
6	10.67	9.64	8.79	8.08	7.47	6.95	6.50	6.11	5.76
7	10.59	9.58	8.74	8.04	7.44	6.92	6.47	6.08	5.74
8	10.53	9.52	8.69	8.00	7.41	6.89	6.45	6.06	5.72
9	10.46	9.47	8.65	7.96	7.37	6.86	6.43	6.04	5.70
10	10.39	9.41	8.60	7.92	7.34	6.84	6.40	6.01	5.68
11	10.32	9.36	8.56	7.88	7.31	6.81	6.37	5.98	5.66
12	10.25	9.30	8.51	7.84	7.27	6.78	6.35	5.96	5.64
13	10.19	9.25	8.46	7.80	7.24	6.75	6.32	5.94	5.62
14	10.13	9.19	8.42	7.76	7.21	6.72	6.30	5.92	5.60
15	10.06	9.14	8.38	7.73	7.17	6.69	6.27	5.90	5.58

Ounces	Pounds								
	18	19	20	21	22	23	24	25	26
0	5.56	5.26	5.00	4.76	4.54	4.35	4.16	4.00	3.84
1	5.54	5.24	4.98	4.74	4.53	4.34	4.15	3.99	3.83
2	5.52	5.23	4.96	4.73	4.52	4.33	4.14	3.98	3.82
3	5.50	5.21	4.95	4.71	4.51	4.32	4.13	3.97	3.81
4	5.48	5.19	4.94	4.70	4.50	4.30	4.12	3.96	3.81
5	5.46	5.18	4.92	4.69	4.49	4.29	4.11	3.95	3.80
6	5.44	5.16	4.90	4.68	4.48	4.28	4.10	3.94	3.79
7	5.42	5.14	4.89	4.66	4.46	4.27	4.09	3.93	3.78
8	5.40	5.12	4.88	4.65	4.44	4.25	4.08	3.92	3.77
9	5.38	5.11	4.86	4.64	4.43	4.24	4.07	3.91	3.76
10	5.36	5.09	4.84	4.63	4.42	4.23	4.06	3.90	3.75
11	5.34	5.08	4.83	4.61	4.41	4.22	4.05	3.89	3.74
12	5.32	5.07	4.82	4.60	4.39	4.21	4.04	3.88	3.73
13	5.31	5.05	4.81	4.59	4.38	4.19	4.03	3.87	3.73
14	5.30	5.04	4.79	4.57	4.37	4.18	4.02	3.86	3.72
15	5.28	5.02	4.78	4.56	4.36	4.17	4.01	3.85	3.71

HEAT

Thermometer Scales. — There are three thermometer scales in general use: the Fahrenheit (F.), which is generally used in the English speaking countries; the Centigrade (C.) or Celsius, which is used in several continental countries and in scientific work; and the Réaumur (R.), which is used to some extent on the European continent.

In the Fahrenheit thermometer, the freezing point of water is marked at 32 degrees on the scale and the boiling point, at atmospheric pressure, at 212 degrees. The distance between these two points is divided into 180 degrees. On the Centigrade scale, the freezing point of water is at 0 degrees and the boiling point at 100 degrees. On the Réaumur scale, the freezing point is at 0 degrees and the boiling point at 80 degrees. The following formulas may be used for converting temperatures given on any one of the scales to the other scales:

$$\text{Degrees Fahrenheit} = \frac{9 \times \text{degrees C.}}{5} + 32 = \frac{9 \times \text{degrees R.}}{4} + 32.$$

$$\text{Degrees Centigrade} = \frac{5 \times (\text{degrees F.} - 32)}{9} = \frac{5 \times \text{degrees R.}}{4}$$

$$\text{Degrees Réaumur} = \frac{4 \times \text{degrees C.}}{5} = \frac{4 \times (\text{degrees F.} - 32)}{9}$$

Tables are given herewith for converting degrees Centigrade into degrees Fahrenheit. The tables can, of course, be conveniently used in the reverse order. The table for "Conversion from Degrees Centigrade to Degrees Fahrenheit" covers the whole range of practically or scientifically obtained temperatures. As an example of the use of the table, 1040 degrees Centigrade equals 1904 degrees Fahrenheit, and that −130 degrees Centigrade equals −202 degrees Fahrenheit.

Absolute Temperature and Absolute Zero. — A point has been determined on the thermometer scale, by theoretical considerations, which is called the absolute zero and beyond which a further decrease in temperature is inconceivable. This point is located at −273.2 degrees Centigrade or 459.7 degrees F. A temperature reckoned from this point, instead of from the zero on the ordinary thermometers, is called absolute temperature. Absolute temperature in degrees C. is known as "degrees Kelvin" or the "Kelvin scale" (K) and absolute temperature in degrees F. is known as "degrees Rankine" or the "Rankine scale" (R).

$$\text{Degrees Kelvin} = \text{degrees C.} + 273.2$$
$$\text{Degrees Rankine} = \text{degrees F.} + 459.7$$

Measures of the Quantity of Heat. — The unit of quantity of heat used in the English speaking countries is the British thermal unit, which is the quantity of heat required to raise the temperature of one pound of pure water one degree F. (American Standard abbreviation, Btu; conventional British symbol, B.Th.U.) The French thermal unit or *kilogram calorie*, is the quantity of heat required to raise the temperature of one kilogram of pure water one degree C. One kilogram calorie = 3.968 British thermal units = 1000 gram calories.

The number of foot-pounds of mechanical energy equivalent to one British thermal unit is called the *mechanical equivalent of heat*, and equals 778 foot-pounds. One foot-pound equals 0.001285 heat unit.

Comparison Between Degrees Centigrade and Degrees Fahrenheit

Deg. C.	Deg. F.	Deg. C.	Deg. F.	Deg. C.	Deg. F.	Deg. C.	Deg. F.	Deg. C.	Deg. F.	Deg. C.	Deg. F.
−40	−40.0	8	46.4	56	132.8	104	219.2	152	305.6	200	392.0
−39	−38.2	9	48.2	57	134.6	105	221.0	153	307.4	201	393.8
−38	−36.4	10	50.0	58	136.4	106	222.8	154	309.2	202	395.6
−37	−34.6	11	51.8	59	138.2	107	224.6	155	311.0	203	397.4
−36	−32.8	12	53.6	60	140.0	108	226.4	156	312.8	204	399.2
−35	−31.0	13	55.4	61	141.8	109	228.2	157	314.6	205	401.0
−34	−29.2	14	57.2	62	143.6	110	230.0	158	316.4	206	402.8
−33	−27.4	15	59.0	63	145.4	111	231.8	159	318.2	207	404.6
−32	−25.6	16	60.8	64	147.2	112	233.6	160	320.0	208	406.4
−31	−23.8	17	62.6	65	149.0	113	235.4	161	321.8	209	408.2
−30	−22.0	18	64.4	66	150.8	114	237.2	162	323.6	210	410.0
−29	−20.2	19	66.2	67	152.6	115	239.0	163	325.4	211	411.8
−28	−18.4	20	68.0	68	154.4	116	240.8	164	327.2	212	413.6
−27	−16.6	21	69.8	69	156.2	117	242.6	165	329.0	213	415.4
−26	−14.8	22	71.6	70	158.0	118	244.4	166	330.8	214	417.2
−25	−13.0	23	73.4	71	159.8	119	246.2	167	332.6	215	419.0
−24	−11.2	24	75.2	72	161.6	120	248.0	168	334.4	216	420.8
−23	− 9.4	25	77.0	73	163.4	121	249.8	169	336.2	217	422.6
−22	− 7.6	26	78.8	74	165.2	122	251.6	170	338.0	218	424.4
−21	− 5.8	27	80.6	75	167.0	123	253.4	171	339.8	219	426.2
−20	− 4.0	28	82.4	76	168.8	124	255.2	172	341.6	220	428.0
−19	− 2.2	29	84.2	77	170.6	125	257.0	173	343.4	221	429.8
−18	− 0.4	30	86.0	78	172.4	126	258.8	174	345.2	222	431.6
−17	+ 1.4	31	87.8	79	174.2	127	260.6	175	347.0	223	433.4
−16	3.2	32	89.6	80	176.0	128	262.4	176	348.8	224	435.2
−15	5.0	33	91.4	81	177.8	129	264.2	177	350.6	225	437.0
−14	6.8	34	93.2	82	179.6	130	266.0	178	352.4	226	438.8
−13	8.6	35	95.0	83	181.4	131	267.8	179	354.2	227	440.6
−12	10.4	36	96.8	84	183.2	132	269.6	180	356.0	228	442.4
−11	12.2	37	98.6	85	185.0	133	271.4	181	357.8	229	444.2
−10	14.0	38	100.4	86	186.8	134	273.2	182	359.6	230	446.0
− 9	15.8	39	102.2	87	188.6	135	275.0	183	361.4	231	447.8
− 8	17.6	40	104.0	88	190.4	136	276.8	184	363.2	232	449.6
− 7	19.4	41	105.8	89	192.2	137	278.6	185	365.0	233	451.4
− 6	21.2	42	107.6	90	194.0	138	280.4	186	366.3	234	453.2
− 5	23.0	43	109.4	91	195.8	139	282.2	187	368.6	235	455.0
− 4	24.8	44	111.2	92	197.6	140	284.0	188	370.4	236	456.8
− 3	26.6	45	113.0	93	199.4	141	285.8	189	372.2	237	458.6
− 2	28.4	46	114.8	94	201.2	142	287.6	190	374.0	238	460.4
− 1	30.2	47	116.6	95	203.0	143	289.4	191	375.8	239	462.2
0	32.0	48	118.4	96	204.8	144	291.2	192	377.6	240	464.0
+ 1	33.8	49	120.2	97	206.6	145	293.0	193	379.4	241	465.8
2	35.6	50	122.0	98	208.4	146	294.8	194	381.2	242	467.6
3	37.4	51	123.8	99	210.2	147	296.6	195	383.0	243	469.4
4	39.2	52	125.6	100	212.0	148	298.4	196	384.8	244	471.2
5	41.0	53	127.4	101	213.8	149	300.2	197	386.6	246	474.8
6	42.8	54	129.2	102	215.6	150	302.0	198	388.4	248	478.4
7	44.6	55	131.0	103	217.4	151	303.8	199	390.2	250	482.0

Table for Conversion from Degrees Centigrade to Degrees Fahrenheit

Degrees Centi- grade	0	10	20	30	40	50	60	70	80	90
	Degrees Fahrenheit									
−200	−328	−346	−364	−382	−400	−418	−436	−454	.....	.....
−100	−148	−166	−184	−202	−220	−238	−256	−274	−292	−310
−0	+32	+14	−4	−22	−40	−58	−76	−94	−112	−130
0	32	50	68	86	104	122	140	158	176	194
100	212	230	248	266	284	302	320	338	356	374
200	392	410	428	446	464	482	500	518	536	554
300	572	590	608	626	644	662	680	698	716	734
400	752	770	788	806	824	842	860	878	896	914
500	932	950	968	986	1004	1022	1040	1058	1076	1094
600	1112	1130	1148	1166	1184	1202	1220	1238	1256	1274
700	1292	1310	1328	1346	1364	1382	1400	1418	1436	1454
800	1472	1490	1508	1526	1544	1562	1580	1598	1616	1634
900	1652	1670	1688	1706	1724	1742	1760	1778	1796	1814
1000	1832	1850	1868	1886	1904	1922	1940	1958	1976	1994
1100	2012	2030	2048	2066	2084	2102	2120	2138	2156	2174
1200	2192	2210	2228	2246	2264	2282	2300	2318	2336	2354
1300	2372	2390	2408	2426	2444	2462	2480	2498	2516	2534
1400	2552	2570	2588	2606	2624	2642	2660	2678	2696	2714
1500	2732	2750	2768	2786	2804	2822	2840	2858	2876	2894
1600	2912	2930	2948	2966	2984	3002	3020	3038	3056	3074
1700	3092	3110	3128	3146	3164	3182	3200	3218	3236	3254
1800	3272	3290	3308	3326	3344	3362	3380	3398	3416	3434
1900	3452	3470	3488	3506	3524	3542	3560	3578	3596	3614
2000	3632	3650	3668	3686	3704	3722	3740	3758	3776	3794
2100	3812	3830	3848	3866	3884	3902	3920	3938	3956	3974
2200	3992	4010	4028	4046	4064	4082	4100	4118	4136	4154
2300	4172	4190	4208	4226	4244	4262	4280	4298	4316	4334
2400	4352	4370	4388	4406	4424	4442	4460	4478	4496	4514
2500	4532	4550	4568	4586	4604	4622	4640	4658	4676	4694
2600	4712	4730	4748	4766	4784	4802	4820	4838	4856	4874
2700	4892	4910	4928	4946	4964	4982	5000	5018	5036	5054
2800	5072	5090	5108	5126	5144	5162	5180	5198	5216	5234
2900	5252	5270	5288	5306	5324	5342	5360	5378	5396	5414
3000	5432	5450	5468	5486	5504	5522	5540	5558	5576	5594
3100	5612	5630	5648	5666	5684	5702	5720	5738	5756	5774
3200	5792	5810	5828	5846	5864	5882	5900	5918	5936	5954
3300	5972	5990	6008	6026	6044	6062	6080	6098	6116	6134
3400	6152	6170	6188	6206	6224	6242	6260	6278	6296	6314
3500	6332	6350	6368	6386	6404	6422	6440	6458	6476	6494
3600	6512	6530	6548	6566	6584	6602	6620	6638	6656	6674
3700	6692	6710	6728	6746	6764	6782	6800	6818	6836	6854
3800	6872	6890	6908	6926	6944	6962	6980	6998	7016	7034
3900	7052	7070	7088	7106	7124	7142	7160	7178	7196	7214
4000	7232	7250	7268	7286	7304	7322	7340	7358	7376	7394

Coefficients of Heat Transmission

Heat transmitted, in British thermal units, per second, through metal 1 inch thick, per square inch of surface, for a temperature difference of 1° F.

Metal	Btu per Second	Metal	Btu per Second	Metal	Btu per Second
Aluminum.......	0.00203	German silver....	0.00050	Steel, soft......	0.00062
Antimony........	0.00022	Iron.............	0.00089	Silver..........	0.00610
Brass, yellow.....	0.00142	Lead.............	0.00045	Tin............	0.00084
Brass, red........	0.00157	Mercury..........	0.00011	Zinc...........	0.00170
Copper..........	0.00404	Steel, hard.......	0.00034	....	....

Coefficients of Heat Radiation

Heat radiated, in British thermal units, per square foot of surface per hour, for a temperature difference of 1° F.

Surface	Btu per Hour	Surface	Btu per Hour
Cast-iron, new...............	0.6480	Sawdust....................	0.7215
Cast-iron, rusted............	0.6868	Sand, fine..................	0.7400
Copper, polished............	0.0327	Silver, polished.............	0.0266
Glass......................	0.5948	Tin, polished...............	0.0439
Iron, ordinary...............	0.5662	Tinned iron, polished.......	0.0858
Iron, sheet-, polished.......	0.0920	Water......................	1.0853
Oil........................	1.4800	....	....

Freezing Mixtures

Mixture	Temperature Change, Degrees F.	
	From	To
Common salt (NaCl), 1 part; snow, 3 parts........................	32	±0
Common salt (NaCl), 1 part; snow, 1 part..........................	32	−0.4
Calcium chloride (CaCl₂), 3 parts; snow, 2 parts..................	32	−27
Calcium chloride (CaCl₂), 2 parts; snow, 1 part...................	32	−44
Sal ammoniac (NH₄Cl), 5 parts; saltpeter (KNO₃), 5 parts; water, 16 parts	50	+10
Sal ammoniac (NH₄Cl), 1 part; saltpeter (KNO₃), 1 part; water, 1 part	46	−11
Ammonium nitrate (NH₄NO₃), 1 part; water, 1 part..............	50	+ 3
Potassium hydrate (KOH), 4 parts; snow, 3 parts	32	−35

Ignition Temperatures. — The following temperatures are required to ignite the different substances specified: Phosphorus, transparent, 120 degrees F.; bisulphide of carbon, 300 degrees F.; gun cotton, 430 degrees F.; nitro-glycerine, 490 degrees F.; phosphorus, amorphous, 500 degrees F.; rifle powder, 550 degrees F.; charcoal, 660 degrees F.; dry pine wood, 800 degrees F.; dry oak wood, 900 degrees F.

1740 HEAT

Latent Heat. — When a body changes from the solid to the liquid state, or from the liquid to the gaseous state, a certain amount of heat is used to accomplish this change. This heat does not raise the temperature of the body and is called latent heat. When the body changes again from the gaseous to the liquid, or from the liquid to the solid state, this quantity of heat is given out by it. The *latent heat of fusion* is the heat supplied to a solid body at the melting point; this heat is absorbed by the body although its temperature remains nearly stationary during the whole operation of melting. The *latent heat of evaporation* is the heat that must be supplied to a liquid at the boiling point to transform the liquid into a vapor. The latent heat is generally given in British thermal units per pound. When it is said that the latent heat of evaporation of water is 966.6, this means that it takes 966.6 heat units to evaporate one pound of water after it has been raised to the boiling point, 212 degrees F.

Latent Heat of Fusion

Substance	Btu per Pound	Substance	Btu per Pound	Substance	Btu per Pound
Bismuth	22.75	Paraffine	63.27	Sulphur	16.86
Beeswax	76.14	Phosphorus	9.06	Tin	25.65
Cast iron, gray	41.40	Lead	10.00	Zinc	50.63
Cast iron, white	59.40	Silver	37.92	Ice	144.00

Latent Heat of Evaporation

Liquid	Btu per Pound	Liquid	Btu per Pound	Liquid	Btu per Pound
Alcohol, ethyl	371.0	Bisulphide of carbon	160.0	Sulphur dioxide	164.0
Alcohol, methyl	481.0	Ether	162.8	Turpentine	133.0
Ammonia	529.0			Water	966.6

Boiling Points of Various Substances at Atmospheric Pressure

Substance	Boiling Point, Degrees F.	Substance	Boiling Point, Degrees F.	Substance	Boiling Point, Degrees F.
Aniline	363	Chloroform	140	Saturated brine	226
Alcohol	173	Ether	100	Sulphur	833
Ammonia	−28	Linseed oil	597	Sulphuric acid	590
Benzine	176	Mercury	676	Water, pure	212
Bromine	145	Napthaline	428	Water, sea	213.2
Carbon bisulphide	118	Nitric acid	248	Wood alcohol	150
		Oil of turpentine	315		

Specific Heat. — The specific heat of a substance is the ratio of the heat required to raise the temperature of a certain weight of the given substance one degree F. to that required to raise the temperature of the same weight of water one degree. As the specific heat is not constant at all temperatures, it is generally assumed that it is determined by raising the temperature from 62 to 63 degrees F. For most substances, however, it is practically constant for temperatures up to 212 degrees F.

Average Specific Heats of Various Substances

Substance	Specific Heat	Substance	Specific Heat
Alcohol (absolute)............	0.700	Kerosene...................	0.500
Alcohol (density 0.8).........	0.622	Lead.....................	0.031
Aluminum...................	0.214	Limestone................	0.217
Antimony...................	0.051	Magnesia.................	0.222
Benzine....................	0.450	Marble...................	0.210
Brass......................	0.094	Masonry, brick............	0.200
Brickwork..................	0.200	Mercury..................	0.033
Cadmium...................	0.057	Naphtha..................	0.310
Charcoal...................	0.200	Nickel....................	0.109
Chalk......................	0.215	Oil, machine..............	0.400
Coal.......................	0.240	Oil, olive.................	0.350
Coke......................	0.203	Phosphorus...............	0.189
Copper, 32° to 212° F........	0.094	Platinum.................	0.032
Copper, 32° to 572° F........	0.101	Quartz...................	0.188
Corundum..................	0.198	Sand.....................	0.195
Ether......................	0.503	Silica....................	0.191
Fusel oil...................	0.564	Silver....................	0.056
Glass......................	0.194	Soda.....................	0.231
Gold.......................	0.031	Steel, mild...............	0.116
Graphite...................	0.201	Steel, high carbon.........	0.117
Ice........................	0.504	Stone (generally)..........	0.200
Iron, cast..................	0.130	Sulphur..................	0.178
Iron, wrought, 32° to 212° F....	0.110	Sulphuric acid............	0.330
32° to 392° F............	0.115	Tin......................	0.056
32° to 572° F............	0.122	Turpentine...............	0.472
32° to 662° F............	0.126	Water....................	1.000
Iron, at high temperatures:		Wood, fir.................	0.650
1382° to 1832° F...........	0.213	Wood, oak................	0.570
1750° to 1840° F...........	0.218	Wood, pine...............	0.467
1920° to 2190° F...........	0.199	Zinc.....................	0.095

Specific Heat of Gases

Gas	Constant Pressure	Constant Volume	Gas	Constant Pressure	Constant Volume
Acetic acid.........	0.412	....	Chloroform...........	0.157	....
Air.................	0.238	0.168	Hydrogen..........	3.409	2.412
Alcohol............	0.453	0.399	Nitrogen...........	0.244	0.173
Ammonia...........	0.508	0.399	Oxygen............	0.217	0.155
Carbonic acid......	0.217	0.171	Ethylene...........	0.404	0.332
Carbonic oxide.....	0.245	0.176	Steam..............	0.480	0.346
Chlorine..........	0.121	....			

Heat Loss from Uncovered Steam Pipes. — The loss of heat from a bare steam or hot water pipe varies with the difference between the temperature inside the pipe and that of the surrounding air. The loss is 2.15 Btu per hour, per square foot of pipe surface, per degree F. of temperature difference when the latter is 100 degrees; for a difference of 200 degrees, the loss is 2.66 Btu; for 300 degrees, 3.26 Btu; for 400 degrees, 4.03 Btu; for 500 degrees, 5.18 Btu. Thus, if the pipe area is 1.18 square feet per foot of length, and the temperature difference 300 degrees F., the loss per hour per foot of length = 1.18 × 300 × 3.26 = 1154 Btu.

Values of Heat Conductivity (k) and of Conductance (C) of Common Building and Heat Insulating Materials

Units are Btu per hour per degree temperature difference per square foot area and for 1 inch thickness except when otherwise noted.

Common Building Materials	Thickness, Inches	k or C*	Heat Insulating Materials	Density, Lb. per Cu. Ft.	k*
Blocks, Cinder....	8	0.62	Asbestos wood.........	123	2.70
	12	0.51	Balsa wood............	20.0	0.58
Blocks, Concrete..	8	1.00	Balsa wood............	7.3	0.33
	12	0.80	Balsam wool...........	2.2	0.27
Bricks,			Cabot's quilt..........	4	0.255
Common (clay).	1	5.0	Celotex...............	13.2	0.34
Bricks, Face (clay)	1	9.2	Corkboard (pure)......	14.0 to 10.6	0.34 to 0.30
Bricks, Glass.....	—		Dry Zero..............	1.0	0.24
Cement mortar....	1	12.0	Fibrofelt.............	13.6	0.32
Concrete...........	1	12.0	Glass wool............	1.5 to 0.85	0.27 to 0.25
Plaster (gypsum)..	1	3.3	Hairinsul (75% hair,		
Plasterboard......	3/8	3.73	25% jute)...........	6.3	0.27
	1/2	2.82	Hairinsul (50% hair,		
Plaster and wood			50% jute)...........	6.1	0.26
lath...........	A†	2.0	Hairfelt..............	13.0 to 11.0	0.26
Roofing materials			Insulite.............	16.9	0.34
Built-up roofing.	3/8	3.53	Linofelt..............	4.9	0.28
Composition			Lith.................	14.3	0.40
roofing........	A†	6.5	Maftex...............	16.1	0.34
Shingles,			Magnesia (rigid),		
Asbestos......	A†	6.0	15% asbestos........	13.2	0.39
Shingles, Slate....	1	10.37	Masonite.............	19.8	0.33
Shingles, Wood....	A†	1.28	Regranulated cork.....	8.1	0.31
Stone.............	1	12.0	Rock cork............	14.5	0.33
Stucco............	1	12.0	Rock wool............	10.0	0.27
Tile or terrazzo....	1	12.0	Rock wool............	21.0	0.30
Tile, hollow clay..	4	1.0	Sawdust..............	—	1.04
	6	0.64	Shavings.............	—	0.71
	12	0.40	Thermofelt (jute and		
Tile, hollow			asbestos fibers)......	10.0	0.37
gypsum.........	4	0.46	Thermofelt (hair and		
Wood or lumber			asbestos fibers)......	7.8	0.28
Maple..........	1	1.15	Thermofill		
Yellow pine...	1	0.80	(flaked gypsum).....	34.0	0.23
Yellow pine lap				19.8	0.35
siding.........	A†	1.28	Torfoleum............	10.2	0.29

* Where thickness is 1 inch, the value given is heat conductivity (k); for other thicknesses, the value given is heat conductance (C). Values of k are for thickness of 1 in., reported by various laboratories but principally from tests at the Bureau of Standards. Tests at mean temperature of 90° F. mainly, but at 75° F. in a few cases.

† A indicates average thickness.

Linear Expansion of Various Substances Between 32 and 212 Deg. Fahr.

(For linear expansion of metals see "Specific Gravity and Properties of Metals")

Expansion of volume = 3 × linear expansion.

Substance	Linear Expansion for 1 Deg. Fahr.	Substance	Linear Expansion for 1 Deg. Fahr.
Brick.....................	0.0000030	Masonry, brick, from....	0.0000026
Cement, Portland.......	0.0000060	to......	0.0000050
Concrete................	0.0000080	Plaster..................	0.0000092
Ebonite.................	0.0000428	Porcelain................	0.0000020
Glass, thermometer.....	0.0000050	Quartz, from............	0.0000043
Glass, hard.............	0.0000050	to............	0.0000079
Granite..................	0.0000044	Slate....................	0.0000058
Marble, from............	0.0000031	Sandstone...............	0.0000065
to.................	0.0000079	Wood (pine).............	0.0000028

PROPERTIES, COMPRESSION AND FLOW OF AIR

Properties of Air. — Air is a mechanical mixture composed of 78 per cent, by volume, of nitrogen, 21 per cent of oxygen and 1 per cent of argon. The weight of pure air at 32 degrees F. and atmospheric pressure (29.92 inches of mercury or 14.70 pounds per square inch) is 0.08073 pound per cubic foot. The volume of a pound of air at the same temperature and pressure is 12.387 cubic feet. The weight of air at any other temperature or pressure is:

$$W = \frac{1.325 \times B}{T}$$

in which W = weight in pounds per cubic foot; B = height of barometric pressure in inches of mercury; T = absolute temperature Fahrenheit.

Volume and Weight of Air at Different Temperatures, at Atmospheric Pressure

Temperature, Degrees Fahr.	Volume of 1 Pound of Air in Cubic Feet	Weight per Cubic Foot, Pounds	Temperature, Degrees Fahr.	Volume of 1 Pound of Air in Cubic Feet	Weight per Cubic Foot, Pounds	Temperature, Degrees Fahr.	Volume of 1 Pound of Air in Cubic Feet	Weight per Cubic Foot, Pounds
0	11.57	0.0864	172	15.92	0.0628	800	31.75	0.0315
12	11.88	0.0842	182	16.18	0.0618	900	34.25	0.0292
22	12.14	0.0824	192	16.42	0.0609	1000	37.31	0.0268
32	12.39	0.0807	202	16.67	0.0600	1100	39.37	0.0254
42	12.64	0.0791	212	16.92	0.0591	1200	41.84	0.0239
52	12.89	0.0776	230	17.39	0.0575	1300	44.44	0.0225
62	13.14	0.0761	250	17.89	0.0559	1400	46.95	0.0213
72	13.39	0.0747	275	18.52	0.0540	1500	49.51	0.0202
82	13.64	0.0733	300	19.16	0.0522	1600	52.08	0.0192
92	13.89	0.0720	325	19.76	0.0506	1700	54.64	0.0183
102	14.14	0.0707	350	20.41	0.0490	1800	57.14	0.0175
112	14.41	0.0694	375	20.96	0.0477	2000	62.11	0.0161
122	14.66	0.0682	400	21.69	0.0461	2200	67.11	0.0149
132	14.90	0.0671	450	22.94	0.0436	2400	72.46	0.0138
142	15.17	0.0659	500	24.21	0.0413	2600	76.92	0.0130
152	15.41	0.0649	600	26.60	0.0376	2800	82.64	0.0121
162	15.67	0.0638	700	29.59	0.0338	3000	87.72	0.0114

The absolute zero from which all temperatures must be counted when dealing with the weight and volume of gases is assumed to be −459.2 degrees F. Hence, to obtain the absolute temperature T used in the formula above, add to the temperature observed on a regular Fahrenheit thermometer the value 459.2.

In obtaining the value of B, 1 inch of mercury at 32 degrees F. may be taken as equal to a pressure of 0.491 pound per square inch.

Example. — What would be the weight of a cubic foot of air at atmospheric pressure (29.92 inches of mercury) at 100 degrees F.?

$$W = \frac{1.325 \times 29.92}{100 + 459.2} = 0.0709 \text{ pound.}$$

Weight of Air at Different Pressures and Temperatures

Weight in Pounds per Cubic Foot

Temp. of Air, Degrees Fahr.	Gage Pressure, Pounds														
	0	5	10	20	30	40	50	60	80	100	120	150	200	250	300
−20	0.0900	0.1205	0.1515	0.2125	0.274	0.336	0.397	0.458	0.580	0.702	0.825	1.010	1.318	1.625	1.930
−10	0.0882	0.1184	0.1485	0.2090	0.268	0.328	0.388	0.448	0.567	0.687	0.807	0.989	1.288	1.588	1.890
0	0.0864	0.1160	0.1455	0.2040	0.263	0.321	0.380	0.438	0.555	0.672	0.790	0.968	1.260	1.553	1.850
10	0.0846	0.1136	0.1425	0.1995	0.257	0.314	0.372	0.429	0.543	0.658	0.774	0.947	1.233	1.520	1.810
20	0.0828	0.1112	0.1395	0.1955	0.252	0.307	0.364	0.420	0.533	0.645	0.757	0.927	1.208	1.489	1.770
30	0.0811	0.1088	0.1366	0.1916	0.246	0.301	0.357	0.412	0.522	0.632	0.742	0.908	1.184	1.460	1.735
40	0.0795	0.1067	0.1338	0.1876	0.241	0.295	0.350	0.404	0.511	0.619	0.727	0.890	1.161	1.431	1.701
50	0.0780	0.1045	0.1310	0.1839	0.237	0.290	0.343	0.396	0.501	0.607	0.713	0.873	1.139	1.403	1.668
60	0.0764	0.1025	0.1283	0.1803	0.232	0.284	0.336	0.388	0.493	0.596	0.700	0.856	1.116	1.376	1.636
80	0.0736	0.0988	0.1239	0.1738	0.224	0.274	0.324	0.374	0.473	0.572	0.673	0.824	1.074	1.325	1.573
100	0.0710	0.0954	0.1197	0.1676	0.215	0.264	0.312	0.360	0.455	0.551	0.648	0.794	1.035	1.276	1.517
120	0.0686	0.0921	0.1155	0.1618	0.208	0.255	0.302	0.348	0.440	0.533	0.626	0.767	1.001	1.234	1.465
140	0.0663	0.0889	0.1115	0.1565	0.201	0.246	0.291	0.336	0.426	0.516	0.606	0.742	0.968	1.194	1.416
150	0.0652	0.0874	0.1096	0.1541	0.198	0.242	0.286	0.331	0.419	0.508	0.596	0.730	0.953	1.175	1.392
175	0.0626	0.0840	0.1054	0.1482	0.191	0.233	0.275	0.318	0.403	0.488	0.573	0.701	0.914	1.128	1.337
200	0.0603	0.0809	0.1014	0.1427	0.184	0.225	0.265	0.305	0.388	0.470	0.552	0.674	0.879	1.084	1.287
225	0.0581	0.0779	0.0976	0.1373	0.177	0.216	0.255	0.295	0.374	0.452	0.531	0.649	0.846	1.043	1.240
250	0.0560	0.0751	0.0941	0.1323	0.170	0.208	0.247	0.284	0.369	0.436	0.513	0.627	0.817	1.007	1.197
275	0.0541	0.0726	0.0910	0.1278	0.164	0.201	0.233	0.274	0.343	0.421	0.494	0.605	0.789	0.972	1.155
300	0.0523	0.0707	0.0883	0.1237	0.159	0.194	0.230	0.265	0.336	0.407	0.478	0.585	0.762	0.940	1.118
350	0.0491	0.0658	0.0825	0.1160	0.149	0.183	0.216	0.240	0.316	0.382	0.449	0.549	0.715	0.883	1.048
400	0.0463	0.0621	0.0779	0.1090	0.140	0.172	0.203	0.235	0.297	0.360	0.423	0.517	0.674	0.831	0.987
450	0.0437	0.0586	0.0735	0.1033	0.133	0.163	0.192	0.222	0.281	0.340	0.399	0.488	0.637	0.786	0.934
500	0.0414	0.0555	0.0696	0.0978	0.126	0.154	0.182	0.210	0.266	0.322	0.379	0.463	0.604	0.746	0.885
550	0.0394	0.0528	0.0661	0.0930	0.120	0.146	0.173	0.200	0.253	0.306	0.359	0.440	0.573	0.709	0.841
600	0.0376	0.0504	0.0631	0.0885	0.114	0.139	0.165	0.190	0.241	0.292	0.343	0.419	0.547	0.675	0.801

Relation between Pressure, Temperature and Volume of Air. — This relationship is expressed by the formula:

$$\frac{P \times V}{T} = 53.3,$$

in which P = absolute pressure in pounds per square foot; V = volume in cubic feet of one pound of air at the given pressure and temperature; T = absolute temperature in degrees F.

Example. — What is the volume of one pound of air at a pressure of 24.7 pounds per square inch and at a temperature of 210 degrees F.?

$$\frac{24.7 \times 144 \times V}{210 + 459.2} = 53.3, \text{ or } V = \frac{53.3 \times 669.2}{24.7 \times 144} = 10.03 \text{ cubic feet.}$$

Relation Between Barometric Pressure, and Pressures in Pounds per Square Inch and Square Foot

Barometer, Inches	Pressure in Pounds per Square Inch	Pressure in Pounds per Square Foot	Barometer, Inches	Pressure in Pounds per Square Inch	Pressure in Pounds per Square Foot	Barometer, Inches	Pressure in Pounds per Square Inch	Pressure in Pounds per Square Foot
28.00	13.75	1980	29.25	14.36	2068	30.50	14.98	2156
28.25	13.87	1997	29.50	14.48	2086	30.75	15.10	2174
28.50	13.99	2015	29.75	14.61	2103	31.00	15.22	2192
28.75	14.12	2033	30.00	14.73	2121	31.25	15.34	2210
29.00	14.24	2050	30.25	14.85	2139	.....	.....	......

Expansion and Compression of Air. — The formula for the relationship of pressure, temperature and volume of air just given indicates that when the pressure remains constant the volume is directly proportional to the absolute temperature. If the temperature remains constant, the volume is inversely proportional to the absolute pressure. Theoretically, air (as well as other gases) can be expanded or compressed according to two different laws. *Adiabatic* expansion or compression takes place when the air is expanded or compressed without transmission of heat to or from it; as for example, if the air could be expanded or compressed in a cylinder of an absolutely non-conducting material. Let:

P_1 = initial absolute pressure in pounds per square foot;
V_1 = initial volume in cubic feet;
T_1 = initial absolute temperature in degrees F.;
P_2 = absolute pressure in pounds per square foot, after compression;
V_2 = volume in cubic feet, after compression;
T_2 = absolute temperature in degrees F., after compression.

Then:

$$\frac{V_2}{V_1} = \left(\frac{P_1}{P_2}\right)^{0.71} \qquad \frac{P_2}{P_1} = \left(\frac{V_1}{V_2}\right)^{1.41} \qquad \frac{T_2}{T_1} = \left(\frac{V_1}{V_2}\right)^{0.41}$$

$$\frac{V_2}{V_1} = \left(\frac{T_1}{T_2}\right)^{2.46} \qquad \frac{P_2}{P_1} = \left(\frac{T_2}{T_1}\right)^{3.46} \qquad \frac{T_2}{T_1} = \left(\frac{P_2}{P_1}\right)^{0.29}$$

These formulas are also applicable if all pressures are in pounds per square inch or if all volumes are in cubic inches.

Isothermal expansion or compression takes place when the gas is expanded or compressed with an addition or transmission of sufficient heat to maintain a constant temperature. Let:

P_1 = initial pressure in pounds per square foot;
V_1 = initial volume in cubic feet;
P_2 = absolute pressure in pounds per square foot, after compression;
V_2 = volume in cubic feet, after compression;
C = constant depending on the temperature.

Then:

$$P_1 \times V_1 = P_2 \times V_2 = C.$$

For a temperature of 32 degrees F., constant C equals 26,200 foot-pounds, and for other temperatures it may be found from the formula, $C = 53.3\,T$, in which T is the absolute temperature which is maintained during the expansion or compression.

Example. — A volume of 165 cubic feet of air, at a pressure of 15 pounds per square inch, is compressed adiabatically to a pressure of 80 pounds per square inch. What will be the volume at this pressure?

$$V_2 = V_1 \left(\frac{P_1}{P_2}\right)^{0.71} = 165 \left(\frac{15}{80}\right)^{0.71} = 50 \text{ cubic feet, approx.}$$

Example. — The same volume of air is compressed isothermally from 15 to 80 pounds per square inch. What will be the volume after compression?

$$V_2 = \frac{P_1 \times V_1}{P_2} = \frac{15 \times 165}{80} = 31 \text{ cubic feet.}$$

Foot-pounds of Work Required in Compression of Air
Initial Pressure = 1 atmosphere = 14.7 pounds per square inch

Gage Pressure in Pounds per Square Inch	Foot-pounds Required per Cubic Foot of Air at Initial Pressure			Gage Pressure in Pounds per Square Inch	Foot-pounds Required per Cubic Foot of Air at Initial Pressure		
	Isothermal Compression	Adiabatic Compression	Actual Power Required		Isothermal Compression	Adiabatic Compression	Actual Power Required
5	619.6	649 5	637.5	55	3393.7	4188.9	3870.8
10	1098.2	1192.0	1154.6	60	3440.4	4422.8	4029.8
15	1488.3	1661.2	1592.0	65	3577.6	4645.4	4218.2
20	1817.7	2074.0	1971.4	70	3706.3	4859.6	4398.1
25	2102.6	2451.6	2312.0	75	3828.0	5063.9	4569.5
30	2353.6	2794.0	2617.8	80	3942.9	5259.7	4732.9
35	2578.0	3111.0	2897.8	85	4051.5	5450.0	4890.1
40	2780.8	3405.5	3155.6	90	4155.7	5633.1	5042.1
45	2966.0	3681.7	3395.4	95	4254.3	5819.3	5187.3
50	3136.2	3942.3	3619.8	100	4348.1	5981.2	5327.9

Work Required in Compression of Air. — The total work required for compression and expulsion of air, adiabatically compressed, is:

$$\text{Total work in foot-pounds} = 3.46\, P_1 V_1 \left[\left(\frac{P_2}{P_1}\right)^{0.29} - 1\right]$$

in which P_1 = initial absolute pressure in pounds per square foot;
P_2 = absolute pressure in pounds per square foot, after compression;
V_1 = initial volume in cubic feet.

The total work required for isothermal compression is:

$$\text{Total work in foot-pounds} = P_1 V_1 \text{ hyp. log. } \frac{V_1}{V_2}$$

in which P_1, P_2 and V_1 denote the same quantities as in the previous equation, and V_2 = volume of air in cubic feet, after compression.

The work required to compress air isothermally, that is, when the heat of compression is removed as rapidly as produced, is considerably less than the work required for compressing air adiabatically, or when all the heat is retained. In actual practice, neither of these two theoretical extremes are obtainable, but the power required for air compression is about the medium between the powers that would be required for each. The accompanying table gives the average number of foot-pounds of work required to compress air.

Horsepower Required to Compress Air. — In the accompanying tables is given the horsepower required for compressing one cubic foot of free air per minute (isothermally and adiabatically) from atmospheric pressure (14.7 pounds per square inch) to various gage pressures, for one-, two- and three-stage compression. The formula for calculating the horsepower required to compress, adiabatically, a given volume of free air to a given pressure is:

$$\text{H. P.} = \frac{144 \, NPVn}{33000 \, (n-1)} \left[\left(\frac{P_2}{P} \right)^{\frac{n-1}{Nn}} - 1 \right]$$

in which N = number of stages in which compression is accomplished;

P = atmospheric pressure in pounds per square inch;

P_2 = absolute terminal pressure in pounds per square inch;

V = volume of air, in cubic feet, compressed per minute, at atmospheric pressure;

n = exponent of the compression curve = 1.41 for adiabatic compression.

For different methods of compression and for one cubic foot of air per minute, this formula may be simplified as follows:

For one-stage compression: H. P. = 0.015 P $(R^{0.29} - 1)$

For two-stage compression: H. P. = 0.030 P $(R^{0.145} - 1)$

For three-stage compression: H. P. = 0.045 P $(R^{0.0975} - 1)$

For four-stage compression: H. P. = 0.060 P $(R^{0.0725} - 1)$

In these latter formulas $R = \frac{P_2}{P}$ = number of atmospheres to be compressed.

The formula for calculating the horsepower required to compress isothermally a given volume of free air to a given pressure is:

$$\text{H. P.} = \frac{144 \, PV}{33000} \left(\text{hyp. log. } \frac{P_2}{P} \right)$$

Hyperbolic logarithms are obtained by multiplying common logarithms by 2.302585. See also the tables of hyperbolic logarithms, page 144.

Horsepower Required to Compress Air

Horsepower Required for Compressing One Cubic Foot of Free Air per Minute (Isothermally and Adiabatically) from Atmospheric Pressure (14.7 pounds per square inch) to Various Gage Pressures. — Single-stage Compression

(Initial Temperature of Air, 60° F. — Jacket-cooling not considered)

Gage Pressure, Pounds	Absolute Pressure, Pounds	Number of Atmospheres	Isothermal Compression		Adiabatic Compression			
			Mean Effective Pressure	Horsepower	Mean Effective Pressure, Theoretical	Mean Eff. Pressure plus 15 per cent Friction	Horsepower, Theoretical	Horsepower plus 15 per cent Friction
5	19.7	1.34	4.13	0.018	4.46	5.12	0.019	0.022
10	24.7	1.68	7.57	0.033	8.21	9.44	0.036	0.041
15	29.7	2.02	11.02	0.048	11.46	13.17	0.050	0.057
20	34.7	2.36	12.62	0.055	14.30	16.44	0.062	0.071
25	39.7	2.70	14.68	0.064	16.94	19.47	0.074	0.085
30	44.7	3.04	16.30	0.071	19.32	22.21	0.084	0.096
35	49.7	3.38	17.90	0.078	21.50	24.72	0.094	0.108
40	54.7	3.72	19.28	0.084	23.53	27.05	0.103	0.118
45	59.7	4.06	20.65	0.090	25.40	29.21	0.111	0.127
50	64.7	4.40	21.80	0.095	27.23	31.31	0.119	0.136
55	69.7	4.74	22.95	0.100	28.90	33.23	0.126	0.145
60	74.7	5.08	23.90	0.104	30.53	35.10	0.133	0.153
65	79.7	5.42	24.80	0.108	32.10	36.91	0.140	0.161
70	84.7	5.76	25.70	0.112	33.57	38.59	0.146	0.168
75	89.7	6.10	26.62	0.116	35.00	40.25	0.153	0.175
80	94.7	6.44	27.52	0.120	36.36	41.80	0.159	0.182
85	99.7	6.78	28.21	0.123	37.63	43.27	0.164	0.189
90	104.7	7.12	28.93	0.126	38.89	44.71	0.169	0.195
95	109.7	7.46	29.60	0.129	40.11	46.12	0.175	0.201
100	114.7	7.80	30.30	0.132	41.28	47.46	0.180	0.207
110	124.7	8.48	31.42	0.137	43.56	50.09	0.190	0.218
120	134.7	9.16	32.60	0.142	45.69	52.53	0.199	0.229
130	144.7	9.84	33.75	0.147	47.72	54.87	0.208	0.239
140	154.7	10.52	34.67	0.151	49.64	57.08	0.216	0.249
150	164.7	11.20	35.59	0.155	51.47	59.18	0.224	0.258
160	174.7	11.88	36.30	0.158	53.70	61.80	0.234	0.269
170	184.7	12.56	37.20	0.162	55.60	64.00	0.242	0.278
180	194.7	13.24	38.10	0.166	57.20	65.80	0.249	0.286
190	204.7	13.92	38.80	0.169	58.80	67.70	0.256	0.294
200	214.7	14.60	39.50	0.172	60.40	69.50	0.263	0.303

Horsepower Required to Compress Air

Horsepower Required for Compressing One Cubic Foot of Free Air per Minute (Isothermally and Adiabatically) from Atmospheric Pressure (14.7 pounds per square inch) to Various Gage Pressures. — Two-stage Compression

(Initial Temperature of Air, 60° F. — Jacket-cooling not considered)

Gage Pressure, Pounds	Absolute Pressure, Pounds	Number of Atmospheres	Correct Ratio of Cylinder Volumes	Intercooler Gage Pressure	Isothermal Compression		Adiabatic Compression					Percentage of Saving over One-stage Compression
					Mean Effective Pressure	Horsepower	Mean Eff. Pressure, Theoretical	Mean Eff. Pressure plus 15 per cent Friction	Horsepower, Theoretical	H.P. plus 15 per cent Friction		
50	64.7	4.40	2.10	16.2	21.80	0.095	24.30	27.90	0.106	0.123		10.9
60	74.7	5.08	2.25	18.4	23.90	0.104	27.20	31.30	0.118	0.136		11.3
70	84.7	5.76	2.40	20.6	25.70	0.112	29.31	33.71	0.128	0.147		12.3
80	94.7	6.44	2.54	22.7	27.52	0.120	31.44	36.15	0.137	0.158		13.8
90	104.7	7.12	2.67	24.5	28.93	0.126	33.37	38.36	0.145	0.167		14.2
100	114.7	7.80	2.79	26.3	30.30	0.132	35.20	40.48	0.153	0.176		15.0
110	124.7	8.48	2.91	28.1	31.42	0.137	36.82	42.34	0.161	0.185		15.2
120	134.7	9.16	3.03	29.8	32.60	0.142	38.44	44.20	0.168	0.193		15.6
130	144.7	9.84	3.14	31.5	33.75	0.147	39.86	45.83	0.174	0.200		16.3
140	154.7	10.52	3.24	32.9	34.67	0.151	41.28	47.47	0.180	0.207		16.7
150	164.7	11.20	3.35	34.5	35.59	0.155	42.60	48.99	0.186	0.214		16.9
160	174.7	11.88	3.45	36.1	36.30	0.158	43.82	50.39	0.191	0.219		18.4
170	184.7	12.56	3.54	37.3	37.20	0.162	44.93	51.66	0.196	0.225		19.0
180	194.7	13.24	3.64	38.8	38.10	0.165	46.05	52.95	0.201	0.231		19.3
190	204.7	13.92	3.73	40.1	38.80	0.169	47.16	54.22	0.206	0.236		19.5
200	214.7	14.60	3.82	41.4	39.50	0.172	48.18	55.39	0.210	0.241		20.1
210	224.7	15.28	3.91	42.8	40.10	0.174	49.35	56.70	0.216	0.247		.....
220	234.7	15.96	3.99	44.0	40.70	0.177	50.30	57.70	0.220	0.252		.....
230	244.7	16.64	4.08	45.3	41.30	0.180	51.30	59.10	0.224	0.257		.....
240	254.7	17.32	4.17	46.6	41.90	0.183	52.25	60.10	0.228	0.262		.....
250	264.7	18.00	4.24	47.6	42.70	0.186	52.84	60.76	0.230	0.264		.....
260	274.7	18.68	4.32	48.8	43.00	0.188	53.85	62.05	0.235	0.270		.....
270	284.7	19.36	4.40	50.0	43.50	0.190	54.60	62.90	0.238	0.274		.....
280	294.7	20.04	4.48	51.1	44.00	0.192	55.50	63.85	0.242	0.278		.....
290	304.7	20.72	4.55	52.2	44.50	0.194	56.20	64.75	0.246	0.282		.....
300	314.7	21.40	4.63	53.4	45.80	0.197	56.70	65.20	0.247	0.283		.....
350	364.7	24.80	4.98	58.5	47.30	0.206	60.15	69.16	0.262	0.301		.....
400	414.7	28.20	5.31	63.3	49.20	0.214	63.19	72.65	0.276	0.317		.....
450	464.7	31.60	5.61	67.8	51.20	0.223	65.93	75.81	0.287	0.329		.....
500	514.7	35.01	5.91	72.1	52.70	0.229	68.46	78.72	0.298	0.342		.....

Horsepower Required to Compress Air

Horsepower Required for Compressing One Cubic Foot of Free Air per Minute (Isothermally and Adiabatically) from Atmospheric Pressure (14.7 pounds per square inch) to Various Gage Pressures. — Three-stage Compression

(Initial Temperature of Air, 60° F. — Jacket-cooling not considered)

Gage Pressure, Pounds	Absolute Pressure, Pounds	Number of Atmospheres	Correct Ratio of Cylinder Volumes	Intercooler Gage Pressure, First and Second Stages	Isothermal Compression		Adiabatic Compression				Percentage of Saving over Two-stage Compression
					Mean Effective Pressure	Horsepower	Mean Eff. Pressure, Theoretical	Mean Eff. Pressure plus 15 per cent Friction	Horsepower, Theoretical	H.P. plus 15 per cent Friction	
100	114.7	7.8	1.98	14.4– 42.9	30.30	0.132	33.30	38.30	0.145	0.167	5.23
150	164.7	11.2	2.24	18.2– 59.0	35.59	0.155	40.30	46.50	0.175	0.202	5.92
200	214.7	14.6	2.44	21.2– 73.0	39.50	0.172	45.20	52.00	0.196	0.226	6.67
250	264.7	18.0	2.62	23.8– 86.1	42.70	0.186	49.20	56.60	0.214	0.246	6.96
300	314.7	21.4	2.78	26.1– 98.7	45.30	0.197	52.70	60.70	0.229	0.264	7.28
350	364.7	24.8	2.92	28.2–110.5	47.30	0.206	55.45	63.80	0.242	0.277	7.64
400	414.7	28.2	3.04	30.0–121.0	49.20	0.214	58.25	66.90	0.253	0.292	8.33
450	464.7	31.6	3.16	31.8–132.3	51.20	0.223	60.40	69.40	0.263	0.302	8.36
500	514.7	35.0	3.27	33.4–142.4	52.70	0.229	62.30	71.70	0.273	0.314	8.38
550	564.7	38.4	3.38	35.0–153.1	53.75	0.234	65.00	74.75	0.283	0.326	8.80
600	614.7	41.8	3.47	36.3–162.3	54.85	0.239	66.85	76.90	0.291	0.334	8.86
650	664.7	45.2	3.56	37.6–171.5	56.00	0.244	67.90	78.15	0.296	0.340	9.02
700	714.7	48.6	3.65	38.9–180.8	57.15	0.249	69.40	79.85	0.303	0.348	9.18
750	764.7	52.0	3.73	40.1–189.8	58.10	0.253	70.75	81.40	0.309	0.355	....
800	814.7	55.4	3.82	41.4–199.5	59.00	0.257	72.45	83.25	0.315	0.362	....
850	864.7	58.8	3.89	42.5–207.8	60.20	0.262	73.75	84.90	0.321	0.369	....
900	914.7	62.2	3.95	43.4–214.6	60.80	0.265	74.80	86.00	0.326	0.375	....
950	964.7	65.6	4.03	44.6–224.5	61.72	0.269	76.10	87.50	0.331	0.381	....
1000	1014.7	69.0	4.11	45.7–233.3	62.40	0.272	77.20	88.80	0.336	0.383	....
1050	1064.7	72.4	4.15	46.3–238.3	63.10	0.275	78.10	90.10	0.340	0.391	....
1100	1114.7	75.8	4.23	47.5–248.3	63.80	0.278	79.10	91.10	0.344	0.396	....
1150	1164.7	79.2	4.30	48.5–256.8	64.40	0.281	80.15	92.20	0.349	0.401	....
1200	1214.7	82.6	4.33	49.0–261.3	65.00	0.283	81.00	93.15	0.353	0.405	....
1250	1264.7	86.0	4.42	50.3–272.3	65.60	0.286	82.00	94.30	0.357	0.411	....
1300	1314.7	89.4	4.48	51.3–280.8	66.30	0.289	82.90	95.30	0.362	0.416	....
1350	1364.7	92.8	4.53	52.0–287.3	66.70	0.291	84.00	96.60	0.366	0.421	....
1400	1414.7	96.2	4.58	52.6–293.5	67.00	0.292	84.60	97.30	0.368	0.423	....
1450	1464.7	99.6	4.64	53.5–301.5	67.70	0.295	85.30	98.20	0.371	0.426	....
1500	1514.7	103.0	4.69	54.3–309.3	68.30	0.298	85.80	98.80	0.374	0.430	....
1550	1564.7	106.4	4.74	55.0–317.3	68.80	0.300	86.80	99.85	0.378	0.434	....
1600	1614.7	109.8	4.79	55.8–323.3	69.10	0.302	87.60	100.80	0.382	0.438	....

Flow of Air in Pipes. — The following formulas are used by the B. F. Sturtevant Co.:

$$v = \sqrt{\frac{25,000\,dp}{L}} \qquad p = \frac{Lv^2}{25,000\,d}$$

in which v = velocity of air in feet per second;

p = loss of pressure due to flow through the pipes in ounces per square inch;

d = inside diameter of pipe in inches;

L = length of pipe in feet.

The quantity of air discharged in cubic feet per second is the product of the velocity as obtained from the formula above and the area of the pipe in square feet. The horsepower required to drive air through a pipe equals the volume of air in cubic feet per second multiplied by the pressure in pounds per square foot, and this product divided by 550.

Volume of Air Transmitted, in Cubic Feet per Minute, Through Pipes

Velocity of Air in Feet per Second	Actual Inside Diameter of Pipe, Inches									
	1	2	3	4	6	8	10	12	16	24
1	0.33	1.31	2.95	5.2	11.8	20.9	32.7	47.1	83.8	188
2	0.65	2.62	5.89	10.5	23.6	41.9	65.4	94.2	167.5	377
3	0.98	3.93	8.84	15.7	35.3	62.8	98.2	141.4	251.3	565
4	1.31	5.24	11.78	20.9	47.1	83.8	131.0	188.0	335.0	754
5	1.64	6.55	14.7	26.2	59.0	104.0	163.0	235.0	419.0	942
6	1.96	7.85	17.7	31.4	70.7	125.0	196.0	283.0	502.0	1131
7	2.29	9.16	20.6	36.6	82.4	146.0	229.0	330.0	586.0	1319
8	2.62	10.50	23.5	41.9	94.0	167.0	262.0	377.0	670.0	1508
9	2.95	11.78	26.5	47.0	106.0	188.0	294.0	424.0	754.0	1696
10	3.27	13.1	29.4	52.0	118.0	209.0	327.0	471.0	838.0	1885
12	3.93	15.7	35.3	63.0	141.0	251.0	393.0	565.0	1005.0	2262
15	4.91	19.6	44.2	78.0	177.0	314.0	491.0	707.0	1256.0	2827
18	5.89	23.5	53.0	94.0	212.0	377.0	589.0	848.0	1508.0	3393
20	6.55	26.2	59.0	105.0	235.0	419.0	654.0	942.0	1675.0	3770
24	7.86	31.4	71.0	125.0	283.0	502.0	785.0	1131.0	2010.0	4524
25	8.18	32.7	73.0	131.0	294.0	523.0	818.0	1178.0	2094.0	4712
28	9.16	36.6	82.0	146.0	330.0	586.0	916.0	1319.0	2346.0	5278
30	9.80	39.3	88.0	157.0	353.0	628.0	982.0	1414.0	2513.0	5655

Flow of Compressed Air in Pipes. — When there is a comparatively small difference of pressure at the two ends of the pipe, the volume of flow in cubic feet per minute is found by the formula:

$$V = 58 \sqrt{\frac{pd^5}{WL}}$$

in which V = volume of air in cubic feet per minute;

p = difference in pressure at the two ends of the pipe in pounds per square inch;

d = inside diameter of pipe in inches;

W = weight in pounds of one cubic foot of entering air;

L = length of pipe in feet.

Velocity of Escaping Compressed Air

Pressure Above Atmospheric Pressure			Theoretical Velocity, Feet per Second	Pressure Above Atmospheric Pressure			Theoretical Velocity, Feet per Second
In Atmospheres	In Inches Mercury	In Lbs. per Sq. In.		In Atmospheres	In Inches Mercury	In Lbs. per Sq. In.	
0.010	0.30	0.147	94.4	0.680	20.4	10.0	780
0.066	2.10	1.00	246.0	0.809	24.3	12.0	855
0.100	3.00	1.47	299.0	1.0	30.0	14.7	946
0.136	4.08	2.00	348.0	2.0	60.0	29.4	1094
0.204	6.12	3.00	427.0	5.0	150.0	73.5	1219
0.272	8.16	4.00	493.0	10.0	300.0	147.0	1275
0.340	10.20	5.00	552.0	20.0	600.0	294.0	1304
0.408	12.24	6.00	604.0	40.0	1200.0	588.0	1323
0.500	15.00	7.35	673.0	100.0	3000.0	1470.0	1331
0.544	16.32	8.00	697.0	200.0	6000.0	2940.0	1334
0.611	18.34	9.00	741.0	......	......	......	......

The theoretical velocities in the table above must be reduced by multiplying by a "factor of discharge," which varies with the orifice and the pressure. The following factors are used for orifices in thin plate and short tubes.

Type of Orifice	Pressures in Atmospheres Above Atmospheric Pressure						
	0.01	0.1	0.5	1	5	10	100
Orifice in thin plate........	0.65	0.64	0.57	0.54	0.45	0.44	0.42
Orifice in short tube......	0.83	0.82	0.71	0.67	0.53	0.51	0.49

Velocity of Air under Low Pressures. — The table "Velocity of Air under Low Pressures" gives the theoretical velocity for the discharge of air into the atmosphere. These theoretical velocities are modified by multiplying them by a factor varying with the form of the orifice. For an orifice with sharp edges in a thin plate, this factor equals 0.65. For a plate with the inside of the orifice rounded, the factor equals 0.70 to 0.75, and for a well-shaped nozzle, 0.93.

Velocity of Air Under Low Pressures
(Temperature 62° F.)

Gage Pressure, Ounces per Square Inch	Theoretical Velocity, Feet per Second	Gage Pressure, Ounces per Square Inch	Theoretical Velocity, Feet per Second	Gage Pressure, Ounces per Square Inch	Theoretical Velocity, Feet per Second	Gage Pressure, Ounces per Square Inch	Theoretical Velocity, Feet per Second	Gage Pressure, Ounces per Square Inch	Theoretical Velocity, Feet per Second
0.006	6.61	0.115	29.5	0.346	51.2	0.866	80.9	2.308	132.0
0.012	9.35	0.173	36.2	0.404	55.3	1.153	93.5	2.597	140.0
0.023	13.20	0.231	41.8	0.461	59.1	1.442	104.0	2.885	148.0
0.040	17.40	0.260	44.3	0.519	62.7	1.731	114.0	3.462	162.0
0.058	20.90	0.289	46.7	0.577	66.1	2.020	124.0	....	....

Loss of Pressure Due to Flow through Pipes. — The table "Loss of Pressure by Friction in Pipes" is based on data published by the B. F. Sturtevant Co., and gives the loss in pressure due to friction of air in pipes 100 feet long. For any other length the loss is proportional to the length.

Loss of Pressure by Friction in Pipes

Velocity, Feet per Minute	Diameter of Pipe in Inches											
	1	2	3	4	5	6	7	8	9	10	11	12
	Loss in Ounces per Square Inch per 100 Feet											
600	0.4	0.2	0.13	0.1	0.08	0.07	0.06	0.05	0.04	0.04	0.04	0.03
1200	1.6	0.8	0.53	0.4	0.32	0.27	0.23	0.20	0.18	0.16	0.14	0.13
1800	3.6	1.8	1.20	0.9	0.72	0.60	0.51	0.45	0.40	0.36	0.33	0.30
2400	6.4	3.2	2.13	1.6	1.28	1.07	0.91	0.80	0.71	0.64	0.58	0.53
3000	10.0	5.0	3.33	2.5	2.00	1.67	1.43	1.25	1.11	1.00	0.91	0.83
3600	14.4	7.2	4.80	3.6	2.88	2.40	2.06	1.80	1.60	1.44	1.31	1.20
4200	...	9.8	6.53	4.9	3.92	3.27	2.80	2.45	2.18	1.96	1.78	1.63
4800	...	12.8	8.53	6.4	5.12	4.27	3.66	3.20	2.84	2.56	2.33	2.13
6000	...	20.0	13.33	10.0	8.00	6.67	5.71	5.00	4.44	4.00	3.64	3.33

Velocity, Feet per Minute	Diameter of Pipe in Inches									
	14	16	20	24	28	32	36	40	44	48
	Loss in Ounces per Square Inch per 100 Feet									
600	0.029	0.025	0.02	0.017	0.014	0.012	0.011	0.01	0.009	0.008
1200	0.114	0.100	0.08	0.067	0.057	0.050	0.044	0.04	0.036	0.033
1800	0.257	0.225	0.18	0.150	0.129	0.112	0.100	0.09	0.082	0.075
2400	0.457	0.400	0.32	0.267	0.239	0.200	0.178	0.16	0.145	0.133
3000	0.714	0.625	0.50	0.417	0.357	0.312	0.278	0.25	0.227	0.208
3600	1.029	0.900	0.72	0.600	0.514	0.450	0.400	0.36	0.327	0.300
4200	1.400	1.225	0.98	0.817	0.700	0.612	0.544	0.49	0.445	0.408
4800	1.829	1.600	1.28	1.067	0.914	0.800	0.711	0.64	0.582	0.533
6000	2.857	2.500	2.00	1.667	1.429	1.250	1.111	1.00	0.909	0.833

Effect of Bends on the Flow of Air. — The formulas given for the flow of air through pipes relate to straight pipes only. The effect of a bend in a fitting or pipe varies to a great extent with the character of the bend. The resistance offered is least when the radius of the bend is equal to five times the radius of the pipe. The usual way for stating the resistance offered by a bend is in terms of the equivalent length of straight pipe which offers the same frictional resistance to the flow of air as does the bend. The following formula may be used:

$$L = 12.85\, l \left(\frac{r}{R}\right)^{0.83}$$

in which L = equivalent length of straight pipe in feet; R = mean radius of bend in feet or inches; r = inside radius of pipe in feet or inches; l = length of bend in feet measured along the center line.

The resistance of a bend, the radius of which is five times the radius of the pipe, is equal to the resistance of a straight length of pipe, 3⅓ times the length of the bend measured along the center line.

Effect of Fittings. — The reduction of pressure produced by elbows, tees and globe valves may also be stated in an equivalent length of straight pipe. The following table (National Tube Co.) gives the additional length required to equal the friction due to globe valves. For elbows and tees, take two-thirds of the length given in the table.

Diam. of Pipe,	1	1½	2	3	4	5	6	8	10	12	15	18	24
Additional Length, Feet	2	4	7	13	20	28	36	53	70	88	115	143	200

Loss of Pressure in Pounds per Square Inch of Air at 80 Pounds Gage Pressure in 1000 Feet of Pipe

(Ingersoll-Rand Co.)

Size of Pipe	Delivery in Cubic Feet of Compressed Air per Minute at 80 Pounds Gage									
	7.74	11.3	15.2	19.4	23.2	27.2	31.0	38.7	46.5	62.0
	Equivalent Delivery in Cubic Feet of Free Air per Minute									
	50	75	100	125	150	175	200	250	300	400
1	14.31	.....	.....	.....	.....	.....	.....	.....	.....	.....
1¼	3.96	8.46	15.31	.....	.....	.....	.....	.....	.....	.....
1½	1.53	3.26	5.92	9.64	13.79	.....	.....	.....	.....	.....
2	0.33	0.71	1.28	2.09	2.99	4.09	5.34	8.32	12.01	.....
2½	0.10	0.21	0.39	0.64	0.91	1.25	1.63	2.54	3.67	6.53
3	0.03	0.08	0.14	0.24	0.34	0.47	0.61	0.96	1.38	2.45
3½	0.01	0.03	0.06	0.11	0.15	0.21	0.27	0.43	0.62	1.11
4	.....	0.01	0.03	0.05	0.07	0.10	0.13	0.21	0.30	0.54
4½	.....	.....	0.02	0.03	0.04	0.06	0.07	0.12	0.17	0.30
5	.....	.....	0.01	0.01	0.02	0.03	0.04	0.07	0.09	0.17
6	.....	.....	.....	.....	0.01	0.01	0.01	0.02	0.03	0.06
7	.....	.....	.....	.....	.....	.....	.....	0.01	0.01	0.03
8	.....	.....	.....	.....	.....	.....	.....	.....	.....	0.01

Size of Pipe	Delivery in Cubic Feet of Compressed Air per Minute at 80 Pounds Gage									
	77.4	92.9	124.0	152	232	310	387	465	620	774
	Equivalent Delivery in Cubic Feet of Free Air per Minute									
	500	600	800	1000	1500	2000	2500	3000	4000	5000
2½	10.81	.....	.....	.....	.....	.....	.....	.....	.....	.....
3	3.83	5.61	9.86	.....	.....	.....	.....	.....	.....	.....
3½	1.73	2.46	4.42	6.64	15.41	.....	.....	.....	.....	.....
4	0.85	1.22	2.18	3.29	7.62	13.62	.....	.....	.....	.....
4½	0.47	0.68	1.19	1.82	4.24	7.58	11.79	.....	.....	.....
5	0.27	0.39	0.69	1.04	2.43	4.32	6.88	9.72	.....	.....
6	0.10	0.15	0.27	0.40	0.95	1.69	2.64	3.79	6.78	10.55
7	0.05	0.06	0.12	0.18	0.43	0.77	1.19	1.73	3.07	4.79
8	0.02	0.03	0.06	0.09	0.22	0.39	0.60	0.87	1.55	2.46
9	0.01	0.02	0.03	0.05	0.12	0.21	0.33	0.48	0.85	1.33
10	.....	0.01	0.02	0.03	0.06	0.12	0.19	0.28	0.49	0.77
12	.....	.....	0.01	0.01	0.02	0.04	0.07	0.11	0.19	0.30
14	.....	.....	.....	.....	0.01	0.02	0.03	0.05	0.09	0.14
16	.....	.....	.....	.....	.....	0.01	0.01	0.02	0.04	0.07

Inside Diameter of Pipes, in Inches, Required to Transmit Air at Given Velocities

(Buffalo Forge Co.)

Cubic Feet of Air Transmitted per Minute	Velocity of Air, Feet per Minute											
	500	600	800	1000	1200	1500	1800	2000	2500	3000	3500	4000
	Diameter of Pipe, Inches											
200	9	8	7	7	6	6	6	6	6	6	6	6
400	13	11	10	9	8	8	7	7	6	6	6	6
600	15	14	12	11	10	9	8	8	7	7	6	6
800	18	16	14	13	12	10	9	9	8	8	7	7
1000	20	18	16	14	13	12	10	10	9	8	8	7
1200	21	20	17	15	14	13	11	11	10	9	9	8
1400	23	21	18	16	15	14	12	12	11	10	9	9
1600	25	23	20	18	16	15	13	13	11	11	10	9
1800	26	24	21	19	17	16	14	13	12	11	10	10
2000	28	25	22	20	18	16	15	14	13	12	11	10
2200	29	27	23	21	19	17	15	15	13	12	11	11
2400	30	28	24	21	20	18	16	15	14	13	12	11
2600	31	29	25	22	20	18	17	16	15	13	12	11
2800	33	30	26	23	21	19	18	16	15	14	13	12
3000	34	31	27	24	22	20	18	17	15	14	13	12
3200	34	32	28	25	23	20	19	18	15	15	13	13
3400	36	33	28	25	23	21	19	18	16	15	14	13
3600	37	34	29	26	24	21	20	19	16	15	14	13
3800	38	35	30	27	25	22	21	19	17	16	15	14
4000	39	35	31	28	25	22	21	20	18	16	15	14
4200	40	36	32	28	26	23	21	20	18	16	15	14
4400	41	37	32	29	26	24	22	21	18	17	16	15
4600	42	38	33	30	27	24	22	21	19	17	16	15
4800	42	39	34	30	28	25	22	21	19	18	16	15
5000	43	40	34	31	28	25	23	22	20	18	17	16
5200	44	40	35	31	29	25	24	22	20	18	17	16
5400	..	..	35	32	29	26	24	23	21	18	18	16
5600	..	..	36	33	30	27	24	23	21	19	18	17
5800	..	..	37	33	30	27	25	24	21	19	18	17
6000	..	..	38	34	31	28	25	24	21	20	18	17
6200	..	..	38	34	31	28	25	24	21	20	18	17
6400	..	..	39	35	32	28	26	25	22	20	19	18
6600	..	..	39	36	32	29	26	25	22	21	19	18
6800	..	..	40	36	33	29	27	25	23	21	19	18
7000	..	..	40	36	33	30	27	26	23	21	19	18
7200	..	..	41	37	34	30	28	26	23	21	20	19
7400	..	..	41	37	34	30	28	27	24	21	20	19
7600	..	..	42	38	34	31	28	27	24	22	20	19
7800	..	..	43	38	36	31	29	27	24	22	21	19
8000	..	..	43	39	36	32	29	28	25	22	21	20
8200	..	..	..	39	36	32	29	28	25	23	21	20
8400	..	..	..	40	36	33	30	28	25	23	21	20

Care of Pneumatic Hammers. — The life of pneumatic hammers can be greatly prolonged, and the necessity for making repairs largely eliminated, by keeping the working parts clean and well lubricated. It is a good plan to occasionally submerge the hammer in a bath of benzine for a few hours, and then blow it out under pressure to dislodge any foreign matter that may have entered. Before using the hammer, the working parts should be lubricated with a good quality of light machine oil. The source of pneumatic hammer troubles is sometimes in the pipe line. The moisture in the air rusts the pipes, and if a hammer is connected without first blowing out the pipes, the sediment is liable to enter the working parts and cause the valve or piston to stick. Rubber also deteriorates rapidly, and particles of the hose may blow into the valve box and interfere with the operation of the hammer. The use of a poor grade of heavy-bodied oil will also cause the ports to become clogged and render the hammer inoperative. In such cases, it is a good plan to clean the working parts by injecting a liberal quantity of benzine through the throttle handle, as this dislodges the foreign matter and "cuts" the thick oil, which can then be removed by blowing air through the hammer.

The use of strainers or filters attached to the hammer or placed in the supply pipe is to be recommended. Perhaps the most serious abuse to which riveting hammers are subjected is the use of short pistons. When the length of the piston is reduced, the hammer delivers a more rapid blow and, for a time, facilitates the work; hence workmen sometimes substitute short pistons to increase their output, especially when working on a piece-work basis. Short pistons are objectionable as they tend to crumble, and the broken parts will cut the inner casing of the cylinder. If the latter is not damaged beyond repair from this cause, it is soon cracked or the hammer is otherwise broken.

Pneumatic Hammer Capacity and Air Consumption *

Piston Diam., Inches	Stroke, Inches	Weight, Pounds	Cu. Ft. of Free Air per Min.	Blows per Minute	Size of Hose Required	Work Adapted for
Riveting Hammers							
1 1/16	1	10 1/4	15	3100	1/2	Driving 1/4-inch Hot Rivets
1 1/16	2	11 1/4	15	2200	1/2	Driving 5/16-inch Hot Rivets
1 1/16	3	12 1/2	15	1600	1/2	Driving 3/8-inch Hot Rivets
1 1/16	4	15	15	1100	1/2	Driving 1/2-inch Hot Rivets
1 1/8	5	17	20	1000	3/4	Driving 3/4-inch Hot Rivets
1 1/16	6	19	21	900	3/4	Driving 7/8-inch Hot Rivets
1 1/16	8	21	22	770	3/4	Driving 1-inch Hot Rivets
1 1/16	9	22	23	700	3/4	Driving 1 1/8-inch Hot Rivets
1 1/8	9	22	25	700	3/4	Driving 1 1/4-inch Hot Rivets
1 1/16	9	42	22	800	3/4	Driving Stay-bolts — All Sizes
Chipping and Calking Hammers							
3/4	1 9/16	5 1/2	7	5000	1/2	Very Light Chipping and Calking
15/16	1 1/4	7	10	4000	1/2	Very Light Chipping and Calking
1 1/16	1	10 1/4	15	3100	1/2	Very Light Chipping and Calking
1 1/16	2	11 1/4	15	2200	1/2	Medium Chipping, Calking and Beading
1 1/16	3	12 1/2	15	1600	1/2	General Chipping and Calking
1 1/16	4	15	15	1100	1/2	Heavy Chipping and Calking

* Independent Pneumatic Tool Co.

Pneumatic Hammer Capacity and Air Consumption *

Diam. of Piston, Inches	Length of Stroke, Inches	Blows per Minute	Cu. Ft. of Free Air per Minute †	Size of Hose Connection	Diam. of Piston, Inches	Length of Stroke, Inches	Capacity, Rivet Diam.	Blows per Minute	Cu. Ft. of Free Air per Minute	Size of Hose Connection
Chipping and Calking Hammers					Riveting Hammers					
3/4	1 3/8	2900	6	1/4	1 1/16	5	3/4	1000	25	3/8
15/16	1 1/4	2200	8	1/4	1 1/16	6	7/8	760	25	3/8
1 1/16	1 1/2	2800	12	1/4	1 1/16	8	1 1/8	700	25	3/8
1 1/8	1	3200	10	1/4	1 1/16	9	1 1/4	620	25	3/8
1 1/8	2	2800	12	1/4	1 1/16	6	7/8	760	25	3/8
1 1/8	3	2400	13	1/4	1 1/16	8	1 1/8	700	25	3/8
1 1/8	4	1600	14	1/4	1 1/16	9	1 1/4	620	25	3/8
1 1/8	1	3200	21	1/4	1 3/16	8	1 1/2	800	28	3/8
1 1/8	2	2800	23	1/4	....	....	....	....	....	....
1 1/8	4	1300	26	1/4	....	....	....	....	....	....
1 3/16	2	2800	10	1/4	....	....	....	....	....	....

* Chicago Pneumatic Tool Co. † Air consumption based upon an air pressure of 80 pounds per square inch.

Air Consumption of Pneumatic Drills. — A general idea of the number of cubic feet of free air per minute required for operating pneumatic drilling machines may be obtained from the following figures. The air consumption of drills made by different manufacturers is, of course, subject to some variation. These figures are based upon an initial air pressure of 80 pounds per square inch:

1. Cylinder diameter, 1 1/4 inch; stroke, 7/8 inch; size of hose connection, 1/4 inch; air consumption, 15 cubic feet per minute.

2. Cylinder diameter, 1 1/2 inch; stroke, 1 1/4 inch; size of hose connection, 1/2 inch; air consumption, from 18 to 20 cubic feet per minute.

3. Cylinder diameter, 1 11/16 inch; stroke, 1 5/8 inch; size of hose connection, 1/2 inch; air consumption, from 20 to 25 cubic feet per minute.

4. Cylinder diameter, 2 inches; stroke, 1 7/8 inch; size of hose connection, 1/2 inch; air consumption, from 30 to 35 cubic feet per minute.

Pneumatic Hoists. — The air-motor or pneumatic geared type of hoist is equipped with some form of air motor which drives the lifting drum through suitable reduction gearing. There are three general classes of air hoists of the cylinder type. With the *single-acting type*, compressed air is admitted to the lower or stuffing-box side of the piston only, and when lowering the hoist, this air is exhausted. This type is intended for ordinary work, especially where a delicate control is not necessary. The *air-balanced type* of hoist is so arranged that there is full air pressure on the stuffing-box side of the piston at all times. The load is hoisted by exhausting air from the space above the piston; the unbalanced area due to the space occupied by the piston-rod aids in forcing the piston downward. The advantage of this arrangement is accuracy of control. The *double-acting type* differs from the balanced type in that air may be admitted and exhausted from either side of the piston, so that the latter may be moved in either direction with equal power. Thus, with a balanced hoist, there is a constant pressure on one side of the piston and a variable pressure on the other, whereas, with a double-acting type, the pressure on either side of the piston may be varied in accordance with the amount of the load and the direction in which the force must be applied.

PRESSURES AND FLOW OF WATER

Water Pressures. — Water is composed of two gases, hydrogen and oxygen, in the ratio of two volumes of the former to one of the latter. Water boils under atmospheric pressure at 212 degrees F. and freezes at 32 degrees F. Its greatest density is at 39.1 degrees F., when it weighs 62.425 pounds per cubic foot. The pressure in pounds per square inch of water that is not moving, against the sides of any pipe, vessel, container or dam, is due solely to the "head," or height of the surface of the water above the point at which the pressure is considered. The pressure is equal to 0.433 pound per square inch for every foot of the head, at a temperature of 62 degrees F. For higher temperatures, the pressure slightly decreases in the proportion indicated by the table "Weight of Water per Cubic Foot at Different Temperatures." The pressure per square inch is equal in all directions, downwards, upwards and sideways. Water can be compressed only in a very slight degree, the compressibility being so slight that even at the depth of a mile, a cubic foot of water weighs only about one-half pound more than at the surface.

Pressure in Pounds per Square Inch for Different Heads of Water

Head, Feet	0	1	2	3	4	5	6	7	8	9
0	....	0.43	0.87	1.30	1.73	2.16	2.60	3.03	3.46	3.90
10	4.33	4.76	5.20	5.63	6.06	6.49	6.93	7.36	7.79	8.23
20	8.56	9.09	9.53	9.96	10.39	10.82	11.26	11.69	12.12	12.56
30	12.99	13.42	13.86	14.29	14.72	15.15	15.59	16.02	16.45	16.89
40	17.32	17.75	18.19	18.62	19.05	19.48	19.92	20.35	20.78	21.22
50	21.65	22.08	22.52	22.95	23.38	23.81	24.25	24.68	25.11	25.55
60	25.98	26.41	26.85	27.28	27.71	28.14	28.58	29.01	29.44	29.88
70	30.31	30.74	31.18	31.61	32.04	32.47	32.91	33.34	33.77	34.21
80	34.64	35.07	35.51	35.94	36.37	36.80	37.24	37.67	38.10	38.54
90	38.97	39.40	39.84	40.27	40.70	41.13	41.57	42.00	42.43	42.87

Heads of Water in Feet Corresponding to Certain Pressures in Pounds per Square Inch

Pressure, Lbs.	0	1	2	3	4	5	6	7	8	9
0	....	2.3	4.6	6.9	9.2	11.5	13.9	16.2	18.5	20.8
10	23.1	25.4	27.7	30.0	32.3	34.6	36.9	39.3	41.6	43.9
20	46.2	48.5	50.8	53.1	55.4	57.7	60.0	62.4	64.7	67.0
30	69.3	71.6	73.9	76.2	78.5	80.8	83.1	85.4	87.8	90.1
40	92.4	94.7	97.0	99.3	101.6	103.9	106.2	108.5	110.8	113.2
50	115.5	117.8	120.1	122.4	124.7	127.0	129.3	131.6	133.9	136.3
60	138.6	140.9	143.2	145.5	147.8	150.1	152.4	154.7	157.0	159.3
70	161.7	164.0	166.3	168.6	170.9	173.2	175.5	177.8	180.1	182.4
80	184.8	187.1	189.4	191.7	194.0	196.3	198.6	200.9	203.2	205.5
90	207.9	210.2	212.5	214.8	217.1	219.4	221.7	224.0	226.3	228.6

Comparison of Different Methods of Measuring Pressures

Ounces and Pounds per Square Inch, and Inches of Water and Mercury

Ounces per Square Inch	Pounds per Square Inch	Inches of Water	Inches of Mercury	Ounces per Square Inch	Pounds per Square Inch	Inches of Water	Inches of Mercury
0.25	0.016	0.433	0.0310	8	0.500	13.856	1.020
0.50	0.031	0.866	0.0638	9	0.562	15.588	1.148
1	0.062	1.732	0.1275	10	0.625	17.320	1.275
2	0.125	3.464	0.2551	11	0.687	19.052	1.403
3	0.187	5.196	0.3826	12	0.750	20.784	1.531
4	0.250	6.928	0.5102	13	0.812	22.516	1.658
5	0.312	8.660	0.6377	14	0.875	24.248	1.786
6	0.375	10.392	0.7653	15	0.937	25.980	1.913
7	0.437	12.124	0.8928	16	1.000	27.712	2.041

Pounds per Square Inch, Inches and Feet of Water and Inches of Mercury

Pounds per Square Inch	Inches of Water	Feet of Water	Inches of Mercury	Pounds per Square Inch	Inches of Water	Feet of Water	Inches of Mercury
1	27.71	2.31	2.041	14	387.97	32.33	28.57
2	55.42	4.62	4.081	14.7	407.37	33.95	30.00
3	83.14	6.93	6.122	15	415.68	34.64	30.61
4	110.85	9.24	8.163	16	443.40	36.95	32.65
5	138.56	11.55	10.20	17	471.11	39.26	34.69
6	166.27	13.86	12.24	18	498.82	41.57	36.73
7	193.99	16.17	14.28	19	526.53	43.88	38.77
8	221.70	18.47	16.33	20	554.25	46.19	40.81
9	249.41	20.78	18.37	21	581.96	48.50	42.85
10	277.12	23.09	20.41	22	609.67	50.81	44.89
11	304.84	25.40	22.45	23	637.38	53.12	46.94
12	332.55	27.71	24.49	24	665.10	55.42	48.98
13	360.26	30.02	26.53	25	692.81	57.73	51.02

Volume of Water at Different Temperatures

Degrees Fahr.	Volume	Degrees Fahr.	Volume	Degrees Fahr.	Volume	Degrees Fahr.	Volume
39.1	1.00000	86	1.00425	131	1.01423	176	1.02872
50	1.00025	95	1.00586	140	1.01678	185	1.03213
59	1.00083	104	1.00767	149	1.01951	194	1.03570
68	1.00171	113	1.00967	158	1.02241	203	1.03943
77	1.00286	122	1.01186	167	1.02548	212	1.04332

Weight of Water per Cubic Foot at Different Temperatures

Temperature, Degrees F.	Weight per Cubic Foot, Pounds	Temperature, Degrees F.	Weight per Cubic Foot, Pounds	Temperature, Degrees F.	Weight per Cubic Foot, Pounds	Temperature, Degrees F.	Weight per Cubic Foot, Pounds	Temperature, Degrees F.	Weight per Cubic Foot, Pounds	Temperature, Degrees F.	Weight per Cubic Foot, Pounds
32	62.42	130	61.56	220	59.63	320	56.66	420	52.6	520	47.6
40	62.42	140	61.37	230	59.37	330	56.30	430	52.2	530	47.0
50	62.41	150	61.18	240	59.11	340	55.94	440	51.7	540	46.3
60	62.37	160	60.98	250	58.83	350	55.57	450	51.2	550	45.6
70	62.31	170	60.77	260	58.55	360	55.18	460	50.7	560	44.9
80	62.23	180	60.55	270	58.26	370	54.78	470	50.2	570	44.1
90	62.13	190	60.32	280	57.96	380	54.36	480	49.7	580	43.3
100	62.02	200	60.12	290	57.65	390	53.94	490	49.2	590	42.6
110	61.89	210	59.88	300	57.33	400	53.50	500	48.7	600	41.8
120	61.74	212	59.83	310	57.00	410	53.00	510	48.1	...	...

Table of Horsepower Due to Certain Head of Water

The table gives the horsepower of 1 cubic foot of water per minute, and is based on an efficiency of 85 per cent.

Heads in Feet	Horse-power	Heads in Feet	Horse-power	Heads in Feet	Horse-power	Heads in Feet	Horse-power	Heads in Feet	Horse-power
1	0.0016	170	0.274	340	0.547	520	0.837	1250	2.012
10	0.0161	180	0.290	350	0.563	540	0.869	1300	2.093
20	0.0322	190	0.306	360	0.580	560	0.901	1350	2.173
30	0.0483	200	0.322	370	0.596	580	0.934	1400	2.254
40	0.0644	210	0.338	380	0.612	600	0.966	1450	2.334
50	0.0805	220	0.354	390	0.628	650	1.046	1500	2.415
60	0.0966	230	0.370	400	0.644	700	1.127	1550	2.495
70	0.1127	240	0.386	410	0.660	750	1.207	1600	2.576
80	0.1288	250	0.402	420	0.676	800	1.288	1650	2.656
90	0.1449	260	0.418	430	0.692	850	1.368	1700	2.737
100	0.1610	270	0.435	440	0.708	900	1.449	1750	2.818
110	0.1771	280	0.451	450	0.724	950	1.529	1800	2.898
120	0.1932	290	0.467	460	0.740	1000	1.610	1850	2.978
130	0.2093	300	0.483	470	0.757	1050	1.690	1900	3.059
140	0.2254	310	0.499	480	0.773	1100	1.771	1950	3.139
150	0.2415	320	0.515	490	0.789	1150	1.851	2000	3.220
160	0.2576	330	0.531	500	0.805	1200	1.932	2100	3.381

Flow of Water in Pipes. — The quantity of water that will be discharged through a pipe depends primarily on the head and also upon the diameter of the pipe, the character of the interior surface, and the number and shape of the bends. The head may be either the actual distance between the levels of the surface of water in a reservoir and the point of discharge, or it may be caused by mechanically applied pressure, as by pumping, in which case the head is calculated as the vertical distance corresponding to the pressure. One pound per square inch is equal to 2.309 feet head, or 1 foot head is equal to a pressure of 0.433 pound per square inch.

All formulas for finding the amount of water that will flow through a pipe in a given time are approximate. The formula below will give results within 5 or 10 per cent of actual results, if applied to pipe lines carefully laid and in a fair condition.

$$V = C \sqrt{\frac{hD}{L + 54 D}}$$

in which V = approximate mean velocity in feet per second;

C = coefficient from the accompanying table;

D = diameter of pipe in feet;

h = total head in feet;

L = total length of pipe line in feet.

Values of Coefficient C

Diam. of Pipe		C	Diam. of Pipe		C	Diam. of Pipe		C
Feet	Inches		Feet	Inches		Feet	Inches	
0.1	1.2	23	0.8	9.6	46	3.5	42	64
0.2	2.4	30	0.9	10.8	47	4.0	48	66
0.3	3.6	34	1.0	12.0	48	5.0	60	68
0.4	4.8	37	1.5	18.0	53	6.0	72	70
0.5	6.0	39	2.0	24.0	57	7.0	84	72
0.6	7.2	42	2.5	30.0	60	8.0	96	74
0.7	8.4	44	3.0	36.0	62	10.0	120	77

Example. — A pipe line, 1 mile long, 12 inches in diameter, discharges water under a head of 100 feet. Find the velocity and quantity of discharge.

From the table, the coefficient C is found to be 48 for a pipe 1 foot in diameter, hence:

$$V = 48 \sqrt{\frac{100 \times 1}{5280 + 54 \times 1}} = 6.57 \text{ feet per second.}$$

To find the discharge in cubic feet per second, multiply the velocity found by the area of cross-section of the pipe in square feet:

$$6.57 \times 0.7854 = 5.16 \text{ cubic feet per second.}$$

The loss of head due to a bend in the pipe is most frequently given in the equivalent length of straight pipe, which would cause the same loss in head as the bend. Experiments show that a right-angle bend should have a radius of about three times the diameter of the pipe. Assuming this curvature, then, if D is the diameter of the pipe in inches and L is the length of straight pipe in feet, which causes the same loss of head as the bend in the pipe, the following formula gives the equivalent length of straight pipe that should be added to compensate for a right-angle bend:

$$L = 4 D \div 3.$$

Thus the loss of head due to a right-angle bend in a six-inch pipe would be equal to that in 8 feet of straight pipe. Experiments undertaken to determine the losses due to valves in pipe lines indicate that a fully open gate valve in a pipe causes a loss of head corresponding to that in a length of pipe equal to six diameters.

Flow of Water Through Nozzles in Cubic Feet per Second

Head in Feet, at Nozzle	Pressure, Pounds per Square Inch	Theoretical Velocity, Feet per Second	Diameter of Nozzle, Inches							
			1	1½	2	2½	3	3½	4	4½
5	2.17	17.93	0.10	0.22	0.39	0.61	0.88	1.20	1.56	2.04
10	4.33	25.36	0.14	0.31	0.55	0.86	1.24	1.69	2.21	2.87
20	8.66	35.86	0.19	0.44	0.78	1.22	1.76	2.39	3.13	4.07
30	12.99	43.92	0.24	0.54	0.96	1.50	2.16	2.93	3.83	4.98
40	17.32	50.72	0.28	0.62	1.10	1.73	2.49	3.39	4.43	5.75
50	21.65	56.71	0.31	0.70	1.24	1.93	2.78	3.79	4.95	6.43
60	25.99	62.12	0.34	0.76	1.35	2.12	3.05	4.15	5.42	7.04
70	30.32	67.10	0.37	0.82	1.46	2.29	3.29	4.48	5.86	7.61
80	34.65	71.73	0.39	0.88	1.56	2.44	3.52	4.79	6.26	8.13
90	38.98	76.08	0.42	0.94	1.66	2.59	3.73	5.08	6.64	8.63
100	43.31	80.20	0.44	0.99	1.75	2.73	3.94	5.38	7.00	9.09
120	51.97	87.88	0.49	1.08	1.87	3.00	4.31	5.87	7.67	9.96
140	60.63	94.89	0.52	1.17	2.07	3.23	4.66	6.35	8.28	10.76
160	69.29	101.45	0.56	1.25	2.21	3.46	4.98	6.78	8.86	11.50
180	77.96	107.59	0.59	1.32	2.34	3.67	5.28	7.19	9.39	12.20
200	86.62	113.41	0.62	1.39	2.47	3.87	5.57	7.57	9.90	12.86
250	108.50	126.80	0.70	1.56	2.76	4.32	6.22	8.47	11.07	14.38
300	130.20	138.91	0.76	1.71	3.03	4.74	6.82	9.27	12.13	15.75
350	151.90	150.04	0.82	1.84	3.27	5.12	7.37	10.02	13.10	17.01
400	173.60	160.40	0.88	1.97	3.50	5.47	7.87	10.71	14.00	18.19
450	195.30	170.12	0.93	2.09	3.71	5.80	8.35	11.36	14.85	19.39
500	216.00	179.33	0.99	2.21	3.91	6.11	8.80	11.98	15.65	20.34

Head in Feet, at Nozzle	Pressure, Pounds per Square Inch	Theoretical Velocity, Feet per Second	Diameter of Nozzle, Inches							
			5	6	7	8	9	10	11	12
5	2.17	17.93	2.44	3.52	4.81	6.3	7.9	9.8	12.8	14.1
10	4.33	25.36	3.46	4.98	6.78	8.8	11.2	13.8	16.7	19.9
20	8.66	35.86	4.88	7.04	9.58	12.5	15.8	19.6	23.7	28.2
30	12.99	43.92	5.99	8.62	11.74	15.3	19.4	23.9	29.0	34.5
40	17.32	50.72	6.92	9.96	13.56	17.7	22.4	27.7	33.5	39.8
50	21.65	56.71	7.73	11.13	15.16	19.8	25.0	30.9	37.4	44.5
60	25.99	62.12	8.44	12.19	16.60	21.7	27.4	33.9	41.0	48.8
70	30.32	67.10	9.15	13.17	17.93	23.4	29.6	36.6	44.3	52.7
80	34.65	71.73	9.78	14.08	19.17	25.0	31.7	39.1	47.3	56.4
90	38.98	76.08	10.38	14.93	20.35	26.6	33.6	41.5	50.2	59.7
100	43.31	80.20	10.94	15.74	21.44	28.0	35.4	43.7	52.9	63.0
120	51.97	87.88	11.99	17.25	23.49	30.7	38.8	47.9	58.0	69.0
140	60.63	94.89	12.94	18.63	25.36	33.1	41.9	51.7	62.6	74.5
160	69.29	101.45	13.84	19.91	27.12	35.4	44.8	55.3	67.0	79.7
180	77.96	107.59	14.67	21.12	28.76	37.6	47.5	58.7	71.0	84.5
200	86.62	113.41	15.47	22.26	30.31	39.6	50.1	61.8	74.8	89.1
250	108.50	126.80	17.29	24.86	33.89	44.3	56.0	69.2	83.7	99.6
300	130.20	138.91	18.90	27.27	37.13	48.5	61.4	75.8	91.7	109.1
350	151.90	150.04	20.46	29.45	40.10	52.4	66.3	81.8	99.0	117.8
400	173.60	160.40	21.88	31.49	42.87	56.0	70.9	87.5	105.9	126.0
450	195.30	170.12	23.20	33.39	45.26	59.4	75.2	92.8	112.2	133.6
500	216.00	179.33	24.46	35.20	47.93	62.6	79.2	97.8	118.4	140.8

Theoretical Velocity of Water Due to Head in Feet

Head in Feet	Theoretical Velocity, Feet per Second	Theoretical Velocity, Feet per Minute	Head in Feet	Theoretical Velocity, Feet per Second	Theoretical Velocity, Feet per Minute	Head in Feet	Theoretical Velocity, Feet per Second	Theoretical Velocity, Feet per Minute
1	8.02	481	48	55.60	3336	95	78.22	4693
2	11.34	682	49	56.17	3370	96	78.63	4718
3	13.90	834	50	56.74	3405	97	79.04	4742
4	16.05	963	51	57.31	3438	98	79.44	4767
5	17.94	1077	52	57.87	3472	99	79.85	4791
6	19.66	1179	53	58.42	3505	100	80.25	4815
7	21.23	1274	54	58.97	3538	105	82.23	4934
8	22.70	1362	55	59.51	3571	110	84.17	5050
9	24.07	1445	56	60.05	3603	115	86.06	5163
10	25.38	1523	57	60.59	3635	120	87.91	5274
11	26.61	1597	58	61.12	3667	125	89.72	5383
12	27.80	1668	59	61.64	3698	130	91.50	5490
13	28.93	1736	60	62.16	3730	135	93.24	5594
14	30.03	1802	61	62.68	3761	140	94.95	5697
15	31.08	1865	62	63.19	3791	145	96.63	5798
16	32.10	1926	63	63.70	3822	150	98.28	5897
17	33.09	1985	64	64.20	3852	155	99.91	5994
18	34.05	2043	65	64.70	3882	160	101.50	6090
19	34.98	2099	66	65.19	3912	165	103.08	6185
20	35.89	2153	67	65.69	3941	170	104.63	6278
21	36.77	2206	68	66.17	3970	175	106.16	6370
22	37.64	2258	69	66.66	4000	180	107.66	6460
23	38.49	2309	70	67.14	4028	185	109.15	6549
24	39.31	2359	71	67.62	4057	190	110.61	6637
25	40.12	2407	72	68.09	4086	195	112.06	6724
26	40.92	2455	73	68.56	4114	200	113.49	6809
27	41.70	2502	74	69.03	4142	205	114.90	6894
28	42.46	2548	75	69.50	4170	210	116.29	6978
29	43.21	2593	76	69.96	4198	215	117.66	7060
30	43.95	2637	77	70.42	4225	220	119.03	7142
31	44.68	2681	78	70.87	4252	225	120.38	7222
32	45.40	2724	79	71.33	4280	230	121.70	7302
33	46.10	2766	80	71.78	4307	235	123.02	7381
34	46.79	2783	81	72.22	4333	240	124.32	7459
35	47.48	2848	82	72.67	4360	245	125.60	7537
36	48.15	2889	83	73.11	4387	250	126.88	7613
37	48.81	2929	84	73.55	4413	255	128.15	7649
38	49.47	2968	85	73.99	4439	260	129.39	7764
39	50.12	3007	86	74.42	4465	270	131.86	7912
40	50.75	3045	87	74.85	4491	280	134.28	8057
41	51.38	3083	88	75.28	4517	290	136.66	8200
42	52.01	3120	89	75.71	4542	300	138.99	8340
43	52.62	3157	90	76.13	4568	310	141.29	8478
44	53.23	3194	91	76.55	4593	320	143.55	8613
45	53.83	3230	92	76.97	4618	330	145.78	8761
46	54.43	3266	93	77.39	4643	340	147.97	8878
47	55.02	3301	94	77.80	4668	350	150.13	9008

Loss of Head in Pipes by Friction

(Pelton Water-wheel Co.)

L = loss of head, in feet, for 100 feet length of pipe.
Q = quantity of water discharged per minute, in cubic feet.

Velocity, Feet per Second	Inside Diameter of Pipe in Inches											
	1		2		3		4		5		6	
	L	Q	L	Q	L	Q	L	Q	L	Q	L	Q
2.0	2.37	0.65	1.18	2.62	0.79	5.9	0.59	10.4	0.47	16.3	0.39	23.5
2.2	2.80	0.73	1.40	2.88	0.94	6.5	0.70	11.5	0.56	18.0	0.47	25.9
2.4	3.27	0.79	1.64	3.14	1.09	7.1	0.82	12.5	0.65	19.6	0.55	28.2
2.6	3.78	0.86	1.89	3.40	1.26	7.6	0.94	13.6	0.76	21.3	0.63	30.6
2.8	4.32	0.92	2.16	3.66	1.44	8.2	1.08	14.6	0.86	22.9	0.72	32.9
3.0	4.89	0.99	2.44	3.92	1.62	8.8	1.22	15.7	0.98	24.5	0.81	35.3
3.2	5.47	1.06	2.73	4.18	1.82	9.4	1.37	16.7	1.10	26.2	0.91	37.7
3.4	6.09	1.12	3.05	4.45	2.04	10.0	1.52	17.8	1.22	27.8	1.02	40.0
3.6	6.76	1.19	3.38	4.71	2.26	10.6	1.69	18.8	1.35	29.4	1.13	42.4
3.8	7.48	1.26	3.74	4.97	2.49	11.2	1.87	19.9	1.49	31.0	1.25	44.7
4.0	8.20	1.32	4.10	5.23	2.73	11.8	2.05	20.9	1.64	32.7	1.37	47.1
4.4	9.77	1.45	4.89	5.76	3.25	12.9	2.43	23.0	1.95	36.0	1.62	51.8
4.8	11.45	1.58	5.72	6.28	3.81	14.1	2.85	25.1	2.27	39.2	1.90	56.5
5.0	12.33	1.65	6.17	6.54	4.11	14.7	3.08	26.2	2.46	40.9	2.05	58.9
5.2	13.24	1.72	6.62	6.80	4.41	15.3	3.31	27.2	2.65	42.5	2.21	61.2
5.6	15.16	1.85	7.58	7.32	5.06	16.5	3.79	29.3	3.03	45.8	2.53	65.9
6.0	17.23	1.98	8.61	7.85	5.74	17.7	4.31	31.4	3.45	49.1	2.87	70.7
7.0	22.89	2.31	11.45	9.16	7.62	20.6	5.72	36.6	4.57	57.2	3.81	82.4

Velocity, Feet per Second	Inside Diameter of Pipe in Inches											
	7		8		9		10		12		14	
	L	Q	L	Q	L	Q	L	Q	L	Q	L	Q
2.0	0.34	32.0	0.30	41.9	0.26	53	0.24	65	0.20	94	0.17	128
2.2	0.40	35.3	0.35	46.1	0.31	58	0.28	72	0.23	103	0.20	141
2.4	0.47	38.5	0.41	50.2	0.36	64	0.33	78	0.27	113	0.23	154
2.6	0.54	41.7	0.47	54.4	0.42	69	0.38	85	0.31	122	0.27	167
2.8	0.62	44.9	0.54	58.6	0.48	74	0.43	92	0.36	132	0.31	179
3.0	0.70	48.1	0.61	62.8	0.54	79	0.49	98	0.41	141	0.35	192
3.2	0.78	51.3	0.69	67.0	0.61	85	0.55	105	0.46	151	0.39	205
3.4	0.87	54.5	0.76	71.2	0.68	90	0.61	111	0.51	160	0.44	218
3.6	0.97	57.7	0.85	75.4	0.75	95	0.68	118	0.57	169	0.48	231
3.8	1.07	60.9	0.94	79.6	0.83	101	0.75	124	0.62	179	0.53	243
4.0	1.17	64.1	1.03	83.7	0.91	106	0.82	131	0.68	188	0.59	256
4.4	1.39	70.5	1.22	92.1	1.09	116	0.98	144	0.81	207	0.70	282
4.8	1.63	76.9	1.43	100.0	1.27	127	1.14	157	0.95	226	0.82	308
5.0	1.76	80.2	1.54	105.0	1.37	132	1.23	163	1.03	235	0.88	321
5.2	1.89	83.3	1.65	109.0	1.47	138	1.32	170	1.10	245	0.95	333
5.6	2.17	89.8	1.89	117.0	1.68	148	1.51	183	1.26	264	1.08	359
6.0	2.46	96.2	2.15	125.0	1.92	159	1.71	196	1.43	283	1.23	385
7.0	3.26	112.0	2.85	146.0	2.52	185	2.28	229	1.91	330	1.63	449

FLOW OF WATER

Loss of Head in Pipes by Friction

(Pelton Water-wheel Co.)

L = loss of head, in feet, for 100 feet length of pipe.
Q = quantity of water discharged per minute, in cubic feet.

Velocity, Feet per Second	Inside Diameter of Pipe in Inches									
	15		16		18		20		24	
	L	Q	L	Q	L	Q	L	Q	L	Q
2.0	0.158	147	0.147	167	0.132	212	0.119	262	0.098	377
2.2	0.187	162	0.175	184	0.156	233	0.140	288	0.116	414
2.4	0.218	176	0.205	201	0.182	254	0.164	314	0.136	452
2.6	0.252	191	0.236	218	0.210	275	0.189	340	0.157	490
2.8	0.288	206	0.270	234	0.240	297	0.216	366	0.180	528
3.0	0.325	221	0.306	251	0.271	318	0.245	393	0.204	565
3.2	0.366	235	0.343	268	0.305	339	0.275	419	0.229	603
3.4	0.408	250	0.383	284	0.339	360	0.306	445	0.255	641
3.6	0.452	265	0.425	301	0.377	382	0.339	471	0.283	678
3.8	0.499	280	0.468	318	0.416	403	0.374	497	0.312	716
4.0	0.548	294	0.513	335	0.456	424	0.410	523	0.342	754
4.4	0.651	324	0.611	368	0.542	466	0.488	576	0.407	829
4.8	0.763	353	0.715	402	0.636	509	0.572	628	0.476	905
5.0	0.822	368	0.770	419	0.685	530	0.617	654	0.513	942
5.2	0.883	383	0.828	435	0.736	551	0.662	680	0.552	980
5.6	1.011	412	0.949	469	0.843	594	0.758	733	0.632	1055
6.0	1.148	442	1.076	502	0.957	636	0.861	785	0.717	1131
7.0	1.520	515	1.430	586	1.270	742	1.143	916	0.953	1319

Velocity, Feet per Second	Inside Diameter of Pipe in Inches									
	28		30		36		42		48	
	L	Q	L	Q	L	Q	L	Q	L	Q
2.0	0.084	513	0.079	589	0.066	848	0.057	1155	0.050	1508
2.2	0.099	564	0.093	648	0.078	933	0.067	1270	0.059	1658
2.4	0.116	616	0.109	707	0.091	1018	0.079	1385	0.069	1809
2.6	0.134	667	0.126	766	0.104	1100	0.090	1500	0.079	1960
2.8	0.153	718	0.144	824	0.119	1188	0.103	1617	0.090	2110
3.0	0.174	770	0.163	883	0.135	1273	0.117	1730	0.102	2260
3.2	0.195	821	0.182	942	0.152	1357	0.131	1845	0.115	2410
3.4	0.218	872	0.204	1001	0.169	1442	0.146	1961	0.128	2560
3.6	0.242	923	0.226	1060	0.188	1527	0.162	2079	0.142	2715
3.8	0.267	974	0.249	1119	0.207	1612	0.178	2190	0.156	2865
4.0	0.293	1026	0.273	1178	0.228	1697	0.195	2310	0.171	3016
4.4	0.348	1129	0.325	1296	0.271	1866	0.232	2540	0.203	3318
4.8	0.409	1231	0.381	1414	0.318	2036	0.270	2770	0.238	3619
5.0	0.440	1283	0.411	1472	0.342	2121	0.294	2885	0.256	3770
5.2	0.473	1334	0.441	1531	0.368	2206	0.317	3000	0.278	3920
5.6	0.542	1437	0.506	1649	0.421	2376	0.374	3230	0.319	4222
6.0	0.615	1539	0.574	1767	0.479	2545	0.408	3461	0.358	4524
7.0	0.817	1796	0.762	2061	0.636	2868	0.545	4030	0.476	5277

Capacity of Hydraulic Presses

Diam. of Ram, Inches	Area of Ram, Sq. Ins.	Pressure in Pounds per Square Inch on End of Ram										
		2000	2100	2200	2300	2400	2500	2600	2700	2800	2900	3000
		Capacity of Hydraulic Press in Tons										
1	0.785	0.8	0.8	0.9	0.9	0.9	1.0	1.0	1.1	1.1	1.1	1.2
2	3.142	3.1	3.3	3.5	3.6	3.8	3.9	4.1	4.2	4.4	4.5	4.7
3	7.069	7.0	7.4	7.8	8.1	8.5	8.8	9.2	9.5	9.9	10.2	10.6
4	12.566	12.5	13	14.0	14.5	15.0	15.5	16.0	17.0	17.5	18.0	19
5	19.635	20	21	21.5	22.5	23.5	24.5	25.5	26.5	27.5	28.5	29
6	28.274	28	30	31	33	34	35	37	38	40	41	42
7	38.484	38	40	42	44	46	48	50	52	54	56	58
8	50.265	50	53	55	58	60	63	65	68	70	73	75
9	63.617	63	67	70	73	76	80	83	86	89	92	95
10	78.540	78	82	86	90	94	98	102	106	110	114	118
11	95.033	95	100	105	109	114	119	124	128	133	138	143
12	113.097	113	119	124	130	136	141	147	153	158	164	170
13	132.732	132	139	146	153	159	166	172	179	186	193	199
14	153.938	154	162	169	177	185	192	200	208	216	223	231
15	176.715	177	185	194	203	212	221	230	239	247	256	265
16	201.062	201	211	221	231	241	251	261	271	281	292	302
17	226.980	227	238	250	261	272	284	295	306	318	329	340
18	254.469	254	267	280	293	305	318	331	344	356	369	382
19	283.529	284	298	312	326	340	354	369	383	397	411	425
20	314.160	314	330	346	361	377	393	408	424	440	456	471
21	346.361	346	364	381	398	416	433	450	468	485	502	520
22	380.133	380	399	418	437	456	475	494	513	532	551	570
23	415.476	415	436	457	478	499	519	540	561	582	602	623
24	452.390	452	475	498	520	543	565	588	611	633	656	679
25	490.875	491	515	540	565	589	614	638	663	687	712	736
26	530.930	531	557	584	612	637	664	690	717	743	770	796
27	572.556	573	601	630	658	687	716	744	773	802	830	859
28	615.753	616	647	677	708	739	770	800	831	862	893	924
29	660.521	661	694	727	760	793	826	859	892	925	958	991
30	706.860	707	742	778	813	848	884	919	954	990	1025	1060

Rules and Formulas for Hydraulic Press Calculations. — To find the total pressure of a hydraulic press when the diameter of the ram in inches and the water pressure (gage pressure) in pounds per square inch are given, multiply the area of the cross-section of the ram by the pressure per square inch, and divide by 2000. The result is the capacity of the hydraulic press in tons. The same result may be obtained as follows: Multiply the square of the diameter of the ram by the pressure per square inch, and multiply this product by 0.00039. The result is the total pressure of the press in tons.

The pressure per square inch on the material under pressure in the press can be determined when the total pressure of the press and the area of the material under pressure are known. Multiply the total pressure of the press in tons by 2000, and divide the product by the area of the material to be pressed. The quotient is the pressure in pounds per square inch on the surface of the material.

Capacity of Hydraulic Presses

Diam. of Ram, Inches	Area of Ram, Sq. Ins.	Pressure in Pounds per Square Inch on End of Ram									
		3100	3200	3300	3400	3500	3600	3700	3800	3900	4000
		Capacity of Hydraulic Press in Tons									
1	0.785	1.2	1.3	1.3	1.3	1.4	1.4	1.4	1.5	1.5	1.6
2	3.142	4.9	5.0	5.2	5.3	5.5	5.7	5.8	6.0	6.1	6.3
3	7.069	10.9	11.3	11.7	12.0	12.4	12.7	13.1	13.4	13.8	14.1
4	12.566	19.5	20	20.5	21	22	22.5	23	24	24.5	25
5	19.635	30	31	32	33	34	35	36	37	38	39
6	28.274	44	45	47	48	49	51	52	54	55	56
7	38.484	60	62	64	66	67	69	71	73	75	77
8	50.265	78	80	83	85	88	90	93	95	98	100
9	63.617	99	102	105	108	111	115	118	121	124	127
10	78.540	122	126	130	134	137	141	145	149	153	157
11	95.033	147	152	157	162	166	171	176	181	185	190
12	113.097	175	181	187	192	198	204	209	215	221	226
13	132.732	206	212	219	226	232	238	245	252	259	265
14	153.938	239	246	254	262	269	277	285	293	300	308
15	176.715	274	283	292	300	309	318	327	336	345	353
16	201.062	312	322	332	342	352	362	372	382	392	402
17	226.980	352	363	375	386	397	409	420	431	443	454
18	254.469	394	407	420	433	445	458	471	483	496	509
19	283.529	439	452	468	482	496	510	525	539	553	567
20	314.160	487	503	518	534	550	566	581	597	613	628
21	346.361	537	554	571	589	606	623	641	658	675	693
22	380.133	589	608	627	646	665	684	703	722	741	760
23	415.476	644	665	686	706	727	748	769	789	810	831
24	452.390	701	724	746	769	792	814	837	860	882	905
25	490.875	761	785	810	834	859	884	908	933	957	982
26	530.930	823	850	876	903	929	956	982	1009	1035	1062
27	572.556	887	916	945	973	1002	1031	1059	1088	1116	1145
28	615.753	954	985	1016	1047	1078	1108	1139	1170	1201	1232
29	660.521	1024	1057	1090	1123	1156	1189	1222	1255	1288	1321
30	706.860	1096	1131	1166	1202	1237	1272	1308	1343	1378	1414

When a certain pressure per square inch on the material under pressure is required, the gage pressure of the press necessary to obtain this pressure may be calculated as follows: Multiply the area of the surface under pressure by the pressure per square inch desired on the material. Divide this product by 0.7854 times the square of the diameter of the ram. The quotient will be the desired gage pressure.

Expressing these rules as formulas, let D = diameter of ram in inches; P = water pressure in pounds per square inch (gage pressure); C = total pressure or capacity of press in tons; A = area of material to be pressed, in square inches; P_a = pressure in pounds per square inch on material under pressure; then:

$$C = 0.00039 \, D^2 \times P; \quad P_a = \frac{2000 \, C}{A}; \quad P = \frac{A \times P_a}{0.7854 \, D^2}$$

PIPE AND PIPE FITTINGS

Standard Weights and Dimensions of Welded and Seamless Steel Pipe.
(ASA B36.1)

Size (Nom. Inside Diam.) In.	Outside Diam. In.	"Standard Weight" (Standard Wall) Pipe			"Extra Strong" Pipe		"Double Extra Strong" Pipe	
		Threads per Inch	Thickness,† In.	Weight per Foot, with Couplings Lb.	Thickness,† In.	Weight per Foot, Plain Ends, Lb.	Thickness, In.	Weight per Foot, Plain Ends, Lb.
⅛	0.405	27	**0.068**	0.24	**0.095**	0.31	.....	......
¼	0.540	18	**0.088**	0.42	**0.119**	0.54	.....	......
⅜	0.675	18	**0.091**	0.57	**0.126**	0.74	.....	......
½	0.840	14	**0.109**	0.85	**0.147**	1.09	0.294	1.71
¾	1.050	14	**0.113**	1.13	**0.154**	1.47	0.308	2.44
1	1.315	11½	**0.133**	1.68	**0.179**	2.17	0.358	3.66
1¼	1.660	11½	**0.140**	2.28	**0.191**	3.00	0.382	5.21
1½	1.900	11½	**0.145**	2.73	**0.200**	3.63	0.400	6.41
2	2.375	11½	**0.154**	3.68	**0.218**	5.02	0.436	9.03
2½	2.875	8	**0.203**	5.82	**0.276**	7.66	0.552	13.70
3	3.500	8	**0.216**	7.62	**0.300**	10.25	0.600	18.58
3½	4.000	8	**0.226**	9.20	**0.318**	12.51	.....	......
4	4.500	8	**0.237**	10.89	**0.337**	14.98	0.674	27.54
5	5.563	8	**0.258**	14.81	**0.375**	20.78	0.750	38.55
6	6.625	8	**0.280**	19.18	**0.432**	28.57	0.864	53.16
8	8.625	8	**0.322**	29.35	**0.500**	43.39	0.875	72.42
10	10.750	8	**0.365**	41.85	0.500	54.74	.....	......
12	12.750	8	**0.375**	51.15	0.500	65.42	.....	......
14	14.000	8	**0.375**	*54.57	0.500	72.09	.....	......
16	16.000	8	**0.375**	*62.58	0.500	82.77	.....	......
18	18.000	8	**0.375**	*70.59	0.500	93.45	.....	......
20	20.000	8	**0.375**	*78.60	0.500	104.13	.....	......
24	24.000	8	**0.375**	*94.62	0.500	125.49	.....	......

The decimal thicknesses listed for the respective pipe sizes represent their nominal or average wall dimensions.

* Denotes pipe with plain ends, i.e., without thread or coupling.

† Thicknesses shown in **bold face** type for *Standard Wall* are identical with corresponding thicknesses shown in **bold face** type for Schedule 40 pipe. Those shown in **bold face** for *Extra Strong Wall* are identical with corresponding thicknesses shown in **bold face** type for Schedules 60 and 80 pipe.

Double Extra Strong Wall has no corresponding Schedule number.

Welded Wrought Iron Pipe (ASA B36.2).—The wall thicknesses for wrought iron pipe and the weights per foot are those which have always been customary for this commodity. The weights per foot correspond to those for welded and seamless steel pipe in the above table, but because of the difference in weight per cubic foot of the two materials, the wall thickness for wrought iron pipe is slightly greater than that for steel pipe given in the above table.

American Standard Welded and Seamless Steel Pipe (ASA B36.1)

Thicknesses shown in **bold face** type in Schedule 40 are identical with thicknesses for "standard weight" pipe; those shown in **bold face** in Schedules 60 and 80 are identical with thicknesses for "extra strong" pipe.

Nom. Pipe Size, In.	Outside Diam. In.	Nominal Wall Thickness, Inches									
		Schedule Number									
		10	20	30	40	60	80	100	120	140	160
1/8	0.405	...	...	...	**0.068**	...	**0.095**	...	...	...	....
1/4	0.540	...	...	...	**0.088**	...	**0.119**	...	...	...	....
3/8	0.675	...	...	...	**0.091**	...	**0.126**	...	...	...	....
1/2	0.840	...	...	...	**0.109**	...	**0.147**	...	...	...	0.187
3/4	1.050	...	...	...	**0.113**	...	**0.154**	...	...	...	0.218
1	1.315	...	...	...	**0.133**	...	**0.179**	...	...	...	0.250
1 1/4	1.660	...	...	...	**0.140**	...	**0.191**	...	...	...	0.250
1 1/2	1.900	...	...	...	**0.145**	...	**0.200**	...	...	...	0.281
2	2.375	...	...	...	**0.154**	...	**0.218**	...	...	...	0.343
2 1/2	2.875	...	...	...	**0.203**	...	**0.276**	...	...	...	0.375
3	3.500	...	...	...	**0.216**	...	**0.300**	...	...	...	0.438
3 1/2	4.000	...	...	...	**0.226**	...	**0.318**	...	...	...	....
4	4.500	...	...	...	**0.237**	...	**0.337**	...	0.438	...	0.531
5	5.563	...	...	...	**0.258**	...	**0.375**	...	0.500	...	0.625
6	6.625	...	...	...	**0.280**	...	**0.432**	...	0.562	...	0.718
8	8.625	...	0.250	0.277	**0.322**	0.406	**0.500**	0.593	0.718	0.812	0.906
10	10.75	...	0.250	0.307	**0.365**	**0.500**	0.593	0.718	0.843	1.000	1.125
12	12.75	...	0.250	0.330	0.406	0.562	0.687	0.843	1.000	1.125	1.312
*14	14.0	0.250	0.312	0.375	0.438	0.593	0.750	0.937	1.093	1.250	1.406
*16	16.0	0.250	0.312	0.375	0.500	0.656	0.843	1.031	1.218	1.438	1.593
*18	18.0	0.250	0.312	0.438	0.562	0.750	0.937	1.156	1.375	1.562	1.781
*20	20.0	0.250	0.375	0.500	0.593	0.812	1.031	1.281	1.500	1.750	1.968
*24	24.0	0.250	0.375	0.562	0.687	0.968	1.218	1.531	1.812	2.062	2.343
*30	30.0	0.312	0.500	0.625	...	...	...	...	...	...	....

The nominal sizes of pipes larger than 12 inches are the same as the outside diameters. These large sizes commonly are designated as O.D. pipe. The inside diameter depends upon the wall thickness. The standard includes six sizes of O.D. pipe. Each of these sizes has a range of ten wall thicknesses, excepting the 30-inch size which has a range of three thicknesses. These O.D. pipes (marked * in table) all have 8 threads per inch. They will be furnished with plain ends unless otherwise specified.

The decimal thicknesses listed for the respective pipe sizes represent their nominal or average wall dimensions and include an allowance for mill tolerance of 12.5 per cent under the nominal thicknesses.

These specifications cover welded and seamless steel pipe. The "Schedule Numbers" indicate approximate values of the expression $1000 \times P/S$, in which P = internal pressure in pounds per square inch and S = allowable fiber stress in pounds per square inch.

Weight of Pipe per Foot. — The weight of pipe per linear foot for pipe with plain ends or without couplings, can be determined by the following formula:

$$W = K (D^2 - d^2)$$

in which D = outside diameter; d = inside diameter; W = weight per running foot; $K = 2.67$ for steel pipe; $K = 2.45$ for cast iron; $K = 2.82$ for brass;

K = 3.03 for copper; K = 3.86 for lead. The constant for cast iron (2.45) is based on cast iron weighing 0.26 pound per cubic inch, or 450 pounds per cubic foot, and it is advisable to add 10 per cent to the figures obtained for cast iron from the formula, to allow for overweight in the castings.

Bursting Pressure of Pipes. — The bursting pressure of pipes can be determined approximately by the following formula (Barlow's):

$$P = \frac{2\,T \times S}{O}$$

in which P = bursting pressure in pounds per square inch; T = thickness of wall, in inches; O = outside diameter of pipe, in inches; S = tensile strength of material, in pounds per square inch. The value of S as determined by actual bursting tests is 40,000 pounds for butt-welded steel pipe, and 50,000 pounds for lap-welded steel pipe. The accompanying table, "Bursting and Working Pressures for Pipes," is based on the foregoing formula, the accuracy of which has been tested by an exhaustive series of tests conducted by the National Tube Co. In these tests, all types of pipe and tubing were burst, and a number of different methods of plugging the ends were employed, to obtain results for different strains. These results were carefully checked with all available formulas and the Barlow formula came nearer to the experimental results than any of the others.

The Tensile Strength of Non-ferrous Piping. — The strength should be as follows: Brass piping 7000 pounds per square inch; copper piping, 6000 pounds per square inch; Benedict nickel piping, 14,000 pounds per square inch; and Monel metal piping, 20,000 pounds per square inch. Brass and copper pipe should not be tested, however, beyond 1000 pounds per square inch, and Benedict and Monel metal pipes should not be tested beyond 2000 pounds per square inch.

Riveted Steel and Spiral Pipe. — Pipe made of sheet steel (1) may be formed of straight riveted sections; (2) it may have a spiral (helical) riveted seam; or (3) the joint of the spiral pipe may be formed by an interlocking seam. Pipes of this general class are used for low-pressure work in connection with exhaust steam mains, irrigation and dredging, hydraulic mining, exhaust systems, etc.

Approximate Bursting Pressure for Spiral Pipe

Inside Diam., Inches	Thickness, U.S. Gage	Bursting Pressure Lb., Sq. Ft.	Inside Diam., Inches	Thickness, U.S. Gage	Bursting Pressure Lb., Sq. Ft.	Inside Diam., Inches	Thickness, U.S. Gage	Bursting Pressure Lb., Sq. Ft.
Spiral Riveted Pipe — American Spiral Pipe Works								
4	16	1875	12	16	625	24	12	540
6	16	1250	14	14	670	28	10	605
8	16	935	16	14	585	32	10	525
10	16	750	20	14	470	40	10	420
Interlocking Seam — Standard Spiral Pipe Works								
4	16	1875	12	10	1400	26	10	635
4	22	845	12	20	280	26	20	153
6	16	1250	14	10	1200	30	10	540
6	22	470	14	20	240	30	18	180
8	16	935	18	10	930	34	10	475
8	22	350	18	20	235	34	18	158
10	10	1510	22	10	760	40	10	410
10	20	405	22	20	190	40	18	144

Bursting and Working Pressures for Pipes

Size of Pipe, Inches	Bursting Pressure, Pounds per Sq. In.	Working Pressures			Size of Pipe, Inches	Bursting Pressure, Pounds per Sq. In.	Working Pressures		
		Factor of Safety 6	Factor of Safety 8	Factor of Safety 10			Factor of Safety 6	Factor of Safety 8	Factor of Safety 10
Standard Pipe									
¼	13,032	2172	1629	1303	3½	5610	935	701	561
⅜	10,784	1797	1348	1078	4	5266	877	658	526
½	10,384	1731	1298	1038	4½	4940	823	618	494
¾	8,608	1434	1076	860	5	4630	772	579	463
1	8,088	1348	1011	808	6	4220	703	528	422
1¼	6,744	1124	843	674	7	3940	657	493	394
1½	6,104	1017	763	610	8	3730	622	466	373
2	5,184	864	648	518	9	3550	591	444	355
2½	5,648	941	706	564	10	3390	565	424	339
3	4,936	823	617	493	12	2940	490	368	294
Extra Strong									
¼	17,624	2937	2203	1762	3½	7950	1325	994	795
⅜	14,928	2488	1866	1492	4	7480	1246	935	748
½	14,000	2333	1750	1400	4½	7100	1183	887	710
¾	11,728	1954	1716	1172	5	6740	1123	842	674
1	10,888	1814	1611	1088	6	6550	1091	819	655
1¼	9,200	1533	1150	920	7	6520	1086	815	652
1½	8,416	1403	1052	841	8	5780	963	722	578
2	7,336	1223	917	733	9	5190	865	649	519
2½	7,680	1280	960	768	10	4650	775	581	465
3	6,856	1142	857	685	12	3920	653	490	392
Double Extra Strong									
½	28,000	4666	3500	2800	3½	15,900	2650	1987	1590
¾	23,464	3910	2933	2346	4	14,970	2495	1871	1497
1	21,776	3629	2722	2177	4½	14,200	2367	1775	1420
1¼	18,408	3068	2301	1840	5	13,480	2247	1685	1348
1½	16,840	2807	2105	1684	6	13,040	2173	1630	1304
2	15,360	2560	1920	1536	7	11,470	1912	1434	1147
2½	14,680	2447	1835	1468	8	10,140	1690	1267	1014
3	13,714	2285	1714	1371	......	......	......	......	......
Large O. D. Pipe — ⅜ inch Thick					Large O. D. Pipe — ½ inch Thick				
14	2680	447	335	268	14	3570	595	446	357
15	2500	417	313	250	15	3333	556	417	333
16	2340	390	293	234	16	3120	520	390	312
18	2080	347	260	208	18	2770	462	346	277
20	1870	312	234	187	20	2500	417	313	250
22	1700	283	213	170	22	2270	378	284	227
24	1560	260	195	156	24	2080	347	260	208

Transverse and Surface Areas of Standard and Extra Strong Pipe

Nominal Size of Pipe, Inches	Diameters, Inches		Transverse Areas, Sq. In.			Length of Pipe in Feet per Sq. Ft. of Surface Area		Length in Feet Containing One Cu. Ft.
	External	Internal	External	Internal	Metal	External	Internal	
Standard Wrought Pipe								
⅛	0.405	0.269	0.129	0.057	0.072	9.431	14.199	2533.775
¼	0.540	0.364	0.229	0.104	0.125	7.073	10.493	1383.789
⅜	0.675	0.493	0.358	0.191	0.167	5.658	7.747	754.360
½	0.840	0.622	0.554	0.304	0.250	4.547	6.141	473.906
¾	1.050	0.824	0.866	0.533	0.333	3.637	4.635	270.034
1	1.315	1.049	1.358	0.864	0.494	2.904	3.641	166.618
1¼	1.660	1.380	2.164	1.495	0.669	2.301	2.767	96.275
1½	1.900	1.610	2.835	2.036	0.799	2.010	2.372	70.733
2	2.375	2.067	4.430	3.355	1.075	1.608	1.847	42.913
2½	2.875	2.469	6.492	4.788	1.704	1.328	1.547	30.077
3	3.500	3.068	9.621	7.393	2.228	1.091	1.245	19.479
3½	4.000	3.548	12.566	9.886	2.680	0.954	1.076	14.565
4	4.500	4.026	15.904	12.730	3.174	0.848	0.948	11.312
4½	5.000	4.506	19.635	15.947	3.688	0.763	0.847	9.030
5	5.563	5.047	24.306	20.006	4.300	0.686	0.756	7.198
6	6.625	6.065	34.472	28.891	5.581	0.576	0.629	4.984
7	7.625	7.023	45.664	38.738	6.926	0.500	0.543	3.717
8	8.625	8.071	58.426	51.161	7.265	0.442	0.473	2.815
8	8.625	7.981	58.426	50.027	8.399	0.442	0.478	2.878
9	9.625	8.941	72.760	62.786	9.974	0.396	0.427	2.294
10	10.750	10.192	90.763	81.585	9.178	0.355	0.374	1.765
10	10.750	10.136	90.763	80.691	10.072	0.355	0.376	1.785
10	10.750	10.020	90.763	78.855	11.908	0.355	0.381	1.826
11	11.750	11.000	108.434	95.033	13.401	0.325	0.347	1.515
12	12.750	12.090	127.676	114.800	12.876	0.299	0.315	1.254
12	12.750	12.000	127.676	113.097	14.579	0.299	0.318	1.273
Extra Strong Wrought Pipe								
⅛	0.405	0.215	0.129	0.036	0.093	9.431	17.766	3966.392
¼	0.540	0.302	0.229	0.072	0.157	7.073	12.648	2010.290
⅜	0.675	0.423	0.358	0.141	0.217	5.658	9.030	1024.689
½	0.840	0.546	0.554	0.234	0.320	4.547	6.995	615.017
¾	1.050	0.742	0.866	0.433	0.433	3.637	5.147	333.016
1	1.315	0.957	1.358	0.719	0.639	2.904	3.991	200.193
1¼	1.660	1.278	2.164	1.283	0.881	2.301	2.988	112.256
1½	1.900	1.500	2.835	1.767	1.068	2.010	2.546	81.487
2	2.375	1.939	4.430	2.953	1.477	1.608	1.969	48.766
2½	2.875	2.323	6.492	4.238	2.254	1.328	1.644	33.976
3	3.500	2.900	9.621	6.605	3.016	1.091	1.317	21.801
3½	4.000	3.364	12.566	8.888	3.678	0.954	1.135	16.202
4	4.500	3.826	15.904	11.497	4.407	0.848	0.998	12.525
4½	5.000	4.290	19.635	14.455	5.180	0.763	0.890	9.962
5	5.563	4.813	24.306	18.194	6.112	0.686	0.793	7.915
6	6.625	5.761	34.472	26.067	8.405	0.576	0.663	5.524
7	7.625	6.625	45.664	34.472	11.192	0.500	0.576	4.177
8	8.625	7.625	58.426	45.663	12.763	0.442	0.500	3.154
9	9.625	8.625	72.760	58.426	14.334	0.396	0.442	2.464
10	10.750	9.750	90.763	74.662	16.101	0.355	0.391	1.929
11	11.750	10.750	108.434	90.763	17.671	0.325	0.355	1.587
12	12.750	11.750	127.676	108.434	19.242	0.299	0.325	1.328

Steel and Wrought-iron Pipe. — The term "wrought-iron pipe" is often used indiscriminately to designate all butt- or lap-welded pipe whether made from wrought iron or steel, but the term "wrought pipe" is preferable for designating either steel or wrought-iron pipe. A large percentage of the "wrought pipe" now used is made of steel. When wrought-iron pipe is desired the term "genuine wrought iron" or "guaranteed wrought iron" should be used.

Formerly wrought iron was preferred for the best classes of work, but records of installations and tests have demonstrated that steel pipe is equal to wrought-iron pipe for general work and, according to some authorities, resists corrosion, in the average case, as well as wrought iron; the steel pipe is also cheaper than wrought iron, and most of the wrought pipe made in the United States is of steel.

Pipe Wall Thickness Numbers. — According to the American Standard (ASA B36.10), the wall thicknesses available for a given nominal pipe size, are designated by wall thickness "Schedule Numbers" as shown by the table on page 1769. These thickness schedules were intended, originally, to supersede the general terms which have been widely used, such as "standard weight," "extra strong," and "double extra strong." The thicknesses shown in bold-face type under schedule number 40 are identical with the thicknesses for "standard weight" pipe shown in former lists, whereas the thicknesses in bold-face type under schedule numbers 60 and 80 are identical with the thicknesses for "extra strong" pipe. Changes in thickness and weight of the various grades are made by varying the inside diameter only. The outside diameter remains constant so that any grade of pipe may be used with any grade of fitting, flange, coupling, or valve. Standard weight pipe is commonly used for heating work, exhaust lines, and all pressures below 100 pounds per square inch; extra heavy pipe should be employed for pressures from 100 to 200 pounds per square inch, and where there is liable to be considerable corrosion. These pressures are far below the ultimate strength of the pipe.

Making Screwed Joints Tight. — When making up screwed joints, the threads should be clean, and red or white lead, or some standard pipe joint cement or lubricant, should be applied to the threads in order to decrease the friction of the bearing surfaces of the threads; the joint should not be screwed up fast enough to produce excessive friction. Friction of the threads produces heat, thus causing the metal of the pipe to expand before the joint is properly made, with the result that, when the pipe cools again and contracts in the flange or fitting, the joint may be loose and cause leakage when the pressure is turned on the piping system.

Pipe Coverings. — Steam and feed-water pipes are protected with heat-insulating coverings in order to prevent loss of heat by radiation. Under ordinary conditions, about 3 British thermal units per square foot per hour, per degree difference in temperature, radiate from a bare steam pipe. Good commercial heat-insulating materials used for pipe covering will save from 75 to 85 per cent of this loss. Among the various materials used for covering pipe may be mentioned hair felt, cork, magnesia, and mineral wool. Asbestos is a very poor non-conductor of heat, but it may be used to advantage as a binder in other insulating substances. A common covering consists of 85 per cent carbonate of magnesia mixed with 15 per cent of asbestos. The covering should be at least 1 inch thick and preferably from 2 to 3 inches, depending on the size of the pipe. It is generally manufactured in sections molded in halves to fit the pipe. Valves and fittings may be covered with the same material in a plastic state. The covering is secured in place by means of heavy duck or canvas and bands made of brass or sheet iron placed at regular intervals along the pipes. Many commercial pipe coverings are made from two or more of these substances. Pipe laid in trenches may be insulated by the use of ashes, coke, loam, or charcoal.

Lap-welded and Seamless Boiler Tubes. — The following specifications for lap-welded and seamless boiler tubes have been approved by the Boiler Tube Manufacturers of America. Lap-welded tubes shall be made of open-hearth steel or knobbled hammered charcoal iron. Seamless tubes shall be made of open-hearth steel. The steel shall conform to the following requirements as to chemical composition: Carbon, from 0.08 to 0.18 per cent; manganese, from 0.30 to 0.50 per cent; phosphorus, not over 0.04 per cent; and sulphur, not over 0.045 per cent.

Thicknesses of Tubes for Water-tube Boilers.—According to the A. S. M. E. "Boiler Code," the minimum thicknesses of tubes used in water-tube boilers, measured by the Birmingham wire gage, for maximum allowable working pressures not exceeding 165 pounds per square inch, shall be as follows: Diameters less than 3 inches, No. 12 B.W.G.; 3 inches or over but less than 4 inches, No. 11 B.W.G.; 4 inches or over but less than 5 inches, No. 10 B.W.G.; 5 inches, No. 9 B.W.G. The foregoing gages shall be increased as follows for maximum allowable working pressures higher than 165 pounds per square inch: Over 165 pounds but not exceeding 235 pounds, 1 gage; over 235 pounds but not exceeding 285 pounds, 2 gages; over 285 pounds but not exceeding 400 pounds, 3 gages. Tubes over 4 inches in diameter shall not be used for maximum allowable working pressures above 285 pounds per square inch.

Thicknesses of Tubes for Fire-tube Boilers. — The minimum thicknesses of tubes used in fire-tube boilers, measured by the Birmingham wire gage, for maximum allowable working pressures not exceeding 175 pounds per square inch, shall be as follows: Diameters less than 2½ inches, No. 13 B.W.G.; 2½ inches or over but less than 3¼ inches, No. 12 B.W.G.; 3¼ inches or over but less than 4 inches, No. 11 B.W.G.; 4 inches or over but less than 5 inches, No. 10 B.W.G.; 5 inches, No. 9 B.W.G. For higher maximum allowable working pressures than previously given, the thicknesses shall be increased one gage.

Lap-welded Steel or Charcoal Iron Boiler Tubes

External Diameter, Inches	Standard Thickness		Nominal Weight per Foot — Pounds		External Diameter, Inches	Standard Thickness		Nominal Weight per Foot — Pounds	
	Birmingham Wire Gage	Inches	Standard Thickness	One Extra Wire Gage		Birmingham Wire Gage	Inches	Standard Thickness	One Extra Wire Gage
1¾	13	0.095	1.679	1.910	4½	10	0.134	6.248	6.879
2	13	0.095	1.932	2.201	5	9	0.148	7.669	8.520
2¼	13	0.095	2.186	2.492	6	8	0.165	10.282	11.188
2½	12	0.109	2.783	3.050	7	8	0.165	12.044	13.110
2¾	12	0.109	3.074	3.370	8	8	0.165	13.807	15.033
3	12	0.109	3.365	3.691	9	7	0.180	16.955	19.072
3¼	11	0.120	4.011	4.459	10	6	0.203	21.240	22.979
3½	11	0.120	4.331	4.817	11	5	0.220	25.329	27.355
3¾	11	0.120	4.652	5.175	12	......	0.229	28.788	31.188
4	10	0.134	5.532	6.088	13	4	0.238	32.439	35.243

Relative Strengths of Lap- and Butt-welded Pipe. — If seamless steel tubes are assumed to have a strength of 100 per cent, butt-welded steel pipe has a comparative strength of 73 per cent, and lap-welded steel pipe of 92 per cent. From this it will be seen that the strength of a butt-weld is only about 80 per cent of that of a lap-weld. The relative strengths of wrought iron and steel pipe are as follows: Butt-welded wrought-iron pipe has 70 per cent of the strength of similar butt-welded steel pipe, and lap-welded wrought-iron pipe has 57 per cent of the strength of similar lap-welded steel pipe.

American Standard Pipe Flanges and Flanged Fittings. — The American standard fittings (see following tables) have been approved by the American Standards Association and also by the Heating, Piping, and Air Conditioning Contractors National Association; Manufacturers' Standardization Society of Valve and Fittings Industry; and by the American Society of Mechanical Engineers.

Sizes of Fittings. — Sizes of all fittings are designated by giving the corresponding nominal pipe size, which is the same as the port diameter of the fittings for pipe sizes of 12 inches or smaller. When the nominal pipe size is based upon the outside diameter (O.D. pipe), the corresponding fittings will have a smaller port diameter than indicated by the nominal size.

Material for Cast-iron Fittings. — The dimensions of American Standard cast-iron flanges and fittings are based on material equal to the requirements of class "A" regular gray iron for sizes 12 inches and smaller, and class "B" higher strength gray iron for sizes 14 inches and larger, as covered by A.S.T.M. Specification A 126. Requirements of A.S.T.M. A 126 are: maximum sulphur content 0.12 per cent, maximum phosphorus content 0.75 per cent, and a minimum tensile strength of 21,000 pounds per square inch for Class A and 31,000 pounds per square inch for Class B.

Material for Steel Castings. — The dimensions of American standard steel flange fittings are based upon material equal to that covered by the A.S.T.M. Specification for Carbon-steel Castings for Valves, Flanges and Fittings for High Temperature Service (A 95–36). These castings are to be heat-treated and conform to the following requirements: Minimum tensile strength 70,000 pounds per square inch; minimum yield point, 36,000 pounds per square inch; minimum elongation in 2 inches, 22 per cent; minimum reduction of area, 30 per cent; maximum phosphorus content, 0.05 per cent and maximum sulphur content 0.06 per cent.

Tolerances. — An inspection tolerance of plus or minus $\frac{1}{32}$ inch is allowable on all center-to-contact-surface dimensions for sizes of fittings up to and including 10 inches, and plus or minus $\frac{1}{16}$ inch on larger sizes.

Bolting. — Bolt holes straddle the center-lines and are in multiples of four, so that fittings may be made to face in any quarter position. The dimensions of bolts for steel fittings are based on a product equal to the A.S.T.M. Standard Specifications for Alloy Steel Bolting Material for High Temperature Service No. A 96–33. This steel has the following minimum tensile strength: Class A, 95,000 pounds; Class B, 105,000 pounds; and Class C, 125,000 pounds per square inch.

Pressure Ratings. — The steel flanged fittings covered by Tables 8 to 11 inclusive, have the following pressure-temperature ratings: All pressures in this table are in

Maximum, Non-shock, Service Pressure Ratings for Water, Steam and Oil			Hydrostatic Shell Test Pressure; Max. at 125 deg. F. or less
At 750 deg. F. Service Temp.	At 450 deg. F. Service Temp.	At 100 deg. F. Service Temp.	
100	160	230	350
300	390	500	750
400	520	670	1000
600	780	1000	1500
900	1170	1500	1500
1500	1950	2500	2000
2500	3250	4170	3500
			6000

pounds per square inch and represent gage pressures. Except for 100, the values shown for 750 deg. F. temperature are primary service pressure ratings. The pressure values shown for 450 deg. F., apply to boiler feed lines, etc.

Table 1.   American Standard Class 125 Cast-iron Pipe Flanges (ASA B16.1)

Nominal Pipe Size	Diam. of Flange	Thickness of Flange (Min.)	Diam. of Bolt Circle	Number of Bolts	Diam. of Bolts	Diam. of Drilled Bolt Holes	Length of Bolts	Size of Ring Gasket
1	4¼	7⁄16	3⅛	4	½	⅝	1¾	1 × 2⅝
1¼	4⅝	½	3½	4	½	⅝	2	1¼ × 3
1½	5	9⁄16	3⅞	4	½	⅝	2	1½ × 3⅜
2	6	⅝	4¾	4	⅝	¾	2¼	2 × 4⅛
2½	7	11⁄16	5½	4	⅝	¾	2½	2½ × 4⅞
3	7½	¾	6	4	⅝	¾	2½	3 × 5⅜
3½	8½	13⁄16	7	8	⅝	¾	2¾	3½ × 6⅜
4	9	15⁄16	7½	8	⅝	¾	3	4 × 6⅞
5	10	15⁄16	8½	8	¾	⅞	3	5 × 7¾
6	11	1	9½	8	¾	⅞	3¼	6 × 8¾
8	13½	1⅛	11¾	8	¾	⅞	3½	8 × 11
10	16	1 3⁄16	14¼	12	⅞	1	3¾	10 × 13⅜
12	19	1¼	17	12	⅞	1	3¾	12 × 16⅛
14 O.D.	21	1⅜	18¾	12	1	1⅛	4¼	14 × 17¾
16 O.D.	23½	1 7⁄16	21¼	16	1	1⅛	4½	16 × 20¼
18 O.D.	25	1 9⁄16	22¾	16	1⅛	1¼	4¾	18 × 21⅝
20 O.D.	27½	1 11⁄16	25	20	1⅛	1¼	5	20 × 23⅞
24 O.D.	32	1⅞	29½	20	1¼	1⅜	5½	24 × 28¼
30 O.D.	38¾	2⅛	36	28	1¼	1⅜	6¼	30 × 34¾
36 O.D.	46	2⅜	42¾	32	1½	1⅝	7	36 × 41¼
42 O.D.	53	2⅝	49½	36	1½	1⅝	7½	42 × 48
48 O.D.	59½	2¾	56	44	1½	1⅝	7¾	48 × 54½
54 O.D.	66¼	3	62¾	44	1¾	2	8½	54 × 61
60 O.D.	73	3⅛	69¼	52	1¾	2	8¾	60 × 67½
72 O.D.	86½	3½	82½	60	1¾	2	9½	72 × 80¾
84 O.D.	99¾	3⅞	95½	64	2	2¼	10½	84 × 93½
96 O.D.	113¼	4¼	108½	68	2¼	2½	11½	96 × 106¼

All dimensions given in inches.

Class 125 cast-iron pipe flanges and fittings are rated as follows for maximum saturated steam service pressures (gage): 125 pounds per square inch for sizes 1 to 12 inches, inclusive; 100 pounds per square inch for sizes 14 to 24 inches, inclusive; and 50 pounds per square inch for sizes 30 to 48 inches, inclusive.   For maximum water service pressures (gage) at or near the ordinary range of air temperature: 175 pounds per square inch for sizes 1 to 12 inches, inclusive, and 150 pounds per square inch for sizes 14 to 48 inches, inclusive, for flanges only.

The sizes from 54 to 96 inches are included for convenience where special fittings with larger flanges are required and do not necessarily carry a definite rating.

Bolt holes straddle the center lines and are in multiples of four, so that fittings may be made to face in any quarter.   For bolts smaller than 1¾ inches the bolt holes shall be drilled ⅛ inch larger in diameter than the nominal diameter of the bolt.   Holes for bolts 1¾ inches and larger shall be drilled ¼ inch larger than nominal diameter of bolts.

The bolt holes of these cast-iron flanges and flanged fittings need not be spot faced for ordinary service except as follows: In sizes 12 inches and smaller when rough flanges, after facing, are oversize more than ⅛ inch in thickness, they shall be spot faced to the specified thickness of flange (minimum) with a plus tolerance of ¹⁄16 inch.   In sizes 14 inches to 24 inches, inclusive, when rough flanges, after facing, are oversize more than ³⁄16 inch in thickness they shall be spot faced to the specified thickness of flange (minimum) with a plus tolerance of ¹⁄16 inch.   In sizes 30 inches and larger when rough flanges, after facing, are oversize more than ¼ inch in thickness they shall be spot faced to the specified thickness of flange (minimum) with a plus tolerance of ⅛ inch.

Bolts shall be of steel with American Standard Regular or Heavy Unfinished Square Heads and the nuts shall be of steel with American Standard Heavy Unfinished Hexagonal dimensions, all as specified in American Standard for Wrench-Head Bolts and Nut and Wrench Openings (ASA B18.2).   For bolts 1¾ inches in diameter and larger, bolt-studs with a nut on each end are recommended.

Table 2. American Standard Class 25 Cast-iron Flanged Fittings (ASA B16b2)

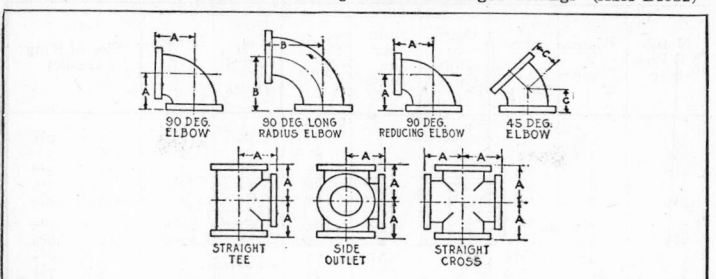

Nominal Pipe Size	Center to Face A	Center to Face B	Center to Face C	Face to Face A + A	Diam. of Flange	Thickness of Flange (Min.)	Body Wall Thickness (Min.)
4	6½	9	4	13	9	¾	0.42
5	7½	10¼	4½	15	10	¾	0.44
6	8	11½	5	16	11	¾	0.44
8	9	14	5½	18	13½	¾	0.46
10	11	16½	6½	22	16	⅞	0.50
12	12	19	7½	24	19	1	0.54
14	14	21½	7½	28	21	1⅛	0.57
16	15	24	8	30	23½	1⅛	0.60
18	16½	26½	8½	33	25	1¼	0.64
20	18	29	9½	36	27½	1¼	0.67
24	22	34	11	44	32	1⅜	0.76
30	25	41½	15	50	38¾	1½	0.88
36	28	49	18	56	46	1⅝	0.99
42	31	56½	21	62	53	1¾	1.10
48	34	64	24	68	59½	2	1.26
54	39	71½	27	78	66¼	2¼	1.35
60	44	79	30	88	73	2¼	1.39
72	53	94	36	106	86½	2½	1.62

All dimensions given in inches. Size of all fittings listed indicates nominal inside diameter of port.

Maximum Pressures (gage): Fittings of all sizes, 25 pounds per square inch for saturated steam; sizes 36 inches and smaller, 43 pounds per square inch maximum non-shock working hydraulic pressure or 25 pounds per square inch maximum gas pressure at or near the ordinary range of air temperatures.

The flange diameters, bolt circles, and number of bolts are the same as the " 125 Lb. American Standard " in Table 1 with a reduction in the thickness of flanges and the bolt diameters, thereby maintaining interchangeability with the "125 Lb. American Standard " flanges. The face to face and center to face dimensions of fittings are the same as the " 125 Lb. American Standard " (Class 125) cast iron flanged fittings.

Special degree elbows, ranging from 1 to 45 degrees inclusive shall have the same center to face dimensions given for 45-degree elbows and those over 45 degrees and up to 90 degrees inclusive shall have the same center to face dimensions as given for 90-degree elbows. The angle designation of an elbow is its deflection from straight line flow and is the angle between the flange faces.

Side outlet elbows and side outlet tees shall have all openings on intersecting center lines.

Tees, side outlet tees, and crosses, 16 inches and smaller, reducing on the outlet or branch, have the same dimensions center to face, and face to face as straight size fittings, corresponding to the size of the larger opening. Sizes 18 inches and larger, reducing on the outlet, are made in two lengths, depending on the size of the outlet.

Tees and crosses, reducing on the run only, carry same dimensions center to face and face to face as a straight size fitting of the larger opening.

Table 3. American Standard Class 125 Cast-iron Flanged Fittings (ASA B16.1)

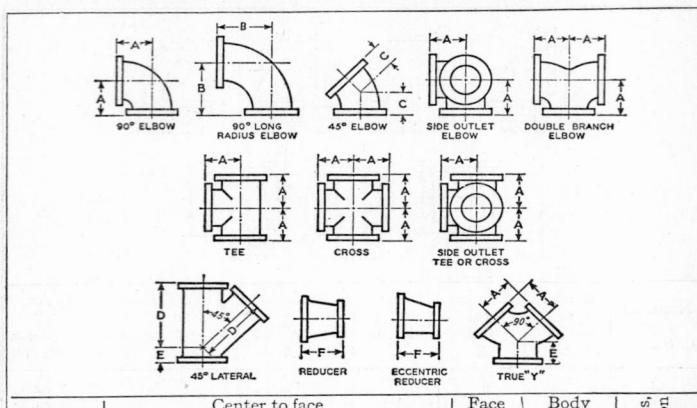

90° ELBOW   90° LONG RADIUS ELBOW   45° ELBOW   SIDE OUTLET ELBOW   DOUBLE BRANCH ELBOW

TEE   CROSS   SIDE OUTLET TEE OR CROSS

45° LATERAL   REDUCER   ECCENTRIC REDUCER   TRUE "Y"

Nominal Pipe Size	Center to face					Face to Face F	Body Wall Thickness†	
	A	B	C	D	E			Fitting flange dimensions are same as pipe flange dimensions, see Table 1 which also gives bolt, gasket and hole location dimensions.
1	3½	5	1¾	5¾	1¾	....	5⁄16	
1¼	3¾	5½	2	6¼	1¾	....	5⁄16	
1½	4	6	2¼	7	2	....	5⁄16	
2	4½	6½	2½	8	2½	5	5⁄16	
2½	5	7	3	9½	2½	5½	5⁄16	
3	5½	7¾	3	10	3	6	3⁄8	
3½	6	8½	3½	11½	3	6½	7⁄16	
4	6½	9	4	12	3	7	½	
5	7½	10¼	4½	13½	3½	8	½	
6	8	11½	5	14½	3½	9	9⁄16	
8	9	14	5½	17½	4½	11	5⁄8	
10	11	16½	6½	20½	5	12	3⁄4	
12	12	19	7½	24½	5½	14	13⁄16	
14 OD	14	21½	7½	27	6	16	7⁄8	
16 OD	15	24	8	30	6½	18	1	
18 OD	16½	26½	8½	32	7	19	1 1⁄16	
20 OD	18	29	9½	35	8	20	1⅛	
24 OD	22	34	11	40½	9	24	1¼	
30 OD	25	41½	15	49	10	30	1 7⁄16	
36 OD	28*	49	18	....	....	36	1⅝	
42 OD	31*	56½	21	....	....	42	1 13⁄16	
48 OD	34*	64	24	....	....	48	2	

All dimensions given in inches.

For pressure ratings, see footnote of Table 1.

* Does not apply to true Y's or double branch elbows.

† Body thickness not to be less than 87½ percent of tabulated value.

Elbows: Reducing elbows and side outlet elbows have the same dimensions center-to-face as straight size elbows, corresponding to the size of the larger opening.

Special degree elbows, ranging from 1 to 45 degrees inclusive, have the same center-to-face dimensions as 45 degree elbows and those over 45 degrees and up to 90 degrees inclusive have the same center-to-face dimensions as 90 degree elbows. The angle designation of an elbow is its deflection from straight line flow and is the angle between the flange faces.

Side outlet elbows, tees, and crosses have all openings on intersecting center-lines.

For dimensions of other reducing fittings, see Table 4.

Table 4. American Standard Class 125 Cast-iron Flanged Fittings — Reducing Tees, Crosses and Laterals (ASA B16.1)

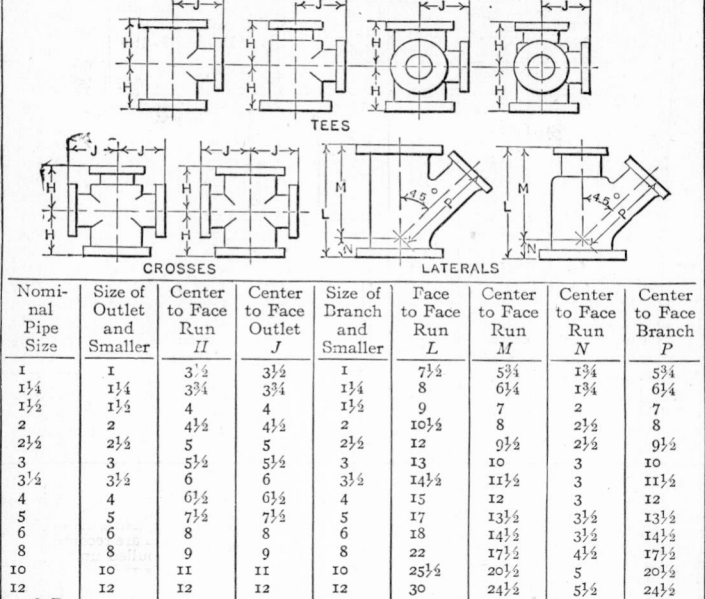

Nominal Pipe Size	Size of Outlet and Smaller	Center to Face Run *H*	Center to Face Outlet *J*	Size of Branch and Smaller	Face to Face Run *L*	Center to Face Run *M*	Center to Face Run *N*	Center to Face Branch *P*
1	1	3½	3½	1	7½	5¾	1¾	5¾
1¼	1¼	3¾	3¾	1¼	8	6¼	1¾	6¼
1½	1½	4	4	1½	9	7	2	7
2	2	4½	4½	2	10½	8	2½	8
2½	2½	5	5	2½	12	9½	2½	9½
3	3	5½	5½	3	13	10	3	10
3½	3½	6	6	3½	14½	11½	3	11½
4	4	6½	6½	4	15	12	3	12
5	5	7½	7½	5	17	13½	3½	13½
6	6	8	8	6	18	14½	3½	14½
8	8	9	9	8	22	17½	4½	17½
10	10	11	11	10	25½	20½	5	20½
12	12	12	12	12	30	24½	5½	24½
14 O.D.	14	14	14	14	33	27	6	27
16 O.D.	16	15	15	16	36½	30	6½	30
18 O.D.	12	13	15½	8	26	25	1	27½
20 O.D.	14	14	17	10	28	27	1	29½
24 O.D.	16	15	19	12	32	31½	½	34½
30 O.D.	20	18	23	14	20	39	0	42
36 O.D.	24	20	25	......	......	......	......	......

All dimensions given in inches.

Tees and Crosses: Short body patterns are used for sizes 18 inches and larger. Long body patterns are used when outlets are larger than given in the above table, the dimensions being the same as for straight-size fittings.

Fittings reducing on the run only have the same dimensions center-to-face as straight-size fittings corresponding to size of the larger opening. Tees increasing on outlet, known as "bull head tees," have same center-to-face dimensions as a straight fitting of the size of the outlet. For example: a 12 × 12 × 18-inch tee will be governed by the dimensions of the 18-inch long body tee, given in Table 3; namely 16½ inches center-to-face of all openings.

Side outlet tees, with outlet at 90 degrees or any other angle, straight or reducing, have the same dimensions center-to-face as regular tees having the same reductions.

In a side outlet tee the larger of the two side outlets governs the center-to-face dimension "*J*."

Laterals: Long body patterns are used when branches are larger than given in the above table and therefore have same dimensions as straight-size fittings. Long body patterns shall be used for fittings which are reducing on the run only.

All reducing fittings, 1 to 16 inches inclusive, have the same center-to-face dimensions as straight-size fittings.

Crosses and laterals, both straight and reducing, shall be reinforced where necessary to compensate for the inherent weakness in the casting design.

Table 5. American Standard Class 250 Cast-iron Flanges (ASA B16b)

Nominal Pipe Size	Diam. of Flange	Thickness of Flange[3] (Min.)	Diam. of Bolt Circle	Diam. of Bolt Holes[1]	Number of Bolts[1]	Size of Bolts	Length of Bolts[2]	Size Ring of Gasket
1	4⅞	1 1/16	3½	¾	4	⅝	2½	1 × 2⅞
1¼	5¼	¾	3⅞	¾	4	⅝	2½	1¼ × 3¼
1½	6⅛	13/16	4½	⅞	4	¾	2¾	1½ × 3¾
2	6½	⅞	5	¾	8	⅝	2¾	2 × 4⅜
2½	7½	1	5⅞	⅞	8	¾	3¼	2½ × 5⅛
3	8¼	1⅛	6⅝	⅞	8	¾	3½	3 × 5⅞
3½	9	1 3/16	7¼	⅞	8	¾	3½	3½ × 6½
4	10	1¼	7⅞	⅞	8	¾	3¾	4 × 7⅛
5	11	1⅜	9¼	⅞	8	¾	4	5 × 8½
6	12½	1 7/16	10⅝	⅞	12	¾	4	6 × 9⅞
8	15	1⅝	13	1	12	⅞	4½	8 × 12⅛
10	17½	1⅞	15¼	1⅛	16	1	5¼	10 × 14¼
12	20½	2	17¾	1¼	16	1⅛	5½	12 × 16⅝
14 OD	23	2⅛	20¼	1¼	20	1⅛	6	13¼ × 19⅛
16 OD	25½	2¼	22½	1⅜	20	1¼	6¼	15¼ × 21¼
18 OD	28	2⅜	24¾	1⅜	24	1¼	6½	17 × 23½
20 OD	30½	2½	27	1⅜	24	1¼	6¾	19 × 25¾
24 OD	36	2¾	32	1 11/16	24	1½	7¾	23 × 30½
*30 OD	43	3	39¼	2	28	1¾	8½	29 × 37½
*36 OD	50	3⅜	46	2¼	32	2	9½	34½ × 44
*42 OD	57	3 11/16	52¾	2¼	36	2	10¼	40¼ × 50¾
*48 OD	65	4	60¾	2¼	40	2	10¾	46 × 58¾

All dimensions given in inches.

[1] Drilling templates are in multiples of four, so that fittings may be made to face in any quarter, and bolt holes straddle the center line. For bolts smaller than 1½ in. the bolt holes shall be drilled ⅛ in. larger in diameter than the nominal diameter of the bolt. Holes for bolts 1½ in. shall be drilled 3/16 in. larger in diameter than the nominal diameter of the bolt. Holes for bolts 1¾ in. and larger shall be drilled ¼ in. larger than nominal diameter of bolts.

[2] The bolt holes of these cast-iron flanges and flanged fittings need not be spot faced for ordinary service except as follows: In sizes 12 in. and smaller when rough flanges, after facing, are oversize more than ⅛ in. in thickness, they shall be spot faced to the specified thickness of flange (minimum) with a plus tolerance of 1/16 in. In sizes 14 to 24 in., inclusive, when rough flanges, after facing, are oversize more than 3/16 in. in thickness they shall be spot faced to the specified thickness of flange (minimum) with a plus tolerance of 1/16 in. In sizes 30 in. and larger when rough flanges, after facing, are oversize more than ¼ in. in thickness they shall be spot faced to the specified thickness of flange (minimum) with a plus tolerance of ⅛ in.

[3] All Class 250 cast-iron flanges have a 1/16-in. raised face. This raised face is included in the face-to-face, center-to-face, and the minimum thickness of flange dimensions.

Bolts shall be of carbon steel with American Standard regular unfinished square heads or American Standard heavy unfinished hexagonal heads and the nuts shall be of carbon steel with American Standard heavy hexagonal dimensions, all as specified in American Standard for Wrench Head Bolts and Nuts and Wrench Openings (ASA B18.2). For bolts 1¾ in. in diameter and larger, bolt-studs with a nut on each end are recommended.

Hexagonal nuts for pipe sizes 1 in. to 16 in. can be conveniently pulled up with open wrenches of minimum design of heads. Hexagonal nuts for pipe sizes 18 in. to 48 in. can be conveniently pulled up with box wrenches. All bolts, or bolt-studs if used, and all nuts shall be threaded in accordance with American Standard for Screw Threads (ASA B1.1) Coarse-Thread Series, Class 2 Fit (see also pages 1108 and 1109).

Class 250 pipe flanges and fittings are rated as follows for maximum saturated steam service pressures (gage): 250 pounds per square inch for sizes 1 to 12 inches, inclusive; 200 pounds per square inch for sizes 14 to 24 inches, inclusive; 100 pounds per square inch for sizes 30 to 48 inches, inclusive. For maximum water service pressures (gage) at or near the ordinary range of air temperature: 400 pounds per square inch for sizes 1 to 12 inches, inclusive; 300 pounds per square inch for sizes 14 to 48 inches, inclusive, for flanges only.

* These sizes are included for convenience where special fittings larger than 24 in. are required.

Table 6. American Standard Class 250 Cast-iron Flanged Fittings (ASA B16b)

Nominal Pipe Size	Inside Diam. of Fitting (Min.)	Wall Thickness of Body*	Diam. of Raised Face	Center to Face			Face to Face G	Fitting flange dimensions are same as pipe flange dimensions, see Table 5, which also gives bolt, gasket, and hole location dimensions.
				A	*B*	*C*		
2	2	$7/16$	$4^{3}/16$	5	$6\frac{1}{2}$	3	5	
$2\frac{1}{2}$	$2\frac{1}{2}$	$\frac{1}{2}$	$4^{15}/16$	$5\frac{1}{2}$	7	$3\frac{1}{2}$	$5\frac{1}{2}$	
3	3	$9/16$	$5^{11}/16$	6	$7\frac{3}{4}$	$3\frac{1}{2}$	6	
$3\frac{1}{2}$	$3\frac{1}{2}$	$9/16$	$6^{5}/16$	$6\frac{1}{2}$	$8\frac{1}{2}$	4	$6\frac{1}{2}$	
4	4	$5/8$	$6^{15}/16$	7	9	$4\frac{1}{2}$	7	
5	5	$11/16$	$8^{5}/16$	8	$10\frac{1}{4}$	5	8	
6	6	$3/4$	$9^{11}/16$	$8\frac{1}{2}$	$11\frac{1}{2}$	$5\frac{1}{2}$	9	
8	8	$13/16$	$11^{15}/16$	10	14	6	11	
10	10	$15/16$	$14^{1}/16$	$11\frac{1}{2}$	$16\frac{1}{2}$	7	12	
12	12	I	$16^{7}/16$	13	19	8	14	
14 OD	$13\frac{1}{4}$	$1\frac{1}{8}$	$18^{15}/16$	15	$21\frac{1}{2}$	$8\frac{1}{2}$	16	
16 OD	$15\frac{1}{4}$	$1\frac{1}{4}$	$21^{1}/16$	$16\frac{1}{2}$	24	$9\frac{1}{2}$	18	
18 OD	17	$1\frac{3}{8}$	$23^{3}/16$	18	$26\frac{1}{2}$	10	19	
20 OD	19	$1\frac{1}{2}$	$25^{5}/16$	$19\frac{1}{2}$	29	$10\frac{1}{2}$	20	
24 OD	23	$1\frac{5}{8}$	$30\frac{1}{4}$	$22\frac{1}{2}$	34	12	24	

All dimensions given in inches.

All Class 250 cast-iron flanges have a $\frac{1}{16}$-in. raised face. This raised face is included in the face-to-face, center-to-face, and the minimum thickness of flange dimensions.

Reducing elbows carry the same dimensions center to face as regular straight size elbows corresponding to the size of the larger opening. Tees 16 in. and smaller reducing on the outlet have the same dimensions center to face and face to face as straight size fittings corresponding to the size of the larger opening. Sizes 18 in. and larger reducing on the outlet are made in two lengths depending on the size of the outlet.

Special degree elbows ranging from 1 to 45 deg, inclusive, have the same center-to-face dimensions given for 45-deg elbows, and those over 45 deg and up to 90-deg, inclusive, shall have the same center-to-face dimensions given for 90-deg elbows. The angle designation of an elbow is its deflection from straight line flow and is the angle between the flange faces.

Reducers, for all reductions, use the same face-to-face dimensions given in the above table of dimensions for the larger opening.

For drilling templates, refer to Table 5 footnotes.

For pressure ratings refer to Table 5 footnotes.

For bolt sizes refer to Table 5 footnotes.

* Wall thickness at no point shall be less than $87\frac{1}{2}$ per cent of the dimensions given in the table.

Maximum Size of Hole that can be Tapped in Fitting Without Adding Bosses.

Size of Fitting (inches)	2 to 3	4 to 5	6	8	10	21	14 to 24
Size of Tapped Hole (inches)	$3/8$	$\frac{1}{2}$	$3/4$	1	$1\frac{1}{4}$	$1\frac{1}{2}$	2

Table 7. Facing Dimensions for American Standard Steel Pipe Flanges — All Pressures

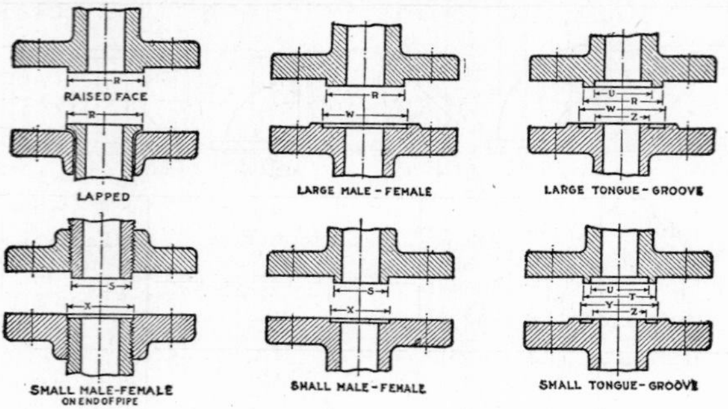
R
RAISED FACE
R
LAPPED
R
W
LARGE MALE - FEMALE
U
R
W
Z
LARGE TONGUE - GROOVE
S
X
SMALL MALE-FEMALE
ON END OF PIPE
S
X
SMALL MALE - FEMALE
U
T
Y
Z
SMALL TONGUE - GROOVE

Pipe Size	*R*	*S*	*T*	*U*	*W*	*X*	*Y*	*Z*
1/2	1 3/8	23/32	1 3/8	1	1 7/16	25/32	1 7/16	15/16
3/4	1 11/16	15/16	1 11/16	1 5/16	1 3/4	1	1 3/4	1 1/4
1	2	1 3/16	1 7/8	1 1/2	2 1/16	1 1/4	1 15/16	1 7/16
1 1/4	2 1/2	1 1/2	2 1/4	1 7/8	2 9/16	1 9/16	2 5/16	1 13/16
1 1/2	2 7/8	1 3/4	2 1/2	2 1/8	2 15/16	1 13/16	2 9/16	2 1/16
2	3 5/8	2 1/4	3 1/4	2 7/8	3 11/16	2 5/16	3 5/16	2 13/16
2 1/2	4 1/8	2 11/16	3 3/4	3 3/8	4 3/16	2 3/4	3 13/16	3 5/16
3	5	3 5/16	4 5/8	4 1/4	5 1/16	3 3/8	4 11/16	4 3/16
3 1/2	5 1/2	3 13/16	5 1/8	4 3/4	5 9/16	3 7/8	5 3/16	4 11/16
4	6 3/16	4 5/16	5 11/16	5 3/16	6 1/4	4 3/8	5 3/4	5 1/8
5	7 5/16	5 3/8	6 13/16	6 5/16	7 3/8	5 7/16	6 7/8	6 1/4
6	8 1/2	6 3/8	8	7 1/2	8 9/16	6 7/16	8 1/16	7 7/16
8	10 5/8	8 3/8	10	9 3/8	10 11/16	8 7/16	10 1/16	9 5/16
10	12 3/4	10 1/2	12	11 1/4	12 13/16	10 9/16	12 1/16	11 3/16
12	15	12 1/2	14 1/4	13 1/2	15 1/16	12 9/16	14 5/16	13 7/16
14 O.D.	16 1/4	13 3/4	15 1/2	14 3/4	16 5/16	13 13/16	15 9/16	14 11/16
16 O.D.	18 1/2	15 3/4	17 5/8	16 3/4	18 9/16	15 13/16	17 11/16	16 11/16
18 O.D.	21	17 3/4	20 1/8	19 1/4	21 1/16	17 13/16	20 3/16	19 3/16
20 O.D.	23	19 3/4	22	21	23 1/16	19 13/16	22 1/16	20 15/16
24 O.D.	27 1/4	23 3/4	26 1/4	25 1/4	27 5/16	23 13/16	26 5/16	25 3/16

All dimensions given in inches.

Raised Face: The regular facing for the 150 and 300 pound steel flanged fittings and companion flange standards is a raised face 1/16 inch high for all sizes. This face is included in the minimum flange thickness dimension. A 1/16-inch raised face is also permitted on the 400, 600, 900, 1500 and 2500-pound flange standards, but it must be added to the minimum flange thickness.

The regular facing for 400, 600, 900, 1500 and 2500-pound flanges is a 1/4-inch raised face for all sizes and is not included in minimum flange thickness dimension.

Gaskets: Gaskets for male-female and tongue-groove joints shall cover the bottom of the recess with minimum clearances taking into account the tolerance of plus or minus 0.016 inch is allowed on the inside and outside diameters of all facings. Care should be taken in the use of joints of the dimensions *S* and *X* given for small male-female joints as they apply particularly on lines where the joint is made on the end of pipe, to insure that pipe used is thick enough to permit sufficient bearing surface to prevent crushing the gasket. Screwed companion flanges for small male and female joints are furnished with plain face and are threaded with American Standard Lock-nut Thread.

Table. 8. American Standard 300-Pound Steel Flanged Fittings

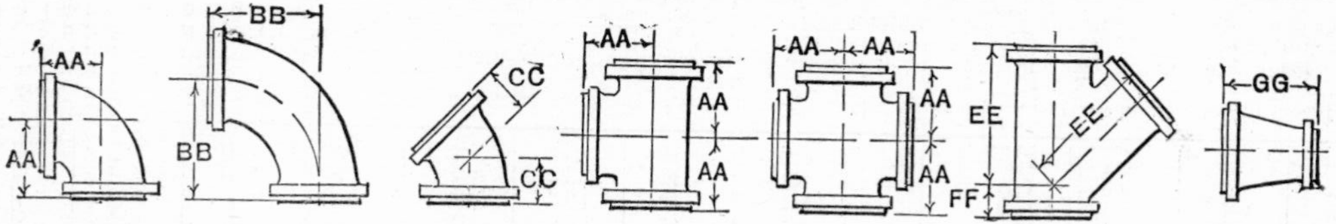

Nom. Pipe Size	Inside Diam. Fitting	Min. Wall Thick-ness	Flange Diam.	Flange Thick-ness	Bolt Circle Diam.	No. of Bolts	Size of Bolts	Dimensions to Contact Surface of Raised Face					
								AA	*BB*	*CC*	*EE*	*FF*	*GG*
1	1	1/4	4 7/8	11/16	3 1/2	4	5/8	4	5	2 1/4	6 1/2	2	4 1/2
1 1/4	1 1/4	1/4	5 1/4	3/4	3 7/8	4	5/8	4 1/4	5 1/2	2 1/2	7 1/4	2 1/4	4 1/2
1 1/2	1 1/2	1/4	6 1/8	13/16	4 1/2	4	3/4	4 1/2	6	2 3/4	8 1/2	2 1/2	4 1/2
2	2	1/4	6 1/2	7/8	5	8	5/8	5	6 1/2	3	9	2 1/2	5
2 1/2	2 1/2	1/4	7 1/2	1	5 7/8	8	3/4	5 1/2	7	3 1/2	10 1/2	2 1/2	5 1/2
3	3	9/32	8 1/4	1 1/8	6 5/8	8	3/4	6	7 3/4	3 1/2	11	3	6
3 1/2	3 1/2	9/32	9	1 3/16	7 1/4	8	3/4	6 1/2	8 1/2	4	12 1/2	3	6 1/2
4	4	5/16	10	1 1/4	7 7/8	8	3/4	7	9	4 1/2	13 1/2	3	7
5	5	3/8	11	1 3/8	9 1/4	8	3/4	8	10 1/4	5	15	3 1/2	8
6	6	3/8	12 1/2	1 7/16	10 5/8	12	3/4	8 1/2	11 1/2	5 1/2	17 1/2	4	9
8	8	7/16	15	1 5/8	13	12	7/8	10	14	6	20 1/2	5	11
10	10	1/2	17 1/2	1 7/8	15 1/4	16	1	11 1/2	16 1/2	7	24	5 1/2	12
12	12	9/16	20 1/2	2	17 3/4	16	1 1/8	13	19	8	27 1/2	6	14
14 O.D.	13 1/4	5/8	23	2 1/8	20 1/4	20	1 1/8	15	21 1/2	8 1/2	31	6 1/2	16
16 O.D.	15 1/4	11/16	25 1/2	2 1/4	22 1/2	20	1 1/4	16 1/2	24	9 1/2	34 1/2	7 1/2	18
18 O.D.	17	3/4	28	2 3/8	24 3/4	24	1 1/4	18	26 1/2	10	37 1/2	8	19
20 O.D.	19	13/16	30 1/2	2 1/2	27	24	1 1/4	19 1/2	29	10 1/2	40 1/2	8 1/2	20
24 O.D.	23	15/16	36	2 3/4	32	24	1 1/2	22 1/2	34	12	47 1/2	10	24

A raised face of 1/16-inch is included in (*a*) minimum thickness of flanges, (*b*) " center-to-contact-surface " dimensions; hence the " center-to-contact-surface " dimensions are the same as the " center-to-flange-edge " dimensions for this type of facing. Where facings other than the 1/16-inch raised face are used, the " center-to-flange-edge " dimensions shall remain unchanged.

Table 9. American Standard 400-Pound Steel Flanged Fittings

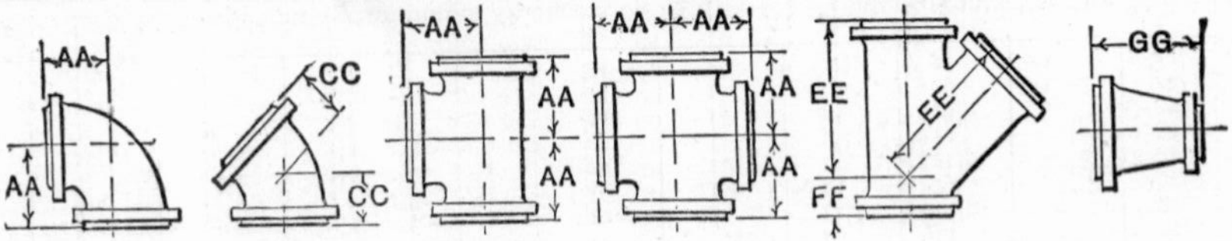

Nominal Pipe Size	Inside Diam. Fitting	Wall Thick-ness	Flange Diam.	Flange Thick-ness	Bolt Circle Diam.	No. of Bolts	Size of Bolts	Dimensions to Contact Surface of Raised Face *AA*	*CC*	*EE*	*FF*	*GG*
For sizes below 4 inches, use the dimensions of 600-pound fittings given in Table 10.												
4	4	3/8	10	1 3/8	7 7/8	8	7/8	8	5 1/2	16	4 1/2	8 1/4
5	5	7/16	11	1 1/2	9 1/4	8	7/8	9	6	16 3/4	5	9 1/4
6	6	7/16	12 1/2	1 5/8	10 5/8	12	7/8	9 3/4	6 1/4	18 3/4	5 1/4	10
8	8	9/16	15	1 7/8	13	12	1	11 3/4	6 3/4	22 1/4	5 3/4	12
10	10	11/16	17 1/2	2 1/8	15 1/4	16	1 1/8	13 1/4	7 3/4	25 3/4	6 1/4	13 1/2
12	12	3/4	20 1/2	2 1/4	17 3/4	16	1 1/4	15	8 3/4	29 3/4	6 1/2	15 1/4
14 O.D.	13 1/8	13/16	23	2 3/8	20 1/4	20	1 1/4	16 1/4	9 1/4	32 3/4	7	16 1/2
16 O.D.	15	7/8	25 1/2	2 1/2	22 1/2	20	1 3/8	17 3/4	10 1/4	36 1/4	8	18 1/2
18 O.D.	17	15/16	28	2 5/8	24 3/4	24	1 3/8	19 1/4	10 3/4	39 1/4	8 1/2	19 1/2
20 O.D.	18 7/8	1 1/16	30 1/2	2 3/4	27	24	1 1/2	20 3/4	11 1/4	42 3/4	9	21
24 O.D.	22 5/8	1 3/16	36	3	32	24	1 3/4	24 1/4	12 3/4	50 1/4	10 1/2	24 1/2

A raised face of 1/4 inch is not included in the minimum thickness of flanges given in the table (column 5) but is included in "center-to-contact-surface" of raised face dimensions.

Note that dimensions such as *AA*, *CC*, etc., are from center-to-*contact-surface* of raised face; hence, all dimensions from center-to-*flange-edges* are 1/4 inch less than *AA*, *CC*, etc., as raised faces of 400-pound fittings are all 1/4 inch high. Where facings other than the 1/4-inch raised face are used, the "center-to-flange-edge" dimensions equal to the dimensions *AA*, *CC*, etc., minus 1/4 inch shall remain unchanged, and the new "center-to-contact-surface" dimensions shall be established to suit the facing used.

Reducing fittings shall have the same "center-to-contact-surface" dimensions as those of straight size fittings of the largest opening.

Table 10. American Standard 600-Pound Steel Flanged Fittings

Nominal Pipe Size	Inside Diam. Fitting	Wall Thickness	Flange Diam.	Flange Thickness	Bolt Circle Diam.	No. of Bolts	Size of Bolts	Dimensions to Contact Surface of Raised Face				
								AA	CC	EE	FF	GG
1/2	1/2	1/4	3 3/4	9/16	2 5/8	4	1/2	3 1/4	2	5 3/4	1 3/4	5
3/4	3/4	1/4	4 5/8	5/8	3 1/4	4	5/8	3 3/4	2 1/4	6 3/4	2	5
1	1	1/4	4 7/8	11/16	3 1/2	4	5/8	4 1/4	2 1/4	7 1/4	2 1/4	5
1 1/4	1 1/4	1/4	5 1/4	13/16	3 7/8	4	5/8	4 1/4	2 3/8	8	2 1/2	5
1 1/2	1 1/2	1/4	6 1/8	7/8	4 1/2	4	3/4	4 1/2	3	9	2 3/4	6
2	2	5/16	6 1/2	1	5	8	5/8	4 3/4	4 1/4	10 1/4	3 1/2	6 3/4
2 1/2	2 1/2	3/8	7 1/2	1 1/8	5 7/8	8	3/4	5 1/4	4 1/2	11 1/2	3 1/2	7 1/4
3	3	3/8	8 1/4	1 1/4	6 5/8	8	3/4	5 3/4	5	12 3/4	4	7 3/4
3 1/2	3 1/2	7/16	9	1 3/8	7 1/4	8	3/4	6 1/2	5 1/2	14	4 1/2	8 3/4
4	4	1/2	10 3/4	1 1/2	8 1/2	8	3/4	7	6	16 1/2	4 1/2	10 1/4
5	5	9/16	13	1 3/4	10 1/2	8	3/4	7 1/2	7	19 1/2	6 1/2	11 1/4
6	6	5/8	14	1 7/8	11 1/2	12	7/8	8 1/2	7 1/2	21	7	13 1/4
8	7 7/8	3/4	16 1/2	2 3/16	13 3/4	12	1	10	8 1/2	24 1/2	8	15 3/4
10	9 3/4	7/8	20	2 1/2	17	16	1 1/8	11	9 1/2	29 1/2	8 1/2	16 3/4
12	11 3/4	1	22	2 5/8	19 1/4	20	1 1/4	13	10	31 1/2	9	17 3/4
14 O.D.	12 7/8	1 1/8	23 3/4	2 3/4	20 3/4	20	1 1/4	15 1/2	10 3/4	34 1/4	10	19 3/4
16 O.D.	14 1/4	1 1/4	27	3	23 3/4	20	1 3/8	16 1/2	11 3/4	38 1/4	10 1/2	21 1/4
18 O.D.	16 1/4	1 3/8	29 1/4	3 1/4	25 3/4	20	1 1/2	17 1/2	12 1/4	42	11	23 3/4
20 O.D.	18 1/4	1 1/2	32	3 1/2	28 1/2	24	1 5/8	19 1/2	13	45 1/4		27 3/4
24 O.D.	22	1 3/4	37	4	33	24	1 7/8	27 1/2	14 3/4	53	13	

Instructions given in foot-notes of Table 9 apply also to the 600-pound fittings.

Table 11. American Standard 900- and 1500-Pound Steel Flanged Fittings

Nominal Pipe Size	Inside Diam. Fitting	Wall Thick-ness	Flange Diam.	Flange Thick-ness	Bolt Circle Diam.	No. of Bolts	Size of Bolts	Dimensions to Contact Surface of Raised Face See illustration of Table 10				
								AA	*CC*	*EE*	*FF*	*GG*
900-pound Fittings. For sizes below 3 inches, use the dimensions of 1500-pound fittings given in lower half of table												
3	2⅞	½	9½	1½	7½	8	⅞	7½	5½	14½	4½	7¾
4	3⅞	⅝	11½	1¾	9¼	8	1⅛	9	6½	17½	5½	9¼
5	4¾	¾	13¾	2	11	8	1¼	11	7½	21	6½	11¼
6	5¾	13/16	15	2 3/16	12½	12	1⅛	12	8	22½	6½	12¼
8	7½	1 1/16	18½	2½	15½	12	1⅜	14½	9	27½	7½	14¾
10	9⅜	1¼	21½	2¾	18½	16	1⅜	16½	10	31½	8½	16¾
12	11⅛	1 7/16	24	3⅛	21	20	1⅜	19	11	34½	9	17¾
14 O.D.	12¼	1 9/16	25¼	3⅜	22	20	1½	20¼	11½	36½	9½	19
16 O.D.	14	1 13/16	27¾	3½	24¼	20	1⅝	22¼	12½	40¾	10½	21
18 O.D.	15¾	2	31	4	27	20	1⅞	24	13¼	45½	12	24½
20 O.D.	17½	2¼	33¾	4¼	29½	20	2	26	14½	50¼	13	26½
24 O.D.	21	2⅝	41	5½	35½	20	2½	30½	18	60	15½	30½
1500-pound Fittings — Standard includes sizes from ½ to 24 inches												
1	⅞	⅜	5⅞	1⅛	4	4	⅞	5	3½	9	2½	5
1¼	1⅛	⅜	6¼	1⅛	4⅜	4	⅞	5½	4	10	3	5¾
1½	1⅜	7/16	7	1¼	4⅞	4	1	6	4¼	11	3½	6¼
2	1⅞	9/16	8½	1½	6½	8	⅞	7¼	4¾	13¼	4	7¼
2½	2¼	11/16	9⅝	1⅝	7½	8	1	8¼	5¼	15¼	4½	8¼
3	2¾	¾	10½	1⅞	8	8	1⅛	9¼	5¾	17¼	5	9¼
4	3⅝	1	12¼	2⅛	9½	8	1¼	10¾	7¼	19¼	6	10¾
5	4⅜	1⅛	14¾	2⅞	11½	8	1½	13¼	8¾	23¼	7½	13¾
6	5⅜	1 5/16	15½	3¼	12½	12	1⅜	13⅞	9⅜	24⅞	8⅛	14½
8	7	1⅝	19	3⅝	15½	12	1⅝	16⅜	10⅞	29⅞	9⅛	17
10	8¾	2	23	4¼	19	12	1⅞	19½	12	36	10¼	20¼
12	10⅜	2 5/16	26½	4⅞	22½	16	2	22¼	13¼	40¾	12	23
14 O.D.	11⅜	2½	29½	5¼	25	16	2¼	24¾	14¼	44	12½	25¾
16 O.D.	13	2⅞	32½	5¾	27¾	16	2½	27¼	16¼	48¼	14¾	28¼

Instructions given in foot-notes of Table 9 apply also to these fittings.

Table 1. British Standard Flanges for Gas and Water Pipes, Valves and Fittings (For Land Use)

Nominal Pipe Size, Inches	Flange Diam.	Bolt Circle Diam.	Bolt Diam.*	Gas Pressures to 30 lbs. sq. in. Water Pressures to 50 lbs.			Water Pressures from 50 to 130 Pounds per Sq. In.			Water Pressures from 130 to 175 Pounds per Sq. In.		
				No. of Bolts	Flange Thickness		No. of Bolts	Flange Thickness		No. of Bolts	Flange Thickness	
					Cast I.	Steel		Cast I.	Steel		Cast I.	Steel
½	3¾	2⅝	½	4	½	3/16	4	½	3/16	4	½	3/16
¾	4	2⅞	½	4	½	3/16	4	½	3/16	4	½	3/16
1	4½	3¼	½	4	½	3/16	4	½	3/16	4	½	3/16
1¼	4¾	3 7/16	½	4	⅝	¼	4	⅝	¼	4	⅝	¼
1½	5¼	3⅞	½	4	⅝	¼	4	⅝	¼	4	⅝	¼
2	6	4½	⅝	4	⅝	5/16	4	11/16	5/16	4	¾	5/16
2½	6½	5	⅝	4	11/16	5/16	4	11/16	5/16	4	¾	5/16
3	7¼	5¾	⅝	4	11/16	⅜	4	¾	⅜	4	¾	⅜
3½	8	6½	⅝	4	¾	⅜	4	¾	⅜	4	¾	⅜
4	8½	7	⅝	4	¾	⅜	4	¾	⅜	4	⅞	⅜
5	10	8¼	⅝	4	¾	½	8	13/16	½	8	⅞	½
6	11	9¼	⅝	4	13/16	½	8	13/16	½	8	⅞	½
7	12	10¼	⅝	8	13/16	½	8	⅞	½	8	1	½
8	13¼	11½	⅝	8	⅞	½	8	⅞	½	8	1	½
9	14½	12¾	⅝	8	⅞	⅝	8	⅞	⅝	8	1	⅝
10	16	14	¾	8	15/16	⅝	8	1	⅝	8	1	⅝
12	18	16	¾	8	15/16	⅝	12	1	⅝	12	1⅛	⅝
14	20¾	18½	⅞	8	1	⅝	12	1⅛	⅝	12	1¼	¾
15	21¾	19½	⅞	8	1	⅝	12	1⅛	⅝	12	1¼	¾
16	22¾	20½	⅞	12	1 1/16	⅝	12	1⅛	⅝	12	1¼	¾
18	25¼	23	⅞	12	1 1/16	⅝	12	1¼	¾	12	1⅜	⅞
20	27¾	25¼	⅞	12	1⅛	⅝	16	1¼	⅞	16	1½	1
21	29	26½	⅞	12	1⅛	⅝	16	1⅜	⅞	16	1½	1
22	30	27½	1	12	1 3/16	⅝	16	1⅜	⅞	16	1½	1
24	32½	29¾	1	12	1 3/16	⅝	16	1⅜	1	16	1⅝	1⅛

This table does not apply to boiler feed pipes or other water pipes subject to exceptional shocks.

* Holes for ½-inch and ⅝-inch bolts are 1/16 inch larger and for larger sizes of bolts, ⅛ inch larger than the bolt diameters. Bolt holes to be drilled off center-lines.

Table 2. British Standard Flanges for Pipes, Valves and Fittings (For Land Use) Steam Pressures up to 100 Pounds per Square Inch

Nominal Pipe Size, Inches	Flange Diam.	Bolt Circle	Number of Bolts		Bolt Diameters*		Flange Thicknesses for Different Materials and Pressures †					
	Working Steam Pressures, Pounds per Square Inch						Cast I.	Cast Steel, Bronze		Steel — Screwed Riveted or Welded		
	Up to 100	Up to 100	Up to 50	50 to 100	Up to 50	50 to 100	Up to 100	Up to 50	50 to 100	Up to 50	50 to 100
½	3¾	2⅝	4	4	½	½	½	⅜	⅜	3/16	¼
¾	4	2⅞	4	4	½	½	½	⅜	⅜	3/16	¼
1	4½	3¼	4	4	½	½	½	⅜	⅜	3/16	9/32
1¼	4¾	3 7/16	4	4	½	½	⅝	½	½	¼	5/16
1½	5¼	3⅞	4	4	½	½	⅝	½	½	¼	11/32
2	6	4½	4	4	⅝	⅝	¾	9/16	9/16	5/16	⅜
2½	6½	5	4	4	⅝	⅝	¾	9/16	9/16	5/16	13/32
3	7¼	5¾	4	4	⅝	⅝	¾	9/16	9/16	⅜	7/16
3½	8	6½	4	8	⅝	⅝	¾	9/16	9/16	⅜	15/32
4	8½	7	4	8	⅝	⅝	⅞	11/16	11/16	⅜	½
5	10	8¼	8	8	⅝	⅝	⅞	11/16	11/16	½	9/16
6	11	9¼	8	8	⅝	¾	⅞	11/16	11/16	½	11/16
7	12	10¼	8	8	⅝	¾	1	¾	¾	½	¾
8	13¼	11½	8	8	⅝	¾	1	¾	¾	½	¾
9	14½	12¾	8	12	⅝	¾	1	¾	13/16	⅝	13/16
10	16	14	8	12	¾	¾	1	¾	⅞	⅝	⅞
12	18	16	12	12	¾	⅞	1⅛	⅞	1	⅝	1
14	20¾	18½	12	12	⅞	⅞	1¼	1	1	¾	1
15	21¾	19½	12	12	⅞	⅞	1¼	1	1	¾	1
16	22¾	20½	12	12	⅞	⅞	1¼	1	1	¾	1
18	25¼	23	12	16	⅞	⅞	1⅜	1⅛	1⅛	⅞	1⅛
20	27¾	25¼	16	16	⅞	⅞	1½	1¼	1¼	1	1¼
21	29	26½	16	16	⅞	1	1½	1¼	1⅜	1	1⅜
24	32½	29¾	16	16	1	1	1⅝	1⅜	1½	1⅛	1½

* Holes for ½-inch and ⅝-inch bolts are 1/16 inch larger and for larger sizes of bolts, ⅛ inch larger than the bolt diameters. Bolt holes to be drilled off center-lines.

† Flange thicknesses include a raised face (if used) not over 1/16 inch high.

Table 3. British Standard Flanges for Pipes, Valves and Fittings (For Land Use) Steam Pressures from 100 to 350 Lbs. per Sq. In.

Nominal Pipe Size, Inches	Flange Diam.		Bolt Circle Diam.		Bolt Diameters*			Number of Bolts	Flange Thicknesses for Different Materials and Pressures †			
	Working Steam Pressures, Pounds per Square Inch								Cast I.	Cast Steel, Bronze, Steel Screwed, Riveted or Welded		
	100 to 150	150 to 350	100 to 150	150 to 350	100 to 150	150 to 250	250 to 350	100 to 350	100 to 150	100 to 150	150 to 250	250 to 350
½	3¾	4½	2⅝	3¼	½	⅝	⅝	4	½	⅜	½	⅝
¾	4	4½	2⅞	3¼	½	⅝	⅝	4	½	⅜	½	⅝
1	4¾	4¾	3 7/16	3 7/16	⅝	⅝	⅝	4	½	⅜	9/16	¾
1¼	5¼	5¼	3⅞	3⅞	⅝	⅝	⅝	4	⅝	½	11/16	¾
1½	5½	5½	4⅛	4⅛	⅝	⅝	⅝	4	⅝	½	11/16	⅞
2	6½	6½	5	5	⅝	⅝	¾	4	¾	⅝	¾	1
2½	7¼	7¼	5¾	5¾	⅝	⅝	¾	8	¾	⅝	¾	1
3	8	8	6½	6½	⅝	⅝	¾	8	¾	⅝	⅞	1¼
3½	8½	8½	7	7	⅝	⅝	¾	8	⅞	¾	⅞	1¼
4	9	9	7½	7½	⅝	⅝	¾	8	⅞	¾	1	1⅜
5	11	11	9¼	9¼	¾	¾	⅞	8	1	⅞	1⅛	1½
6	12	12	10¼	10¼	¾	¾	⅞	12	1	⅞	1⅛	1½
7	13¼	13¼	11½	11½	¾	¾	⅞	12	1	⅞	1¼	1⅝
8	14½	14½	12¾	12¾	¾	¾	⅞	12	1⅛	1	1¼	1⅝
9	16	16	14	14	⅞	⅞	1	12	1⅛	1	1⅜	1¾
10	17	17	15	15	⅞	⅞	1	12	1⅛	1	1⅜	1⅞
12	19¼	19¼	17¼	17¼	⅞	⅞	1	16	1¼	1⅛	1½	2
14	21¾	21¾	19½	19½	1	1	1⅛	16	1⅜	1¼	1⅝	2⅛
15	22¾	22¾	20½	20½	1	1	1⅛	16	1⅜	1¼	1¾	2⅛
16	24	24	21¾	21¾	1	1	1⅛	20	1⅜	1¼	1¾	2¼
18	26½	26½	24	24	1⅛	1⅛	1¼	20	1½	1⅜	1⅞	2⅜
20	29	29	26½	26½	1⅛	1⅛	1¼	24	1⅝	1½	2	2½
21	30	30	27½	27½	1⅛	1⅛	1¼	24	1⅝	1½	2⅛	2⅝
24	33½	33½	30¾	30¾	1¼	1¼	1⅜	24	1¾	1⅝	2¼	2¾

* Holes for ½-inch and ⅝-inch bolts are 1/16 inch larger, and for larger sizes of bolts, ⅛ inch larger than the bolt diameters. Bolt holes to be drilled off center-lines.

† Flange thicknesses include a raised face (if used) not over 1/16 inch high.

Table 4. British Standard Flanges for Pipes, Valves and Fittings

(For land use) Steam pressures above 350 and up to 450 pounds per square inch

Nominal Pipe Size	Flange Diameter	Bolt Circle Diameter	Number of Bolts	Bolt Diameter	Flange Thickness*	Nominal Pipe Size	Flange Diameter	Bolt Circle Diameter	Number of Bolts	Bolt Diameter	Flange Thickness*
½	4½	3¼	4	5/8	3/4	5	11	9¼	12	7/8	1⅝
¾	4½	3¼	4	5/8	3/4	6	12	10¼	12	7/8	1⅝
1	5	3¾	4	5/8	7/8	7	13½	11½	12	1	1¾
1¼	5¼	3⅞	4	5/8	7/8	8	14½	12½	12	1	1⅞
1½	6	4½	4	3/4	1	9	16	14	16	1	2
2	6½	5	8	5/8	1	10	17	15	16	1	2
2½	7¼	5¾	8	3/4	1⅛	12	19¼	17	16	1⅛	2¼
3	8	6½	8	3/4	1¼	14	22½	20	16	1¼	2⅜
3½	9	7¼	8	7/8	1¼	15	23¾	21¼	20	1¼	2½
4	9½	7¾	8	7/8	1⅜	16	24¾	22¼	20	1¼	2⅝

* Flange thicknesses apply to cast steel, bronze, steel (stamped or forged) either screwed or riveted on with boss or welded on with fillet.

Holes for ½-inch and ⅝-inch bolts are 1/16 inch larger, and for larger sizes of bolts, ⅛ inch larger than the bolt diameters. Bolt holes to be drilled off center-lines.

Dimensions of British Standard Welded-on Flanges for Pipe Lines

(For working steam pressures up to 150 lbs., 250 lbs. and 350 lbs. per square inch)

Inside Diam. of Pipe	Diam. of Flange	Diam. of Bolt Circle	Number of Bolts	Diameter of Bolts†		Thickness of Steel or Iron Welded-on Flanges		
				Up to 250 Lbs.	250 to 350 Lbs.	Up to 150 Lbs.	150 to 250 Lbs.	250 to 350 Lbs.
2″	6″	4½″	4	5/8″	5/8″	1/2″	11/16″	7/8″
2½	6½	5	4	5/8	3/4	5/8	3/4	1
3	7¼	5¾	8	5/8	3/4	5/8	3/4	1
3½	8	6½	8	5/8	3/4	5/8	7/8	1¼
4	8½	7	8	5/8	3/4	3/4	7/8	1¼
*4½	9	7½	8	5/8	3/4	3/4	1	1⅜
5	10	8¼	8	3/4	7/8	3/4	1	1⅜
6	11	9¼	8	3/4	7/8	7/8	1⅛	1½
7	12	10¼	12	3/4	7/8	7/8	1⅛	1½
8	13¼	11½	12	3/4	7/8	7/8	1¼	1⅝
9	14½	12¾	12	3/4	7/8	1	1¼	1⅝
10	16	14	12	7/8	1	1	1⅜	1¾
*11	17	15	12	7/8	1	1	1⅜	1⅞
12	18	16	16	7/8	1	1⅛	1½	1⅞
*13	19¼	17¼	16	7/8	1	1⅛	1½	2
14	20¾	18½	16	1	1⅛	1⅛	1⅝	2
15	21¾	19½	16	1	1⅛	1¼	1⅝	2⅛
16	22¾	20½	16	1	1⅛	1¼	1¾	2⅛
*17	24	21¾	20	1	1⅛	1¼	1¾	2¼
18	25¼	23	20	1	1⅛	1⅜	1⅞	2⅜
*19	26½	24	20	1⅛	1¼	1⅜	1⅞	2⅜
20	27¾	25¼	20	1⅛	1¼	1⅜	2	2½
21	29	26½	24	1⅛	1¼	1½	2	2½
*22	30	27½	24	1⅛	1¼	1½	2⅛	2⅝
*23	31	28½	24	1⅛	1¼	1½	2⅛	2⅝
24	32½	29¾	24	1¼	1⅜	1⅝	2¼	2¾

* These sizes not recommended for general use.

† The diameters of the holes for ½-in. and ⅝-in. bolts to be 1/16 in. larger than the diameters of the bolts, and for larger sizes of bolts, ⅛ in. Bolt holes to be drilled off center-lines.

British Standards for Flanged Bends and Tees. — The standards recommended by the British Engineering Standards Association for short bends and tees of cast metal and for long bends of wrought iron and steel are given in the accompanying table. For short bends and tees the dimensions from the center line to the face of the flange are equal to the pipe diameter plus three inches. The dimensions of long bends of wrought iron and steel were determined with reference to the requirements of manufacture and are given for pipe sizes up to and including 20 inches which is considered the maximum for bends of this type.

Dimensions of British Standard Short Bends, Long Bends, and Tees

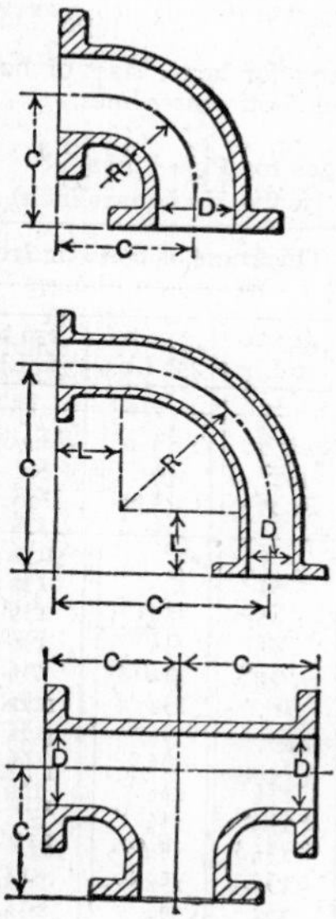

Inside Diam. of Pipe, *D*	Short Bends and Tees †		Long Bends Wrought Iron and Steel		
	C	*R*	*L*	*C*	*R*
½″	3½″	2½″	2½″	4½″	2″
¾	3¾	2¾	2½	5	2½
1	4	2¾	3	6	3
1¼	4¼	3	3	6¾	3¾
1½	4½	3	3	7½	4½
*1¾	4¾	3¼	3½	8¾	5¼
2	5	3¼	3½	9½	6
2½	5½	3¾	4	11½	7½
3	6	4	4	13	9
3½	6½	4½	5	15½	10½
4	7	4¾	5	17	12
*4½	7½	5¼	6	19½	13½
5	8	5½	6	21	15
6	9	6½	7	25	18
7	10	7¼	7	31½	24½
8	11	8¼	8	36	28
9	12	9	8	39½	31½
10	13	10	9	49	40
*11	14	10¾	9	53	44
12	15	11¾	10	58	48
*13	16	12½	11	69½	58½
14	17	13½	11	74	63
15	18	14¼	12	79½	67½
16	19	15¼	13	93	80
*17	20	16	14	99	85
18	21	17	14	104	90
*19	22	17¾	15	119½	104½
20	23	18¾	16	126	110
21	24	19½	.....	.....	.....
*22	25	20½	.....	.....	.....
*23	26	21¼	.....	.....	.....
24	27	22¼	.....	.....	.....

* These sizes not recommended for general use.

† The dimensions of unequal tees having branches which do not vary in diameter more than 3 to 1, are the same as the dimensions given in the table for the largest branch diameter.

Cast-iron Pipe. — Cast-iron pipe is used instead of wrought pipe where the pipes must be placed under ground or submerged, and also for main steam pipes and branches which are subjected to acids. Cast-iron pipe is extensively employed for cold water on lines 4 inches in diameter and above. Commercial cast-iron pipe is unsuitable for lines subjected to expansion strains, contraction, and vibration unless the pipe is very heavy. It is not suitable for superheated steam or for temperatures above 575 degrees F. The cast-iron pipe used for underground work generally has the *bell-and-spigot* ends which are leaded and calked to secure a tight joint. Exposed cast-iron pipes usually have flanged ends.

Thickness Formula for Cast-iron Pipe. — The following formula for determining the thickness of cast-iron pipe was adopted by the American Water Works Association, and is in general use.

$$T = 0.25 + \frac{(P + X) R}{3300}$$

T = pipe thickness in inches; P = maximum static pressure in pounds per square inch for which the pipe is intended; X = allowance made for water ram; and R = inside radius in inches. For ordinary water-works conditions and pipe diameters from 42 to 60 inches, 70 pounds per square inch is a conservative value for X, but for smaller pipe, Brackett allows the following values:

Diameter of pipe, inches,	= 36	30	24	20	16	12	10 to 3
Values of X	= 75	80	85	90	100	110	120

Standard Thickness and Weights of Cast-iron Pipe — Bell-and-spigot Joint

Nominal Inside Diam., In.	Class A 100-Feet Head 43 Lb. Pressure		Class B 200-Feet Head 86 Lb. Pressure		Class C 300-Feet Head 130 Lb. Pressure		Class D 400-Feet Head 173 Lb. Pressure	
	Thickness, Inches	Weight per Foot	Thickness, Inches	Weight per Foot	Thickness, Inches	Weight per Foot	Thickness, Inches	Weight per Foot
4	0.42	20.0	0.45	21.7	0.48	23.3	0.52	25.0
6	0.44	30.8	0.48	33.3	0.51	35.8	0.55	38.3
8	0.46	42.9	0.51	47.5	0.56	52.1	0.60	55.8
10	0.50	57.1	0.57	63.8	0.62	70.8	0.68	76.7
12	0.54	72.5	0.62	82.1	0.68	91.7	0.75	100.0
14	0.57	89.6	0.66	102.5	0.74	116.7	0.82	129.2
16	0.60	108.3	0.70	125.0	0.80	143.8	0.89	158.3
18	0.64	129.2	0.75	150.0	0.87	175.0	0.96	191.7
20	0.67	150.0	0.80	175.0	0.92	208.3	1.03	229.2
24	0.76	204.2	0.89	233.3	1.04	279.2	1.16	306.7
30	0.88	291.7	1.03	333.3	1.20	400.0	1.37	450.0
36	0.99	391.7	1.15	454.2	1.36	545.8	1.58	625.0
42	1.10	512.5	1.28	591.7	1.54	716.7	1.78	825.0
48	1.26	666.7	1.42	750.0	1.71	908.3	1.96	1050.0
54	1.35	800.0	1.55	933.3	1.90	1141.7	2.23	1341.7
60	1.39	916.7	1.67	1104.2	2.00	1341.7	2.38	1583.3
72	1.62	1283.4	1.95	1545.8	2.39	1904.2	.....	......
84	1.72	1633.4	2.22	2104.2	.....	......	.....	......

The approximate "laying length" for all diameters is 12 feet. The weights given include an allowance for the bell.

Table 1. American Standard Pipe Plugs — Square Head (ASA B16.14)

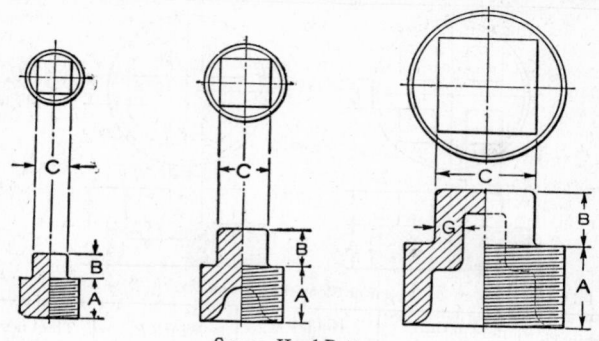

Square Head Patterns

| Nominal[1,2] Pipe Size | Length A of Thread, Min. | Height B of Square, Min. | Width C Across Flats | | Thickness G, Min.[4] |
			Nom.[3]	Max.	
⅛	0.37	0.24	⁹⁄₃₂	0.281	....
¼	0.44	0.28	⅜	0.375	....
⅜	0.48	0.31	⁷⁄₁₆	0.438	....
½	0.56	0.38	⁹⁄₁₆	0.563	0.16
¾	0.63	0.44	⅝	0.625	0.18
1	0.75	0.50	¹³⁄₁₆	0.813	0.20
1¼	0.80	0.56	¹⁵⁄₁₆	0.938	0.22
1½	0.83	0.62	1⅛	1.125	0.24
2	0.88	0.68	1⁵⁄₁₆	1.313	0.26
2½	1.07	0.74	1½	1.500	0.29
3	1.13	0.80	1¹¹⁄₁₆	1.688	0.31
3½	1.18	0.86	1⅞	1.875	0.34

All dimensions given in inches.

Material to be cast iron, malleable iron, or steel.

These plugs are threaded with American Standard tapered pipe threads. (ASA B2.1.)

[1] Solid plugs are provided in sizes ⅛ to 3½ in., incl.; cored plugs, ½ to 3½ in. incl.

[2] For sizes 4-in. and larger slotted or bar pattern plugs are provided. (See Table 2.)

[3] Except for the ⅛ nominal pipe size, these dimensions are the nominal size of wrench as given in the table of American Standard Open End Wrench Openings (ASA B18.2). Square head plugs are designed to fit these wrenches.

[4] Cored plugs have minimum metal thickness at all points, equal to dimension G, except at the end of the thread. Metal thickness at no point shall be less than 90 per cent of the thickness given in the tables.

Pressure Rating — These standard pipe plugs (Tables 1 and 2) have no definite ratings and are used with regular 125-lb cast-iron and 150-lb malleable-iron screwed fittings. For higher pressures, solid plugs (not cored) are quite commonly used.

Table 2.   American Standard Pipe Plugs (ASA B16.14)

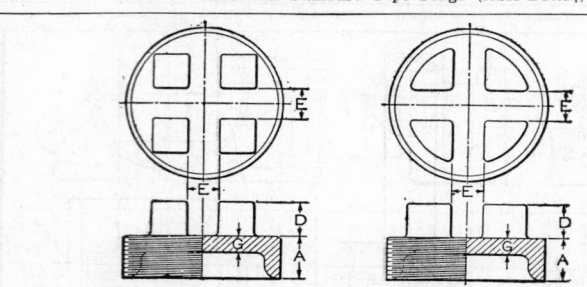

Bar or Slotted Patterns

Nominal Pipe Size	Length A of Thread, Min.	Height D of Lugs, Min.	Width E, Min.	Thickness G, Min.
4	1.22	1.00	0.88	0.37
5	1.31	1.00	0.88	0.46
6	1.40	1.25	1.25	0.52
8	1.57	1.38	1.50	0.66

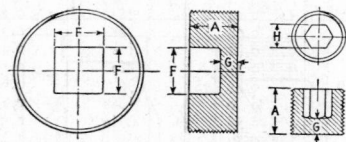

Countersunk Pattern

Nominal Pipe Size	Thread Length, Min. A	Size of Square Socket[1] F		Size of Hexagon[2] H	Metal Thickness Min. G
		Nom.	Min.		
$\frac{1}{8}$	0.37	...	....	$\frac{3}{16}$	0.06
$\frac{1}{4}$	0.44	...	....	$\frac{1}{4}$	0.09
$\frac{3}{8}$	0.48	...	....	$\frac{5}{16}$	0.13
$\frac{1}{2}$	0.56	$\frac{3}{8}$	0.382	$\frac{3}{8}$	0.16
$\frac{3}{4}$	0.63	$\frac{1}{2}$	0.508	$\frac{9}{16}$	0.18
1	0.75	$\frac{1}{2}$	0.508	$\frac{5}{8}$	0.20
$1\frac{1}{4}$	0.80	$\frac{3}{4}$	0.759	...	0.22
$1\frac{1}{2}$	0.83	$\frac{3}{4}$	0.759	...	0.24
2	0.88	$\frac{7}{8}$	0.884	...	0.26
$2\frac{1}{2}$	1.07	$1\frac{1}{8}$	1.137	....	0.29
3	1.13	$1\frac{3}{8}$	1.391	....	0.31
$3\frac{1}{2}$	1.18	$1\frac{1}{2}$	1.518	....	0.34
4	1.22	2	2.022	....	0.37

All dimensions given in inches.
Material to be cast iron, malleable iron, or steel.
These plugs are threaded with American Standard tapered pipe threads.   (ASA B2.1.)
[1] Square socket of countersunk pattern to have dimensions to fit commercial square bars of sizes indicated.
[2] Hexagon socket of countersunk pattern shall have dimensions to fit regular wrenches used with hexagon socket set screws.

Table 1. American Standard 150-Pound Malleable-iron Screwed Fittings

For Maximum Saturated Steam Pressures of 150 Pounds per Square Inch

ELBOW   TEE   CROSS   45° ELBOW

Pipe Size	A	C	B Min.	E Min.	F Min.	F Max.	G Min.	H Min.
1/8	0.69	......	0.25	0.200	0.40	0.43	0.090	0.693
1/4	0.81	0.73	0.32	0.215	0.54	0.58	0.095	0.844
3/8	0.95	0.80	0.36	0.230	0.67	0.71	0.100	1.015
1/2	1.12	0.88	0.43	0.249	0.84	0.89	0.105	1.197
3/4	1.31	0.98	0.50	0.273	1.05	1.10	0.120	1.458
1	1.50	1.12	0.58	0.302	1.31	1.38	0.134	1.771
1¼	1.75	1.29	0.67	0.341	1.66	1.73	0.145	2.153
1½	1.94	1.43	0.70	0.368	1.90	1.97	0.155	2.427
2	2.25	1.68	0.75	0.422	2.37	2.44	0.173	2.963
2½	2.70	1.95	0.92	0.478	2.87	2.97	0.210	3.589
3	3.08	2.17	0.98	0.548	3.50	3.60	0.231	4.285
3½	3.42	2.39	1.03	0.604	4.00	4.10	0.248	4.843
4	3.79	2.61	1.08	0.661	4.50	4.60	0.265	5.401
5	4.50	3.05	1.18	0.780	5.56	5.66	0.300	6.583
6	5.13	3.46	1.28	0.900	6.62	6.72	0.336	7.767

Dimensions of Couplings

Straight and Reducing Sizes

Pipe Size	B Min.	E Min.	G Min.	H Min.	Rib* Thickness	W	M
1/8	0.25	0.200	0.090	0.693	0.090	0.96	......
1/4	0.32	0.215	0.095	0.844	0.095	1.06	1.00
3/8	0.36	0.230	0.100	1.015	0.100	1.16	1.13
1/2	0.43	0.249	0.105	1.197	0.105	1.34	1.25
3/4	0.50	0.273	0.120	1.458	0.120	1.52	1.44
1	0.58	0.302	0.134	1.771	0.134	1.67	1.69
1¼	0.67	0.341	0.145	2.153	0.145	1.93	2.06
1½	0.70	0.368	0.155	2.427	0.155	2.15	2.31
2	0.75	0.422	0.173	2.963	0.173	2.53	2.81
2½	0.92	0.478	0.210	3.589	0.210	2.88	3.25
3	0.98	0.548	0.231	4.285	0.231	3.18	3.69
3½	1.03	0.604	0.248	4.843	0.248	3.43	4.00
4	1.08	0.661	0.265	5.401	0.265	3.69	4.38

The recommended maximum hydraulic service pressure rating (including shock) is 300 pounds per square inch (gage) at or near the ordinary range of air temperatures.

The "size" of the fittings is identified by the corresponding "nominal pipe size."

* Right-hand couplings have 2 ribs, and right- and left-hand couplings have 4 or more ribs.

All dimensions given in inches.

Table 2. American Standard 150-Pound Malleable-iron Screwed Fittings
For Maximum Saturated Steam Pressures of 150 Pounds per Square Inch

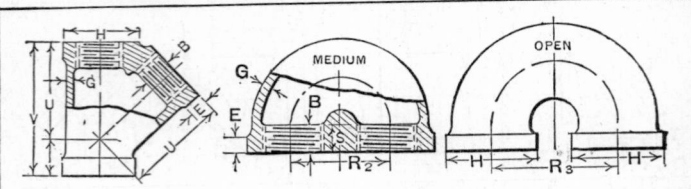

Dimensions of 45 Degree. Y-Branches (Straight Sizes)

Pipe Size	B Min.	E Min.	G Min.	H Min.	T	U	V
⅜	0.36	0.230	0.100	1.015	0.50	1.43	1.93
½	0.43	0.249	0.105	1.197	0.61	1.71	2.32
¾	0.50	0.273	0.120	1.458	0.72	2.05	2.77
1	0.58	0.302	0.134	1.771	0.85	2.43	3.28
1¼	0.67	0.341	0.145	2.153	1.02	2.92	3.94
1½	0.70	0.368	0.155	2.427	1.10	3.28	4.38
2	0.75	0.422	0.173	2.963	1.24	3.93	5.17
2½	0.92	0.478	0.210	3.589	1.52	4.73	6.25
3	0.98	0.548	0.231	4.285	1.71	5.55	7.26
3½	1.03	0.604	0.248	4.843	1.85	6.25	8.10
4	1.08	0.661	0.265	5.401	2.01	6.97	8.98

Return Bends — Close, Medium and Open Patterns

Pipe Size	B* Min.	E Min.	G Min.	H Min.	R₁† Close Pattern	R₂ Medium Pattern	R₃ Open Pattern
½	0.43	0.249	0.116	1.197	1.000	1.25	1.50
¾	0.50	0.273	0.133	1.458	1.250	1.50	2.00
1	0.58	0.302	0.150	1.771	1.500	1.875	2.50
1¼	0.67	0.341	0.165	2.153	1.750	2.25	3.00
1½	0.70	0.368	0.178	2.427	2.188	2.50	3.50
2	0.75	0.422	0.201	2.963	2.625	3.000	4.00
2½	0.92	0.478	0.244	3.589	.....	....	4.50
3	0.98	0.548	0.272	4.285	.....	....	5.00

The recommended maximum hydraulic service pressure rating (including shock) is 300 pounds per square inch (gage) at or near the ordinary range of air temperatures.

The " size " of the fittings is identified by the corresponding " nominal pipe size."

In the case of reducing tees, crosses, and Y-branches (laterals), the size of the largest run opening shall be given first, followed by the size of the opening at the opposite end of the run. Where the fitting is a tee or Y-branch (lateral), the size of the outlet is given last. Where the fitting is a cross, the largest side-outlet opening is the third dimension given followed by the opening opposite.

It is permissible to furnish close pattern return bends not banded. Close pattern return bends will not make up parallel coils, as the distance center-to-center of two adjacent bends is greater than the center-to-center of openings of a single bend.

All dimensions in inches.

American Standard Cast-iron Screwed Fittings (ASA B16.4)
For Maximum Saturated Steam Pressures of 125 and 250 Pounds per Sq. In.

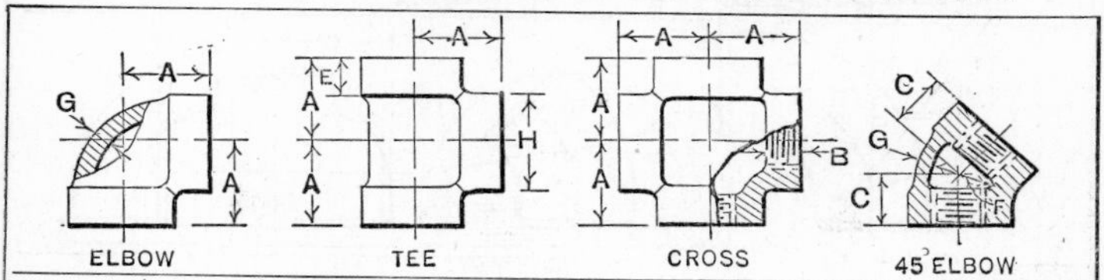

ELBOW   TEE   CROSS   45° ELBOW

Pipe Size	A	C	B Min.	E Min.	F Min.	F Max.	G	H Min.
				Fittings for 125 Pounds per Square Inch				
¼	0.81	0.73	0.32	0.38	0.540	0.584	0.110	0.93
⅜	0.95	0.80	0.36	0.44	0.675	0.719	0.120	1.12
½	1.12	0.88	0.43	0.50	0.840	0.897	0.130	1.34
¾	1.31	0.98	0.50	0.56	1.050	1.107	0.155	1.63
1	1.50	1.12	0.58	0.62	1.315	1.385	0.170	1.95
1¼	1.75	1.29	0.67	0.69	1.660	1.730	0.185	2.39
1½	1.94	1.43	0.70	0.75	1.900	1.970	0.200	2.68
2	2.25	1.68	0.75	0.84	2.375	2.445	0.220	3.28
2½	2.70	1.95	0.92	0.94	2.875	2.975	0.240	3.86
3	3.08	2.17	0.98	1.00	3.500	3.600	0.260	4.62
3½	3.42	2.39	1.03	1.06	4.000	4.100	0.280	5.20
4	3.79	2.61	1.08	1.12	4.500	4.600	0.310	5.79
5	4.50	3.05	1.18	1.18	5.563	5.663	0.380	7.05
6	5.13	3.46	1.28	1.28	6.625	6.725	0.430	8.28
8	6.56	4.28	1.47	1.47	8.625	8.725	0.550	10.63
10	*8.08	5.16	1.68	1.68	10.750	10.850	0.690	13.12
12	*9.50	5.97	1.88	1.88	12.750	12.850	0.800	15.47
				Fittings for 250 Pounds per Square Inch				
¼	0.94	0.81	0.43	0.49	0.540	0.584	0.18	1.17
⅜	1.06	0.88	0.47	0.55	0.675	0.719	0.18	1.36
½	1.25	1.00	0.57	0.60	0.840	0.897	0.20	1.59
¾	1.44	1.13	0.64	0.68	1.050	1.107	0.23	1.88
1	1.63	1.31	0.75	0.76	1.315	1.385	0.28	2.24
1¼	1.94	1.50	0.84	0.88	1.660	1.730	0.33	2.73
1½	2.13	1.69	0.87	0.97	1.900	1.970	0.35	3.07
2	2.50	2.00	1.00	1.12	2.375	2.445	0.39	3.74
2½	2.94	2.25	1.17	1.30	2.875	2.975	0.43	4.60
3	3.38	2.50	1.23	1.40	3.500	3.600	0.48	5.36
3½	3.75	2.63	1.28	1.49	4.000	4.100	0.52	5.98
4	4.13	2.81	1.33	1.57	4.500	4.600	0.56	6.61
5	4.88	3.19	1.43	1.74	5.563	5.663	0.66	7.92
6	5.63	3.50	1.53	1.91	6.625	6.725	0.74	9.24
8	7.00	4.31	1.72	2.24	8.625	8.725	0.90	11.73
10	8.63	5.19	1.93	2.58	10.750	10.850	1.08	14.37
12	10.00	6.00	2.13	2.91	12.750	12.850	1.24	16.84

* This applies to elbows and tees only. All dimensions given in inches.

250 Lb. Brass or Bronze Screwed Fittings. — Dimensions of fittings from ¼ to 4 inches nominal pipe size inclusive, agree with those of 125 Lb. Cast Iron Screwed Fittings, except couplings. Couplings agree with 150 Lb. Malleable Iron Coupling dimensions. 3½-inch size fittings are not available in brass or bronze.

Table 1. Dimensions of Butt-Welding Elbows and Tees — American Standard

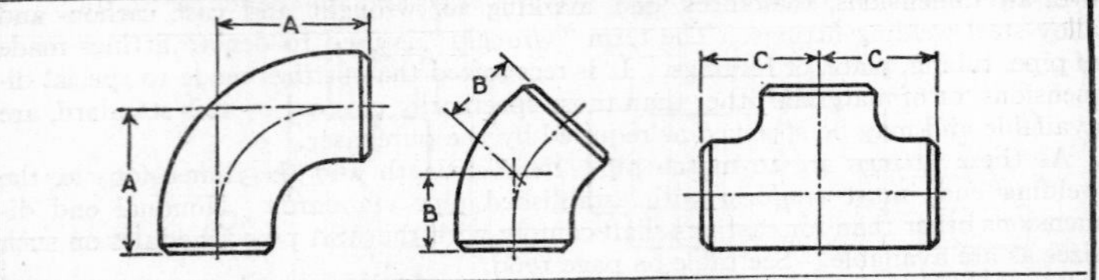

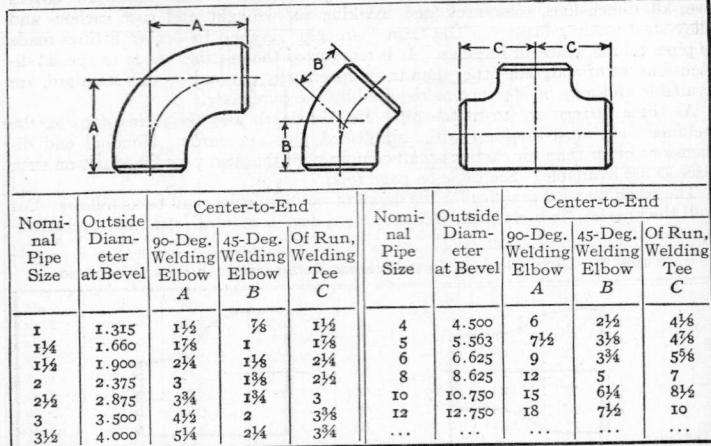

Nominal Pipe Size	Outside Diameter at Bevel	Center-to-End 90-Deg. Welding Elbow *A*	Center-to-End 45-Deg. Welding Elbow *B*	Center-to-End Of Run, Welding Tee *C*	Nominal Pipe Size	Outside Diameter at Bevel	Center-to-End 90-Deg. Welding Elbow *A*	Center-to-End 45-Deg. Welding Elbow *B*	Center-to-End Of Run, Welding Tee *C*
1	1.315	1½	⅞	1½	4	4.500	6	2½	4⅛
1¼	1.660	1⅞	1	1⅞	5	5.563	7½	3⅛	4⅞
1½	1.900	2¼	1⅛	2¼	6	6.625	9	3¾	5⅝
2	2.375	3	1⅜	2½	8	8.625	12	5	7
2½	2.875	3¾	1¾	3	10	10.750	15	6¼	8½
3	3.500	4½	2	3⅜	12	12.750	18	7½	10
3½	4.000	5¼	2¼	3¾	...	...	...	...	...

All dimensions given in inches. The dimensions of welding tees cover those which have branch outlets from one size less than half the size of the runway opening of the tees to full size.

Table 2. Dimensions of Butt-Welding 180-Deg. Return Bends

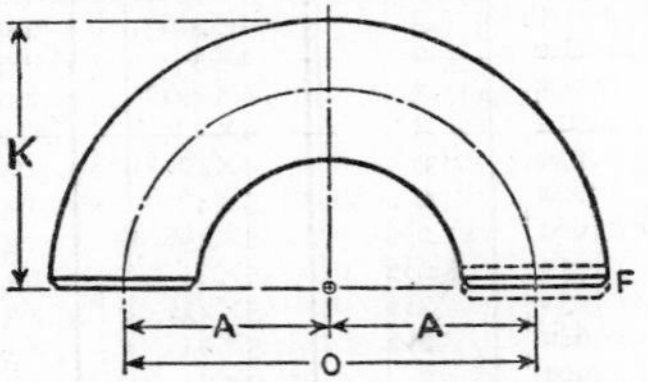

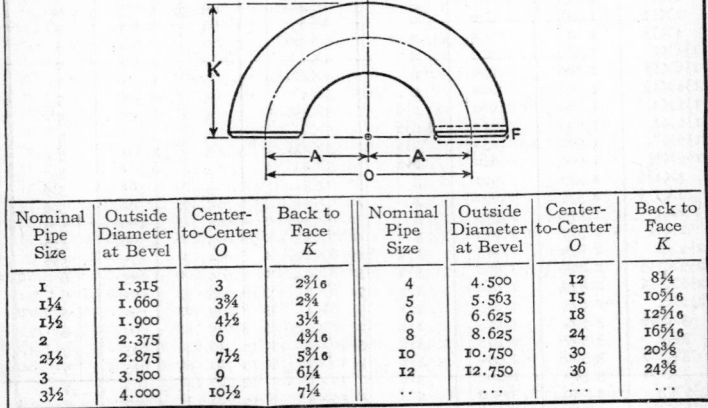

Nominal Pipe Size	Outside Diameter at Bevel	Center-to-Center *O*	Back to Face *K*	Nominal Pipe Size	Outside Diameter at Bevel	Center-to-Center *O*	Back to Face *K*
1	1.315	3	2 3/16	4	4.500	12	8¼
1¼	1.660	3¾	2¾	5	5.563	15	10 5/16
1½	1.900	4½	3¼	6	6.625	18	12 5/16
2	2.375	6	4 3/16	8	8.625	24	16 5/16
2½	2.875	7½	5 3/16	10	10.750	30	20⅜
3	3.500	9	6¼	12	12.750	36	24⅜
3½	4.000	10½	7¼	..	...	...	...

All dimensions given in inches.
Dimension *A* is equal to ½ of dimension *O*.
Tolerance for alignment *F*, ± 1/32 inch for sizes up to 8 inches inclusive, and ± 1/16 inch for sizes 10 inches and larger. Tolerance for *O* is ± ¼ inch for sizes up to 8 inches inclusive, and ± ⅜ inch for sizes 10 inches and larger. Tolerance for *K* is ± ¼ inch.

American Standard Steel Butt-Welding Fittings. — This standard covers over-all dimensions, tolerances, and marking for wrought and cast carbon- and alloy-steel welding fittings. The term "wrought" is used to denote fittings made of pipe, tubing, plate, or forgings. It is recognized that fittings made to special dimensions, or of materials other than those specifically covered by this standard, are available and may be specified as required by the purchaser.

As these fittings are to match pipe, their strength and the dimensions at the welding ends must conform with established pipe standards. Nominal end dimensions other than for castings shall comply with the ASA pipe schedules on such sizes as are available. See table on page 1769.

The recommended practice for the detail of welding bevel shall be as follows: For wall thicknesses 3/16 to 3/4 inch, inclusive, 37½ deg. ± 2½ deg., straight bevel termi-

Table 3. Dimensions of Butt-Welding Reducers — American Standard

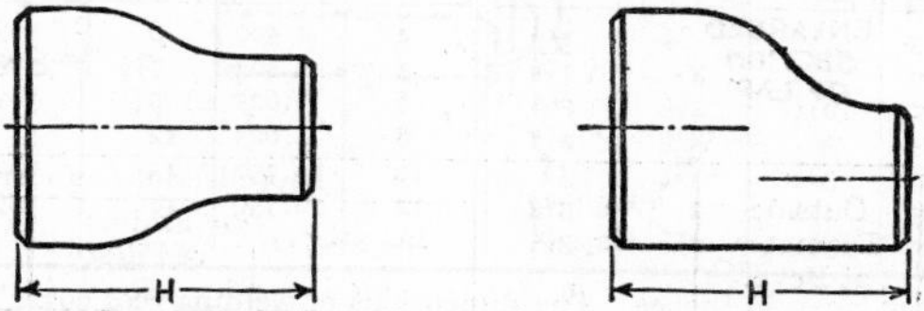

Nominal Pipe Size	Outside Diameter at Bevel		End-to-End H	Nominal Pipe Size	Outside Diameter at Bevel		End-to-End H
	Large End	Small End			Large End	Small End	
1×¾	1.315	1.050	2	4×3½	4.500	4.000	4
1×½	1.315	0.840	2	4×3	4.500	3.500	4
1×⅜	1.315	0.675	2	4×2½	4.500	2.875	4
1¼×1	1.660	1.315	2	4×2	4.500	2.375	4
1¼×¾	1.660	1.050	2	4×1½	4.500	1.900	4
1¼×½	1.660	0.840	2	5×4	5.563	4.500	5
1½×1¼	1.900	1.660	2½	5×3½	5.563	4.000	5
1½×1	1.900	1.315	2½	5×3	5.563	3.500	5
1½×¾	1.900	1.050	2½	5×2½	5.563	2.875	5
1½×½	1.900	0.840	2½	5×2	5.563	2.375	5
2×1½	2.375	1.900	3	6×5	6.625	5.563	5½
2×1¼	2.375	1.660	3	6×4	6.625	4.500	5½
2×1	2.375	1.315	3	6×3½	6.625	4.000	5½
2×¾	2.375	1.050	3	6×3	6.625	3.500	5½
2½×2	2.875	2.375	3½	6×2½	6.625	2.875	5½
2½×1½	2.875	1.900	3½	8×6	8.625	6.625	6
2½×1¼	2.875	1.660	3½	8×5	8.625	5.563	6
2½×1	2.875	1.315	3½	8×4	8.625	4.500	6
3×2½	3.500	2.875	3½	8×3½	8.625	.4.000	6
3×2	3.500	2.375	3½	10×8	10.750	8.625	7
3×1½	3.500	1.900	3½	10×6	10.750	6.625	7
3×1¼	3.500	1.660	3½	10×5	10.750	5.563	7
3½×3	4.000	3.500	4	10×4	10.750	4.500	7
3½×2½	4.000	2.875	4	12×10	12.750	10.750	8
3½×2	4.000	2.375	4	12×8	12.750	8.625	8
3½×1½	4.000	1.900	4	12×6	12.750	6.625	8
3½×1¼	4.000	1.660	4	12×5	12.750	5.563	8

All dimensions given in inches.

nating at the inner part in a land or unbevelled edge 1/16 inch wide. For wall thicknesses greater than ¾ inch, the angle of bevel is 20 deg. (± 2½ deg.) with a 3/16 inch radius or fillet connecting with a 1/16 inch land.

Welding ends having thicknesses less than 3/16 inch shall be prepared with a slight chamfer or square in accordance with manufacturer's practice.

Table 4. Dimensions of Butt-Welding Caps and Lapped-Joint Stub Ends — American Standard

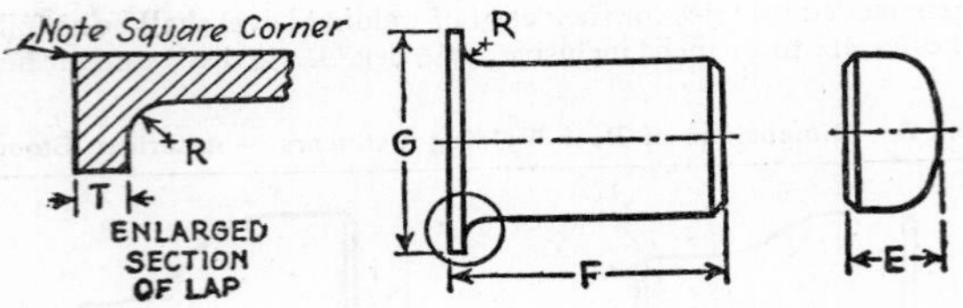

Nominal Pipe Size	Outside Diameter at Bevel	Welding Caps[1,2] E	Lapped-Joint Stub Ends: Length[5] F	Radius of Fillet[3] R	Diameter of Lap[4] G
1	1.315	1½	4	1/8	2
1¼	1.660	1½	4	3/16	2½
1½	1.900	1½	4	1/4	2⅞
2	2.375	1½	6	5/16	3⅝
2½	2.875	1½	6	5/16	4⅛
3	3.500	2	6	3/8	5
3½	4.000	2½	6	3/8	5½
4	4.500	2½	6	7/16	6 3/16
5	5.563	3	8	7/16	7 5/16
6	6.625	3½	8	½	8½
8	8.625	4	8	½	10⅝
10	10.750	5	10	½	12¾
12	12.750	6	10	½	15
14	14.000	6½	12	½	16¼
16	16.000	7	12	½	18½
18	18.000	8	12	½	21
20	20.000	9	12	½	23
24	24.000	10½	12	½	27¼

All dimensions given in inches.

Thickness (*T*). The basic minimum lap thickness (*T*) shall not be less than nominal pipe wall thickness. (See table on page 1769 for nominal pipe wall thickness.)

[1] The shape of these caps shall be ellipsoidal and shall conform to the shape requirements as given in the A.S.M.E. Boiler Construction Code.

[2] Dimension *E* for sizes 12 inches and smaller is applicable only up to and including Schedule 80 pipe wall thickness (see page 1769). For sizes 14 inches and larger, it is applicable for a thickness up to ½ inch only. A thicker wall will require a greater dimension.

[3] These dimensions conform to the radius established for lap joint flanges in American Standard for Steel Pipe Flanges and Flanged Fittings.

[4] This dimension is for standard machined facings in accordance with American Standard for Steel Pipe Flanges and Flanged Fittings (Dimension *G* is the same as *R*, page 1782). Back face of lap shall be machined to conform to surface of flange on which it seats.

[5] Dimension *F* for sizes 12 inches and smaller is applicable only up to and including Schedule 80 pipe wall thickness (see page 1769). For sizes 14 inches and larger, it is applicable for a pipe wall thickness up to ½ inch only.

Pitch of Bolts for Water and Steam Joints

Thickness of Flange for Through Bolts equals 1¼ to 1½ Bolt Diameters.
Thickness of Flange for Through Studs equals 1½ to 2 Stud Diameters.
Width of Flange equals 2¾ to 3½ Bolt or Stud Diameters.

Diameter of Bolt	Pressure in Pounds per Square Inch						Diameter of Bolt	Pressure in Pounds per Square Inch					
	0 to 50	50 to 90	90 to 125	125 to 150	150 to 175	175 to 200		0 to 50	50 to 90	90 to 125	125 to 150	150 to 175	175 to 200
½	3½	3	2⅝	2¼	2	1¾	1¼	8¾	7½	6½	5⅝	5	4⅜
⅝	4⅜	3¾	3¼	2¾	2½	2¼	1⅜	9⅝	8¼	7¼	6¼	5½	4⅞
¾	5¼	4½	4	3½	3	2¾	1½	10½	9	8	7	6	5¼
⅞	6⅛	5¼	4½	4	3½	3⅛	1⅝	11⅜	9¾	8½	7½	6½	5¾
1	7	6	5¼	4½	4	3½	1¾	12¼	10½	9	8	7	6¼
1⅛	7⅞	6¾	5⅞	5	4½	4	2	14	12	10½	9	8	7

Pitch of bolts is determined as follows: For pressures from 0 to 50 pounds, pitch = bolt diameter × 7; pressures from 50 to 90 pounds, pitch = bolt diameter × 6; from 90 to 125 pounds, pitch = bolt diameter × 5¼; from 125 to 150 pounds, pitch = bolt diameter × 4½; from 150 to 175 pounds, pitch = bolt diameter × 4; from 175 to 200 pounds, pitch = bolt diameter × 3½.

Linear Expansion of Steam Pipes*
(Increase of Length, in Inches, per 100 Feet)

Temp. Increase in Degrees Fahr.	Cast Iron	Wrought Iron	Steel	Brass and Copper	Temp. Increase in Degrees Fahr.	Cast Iron	Wrought Iron	Steel	Brass and Copper
50	0.36	0.40	0.38	0.57	450	3.89	4.28	4.08	6.18
100	0.72	0.79	0.76	1.14	475	4.20	4.62	4.41	6.68
125	0.88	0.97	0.92	1.40	500	4.45	4.90	4.67	7.06
150	1.10	1.21	1.15	1.75	525	4.75	5.22	4.99	7.55
175	1.28	1.41	1.34	2.04	550	5.05	5.55	5.30	8.03
200	1.50	1.65	1.57	2.38	575	5.36	5.90	5.63	8.52
225	1.70	1.87	1.78	2.70	600	5.70	6.26	5.98	9.06
250	1.90	2.09	1.99	3.02	625	6.05	6.65	6.35	9.62
275	2.15	2.36	2.26	3.42	650	6.40	7.05	6.71	10.18
300	2.35	2.58	2.47	3.74	675	6.78	7.46	7.12	10.78
325	2.60	2.86	2.73	4.13	700	7.15	7.86	7.50	11.37
350	2.80	3.08	2.94	4.45	725	7.58	8.33	7.96	12.06
375	3.15	3.46	3.31	5.01	750	7.96	8.75	8.36	12.66
400	3.30	3.63	3.46	5.24	775	8.42	9.26	8.84	13.38
425	3.68	4.05	3.86	5.85	800	8.87	9.76	9.31	14.10

* The expansion, for any length, between two temperatures, is found by dividing the difference in length at these temperatures by 100, and multiplying by length of pipe in feet.

Dimensions of Lead Pipe

Tensile strength of lead, 2240 pounds per square inch. Safe working pressures are based on a factor of safety of 5.

Inside Diameter, Inches	Outside Diameter, Inches	Thickness, Inches	Weight per Foot		Approximate Bursting Pressure in Pounds per Square Inch	Safe Working Pressure in Pounds per Square Inch	Commercial Designations	
			Lbs.	Oz.			Lead Pipe Manufacturers	Plumbing Supplies Catalogues*
⅜	0.74	0.183	1	12	2150	430	AAA	D. E. S.
⅜	0.72	0.173	1	8	2000	400	AA	E. S.
⅜	0.66	0.143	1	4	1650	330	A	Strong
⅜	0.63	0.128	1	0	1500	300	B	Medium
⅜	0.58	0.103	0	12	1250	250	C	Light
⅜	0.55	0.088	0	10	1050	210	D	E. L.
⅜	0.51	0.068	0	7	800	160	E	Aqueduct
7/16	0.66	0.111	1	0	1165	230	B	Medium
7/16	0.63	0.096	0	13	1000	200	C	Light
½	1.01	0.255	3	0	2000	400	AAA	D. E. S
½	0.87	0.185	2	0	1600	320	AA	E. S.
½	0.84	0.170	1	12	1500	300	A	Strong
½	0.76	0.130	1	4	1150	230	B	Medium
½	0.71	0.105	1	0	900	180	C	Light
½	0.67	0.085	0	12	700	140	D	E. L.
½	0.63	0.065	0	9	550	110	E	Aqueduct
⅝	1.13	0.253	3	8	1700	340	AAA	D. E. S.
⅝	1.05	0.213	2	12	1500	300	AA	E. S.
⅝	1.02	0.198	2	8	1300	260	A	Strong
⅝	0.96	0.167	2	0	1150	230	B	Medium
⅝	0.88	0.128	1	8	900	180	C	Light
⅝	0.80	0.088	1	0	600	120	D	E. L.
⅝	0.77	0.073	0	12	500	100	E	Aqueduct
¾	1.31	0.280	4	12	1900	380	AAA	D. E. S.
¾	1.21	0.230	3	8	1400	280	AA	E. S.
¾	1.16	0.205	3	0	1150	230	A	Strong
¾	1.07	0.160	2	4	950	190	B	Medium
¾	1.01	0.130	1	12	750	150	C	Light
¾	0.94	0.095	1	4	550	110	D	E. L.
¾	0.91	0.080	1	0	450	90	E	Aqueduct
1	1.59	0.295	6	0	1300	260	AAA	D. E. S.
1	1.51	0.255	4	12	1100	220	AA	E. S.
1	1.42	0.210	4	0	900	180	A	Strong
1	1.36	0.180	3	4	775	155	B	Medium
1	1.28	0.140	2	8	600	120	C	Light
1	1.23	0.115	2	0	500	100	D	E. L.
1	1.17	0.085	1	8	400	80	E	Aqueduct

* D. E. S. = double extra strong; E. S. = extra strong; E. L. = extra light.

Dimensions of Lead Pipe (*Continued*)

Inside Diameter, Inches	Outside Diameter, Inches	Thickness, Inches	Weight per Foot		Approximate Bursting Pressure in Pounds per Square Inch	Safe Working Pressure in Pounds per Square Inch	Commercial Designations	
							Lead Pipe Manufacturers	Plumbing Supplies Catalogues*
			Lbs.	Oz.				
1¼	1.82	0.285	6	12	1000	200	AAA	D. E. S.
1¼	1.75	0.250	5	12	900	180	AA	E. S.
1¼	1.67	0.210	4	12	750	150	A	Strong
1¼	1.59	0.170	3	12	600	120	B	Medium
1¼	1.52	0.135	3	0	475	95	C	Light
1¼	1.50	0.125	2	8	450	90	D	E. L.
1¼	1.45	0.100	2	0	350	70	E	Aqueduct
1½	2.11	0.305	8	8	900	180	AAA	D. E. S.
1½	2.04	0.270	7	8	800	160	AA	E. S.
1½	1.96	0.230	6	8	700	140	A	Strong
1½	1.88	0.190	5	0	550	110	B	Medium
1½	1.82	0.160	4	4	475	95	C	Light
1½	1.78	0.140	3	8	400	80	D	E. L.
1½	1.75	0.125	3	0	350	70	E	Aqueduct
1¾	2.42	0.335	10	0	850	170	AAA	D. E. S.
1¾	2.26	0.255	8	8	650	130	AA	E. S.
1¾	2.21	0.230	7	0	600	120	A	Strong
1¾	2.15	0.200	6	0	500	100	B	Medium
1¾	2.09	0.170	5	0	450	90	C	Light
1¾	2.03	0.140	4	0	375	75	D	E. L.
2	2.59	0.295	11	12	650	130	AAA	D. E. S.
2	2.51	0.255	9	0	550	110	AA	E. S.
2	2.45	0.225	8	0	500	100	A	Strong
2	2.41	0.205	7	0	450	90	B	Medium
2	2.37	0.185	6	0	375	75	C	Light
2	2.26	0.130	4	12	275	55	D	E. L.

* D. E. S. = double extra strong; E. S. = extra strong; E. L. = extra light.

Brass and Copper Pipes and Tubes. — Seamless brass and copper tubes for use in plumbing, boiler feed lines, etc., have the same outside diameter as standard steel pipe and may be used with the same fittings, but the wall thicknesses for most diameters are less according to A.S.T.M. Specifications B 42–33 and B–43–33. Seamless copper water tubes intended especially for plumbing purposes, underground water service, etc., and suitable for water-heater coils, fuel and gas lines, are made in three classes (*K*, *L*, and *M*) or ranges of wall thicknesses according to A.S.T.M. Specifications B 88–33. The thickest tubing (*K*) is for underground service and general plumbing; Class *L* is for general plumbing; and Class *M* for use with soldered fittings only. The actual outside diameters are not like the standard for steel and range from 0.5000 inch to 6.125 inches. Seamless copper and brass tubes for general engineering use, condenser tubes, etc., are available for commercial use in a wide range of diameters and thicknesses. The American practice is to make the wall thicknesses conform to the Birmingham or Stubbs iron wire gage. The nominal diameter usually indicates the outside diameter.

Sizes and Weights in Pounds per Foot of Seamless Brass Tubes *

Outside Diam. of Tube, Inches	Thickness — Stub's or Birmingham Gage											
	3	4	5	6	7	8	9	10	11	12	13	14
	Decimal Equivalent of Gage Number, Inch											
	0.259	0.238	0.220	0.203	0.180	0.165	0.148	0.134	0.120	0.109	0.095	0.083
⅛	....	....	....	....	....	....	....	....	....	....	....	....
3/16	....	....	....	....	....	....	....	....	....	....	....	....
¼	....	....	....	....	....	....	....	....	0.18	0.177	0.170	0.160
5/16	....	....	....	....	....	....	....	....	0.27	0.256	0.238	0.220
⅜	....	....	....	....	....	0.40	0.39	0.37	0.35	0.335	0.307	0.280
7/16	....	....	....	....	....	0.52	0.49	0.47	0.44	0.413	0.376	0.340
½	....	....	....	0.70	0.66	0.64	0.60	0.57	0.53	0.492	0.444	0.400
9/16	....	....	....	0.84	0.79	0.76	0.71	0.66	0.61	0.571	0.513	0.460
⅝	1.09	1.06	1.03	0.99	0.92	0.88	0.81	0.76	0.70	0.649	0.581	0.520
11/16	1.28	1.23	1.19	1.13	1.05	0.99	0.92	0.86	0.79	0.728	0.650	0.580
¾	1.47	1.41	1.35	1.28	1.18	1.11	1.03	0.95	0.87	0.807	0.718	0.640
13/16	1.65	1.58	1.50	1.43	1.31	1.23	1.13	1.05	0.96	0.885	0.787	0.700
⅞	1.84	1.75	1.66	1.57	1.44	1.35	1.24	1.15	1.04	0.964	0.855	0.759
15/16	2.03	1.92	1.82	1.72	1.57	1.47	1.35	1.24	1.13	1.042	0.924	0.819
1	2.22	2.09	1.98	1.87	1.70	1.59	1.45	1.34	1.22	1.12	0.99	0.88
1⅛	2.60	2.44	2.30	2.16	1.96	1.83	1.67	1.53	1.39	1.28	1.13	1.00
1¼	2.97	2.78	2.61	2.45	2.22	2.07	1.88	1.73	1.56	1.44	1.27	1.12
1⅜	3.35	3.12	2.93	2.75	2.48	2.30	2.10	1.92	1.74	1.59	1.40	1.24
1½	3.72	3.47	3.25	3.04	2.74	2.54	2.31	2.11	1.91	1.75	1.54	1.36
1⅝	4.09	3.81	3.57	3.33	3.00	2.78	2.52	2.31	2.08	1.91	1.68	1.48
1¾	4.47	4.15	3.88	3.62	3.26	3.02	2.74	2.50	2.26	2.06	1.82	1.60
1⅞	4.84	4.50	4.20	3.92	3.52	3.26	2.95	2.69	2.43	2.22	1.95	1.72
2	5.21	4.84	4.52	4.21	3.78	3.50	3.16	2.89	2.60	2.38	2.09	1.84
2⅛	5.59	5.18	4.84	4.50	4.04	3.73	3.38	3.08	2.78	2.54	2.23	1.96
2¼	5.96	5.53	5.15	4.80	4.30	3.97	3.59	3.27	2.95	2.69	2.36	2.08
2⅜	6.34	5.87	5.47	5.09	4.56	4.21	3.80	3.47	3.12	2.85	2.50	2.20
2½	6.71	6.21	5.79	5.38	4.82	4.45	4.02	3.66	3.30	3.01	2.64	2.32
2⅝	7.08	6.56	6.11	5.67	5.08	4.69	4.23	3.85	3.47	3.17	2.77	2.44
2¾	7.46	6.90	6.42	5.97	5.34	4.92	4.44	4.05	3.64	3.32	2.91	2.56
2⅞	7.83	7.24	6.74	6.26	5.60	5.16	4.66	4.24	3.81	3.48	3.05	2.68
3	8.20	7.59	7.06	6.55	5.86	5.40	4.87	4.43	3.99	3.64	3.19	2.79
3⅛	8.58	7.93	7.38	6.85	6.12	5.64	5.08	4.63	4.16	3.79	3.32	2.91
3¼	8.95	8.27	7.69	7.14	6.38	5.88	5.30	4.82	4.33	3.95	3.46	3.03
3⅜	9.33	8.62	8.01	7.43	6.64	6.11	5.51	5.01	4.51	4.11	3.60	3.15
3½	9.70	8.96	8.33	7.72	6.90	6.35	5.72	5.21	4.68	4.27	3.73	3.27
3⅝	10.07	9.30	8.65	8.02	7.16	6.59	5.94	5.40	4.85	4.42	3.87	3.39
3¾	10.45	9.65	8.96	8.31	7.42	6.83	6.15	5.59	5.03	4.58	4.01	3.51
3⅞	10.82	9.99	9.28	8.60	7.68	7.07	6.37	5.79	5.20	4.74	4.15	3.63

To determine weight per foot of a tube of a given *inside diameter*, add to weights in above list the weights in pounds per foot given below under corresponding gage numbers.

Gage No.	3	4	5	6	7	8	9	10	11	12	13	14
Weight Added	1.549	1.308	1.117	0.951	0.748	0.628	0.506	0.414	0.332	0.274	0.208	0.159

* Bridgeport Brass Co.

Sizes and Weights in Pounds per Foot of Seamless Brass Tubes

Outside Diam. of Tube, Inches	Thickness — Stub's or Birmingham Gage										
	15	16	17	18	19	20	21	22	23	24	25
	Decimal Equivalent of Gage Number, Inch										
	0.072	0.065	0.058	0.049	0.042	0.035	0.032	0.028	0.025	0.022	0.020
⅛	....	0.045	0.045	0.043	0.040	0.036	0.034	0.031	0.029	0.026	0.024
3⁄16	0.096	0.092	0.087	0.078	0.070	0.062	0.057	0.051	0.047	0.042	0.039
¼	0.148	0.139	0.129	0.114	0.101	0.087	0.080	0.072	0.065	0.058	0.053
5⁄16	0.200	0.186	0.170	0.149	0.131	0.112	0.104	0.092	0.083	0.074	0.067
⅜	0.252	0.233	0.212	0.184	0.161	0.137	0.127	0.112	0.101	0.090	0.082
7⁄16	0.304	0.279	0.254	0.220	0.192	0.163	0.150	0.132	0.119	0.106	0.096
½	0.356	0.326	0.296	0.255	0.222	0.188	0.173	0.152	0.137	0.121	0.111
9⁄16	0.408	0.373	0.338	0.290	0.252	0.213	0.196	0.173	0.155	0.137	0.125
⅝	0.460	0.420	0.380	0.326	0.283	0.238	0.219	0.193	0.173	0.153	0.140
11⁄16	0.511	0.467	0.421	0.361	0.313	0.264	0.242	0.213	0.191	0.169	0.154
¾	0.563	0.514	0.463	0.396	0.343	0.289	0.265	0.233	0.209	0.185	0.169
13⁄16	0.615	0.561	0.505	0.432	0.373	0.314	0.288	0.253	0.227	0.201	0.183
⅞	0.667	0.608	0.547	0.467	0.404	0.339	0.311	0.274	0.245	0.217	0.197
15⁄16	0.719	0.655	0.589	0.502	0.434	0.365	0.334	0.294	0.263	0.232	0.211
1	0.77	0.70	0.63	0.54	0.46	0.389	0.358	0.314	0.281	0.248	0.226
1⅛	0.87	0.79	0.71	0.61	0.52	0.439	0.404	0.354	0.317	0.280	0.255
1¼	0.98	0.89	0.80	0.68	0.59	0.490	0.450	0.395	0.354	0.312	0.284
1⅜	1.08	0.98	0.88	0.75	0.65	0.540	0.496	0.435	0.390	0.343	0.313
1½	1.19	1.08	0.96	0.82	0.71	0.591	0.542	0.476	0.426	0.375	0.342
1⅝	1.29	1.17	1.05	0.89	0.77	0.641	0.588	0.516	0.462	0.407	0.371
1¾	1.39	1.26	1.13	0.96	0.83	0.692	0.635	0.556	0.498	0.439	0.399
1⅞	1.50	1.36	1.22	1.03	0.89	0.742	0.681	0.597	0.534	0.470	0.428
2	1.60	1.45	1.30	1.10	0.95	0.793	0.727	0.637	0.570	0.502	0.457
2⅛	1.71	1.55	1.38	1.17	1.01	0.843	0.773	0.678	0.606	0.534	0.486
2¼	1.81	1.64	1.47	1.24	1.07	0.894	0.819	0.718	0.642	0.566	0.515
2⅜	1.91	1.73	1.55	1.32	1.13	0.944	0.866	0.758	0.678	0.597	0.544
2½	2.02	1.83	1.63	1.39	1.19	0.995	0.912	0.799	0.714	0.629	0.573
2⅝	2.12	1.92	1.72	1.46	1.25	1.045	0.958	0.839	0.750	0.661	.....
2¾	2.23	2.01	1.80	1.53	1.31	1.096	1.004	0.880	0.786	0.693	.....
2⅞	2.33	2.11	1.89	1.60	1.37	1.146	1.050	0.920	0.822	0.724	.....
3	2.43	2.20	1.97	1.67	1.43	1.197	1.096	0.960	0.859	0.756	.....
3⅛	2.54	2.30	2.05	1.74	1.49	1.247	1.143	1.001	0.895	0.788	.....
3¼	2.64	2.39	2.14	1.81	1.55	1.298	1.189	1.041	0.931	0.820	.....
3⅜	2.74	2.48	2.22	1.88	1.62	1.348	1.235	1.082	0.967	0.851	.....
3½	2.85	2.58	2.30	1.95	1.68	1.399	1.281	1.122	1.003	0.883	.....
3⅝	2.95	2.67	2.39	2.02	1.74	1.449	1.327	1.162	1.039	0.915	.....
3¾	3.06	2.76	2.47	2.09	1.80	1.50	1.373	1.203	1.075	0.946	.....
3⅞	3.16	2.86	2.56	2.16	1.86	1.55	1.42	1.243	1.111	0.978	.....

To determine weight per foot of a tube of a given *inside diameter*, add to weights in above list the weights in pounds per foot given below under corresponding gage numbers.

Gage No.	15	16	17	18	19	20	21	22	23	24	25
Weight Added	0.120	0.097	0.078	0.055	0.041	0.028	0.024	0.018	0.014	0.011	0.009

Sizes and Weights in Pounds per Foot of Seamless Brass Tubes

Outside Diam. of Tube, Inches	Thickness — Stub's or Birmingham Gage									
	3	4	5	6	7	8	9	10	11	12
	Decimal Equivalent of Gage Number, Inch									
	0.259	0.238	0.220	0.203	0.180	0.165	0.148	0.134	0.120	0.109
4	11.19	10.33	9.60	8.90	7.94	7.31	6.58	5.98	5.37	4.89
4⅛	11.57	10.68	9.91	9.19	8.20	7.54	6.79	6.17	5.55	5.05
4¼	11.94	11.02	10.23	9.48	8.46	7.78	7.01	6.37	5.72	5.21
4⅜	12.32	11.36	10.55	9.77	8.72	8.02	7.22	6.56	5.89	5.37
4½	12.69	11.71	10.87	10.07	8.98	8.26	7.43	6.75	6.06	5.52
4⅝	13.06	12.05	11.18	10.36	9.24	8.50	7.65	6.94	6.24	5.68
4¾	13.44	12.39	11.50	10.65	9.50	8.73	7.86	7.14	6.41	5.84
4⅞	13.81	12.74	11.82	10.95	9.76	8.97	8.07	7.33	6.58	6.00
5	14.18	13.08	12.14	11.24	10.02	9.21	8.29	7.53	6.76	6.15
5⅛	14.56	13.42	12.45	11.53	10.28	9.45	8.50	7.72	6.93	6.31
5¼	14.93	13.77	12.77	11.82	10.53	9.69	8.71	7.91	7.10	6.47
5⅜	15.31	14.11	13.09	12.12	10.79	9.92	8.93	8.11	7.28	6.62
5½	15.68	14.45	13.41	12.41	11.05	10.16	9.14	8.30	7.45	6.78
5⅝	16.05	14.80	13.72	12.70	11.31	10.40	9.35	8.49	7.62	6.94
5¾	16.43	15.14	14.04	13.00	11.57	10.64	9.57	8.69	7.80	7.10
5⅞	16.80	15.48	14.36	13.29	11.83	10.88	9.78	8.88	7.97	7.25
6	17.17	15.83	14.67	13.58	12.09	11.12	9.99	9.07	8.14	7.41
6⅛	17.55	16.17	14.99	13.87	12.35	11.35	10.21	9.27	8.32	7.57
6¼	17.92	16.51	15.31	14.17	12.61	11.59	10.42	9.46	8.49	7.72
6⅜	18.30	16.86	15.63	14.46	12.87	11.83	10.64	9.65	8.66	7.88
6½	18.67	17.20	15.94	14.75	13.13	12.07	10.85	9.85	8.84	8.04
6⅝	19.04	17.54	16.26	15.05	13.39	12.31	11.06	10.04	9.01	8.20
6¾	19.42	17.89	16.58	15.34	13.65	12.54	11.28	10.23	9.18	8.35
6⅞	19.79	18.23	16.90	15.63	13.91	12.78	11.49	10.43	9.35	8.51
7	20.16	18.57	17.21	15.92	14.17	13.02	11.70	10.62	9.53	8.67
7⅛	20.54	18.92	17.53	16.22	14.43	13.26	11.92	10.81	9.70	8.83
7¼	20.91	19.26	17.85	16.51	14.69	13.50	12.13	11.01	9.87	8.98
7⅜	21.29	19.60	18.17	16.80	14.95	13.73	12.34	11.20	10.05	9.14
7½	21.66	19.95	18.48	17.10	15.21	13.97	12.56	11.39	10.22	9.30
7⅝	22.03	20.29	18.80	17.39	15.47	14.21	12.77	11.59	10.39	9.45
7¾	22.41	20.64	19.12	17.68	15.73	14.45	12.98	11.78	10.57	9.61
7⅞	22.78	20.98	19.44	17.98	15.99	14.69	13.20	11.97	10.74	9.77
8	23.15	21.32	19.75	18.27	16.25	14.93	13.41	12.17	10.91	9.93

To determine weight per foot of a tube of a given *inside diameter*, add to weights in above list the weights in pounds per foot given below under corresponding gage numbers.

Gage No.	3	4	5	6	7	8	9	10	11	12
Weight Added	1.549	1.308	1.117	0.951	0.748	0.628	0.506	0.414	0.332	0.274

Sizes and Weights in Pounds per Foot of Seamless Brass Tubes

Outside Diam. of Tube, Inches	Thickness — Stub's or Birmingham Gage											
	13	14	15	16	17	18	19	20	21	22	23	24
	Decimal Equivalent of Gage Number, Inch											
	0.095	0.083	0.072	0.065	0.058	0.049	0.042	0.035	0.032	0.028	0.025	0.022
4	4.28	3.75	3.26	2.95	2.64	2.23	1.92	1.601	1.466	1.284	1.147	1.010
4⅛	4.42	3.87	3.37	3.05	2.72	2.30	1.98	1.651	1.512	1.324	1.183	....
4¼	4.56	3.99	3.47	3.14	2.81	2.38	2.04	1.702	1.558	1.364	1.219	....
4⅜	4.69	4.11	3.58	3.23	2.89	2.45	2.10	1.752	1.604	1.405	1.255	....
4½	4.83	4.23	3.68	3.33	2.97	2.52	2.16	1.803	1.650	1.445	1.291	....
4⅝	4.97	4.35	3.78	3.42	3.06	2.59	2.22	1.853	1.697	1.486	...	....
4¾	5.11	4.47	3.89	3.52	3.14	2.66	2.28	1.904	1.743	1.526	...	....
4⅞	5.24	4.59	3.99	3.61	3.22	2.73	2.34	1.954	1.789	1.566	...	....
5	5.38	4.71	4.09	3.70	3.31	2.80	2.40	2.005	1.835	1.607	...	....
5⅛	5.52	4.83	4.20	3.79	3.39	2.87	2.46	2.055	1.881	....	...	....
5¼	5.65	4.95	4.30	3.89	3.48	2.94	2.52	2.106	1.928	....	...	....
5⅜	5.79	5.07	4.41	3.98	3.56	3.01	2.58	2.156	1.974	....	...	....
5½	5.93	5.19	4.51	4.08	3.64	3.08	2.65	2.207	2.02	....	...	....
5⅝	6.07	5.31	4.61	4.17	3.73	3.15	2.71	2.257	....	....	...	....
5¾	6.20	5.43	4.72	4.26	3.81	3.22	2.77	2.308	....	....	...	....
5⅞	6.34	5.55	4.82	4.36	3.89	3.29	2.83	2.358	....	....	...	....
6	6.48	5.67	4.93	4.45	3.98	3.37	2.89	2.409	....	....	...	....
6⅛	6.61	5.79	5.03	4.54	4.06	3.44	....	....	....	....	...	....
6¼	6.75	5.91	5.13	4.64	4.15	3.51	....	....	....	....	...	....
6⅜	6.89	6.03	5.24	4.73	4.23	3.58	....	....	....	....	...	....
6½	7.03	6.15	5.34	4.83	4.31	3.65	....	....	....	....	...	....
6⅝	7.16	6.27	5.45	4.92	4.40	3.72	....	....	....	....	...	....
6¾	7.30	6.39	5.55	5.01	4.48	3.79	....	....	....	....	...	....
6⅞	7.44	6.51	5.65	5.11	4.56	3.86	....	....	....	....	...	....
7	7.57	6.63	5.76	5.20	4.65	3.93	....	....	....	....	...	....
7⅛	7.71	6.75	5.86	5.29	....	....						
7¼	7.85	6.87	5.96	5.39	....	....						
7⅜	7.99	6.99	6.07	5.48	....	....						
7½	8.12	7.11	6.17	5.58	....	....						
7⅝	8.26	7.23	6.28	5.67	....	....						
7¾	8.40	7.35	6.38	5.76	....	....						
7⅞	8.53	7.47	6.48	5.86	....	....						
8	8.67	7.58	6.59	5.95	....	....						

To determine weight per foot of a tube of a given *inside diameter*, add to weights in above list the weights in pounds per foot given below under corresponding gage numbers.

Gage No.	13	14	15	16	17	18	19	20	21	22	23	24
Weight Added	0.208	0.159	0.120	0.097	0.078	0.055	0.041	0.028	0.024	0.018	0.014	0.011

Seamless Drawn Brass and Copper Pipe

Made to correspond with iron pipe and to fit iron pipe fittings (American Tube Works).

Diameter			Approximate Weight per Foot, Pounds		Diameter			Approximate Weight per Foot, Pounds	
Iron Pipe Size	Approx. Outside Diam.	Exact Outside Diam.	Brass	Copper	Iron Pipe Size	Approx. Outside Diam.	Exact Outside Diam.	Brass	Copper
$\frac{1}{8}$	$\frac{3}{8}$	0.405	0.25	0.26	$2\frac{1}{2}$	$2\frac{7}{8}$	2.875	5.75	6.05
$\frac{1}{4}$	$\frac{9}{16}$	0.540	0.43	0.45	3	$3\frac{1}{2}$	3.500	8.30	8.74
$\frac{3}{8}$	$\frac{11}{16}$	0.675	0.62	0.65	$3\frac{1}{2}$	4	4.000	10.90	11.47
$\frac{1}{2}$	$\frac{13}{16}$	0.840	0.90	0.95	4	$4\frac{1}{2}$	4.500	12.70	13.37
$\frac{3}{4}$	$1\frac{1}{16}$	1.050	1.25	1.32	$4\frac{1}{2}$	5	5.000	13.90	14.63
1	$1\frac{5}{16}$	1.315	1.70	1.79	5	$5\frac{9}{16}$	5.563	15.75	16.58
$1\frac{1}{4}$	$1\frac{5}{8}$	1.660	2.50	2.63	6	$6\frac{5}{8}$	6.625	18.31	19.27
$1\frac{1}{2}$	$1\frac{7}{8}$	1.900	3.00	3.16	7	$7\frac{5}{8}$	7.625	23.73	24.98
2	$2\frac{3}{8}$	2.375	4.00	4.21	.....	.....	.....	....	....

Threading Pipe. — Clean, smooth pipe threads are essential to a good joint and depend largely upon the rake or lip angle and lead of the chasers, and the clearance, chip space and number of chasers in the die-head. The lip angle should vary from 15 to 25 degrees, depending upon the style and condition of the chasers and chaser holders. The chip space in front of the chasers should be large enough to allow room for accumulation of chips and at the same time provide means of

Length of Thread on Pipe Required to Make a Tight Joint

(Crane Co.)

Size of Pipe, Inches	Dimension A, Inches	Size of Pipe, Inches	Dimension A, Inches	Size of Pipe, Inches	Dimension A, Inches
$\frac{1}{8}$	$\frac{1}{4}$	$1\frac{1}{2}$	$1\frac{1}{16}$	5	$1\frac{1}{4}$
$\frac{1}{4}$	$\frac{3}{8}$	2	$\frac{3}{4}$	6	$1\frac{5}{16}$
$\frac{3}{8}$	$\frac{3}{8}$	$2\frac{1}{2}$	$\frac{15}{16}$	7	$1\frac{3}{8}$
$\frac{1}{2}$	$\frac{1}{2}$	3	1	8	$1\frac{7}{16}$
$\frac{3}{4}$	$\frac{9}{16}$	$3\frac{1}{2}$	$1\frac{1}{16}$	9	$1\frac{1}{2}$
1	$1\frac{1}{16}$	4	$1\frac{1}{8}$	10	$1\frac{5}{8}$
$1\frac{1}{4}$	$1\frac{1}{16}$	$4\frac{1}{2}$	$1\frac{3}{16}$	12	$1\frac{3}{4}$

Dimensions do not allow for variation in tapping or threading.

lubricating the chasers. This is an important point, as insufficient chip space will cause the chips to clog and tear the threads. The lead of the chaser is the angle which is machined or ground on the leading or front side, to enable the die to start readily on the pipe, and also to distribute the work of cutting over a number of threads. To secure a good thread, the lead should cover the first three threads. As the heaviest cutting is done by this beveled part, it should have a slightly greater clearance angle than the rest of the threads on the chaser. When re-grinding chasers which have become dull on the lead, care should be taken to give each chaser the same length of lead, as otherwise the work will be unevenly distributed.

The number of chasers with which a die should be equipped depends upon the size of the die. The number recommended for different sizes is as follows:

Size of Die	Number of Chasers	Size of Die	Number of Chasers
Up to 1¼ inch	4	10 to 12 inches	12
1¼ to 4 inches	6	12 to 14 inches	14
4 to 7 inches	8	14 to 18 inches	16
7 to 10 inches	10	18 to 20 inches	18

Pipe threading dies should be lubricated with a good quality of lard oil or crude cotton-seed oil, the lubricant being used in liberal quantities.

Pipe and Tube Bending. — In bending a pipe or tube, the outer part of the bend is stretched and the inner section compressed, and as the result of opposite and unequal stresses, the pipe or tube tends to flatten or collapse. To prevent such distortion, the common practice is to support the wall of the pipe or tube in some manner during the bending operation. This support may be in the form of a filling material, or, when a bending machine or fixture is used, an internal mandrel or ball-shaped member may support the inner wall when required. If a filling material is used, it is melted and poured into the pipe or tube. One filler material (a commercial alloy known as "Bendalloy") has a melting point of only 160 degrees F. and is composed of bismuth, lead, tin, and cadmium. With this material, tubes having very thin walls have been bent to small radii. The metal filler conforms to the inside of the tube so closely that the tube can be bent just as though it were a solid rod. The filler is removed readily by melting. This method has been applied to the bending of copper, brass, duralumin, plain steel, and stainless steel tubes with uniform success. Tubes plated with chromium or nickel can be bent without danger of the plate flaking off.

Other filling materials such as resin, tar, lead, and dry sand have also been used.

Pipes are often bent to avoid the use of fittings, thus eliminating joints, providing a smooth unobstructed passage for fluids, and resulting in certain other advantages.

Minimum Radius: The safe minimum radius for a given diameter, material, and method of bending depends upon the thickness of the pipe wall, it being possible, for example, to bend extra heavy pipe to a smaller radius than pipe of standard weight. As a general rule, wrought iron or steel pipe of standard weight may readily be bent to a radius equal to five or six times the nominal pipe diameter. The minimum radius for standard weight pipe should, as a rule, be three and one-half to four times the diameter. It will be understood, however, that the minimum radius may vary considerably, depending upon the method of bending. Extra heavy pipe may be bent to radii varying from two and one-half times the diameter for smaller sizes to three and one-half to four times the diameter for larger sizes.

Rules for Finding Lengths of Bends: In determining the required length of a pipe or tube before bending, the lengths of the straight sections are, of course, added to the lengths required for the curved sections in order to make the proper allowance for bends. The following rules are for finding the lengths of the curved sections.

Rule for 90-Degree Bend: To find the length of a 90-degree or right-angle bend, multiply the radius of the bend by 1.57 (the radius is measured to the center of the pipe or to a point midway between the inner and outer walls).

Rule for 180-Degree Bend: To find the length of a 180-degree or U bend, multiply the radius of the bend by 3.14.

General Rule: A general rule for finding the lengths of sections having degrees of curvature other than 90 and 180 is as follows: Multiply the radius of the bend by the included angle, and then multiply the product by the constant 0.01745. The result is the length of the curved section.

Inside Diameter of Shelby Standard Cold-drawn Tubing

Figures in Body of Table give Inside Diameter in Inches

Thickness in Gage and Fractions of an Inch

Outside Diameter, Inches	22 B.W.G.	20 B.W.G.	18 B.W.G.	1/16	3/32	1/8	5/32	3/16	7/32	1/4	5/16	3/8	1/2	5/8	3/4	7/8	1
1/2	0.444	0.430	0.402	0.375	0.3125	0.250											
5/8	0.569	0.555	0.527	0.500	0.4375	0.375											
3/4	0.694	0.680	0.652	0.625	0.5625	0.500	0.4375	0.375									
7/8	0.819	0.805	0.777	0.750	0.6875	0.625	0.5625	0.500	0.4375								
1	0.944	0.930	0.902	0.875	0.8125	0.750	0.6875	0.625	0.5625	0.500							
1 1/8	1.069	1.055	1.027	1.000	0.9375	0.875	0.8125	0.750	0.6875	0.625							
1 1/4	1.194	1.180	1.152	1.125	1.0625	1.000	0.9375	0.875	0.8125	0.750	0.625	0.500					
1 3/8		1.305	1.277	1.250	1.1875	1.125	1.0625	1.000	0.9375	0.875	0.750	0.625					
1 1/2		1.430	1.402	1.375	1.3125	1.250	1.1875	1.125	1.0625	1.000	0.875	0.750	0.500				
1 3/4				1.625	1.5625	1.500	1.4375	1.375	1.3125	1.250	1.125	1.000	0.750				
2				1.875	1.8125	1.750	1.6875	1.625	1.5625	1.500	1.375	1.250	1.000	0.750			
2 1/4				2.125	2.0625	2.000	1.9375	1.875	1.8125	1.750	1.625	1.500	1.250	1.000			
2 1/2				2.375	2.3125	2.250	2.1875	2.125	2.0625	2.000	1.875	1.750	1.500	1.250			
2 3/4				2.625	2.5625	2.500	2.4375	2.375	2.3125	2.250	2.125	2.000	1.750	1.500			
3					2.8125	2.750	2.6875	2.625	2.5625	2.500	2.375	2.250	2.000	1.750	1.500	1.250	1.000
3 1/4					3.0625	3.000	2.9375	2.875	2.8125	2.750	2.625	2.500	2.250	2.000	1.750	1.500	1.250
3 1/2					3.3125	3.250	3.1875	3.125	3.0625	3.000	2.875	2.750	2.500	2.250	2.000	1.750	1.500
3 3/4						3.500	3.4375	3.375	3.3125	3.250	3.125	3.000	2.750	2.500	2.250	2.000	1.750
4						3.750	3.6875	3.625	3.5625	3.500	3.375	3.250	3.000	2.750	2.500	2.250	2.000
4 1/4							3.9375	3.875	3.8125	3.750	3.625	3.500	3.250	3.000	2.750	2.500	2.250
4 1/2							4.1875	4.125	4.0625	4.000	3.875	3.750	3.500	3.250	3.000	2.750	2.500
4 3/4							4.4375	4.375	4.3125	4.250	4.125	4.000	3.750	3.500	3.250	3.000	2.750
5							4.6875	4.625	4.5625	4.500	4.375	4.250	4.000	3.750	3.500	3.250	3.000
5 1/2							5.1875	5.125	5.0625	5.000	4.875	4.750	4.500	4.250	4.000	3.750	3.500

Relative Discharging Capacities of Pipes

Figures in body of table represent number of small pipes having a discharging capacity equivalent to one large pipe of given diameter.

Actual Internal Diam., Inches	7.981	7.023	6.665	5.047	4.506	4.026	3.548	3.068	2.469	2.067	1.610	1.380	1.049	0.824	0.622	0.493	0.364	0.269
Nom. Internal Diam.	8	7	6	5	4½	4	3½	3	2½	2	1½	1¼	1	¾	½	⅜	¼	⅛
¼	…	…	…	…	…	…	…	…	…	…	…	…	…	…	…	…	1	2.1
⅜	…	…	…	…	…	…	…	…	…	…	…	…	…	…	…	1	2.1	4.5
½	…	…	…	…	…	…	…	…	…	…	…	…	…	…	1	1.8	3.8	8
¾	…	…	…	…	…	…	…	…	…	…	…	…	…	1	2	3.6	8	16
1	…	…	…	…	…	…	…	…	…	…	…	…	1	1.8	3.7	6.6	14	30
1¼	…	…	…	…	…	…	…	…	…	…	…	1	2	3.6	7	13	28	60
1½	…	…	…	…	…	…	…	…	…	…	1	1.5	2.9	5.3	11	19	41	88
2	…	…	…	…	…	…	…	…	…	1	1.9	2.7	5.5	10	20	36	77	164
2½	…	…	…	…	…	…	…	…	1	1.6	2.9	4.3	8	16	31	56	120	255
3	…	…	…	…	…	…	…	1	1.7	2.7	5	7	15	27	54	97	206	439
3½	…	…	…	…	…	…	1	1.4	2.5	3.9	7	11	21	38	78	139	297	632
4	…	…	…	…	…	1	1.4	2.0	3.4	5.3	10	15	29	53	107	191	407	867
4½	…	…	…	…	1	1.3	1.8	2.6	4.5	7	13	19	38	70	141	253	539	1148
5	…	…	…	1	1.3	1.8	2.4	3.5	6	9	17	26	51	93	188	335	716	1525
6	…	…	1	1.6	2.1	2.8	3.8	5.5	9	15	28	40	80	147	297	531	1133	2414
7	…	1	1.4	2.3	3.0	4.0	5.5	8.0	14	21	40	58	116	212	428	766	1635	3483
8	1	1.3	2.0	3.1	4.2	5.5	7.6	10.9	19	29	55	80	160	292	590	1054	2251	4795
9	1.3	1.8	2.6	4.2	5.5	7.3	10	14	25	39	73	107	212	388	783	1401	2990	6369
10	1.8	2.4	3.5	5.6	7.4	10	13	19	33	52	97	142	282	516	1042	1862	3976	8468
11	2.2	3.0	4.4	7.0	9.3	12	17	24	42	65	122	179	356	651	1315	2352	5020	10693
12	2.8	3.8	5.5	8.7	12.0	15	21	30	52	81	152	223	443	809	1635	2923	6240	13292
13	3.6	4.9	7.0	11.0	15.0	20	27	39	67	104	194	286	567	1037	2094	3745	7994	17028
14	4.3	5.9	8.5	13.0	18.0	24	32	46	80	125	233	343	680	1244	2512	4492	9589	20425
15	5.0	6.9	10.0	16.0	21.0	28	38	55	95	148	276	406	806	1474	2976	5322	11361	24199

Definitions of Pipe Fittings

The following definitions for various pipe fittings are given by the National Tube Co.:

Armstrong Joint. — A two-bolt, flanged or lugged connection for high pressures. The ends of the pipes are peculiarly formed to properly hold a gutta-percha ring. It was originally made for cast-iron pipe. The two-bolt feature has much to commend it. There are various substitutes for this joint, many of which employ rubber in place of gutta-percha; others use more bolts in order to reduce the cost.

Bell and Spigot Joint. — (1) The usual term for the joint in cast-iron pipe. Each piece is made with an enlarged diameter or bell at one end into which the plain or spigot end of another piece is inserted when laying. The joint is then made tight by cement, oakum, lead, rubber or other suitable substance, which is driven in or calked into the bell and around the spigot. When a similar joint is made in wrought pipe by means of a cast bell (or hub), it is at times called hub and spigot joint (poor usage). Matheson joint is the name applied to a similar joint in wrought pipe which has the bell formed from the pipe. (2) Applied to fittings or valves, means that one end of the run is a "bell," and the other end is a "spigot," similar to those used on regular cast-iron pipe.

Bonnet. — (1) A cover used to guide and enclose the tail end of a valve spindle. (2) A cap over the end of a pipe (poor usage).

Branch. — The outlet or inlet of a fitting not in line with the run, but which may make any angle.

Branch Ell. — (1) Used to designate an elbow having a back outlet in line with one of the outlets of the "run." It is also called a heel outlet elbow. (2) Incorrectly used to designate side outlet or back outlet elbow.

Branch Pipe. — A very general term used to signify a pipe either cast or wrought, that is equipped with one or more branches. Such pipes are used so frequently that they have acquired common names such as tees, crosses, side or back outlet elbows, manifolds, double-branch elbows, etc. The term branch pipe is generally restricted to such as do not conform to usual dimensions.

Branch Tee (Header). — A tee having many side branches. (See Manifold.)

Bull Head Tee. — A tee the branch of which is larger than the run.

Bushing. — A pipe fitting for the purpose of connecting a pipe with a fitting of larger size, being a hollow plug with internal and external threads to suit the different diameters.

Card Weight Pipe. — A term used to designate standard or full weight pipe, which is the Briggs' standard thickness of pipe.

Close Nipple. — One the length of which is about twice the length of a standard pipe thread and is without any shoulder.

Coupling. — A threaded sleeve used to connect two pipes. Commercial couplings are threaded inside to suit the exterior thread of the pipe. The term coupling is occasionally used to mean any jointing device and may be applied to either straight or reducing sizes.

Cross. — A pipe fitting with four branches arranged in pairs, each pair on one axis, and the axes at right angles. When the outlets are otherwise arranged the fittings are branch pipes or specials.

Cross-over. — A small fitting with a double offset, or shaped like the letter U with the ends turned out. It is only made in small sizes and used to pass the flow of one pipe past another when the pipes are in the same plane.

Cross-over Tee. — A fitting made along lines similar to the cross-over, but having at one end two openings in a tee-head the plane of which is at right angles to the plane of the cross-over bend.

Cross Valve. — (1) A valve fitted on a transverse pipe so as to open communication at will between two parallel lines of piping. Much used in connection with oil and water pumping arrangements, especially on ship board. (2) Usually considered as an angle valve with a back outlet in the same plane as the other two openings.

Crotch. — A fitting that has the general shape of the letter *Y*. Caution should be exercised not to confuse the crotch and wye.

Double-branch Elbow. — A fitting that, in a manner, looks like a tee, or as if two elbows had been shaved and then placed together, forming a shape something like the letter *Y* or a crotch.

Double Sweep Tee. — A tee made with easy curves between body and branch, *i.e.*, the center of the curve between run and branch lies outside the body.

Drop Elbow. — A small sized ell that is frequently used where gas is put into a building. These fittings have wings cast on each side. The wings have small countersunk holes so that they may be fastened by wood screws to a ceiling or wall or framing timbers.

Drop Tee. — One having the same peculiar wings as the drop elbow.

Dry Joint. — One made without gasket or packing or smear of any kind, as a ground joint.

Elbow (Ell). — A fitting that makes an angle between adjacent pipes. The angle is always 90 degrees, unless another angle is stated. (See Branch, Service, and Union Ell.)

Extra Heavy. — When applied to pipe, means pipe thicker than standard pipe; when applied to valves and fittings, indicates goods suitable for a working pressure of 250 pounds per square inch.

Header. — A large pipe into which one set of boilers is connected by suitable nozzles or tees, or similar large pipes from which a number of smaller ones lead to consuming points. Headers are often used for other purposes — for heaters or in refrigeration work. Headers are essentially branch pipes with many outlets, which are usually parallel. Largely used for tubes of water-tube boilers.

Hydrostatic Joint. — Used in large water mains, in which sheet lead is forced tightly into the bell of a pipe by means of the hydrostatic pressure of a liquid.

Kewanee Union. — A patented pipe union having one pipe end of brass and the other of malleable iron, with a ring or nut of malleable iron, in which the arrangement and finish of the several parts is such as to provide a non-corrosive ball-and-socket joint at the junction of the pipe ends, and a non-corrosive connection between the ring and brass pipe end.

Lead Joint. — (1) Generally used to signify the connection between pipes which is made by pouring molten lead into the annular space between a bell and spigot, and then making the lead tight by calking. (2) Rarely used to mean the joint made by pressing the lead between adjacent pieces, as when a lead gasket is used between flanges.

Lead Wool. — A material used in place of molten lead for making pipe joints. It is lead fiber, about as coarse as fine excelsior, and when made in a strand, it can be calked into the joints, making them very solid.

Line Pipe. — Special brand of pipe that employs recessed and taper thread couplings, and usually greater length of thread than Briggs' standard. The pipe is also subjected to higher test.

Lip Union. — (1) A special form of union characterized by the lip that prevents the gasket from being squeezed into the pipe so as to obstruct the flow. (2) A ring union, unless flange is specified.

Manifold. — (1) A fitting with numerous branches used to convey fluids between a large pipe and several smaller pipes. (See Branch Tee.) (2) A header for a coil.

Matheson Joint. — A wrought pipe joint made by enlarging one end of the pipe to form a suitable lead recess, similar to the bell end of a cast-iron pipe, and which receives the male or spigot end of the next length. Practically the same style of a joint as used for cast-iron pipe.

Medium Pressure. — When applied to valves and fittings, means suitable for a working pressure of from 125 to 175 pounds per square inch.

Needle Valve. — A valve provided with a long tapering point in place of the ordinary valve disk. The tapering point permits fine graduation of the opening. At times called a needle point valve.

Nipple. — (1) A tubular pipe fitting usually threaded on both ends and under 12 inches in length. Pipe over 12 inches long is regarded as cut pipe. (See Close, Short, Shoulder and Space Nipple.)

Reducer. — (1) A fitting having a larger size at one end than at the other. Some have tried to establish the term "increaser" — thinking of direction of flow — but this has been due to a misunderstanding of the trade custom of always giving the largest size of run of a fitting first; hence, all fittings having more than one size are reducers. They are always threaded inside, unless specified flanged or for some special joint. (2) Threaded type, made with abrupt reduction. (3) Flanged pattern with taper body. (4) Flanged eccentric pattern with taper body, but flanges at 90 degrees to one side of body. (5) Misapplied at times, to a reducing coupling.

Run. — (1) A length of pipe that is made of more than one piece of pipe. (2) The portion of any fitting having its ends "in line" or nearly so, in contradistinction to the branch or side opening, as of a tee. The two main openings of an ell also indicate its run, and when there is a third opening on an ell, the fitting is a "side outlet" or "back outlet" elbow, except that when all three openings are in one plane and the back outlet is in line with one of the run openings, the fitting is a "heel outlet elbow" or a "single sweep tee" or sometimes a "branch tee."

Rust Joint. — Employed to secure rigid connection. The joint is made by packing an intervening space tightly with a stiff paste which oxidizes the iron, the whole rusting together and hardening into a solid mass. It generally cannot be separated except by destroying some of the pieces. One recipe is 80 pounds cast-iron borings or filings, 1 pound sal-ammoniac, 2 pounds flowers of sulphur, mixed to a paste with water.

Service Ell. — An elbow having an outside thread on one end. Also known as street ell.

Service Pipe. — A pipe connecting mains with a dwelling.

Service Tee. — A tee having inside thread on one end and on branch, but outside thread on other end of run. Also known as street tee.

Short Nipple. — One whose length is a little greater than that of two threaded lengths or somewhat longer than a close nipple. It always has some unthreaded portion between the two threads.

Shoulder Nipple. — A nipple of any length, which has a portion of pipe between two pipe threads. As generally used, however, it is a nipple about halfway between the length of a close nipple and a short nipple.

Space Nipple. — A nipple with a portion of pipe or shoulder between the two threads. It may be of any length long enough to allow a shoulder.

Standard Pressure. — A term applied to valves and fittings suitable for a working steam pressure of 125 pounds per square inch.

Tee. — A fitting, either cast or wrought, that has one side outlet at right angles to the run. A single outlet branch pipe. (See Branch, Bull Head, Cross-over, Double Sweep, Drop, Service and Union Tee.)

Union. — (1) The usual trade term for a device used to connect pipes. It commonly consists of three pieces which are, first, the thread end fitted with exterior and interior threads; second, the bottom end fitted with interior threads and a small exterior shoulder; and third, the ring which has an inside flange at one end while the other end has an inside thread like that on the exterior of the thread end. A gasket is placed between the thread and bottom ends, which are drawn together by the ring. Unions are very extensively used, because they permit of connections with little disturbance of the pipe positions.

Union Ell. — An ell with a male or female union at one end.

Union Joint. — A pipe coupling, usually threaded, which permits disconnection without disturbing other sections.

Union Tee. — A tee with male or female union at connection on one end of run.

Wiped Joint. — A lead joint in which the molten solder is poured upon the desired place, after scraping and fitting the parts together, and the joint is wiped up by hand with a moleskin or cloth pad while the metal is in a plastic condition.

Wye (Y). — A fitting either cast or wrought that has one side outlet at any angle other than 90 degrees. The angle is usually 45 degrees, unless another angle is specified. The fitting is usually indicated by the letter Y.

Lutes and Cements

Luting and cementing materials for various purposes in the laboratory and shops may be classified as follows: Water- and steam-proof; oil-proof; acid-proof; proof to hydrocarbon gases; chlorine-proof; elastic; general purposes; marine glue; gaskets; machinists'; leather (belting); crucible; iron; and stone.

Water-proof Compositions. — The asphalt fluid coatings for reservoir walls, concrete foundations, brick, wood, etc., are often of use to engineers. Asphalt only partly dissolves in petroleum naphtha, but when heated in a steam-jacketed kettle and not thinned out too much, a mixture of the two may be obtained in which the part of the asphalt not dissolved is held in suspension. Asphalt is entirely soluble in benzol or toluol, which are about the cheapest solvents for all the constituents of asphalt. Tar and pitch are sometimes used in this connection, but tar contains water, light oils and free carbon, and does not wear as well as good refined asphalt; pitch also contains free carbon, which is sometimes objectionable when it is thinned out with a solvent. Asphalt alone is somewhat pervious to water, but it can be improved in this respect by adding about one-fourth its weight of paraffin; it is also well to add a little boiled linseed oil. For thicker compositions, where body is required, asbestos, stone powder, cement, etc., may be added as fillers. Lutes of linseed oil thickened with clay, asbestos, red or white lead, etc., are water-proof if made thick enough. These are much used for steam joints. Flaxseed meal made into a paste with water is often serviceable, the oil contained serving as a binder as the water evaporates.

Oil-proof Cements. — The well-known "hektograph composition" is the most useful lute for small leaks, etc. It consists of the following ingredients: Good glue or gelatin, 2 parts; glycerin, 1 part; water, 7 parts. This preparation is applied warm and stiffens quickly on cooling. Another very useful composition is a stiff paste of molasses and flour. Another preparation, impervious to oil vapors, is the "flaxseed poultice," mentioned in the preceding paragraph, which is proof to oil vapors. One of the strongest cements, and one which is really oil-proof, water-proof and acid-proof, is a stiff paste of glycerin and litharge. These form a chemical combination which sets in a few minutes. If a little water is added, it sets more slowly, which is often an advantage. This cement is mixed when required for use. A mixture of plaster-of-paris and water is useful, and it is sometimes advantageous to mix asbestos, straw or hair with it. A solution of silicate of soda made into a stiff paste with carbonate of lime gets hard in six to eight hours.

Acid-proof Cements. — The asphalt compositions already mentioned, compositions of melted sulphur with fillers of stone powder, cement, sand, etc., may be used, and also the following, which withstands hydrochloric acid vapors: Rosin, 1 part; sulphur, 1 part; fireclay, 2 parts. The lute composed of boiled linseed oil and fireclay acts well with most acid vapors. The composition of glycerin and litharge previously referred to is useful in this connection, especially when made up according to the following formula: Litharge, 80 pounds; red lead, 8 pounds; "flock" asbestos, 10 pounds. It should be fed into a mixer, a little at a time, with small quantities of boiled oil (about six quarts of oil being used). Sockets in 3-inch pipes carrying nitric acid, calked with this preparation, showed no leaks in nine months.

A particularly useful cement for withstanding acid vapors, which is tough and elastic, is composed of crude rubber, cut fine, 1 part; linseed oil, boiled, 4 parts; fireclay, 6 parts. The rubber is dissolved in carbon disulphide to the consistency of molasses and is then mixed with the oil. Other acid-proof cements are as follows: "Black putty" made by carefully mixing equal portions of china-clay, gas-tar and linseed oil. The china-clay must be well dried by placing it over a boiler or by other means. Barytes cement is composed of pure, finely ground sulphate of barium, and is made into a putty with a solution of silicate of soda. This sets very hard when moderately heated, and is then proof against acids. The gravity of the silicate of soda should be between 1.2 and 1.4, 24 degrees to 42 degrees Baumé. If too thin, it does not hold; and when thicker than 1.4, it expands and breaks.

Gasket Compositions. — Almost any cementing substance may be used with rings of asbestos, etc., for gaskets, but some are especially adapted for the purpose. Asphalt, tar, petroleum residuum and soft or hard pitch are recommended. Silicate of soda is much used, and is sometimes advantageously mixed with casein, fine sand, clay, asbestos, carbonate of lime, caustic lime, magnesia, oxides of heavy metals, such as lead, zinc, iron and powdered barytes. A few mixtures that might be selected are: Silicate of soda and asbestos; silicate of soda, asbestos and slaked lime; silicate of soda and fine sand; silicate of soda and fireclay.

Machinists' Cements. — These are the well-known red and white leads. The red lead is often diluted with an equal bulk of silica or other inert substance to make it less powdery. The best way to do this is to add rubber or gutta-percha to the oil as follows: Linseed oil, 6 parts, by weight; rubber or gutta-percha, 1 part by weight. The rubber or gutta-percha is dissolved in sufficient carbon disulphide to give it the consistency of molasses, mixed with the oil, and left exposed to the air for about twenty-four hours. The red lead is then mixed to a putty. Oxide of iron makes a less brittle cement than red lead.

Leather Cements. — 1. Equal parts of good hide glue and American isinglass, softened in water for ten hours and then boiled with pure tannin until the whole mass is sticky. The surface of the joint should be roughened and the cement applied hot. 2. One pound of finely shredded gutta-percha digested over a water-bath with 10 pounds of benzol, until dissolved, and 12 pounds of linseed oil varnish stirred in. 3. Seven and one-half pounds of finely shredded india-rubber is completely dissolved in 10 pounds of carbon disulphide by treating while hot; 1 pound of shellac and 1 pound of turpentine are added, and the hot solution heated until the two latter ingredients are also dissolved.

Another leather cement is as follows: Gutta-percha, 8 ounces; pitch, 1 ounce; shellac, 1 ounce; sweet oil, 1 ounce. These are melted together. Still another is as follows: Fish glue is soaked in water twenty-four hours, allowed to drain for a like period, boiled well, and a previously melted mixture of 2 ounces of rosin and ½ ounce of boiled oil is added to every two pounds of glue solution.

Iron and Stone Cements. — When finely divided iron, such as filings or cast-iron borings that have been powdered, is mixed with an oxidizing agent, such as manganese dioxide, or a substance electro-negative to iron, such as sulphur, in a good conducting solution like salt or sal-ammoniac, galvanic action sets in very rapidly and the iron swells, by forming iron oxide, and cements the mass together. It is best diluted with Portland cement, the proportions being as follows: Iron filings, 40 parts; manganese dioxide or flowers of sulphur, 10 parts; sal-ammoniac, 1 part; Portland cement, 20 to 40 parts; water to form a paste. A hard stone-like composition is made as follows: Zinc oxide, 2 parts; zinc chloride, 1 part; water to make a paste. Magnesium oxide and chloride may also be used in like proportions. When used in considerable quantity, this cement is mixed with powdered stone, for reasons of economy, the proportions depending upon the character of the work.

Cement proof to Hydrocarbon Gases. — Compositions of plaster and cement, the former setting more quickly, are used; also compositions of casein, such as finely powdered casein, 2 parts; fresh slaked lime, 50 parts; fine sand, 50 parts. Water is added, when used, to form a thick mass. Various mixtures of silicate of soda are employed in which the thick silicate is absorbed in some inert material such as clay, sand or asbestos.

Cements proof to Chlorine. — The best and only reliable compositions are a few made with Portland cement, and the following is much used for electrolytic and chemical plants: Powdered glass, 1 part; Portland cement, 1 part; silicate of soda, 1 part; a small amount of powdered slate. This lute is said to stand acids and alkalies, as well as the influences of chlorine. Linseed oil made into a paste with fireclay serves for a time.

Elastic Cements. — The various cements containing rubber are elastic, if the rubber is in a predominating amount; many containing boiled linseed oil and the hektograph composition already mentioned are quite elastic. The rubber and linseed-oil cement, given in the paragraph headed "Acid-proof Cements," is very tough and useful for nearly all purposes except when oil vapors are to be confined. The most useful single rubber lute is probably the so-called Hart's india-rubber cement. Equal parts of raw linseed oil and pure masticated rubber are digested together by heating, and this mixture is made into a stiff putty with fine "paper stock" asbestos. It is more convenient, however, to dissolve the rubber first in carbon disulphide, and, after mixing the oil with it, to let the solvent evaporate spontaneously.

General Purposes. — Plaster-of-paris, especially when mixed with asbestos, straw, flush trimmings, hair, broken stone, etc., and used according to temperature, strain and other conditions, is one of the most useful preparations for general purposes. A putty of flour and molasses is a good composition to keep in a works ready for quick application when needed. It serves, for a time, almost any purpose at moderate temperatures. Casein compositions have great strength. The white of an egg made into a paste with slaked lime is strong and efficient, but must be used promptly on account of its quick setting qualities.

Marine Glue. — This can be purchased almost as cheaply as made. It consists of crude rubber, 1 part; shellac, 2 parts; pitch, 3 parts. The rubber must first be dissolved in carbon disulphide or turpentine before mixing with the heated combination of the other two ingredients.

Acid-proof Lining. — A lining for protecting tanks from the influence of acids is made from a mixture consisting of 75 parts (by weight), of pitch; 9 parts plaster-of-paris; 9 parts ochre; 15 parts beeswax; and 3 parts litharge. The tanks are covered on the inside with a thick coat of this mixture.

Cements for Pipe Joints. — A strong cement which is oil-proof, waterproof, and acid-proof, consists of a stiff paste of glycerin and litharge. These form a chemical combination which sets in a few minutes. If a little water is added, it sets more slowly, which is often an advantage. This cement is mixed when required for use.

Mixture for Threaded Pipe Joints. — A good material to apply to pipe threads before making up the joints, in order to obtain a tight joint that will resist the action of gases or liquids, is made of red lead mixed with pure boiled linseed oil. This mixture has been widely used and is very satisfactory. It should have a heavy fluid-like consistency, and if applied to a clean, well-cut thread will give an excellent joint.

Shellac for Pipe Connections. — Shellac has proved to be a very satisfactory substitute for lead in sealing air and gas pipe connections. It is applied with a brush to the joints and hardens very rapidly, and being brittle, the pipes can be readily disconnected.

Graphite, Litharge, Chalk Cement. — A good cement for use in making steam pipe joints is made in the following manner: Grind and wash in clean cold water 15 parts of chalk and 50 parts of graphite; mix the two together thoroughly and allow to dry. When dry regrind to a fine powder, to which add 20 parts of ground litharge and mix to a stiff paste with 15 parts of boiled linseed oil. The preparation may be set aside for future use, as it will remain plastic for a long time, if placed in a cool place. It is applied to the joint packing as any ordinary cement.

White and Red Lead Mixture. — Mix in ordinary white lead, enough powdered red lead to make a paste the consistency of putty. Spread this mixture on the joint, and when it hardens, the joint will be water tight. This mixture was used on stand-pipe flanges after testing all kinds of rubber gaskets without success. The mixture hardened and made a tight joint, never leaking afterward.

Permanent Cement for Steam Pipes. — To make a permanent cement used for stopping leaks in steam pipes where calking or plugging is impossible, mix black oxide of manganese and raw linseed oil, using enough oil with the manganese to bring it to a thick paste; apply to the pipe or joint at leak. It is best to remove pressure from the pipe and keep it sufficiently warm to absorb the oil from the manganese. In twenty-four hours the cement will be very hard.

High-Pressure Water Pipes. — A highly recommended packing and cement, combined, for making tight joints in high-pressure water pipes, is made as follows: Mix with boiled linseed oil, to the consistency of putty, these ingredients: Ground litharge, 10 pounds; plaster-of-paris, 4 pounds; yellow ochre, ½ pound; red lead, 2 pounds; cut hemp fiber, ½ ounce. The hemp fiber should be cut in lengths of about ½ inch, and thoroughly mixed into the putty material. Its office is to give consistency to the cement. The cement is applied to the joint similarly to any other cement. It dries thoroughly in from 10 to 12 hours.

Cement to Resist Acids. — A cement that withstands hydrochloric acid vapors consists of rosin, 1 part; sulphur, 1 part; fireclay, 2 parts. A cement composed of boiled linseed oil and fireclay acts well with most acid vapors. A composition of glycerin and litharge is useful in this connection, especially when made up according to the following formula: Litharge, 80 pounds; red lead, 8 pounds; "flock" asbestos, 10 pounds. It should be fed into a mixer, a little at a time, with small quantities of boiled oil (about six quarts of oil being used). Sockets in 3-inch pipes carrying nitric acid, calked with this preparation, showed no leaks in nine months.

Packing to Resist Gasoline Vapor. — To prepare packing for joints in pipes, etc., carrying gasoline vapor, mix a quantity of graphite and kerosene to a thick paste and apply the paste to both sides of sheet asbestos. When dry, the packing may be cut to the shape desired. The graphite helps the asbestos to make intimate contact with the iron and thus maintain a tight joint continuously at high temperature for an indefinite time.

STANDARDS FOR ELECTRIC MOTORS

The mounting dimensions for electric motors as standardized in the United States by the National Electrical Manufacturers Association (N.E.M.A.) will be found in Tables 1 and 2. These dimensions include the spacing of bolt holes in the foot of the motor, the distance from the bottom of the foot to the center-line of the motor shaft, the size of the conduit, the length of hub, and other dimensions likely to be required by designers or manufacturers of motor-driven equipment. The standard motor frame number is given in the first column and opposite this number the mounting and other essential dimensions. A given frame number may represent either a direct- or alternating-current motor, and also different horsepower and speed ratings. The standard frame numbers for different types of motors will be found in Tables 3 to 7 inclusive. For horsepower and speed ratings, see Tables 8 to 13.

To illustrate the application of these tables, determine the standard frame size and mounting dimensions for a direct-current general-purpose motor having a horse-power rating of 5 and a speed of 1150 R.P.M.

Table 3 shows that the frame number is 284 and Table 1 gives the mounting dimensions of any motor having this frame size. If the motor is to be mounted upon a belt-tightening base or upon rails, the standard dimensions of the base or rails for different motor frame numbers will be found in Table 2.

Maximum Motor and Generator Ratings for Different Types of Drives. — The following data represent good practice (under normal operations conditions) for the use of (1) flat-belt drives; (2) V-belt drives; (3) chain drives, and (4) gear drives on motors and generators which are not equipped with outboard bearings. (Recommended standards of National Electrical Manufacturers Association.)

Full Load Rpm of Motor or Generator	Maximum Hp Rating of Motor	Maximum Kw Rating Generator	Full Load Rpm of Motor or Generator	Maximum Hp Rating of Motor	Maximum Kw Rating Generator
FLAT-BELT DRIVES					
2400–3600	20	15	750–900	125	75
1800–2400	30	20	720–750	150	100
1200–1800	40	30	560–720	200	150
900–1200	75	50	....	...	...
V-BELT DRIVES					
2400–3600	20	15	750–900	200	100
1800–2400	40	30	720–750	250	150
1200–1800	75	40	560–720	300	200
900–1200	125	75	....	...	...
CHAIN DRIVES					
2400–3600	20	15	750–900	200	100
1800–2400	40	30	720–750	250	150
1200–1800	75	40	560–720	300	200
900–1200	125	75	....	...	...
GEAR DRIVES*					
1500–1800	5	..	750–900	50	...
1200–1500	10	..	560–750	75	...
900–1200	25	..	....	...	...

* These values for gear drives are based upon the use of steel pinions.

Table 1. Standard Dimensions for D-C and A-C Motors
(Adoped Standard of National Electrical Manufacturers Association)

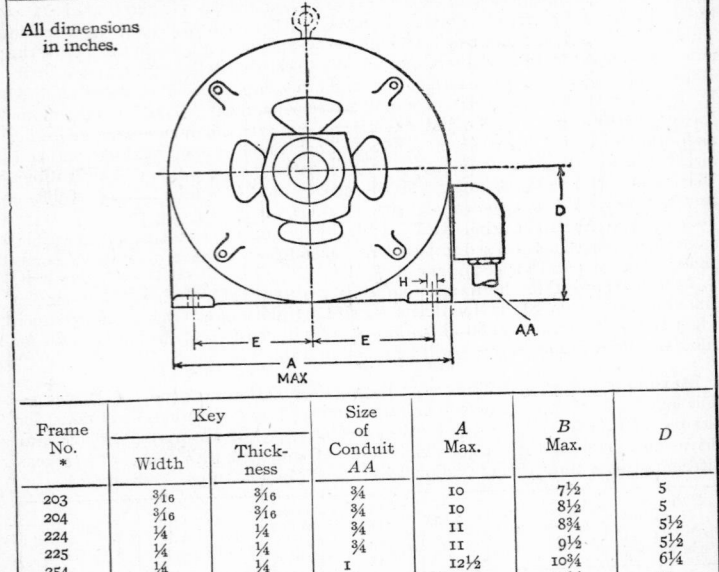

All dimensions in inches.

Frame No. *	Key		Size of Conduit AA	A Max.	B Max.	D
	Width	Thickness				
203	³⁄₁₆	³⁄₁₆	¾	10	7½	5
204	³⁄₁₆	³⁄₁₆	¾	10	8½	5
224	¼	¼	¾	11	8¾	5½
225	¼	¼	¾	11	9½	5½
254	¼	¼	1	12½	10¾	6¼
284	¼	¼	1	14	12½	7
324	⅜	⅜	1¼	16	14	8
326	⅜	⅜	1¼	16	15½	8
364	½	½	1½	18	15¼	9
364S	⅜	⅜	1½	18	15¼	9
365	½	½	1½	18	16¼	9
365S	⅜	⅜	1½	18	16¼	9
404	½	½	2	20	16¼	10
404S	½	½	2	20	16¼	10
405	½	½	2	20	17¾	10
405S	½	½	2	20	17¾	10
444	⅝	⅝	2	22	18½	11
444S	½	½	2	22	18½	11
445	⅝	⅝	2	22	20½	11
445S	½	½	2	22	20½	11
504U	¾	¾	2½	25	21	12½
504S	½	½	2½	25	21	12½
505	¾	¾	2½	25	23	12½
505S	½	½	2½	25	23	12½

* Dimensions for frame No. 504U are a recommended standard of the National Electrical Manufacturers Association (June, 1946 recommendation).

Tolerances on keyways: Width ³⁄₁₆ inch to ¾ inch inclusive +.000 inch, −.002 inch. Tolerances in making keyways parallel to center line of shaft: Shaft diameters ¾ inches to 1½ inches inc. .002 inches; shaft diameters 1⅝ inches to 3⅜ inches inc. .003 inches. Dimension D will never be greater than the above values and may be less so that shims

Table 1 (*Continued*). **Standard Dimensions for D-C and A-C Motors**
(Adopted Standard of National Electrical Manufacturers Association)

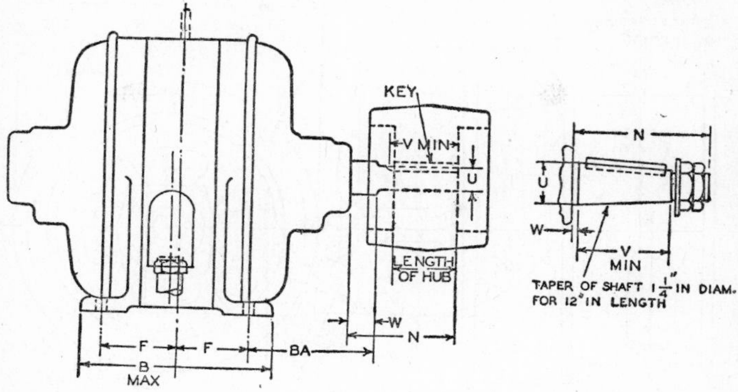

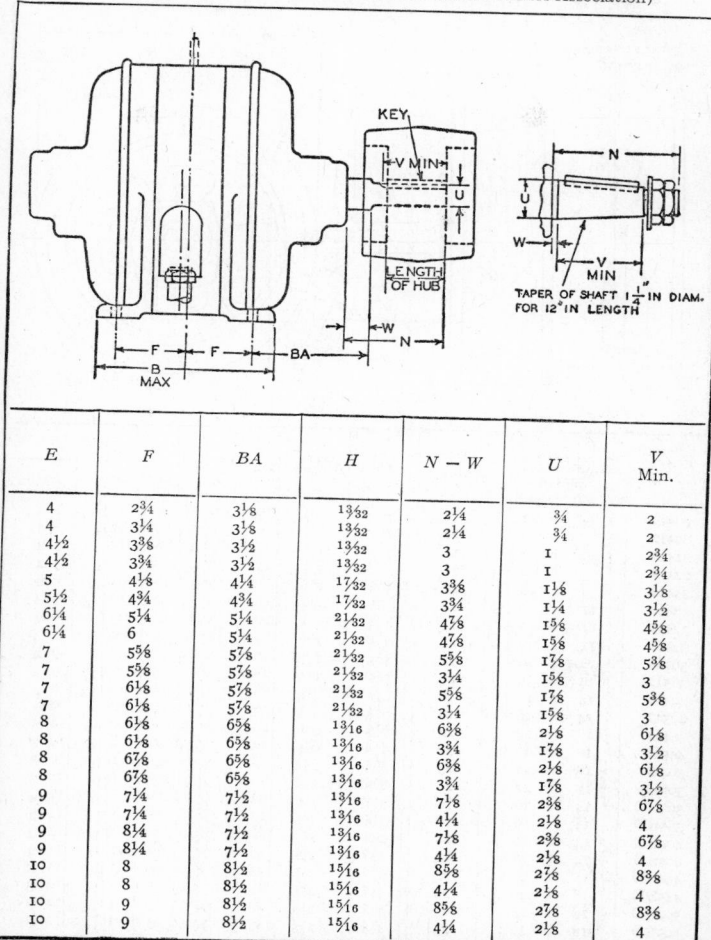

E	*F*	*BA*	*H*	*N − W*	*U*	*V* Min.
4	2¾	3⅛	1 3/32	2¼	¾	2
4	3¼	3⅛	1 3/32	2¼	¾	2
4½	3⅜	3½	1 3/32	3	1	2¾
4½	3¾	3½	1 3/32	3	1	2¾
5	4⅛	4¼	1 7/32	3⅜	1⅛	3⅛
5½	4¾	4¾	1 7/32	3¾	1¼	3½
6¼	5¼	5¼	2 1/32	4⅞	1⅝	4⅝
6¼	6	5¼	2 1/32	4⅞	1⅝	4⅝
7	5⅝	5⅞	2 1/32	5⅝	1⅞	5⅜
7	5⅝	5⅞	2 1/32	3¼	1⅝	3
7	6⅛	5⅞	2 1/32	5⅝	1⅞	5⅜
7	6⅛	5⅞	2 1/32	3¼	1⅝	3
8	6⅛	6⅝	1 3/16	6⅜	2⅛	6⅛
8	6⅛	6⅝	1 3/16	3¾	1⅞	3½
8	6⅞	6⅝	1 3/16	6⅜	2⅛	6⅛
8	6⅞	6⅝	1 3/16	3¾	1⅞	3½
9	7¼	7½	1 3/16	7⅛	2⅜	6⅞
9	7¼	7½	1 3/16	4¼	2⅛	4
9	8¼	7½	1 3/16	7⅛	2⅜	6⅞
9	8¼	7½	1 3/16	4¼	2⅛	4
10	8	8½	1 5/16	8⅝	2⅞	8⅜
10	8	8½	1 5/16	4¼	2⅛	4
10	9	8½	1 5/16	8⅝	2⅞	8⅜
10	9	8½	1 5/16	4¼	2⅛	4

are usually required for coupled or geared machines. When exact dimension is required, shims up to 1/32 inch may be necessary on frame sizes whose dimension *D* is 8 inches and less, and on larger frame shims up to 1/16 inch may be necessary.

Tolerances on shaft extension diameters are: Shaft diameter ¼ inch to 1½ inches inclusive +.0000 inches, −.0005 inches. Shaft diameters 1⅝ inches to 3⅜ inches inclusive +.000 inch −.001 inch.

Table 1a. Flange-Mounting (Type D) for D-C and A-C Electric Motors*
(Standard Dimensions of National Electrical Manufacturers Association)

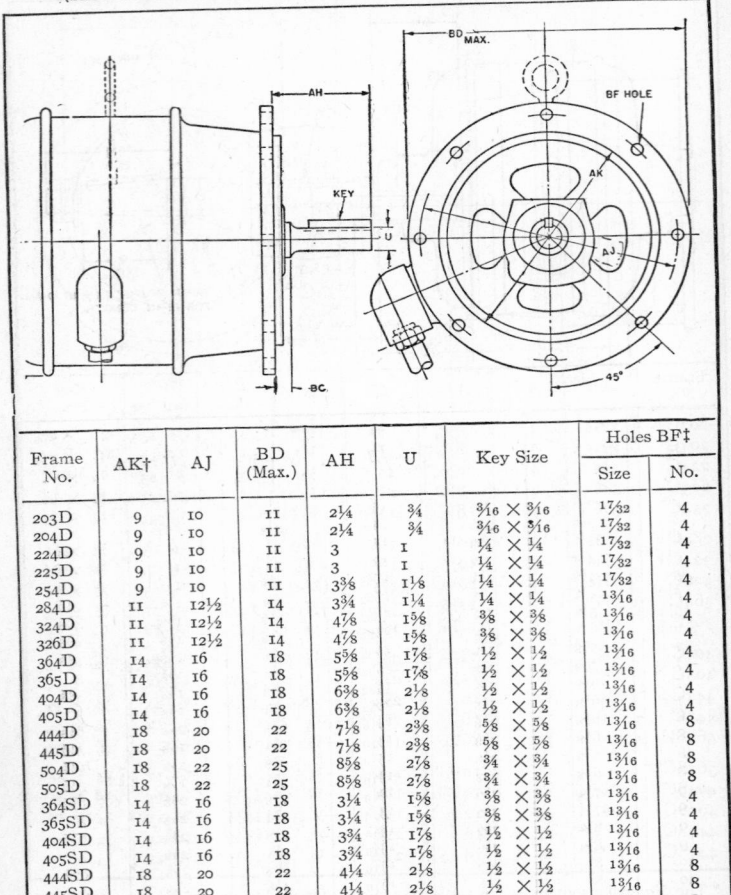

Frame No.	AK†	AJ	BD (Max.)	AH	U	Key Size	Holes BF‡	
							Size	No.
203D	9	10	11	2¼	¾	3/16 × 3/16	17/32	4
204D	9	10	11	2¼	¾	3/16 × 3/16	17/32	4
224D	9	10	11	3	1	¼ × ¼	17/32	4
225D	9	10	11	3	1	¼ × ¼	17/32	4
254D	9	10	11	3⅜	1⅛	¼ × ¼	17/32	4
284D	11	12½	14	3¾	1¼	¼ × ¼	13/16	4
324D	11	12½	14	4⅞	1⅝	⅜ × ⅜	13/16	4
326D	11	12½	14	4⅞	1⅝	⅜ × ⅜	13/16	4
364D	14	16	18	5⅝	1⅞	½ × ½	13/16	4
365D	14	16	18	5⅝	1⅞	½ × ½	13/16	4
404D	14	16	18	6⅜	2⅛	½ × ½	13/16	4
405D	14	16	18	6⅜	2⅛	½ × ½	13/16	4
444D	18	20	22	7⅛	2⅜	⅝ × ⅝	13/16	8
445D	18	20	22	7⅛	2⅜	⅝ × ⅝	13/16	8
504D	18	22	25	8⅝	2⅞	¾ × ¾	13/16	8
505D	18	22	25	8⅝	2⅞	¾ × ¾	13/16	8
364SD	14	16	18	3¼	1⅝	⅜ × ⅜	13/16	4
365SD	14	16	18	3¼	1⅝	⅜ × ⅜	13/16	4
404SD	14	16	18	3¾	1⅞	½ × ½	13/16	4
405SD	14	16	18	3¾	1⅞	½ × ½	13/16	4
444SD	18	20	22	4¼	2⅛	½ × ½	13/16	8
445SD	18	20	22	4¼	2⅛	½ × ½	13/16	8
504SD	18	22	25	4¼	2⅛	½ × ½	13/16	8
505SD	18	22	25	4¼	2⅛	½ × ½	13/16	8

* Flange mounting applicable to both horizontal and vertical motors. Frame numbers for vertical motors may have suffix letters DV or SDV.
† The tolerance for the AK dimension is +.000, −.005 inch.
‡ Holes in 4-hole flange are midway between horizontal and vertical centerlines. Flange face is in line with shaft shoulder; hence dimension BC = 0.
Motors with flange mountings may or may not have feet.

Table 1b. Face Mounting (Type C) for D-C and A-C Electric Motors*
(Standard Dimensions of National Electrical Manufacturers Association)

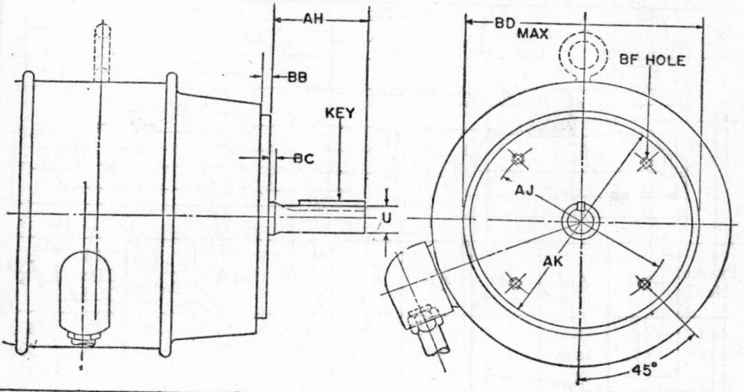

Frame No.	*AH*	*AJ*	*AK*	*U*	*BC*	*BD* Max.	*BF*† Tap Size	Key Size
203C	2 5/16	7 1/4	8 1/2	3/4	1/16	9	1/2–13	3/16 × 3/16
204C	2 5/16	7 1/4	8 1/2	3/4	1/16	9	1/2–13	3/16 × 3/16
224C	3 1/8	7 1/4	8 1/2	1	1/8	9	1/2–13	1/4 × 1/4
225C	3 1/8	7 1/4	8 1/2	1	1/8	9	1/2–13	1/4 × 1/4
254C	3 3/4	7 1/4	8 1/2	1 1/8	3/8	10	1/2–13	1/4 × 1/4
284C	4 7/16	9	10 1/2	1 1/4	1 1/16	11 1/4	1/2–13	1/4 × 1/4
324C	5 5/16	9	10 1/2	1 5/8	7/16	12 1/2	1/2–13	3/8 × 3/8
326C	5 5/16	9	10 1/2	1 5/8	7/16	12 1/2	1/2–13	3/8 × 3/8
364C	5 3/8	11	12 1/2	1 7/8	—1/4	14	5/8–11	1/2 × 1/2
365C	5 3/8	11	12 1/2	1 7/8	—1/4	14	5/8–11	1/2 × 1/2
404C	6 1/8	11	12 1/2	2 1/8	—1/4	15 1/2	5/8–11	1/2 × 1/2
405C	6 1/8	11	12 1/2	2 1/8	—1/4	15 1/2	5/8–11	1/2 × 1/2
444C	6 7/8	14	16	2 3/8	—1/4	17 1/2	5/8–11	5/8 × 5/8
445C	6 7/8	14	16	2 3/8	—1/4	17 1/2	5/8–11	5/8 × 5/8
364SC	3	11	12 1/2	1 5/8	—1/4	14	5/8–11	3/8 × 3/8
365SC	3	11	12 1/2	1 5/8	—1/4	14	5/8–11	3/8 × 3/8
404SC	3 1/2	11	12 1/2	1 7/8	—1/4	15 1/2	5/8–11	1/2 × 1/2
405SC	3 1/2	11	12 1/2	1 7/8	—1/4	15 1/2	5/8–11	1/2 × 1/2
444SC	4	14	16	2 1/8	—1/4	17 1/2	5/8–11	1/2 × 1/2
445SC	4	14	16	2 1/8	—1/4	17 1/2	5/8–11	1/2 × 1/2

* The dimensions given in this table may also be applied to vertical motors, in which case the frame designation may have suffix letters *CV* or *SCV*.

† There are four equally spaced holes *BF* for all frames. Minimum depth of hole is 3/4 inch for frames 203*C* to 326*C* incl. and 15/16 inch for all others.

Dimension *BB* is 1/4 inch for all frame sizes.

Tolerances. *AK* dimension: 203–326 frames, incl., +.000, −.003 inch; 364–445 frames, incl., +.000, −.005 inch.

Permissible Shaft Runout: 203–326 frames, incl., .002 inch indicator reading; 364–445 frames, incl., .003 inch indicator reading.

Table 2. Dimensions of Belt-tightening Slide Rails or Base for D-C and A-C Motors
(Adopted Standard of National Electrical Manufacturers Association)

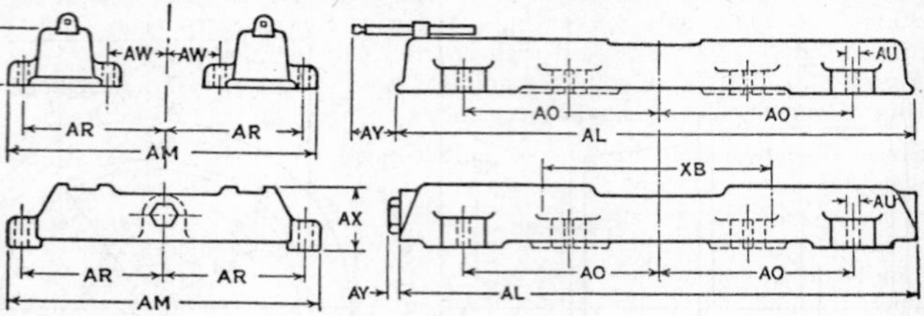

Frame No. †	AL	AM	AO	AR	AU	AW	AX	AY Bases	AY Max. Rails	XB *
204	14	12	5	5¼	½	1¼	1¾	½	4	3
224	15½	12¼	5½	5⅜	½	1⅜	1¾	½	4¼	3½
225	15½	13	5½	5¾	½	1¾	1¾	½	4¼	3½
254	17¾	15⅛	6¼	6⅝	⅝	1⅝	2	⅝	5	4
284	19¾	16⅞	7	7½	⅝	2	2	⅝	5¾	4½
324	22¾	19¼	8	8½	¾	2	2½	¾	6½	5¼
326	22¾	20¾	8	9¼	¾	2¾	2½	¾	6½	5¼
364	25½	20½	9	9⅛	¾	2⅛	2½	¾	7½	6
365	25½	21½	9	9⅝	¾	2⅝	2½	¾	7½	6
404	28¾	22⅜	10	9⅞	⅞	2⅜	3	⅞	7⅞	7
405	28¾	23⅞	10	10⅝	⅞	3⅛	3	⅞	7⅞	7
444	31¼	24⅝	11	11	⅞	3½	3	⅞	8⅜	7½
445	31¼	26⅝	11	12	⅞	4½	3	⅞	8⅜	7½
504U	35	28	12½	12½	1	3½	3½	1	9	8
505	35	30	12½	13½	1	4½	3½	1	9	8

* Column *XB* gives movement of motor on base.
† Frame No. 203 (not listed in this table) is same as No. 204, excepting $AM = 11$ inches, $AR = 4\frac{3}{4}$ inches, and $AW = \frac{3}{4}$ inch.

The use of outboard bearings should be specified for general purpose motors with gear drive in frame sizes 75 H.P., 850 to 900 R.P.M. and larger.

For quiet operation and freedom from severe vibration when using gear drive, the speed of the motor should be selected such that with the pinion or gear used the peripheral speed at the pitch diameter will not exceed 1300 feet per minute when using cut steel spur gearings.

Standard Direction of Motor Rotation. — The standard direction of rotation for all non-reversing direct-current motors, all alternating-current single-phase motors, all synchronous motors, and all universal motors, is *counter clockwise* when facing that end of the motor opposite the drive.

This rule does not apply to two- and three-phase induction motors as most applications on which they are used are of such a nature that either or both directions of rotation may be required, and the phase sequence of the power lines is rarely known. (This is the adopted standard of the National Electrical Manufacturers Association.)

Small-power Universal Motors. — A small-power motor, is described in the adopted standard of the National Electrical Manufacturers Association, as a motor built on a frame smaller than that having a continuous rating of one horsepower, open type, at 1700–1800 R.P.M. The classification of small universal motors includes: (a) Plain series — varying-speed with concentrated poles, and (b) compensated series — varying-speed with distributed windings.

Rating Standards: The standard voltages are 115 and 230 volts (direct and alternating current). The standard frequencies are from zero to 60 cycles per second.

Small Direct-Current Motors. — Direct-current motors of less than one horsepower may have constant speed, varying speed, adjustable speed, or adjustable varying speed characteristics. The standard voltages are 32, 115, and 230 volts. The fields of 32-volt standard motors are so designed that they can be run continuously on 40 volts without injury.

The recommended full-load speed ratings follow: 1 H.P. — 3450 R.P.M.; ¾ H.P. — 3450 and 1725 R.P.M.; ½ H.P. — 3450, 1725, and 1140 R.P.M.; and ⅓ to ½0 H.P. — 3450, 1725, 1140, and 860 R.P.M. When motors are required to operate at other than these standard speeds, full-load speeds approximating those of 25- or 60-cycle alternating-current motors shall be given preference. At normal operating temperature, rated load and voltage, a variation of 7½ per cent above or below any rated speed is permissible according to the N.E.M.A. standard.

Small Alternating-Current Motors. — Motors of less than one horsepower and for alternating current are made in various types with either constant speed, varying speed, or adjustable varying speed characteristics. The standard voltages are 115 and 230 volts for single-phase motors, and 110, 208 (for 60 cycles only) and 220 volts for polyphase motors. The standard frequencies are 25, 50 and 60 cycles per second. Horsepower and speed ratings are as given in Table 10.

Large Direct-Current Motors. — Large power direct-current motors are defined as motors built in frames one horsepower, 1700–1750 R.P.M. up to and including motors built in frames corresponding to 200 horsepower at speeds higher than 450 R.P.M., open type, having a continuous time rating but not exceeding 200 horsepower. Standard voltages are 115 and 230 volts. The standard voltage limits for constant-speed motors of the horsepower and speed ratings given in Table 8 are: 115 volts for motors of 1½ to 20 horsepower, incl. — 3500 R.P.M.; 1 to 30 horsepower, incl. — 1750 R.P.M.; ¾ to 40 horsepower, incl. — 1150 R.P.M.; ½ to 40 horsepower, incl. — 850 R.P.M. and all lower speeds, and 230 volts for all ratings.

Adjustable-Speed Motors, 3-to-1 and Higher Ratios. — The standard horsepower and speed ratings are as given in Table 9. The standard voltage limits are: 115 volts for ½ to 20 horsepower, inclusive, at all speeds, and 230 volts for all ratings.

Rating Standards for Planer Motors. — Planer motors of 4-to-1 speed ratio (250 to 1000 R.P.M.) have cutting speeds of 250 to 750 R.P.M. and return speeds of 500 to 1000 R.P.M. Motors of 6-to-1 ratio (200 to 1200 R.P.M.) have cutting speeds of 200 to 750 R.P.M. and return speeds of 500 to 1200 R.P.M. Planer motors are given a one-hour rating on a 50 deg. C. rise basis at full rated load at one-half maximum rated speed.

Variation from Rated Speed: At normal operating temperature, rated load and voltage and at full field, the variation above or below the rated full-field speed of *constant-speed motors* is not to exceed 7½ per cent for motors built in frame sizes which are the same size as or smaller than that used for the general-purpose open-type, 7½-H.P., 1150-R.P.M. motor; for motors built in larger frames, the variation is not to exceed 5 per cent.

Adjustable-speed motors have the same allowable variation from rated speed as do constant speed motors.

Large Single-Phase Motors. — For motors of this general class and of one horsepower rating or larger, the standard voltages are 115 and 230 volts. The

Table 3. Standard Frame Sizes for Direct-Current Motors

Constant speed motors of horizontal and vertical designs for continuous duty — Adopted Standard of National Electrical Manufacturers Association

Rating H.P.	Speed in Revolutions per Minute						
	3500	1750	1150	850	690	575	500
	Frame Number						
½	...	...	...	204	224	225	...
¾	...	...	203*	224	225	254	284
1	...	203*	204	225	254	254	284
1½	203*	204*	224	254	254	...	...
2	204*	224*	225	254	284	...	...
3	224	225	254	284	...	...	...
5	225	254	284	...	...	...	...
7½	254	284	...	...	...	...	...
10	284	...	...	...	...	...	...

Standard dimensions for these frame numbers are given in Table 1. Revised numbers marked (*) effective October 1, 1940.

Table 4. Standard Frame Sizes for Two- and Three-Phase Squirrel-Cage Motors
(Adopted Standard of National Electrical Manufacturers Association)

Rating H.P.	Totally Enclosed, Low Voltage, 60 Cycles, 550 Volts or Less				Rating H.P.	General-Purpose Motors, Open Type, 25 Cycles		
	Frame Number					Frame Number		
	3600 R.P.M.	1800 R.P.M.	1200 R.P.M.	900 R.P.M.		1500 R.P.M.	750 R.P.M.	500 R.P.M.
½	....	....	....	204	½	.....	204	224
¾	....	....	203	224	¾	.....	224	225
1	....	203	204	225	1	224	225	254
1½	203	204	224	254	1½	225	254	284
2	204	224	225	254	2	225	254	284
3	284	284	324	324	3	254	284	326
....	....	....	....	....	5	284	324	365
....	....	....	....	....	7½	326	326	404
....	....	....	....	....	10	364	365	405
....	....	....	....	....	15	365	405	445
....	....	....	....	....	20	404	444	504
....	....	....	....	....	25	405	445	505
....	....	....	....	....	30	445	504	......
....	....	....	....	....	40	504	505	......
....	....	....	....	....	50	505S	....	....

Standard dimensions for all of these frame numbers are given in Table 1.

Frame numbers above the zigzag line (section of table at right) have been standardized for 110, 220, 440 and 550 volts and those below for 220, 440 and 550 volts.

If motor is to be mounted upon a belt-tightening base (or upon rails) see standard dimensions in Table 2 for any given frame number.

standard frequencies are 25, 50 and 60 cycles per second.   The standard horsepower and speed ratings are given in Table 12.

Large Polyphase Motors. — These induction motors include the squirrel-cage type with constant-speed characteristics, the wound rotor type with constant speed and adjustable varying speed characteristics, and automatic start polyphase.

The standard voltages are 110, 208 (60 cycles only) 220, 440, 550, and 2300 volts. The standard frequencies are 25, 50 and 60 cycles per second.   The standard horsepower and speed ratings are given in Table 11 for 60 and 25 cycles.

Large Synchronous Motors. — (The following does not apply to motors of the self-excited or non-excited synchronous types.)   Synchronous motors separately excited may be classed as (a) revolving field (rotor); (b) stationary field (stator). The standard voltages are 208 (60 cycles only) 220, 440, 550 and 2300 volts for ratings up to 200 horsepower.   Above 200 horsepower, the standard voltages are 208 (60 cycles only) 220, 440, 550, 2300, 4000, 6600, 11000 and 13200 volts.   The standard frequencies are 25, 50 and 60 cycles per second.   See Table 13.

Crane Motors — Alternating Current. — The standard voltages for crane motors are 110, 208 (60 cycles only) 220, 440 and 550 volts, and the standard frequencies are 25 and 60 cycles per second.

Standard Definitions of Motor Terms. — The definitions which follow have been adopted as standard by the National Electrical Manufacturers Association.

Locked-Rotor or Static Torque: The locked-rotor torque of a motor is the minimum torque which it will develop at rest for all angular positions of the rotor with rated voltage applied at rated frequency.

Breakdown Torque: The breakdown torque of a motor is the maximum torque which the motor will develop, with rated voltage and frequency applied to the motor, without an abrupt drop in speed.

Pull-Out Torque — Synchronous Motor: The pull-out torque of a synchronous motor is the maximum sustained torque which the motor will develop at synchronous speed for one minute with rated voltage, frequency, and normal excitation applied.

Pull-In Torque — Synchronous Motor: The pull-in torque of a synchronous motor is the maximum constant torque under which the motor will pull its connected inertia load into synchronism, at rated voltage and frequency, when its field excitation is applied.

The speed to which a motor will bring its load depends on the power required to drive it and whether the motor can pull the load into step from this speed depends on the inertia of the revolving parts, so that the pull-in torque cannot be determined without having the WR² value as well as the torque of the load. (W = weight of all revolving parts in pounds; R = radius of gyration in feet.)

Full-Load Torque: The full-load torque of a motor is the torque necessary to produce its rated horsepower at full load speed.   In pounds at 1-foot radius it is equal to the horsepower times 5250 divided by the full-load speed.

Pull-Up Torque: The pull-up torque of an alternating current motor is the minimum external torque developed by the motor during the period of acceleration from rest to the speed at which breakdown torque occurs.   For motors which do not have a definite breakdown torque, the pull-up torque is the minimum torque developed up to rated speed.

Locked Rotor Current — A.C. Motor: The locked rotor current of a squirrel cage induction or other internally short-circuited motor is the current taken from the line with the rotor locked and with rated voltage and frequency applied to the motor.

Locked-Rotor Current — Motor and Starter: The locked rotor current of a motor and starter is the current taken from the line with the rotor locked, with the starting device in the starting position, and with rated voltage and frequency applied.

Table 5. Standard Frame Sizes for Two- and Three-Phase Squirrel-Cage Motors
(Adopted Standard of National Electrical Manufacturers Association)

Rating H.P.	General Purpose Motors — Open Type, 60 Cycles							
	Revolutions per Minute							
	3600	1800	1200	900	720	600	514	450
	Frame Number							
½	......	......	......	204	224	225	284	284
¾	......	......	203	224	225	254	284	324
1	......	203	204	225	254	254	284	326
1½	203	204	224	254	254	284	324	365
2	204	224	225	254	284	324	326	404
3	224	225	254	284	324	326	365	405
5	225	254	284	324	326	*364*	404	405
7½	254	284	324	326	*364*	*365*	405	444
10	284	324	326	*364*	*365*	404	444	445
15	324	326	*364*	*365*	404	405	445	*504U*
20	326	*364*	*365*	404	405	444	*504U*	505
25	*364S*	*364*	404	405	444	445	505	......
30	*364S*	*365*	405	444	445	*504U*	......	......
40	*365S*	404	444	445	*504U*	505	......	......
50	*404S*	*405S*	445	*504U*	505	......	......	......
60	*405S*	*444S*	*504U*	505	......	......	......	......
75	*444S*	*445S*	505	......	......	......	......	......
100	*445S*	*504S*	......	......	......	......	......	......
125	*504S*	*505S*	......	......	......	......	......	......
150	*505S*	......	......	......	......	......	......	......

Standard dimensions for frame numbers are given in Table 1. Frame numbers above the zigzag line have been standardized for 110, 208, 220, 440 and 550 volts. Those below for 208, 220, 440, 550 volts. Figures in italics indicate a former recommended standard that became an adopted standard in 1947.

Table 6. Standard Frame Sizes for Single-Phase Motors
(Adopted Standard of National Electrical Manufacturers Association)

Rating H.P.	General Purpose Motors Open Type, 60 Cycles, 115 and 230 V				Rating H.P.	Totally-enclosed, Fan-cooled Motors 60 Cycles, 115 and 230 V			
	Speed — R.P.M.					Speed — R.P.M.			
	3600	1800	1200	900		3600	1800	1200	900
	Frame Number*					Frame Number			
½	......	......	......	224	½	......	......	......	224
¾	......	......	203	225	¾	......	......	......	225
1	......	203	224	254	1	......	......	224	254
1½	203	204	225	254	1½	......	......	225	254
2	204	224	254	......	2	......	224	254	......
3	224	225	......	......	3	224	225	......	......
5	225	254	......	......	5	225	254	......	......
7½	254	......	......	......	7½	254	......	......	......

* Standard dimensions for these frame numbers are given in Table 1.

General Purpose Motors: (a) A general purpose motor (except synchronous motor) is any motor of 200 H.P. or less and speeds of 450 R.P.M. or more having a continuous rating and designed, listed or offered in standard ratings for use without restriction to a particular application.

(b) A general purpose synchronous motor is any motor rated 200 H.P. or less at 1.0 power factor or 150 H.P. or less at 0.8 power factor and speeds higher than 450 R.P.M. having a continuous time rating and designed, listed or offered in standard ratings for use without restriction to a particular application.

Service Factor — General-Purpose Motors: A service factor of a general-purpose motor is a multiplier which, applied to the normal horsepower rating, indicates a permissible loading which may be carried under the conditions specified.

Special Purpose Motor: An industrial power motor specifically designated and listed for a specific power application (where the load requirements and duty cycle are definitely known) is termed a " special purpose motor."

Small-power Motor: A small-power motor is a motor built in a frame smaller than that having a continuous rating of 1 H.P., open type, at 1700–1800 R.P.M.

Large-power Motor: A large-power motor is a motor built in a frame having a continuous rating of 1 H.P., open type, at 1700–1800 R.P.M., or in a larger frame.

Universal Motor: A universal motor is a series wound or a compensated series wound motor which may be operated either upon direct current or alternating single-phase current at approximately the same speed and output. These conditions must be met when the alternating and direct current voltages are about the same, and the alternating-current frequency is not greater than 60 cycles per second.

Constant Speed Motor: A constant speed motor is a motor in which the speed at normal operation is constant or practically constant; for example, a synchronous motor, an induction motor with small slip, or an ordinary direct-current shunt wound motor.

Varying Speed Motor: A motor in which the speed varies with the load, ordinarily decreasing as the load increases; for example, a series-wound or repulsion motor.

Adjustable Speed Motor: An adjustable speed motor is a motor in which the speed can be varied gradually over a considerable range, but when once adjusted, remains practically unaffected by the load; such as a direct-current shunt-wound motor with field resistance control, designed for a considerable range of speed adjustment.

Base Speed of an Adjustable-Speed Motor: The base speed of an adjustable speed motor is the lowest rated speed obtained at rated load and rated voltage at the temperature rise specified in the rating.

Open Machine: An open machine is one having ventilating openings which permit passage of external cooling air over and around the windings.

Totally-Enclosed Machine: A totally enclosed machine is one so enclosed as to prevent exchange of air between the inside and the outside of the case, but not sufficiently enclosed to be termed air-tight.

Adjustable Varying Speed Motor: An adjustable varying speed motor is a motor in which the speed can be adjusted gradually, but in which the speed, when once adjusted to a given load, will vary in considerable degree with change in the load; such as a compound wound D.C. motor adjusted by field control or a wound-rotor induction motor with rheostatic speed control.

Multi-speed Motor: A multi-speed motor is a motor which can be operated at any one of two or more definite speeds, each being practically independent of the load; for example, a direct-current motor with two armature windings, or an induction motor with windings capable of various pole groupings.

Dielectric Test: Dielectric tests consist of the application of a voltage higher than the rated voltage for a specified time and designed to determine the adequacy against breakdown of insulating materials and spacings under normal conditions.

Standard Speeds for Gearmotors.—The terms "gearmotor" and "motoreducer" are used to designate an electric motor and geared speed reducer (or speed-increasing drive in some cases) combined in a single compact unit. Gearmotors are made both in horizontal and vertical designs and in a wide range of sizes and speed ratios. They are obtainable in polyphase, single phase, and direct-current types.

Speeds: Standard speeds have been adopted by the National Electrical Manufacturers Association. Each speed in the series is an approximate multiple of 1.225. With 1750 R.P.M. as the starting point, the first reduction = 1750 ÷ 1.225 = 1430 (rounded number); the next speed = 1430 ÷ 1.225 = 1170, etc. The following series of output or driven shaft speeds, based upon the 1.225 factor, are from the General Electric Company and apply to gearmotors ranging from 1/8 to 75 H.P.: 780, 640, 520, 420, 350, 280, 230, 190, 155, 125, 100, 84, 68, 56, 45, 37, 30, 25, 20, 16.5, 13.5.

Effects of Voltage Variation Upon Performance of Induction Motors.—Electric motors of the induction type are at times operated on circuits of voltage or frequency other than those for which the motors are rated. Under such conditions, the performance of the motor will vary from the standard rating. Voltage variations of 10 per cent on power circuits are allowed in most commission rules. However, changing the voltage applied to an induction motor has the effect of changing its proper rating as to power factor and efficiency in proportion to the square of the applied voltage. Thus a 5 horsepower motor, operated at 10 per cent above the rated voltage, would have characteristics proper for a 6 horsepower motor (6.05 horsepower to be exact); and at 10 per cent below the rated voltage, those of a 4 horsepower motor.

Table 7. Standard Frame Sizes for Two- and Three-Phase Wound Rotor General-Purpose Motors

Rating H.P.	Open Type, 60 Cycles					Rating H.P.	Open Type, 25 Cycles, 550 V, or Less	
	1800 R.P.M.	1200 R.P.M.	900 R.P.M.	720 R.P.M.	600 R.P.M.		750 R.P.M.	500 R.P.M.
	Frame Number						Frame No.	
1	....	....	225	....	....	2	284	....
1½	....	....	254	....	....	3	324	....
2	224	225	254	324	....	5	326	....
3	225	254	284	326	365	7½	365	....
5	254	284	324	365	404	10	405	....
7½	284	324	326	404	405	15	444	....
10	324	326	365	405	444	20	445	505
15	326	365	404	444	445	25	504	....
20	364	404	405	445	504U	30	505	....
25	365	405	444	504U	505			
30	404	444	445	505	....			
40	405	*445	*504U	....	....			
50	444S	*504U	*505	....	....			
60	445S	*505	....	....	....			
75	504S	....	....	....	....			
100	505S	....	....	....	....			

* Frame numbers also apply for 2300 volt motors. Standard dimensions for frame numbers are given in Table 1. Frame numbers above zigzag line have been standardized for 110, 208, 220, 440 and 550 volts. Those below, for 208, 220, 440 and 550 volts.

Table 8. Standard Horsepower and Speed Ratings for Constant-Speed Direct-Current Motors

Recommended Practice of National Electrical Manufacturers Association

Rating H.P.	Minimum Speed Ratings — R.P.M.						
	3500	1750	1150	850	690	575	500
	Maximum speeds in R.P.M., obtained by field-weakening of shunt-wound motors when delivering full-rated horsepower						
½	....	....	....	1700	1380	1150	1000
¾	....	....	2300	1700	1380	1150	1000
1	....	2190	2300	1700	1380	1150	1000
1½	3500	2190	2300	1700	1380	1150	1000
2	3500	2190	2300	1700	1380	1150	1000
3	3500	2190	2300	1700	1380	1150	1000
5	3500	2190	2300	1700	1380	1150	1000
7½	3500	2190	1725	1700	1380	1150	1000
10	3500	2190	1725	1700	1380	1150	1000
15	3500	2190	1725	1700	1380	1150	1000
20	3500	2190	1725	1700	1380	1150	1000
25	3500	2190	1725	1700	1380	1150	1000
30	3500	1925	1725	1700	1380	1150	1000
40	3500	1925	1440	1275	1380	1150	1000
50	3500	1925	1440	1275	1035	1150	1000
60	....	1925	1440	1065	1035	865	1000
75	....	1925	1440	1065	1035	865	1000
100	....	1925	1440	1065	1035	865	750
125	....	1925	1325	1065	865	720	750
150	....	1925	1325	1065	865	720	750
200	....	1925	1325	1065	865	720	750

Rating H.P.	Minimum Speed Ratings — R.P.M.						
	450	400	350	300	250	200	150	100
	Maximum speeds in R.P.M., obtained by field-weakening of shunt-wound motors when delivering full-rated horsepower						
½	900	800	700	600	500	400	300	200
¾	900	800	700	600	500	400	300	200
1	900	800	700	600	500	400	300	200
1½	900	800	700	600	500	400	300	300
2	900	800	700	600	500	400	300	200
3	900	800	700	600	500	400	300	200
5	900	800	700	600	500	400	300	200
7½	900	800	700	600	500	400	300	200
10	900	800	700	600	500	400	300	200
15	900	800	700	600	500	400	300	200
20	900	800	700	600	500	400	300	200
25	900	800	700	600	500	400	300	200
30	900	800	700	600	500	400	300	200
40	900	800	700	600	500	400	300	200
50	900	800	700	600	500	400	300	...
60	900	800	700	600	500	400	300	...
75	900	800	700	600	500	400	...	...
100	900	800	700	600	500	...	...	...
125	900	800	700	600	...	...	...	...
150	675	800	700	...	...	...	...	...
200	675	...	...	...	...	...	...	...

NOTE: All motors are for either belted or direct-connected service except the following ratings, which are recommended for direct connection only:

1½ to 50 H.P., inclusive — 3500 R.P.M.
50 to 200 H.P., inclusive — 1750 R.P.M.
100 to 200 H.P., inclusive — 1150 R.P.M.
150 to 200 H.P., inclusive — 850 R.P.M.

Table 9. Standard Horsepower and Speed Ratings for Adjustable-Speed Direct-Current Motors, 3-to-1 and Higher Ratios

Recommended Practice of National Electrical Manufacturers Association

Continuous (Note 1)	1-Hour (Note 2)	1150	850	690	575	500	450	400
H.P. Ratings		Minimum Speed Ratings — R.P.M.						
		Maximum Speed Ratings — R.P.M.						
½	¾	....	3400	3450	3450	3000	2700	2400
¾	1	3450	3400	3450	3450	3000	2700	2400
1	1½	3450	3400	3450	2875	2500	2700	2400
1½	2	3450	2550	2760	2875	2500	2250	2400
2	3	3450	2550	2760	2875	2500	2250	2400
3	5	....	2550	2300	2300	2500	2250	2400
5	7½	....	....	2300	2300	2000	2250	2000
7½	10	....	....	2300	2300	2000	1800	2000
10	15	....	....	....	2300	2000	1800	2000
15	20	....	....	....	1800	1800	1800	1600
20	25	....	....	....	1800	1800	1800	1600
25	30	....	....	....	1800	1500	1500	1600
30	40	....	....	....	1800	1500	1500	1600
40	50	....	....	....	....	1500	1500	1600
50	60	....	....	....	....	1500	1500	1200
60	75	....	....	....	....	1500	1350	1200
75	100	....	....	....	....	....	....	1200
100	125	....	....	....	....	....	....	1200
125	150	....	....	....	....	....	....	1200
150	200	....	....	....	....	....	....	1200

Continuous (Note 1)	1-Hour (Note 2)	350	300	250	200	150	100
H.P. Ratings		Minimum Speed Ratings — R.P.M.					
		Maximum Speed Ratings — R.P.M.					
½	¾	2100	1800	1500	1200	900	600
¾	1	2100	1800	1500	1200	900	600
1	1½	2100	1800	1500	1200	900	600
1½	2	2100	1800	1500	1200	900	600
2	3	2100	1800	1500	1200	900	600
3	5	2100	1800	1500	1200	900	600
5	7½	2100	1800	1500	1200	900	600
7½	10	2100	1800	1500	1200	900	600
10	15	1750	1800	1500	1200	900	600
15	20	1750	1500	1500	1200	900	600
20	25	1750	1500	1500	1200	900	600
25	30	1500	1500	1200	1200	900	600
30	40	1500	1500	1200	1200	900	600
40	50	1500	1200	1200	1200	900	600
50	60	1200	1200	1200	1200	900	...
60	75	1200	1200	1200	1200	900	...
75	100	1200	1200	1200	1200	...	...
100	125	1200	1200	1200	....	...	...
125	150	1200	1200	....	....	...	...
150	200	1200	....	....	....	...	...

NOTE 1: The horsepower figures given in this column are for continuous rating with a temperature rise of 40 deg. C. at one and one-half times minimum speed.

NOTE 2: The horsepower figures given in this column are for one-hour rating with temperature rise of 50 deg. C. throughout the entire speed range.

The figures in both columns one and two, taken together, give the limits between which the continuous horsepower rating will vary in a straight line with speed from one and one-half times minimum to three times minimum speed with a temperature rise of 40 deg. C. No further increase in horsepower is recognized above three times minimum speed.

These motors may be equipped with semi-enclosing covers without change in horsepower rating, but the continuous temperature rating will be 50 deg. C. rise over entire speed range.

Table 10. Horsepower and Speed Ratings for Alternating-Current Motors

Alternating-current motors of less than one horsepower. Recommended practice of National Electrical Manufacturers Association

Brake H.P. Rating	60 Cycle		25 Cycle		Brake H.P. Rating *	60 Cycle		25 Cycle	
	Synchronous R.P.M.	Appr. Full Load R.P.M.	Synchronous R.P.M	Appr. Full Load R.P.M		Synchronous R.P.M.	Appr. Full Load R.P.M.	Synchronous R.P.M.	Appr. Full Load R.P.M.
1....	3600	3450	....	....	1/3	3600	3450		
3/4..	3600	3450	1500	1425	1/4			1500	1425
	1800	1725			1/6	1800	1725		
1/2..	3600	3450			1/8				
	1800	1725	1500	1425	1/12	1200	1140		
	1200	1140			1/20	900	860		

* Motors with H.P. ratings from 1/8 down to 1/20 all have the same speed ratings.

Table 11. Horsepower and Speed Ratings for Polyphase Induction Motors
(Adopted Standard of National Electrical Manufacturers Association)

Standard horsepower and speed ratings for protected and semi-protected continuous duty constant speed motors.

Rating H.P.	Revolutions per Minute										
	60 Cycles								25 Cycles		
1/2	.....	....	....	900	720	600	514	450	.....	750	500
3/4	.....	....	1200	900	720	600	514	450	.....	750	500
1	.....	1800	1200	900	720	600	514	450	.....	750	500
1½	*3600	1800	1200	900	720	600	514	450	*1500	750	500
2	*3600	1800	1200	900	720	600	514	450	*1500	750	500
3	*3600	1800	1200	900	720	600	514	450	*1500	750	500
5	*3600	1800	1200	900	720	600	514	450	*1500	750	500
7½	*3600	1800	1200	900	720	600	514	450	*1500	750	500
10	*3600	1800	1200	900	720	600	514	450	*1500	750	500
15	*3600	1800	1200	900	720	600	514	450	*1500	750	500
20	*3600	1800	1200	900	720	600	514	450	*1500	750	500
25	.....	1800	1200	900	720	600	514	450	*1500	750	500
30	.....	1800	1200	900	720	600	514	450	*1500	750	500
40	.....	1800	1200	900	720	600	514	450	*1500	750	500
50	.....	....	1200	900	720	600	514	450	.....	750	500
60	.....	....	1200	900	720	600	514	450	.....	750	500
75	.....	....	1200	900	720	600	514	450	.....	750	500
100	.....	....	....	900	720	600	514	450	.....	750	500
125	.....	....	....	900	720	600	514	450	.....	750	500
150	.....	....	....	...	720	600	514	450	.....	750	500
200	.....	....	....	...	720	600	514	...	.....	...	500

* The 3600 and 1500 R.P.M. ratings apply to squirrel-cage motors only.

Table 12. Standard Horsepower and Speed Ratings for Single-Phase Motors
(National Electrical Manufacturers Association)

Standard horsepower and speed ratings for open, protected and semi-protected continuous-duty constant-speed motors.

60 Cycles					50 Cycles					25 Cycles		
H.P.	R.P.M.*				H.P.	R.P.M.*				H.P.	R.P.M.*	
½	....	....	....	900	½	....	....	1000	750		....	...
¾	....	....	1200	900	¾	....	1500	1000	750		....	...
1	....	1800	1200	900	1	3000	1500	1000	750	1	1500	...
1½	3600	1800	1200	900	1½	3000	1500	1000	750	1½	1500	...
2	3600	1800	1200	900	2	3000	1500	1000	750	2	1500	750
3	3600	1800	1200	900	3	3000	1500	1000	750	3	1500	750
5	3600	1800	1200	900	5	3000	1500	1000	750	5	1500	750
7½	3600	1800	1200	900	7½	3000	1500	1000	750	7½	1500	750
10	3600	1800	1200	900	10	3000	1500	1000	750	10	1500	750
15	3600	1800	1200	900	15	3000	1500	1000	750	15	1500	750
20	3600	1800	1200	900	20	3000	1500	1000	750	20	1500	750
25	3600	1800	1200	900								

* The speeds listed are synchronous speeds.

The single-phase classification includes (1) split-phase; (2) resistance-start; (3) reactor-start; (4) capacitor-start; (5) capacitor; (6) series; (7) repulsion; (8) compensated-repulsion; (9) repulsion-start induction; and (10) repulsion-induction.

The standard voltages for single-phase motors are 115 and 230 volts.

Table 13. Standard Horsepower and Speed Ratings for Synchronous Motors
Horsepower and speed ratings for open type synchronous motors with continuous time rating. (National Electrical Manufacturers Association)

	General Purpose Synchronous Motors												
	60 Cycles						50 Cycles					25 Cycles	
	Number of Poles												
H.P.	4	6	8	10	12	14	4	6	8	10	12	4	6
	Speed—R.P.M.												
20	1800	1200	...	...	...	...	1500	...	...	...	...	...	...
25	1800	1200	...	...	...	...	1500	1000	...	...	...	...	...
30	1800	1200	900	...	...	...	1500	1000	...	...	...	...	...
40	1800	1200	900	720	...	...	1500	1000	750	...	...	750	...
50	1800	1200	900	720	600	...	1500	1000	750	600	...	750	...
60	1800	1200	900	720	600	...	1500	1000	750	600	...	750	...
75	1800	1200	900	720	600	...	1500	1000	750	600	...	750	...
100	1800	1200	900	720	600	514	1500	1000	750	600	500	750	500
125	1800	1200	900	720	600	514	1500	1000	750	600	500	750	500
150	1800	1200	900	720	600	514	1500	1000	750	600	500	750	500
200	1800	1200	900	720	600	514	1500	1000	750	600	500	750	500

TYPES AND CHARACTERISTICS
OF ELECTRIC MOTORS

Types of Direct-Current Motors. — Direct-current motors may be grouped into three general classes: series-wound, shunt-wound and compound-wound. In the *series-wound motor* the field windings, which are fixed in the stator frame, and the armature windings, which are placed around the rotor, are connected in series so that all current passing through the armature also passes through the field. In the *shunt-wound motor*, both armature and field are connected across the main power supply so that the armature and field currents are separate. In the *compound-wound motor*, both series and shunt field windings are provided and these may be connected so that the currents in both are flowing in the same direction, called *cumulative compounding*, or so that the currents in each are flowing in opposite directions, called *differential compounding*.

Characteristics of Series-wound Direct-Current Motors. — In the series-wound motor, any increase in load results in more current passing through the armature and the field windings. As the field is strengthened by this increased current, the motor speed decreases. Conversely, as the load is decreased the field is weakened and the speed increases and at very light loads may become excessive. For this reason, series-wound direct-current motors are usually directly connected or geared to the load to prevent " runaway." (A series-wound motor designated as series-shunt wound, is sometimes provided with a light shunt field winding to prevent dangerously high speeds at light loads.) The increase in armature current with increasing load produces increased torque, so that the series-wound motor is particularly suited to heavy starting duty and where severe overloads may be expected. Its speed may be adjusted by means of a variable resistance placed in series with the motor, but due to variation with load, the speed cannot be held at any constant value. This variation of speed with load becomes greater as the speed is reduced. Series-wound motors are used where the load is practically constant and can easily be controlled by hand. They are usually limited to traction and lifting service.

Shunt-wound Direct-Current Motors. — In the shunt-wound motor, the strength of the field is not affected appreciably by change in the load, so that a fairly constant speed (about 10 to 12 per cent drop from no load to full load speed) is obtainable. This type of motor may be used for the operation of machines requiring an approximately constant speed and imposing low starting torque and light overload on the motor.

The shunt-wound motor becomes an adjustable-speed motor by means of field control or by armature control. If a variable resistance is placed in the field circuit, the amount of current in the field windings and hence the speed of rotation can be controlled. As the speed increases, the torque decreases proportionately, resulting in nearly constant horsepower. A speed range of 6 to 1 is possible using field control, but 4 to 1 is more common. Speed regulation is somewhat greater than in the constant-speed shunt-wound motors, ranging from about 15 to 22 per cent. If a variable resistance is placed in the armature circuit, the voltage applied to the armature can be reduced and hence the speed of rotation can be reduced over a range of about 2 to 1. With armature control, speed regulation becomes poorer as speed is decreased, and is about 100 per cent for a 2 to 1 speed range. Since the current through the field remains unchanged, the torque remains constant.

Machine Tool Applications: The adjustable-speed shunt-wound motors are useful on larger machines of the boring mill, lathe and planer type and are particularly adapted to spindle drives because constant horsepower characteristics permit heavy cuts at low speed and light or finishing cuts at high speed. They have long been used for planer drives because they can provide an adjustable low speed for the cutting stroke and a high speed for the return stroke. Their application has been limited, however, to plants in which direct-current power is available.

Adjustable-voltage Shunt-wound Motor Drive. — More extensive use of the shunt-wound motor has been made possible by a combination drive that includes a means of converting alternating-current to direct-current. This conversion may be effected by a self-contained unit consisting of a separately excited direct-current generator driven by a constant speed alternating-current motor connected to the regular alternating-current line, or by an electronic rectifier with suitable controls connected to the regular alternating-current supply lines. The latter has the advantage of causing no vibration when mounted directly on the machine tool, an important factor in certain types of grinders.

In this type of adjustable-speed, shunt-wound motor drive, speed control is effected by varying the voltage applied to the armature while supplying constant voltage to the field. In addition to providing for the adjustment of the voltage supplied by the conversion unit to the armature of the shunt-wound motor, the amount of current passing through the motor field may also be controlled. In fact, a single control may be provided to vary the motor speed from minimum to base speed (speed of the motor at full load with rated voltage on armature and field) by varying the voltage applied to the armature and from base speed to maximum speed by varying the current flowing through the field. When so controlled, the motor operates at constant torque up to base speed and at constant horsepower above base speed.

Speed Range: Speed ranges of at least 20 to 1 below base speed and 4 or 5 to 1 above base speed (a total range of 100 to 1, or more) are obtainable as compared with about 2 to 1 below normal speed and 3 or 4 to 1 above normal speed for the conventional type of control. Speed regulation may be as great as 25 per cent at high speeds. Special electronic controls, when used with this type shunt motor drive, make possible maintenance of motor speeds with as little variation as ½ to 1 per cent of full load speed from full load to no load over a line voltage variation of ±10 per cent and over any normal variation in motor temperature and ambient temperature.

Applications: These direct-current, adjustable-voltage drives, as they are sometimes called, have been applied successfully to such machine tools as planers, milling machines, boring mills and lathes, as well as to other industrial machines where wide, stepless speed control, uniform speed under all operating conditions, constant torque acceleration and adaptability to automatic operation are required.

Compound-wound Motors. — In the compound-wound motor, the speed variation due to load changes is much less than in the series-wound motor, but greater than in the shunt-wound motor (ranging up to 25 per cent from full load to no load). It has a greater starting torque than the shunt-wound motor, is able to withstand heavier overloads, but has a narrower adjustable speed range. Standard motors of this type have a cumulative-compound winding, the differential-compound winding being limited to special applications. They are used where the starting load is very heavy or where the load changes suddenly and violently as with reciprocating pumps, printing presses and punch presses.

Types of Polyphase Alternating-Current Motors. — The most widely used polyphase motors are of the induction type. The "*squirrel cage*" *induction motor* consists of a wound stator which is connected to an external source of alternating-current power and a laminated steel core rotor with a number of heavy aluminum or copper conductors set into the core around its periphery and parallel to its axis. These conductors are connected together at each end of the rotor by a heavy ring which provides closed paths for the currents induced in the rotor to circulate. This forms, in effect, a " squirrel-cage " from which the motor takes its name.

Wound-rotor type of *Induction motor:* This type has in addition to a squirrel cage, a series of coils set into the rotor which are connected through slip-rings to external variable resistors. By varying the resistance of the wound-rotor circuits, the amount of current flowing in these circuits and hence the speed of the motor can be controlled. Since the rotor of an induction motor is not connected to the power supply, the motor is said to operate by transfer action and is analogous to a transformer with a short-circuited secondary that is free to rotate. Induction motors are built with a wide range of speed and torque characteristics which are discussed under " Operating Characteristics of Polyphase Induction Motors."

Synchronous Motor: The other type of polyphase alternating-current motor used industrially is the *synchronous motor.* In contrast to the induction motor, the rotor of the synchronous motor is connected to a direct-current supply which provides a field that rotates in step with the alternating-current field in the stator. After having been brought up to synchronous speed, which is governed by the frequency of the power supply and the number of poles in the rotor, the synchronous motor operates at this constant speed throughout its entire load range.

Operating Characteristics of Squirrel-cage Induction Motors. — In general, squirrel-cage induction motors are simple in design and construction and offer rugged service. They are essentially constant-speed motors, their speed changing very little with load and not being subject to adjustment. They are used for a wide range of industrial applications calling for integral horsepower ratings. According to the NEMA (National Electrical Manufacturers Association) Standards, there are five classes of squirrel-cage induction motors designated respectively as *A*, *B*, *C*, *D*, and *F*.

Design A motors are not commonly used since Design *B* has similar characteristics with the advantage of lower starting current.

Design B motors may be designated as a general purpose type suitable for the majority of polyphase alternating-current applications such as blowers, compressors, drill presses, grinders, hammer mills, lathes, planers, polishers, saws, screw machines, shakers, stokers, etc. The starting torque at 1800 R.P.M. is 250 to 275 per cent of full load torque for 3 H.P. and below; for 5 H.P. to 75 H.P. ratings the starting torque ranges from 185 to 150 per cent of full load torque. They have low starting current requirements, usually no more than 5 to 6 times full load current and can be started at full voltage. Their slip (difference between synchronous speed and actual speed at rated load) is relatively low.

Design C motors have high starting torque (up to 250 per cent of full load torque) but low starting current. They can be started at full voltage. Slip at rated load is relatively low. They are used for compressors requiring a loaded start, heavy conveyors, reciprocating pumps and other applications requiring high starting torque.

Design D motors have high slip at rated load, that is the motor speed drops off appreciably as the load increases, permitting use of the stored energy of a flywheel. They provide heavy starting torque, up to 275 per cent of full load torque, are quiet in operation and have relatively low starting current. Applications are for impact, shock and other high peak loads or flywheel drives such as trains, elevators, hoists, punch and drawing presses, shears, etc.

Design F motors provide low starting torque, about 125 per cent of full load torque, and low starting current. They are used to drive machines which start infrequently either at no load or very light load.

Multiple Speed Induction Motors. — This type has a number of windings in the stator so arranged and connected that the number of effective poles and hence the speed can be changed. These motors are for the same types of starting conditions as the conventional squirrel cage induction motors and are available in designs which provide constant horsepower at all rated speeds and in designs which provide constant torque at all rated speeds. Typical speed combinations obtainable in these motors are 600, 900, 1200 and 1800 R.P.M.; 450, 600, 900 and 1200 R.P.M.; and 600, 720, 900 and 1200 R.P.M. Where a gradual change in speed is called for, a wound rotor may be provided in addition to the multiple stator windings.

Wound Rotor Induction Motors. — These motors are designed for applications where extremely low starting current with high starting torque are called for, such as in blowers, conveyors, compressors, fans and pumps. They may be employed for adjustable-varying speed service where the speed range does not extend below 50 per cent of synchronous speed, as for steel plate-forming rolls, printing presses, cranes, blowers, stokers, lathes and milling machines of certain types. The speed regulation of a wound rotor induction motor ranges from 5 to 10 per cent at maximum speed and from 18 to 30 per cent at low speed. They are also employed for reversing service as in cranes, gates, hoists and elevators.

High Frequency Induction Motors. — This type is used in conjunction with frequency changers when very high speeds are desired, as on grinders, drills, routers, portable tools or woodworking machinery. These motors have an advantage over the series-wound or universal type of high speed motor in that they operate at a relatively constant speed over the entire load range. A motor-generator set, a two-unit frequency converter or a single unit inductor frequency converter may be used to supply three-phase power at the frequency required. The single unit frequency converter may be obtained for delivering any one of a number of frequencies ranging from 360 to 2160 cycles and it is self-driven and self-excited from the general polyphase power supply.

Synchronous Motors. — These are widely used in electric timing devices; to drive machines that must operate in synchronism; and also to operate compressors, rolling mills, crushers which are started without load, paper mill screens, shredders, vacuum pumps and motor-generator sets. They have an inherently high power factor and are often employed to make corrections for the low power factor of other types of motors on the same system.

Types of Single Phase Alternating Current Motors. — Most of the single-phase alternating-current motors are basically induction motors distinguished by different arrangements for starting. (A single-phase induction motor with only a squirrel cage rotor has no starting torque.) In the *capacitor-start* single-phase motor, an auxiliary winding in the stator is connected in series with a capacitor and a centrifugal switch. During the starting and accelerating period the motor operates as a two-phase induction motor. At about two-thirds full-load speed, the auxiliary circuit is disconnected by the switch and the motor then runs as a single phase induction motor. In the *capacitor-start, capacitor-run* motor, the auxiliary circuit is arranged to provide high effective capacity for high starting torque and to remain connected to the line but with reduced capacity during the running period. In the *single-value capacitor* or *capacitor split-phase* motor, a relatively small continuously-rated capacitor is permanently included in one of the two stator windings and the motor both starts and runs like a two-phase motor.

In the *repulsion-start* single-phase motor, a drum-wound rotor circuit is connected to a commutator with a pair of short-circuited brushes set so that the magnetic axis of the rotor winding is inclined to the magnetic axis of the stator winding.

The current flowing in this rotor circuit reacts with the field to produce a starting and accelerating torque. At about two-thirds full load speed the brushes are lifted, the commutator is short circuited and the motor runs as a single-phase squirrel-cage motor. The *repulsion* motor employs a repulsion winding on the rotor for both starting and running. The *repulsion-induction* motor has an outer winding on the rotor acting as a repulsion winding and an inner squirrel cage winding. As the motor comes up to speed, the induced rotor current partially shifts from the repulsion winding to the squirrel cage winding and the motor runs partly as an induction motor.

In the *split-phase* motor, an auxiliary winding in the stator is used for starting with either a resistance connected in series with the auxiliary winding (*resistance-start*) or a reactor in series with the main winding (*reactor-start*).

The *series wound* single-phase motor has a rotor winding in series with the stator winding as in the series-wound direct-current motor. Since this motor may also be operated on direct-current, it is called a *universal* motor.

Characteristics of Single-Phase Alternating Current Motors. — Single-phase motors are used in sizes up to about 7½ horsepower for heavy starting duty chiefly in home and commercial appliances for which polyphase power is not available. The *capacitor-start* motor is available in normal starting torque designs for such applications as centrifugal pumps, fans, and blowers and in high-starting torque designs for reciprocating compressors, pumps, loaded conveyors, or belts. The *capacitor-start, capacitor-run* motor is exceptionally quiet in operation when loaded to at least 50 per cent of capacity. It is available in low-torque designs for fans and centrifugal pumps and in high-torque designs for applications similar to those of the capacitor-start motor.

The *capacitor split-phase* motor requires the least maintenance of all single-phase motors but has very low starting torque. Its high maximum torque makes it potentially useful in floor sanders or in grinders where momentary overloads due to excessive cutting pressure are experienced. It is also used for slow-speed direct connected fans.

The *repulsion-start, induction-run* motor has higher starting torque than the capacitor motors, although for the same current, the capacitor motors have equivalent pull-up and maximum torque. Electrical and mechanical noise and the extra maintenance sometimes required are disadvantages. These motors are used for compressors, conveyors and stokers starting under full load. The *repulsion-induction* motor has relatively high starting torque and low starting current. It also has a smooth speed-torque curve with no break and a greater ability to withstand long accelerating periods than capacitor type motors. It is particularly suitable for severe starting and accelerating duty and for high inertia loads such as laundry extractors. Brush noise is, however, continuous.

The *repulsion* motor has no limiting synchronous speed and the speed changes with the load. At certain loads, slight changes in load cause wide changes in speed. A brush shifting arrangement may be provided to adjust the speed which may have a range of 4 to 1 if full rated constant torque is applied but a decreasing range as the torque falls below this value. This type of motor may be reversed by shifting the brushes beyond the neutral point. These motors are suitable for machines requiring constant-torque and adjustable speed.

The *split-phase* and *universal* motors are limited to about ⅓ H.P. ratings and are used chiefly for small appliance and office machine applications.

Motors with Built-in Speed Reducers. — Electric motors having built-in speed-changing units are compact and the design of these motorized speed reducers tends to improve the appearance of the machines which they drive. There are several types of these speed reducers; they may be classified according to whether they are equipped with a worm-gear drive, a regular gear train with parallel shafts, or planetary gearing.

The claims made for the worm-gear type of reduction unit are that the drive is quiet in operation and well adapted for cases where the slow-speed shaft must be at right angles to the motor shaft and where a high speed ratio is essential.

For very low speeds, the double reduction worm-gear units are suitable. In these units two sets of worm-gearing form the gear train, and both the slow-speed shaft and the armature shaft are parallel. The intermediate worm-gear shaft can be built to extend from the housing, if required, so as to make two countershaft speeds available on the same unit.

In the parallel-shaft type of speed reducer, the slow-speed shaft is parallel with the armature shaft. The slow-speed shaft is rotated by a pinion on the armature shaft, this pinion meshing with a larger gear on the slow-speed shaft.

Geared motors having built-in speed-changing units are available with constant-mesh change-gears for varying the speed ratio.

Planetary gearing permits a large speed reduction with few parts; hence, it is well adapted for geared-head motor units where economy and compactness are essential. The slow-speed shaft is in line with the armature shaft.

Factors Governing Motor Selection

Speed, Horsepower, Torque and Inertia Requirements. — Where more than one speed or a range of speeds are called for, one of the following types of motors may be selected, depending upon other requirements: For direct-current, the standard shunt-wound motor with field control has a 2 to 1 range in some cases; the adjustable speed motor may have a range of from 3 to 1 up to 6 to 1; the shunt motor with adjustable voltage supply has a range up to 20 to 1 or more below base speed and 4 or 5 to 1 above base speed, making a total range of up to 100 to 1 or more. For polyphase alternating current, multi-speed squirrel cage induction motors have 2, 3 or 4 fixed speeds; the wound-rotor motor has a 2 to 1 range. The two-speed wound rotor motor has a 4 to 1 range. The brush-shifting shunt motor has a 4 to 1 range. The brush-shifting series motor has a 3 to 1 range; and the squirrel-cage motor with a variable frequency supply has a very wide range. For single phase alternating current, the brush-shifting repulsion motor has a 2½ to 1 range; the capacitor motor with tapped winding has a 2 to 1 range and the multi-speed capacitor motor has 2 or 3 fixed speeds. Speed regulation (variation in speed from no load to full load) is greatest with motors having series field windings and entirely absent with synchronous motors.

Horsepower: Where the load to be carried by the motor is not constant but follows a definite cycle, a horsepower-time curve enables the peak horsepower to be determined as well as the root-mean-square average horsepower, which indicates the proper motor rating from a heating standpoint. Where the load is maintained at a constant value for a period of from 15 minutes to 2 hours depending on the size, the horsepower rating required will usually not be less than this constant value. When selecting the size of an induction motor, it should be kept in mind that this type of motor operates at maximum efficiency when it is loaded to full capacity. Where operation is to be at several speeds, the horsepower requirement for each should be determined.

Torque: Starting torque requirements may vary from 10 per cent of full load to 250 per cent of full load torque depending upon the type of machine being driven. Starting torque may vary for a given machine because of frequency of start, temperature, type and amount of lubricant, etc. and such variables should be taken into account. The motor torque supplied to the machine must be well above that required by the driven machine at all points up to full speed. The greater the excess torque, the more rapid the acceleration. The approximate time required for acceleration from rest to full speed is given by the formula:

$$\text{Time} = \frac{N \times WR^2}{T_a \times 308} \text{ seconds}$$

where N = Full load speed in R.P.M.

T_a = Torque = average foot-pounds available for acceleration.

WR^2 = Inertia of rotating part in pounds feet squared (W = weight and R = radius of gyration of rotating part).

308 = Combined constant converting minutes into seconds, weight into mass and radius into circumference.

If the time required for acceleration is greater than 20 seconds, special motors or starters may be required to avoid overheating.

The running torque T_r is found by the formula:

$$T_r = \frac{5250 \times \text{H.P.}}{N} \text{ foot pounds}$$

where H.P. = Horsepower being supplied to the driven machine

N = Running speed in R.P.M.

5250 = Combined constant converting horsepower to foot-pounds per minute and work per revolution into torque.

The peak horsepower determines the maximum torque required by the driven machine and the motor must have a maximum running torque in excess of this. *Inertia:* The inertia or flywheel effect of the rotating parts of a driven machine will, if large, appreciably affect the accelerating time and hence, the amount of heating in the motor. If synchronous motors are used, the inertia (WR^2) of both the motor rotor and the rotating parts of the machine must be known since the pull-in torque (torque required to bring the driven machine up to synchronous speed) varies approximately as the square root of the total inertia of motor and load.

Space Limitations in Motor Selection. — If the motor is to become an integral part of the machine which it drives and space is at a premium, a partial motor may be called for. A complete motor is one made up of a stator, a rotor, a shaft, and two end shields with bearings. A *partial motor* is without one or more of these elements. One common type is furnished without drive-end end shield and bearing and is directly connected to the end or side of the machine which it drives, such as the headstock of a lathe. A so-called *shaftless type of motor* is supplied without shaft, end shields or bearings and is intended for built-in application in such units as multiple drilling machines, precision grinders, deep well pumps, compressors and hoists where the rotor is actually made a part of the driven machine. Where partial motors are used, however, proper ventilation, mounting, alignment and bearings must be arranged for by the designer of the machine to which it is applied.

Sometimes it is possible to use a motor having a smaller frame size and wound with Class B insulation, permitting it to be subjected to a higher temperature rise than the larger frame Class A insulated motor having the same horsepower rating.

Temperatures. — The applicability of a given motor is limited not only by its load starting and carrying ability, but also by the temperature which it reaches under load. Motors are given temperature ratings which are based upon the type of insulation (Class A or Class B are the most common) used in their construction and their type of frame (open, semi-enclosed or enclosed).

Insulating Materials: Class A materials are: (1) Cotton, silk, paper and similar organic materials when either impregnated or immersed in a liquid dielectric; (2) molded and laminated materials with cellulose filler, phenolic resins and other resins of similar properties; (3) films and sheets of cellulose acetate and other cellulose derivatives of similar properties; (4) varnishes (enamel) as applied to conductors.

Class B insulating materials are: Mica, asbestos, fiber glass and similar inorganic materials in built-up form with organic binding substances. A small proportion of Class A materials may be used for structural purposes only.

Ambient Temperature and Allowable Temperature Rise: Normal ambient temperature is taken to be 40° C. (104° F.). For open general-purpose motors with Class A insulation, the normal temperature rise on which the performance guarantees are based is 40° C. (72° F.).

Motors with Class A insulation having protected, semi-protected, drip-proof, splash-proof, or drip-proof protected enclosures have a 50° C. (90° F.) rise rating.

Motors with Class A insulation and having totally enclosed, totally enclosed fan-cooled, explosion-proof, water-proof, dust-tight, submersible or dust-explosion-proof enclosures have a 55° C. (99° F.) rise rating.

Motors with Class B insulation are permissible for total temperatures up to 110 degrees C. (230° F.) for open motors and 115° C. (239° F.) for enclosed motors.

Motors Exposed to Injurious Conditions. — Where motors are to be used in locations imposing unusual operating conditions, the manufacturer should be consulted, especially where any of the following conditions apply: (1) exposed to chemical fumes; (2) operated in damp places; (3) operated at speeds in excess of specified overspeed; (4) exposed to combustible or explosive dust; (5) exposed to gritty or conducting dust; (6) exposed to lint; (7) exposed to steam; (8) operated in poorly ventilated rooms; (9) operated in pits, or where entirely enclosed in boxes; (10) exposed to inflammable or explosive gases; (11) exposed to temperatures below 10° C. (50° F.); (12) exposed to oil vapor; (13) exposed to salt air; (14) exposed to abnormal shock or vibration from external sources; (15) where the departure from rated voltage is excessive; (16) where the alternating-current supply voltage is unbalanced.

Improved insulating materials and processes and greater mechanical protection against falling materials and liquids make it possible to use general-purpose motors in many locations where special purpose motors were previously considered necessary. *Splash-proof motors* having well protected ventilated openings and specially treated windings are used where they are to be subjected to falling and splashing water or are to be washed down as with a hose. Where climatic conditions are not severe, this type of motor is also successfully used in unprotected out-of-door installations.

If the surrounding atmosphere carries abnormal quantities of metallic, abrasive or non-explosive dust or acid or alkali fumes, a *totally enclosed fan-cooled motor* may be called for. In this type, the motor proper is completely enclosed but air is blown through an outer shell which completely or partially surrounds the inner case. Where the dust in the atmosphere is of a kind which tends to pack or solidify and close the air passages of open splash-proof or totally enclosed fan-cooled motors, *totally enclosed (non-ventilated) motors* are used. This type, which is limited to low horsepower ratings, is also used for outdoor service in mild or severe climates.

In addition to these special-purpose motors there are two types *of explosion-proof motors* designed for hazardous locations. One type is for operation in hazardous dust locations (Class II, Group *G* of the National Electrical Code) while the other is for atmospheres containing explosive vapors and fumes classified as Class I, Group *D* (gasoline, naptha, alcohols, acetone, lacquer-solvent vapors, natural gas).

Table 1. Characteristics and Applications of D.C. Motors, 1-300 H.P.

Type	Starting Duty	Maximum Momentary Running Torque	Speed Regulation	Speed Control†	Applications
Shunt-wound, constant-speed	Medium starting torque. Varies with voltage supplied to armature, and is limited by starting resistor to 125 to 200 per cent full-load torque	125 to 200 per cent. Limited by commutation	8 to 12 per cent	Basic speed to 200 per cent basic speed by field control	Drives where starting requirements are not severe. Use constant-speed or adjustable-speed, depending on speed required. Centrifugal pumps, fans, blowers, conveyors, elevators, wood- and metal-working machines
Shunt-wound, adjustable-speed			10 to 20 per cent, increases with weak fields	Basic speed to 60 per cent basic speed (lower for some ratings) by field control	
Shunt-wound, adjustable voltage control			Up to 25 per cent. Less than 5 per cent obtainable with special rotating regulator	Basic speed to 2 per cent basic speed and basic speed to 200 per cent basic speed	Drives where wide, stepless speed control, and uniform speed, constant-torque acceleration and adaptability to automatic operation are required. Planers, milling machines, boring machines, lathes, etc.
Compound-wound, constant-speed	Heavy starting torque. Limited by starting resistor to 130 to 260 per cent of full-load torque	130 to 260 per cent. Limited by commutation	Standard compounding 25 per cent. Depends on amount of series winding	Basic speed to 125 per cent basic speed by field control	Drives requiring high starting torque and fairly constant speed. Pulsating loads. Shears, bending rolls, pumps, conveyors, crushers, etc.
Series-wound, varying-speed	Very heavy starting torque. Limited to 300 per cent to 350 per cent full-load torque	300 to 350 per cent. Limited by commutation	Very high. Infinite no-load speed	From zero to maximum speed, depending on control and load	Drives where very high starting torque is required and speed can be regulated. Cranes, hoists, gates, bridges, car dumpers, etc.

† Minimum speed below basic speed by armature control limited by heating.

Table 2.   Characteristics and Applications of Polyphase A.C. Motors

Polyphase Type	Ratings Hp	Speed Regulation	Speed Control	Starting Torque	Breakdown Torque	Applications
General-purpose squirrel cage, normal stg current, normal stg torque, Design B	0.5 to 200 hp	Less than 5%	None, except multi-speed types, designed for 2 to 4 fixed speeds	100 to 250% of full-load	200 to 300% of full-load	Constant-speed service where starting torque is not excessive. Fans, blowers, rotary compressors, centrifugal pumps, wood-working machines, machine tools, line shafts
Full-voltage starting, high stg torque, normal stg current, squirrel-cage, Design C	3 to 150 hp	Less than 5%	None, except multi-speed types, designed for 2 to 4 fixed speeds	200 to 250% of full-load	190 to 225% of full-load	Constant-speed service where fairly high starting torque is required at infrequent intervals with starting current of about 500% full load. Reciprocating pumps and compressors, conveyors, crushers, pulverizers, agitators, etc.
Full-voltage starting, high stg torque, high-slip squirrel-cage, Design D	0.5 to 150 hp	Drops about 7 to 12% from no load to full load	None, except multi-speed types, designed for 2 to 4 fixed speeds	275% of full load, depending upon speed and resistance	275%. This motor will usually not stall until loaded to its maximum torque, which occurs at standstill	Constant-speed service and high starting torque if starting not too frequent, and for taking high-peak loads with or without flywheels. Punch presses, die stamping, shears, bulldozers, bailers, hoists, cranes, elevators, etc.
Wound-rotor, external-resistance starting	0.5 to several thousand	With rotor rings short-circuited drops about 3% for large to 5% for small sizes	Speed can be reduced to 50% of normal by rotor resistance. Speed varies inversely as resistance and how distributed the load	Up to 300% depending upon external resistance in rotor circuit	200% when rotor slip rings are short circuited	Where high-starting torque with low-starting current or where limited speed control is required. Fans, centrifugal and plunger pumps, compressors, conveyors, hoists, cranes, ball mills, gate hoists, etc.
Synchronous	25 to several thousand	Constant	None, except special motors designed for 2 fixed speeds	40% for slow speed to 160% for medium speed 80% p-f designs. Special high torque designs	Pull-out torque of unity-p-f motors 170%; 80%—p-f motors 225%. Special designs up to 300%	For constant-speed service, direct connection to slow-speed machines and where power-factor correction is required.

General Electric Co.

Sizes of Motors for Machine Tools
and Forging Machinery

The number of kinds and wide range of sizes of motor-driven machines is so large as to make a complete listing impractical. The machines for which suitable types and sizes of motors are listed below are typical applications and are based upon information supplied by Westinghouse Electric Corporation. The horsepower values shown are for average practice. They may be decreased for very light work and must often be increased for heavy work. The type of motor to be used in each case is indicated by symbols A, B, C, etc. The meaning of these symbols is as follows:

A. Adjustable speed, shunt-wound, direct-current motor, wherever a number of speeds are essential.

B. Constant speed, shunt-wound, direct-current motor, when the required speeds are obtainable by a gear-box or other adjustable speed transmission or when only one speed is required.

C. Squirrel-cage induction motor, when direct current is not available; a gear-box or other adjustable speed transmission must be used to obtain different speeds.

D. Constant speed, compound-wound, direct-current motor, when speeds are obtainable by a gear-box or other adjustable speed transmission or when only one speed is required.

E. Wound secondary or squirrel-cage induction motor with approximately 10 per cent slip, when direct current is not available.

F. Adjustable speed, compound-wound, direct-current motor.

Motor Power for Machine Tools and Forging Machinery — 1

Engine Lathes			Punch Presses		
Type of Motor: *A, B* or *C*			Type of Motor: *A, C, D* or *E*		
Swing of Lathe, Inches	Service and H.P.		Soft Steel, Hole Diam., Inches	Thickness of Plate, Inches	Horse-power*
	Average	Heavy			
12	3	5	¼	¼	½ to 1
14–16	5–7½	7½–10	⅜	⅜	½ to 1½
18–24	10–15	15–25	½	½	¾ to 3
27–36	20–25	30	⅝	⅝	1½ to 2
42–54	30–40	50	¾	¾	1 to 5
60–72	40–60	....	⅞	⅞	1½ to 5

Cylindrical Grinding Machines					
Type of Motor: *A, B* or *C*			1	1	2 to 6
Size of Wheel, Inches	Distance between Centers, Inches	Horse-power	1¼	1	3 to 8
			1½	1	7½
			1¾	1	10
10 × ¾	20 to 30	2 to 4	2	1	10
10 × 1½	20 to 30	2 to 4	2¼	1⅛	10 to 15
12 × 1¼	32 to 66	5 to 8	2¼	1⅜	15 to 20
12 × 1½	32 to 66	5 to 8	2½	1½	15 to 20
12 × 2½	32 to 96	10 to 12	3	2	20 to 25
14 × 1½	20 to 86	5 to 8	4	1½	25
16 × 3	30 to 90	7½ to 10	6	1½	40
18 × 2	27 to 120	7½ to 10			
20 × 2	36 to 96	10 to 15	* The variations in horsepower are due entirely to the design of the press, especially with regard to flywheel and speed.		
20 × 2½	39 to 123	12 to 15			
24 × 2	96 to 168	15 to 20			
24 × 3	98 to 172	25 to 35			

Motor Power for Machine Tools and Forging Machinery — 2

Milling Machines
Type of Motor: A, B or C

Universal Milling Machines

Max. Feeding Movements, Inches			Horse-power
Length-wise	Lateral	Vertical	
22	8	18	3 to 5
28	10	18	5 to 7½
34	12	19	7½ to 10
42	14	20	10 to 15
50	14	20	15 to 20

Plain Milling Machines

Max. Feeding Movements, Inches			Horse-power
Length-wise	Lateral	Vertical	
22	8	19	3
28	10	19	5 to 7½
34	12	20	7½ to 10
42	14	20	10 to 15
50	14	21	15 to 20

Vertical Milling Machines

Max. Feeding Movements, Inches			Horse-power
Length-wise	Lateral	Vertical	
22	12	18	3 to 5
22	13	20	5 to 7½
34	14	22	7½ to 10
42	15	22	10 to 15
52	12	24	15 to 20

Horizontal Boring, Drilling and Milling Machines
Type of Motor: A, B or C

Spindle Diam., Inches	Horse-power	Spindle Diam., Inches	Horse-power
3½–4½	15–25	6½	20–30
5	20–30	7–9½	30–40

Hydraulic Wheel Presses
Type of Motor: B or C

Capac-ity, Tons	Horse-power	Capac-ity, Tons	Horse-power
100	3 to 3½	400	7½ to 10
200	5 to 7½	500	10 to 15
300	6 to 7½	600	12½ to 15

Shears
Type of Motor: C, D or E

Vertical Type

Soft Steel, Width, Inches	Thickness of Plate, Inches	Horsepower
30 to 42	1/32	¾ to 1
36 to 62	1/16	2 to 3
36 to 144	⅛	3 to 10
36 to 144	3/16	4 to 12
42 to 168	¼	6 to 20
54 to 126	⅜	15 to 20

Lever Type

Soft Steel, Square Bar, Size, Inches	Horse-power	Soft Steel, Square Bar, Size, Inches	Horse-power
¾	2 to 5	2½	10 to 20
1	3 to 5	2¾	15 to 20
1¼	5 to 7½	3	15 to 25
1½	5 to 7½	3¼	20 to 30
1¾	5 to 10	3½	20 to 40
2	7½ to 10	4	30 to 50
2¼	10 to 15	....	....

Bolt Heading, Upsetting and Forging Machinery
Type of Motor: D, E or F

Size, Inches	Horse-power	Size, Inches	Horse-power
1¼	10	3	30
1½	15	4	50
2	20	5	60
2½	25	6	75

Bulldozers or Forming or Bending Machines
Type of Motor: D or E

Width, Inches	Head Move-ment, Inches	Horse-power
29	14	5
34	16	7½
39	16	10
45	18	15
63	20	20

ELECTRIC MOTOR MAINTENANCE

Electric Motor Inspection Schedule. — Frequency and thoroughness of inspection depend upon such factors as; (1) importance of the motor in the production scheme; (2) percentage of days the motor operates; (3) nature of service; (4) winding conditions. The following schedules, recommended by the General Electric Company, and covering both A.C. and D.C. motors are based on average conditions in so far as duty and dirt are concerned.

Weekly Inspection. — (1) *Surroundings.* Check to see if the windings are exposed to any dripping water, acid or alcoholic fumes; also, check for any unusual amount of dust, chips or lint on or about the motor. See if any boards, covers, canvas, etc., have been left about that might interfere with the motor ventilation or jam moving parts.

(2) *Lubrication of sleeve bearing motors.* In sleeve-bearing motors check oil level, if a gage is used, and fill to the specified line. If the journal diameter is less than 2 inches, the motor should be stopped before checking the oil level. For special lubricating systems, such as wool-packed, forced lubrication, flood and disk lubrication, follow instruction book. Oil should be added to bearing housing only when motor is at rest. A check should be made to see if oil is creeping along the shaft toward windings where it may harm the insulation.

(3) *Mechanical condition.* — Note any unusual noise which may be caused by metal to metal contact or any odor as from scorching insulation varnish.

(4) *Ball or roller bearings.* Feel ball- or roller-bearing housings for evidence of vibration, and listen for any unusual noise. Inspect for creepage of grease on inside of motor.

(5) *Commutators and brushes.* Check brushes and commutator for sparking. If the motor is on cyclic duty it should be observed through several cycles. Note color and surface condition of the commutator. A stable copper oxide-carbon film (as distinguished from a pure copper surface) on the commutator is an essential requirement for good commutation. Such a film may vary in color all the way from copper to straw, chocolate to black. It should be clean and smooth and have a high polish. All brushes should be checked for wear and pigtail connections for looseness. The commutator surface may be cleaned by using a piece of dry canvas or other hard, nonlinting material which is wound around and securely fastened to a wooden stick, and held against the rotating commutator.

(6) *Rotors and armatures.* The air gap on sleeve bearing motors should be checked, especially if they have been recently overhauled. After installing new bearings, make sure that the average reading is within 10 per cent, provided reading should be less than 0.020 inch. Check air passages through punchings and make sure they are free of foreign matter.

(7) *Windings.* If necessary clean windings by suction or mild blowing. After making sure that the motor is dead, wipe off windings with dry cloth, note evidence of moisture and see if any water has accumulated in the bottom of frame. Check also and see if any oil or grease has worked its way up to the rotor or armature windings. Clean with carbon tetrachloride in a well-ventilated room.

(8) *General.* This is a good time to check the belt, gears, flexible couplings, chain and sprockets for excessive wear or improper location. The motor starting should be checked to make sure that it comes up to proper speed each time power is applied.

Monthly or Bi-Monthly Inspection. — (1) *Windings.* Check shunt, series and commutating field windings for tightness. Try to move field spools on the poles, as drying out may have caused some play. If this condition exists, a service shop should be consulted. The motor cable connections should be checked for tightness.

(2) *Brushes*. Check brushes in holders for fit and free play. Also check the brush-spring pressure. Tighten brush studs in holders to take up slack from drying out of washers, making sure that studs are not displaced, particularly on D.C. motors. Replace brushes that are worn down almost to the brush rivet, examine brush faces for chipped toes or heels, and for heat cracks. Damaged brushes should be replaced immediately.

(3) *Commutators*. Examine commutator surface for high bars and high mica, or evidence of scratches or roughness. See that the risers are clean and have not been damaged in any way.

(4) *Ball or roller bearings*. On hard-driven, 24-hour service ball- or roller-bearing motors, purge out old grease through drain hole and apply new grease. Check to make sure grease or oil is not leaking out of the bearing housing. If any leakage is present, correct the condition before continuing to operate.

(5) *Sleeve bearings*. Check sleeve bearings for wear, including end-play bearing surfaces. Clean out oil wells if there is evidence of dirt or sludge. Flush with lighter oil before refilling.

(6) *Enclosed gears*. For motors with enclosed gears, open drain plug and check oil flow for presence of metal scale, sand or water. If condition of oil is bad, drain, flush and refill as directed. Rock rotor to see if slack or backlash is increasing.

(7) *Loads*. Check loads for changed conditions, bad adjustment, poor handling or control.

(8) *Couplings and other drive details*. Note if belt-tightening adjustment is all used up. Shorten belt if this condition exists. See if belt runs steadily and close to inside (motor edge) of pulley. Chain should be checked for evidence of wear and stretch. Clean inside of chain housing. Check chain-lubricating system. Note incline of slanting base to make sure it does not cause oil rings to rub on housing.

Annual or Bi-Annual Inspection. — (1) *Windings*.

Check insulation resistance by using either a megohmmeter or a volt meter having a resistance of about 100 ohms per volt. Check insulation surfaces for dry cracks and other evidence of need for coatings of insulating material. Clean surfaces and ventilating passages thoroughly if inspection shows accumulation of dust. Check for mold or water standing in frame to determine if windings need to be dried out, varnished and baked.

(2) *Air gap and bearings*. Check air gap to make sure that average reading is within 10 per cent, provided reading should be less than 0.020 inch. All bearings, ball, roller and sleeve should be thoroughly checked and defective ones replaced. Waste-packed and wick-oiled bearings should have waste or wicks renewed, if they have become glazed or filled with metal or dirt, making sure that new waste bears well against shaft.

(3) *Rotors (squirrel-cage)*. Check squirrel-cage rotors for broken or loose bars and evidence of local heating. If fan blades are not cast in place, check for loose blades. Look for marks on rotor surface indicating foreign matter in air gap or a worn bearing.

(4) *Rotors (wound)*. Clean wound rotors thoroughly around collector rings, washers and connections. Tighten connections if necessary. If rings are rough, spotted or eccentric, refer to service shop for refinishing. See that all top sticks or wedges are tight. If any are loose, refer to service shop.

(5) *Armatures*. Clean all armature air passages thoroughly if any are obstructed. Look for oil or grease creeping along shaft, checking back to bearing. Check commutator for surface condition, high bars, high mica or eccentricity. If necessary, turn down the commutator to secure a smooth fresh surface.

(6) *Loads*. Read load on motor with instruments at no load, full load or through an entire cycle, as a check on the mechanical condition of the driven machine.

MANUFACTURING PLANT APPRAISAL

The method of appraising manufacturing plants depends somewhat upon the purpose of the appraisal. When making an appraisal for a prospective buyer, the appraiser will naturally decide upon a comparatively low range of values, knowing that the expert retained by the owners will decide upon the upper range, and *vice versa*. It may be impossible to determine absolutely the value of a machine, and the variation of a few dollars, one way or the other, might be equally justifiable under certain conditions. If the appraisal is made for the owners for purposes of taxation, accounting and insurance, it is well to take average values.

Terms used in Appraisal Work. — The meaning or definition of terms used in appraisal work and a brief explanation of the underlying theories are given in the following: *Unit Plant:* A unit portion of the plant equipment. *Replacement Value:* Actual cost of replacing a unit plant with one of the same type at prevalent market prices at time of appraisal. The replacement value, then, is the market price of the machine plus freight plus cost of installation In the case of large machine tools, the freight and installation items are large enough to be worth considering, especially when expensive foundations are necessary. When appraising small parts of machinery and small tools, these items are practically negligible when considering individual tools, but in appraising the contents of a tool-room, where large quantities of tools have been purchased in bulk, some allowance should be made for freight. *First Cost Installed:* The original cost of unit plant at market prices prevalent at the time of purchase of the plant under consideration plus freight and cost of installation. The "first cost installed" can often be obtained directly from the books of the business. *Scrap Value:* The actual cash return brought by the sale of materials (iron, copper, etc.) used in the construction of a machine or tool at current market prices, less cost of junking. The cost of junking will be high in the case of large and unwieldy machines, and in some cases will offset the return from sale of scrap, making the net scrap value zero or even a negative quantity. *Depreciation:* The lessening in value of unit plant due to (1) wear and tear; (2) age and deterioration; (3) inefficiency and inferiority in design. *Depreciable or Wearing Value:* The replacement value of plant less the scrap value. *Depreciated or Present Value:* Value of unit plant at the time of appraisal. Present value equals the replacement value less the accrued depreciation at time of appraisal.

Replacement Value. — The determination of the replacement value is simply a matter of applying unit prices to the machine or tool in question with proper additions for freight and installation. A careful check of unit prices is, of course, necessary to ascertain their accuracy at the time of the appraisal. The increased costs of material and labor have caused a marked rise in the prices of some of the larger machine tools within the past decade. In the case of small machine tools, prices, in many instances, have decreased within the past few years.

Present Value. — The computation of the theoretical present value can be most easily done by applying an annual rate of depreciation directly to the wearing value and subtracting the result from the replacement value. The wearing value equals the replacement value less the scrap value. The scrap value has a definite ratio to the replacement value for each type of plant. The reciprocal of the life of a machine or tool gives the rate per cent which, when applied to the wearing value and multiplied by the age in years, gives the accrued depreciation. This latter subtracted from the replacement value gives the present value. The present value can be obtained directly by applying the following formula: Present value = $\dfrac{a\,(l-f)+fb}{l}$, where a = replacement value; b = scrap value; f = age of machine;

l = life of machine. After the present value has been obtained by either of the methods outlined, allowance should be made for the actual condition of the machine or tool in question, as ascertained by careful inspection. For example, two drill presses of the same make and size, recently installed, are operating side by side. One is found to be in excellent condition while the other has a table badly mutilated by careless operators. Obviously, the accrued depreciation on the second should be greater and the present value less than on the first. It is in cases of this kind that the appraiser's judgment comes into play.

Depreciation of Mechanical Equipment. — The depreciation or reduction in value of mechanical apparatus is estimated in advance in order to determine what funds should be set aside periodically to provide ultimately for the purchase of new equipment. Depreciation percentages, even for the same types of equipment, vary considerably because they are affected by certain variable factors, such, for example, as (1) extent of wear resulting from use or location of equipment; (2) obsolescence or reduction in value due to development of more efficient apparatus (in this connection either a reduction or an increase in replacement value of new apparatus may have to be considered); (3) care of equipment, both as regards operating conditions and maintenance or repairs. These factors vary widely for different classes of equipment. Certain types of machines and tools, for example, depreciate in value as the result of wear only; whereas other types become obsolete and are uneconomical to use because an improved design or type has been developed. The following depreciation rates, all of which are given as percentages of the original cost, have been obtained from various sources. The extreme variations recommended by various authorities are given to indicate the fluctuations under different conditions. The average percentages, together with the number of sources upon which the averages are based, are also included.

Belting. — Main belts, range 5 to 25 per cent; average from eleven sources, 12 per cent. Machine belts, 25 to 50 per cent.

Motors. — Range 4 to 10 per cent; average from twelve sources, 7 per cent.

Engines, Reciprocating Steam. — Range 4 to 10 per cent; average from thirteen sources, 6 per cent. *Engines, Turbine Type.* — Range 3 to 7 per cent; average from thirteen sources, 5 per cent. *Engines, Gas.* — Range 5 to 10 per cent; average from eight sources, 7 per cent.

Boilers. — Range 4 to 10 per cent; average from eighteen sources, 6 per cent.

Pumps. — Range 3½ to 8 per cent; average from nine sources, 5 per cent.

Hoists. — Range 7 to 12 per cent.

Cranes. — Range 2 to 10 per cent; average from eight sources, 6 per cent.

Machine Tools. — Common range for standard types subject to normal usage, 5 to 10 per cent. For manufacturing types or special designs used continuously, the range may vary from 15 to 30 per cent. Each type of machine tool must be considered separately because of the wide variety of operating conditions and also on account of the numerous developments in the machine tool industry which cannot be predetermined.

Machinery in General. — Range 5 to 13 per cent; average from eight sources, 9 per cent.

Dies. — Range 25 to 50 per cent; average from four sources, 40 per cent. The cost of tools of this class, when made for a particular order, should be charged to that order.

Hammers, Drop and Steam. — 10 per cent.

Patterns. — Range 20 to 100 per cent; average from six sources, 65 per cent. Metal patterns have a lower depreciation rate than wood patterns, but in any case when patterns are for a particular job, the entire cost should be charged to that job.

The foregoing figures are intended chiefly as a general guide.

Depreciation Charges. — The depreciation in value of mechanical equipment takes place at a variable rate and is more or less compensated for by repairs and renewals, but an average can be determined by estimating the probable working life of the machine and then distributing over this period the difference between the cost of the machine and its scrap or junk value. The *replacement cost* of the machine includes the original price, the expense of installation, the cost of all repairs and renewals, and the expenditure for special tools and fixtures.

Replacements of expensive machinery, which is either worn out or obsolete, are generally provided for by setting aside annually a certain *depreciation charge*, thus creating a *depreciation fund* or reserve. The object of this plan is to avoid excessive operating charges during the years when replacements of expensive equipment are necessary. The depreciation fund may be invested in securities having a regular market value or it may be invested in the company's own business, preferably in such a way as to be available when needed.

Formulas for Determining Depreciation Charges. — If the value of a machine or other property is assumed to decrease at a uniform rate (which is the most common method), the annual depreciation in dollars, not considering interest on invested funds, may be found by subtracting the scrap value from the replacement cost, and dividing the difference by the estimated life of the machine in years. Thus, if D = annual depreciation in dollars; P = depreciation expressed on a percentage basis (decimal fraction); C = replacement cost; S = scrap value; n = number of years of useful life; then $D = \dfrac{C - S}{n}$. This is sometimes called the *straight line method*, because the depreciation charges are the same each year and if plotted would lie along a straight line; hence the name. When the depreciation charge is invested at a given percentage rate P, compounded annually, the depreciation charge may be determined by one of the following formulas: If the annual payments are made at the *end* of each year, then:

$$D = (C - S) \frac{P}{(1 + P)^n - 1}$$

If the annual payments are made at the *beginning* of each year, then:

$$D = (C - S) \frac{P}{(1 + P)^{n+1} - (1 + P)}$$

Example: The replacement cost of a machine is $6000; the scrap value is $100; and the useful life of the machine is estimated to be 20 years. Determine the annual depreciation charge, assuming that these sums are to be invested at the end of each year at six per cent compounded annually.

$$D = (6000 - 100) \frac{0.06}{(1 + 0.06)^{20} - 1} = \$160 \text{ approx.}$$

Diminishing Depreciation Charges. — When the depreciation charges are to be calculated on the decreasing value of equipment or its value at the beginning of each year, instead of taking a fixed replacement or original value as the basis, the following formulas may be used. The notation is similar to that previously given.

$$P = 1 - \sqrt[n]{\frac{S}{C}}$$

The depreciation charge at the end of a given number of years x is found by one of the following formulas:

$$D = PC \left(\frac{S}{C}\right)^{\frac{x-1}{n}} = PC \sqrt[n]{\left(\frac{S}{C}\right)^{x-1}}$$

Economical Production Cycle

Nearly all manufacturing concerns are confronted with the problem of determining how many parts of one kind should be made at one time before re-tooling and re-setting the machine for another part. It is evident that the set-up cost per part is less as the number of parts in a run increases; therefore, if there are too few pieces in a run, the part becomes very costly. It is also evident that if too many pieces are made in a run, the pieces will be in storage a long time before they are used, causing the cost of the part to be increased due to interest on money invested in parts and storage space cost; therefore, too many pieces in a run will also make the parts very costly.

Most Economical Number. — If too few or too many pieces are made in one run the parts become more costly. There is, however, one quantity where the sum of the set-up cost and the increased cost due to interest and floor space is a minimum, and this quantity is known as the "economical cycle." By the use of higher mathematics it can be proved that:

$$\text{Economical cycle} = \sqrt{\frac{BFD \times 560}{C \times (D - F) \times A}}$$

B = total cost of set-up, in dollars;
F = number of parts used per day;
D = number of parts that can be made per day;
C = total cost of material, labor, and overhead *per part*; the set-up cost per part can be neglected at this point, as it would change the economical cycle but little.
A = fraction by which the cost of the part is increased if kept in storage for one year; this increase is caused by interest on money invested, insurance and value of floor space. For example, assume that C equals \$0.25, the interest rate is 6 per cent, and insurance and floor space costs \$0.01 per part per year; then the cost of one part, if in storage one year, would be increased $0.25 \times 0.06 + 0.01 = 0.025$, which equals 10 per cent, or $A = 0.1$.

Example Showing Application: For the purpose of explaining the use of the formula, assume that $B = \$16$, $F = 20$, $D = 200$, C equals \$0.25 and $A = 0.1$ (10 per cent). Then

$$\sqrt{\frac{16 \times 20 \times 200 \times 560}{0.25 \times (200 - 20) \times 0.1}} = \sqrt{7,964,444} = 2822$$

or 2800 approximately.

If the parts in the problem considered were made in lots of 2822 pieces, the set-up cost per part would be $16 \div 2822$ or \$0.0056. Since $\frac{2822}{20}$ days are required to use the parts in the cycle and since $\frac{2822}{200}$ days are required to make the parts, it is evident that the last part made would be in storage $\left(\frac{2822}{20} - \frac{2822}{200}\right)$ days. The first part made is in storage no time. Knowing the time the first and last parts are in storage, the average storage time can be obtained by taking one-half of the sum, thus: $\frac{1}{2}\left(\frac{2822}{20} - \frac{2822}{200}\right)$ days. Taking 280 as the number of production days per year, the average time would be $\frac{1/2}{280}\left(\frac{2822}{20} - \frac{2822}{200}\right)$ years.

Since the storage and interest increase the cost of the parts 10 per cent per year, the storage charge on the parts would be $0.25 \times 0.1 \times \frac{1/2}{280}\left(\frac{2822}{20} - \frac{2822}{200}\right)$ or \$0.0056 per part. It can be seen that the set-up cost, \$0.0056, and the storage charge, \$0.0056, are equal when the most economical number of parts are made. This can be proved mathematically, but requires a very complicated mathematical analysis.

WEIGHTS AND MEASURES

Measures of Length

1 mile = 1760 yards = 5280 feet.
1 yard = 3 feet = 36 inches.   1 foot = 12 inches.
  1 mil = 0.001 inch.   1 fathom = 2 yards = 6 feet.
  1 rod = 5.5 yards = 16.5 feet.   1 hand = 4 inches.   1 span = 9 inches.
  1 micro-inch = one millionth inch or 0.000001 inch.   (1 micron = one millionth meter = 0.00003937 inch.)

Surveyor's Measure

  1 mile = 8 furlongs = 80 chains.
  1 furlong = 10 chains = 220 yards.
  1 chain = 4 rods = 22 yards = 66 feet = 100 links.
  1 link = 7.92 inches.

Nautical Measure

  1 league = 3 nautical miles.
  1 nautical mile = 6080.2 feet = 1.1516 statute mile.   (The *knot*, which is a nautical unit of speed, is equivalent to a speed 1 nautical mile per hour.)
  One degree at the equator = 60 nautical miles = 69.096 statute miles.   360 degrees = 21,600 nautical miles = 24,874.5 statute miles = circumference at equator.

Square Measure

  1 square mile = 640 acres = 6400 square chains.
  1 acre = 10 square chains = 4840 square yards = 43,560 square feet.
  1 square chain = 16 square rods = 484 square yards = 4356 square feet.
  1 square rod = 30.25 square yards = 272.25 square feet = 625 square links.
  1 square yard = 9 square feet.
  1 square foot = 144 square inches.
An acre is equal to a square, the side of which is 208.7 feet.

Measure used for Diameters and Areas of Electric Wires

  1 circular inch = area of circle 1 inch in diameter = 0.7854 square inch.
  1 circular inch = 1,000,000 circular mils.
  1 square inch = 1.2732 circular inch = 1,273,239 circular mils.
A circular mil is the area of a circle 0.001 inch in diameter.

Cubic Measure

  1 cubic yard = 27 cubic feet.
  1 cubic foot = 1728 cubic inches.
The following measures are also used for wood and masonry:
  1 cord of wood = 4 × 4 × 8 feet = 128 cubic feet.
  1 perch of masonry = $16\frac{1}{2} × 1\frac{1}{2} × 1$ foot = $24\frac{3}{4}$ cubic feet.

Shipping Measure

For measuring entire internal capacity of a vessel:
  1 register ton = 100 cubic feet.
For measurement of cargo:
  Approximately 40 cubic feet of merchandise is considered a shipping ton, unless that bulk would weigh more than 2000 pounds, in which case the freight charge may be based upon weight.
  40 cubic feet = 32.143 U. S. bushels = 31.16 Imperial bushels.

Dry Measure

1 bushel (U. S. or Winchester struck bushel) = 1.2445 cubic foot = 2150.42 cubic inches.
1 bushel = 4 pecks = 32 quarts = 64 pints.
1 peck = 8 quarts = 16 pints.
1 quart = 2 pints.
1 heaped bushel = $1\frac{1}{4}$ struck bushel.
1 cubic foot = 0.8036 struck bushel.
1 British Imperial bushel = 8 Imperial gallons = 1.2837 cubic foot = 2218.19 cubic inches.

Liquid Measure

1 U. S. gallon = 0.1337 cubic foot = 231 cubic inches = 4 quarts = 8 pints.
1 quart = 2 pints = 8 gills.
1 pint = 4 gills.
1 British Imperial gallon = 1.2009 U. S. gallon = 277.42 cubic inches.
1 cubic foot = 7.48 U. S. gallons.

Old Liquid Measure

1 tun = 2 pipes = 3 puncheons.
1 pipe or butt = 2 hogsheads = 4 barrels = 126 gallons.
1 puncheon = 2 tierces = 84 gallons.
1 hogshead = 2 barrels = 63 gallons.
1 tierce = 42 gallons.
1 barrel = $31\frac{1}{2}$ gallons.

Apothecaries' Fluid Measure

1 U. S. fluid ounce = 8 drachms = 1.805 cubic inch = $\frac{1}{128}$ U. S. gallon.
1 fluid drachm = 60 minims.
1 British fluid ounce = 1.732 cubic inch.

Measures of Weight

Avoirdupois or Commercial Weight

1 gross or long ton = 2240 pounds.
1 net or short ton = 2000 pounds.
1 pound = 16 ounces = 7000 grains.
1 ounce = 16 drachms = 437.5 grains.

The following measures for weight are now seldom used in the United States:
1 hundred-weight = 4 quarters = 112 pounds (1 gross or long ton = 20 hundred-weights); 1 quarter = 28 pounds; 1 stone = 14 pounds; 1 quintal = 100 pounds.

Troy Weight, used for Weighing Gold and Silver

1 pound = 12 ounces = 5760 grains.
1 ounce = 20 pennyweights = 480 grains.
1 pennyweight = 24 grains.
1 carat (used in weighing diamonds) = 3.086 grains.
1 grain Troy = 1 grain avoirdupois = 1 grain apothecaries' weight.

Apothecaries' Weight

1 pound = 12 ounces = 5760 grains.
1 ounce = 8 drachms = 480 grains.
1 drachm = 3 scruples = 60 grains.
1 scruple = 20 grains.

Measures of Pressure

1 pound per square inch = 144 pounds per square foot = 0.068 atmosphere = 2.042 inches of mercury at 62 degrees F. = 27.7 inches of water at 62 degrees F. = 2.31 feet of water at 62 degrees F.

1 atmosphere = 30 inches of mercury at 62 degrees F. = 14.7 pounds per square inch = 2116.3 pounds per square foot = 33.95 feet of water at 62 degrees F.

1 foot of water at 62 degrees F. = 62.355 pounds per square foot = 0.432 pound per square inch.

1 inch of mercury at 62 degrees F. = 1.132 foot of water = 13.58 inches of water = 0.491 pound per square inch.

Miscellaneous

1 great gross = 12 gross = 144 dozen.
1 gross = 12 dozen = 144 units.
1 dozen = 12 units.
1 score = 20 units.

1 quire = 24 sheets.
1 ream = 20 quires = 480 sheets.
1 ream printing paper = 500 sheets.

Decimal Equivalents of Fractions of an Inch

1/64	0.015 625	11/32	0.343 75	43/64	0.671 875
1/32	0.031 25	23/64	0.359 375	11/16	0.687 5
3/64	0.046 875	3/8	0.375	45/64	0.703 125
1/16	0.062 5	25/64	0.390 625	23/32	0.718 75
5/64	0.078 125	13/32	0.406 25	47/64	0.734 375
3/32	0.093 75	27/64	0.421 875	3/4	0.750
7/64	0.109 375	7/16	0.437 5	49/64	0.765 625
1/8	0.125	29/64	0.453 125	25/32	0.781 25
9/64	0.140 625	15/32	0.468 75	51/64	0.796 875
5/32	0.156 25	31/64	0.484 375	13/16	0.812 5
11/64	0.171 875	1/2	0.500	53/64	0.828 125
3/16	0.187 5	33/64	0.515 625	27/32	0.843 75
13/64	0.203 125	17/32	0.531 25	55/64	0.859 375
7/32	0.218 75	35/64	0.546 875	7/8	0.875
15/64	0.234 375	9/16	0.562 5	57/64	0.890 625
1/4	0.250	37/64	0.578 125	29/32	0.906 25
17/64	0.265 625	19/32	0.593 75	59/64	0.921 875
9/32	0.281 25	39/64	0.609 375	15/16	0.937 5
19/64	0.296 875	5/8	0.625	61/64	0.953 125
5/16	0.312 5	41/64	0.640 625	31/32	0.968 75
21/64	0.328 125	21/32	0.656 25	63/64	0.984 375

Table of Decimal Equivalents of a Foot Corresponding to Inches and Fractions of Inches. — Assume, for example, that it is required to find the equivalent of 6 7/32 inches in decimals of a foot. Locate 7/32 in the left-hand column and follow the horizontal line until the column headed "6" is reached. The figures 0.5182 read off in this column are the decimals of a foot corresponding to 6 7/32; in other words, 6 7/32 inches equals 0.5182 foot.

Inches into Decimals of a Foot

Inch	0	1	2	3	4	5	6	7	8	9	10	11
....		0.0833	0.1667	0.2500	0.3333	0.4167	0.5000	0.5833	0.6667	0.7500	0.8333	0.9167
1/32	0.0026	0.0859	0.1693	0.2526	0.3359	0.4193	0.5026	0.5859	0.6693	0.7526	0.8359	0.9193
1/16	0.0052	0.0885	0.1719	0.2552	0.3385	0.4219	0.5052	0.5885	0.6719	0.7552	0.8385	0.9219
3/32	0.0078	0.0911	0.1745	0.2578	0.3411	0.4245	0.5078	0.5911	0.6745	0.7578	0.8411	0.9245
1/8	0.0104	0.0938	0.1771	0.2604	0.3438	0.4271	0.5104	0.5938	0.6771	0.7604	0.8438	0.9271
5/32	0.0130	0.0964	0.1797	0.2630	0.3464	0.4297	0.5130	0.5964	0.6797	0.7630	0.8464	0.9297
3/16	0.0156	0.0990	0.1823	0.2656	0.3490	0.4323	0.5156	0.5990	0.6823	0.7656	0.8490	0.9323
7/32	0.0182	0.1016	0.1849	0.2682	0.3516	0.4349	0.5182	0.6016	0.6849	0.7682	0.8516	0.9349
1/4	0.0208	0.1042	0.1875	0.2708	0.3542	0.4375	0.5208	0.6042	0.6875	0.7708	0.8542	0.9375
9/32	0.0234	0.1068	0.1901	0.2734	0.3568	0.4401	0.5234	0.6068	0.6901	0.7734	0.8568	0.9401
5/16	0.0260	0.1094	0.1927	0.2760	0.3594	0.4427	0.5260	0.6094	0.6927	0.7760	0.8594	0.9427
11/32	0.0286	0.1120	0.1953	0.2786	0.3620	0.4453	0.5286	0.6120	0.6953	0.7786	0.8620	0.9453
3/8	0.0313	0.1146	0.1979	0.2813	0.3646	0.4479	0.5313	0.6146	0.6979	0.7813	0.8646	0.9479
13/32	0.0339	0.1172	0.2005	0.2839	0.3672	0.4505	0.5339	0.6172	0.7005	0.7839	0.8672	0.9505
7/16	0.0365	0.1198	0.2031	0.2865	0.3698	0.4531	0.5365	0.6198	0.7031	0.7865	0.8698	0.9531
15/32	0.0391	0.1224	0.2057	0.2891	0.3724	0.4557	0.5391	0.6224	0.7057	0.7891	0.8724	0.9557
1/2	0.0417	0.1250	0.2083	0.2917	0.3750	0.4583	0.5417	0.6250	0.7083	0.7917	0.8750	0.9583
17/32	0.0443	0.1276	0.2109	0.2943	0.3776	0.4609	0.5443	0.6276	0.7109	0.7943	0.8776	0.9609
9/16	0.0469	0.1302	0.2135	0.2969	0.3802	0.4635	0.5469	0.6302	0.7135	0.7969	0.8802	0.9635
19/32	0.0495	0.1328	0.2161	0.2995	0.3828	0.4661	0.5495	0.6328	0.7161	0.7995	0.8828	0.9661
5/8	0.0521	0.1354	0.2188	0.3021	0.3854	0.4688	0.5521	0.6354	0.7188	0.8021	0.8854	0.9688
21/32	0.0547	0.1380	0.2214	0.3047	0.3880	0.4714	0.5547	0.6380	0.7214	0.8047	0.8880	0.9714
11/16	0.0573	0.1406	0.2240	0.3073	0.3906	0.4740	0.5573	0.6406	0.7240	0.8073	0.8906	0.9740
23/32	0.0599	0.1432	0.2266	0.3099	0.3932	0.4766	0.5599	0.6432	0.7266	0.8099	0.8932	0.9766
3/4	0.0625	0.1458	0.2292	0.3125	0.3958	0.4792	0.5625	0.6458	0.7292	0.8125	0.8958	0.9792
25/32	0.0651	0.1484	0.2318	0.3151	0.3984	0.4818	0.5651	0.6484	0.7318	0.8151	0.8984	0.9818
13/16	0.0677	0.1510	0.2344	0.3177	0.4010	0.4844	0.5677	0.6510	0.7344	0.8177	0.9010	0.9844
27/32	0.0703	0.1536	0.2370	0.3203	0.4036	0.4870	0.5703	0.6536	0.7370	0.8203	0.9036	0.9870
7/8	0.0729	0.1563	0.2396	0.3229	0.4063	0.4896	0.5729	0.6563	0.7396	0.8229	0.9063	0.9896
29/32	0.0755	0.1589	0.2422	0.3255	0.4089	0.4922	0.5755	0.6589	0.7422	0.8255	0.9089	0.9922
15/16	0.0781	0.1615	0.2448	0.3281	0.4115	0.4948	0.5781	0.6615	0.7448	0.8281	0.9115	0.9948
31/32	0.0807	0.1641	0.2474	0.3307	0.4141	0.4974	0.5807	0.6641	0.7474	0.8307	0.9141	0.9974

Inches

Decimals of a Foot

Decimal Equivalents of 6ths, 12ths, and 24ths of an Inch

1/24	0.041 667	9/24	0.375	17/24	0.708 333
1/12...	0.083 333	5/12....	0.416 667	9/12...	0.75
3/24	0.125	11/24	0.458 333	19/24	0.791 667
1/6......	0.166 667	3/8......	0.5	5/6......	0.833 333
5/24	0.208 333	13/24	0.541 667	21/24	0.875
3/12...	0.25	7/12....	0.583 333	11/12...	0.916 667
7/24	0.291 667	15/24	0.625	23/24	0.958 333
2/6......	0.333 333	4/6......	0.666 667	......	....

Decimal Equivalents of 7ths, 14ths, and 28ths of an Inch

1/28	0.035 714	5/14..	0.357 143	19/28	0.678 571
1/14..	0.071 429	11/28	0.392 857	5/7....	0.714 286
3/28	0.107 143	3/7....	0.428 571	21/28	0.75
1/7....	0.142 857	13/28	0.464 286	11/14..	0.785 714
5/28	0.178 571	7/14..	0.5	23/28	0.821 429
3/14..	0.214 286	15/28	0.535 714	6/7....	0.857 143
7/28	0.25	4/7....	0.571 429	25/28	0.892 857
2/7....	0.285 714	17/28	0.607 143	13/14..	0.928 571
9/28	0.321 429	9/14..	0.642 867	27/28	0.964 286

U. S. Gallons into Cubic Feet

Gallons	Cubic Feet	Gallons	Cubic Feet	Gallons	Cubic Feet	Gallons	Cubic Feet
1	0.134	20	2.674	300	40.10	4,000	534.72
2	0.267	30	4.010	400	53.47	5,000	668.40
3	0.401	40	5.347	500	66.84	6,000	802.08
4	0.535	50	6.684	600	80.21	7,000	935.76
5	0.668	60	8.021	700	93.58	8,000	1,069.44
6	0.802	70	9.358	800	106.94	9,000	1,203.12
7	0.936	80	10.694	900	120.31	10,000	1,336.81
8	1.069	90	12.031	1000	133.68	50,000	6,684.03
9	1.203	100	13.368	2000	267.36	100,000	13,368.06
10	1.337	200	26.736	3000	401.04	500,000	66,840.28

Cubic Feet into Gallons

(1 cubic foot = 7.4805 U. S. gallons; 1 gallon = 231 cubic inches = 0.13368 cubic foot.)

Cubic Feet	Gallons	Cubic Feet	Gallons	Cubic Feet	Gallons	Cubic Feet	Gallons
0.1	0.75	2	14.96	30	224.4	400	2,992.2
0.2	1.50	3	22.44	40	299.2	500	3,740.3
0.3	2.24	4	29.92	50	374.0	600	4,488.3
0.4	2.99	5	37.40	60	448.8	700	5,236.4
0.5	3.74	6	44.88	70	523.6	800	5,984.4
0.6	4.49	7	52.36	80	598.4	900	6,732.5
0.7	5.24	8	59.84	90	673.2	1,000	7,480.5
0.8	5.98	9	67.32	100	748.1	5,000	37,402.6
0.9	6.73	10	74.81	200	1496.1	10,000	74,805.2
1.0	7.48	20	149.61	300	2244.2	50,000	374,025.9

Contents in Cubic Feet and U. S. Gallons of Pipes and Cylinders One Foot in Length

Diam. in Inches	For 1 Foot in Length		Diam. in Inches	For 1 Foot in Length		Diam. in Inches	For 1 Foot in Length	
	Cubic Feet	U. S. Gallons		Cubic Feet	U. S. Gallons		Cubic Feet	U. S. Gallons
¼	0.0003	0.0025	6¾	0.2485	1.859	19	1.969	14.73
5⁄16	0.0005	0.0040	7	0.2673	1.999	19½	2.074	15.51
⅜	0.0008	0.0057	7¼	0.2867	2.145	20	2.182	16.32
7⁄16	0.0010	0.0078	7½	0.3068	2.295	20½	2.292	17.15
½	0.0014	0.0102	7¾	0.3276	2.450	21	2.405	17.99
9⁄16	0.0017	0.0129	8	0.3491	2.611	21½	2.521	18.86
⅝	0.0021	0.0159	8¼	0.3712	2.777	22	2.640	19.75
11⁄16	0.0026	0.0193	8½	0.3941	2.948	22½	2.761	20.66
¾	0.0031	0.0230	8¾	0.4176	3.125	23	2.885	21.58
13⁄16	0.0036	0.0269	9	0.4418	3.305	23½	3.012	22.53
⅞	0.0042	0.0312	9¼	0.4667	3.491	24	3.142	23.50
15⁄16	0.0048	0.0359	9½	0.4922	3.682	25	3.409	25.50
1	0.0055	0.0408	9¾	0.5185	3.879	26	3.687	27.58
1¼	0.0085	0.0638	10	0.5454	4.080	27	3.976	29.74
1½	0.0123	0.0918	10¼	0.5730	4.286	28	4.276	31.99
1¾	0.0167	0.1249	10½	0.6013	4.498	29	4.587	34.31
2	0.0218	0.1632	10¾	0.6303	4.715	30	4.909	36.72
2¼	0.0276	0.2066	11	0.6600	4.937	31	5.241	39.21
2½	0.0341	0.2550	11¼	0.6903	5.164	32	5.585	41.78
2¾	0.0412	0.3085	11½	0.7213	5.396	33	5.940	44.43
3	0.0491	0.3672	11¾	0.7530	5.633	34	6.305	47.16
3¼	0.0576	0.4309	12	0.7854	5.875	35	6.681	49.98
3½	0.0668	0.4998	12½	0.8522	6.375	36	7.069	52.88
3¾	0.0767	0.5738	13	0.9218	6.895	37	7.467	55.86
4	0.0873	0.6528	13½	0.9940	7.436	38	7.876	58.92
4¼	0.0985	0.7369	14	1.069	7.997	39	8.296	62.06
4½	0.1104	0.8263	14½	1.147	8.578	40	8.727	65.28
4¾	0.1231	0.9206	15	1.227	9.180	41	9.168	68.58
5	0.1364	1.020	15½	1.310	9.801	42	9.621	71.97
5¼	0.1503	1.125	16	1.396	10.44	43	10.085	75.44
5½	0.1650	1.234	16½	1.485	11.11	44	10.559	78.99
5¾	0.1803	1.349	17	1.576	11.79	45	11.045	82.62
6	0.1963	1.469	17½	1.670	12.49	46	11.541	86.33
6¼	0.2131	1.594	18	1.767	13.22	47	12.048	90.13
6½	0.2304	1.724	18½	1.867	13.96	48	12.566	94.00

One cubic foot of water at 39.1 degrees F. weighs 62.4245 pounds.

One cubic foot of air at 32 degrees F., atmospheric pressure, weighs 0.08073 pound.

One pound of water at 39.1 degrees F. has a volume of 0.01602 cubic foot.

One pound of air at 32 degrees F., atmospheric pressure, has a volume of 12.387 cubic feet.

One gallon of water at 62 degrees F. weighs 8.336 pounds.

One pound of water at 62 degrees F. has a volume of 0.1199 U. S. gallon.

Contents of Cylindrical Tanks in U. S. Gallons

Depth of Tank, Feet	Diameter of Tank, Feet								
	5	6	7	8	9	10	11	12	13
	Contents of Tank, U. S. Gallons								
5	734	1058	1439	1880	2379	2,938	3,555	4,230	4,965
6	881	1269	1727	2256	2855	3,525	4,265	5,076	5,957
7	1028	1481	2015	2632	3331	4,113	4,976	5,922	6,950
8	1175	1692	2303	3008	3807	4,700	5,687	6,768	7,943
9	1322	1904	2591	3384	4283	5,288	6,398	7,614	8,936
10	1469	2115	2879	3760	4759	5,875	7,109	8,460	9,929
11	1616	2327	3167	4136	5235	6,463	7,820	9,306	10,922
12	1763	2538	3455	4512	5711	7,050	8,531	10,152	11,915
13	1909	2750	3742	4888	6187	7,638	9,242	10,998	12,808
14	2056	2961	4030	5264	6662	8,225	9,953	11,844	13,801
15	2203	3173	4318	5640	7138	8,813	10,664	12,690	14,894
16	2350	3384	4606	6016	7614	9,400	11,374	13,536	15,887
17	2497	3596	4894	6392	8090	9,988	12,085	14,383	16,879
18	2644	3807	5182	6768	8566	10,575	12,796	15,229	17,872
19	2791	4019	5480	7144	9042	11,163	13,507	16,075	18,865
20	2938	4230	5758	7520	9518	11,750	14,218	16,921	19,858

Depth of Tank, Feet	Diameter of Tank, Feet							
	14	15	16	18	20	22	24	25
	Contents of Tank, U. S. Gallons							
5	5,758	6,610	7,521	9,518	11,751	14,218	16,921	18,360
6	6,909	7,931	9,025	11,422	14,101	17,062	20,305	22,032
7	8,061	9,253	10,529	13,325	16,451	19,905	23,689	25,704
8	9,212	10,575	12,033	15,229	18,801	22,749	27,073	29,376
9	10,364	11,897	13,537	17,132	21,151	25,592	30,457	33,048
10	11,515	13,219	15,041	19,036	23,501	28,436	33,841	36,720
11	12,667	14,541	16,545	20,940	25,851	31,280	37,225	40,392
12	13,818	15,863	18,049	22,843	28,201	34,123	40,609	44,064
13	14,970	17,185	19,553	24,747	30,551	36,967	43,993	47,736
14	16,121	18,507	21,057	26,650	32,901	39,810	47,377	51,408
15	17,273	19,829	22,562	28,554	35,252	42,654	50,762	55,080
16	18,424	21,150	24,066	30,458	37,602	45,498	54,146	58,752
17	19,576	22,472	25,570	32,361	39,952	48,341	57,530	62,424
18	20,727	23,794	27,074	34,265	42,302	51,185	60,914	66,096
19	21,879	25,116	28,578	36,168	44,652	54,028	64,298	69,768
20	23,030	26,438	30,082	38,072	47,002	56,872	67,682	73,440

A cylinder 7 inches in diameter and 6 inches high contains one gallon within 0.1 of a cubic inch.

The volume, in U. S. gallons, of a cylinder, equals the square of the diameter in inches × height of cylinder in inches × 0.0034.

Circular Mil Gage for Electrical Wires*

A.W.G. or B. & S. Gage	Diam. Mils	Circular Mils	A.W.G. or B. & S. Gage	Diam. Mils	Circular Mils	A.W.G. or B. & S. Gage	Diam. Mils	Circular Mils
0000	460	212,000	12	81	6530	27	14.2	202.
000	410	168,000	13	72	5180	28	12.6	160.
00	365	133,000	14	64	4110	29	11.3	127.
0	325	106,000	15	57	3260	30	10.0	101.
1	289	83,700	16	51	2580	31	8.9	79.7
2	258	66,400	17	45	2050	32	8.0	63.2
3	229	52,600	18	40	1620	33	7.1	50.1
4	204	41,700	19	36	1290	34	6.3	39.8
5	182	33,100	20	32	1020	35	5.6	31.5
6	162	26,300	21	28.5	810	36	5.0	25.0
7	144	20,800	22	25.3	642	37	4.5	19.8
8	128	16,500	23	22.6	509	38	4.0	15.7
9	114	13,100	24	20.1	404	39	3.5	12.5
10	102	10,400	25	17.9	320	40	3.1	9.9
11	91	8,230	26	15.9	254	..	....	....

* A circular mil is a unit of area that is applied to electrical wires and cables and is equal to the area of a circle one mil (.001 inch) in diameter. The area of any circle in circular mils is equal to the square of its diameter in mils.

METRIC SYSTEM OF MEASUREMENTS

In the metric system of measurements, the principal unit for length is the meter; the principal unit for capacity, the liter; and the principal unit for weight, the gram. The following prefixes are used for sub-divisions and multiples: milli = $\frac{1}{1000}$; centi = $\frac{1}{100}$; deci = $\frac{1}{10}$; deca = 10; hecto = 100; kilo = 1000. In abbreviations, the sub-divisions are frequently used with a small letter and the multiples with a capital letter, although this practice is not universally followed everywhere where the metric system is used.

All the multiples and sub-divisions are not used commercially. Those ordinarily used for length are kilometer, meter, centimeter and millimeter; for capacity, square meter, square centimeter and square millimeter; for cubic measures, cubic meter, cubic decimeter (liter), cubic centimeter, and cubic millimeter. The most commonly used weights are the kilogram and gram. The metric system was legalized in the United States by an Act of Congress in 1866.

Measures of Length

10 millimeters (mm.) = 1 centimeter (cm.).
10 centimeters = 1 decimeter (dm.).
10 decimeters = 1 meter (m.).
1000 meters = 1 kilometer (Km.).

Square Measure

100 square millimeters (mm.^{2}) = 1 square centimeter (cm.^{2}).
100 square centimeters = 1 square decimeter (dm.^{2}).
100 square decimeters = 1 square meter (m.^{2}).

Surveyor's Square Measure

100 square meters (m.^{2}) = 1 are (ar.).
100 ares = 1 hectare (har.).
100 hectares = 1 square kilometer (Km.^{2}).

Cubic Measure

1000 cubic millimeters (mm.³) = 1 cubic centimeter (cm.³).
1000 cubic centimeters = 1 cubic decimeter (dm.³).
1000 cubic decimeters = 1 cubic meter (m.³).

Dry and Liquid Measure

10 milliliters (ml.) = 1 centiliter (cl.).
10 centiliters = 1 deciliter (dl.).
10 deciliters = 1 liter (l.).
100 liters = 1 hectoliter (Hl.).

1 liter = 1 cubic decimeter = the volume of 1 kilogram of pure water at a temperature of 39.2 degrees F.

Measures of Weight

10 milligrams (mg.) = 1 centigram (cg.).
10 centigrams = 1 decigram (dg.).
10 decigrams = 1 gram (g.).
10 grams = 1 decagram (Dg.).
10 decagrams = 1 hectogram (Hg.).
10 hectograms = 1 kilogram (Kg.).
1000 kilograms = 1 (metric) ton (T.).

Metric and English Conversion Table

Linear Measure

1 kilometer = 0.6214 mile.
1 meter = { 39.37 inches.
3.2808 feet.
1.0936 yard.
1 centimeter = 0.3937 inch.
1 millimeter = 0.03937 inch.

1 mile = 1.609 kilometer.
1 yard = 0.9144 meter.
1 foot = 0.3048 meter.
1 foot = 304.8 millimeters.
1 inch = 2.54 centimeters.
1 inch = 25.4 millimeters.

Square Measure

1 square kilometer = 0.3861 square mile = 247.1 acres.
1 hectare = 2.471 acre = 107,640 square feet.
1 are = 0.0247 acre = 1076.4 square feet.
1 square meter = 10.764 square feet = 1.196 square yard.
1 square centimeter = 0.155 square inch.
1 square millimeter = 0.00155 square inch.

---

1 square mile = 2.5899 square kilometers.
1 acre = 0.4047 hectare = 40.47 ares.
1 square yard = 0.836 square meter.
1 square foot = 0.0929 square meter = 929 square centimeters.
1 square inch = 6.452 square centimeters = 645.2 square millimeters.

Cubic Measure

1 cubic meter = 35.314 cubic feet = 1.308 cubic yard.
1 cubic meter = 264.2 U. S. gallons.
1 cubic centimeter = 0.061 cubic inch.
1 liter (cubic decimeter) = 0.0353 cubic foot = 61.023 cubic inches.
1 liter = 0.2642 U. S. gallon = 1.0567 U. S. quart.

1 cubic yard = 0.7645 cubic meter.
1 cubic foot = 0.02832 cubic meter = 28.317 liters.
1 cubic inch = 16.38716 cubic centimeters.
1 U. S. gallon = 3.785 liters.
1 U. S. quart = 0.946 liter.

Weight

1 metric ton = 0.9842 ton (of 2240 pounds) = 2204.6 pounds.
1 kilogram = 2.2046 pounds = 35.274 ounces avoirdupois.
1 gram = 0.03215 ounce troy = 0.03527 ounce avoirdupois.
1 gram = 15.432 grains.

---

1 ton (of 2240 pounds) = 1.016 metric ton = 1016 kilograms.
1 pound = 0.4536 kilogram = 453.6 grams.
1 ounce avoirdupois = 28.35 grams.
1 ounce troy = 31.103 grams.
1 grain = 0.0648 gram.

---

1 kilogram per square millimeter = 1422.32 pounds per square inch.
1 kilogram per square centimeter = 14.223 pounds per square inch.
1 kilogram-meter = 7.233 foot-pounds.
1 pound per square inch = 0.0703 kilogram per square centimeter.
1 calorie (kilogram calorie) = 3.968 B.T.U. (British thermal unit).

The C.G.S. System of Measurement

The C.G.S. (centimeter-gram-second) system, frequently known as the absolute system of measurement, is based upon the length and weight units of the metric system, and the second as the time unit. In this system, the unit of distance is one centimeter, the unit of mass (or weight) is one gram, and the unit of time, one second. From these fundamental units are derived:

Unit of velocity = 1 centimeter in one second.
Acceleration due to gravity (at Paris) = 981 centimeters in one second.
Unit of force = 1 dyne = 1/981 gram.
Unit of work = 1 erg = 1 dyne-centimeter.
Unit of power = 1 watt = 10,000,000 ergs per second.

The C.G.S. system of power measurements is becoming more and more used in the engineering field. It is used exclusively for electrical machines and apparatus on account of the simple relationship which exists between the various units. It is likely to be soon adopted in many other fields. The unit of work, erg, is so small that in practical work the joule is usually employed instead. One joule equals 10,000,000 ergs.

Standard of Length. — In 1866 the United States, by act of Congress, passed a law making legal the meter, the only measure of length that has been legalized by the United States Government. The United States yard is defined by the relation: 1 yard = $\frac{3600}{3937}$ meter. The legal equivalent of the meter for commercial purposes was fixed as 39.37 inches, by law, in July, 1866, and experience having shown that this value was exact within the error of observation, the United States

Office of Standard Weights and Measures was, in 1893, authorized to derive the yard from the meter by the use of this relation. The United States prototype meters Nos. 27 and 21 were received from the International Bureau of Weights and Measures in 1889. Meter No. 27, sealed in its metal case, is preserved in a fire-proof vault at the Bureau of Standards.

Comparisons made prior to 1893 indicated that the relation of the yard to the meter, fixed by the act of 1866, was by chance the exact relation between the international meter and the British imperial yard, within the error of observation. A subsequent comparison made between the standards just mentioned indicates that the legal relation adopted by Congress is in error 0.0001 inch; but, in view of the fact that certain comparisons made by the English Standards Office between the imperial yard and its authentic copies show variations as great if not greater than this, it cannot be said with certainty that there is a difference between the imperial yard of Great Britain and the United States yard derived from the meter. The bronze yard No. 11, which was an exact copy of the British imperial yard both in form and material, had shown changes when compared with the imperial yard in 1876 and 1888, which could not reasonably be said to be entirely due to changes in Bronze No. 11. On the other hand, the new meters represented the most advanced ideas of standards, and it therefore seemed that greater stability as well as higher accuracy would be secured by accepting the international meter as a fundamental standard of length.

Application of the Metric System.

Application of the Metric System. — In the practical application of the metric system in machine shop and drafting-room work, the part of the system with which the draftsman and machinist come into direct contact is the length measurements. The length units of the metric system that are most generally used in connection with any work relating to mechanical engineering are the meter, the centimeter, and the millimeter. The decimeter is not commonly used as a length measurement. On mechanical drawings all dimensions are generally given in millimeters, no matter how large they may be. In fact, dimensions of such machines as locomotives and large electrical apparatus are given exclusively in millimeters. This practice is adopted to avoid mistakes due to misplacing decimal points, or mis-reading dimensions if other units are used as well. When dimensions are given in millimeters, the majority can be given without resorting to decimal points, as a millimeter is only a trifle more than 1/32 inch. Only dimensions of precision need be given in decimals of a millimeter; such dimensions are generally given in hundredths of a millimeter — for example, 0.02 millimeter. As 0.01 millimeter is equal to 0.0004 inch, it is seldom that dimensions would be given with greater accuracy than to hundredths of a millimeter.

Drawings made to the metric system are not made to scales of 1/2, 1/4, 1/8, etc., as in the case of drawings made to the English system. If the object cannot be drawn full size, it is generally drawn one-fifth size, and, if this is too large, it is drawn one-tenth size. In exceptional cases, when very large objects are to be shown on a drawing, scales of one-twentieth, one-fiftieth, and one-one-hundredth may be used.

Tables of Metric Equivalents. — The following tables for converting milli-meters to inches are based on the equivalent of the meter as legalized by the United States Government, according to which 1 meter = 39.37 inches and 1 inch = 25.4000508 + or practically 25.4 millimeters. The use in industry of 25.4 millimeters as a simplified practical equivalent of one inch has been approved by the American Standards Association. This equivalent has also been adopted by industry in Great Britain (where the legal equivalent of one inch is 25.39998 millimeters) and in Germany, Italy, Russia, Switzerland, Sweden, and other countries.

Table for Converting Millimeters into Inches

Milli-meters	Inches	Milli-meters	Inches	Milli-meters	Inches	Milli-meters	Inches	Milli-meters	Inches
1	0.0394	51	2.0079	101	3.9764	151	5.9449	201	7.9134
2	0.0787	52	2.0472	102	4.0157	152	5.9842	202	7.9527
3	0.1181	53	2.0866	103	4.0551	153	6.0236	203	7.9921
4	0.1575	54	2.1260	104	4.0945	154	6.0630	204	8.0315
5	0.1968	55	2.1653	105	4.1338	155	6.1023	205	8.0708
6	0.2362	56	2.2047	106	4.1732	156	6.1417	206	8.1102
7	0.2756	57	2.2441	107	4.2126	157	6.1811	207	8.1496
8	0.3150	58	2.2835	108	4.2520	158	6.2205	208	8.1890
9	0.3543	59	2.3228	109	4.2913	159	6.2598	209	8.2283
10	0.3937	60	2.3622	110	4.3307	160	6.2992	210	8.2677
11	0.4331	61	2.4016	111	4.3701	161	6.3386	211	8.3071
12	0.4724	62	2.4409	112	4.4094	162	6.3779	212	8.3464
13	0.5118	63	2.4803	113	4.4488	163	6.4173	213	8.3858
14	0.5512	64	2.5197	114	4.4882	164	6.4567	214	8.4252
15	0.5905	65	2.5590	115	4.5275	165	6.4960	215	8.4645
16	0.6299	66	2.5984	116	4.5669	166	6.5354	216	8.5039
17	0.6693	67	2.6378	117	4.6063	167	6.5748	217	8.5433
18	0.7087	68	2.6772	118	4.6457	168	6.6142	218	8.5827
19	0.7480	69	2.7165	119	4.6850	169	6.6535	219	8.6220
20	0.7874	70	2.7559	120	4.7244	170	6.6929	220	8.6614
21	0.8268	71	2.7953	121	4.7638	171	6.7323	221	8.7008
22	0.8661	72	2.8346	122	4.8031	172	6.7716	222	8.7401
23	0.9055	73	2.8740	123	4.8425	173	6.8110	223	8.7795
24	0.9449	74	2.9134	124	4.8819	174	6.8504	224	8.8189
25	0.9842	75	2.9527	125	4.9212	175	6.8897	225	8.8582
26	1.0236	76	2.9921	126	4.9606	176	6.9291	226	8.8976
27	1.0630	77	3.0315	127	5.0000	177	6.9685	227	8.9370
28	1.1024	78	3.0709	128	5.0394	178	7.0079	228	8.9764
29	1.1417	79	3.1102	129	5.0787	179	7.0472	229	9.0157
30	1.1811	80	3.1496	130	5.1181	180	7.0866	230	9.0551
31	1.2205	81	3.1890	131	5.1575	181	7.1260	231	9.0945
32	1.2598	82	3.2283	132	5.1968	182	7.1653	232	9.1338
33	1.2992	83	3.2677	133	5.2362	183	7.2047	233	9.1732
34	1.3386	84	3.3071	134	5.2756	184	7.2441	234	9.2126
35	1.3779	85	3.3464	135	5.3149	185	7.2834	235	9.2519
36	1.4173	86	3.3858	136	5.3543	186	7.3228	236	9.2913
37	1.4567	87	3.4252	137	5.3937	187	7.3622	237	9.3307
38	1.4961	88	3.4646	138	5.4331	188	7.4016	238	9.3701
39	1.5354	89	3.5039	139	5.4724	189	7.4409	239	9.4094
40	1.5748	90	3.5433	140	5.5118	190	7.4803	240	9.4488
41	1.6142	91	3.5827	141	5.5512	191	7.5197	241	9.4882
42	1.6535	92	3.6220	142	5.5905	192	7.5590	242	9.5275
43	1.6929	93	3.6614	143	5.6299	193	7.5984	243	9.5669
44	1.7323	94	3.7008	144	5.6693	194	7.6378	244	9.6063
45	1.7716	95	3.7401	145	5.7086	195	7.6771	245	9.6456
46	1.8110	96	3.7795	146	5.7480	196	7.7165	246	9.6850
47	1.8504	97	3.8189	147	5.7874	197	7.7559	247	9.7244
48	1.8898	98	3.8583	148	5.8268	198	7.7953	248	9.7638
49	1.9291	99	3.8976	149	5.8661	199	7.8346	249	9.8031
50	1.9685	100	3.9370	150	5.9055	200	7.8740	250	9.8425

Table for Converting Millimeters into Inches (Continued)

Millimeters	Inches	Millimeters	Inches	Millimeters	Inches	Millimeters	Inches	Millimeters	Inches
251	9.8819	301	11.8504	351	13.8189	401	15.7874	451	17.7559
252	9.9212	302	11.8897	352	13.8582	402	15.8267	452	17.7952
253	9.9606	303	11.9291	353	13.8976	403	15.8661	453	17.8346
254	10.0000	304	11.9685	354	13.9370	404	15.9055	454	17.8740
255	10.0393	305	12.0078	355	13.9763	405	15.9448	455	17.9133
256	10.0787	306	12.0472	356	14.0157	406	15.9842	456	17.9527
257	10.1181	307	12.0866	357	14.0551	407	16.0236	457	17.9921
258	10.1575	308	12.1260	358	14.0945	408	16.0630	458	18.0315
259	10.1968	309	12.1653	359	14.1338	409	16.1023	459	18.0708
260	10.2362	310	12.2047	360	14.1732	410	16.1417	460	18.1102
261	10.2756	311	12.2441	361	14.2126	411	16.1811	461	18.1496
262	10.3149	312	12.2834	362	14.2519	412	16.2204	462	18.1889
263	10.3543	313	12.3228	363	14.2913	413	16.2598	463	18.2283
264	10.3937	314	12.3622	364	14.3307	414	16.2992	464	18.2677
265	10.4330	315	12.4015	365	14.3700	415	16.3385	465	18.3070
266	10.4724	316	12.4409	366	14.4094	416	16.3779	466	18.3464
267	10.5118	317	12.4803	367	14.4488	417	16.4173	467	18.3858
268	10.5512	318	12.5197	368	14.4882	418	16.4567	468	18.4252
269	10.5905	319	12.5590	369	14.5275	419	16.4960	469	18.4645
270	10.6299	320	12.5984	370	14.5669	420	16.5354	470	18.5039
271	10.6693	321	12.6378	371	14.6063	421	16.5748	471	18.5433
272	10.7086	322	12.6771	372	14.6456	422	16.6141	472	18.5826
273	10.7480	323	12.7165	373	14.6850	423	16.6535	473	18.6220
274	10.7874	324	12.7559	374	14.7244	424	16.6929	474	18.6614
275	10.8267	325	12.7952	375	14.7637	425	16.7322	475	18.7007
276	10.8661	326	12.8346	376	14.8031	426	16.7716	476	18.7401
277	10.9055	327	12.8740	377	14.8425	427	16.8110	477	18.7795
278	10.9449	328	12.9134	378	14.8819	428	16.8504	478	18.8189
279	10.9842	329	12.9527	379	14.9212	429	16.8897	479	18.8582
280	11.0236	330	12.9921	380	14.9606	430	16.9291	480	18.8976
281	11.0630	331	13.0315	381	15.0000	431	16.9685	481	18.9370
282	11.1023	332	13.0708	382	15.0393	432	17.0078	482	18.9763
283	11.1417	333	13.1102	383	15.0787	433	17.0472	483	19.0157
284	11.1811	334	13.1496	384	15.1181	434	17.0866	484	19.0551
285	11.2204	335	13.1889	385	15.1574	435	17.1259	485	19.0944
286	11.2598	336	13.2283	386	15.1968	436	17.1653	486	19.1338
287	11.2992	337	13.2677	387	15.2362	437	17.2047	487	19.1732
288	11.3386	338	13.3071	388	15.2756	438	17.2441	488	19.2126
289	11.3779	339	13.3464	389	15.3149	439	17.2834	489	19.2519
290	11.4173	340	13.3858	390	15.3543	440	17.3228	490	19.2913
291	11.4567	341	13.4252	391	15.3937	441	17.3622	491	19.3307
292	11.4960	342	13.4645	392	15.4330	442	17.4015	492	19.3700
293	11.5354	343	13.5039	393	15.4724	443	17.4409	493	19.4094
294	11.5748	344	13.5433	394	15.5118	444	17.4803	494	19.4488
295	11.6141	345	13.5826	395	15.5511	445	17.5196	495	19.4881
296	11.6535	346	13.6220	396	15.5905	446	17.5590	496	19.5275
297	11.6929	347	13.6614	397	15.6299	447	17.5984	497	19.5669
298	11.7323	348	13.7008	398	15.6693	448	17.6378	498	19.6063
299	11.7716	349	13.7401	399	15.7086	449	17.6771	499	19.6456
300	11.8110	350	13.7795	400	15.7480	450	17.7165	500	19.6850

Table for Converting Millimeters into Inches (Continued)

Millimeters	Inches	Millimeters	Inches	Millimeters	Inches	Millimeters	Inches	Millimeters	Inches
501	19.7244	551	21.6929	601	23.6614	651	25.6299	701	27.5984
502	19.7637	552	21.7322	602	23.7007	652	25.6692	702	27.6377
503	19.8031	553	21.7716	603	23.7401	653	25.7086	703	27.6771
504	19.8425	554	21.8110	604	23.7795	654	25.7480	704	27.7165
505	19.8818	555	21.8503	605	23.8188	655	25.7873	705	27.7558
506	19.9212	556	21.8897	606	23.8582	656	25.8267	706	27.7952
507	19.9606	557	21.9291	607	23.8976	657	25.8661	707	27.8346
508	20.0000	558	21.9685	608	23.9370	658	25.9055	708	27.8740
509	20.0393	559	22.0078	609	23.9763	659	25.9448	709	27.9133
510	20.0787	560	22.0472	610	24.0157	660	25.9842	710	27.9527
511	20.1181	561	22.0866	611	24.0551	661	26.0236	711	27.9921
512	20.1574	562	22.1259	612	24.0944	662	26.0629	712	28.0314
513	20.1968	563	22.1653	613	24.1338	663	26.1023	713	28.0708
514	20.2362	564	22.2047	614	24.1732	664	26.1417	714	28.1102
515	20.2755	565	22.2440	615	24.2125	665	26.1810	715	28.1495
516	20.3149	566	22.2834	616	24.2519	666	26.2204	716	28.1889
517	20.3543	567	22.3228	617	24.2913	667	26.2598	717	28.2283
518	20.3937	568	22.3622	618	24.3307	668	26.2992	718	28.2677
519	20.4330	569	22.4015	619	24.3700	669	26.3385	719	28.3070
520	20.4724	570	22.4409	620	24.4094	670	26.3779	720	28.3464
521	20.5118	571	22.4803	621	24.4488	671	26.4173	721	28.3858
522	20.5511	572	22.5196	622	24.4881	672	26.4566	722	28.4251
523	20.5905	573	22.5590	623	24.5275	673	26.4960	723	28.4645
524	20.6299	574	22.5984	624	24.5669	674	26.5354	724	28.5039
525	20.6692	575	22.6377	625	24.6062	675	26.5747	725	28.5432
526	20.7086	576	22.6771	626	24.6456	676	26.6141	726	28.5826
527	20.7480	577	22.7165	627	24.6850	677	26.6535	727	28.6220
528	20.7874	578	22.7559	628	24.7244	678	26.6929	728	28.6614
529	20.8267	579	22.7952	629	24.7637	679	26.7322	729	28.7007
530	20.8661	580	22.8346	630	24.8031	680	26.7716	730	28.7401
531	20.9055	581	22.8740	631	24.8425	681	26.8110	731	28.7795
532	20.9448	582	22.9133	632	24.8818	682	26.8503	732	28.8188
533	20.9842	583	22.9527	633	24.9212	683	26.8897	733	28.8582
534	21.0236	584	22.9921	634	24.9606	684	26.9291	734	28.8976
535	21.0629	585	23.0314	635	24.9999	685	26.9684	735	28.9369
536	21.1023	586	23.0708	636	25.0393	686	27.0078	736	28.9763
537	21.1417	587	23.1102	637	25.0787	687	27.0472	737	29.0157
538	21.1811	588	23.1496	638	25.1181	688	27.0866	738	29.0551
539	21.2204	589	23.1889	639	25.1574	689	27.1259	739	29.0944
540	21.2598	590	23.2283	640	25.1968	690	27.1653	740	29.1338
541	21.2992	591	23.2677	641	25.2362	691	27.2047	741	29.1732
542	21.3385	592	23.3070	642	25.2755	692	27.2440	742	29.2125
543	21.3779	593	23.3464	643	25.3149	693	27.2834	743	29.2519
544	21.4173	594	23.3858	644	25.3543	694	27.3228	744	29.2913
545	21.4566	595	23.4251	645	25.3936	695	27.3621	745	29.3307
546	21.4960	596	23.4645	646	25.4330	696	27.4015	746	29.3700
547	21.5354	597	23.5039	647	25.4724	697	27.4409	747	29.4094
548	21.5748	598	23.5433	648	25.5118	698	27.4803	748	29.4487
549	21.6141	599	23.5826	649	25.5511	699	27.5196	749	29.4881
550	21.6535	600	23.6220	650	25.5905	700	27.5590	750	29.5275

Table for Converting Millimeters into Inches (Continued)

Milli-meters	Inches	Milli-meters	Inches	Milli-meters	Inches	Milli-meters	Inches	Milli-meters	Inches
751	29.5669	801	31.5354	851	33.5039	901	35.4728	951	37.4409
752	29.6062	802	31.5747	852	33.5432	902	35.5117	952	37.4802
753	29.6456	803	31.6141	853	33.5826	903	35.5511	953	37.5196
754	29.6850	804	31.6535	854	33.6220	904	35.5905	954	37.5590
755	29.7243	805	31.6928	855	33.6613	905	35.6298	955	37.5983
756	29.7637	806	31.7322	856	33.7007	906	35.6692	956	37.6377
757	29.8031	807	31.7716	857	33.7401	907	35.7086	957	37.6771
758	29.8425	808	31.8110	858	33.7795	908	35.7480	958	37.7165
759	29.8818	809	31.8503	859	33.8188	909	35.7873	959	37.7558
760	29.9212	810	31.8897	860	33.8582	910	35.8267	960	37.7952
761	29.9606	811	31.9291	861	33.8976	911	35.8661	961	37.8346
762	29.9999	812	31.9684	862	33.9369	912	35.9054	962	37.8739
763	30.0393	813	32.0078	863	33.9763	913	35.9448	963	37.9133
764	30.0787	814	32.0472	864	34.0157	914	35.9842	964	37.9527
765	30.1180	815	32.0865	865	34.0550	915	36.0235	965	37.9920
766	30.1574	816	32.1259	866	34.0944	916	36.0629	966	38.0314
767	30.1968	817	32.1653	867	34.1338	917	36.1023	967	38.0708
768	30.2362	818	32.2047	868	34.1732	918	36.1417	968	38.1102
769	30.2755	819	32.2440	869	34.2125	919	36.1810	969	38.1495
770	30.3149	820	32.2834	870	34.2519	920	36.2204	970	38.1889
771	30.3543	821	32.3228	871	34.2913	921	36.2598	971	38.2283
772	30.3936	822	32.3621	872	34.3306	922	36.2991	972	38.2676
773	30.4330	823	32.4015	873	34.3700	923	36.3385	973	38.3070
774	30.4724	824	32.4409	874	34.4094	924	36.3779	974	38.3464
775	30.5117	825	32.4802	875	34.4487	925	36.4172	975	38.3857
776	30.5511	826	32.5196	876	34.4881	926	36.4566	976	38.4251
777	30.5905	827	32.5590	877	34.5275	927	36.4960	977	38.4645
778	30.6299	828	32.5984	878	34.5669	928	36.5354	978	38.5039
779	30.6692	829	32.6377	879	34.6062	929	36.5747	979	38.5432
780	30.7086	830	32.6771	880	34.6456	930	36.6141	980	38.5826
781	30.7480	831	32.7165	881	34.6850	931	36.6535	981	38.6220
782	30.7873	832	32.7558	882	34.7243	932	36.6928	982	38.6613
783	30.8267	833	32.7952	883	34.7637	933	36.7322	983	38.7007
784	30.8661	834	32.8346	884	34.8031	934	36.7716	984	38.7401
785	30.9054	835	32.8739	885	34.8424	935	36.8109	985	38.7794
786	30.9448	836	32.9133	886	34.8818	936	36.8503	986	38.8188
787	30.9842	837	32.9527	887	34.9212	937	36.8897	987	38.8582
788	31.0236	838	32.9921	888	34.9606	938	36.9291	988	38.8976
789	31.0629	839	33.0314	889	34.9999	939	36.9684	989	38.9369
790	31.1023	840	33.0708	890	35.0393	940	37.0078	990	38.9763
791	31.1417	841	33.1102	891	35.0787	941	37.0472	991	39.0157
792	31.1810	842	33.1495	892	35.1180	942	37.0865	992	39.0550
793	31.2204	843	33.1889	893	35.1574	943	37.1259	993	39.0944
794	31.2598	844	33.2283	894	35.1968	944	37.1653	994	39.1338
795	31.2991	845	33.2676	895	35.2361	945	37.2046	995	39.1731
796	31.3385	846	33.3070	896	35.2755	946	37.2440	996	39.2125
797	31.3779	847	33.3464	897	35.3149	947	37.2834	997	39.2519
798	31.4173	848	33.3858	898	35.3543	948	37.3228	998	39.2913
799	31.4566	849	33.4251	899	35.3936	949	37.3621	999	39.3306
800	31.4960	850	33.4645	900	35.4330	950	37.4015	1000	39.3700

Inches into Millimeters

Inches	Millimeters	Inches	Millimeters	Inches	Millimeters	Inches	Millimeters	Inches	Millimeters
1/64	0.3969	51/64	20.2406	2 5/32	54.7688	3 23/32	94.4564	5 9/32	134.144
1/32	0.7937	13/16	20.6375	2 3/16	55.5626	3 3/4	95.2502	5 5/16	134.938
3/64	1.1906	53/64	21.0344	2 7/32	56.3564	3 25/32	96.0439	5 11/32	135.732
1/16	1.5875	27/32	21.4312	2 1/4	57.1501	3 13/16	96.8377	5 3/8	136.525
5/64	1.9844	55/64	21.8281	2 9/32	57.9439	3 27/32	97.6314	5 13/32	137.319
3/32	2.3812	7/8	22.2250	2 5/16	58.7376	3 7/8	98.4252	5 7/16	138.113
7/64	2.7781	57/64	22.6219	2 11/32	59.5314	3 29/32	99.2189	5 15/32	138.907
1/8	3.1750	29/32	23.0187	2 3/8	60.3251	3 15/16	100.013	5 1/2	139.700
9/64	3.5719	59/64	23.4156	2 13/32	61.1189	3 31/32	100.806	5 17/32	140.494
5/32	3.9687	15/16	23.8125	2 7/16	61.9126	4	101.600	5 9/16	141.288
11/64	4.3656	61/64	24.2094	2 15/32	62.7064	4 1/32	102.394	5 19/32	142.082
3/16	4.7625	31/32	24.6062	2 1/2	63.5001	4 1/16	103.188	5 5/8	142.875
13/64	5.1594	63/64	25.0031	2 17/32	64.2939	4 3/32	103.981	5 21/32	143.669
7/32	5.5562	1	25.4001	2 9/16	65.0876	4 1/8	104.775	5 11/16	144.463
15/64	5.9531	1 1/32	26.1938	2 19/32	65.8814	4 5/32	105.569	5 23/32	145.257
1/4	6.3500	1 1/16	26.9876	2 5/8	66.6751	4 3/16	106.363	5 3/4	146.050
17/64	6.7469	1 3/32	27.7813	2 21/32	67.4689	4 7/32	107.156	5 25/32	146.844
9/32	7.1437	1 1/8	28.5751	2 11/16	68.2626	4 1/4	107.950	5 13/16	147.638
19/64	7.5406	1 5/32	29.3688	2 23/32	69.0564	4 9/32	108.744	5 27/32	148.432
5/16	7.9375	1 3/16	30.1626	2 3/4	69.8501	4 5/16	109.538	5 7/8	149.225
21/64	8.3344	1 7/32	30.9563	2 25/32	70.6439	4 11/32	110.331	5 29/32	150.019
11/32	8.7312	1 1/4	31.7501	2 13/16	71.4376	4 3/8	111.125	5 15/16	150.813
23/64	9.1281	1 9/32	32.5438	2 27/32	72.2314	4 13/32	111.919	5 31/32	151.607
3/8	9.5250	1 5/16	33.3376	2 7/8	73.0251	4 7/16	112.713	6	152.400
25/64	9.9219	1 11/32	34.1313	2 29/32	73.8189	4 15/32	113.506	6 1/16	153.988
13/32	10.3187	1 3/8	34.9251	2 15/16	74.6126	4 1/2	114.300	6 1/8	155.575
27/64	10.7156	1 13/32	35.7188	2 31/32	75.4064	4 17/32	115.094	6 3/16	157.163
7/16	11.1125	1 7/16	36.5126	3	76.2002	4 9/16	115.888	6 1/4	158.750
29/64	11.5094	1 15/32	37.3063	3 1/32	76.9939	4 19/32	116.681	6 5/16	160.338
15/32	11.9062	1 1/2	38.1001	3 1/16	77.7877	4 5/8	117.475	6 3/8	161.925
31/64	12.3031	1 17/32	38.8938	3 3/32	78.5814	4 21/32	118.269	6 7/16	163.513
1/2	12.7000	1 9/16	39.6876	3 1/8	79.3752	4 11/16	119.063	6 1/2	165.100
33/64	13.0969	1 19/32	40.4813	3 5/32	80.1689	4 23/32	119.856	6 9/16	166.688
17/32	13.4937	1 5/8	41.2751	3 3/16	80.9627	4 3/4	120.650	6 5/8	168.275
35/64	13.8906	1 21/32	42.0688	3 7/32	81.7564	4 25/32	121.444	6 11/16	169.863
9/16	14.2875	1 11/16	42.8626	3 1/4	82.5502	4 13/16	122.238	6 3/4	171.450
37/64	14.6844	1 23/32	43.6563	3 9/32	83.3439	4 27/32	123.031	6 13/16	173.038
19/32	15.0812	1 3/4	44.4501	3 5/16	84.1377	4 7/8	123.825	6 7/8	174.625
39/64	15.4781	1 25/32	45.2438	3 11/32	84.9314	4 29/32	124.619	6 15/16	176.213
5/8	15.8750	1 13/16	46.0376	3 3/8	85.7252	4 15/16	125.413	7	177.800
41/64	16.2719	1 27/32	46.8313	3 13/32	86.5189	4 31/32	126.206	7 1/16	179.388
21/32	16.6687	1 7/8	47.6251	3 7/16	87.3127	5	127.000	7 1/8	180.975
43/64	17.0656	1 29/32	48.4188	3 15/32	88.1064	5 1/32	127.794	7 3/16	182.563
11/16	17.4625	1 15/16	49.2126	3 1/2	88.9002	5 1/16	128.588	7 1/4	184.150
45/64	17.8594	1 31/32	50.0063	3 17/32	89.6939	5 3/32	129.382	7 5/16	185.738
23/32	18.2562	2	50.8001	3 9/16	90.4877	5 1/8	130.175	7 3/8	187.325
47/64	18.6531	2 1/32	51.5939	3 19/32	91.2814	5 5/32	130.969	7 7/16	188.913
3/4	19.0500	2 1/16	52.3876	3 5/8	92.0752	5 3/16	131.763	7 1/2	190.500
49/64	19.4469	2 3/32	53.1814	3 21/32	92.8689	5 7/32	132.557	7 9/16	192.088
25/32	19.8437	2 1/8	53.9751	3 11/16	93.6627	5 1/4	133.350	7 5/8	193.675

Feet and Inches into Millimeters

Inches	Millimeters	Inches	Millimeters	Ft. In.	Millimeters	Ft. In.	Millimeters	Feet	Millimeters
7 11/16	195.263	10 13/16	274.638	3 7	1092.20	7 9	2362.20	33	10,058.4
7 3/4	196.850	10 7/8	276.226	3 8	1117.60	7 10	2387.60	34	10,363.2
7 13/16	198.438	10 15/16	277.813	3 9	1143.00	7 11	2413.00	35	10,668.0
7 7/8	200.025	11	279.401	3 10	1168.40	8 0	2438.40	36	10,972.8
7 15/16	201.613	11 1/16	280.988	3 11	1193.80	8 1	2463.80	37	11,277.6
8	203.200	11 1/8	282.576	4 0	1219.20	8 2	2489.20	38	11,582.4
8 1/16	204.788	11 3/16	284.163	4 1	1244.60	8 3	2514.61	39	11,887.2
8 1/8	206.375	11 1/4	285.751	4 2	1270.00	8 4	2540.01	40	12,192.0
8 3/16	207.963	11 5/16	287.338	4 3	1295.40	8 5	2565.41	41	12,496.8
8 1/4	209.550	11 3/8	288.926	4 4	1320.80	8 6	2590.81	42	12,801.6
8 5/16	211.138	11 7/16	290.513	4 5	1346.20	8 7	2616.21	43	13,106.4
8 3/8	212.725	11 1/2	292.101	4 6	1371.60	8 8	2641.61	44	13,411.2
8 7/16	214.313	11 9/16	293.688	4 7	1397.00	8 9	2667.01	45	13,716.0
8 1/2	215.900	11 5/8	295.276	4 8	1422.40	8 10	2692.41	46	14,020.8
8 9/16	217.488	11 11/16	296.863	4 9	1447.80	8 11	2717.81	47	14,325.6
8 5/8	219.075	11 3/4	298.451	4 10	1473.20	9 0	2743.21	48	14,630.4
8 11/16	220.663	11 13/16	300.038	4 11	1498.60	9 1	2768.61	49	14,935.2
8 3/4	222.250	11 7/8	301.626	5 0	1524.00	9 2	2794.01	50	15,240.0
8 13/16	223.838	11 15/16	303.213	5 1	1549.40	9 3	2819.41	51	15,544.8
8 7/8	225.425	12	304.801	5 2	1574.80	9 4	2844.81	52	15,849.6
8 15/16	227.013	13	330.201	5 3	1600.20	9 5	2870.21	53	16,154.4
9	228.600	14	355.601	5 4	1625.60	9 6	2895.61	54	16,459.2
9 1/16	230.188	15	381.001	5 5	1651.00	9 7	2921.01	55	16,764.0
9 1/8	231.775	16	406.401	5 6	1676.40	9 8	2946.41	56	17,068.8
9 3/16	233.363	17	431.801	5 7	1701.80	9 9	2971.81	57	17,373.6
9 1/4	234.950	18	457.201	5 8	1727.20	9 10	2997.21	58	17,678.4
9 5/16	236.538	19	482.601	5 9	1752.60	9 11	3022.61	59	17,983.2
9 3/8	238.125	20	508.001	5 10	1778.00	10 0	3048.01	60	18,288.0
9 7/16	239.713	21	533.401	5 11	1803.40	11 0	3352.81	61	18,592.8
9 1/2	241.300	22	558.801	6 0	1828.80	12 0	3657.61	62	18,897.6
9 9/16	242.888	23	584.201	6 1	1854.20	13 0	3962.41	63	19,202.4
9 5/8	244.475	24	609.601	6 2	1879.60	14 0	4267.21	64	19,507.2
9 11/16	246.063	25	635.001	6 3	1905.00	15 0	4572.01	65	19,812.0
9 3/4	247.650	26	660.401	6 4	1930.40	16 0	4876.81	66	20,116.8
9 13/16	249.238	27	685.801	6 5	1955.80	17 0	5181.61	67	20,421.6
9 7/8	250.825	28	711.201	6 6	1981.20	18 0	5486.41	68	20,726.4
9 15/16	252.413	29	736.601	6 7	2006.60	19 0	5791.21	69	21,031.2
10	254.001	30	762.002	6 8	2032.00	20 0	6096.01	70	21,336.0
10 1/16	255.588	31	787.402	6 9	2057.40	21 0	6400.81	71	21,640.8
10 1/8	257.176	32	812.802	6 10	2082.80	22 0	6705.61	72	21,945.6
10 3/16	258.763	33	838.202	6 11	2108.20	23 0	7010.41	73	22,250.4
10 1/4	260.351	34	863.602	7 0	2133.60	24 0	7315.21	74	22,555.2
10 5/16	261.938	35	889.002	7 1	2159.00	25 0	7620.02	75	22,860.0
10 3/8	263.526	36	914.402	7 2	2184.40	26 0	7924.82	76	23,164.8
10 7/16	265.113	37	939.802	7 3	2209.80	27 0	8229.62	77	23,469.6
10 1/2	266.701	38	965.202	7 4	2235.20	28 0	8534.42	78	23,774.4
10 9/16	268.288	39	990.602	7 5	2260.60	29 0	8839.22	79	24,079.2
10 5/8	269.876	40	1016.00	7 6	2286.00	30 0	9144.02	80	24,384.0
10 11/16	271.463	41	1041.40	7 7	2311.40	31 0	9448.82	81	24,688.8
10 3/4	273.051	42	1066.80	7 8	2336.80	32 0	9753.62	82	24,993.6

Hundredths of a Millimeter into Inches

Millimeters	Inches	Millimeters	Inches	Millimeters	Inches	Millimeters	Inches	Millimeters	Inches
0.01	0.0004	0.21	0.0083	0.41	0.0161	0.61	0.0240	0.81	0.0319
0.02	0.0008	0.22	0.0087	0.42	0.0165	0.62	0.0244	0.82	0.0323
0.03	0.0012	0.23	0.0091	0.43	0.0169	0.63	0.0248	0.83	0.0327
0.04	0.0016	0.24	0.0094	0.44	0.0173	0.64	0.0252	0.84	0.0331
0.05	0.0020	0.25	0.0098	0.45	0.0177	0.65	0.0256	0.85	0.0335
0.06	0.0024	0.26	0.0102	0.46	0.0181	0.66	0.0260	0.86	0.0339
0.07	0.0028	0.27	0.0106	0.47	0.0185	0.67	0.0264	0.87	0.0343
0.08	0.0031	0.28	0.0110	0.48	0.0189	0.68	0.0268	0.88	0.0346
0.09	0.0035	0.29	0.0114	0.49	0.0193	0.69	0.0272	0.89	0.0350
0.10	0.0039	0.30	0.0118	0.50	0.0197	0.70	0.0276	0.90	0.0354
0.11	0.0043	0.31	0.0122	0.51	0.0201	0.71	0.0280	0.91	0.0358
0.12	0.0047	0.32	0.0126	0.52	0.0205	0.72	0.0283	0.92	0.0362
0.13	0.0051	0.33	0.0130	0.53	0.0209	0.73	0.0287	0.93	0.0366
0.14	0.0055	0.34	0.0134	0.54	0.0213	0.74	0.0291	0.94	0.0370
0.15	0.0059	0.35	0.0138	0.55	0.0217	0.75	0.0295	0.95	0.0374
0.16	0.0063	0.36	0.0142	0.56	0.0220	0.76	0.0299	0.96	0.0378
0.17	0.0067	0.37	0.0146	0.57	0.0224	0.77	0.0303	0.97	0.0382
0.18	0.0071	0.38	0.0150	0.58	0.0228	0.78	0.0307	0.98	0.0386
0.19	0.0075	0.39	0.0154	0.59	0.0232	0.79	0.0311	0.99	0.0390
0.20	0.0079	0.40	0.0157	0.60	0.0236	0.80	0.0315	1.00	0.0394

Decimals of an Inch into Millimeters

Inches	Millimeters	Inches	Millimeters	Inches	Millimeters	Inches	Millimeters	Inches	Millimeters
0.001	0.025	0.140	3.56	0.360	9.14	0.580	14.73	0.800	20.32
0.002	0.051	0.150	3.81	0.370	9.40	0.590	14.99	0.810	20.57
0.003	0.076	0.160	4.06	0.380	9.65	0.600	15.24	0.820	20.83
0.004	0.102	0.170	4.32	0.390	9.91	0.610	15.49	0.830	21.08
0.005	0.127	0.180	4.57	0.400	10.16	0.620	15.75	0.840	21.34
0.006	0.152	0.190	4.83	0.410	10.41	0.630	16.00	0.850	21.59
0.007	0.178	0.200	5.08	0.420	10.67	0.640	16.26	0.860	21.84
0.008	0.203	0.210	5.33	0.430	10.92	0.650	16.51	0.870	22.10
0.009	0.229	0.220	5.59	0.440	11.18	0.660	16.76	0.880	22.35
0.010	0.254	0.230	5.84	0.450	11.43	0.670	17.02	0.890	22.61
0.020	0.508	0.240	6.10	0.460	11.68	0.680	17.27	0.900	22.86
0.030	0.762	0.250	6.35	0.470	11.94	0.690	17.53	0.910	23.11
0.040	1.016	0.260	6.60	0.480	12.19	0.700	17.78	0.920	23.37
0.050	1.270	0.270	6.86	0.490	12.45	0.710	18.03	0.930	23.62
0.060	1.524	0.280	7.11	0.500	12.70	0.720	18.29	0.940	23.88
0.070	1.778	0.290	7.37	0.510	12.95	0.730	18.54	0.950	24.13
0.080	2.032	0.300	7.62	0.520	13.21	0.740	18.80	0.960	24.38
0.090	2.286	0.310	7.87	0.530	13.46	0.750	19.05	0.970	24.64
0.100	2.540	0.320	8.13	0.540	13.72	0.760	19.30	0.980	24.89
0.110	2.794	0.330	8.38	0.550	13.97	0.770	19.56	0.990	25.15
0.120	3.048	0.340	8.64	0.560	14.22	0.780	19.81	1.000	25.40
0.130	3.302	0.350	8.89	0.570	14.48	0.790	20.07	....	....

Example: — Find 0.856 inch in millimeters; 0.850 inch = 21.59 millimeters; 0.006 inch = 0.152 millimeter. Hence 21.59 + 0.152 = 21.742 millimeters = 0.856 inch.

Inches into Centimeters

Inches	0	1	2	3	4	5	6	7	8	9
	Cm.	Cm.	Cm.	Cm.	Cm.	Cm.	Cm.	Cm.	Cm.	Cm.
0	.....	2.54	5.08	7.62	10.16	12.70	15.24	17.78	20.32	22.86
10	25.40	27.94	30.48	33.02	35.56	38.10	40.64	43.18	45.72	48.26
20	50.80	53.34	55.88	58.42	60.96	63.50	66.04	68.58	71.12	73.66
30	76.20	78.74	81.28	83.82	86.36	88.90	91.44	93.98	96.52	99.06
40	101.60	104.14	106.68	109.22	111.76	114.30	116.84	119.38	121.92	124.46
50	127.00	129.54	132.08	134.62	137.16	139.70	142.24	144.78	147.32	149.86
60	152.40	154.94	157.48	160.02	162.56	165.10	167.64	170.18	172.72	175.26
70	177.80	180.34	182.88	185.42	187.96	190.50	193.04	195.58	198.12	200.66
80	203.20	205.74	208.28	210.82	213.36	215.90	218.44	220.98	223.52	226.06
90	228.60	231.14	233.68	236.22	238.76	241.30	243.84	246.38	248.92	251.46
100	254.00	256.54	259.08	261.62	264.16	266.70	269.24	271.78	274.32	276.86

Centimeters into Inches

Cm.	0	1	2	3	4	5	6	7	8	9
	Inch	Inch	Inch	Inch	Inch	Inch	Inch	Inch	Inch	Inch
0	.....	0.394	0.787	1.181	1.575	1.969	2.362	2.756	3.150	3.543
10	3.937	4.331	4.724	5.118	5.512	5.906	6.299	6.693	7.087	7.480
20	7.874	8.268	8.661	9.055	9.449	9.843	10.236	10.630	11.024	11.417
30	11.811	12.205	12.598	12.992	13.386	13.780	14.173	14.567	14.961	15.354
40	15.748	16.142	16.535	16.929	17.323	17.717	18.110	18.504	18.898	19.291
50	19.685	20.079	20.472	20.866	21.260	21.654	22.047	22.441	22.835	23.228
60	23.622	24.016	24.409	24.803	25.197	25.591	25.984	26.378	26.772	27.164
70	27.559	27.953	28.346	28.740	29.134	29.528	29.921	30.315	30.709	31.102
80	31.496	31.890	32.283	32.677	33.071	33.465	33.858	34.252	34.646	35.039
90	35.433	35.827	36.220	36.614	37.008	37.402	37.795	38.189	38.583	38.976
100	39.370	39.764	40.157	40.551	40.945		41.732	42.126	42.520	42.913

Feet into Meters

Feet	0	1	2	3	4	5	6	7	8	9
	Meters	Meters	Meters	Meters	Meters	Meters	Meters	Meters	Meters	Meters
0	.....	0.305	0.610	0.914	1.219	1.524	1.829	2.134	2.438	2.743
10	3.048	3.353	3.658	3.962	4.267	4.572	4.877	5.182	5.486	5.791
20	6.096	6.401	6.706	7.010	7.315	7.620	7.925	8.229	8.534	8.839
30	9.144	9.449	9.753	10.058	10.363	10.668	10.972	11.277	11.582	11.887
40	12.192	12.496	12.801	13.106	13.411	13.716	14.020	14.325	14.630	14.935
50	15.239	15.544	15.849	16.154	16.459	16.763	17.068	17.373	17.678	17.983
60	18.287	18.592	18.897	19.202	19.507	19.811	20.116	20.421	20.726	21.031
70	21.335	21.640	21.945	22.250	22.555	22.859	23.164	23.469	23.774	24.079
80	24.383	24.688	24.993	25.298	25.602	25.907	26.212	26.517	26.822	27.126
90	27.431	27.736	28.041	28.346	28.651	28.955	29.260	29.565	29.870	30.174
100	30.479	30.784	31.089	31.394	31.698	32.003	32.308	32.613	32.918	33.222

Meters into Feet

Meters	0	1	2	3	4	5	6	7	8	9
	Feet	Feet	Feet	Feet	Feet	Feet	Feet	Feet	Feet	Feet
0	.....	3.281	6.562	9.842	13.123	16.404	19.685	22.966	26.247	29.527
10	32.808	36.089	39.370	42.651	45.932	49.212	52.493	55.774	59.055	62.336
20	65.617	68.897	72.178	75.459	78.740	82.021	85.302	88.582	91.863	95.144
30	98.425	101.71	104.99	108.27	111.55	114.83	118.11	121.39	124.67	127.95
40	131.23	134.51	137.79	141.08	144.36	147.64	150.92	154.20	157.48	160.76
50	164.04	167.32	170.60	173.88	177.16	180.45	183.73	187.01	190.29	193.57
60	196.85	200.13	203.41	206.69	209.97	213.25	216.53	219.82	223.10	226.38
70	229.66	232.94	236.22	239.50	242.78	246.06	249.34	252.62	255.90	259.19
80	262.47	265.75	269.03	272.31	275.59	278.87	282.15	285.43	288.71	291.99
90	295.27	298.56	301.84	305.12	308.40	311.68	314.96	318.24	321.52	324.80
100	328.08	331.36	334.64	337.93	341.21	344.49	347.77	351.05	354.33	357.61

Square Inches into Square Centimeters

Square Inches	0 Sq. Cm.	1 Sq. Cm.	2 Sq. Cm.	3 Sq. Cm.	4 Sq. Cm.	5 Sq. Cm.	6 Sq. Cm.	7 Sq. Cm.	8 Sq. Cm.	9 Sq. Cm.
0		6.45	12.90	19.36	25.81	32.26	38.71	45.16	51.61	58.07
10	64.52	70.97	77.42	83.87	90.32	96.77	103.23	109.68	116.13	122.58
20	129.03	135.48	141.94	148.39	154.84	161.29	167.74	174.19	180.65	187.10
30	193.55	200.00	206.45	212.90	219.36	225.81	232.26	238.71	245.16	251.61
40	258.07	264.52	270.97	277.42	283.87	290.32	296.77	303.23	309.68	316.13
50	322.58	329.03	335.48	341.93	348.39	354.84	361.29	367.74	374.19	380.65
60	387.10	393.55	400.00	406.45	412.90	419.36	425.81	432.26	438.71	445.16
70	451.61	458.07	464.52	470.97	477.42	483.87	490.32	496.78	503.23	509.68
80	516.13	522.58	529.03	535.48	541.94	548.39	554.84	561.29	567.74	574.19
90	580.65	587.10	593.55	600.00	606.45	612.90	619.36	625.81	632.26	638.71
100	645.17	651.62	658.07	664.52	670.97	677.42	683.88	690.33	696.78	703.23

Square Centimeters into Square Inches

Square Cm.	0 Sq. In.	1 Sq. In.	2 Sq. In.	3 Sq. In.	4 Sq. In.	5 Sq. In.	6 Sq. In.	7 Sq. In.	8 Sq. In.	9 Sq. In.
0	.....	0.155	0.310	0.465	0.620	0.775	0.930	1.085	1.240	1.395
10	1.550	1.705	1.860	2.015	2.170	2.325	2.480	2.635	2.790	2.945
20	3.100	3.255	3.410	3.565	3.720	3.875	4.030	4.185	4.340	4.495
30	4.650	4.805	4.960	5.115	5.270	5.425	5.580	5.735	5.890	6.045
40	6.200	6.355	6.510	6.665	6.820	6.975	7.130	7.285	7.440	7.595
50	7.750	7.905	8.060	8.215	8.370	8.525	8.680	8.835	8.990	9.145
60	9.300	9.455	9.610	9.765	9.920	10.075	10.230	10.385	10.540	10.695
70	10.850	11.005	11.160	11.315	11.470	11.625	11.780	11.935	12.090	12.245
80	12.400	12.555	12.710	12.865	13.020	13.175	13.330	13.485	13.640	13.795
90	13.950	14.105	14.260	14.415	14.570	14.725	14.880	15.035	15.190	15.345
100	15.500	15.655	15.810	15.965	16.120	16.275	16.430	16.585	16.740	16.895

Square Feet into Square Meters

Square Feet	0 Sq. Meters	1 Sq. Meters	2 Sq. Meters	3 Sq. Meters	4 Sq. Meters	5 Sq. Meters	6 Sq. Meters	7 Sq. Meters	8 Sq. Meters	9 Sq. Meters
0	.....	0.0929	0.1858	0.2787	0.3716	0.4645	0.5574	0.6503	0.7432	0.8361
10	0.9290	1.0219	1.1148	1.2077	1.3006	1.3936	1.4865	1.5794	1.6723	1.7652
20	1.8581	1.9510	2.0439	2.1368	2.2297	2.3226	2.4155	2.5084	2.6013	2.6942
30	2.7871	2.8800	2.9729	3.0658	3.1587	3.2516	3.3445	3.4374	3.5303	3.6232
40	3.7161	3.8090	3.9019	3.9948	4.0878	4.1807	4.2736	4.3665	4.4594	4.5523
50	4.6452	4.7381	4.8310	4.9239	5.0168	5.1097	5.2026	5.2955	5.3884	5.4813
60	5.5742	5.6671	5.7600	5.8529	5.9458	6.0387	6.1316	6.2245	6.3174	6.4103
70	6.5032	6.5961	6.6890	6.7819	6.8749	6.9678	7.0607	7.1536	7.2465	7.3394
80	7.4323	7.5252	7.6181	7.7110	7.8039	7.8968	7.9897	8.0826	8.1755	8.2684
90	8.3613	8.4542	8.5471	8.6400	8.7329	8.8258	8.9187	9.0116	9.1045	9.1974
100	9.2903	9.3832	9.4761	9.5690	9.6619	9.7548	9.8477	9.9406	10.0335	10.1264

Square Meters into Square Feet

Square Meters	0 Sq. Ft.	1 Sq. Ft.	2 Sq. Ft.	3 Sq. Ft.	4 Sq. Ft.	5 Sq. Ft.	6 Sq. Ft.	7 Sq. Ft.	8 Sq. Ft.	9 Sq. Ft.
0	.....	10.76	21.53	32.29	43.06	53.82	64.58	75.35	86.11	96.88
10	107.64	118.40	129.17	139.93	150.69	161.46	172.22	182.99	193.75	204.51
20	215.28	226.04	236.81	247.57	258.33	269.10	279.86	290.62	301.39	312.15
30	322.92	333.68	344.44	355.21	365.97	376.74	387.50	398.26	409.03	419.79
40	430.55	441.32	452.08	462.85	473.61	484.37	495.14	505.90	516.67	527.43
50	538.19	548.96	559.72	570.48	581.25	592.01	602.78	613.54	624.30	635.07
60	645.83	656.60	667.36	678.12	688.89	699.65	710.42	721.18	731.94	742.71
70	753.47	764.23	775.00	785.76	796.53	807.29	818.05	828.82	839.58	850.35
80	861.11	871.87	882.64	893.40	904.16	914.93	925.69	936.46	947.22	957.98
90	968.75	979.51	990.28	1001.04	1011.80	1022.57	1033.33	1044.10	1054.86	1065.62
100	1076.39	1087.15	1097.92	1108.68	1119.44	1130.21	1140.97	1151.74	1162.50	1173.26

Cubic Inches into Cubic Centimeters

Cubic Inches	0 Cubic Cm.	1 Cubic Cm.	2 Cubic Cm.	3 Cubic Cm.	4 Cubic Cm.	5 Cubic Cm.	6 Cubic Cm.	7 Cubic Cm.	8 Cubic Cm.	9 Cubic Cm.
0	.....	16.38	32.77	49.16	65.55	81.93	98.32	114.71	131.09	147.48
10	163.87	180.26	196.64	213.03	229.41	245.80	262.19	278.58	294.88	311.35
20	327.73	344.12	360.50	376.89	393.27	409.66	426.05	442.44	458.74	475.21
30	491.60	507.99	524.37	540.76	557.14	573.53	589.92	606.31	622.61	639.08
40	655.46	671.85	688.23	704.52	721.00	737.39	753.78	770.17	786.47	802.94
50	819.33	835.72	851.10	868.49	884.87	901.26	917.65	934.04	950.34	966.81
60	983.20	999.59	1016.0	1032.4	1048.7	1065.1	1081.5	1097.9	1114.2	1130.7
70	1147.1	1163.5	1179.9	1196.3	1212.6	1229.0	1245.4	1261.8	1278.1	1294.6
80	1310.9	1327.3	1343.7	1360.1	1376.4	1392.8	1409.2	1425.6	1441.9	1458.4
90	1474.8	1491.2	1507.6	1524.0	1540.3	1556.7	1573.1	1589.5	1605.8	1622.3
100	1638.7	1655.1	1671.5	1687.9	1704.2	1720.6	1737.0	1753.4	1769.7	1786.2

Cubic Centimeters into Cubic Inches

Cubic Cm.	0 Cubic Inches	1 Cubic Inches	2 Cubic Inches	3 Cubic Inches	4 Cubic Inches	5 Cubic Inches	6 Cubic Inches	7 Cubic Inches	8 Cubic Inches	9 Cubic Inches
0	.....	0.0610	0.1221	0.1831	0.2441	0.3051	0.3661	0.4272	0.4882	0.5492
10	0.6102	0.6712	0.7323	0.7933	0.8543	0.9153	0.9763	1.0374	1.0984	1.1594
20	1.2205	1.2815	1.3426	1.4036	1.4646	1.5256	1.5866	1.6477	1.7087	1.7697
30	1.8308	1.8918	1.9529	2.0139	2.0749	2.1359	2.1969	2.2580	2.3190	2.3800
40	2.4410	2.5020	2.5631	2.6241	2.6851	2.7461	2.8071	2.8682	2.9292	2.9902
50	3.0513	3.1123	3.1734	3.2344	3.2954	3.3564	3.4174	3.4785	3.5395	3.6005
60	3.6615	3.7225	3.7836	3.8446	3.9056	3.9666	4.0276	4.0887	4.1497	4.2107
70	4.2718	4.3328	4.3939	4.4549	4.5159	4.5769	4.6379	4.6990	4.7600	4.8210
80	4.8820	4.9430	5.0041	5.0651	5.1261	5.1871	5.2481	5.3092	5.3702	5.4312
90	5.4923	5.5533	5.6144	5.6754	5.7364	5.7974	5.8584	5.9195	5.9805	6.0415
100	6.1025	6.1635	6.2246	6.2856	6.3466	6.4076	6.4686	6.5297	6.5907	6.6517

Cubic Feet into Cubic Meters

Cubic Feet	0 Cubic Meters	1 Cubic Meters	2 Cubic Meters	3 Cubic Meters	4 Cubic Meters	5 Cubic Meters	6 Cubic Meters	7 Cubic Meters	8 Cubic Meters	9 Cubic Meters
0	.....	0.0283	0.0566	0.0850	0.1133	0.1416	0.1699	0.1982	0.2265	0.2549
10	0.2832	0.3115	0.3398	0.3681	0.3964	0.4248	0.4531	0.4814	0.5097	0.5380
20	0.5663	0.5947	0.6230	0.6513	0.6796	0.7079	0.7362	0.7646	0.7929	0.8212
30	0.8495	0.8778	0.9061	0.9345	0.9628	0.9911	1.0194	1.0477	1.0760	1.1044
40	1.1327	1.1610	1.1893	1.2176	1.2459	1.2743	1.3026	1.3309	1.3592	1.3875
50	1.4159	1.4442	1.4725	1.5008	1.5291	1.5574	1.5858	1.6141	1.6424	1.6707
60	1.6990	1.7273	1.7557	1.7840	1.8123	1.8406	1.8689	1.8972	1.9256	1.9539
70	1.9822	2.0105	2.0388	2.0671	2.0955	2.1238	2.1521	2.1804	2.2087	2.2370
80	2.2654	2.2937	2.3220	2.3503	2.3786	2.4069	2.4353	2.4636	2.4919	2.5202
90	2.5485	2.5768	2.6052	2.6335	2.6618	2.6901	2.7184	2.7468	2.7751	2.8034
100	2.8317	2.8600	2.8884	2.9167	2.9450	2.9733	3.0016	3.0300	3.0583	3.0866

Cubic Meters into Cubic Feet

Cubic Meters	0 Cubic Feet	1 Cubic Feet	2 Cubic Feet	3 Cubic Feet	4 Cubic Feet	5 Cubic Feet	6 Cubic Feet	7 Cubic Feet	8 Cubic Feet	9 Cubic Feet
0	.....	35.3	70.6	105.9	141.3	176.6	211.9	247.2	282.5	317.8
10	353.1	388.5	423.8	459.1	494.4	529.7	565.0	600.3	635.7	671.0
20	706.3	741.6	776.9	812.2	847.5	882.9	918.2	953.5	988.8	1024.1
30	1059.4	1094.7	1130.1	1165.4	1200.7	1236.0	1271.3	1306.6	1341.9	1377.3
40	1412.6	1447.9	1483.2	1518.5	1553.8	1589.2	1624.5	1659.8	1695.1	1730.4
50	1765.7	1801.0	1836.4	1871.7	1907.0	1942.3	1977.6	2012.9	2048.2	2083.6
60	2118.9	2154.2	2189.5	2224.8	2260.1	2295.4	2330.8	2366.1	2401.4	2436.7
70	2472.0	2507.3	2542.6	2578.0	2613.3	2648.6	2683.9	2719.2	2754.5	2789.8
80	2825.2	2860.5	2895.8	2931.1	2966.4	3001.7	3037.0	3072.4	3107.7	3143.0
90	3178.3	3213.6	3248.9	3284.2	3319.6	3354.9	3390.2	3425.5	3460.8	3496.1
100	3531.4	3566.7	3602.0	3637.3	3672.7	3708.0	3743.3	3778.6	3813.9	3849.2

Cubic Feet into Liters (Cubic Decimeters)

Cubic Feet	0	1	2	3	4	5	6	7	8	9
	Liters	Liters	Liters	Liters	Liters	Liters	Liters	Liters	Liters	Liters
0	.....	28.32	56.63	84.95	113.26	141.58	169.89	198.21	226.53	254.84
10	283.16	311.47	339.79	368.11	396.42	424.74	453.06	481.37	509.69	538.0
20	566.32	594.64	622.95	651.27	679.58	707.90	736.22	764.53	792.85	821.16
30	849.48	877.80	906.11	934.43	962.74	991.06	1019.4	1047.7	1076.0	1104.3
40	1132.6	1160.8	1189.2	1217.5	1245.9	1274.2	1302.5	1330.8	1359.1	1387.4
50	1415.8	1444.0	1472.4	1500.7	1529.1	1557.4	1585.7	1614.0	1642.3	1670.6
60	1698.9	1727.2	1755.5	1783.8	1812.2	1840.5	1868.8	1897.1	1925.4	1953.7
70	1982.1	2010.3	2038.7	2067.0	2095.4	2123.7	2152.0	2180.3	2208.6	2236.9
80	2265.3	2293.5	2321.9	2350.2	2378.6	2406.9	2435.2	2463.5	2491.8	2520.1
90	2548.4	2576.6	2605.0	2633.3	2661.6	2690.0	2718.3	2746.6	2774.9	2803.2
100	2831.6	2859.8	2888.2	2916.5	2944.9	2973.2	3001.5	3029.8	3058.1	3086.4

Liters (Cubic Decimeters) into Cubic Feet

Liters	0	1	2	3	4	5	6	7	8	9
	Cubic Feet	Cubic Feet	Cubic Feet	Cubic Feet	Cubic Feet	Cubic Feet	Cubic Feet	Cubic Feet	Cubic Feet	Cubic Feet
0	.....	0.0353	0.0706	0.1059	0.1413	0.1766	0.2119	0.2472	0.2825	0.3178
10	0.3531	0.3884	0.4237	0.4590	0.4944	0.5297	0.5650	0.6003	0.6356	0.6709
20	0.7063	0.7416	0.7766	0.8122	0.8476	0.8829	0.9182	0.9535	0.9888	1.0241
30	1.0594	1.0947	1.1300	1.1653	1.2007	1.2360	1.2713	1.3066	1.3419	1.3772
40	1.4126	1.4479	1.4832	1.5185	1.5539	1.5892	1.6245	1.6598	1.6951	1.7304
50	1.7658	1.8011	1.8364	1.8717	1.9071	1.9424	1.9777	2.0130	2.0483	2.0836
60	2.1189	2.1542	2.1895	2.2248	2.2602	2.2955	2.3308	2.3661	2.4014	2.4367
70	2.4721	2.5074	2.5427	2.5780	2.6134	2.6487	2.6840	2.7193	2.7546	2.7899
80	2.8252	2.8605	2.8958	2.9311	2.9665	3.0018	3.0371	3.0724	3.1077	3.1430
90	3.1784	3.2137	3.2490	3.2843	3.3197	3.3550	3.3903	3.4256	3.4609	3.4962
100	3.5315	3.5668	3.6021	3.6374	3.6728	3.7081	3.7434	3.7787	3.8140	3.8493

U. S. Gallons into Liters

Gallons	0	1	2	3	4	5	6	7	8	9
	Liters	Liters	Liters	Liters	Liters	Liters	Liters	Liters	Liters	Liters
0	.....	3.785	7.571	11.356	15.142	18.927	22.713	26.498	30.283	34.069
10	37.854	41.640	45.425	49.211	52.996	56.781	60.567	64.352	68.138	71.923
20	75.709	79.494	83.280	87.065	90.850	94.636	98.421	102.21	105.99	109.78
30	113.56	117.35	121.13	124.92	128.70	132.49	136.28	140.06	143.85	147.63
40	151.42	155.20	158.99	162.77	166.56	170.34	174.13	177.92	181.70	185.49
50	189.27	193.06	196.84	200.63	204.41	208.20	211.98	215.77	219.56	223.34
60	227.13	230.91	234.70	238.48	242.27	246.05	249.84	253.62	257.41	261.19
70	264.98	268.77	272.55	276.34	280.12	283.91	287.69	291.48	295.26	299.05
80	302.83	306.62	310.41	314.19	317.98	321.76	325.55	329.33	333.12	336.90
90	340.69	344.47	348.26	352.05	355.83	359.62	363.40	367.19	370.97	374.76
100	378.54	382.33	386.11	389.90	393.69	397.47	401.26	405.04	408.83	412.61

Liters into U. S. Gallons

Liters	0	1	2	3	4	5	6	7	8	9
	Gallons	Gallons	Gallons	Gallons	Gallons	Gallons	Gallons	Gallons	Gallons	Gallons
0	.....	0.264	0.528	0.793	1.057	1.321	1.585	1.849	2.113	2.378
10	2.642	2.906	3.170	3.434	3.698	3.963	4.227	4.491	4.755	5.019
20	5.283	5.548	5.812	6.076	6.340	6.604	6.868	7.133	7.397	7.661
30	7.925	8.189	8.453	8.718	8.982	9.246	9.510	9.774	10.038	10.303
40	10.567	10.831	11.095	11.359	11.623	11.888	12.152	12.416	12.680	12.944
50	13.209	13.473	13.737	14.001	14.265	14.529	14.794	15.058	15.322	15.586
60	15.850	16.114	16.379	16.643	16.907	17.171	17.435	17.699	17.964	18.228
70	18.492	18.756	19.020	19.284	19.549	19.813	20.077	20.341	20.605	20.869
80	21.134	21.398	21.662	21.926	22.190	22.454	22.719	22.983	23.247	23.511
90	23.775	24.040	24.304	24.568	24.832	25.096	25.360	25.625	25.889	26.153
100	26.417	26.681	26.945	27.210	27.474	27.738	28.002	28.266	28.530	28.795

Pounds into Kilograms

Pounds	0 Kilograms	1 Kilograms	2 Kilograms	3 Kilograms	4 Kilograms	5 Kilograms	6 Kilograms	7 Kilograms	8 Kilograms	9 Kilograms
0	....	0.454	0.907	1.361	1.814	2.268	2.722	3.175	3.629	4.082
10	4.536	4.990	5.443	5.897	6.350	6.804	7.257	7.711	8.165	8.618
20	9.072	9.525	9.979	10.433	10.886	11.340	11.793	12.247	12.701	13.154
30	13.608	14.061	14.515	14.969	15.422	15.876	16.329	16.783	17.237	17.690
40	18.144	18.597	19.051	19.504	19.958	20.412	20.865	21.319	21.772	22.226
50	22.680	23.133	23.587	24.040	24.494	24.948	25.401	25.855	26.308	26.762
60	27.216	27.669	28.123	28.576	29.030	29.484	29.937	30.391	30.844	31.298
70	31.751	32.205	32.659	33.112	33.566	34.019	34.473	34.927	35.380	35.834
80	36.287	36.741	37.195	37.648	38.102	38.555	39.009	39.463	39.916	40.370
90	40.823	41.277	41.730	42.184	42.638	43.091	43.545	43.998	44.453	44.906
100	45.359	45.813	46.266	46.720	47.174	47.627	48.081	48.534	48.988	49.442

Kilograms into Pounds

Kilograms	0 Lbs.	1 Lbs.	2 Lbs.	3 Lbs.	4 Lbs.	5 Lbs.	6 Lbs.	7 Lbs.	8 Lbs.	9 Lbs.
0	....	2.205	4.409	6.614	8.818	11.023	13.228	15.432	17.637	19.842
10	22.046	24.251	26.455	28.660	30.865	33.069	35.274	37.479	39.683	41.888
20	44.092	46.297	48.502	50.706	52.911	55.116	57.320	59.525	61.729	63.934
30	66.139	68.343	70.548	72.752	74.957	77.162	79.366	81.571	83.776	85.980
40	88.185	90.389	92.594	94.799	97.003	99.208	101.41	103.62	105.82	108.03
50	110.23	112.44	114.64	116.84	119.05	121.25	123.46	125.66	127.87	130.07
60	132.28	134.48	136.69	138.89	141.10	143.30	145.51	147.71	149.91	152.12
70	154.32	156.53	158.73	160.94	163.14	165.35	167.55	169.76	171.96	174.17
80	176.37	178.57	180.78	182.98	185.19	187.39	189.60	191.80	194.01	196.21
90	198.42	200.62	202.83	205.03	207.23	209.44	211.64	213.85	216.05	218.26
100	220.46	222.67	224.87	227.08	229.28	231.49	233.69	235.89	238.10	240.30

Ounces Avoirdupois into Grams

Ounces	0 Grams	1 Grams	2 Grams	3 Grams	4 Grams	5 Grams	6 Grams	7 Grams	8 Grams	9 Grams
0	....	28.35	56.70	85.05	113.39	141.74	170.09	198.44	226.79	255.14
10	283.48	311.83	340.18	368.52	396.87	425.22	453.57	481.92	510.27	538.62
20	566.97	595.32	623.67	652.01	680.36	708.71	737.06	765.41	793.76	822.11
30	850.46	878.81	907.16	935.50	963.85	992.20	1020.5	1048.9	1077.2	1105.6
40	1133.9	1162.2	1190.6	1218.90	1247.3	1275.6	1304.0	1332.3	1360.7	1389.0
50	1417.4	1445.7	1474.1	1502.4	1530.8	1559.1	1587.5	1615.8	1644.2	1672.5
60	1700.9	1729.2	1756.6	1785.9	1814.3	1842.9	1871.0	1899.3	1927.7	1956.0
70	1984.4	2012.7	2041.1	2079.4	2097.8	2126.1	2154.5	2182.8	2211.2	2239.5
80	2267.9	2296.2	2324.6	2352.9	2381.3	2409.6	2438.0	2466.3	2494.7	2523.0
90	2551.4	2579.7	2608.1	2636.4	2664.8	2693.1	2721.5	2739.8	2778.2	2806.5
100	2834.8	2863.1	2891.5	2919.8	2948.2	2976.5	3004.9	3033.2	3061.6	3089.9

Grams into Ounces Avoirdupois

Grams	0 Oz.	1 Oz.	2 Oz.	3 Oz.	4 Oz.	5 Oz.	6 Oz.	7 Oz.	8 Oz.	9 Oz.
0	....	0.0353	0.0705	0.1058	0.1411	0.1764	0.2116	0.2469	0.2822	0.3175
10	0.3527	0.3880	0.4232	0.4585	0.4938	0.5295	0.5643	0.5996	0.6349	0.6702
20	0.7055	0.7408	0.7760	0.8113	0.8466	0.8823	0.9171	0.9524	0.9877	1.0230
30	1.0582	1.0935	1.1287	1.1640	1.1993	1.2350	1.2698	1.3051	1.3404	1.3757
40	1.4110	1.4463	1.4815	1.5168	1.5521	1.5878	1.6226	1.6579	1.6932	1.7285
50	1.7637	1.8040	1.8392	1.8745	1.9098	1.9455	1.9803	2.0156	2.0509	2.0862
60	2.1165	2.1518	2.1870	2.2223	2.2576	2.2933	2.3281	2.3634	2.3987	2.4340
70	2.4692	2.5045	2.5397	2.5750	2.6103	2.6460	2.6808	2.7161	2.7514	2.7867
80	2.8220	2.8573	2.8925	2.9278	2.9631	2.9988	3.0336	3.0689	3.1042	3.1395
90	3.1747	3.2100	3.2452	3.2805	3.3158	3.3515	3.3863	3.4216	3.4569	3.4922
100	3.5275	3.5628	3.5980	3.6333	3.6686	3.7043	3.7391	3.7744	3.8097	3.8450

Pounds per Square Inch into Kilograms per Square Centimeter

Pounds per Square Inch	0 Kg.per Sq. Cm.	1 Kg.per Sq. Cm.	2 Kg.per Sq. Cm.	3 Kg.per Sq. Cm.	4 Kg.per Sq. Cm.	5 Kg.per Sq. Cm.	6 Kg.per Sq. Cm.	7 Kg.per Sq. Cm.	8 Kg.per Sq. Cm.	9 Kg.per Sq. Cm.
0	.....	0.0703	0.1406	0.2109	0.2812	0.3515	0.4218	0.4921	0.5625	0.6328
10	0.7031	0.7734	0.8437	0.9140	0.9843	1.0546	1.1249	1.1952	1.2655	1.3358
20	1.4062	1.4765	1.5468	1.6171	1.6874	1.7577	1.8280	1.8983	1.9686	2.0389
30	2.1092	2.1795	2.2498	2.3202	2.3905	2.4608	2.5311	2.6014	2.6717	2.7420
40	2.8123	2.8826	2.9529	3.0232	3.0935	3.1639	3.2342	3.3045	3.3748	3.4451
50	3.5154	3.5857	3.6560	3.7263	3.7966	3.8669	3.9372	4.0075	4.0779	4.1482
60	4.2185	4.2888	4.3591	4.4294	4.4997	4.5700	4.6403	4.7106	4.7809	4.8512
70	4.9216	4.9919	5.0622	5.1325	5.2028	5.2731	5.3434	5.4137	5.4840	5.5543
80	5.6246	5.6949	5.7652	5.8356	5.9059	5.9762	6.0465	6.1168	6.1871	6.2574
90	6.3277	6.3980	6.4683	6.5386	6.6089	6.6793	6.7496	6.8199	6.8902	6.9605
100	7.0308	7.1011	7.1714	7.2417	7.3120	7.3823	7.4526	7.5229	7.5933	7.6636

Kilograms per Square Centimeter into Pounds per Square Inch

Kilograms per Sq. Cm.	0 Lbs. per Sq. In.	1 Lbs. per Sq. In.	2 Lbs. per Sq. In.	3 Lbs. per Sq. In.	4 Lbs. per Sq. In.	5 Lbs. per Sq. In.	6 Lbs. per Sq. In.	7 Lbs. per Sq. In.	8 Lbs. per Sq. In.	9 Lbs. per Sq. In.
0	.....	14.22	28.45	42.67	56.89	71.12	85.34	99.56	113.78	128.01
10	142.23	156.45	170.68	184.90	199.12	213.35	227.57	241.79	256.02	270.24
20	284.46	298.69	312.91	327.13	341.36	355.58	369.80	384.03	398.25	412.47
30	426.70	440.92	455.14	469.36	483.59	497.81	512.03	526.26	540.48	554.70
40	568.93	583.15	597.37	611.60	625.82	640.04	654.27	668.49	682.71	696.94
50	711.16	725.38	739.61	753.83	768.05	782.28	796.50	810.72	824.94	839.17
60	853.39	867.61	881.84	896.06	910.28	924.51	938.73	952.95	967.18	981.40
70	995.62	1009.8	1024.1	1038.3	1052.5	1066.7	1081.0	1095.2	1109.4	1123.6
80	1137.8	1152.1	1166.3	1180.5	1194.7	1209.0	1223.2	1237.4	1251.6	1265.9
90	1280.1	1294.3	1308.5	1322.7	1337.0	1351.2	1365.4	1379.6	1393.9	1408.1
100	1422.3	1436.5	1450.8	1465.0	1479.2	1493.4	1507.7	1521.9	1536.1	1550.3

Pounds per Square Foot into Kilograms per Square Meter

Pounds per Square Foot	0 Kg.per Sq. Meter	1 Kg.per Sq. Meter	2 Kg.per Sq. Meter	3 Kg.per Sq. Meter	4 Kg.per Sq. Meter	5 Kg.per Sq. Meter	6 Kg.per Sq. Meter	7 Kg.per Sq. Meter	8 Kg.per Sq. Meter	9 Kg.per Sq. Meter
0	.....	4.88	9.76	14.65	19.53	24.41	29.30	34.18	39.06	43.94
10	48.83	53.71	58.59	63.47	68.36	73.24	78.12	83.00	87.88	92.77
20	97.65	102.53	107.41	112.30	117.18	122.06	126.94	131.83	136.71	141.59
30	146.47	151.35	156.23	161.12	166.00	170.88	175.76	180.65	185.53	190.41
40	195.30	200.18	205.06	209.95	214.83	219.71	224.59	229.48	234.36	239.24
50	244.12	249.01	253.89	258.78	263.66	268.54	273.42	278.31	283.18	288.06
60	292.95	297.83	302.71	307.60	312.48	317.36	322.24	327.13	332.00	336.89
70	341.77	346.65	351.53	356.42	361.30	366.18	371.06	375.95	380.83	385.71
80	390.59	395.48	400.36	405.24	410.12	415.00	419.89	424.77	429.65	434.53
90	439.43	444.31	449.19	454.08	458.96	463.84	468.72	473.61	478.48	483.37
100	488.25	493.13	498.00	502.90	507.78	512.66	517.54	522.43	527.31	532.19

Kilograms per Square Meter into Pounds per Square Foot

Kilograms per Square Meter	0 Lbs. per Sq. Ft.	1 Lbs. per Sq. Ft.	2 Lbs. per Sq. Ft.	3 Lbs. per Sq. Ft.	4 Lbs. per Sq. Ft.	5 Lbs. per Sq. Ft.	6 Lbs. per Sq. Ft.	7 Lbs. per Sq. Ft.	8 Lbs. per Sq. Ft.	9 Lbs. per Sq. Ft.
0	.....	0.2048	0.4096	0.6144	0.8192	1.0240	1.2289	1.4337	1.6385	1.8433
10	2.0481	2.2529	2.4577	2.6625	2.8673	3.0721	3.2770	3.4818	3.6866	3.8914
20	4.0962	4.3010	4.5058	4.7106	4.9154	5.1202	5.3251	5.5299	5.7347	5.9395
30	6.1444	6.3492	6.5540	6.7588	6.9636	7.1684	7.3733	7.5781	7.7829	7.9877
40	8.1925	8.3973	8.6021	8.8069	9.0117	9.2165	9.4214	9.6262	9.8310	10.036
50	10.240	10.445	10.649	10.854	11.059	11.264	11.469	11.674	11.878	12.083
60	12.289	12.494	12.698	12.903	13.108	13.313	13.518	13.723	13.927	14.132
70	14.337	14.542	14.746	14.951	15.156	15.361	15.565	15.771	15.975	16.180
80	16.385	16.590	16.794	16.999	17.204	17.409	17.614	17.819	18.023	18.228
90	18.433	18.638	18.842	19.047	19.252	19.457	19.662	19.867	20.071	20.276
100	20.481	20.686	20.890	21.095	21.300	21.505	21.710	21.915	22.119	22.324

Foot-pounds into Meter-Kilograms

Foot-pounds	0 Meter-kilogr.	1 Meter-kilogr.	2 Meter-kilogr.	3 Meter-kilogr.	4 Meter-kilogr.	5 Meter-kilogr.	6 Meter-kilogr.	7 Meter-kilogr.	8 Meter-kilogr.	9 Meter-kilogr.
0	.....	0.138	0.276	0.415	0 553	0.691	0.829	0.967	1.06	1.244
10	1.382	1.520	1.658	1.796	1.934	2.073	2.211	2.349	2.487	2.625
20	2.764	2.902	3.040	3.178	3.316	3.455	3.593	3 731	3.869	4.007
30	4.146	4.284	4.422	4.560	4.698	4.837	4.975	5.113	5.251	5.389
40	5.528	5.666	5.804	5.942	6.080	6.219	6.357	6.495	6.633	6.771
50	6.910	7.048	7.186	7.324	7.462	7.601	7.739	7.877	8.015	8.153
60	8.292	8.430	8.568	8.706	8.844	8.983	9.121	9.259	9.397	9.535
70	9.674	9.812	9.950	10.088	10.227	10.365	10.503	10.641	10.779	10.918
80	11.056	11.194	11.332	11.470	11.609	11.747	11.885	12.023	12.161	12.300
90	12.438	12.576	12.714	12.855	12.991	13.129	13.267	13.405	13.544	13.682
100	13.820	13.958	14.096	14.235	14.373	14.511	14.649	14.787	14.925	14.064

Meter-Kilograms into Foot-pounds

Meter-kilograms	0 Foot-lbs.	1 Foot-lbs.	2 Foot-lbs.	3 Foot-lbs.	4 Foot-lbs.	5 Foot-lbs.	6 Foot-lbs.	7 Foot-lbs.	8 Foot-lbs.	9 Foot-lbs.
0	.....	7.23	14.47	21.70	28.93	36.17	43.40	50.63	57.87	65.10
10	72.33	79.57	86.80	94.03	101.27	108.50	115.74	122.97	130.20	137.43
20	144.67	151.90	159.13	166.37	173.60	180.84	188.08	195.30	202.54	209.77
30	217.00	224.23	231.46	238.70	245.93	253.17	260.41	267.63	274.87	282.10
40	289.34	296.57	303.79	311.04	318.27	325.50	332.75	339.98	347.21	354.44
50	361.66	368.89	376.12	383.36	390.59	397.82	405.07	412.30	419.53	426.76
60	434.00	441.23	448.45	455.70	462.93	470.17	477.41	484.64	491.87	499.10
70	506.34	513.57	520.80	528.04	535.27	542.50	549.75	556.98	564.21	571.44
80	578.68	585.91	593.14	600.38	607.61	614.85	622.09	629.41	636.55	643.78
90	651.00	658.23	665.46	672.70	679.93	687.17	694.41	701.63	708.87	716.10
100	723.34	730.57	737.80	745.04	752.27	759.51	766.75	774.07	781.21	788.44

Foot-pounds into British Thermal Units

Foot-pounds	0 B.T.U.	1 B.T.U.	2 B.T.U.	3 B.T.U.	4 B.T.U.	5 B.T.U.	6 B.T.U.	7 B.T.U.	8 B.T.U.	9 B.T.U.
0	.....	0.0013	0.0026	0.0039	0.0051	0.0064	0.0077	0.0090	0.0103	0.0116
10	0.0129	0.0141	0.0154	0.0167	0.0180	0.0193	0.0206	0.0218	0.0231	0.0244
20	0.0257	0.0270	0.0283	0.0296	0.0308	0.0321	0.0334	0.0347	0.0360	0.0373
30	0.0385	0.0398	0.0411	0.0424	0.0437	0.0450	0.0463	0.0475	0.0488	0.0501
40	0.0514	0.0527	0.0540	0.0552	0.0565	0.0578	0.0591	0.0604	0.0617	0.0630
50	0.0642	0.0655	0.0668	0.0681	0.0694	0.0707	0.0719	0.0732	0.0745	0.0758
60	0.0771	0.0784	0.0797	0.0809	0.0822	0.0835	0.0848	0.0861	0.0874	0.0886
70	0.0899	0.0913	0.0925	0.0938	0.0951	0.0964	0.0976	0.0989	0.1002	0.1015
80	0.1028	0.1040	0.1054	0.1066	0.1079	0.1092	0.1105	0.1118	0.1131	0.1143
90	0.1156	0.1169	0.1182	0.1195	0.1208	0.1221	0.1233	0.1246	0.1259	0.1272
100	0.1285	0.1298	0.1311	0.1324	0.1337	0.1350	0.1362	0.1375	0.1388	0.1401

British Thermal Units into Foot-pounds

B.T.U.	0 Foot-lbs.	1 Foot-lbs.	2 Foot-lbs.	3 Foot-lbs.	4 Foot-lbs.	5 Foot-lbs.	6 Foot-lbs.	7 Foot-lbs.	8 Foot-lbs.	9 Foot-lbs.
0	.....	778	1,557	2,335	3,114	3,892	4,670	5,449	6,227	7,006
10	7,784	8,562	9,341	10,119	10,897	11,676	12,454	13,233	14,011	14,789
20	15,568	16,346	17,125	17,903	18,681	19,460	20,238	21,017	21,795	22,573
30	23,352	24,130	24,909	25,687	26,465	27,244	28,022	28,800	29,579	30,357
40	31,136	31,914	32,692	33,471	34,249	35,028	35,806	36,584	37,363	38,141
50	38,920	39,698	40,476	41,255	42,033	42,811	43,590	44,368	45,147	45,925
60	46,703	47,482	48,260	49,039	49,817	50,595	51,374	52,152	52,931	53,709
70	54,487	55,266	56,044	56,823	57,601	58,379	59,158	59,936	60,714	61,493
80	62,271	63,050	63,828	64,606	65,385	66,163	66,942	67,720	68,498	69,277
90	70,055	70,834	71,612	72,390	73,169	73,947	74,726	75,504	76,282	77,061
100	77,839	78,618	79,396	80,174	80,953	81,731	82,510	83,288	84,066	84,845

Horsepower into Kilowatts

H.P.	0 K.W.	1 K.W.	2 K.W.	3 K.W.	4 K.W.	5 K.W.	6 K.W.	7 K.W.	8 K.W.	9 K.W.
0	.....	0.746	1.491	2.237	2.983	3.729	4.474	5.220	5.966	6.711
10	7.457	8.203	8.948	9.694	10.440	11.186	11.931	12.677	13.423	14.168
20	14.914	15.660	16.405	17.151	17.897	18.643	19.388	20.134	20.880	21.625
30	22.371	23.117	23.862	24.608	25.354	26.100	26.845	27.591	28.337	29.082
40	29.828	30.574	31.319	32.065	32.811	33.557	34.302	35.048	35.794	36.539
50	37.285	38.031	38.776	39.522	40.268	41.014	41.759	42.505	43.251	43.996
60	44.742	45.488	46.233	46.979	47.725	48.471	49.216	49.962	50.708	51.453
70	52.199	52.945	53.691	54.436	55.182	55.928	56.673	57.419	58.165	58.910
80	59.656	60.402	61.148	61.893	62.639	63.385	64.130	64.876	65.622	66.367
90	67.113	67.859	68.605	69.350	70.096	70.842	71.587	72.333	73.079	73.824
100	74.570	75.316	76.062	76.807	77.553	78.299	79.044	79.790	80.536	81.281

Kilowatts into Horsepower

K.W.	0 H.P.	1 H.P.	2 H.P.	3 H.P.	4 H.P.	5 H.P.	6 H.P.	7 H.P.	8 H.P.	9 H.P.
0	.....	1.341	2.682	4.023	5.364	6.705	8.046	9.387	10.728	12.069
10	13.410	14.751	16.092	17.433	18.774	20.115	21.456	22.797	24.138	25.479
20	26.820	28.161	29.502	30.843	32.184	33.525	34.866	36.208	37.549	38.890
30	40.231	41.572	42.913	44.254	45.595	46.936	48.277	49.618	50.959	52.300
40	53.641	54.982	56.323	57.664	59.005	60.346	61.687	63.028	64.369	65.710
50	67.051	68.392	69.733	71.074	72.415	73.756	75.097	76.438	77.779	79.120
60	80.461	81.802	83.143	84.484	85.825	87.166	88.507	89.848	91.189	92.530
70	93.871	95.212	96.553	97.894	99.235	100.58	101.92	103.26	104.60	105.94
80	107.28	108.62	109.96	111.30	112.65	113.99	115.33	116.67	118.01	119.35
90	120.69	122.03	123.37	124.71	126.06	127.40	128.74	130.08	131.42	132.76
100	134.10	135.44	136.78	138.12	139.47	140.81	142.15	143.49	144.83	146.17

Miles into Kilometers

Miles	0 Km.	1 Km.	2 Km.	3 Km.	4 Km.	5 Km.	6 Km.	7 Km.	8 Km.	9 Km.
0	.....	1.609	3.219	4.828	6.437	8.047	9.656	11.265	12.875	14.484
10	16.093	17.703	19.312	20.921	22.531	24.140	25.750	27.359	28.968	30.578
20	32.187	33.796	35.406	37.015	38.624	40.234	41.843	43.452	45.062	46.671
30	48.280	49.890	51.499	53.108	54.718	56.327	57.936	59.546	61.155	62.764
40	64.374	65.983	67.593	69.202	70.811	72.421	74.030	75.639	77.249	78.858
50	80.467	82.077	83.686	85.295	86.905	88.514	90.123	91.733	93.342	94.951
60	96.561	98.170	99.779	101.39	103.00	104.61	106.22	107.83	109.44	111.04
70	112.65	114.26	115.87	117.48	119.09	120.70	122.31	123.92	125.53	127.14
80	128.75	130.36	131.97	133.58	135.19	136.79	138.40	140.01	141.62	143.23
90	144.84	146.45	148.06	149.67	151.28	152.89	154.50	156.11	157.72	159.33
100	160.93	162.54	164.15	165.76	167.37	168.98	170.59	172.20	173.81	175.42

Kilometers into Miles

Km.	0 Miles	1 Miles	2 Miles	3 Miles	4 Miles	5 Miles	6 Miles	7 Miles	8 Miles	9 Miles
0	......	0.621	1.243	1.864	2.486	3.107	3.728	4.350	4.971	5.592
10	6.214	6.835	7.457	8.078	8.699	9.321	9.942	10.562	11.185	11.805
20	12.427	13.049	13.670	14.292	14.913	15.534	16.156	16.776	17.399	18.019
30	18.641	19.263	19.884	20.506	21.127	21.748	22.370	22.990	23.613	24.233
40	24.855	25.477	26.098	26.720	27.341	27.962	28.584	29.204	29.827	30.447
50	31.069	31.690	32.311	32.933	33.554	34.175	34.797	35.417	36.040	36.660
60	37.282	37.904	38.525	39.147	39.768	40.389	41.011	41.631	42.254	42.874
70	43.497	44.118	44.739	45.361	45.982	46.603	47.225	47.845	48.468	49.088
80	49.711	50.332	50.953	51.575	52.196	52.817	53.439	54.059	54.682	55.302
90	55.924	56.545	57.166	57.788	58.409	59.030	59.652	60.272	60.895	61.515
100	62.138	62.759	63.380	64.002	64.623	65.244	65.866	66.486	67.109	67.729

Fundamental Electrical Units. — *Ohm:* The unit of resistance to the flow of an electric current. The international ohm has been defined as the resistance at zero degrees Centigrade of a column of mercury of uniform cross-section having a length of 106.300 centimeters and a mass of 14.4521 grams.

Ampere: The unit of the rate of flow of an electric current. A current of one ampere, when passed through a solution of nitrate of silver in water, deposits silver at the rate of 0.001118 gram per second. An ampere is equal to the flow of a quantity of electricity of one coulomb per second.

Volt: The unit of electromotive force. An electromotive force of one volt, when steadily applied to a conductor the resistance of which is one ohm, will produce a current of one ampere. The electromotive force between the poles or electrodes of the voltaic cell known as the Weston normal cell, at a temperature of 20 degrees C., which is 1.0183 volts, is used as a reference standard.

Coulomb: The unit of quantity. A coulomb is the quantity of electricity transmitted by a current of one ampere in one second. It is also equal to the quantity of electricity contained in a condenser with a capacity of one farad, when the same is subject to an electromotive force of one volt.

Farad: The unit of capacity. A farad is the capacity of a condenser charged to a potential of one volt by one coulomb of electricity.

Henry: The unit of inductance. A henry is the inductance of a coil in which a current varying at the rate of one ampere per second will induce one volt. The one volt induced does not include the electromotive force necessary to overcome the resistance of the circuit. A more practical unit, the millihenry (one thousandth of a henry) is the unit used in rating coils and electromagnets.

Watt: The unit of electric power. A watt is equivalent to the work done at the rate of one joule per second. It is also equal to the power expended by an electric current of one ampere flowing through a resistance of one ohm. One kilowatt is equal to one thousand watts.

Power and Heat Equivalents

1 horsepower-hour = 0.746 kilowatt-hour = 1,980,000 foot-pounds = 2545 Btu (British thermal units) = 2.64 pounds of water evaporated at 212° F. = 17 pounds of water raised from 62° to 212° F.

1 kilowatt-hour = 1000 watt-hours = 1.34 horsepower-hour = 2,655,200 foot-pounds = 3,600,000 joules = 3415 Btu = 3.54 pounds of water evaporated at 212° F. = 22.8 pounds of water raised from 62° to 212° F.

1 horsepower = 746 watts = 0.746 kilowatt = 33,000 foot-pounds per minute = 550 foot-pounds per second = 2545 Btu per hour = 42.4 Btu per minute = 0.71 Btu per second = 2.64 pounds of water evaporated per hour at 212° F.

1 kilowatt = 1000 watts = 1.34 horsepower = 2,655,200 foot-pounds per hour = 44,200 foot-pounds per minute = 737 foot-pounds per second = 3415 Btu per hour = 57 Btu per minute = 0.95 Btu per second = 3.54 pounds of water evaporated per hour at 212° F.

1 watt = 1 joule per second = 0.00134 horsepower = 0.001 kilowatt = 3.42 Btu per hour = 44.22 foot-pounds per minute = 0.74 foot-pounds per second = 0.0035 pound of water evaporated per hour at 212° F.

1 Btu (British thermal unit) = 1052 watt-seconds = 778 foot-pounds = 0.252 kilogram-calorie = 0.000292 kilowatt-hour = 0.000393 horsepower-hour = 0.00104 pound of water evaporated at 212° F.

1 foot-pound = 1.36 joule = 0.000000377 kilowatt-hour = 0.00129 Btu = 0.0000005 horsepower-hour.

1 joule = 1 watt-second = 0.000000278 kilowatt-hour = 0.00095 Btu = 0.74 foot-pound.

PATENTS

Patentable Inventions. — Patents are issued by the United States Patent Office to any person who has invented or discovered any new and useful art, machine, method of manufacture, composition of matter, or any new and useful improvement along these lines. In order to obtain a patent for an invention, the latter must not have been known or used by others in this country previous to the time the invention was made by the person applying for the patent; nor must it have been described in any printed publication in this or any foreign country before the invention was made by the person applying for a patent in this country, or more than one year prior to the application for a patent. A patent cannot be granted if the article has been in public use or for sale in the United States for more than one year prior to the application for a patent.

A patent contains a grant to the patentee, his heirs or assigns, for a term of seventeen years, for the exclusive right to make, use or sell the invention or discovery throughout the United States. In case the inventor at the time of making his application believed himself to be the first inventor or discoverer, but it is subsequently found that the invention or discovery has been known or used in a foreign country before the time of his invention, he will not be refused a patent providing the article has not previously been patented or described in any printed publication. The application for a patent in this country must be filed within 12 months after an application for a patent may have been filed in a foreign country.

Applications for Patents. — An inventor who wishes to apply for a patent, and is not familiar with the rules of patent practice, should apply to the Patent Office, for a copy of the "Rules of Practice," which will be sent upon request. It is also advisable that the services of a competent and duly registered patent attorney be secured, as the values of patents depend largely upon the preparation of the specifications and the claims. An inexperienced person will often prepare claims which cover only the particular design for the apparatus in which the invention at first may have been executed. The invention, however, may be much more fundamental in character, and the claims should cover all possible designs by means of which the same end may be obtained with the same fundamental principles of action of the device. The patent office, while it will not recommend any particular patent attorney or firm, advises applicants to avoid doing business with those attorneys who advertise the possession of unusual facilities for obtaining patents.

Applications for a patent must be made in writing to the Commissioner of Patents. The applicant must also file in the patent office a written description of the invention or discovery, in clear, concise and exact terms. In the case of a machine, it is necessary to particularly point out and distinctly claim the particular improvement or combination of which the inventor claims to be the discoverer. The specification and claim must be signed by the inventor. When the nature of the invention is such that drawings will make the description clearer, the applicant must furnish a drawing signed by the inventor or his attorney. If the patent office so requires, the applicant must also furnish a model of convenient size to exhibit advantageously the several parts of the invention, but a model should not be sent unless first called for by the patent office.

Fees. — All fees must be paid in advance and are as follows: On filing each *original application* for patent, $30, plus $1 for each claim in excess of 20; on filing each *reissue application* for patent, $30, regardless of the number of claims; on issuing each *original patent*, $30, plus $1 for each claim in excess of 20. In *design cases*: For 3 years and 6 months, $10; for 7 years, $15; for 14 years, $30.

INDEX

G